NCIPAL SUBJECTS

Machining Processes and Their Application to Steel and Cast Iron

Grinding, Honing, Lapping

Cutting-Tool Materials

Machining of:

METALS HANDBOOK

8th Edition

VOL. 3

Machining

prepared under the direction of the

ASM HANDBOOK COMMITTEE

Taylor Lyman, Editor
Howard E. Boyer, Managing Editor
Associate Editors: William J. Carnes, Louis Carr, Margaret W. Chevalier, Edward A. Durand, Philip D. Harvey, Helen Lawton, Theodore M. Leach and Carl H. Willer. Assistant Editors: Ian A. Anderson, Helen V. Bukovics, Barbara A. Caldwell and Jean S. Elliot

AMERICAN SOCIETY FOR METALS
Metals Park, Ohio 44073

First printing, October 1967
Second printing, May 1968

Nothing contained in the Metals Handbook is to be construed as a grant of any right of manufacture, sale, or use in connection with any method, process, apparatus, product, or composition, whether or not covered by letters patent or registered trade mark, nor as a defense against liability for the infringement of letters patent or registered trade mark.

Library of Congress Catalog Card Number: 27-12046

PRINTED IN THE UNITED STATES OF AMERICA

MEMBERS OF ASM HANDBOOK COMMITTEE (1964 to 1967)

D. J. WRIGHT
CHAIRMAN (1964-1965)
Caterpillar Tractor Co.
(Member, 1959-1967)

J. D. GRAHAM
CHAIRMAN (1965-)
International Harvester Co.
(Member, 1961-)

W. A. STADTLER
VICE CHAIRMAN (1965-)
International Business Machines Corp.
(Member, 1962-)

RALPH W. E. LEITER
PAST CHAIRMAN (1964)
The Budd Co.
(Chairman, 1962-1963)

TAYLOR LYMAN
SECRETARY (1945-)
Editor – Metals Handbook
American Society for Metals

WILLIAM W. AUSTIN (1961-1967)
North Carolina State College

H. J. BATES (1966-)
Fairfield Manufacturing Co.

MICHAEL B. BEVER (1965-)
Massachusetts Institute of Technology

R. B. BOSWELL (1964-)
Chrysler Corp.

CARSON L. BROOKS (1966-)
Reynolds Metals Co.

ROBERT DALLMAN (1965-1966)
Robert W. Hunt Co.

D. A. DASHFIELD (1966-)
Bell Helicopter Co.

R. DOUGHTON, JR. (1959-1964)
Jones & Laughlin Steel Corp.

W. O. DOW, JR. (1965-)
Manning Products Co.

W. D. FRANCE (1964-1965)
Scovill Manufacturing Co.

D. J. GIRARDI (1961-1965)
Timken Roller Bearing Co.

WILSON T. GROVES (1963-)
Dana Corp.

ROBERT L. HADLEY (1962-)
General Electric Co.

EARL J. HAGAN (1965-)
AMP Inc.

BRUCE M. HAMILTON (1963-)
Crucible Steel Co. of America

G. F. KAPPELT (1956-1958, 1961-1964)
Bell Aerosystems Co.

RUPERT KLEIN (1966-)
Crane Co.

JACK E. LABELLE (1965-)
General Motors Corp.

L. R. MAITLAND (1964-1967)
Talon, Inc.

T. W. MORRISON (1964-)
SKF Industries, Inc.

A. H. RAUCH (1962-1965)
Deere & Co.

JOHN H. RIZLEY (1963-1966)
General Dynamics/Pomona

JACK D. ROBINSON (1963-1966)
Bendix Corp.

KENNETH E. ROSE (1962-1965)
University of Kansas

S. A. ROSECRANS (1963-1966)
Westinghouse Electric Corp.

WILLIAM C. SCHULTE (1962-1965)
Curtiss-Wright Corp.

BRUCE M. SHIELDS (1965-)
United States Steel Corp.

GEORGE J. SHUBAT (1966-)
Diamond Chain Co.

ROBERT L. SPROAT (1965-)
Standard Pressed Steel Co.

PREVIOUS CHAIRMEN OF ASM HANDBOOK COMMITTEE

R. S. ARCHER* (1940-1942)
(Member, 1937-1942)

L. B. CASE (1931-1933)
(Member, 1928-1933)

E. O. DIXON* (1952-1954)
(Member, 1947-1955)

R. L. DOWDELL (1938-1939)
(Member, 1935-1939)

J. P. GILL* (1937)
(Member, 1934-1937)

J. F. HARPER* (1923-1926)
(Member, 1923-1926)

C. H. HERTY, JR.* (1934-1936)
(Member, 1930-1936)

J. B. JOHNSON (1948-1951)
(Member, 1944-1951)

*Deceased

R. W. E. LEITER (1962-1963)
(Member, 1955-1958, 1960-1964)

G. V. LUERSSEN (1943-1947)
(Member, 1942-1947)

W. J. MERTEN* (1927-1930)
(Member, 1923-1933)

N. E. PROMISEL (1955-1961)
(Member, 1954-1963)

J. EDWARD DONNELLAN
(Secretary, 1924-1945)

Contributors to This Volume

Numbers refer to first page of each article in which contributor participated. Names of author committee chairmen are printed in capital letters.

FOREWORD

IN VOLUME 1 of this 8th edition of METALS HANDBOOK, machining is defined as removing material, in the form of chips, from work, usually through the use of a machine. Within the generally accepted or traditional scope of this definition, the factors involved in machining are work material, machine tool, cutting tool, and cutting fluid. Great efforts have continuously been made to evaluate these factors and, through new knowledge and improvements, to ensure the attainment of the high rates of material removal demanded by the economic pressures that are so closely allied with machining operations. Under these pressures, machining technology has always remained dynamic and great progress has been made in meeting every challenge that has arisen from our industrial environment. Requirements for high-strength materials suitable for the severe service applications introduced by the space age have exerted new and greater demands on machining technology. Thus a new impetus has been given to machining development, and with the space age significant advances have been made in material-removal techniques.

This third volume of the 8th edition of METALS HANDBOOK is an endeavor by the American Society for Metals to present a comprehensive, up-to-date treatment of the dynamic subject of machining. Through their combined efforts, the ASM Handbook Committee, author committees, contributors, and editorial staff have produced a book that makes available to the reader much valuable information on all phases of conventional machining, including the machinability of materials and the application of machine tools, cutting tools, and cutting fluids. In addition, the book presents information on recent developments such as electrical discharge machining, chemical and electrochemical machining, which are processes dictated by the parts and sometimes by economics when conventional methods are not productive.

This volume is a significant step toward the fulfillment of ASM's commitment to provide its members — and other interested individuals — with improved information on the processing and fabrication of metals. It is a worthy forerunner of the two projected companion volumes on forming and welding that are to complete the coverage of this branch of metalworking technology. To all the men and women who contributed in the preparation and production of this volume, we extend our sincere thanks.

JOHN CONVEY
President – American Society for Metals

ALLAN RAY PUTNAM
Managing Director

PREFACE

THIS IS THE THIRD in a series of volumes that will supersede and expand the single-volume 7th edition of METALS HANDBOOK. In preparing this new volume, the aim of the ASM Handbook Committee and the authors has been to provide the reader with practical information that will help him select and control processes for machining ferrous and nonferrous metals.

As it was for the first two volumes of this 8th edition, principal reliance for authorship has again been placed on committees of engineers and production managers from industry, in order to arrive at a balanced presentation of divergent viewpoints and to achieve realism in relation to practice. More than 300 plants, large and small, are represented in the authorship of this third volume; 26 committees and 348 individuals are named herein as contributors. In addition to the contributors credited throughout these pages, many other members and friends of ASM — including, especially, numerous colleagues of the authors cited — have supplied valuable information and have reviewed manuscripts for accuracy and clarity.

The table at the foot of this page compares in detail the subject coverage in this third volume of the 8th edition with the coverage of corresponding subject matter in the 7th edition. As measured by the number of illustrations and tables, more than 20 times as much numerical information has been included in this volume as in the corresponding subject areas of the 7th edition. Apart from expanded coverage of subjects, this increased emphasis on easily accessible data (as distinguished from descriptive text), together with the closer relation of this volume to industrial practice (demonstrated by the large number of specific examples, applications and comparisons), constitutes the important difference between the 7th edition of METALS HANDBOOK and this 8th edition.

This volume represents the first major contribution of the American Society for Metals in the field of machining. The information presented and the associated index entries would fill a 2000-page book published in the conventional format of 6-by-9-in. pages. And yet a space allocation of this magnitude is none too generous for the presentation of a clear account of the great number of processes now in widespread industrial use for machining the growing variety of ferrous and nonferrous metals and alloys.

The first 310 pages of this book contain 40 articles, each dealing with a single process and its application primarily to steel and cast iron. Twelve of the 40 processes are so-called nontraditional or unconventional ones, such as machining and grinding by electrical discharge and electrochemical methods.

The next section (pages 311 to 332) consists of five articles on the properties and selection of materials for cutting tools.

The remainder of the book (180 pages) contains 18 articles on machining and grinding of metals other than carbon and low-alloy steels. The titles of these articles refer to the type of metal being machined — cast iron, tool steel, and stainless steel; and aluminum alloys, beryllium, copper and copper alloys, and other nonferrous metals.

Comparison of Volume 3 of the 8th Edition With Corresponding Subject Matter on Machining in the 7th Edition

Subject matter (page reference, 8th edition)	Illustrations		Tables		Examples		Contributors		Pages	
	8th ed	7th ed	8th ed	7th ed	8th ed	7th ed	3th ed	7th ed	8th ed	7th ed
Machining processes using conventional tools (1 to 226)	1335	14	412	10	448	0	134	11	226	15
Electrical, electrochemical and other nontraditional processes (227 to 256; 280 to 287)	115	0	63	0	21	0	19	0	38	0
Grinding, honing and lapping (257 to 279; 288 to 310)	232	0	76	0	110	0	30	1	46	2
Materials for cutting tools (311 to 332)	173	3	26	7	61	0	54	19	22	7
Machining of cast iron (333 to 352)	87	1	65	0	36	0	10	0	20	2
Machining and grinding of tool steel (353 to 374)	74	0	52	0	63	0	10	0	22	0
Machining of stainless steel and heat-resisting alloys (375 to 438)	353	0	197	0	127	0	25	0	64	0
Machining of nonferrous metals (439 to 512)	467	143	208	18	143	0	66	11	74	17
Total	2836	161	1099	35	1009	0	348	42	512	43

The principal new contribution made in this volume is the multiplicity of examples that describe machining practice. Numbered consecutively from 1 through 1009 from the front to the back of the book, these examples deal with methods used, improvements made or problems solved in specific operations and applications, and they emphasize the results obtained in the manufacture of a great variety of metal parts.

To tie the various sections of the book together and make a more unified whole, the editors have used several techniques, the three principal ones of which are as follows:

First, each major article is concluded with a tabulation of example numbers that refers the reader to closely related examples presented elsewhere in the book. Thus, at the end of the article "Drilling" is a table that lists 49 examples of drilling practice located elsewhere, in the various articles on machining of metals other than carbon and low-alloy steels. Similarly, a table at the end of the article "Machining of Stainless Steel" directs the reader to 51 examples in the first half of the book that deal with machining of stainless steel.

Second, to make it easy for the reader to find any of the 1009 consecutively numbered examples without having to consult the index or the table of contents, the span of example numbers presented on each pair of facing pages is indicated at the tops of those pages, near the inside margins.

Third, the index (printed on colored paper) has been expanded more than 20% over those in Volumes 1 and 2, in terms of the number of index entries per page of book. Suggestions for effective use of the index are given on the first index page.

In compiling this new work on machining, and in orienting the subject matter strongly toward industrial practice, the authors have omitted discussions of the underlying fundamentals of the physics of metal cutting. This omission is justified by the need to conserve space and by the availability of the more fundamental physical data in journal articles and other sources.

IN CONCLUDING this preface, we borrow the words of the final paragraph of the Preface to Volume 1: The extensive range of data and examples presented in this book reflects the specialized knowledge of its 348 contributors. Upon the collective experience and high competence of these specialists rest the accuracy and authority of the volume.

TAYLOR LYMAN
Editor – Metals Handbook

Contents of Metals Handbook Volume 3

Machining Processes and Their Application to Steel and Cast Iron

Machining Processes, Steel and Cast Iron (cont'd)

Grinding, Honing and Lapping

Materials for Cutting Tools

Machining of Cast Iron

Machining and Grinding of Tool Steel

Machining of Stainless Steel and Heat-Resisting Alloys

Machining of Nonferrous Metals

MACHINING PROCESSES AND THEIR APPLICATION TO STEEL AND CAST IRON

CONTENTS

Turning

*By the ASM Committee on Turning**

TURNING is a machining process for generating external surfaces of revolution by the action of a cutting tool on a rotating workpiece, usually in a lathe. When this same action is applied to internal surfaces of revolution, the process is termed boring. In many instances, turning and boring are performed simultaneously or consecutively in the same setup. This article discusses applications in which turning is the sole operation or is the major operation in a machining sequence.

Process Capabilities

Several other machining operations are often performed in conjunction with turning. These include facing, longitudinal drilling, boring, reaming, tapping, threading, chamfering and knurling. Also, accessories can be obtained for milling, grinding and cross drilling, although these operations are less frequently combined with turning. When more than two or three different operations are performed on identical parts, it is usually more practical to employ the processes described in the article on Multiple-Operation Machining (page 147).

Size and Shape of Workpiece. Availability of equipment that can hold and rotate the workpiece is the major restriction on the size of workpiece that can be turned. Turning is done on parts ranging in size from those used in watches up to steel propeller shafts more than 80 ft long. Aluminum parts (about one third the density of steel or brass) over 10 ft in diameter have been successfully turned. In practice, weight of the work metal per unit of volume may restrict the size of workpiece that is practical to turn. Problems in holding and handling increase as weight and size increase. Some large parts are turned in vertical boring mills (see Example 32, involving a 60-ton workpiece, in the article on Boring).

Sometimes the entire workpiece is so unwieldy that rotating is virtually impossible. A notable example is in the turning of crankpin diameters on large crankshafts. This condition, however, usually can be overcome, and an acceptable degree of dynamic balance obtained, by counterweighting. Counterweights may be attached either to the spindle of the machine or to the work.

Power Required. Engagement of the cutting tool with the rotating work results in a tangential force that, for a specific work metal, tool shape and feed rate, generally is independent of the cutting speed and directly proportional to the depth of cut. That force multiplied by the surface speed of the workpiece serves as a basis for calculating the net horsepower required to remove metal from the piece being turned. Power required to move the tool longitudinally usually is negligible.

The effects of composition and hardness of work metal on power requirements for turning are illustrated in Fig. 1, for a fixed tool design, speed and feed. Power requirements differ greatly for the different families of alloys, averaging about 0.1, 0.25 and 0.8 hp per cu in. per min for magnesium alloys, copper alloys, and steels, respectively. As also shown in Fig. 1, the power values increase with increasing hardness within each family of alloys, the rate of increase being greatest for cast irons and for steels harder than 350 Bhn. Besides having significance for the design of lathes, these data on power requirements provide an indication of the relative ease and cost of turning various metals.

The effect of cutting tool design on power requirements is discussed and illustrated under "Design of Single-Point Tools", on page 4. The use of cutting fluids can have an indirect effect on power requirements through its effect on speed and feed.

*Harold A. Maloney, *Chairman,* Plant Metallurgist, Transmission Div., Clark Equipment Co.; Homer Briggs, Tool Engineer, W-K-M Div., ACF Industries Inc.; C. C. Collins, Foreman, Experimental Machine Shop, Ingersoll-Rand Co.; S. S. Cowell, Tool and Field Representative, Transmission and Chassis Div., Ford Motor Co.

Leslie J. Goplen, Engineering Dept., Gisholt Machine Co.; F. H. Lockard, Methods Dept., John Deere Waterloo Tractor Works; William W. Parr, Department Head, Machine Dept., Kodak Park Works, Eastman Kodak Co.; H. F. Scheeler, Superintendent, Machining Div., Fort Wayne Works, International Harvester Co.

Homer J. Terhaar, Manager, Machine Div., Gleason Works; Donald D. Tome, Process Engineer, Aero Engineering Model Shop, Aeronautical Div., Honeywell Inc.; C. G. Wood, Assistant Factory Superintendent, Commercial Aircraft Div., Cessna Aircraft Co.; Harold E. Wright, Jr., Superintendent, Production Engineering, Milwaukee Plant, AC Electronics Div., General Motors Corp.

Depth of Cut, Feed and Speed. To minimize the number of cuts required, the depth of cut should be as great as is consistent with the strength of the part and the chucking equipment, the power of the machine tool, and the amount of stock to be removed. As depth of cut is increased, the cutting force becomes larger. This must be limited to a value that will not distort the part, pull it from the chuck, or overload the machine. Depth of cut ordinarily ranges from a few mils to about ¼ in., but can be an inch or more in roughing cuts on large pieces.

The feed depends on the finish desired and the strength and rigidity of the part and the machine. Feed in most applications varies between 0.005 and 0.020 ipr. Finishing cuts require a light feed and may be at 0.001 ipr or less; roughing cuts on large workpieces are often taken at a feed rate of 0.25 ipr or more. Cutting speed depends primarily on workpiece hardness. Speed and feed are discussed in detail on pages 6 to 11.

Lathes

An engine lathe consists basically of a bed (including two ways), a headstock, a tailstock, a compound slide (carriage), a cross slide, a tool holder mounted on the cross slide, and a source of power for rotating the workpiece. Most engine lathes also incorporate a lead screw that moves the compound slide uniformly along the bed.

Engine lathes are available with an almost infinite number of modifications, and also have provided the basis for the development of another group of machine tools that includes turret lathes and single-spindle or multiple-spindle bar and chucking machines (see the article that begins on page 147). The main feature that distinguishes the latter group of machines from the engine lathe or any of its modifications is that none of the turret lathes or bar and chucking machines utilizes a tailstock.

Regardless of other modifications, engine lathes are provided with only two types of headstocks — chucking and centering. The chucking type of headstock incorporates a work-holding device that grips the workpiece, thus providing centering and clamping for positive rotation. This type is most used for turning castings or forgings.

In a lathe having the centering type of headstock, the workpiece is secured in position between a pointed center in the headstock and a counterpart center in the tailstock. The workpiece is gripped for rotation by means of a drive dog, which locks into the face plate. The centering type is most commonly used for turning long, symmetrical workpieces, such as shafts. In common practice, the workpiece is turned for most of its length, after which the drive dog is removed, the workpiece reversed and the operation completed.

Two of the more common modifications of the basic engine lathe are hollow-spindle lathes and gap-frame lathes. Both modifications permit the lathe to accommodate specific shapes.

Hollow-spindle lathes are constructed so as to permit the loading of tubular or shaftlike workpieces through a hollow spindle in the rear of the headstock. Workpieces may then be extended as required through the headstock into the work area, gripped by jaw-type holders. With this type of lathe, the ends of long members can be turned without the need for a lathe long enough to accommodate the entire length of the workpiece between centers. The distance that the workpiece may extend from the rear of the headstock is virtually unlimited. However, as the unsupported length becomes unwieldy, steady rests or some other means of outboard support must be provided. Hollow-spindle lathes often are referred to as "oil-country" lathes, because of their extensive use for turning sections of long members such as drill pipes and sucker rods.

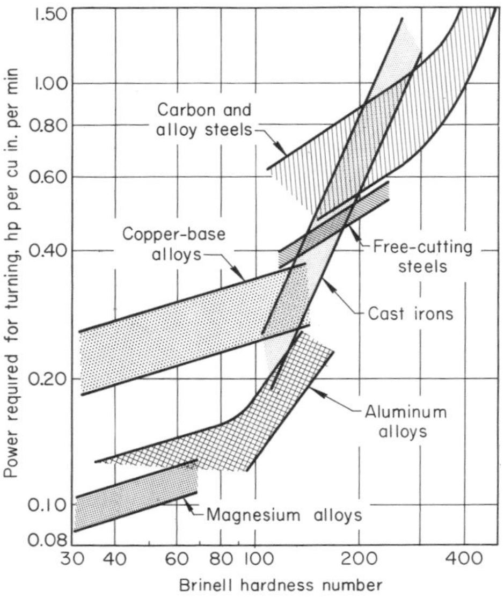

Data plotted are for 0.100-in. depth of cut at a feed of 0.0125 ipr, with tools of the following geometry: 8°, 14°, 6°, 6°, 6°, 0°, 3⁄64 in.— except on aluminum, for which tool geometry was 20°, 40°, 10°, 10°, 10°, 15°, 0 in. (See Table 1 for identification of tool angles.)

Fig. 1. Effect of composition and hardness of work metal on horsepower requirements

Gap-frame lathes, sometimes called "gap-bed" lathes, have been modified to provide greater diametral clearance adjacent to the headstock. With a gap-frame lathe, workpieces that require off-center mounting, or that have irregular protrusions, can be turned by utilizing this additional clearance. Otherwise, a larger lathe would be required to rotate the same workpiece. However, this does not mean that the gap-frame lathe can turn the extremes of any workpiece that can be accommodated by the larger clearance. Travel of the compound slide is restricted to the length of the ways. Therefore, as the slide approaches the headstock, it is stopped at the gap, which may not be as far as desired. This disadvantage can be partly overcome by the use of accessories that permit further travel of the tool from the compound slide. However, this involves tool overhang and decreases rigidity.

Methods of Control. Regardless of size and design, lathes are classified by method of control in operation; that is, manual, semiautomatic and automatic.

Manual lathes have no automatic controls; all operations are controlled by the operator. Manual lathes are most commonly used for one of three applications: (*a*) machining one or, at most, fewer than a dozen small parts; (*b*) producing prototypes in model shops or toolrooms; and (*c*) turning large components for which one turning cut may require one or more hours. For turning the same workpieces, setup time for manual operation is low compared with that for semiautomatic or automatic operation.

Semiautomatic lathes may vary considerably in the degree to which the operation has been automated. However, all semiautomatic machines require some operator attention during the machining cycle (in addition to loading and unloading). In some instances, the operator may be required only to initiate the action of a cross-slide tool at a specific point in the operation. In other instances, the operator may have to stop the cycle, remove the drive dog, and reverse the workpiece for the next operation in a sequence. Setup time for a semiautomatic lathe is greater than for a manual lathe but is less than for an automatic lathe.

Automatic lathes require no operator attention during the machining cycle. With most types, however, workpieces are loaded and unloaded manually. The cycle also is started manually, but the operations are completed (and the machine is stopped) automatically.

For turning several diameters on a workpiece that cannot be placed between the lathe centers but can be secured on an arbor, a logical procedure is: (*a*) operator assembles workpiece on arbor, (*b*) operator places loaded arbor in lathe and touches start button, and (*c*) machining operations take place in a predetermined sequence and lathe stops automatically. During the machining cycle, the operator prepares another workpiece-and-arbor assembly to permit immediate reloading. It is often possible (depending on the time consumed in the machining cycle) for one operator to handle two machines.

For some high-production operations, automatic lathes are available that incorporate automatic loading and unloading devices, thus demanding a minimum of operator attention. With these devices, one operator can handle two or more machines. In all instances, setup time is greater for automatic lathes than for manual or semiautomatic types.

Duplicating lathes include copying, tracer, profiling, numerical-control, and continuous-path turning lathes. All are versatile production machines and are adaptable to the turning of external and internal contours. Tracer and numerical-control lathes are the most commonly used types of duplicating lathes. Each employs a different actuating system to guide the single-point cutting tool that generates the desired profile as the workpiece is rotated.

Tracer Lathes. With tracer equipment, the tool slide is controlled by means of a sensitive stylus, usually hydraulically connected, which follows an accurate template. The template may be a finish-turned workpiece or a profile cut from a flat, thin steel plate.

Tracer equipment is available either as units to be attached to standard lathes or as complete, specially engineered machine tools. The combinations of feeds, speeds and number of cuts that can be accomplished automatically are almost unlimited. For instance, some tracer lathes can be controlled for making six or more passes to permit roughing, semifinishing and finishing. These cuts may be coordinated with three or more automatic changes of speed or feed, or both, during one machining cycle.

Tracer lathes can be equipped with two tracer units to operate from both ends or both sides of a workpiece, for completely turning the part on one machine. A fully equipped tracer lathe incorporates one or more cross slides for use in rough or finish facing, back chamfering, grooving or undercutting. Optional equipment includes automatic-positioning steady rests, and an automatic-indexing tool head that contains roughing and finishing tools.

Numerical-control lathes differ from hydraulically controlled tracer lathes primarily in that their cutting tools are controlled by an electronic remote-control system. All tool movements during cuts, as well as all tool indexing, cross-slide operations, and changes of speed and feed, are pre-engineered and programmed on a punched tape for electronic control of all machine movements. Advantages of the numerical-control lathe include low inventory of tooling (no templates are required, for example) and fully controlled cutting conditions (because speed and feed changes, for example, can be made only by reprogramming and punching the tape accordingly).

Attachments that increase the capabilities of engine lathes include:

1 **Grinding attachments**, of several types and sizes, make it possible to perform many grinding operations without removing the workpiece from the lathe. These attachments, however, do not provide the rigidity of grinding machines, and light grinding cuts therefore are advisable.
2 **Milling attachments** permit keyway cutting, T-slotting, dovetailing, angle milling, and thread milling. With one type, the cutter is held in the headstock and the workpiece is held and correctly positioned by a device attached to the cross slide. With another, the cutter and driving arrangement are mounted on the cross slide, and the workpiece is held between the lathe centers.
3 **Taper attachments** are controlled by a guide to which the cross slide is attached. This guide is adjustable to various angles, to permit turning or boring of tapers on the workpiece.
4 **Turret attachments**, of several types, may be added to engine lathes to provide them with some of the multiple-operation versatility of turret lathes.
5 **Gear-cutting attachments** make it possible to cut spur gears on an engine lathe.
6 **Ball-turning rests** replace the compound slide and enable turning or boring of spherical shapes.
7 **Contouring attachments** follow a flat or three-dimensional template or sample part by means of a servomechanism that positions the tool for turning of shafts, radii or irregular shapes.

Tools

Although form tools ground to specific shapes are frequently used to produce contours on workpieces when tool travel is limited to straight-line movement, most metal removal in lathe turning is accomplished with single-point tools.

Single-point tools may be produced from a solid bar of tool steel, by grinding the appropriate cutting edge on one end (Fig. 2a), or they may be made of less costly stock and provided with a tip, or insert, of carbide or other cutting material (Fig. 2b). The insert may be held in place mechanically, or by brazing, soldering or welding. Brazed, soldered or welded inserts are resharpened after becoming dull through use; inserts held in place mechanically are usually of the disposable (throwaway) type. (See Examples 605, 606, 640, 647 and 648 for comparisons involving disposable inserts.)

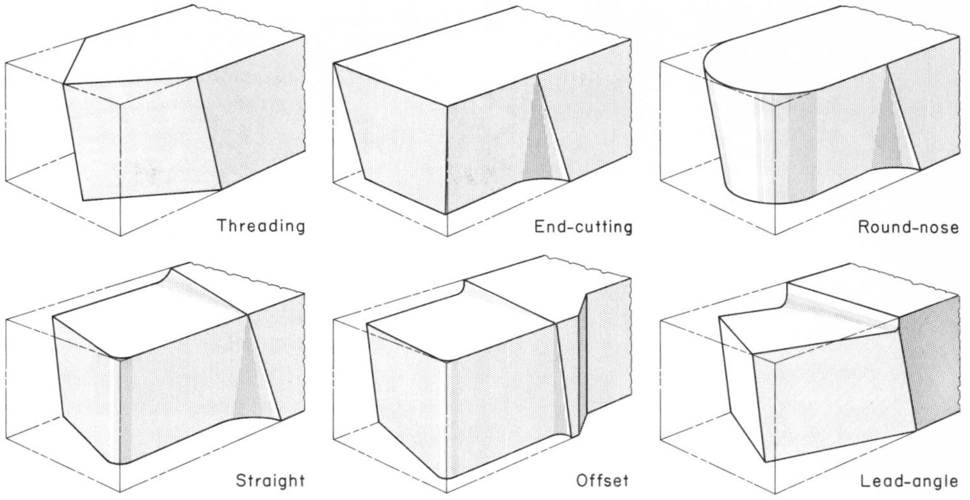

(a) Six common shapes of tools ground from solid bars

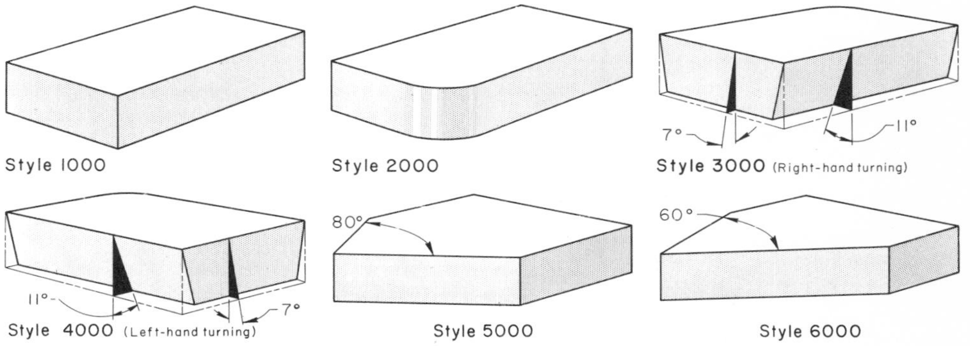

(b) Standard shapes of carbide tips

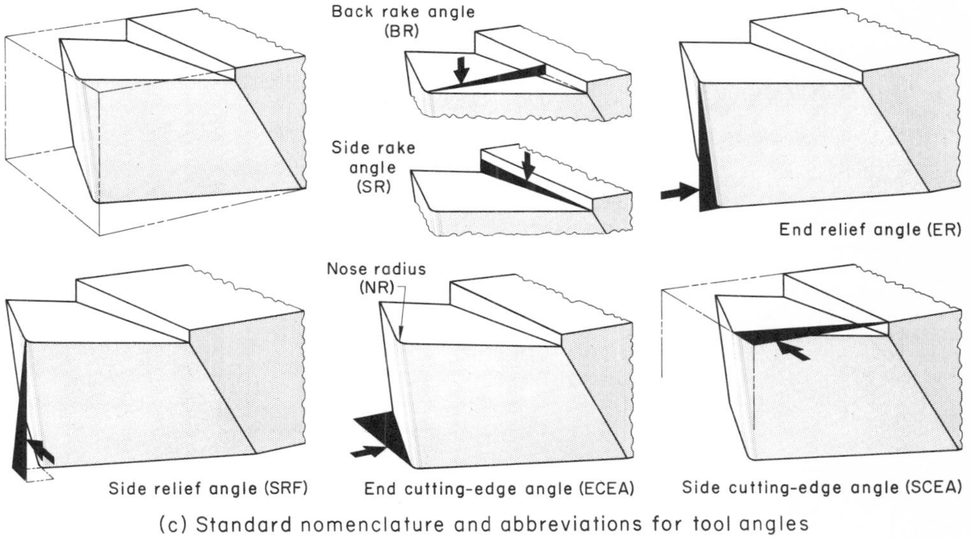

(c) Standard nomenclature and abbreviations for tool angles

Back rake angle (BR) is the angle between the cutting face of the tool and the shank or holder, measured parallel to the side of the shank or holder. The angle is positive if, as in sketch above, it slopes from the cutting point downward toward the shank, and negative if it slopes upward toward the shank.

Side rake angle (SR) is the angle between the cutting face of the tool and the shank or holder, measured perpendicular to the side of the shank or holder. The angle is positive if, as in sketch above, it slopes downward away from the cutting edge to the opposite side of the shank, and negative if it slopes upward.

End relief angle (ER) is the angle between the end face of the tool and a line drawn from the cutting edge perpendicular to the base of the shank or holder, and usually is measured at right angles to the end cutting edge.

Side relief angle (SRF) is the angle between the side flank immediately below the side cutting edge and a line drawn through the side cutting edge perpendicular to the base of the tool or tool holder, and usually is measured at right angles to the side flank.

End cutting-edge angle (ECEA) is the angle between the end cutting edge of the tool and a line perpendicular to the side of the shank.

Side cutting-edge angle (SCEA), called also "lead angle", is the angle between the side cutting edge and the projected side of the shank or holder.

Nose radius (NR) is the radius on the tool between the end and the side cutting edges.

Fig. 2. Common shapes and standard angles of single-point tools

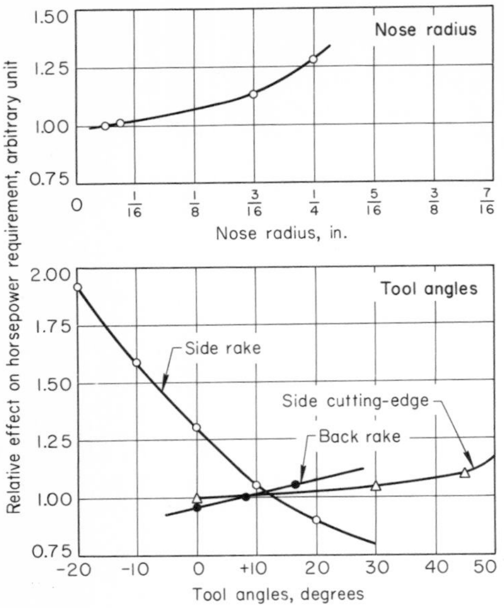

Data show effects of deviations from standard single-point tool shape of 8°, 14°, 6°, 6°, 6°, 0°, 1/16 in. (See Table 1 for identification of tool angles.) Depth of cut, 0.100 in.; feed, 0.0125 ipr.

Fig. 3. Effect of tool angles and nose radius on horsepower required for turning

Design of Single-Point Tools

Standard angles for single-point tools are illustrated and named in Fig. 2(c), and are further explained in the accompanying caption. The conventional order in which these angles are listed in specific identifications (the "tool signature") is given in Table 1.

On a single-point tool feeding to the side, the back rake (sometimes called "top rake") turns the chip away from the finished work and gives the tool a slicing action. Zero back rake makes the chip spiral more tightly, whereas a positive back rack stretches the spiral chip into a longer helix.

Side rake controls the thickness of the tool behind the cutting edge. A thick tool associated with a small rake angle provides maximum strength, but the small angle produces higher cutting forces than a larger one (Fig. 3).

The end relief angle (also called "front clearance") provides clearance between the tool and the finished surface of the work. Wear reduces the angle. If the angle is too small, the tool rubs on the surface of the work and mars the finish. If the angle is too large, the tool may dig into the work and chatter, or show weakness and fail through chipping. If the tool is set above the center of rotation, effective end relief angle is reduced; this must be considered in choosing the value.

The side relief angle provides clearance between the cut surface of the work and the flank of the tool. Tool wear reduces the effective portion of the angle close to the work. If this angle is too small, the cutter rubs and heats. If it is too large, the cutting edge is weak and the tool may dig in, particularly with a large side rake angle or with play in the feed mechanism. When threads or other helices are being cut, the effective side relief angle is reduced by the helix angle, which should be added to the recommended angle.

The end cutting-edge angle provides clearance between the cutter and the finished surface of the work. An angle too close to zero may cause chatter with heavy feeds, but for a smooth finish the angle on light finishing cuts should be small.

The side cutting-edge angle turns the chip away from the finished surface. If this angle is enlarged, the width of the chip is increased inversely with the cosine of the angle, and the chip thickness is reduced proportionately.

The nose contour, normally specified as a radius, removes the fragile corner of the tool, prolongs tool life, and improves finish. The radius may be large for maximum strength or for rough-cutting tools, but it may be reduced for light feeds. A radius too large may cause chatter, but the larger it is without chattering, the better the finish is, as discussed later, on pages 18 and 19.

Tool design influences the power required at the tool point for turning. Effects of three tool angles and the nose radius are plotted in Fig. 3; side rake angle has the greatest effect.

Tool design is particularly important in tracer-lathe turning. Because only one tool is used to make all cuts, and the minimum number of passes is desirable, the fastest rate of metal removal is used that is compatible with maintenance of dimensional and finish requirements. The use of only one cutting tool imposes severe restrictions on the shape of the tool. A tool often must be provided with a −3° side cutting-edge angle and a 30° minimum end cutting-edge angle, which results in a weak structure at the nose of the cutting edge. For this reason, heavy feed forces often must be avoided, if not already ruled out because of required finish. Thus, surface speed becomes the criterion for determining maximum rate of metal removal, and the design of the cutting tool becomes vitally important in obtaining maximum metal removal and tool life.

The influence of tool design on efficiency in turning is illustrated in the following example:

Table 1. Conventional Order of Listing Angles of Single-Point Tools in the Tool Signature

Order listed	Angle	Abbreviation
1	Back rake	BR
2	Side rake	SR
3	End relief	ER
4	Side relief	SRF
5	End cutting edge	ECEA
6	Side cutting edge	SCEA
7	Nose radius	NR

Example 1. Effective Side Rake Angle (Fig. 4)

Figure 4 shows the results of a study made in one plant to determine the influence of the effective side rake angle ("top" rake) of tungsten carbide rhomboid inserts on power requirements, tool erosion, and total tool life in turning the drive end of a rear-axle shaft in a tracer lathe. With a back rake of −7°, the three chip-breaker grinds tested (see Fig. 4) had effective side rake angles of +6°, 0°, and −7°, respectively.

The shaft, shown at the top of Fig. 4, was made from a hot rolled 1037 steel bar 3.375 in. in diameter. The drive end was machined in one automatic machine cycle that consisted of: turning the 3.366-in.-diam steady-rest section, rough turning a 3.205-in. diameter (for the 2.985-in. and 3.027-in. diameters), chamfering the end, finish turning the 2.985-in. and 3.027-in. diameters, turning the 0.12-in. radius, and one-pass turning of the 3.160-in. and 3.215-in. diameters. Depths of cut varied from 0.085 to 0.110 in. To assure a satisfactory surface finish (250 micro-in.) with tools having a 0.06-in. nose radius, feed rate was held to 0.016 ipr. Speeds were 690 and 725 sfm, for the 3.205-in. and the 3.375-in. diameters, respectively [as compared to the nominal speed of 335 sfm shown in Table 4].

Because of the high surface speeds, tool life was governed entirely by the rate of crater formation. As shown in Fig. 4, by changing the effective side rake angle from −7° to +6°, increases of 43% and 55% in tool life were obtained at 725 and 690 sfm, respectively. Also, at 725 sfm the change from negative to positive rake resulted in a 15% reduction in required horsepower.

When single-point tools of the insert type are used, tool-holder design can affect tool life, as in the next example:

Example 2. Improved Tool Holder (Fig. 5)

In profile-lathe turning the 6118 steel steering-gear sector shaft shown in Fig. 5 tool life was increased 25%, from 375 to 470 pieces, by changing the design of the holder

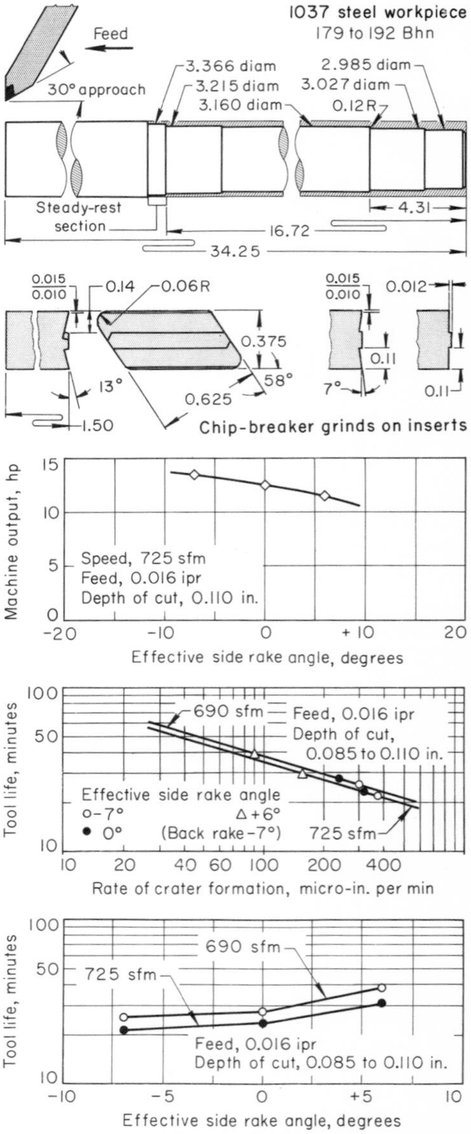

Fig. 4. Influence of effective side rake angle on horsepower consumption, rate of crater formation (tool erosion), and total tool life, in turning a 1037 steel rear-axle shaft in a tracer lathe **(Example 1)**

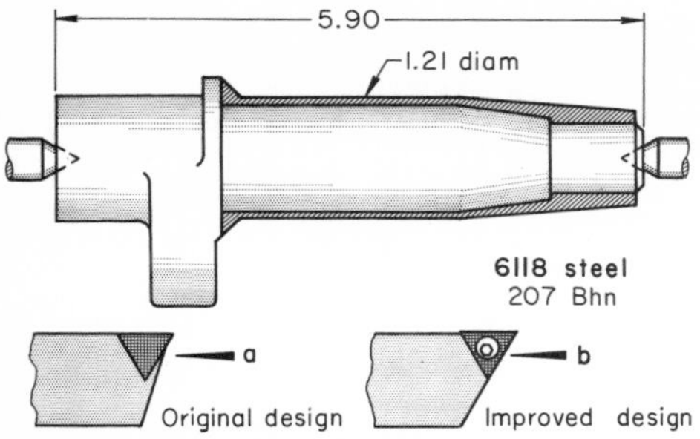

Fig. 5. Redesign of holder increased insert life 25% in turning this shaft on a profile lathe. (Example 2)

for the disposable carbide inserts used. With the holder originally used, which had standard negative rake (−5°), chip wash caused breakdown of the edge indicated as "a" in Fig. 5. After the holder had eroded sufficiently, the insert lost its support and pulled out. This problem was eliminated by redesigning the holder to use a cam lock ("b" in Fig. 5). The redesigned holder also had a −5° rake angle.

Turning speed was 1700 rpm (540 sfm), feed was 0.030 ipr, and depth of cut ranged from 0.12 to 0.25 in. [These conditions correspond to a speed about 30% above nominal and feed rate twice the nominal value given in Table 6.]

Designs of tool holders with round, square, and triangular inserts, respectively, are shown in Examples 801, 802 and 804, in the article "Machining of Heat-Resisting Alloys". A tool holder and flush-pin gage used in plunge cutting are described in Example 805 in the same article.

Cutoff Tools. Successive pieces of turned, faced or bored work frequently are separated or cut away by a radially plunging tool. Providing a front angle of about 15° on parting tools minimizes the size of the teat on the piece as it breaks off; this is not done with thin cutoff blades, because the resulting lateral force might cause the parting tool to lead sidewise.

The two examples that follow present design details of tools that have performed successfully in cutoff operations in production applications:

Examples 3 and 4. Cutoff Tools

Example 3 (Fig. 6). For martensitic and austenitic stainless steels, the carbide tool shown in Fig. 6 proved useful for various cutoff operations. Carbide was grade C-2 (88.25 W, 5.75 C, 6.0 Co). The curved back rake (5⁄16-in. radius) gave good chip control, and the 4° side cutting clearance assured desired finish. Speeds used with this tool ranged from 150 to 250 sfm; feeds were light, ranging from 0.002 to 0.003 ipr.

Example 4 (Fig. 7). The tool shown in Fig. 7 was provided with the 0.020-in.-by-5° chamfer to eliminate chipping of tool edges at breakthrough in cutoff and trimming operations on cylindrical sheet metal parts or thin-wall tubing. Other design features for this tool varied (as shown in Fig. 7) depending on whether the tool was made of steel or carbide. Carbide used was grade C-2 (88.25 W, 5.75 C, 6.0 Co).

Tools of this design were used successfully on types 410, 321 and 316 stainless steels and on A-286 alloy, for cutting walls 0.040 to 0.090 in. thick. When both ends of a cylinder required cutoff at the same setting, left-hand and right-hand tools of this design were used.

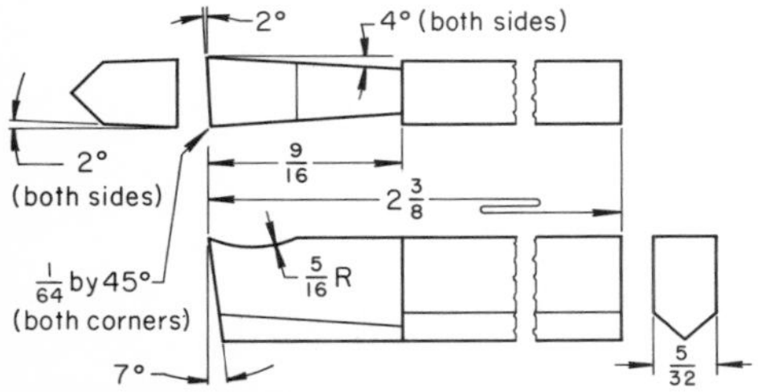

Fig. 6. Design of carbide cutoff tool for stainless steel (Example 3)

A special tool to cut off and trim tubing and deep-drawn cups of 317 stainless is shown in Example 742, in the article "Machining of Stainless Steel". Figure 9(b) in "Machining of Heat-Resisting Alloys" shows a cast alloy tool used for cutting off Inconel 600 tubing.

Facing Tools. Special attention to the elements of the tool form that turn the chip away from the work (described above under tool design) is necessary in facing cuts, to prevent the strain-hardened chips from scratching the finished surface of the work. The tool holder and tool material also may be important considerations, as in the example that follows.

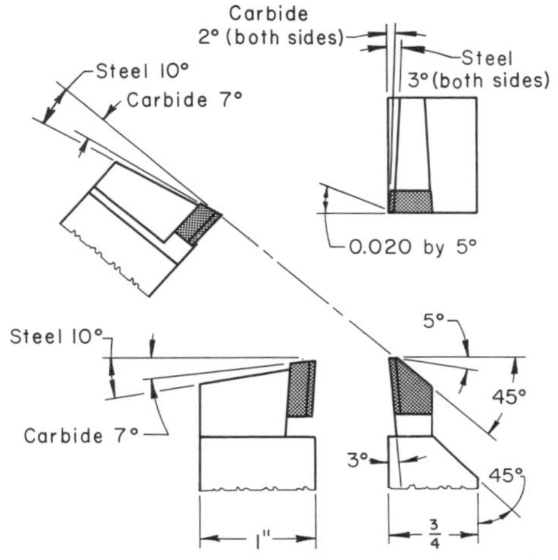

Fig. 7. Design of tool for cutoff and trimming of thin-wall cylinders and tubing. Chamfer (0.020 in. by 5°) eliminated chipping of tool edges at breakthrough. (Example 4)

Example 5. Tool and Holder for Facing (Fig. 8)

The tool holder and high speed steel insert tool shown in Fig. 8 were designed to eliminate tool breakage in interrupted facing cuts on irregularly shaped parts made of type 410 stainless steel at Rockwell C 20 to 25. In facing at a speed of 146 sfm and a feed of 0.0045 ipr, this design served to reduce cross-slide vibration caused by the intermittent cuts, and provided an acceptable finish and an average tool life of 95 pieces per grind. Tool cost per piece machined was slightly less than 1¢.

Several grades of carbide were tried, in the form of triangular inserts having a nose radius of ⅛ in. Although these could be operated at higher speeds than the high speed steel inserts, the cutting edges chipped excessively, and tooling costs were doubled.

Details of the design of single-point tools used in two applications involving multiple machining operations are given in the tabulations accompanying Fig. 24 (page 15) and Fig. 28 (page 16), in this article.

Chip Breakers. In most turning, it is preferable to break chips into small pieces rather than to permit them to form a continuous chip, because: (*a*) broken chips can be flushed away more readily by the cutting fluid, and thus tangling of stringy chips in the machine is avoided; (*b*) small, broken chips are more easily handled and stored; and (*c*) broken chips permit the cutting fluid to lubricate and cool better, thus increasing tool life.

Chips are broken by one of two methods: the chip may be bent to the limit of its ductility, or it may be jammed into a tight corner as it leaves the workpiece. The second method is seldom recommended.

In lathe turning, chips ordinarily curl across the face of the cutting tool. In some instances, particularly with brittle metals, chips break as they are deflected by the tool face. When heavier cuts are taken by increasing the feed, the thicker chip may break as it impinges against the tool face. Where the cut may not be made heavier, or the chip does not break by deflection, the tool must be provided with a chip breaker. Chip breakers may either be ground into the tool or be separate additions to the tool or tool holder. Several types of chip breakers are illustrated and described in Fig. 9. (See also Fig. 4.)

The efficiency of chip breakers is markedly affected by their design. A step that is too wide or too shallow will permit chips of the more ductile metals to flow over the intended obstruction without breaking. A step that is too narrow will cause the chips to crowd between the tool and the workpiece, resulting in galling of the turned surface and reduced tool life. Generally, the optimum width and depth of a chip breaker are governed by depth of cut and rate of feed. Usually, the depth is maintained between 0.015 and 0.030 in. The fillet radius should be two to four times the depth of the chip breaker, and the width should be eight to nine times the feed per revolution. All cutting angles of the tools should be maintained.

Chip Curlers. With ductile metals, and especially with metals that combine strength and ductility (such as annealed stainless steel), breaking of chips is often not feasible, and partic-

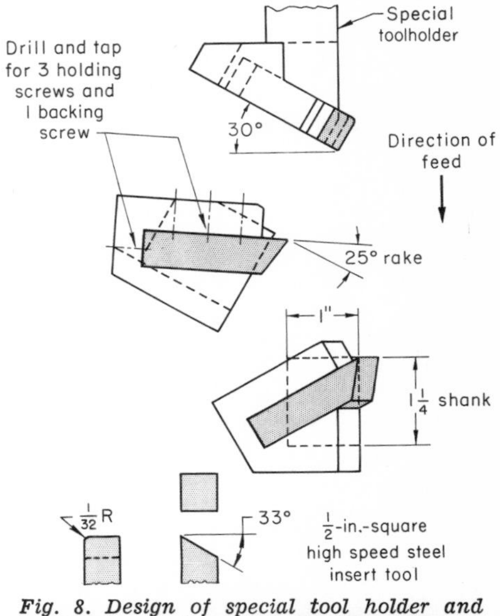

Fig. 8. Design of special tool holder and insert for interrupted facing cuts on irregularly shaped parts made of type 410 stainless steel (Example 5)

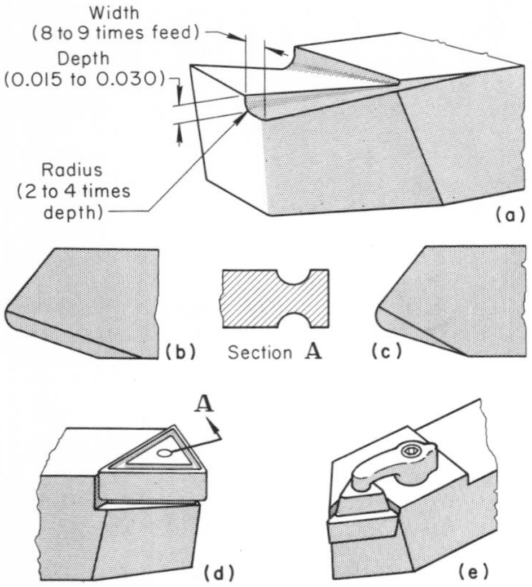

(a) Details of a typical ground-in chip breaker. (b) Parallel ground-in chip breaker. (c) Angular ground-in chip breaker. (d) Grooved chip-breaker on carbide. (e) Mechanically held chip breaker for carbide insert.

Fig. 9. Typical chip breakers for turning tools. See also Fig. 4.

ular attention must be directed to the handling of continuous curls.

The characteristics of the spiral chip and its direction of release can be regulated to some extent by adjusting rake and side cutting-edge angles. Further control can be obtained through chip-curler grooves in the tool, as illustrated in Example 6, which follows. These grooves are similar to the chip-breaker groove shown in Fig. 9(d).

Example 6. Design for Chip-Curler Groove (Fig. 10)

A box tool with a chip-curler groove of the design shown in Fig. 10(a) was not satisfactory for reducing the diameter of annealed type 304 stainless steel bar stock from 1½ to 1⅛ in. over a length of 3 in. The groove design impeded chip flow and caused crowding of the chip and breakage of tools. Adequate chip elimination was obtained when the design of the chip-curler groove was changed to that shown in Fig. 10(b). Other processing details are given in the table accompanying Fig. 10.

Speed and Feed

Carbon and low-alloy steels are classified into ten groups in Table 2. In each group the steels listed are similar with respect to the nominal speeds and feeds that are appropriate in starting to machine parts for which previous experience is lacking. Each of the ten groups of steels is identified in subsequent discussion of speed and feed by the typical steel listed in the first column.

Tables 3, 4 and 5 present nominal speeds and feeds for turning carbon and low-alloy steels at various hardness levels, using high speed steel, carbide or ceramic tools. (Similar information for turning other metals is given in articles on the machining of specific types of alloys — cast iron, stainless steel, aluminum alloys or copper alloys, for example.) These nominal values apply primarily to the turning of diameters of 1 to 3 in. and are based on a tool life of 1 to 2 hr. The tabulated values are intended to serve as starting points for the selection of optimum machining conditions. More exact settings can be made with experience. In

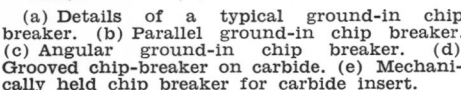

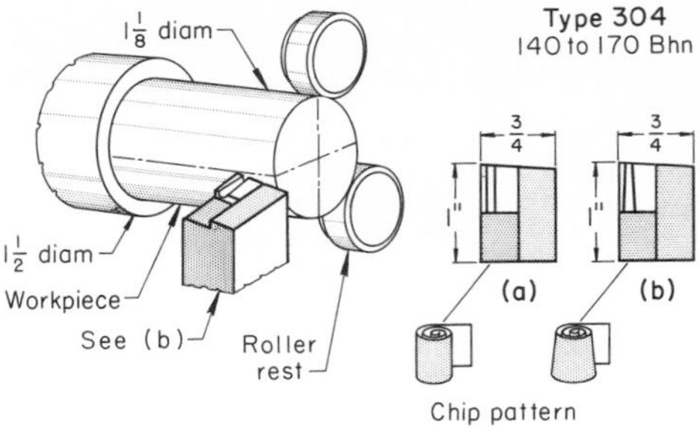

Speed	250 sfm
Feed	0.011 ipr
Metal removed per cut	3/16 in.
Cutting fluid	Mixture of soluble oil and water

NOTE: Bar stock was turned on a turret lathe with spindle capacity of 2 in. A standard carbide-tipped box tool was mounted in the turret.

Fig. 10. Box tool and improperly designed chip-curling groove (a) *and improved design* (b) (Example 6)

commercial practice, speeds and feeds often differ widely from the values given in Tables 3, 4 and 5. The magnitude of these differences is illustrated in Table 6, which compares nominal values of speed and feed from Tables 3 and 4 with the actual values used in turning carbon and low-alloy steels in the examples included in this article. The factors responsible for large deviations from nominal values are considered in the individual examples.

Selection of Speed and Feed. The nominal speed and feed shown in Table 3, 4 or 5 for a given application reflect only the effect of steel group (general chemical type), hardness, type of operation, and tool material. The final selection of speed and feed is usually made on the basis of experience with similar parts or from production trials, and is influenced by: (*a*) work metal, (*b*) type of operation, (*c*) tool material, (*d*) tool design, (*e*) shape of workpiece, (*f*) tool life desired, (*g*) machine condition, (*h*) power of available machines, and (*i*) surface finish required.

Work Metal. With the exception of free-cutting additions, the *direct* effect of chemical composition on optimum speed and feed is small and of little significance in comparison with the normal variation in properties of commercial grades of steel or the larger changes that can be obtained by heat treatment or by cold reduction. Accordingly, all of the carbon and low-alloy steels except free-cutting grades are grouped together in Tables 3, 4 and 5.

Free-cutting grades are usually produced by the addition of 0.10 to 0.30% sulfur or 0.20 to 0.30% lead (or both) to carbon or low-alloy steel (see Table 2). Except at high hardness, the nominal turning speeds for resulfurized or leaded carbon steels shown in Tables 3, 4 and 5 are substantially higher than the values for corresponding plain carbon steels. (See also Examples 309 to 314.) A similar but somewhat smaller increase in permissible speed results from additions of sulfur or lead to low-alloy steels, as compared with corresponding plain low-alloy steels.

Table 7 compares speed-feed-depth relations for a resulfurized free-cutting steel (1112) and a plain carbon steel (1020), using high speed steel tools for 60-min tool life. Over a range of feed

Table 2. Groups of Carbon and Low-Alloy Steels Referred to in Tables of Nominal Speeds and Feeds

Typical steel	Other steels in the group
	Carbon Steels (Low Carbon)
1020	1006, 1008, 1009, 1010, 1012, 1015, 1016, 1017, 1018, 1019, 1021, 1022, 1023, 1024, 1025, 1026
	Carbon Steels (Medium and High Carbon)
1045	1027, 1030, 1033, 1034, 1035, 1036, 1037, 1038, 1039, 1040, 1041, 1042, 1043, 1046, 1049, 1050, 1052, 1055, 1060, 1062, 1064, 1065, 1066, 1070, 1074, 1078, 1080, 1084, 1085, 1086, 1090, 1095
	Resulfurized (Free-Cutting) Low-Carbon Steels
1112	1111, 1113, 1119, 1212, 1213, 1213+Te
1117	1108, 1109, 1115, 1118, 1120, 1126, 1144, 1211
	Resulfurized (Free-Cutting) Medium-Carbon Steels
1137	1132, 1138, 1139, 1140, 1141, 1145, 1146, 1151
	Leaded (Free-Cutting) Low-Carbon Steels
12L14	10L18, 10L20, 12L13
	Low-Alloy Steels (Medium and High Carbon)
4140	1330, 1332, 1335, 1340, 1345, 2330, 2335, 2340, 2345, 3130, 3135, 3140, 3141, 3145, 3150, 4030, 4032, 4037, 4042, 4047, 4063, 4130, 4135, 4137, 4142, 4145, 4147, 4150, 4337, 4340, 4640, 50B40, 50B44, 5046, 50B46, 50B50, 50B60, 5075, 5080, 5130, 5132, 5135, 5140, 5145, 5147, 5150, 5155, 5160, 51B60, 50100, 51100, 52100, 6145, 6150, 6180, 6240, 6250, 6260, 6270, 6290, 6342, 6382, 6440, 6475, 81B45, 8630, 8637, 8640, 8642, 8645, 86B45, 8650, 8655, 8660, 8740, 8742, 9255, 9260, 9262, 94B30, 94B40, 9445, 9840, 9845, 9850
	Resulfurized (Free-Cutting) Low-Alloy Steels
4140+S	Same steels as in group following 4140, but with sulfur added
	Leaded (Free-Cutting) Low-Alloy Steels
41L40	41L30, 41L47, 41L50, 43L47, 51L32, 86L20, 86L40, 52L100
	Low-Alloy Nitriding Steels
7140	All grades
	Low-Alloy Carburizing Steels
8620	1320, 2317, 2512, 2515, 2517, 3115, 3120, 3125, 3310, 3316, 4012, 4017, 4023, 4024, 4027, 4028, 4118, 4125, 4128, 4317, 4320, 4608, 4615, 4617, 4620, 4621, 4720, 4815, 4817, 4820, 5015, 5020, 5024, 5120, 6118, 6120, 6317, 6325, 6415, 8115, 8615, 8617, 8622, 8625, 8627, 8720, 8822, 9310, 9315, 94B15, 94B17

rate and depth of cut, turning speed for the 1112 steel was about twice that for a comparable operation on 1020 steel.

Carbon and other alloying elements in carbon and low-alloy steels have only a small *direct* effect on speed and feed in turning. Plain carbon steels containing less than about 0.15% carbon machine to give soft, gummy chips that are likely to adhere to the cutting tool, and these steels require relatively low speed and feed. Up to about 0.25% carbon, optimum speed and feed increase with increasing carbon content, because of the corresponding decrease in chip ductility. A further rise in carbon content leads to the use of lower speed and feed, because of greatly increased strength, hardness and abrasive characteristics of the metal. The addition of other alloying elements lowers optimum speed and feed by increasing the strength and hardness of the metal. These effects of chemical composition on optimum speed and feed are too small to affect the nominal values in Tables 3, 4 and 5.

Hardness exerts a major effect on the selection of speed and feed. In fact, as a first approximation, speed and feed for turning carbon and low-alloy steels (in the absence of free-cutting additives) can be considered as functions of hardness only; nominal speed and feed values are identical at equal hardness.

Figure 11 shows the effect of hardness on speed and feed for rough and finish turning of hardened steel

Table 3. Nominal Speeds and Feeds for Turning of Carbon and Low-Alloy Steels With High Speed Steel Tools (a)

Typical steel (b)	Brinell hardness	Single-point and box tools, Speed, sfm: Roughing (0.150-in. cut; feed, 0.015 ipr)	Single-point and box tools, Speed, sfm: Finishing (0.025-in. cut; feed, 0.007 ipr)	Form tools: Speed, sfm	Form tools: Feed (ipr) for tool width (in.) of: 0.500	1.000	2.000	Cutoff tools: Speed, sfm	Cutoff tools: Feed (ipr) for tool width (in.) of: 0.062	0.125	0.250
Carbon and Low-Alloy Steels (Except Free-Cutting Grades)											
1020, 1045, 4140, 7140 and 8620, at hardness ranges listed at right	85 to 125	135	180	100	0.0025	0.0015	0.001	100	0.0015	0.002	0.0025
	125 to 175	110	150	80	0.0025	0.0015	0.001	80	0.0015	0.002	0.0025
	175 to 225	90	125	65	0.0025	0.0015	0.001	65	0.0015	0.002	0.0025
	225 to 275	75	105	55	0.0015	0.001	0.0007	55	0.001	0.0015	0.002
	275 to 325	65	85	50	0.0015	0.001	0.0007	50	0.001	0.0015	0.002
	325 to 375	55	70	40	0.0015	0.001	0.0007	40	0.001	0.001	0.0015
	375 to 425	40 (c)	55 (d)	30	0.001	0.0007	0.0005	30	0.001	0.001	0.001
	Rc 50 to 52	20 (c)	30 (d)	...	...	...	...	...	...	...	...
Free-Cutting Carbon and Low-Alloy Steels											
1112, 12L14	100 to 150	155	205	115	0.003	0.0025	0.0015	115	0.002	0.0025	0.003
	150 to 200	170	230	125	0.003	0.0025	0.0015	125	0.002	0.0025	0.003
	200 to 250	105	145	80	0.0025	0.002	0.001	80	0.0015	0.002	0.0025
1117	100 to 150	140	180	105	0.003	0.0025	0.0015	105	0.002	0.0025	0.003
	150 to 200	150	205	110	0.003	0.0025	0.0015	110	0.002	0.0025	0.003
1137	175 to 225	130	190	95	0.003	0.0025	0.0015	95	0.002	0.0025	0.003
	275 to 325	90	110	70	0.0015	0.001	0.0007	70	0.001	0.0015	0.002
	325 to 375	55	70	40	0.0015	0.001	0.0007	40	0.001	0.001	0.0015
	375 to 425	40	55	30	0.001	0.0007	0.0005	30	0.001	0.001	0.001
4140+S and 41L40	150 to 200	115	160	80	0.003	0.0025	0.0015	80	0.002	0.0025	0.003
	200 to 250	95	135	70	0.0025	0.002	0.001	65	0.001	0.002	0.0025
	275 to 325	70	90	50	0.0015	0.001	0.0007	50	0.001	0.0015	0.002
	375 to 425	40 (c)	55 (d)	30	0.001	0.0007	0.0005	30	0.001	0.001	0.001
	Rc 48 to 50	25 (c)	35 (d)	...	...	...	...	...	...	...	...

NOTE: Table 6 contains a comparison of actual speeds and feeds used in examples in this article with the nominal values in this table; see the text for a discussion of the conditions that affect speeds and feeds.

(a) High speed steels M2 and T5, except that the more highly alloyed steels T15, M41, M42, M43 and M44 are often used for turning steel harder than about 225 Bhn. (b) Each steel listed is a frequently used grade in a group of similar steels. For a listing of the steels in the various groups, see Table 2 in this article. (c) Feed, 0.010 ipr. (d) Feed, 0.005 ipr. (Source of data: same as for Table 4)

Table 4. Nominal Speeds and Feeds for Turning of Carbon and Low-Alloy Steels With Carbide Tools (a)

Typical steel (b)	Brinell hardness	Speed, sfm: Single-point and box tools, Brazed: Roughing (0.150-in. cut; feed, 0.015 ipr)	Brazed: Finishing (0.025-in. cut; feed, 0.007 ipr)	Disposable: Roughing (0.150-in. cut; feed, 0.015 ipr)	Disposable: Finishing (0.025-in. cut; feed, 0.007 ipr)	Form tools: Speed, sfm	Form tools: Feed (ipr) for tool width (in.) of: 0.500	1.000	2.000	Cutoff tools: Speed, sfm	Cutoff tools: Feed (ipr) for tool width (in.) of: 0.062	0.125	0.250
Carbon and Low-Alloy Steels (Except Free-Cutting Grades)													
1020, 1045, 4140, 7140 and 8620, at hardness ranges listed at right	85 to 125	460	540	600	675	345	0.005	0.0035	0.0025	345	0.0035	0.006	0.0075
	125 to 175	380	450	465	590	285	0.005	0.0035	0.0025	285	0.0045	0.006	0.0075
	175 to 225	335	420	420	525	250	0.005	0.0035	0.0025	250	0.0045	0.006	0.0075
	225 to 275	310	390	395	475	230	0.003	0.0025	0.0015	230	0.003	0.0045	0.006
	275 to 325	270	350	340	440	200	0.003	0.0025	0.0015	200	0.003	0.0045	0.006
	325 to 375	225	290	275	365	170	0.003	0.002	0.0015	170	0.003	0.003	0.0045
	375 to 425	175	225	215	280	130	0.0025	0.0015	0.001	130	0.002	0.002	0.003
	Rc 50 to 52	100 (c)	125 (d)	125 (c)	150 (d)	...	...	...	...	...	...	...	...
	Rc 54 to 56	60 (d)	75 (d)	70 (d)	90 (d)	...	...	...	...	...	...	...	...
Free-Cutting Carbon and Low-Alloy Steels													
1112, 1117 and 12L14, at hardness ranges listed at right	100 to 150	550	735	685	925	410	0.007	0.006	0.004	410	0.007	0.008	0.009
	150 to 200	610	820	750	1010	460	0.007	0.006	0.004	460	0.007	0.008	0.009
	200 to 250	360	435	440	550	270	0.005	0.004	0.002	270	0.005	0.006	0.007
1137	175 to 225	490	710	610	890	370	0.007	0.006	0.004	370	0.007	0.008	0.009
	275 to 325	340	415	425	520	255	0.003	0.0025	0.0015	255	0.0035	0.0045	0.006
	325 to 375	225	290	275	365	170	0.003	0.002	0.0015	170	0.003	0.003	0.0045
	375 to 425	175	225	215	280	130	0.0025	0.0015	0.001	130	0.002	0.002	0.003
4140+S and 41L40	150 to 200	400	475	500	600	300	0.007	0.006	0.004	300	0.007	0.008	0.009
	275 to 325	300	385	375	470	225	0.003	0.0025	0.0015	225	0.0035	0.0045	0.006
	375 to 425	175	225	215	280	130	0.0025	0.0015	0.001	130	0.002	0.002	0.003
	Rc 48 to 50	120 (c)	140 (d)	150 (c)	175 (d)	...	...	...	...	...	...	...	...
	Rc 52 to 54	75 (e)	85 (d)	90 (e)	105 (d)	...	...	...	...	...	...	...	...

NOTE: Table 6 contains a comparison of actual speeds and feeds used in examples in this article with the nominal values in this table; see the text for a discussion of the conditions that affect speeds and feeds.

(a) For carbide grades C-6 and C-7, except that grade C-8 is more suitable for turning steel harder than about Rc 48. (b) Each steel listed is a frequently used grade in a group of similar steels. For a listing of the steels in the various groups, see Table 2 in this article. (c) Feed, 0.010 ipr. (d) Feed, 0.005 ipr. (e) Feed, 0.007 ipr. (Data are adapted from tables compiled by Metcut Research Associates, Inc.)

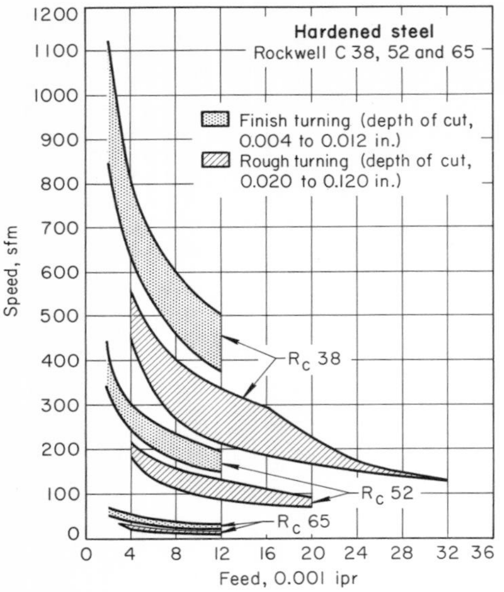

Speed and feed combinations for 60-min tool life. Data are based on turning with carbide tools (79 WC, 15 TiC, 6 Co) lapped with boron carbide. Tools for steels of all hardnesses had 45° side cutting-edge angle, 15° end cutting-edge angle, 0.040-in. nose radius, 0° side rake, and relief angle of either 15° (for 0.008 ipr or less) or 10° (for feeds over 0.008 ipr). Back rake varied with hardness, being 0° for Rc 38, —5° for Rc 52, and —10° for Rc 65.

Fig. 11. Effect of hardness on speeds and feeds used in rough and finish turning

Table 5. Nominal Speeds and Feeds for Turning of Carbon and Low-Alloy Steels With Ceramic Tools(a)

Brinell hardness	Rough turning (depth of cut, over 0.062 in.) Speed, sfm	Rough turning Feed, ipr	Finish turning (depth of cut, under 0.062 in.) Speed, sfm	Finish turning Feed, ipr
Carbon and Low-Alloy Steels, Except Free-Cutting Grades (Typical steels: 1020, 1045, 4140, 7140 and 8620)				
85 to 125	450 to 1300	0.005 to 0.020	650 to 1600	0.004 to 0.010
125 to 175	450 to 1300	0.005 to 0.020	550 to 1550	0.004 to 0.010
175 to 225	350 to 1000	0.005 to 0.020	450 to 1200	0.004 to 0.010
225 to 275	300 to 900	0.005 to 0.020	400 to 1100	0.004 to 0.010
275 to 325	300 to 800	0.005 to 0.020	350 to 900	0.004 to 0.010
Free-Cutting Carbon and Low-Alloy Steels (Typical steels: 1112, 1117, 1137, 12L14, 4140+S and 41L40)				
100 to 150	600 to 1600	0.005 to 0.020	1000 to 2200	0.004 to 0.010
150 to 200	500 to 1500	0.005 to 0.020	900 to 1900	0.004 to 0.010
200 to 250	400 to 1200	0.005 to 0.020	800 to 1800	0.004 to 0.010
275 to 325	400 to 1000	0.005 to 0.020	500 to 1500	0.004 to 0.010
All Steels Listed Above, at Higher Hardness				
325 to 375	250 to 650	0.005 to 0.015	300 to 800	0.004 to 0.010
375 to 425	200 to 600	0.005 to 0.015	250 to 700	0.004 to 0.010
Rc 45 to 48	175 to 550	0.005 to 0.012	225 to 650	0.004 to 0.008
Rc 48 to 52	150 to 500	0.004 to 0.010	200 to 600	0.003 to 0.006
Rc 52 to 56	100 to 350	0.003 to 0.008	150 to 500	0.003 to 0.006

(a) Each typical steel listed is a frequently used grade in a group of similar steels. For a listing of the steels in the various groups, see Table 2 in this article. (Data are adapted from tables compiled by Metcut Research Associates, Inc.)

(quenched and tempered to Rockwell C 38, 52 and 65), regardless of variation in composition. As hardness increases, speed and feed for rough turning decrease, speed for finish turning decreases, and the ranges of speed and feed become progressively narrower.

Figure 12 shows a decrease in speed and feed with increasing hardness (Rockwell C 15, 47 and 52) and also shows the resulting decrease in metal removal rate and tool life and the increase in machining cost.

The effect of a difference in hardness associated with carbon content is illustrated by the comparison in Table 7 of turning speeds for 60-min tool life for hot rolled 1020 steel (127 Bhn) and hot rolled 1050 steel (201 Bhn). Over a wide range of feed and depth of cut, the speed shown for 1050 is about half that for a comparable operation on 1020.

Other Metallurgical Considerations. The need for low speed and feed in turning annealed carbon steel of low carbon content results principally from microstructural considerations. Higher speed and feed can be employed after normalizing or oil quenching such steels. Cold reduction of low-carbon steel also permits higher speed and feed by lowering chip ductility.

Medium-carbon and high-carbon steels also can be heat treated to allow higher speed and feed; the most machinable microstructures for various carbon contents are listed on page 303 in Volume 1 of this Handbook.

The presence of manganese, chromium, nickel or molybdenum in the carbide phase of low-alloy steel affects machining behavior in the same way as does the presence of carbon; in solid solution alloying elements toughen and strengthen the ferrite phase, thus reducing permissible speed and feed.

For further information on the effect of metallurgical factors in the machining of steel, see pages 302 to 316 in Volume 1 of this Handbook.

Type of Operation. For a given work metal, speed is highest for turning with single-point or box tools, and feed is also relatively high for this type of operation. Higher speed and lower feed are used for shallow finishing cuts with these tools than for roughing cuts (Tables 3, 4 and 5). As shown in Table 4, brazed carbide tools are used at lower speeds than disposable carbide tools, primarily to increase tool life and thereby minimize tool changing.

Speeds for turning with form tools or cutoff tools are usually about 40 to 60% of the finish-turning speed with single-point tools. Feed rate in form turning varies inversely with tool width, as would be expected, but feed rate for cutoff turning varies directly with tool width, for the range of widths shown. Feed rate is usually lower for these tools than for single-point or box tools.

Tool Material. Tables 3, 4 and 5 show ranges of nominal speed for the three basic tool materials as: high speed steel, 20 to 230 sfm; carbide, 60 to 1010 sfm; and ceramic, 100 to 2200 sfm. Nominal feeds range as follows:

Single-Point and Box Tools

High speed steel	0.005 to 0.015 ipr
Carbide	0.005 to 0.015
Ceramic	0.003 to 0.020

Form Tools

High speed steel	0.0005 to 0.003
Carbide	0.001 to 0.007

Cutoff Tools

High speed steel	0.001 to 0.003
Carbide	0.002 to 0.009

High speed steel cutting tools — although versatile, shock-resistant, and readily forged and machined to a wide variety of forms — are limited to relatively low turning speeds. Although carbide tools are more economical than high speed steel tools in most high-production turning applications, they require a rigid setup and freedom from chatter, to avoid chipping or breaking, and they do not perform well at low turning speed. Ceramic tools are used at still higher speeds, but they are subject to the limitations of carbide

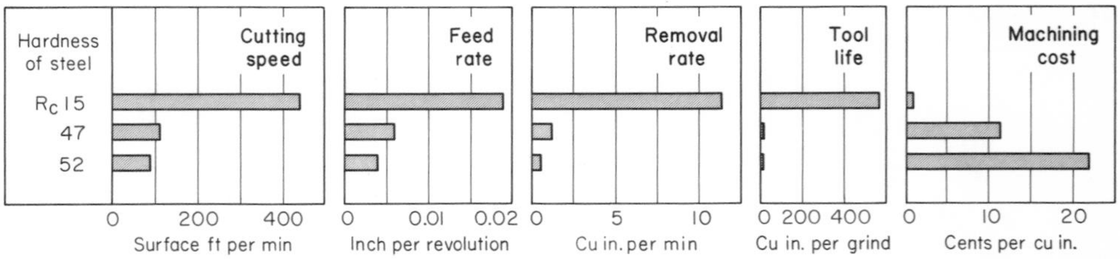

Condition or result	Rockwell C hardness of steel turned(a) Rc 15	Rc 47	Rc 52
Machining Conditions			
Speed, rpm	1090	350	226
Speed, sfm	445	115	90
Feed, ipr	0.019	0.006	0.004
Depth of cut, in.	0.120	0.120	0.120
Cutting fluid	None	(b)	(b)
Results, Based on Metal Removal			
Rate, cu in. per min ..	11.5	1.24	0.62
Tool life, cu in.(c) ...	576.0	18.6	17.0
Cost per cu in.	$0.010	$0.115	$0.220

Footnotes

(a) Steels were 4130 at Rockwell C 15, 4330 at Rockwell C 47, and 4340 at Rockwell C 52. All three steels were turned on a 16-in. lathe with C-6 carbide (77 W, 8 Ti, 7 C, 8 Co) tool bits ½-in. IC by 3⁄16 in. All tools had —7° back and side rake angles, +7° end and side relief angles, 15° side cutting-edge angle, and 0.030-in. nose radius; height above center was 0.005 in. (b) 1-to-1 mixture of sulfurized oil and mineral oil. (c) Amount of metal removed before tool developed wear land of 0.018 in. and thus required resharpening or replacement.

Fig. 12. Effect of hardness on speed, feed and results in turning

tools in greater degree. Cast cobalt-base alloy tools are usually operated at speeds intermediate between those used with high speed steel tools and carbide tools, but have only a narrow range of application, chiefly where tool temperatures are high and cooling is not feasible.

Data on the relative performance of different tool materials in several turning applications are given in "Selection of Material for Cutting Tools", page 325. See also entries under *Tool Material Comparisons* in the index.

In multiple-tool setups, advantage is sometimes taken of the relation between optimum speed and tool material in machining two or more diameters at the same spindle speed. For instance, on a workpiece having a 1-in. diameter and a 4-in. diameter, both diameters could not be turned efficiently with the same tool material at the same time. If the speed were selected for the larger diameter, it would be too slow for the smaller diameter, and vice versa. However, both diameters can be turned efficiently at the same time when a high speed steel tool is used for the 1-in. diameter and a carbide tool for the 4-in. diameter.

Tool Design. Single-point tools have already been described in a general way. Figure 2 shows the common shapes and defines the standard angles for these tools, and the function of each tool angle is explained under "Design of Single-Point Tools", pages 4 to 6. The effects of tool angles and nose radius on power requirements are illustrated in Fig. 3. Permissible speed becomes greater as nose radius is increased, up to the radius at which chatter begins. The effect on speed is most pronounced for shallow cuts, and speed is inversely related to feed.

The same relations hold for side cutting-edge angle, up to the angle at which chatter is encountered. This limiting angle is usually above 30° (tool shank perpendicular to work surface) and is lowest for deep cuts and low feeds.

As side rake angle (or back rake angle in end-cutting applications) is increased, speed increases at first and then decreases. The side rake angle for which speed is a maximum varies with the operation, but usually is in the range of 8° to 22°. Side cutting-edge angle and side rake angle for a given speed are likely to be lower in turning hard steel than in turning soft steel.

The remaining standard angles of single-point tools have little or no effect on speed and feed.

The effect of nose radius on speed and feed is illustrated in Tables 8 and 9, where speeds corresponding to 60-min tool life are tabulated over a range of feed and depth of cut for nose radii of 0, 1/16, 1/8 and 1/4 in. As mentioned previously, speed can be increased as nose radius is increased, and speeds for carbide tools are about three times those for high speed steel tools. Speeds for the finishing tool are relatively high, in spite of the 0° side rake and side cutting-edge angles, in order to produce a smooth surface.

Configuration of the workpiece, or of that portion of the workpiece being machined, sometimes influences optimum speed or feed (or both), as demonstrated in the following example:

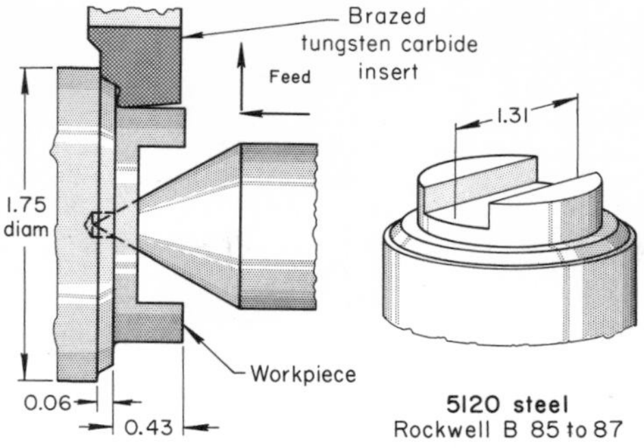

Spindle speed	3000 rpm
Surface speed:	
Turned diameter	1025 sfm
Formed diameter	1375 sfm
Feed	0.012 ipr (a)
Depth of cut:	
Turned diameter	0.025 in.
Formed diameter	0.225 in.
Cutting fluid	None (a)
Tool life per insert (b)	500 pieces (a)

(a) At the 0.005-ipr feed originally used, with water-soluble oil cutting fluid, tool life per insert was only 30 to 45 pieces.
(b) Three adjustments were made between tool changes, to maintain the specified dimensional tolerance.

Fig. 13. Interrupted-cut turning operation in which tool life was increased by use of heavier feed and elimination of cutting fluid (Example 7)

Example 7. Heavier Feed for Interrupted Cutting (Fig. 13)

In turning and forming the workpiece illustrated in Fig. 13, the tool was subjected to severe interrupted cutting (two wide interruptions per revolution) for about two-thirds of the turned length. [Surface speeds are much higher than the nominal values (see comparison in Table 6) because of the interrupted cutting.] At a feed rate of 0.005 ipr, and with the workpiece flooded with soluble-oil cutting fluid, life of the brazed carbide inserts used was unacceptably low (30 to 45 parts per insert). Tools failed from edge chipping.

Without any other processing changes, raising the feed to 0.012 ipr and eliminating the cutting fluid (which resulted in higher working temperatures) increased tool life to 500 parts per insert. Processing details are given with Fig. 13.

When large and small diameters are to be machined within the same cycle, a change in speed during the cycle may be necessary to provide the most suitable speed for each diameter. This can be accomplished by the use of a two-speed drive motor or, more effectively, by the use of an electronically controlled variable-speed unit:

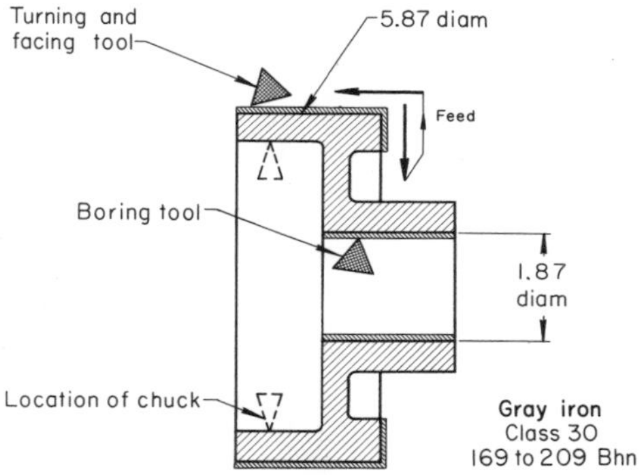

Item	Two-speed motor 5.87-in. OD	Two-speed motor 1.87-in. ID	Variable speed control 5.87-in. OD	Variable speed control 1.87-in. ID
Speed, rpm	280	560	280	775
Speed, sfm	430	275	430	380
Feed, ipr	0.012	0.014	0.012	0.018
Depth of cut, in.	0.020	0.020	0.020	0.020
Machine cycle, sec	105		80	

Fig. 14. Comparison of machining conditions and cycle time using two-speed motor versus variable speed control (Example 8)

Example 8. Variable Speed Control Reduces Machining Time (Fig. 14)

The gray iron casting shown in Fig. 14 was consecutively turned on the 5.87-in. diameter and bored on the 1.87-in. diameter. Originally, the lathe on which these operations were performed was powered by a two-speed motor rated at 1800 and 900 rpm. By providing the lathe with a variable speed control, a more nearly optimum speed could be used for the 1.87-in. diameter, and this resulted in about

Table 6. Comparison of Actual and Nominal Speeds and Feeds for Turning of Carbon and Low-Alloy Steels (a)

Example No. (a)	Steel	Average hardness, Bhn	Comparable steel in Table 3 or 4	Operation	Tool Material	Tool Type	Speed, sfm Actual (a)	Speed, sfm Nominal (b)	Feed, ipr Actual (a)	Feed, ipr Nominal (b)
1	1037	186	1045	Roughing	Carbide	Brazed	725	335	0.016	0.015
2	6118	207	8620	Roughing	Carbide	Disposable	540	420	0.030	0.015
7	5120	167	8620	Finishing	Carbide	Brazed	1025	450	0.012	0.007
				Forming (c)	Carbide	Brazed	1375	280	0.012	0.005
9	1045	194	1045	Roughing	Carbide	Brazed	430	335	0.016	0.015
				Roughing	Carbide	Brazed	530	335	0.018	0.015
13	4130	318	4140	Finishing	Carbide	Brazed	190	350	0.004	0.007
				Finishing	Carbide	Brazed	270	350	0.004	0.007
18	4820	228	8620	Roughing	HSS	...	83	75	0.010	0.015
				Roughing	Carbide	Disposable	405	395	0.014	0.015
20	8622	187	8620	Roughing	HSS	...	115	90	0.012	0.015
				Roughing	Carbide	Disposable	655	420	0.010	0.015
21	4320	227	8620	Roughing	Carbide	Brazed	392	310	0.015	0.015
25	1035	150	1045	Roughing	Carbide	Brazed	495	380	0.020	0.015
26	1141	207	1137	Roughing	Carbide	Brazed	540	490	0.008	0.015
27	8620	169	8620	Finishing	Carbide	Brazed	639	450	0.008	0.007
				Finishing	Carbide	Brazed	1125	450	0.008	0.007

(a) From examples that appear in this article. (b) From Table 3 or 4. (c) Tool width, 0.500 in.

Table 7. Comparison of Cutting Speeds for 60-Min Tool Life in Turning Three Different Hot Rolled Steels With T1 High Speed Steel Tools(a)

Depth of cut, in.	Speed (sfm) for feed (ipr) of: 0.002	0.004	0.008	1/64	1/32	1/16	1/8
1112 Steel (130 Bhn)							
1/32 ...	2004	1290	816	540	363	255	219
1/16 ...	1401	930	597	390	258	186	150
1/8	1215	774	534	327	216	150	114
1/4	1107	690	444	288	189	129	93
1/2	1038	654	411	267	171	111	75
1	999	627	396	252	159	99	63
1020 Steel (127 Bhn)							
1/32 ...	944	607	384	254	171	120	103
1/16	660	438	281	184	114	88	71
1/8	572	364	251	154	102	71	54
1/4	521	325	209	136	89	61	44
1/2	489	308	194	126	80	52	35
1	471	295	187	119	75	47	30
1050 Steel (201 Bhn)							
1/32 ...	464	298	189	125	84	59	51
1/16 ...	324	215	138	90	60	43	35
1/8	281	179	124	76	50	35	26
1/4	254	160	103	67	44	30	22
1/2	240	151	95	62	40	26	17
1	231	145	92	58	37	23	15

(a) Tool angles: BR, 8°; SR, 14°; ER, 6°; SRF, 6°; ECEA, 6°; SCEA, 30°; NR, 1/8 in. No cutting fluid used. (Source of data for this table: ASME Manual on Cutting of Metals, 2nd Ed, 1952)

a 25% reduction in machine cycle time. Comparative data for the two methods are presented in the table that accompanies Fig. 14. [In some applications of this kind, simultaneous turning with a carbide tool and boring with a high speed steel tool is efficient.]

Tool Life Desired. Analyses are often made with specific setups to determine the optimum feed and speed for maximum tool life, because tool life is many times more sensitive to changes in cutting speed than to any other single factor. However, it is common practice to sacrifice some tool life by purposely increasing speeds (often by as much as 50%) to shorten cycle time and increase productivity. This practice is most often used when tools can be changed readily, with a minimum of downtime.

In any specific application, however, over-all cost must be examined to determine whether the gains in productivity outweigh the added cost of sharpening or replacing tools. Details of a cost-and-productivity analysis are given in the following example:

Example 9. Decrease in Over-All Cost Despite 50% Lower Tool Life (Fig. 15)

The speed initially used to meet production requirements in turning the 1045 steel shaft shown in Fig. 15 was somewhat higher than the nominal value (see comparison in Table 6). It was found that a further increase in speed and a 13% increase in feed enabled a 30% increase in production rate and a 5% decrease in over-all cost, in spite of a 50% drop in tool life.

This part was turned from a hot rolled bar 1.875 in. in diameter by 37.78 in. long. Depth of cut ranged from 0.026 to 0.150 in. The outside diameter was turned completely and grooved on a two-machine battery of copying lathes. Processing and cost data for the original and improved methods are compared in the table accompanying Fig. 15.

Machine Condition. Lathes that are worn may require the use of lower than normal speeds and feeds, mainly because they will develop chatter more readily than machines in good condition. It is not good practice to use worn machines, but at times there is no alternative, and processing must then be modified to accommodate the condition of the equipment.

Horsepower of available machines may limit the speeds and feeds to be used. It may be necessary to turn a part at less than the optimum speed, or to reduce the feed, because adequate power is not available. If purchase of an adequately powered machine is not economically practical, compromises must be made. By reducing the feed, speed may be maintained, but the penalty, of course, is a longer machining cycle.

Surface finish is influenced by feed rate per revolution and by the nose radius of the tool, as discussed in the section on Surface Finish in this article (page 17). For parts that require a tool having a small nose radius (for example, to maintain a small radius between a shaft diameter and a shoulder), compensation must be made by reducing the feed rate to obtain the required surface finish. Usually, the feed rate is the compromise value that allows the attainment of maximum possible production consistent with the specified finish.

Effect of Speed and Feed on Cost

Speeds and feeds that are too low consume excessive time, which usually results in an increase in workpiece cost. However, optimum speeds and feeds are not necessarily the maximum that the workpiece and the machine will tolerate. Excessively high speeds and feeds result in shorter tool life and therefore in increased tool cost.

In turning difficult-to-machine alloys, it is especially important that speed and feed be carefully selected and coordinated, for optimum results at minimum cost. Figure 16 shows the results of tests that were conducted to determine the influence of speed and feed on the cost of turning shafts (average diameter, 1.760 in.) made of alloy A-286. This material, an iron-base heat-resisting alloy containing 15 Cr, 26 Ni, 1.25 Mo, 2 Ti and 0.25 Al, was precipitation hardened to Rockwell C 35 before being machined.

In these tests, to determine optimum speed and feed, three "speed searches" were made with feed fixed at 0.0087 ipr (selected as near-optimum on the basis of extensive previous experience). A speed of 152 sfm was found to be optimum; at this speed, tool life was 25 cu in., and machining cost was $0.079 per cu in. of metal removed. As the chart at the left in Fig. 16 shows, slower speed raised tool life to 36 cu in., but cost increased to $0.097 per cu in. At a faster speed, tool life decreased to 9 cu in., and total cost increased to $0.092 per cu in. (because of the increased cost of tool usage).

When optimum speed had been determined, a check on the estimated feed was conducted. The feed search (chart at right in Fig. 16) confirmed that 0.0087 ipr was most economical.

The total cost of removing one cubic inch of metal in the speed and feed searches can be obtained from the tool life (expressed in cubic inches) shown in the chart and the cost factors listed in the table accompanying Fig. 16.

Table 8. Effect of Variables on Cutting Speed for 60-Min Tool Life in Turning Hot Rolled 1020 Steel With T1 High Speed Steel Tools(a)

Depth of cut, in.	Speed (sfm) for feed (ipr) of: 0.002	0.004	0.008	1/64	1/32	1/16	1/8
Tool No. 1 (SCEA, 0°; NR, 0)(b)							
1/32	420	267	174	117	82	82	82
1/16	418	264	173	116	78	57	54
1/8	418	263	171	112	75	52	40
1/4	416	263	167	110	72	49	34
1/2	412	261	167	107	69	45	30
1	412	260	164	105	65	41	25
Tool No. 2 (SCEA, 0°; NR, 1/16 in.)(b)							
1/32	688	439	285	191	140	109	93
1/16	562	359	232	157	110	82	66
1/8	493	315	202	134	93	66	51
1/4	454	288	185	122	82	57	41
1/2	432	276	175	113	73	49	34
1	424	261	170	107	68	42	27
Tool No. 3 (SCEA, 30°; NR, 1/8 in.)(b)							
1/32	944	607	384	254	171	120	103
1/16	660	438	281	184	114	88	71
1/8	572	364	251	154	102	71	54
1/4	521	325	209	136	89	61	44
1/2	489	308	194	126	80	52	35
1	471	295	187	119	75	47	30
Tool No. 4 (SCEA, 30°; NR, 1/4 in.)(b)							
1/32	1065	680	430	283	188	130	103
1/16	941	596	379	246	161	109	81
1/8	667	434	275	178	117	79	58
1/4	574	365	229	148	97	65	45
1/2	517	326	206	131	85	55	37
1	482	305	191	123	76	48	30
Finishing Tool(c)							
0.005 ..	1303	762	590	431	343	287	...
0.010 ..	1018	668	442	318	243	191	...
0.015 ..	896	574	383	271	199	161	...

(a) No cutting fluid used. (b) Tool angles: BR, 8°; SR, 14°; ER, 6°; SRF, 6°; ECEA, 6°. (c) Tool angles: BR, 20°; SR, 0°; ER, 6°; SRF, 6°; ECEA, 6°; SCEA, 0°; NR, 1/8 in.; flat, 1/8 in. (Source of table: ASME Manual on Cutting of Metals, 1952)

Table 9. Effect of Variables on Cutting Speed for 60-Min Tool Life in Turning Hot Rolled 1020 Steel With Carbide Tools(a)

Depth of cut, in.	Speed (sfm) for feed (ipr) of: 0.002	0.004	0.008	1/64	1/32	1/16	1/8
Tool No. 1 (SCEA, 0°; NR, 0)(b)							
1/32 ...	1438	908	583	379	256	256	256
1/16 ...	1436	906	583	376	245	169	163
1/8 ...	1433	905	577	373	241	159	110
1/4 ...	1433	902	575	369	237	154	102
1/2 ...	1428	901	571	365	232	148	95
1	1427	898	568	362	227	142	89
Tool No. 2 (SCEA, 0°; NR, 1/16 in.)(b)							
1/32 ...	2378	1513	978	651	464	358	311
1/16 ...	1935	1233	792	526	363	262	210
1/8 ...	1702	1084	690	452	306	211	161
1/4 ...	1568	1016	635	411	271	182	129
1/2 ...	1495	951	599	385	249	163	110
1	1439	903	586	372	237	150	93
Tool No. 3 (SCEA, 30°; NR, 1/8 in.)(b)							
1/32 ...	3309	2101	1323	867	581	403	340
1/16 ...	2281	1512	964	625	411	286	229
1/8 ...	1978	1256	865	524	340	230	170
1/4 ...	1788	1124	718	463	299	198	147
1/2 ...	1672	1061	668	430	274	177	119
1	1631	1026	646	414	261	163	105
Tool No. 4 (SCEA, 30°; NR, 1/4 in.)(b)							
1/32 ...	3684	2346	1481	969	638	435	342
1/16 ...	3254	2058	1305	844	545	363	267
1/8 ...	2301	1497	946	611	396	263	187
1/4 ...	1988	1251	787	510	327	214	147
1/2 ...	1788	1116	711	456	290	186	123
1	1674	1061	664	426	269	169	107
Finishing Tool(c)							
0.005	3444	2007	1556	1131	903	752	691
0.010	2694	1760	1162	831	630	516	456
0.015	2360	1515	1007	704	516	416	362

(a) No cutting fluid used. (b) Tool angles: BR, 8°; SR, 14°; ER, 6°; SRF, 6°; ECEA, 6°. (c) Tool angles: BR, 20°; SR, 0°; ER, 6°; SRF, 6°; ECEA, 6°; SCEA, 0°; NR, 1/8 in.; flat, 1/8 in. (Source of table: ASME Manual on Cutting of Metals, 1952)

To show numerically the influence of the three cost factors, calculations of costs for the three turning feeds are presented below:

Feed of 0.0081 Ipr

For the removal rate of 1.66 cu in. per min shown, it would take 1/1.66 or 0.602 min to remove one cubic inch of metal.

Cost per cubic inch:

Operating	$0.116 × 0.602	= $0.070
Tool change	0.10/22	= 0.004
Tool usage	0.258/22	= 0.011
Total		$0.085

Feed of 0.0087 Ipr (Optimum)

Time to remove one cubic inch of metal at this feed rate would be 1/1.79 or 0.559 min.

Cost per cubic inch:

Operating	$0.116 × 0.559	= $0.065
Tool change	0.10/25	= 0.004
Tool usage	0.258/25	= 0.010
Total		$0.079

Feed of 0.0094 Ipr

Time to remove one cubic inch of metal at this feed rate would be 1/1.93 or 0.518 min.

Cost per cubic inch:

Operating	$0.116 × 0.518	= $0.060
Tool change	0.10/5	= 0.020
Tool usage	0.258/5	= 0.051
Total		$0.131

From the foregoing calculations it is evident that:

1. The near-optimum value of the first variable (speed) was confirmed by the test with the second variable (feed). Note that with optimum speed, a slight increase over optimum feed raised total cost by more than 65%.
2. Machining at a feed less than the optimum value was uneconomical because the operating cost increased. Operating cost was the largest of the three items making up total cost.
3. Machining at a feed greater than the optimum value was uneconomical because tool costs increased by much more than operating cost decreased.

Choice of Equipment and Procedure

The selection of equipment and machining procedure for a specific part depends largely on:

- Size of workpiece
- Configuration of workpiece
- Equipment capacity (speed, feed and horsepower range)
- Production quantity
- Dimensional accuracy
- Number of operations
- Surface finish.

The next seven sections of this article discuss the influence of these factors, and present examples that describe or compare equipment and techniques for production applications.

Size of Workpiece

In addition to physically accommodating the work, a well-qualified lathe provides it with firm support, rigidly supports the cutting tools and feeds them into the work at the desired rate, and has enough power to maintain the selected rate of metal removal. Thus, size of the workpiece is usually the first consideration in selecting the most appropriate lathe for a specific job.

Small parts requiring average to close tolerances, such as components of instruments, are commonly produced

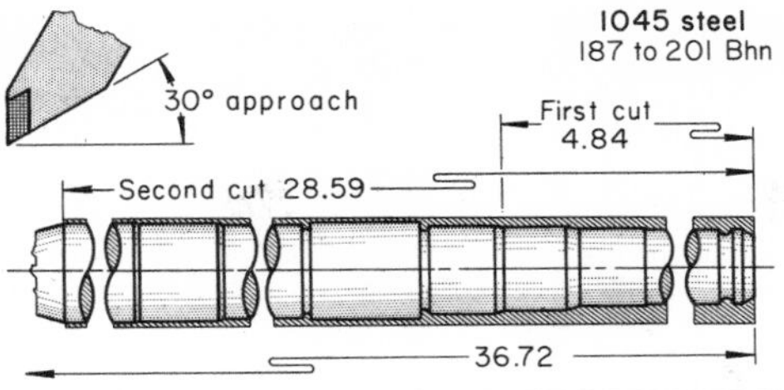

Item	Original method	Improved method
Operating Conditions		
Speed, rpm	872	1080
Speed, sfm	430	530
Feed, ipr	0.0163	0.0185
Feed, ipm	14.21	19.98
Machining time, min	2.4	1.7
Tool life per grind, pieces	40	20
Costs per Piece		
Machining	$0.1710	$0.1485
Tools(a)	0.0126	0.0252
Total	$0.1836	$0.1737

(a) Based on tool cost per edge (including resharpening) of $0.503.

Fig. 15. Turning application in which increase in speed and feed, although reducing tool life, resulted in greater productivity and lower cost (Example 9)

in watchmaker's lathes, bench lathes, or toolroom lathes.

Average-size parts such as automotive spindles and shafts with a length-to-diameter ratio of not more than 10 to 1, axles and drives shafts long enough to require one or more steady rests to prevent flexing, and similar parts turned between centers comprise a substantial percentage of the parts produced in engine lathes. Average-size parts of relatively short length and large diameter, such as gear blanks, are usually chucked on the outside or inside diameter and are turned on regular engine lathes, or on gap-frame, automatic, stub, and copying or tracer lathes.

Large or extremely heavy parts are usually turned on lathes designed specifically for one type of work. Specific examples are oil-country tools, large gun barrels, large steel-mill rolls, press columns, and missile parts. Lathes appropriate for parts of this type are heavy-duty long-bed lathes, hollow-spindle lathes, special roll-turning lathes, and missile lathes.

Workpiece Configuration

Workpiece configurations can be separated into two basic categories: regular and irregular.

Regular-shape workpieces are those on which all turned faces are either parallel or perpendicular to the centerline of rotation. Examples include gear blanks, shafts, flanged axles or other parts, cylinder liners, pistons, bearings on camshafts, and ring-shaped parts. Workpieces of this type have no significant angles or radii except normal corner breaks or angular chamfers, which are easily cut by means of tools having corresponding shapes.

Workpieces with cuts only parallel or perpendicular to the centerline of rotation represent a large percentage of lathe work, and are machinable on a wide range of standard engine lathes whose tool carriage or cross slides operate only parallel or at 90° to the centerline of rotation. For turning workpieces of this class, size is the major factor in choosing the most suitable equipment.

Regular lathes can be altered to generate more complex shapes (such as angles and large radii) by the use of cams and angular slides. For small production quantities, these auxiliary devices may be impractical because of the setup time required for changing over from one shape to another. Large production quantities, however, may justify the use of these modified machines — particularly the duplicating lathes (copying, tracer, profiling, numerical-control, or continuous-path machines).

Irregular-shape workpieces are those that require the use of a specific type of lathe in order to be turned satisfactorily. Crankshafts are notable exam-

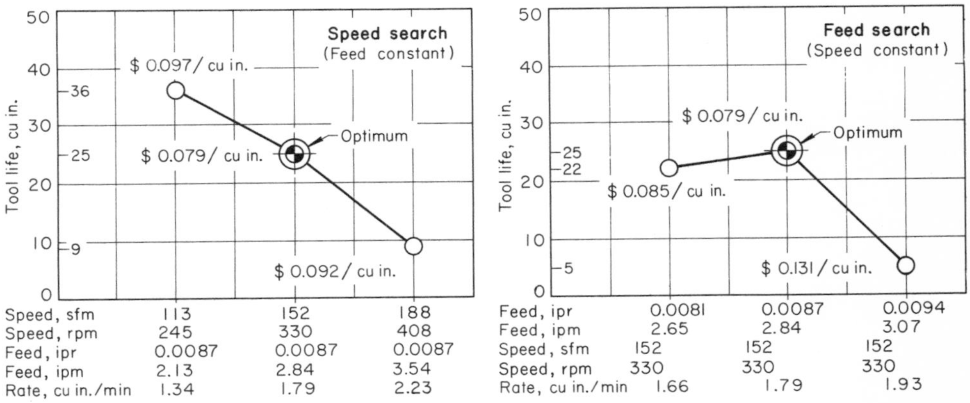

Machining Conditions: 16-in. lathe; 1-to-1 mixture of sulfurized oil and mineral oil, flow application; depth of cut, 0.120 in.

Tool Details

Tool material	C-7 carbide (71 W, 3.5 Ta, 10 Ti, 7.5 C, 8 Co)
Insert size	½ IC by 3/16 in.
Back and side rake angles	−7°
End relief angle	+7°
Side relief angle	+7°
Side cutting-edge angle	15°
Nose radius	0.030 in.
Center height	0.005 in.
Wear land	0.015 in.

Cost Factors

Tool usage, per tool	$0.258
Tool change, per tool	0.10
Operating, per min	0.116

Fig. 16. Influence of speed and feed on cost of turning alloy A-286. *See also text on page 10.*

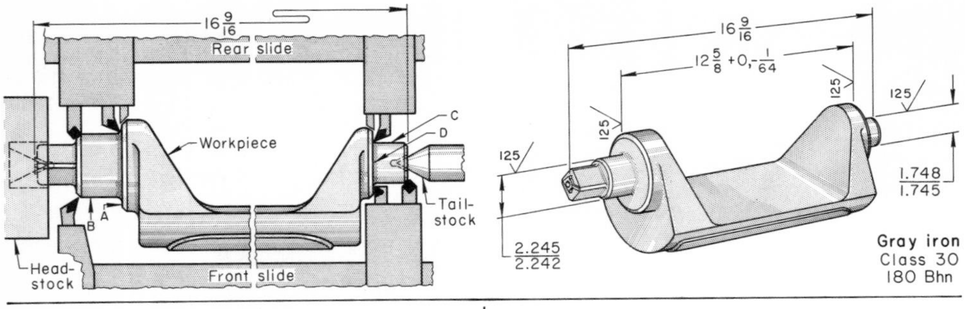

Front-Slide Operations

1. Rough face surface A
2. Finish turn diameters B and C
3. Rough face surface D and chamfer extreme right end

Rear-Slide Operations

1. Finish face surfaces A and D
2. Chamfer remaining three sharp corners (at end of stroke)

Surface speed (at 200 rpm):	
On 1.745-in. diam	92 sfm
On 2.242-in. diam	128 sfm
Feed, front slide	0.013 ipr
Feed, rear slide	0.012 ipr
Depth of cut, turning	0.125 in.
Cutting fluid	Soluble oil
Machining time per piece	3.42 min
Production per hour	17.5 pieces
Tool life per grind	60 to 75 pieces

Fig. 17. Machining an eccentric workpiece without counterbalancing, by the use of subnormal speeds of 92 and 128 sfm for the two diameters (Example 10)

ples. Crankshaft lathes use special center drives to turn and face main bearing sections, and double-end drives to turn and face rod bearing sections.

Many irregular-shape parts are out of balance when rotated, and this may require the application of counterbalances to the spindle, chuck or workpiece. The need for counterbalancing is influenced by degree of out-of-balance, speed of rotation, or available power, or by a combination of these variables. The following example describes an application in which counterbalancing was avoided by turning at low speed:

Example 10. Turning an Eccentric Casting (Fig. 17)

A 20-hp, 12-by-21-in. automatic lathe was used to turn the 35-lb eccentric casting shown in Fig. 17. Workpieces were held between centers and driven by means of a square hole in the face plate that mated with the square stem on the casting.

The sequence of machining operations, and operating conditions and results, are listed below Fig. 17. The machining time of 3.42 min per piece could have been substantially reduced by the use of counterweights, which would have permitted turning at higher speed.

Table 10. Increase in Capabilities of Engine Lathes (a)

	Rating, for year of manufacture: 1936	1967
Horsepower	5 or 7½	7½ to 20(b)
Spindle speed, rpm	16 to 360	24 to 2000
Feed range, ipr	0.0027 to 0.172	0.0007 to 0.187
Thread range per inch	1½ to 92	1 to 256

(a) Data are for lathes with a swing of 20 in. over the bed and of 13 in. over the cross slide. Other sizes have been improved comparably. (b) Optional, within range.

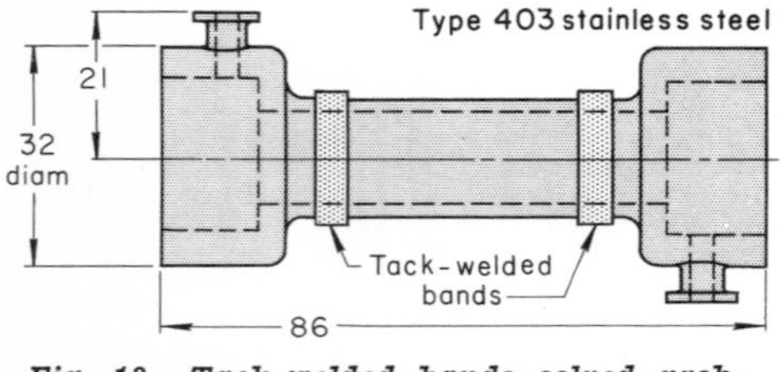

Fig. 18. Tack-welded bands solved problem of chucking this large fabricated part for two-stage machining of both ends in an engine lathe. (Example 11)

Workpieces that have sections of L or T shape, and those with large flanges, may require a swing diameter greatly out of proportion to the stem diameter. Gap-frame lathes often are advantageous for these types of workpiece or for others that require large swing clearances in specific locations along the lathe bed.

Workpieces with extremely high length-to-diameter ratios, such as long sections of pipe or shafting, are also considered irregular. In many instances, such parts require turning only on the ends and can be machined efficiently in a hollow-spindle or center-drive lathe.

Special lathes can be obtained to machine almost any configuration, but their cost usually is justified only when large quantities of similar parts must be produced. The example that follows describes a method devised for adapting an irregular-shape part for machining in a large engine lathe:

Example 11. Special Method of Holding a Large Irregular Part (Fig. 18)

The large (1700 lb) fabricated stainless steel part shown in Fig. 18 required boring, facing and threading at each end. Chucking this part was a problem, because during machining, each end had to be free of centers or chucks, so as not to restrict the tool. The problem was solved by tack welding two bands to the body of the part, as shown in Fig. 18. Each band was rolled of ½-in. plate and was tack welded in two halves.

The part was chucked externally at the headstock, using a four-jaw chuck, and internally at the tailstock, using a revolving three-jaw chuck. The bands were turned true and to the same diameter. The part was then held and driven by the four-jaw chuck at the headstock. A steady rest was used at the farther band to support the part. After one end had been bored, faced and threaded, the part was reversed, end for end, and the opposite end was machined. The bands were then removed by grinding away the tack welds.

Equipment Capacity

The capacity of lathes has been continually increased, as demonstrated in Table 10, which compares power, speed, feed, and thread range for engine lathes produced in 1936 and in 1967.

Horsepower rating must be considered when selecting a lathe, because power consumption is in direct ratio to the rate of metal removal, which in turn is related to production rates. With carbide and ceramic cutting tools, it is practical to use surface speeds ranging from 10 to 2000 sfm. With high speed steel tools, feed rates up to 0.060 ipr on cuts up to, or beyond, 1 in. in depth are commonly used.

Power requirements for one carbide tool, on average work and operating at optimum speeds, can range from 5 to 30 hp; such a range is typical in tracer-lathe turning. In applications involving extremely deep cuts (for example, 2½-in. cuts in turning steel rolls), more than 300 hp may be required.

Spindle-Speed Range. A lathe must be able to rotate a given size of workpiece fast enough to produce the surface speed proper for the tool material, depth of cut and feed rate used. For turning carbon and alloy steels, approximate ranges of surface speeds for various tool materials are as follows:

High speed steel	10 to 200 sfm
Cast cobalt-base alloy	50 to 300
Tungsten carbide	250 to 800
Titanium carbide	250 to 1500
Ceramic	500 to 2000

Production Quantity

Quantity of parts to be machined has a direct bearing on the type of lathe selected, primarily because of cost. Although setup time for an engine lathe is usually less than for a comparable job on any other lathe, it calls for more operator supervision, and

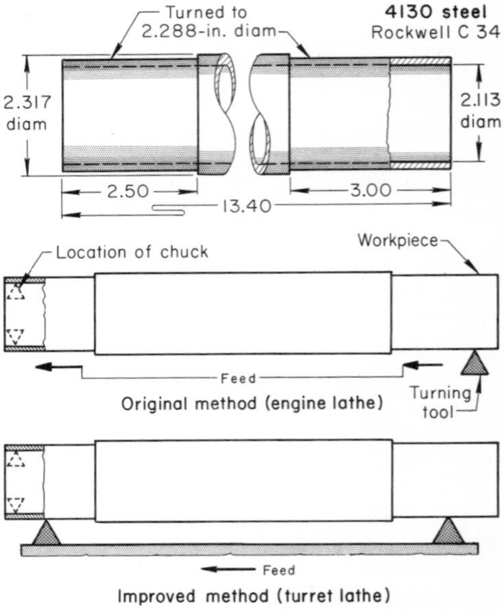

Item	Method(a): Engine lathe	Turret lathe
Speed, rpm	320	450
Speed, sfm	190	270
Feed, ipr	0.004	0.004
Setup time, min	45.6	68
Production per hour, pieces	9	20
Setup cost	$4.76	$7.09
Cost per piece(b)	$0.60	$0.32

(a) For both methods, carbide tools were used and produced about 50 pieces per grind; tool-change time was the same, and water-soluble oil was used as the cutting fluid. (b) Includes labor, material and burden.

Fig. 19. Comparison of setups, operating conditions, and costs for turning a tubular part in an engine lathe and in a turret lathe (Example 13)

Table 11. Effect of Quantity on Choice of Machine (Example 12) (a)

Production quantity, pieces	Most suitable machine	Pieces per hour — Per machine	Pieces per hour — Per man	Setup time, hr
Under 10	Engine lathe	2	2	½
10 to 100	Turret lathe	4	4	4
100 to 10,000	Single-spindle automatic	7	28	6
10,000 to 100,000	Six-spindle automatic (b)	15	45	12

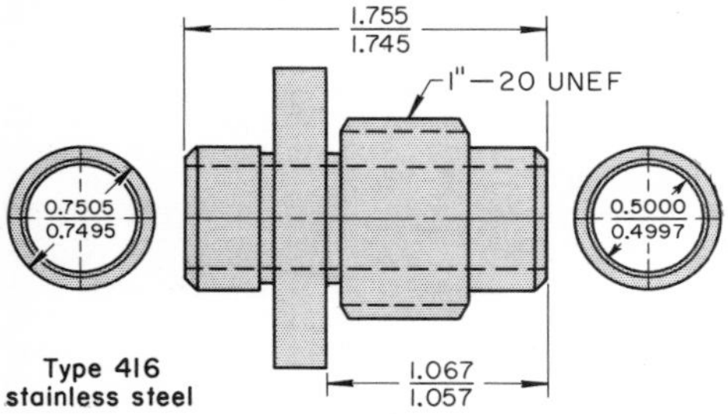

(a) Data are based on turning (at 370 sfm), drilling (at 150 sfm), and threading (at 25 sfm) the part illustrated above. (b) Estimated; the part was not actually machined on a six-spindle automatic machine.

production time per piece is usually greater; consequently, for a majority of parts, it is economical to produce only small quantities on engine lathes. This is demonstrated in the six examples that follow.

Example 12. Engine Lathe vs Turret Lathe and Single-Spindle and Six-Spindle Automatics (Table 11)

The data in Table 11 compare productivity and setup times for four different types of machines, for turning, drilling and threading a small stainless steel part (inset sketch in Table 11). From this comparison it is evident that for machining this part in quantities of more than ten, machines other than an engine lathe are more efficient. For the engine and turret lathes, one operator was required for each machine, whereas one operator could handle four single-spindle automatics or (by estimate) three six-spindle automatics.

Example 13. Engine Lathe vs Turret Lathe (Fig. 19)

The tubular part shown in Fig. 19 was produced in annual quantities of about 1600, in lots of 200 pieces. Originally, a 5-hp engine lathe was used (center sketch in Fig. 19). [Speed and feed were restricted to values substantially below the nominal (see comparison in Table 6), because of problems in maintaining rigidity.] Changing to a more rugged 15-hp turret lathe (bottom sketch in Fig. 19) permitted turning at a 50% increase in speed, and also allowed both ends of the part to be turned simultaneously. Processing details, productivity and costs for the two methods are compared in the table accompanying Fig. 19.

Because both tools were operated from the cross slide, an engine lathe rated at 15 hp could have been used. However, a turret lathe was preferred because the turret could be manipulated in less time than a tailstock, thus reducing loading and unloading time.

Example 14. Engine Lathe vs Chucking Machine (Fig. 20)

Figure 20 compares an engine lathe with an eight-spindle chucking machine, with respect to time per piece in various production quantities, for machining a stainless steel part. Machining of this part (see inset in Fig. 20) entailed nine operations, including facing, turning, undercutting, chamfering and threading; on both machines, chucks that were bored and faced during the setup were used to hold the blanks (bar slugs). As the data in Fig. 20 show, for fewer than 11 parts (the break point), the engine lathe was the more economical; and for more than 11, the chucking machine was.

Both were 10-in. machines, rated at 3 hp. For both machines, speed was 400 rpm (240 sfm); feed was 0.001 ipr for facing, undercutting and chamfering, 0.002 ipr for rough turning the outside diameter and 0.0006 ipr for finish turning, and 0.031 ipr for threading; and carbide tools were used for all operations except threading. The six tools used for the nine operations required grinding after 10 to 15 pieces, except for the chamfering tool, which machined 50 pieces per grind.

Examples 15, 16 and 17. Cost of Machining in Engine Lathe vs Single-Spindle Automatic (Table 12)

The capabilities of an engine lathe and a single-spindle automatic chucking machine were compared for producing three different parts (shown as Examples 15, 16 and 17 in Table 12). In all instances, machining cuts were made individually in the engine lathe, whereas in the single-spindle automatic, turning was combined with other required operations, such as boring, facing and chamfering. Results are compared in Table 12.

Example 15, the bearing housing illustrated in the left-hand sketch in Table 12, was machined from 5-in.-diam, 2⅛-in.-long bar slugs. The hole was rough drilled previously, then bored to finish size (2.178/2.177 in.).

Example 16, the adapter shown in the center sketch in Table 12, was made from a flat blank. Prior to turning, a hole was drilled to permit boring to the finished diameter of 2.272/2.270 in. Approximately ⅛ in. was machined from all surfaces.

Example 17, the roll-centering piston shown in the right-hand sketch in Table 12, was machined from a forging. Machining entailed the removal of ⅜ to ½ in. of stock from all surfaces.

Dimensional Accuracy

In turning a simple cylinder with a single-point tool cutting perpendicular to the axis of rotation, straightness of cut will depend on: (*a*) squareness of the cross slide to the spindle centerline, (*b*) axial movement of the spindle, and (*c*) vibration of the cutting tool at the tip. Assuming that inaccuracy was 0.0001 in. for each of these three factors, minimum variation in machined dimension could not be less than 0.0001 in., and might equal the sum of these three inaccuracies, or 0.0003 in.

Diametral roundness is related directly to the lathe spindle runout. Most spindles rotate in a preloaded angular bearing to eliminate side and end movement. Lathes are available with

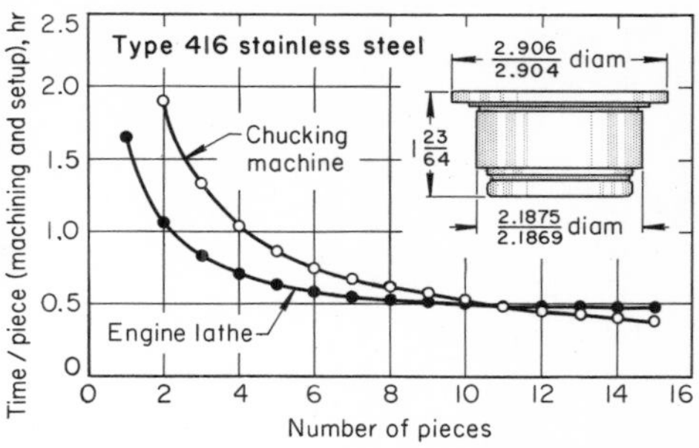

Item	Engine lathe	Chucking machine
Setup time, hr	1.3	3.6
Setup cost	$13.00	$36.00
Tool cost	$30.00	$45.00

Fig. 20. Time per piece as affected by quantity, for an engine lathe vs an eight-spindle chucking machine (Example 14)

spindles that do not exceed 20 millionths of an inch runout, total indicator reading. Relationship of workpiece roundness to spindle runout is shown graphically in Fig. 21(a).

Diameter variation (taper) depends on the relationship of the axis of rotation of the workpiece, in both the vertical and the horizontal planes, to the longitudinal travel of the tool and carriage. Any relationship other than true parallelism will result in taper of the workpiece. The relationship is shown graphically in Fig. 21(b).

Face flatness is influenced by the alignment of the cross slide with the axis of rotation of the workpiece. Any variation from a true perpendicular relationship results in either a high or a low center, depending on the direction of misalignment. Alignment is checked by facing a surface on a dummy blank approximately 4 in. in diameter. An indicator is then mounted on the cross slide and traveled completely across the machined face. The total indicator movement registers face flatness resulting both from vibration and from misalignment of the cross slide due to cam action. Cam action, or "end camming", is the amount of movement of the spindle along the spin axis under dynamic

Table 12. Productivity and Cost Comparison of Engine Lathe and Single-Spindle Automatic Chucking Machine for Producing Three Different Parts (Examples 15, 16 and 17)

Item	Example 15 — Engine lathe	Example 15 — Single-spindle automatic	Example 16 — Engine lathe	Example 16 — Single-spindle automatic	Example 17 — Engine lathe	Example 17 — Single-spindle automatic
Cycle time per piece, min	13	8	11	6.5	34	21.5
Production per hour, pieces	4½	7½	5½	9	2	3
Rate per hour(a)	$7.50	$9.75	$7.50	$9.75	$7.50	$9.75
Cost per piece(b)	$1.63	$1.30	$1.38	$1.06	$4.25	$3.49

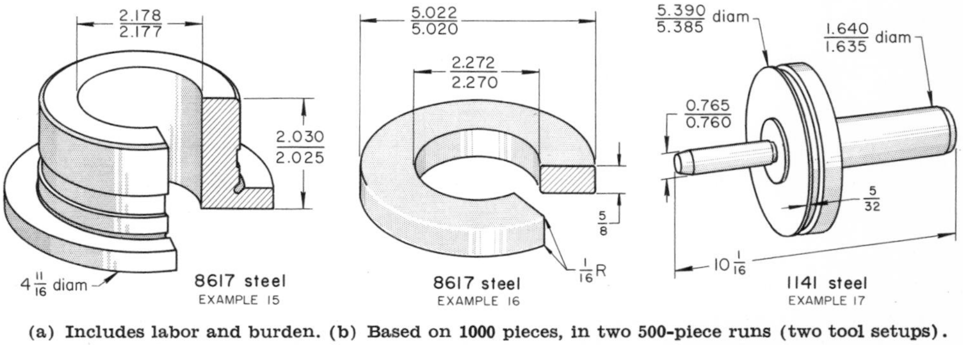

(a) Includes labor and burden. (b) Based on 1000 pieces, in two 500-piece runs (two tool setups).

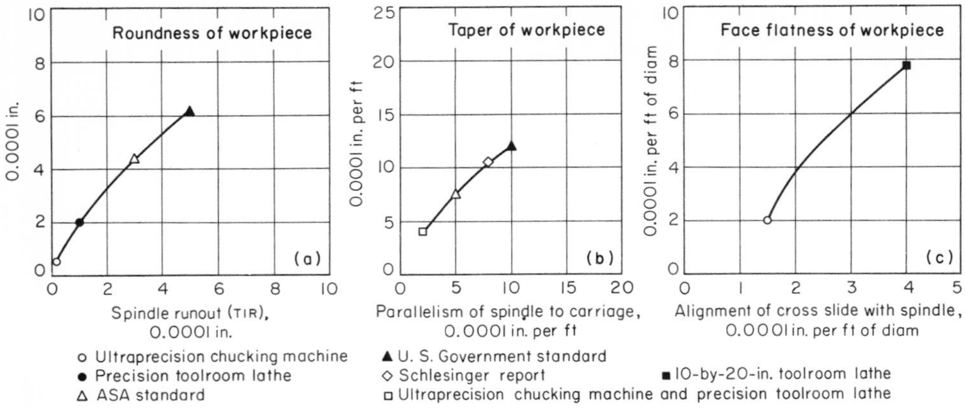

Fig. 21. Effect of machine variables on roundness, taper and face flatness of workpieces

conditions; cam action of the spindle on a precision lathe should be less than 0.0001 in. The effect of cross-slide alignment on face flatness of the workpiece is shown in Fig. 21(c).

Diameter accuracy depends to some degree on operator skill. The cross-slide-positioning dial on precision lathes is graduated in 0.001-in. increments, but these increments are about ⅛ in. apart on the dial. A capable operator can control turned diameters within 0.0003 in. by estimating settings between dial markings. With precision gaging, an experienced operator can sometimes hold diameters within 0.0001 in. Repeatability of the lathe should be within half of the lowest divisional value on the cross-slide dial.

Length dimensions are measured parallel to the axis of rotation. Accuracy depends on positioning of the longitudinal slide. Precision lathes are capable of holding a tolerance of 0.0005 in. on length. On manually operated lathes, however, an experienced operator can usually improve this capability. Control of manually operated lathes can be improved by dial gages on machine slides for reference positioning.

Relationship of tolerances to each other are often more meaningful than tolerances on individual dimensions.

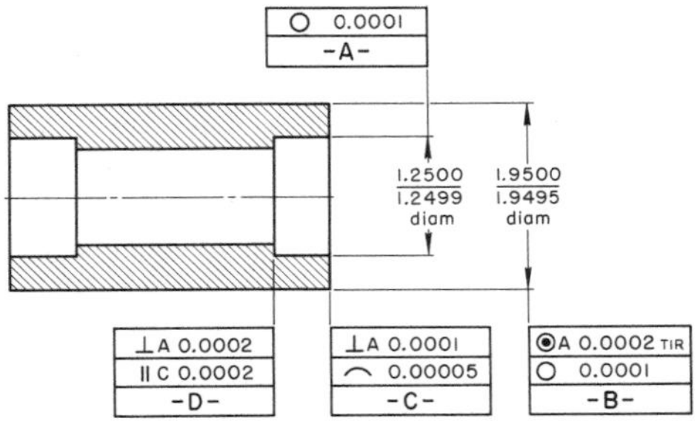

Fig. 22. Typical tolerance relationships that can be held in precision turning.

Tolerance relationships that can be maintained in precision turning are given in Fig. 22. The data in the charts in Fig. 21 show that tolerances of this order of magnitude can be maintained with precision lathes.

Lathe selection on the basis of dimensional accuracy required is illustrated in Example 927 in the article "Machining of Beryllium", which describes an application in which diametral tolerances were held within 0.0001 in. by the use of a lathe having a preloaded spindle that kept runout error below 20 millionths of an inch. Example 29 also involves the use of a lathe with preloaded spindle, for close tolerance and a finish of 10 to 16 micro-in.

The example that follows describes an application in which reselection of machine was necessary for meeting a more usual tolerance of 0.005 in.:

Example 18. Change From Automatic to Tracer Lathes for Rigidity (Fig. 23)

A tolerance of 0.005 in. was specified for all finish-machined dimensions on the forged 4820 steel pinion-gear blank shown in Fig. 23. Machining operations included turning, chamfering, facing and grooving; stock removal ranged from 3/32 to 1/4 in. per side.

Originally, three 15-hp automatic lathes and a total of 20 tools were used to complete the sequence of operations (top row of sketches in Fig. 23). These machines, however, were not rigid enough to withstand the forces from the heavy stock removal. Consequently, size variation of the workpieces and tool breakage were constant problems, despite the use of a feed rate two thirds the nominal value (see comparison in Table 6).

To improve dimensional accuracy and decrease tool breakage, as well as to improve production efficiency, the job was transferred to two 40-hp tracer lathes using only eight tools (sketches at lower left in Fig. 23). The superior rigidity of these machines eliminated tolerance and tool breakage problems, and made it possible to change from high speed steel to carbide tools, and thus increase speed and feed. The change to the tracer lathes reduced machining time per piece by 40%.

Number of Operations

The number of operations that can be performed on an engine lathe is almost limitless. The unmodified engine lathe, however, utilizing one single-point tool, can generate only one surface at a time, and the tool or tool position (or both) must be changed before another surface can be generated. There are two methods for increasing the efficiency of an engine lathe: (*a*) by the use of a duplicating attachment, which can do several operations consecutively by means of program control; and (*b*) by the use of multiple-operation accessories and attachments, such as a turret, so as to permit simultaneous or consecutive operations by two or more different tools. The eight examples that comprise the remainder of this section

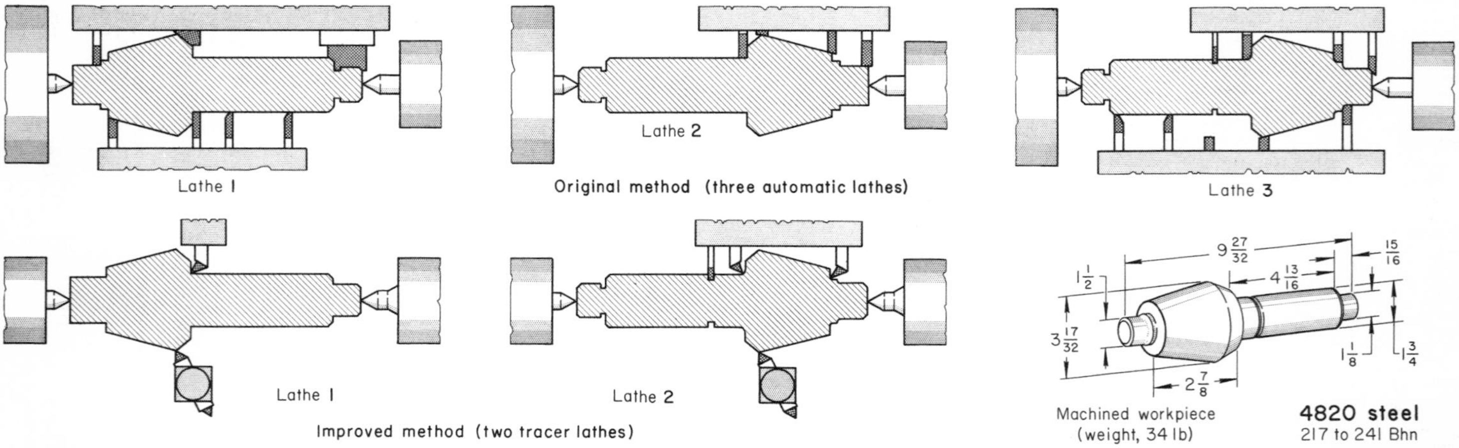

Method	Speed, Rpm	Speed, Sfm	Feed, ipr	Cutting fluid	Tool material	Tool life, pieces	Tool changing, min/8 hr	Machining time per piece, min
Original (three automatic lathes)	90	83 max	0.010	Soluble-oil:water (1:25)	High speed steel	100 per grind	62	4.124
Improved (two tracer lathes) ...	440,880	405	0.014	Soluble-oil:water (1:25)	Disposable carbide	50 per insert	90	2.477

Fig. 23. Change from three automatic lathes to two tracer lathes that provided rigidity required for obtaining dimensional accuracy in machining a forged pinion-gear blank (Example 18)

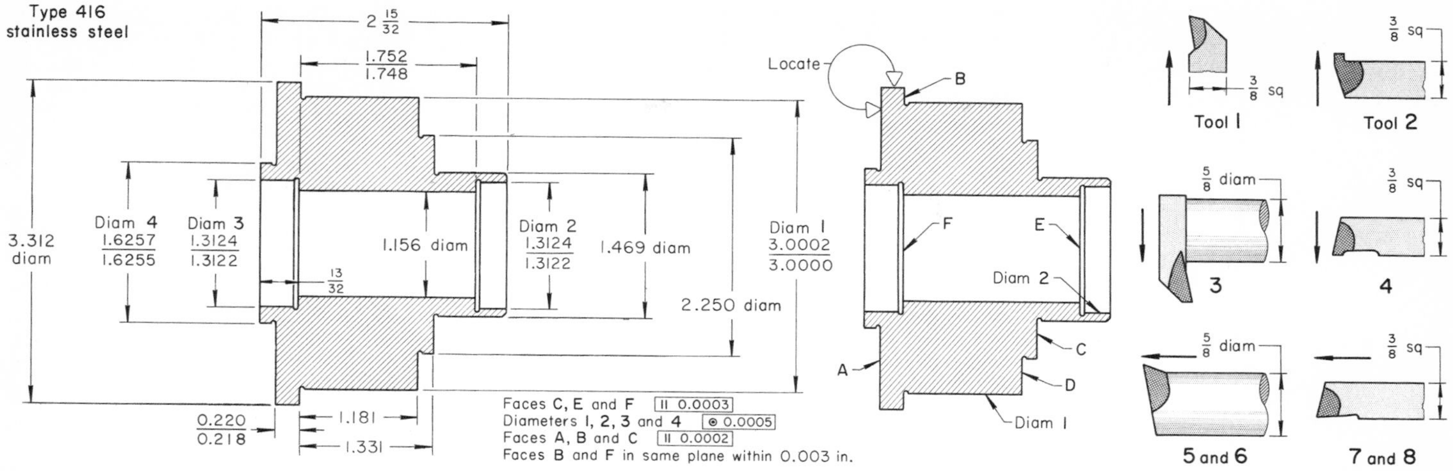

Tool(a)	Operation(b)	Speed Rpm	Speed Sfm	Feed, ipr	Tool details(c) BR	SR	ER	SRF	ECEA	SCEA	NR, in.	Tool life(d)
1..........	Face B, and undercut	130	115	0.0007	5°	3°	6°	3°	0°	0°	0.010	30
2..........	Face C and D, and undercut	130	100, 60	0.0015	5°	3°	6°	3°	0°	0°	0.010	30
3..........	Backface F, and undercut	400	135	0.001	5°	3°	6°	3°	0°	0°	0.010	30
4..........	Face E, and undercut	400	135	0.001	5°	3°	6°	3°	0°	0°	0.010	30
5..........	Rough turn diameter 1	130	100	0.003	5°	8°	6°	6°	0°	5°	0.020	20
6..........	Finish turn diameter 1	130	100	0.001	5°	8°	6°	6°	0°	5°	0.010	20
7..........	Rough bore diameter 2	400	135	0.003	5°	8°	6°	6°	0°	5°	0.010	80
8..........	Finish bore diameter 2	400	135	0.001	5°	8°	6°	6°	0°	5°	0.010	80

(a) All tools were carbide-tipped (steel-cutting grade) and, for maximum tool life and for producing the best surface finish on the workpiece, were ground on the top face to a 4-micro-in. finish, using a 500-grit diamond wheel. Clearance angles and nose radii, 8-micro-in. finish.

(b) Setup time was 4.5 hr; machining time, 30 min per piece. Cutting fluid was a 1-to-20 mixture of soluble oil and water. (c) See caption for Fig. 2 (page 3) for explanation of standard abbreviations used here for tool angles. (d) Average number of pieces machined per grind.

Fig. 24. Stainless steel pivot on which second-machining operations with eight tools shown (details in table) were performed in one chucking by use of a manual lathe equipped with an eight-station turret (Example 19)

describe applications in which lathe efficiency was increased by various methods that made it possible to perform several operations in one setup.

Example 19. Operations With Eight Tools in One Chucking (Fig. 24)

A manually operated chucking lathe having an eight-station turret proved to be an efficient method for performing secondary operations on the 2.65-lb stainless steel mirror-platform pivot illustrated in Fig. 24. Prior operations performed on the larger end allowed the part to be secured in a step chuck that was bored and faced in the setup operation.

The eight standard tools used also are shown in Fig. 24; the operations performed by the tools, together with details of tool design and operating conditions, are given in the table accompanying the illustrations.

Example 20. Three Operations With One Tool in Tracer Lathe (Fig. 25)

Originally, a 5-hp stub lathe was used for machining the four arms of a differential cross forged from 8622 steel. By this method (see upper sketch in Fig. 25), three high speed steel tools were required for turning, chamfering and facing each of the four sections in separate chuckings.

The job was transferred to a 15-hp tracer lathe, which performed all three operations with one tool, and which also used a double, rather than a single, driving arm (see lower sketch in Fig. 25). The changes in machine and driving mechanism increased rigidity enough to permit the use of a carbide tool, which in turn allowed higher speed and shorter machining time. [Operations at a feed rate below nominal with carbide tools made possible a speed 50% greater than nominal (see Table 6), and five times that used with the high speed steel tools in the stub lathe.] Processing details for the two methods are compared below Fig. 25.

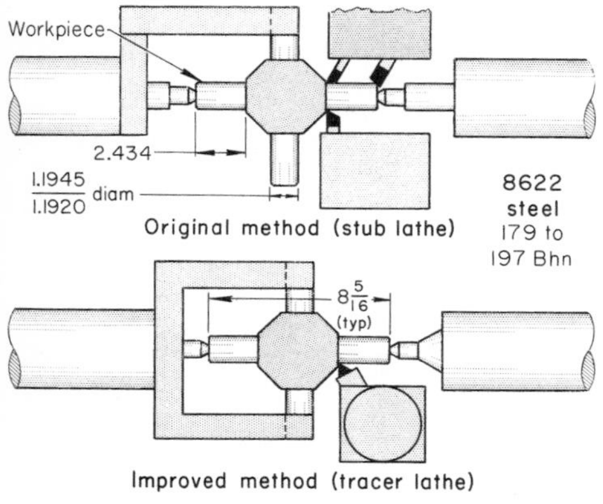

Item	Stub lathe	Tracer lathe
Speed, rpm	366	2100
Speed, sfm	115	655
Feed, ipr	0.0118	0.010
Depth (turning), in. ...	3/32	3/32
Cutting fluid(a)	Soluble-oil:water (1:25)	
Tool material	HSS	Carbide
Tool life, pieces	75(b)	78(c)
Setup time, min	24	24
Downtime for tool change, min(d)	8	15
Machining time, min ...	3.029	1.476

(a) For both methods. (b) Per grind. (c) Per tip (disposable type). (d) Per 8-hr shift.

Fig. 25. Comparison of setup and processing details for machining differential-cross arms in a stub lathe and in a tracer lathe (Example 20)

Example 21. Use of Four Tools in a Threading Lathe (Fig. 26)

A 20-hp semiautomatic hollow-spindle threading lathe was used to machine the forged ends of jack rods. From the standpoint of space, the four tools, plus stock stop, used in this operation (see Fig. 26) represent tooling to near maximum capacity for this type of lathe in a single chucking.

Special features of the machine included: a three-jaw, air-operated chuck, 20 in. in outside diameter and with a 6-in.-diam through bore that permitted loading through the headstock; a longitudinal rear slide with four-pass hydraulic tracer; an overhead facing slide; an overhead retractable stop; and a tailstock-mounted center-generating tool. The sequence of operations, and operating condi-

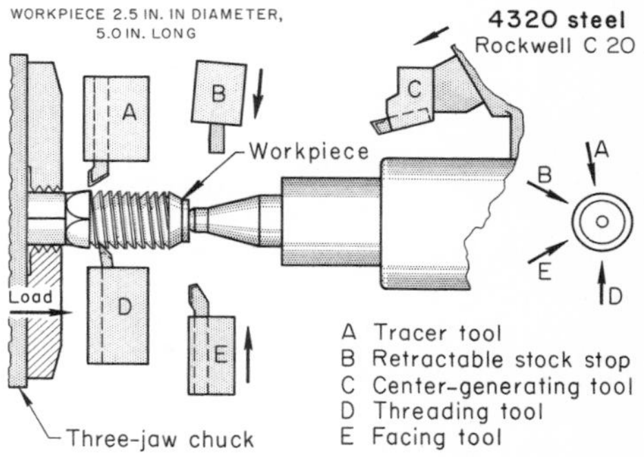

Operation(a)	Speed Rpm	Speed Sfm	Feed, ipr	Depth of cut, in.	Time, min(b)
Facing	600	392	0.012	0.060	0.25
Centering	600	140	0.010	0.150	0.10
Tracer turning	600	392	0.0075 to 0.015	0.125	0.80
Threading ...	300	196	....	0.005	1.60

Sequence of Operations(c)

1 Load workpiece through spindle, and locate against stock stop (B). Close chuck jaws and retract stop.
2 Face end with tool E (tool fed and retracted in one pass).
3 Generate a 60° center with tool C (center-generating tool, mounted on the tailstock, is fed and retracted in one pass).
4 Advance tailstock center (shown already in position) to use 60° center produced in step 3.
5 Turn outside contour with tracer tool A (three passes).
6 Cut threads with tool D (28 passes).
7 Inspect and unload.

(a) For all operations, carbide tools were used and a 25-to-1 mixture of water and soluble oil was the cutting fluid. (b) Total floor-to-floor time was 4.92 min. This included, in addition to machining times listed for the four operations, 0.67 min for tool traverse and 1.50 min for loading, gaging and unloading. (c) The diagram at the right of the drawing shows the relative position of the various tools.

Fig. 26. Use of four tools in a threading lathe for multiple-operation machining of a jack rod (Example 21)

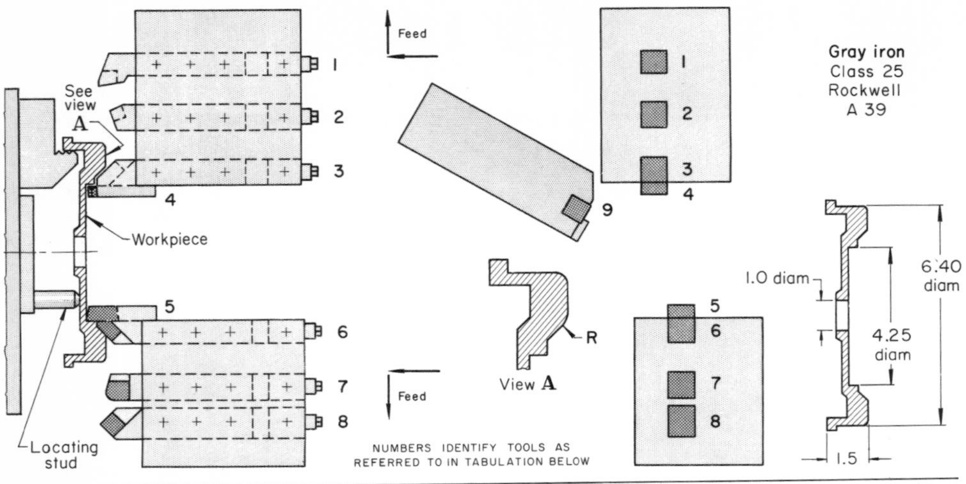

Sequence of Operations

1 Part is placed in air chuck, locating against three studs. Chuck is closed, and machine cycle is started.
2 Table traverses, then feeds to depth. Tool 1 turns outside diameter; tool 8 chamfers.
3 When table reaches predetermined depth, center slide begins to feed, giving transverse action to cam-operated front and rear slides.
4 Rear-slide tools 2 and 4 rough face, and tool 3 rough forms the chamfer. Tools 5, 6 and 7 finish roughed surfaces. When center slide bottoms, overhead tool 9 forms the radius shown in "View A" above.
5 Table returns to rear position, and center slide returns all slides to starting position.
6 Chuck is opened, and workpiece is removed.

Tool No.	Speed, sfm(a)	Feed, ipr	Depth of cut, in.
Machining Conditions(b)			
1 and 8	300	0.018	0.180
2	240 to 300	0.0175	0.180
3	200 to 240	0.0175	0.400
4	47 to 200	0.0175	0.180
5	47 to 200	0.0175	0.020
6	200 to 240	0.0175	0.040
7	240 to 300	0.0175	0.020
9	240	0.025	....

(a) Spindle speed, 180 rpm. (b) For all operations, carbide tools were used, and cutting fluid was a 25-to-1 mixture of water and soluble oil. Floor-to-floor time per piece was 1 minute; production rate: 48 pieces per hour.

Fig. 27. Machining of a cast type-bar segment in an engine lathe modified by replacement of tailstock with a platen table for holding tool slides (Example 22)

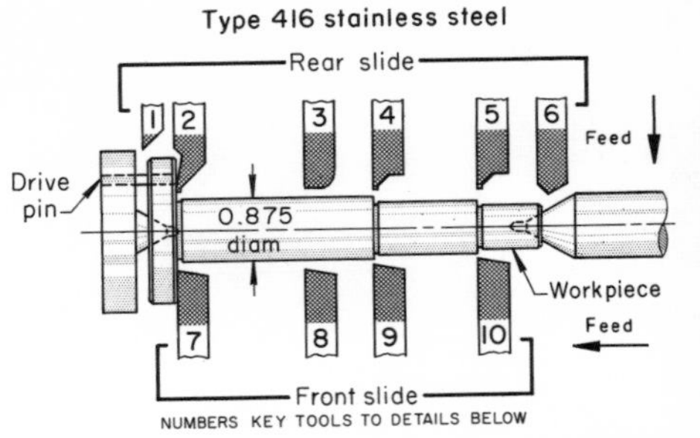

Tool angle(a)	Tools (operations performed are as footnoted): 7, 8, 9 & 10(b)	1, 4 & 5(c)	2 & 6(d)	3(e)
BR	8°	8°	8°	8°
SR	8°	3°	8°	0°
ER	6°	6°	6°	6°
SRF	8°	3°	4°	3°
ECEA	6°	0°	5°	0°
SCEA	5°	0°	0°	0°
NR, in.	0.015	0.010	0.010	0.010

Machining Conditions

Speed ....600 rpm (140 sfm)
Feed, turning ....0.003 ipr
Feed, facing and undercutting ....0.002 ipr
Tool material ....Carbide (brazed)
Setup time ....1 hr
Time per piece, floor-to-floor ....90 sec

(a) See caption for Fig. 2 on page 3 for explanation of standard abbreviations used here for tool angles. (b) Turning. (c) Tool 1, chamfering; tools 4 and 5, undercutting. (d) Facing and chamfering. (e) Forming.

Fig. 28. Setup, tool details, and conditions, for machining shafts in a stub lathe with ten tools in special front and rear holders (Example 23)

tions, are given with Fig. 26. [Speed was slightly above nominal, as shown in Table 6.]

Example 22. Replacement of Tailstock With Platen Table for Increased Tool Capacity (Fig. 27)

For machining gray iron type-bar segments, a 15-hp engine lathe with a 16¾-in. swing was modified by replacing the tailstock with a platen table mounted on the lathe ways. The workpiece and tooling setup are shown in Fig. 27; sequence and details of operations are presented in the tabular caption. A hydraulically operated center slide and cam-operated front and rear slides were mounted on the table and received their motion from the center slide. A slide carrying a radius-forming tool (tool 9 in Fig. 27) was mounted on two overhead bars from the headstock end.

The face finished by tool 5 required a flatness tolerance of 0.0002 in. TIR. This presented a problem, because the thin section would have warped (because of unbalanced stresses) had heavy cuts been taken. Flatness tolerance was maintained by removing only a small amount of metal with the finish cut, thus reducing tool pressure.

Example 23. Use of Special Tool Holders to Increase Machine Efficiency (Fig. 28)

A shaft of 416 stainless steel was machined automatically by using special tool holders in the front and rear tool slides of a 6-in. stub lathe, as shown in Fig. 28. The part was first machined without form tool 3 and turning tool 8. Tools 3 and 8 were added to reduce the cycle time, dividing the longest operation between turning tools 7 and 8. Form tool 3, on the rear slide, took a light forming cut as needed, to remove any metal left between the cuts of turning tools 7 and 8.

The lathe operated on an automatic cycle, requiring only loading and unloading by an operator. Tool details and machining conditions are given with Fig. 28.

Example 24. Special Chuck for Ring-Gear Blanks (Fig. 29)

Ring-gear blanks that required machining all over were formerly machined by means of two chucks and two setups. To reduce han-

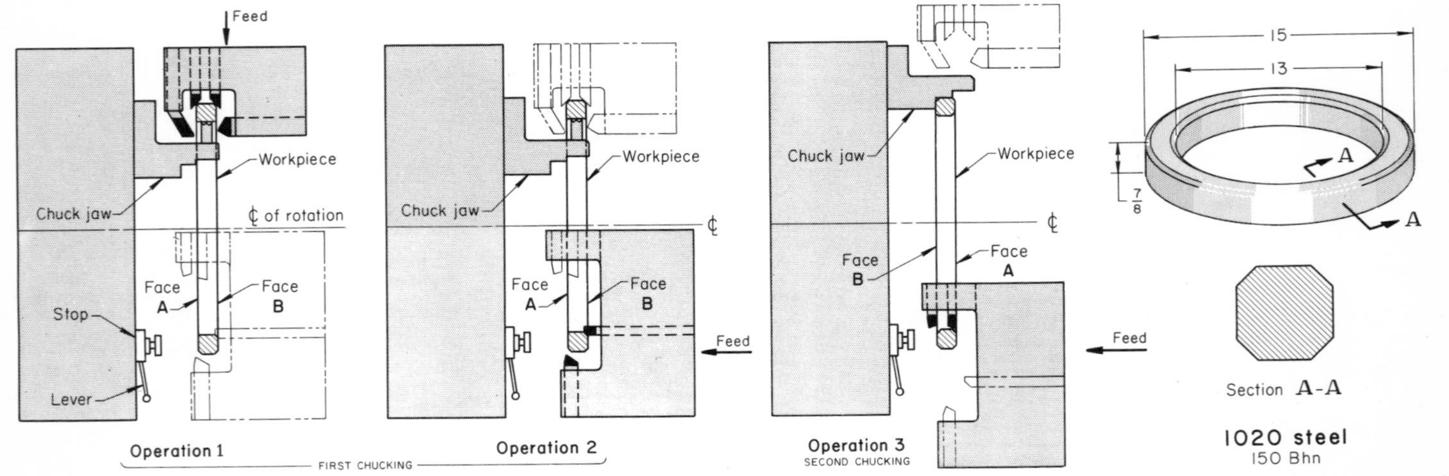

Operation 1: Face A is positioned against three retractable stops; then three chuck jaws grip workpiece on inside diameter, and stops are retracted by lever. In this position, both sides are faced and outside-diameter edges are chamfered.

Operation 2: Outside diameter is turned, edge of face B chamfered. **Operation 3:** Workpiece is reversed, and face B is placed against stops; then chuck jaws grip workpiece on outside diameter, and stops are retracted. Inside diameter is bored, and edge of face A is chamfered.

Fig. 29. Setup, employing specially designed chuck, and sequence of operations for machining ring-gear blanks in two chuckings (Example 24)

dling and permit machining of all faces in one setup, a special hydraulically operated chuck having three inches of jaw travel was designed. This chuck permitted the machining of all surfaces in two chuckings. Setup and sequence of operations are given in Fig. 29.

Example 25. Seven Operations in One Chucking, Using Threaded Adapter (Fig. 30)

By using a threaded adapter at the headstock end of an engine lathe, and a male center in the tailstock, it was feasible to perform seven operations on tubular parts in a single chucking (Fig. 30). The workpiece had been previously bored and internally threaded to permit use of the threaded adapter. Machining details are given in the tabular caption for Fig. 30.

The first six operations included turning, undercutting, chamfering and threading. After completion of these operations, rotation was stopped and eight cross-holes, equally spaced around the periphery, were drilled through the cylinder wall. The cross-hole drill was powered separately and mounted on a quick-change holder. Adequate accuracy for radial spacing of the holes was obtained from marks on the adapter and a fixed pointer on the headstock. [Speed and feed for the turning operation were about one third higher than the nominal values shown in Table 6.]

Example 26. Expanding Collet Increases Machining Efficiency (Fig. 31)

After being broached to produce the 1.121/1.119-in. ID, the gear blank shown in Fig. 31 was turned, faced and chamfered in a 6-in. automatic stub lathe. Changing the method of holding the workpiece for machining, with no change of machine or of operating conditions (see caption for Fig. 31), resulted in the benefits detailed in the following comparison:

Original Method. The gear blank was first pressed onto an arbor (see Fig. 31), and was then machined on the stub lathe, which had a splined arbor driver adapted to the headstock, an air-operated tailstock with a live center, a 4-in. air cylinder to operate the tailstock, and two turning arbors on which the workpieces were pressed. Also required was one 8-ton hydraulic press, which was equipped with a base square to the ram, and was tooled with a press-off fixture, a spacing collar, and a slip-fit bushing (which was required for holding the arbor in alignment with the bore as it was being pressed into the unturned part).

For this operation, it was necessary for the operator to unload and load the lathe; and while the lathe was machining the part, to unload and load the second arbor, using the press provided. Cycle time for the lathe was 0.43 min. The usual time for unloading and loading the second arbor was 0.34 min. Each part was handled six times from floor to floor. Incentive standards for this operation were set at 1.65 standard hours per hundred pieces. At $2.50 per hour, this was a direct labor cost of $4.13 per hundred pieces turned.

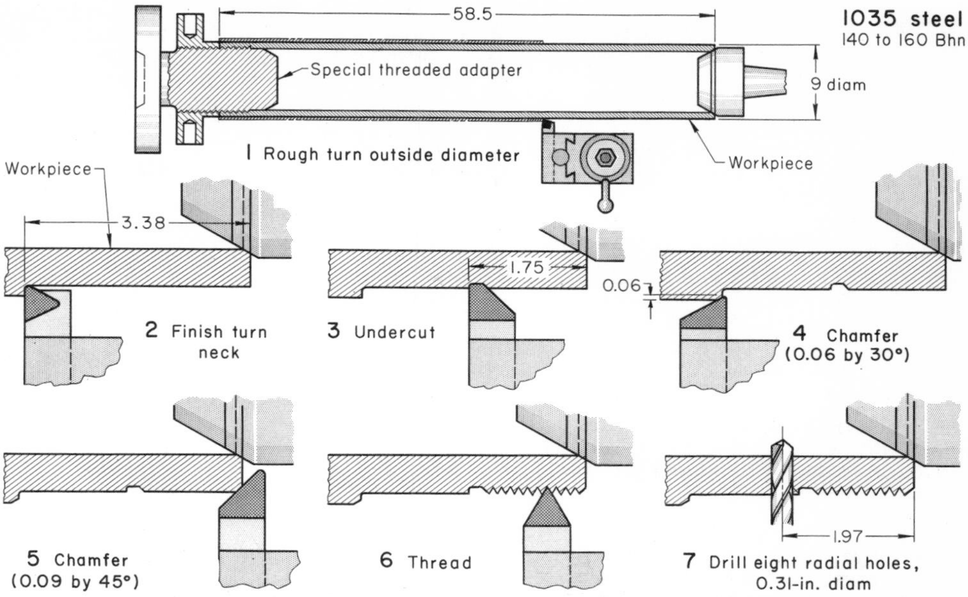

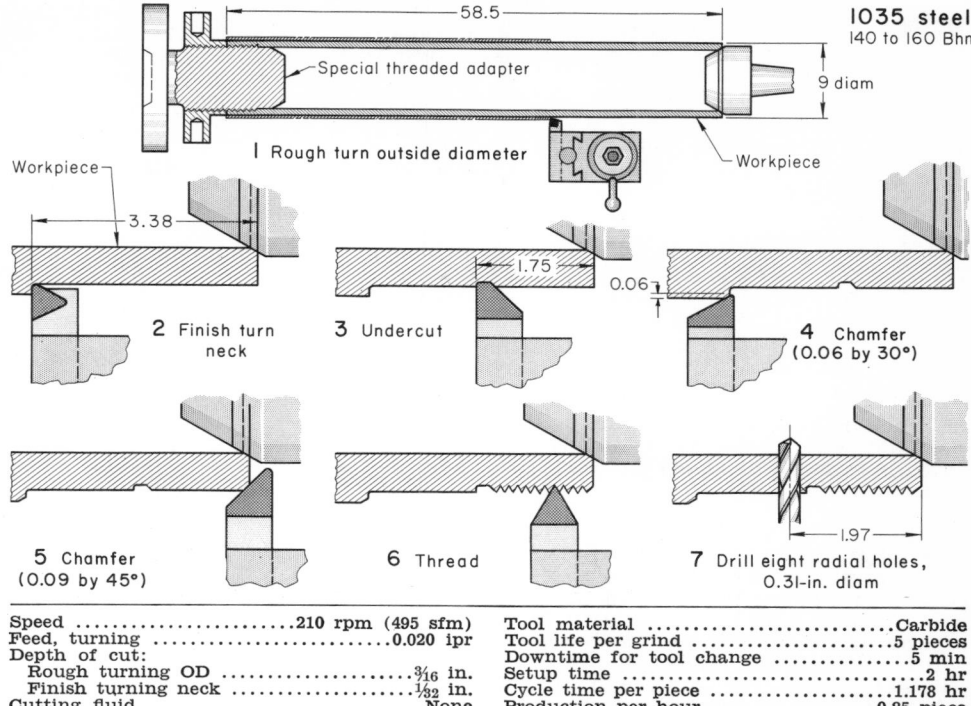

Speed	210 rpm (495 sfm)	Tool material	Carbide
Feed, turning	0.020 ipr	Tool life per grind	5 pieces
Depth of cut:		Downtime for tool change	5 min
Rough turning OD	3/16 in.	Setup time	2 hr
Finish turning neck	1/32 in.	Cycle time per piece	1.178 hr
Cutting fluid	None	Production per hour	0.85 piece

Fig. 30. Setup and conditions for performing seven machining operations in one chucking in an engine lathe, by the use of a special threaded adapter at headstock (Example 25)

Improved Method. The improved method consisted of changing to an expanding collet for holding the workpiece (Fig. 31). This change eliminated the need for the arbor press, which cost $2008, and its tooling, which cost $250, as well as the two arbors, which cost $50 each. Total cost of the eliminated machinery was $2358.

Installing the expanding collet in the headstock of the lathe cost a total of $483 ($100 for the 8-in. air cylinder required, and $383 for the collet and mandrel with drawbar). Net saving in equipment was thus $1875.

By the improved method, the incentive rate was 1.54 standard hours per hundred pieces, or 0.11 standard hour less than by the original method. However, by eliminating the arbor-press operation, another automatic lathe could be added — and one operator could handle both lathes. The incentive rate was thus reduced to 1.11 standard hours per hundred pieces, which provided a direct cost saving of $1.35 per hundred pieces, compared with the original method.

Surface Finish

The surface roughness obtained in lathe turning, aside from being dependent on workpiece material and hardness, is influenced by tool material and its relation to speed and feed rate, by tool design (particularly, tool nose radius), by the rigidity of the machine and the tool, and by the type and effectiveness of the cutting fluid used.

Tool Material, and Speed and Feed. Welding of chips to cutting tool ("edge buildup") is the major cause of surface roughness. Because the speed at which buildup occurs varies for different tool materials, selection of tool material for obtaining smoothest finishes depends on the surface speed to be used.

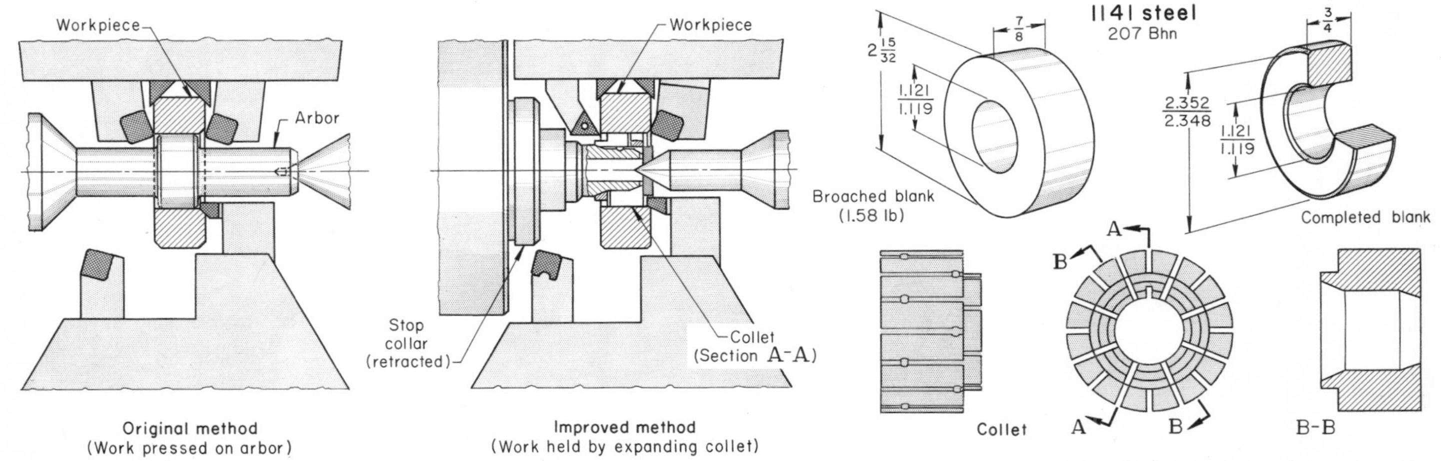

For both methods, speed was 824 rpm (540 sfm for turning and chamfering, 430 sfm average for facing); feed, 0.008 ipr for turning and chamfering, 0.007 ipr for facing; depth of cut, 0.060 in max; cutting fluid, 1-to-40 mixture of heavy-duty soluble oil and water; tool material, carbide.

Fig. 31. Change from original method of holding gear blank (pressed on arbor of stub lathe) to improved method (use of expanding collet) increased productivity and reduced cost, as indicated in Example 26.

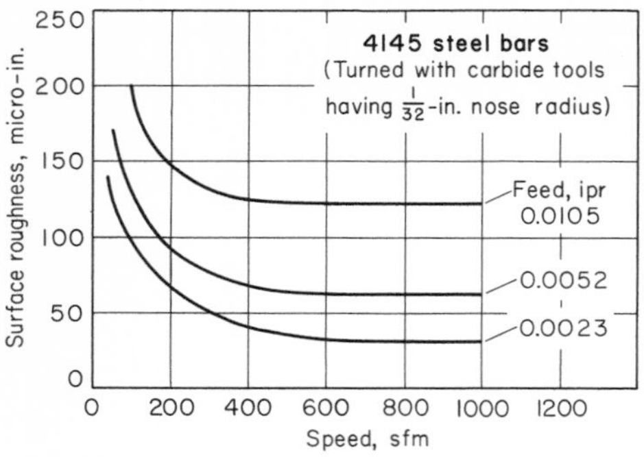

Fig. 32. Influence of speed on surface finish, at constant feed

With high speed steel tools, a built-up edge forms more readily as speed increases. The smoothest surfaces possible using high speed steel tools are obtained at speeds of 5 to 10 sfm, which are too low to be practical for most production applications.

Conversely, edge buildup on carbide tools is minimized by using a surface speed high enough to cause plastic flow of the chip (for ductile metals). A satisfactory guide for determining whether speeds are high enough in machining steel is the color of the chip after cooling. Steel chips that do not show some heat color (at least, a straw color) were removed at a surface speed too low for the material being turned — a practice that usually results in poor finish and short tool life.

The relation between finish and surface speed is shown graphically in Fig. 32; at any specific feed rate, surface finish stabilizes at 400 to 500 sfm. These data also show the pronounced influence of feed rate on surface finish.

For any given workpiece material, the finish obtained in turning with carbide tools is influenced also by the composition of the carbide. Straight tungsten carbide is suitable for brittle metals like cast iron, but tools that contain titanium carbide will give much better results, in terms of finish, allowable speed and tool life, for turning steel and other ductile metals.

In addition to conventional steel-cutting grades of carbide (all of which contain titanium carbide), special grades are available that more strongly resist adhering to steel workpieces over a wide range of speeds (250 to 1200 sfm), compared with conventional grades. As a result, these special grades are sometimes used for the primary purpose of obtaining better finishes, the higher speeds they can withstand being an added benefit in some instances. These special grades, however, are more brittle than conventional grades, and consequently they must be used for relatively light feeds and under conditions of maximum rigidity.

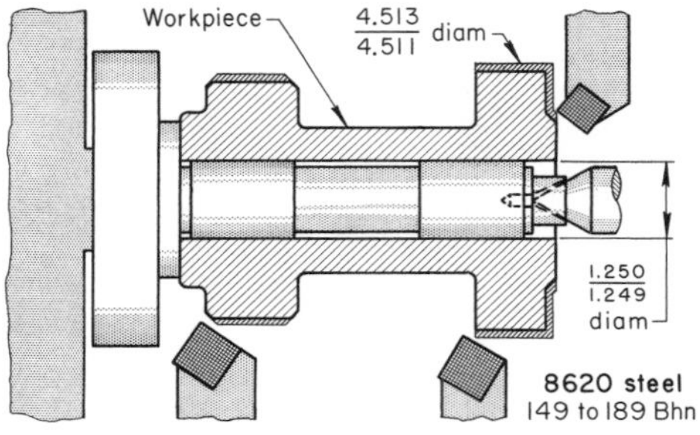

Item	Type of carbide tool: Steel-cutting grade (C-8)	Type of carbide tool: Special TiC grade
Speed, rpm	575	1040
Speed, sfm	639	1125
Feed, ipr	0.008	0.008
Depth of cut, in.	0.020	0.020
Finish obtained, micro-in.	180	80
Cycle time per piece, sec	18	10

Fig. 33. Improvement in surface finish and machining efficiency that resulted from change in composition of carbide tools used for turning, facing and chamfering cluster-gear blanks (Example 27)

The following example describes an application in which a special grade of titanium carbide proved advantageous:

Example 27. Improved Finish and Higher Speeds With Special Carbide (Fig. 33)

The tools originally used for turning, facing and chamfering cluster-gear blanks in an automatic lathe (setup shown in Fig. 33) were made of a conventional steel-cutting grade of carbide. As shown by the comparison of operating details in the tabular caption for Fig. 33, changing to tools made of a special grade of titanium carbide allowed higher speed and decreased cycle time, and also resulted in an improvement in surface finish.

Depth of cut (within any reasonable operating range) has little influence on the finish obtained when carbide tools are used. However, as the depth of cut increases, chip control becomes more critical. The chip breaker must provide a uniform movement of the chips away from the turned surface, because chips that are directed onto the turned surface will scratch the workpiece, and particles of these chips will weld to the workpiece surface.

Nose radius of the tool exerts an important influence on the surface finish obtainable, as demonstrated in the example that follows:

Example 28. Effect of Tool Nose on Finish

A shaft made of 4130 steel (hardness, Rockwell C 34) was turned in an engine lathe with carbide tools. Specified finish was 50 micro-in. At a speed of 712 rpm (270 sfm), feed of 0.0075 ipr, and depth of cut of 0.025 in., tools ground with a nose radius of ⅛ in. could produce only an unacceptable 100-micro-in. finish. This was reduced to 75 micro-in. by grinding the tool nose to a ¼-in. radius. The specified 50-micro-in. finish finally was obtained by using a ⅛-in.-radius tool on which a small flat had been ground. The flat, 0.005 to 0.008 in. wide to correspond with feed rate, produced a skiving action on the work surface.

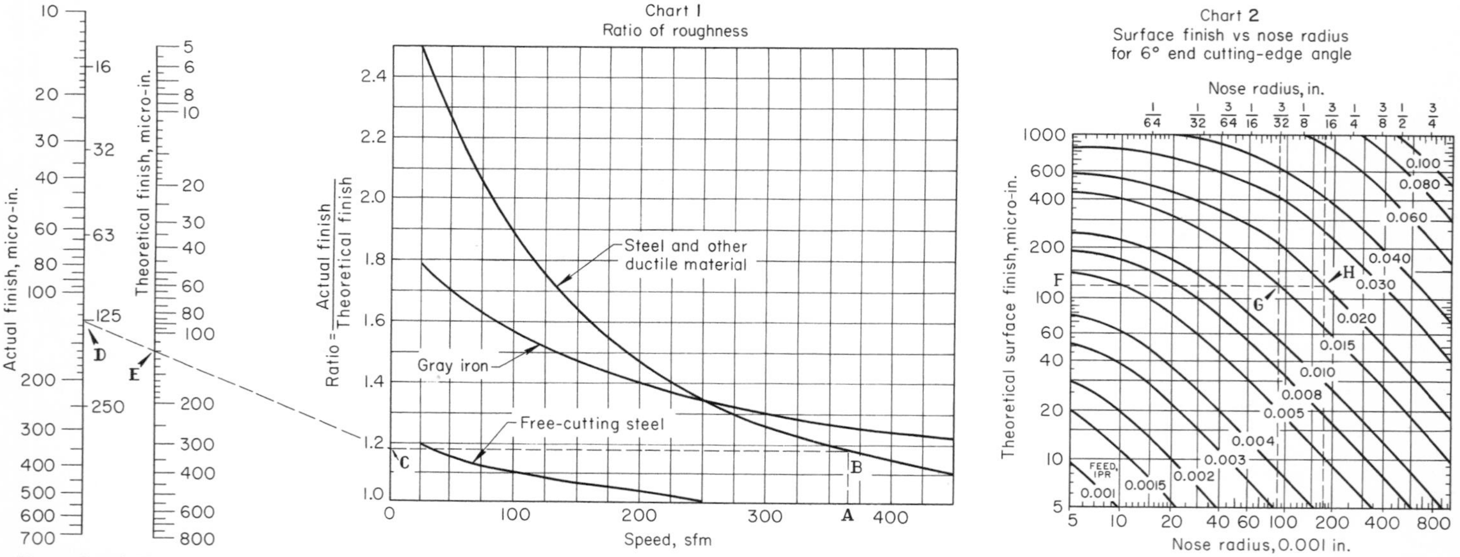

Example of Use. To determine the nose radius required for obtaining a finish of 125 micro-in. when turning 1095 steel at a speed of 365 sfm and a feed of 0.015 ipr:

1 On chart 1, locate 365 sfm (point A). From point A, follow a vertical line to its intersection with the "Steel and other ductile material" curve (point B). Follow a horizontal line to determine the ratio of actual to theoretical finish (point C).

2 Locate the specified 125-micro-in. finish on the "Actual finish" scale (Point D), then draw a line from point D to point C. This line crosses the "Theoretical finish" scale at 120 micro-in. (point E).

3 On chart 2, locate the theoretical finish of 120 micro-in. (point F). Follow a horizontal line to its intersection with the 0.015-ipr feed curve (point G). Follow a vertical line and find that required nose radius is 0.090 in.; the nearest standard radius is $\frac{3}{32}$ in.

4 If machine and work conditions are such that a heavier feed rate could be used, extend line F — G to intersect the 0.020-ipr feed curve (point H). From point H, the vertical line indicates a required nose radius of 0.175 in.; the standard radius is $\frac{3}{16}$ in.

Fig. 34. Nomograph for estimating nose radius required for obtaining specified surface finish

The nose radius required for obtaining a specified surface finish may be estimated by means of the nomograph presented in Fig. 34.

Rigidity of machines and tools has a large influence on surface finish, other factors remaining constant. Chatter develops at lower speeds in machines that have loose bearings, or other vital parts that need repair, than in well-maintained machines. Nonrigid tools and holders also allow chatter to develop at lower speeds than when rigidity is good. Roughness of machined surfaces is the immediate result of chatter, and short tool life follows.

Machines having preloaded ball-bearing (or roller-bearing) spindles provide the rigidity necessary for meeting stringent requirements on finish and tolerance; the use of a machine of this type is described in the example that follows. (See also Example 927.)

Example 29. Turning Shafts to 10 and 16 Micro-In. (Table 13)

In turning the stainless steel shaft illustrated in Table 13, it was required that a finish of 10 to 12 micro-in. be obtained on the taper, and of 16 micro-in. on two 0.7500-in. diameters. The latter also were required to be turned to a tolerance of +0.0000, −0.0002 in. A 10-in. engine lathe with a preloaded ball-bearing spindle having a maximum runout of 0.00002 in. was used to meet these requirements. Other machine features included hardened ways, a precision-ground tailstock center, and a taper attachment.

The workpiece was machined in two setups. In the first, the part was placed in a chuck and the smaller end was faced and center drilled. In the second setup, the part was machined in nine operations (as detailed in Table 13), during which it was held at one end in a 1-in. collet against a fixed stop inside the spindle. The opposite end was supported by a live center from the tailstock.

Cutting Fluid

Although for some applications of lathe turning cutting fluids are neither needed nor desired — most cast iron parts, for example, are machined "dry", and some steel parts (as in Example 7, on page 9) — in most applications, some type of cutting fluid is used. Cutting fluids serve the same purposes in lathe turning as in other metal-cutting operations: to cool workpieces and tools, to flush away chips, and to promote cutting action by minimizing adherence of tool and work.

Surface-finish and tolerance requirements, work-metal composition, and the specific types of operation influence the choice of cutting fluid.

Soluble oil (in mixtures at various concentrations with water) is the most widely used cutting fluid, both because it is the least expensive and because it is unexcelled by any other fluid in ability to cool and to flush away chips. Soluble oils are nonflammable and nontoxic, and are safe to use with virtually all metals without fear of staining. Most soluble oils contain inhibitors that prevent them from causing ferrous metals to rust. The usual mixture is about 1 part oil to 20 parts water; proportions are not critical, however, and in some instances 40 parts water may be used to dilute 1 part oil without significant changes in results.

However, soluble-oil emulsions are far less effective than many other cutting fluids for promoting cutting action and preventing edge buildup. As required smoothness and dimensional accuracy increase, some oil or nonaqueous oil mixture will be needed.

Straight mineral oils are often used when soluble oils do not meet requirements, particularly when the work material is not free-machining or when specified finish exceeds the capability of soluble oil. Mineral oils with a viscosity of about 100 SUS (at 100 F) are most commonly used, although oils with a viscosity of only about 40 SUS (such as mineral seal oil) are used in many applications.

Blended cutting oils of various viscosities are readily available as proprietary compositions. Most of them are basically mineral oils, but are blended with sulfur compounds, animal fats and other materials. They may be used as-purchased or cut back with mineral oils, depending on prior experience with similar jobs.

Although any straight oils are less effective than soluble oils (oil-water emulsions) for cooling and washing away chips, all oils (and particularly those containing sulfur compounds or other special additives) are more effective for improving cutting action. When chatter develops, as the result of vibration or other causes, unacceptable surface finish and short tool life are inevitable. Cutting oils are more effective than soluble-oil emulsions for preventing chatter.

Special Oils and Mixtures. In applications that demand maximum performance of cutting fluids, high-viscosity thread-cutting oils or lard-oil mixtures are preferred. These special cutting fluids are especially effective for cutting threads that require smooth surfaces.

Lard oil is one of the best for promoting cutting action, but because of its high viscosity it is impractical for high-production applications. However, it is often used in small lathes for toolroom or pilot-production applications.

Both thread-cutting oil and lard oil are often mixed with mineral oil, to reduce viscosity to a practical level. These mixtures still retain some of the advantages of the undiluted oils.

Neither of these special oils, however, is equal to a soluble-oil emulsion in ability to cool or to wash away chips.

Compatibility With Metals. All of the cutting fluids discussed above can be used for machining ferrous metals without danger of staining or corroding the work. However, not all of these cutting fluids are compatible with all metals. For instance, sulfurized oils are likely to stain copper-base alloys, beryllium and nickel-base alloys. For information concerning the cutting fluids that are compatible with various nonferrous metals, see articles in this volume on machining of specific metals.

Contamination of cutting fluids may cause excessive variation in workpiece finish or dimensions, short tool life, or corrosion of the workpieces. Common contaminants include: tramp oil, usually from hydraulic systems; water, from any of several sources; fine chips; and bacteria, which cause rancidity and breakdown of cutting fluids by organic decomposition.

Normal preventive maintenance usually is sufficient to forestall serious contamination from tramp oil or water. At a minimum, the circulating system should include a screen (50 to 100 mesh) to prevent chips from being returned to the machining area. For more stringent tolerance and finish requirements, cutting fluids should be circulated through filters. Contamination by bacteria can be prevented by purchasing oils that contain microbe-inhibitors. Water-oil emulsions (soluble oils) used for machining ferrous metals should contain a rust-inhibitor.

Selected References

ASME Research Committee on Metal Cutting Data and Bibliography, "Manual on Cutting of Metals With Single-Point Tools", Second Edition (O. W. Boston, Editor), American Society of Mechanical Engineers, New York, 1952, 546 p. Includes a 191-page section of tabular data giving recommended speeds and power requirements for different feeds and depths or widths of cut in machining steels and cast irons of various compositions and conditions with single-point tools made of carbon steel, high speed steel, cast cobalt-base alloy, or carbide. Also contains more than 180 references to other sources of information.

L. M. Cross, "Numerical Control vs Tracer Control of Machine Tools", ASTME Paper No. 285, 1960. Describes and distinguishes the uses and functions of the two systems; explains, by example, how the two systems are combined to make a "tracer controlled lathe with numerical punched-card function control", and outlines the programming procedure.

D. T. Bisceglia and J. W. Rodd, "Production Application of Ceramics to the Machining of High Strength Steels", ASTME Paper No. 253, 1960. Explains the development and testing of ceramic cutting tools, and describes their techniques and advantages for the turning of gun barrels and precision finishing of hardened steels at Watervliet Arsenal.

D. R. Kibbey and H. D. Moore, "Cutting

Table 13. Turning Shafts to Rigid Finish and Tolerance Specifications (Example 29) (a)

Description of Operations

1 ...... Rough turn two 0.7500-in. diameters
2 ...... Turn ⅞-in. diameter
3 ...... Turn 13⁄16-in. thread diameter
4 ...... Turn 11⁄16-in. diameter
5 ...... Turn ½-in. thread diameter
6 ...... Turn taper (to a finish of 10 to 12 micro-in.)
7 ...... Thread, 13⁄16–16 UN–2A
8 ...... Thread, ½–20 UNF–2A
9 ...... Finish turn two 0.7500-in. diameters (to finish of 16 micro-in. and tolerance of +0.0000, −0.0002 in.)

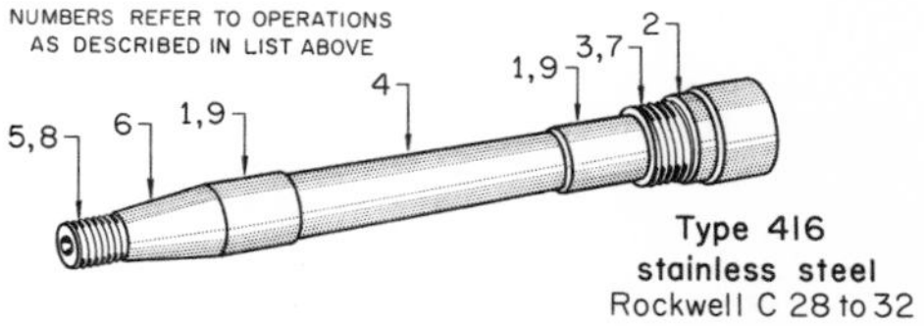

Operating Conditions

Speed, turning ..... 1400 rpm (180 to 320 sfm)
Speed, threading .... 470 rpm
Feed, rough turning .... 0.003 ipr
Feed, finish and taper turning ...... 0.001 ipr
Depth of cut:
  Rough turning .... 0.004 to 0.006 in.
  Finish turning .... 0.002 to 0.003 in.
Cutting fluid .... Soluble oil(b)
Tool life per grind(c):
  Rough turning .... 20 pieces
  Finish and taper turning .... 15 pieces
  Threading .... 30 pieces
Setup time .... 30 min
Cycle time per piece .... 20 min

(a) Operations described here were performed in a 10-in. engine lathe that had a preloaded ball-bearing spindle. (b) Mixed in 1-to-20 ratio with water. (c) For all operations, carbide tools were ground with a 500-grit diamond wheel and honed to a 4-micro-in. finish.

Tool Comparisons at High Speeds", ASTME Paper No. 305, 1960. Compares tool life and other effects obtained with tools of three different ceramics and of two carbide compositions, in lathe turning of 1045 steel at speeds ranging from 500 to 3000 sfm. Based on research conducted at Ohio State University.

D. Kececioglu and A. Sorensen, Jr., "Relative Effect of Dry Cutting, Mist Cooling, and Flood Cooling on Nine Machinability Factors", ASTME Paper No. 308, 1960. Describes test runs on lathe turning of 1045 steel using a carbide cutting tool under the three coolant conditions. Comparative data are plotted showing the effects of these conditions on: tangential, axial and radial forces; specific energy; three power values (shear, friction and total); chip-cutting ratio; and tool wear.

K. J. Trigger and B. T. Chao, "Crater Wear of Cutting Tools", ASTE (ASTME), 1956. Explains theory of crater wear; describes experiments conducted using high speed steel and carbide tools, and shows results in graphs and tables. One conclusion drawn is that temperature has a major effect on crater wear.

Other Examples of Turning Applications in This Volume

Work metal	Example number
Work Metals Compared in Turning	
Cast iron	641, 642, 643, 661, 662, 663
Tool steel	687
Stainless steel	776
Heat-resisting alloys	807, 808, 809
Aluminum	868, 869, 872, 874
Copper	932
Tool Materials Compared in Turning	
Tool steel	692
Stainless steel	743, 774
Tool Design	
Cast iron	647, 648
Tool steel	684, 691
Stainless steel	740, 742, 744
Heat-resisting alloys	801 through 806
Refractory metals	862

Work metal	Example number
Effect of Free-Cutting Additives on Turning	
Cast iron	646
Tool steel	689, 690, 693
Copper	932, 933, 934
Methods	
Cast iron	650
Tool steel	707, 709
Stainless steel	740, 741, 771, 772, 775, 777, 778
Refractory metals	861, 862
Aluminum	875, 903, 905, 906, 908, 909
Beryllium	927, 928
Copper	935, 951, 952, 953
Magnesium	977, 978, 979
Nickel	995, 996, 997
Titanium	998(a)

(a) Also discusses tool design.

Boring

*By the ASM Committee on Boring**

BORING is a machining process in which internal diameters are generated in true relation to the centerline of the spindle by means of single-point cutting tools, and is most commonly used for enlarging or finishing holes or other circular contours. Although most boring operations are done on simple, straight-through holes (ranging upward in diameter from about ¼ in.), the process is also applied to a variety of other configurations. Tooling can be designed for the boring of blind holes, holes with "bottle" configurations, circular-contoured cavities, and bores with numerous steps, undercuts and counterbores. The process is not limited by length-to-diameter ratio of holes; with the workpiece properly supported, holes having diameters that exceed length (or vice versa) by a factor of 50 or more have been successfully bored.

Boring is sometimes used after drilling, to provide drilled holes with greater dimensional accuracy or improved finish. It is more widely used, however, for finishing holes too large to be produced economically by drilling, such as large cored holes in castings or large pierced holes in forgings. In many applications, boring is done in conjunction with turning, facing or other machining operations. The scope of this article is limited to applications in which boring is the sole operation or in which it is the major operation in a machining sequence.

Machines

Metal workpieces have been bored on almost every type of machine that has facilities for rotating a spindle or a workpiece. Most boring, however, is done on the machines (or modifications of them) discussed in the following paragraphs. Electronic (numerical) control can be used with many of these machines.

Engine lathes are versatile, and are used for a variety of boring operations — usually for single-tool jobs. Lathes provide maximum rigidity, because of their massive, single-unit construction, and permit the use of supporting members such as steady rests or boring-bar supports.

In most operations, the workpiece is clamped to the face plate or chuck and is rotated by the spindle in the headstock, the boring tool is secured to a bracket mounted on the tool-post carriage, and power is supplied to the tool from the carriage. Occasionally, however, the workpiece is mounted on the lathe compound and is fed into the rotating boring tool, which is mounted between the headstock and the tailstock and is powered by the headstock spindle.

The use of engine lathes for boring usually is restricted to the machining of a single part (or at most, a few identical parts), because setups are cumbersome and expensive, and because only one hole can be bored at a time. Other limitations on the use of engine lathes for boring are as follows:

1 Swing of the lathe limits maximum projection-from-center of the workpiece.
2 Bed length limits maximum length of carriage feed.
3 Workpieces must be symmetrical, or very nearly so, because off-center configurations cause a serious out-of-balance condition.

Turret lathes are modifications of engine lathes, and are used extensively for boring. The use of turret lathes, however, is subject to the same limitations with respect to workpiece size and configuration as apply to engine lathes (see list above).

Turret lathes are better adapted to high production than engine lathes. The main advantage of a turret lathe is that the rotating turret can be tooled for performing as many as eight different operations in a continuous sequence. This sequence often includes turning, facing, drilling, reaming, tapping or other machining operations, in addition to boring.

Bar machines (screw machines), which in turn are modifications of turret lathes, enable a further increase in production, for parts that are made from bars or tubes. Production can be still further increased by the use of a multiple-spindle automatic bar machine, designed so that every tool is in operation at the same time, but on a different piece of material. This principle is also used on chucking machines.

Vertical boring mills embody the fundamental elements of the lathe. At times the choice between these two types of machines depends on availability, although the vertical boring mill has its own area of application. Vertical machines are more appropriate for workpieces that are so large, heavy, or seriously out of balance that they are easier to lay down on a table than to hang on the face plate of a lathe. Hence vertical boring mills are commonly used for boring and turning operations on heavy workpieces, such as large rings and short cylinders. The weight of a heavy workpiece is distributed uniformly over the table of the boring mill and can easily be supported by the machine base.

*J. J. BARNABEE, *Chairman*, Planning Manager, Manufacturing General Office, Caterpillar Tractor Co.; WAYNE E. BLACKMUN, Manager, Engineering and Manufacturing, Madison Industries Inc.; ROBERT C. BOWEN, Director of Commercial Planning, Ingersoll Milling Machine Co.; H. L. GLEDHILL, Special Project Coordinator, Alexandria Works, Manning, Maxwell & Moore Div., Dresser Industries, Inc.

J. K. LEONOWICZ, Tool Engineer, Euclid Div., General Motors Corp.; W. E. MULLEN, Superintendent of Methods Engineering, Norwood Works, Allis-Chalmers Manufacturing Co.; JOHN POWERS, Vice President – Operations, Verson Allsteel Press Co.; LAWRENCE RANSBERGER, Tooling Supervisor, Dodge Manufacturing Corp.

ELMER STOUT, Process Engineer, Bendix Products Aerospace Div., Bendix Corp.; E. TROBAUGH, Chief Engineer, Robbins Engineering and Development Corp.; K. WINEBRENNER, Superintendent of Machine Shop, East Chicago Works, Blaw-Knox Co.; RALPH A. WISCO, Division Superintendent, Bearing Plant, Link-Belt Co.

Vertical boring mills are especially suited to heavy workpieces that require indicating during setup. With these machines a workpiece can be placed on the horizontal table, set up, leveled and given a trial cut with temporary clamping. Counterbalance can be applied to the top of the work table to compensate for off-center loads. Two or more tools can be operated simultaneously, thus permitting two or more boring operations, or boring and turning operations, to be done at the same time. Another advantage of the vertical mill is that it requires less floor space than an engine lathe of equivalent capacity.

Vertical turret lathes include features of the vertical boring mill. In addition, they are equipped with a turret on the main head and a turret tool holder on the side head. A second vertical head may be mounted on the crossrail and a second side head may be mounted on the opposite side of the machine; these modifications provide the machine with greater flexibility and increase its capacity for simultaneous multiple cutting on a variety of work.

Horizontal boring mills are preferred for a wide variety of production work. In these machines, the workpiece remains stationary and the tool rotates. In some setups the work is fed toward the tool; in others, the tool is fed toward the work.

Horizontal boring mills are of three principal types — table, planer and floor. The table type feeds horizontally on saddle ways, both parallel with and at right angles to the spindle axis. The headstock can be moved vertically on the column, and the spindle is fed horizontally. Because of its flexibility, this type of machine is especially well-suited to work in which other machining operations are performed in conjunction with boring.

The planer type of machine is similar to the table type, except that the supporting table can be moved only at right angles to the spindle. On some planer-type machines, the housing can be fed in and out on a slide, in the same direction as the spindle.

The floor-type machine uses a stationary, T-slotted floor plate, instead of a table, for supporting workpieces. This type of machine is used for machining workpieces that are too large or heavy for reciprocating tables. Horizontal feeds perpendicular to the spindle axis are obtained by movement of the column along the baseways, rather than by movement of the workpiece.

Drill presses, especially of the radial type, are sometimes used for boring, usually when only a few parts require boring. Difficulty of holding tolerances because of lack of rigidity is the main disadvantage in the use of drill presses for boring. This can be partly overcome by clamping workpieces in fixtures that allow the boring-bar extension to enter a bushing in the fixture on the side of the workpiece opposite the spindle.

Precision boring machines are required for boring to tolerances of ten-thousandths of an inch. These machines are available in either vertical or horizontal models with one or more working spindles.

Precision boring machines are of two basic types: (*a*) those in which the spindle is mounted on a fixed bridge and the workpiece is mounted on a reciprocating table, and (*b*) those in which the spindle is mounted on a reciprocating table and the work-holding fixture is mounted on a fixed bridge. In either type, the workpiece may be mounted on the spindle, and rotated, while the tool is mounted on the table or fixed bridge and is nonrotating.

Precision boring machines are much used in tool making.

Special machines include features of the conventional machines discussed above, or are modifications of these machines. Usually, they are "single-purpose" machines, expressly designed either for large-quantity, continuous production of identical parts (as in Example 876, in the article on Machining of Aluminum, which describes the boring of automotive pistons) or for boring work that is too large or unwieldy to be handled in "standard" equipment. An example of the latter is a specially constructed boring mill capable of accommodating workpieces up to 50½ ft in diameter and boring them to a tolerance of ±0.002 in. This machine has two tool heads mounted on an 82-ton crossrail, which is supported by two 21-ft-high columns that span a 35-ft-diam rotary work table. Table speeds range from 0.005 to 0.5 rpm.

Tools

The simplest form of boring tool, shown in Fig. 1(a), consists of a single-point cutter mechanically secured directly to a straight length of the boring bar. The bar can be rotated and fed into the workpiece, or the workpiece can be rotated and moved while the bar remains stationary. However, adjustment is difficult; when the tool becomes worn it must be removed for sharpening and must be reset when returned. Resetting requires a fair degree of skill, and is sometimes tedious. With the boring tool shown in Fig. 1(b), the cutter can be advanced to compen-

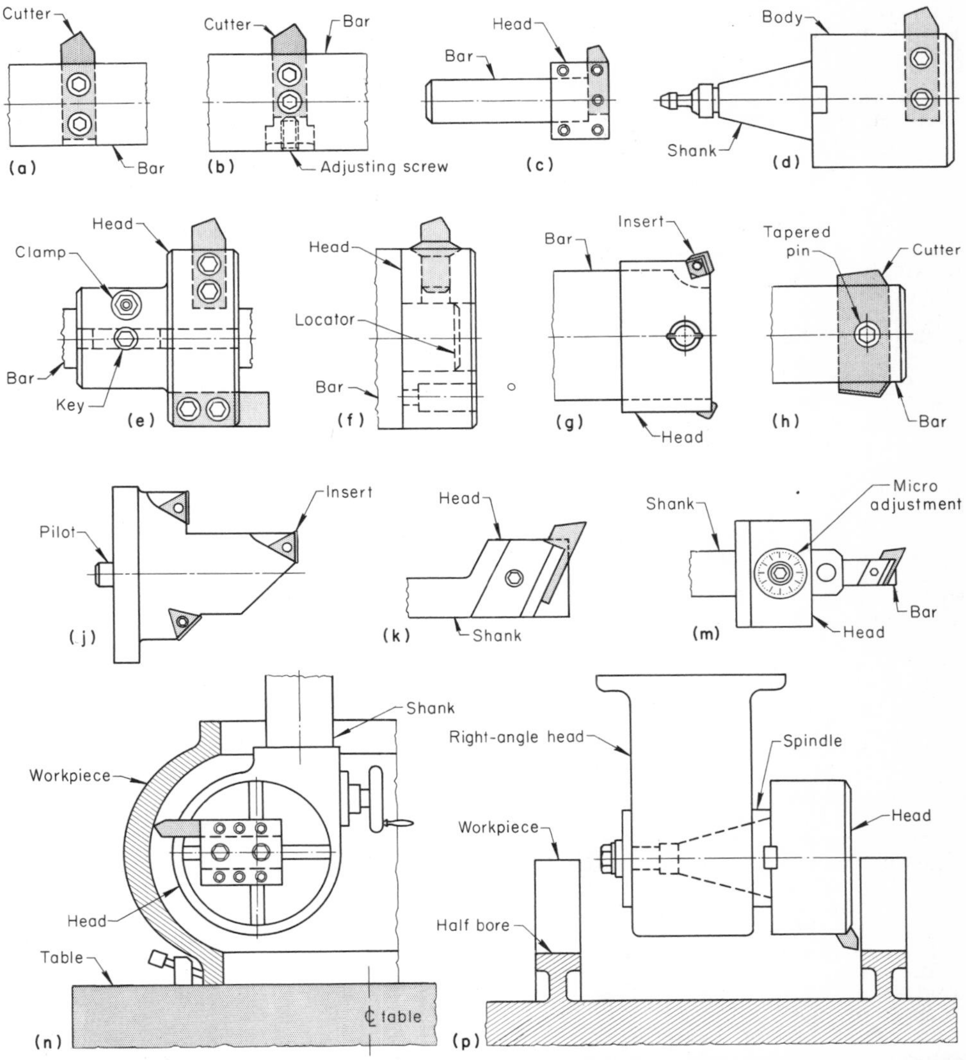

(a) Single-point cutter mechanically secured to boring bar, with no screw for adjustment. (b) Similar to (a), except for adjusting screw, which permits advancement of cutter to compensate for wear. (c) Universal head, or "box tool". (d) Stub boring bar. (e) Detachable head. (f) Detachable head suited to mounting on end of stub or line boring bar. (g) Blade-type tool with two identical cutting inserts 180° apart. (h) Blade-type tool in which cutter is inserted through the body to provide two cutting edges. (j) Multiple-diameter head with indexable inserts. (k) Offset head. (m) Offset head with micro adjustment. (n) Head for generating a radius. (p) Head for boring at right angle to axis of boring bar.

Fig. 1. Thirteen types of boring tools. See text for additional discussion.

sate for wear, by loosening the securing screws and turning the adjusting screw forward.

Increased versatility of operation is provided by a universal boring head (sometimes called a "box tool"), shown in Fig. 1(c). These heads, which are attached to the end of the bar, are designed to hold left-hand or right-hand cutters of a variety of configurations. They also can hold more than one cutter, for multiple-diameter work.

Figure 1(d) shows a type of head known as a stub boring bar. This head has a fixed cutter, and can be used for only a small range of bore sizes. However, it is simple and widely used.

Detachable heads of the type illustrated in Fig. 1(e) are widely used because of their flexibility. These heads can be located at any desired point along the bar and can hold two or more cutters.

The type of detachable head shown in Fig. 1(f) is mounted at the end of a boring bar. These heads can be designed to hold more than one cutter, and their interchangeability permits the boring bar to be used for a range of bore sizes.

The assembly illustrated in Fig. 1(g) is a blade-type tool utilizing two identical cutting inserts 180° apart. The inserts can be either brazed or secured mechanically. The main advantage of this type of tool is that it equalizes the forces imposed on the bar during operation. It is thus possible to maintain closer tolerances with bars having maximum unsupported length than when using a boring tool that has only one cutting edge. Its disadvantage is that the blades cannot be adjusted to compensate for wear, and hence must be removed for grinding and then be reset. This disadvantage is lessened by the use of mechanically held inserts that can be indexed to maintain size.

Figure 1(h) illustrates another style of blade-type tool. The cutter is inserted through the body, thus providing two cutting edges. This tool is sometimes known as a reaming-type boring tool and may be used without support or with a pilot. The two cutting edges often enable a substantial increase in feed rate over that possible when only one cutting edge is used. Advantages and disadvantages of this tool are similar to those described for the tool illustrated in Fig. 1(g).

Numerous modifications of the tool illustrated in Fig. 1(j) are used. This multiple-diameter head may be used with two cutting edges for the same diameter or with two or more cutting edges performing several operations simultaneously or consecutively. Mechanically secured disposable carbide inserts are usually used. These inserts can be indexed, thus using all cutting edges before they are replaced. This is a single-purpose tool and is best suited to high-production boring.

An offset boring head, particularly well-suited to the boring of small holes, is illustrated in Fig. 1(k). This type has no means for fine adjustment. An offset boring head with a micro adjustment is shown in Fig. 1(m). Adjustment is quickly performed by unlocking the dial, turning it to attain the required tool setting, and then relocking it. This head is useful in low-production or toolroom boring in which frequent changes of diameter are required.

A head for generating a radius is shown in Fig. 1(n). This type of head is used to generate an internal or external torus on a workpiece by means of a lathe. The head illustrated in Fig. 1(n) is hand fed and used for low-production boring. For higher production, a power feed can be applied.

Figure 1(p) illustrates a right-angle head, which is often used with stub boring bars on line bores that normally require piloted boring bars. Using a right-angle head helps to minimize bearing and vibration problems often encountered with long boring bars. Right-angle heads are especially suited to machining half bores.

Tool Design

Cutting angles for boring are more critical than for operations such as turning or planing, for at least two reasons: (*a*) boring is more frequently a final machining operation, and (*b*) chip flow is of greater concern in boring. Nomenclature of the angles for boring tools is shown in Fig. 2.

The type and the size of the hole being bored are major factors influencing requirements of tool angles. As noted in the center portion of Fig. 2, the side cutting-edge angle must be varied for through boring, bottoming, or clearing bottom. The end relief angle denoted as angle A in the three lower sketches of Fig. 2 must be sufficient to clear the bore surface. Therefore, this angle must be increased as the bore size is decreased. Excessive end relief is not recommended, however, because it weakens the cutting edge.

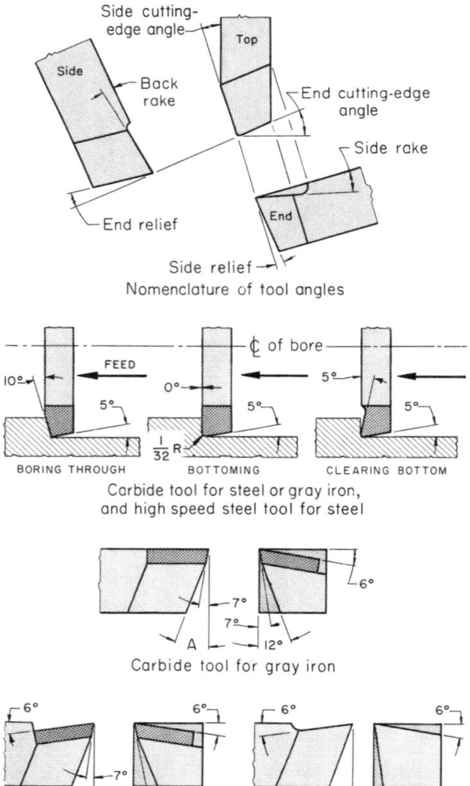

Fig. 2. Nomenclature and typical configurations of boring tools. End relief angle A in lower sketches varies inversely with bore diameter.

Back and side rake angles, in addition to providing cutting action, must act in combination to direct chip flow properly. Chips must flow away from the cut surface toward the center of the bore. If chips are directed toward the side of the bore, they may wrap themselves around the tool in heavy cuts, or mar the finish in a final cut. [Avoidance of chip congestion is of particular importance in boring lead-base bearings. If a lead alloy chip becomes entrapped, it is likely to fuse and promote further congestion, damaging the surface of the workpiece or the tool, or both. Designs of carbide tools for boring lead-base bearing alloys are illustrated on page 482.]

Typical values for boring-tool angles are shown in the lower portion of Fig. 2. These tool angles generally give free-cutting action with minimum resistance to the cutter, thus minimizing the likelihood of chatter. Tool angles may be varied considerably, however.

As boring speeds are increased, and as closer dimensional control is required, it becomes increasingly important that cutting angles be duplicated in regrinding. Random grinding of boring tools can cause variation in surface finish, subnormal tool life, and excessive variation in dimensions.

Tool Materials

High speed steel generally is more suitable than carbide for slow-speed boring of large workpieces. Carbide cutting edges are used almost exclusively for precision boring, in which speeds are high, depth of cut is low, and maximum rigidity is maintained in the setup. Carbide is less suitable for slow speeds and heavier cuts, especially if rigidity cannot be maintained.

There are many exceptions to general rules for selecting cutting-tool materials, as will be noted in the examples in this article that describe specific applications. For more complete information on the characteristics and applicability of cutting-tool materials, see the article that begins on page 325.

Pilots and Supports

Figure 3 illustrates a number of methods that are used for piloting and supporting tools in applications in which long boring bars must be used or close tolerances are required.

In many setups for which it is impractical to use bearing supports, the bar can be supported by the workpiece. Figure 3(a) shows a piloted bar, often known as a "pack head", that uses the workpiece for support. Four or more inserts (usually of nylon or bronze) form the bearing surfaces for the pilot. Another type of head that is piloted by the workpiece is illustrated in Fig. 3(b). This trepanning head is most commonly used for boring large-diameter holes from the solid. Wear pads (usually of carbide) located on the diameter

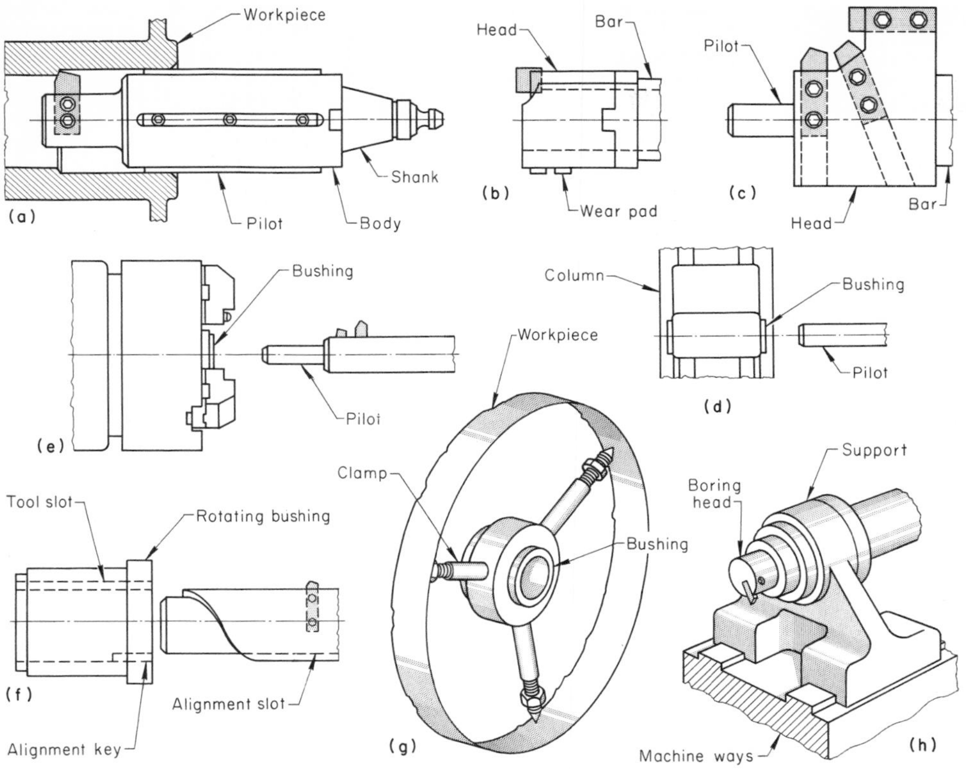

(a) "Pack head" type of pilot. (b) Wear-pad support of trepanning head used for boring large-diameter holes from solid stock. (c) Piloted head capable of using several cutting edges. (d) Bushing mounted on auxiliary column guides pilot on boring bar.

(e) Rotating bushing mounted on front of lathe chuck to receive piloted bar. (f) Rotating bushing aligns boring tool with tool slot in pilot bushing. (g) Three-leg, adjustable spider support. (h) Boring-bar support mounted on machine ways in line with centerline of spindle.

Fig. 3. Methods of piloting or supporting boring tools to maintain alignment. See text for additional discussion.

180° from the cutting edge are used with this type of head to aid in maintaining alignment.

Many modifications of the tool assembly illustrated in Fig. 3(c) are used in production boring applications in which it is practical to precede the cutting edges with a pilot. This type of pilot is usually hardened and ground (and may even be chromium plated) to resist wear.

When it is not feasible to use a portion of the workpiece for the pilot to enter, a guide bushing may be established on an auxiliary column. This principle is illustrated in Fig. 3(d). The type of support shown must be adjusted so that the center of the bushing is accurately aligned with the centerline of the spindle.

Another means of pilot support, for use when machining relatively short bores, is illustrated in Fig. 3(e). As seen in the illustration, the pilot must enter the rotating bushing before the cutting edges begin boring the workpiece, which is held on the front of the rotating chuck.

A rotating bushing used with a line boring bar is illustrated in Fig. 3(f). The spiral on the nose of the bar contacts the alignment key upon entry of the bar and rotates the tool slot into alignment with the cutting tools, thus providing support.

In some applications, workpiece configuration allows the use of a spider support. A three-leg, adjustable support of this type is illustrated in Fig. 3(g). This type of support, however, is difficult to align, and hence is ordinarily used only for extremely low-production or toolroom operations.

Supports mounted on machine ways (Fig. 3h) are in common use, particularly when the boring tools are fed into the rotating workpiece, as on a lathe or similar machine tool.

Maximum unsupported length of a boring bar depends to a great extent on tolerance requirements. Other governing factors are hardness of the metal being bored, speed, depth of cut, and cutting-tool material.

Steel boring bars have a modulus of elasticity of approximately 30 million psi, and although most steel boring bars are heat treated for additional strength or wear resistance, the modulus is unchanged by heat treatment. For maintaining tolerances of the order of ±0.001 in., an unsupported length of four times diameter approaches the practical limit for steel boring bars, and with this much unsupported bar length even minor increases in speed or feed are likely to cause chatter. Less stringent tolerances of ±0.005 in. have been maintained with steel bars having an unsupported length of nearly seven times diameter.

When boring-bar length must be greater than four times diameter and additional support is not feasible, boring bars made from carbide are sometimes used; the modulus of elasticity of carbide is about three times greater than that of steel, and hence rigidity can be maintained for a greater unsupported length, as in the next example:

Example 30. Carbide Boring Bars With 12-to-1 Ratio of Length to Diameter (Table 1)

Formerly, bores up to 40 in. long in powder chambers of guns made of 4140 steel at 375 to 400 Bhn were brought to pregrinding size with a high speed steel contour reamer in four stages — a slow and expensive process.

Reaming was first replaced with a tracer-boring setup, using a carbide cutting tool and a steel boring bar. The length-to-diameter ratio of this bar was 8 to 1. Because of vibration and deflection during cutting, the diameter at the rear of the bore was 0.015 to 0.035 in. less than the specified minimum. Deflection was remedied by taking several light passes, but this method was too slow.

When carbide reinforcing strips were brazed to the bar for added stiffness, machining time was greatly reduced (Table 1). The life of carbide disposable-insert cutters was increased from one cutting edge per pass to one edge per gun tube. The carbide strips on bars up to 25 in. long allowed the use of a smaller-diameter bar, with more room for chip clearance and flow of cutting fluid. But with bore lengths of 40 in. and bar length-to-diameter ratio of 12 to 1, the carbide-reinforced steel boring bar produced excessive variation in bore size. A solid-carbide tapered bar was finally adopted for this application.

With this bar, as Table 1 shows, although overhang was extended from 27 to 43½ in., deflection was only 20% of that for the carbide-reinforced bar. Cost of the solid-carbide bar ($10,700) was amortized in producing 100 guns in a six-month period.

The use of carbide boring bars is extremely limited, however, because *(a)* only small sizes are available, and *(b)* pound for pound, carbide costs about 100 times as much as alloy steel.

Speed and Feed

Speed and feed affect power requirements, tool life, rate of metal removal, machining cost, and tolerances and surface finish obtainable in boring operations. In most applications, speed and feed are selected on the basis of minimum over-all cost, but sometimes a compromise must be made because of hardness of the work material, special product requirements, or production quantity and schedule. For equal depth of cut and rate of feed, boring speeds are substantially lower than turning speeds.

Table 2 presents nominal speeds and feeds for rough boring and finish boring of carbon and low-alloy steels at various hardness levels, using high speed steel or carbide tools. These rates apply primarily to the boring of holes 2 to 4 in. in diameter, and are useful as starting points for the selection of efficient and economical machining conditions. As is evident from many of the examples presented later in this article, speeds and feeds used in com-

Table 1. Steel vs Carbide Bars for Boring Powder Chambers (Example 30) (a)

	Type of boring bar		
Condition	Steel	Carbide-reinforced steel	Solid carbide
Gun size, mm	76	76	120
Speed, rpm	120	196	150
Speed, sfm	94	154	185
Feed, ipr	0.015	0.015	0.020
Depth of cut, in.	0.100	0.125	0.250
Overhang, in.	27	27	43½
Deflection, in.	0.060	0.010	0.002
Number of passes	11	5	7
Time per piece, hr (b)	5	2	4

(a) Work material was 4140 steel at 375 to 400 Bhn; boring was done with carbide cutters. (b) Including setup time.

Table 2. Nominal Speeds and Feeds for Boring of Carbon and Low-Alloy Steels With High Speed Steel and Carbide Tools(a)

Typical steel(b)	Brinell hardness	Rough boring (depth of cut, 0.100 in.) Speed, sfm HSS(c)	Speed, sfm Carbide(d)	Feed, ipr HSS(c)	Feed, ipr Carbide(d)	Finish boring (depth of cut, 0.010 in.) Speed, sfm HSS(c)	Speed, sfm Carbide(d)	Feed, ipr HSS(c)	Feed, ipr Carbide(d)
Carbon and Low-Alloy Steels (Except Free-Cutting Grades)									
1020, 1045, 4140, 7140 and 8620, at hardness ranges listed at right	85 to 125	120	415	0.010	0.015	135	460	0.005	0.006
	125 to 175	100	340	0.010	0.015	110	380	0.005	0.006
	175 to 225	80	305	0.009	0.013	90	335	0.005	0.006
	225 to 275	65	280	0.007	0.009	75	310	0.004	0.005
	275 to 325	60	245	0.007	0.009	65	270	0.004	0.005
	325 to 375	50	205	0.007	0.009	55	225	0.003	0.004
	375 to 425	35	160	0.006	0.007	40	175	0.003	0.004
	Rc 50 to 52	20	90	0.006	0.008	20	100	0.003	0.004
	Rc 54 to 56	..	55	...	0.006	..	60	...	0.003
Free-Cutting Carbon and Low-Alloy Steels									
1112 and 1117	100 to 150	135	505	0.010	0.015	150	560	0.005	0.006
	150 to 200	145	560	0.010	0.015	165	620	0.005	0.006
1137 and 12L14	100 to 150	135	510	0.010	0.015	150	565	0.005	0.006
	150 to 200	115	430	0.010	0.015	125	480	0.005	0.006
	200 to 250	95	325	0.008	0.012	105	360	0.005	0.006
	275 to 325	80	305	0.008	0.010	90	340	0.004	0.005
	325 to 375	50	205	0.007	0.009	55	225	0.003	0.004
	375 to 425	35	155	0.006	0.008	40	175	0.003	0.004
4140+S and 41L40	150 to 200	105	395	0.010	0.015	115	440	0.005	0.006
	275 to 325	60	270	0.008	0.010	70	300	0.004	0.005
	375 to 425	35	155	0.006	0.008	40	175	0.003	0.004
	Rc 50 to 52	20	90	0.006	0.008	20	100	0.003	0.004
	Rc 54 to 56	..	55	...	0.006	..	60	...	0.003

(a) The rates shown here are most applicable to boring of holes 2 to 4 in. in diameter, and are useful as starting points for other applications with comparable steels. See Table 3 for a comparison of actual speeds and feeds used in examples in this article with the nominal values in this table, and see text for a discussion of the conditions that affect speeds and feeds. (b) Each steel listed is a frequently used grade in a group of similar steels. For a listing of the steels in the various groups, see Table 2, page 6. (c) High speed steels M2 and T5, except M2, T5 and T15 for boring steels at hardnesses of 225 to 375 Bhn, and except T15, M41, M42, M43 and M44 for hardnesses above 375 Bhn. (d) Carbide grade C-7, except C-8 for hardnesses above 425 Bhn. (Data are adapted from tables compiled by Metcut Research Associates, Inc.)

mercial practice often differ widely from the nominal values given in Table 2. Some of the reasons for this difference are discussed below.

Size and Bore Diameter. If rugged equipment with adequate power is available, large diameters can be bored at much higher surface speeds and feed rates than those listed in Table 2. Metal can be removed at extremely rapid rates in heavy roughing cuts, and the resulting rough finish and dimensional variation can be corrected by light finishing cuts at slower speeds and higher feeds than normally recommended for finish boring.

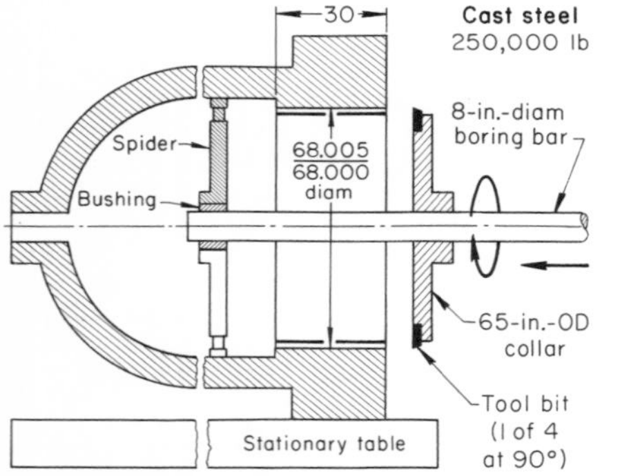

Speed, roughing	6 rpm (107 sfm)
Speed, finishing	17 rpm (302 sfm)
Feed, roughing and finishing	0.050 ipr
Depth of roughing cut per tool bit	0.0625 in. per side
Total depth of roughing cut	0.250 in. per side
Tool material, roughing	High speed steel
Tool material, finishing	Carbide (brazed)
Cutting fluid	Soluble oil
Setup time per piece	15 hr
Total time per piece	25 hr

Workpiece, machined in annealed and normalized condition, was cast from steel of the following composition: 0.35 C, 0.10 Cr, 0.08 Mo.

Fig. 4. Boring a 125-ton cast steel cylinder (Example 31)

These techniques are illustrated in Example 34 (Fig. 7), which describes rough and finish boring of a 180-ton rolling-mill housing made of 1030 steel. Holes 28, 32 and 35 in. in diameter were bored with high speed steel tools. Table 3 compares the speeds and feeds used with nominal rates from Table 2. The high surface speed for roughing this large workpiece (320 sfm) was obtained with a relatively slow rotational speed (35 rpm). The high speed and feed removed metal rapidly in the roughing cut of 3/8 to 1/2 in. A single finishing pass at low speed and high feed removed 0.007 in. for tolerance of +0.003, −0.000 in. on the diameter.

When the workpiece is rotated, its size sometimes limits speeds to below normal values, as in boring a 32-in. diameter on the 15,000-lb 1045 steel forging of Example 33 (Fig. 6) with carbide tools. Table 3 compares the speeds and feeds used for this operation with nominal rates for 1045 steel from Table 2. Speeds were limited by the size of the workpiece to less than half the nominal values. But because of the large bore diameter, feed rates could be substantially higher than the nominal values.

Table 3. Comparison of Nominal and Actual Speeds and Feeds
(Nominal rates from Table 2; actual rates from examples in this article)

Work material	Speed, sfm Nominal	Speed, sfm Actual	Feed, ipr Nominal	Feed, ipr Actual
1030 steel(a):				
Rough boring	100	320	0.010	0.250
Finish boring	110	46	0.005	0.040
1045 steel(b):				
Rough boring	340	150	0.015	0.025
Finish boring	380	150	0.006	0.020
4330 steel(c)	305	230	0.013	0.004
4140 steel(d)	205	75	0.009	0.008

(a) Actual rates, from Example 34 (Fig. 7), were for boring holes 28, 32 and 35 in. in diameter in rolling-mill housings, with high speed steel tools. Nominal rates are for steels in the 1045 group at 125 to 175 Bhn.
(b) Actual rates, from Example 33 (Fig. 6), were for boring a 32-in.-diam hole in a 15,000-lb forging of 1045 steel, with carbide tools. Nominal rates are for 1045 steel at 125 to 175 Bhn.
(c) Actual rates, from Example 62 (Fig. 32), were for boring 2-in.-diam holes in tubes 23 in. long, with carbide tools. Nominal rates are for steels in the 4140 group at 175 to 225 Bhn.
(d) Actual rates, from Example 59 (Fig. 29), were for boring 3.121-in.-diam holes in cylinders 8 ft long, with carbide tools. Nominal rates are for 4140 steel at 325 to 375 Bhn.

Chip Control. In boring tubes of small diameter, chip control is critical, and often governs the selection of feed and speed. This is illustrated in Example 62 (Fig. 32), in which a 23-in.-long tube of normalized 4330 steel was bored to a 2-in. diameter with carbide tools. Speed and feed were established by trial to give effective chip control. As Table 3 shows, the speed used was about 75% of the nominal rate for comparable work material from Table 2, but feed rate was only 33% of nominal.

Tolerances and Bore Length. Close-tolerance bores of high length-to-diameter ratio require slower speed than normal, even though the tool is well supported. Conditions for boring an 8-ft-long hydraulic cylinder of 4140 steel (Rockwell C 38 to 40) to a 3.121-in. diameter are described in Example 59 (Fig. 29). As the comparison in Table 3 shows, the surface speed used in this operation with carbide tools was only about a third of that normally used in boring this material. With this reduced speed, tolerances of ±0.005 in. on the diameter and 0.002 in. per ft on straightness were maintained with this 30-to-1 ratio of length to diameter.

When unsupported boring bars of high length-to-diameter ratio are used in close-tolerance operations, speed and feed are limited by the degree of rigidity of the bar. Example 30 (Table 1) shows how speed, feed and depth of cut were increased by using solid-carbide bars in place of steel bars or reinforced steel bars for boring guns. The unsupported bars had length-to-diameter ratios of 8 to 1 and 12 to 1.

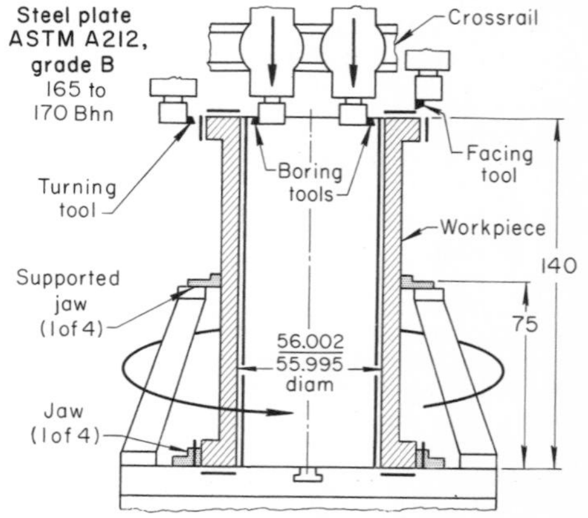

Operating Conditions for Boring

Speed, roughing and finishing	20 rpm (293 sfm)
Feed	0.020 ipr
Depth of roughing cut, each head	0.0625 in.
Total depth of cut	0.125 in.
Tool material	Carbide (brazed)
Cutting fluid	Soluble oil
Setup time per piece	9 hr
Total time per piece	62 hr

Fig. 5. Boring, turning and facing a 60-ton steel pressure vessel (Example 32)

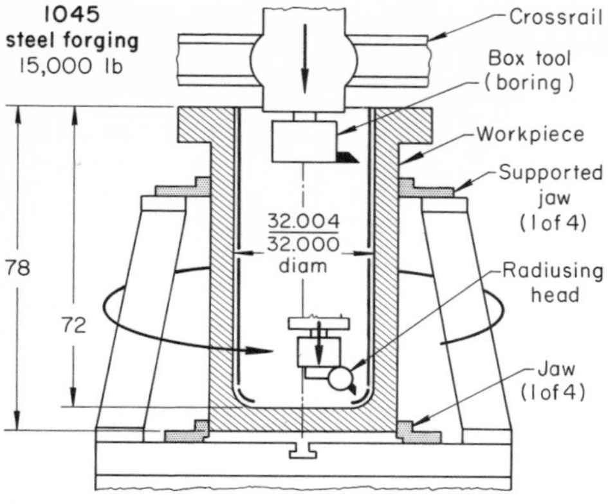

Operating Conditions for Boring

Speed, roughing and semifinishing	18 rpm (150 sfm)
Feed, roughing	0.025 ipr
Feed, semifinishing	0.020 ipr
Depth of each roughing cut (four cuts made)	0.187 in.
Depth of semifinishing cut	0.060 in.
Tool material	Carbide (brazed)
Cutting fluid	Soluble oil
Setup time per piece	3 hr
Total time per piece	25 hr

Fig. 6. Boring and radiusing a 7½-ton steel forging (Example 33)

Other conditions may also demand the use of feeds and speeds substantially different from those shown in Table 2. Tool design can have major effects on feed and speed. In Example 76 (Fig. 46), a change from a single-point to a blade-type cutter for finish boring allowed the feed rate to be increased by 50%.

Surface finish can often be improved by using higher speeds and lower feed rates than normal. With large parts, as in Example 74 (Fig. 44), it may be possible to improve finish by decreasing feed rate without changing speed, but at a sacrifice of production rate.

Production rates in close-tolerance operations can sometimes be increased by using different types of machines for roughing and for finishing, to permit optimum speed and feed for each operation (Examples 67 and 72).

Workpiece Size

In selecting equipment and processing procedure for a specific boring operation, size of workpiece is usually the first factor to consider, because all machines are limited as to swing, speed, height and other capabilities. A small part can be bored on a greater variety of machines than a large part. However, it would be impractical to process a small part on a machine such as a large boring mill, because it would rotate too slowly.

For extremely large workpieces, such as castings weighing many tons, monstrous machines would be needed if the part had to be rotated instead of the tools. For these parts, it is more practical to line up the workpiece and rotate the tools. Part size may also dictate the choice between horizontal and vertical machines. Extremely heavy workpieces impose so great an overhang on spindle bearings in a horizontal machine that chucking or clamping is impractical.

Size may also dictate machine type for parts that, although relatively light in weight, are too long to be bored in machines having short travel, like turret lathes. For these parts, a horizontal machine may be required because of limitations in building height.

The five examples that follow describe specific applications in which size of workpiece was the major factor in choice of equipment and procedure.

Example 31. Boring a 68-In. Diameter in a 125-Ton Cylinder (Fig. 4)

A 15-hp floor-type horizontal boring mill was used with the setup shown in Fig. 4 for boring a 30-in.-long, 68-in.-diam section in a 250,000-lb cast steel main cylinder. Because of its weight, the cylinder was mounted on a stationary table, and the tools were rotated and fed into it. The 8-in.-diam boring bar was locked to the spindle, and was supported at the leading end in an 8.004/8.002-in.-ID bushing mounted in the center of a three-legged spider that was set up at a depth of 45 in. within the cylinder.

Four tool bits were inserted 90° apart in a 65-in.-OD collar mounted on the boring bar. For rough boring, the tools were staggered so that each removed 1/16 in. of metal per side (total depth of cut, ¼ in.). For finish boring, the four tool bits were set the same distance from center, so that only one actually cut while the three others served as backup tools should the leading tool burn or chip. Other processing details are tabulated beneath the illustration for Fig. 4.

Example 32. Boring, Turning and Facing a 60-Ton Vessel in One Setup (Fig. 5)

A 100-hp vertical boring machine with a 20-ft-diam table and 12-ft clearance under the crossrail was used for boring, turning and facing a 140-in.-high pressure vessel made from steel plate and weighing 60 tons. It was feasible to rotate this part, despite its size and weight, because it was symmetrical. The use of four tools on the crossrail, as shown in Fig. 5, made it possible to use the same setup for facing the ends and turning the flanges as for boring the 56-in. ID.

The workpiece was set up and centered on the 20-ft-diam table, and was held in place by four jaws at table level and four other jaws mounted on 75-in.-high supports. The higher, supported jaws were locked against the part, and indicators at these jaws insured that the part was not moved or twisted in machining.

For boring, the workpiece was rotated around the two heads, which were fed downward into it. When 75 in. of the 140-in. length had been machined, the workpiece was turned end for end and the procedure was repeated. Additional processing details for the boring operation are listed below Fig. 5 (see also Fig. 6 for a similar example).

Example 33. Boring a 32-In. Diameter in a 7½-Ton Forging (Fig. 6)

A 50-hp vertical boring mill with a 10-ft-diam table and 8 ft of clearance under the crossrail was used for boring a 15,000-lb forging of 1045 steel. The size, weight and symmetry of this part made it well-suited to the setup used (see Fig. 6), in which the workpiece was rotated and tools were fed downward from the crossrail.

The workpiece was secured to the table by four jaws at table level, and additional bracing was provided by four other jaws mounted on supporting columns about three-fourths as high as the workpiece (see Fig. 5 for a generally similar setup).

A box tool was used for rough and semi-finish boring, after which the 32-in. inside diameter was polished with a sanding belt to a maximum roughness of 32 micro-in. A radius at the bottom of the cylindrical cavity was formed with a separate head (Fig. 6) in a subsequent operation. The swivel radiusing tool, made of high speed steel, was operated with an extension handle, which permitted rotation from above the workpiece, and was used with a rotating head to eliminate tool grooves. Processing conditions and time per piece for the boring operation are listed in the tabulation accompanying Fig. 6.

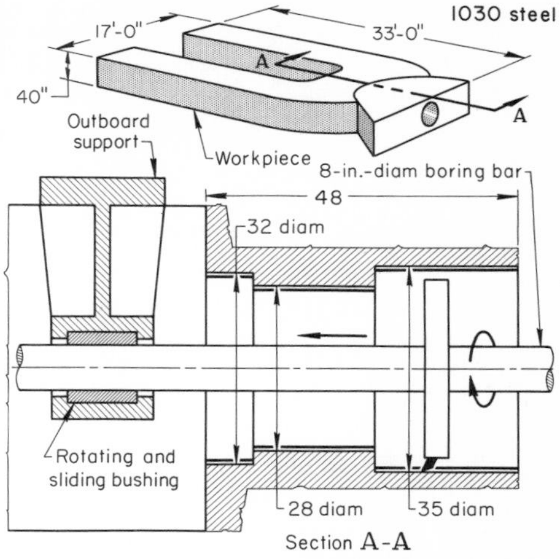

Speed, roughing	35 rpm (320 sfm max)
Speed, finishing	5 rpm (46 sfm max)
Feed, roughing	0.250 ipr
Feed, finishing	0.040 ipr
Depth of cut, roughing	⅜ to ½ in.
Depth of cut, finishing	0.007 in.
Tool material	High speed steel
Setup time per piece	8 hr
Total time per piece	45 hr

Fig. 7. Boring a 180-ton rolling-mill housing (Example 34)

Example 34. Three Diameters in a 180-Ton Housing (Fig. 7)

A horizontal, floor-type mill was used for boring rolling-mill housings made of 1030 steel that weighed up to 180 tons each. Figure 7 shows the setup used for boring three different diameters (nut, clearance and worm-wheel bores) in a housing 33 ft long, 17 ft wide over-all, and up to 40 in. in section

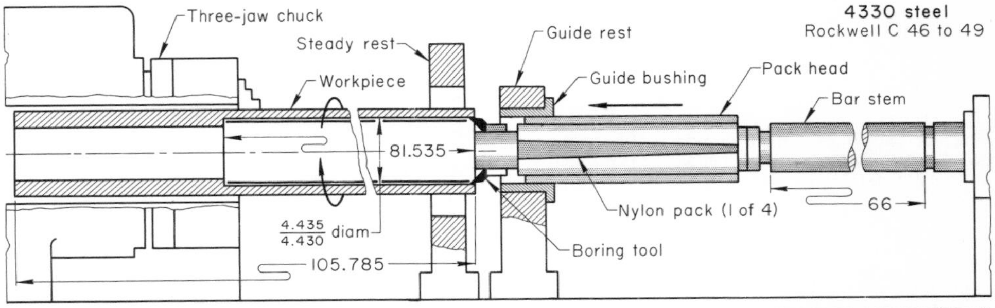

Speed	100 rpm (116 sfm)	Cutting fluid	Soluble oil
Feed	0.012 ipr	Setup time	3.5 hr
Depth of cut	0.125 in.	Handling time per piece(a)	10 min
Tool material	Carbide	Total time per piece	1.4 hr

(a) Loading and unloading, positioning of guide bushing, and tool approach to cutting position

Fig. 8. Boring a long hole to concentricity of 0.020 in. TIR (Example 35)

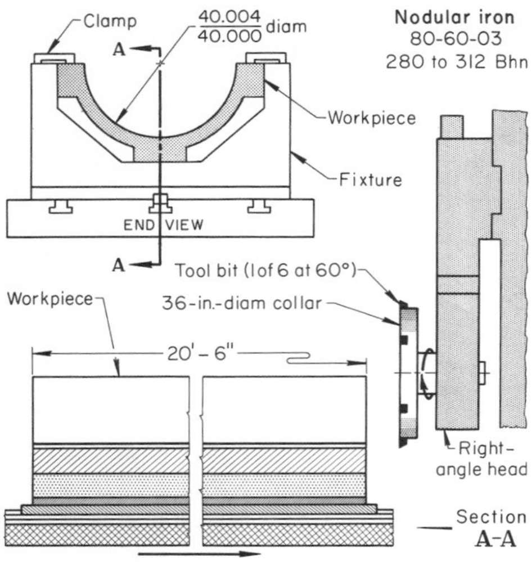

Speed, roughing	17 rpm (175 sfm)
Speed, finishing	19 rpm (200 sfm)
Feed, roughing and finishing	0.030 ipr
Depth of each roughing cut (three cuts made)	0.187 in.
Depth of finishing cut	0.020 in.
Tool material	Carbide (brazed)
Cutting fluid	Soluble oil
Setup time	8 hr
Total time	30 hr

Fig. 9. Boring a long semicylindrical contour in a nodular iron casting (Example 36)

thickness. With this setup, a 7-in. spindle drove an 8-in. boring bar, which was supported by an outboard bearing suspended from the housing face through a window opening in the housing; a bushing in the outboard bearing rotated with the bar but slid on the bar for feed. One roughing pass and one finishing pass were made to complete each bore; tolerances of +0.003, −0.000 in. were maintained. Additional operating conditions are tabulated with Fig. 7.

Example 35. Boring a Hole 18½ Diameters Long in a Large Piston (Fig. 8)

A long-bed horizontal lathe was used to bore the 4330 steel piston shown in Fig. 8. This part posed a problem in boring because of the extreme length (81.535 in.) of the bore to be machined, in relation to its diameter (4.434 in.). Concentricity had to be held within 0.020 in. TIR and diameter within 0.005 in., because the bore would subsequently be honed.

To achieve the critical lineup required for a bore of this length, the soft chuck jaws had to be bored to hold concentricity, and the steady rest and guide bushing had to be in line to prevent the bore from leading off. Boring tools were held on a true centerline by the use of a pack head containing four nylon inserts (Fig. 8). This head was of greater than usual length, to provide more packing area and thus hold pack wear to a minimum. The packs were ground 0.003 in. below tool size, in order to allow for thermal expansion with increasing temperature during operation.

The bore was started by holding the pack head in the guide bushing, and the packs entered the bore before leaving the bushing. Soluble oil was pumped through the boring-bar stem to flush out chips and keep the nylon packs cool.

The tool block held two carbide cutters, 180° apart, that were ground in assembly for the diameter to be bored. Each cutter had a 30° lead angle and a 0.025-in.-deep, 0.060-in.-wide chip breaker with a 0.06-in. base radius and a nose radius of 0.000 to 0.005 in. Additional processing details are listed in the table that accompanies Fig. 8.

[For details of the equipment and procedure used in boring another hole of extreme length-to-diameter ratio (slightly more than 30 to 1), the reader is referred to Example 59 on page 32, in this article.]

Size and configuration of the workpiece often are so closely related that they exert an equal influence on choice of machine and method of boring. Two such instances are described in Examples 36 and 37, which follow. These examples also demonstrate the use of boring for machining contours other than full cylindrical bores.

Example 36. 40-In.-Diam Half-Bore in a 20½-Ft-Long Casting (Fig. 9)

A 30-hp slab mill having a 40-ft-long traveling table, and with 10 ft of clearance between housings and under the rail, was used for boring a long semicylindrical contour, or half-bore, in a nodular iron casting, with the setup shown in Fig. 9. Six carbide tool bits were staggered on the 36-in.-diam boring collar. The casting was clamped to a fixture that was held to the machine table by T-bolts (end view in Fig. 9). Work was fed into the rotating right-angle-head cutter. Additional processing details are listed in the table accompanying Fig. 9.

Example 37. Boring a 30-In.-Radius Contour in a Large Component (Fig. 10)

A 75-hp vertical boring mill with a 10-ft-diam rotary table and 8 ft of clearance under the crossrail was used to bore a contour with a 30-in. radius and a 24-in.-diam opening, in a 4340 steel component for an elbow-die machine (see Fig. 10).

In setting up the piece, a center plug was used to insure an adequate amount of stock for the 30-in. radius. The part was clamped to the table, and jaws were mounted so as not to interfere with the cutting head. The contour was cut using a special radiusing head, which was mounted to a stationary vertical boring head. As table and workpiece revolved at 3 rpm, the radiusing head was hand fed at 0.020 in. per revolution of the workpiece. Additional operating conditions are given in the table with Fig. 10.

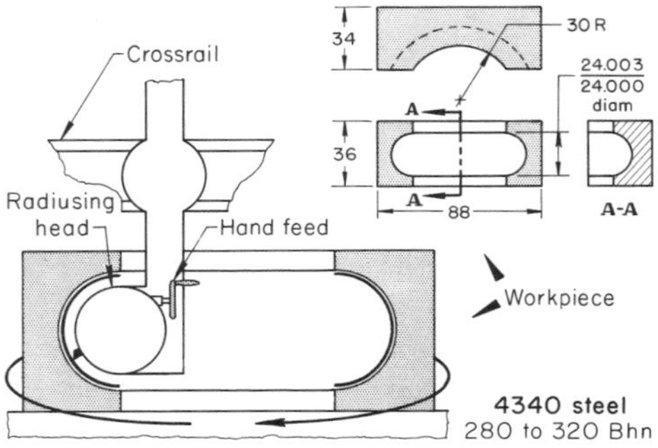

Speed	3 rpm (55 sfm max)
Feed	0.020 ipr
Depth of cut	0.062 in.
Tool material	High speed steel
Cutting fluid	None
Setup time per piece	10 hr
Total time per piece	52 hr

Fig. 10. Boring a radiused contour in a die-machine component (Example 37)

Workpiece Configuration

The configuration of a workpiece, irrespective of its size, may be a major factor in determining the most practical boring method. Configuration may affect the rigidity with which a part can be held while being machined, and thus may create problems even in otherwise simple operations. Other conditions related to configuration that may pose problems in boring are listed at the top of the next column:

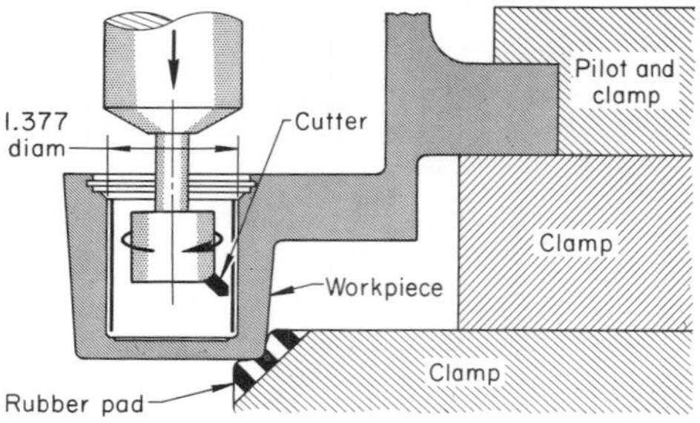

Fig. 11. Work-holding setup used in boring an aircraft brake carrier (Example 38)

1 The maintenance of specific relationships between two or more bored holes in a single part
2 Boring of "bottle" contours and other complex configurations
3 Boring of difficult-to-reach areas.

Examples 38 through 45, which follow, describe equipment and techniques employed in specific production applications to overcome difficulties presented by workpiece configuration.

Example 38. Special Holding Setup for Nonrigid Part (Fig. 11)

Eight equally spaced 1.377-in.-diam holes were bored in an aircraft brake carrier sand cast of magnesium alloy. Because of the shape of this part, it was necessary to devise the special setup shown in Fig. 11 to maintain adequate rigidity during boring. The part was placed on a pilot and air-clamped into position. The inside corner of the overhanging portion to be bored was supported by a rubber pad, which absorbed vibration.

A vertical boring machine equipped with a 3-hp variable-speed motor was used. The boring cutter was a ¼-in. insert tipped with carbide. This tool had a radius of 0.060 in., side rake angle of 15°, and 6° top rake. At a speed of 1200 rpm (433 sfm) and feed of 0.003 ipr, 0.0245 in. of metal was removed in boring, to produce a 12-micro-in. finish.

Example 39. Preventing Distortion in Boring a Long Cylinder (Fig. 12)

A 40-hp horizontal boring mill with a 6-in. spindle and a 6-by-10-ft table was used to bore nodular iron cylinders (Fig. 12). Despite its simple configuration, a part of this type, especially when close tolerances are required, poses problems because of the danger of distortion while it is held in place for machining. The problem was solved here by releasing the holddown clamps after roughing. The part was then reclamped to the supporting V-blocks, but under a much lighter force, which was adequate for semifinishing and finishing because less stock was being removed. Additional processing details are given with Fig. 12.

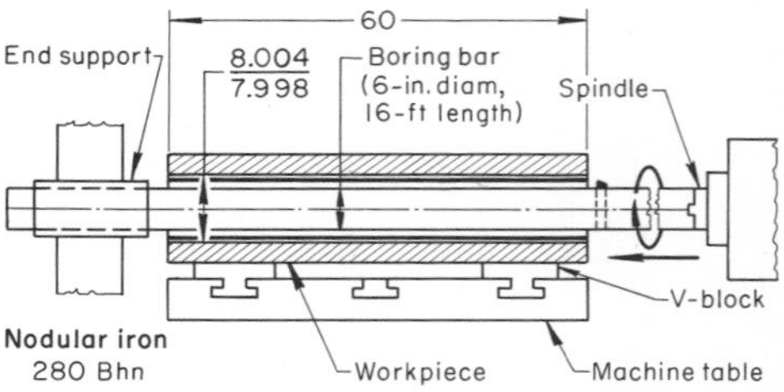

Speed	70 rpm (147 sfm)
Feed, roughing and semifinishing	0.040 ipr
Feed, finishing	0.016 ipr
Depth of roughing cut	0.187 in.
Depth of semifinishing cut	0.031 in.
Depth of finishing cut	0.005 in.
Tool material:	
Roughing and semifinishing	Carbide
Finishing	High speed steel
Cutting fluid	Soluble oil
Setup time per piece	3.5 hr
Total time per piece	8 hr

Fig. 12. Straight-through boring of a nodular iron cylinder (Example 39)

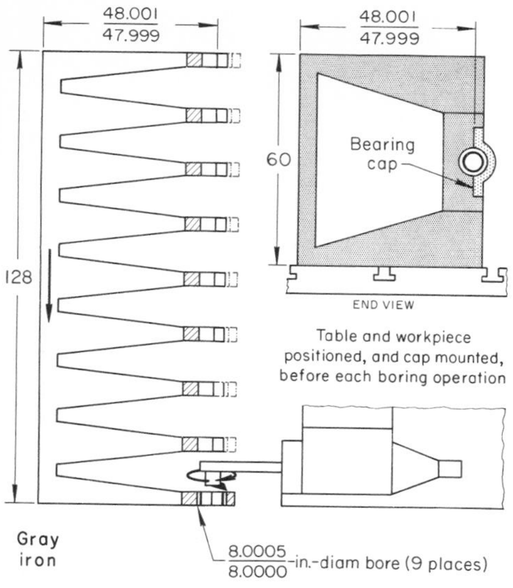

Condition	Roughing	Finishing
Speed, rpm	40	40
Speed, sfm	84	84
Feed, ipr	0.020	0.010
Depth of cut, in.	0.060(a)	0.020(b)
Setup time, hr	4	12
Total time, hr	10	18

(a) For each of four roughing cuts; total, 0.240 in. (b) For single cut taken.

Fig. 13. Roughing and finishing nine in-line bores in a compressor frame (Example 40)

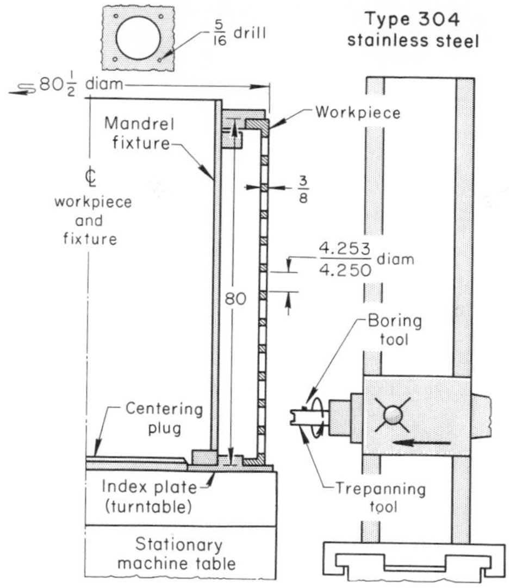

Speed	60 rpm (67 sfm)
Feed	0.006 ipr
Depth of cut, boring	1/16 in. per side
Tool material	High speed steel
Time (trepan, bore, drill and tap):	
Setup	15 hr
Index	48
Machine	76
Total	139 hr

Fig. 14. Boring 576 4¼-in. diam holes in a large drum before drilling and tapping 2304 holes 5⁄16 in. in diameter (Example 41)

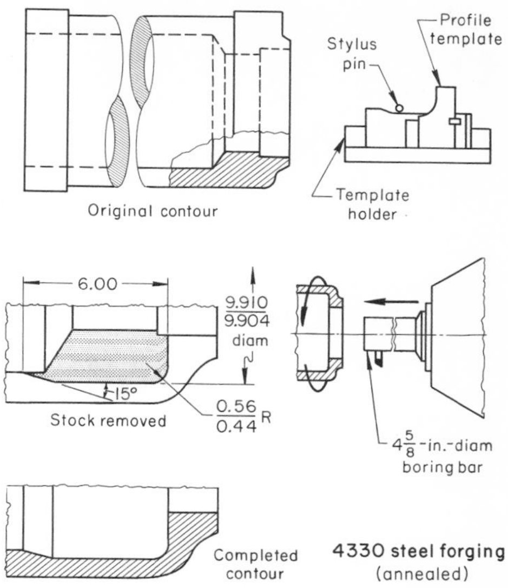

Speed	69 rpm (179 sfm max)
Feed	0.015 ipr
Stock removed in each of six roughing cuts	0.50 in.
Total stock removed in roughing	3.00 in.
Stock removed in finishing cut	0.10 in.
Tool material	Carbide
Cutting fluid	Soluble oil
Setup time	3.5 hr
Time per piece	67 min

Fig. 16. Contour boring setup used to enlarge inside diameter by 3.1 in. in seven passes (Example 43)

Example 40. Sequential Boring of Nine Holes in Line (Fig. 13)

A 40-hp horizontal boring mill that had a 10-by-20-ft table was used for rough and finish boring the nine 8-in.-diam holes in the large gray iron compressor frame shown in Fig. 13. These holes were assigned an in-line tolerance of 0.001 in.

First, the workpiece was placed on a layout table, and a complete layout was made. Then it was set up on the horizontal mill table and secured. All clamps were placed so as not to interfere with the machining operations. Indicators were set at each clamping point to insure that the part was not twisted during clamping.

A right-angle head was then mounted on the face of the mill, and the boring bar was mounted to the right of the head, which was adjusted to center by means of a vernier height gage. A bearing cap was mounted at the extreme outer bore, which was then completed by feeding the table-mounted compressor frame into the rotating single-point carbide tool. Then, until all nine bores were completed, the table and workpiece were repositioned, the next bearing cap was mounted, and the boring operation was repeated. Processing details are listed in the table below Fig. 13.

Example 41. Cutting 576 Holes in a Large Thin-Wall Drum (Fig. 14)

A tape-controlled floor-type horizontal boring mill equipped with an indexing turntable was used for trepanning and boring 576 holes 4¼ in. in diameter in an open-end stainless steel drum. The setup used is shown in Fig. 14. After these holes had been produced, 2304 smaller holes (5⁄16-in. diam) were drilled and tapped; four of these smaller holes were positioned around each of the larger holes as shown in Fig. 14.

The two main problems posed by these operations were: (*a*) providing an effective means of fixturing the workpiece, which lacked rigidity because of its great size in relation to wall thickness (3⁄8 in.); and (*b*) devising a means of indexing to obtain required hole spacing both vertically and horizontally. A mandrel fixture, made to fit the inside diameter of the drum, was set up on the indexing turntable over a centering plug. Then the mandrel was secured to the table, and the drum was secured to the mandrel.

Beginning at the first 4¼-in. hole to be produced, the tape control was set. These holes were produced by a 4⅛-in.-diam trepanning tool and a single-point boring tool bit, both set in the same boring bar (Fig. 14); the spindle was fed into the workpiece. After the first hole was completed, the spindle was retracted and repositioned for the next hole in the vertical line of 12. When all 12 holes had been bored in line, the table was indexed 7° 30′ and the 12 holes in the next vertical row were successively produced. For producing all 576 holes, the table was indexed 48 times.

A similar indexing procedure was followed for drilling and tapping the 5⁄16-in. holes. For drilling, a two-lip end mill was used rather than a drill, because a drill would have readily moved off location on the curved surface of the drum. Additional operating conditions for the trepanning and boring operation are tabulated with Fig. 14.

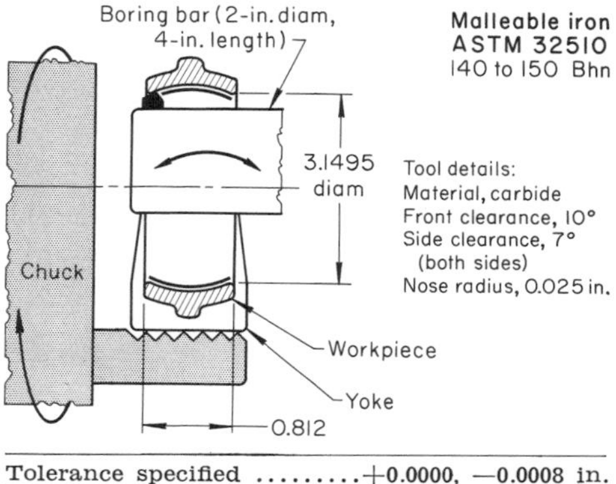

Tolerance specified	+0.0000, −0.0008 in.
Finish specified	125 micro-in.

Operating Conditions

Speed	545 rpm (450 sfm)
Feed	0.008 ipr
Depth of cut	0 to 3⁄32 in.
Cutting fluid	Air-mist soluble oil
Setup time	1½ hr
Downtime for changing tools	½ hr
Production rate	130 pieces per hour
Tool life per grind	900 pieces

Fig. 15. Close-tolerance contour boring in a spherical boring machine (Example 42)

Example 42. Close-Tolerance Contour Boring (Fig. 15)

A precision spherical boring machine was used for contour boring small malleable iron castings to extremely close tolerances (Fig. 15). Workpieces were clamped to the fixture with an air-operated yoke clamping base attached to the rotating air chuck. Processing details are tabulated with Fig. 15.

Example 43. Removal of 3.1 In. of Stock in Seven-Pass Contour Boring (Fig. 16)

A turret lathe equipped with a tracer attachment was used for removing stock to reshape the contour of the bore in a 4330 steel forging (Fig. 16). The 4⅝-in.-diam boring bar used was 15¼ in. in over-all length, and overhung 12¾ in. from the turret face. The bar was made to pilot in the bar holder and was bolted to the face of the turret for maximum rigidity; the tool slot was straight. A triangular carbide insert, secured with a lock-type holder, was used for cutting.

For tracer operation, the machine screws for both longitudinal feed and crossfeed were disengaged, and all feeds were controlled by hydraulic pressure. Six roughing cuts and one finishing cut were used to achieve the completed contour (Fig. 16). The tracer template was designed with a "flipper plate" to allow tools to enter and leave the bore and to move the required distance off centerline. Cutting fluid was forced through the tool. Additional operating conditions are listed in the table accompanying Fig. 16.

Example 44. Three-Operation Boring of "Bottle" Cavity (Fig. 17)

Production of a complex "bottle" configuration in 4340 steel tubing (Fig. 17) was a problem because of the amount of stock to be removed, the depth of the bore, and the necessity for using a small-diameter boring bar. The configuration was produced using a tracer lathe, in three separate operations and with three different tooling setups (Fig. 17).

In the first operation (Fig. 17a), the boring bar used was equipped with a built-in toolset bar for raising and lowering the tool bit. This permitted roughing-out of stock so that profile boring could be done in the third operation. Roughing was accomplished in five cuts, as shown in the top sketch of Fig. 17(a).

In the second operation (Fig. 17b), a taper was bored to a distance of 7.29 in., and a straight bore to 15$^{15}/_{16}$ in., from each end of the workpiece. This was done by removing the cross-slide screw from the lathe and then controlling movement of the cross slide by holding the tracer stylus on the template with hydraulic pressure. Longitudinal feed was controlled by the screw of the lathe.

Profile boring of the roughed-out center section was performed in the third operation (Fig. 17c). The diameter of the boring bar was limited to 2$^{11}/_{16}$ in., because of the depth of the bore and the distance the bar was required to move from the centerline. To obtain maximum rigidity, the bar was bolted to the turret face. This bar was 30½ in. long, and had a 22-in. overhang and a 30°-angle tool slot. Half of the center section was bored from each end; mismatch had to be kept within the amount that could be removed by a subsequent polishing operation. The sequence of steps in the third operation was:

1 Set tracer pin to "start" line and tool bit to end of part, with tool bit set to approximately finish diameter.
2 Turn longitudinal dial clockwise four full turns; turn diameter dial counterclockwise for 0.100-in. depth of cut; then make first cut 2¾ in. long.
3 Turn longitudinal dial one turn counterclockwise, then make second cut 2¾ in. long.
4 Turn longitudinal dial one turn counterclockwise, and turn diameter dial clockwise to leave approximately 0.060 in. of stock. Take full cut of template.
5 Turn both dials to finish setting, and make final cut.

Tool details and operating conditions for the three operations are given in the table accompanying Fig. 17.

Example 45. Use of Boring Bar for Cutting Deep Internal Threads (Fig. 18)

Figure 18 shows the profile of deep internal threads and schematically illustrates the setup used for cutting these threads in the 18-in. inside diameter of a large cylindrical bronze casting by means of a boring tool on an engine lathe. The workpiece was secured to the lathe compound, and the boring bar was held between the headstock and tailstock and was rotated by the headstock spindle. A series of cuts, at a speed of 32 rpm (150 sfm), was required for completing each 1$^{3}/_{16}$-in.-deep thread. Setting up, boring, and removal of the workpiece from the machine required a total of 35 hr per piece.

Number of Operations

In production boring, cost is reduced by combining as many machining operations as possible. Thus, the same machine setup often is used for two or more boring operations, or for boring and other machining operations such as turning, facing, drilling, chamfering and broaching. This may be accomplished in either of two ways: (*a*) having two or more boring or other tools on the same mounting so that they may work simultaneously or consecutively, or (*b*) indexing either the tools or the workpieces so that a number of operations can follow in a cycle.

To achieve these ends, machines such as turret lathes, double-end boring machines, and automatic chucking machines are given primary consideration in selection of equipment. Examples 46 through 55, which follow, describe the equipment and techniques that were employed in specific applications in which two or more boring operations, or boring and other machining operations, were combined.

Examples 46 to 49. Use of Horizontal Turret Lathes

Example 46 — Multiple-Diameter Tools on Six-Station Turret (Fig. 19). A six-station turret lathe was used for machining a complex bore in a gray iron water-pump housing. Operations included core drilling, rough boring of four diameters, reaming of three diameters, recessing of two diameters, cutting a 45°-angle recess, and roller burnishing of two diameters. The workpiece and tools at the six turret stations are shown in Fig. 19.

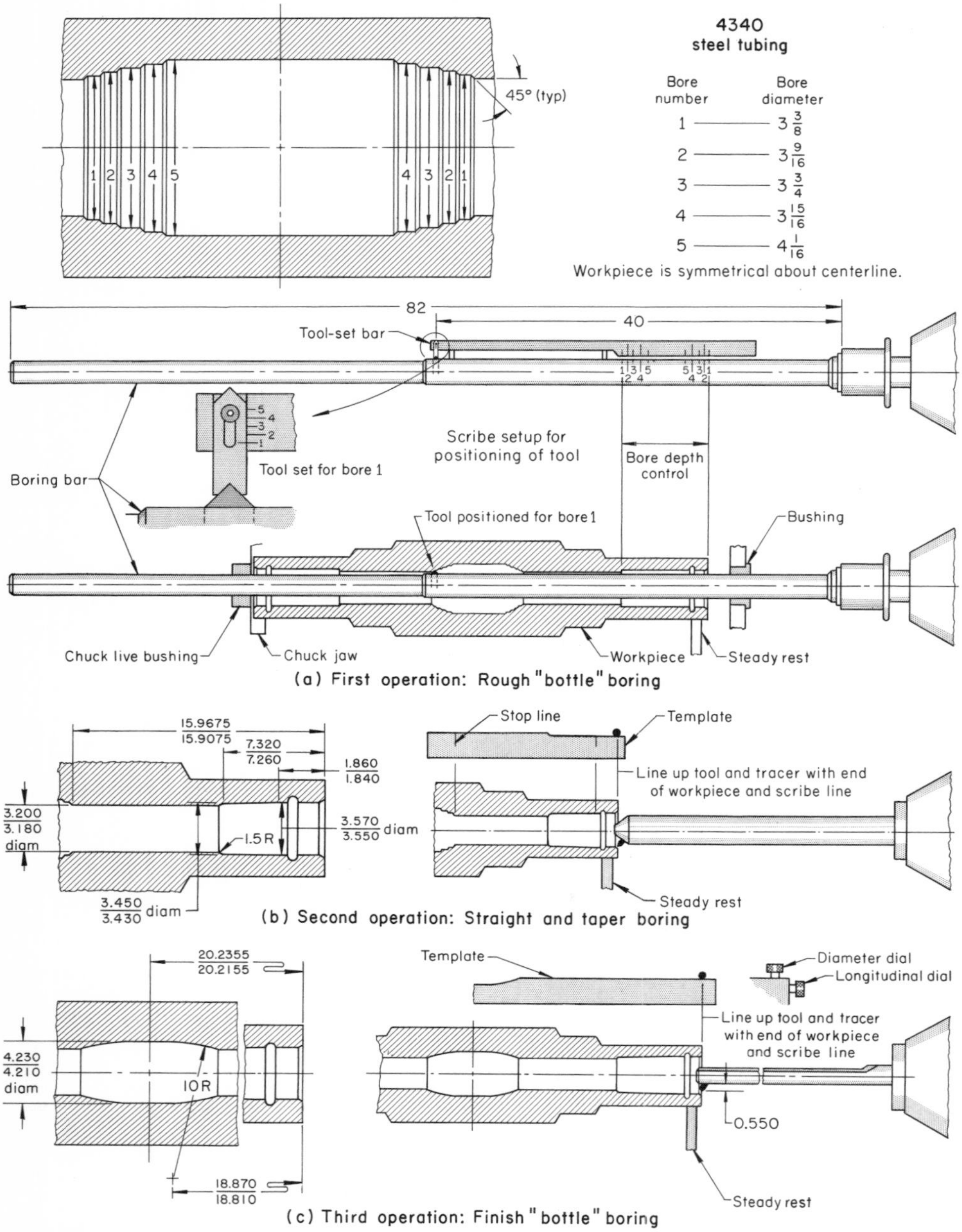

Item	Operation: First	Second	Third
Tool Details			
Length of boring bar, in.	82	24	30½
Diameter of boring bar, in.	2$^{13}/_{16}$	2¾	2$^{11}/_{16}$
Size of tool bit, in.	¾ by ¾	¾ by ¾	½ by ½
Lead angle	45°	15°	15°
Tool material	Carbide	Carbide	Carbide
Chip breaker dimensions:			
Depth, in.	0.025	0.020	0.025
Width, in.	1/16	1/16	5/64
Radius at base, in.	1/32	1/32	1/32
Nose radius, in.	0.005	1/64	0.010 to 0.015
Operating Conditions(a)			
Speed, rpm	307	183	183
Speed, sfm (max)	326	171	202
Feed, ipr	0.009	0.009(b)	0.005
Number of cuts	5	2	4
Production rate, pieces per hour	1¼	1	1

(a) In all operations, a soluble-oil cutting fluid was fed through the center of the bar to the cutting tool. (b) For roughing. Feed for finishing was 0.007 ipr.

Fig. 17. "Bottle" boring of alloy steel tubing in three operations on a tracer lathe (Example 44)

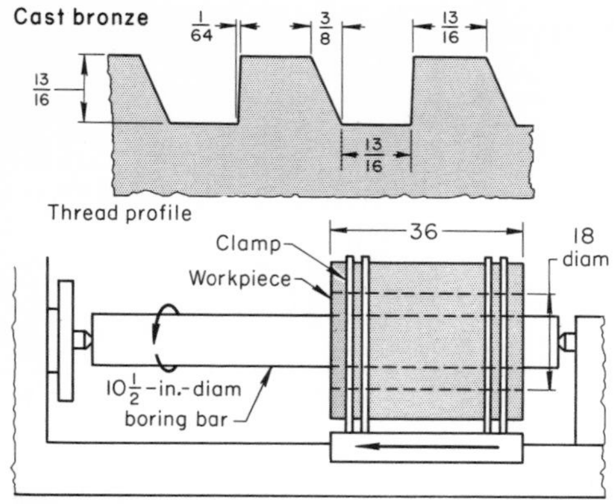

Fig. 18. Use of boring bar on an engine lathe for cutting deep internal threads (Example 45)

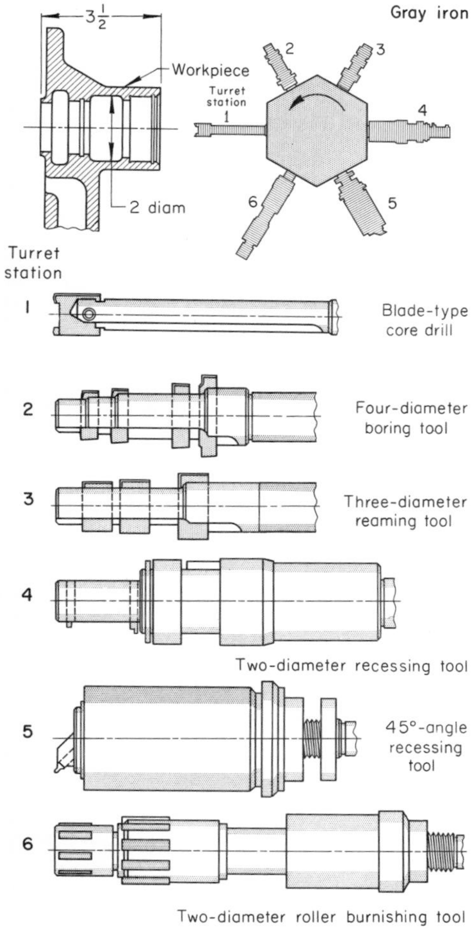

Tolerance on reamed bores .... ±0.001 in.
Tolerance on burnished bores .... ±0.0005 in.

Operating Conditions

Speed:
 Stations 1, 2 and 3 .... 389 rpm (205 sfm)
 Stations 4, 5 and 6 .... 200 rpm (105 sfm)
Feed:
 Stations 1 and 2 .... 0.017 ipr
 Station 3 .... 0.0112 ipr
 Stations 4 and 5 .... 0.0061 ipr
 Station 6 .... 0.0341 ipr
Depth of cut .... 0.015 to 0.125 in.
Tool material .... Carbide
Cutting fluid .... None
Setup time .... 3 hr
Downtime for changing tools .... 10 min
Production rate .... 8 pieces per hour
Tool life per grind .... 75 pieces

Fig. 19. Use of multiple-diameter tools on a horizontal turret lathe for machining a complex bore in a cast water-pump housing (Example 46)

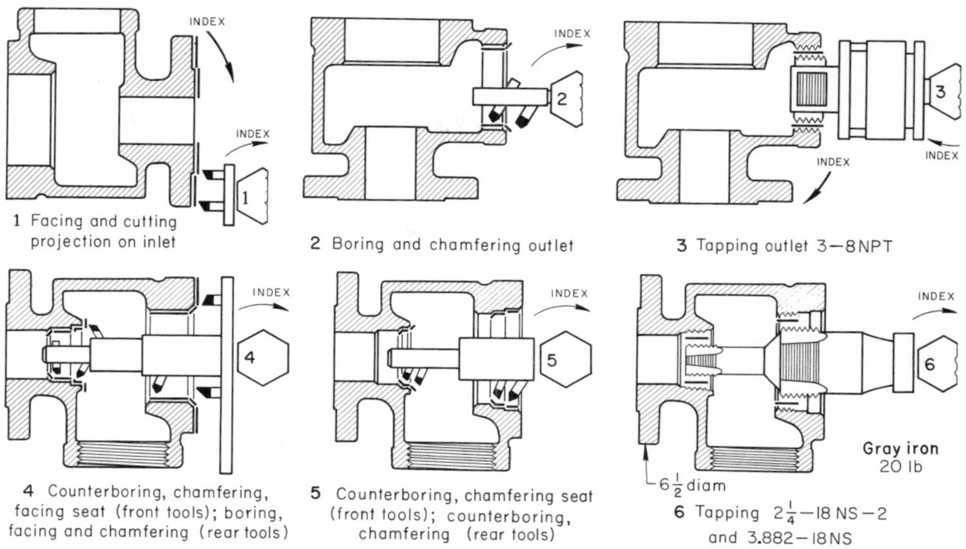

Station	Speed, Rpm	Speed, Sfm, max	Feed, ipr	Work diam, in.(a)	Length of cut, in.(a)	Machining time, min(b)
1 ..	127	216	0.011	6½	1 5/32	1.5
2 ..	127	118	0.011	3 9/16	1 5/16	1.2
3 ..	45	42	(c)	3 9/16	1 5/16	0.5
4 ..	127	200	0.011	6	7/8	1.4
5 ..	127	133	0.011	4 1/16	5/8	1.1
6 ..	45	46	(c)	3 7/8	3/4	0.6

(a) Maximum dimension machined by any one tool in this station. (b) Handling time (not included) for each operation was 0.8 min (48 sec). (c) Feed rate was controlled by the thread pitch.

Fig. 20. Machining a cast valve body, held in a 360°-indexing box chuck, with 17 tools on a six-station turret lathe (Example 47)

The multiple-slot bars (stations 2 and 3) permitted combined cuts and aided in holding bore concentricity. The combined recessing tool and the special 45°-angle recessing tool (stations 4 and 5) eliminated cross-slide operations. Roller burnishing provided control of diameter within ±0.0005 in. and resulted in desirable work-hardened surfaces. Additional processing details are included with Fig. 19.

Example 47 — Use of 17 Tools on Indexing Workpiece (Fig. 20). A 20-lb cast iron valve body was machined in six sequential operations on a horizontal turret lathe, as shown in Fig. 20. The workpiece was held in an adjustable box chuck, indexing 360° around an axis perpendicular to the lathe spindle. Tools operated from the six turret positions as indicated in Fig. 20. All single-point tools were brazed carbide tips, although the use of all cam-locked carbide inserts was later adopted, to eliminate tool grinding and thus avoid disturbing the preset position of the tools in the holder.

Several factors contributed to making this procedure efficient for machining these castings: (*a*) all machined surfaces were indexable around a common center, (*b*) quantity was sufficient to warrant tooling cost, (*c*) reproducibility was improved by using preset tools, and (*d*) only one machine was used, whereas as many as three would have been required for machining by the single-tool method. Refer to Fig. 20 for processing details.

Example 48 — Special Tools for Two-Diameter Boring (Fig. 21). A 15-hp six-station turret lathe having 12 speeds (8 to 212 rpm), and built especially for boring, was used for machining two bores of different diameters in a gray iron special-duty expansion unit. Figure 21 shows the workpiece and the boring tools used for finishing (two tools on one boring bar). Rough and semifinish boring, facing and other machining operations were performed in the same setup, using tools on other stations of the hexagonal turret. For all operations, the workpiece was secured in special interchangeable jaws, using a pin in each jaw for parallelism.

A special boring bar was used that had several detachable tool holders designed for specific products. The tool angles shown in Fig. 21 were necessary because of the 30° angle of the slots in the tool holder and for finishing the square shoulder in the bearing bore. Feed, speed and other operating conditions are tabulated with Fig. 21.

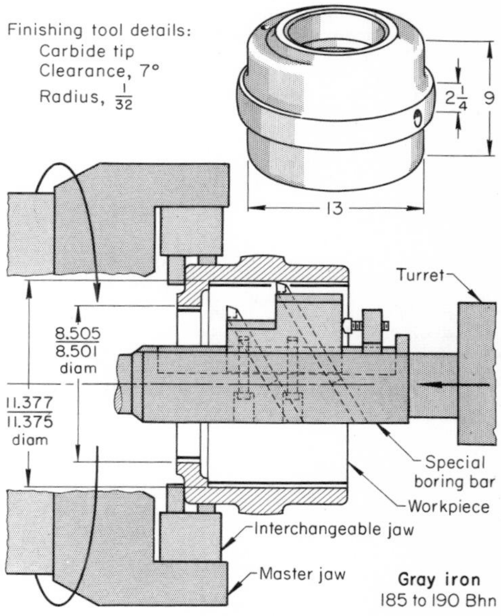

Rough Boring

Speed .... 48 rpm (107 and 143 sfm)
Feed .... 0.017 ipr
Depth of cut, max .... 0.187 in.

Semifinish Boring

Speed .... 87 rpm (194 and 259 sfm)
Feed .... 0.0124 ipr
Depth of cut, max .... 0.030 in.

Finish Boring

Speed .... 87 rpm (194 and 259 sfm)
Feed .... 0.0124 ipr
Depth of cut, max .... 0.020 in.

All Operations

Cutting fluid .... None
Setup time .... 5½ hr
Production rate .... 2½ pieces per hour
Tool life per grind .... 16 pieces

Fig. 21. Simultaneous boring of two diameters in a cast expansion unit, on a horizontal turret lathe (Example 48)

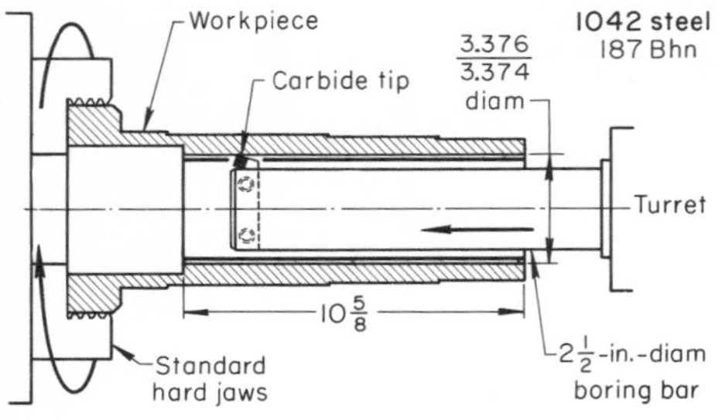

Rough Boring (Two Cuts)

Speed	348 rpm (250 and 278 sfm)
Feed	0.0124 ipr
Depth of first cut	0.125 in.
Depth of second cut	0.150 in.

Semifinish Boring

Speed	456 rpm (400 sfm)
Feed	0.009 ipr
Depth of cut	0.150 in.

Finish Boring

Speed	456 rpm (403 sfm)
Feed	0.009 ipr
Depth of cut	0.0125 in.

All Operations

Cutting fluid	Soluble-oil:water (1:25)
Setup time	2 hr
Time for grinding and resetting tools	0.1 hr
Production rate	1 piece per hour
Tool life per grind	12 pieces

Fig. 22. Four-cut boring of a drive hub, in the second of three chuckings for 17 operations on a horizontal turret lathe (Example 49)

Example 49 — Seventeen Operations in Three Chuckings (Fig. 22). Drive hubs were machined from 6⅜-in.-diam cold drawn 1042 steel bar slugs in three chuckings on a horizontal turret lathe. The setup and conditions used for boring, which was done in the second chucking, are presented in Fig. 22. The lathe had a two-speed motor (15 hp at 900 rpm, and 30 hp at 1800 rpm); 24 different spindle speeds, ranging from 12 to 628 rpm; and 32 different feeds, ranging from 0.0025 to 0.167 ipr. The operations performed in the three chuckings were as follows:

1 Face and turn flange end.
2 Chuck on flange (Fig. 22), using a stepped face on the jaws for assuring parallelism of the bar with the centerline of the spindle. Drill through with 2½-in.-diam spade drill, rough turn outside diameters, bore (two roughing cuts, one semifinishing cut, and one finishing cut), finish turn outside diameters, groove, face hub and flange, and break corners.
3 Chuck on hub, finish turn and face flange, counterbore, and break corners.

This bore represents about the maximum length that is practical to run without a piloted bar when such a close tolerance (±0.001 in.) is required. Had speeds and feeds been increased even as little as 10% over those used (see tabulation with Fig. 22), chatter would probably have occurred.

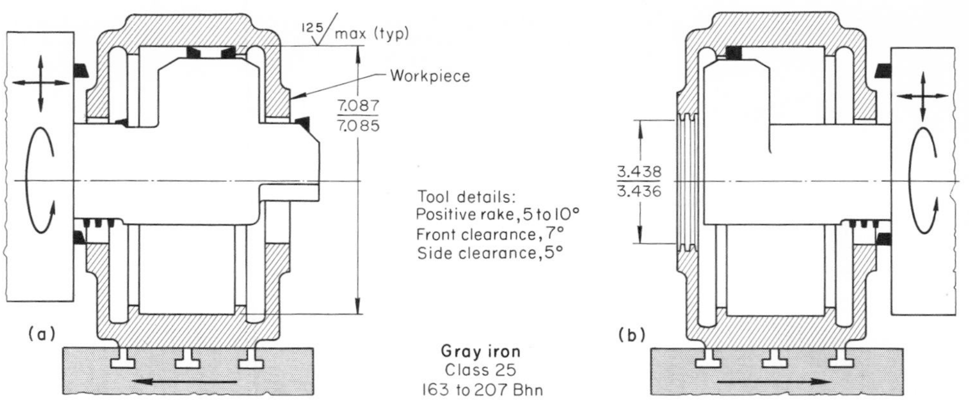

Speed, left head	160 rpm (297 sfm max)
Speed, right head	180 rpm (334 sfm max)
Feed, boring	0.009 ipr
Feed, turning and facing	0.003 ipr
Cutting fluid	None
Tool material	Carbide
Setup time	3 hr
Downtime for changing tools	0.3 hr
Production rate	8 pieces per hour
Tool life per grind	60 to 65 pieces

(a) Tools on left-hand head bored recess bore and both seal bores, turned grooves in left-hand seal bore, and faced the end of the casting. (b) Tools on right-hand head finish bored recess bore, turned right-hand seal-bore grooves, and faced the other end of the casting.

Fig. 24. Double-end boring with different tools on each crossfeed machine head (Example 51)

Examples 50 and 51. Use of Double-End Boring Machines

Example 50 — Identical Tooling on Both Heads (Fig. 23). A double-end horizontal boring machine was used to bore, counterbore and chamfer malleable iron castings, using the setup shown in Fig. 23. Rapid loading and unloading of workpieces were facilitated by holding with air-operated clamps. In this operation, the tools rotated and the heads remained stationary, as the machine table first advanced to one head and then reversed to complete the operation.

Example 51 — Crossfeed Heads With Different Tooling (Fig. 24). A double-end horizontal boring machine having crossfeed head units was used to perform the machining operations shown in Fig. 24. The two-piece (cap and base) gray iron casting being machined was held on the machine table by a cam clamp, and an air-clamp yoke held the cap to the base. After being secured to the machine table, the workpiece was moved to the left (Fig. 24a), for boring the recess bore and both seal bores, and, after the boring tools were retracted, for turning the grooves in the left-hand seal bore and facing. The tools were then retracted, the cap raised, and the workpiece moved to the right (Fig. 24b). Here, after the cap was lowered, the recess bore was finish bored, and this was followed by turning the right-hand seal-bore grooves and facing. Operating conditions are given in the table accompanying Fig. 24.

Examples 52 and 53. Use of Chucking Machines

Example 52 — Five Operations in One Entry of Multiple-Tool Bar (Fig. 25). A single-spindle turret-type chucking machine was used to perform five operations on a gray iron casting, by the procedure illustrated in Fig. 25. The workpiece was held by an air chuck with one platform jaw and a clamping yoke. For all five tools on the bar, it was practical to use triangular disposable carbide inserts, which were reindexed after machining about 550 pieces. The arrangement of the tools is shown in Fig. 25, below which are listed tool data and processing details.

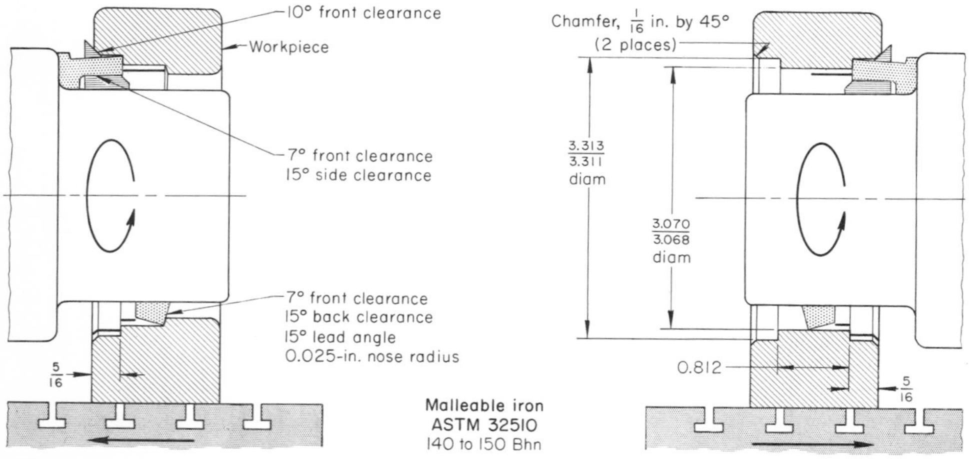

Speed	520 rpm (418 and 450 sfm)
Feed	0.012 ipr
Depth of cut in boring	3/32 in.
Depth of cut in counterboring	⅛ in.
Tool material	Carbide
Cutting fluid	Air-mist soluble oil
Setup time	2 hr
Downtime for changing tools	0.5 hr
Production rate	80 pieces per hour
Tool life per grind	600 pieces

Fig. 23. Double-end boring, counterboring and chamfering with identical tools on both heads (Example 50)

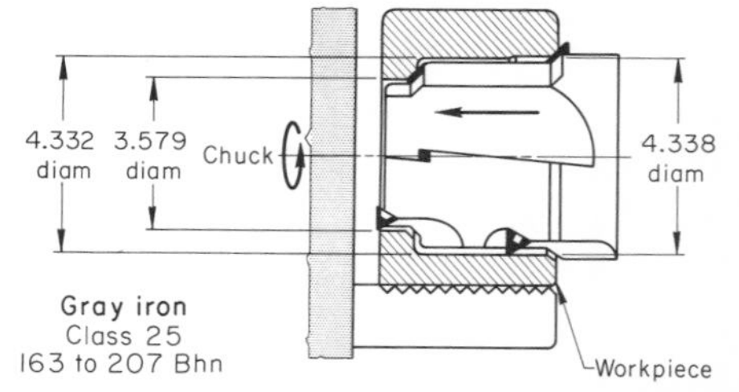

Tolerance specified	±0.001 in.
Finish specified	125 micro-in. (max)

Tool Details

Length of boring bar	6 in.
Diameter of bar	3½ in., stepped to 2¾ in.
Type of cutter	Indexable triangular insert
Cutter material	Carbide
Rake angle	7° (positive)

Operating Conditions

Speed	304 rpm (350 sfm max)
Feed	0.016 ipr
Depth of cut	1/16 to ⅛ in.
Setup time	4 hr
Downtime for changing tools	0.2 hr
Production rate	65 pieces per hour
Tool life per insert edge	550 pieces

Fig. 25. Performing five operations with one boring tool (Example 52)

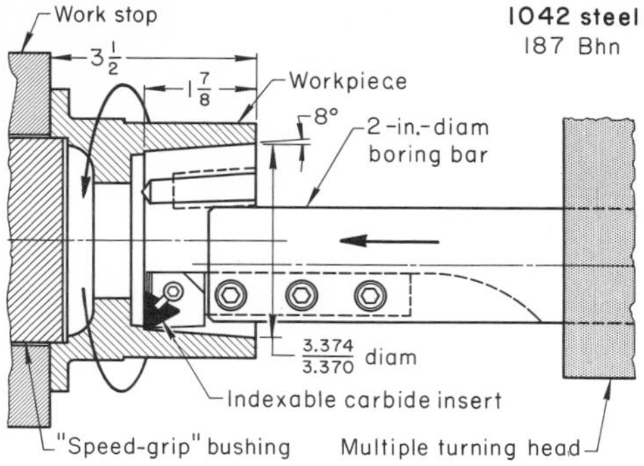

Speed (all four cuts)	622 rpm (550 sfm max)
Feed (all four cuts)	0.006 ipr
Cutting fluid	Soluble-oil:water (1:25)
Setup time	1¾ hr
Time for indexing insert	2 min
Production rate(a)	15.5 pieces per hour
Tool life per insert edge	25 pieces

(a) For complete machining in three chuckings

Fig. 26. Four-cut taper boring of a coupling hub in third chucking in an automatic chucking machine (Example 53)

Example 53 — Third-Chucking Taper Boring After Eight Operations in Two Chuckings (Fig. 26). The taper-boring operation shown and detailed in Fig. 26 was done in the third chucking of the workpiece, a 1042 steel coupling hub, on a 25-hp automatic chucking machine. This machine had high and low speed ranges with six spindle speeds in each (total range, 38 to 1058 rpm), and a selection of 36 different feeds, ranging from 0.0019 to 0.124 ipr.

Operations performed in the three chuckings were as follows:

1. Chuck on outside diameter and rough straight bore, holding diameter to 2.626/2.625 in. (tolerance for drilling and tapping in second chucking); turn outside diameter and face shoulder.
2. Chuck in soft jaw, back face, then rough and finish counterbore. Drill one hole 33/64 in. in diameter and 15/16 in. deep, and two holes 27/64 in. in diameter and 2 in. deep, spaced 95° apart, in end of part to be taper bored in third chucking. Tap the two 27/64-in. holes with ½-13 UNC-2B threads 1 13/16 in. deep.
3. Secure part against work stop by means of a "speed-grip" bushing, inserted in counterbore (see Fig. 26), and complete the tapered bore in four cuts: a straight bore cut, a partial straight bore cut, a rough taper cut, and a finish taper cut.

Cuts in taper boring were interrupted, because half of the drilled, or drilled and tapped, holes were cut away. The rough and finish boring bars were secured in individual spring-loaded pusher heads, which worked off a cam with a drop-off follower.

A conventional turret lathe had originally been used for machining this part, and production rate was about 84 pieces per 8-hr day. With the automatic chucking machine, output was increased to 124 pieces per day. This was attributed to the greater flexibility of tool setup and the greater range of speeds and feeds of the automatic chucking machine (see above) in comparison with the conventional turret lathe.

Examples 54 and 55. Combining Operations on Precision Boring Machines

Example 54 — Five Operations With "Two-in-One" Spindle (Fig. 27). On a single-end precision boring machine, in the setup shown in Fig. 27, boring and counterboring were combined with eccentric turning, boring and facing to form an eccentric lug in a gray iron casting containing a bronze bushing. This was accomplished by the use of a special, "two-in-one" spindle — which was an assembly of two spindles, one mounted within the other, that rotated on different centerlines (Fig. 27).

The inside spindle carried a boring and a counterboring tool, and its centerline coincided with the centerline of the workpiece. The outside spindle carried two tools, spaced 180° apart, swinging eccentric to the workpiece centerline. One of these tools bored the outer wall of the eccentric diameter, while the other turned the inner wall. The tools overlapped slightly, to provide a smooth bottom. The concentric counterbore on the inside, in combination with the eccentric diameter on the outside, gave the lug a crescent shape. The turning tool and the counterboring tool also overlapped. This required that both spindles be driven at the same speed (420 rpm), to prevent interference between the tools.

To machine a part, the operator placed it in the fixture over a locator ring that fit in a previously machined, but larger, counterbore. A radial locating pin fit in a drilled hole to orient the cast lug with the eccentricity in the outer spindle. After clamping, the machine was cycled and all operations were performed simultaneously. Operating conditions are tabulated with Fig. 27.

Example 55 — Four Operations With Three Tools on a Cam-Operated Machine (Fig. 28). Boring, turning, facing and chamfering were combined on a cam-operated single-end precision boring machine; the three-tool setup used and the gray iron casting being machined are shown in Fig. 28. All three tools were in a fixed mounting, and moved as a unit to machine the part. After the casting had been secured in the diaphragm chuck, the machining cycle was begun. The sequence of operations in this cycle was as follows (see Fig. 28 for correlation of tools with surfaces machined, and for operating conditions):

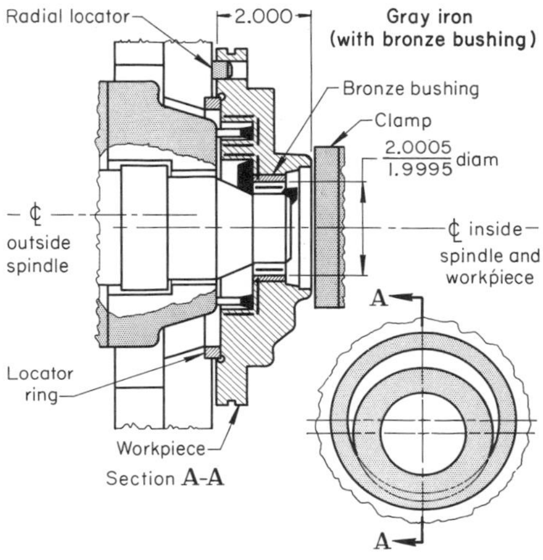

Speed, at 420 rpm:	
Boring	220 sfm
Counterboring	340 sfm
Turning and facing	410 sfm
Feed:	
First (all tools)	0.005 ipr
Second (c'bore, turn, face)	0.001 ipr
Depth of cut	0.012 in. on diam
Cutting fluid	None
Tool material	Carbide(a)
Tool life	8 hr
Production rate	56 pieces per hour

(a) Tools on outside spindle had steel shanks, carbide tips; inside-spindle tools, solid carbide.

Fig. 27. Use of a "two-in-one" spindle for combining boring and counterboring with eccentric turning, boring and facing in a single-end precision boring machine (Example 54)

1. Tool 1 moved to the larger (5½-in.-diam) bore, faced the end, and backed off. Tool 1 reapproached the larger bore at an angle, chamfered the opening, then moved "down" the bore, through a radius and along the "bottom" of the bore. The three-tool unit then backed off.
2. Tool 1 moved to the smaller (2⅛-in.-diam) bore, chamfered the opening, then continued in to finish this bore to size.
3. As tool 1 completed the smaller bore, tool 2 contacted the part in the position shown in Fig. 28. Tool 2 generated the angle and continued along the "bottom" to machine a radius. Tool 2 then turned the outside diameter of the central boss, doubled back, and faced the end of this boss. The tools again backed away, and moved over.
4. Tool 3 approached the part at its outer edge, machined that face, and turned a portion of an outside diameter. Tool 3 continued to move away from the part and was cammed slightly toward the center. The tool reapproached the part and generated two chamfers and a short turned length, to complete the operation.

Although the combination of operations described in Example 55 could be performed on a turret lathe, the assigned tolerances (±0.0005 and ±0.002 in.) would be difficult to attain, repeatability would depend on operator skill rather than on the machine, and production rate would be lower than on the precision boring mill used.

Composition and Hardness of Workpiece Metal

In boring, as in turning, the hardness of steels has a greater effect than composition on their machinability. In general, the harder the steel, the lower are the speed and feed permissible for a given operation. Quantitative data showing the effect of steel hardness on speed, feed, metal-removal rate, and machining cost in turning are presented in Fig. 11 and 12 (page 8) in the article "Turning". Because boring is essentially the turning of inside diameters, effects comparable to those expressed by these data on turning may be expected in boring applications.

The composition and the hardness of the metal being machined are more likely to influence the selection of tool design, tool material and cutting fluid than to determine the type of machine used for a given boring operation. However, metal composition or condition, or both, may dictate the *size* of machine required, because more power is needed as hardness increases. The ease with which a metal can be machined also has a direct influence on costs.

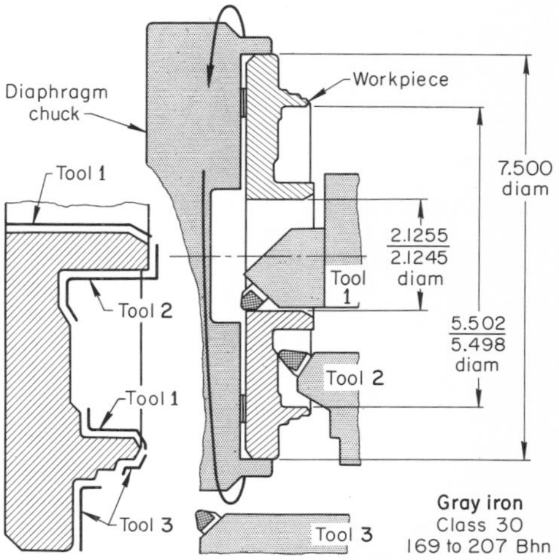

Speed	260 rpm (510 sfm max)
Feed	0.0088 to 0.0091 ipr
Depth of cut on faces	0.010 to 0.015 in.
Depth of cut on diameters	0.020 to 0.030 in.
Cutting fluid	Soluble oil
Tool material	Carbide tips, steel shanks
Production rate	100 pieces per hour

Fig. 28. Boring, turning, facing and chamfering on a cam-operated precision boring machine (Example 55)

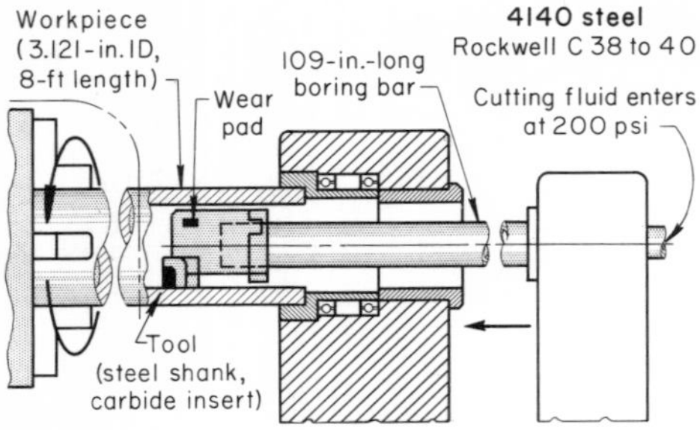

Tolerances Specified on Bore

Diameter	±0.0005 in.
Straightness	0.002 in. per ft

Operating Conditions

Speed	90 rpm (75 sfm)
Feed	0.008 ipr
Depth of cut	0.125 in.
Cutting fluid	Sulfurized oil(a)
Setup time	1½ hr
Downtime for changing tools	10 min
Production rate	2½ hr per piece
Tool life per grind	1 piece

(a) Pumped through bar stem to cutting edge at 50 gal per min, under pressure of 200 psi.

Fig. 29. Setup involving the use of cutting fluid under pressure for accurate boring of a hole 30 diameters long (Example 59)

Rigidity of setup is needed for virtually any metal-cutting operation, but its importance increases as workpiece hardness increases. For example, an annealed alloy steel might be bored without difficulty in a setup having questionable rigidity, whereas if the steel were heat treated to 350 or 400 Bhn, it would probably be impossible to machine in such a setup without tool chatter. If chatter occurs, tolerance, finish and tool life will be impaired.

Reselection of Work Metal. In most instances, work-metal composition and condition are fixed, and processing equipment and techniques must be selected accordingly. Sometimes, however, with no sacrifice in the service performance of a given part, a change in metal composition or condition can be made that will benefit machining so that cost is decreased and productivity is increased. Two applications in which this was possible are described in Examples 56 and 57, which follow; another such application of boring is described in Example 644, on page 335, in the article on Machining of Cast Iron.

Example 56. Change From Steel to Nodular Iron

A large housing for a motor bearing had a rough weight of 190 lb when made of cast steel. Because it was too brittle, gray iron could not be used for this casting, but specifications (withstanding high shock in service without fracture or failure) could be met with nodular iron. As shown in the following comparison, changing to nodular iron not only reduced the weight of this housing without affecting hardness, but also enabled a 22% decrease in boring time and cost:

	Steel	Nodular iron
Rough weight, lb	190	174
Finished weight, lb	178	167
Hardness, Bhn	170	170
Boring time per piece, hr	1.83	1.43
Boring cost per piece	$13.75	$10.75

Example 57. Change From Hot Rolled to Cold Finished Tubing

Parts with a finished weight of 0.6 lb were turned, bored and formed from 1.42-lb blanks of hot rolled 52100 steel tubing at a machining cost of $0.166 each. Changing to cold finished 52100 steel tubing for these parts increased material cost by 11%, but this was more than offset by a 32% decrease in machining time and cost:

	Hot rolled	Cold finished
Material cost per piece	$0.328	$0.364
Machining time, min	1.4	0.95
Machining cost per piece	$0.166	$0.113

Relation Between Work Metal and Cutting Fluid. When difficult-to-machine metals are processed, desired results sometimes can be obtained by changing the grade or type of cutting fluid or by changing the method of delivering the cutting fluid to critical areas. Examples 58, 59 and 60, which follow, deal with the relation between work metal and cutting fluid in three specific applications.

Example 58. Change From Conventional to "Additive-Type" Soluble Oil in Boring 4330 Steel

A special boring bar with a single-point triangular carbide insert was used for boring 3¾–8 UN–3B threads in both ends of a 30-in.-long shaft made of 4330 steel (AMS 6427) and heat treated to Rockwell C 52 to 54. When a conventional soluble oil or mineral oil was used as the cutting fluid, each insert point could bore only one or two complete threads. Finish was 125 to 150 micro-in., and although speed was only 75 sfm (at 75 rpm), chatter was a constant problem and caused unacceptable work.

A proprietary heavy-duty soluble oil containing a stable chlorine additive, and mixed 1-to-5 with water, was substituted as the cutting fluid. Each insert point then bored an average of eight complete threads, and finish was improved to 67 to 100 micro-in. The change also eliminated tool chatter, thus improving size control.

Example 59. Pressurized Cutting Fluid for Close-Tolerance Boring of a Hole 30 Diameters Long in 4140 Steel (Fig. 29)

Figure 29 shows the setup used for boring a 3.121-in.-diam, 8-ft-long hole in a hydraulic cylinder made from 4140 steel tubing, on a 10-hp traveling-head horizontal machine with 16-in. swing. The length-to-diameter ratio of this cylinder represents about the maximum that is practical to bore on a machine of this type when close tolerances must be held.

Because of the high hardness of this cylinder (Rockwell C 38 to 40), a relatively slow boring speed (see operating conditions tabulated with Fig. 29) and special tools were required. The 109-in.-stem boring bar was equipped with a special trepanning-reaming type of head having a single carbide cutting edge and two balanced carbide wear pads. Cutting fluid was pumped through the bar stem to the cutting edge, at 50 gal per min, under a pressure of 200 psi (Fig. 29). This system provided a constant flow of oil.

Example 60. Pressurized Cutting Fluid for Boring Mild Steel Plate (Fig. 30)

Mineral oil under no pressure was used as the cutting fluid in drilling and boring press platens flame-cut to shape from 9-in.-thick mild steel plate (setup shown in Fig. 30). The finish obtained in boring (80 to 120 micro-in.) was unacceptably rough, and the "ball-up" of the stringy chips characteristic of mild steel adversely affected size control.

The problem was solved by the use of a coolant inductor (a commercially available accessory). This forced the mineral oil, at 50-psi pressure, through the boring bar, providing a copious supply at the cutting area to flush away chips. With the pressurized cutting fluid, and no change in tool design, surface roughness was reduced to 40 to 60

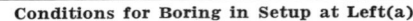

Conditions for Boring in Setup at Left(a)

Speed	249 rpm (240 sfm)
Feed	0.012 ipr
Depth of cut	0.125 in.
Cutting fluid	Mineral oil(b)
Tool material	Carbide
Tool life per grind	30 pieces (60 holes)
Downtime for changing tools	4 min
Boring time per hole	3.5 min

Operating Conditions for Drilling and Boring

Setup time	1 hr
Production rate	3 pieces (6 holes) per hour

(a) Workpieces were drilled and bored, in setup illustrated, on a radial drill press with a 17-in. column and a 5-ft arm. Initial holes were produced with a spade drill, which also was supplied with mineral-oil cutting fluid at 50 psi from a coolant inductor; drilling time per hole was 3.66 min. Boring bar held combination tools for roughing and finishing in one pass. (b) Supplied to bar, at 50 psi, from a coolant inductor.

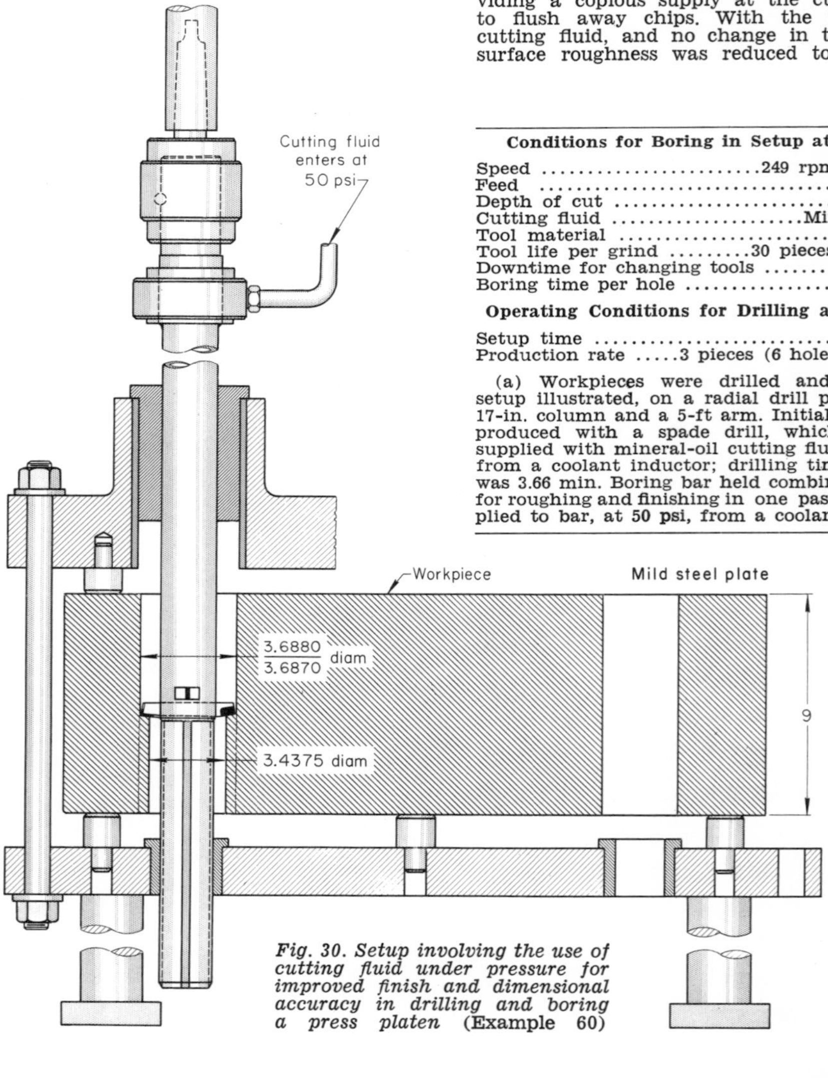

Fig. 30. Setup involving the use of cutting fluid under pressure for improved finish and dimensional accuracy in drilling and boring a press platen (Example 60)

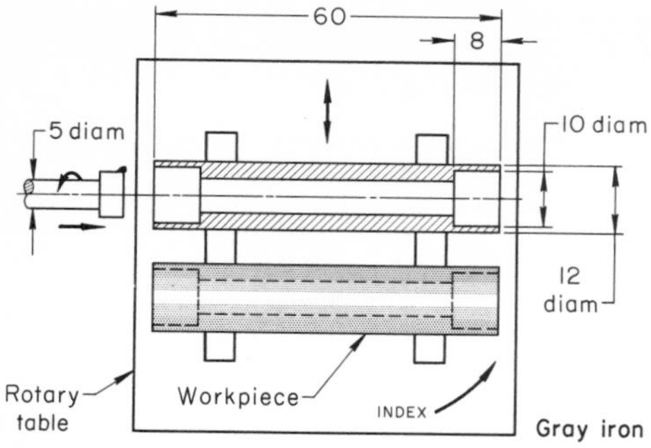

Speed	57 rpm (150 sfm)
Feed	0.015 ipr
Tool material	High speed steel
Cutting fluid	None
Machining time for two-piece load	4 hr(a)

(a) Machining two pieces (four counterbores) on an engine lathe required 11 hr.

Fig. 31. Counterboring tubes two-up on rotary table of a horizontal boring machine (Example 61)

micro-in., and size control was no longer a problem. Operating conditions are given in the table in column 3 alongside Fig. 30.

Production Quantity

The number of identical parts to be bored in a production run is a major factor in the selection of the equipment and procedure to be used. When only one part or only a few identical parts are to be produced and no repeat order is anticipated, the simplest suitable machine available (engine lathe, drill press or boring mill) generally is used, with standard holding devices and boring tools — even though machining time may greatly exceed that on production machines.

As production quantity increases, the need for raising production speed must be weighed against the increased cost of more elaborate tooling. The next step usually is a machine capable of performing a number of operations consecutively (such as a turret lathe, assuming that part size and shape permit). In many instances in which small to intermediate quantities are required, however, radial drill presses may be the most economical machines for boring. This is particularly true when the hole is small in relation to the size of the workpiece or when the configuration of the hole would pose problems for machining in lathes or similar machines.

As requirements are further increased to continuous high production, progressively more complicated machines may be used — up to and including tape-controlled automatic chuckers that are completely programmed for one specific job. Many large-volume applications employ special machines built for efficient boring of identical workpieces in continuous high production; a notable example is the high-production boring of automobile engine blocks.

Examples 61 through 64, which follow, describe specific applications in which quantity to be produced was the deciding factor in selection of equipment and procedure. [For the effect of quantity on selection of machine for lowest overall cost, see Examples 77 and 78 on page 39, in this article.]

Examples 61 and 62. Increases in Production by Changing From Single-Piece Boring on Lathes to Two-Up Boring on Horizontal Machines

Example 61 — Counterboring Gray Iron (Fig. 31). Gray iron tubes 60 in. long required counterboring to a depth of 8 in. from each end. On an engine lathe, 11 hr was required for counterboring two tubes (four counterbores). An increase in production quantity necessitated a reduction in machining time. This was accomplished by the use of a rotary-table horizontal boring machine and the setup shown in Fig. 31. The table of this machine could move sideways as well as rotate 360°, and thus could position the two workpieces for production of all four counterbores. The tool advanced for the completion of each counterbore while the workpiece remained stationary. Using this machine and setup, a two-piece load (four counterbores) was completed in 4 hr, or about one-third the time required on the lathe (see data with Fig. 31).

Example 62 — Boring 4330 Steel (Fig. 32). When 23-in.-long tubes made of 4330 steel were produced in batches of fewer than 100, they were bored on a lathe, one at a time, as shown in Fig. 32(a). The tool block held two carbide tools and chip breakers. The nylon-insert pack head was held rigidly by the guide bushing until it had entered the bore.

As volume increased and production runs exceeded 100 pieces, two tubes at a time were bored with gun reamers on a two-spindle horizontal machine, as shown in Fig. 32(b) — which, in addition to doubling production rate, also enabled the use of a more nearly optimum speed. (Operating details for the two methods are compared in the table accompanying Fig. 32.) Speed and feed for the two-spindle machine were determined by trial to obtain effective chip control, which is mandatory when boring small diameters.

Examples 63 and 64. Use of Radial Drill Presses for Small Production Quantities

Example 63 — Rough and Finish Boring of Gray Iron (Fig. 33). A radial drill press with a 14-in. column and a 36-in. arm was used for one-pass rough and finish boring of 1⅜-in.-diam holes in gray iron end frames for knitting machines, which were produced in small quantities. The setup used is shown in Fig. 33, and processing details are listed in the tabulation accompanying it.

The workpiece was held by means of a raised block fixture. Because accurate hole location, size and straightness were required, it was necessary to use a piloted bar. The boring cutters straightened the predrilled hole and provided accurate hole location. The reaming cutters, allowed to float in the slot of

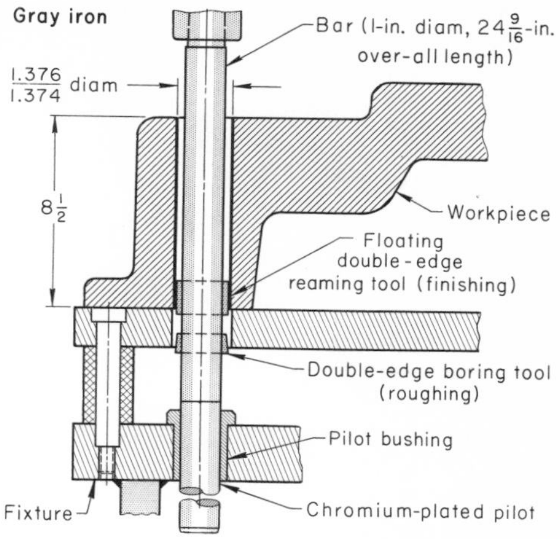

Speed	200 rpm (72 sfm)
Feed	0.012 ipr
Depth of cut, roughing	3/32 in.
Depth of cut, finishing	0.015 in.
Cutting fluid	None
Tool material	M2 high speed steel
Setup time	1½ hr
Downtime for changing tools	1 min
Production rate	12 holes per hour
Tool life per grind	75 holes

Fig. 33. Use of radial drill press for one-pass boring of castings produced in small quantities (Example 63)

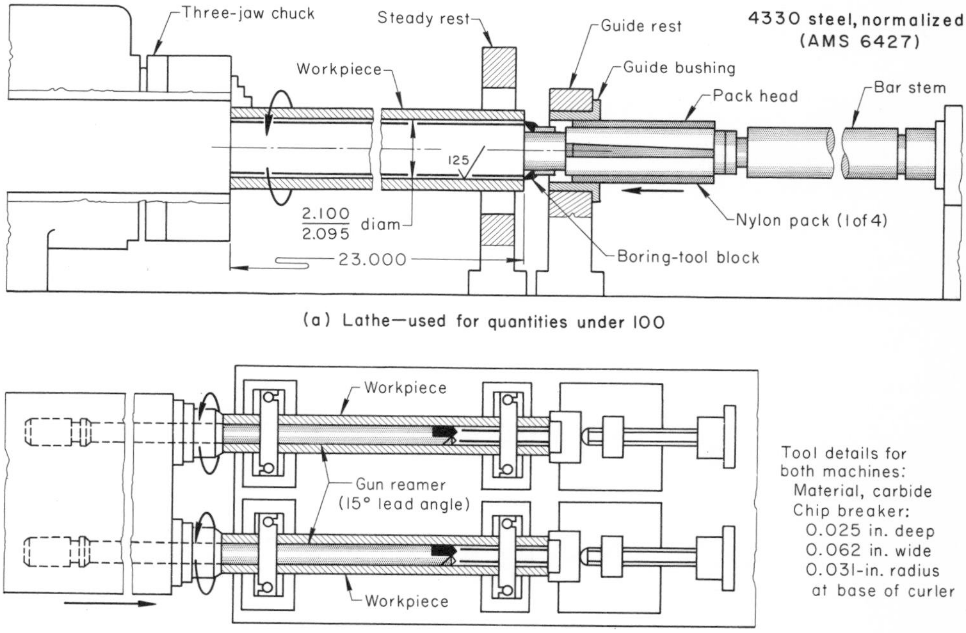

(a) Lathe—used for quantities under 100

(b) Two-spindle horizontal machine—used for quantities over 100

Operating condition(a)	Lathe	Two-spindle machine
Speed, rpm	307	415
Speed, sfm	170	230
Feed, ipr	0.005	0.004
Depth of cut, in.	3/16	3/16
Setup time, hr	2½	4(b)
Production, pieces per hr	3	6

(a) On both machines, soluble-oil cutting fluid was forced, under 200-psi pressure, through stem of boring bar or reamer, to cutting edges. (b) For setting up both fixtures.

Fig. 32. Low-production and high-production methods for boring the same part (Example 62)

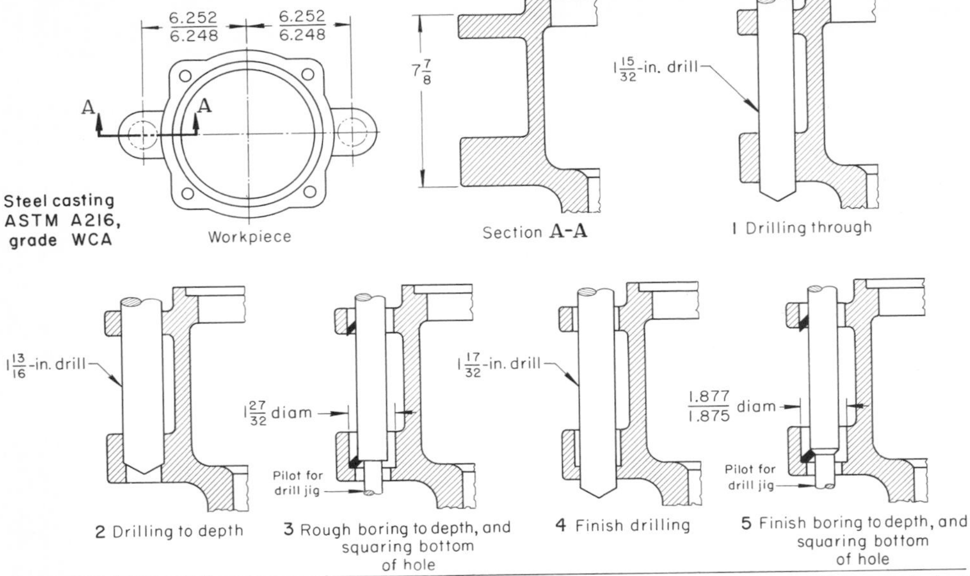

Speed, operation 1 ....125 rpm (48 sfm)	Tool material ....High speed steel
Speed, operations 2 to 5 ..90 rpm (36 to 44 sfm)	Cutting fluid ....Soluble oil
Feed, all operations ....0.011 ipr	Machining time per piece ....86 min

Fig. 34. Sequence of operations for drilling and boring holes in steel castings on a radial drill press — used because of low production quantity (Example 64)

the bar, finished the hole within tolerance (±0.001 in.) without need for a secondary operation.

Speed and feed were established as optimum for machining gray iron with high speed steel cutters. (The feed rate was double that conventionally recommended, because of the two cutting edges available.) Because production quantities were limited, high speed steel cutters were selected as the most economical tools, on the dual basis of ease of regrinding and short downtime for changing tools.

Example 64 — Drilling and Boring Cast Steel (Fig. 34). A 4-ft radial drill press was used for drilling and boring opposing pairs of concentric lugs on steel castings, in five operations as illustrated and detailed in Fig. 34. A special drill jig (not illustrated) having pilot bushings and guides was used to permit achieving the required final tolerance of +0.002, −0.000 in.

A drilling machine was selected primarily because quantities were limited (average production run was six pieces), and because setup time was about 60% less than would have been required had the part been machined on a horizontal boring mill, which could have been used for greater quantities (the configuration of the part precluded the use of machines that require work rotation).

Accuracy of Form and Diameter

Accuracy of boring relates to size, taper, roundness, concentricity, squareness, and parallelism, and to control of vibration that can affect accuracy.

Diameter of the bore can be affected by heat generated at the cut, although an adequate flow of cutting fluid can control heat.

Taper is an error in a cylindrical bore and may be caused by deflection of the boring bar.

To decrease deflection, pilots and bushings (see page 22) are commonly used to reduce the unsupported length of boring bars. Example 31 (Fig. 4) illustrates a bushing supporting the end of a boring bar. Such a setup changes the boring bar from a cantilever beam with end loading to a beam supported at each end with center loading. Although a bar with end supports may be up to twice as long as the cantilever bar, it will deflect only about one tenth as much as the cantilever bar. The deflection will be maximum at the start of the cut and will decrease as the cutting tool moves closer to the end support bushing. An end support bushing at both ends of a workpiece, as in Example 44 (Fig. 17a), may further reduce deflection of the boring bar during cutting.

Deflection can also be reduced by changing the material of the boring bar to one with a higher modulus of elasticity. In Example 30, carbide reinforcing strips were brazed to a bar for added stiffness, and a solid carbide bar permitted a longer overhang with less total deflection than the reinforced bar.

Cutting on the return stroke often will remove stock left in a hole by a deflected bar. The success of this technique depends on the greatly reduced cutting pressure and the proper radial advance of the tool to remove a very slight amount of metal. Return-stroke cutting increases cycle time, because the return stroke is at a low feed rate rather than at the usual rapid traverse.

Roundness of a hole is determined by the variation in radius about a fixed axis. Out-of-roundness (eccentricity) may result when the finish cut is not concentric with the previous cut. Depending on the amount of eccentricity, the depth of cut will vary, which may deflect the tool more during heavy cutting than in a lighter cut. With these conditions it may be necessary to use a semifinish cut and a finish cut and sometimes to cut on the return stroke.

An out-of-balance rotating workpiece or tool holder can produce an out-of-round hole. Careful balancing of the setup can eliminate most such out-of-roundness.

Concentricity of one surface with another is a common specification that can cause production problems. When concentricity must be held to close limits, it is usually desirable to rotate the work. Almost all types of rotating fixtures are applicable to precision boring machines.

Clamping of the workpiece must be such that distortions will not affect hole size and shape. In Example 39 the work was reclamped with a lighter force after the roughing cut. Distortions resulting from a heavy clamping force are released before semifinish and finish cutting and usually are not reinstated by a lighter clamping force.

Multiple-spindle machines or double-end machines can be set up accurately to produce closely concentric surfaces. If the results are not acceptable, it may be possible to plan the sequence of operations so that all close-tolerance surfaces can be machined with tools in the same boring bar.

Squareness and parallelism of holes in relation to other features of the work can be affected by changes in room temperature, in the temperature of control-system oil, and in the temperature of the cutting fluid.

A change in room temperature can cause expansion or contraction of the machine components, with resulting misalignment of the spindle and workpiece centerlines. The temperature of oil in the hydraulic control system can cause deflection of the feed cylinders or the machine slide. Cooling coils in the oil-storage tank can maintain a constant oil temperature.

The heat produced at the tip of the cutting tool may cause a rise in temperature of the cutting fluid. The flow of a warm cutting fluid over the machine components may cause dimensional changes that affect accuracy of operation. Maintaining the cutting fluid at a constant temperature helps to maintain consistent temperature in both the workpiece and the machine tool. The actual temperature of a system is usually less important than the magnitude of temperature variation.

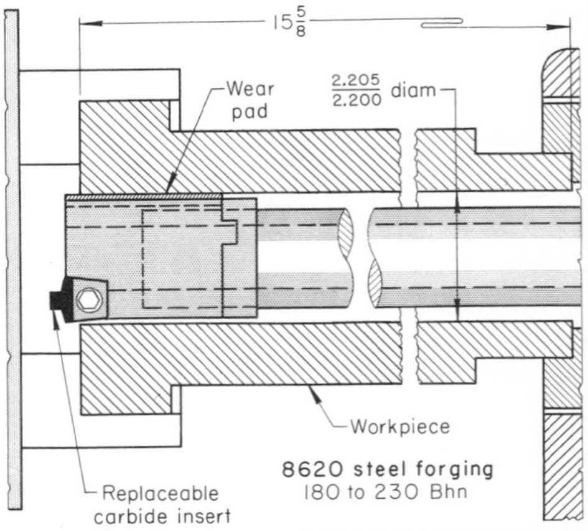

Speed	650 rpm (375 sfm max)
Feed	0.0045 ipr
Cutting fluid	Oil, at 500 psi and 80 gpm(a)
Setup time	2 hr
Downtime for changing tools	5 min
Production rate	6 pieces per hour
Insert life per grind	15 pieces
Regrinds per insert	3

(a) Pumped through stem to cutting edges from 1200-gal system, and maintained at 100 F.

Fig. 35. Use of trepanning head in converted gun-drilling machine for simultaneous drilling and boring to close tolerance (Example 65)

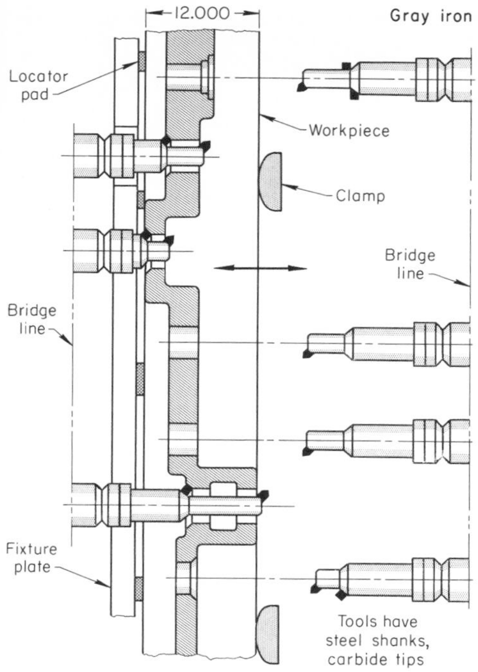

Operating condition	Roughing	Finishing
Spindle speed, rpm	240	380
Surface speed (max), sfm:		
Boring	250	400
Counterboring	284	354
Chamfering	258	...
Feed, all operations, ipr	0.008	0.0028
Depth of cut (max), in.	¼	...
Cutting fluid	None	None
Tolerance, in.	±0.003	±0.001
Production, pcs/hr	11.5	10.3

Fig. 36. Use of 13 tools on seven spindles of a double-end precision boring machine for boring, counterboring and chamfering. Similar setups on two machines were used for roughing and finishing. (Example 66)

Examples Involving Accuracy

As dimensional tolerances become more stringent, machining cost increases. This increase may be caused by the need for more accurate or more rigid tooling and setups, or partly by the need for taking lighter cuts (which slow production, requiring more passes of the tool) for the greater accuracy. The decreased number of parts that can be machined between tool grinds is another important factor, because of increased tool-maintenance cost and loss of machine productivity.

As many of the examples in this article demonstrate, boring to close tolerances with conventional equipment is common practice. The various means of guiding the boring tools, flushing away chips, and other refinements of technique contribute to the maintenance of diametral tolerances of ±0.001 in., or even closer, in production operation.

Precision boring machines are required for meeting tolerances of ±0.0005 in. or less. In many instances such machines are used even when tolerances are no closer than the best obtainable with conventional machines. For example, in high-production boring of relatively small parts to tolerances up to ±0.003 in., the "precision" type of machine usually is preferred, because it offers increased productivity and decreased cost per piece bored. (Precision boring to concentricity within 0.0004 in. TIR is described in Example 878, in the article on Machining of Aluminum.)

Precision boring is closely related to, and frequently overlaps with, gun drilling, as in the following example:

Example 65. Use of Gun-Drilling Machine for Simultaneous Drilling and Boring to ±0.001 In. (Fig. 35)

A 2.205/2.200-in.-diam hole in a pneumatic-hammer housing forged of 8620 steel was simultaneously drilled and bored on a 20-hp converted gun-drilling machine equipped with special tools (Fig. 35). This single-operation procedure replaced drilling, boring and finish reaming, which formerly had been used for producing these holes.

A standard trepanning head with a ¾-in.-wide replaceable carbide insert and preground replaceable wear pads was mounted on a ground, hollow stem. The workpiece was mounted on a special chuck and rotary-bushing carrier with entrance provided for cutting fluid, which was pumped through the stem at 80 gal per min under 500-psi pressure. The tool was piloted both by the bushing and by the wear pads running on the stem. The bushing was mounted in a tapered Teflon collet, which permitted adjustment and damped vibration.

Although specifications permitted a variation of ±0.0025 in. in hole diameter, the finished holes were actually held to ±0.001

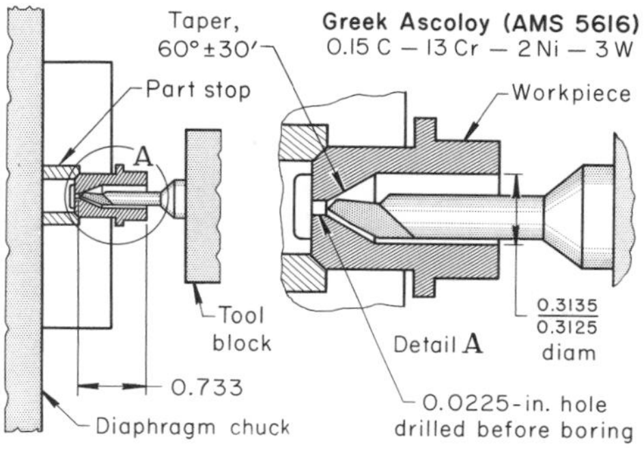

Speed	3600 rpm (295 sfm)
Feed	0.0005 ipr
Depth of cut (on diam)	0.004 to 0.006 in.
Tool material	Carbide (solid)
Cutting fluid	Air-mist soluble oil
Finish specified	16 to 32 micro-in.
Production rate	185 pieces per hour

Fig. 37. Precision boring and tapering of a rotating workpiece in a cam-operated two-station boring machine (Example 67)

in. and within 0.001-in. straightness for the entire length. A surface finish of 40 to 60 micro-in. was obtained. Additional operating conditions are given with Fig. 35.

When close tolerances must be held on complex workpieces, the preferred practice for achieving them at minimum cost is to use a multiple-spindle machine, performing all operations in one setup, as in Example 66, which follows. Had the workpiece in this example been processed on a single-spindle machine, adjustment or changing of tools between holes would have greatly increased the cost.

Example 66. Close-Tolerance Machining With 13 Tools on Seven Spindles (Fig. 36)

Seven holes, ranging from 2¾ to 4 in. in diameter, in a large, complex gray iron casting were machined with 13 single-point cutting tools on a multiple-spindle, double-end precision boring machine. As shown in Fig. 36, all holes were bored through, four holes were also chamfered, and one hole was provided with two counterbores. The workpiece was clamped to a fixture plate on the table. As the table moved to the left, three holes were machined. Direction of table movement was then reversed, and four holes were machined. Boring tools were out of the holes before chamfering or counterboring was begun (Fig. 36).

Roughing operations were performed on one machine with the tool setup shown in Fig. 36; in roughing, tolerance of ±0.003 in. was obtained. The workpiece then was transferred to a similar machine and tool setup, where the holes were finished to ±0.001 in. Additional process details are given with Fig. 36.

When workpiece size and configuration permit, it is usually preferable to rotate the part, rather than the tools, in precision boring, because problems involving concentricity and parallelism thus are minimized. Examples 67 and 68, which follow, describe applications where workpiece rotation was practical.

Examples 67 and 68. Close-Tolerance Boring of Rotated Workpieces

Example 67 — Straight and Taper Boring a Small-Diameter Hole (Fig. 37). The small stainless steel part shown in Fig. 37 was rough machined in an automatic bar machine. Reaming originally had been used for finishing this part (removing 0.004 to 0.006 in. from the inside diameter of the large bore and from the 60° taper). However, because required tolerances (±0.0005 in. on bore, ±0°30′ on taper) were difficult to hold by reaming, boring with a single-point tool was substituted as the method of finishing. Boring was done on a two-station precision machine, which was cam-operated to provide the tool with the necessary longitudinal and lateral movement; the setup is shown in Fig. 37. In addition to providing the required dimensional accuracy, the change of process also provided a fivefold increase in production rate — 185 pieces per hour by boring, as against 37 by reaming.

Example 68 — Boring and Facing With Six Tools on a Vertical Machine (Fig. 38). A special vertical boring machine was used for semifinishing and finishing two bores and facing a large flange on a steel forging. The workpiece and tooling setup are shown in Fig. 38. The special machine used was similar

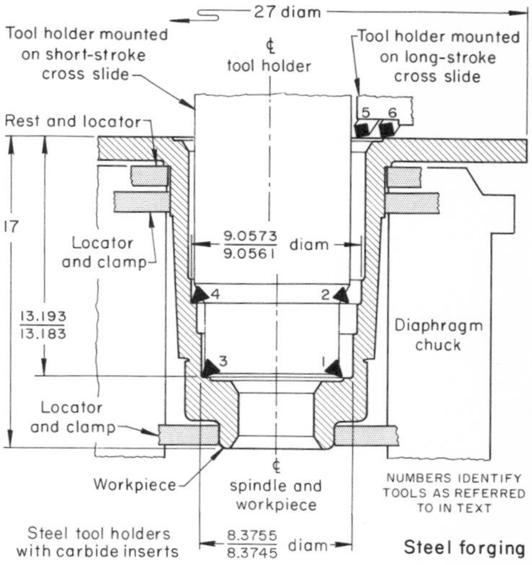

Surface speeds (max):	
Tools 1, 2, 3 and 4	203 sfm(a)
Tools 5 and 6	452 sfm(b)
Feeds:	
Tools 1, 2, 3 and 4 (boring)	0.005 ipr
Tool 1 (facing)	0.002 ipr
Tools 5 and 6 (facing)	0.016 ipr
Depths of cut:	
Tools 1 and 2 (on diameter)	0.070 in.
Tools 3 and 4 (on diameter)	0.020 in.
Tool 1 (on face)	0.020 in.
Tools 5 and 6 (on face)	0.010 in.
Cutting fluid	Soluble oil
Production rate	2.7 pieces per hour

(a) At spindle speed of 92 rpm.
(b) At spindle speed of 64 rpm.

Fig. 38. Precision boring and facing a rotating workpiece with six tools on a special vertical machine (Example 68)

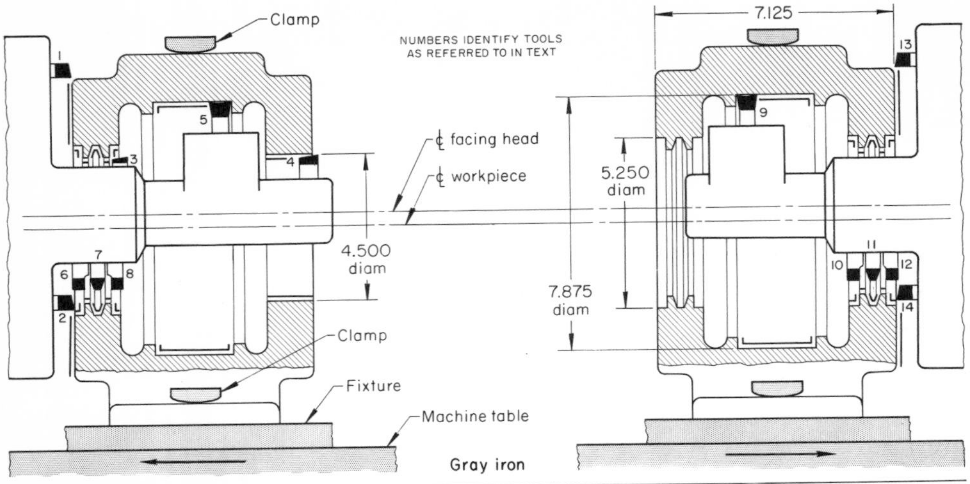

Operations at Left End of Machine(a)
(Tools 1 through 8)

Spindle speed, all operations	120 rpm
Surface speeds:	
Boring (tools 4, 5)	141 and 248 sfm
Facing (tools 1, 2)	165 to 283 sfm
Grooving (tools 6, 7, 8)	165 sfm max
Feeds:	
Boring and facing	0.015 ipr
Grooving	0.007 to 0.010 ipr
Depths of cut:	
Boring	0.250 in. (max) per side
Facing	0.250 in.
Grooving	9/64 in. (3/8-in.-wide plunge)

Operations at Right End of Machine(b)
(Tools 9 through 14)

Spindle speed, all operations	180 rpm
Surface speeds:	
Boring (tool 9)	372 sfm
Facing (tools 13, 14)	248 to 424 sfm
Grooving (tools 10, 11, 12)	248 sfm max
Feeds:	
Boring and facing	0.010 ipr
Grooving	0.007 to 0.010 ipr
Depths of cut:	
Boring	0.015 in. per side
Facing	0.250 in.
Grooving	9/64 in. (3/8-in.-wide plunge)

(a) Tolerance on all dimensions machined at left end was ±0.005 in. (b) Tolerance on finish-bored 7.875-in. ID was ±0.0014 in.; on all other dimensions machined at right end, ±0.005 in.

Fig. 39. Machining a complex casting, using 14 individual tools with two combination boring bars and facing heads on a double-end precision boring machine (Example 69)

in principle to a standard vertical precision boring machine, but requirements for a larger swing and two facing strokes precluded the use of a standard machine.

The part was placed in a double diaphragm chuck against a stop and was clamped when the chuck was closed. After the chucked part had begun rotating, a boring bar with four insert-type carbide tools (Fig. 38) was lowered into the bore. As the bar approached the correct depth, the feed rate was engaged and tools 1 and 2 semifinished the two steps in the bore.

The bar then retracted slightly more than the length of the long bore and moved over; again feed was engaged, and tools 3 and 4 proceeded to finish bore the two diameters. At the bottom of the stroke, the bar again moved over and tool 1 faced the bottom and blended the radius. The bar moved back just short of finish-boring position, and dwelled while the flange was faced.

Semifinish and finish facing of the flange was done by tools 5 and 6, which were mounted in one tool block (Fig. 38). A single horizontal pass with this block completed the part. Additional processing details are tabulated with Fig. 38.

Some complex parts can be efficiently machined to close tolerances by using double-end machines and combination tools. The following example represents about the maximum number of tools that can be made to function effectively in one operation to do boring in the usual manner.

Example 69. Fourteen Tools on Two Heads of a Double-End Precision Boring Machine (Fig. 39)

A double-end precision boring machine was used for boring, facing and grooving a complex casting with a total of 14 tools, as illustrated in Fig. 39. Because of the grooves and the recess, tools had to be fed into the workpiece and then "expanded". To do this, the tools were attached to combination boring bars and facing heads that could be moved eccentrically in two directions from the centerline of spindle and work. The heads were moved by two hydraulic cylinders, which operated while the spindle was rotating.

When the left head was moved, its eccentric swing and that of the boring bar caused the paths described by tools 1, 3, 4 and 5 (Fig. 39) to become larger and the paths described by tools 2, 6, 7 and 8 to become smaller. With the workpiece in position, the left facing head was moved eccentrically and tool 5 plunge faced the inside shoulder. The table feed was engaged and tools 3 and 4 finish bored the inside diameter and tool 5 rough bored the recess. At the end of the table travel, the facing head was moved past center to another eccentric position 180° opposite the first position. This movement faced the end with tools 1 and 2 and plunge formed the grooves with tools 6, 7 and 8.

After the table moved to the right end, a similar facing-head and boring-bar combination was moved into the workpiece. Tool 9 then plunge faced the other inside shoulder, the table feed was engaged, and the interior recess was finish bored. At the end of the table travel, the facing head was moved past center to another eccentric position 180° opposite the first position. This movement faced the end with tools 13 and 14 and plunge formed the grooves with tools 10, 11 and 12.

No cutting fluid was used. See Fig. 39 for process details.

In precision boring, speeds and feeds are based on the use of carbide cutting tools. Consequently, to maintain sufficient tool rigidity when the ratio of the length of the boring bar to hole diameter exceeds 4 to 1, it is generally mandatory that the bar also be made of carbide (as in Example 70) or else that it be piloted (as in Example 71):

Example 70. Precision Boring With Long Carbide Bars (Fig. 40)

A single-end, two-spindle precision boring machine was used for semifinish and finish boring a gray iron casting in the setup shown in Fig. 40. The shape and size of this casting dictated that it be held stationary and the tools rotated. Because the length of the boring bar exceeded hole diameter by slightly more than 6 to 1, a carbide bar was used.

The workpiece was located and clamped to the cross slide. The front spindle was used for semifinish boring, the rear for finishing. To attain the ±0.0005-in. tolerance specified for the finished bore, the machine had to be rigid and the table capable of tracking within two seconds of arc for pitch and yaw in 10 in. of travel. Spindles having no more than 0.0002-in. runout also were required for this job, because of close tolerance on the bore diameter, and because of the excessive whip that more runout would cause in a bar this long. Operating conditions are given with Fig. 40.

Example 71. Precision Boring Four Holes in One Part With Piloted Long Bars (Fig. 41)

A single-end, two-spindle precision boring machine was used for boring four holes in a gray iron casting as shown in Fig. 41. Although the two boring bars had length-to-hole-diameter ratios of 7 to 1 and 14 to 1, respectively, this workpiece required that the boring bars be piloted; hence, carbide bars were not needed. Piloting was done by an assembly, attached to the table, that consisted of a holding fixture and two splined bushings that were ball-bearing mounted. In loading, the part was lowered over this assembly.

In the machining cycle, the table rapidly traversed in, and pointed keys on the bars then engaged pointed ends on the splined pilots (see detail in top left corner of Fig. 41), bringing the two into alignment. Tool interference with the pilot was prevented because the key aligned the tool with one of the splines in the pilot. The lead tools roughed and semifinished the first holes and traversed through the pilots. The table then dropped into feed, and all four holes were finish bored. There was 0.060 in. of stock to be removed on the larger bores and only 0.020 in. on the smaller bores; for this reason, a roughing tool was used only on the larger boring bar. Additional processing details are included with Fig. 41.

In some applications calling for close-tolerance boring, production rate can be increased by the use of two different types of machines — one for roughing, the other for finishing to required dimensions. The procedure employed in one application of this type is described in Example 72, which follows. (Another close-tolerance boring application in which one type of machine was used for roughing, and another type for finishing, is described in Example 67.)

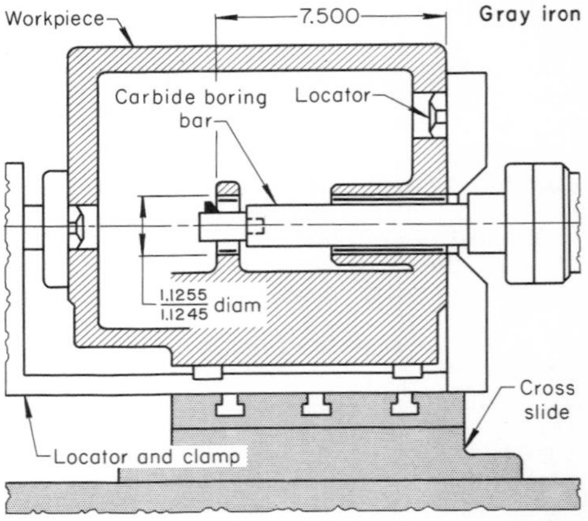

Speed	1360 rpm (400 sfm)
Feed	0.004 ipr
Depth of cut, semifinishing	0.018 in. per side
Depth of cut, finishing	0.005 in. per side
Cutting fluid	None
Tool material	Carbide tip, steel shank
Production rate	26 pieces per hour

Fig. 40. Precision boring in which ratio of bar length to bore diameter dictated the use of a carbide boring bar for maintenance of close tolerance of ±0.0005 in. (Example 70)

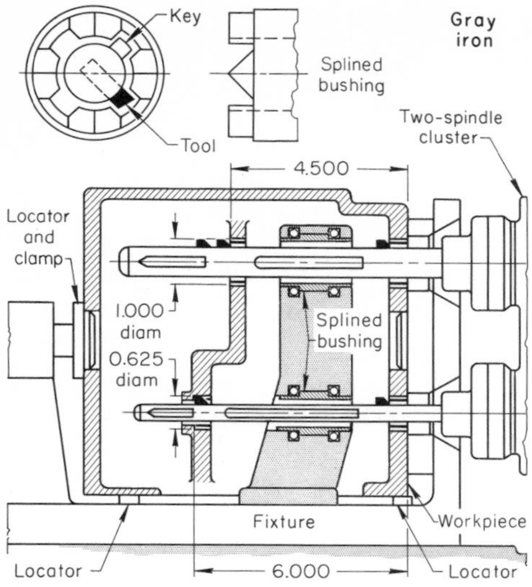

Tolerance on bored holes .....+0.001, —0.000 in.

Operating Conditions

Spindle speeds(a)	1500 and 1000 rpm
Surface speeds(a)	244 and 261 sfm
Feed	0.003 ipr
Depths of cut(a)	0.010 and 0.030 in.
Tool material	Carbide (solid)
Cutting fluid	None
Production rate	50 pieces per hour

(a) For 0.625-in. and 1.000-in. bores, respectively.

Fig. 41. Precision boring with long piloted bars (Example 71)

Example 72. Use of a Precision Boring Machine for Finish Boring a Part Roughed on a Turret Lathe (Fig. 42)

The sleeve in a small stainless steel guide was rough bored on a turret lathe to within 0.006 to 0.007 in. of finished size, and was then semifinish and finish bored on a two-spindle precision boring machine. The high speed and low feed characteristics of the precision machine provided required results in about one-tenth the time that would have been required on the turret lathe.

Figure 42 shows the setup and work-holding collet and fixture common for both spindles of the precision machine. In semifinishing, on the first spindle, 0.005 in. of stock was removed; the finishing cut, on the second spindle, removed 0.001 to 0.0015 in. Additional processing details are given with Fig. 42.

As may be seen from the foregoing examples, it is possible to hold tolerances within 0.001 in. or less in production boring. Quality-control methods usually are used to indicate when adjustments are needed to retain close tolerances, as in the following example:

Example 73. Use of Quality-Control Methods for Maintaining Accuracy in Boring (Fig. 43)

The quality-control chart in Fig. 43 plots the dimensional variations obtained in boring the 5.5125/5.5115-in.-diam hole in the gray iron special-duty adapter illustrated above the chart. These workpieces were bored on a chucking machine. Each of the 18 "sample" points plotted on the vertical axis of the chart represents the average of measurements made on four pieces. The lines at plus and minus 0.0005 in. represent upper and lower specified limits. The line $\overline{X}$ at 0.00017 in. is the estimate of the process capability based on a study of several samples. The line $UCL_{\overline{X}}$ is the upper control limit, and $LCL_{\overline{X}}$ is the lower control limit, calculated from $\overline{X}$. If the process is in control, the average of the samples over a period of time should approach $\overline{X}$.

Charts of this type are valuable in production boring because they indicate trends; any points outside the control limits should be investigated immediately. Here, for example, samples 4 to 9 show a definite trend toward undersize boring, and had the operation been continued unchanged, bores very likely would have been out of tolerance after two or three more four-piece samples had been machined. Therefore, tools were reset toward the upper specified limit before the pieces measured as the tenth sample were machined.

Control of Vibration and Chatter

Vibrations between a tool and a workpiece are either forced or self-excited. In forced vibrations, the alternating force that sustains the motion is created or controlled by the motion itself; when the motion stops, the alternating force disappears. In self-excited vibrations, the sustaining alternating force exists independently of the motion and persists even when the vibratory motion stops.

If an external, periodically varying (cyclic) force is applied to a system such as a machine tool, the mass will oscillate at the frequency of the applied cyclic force. Such forced vibrations can be caused by a passing truck or overhead crane; by machine sources such as faulty bearings or troublesome belts; by loose, worn, or vibrating machine parts; or by interrupted cuts in machining. Such difficulties can be remedied by isolation, by repair or maintenance, or by changing the feed or tool position.

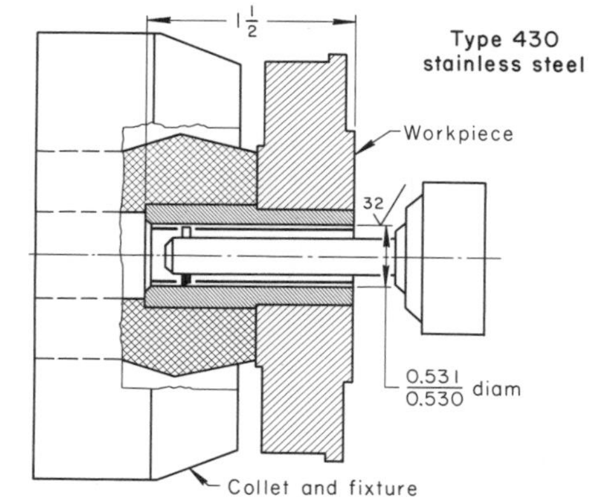

Speed, both operations	4500 rpm (625 sfm)
Feed, both operations	0.0012 ipr
Depths of cut:	
Semifinishing	0.005 in.
Finishing	0.001 to 0.0015 in.
Tool materials:	
Semifinishing	Carbide tip
Finishing	Solid-carbide insert
Production rate	30 pieces per hour

Fig. 42. Setup used on both spindles of a two-spindle precision machine for semifinish and finish boring guide sleeves that were rough bored on a turret lathe (Example 72)

The control of self-excited vibration that builds up in the tool itself is more difficult. In boring bars and quills of unfavorable length-to-diameter ratio, means of controlling self-excited vibration include the use of a boring bar made of material that has a high modulus of elasticity, or the use of an inertia-damped quill, or both.

The static stiffness of a carbide boring bar is three times that of an alloy steel bar because of the difference in modulus of elasticity of the two materials. With its greater static stiffness, a carbide bar can make three times as heavy a cut with the same deflection, or it can make an equal cut with one third as much deflection, and consequently with greater accuracy.

The following data compare the performance of a steel and a carbide bar:

Item	Steel bar	Carbide bar
Rough Boring		
Feed, ipr	0.005	0.007
Speed, rpm	180	350
Depth of cut, in.	3/16-1/4	3/16-1/4
Finish Boring		
Number of cuts	2	1
Feed, ipr	0.005	0.005
Speed, rpm	150	400
Depth of cut, in.	0.030	0.007
Finish, micro-in.	150	90

Each bar had a 5/8-in.-diam head, cutting edges with 30° included angles, and minimum bore diameter of 1 in.

The strength and stiffness of a quill are factors in the deflection caused by cutting forces and have an effect on the frequency of natural vibration. Hence, changing the tool material from steel to carbide will increase stiffness and the frequency of natural vibration but cannot avoid the effects of self-excited vibration.

Use of a Plug Damper. One approach to the problem of self-excited vibration is to bore the unsupported end of the quill and insert a damper (a plug of heavy material) to fit the hole but 0.002 to 0.003 in. smaller in diameter so that it floats in the quill. The end clearance of the damper is approximately the same as the clearance on the diameter.

When the quill starts to vibrate, the plug tends to remain stationary because of its inertia. Thus, the air surrounding the plug is caused to flow from one side of the plug to the other. This air flow tends to dissipate and damp vibration before it can build up or resonate. Any tendency of the quill to vibrate is resisted by the plug in the same manner as a spinning gyroscope resists a change, the air film helping to dissipate the energy that promotes vibration. The vibrations in a quill without a damper die out slowly; in a quill with a damper, the vibrations die out rapidly.

The heavier the weight, the greater the damping effect. Hence the use of a material such as a tungsten alloy (70%

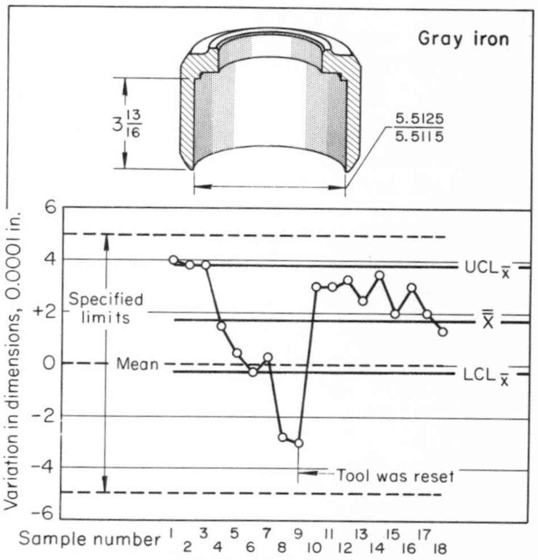

Fig. 43. Quality-control chart showing variations obtained in boring a 5.5125/5.5115-in. hole (Example 73)

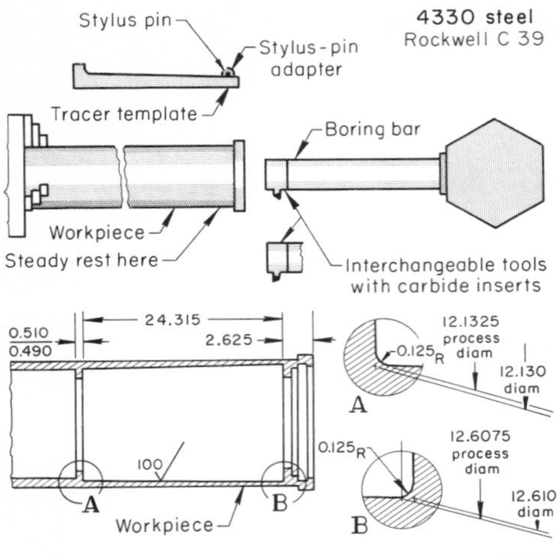

Rough Boring(a)

Speed	69 rpm (217 sfm)
Feed	0.015 ipr
Depth of cut	0.250 in.(b)

Finish Taper Boring(c)

Speed	69 rpm (228 sfm max)
Feed	0.007 ipr
Depth of cut	0.030 in.

Both Operations

Cutting fluid	Soluble oil
Machining time per piece	3 hr

(a) Workpiece, of heat treated tubing, was rough bored in two cuts in a previous operation, to 12-in. ID. (b) Total for the two cuts (0.125 in. each). (c) Finishing, in which the 24.315-in.-long bore was tapered and the two ribs were faced and radiused (see illustration), was done on a long-bed lathe.

Fig. 44. Finish taper boring in which 50% reduction in the roughing feed rate, at the same spindle speed, was required for achieving specified surface finish (Example 74)

heavier than lead) is indicated. The weight should be made as large as possible without appreciably reducing the stiffness of the quill. It is equally important to place the weight where the expected motion is greatest. Both of these considerations indicate that the weight should be placed at the free end of the quill, not at the root where the quill is secured to the spindle.

The damping effect is limited by the amount of weight at the effective damping point. The effective damping force of a given combination of weight and quill increases in direct proportion to the increase in the natural vibration frequency of the quill. By making a portion of the quill of a material having a modulus of elasticity higher than steel, such as tungsten carbide or molybdenum, the natural frequency of vibration is increased, and therefore the same size of weight will provide a greater damping effect.

In horizontal rotating quills, it is advisable to keep the radial clearance of the damper plug small. Or the clearance space around the cylindrical inertia weight can be filled with oil for equal dashpot effect even though there is a much larger clearance than in air. This is advantageous because of the effect of centrifugal force on the damper plug. The damper plug tends to center itself in the quill at low speeds because of the combined action of gravity and centrifugal force. Above a certain speed, centrifugal force overbalances gravity and the weight is pulled to one side and held there, thus reducing its damping effectiveness.

The relation between rotational speed and maximum plug clearance that separates the stable region where gravity keeps the plug centered and the unstable region where centrifugal forces overbalance gravity is indicated by the following approximate values for speed and radial clearance: 10,000 rpm, 0.0003 in.; 6000 rpm, 0.001 in.; 5000 rpm, 0.0014 in.; 4000 rpm, 0.002 in.; and 3000 rpm, 0.003 in. The smaller the clearance, the greater the permissible speed; hence the preference for air as a damping medium rather than oil.

The approximate useful range of the damper appears to be for quill length-to-diameter ratios of 3.5-to-1 to 8-to-1. The tendency of the plug to remain at rest decreases with a decrease in the natural vibration frequency of the quill. Making the quill longer or increasing the weight of the free end of the quill decreases the natural vibration frequency. Thus the damper loses its effectiveness for very long (and consequently low-frequency) quills.

Inertia-Disk Damper. Another device for dissipating vibration consists of a stack of inertia disks of slightly different diameters inside a cavity in the boring bar. Any vibration in the bar causes the disks to slide against each other so that they strike the bar in random timing and thereby reduce the vibration below the magnitude that will cause chatter.

The assembly of disks is held together by a drawbar that extends through the shank and screws into a threaded hole in the cutting head. This arrangement puts the bar under compression, for maximum strength, and permits the shop to change heads for different jobs.

An operation in which a damped boring bar was substituted for a steel bar was the rough and finish boring of a 6½-in.-diam hole 51 in. long in a heat treated 1045 steel compressor body. Two 5-in.-diam openings in the wall presented an interrupted-cutting condition. Boring was done from both ends with a maximum bar overhang of 30 in. A standard square-shank brazed boring tool was used as the cutter. The steel boring bar was run at a speed of 30 rpm and a feed rate of 0.017 ipr for both rough and finish boring.

The roughing operation required three cuts, each 0.125 in. deep. Surface finish was not critical and performance was satisfactory, but slow because of the 30-rpm spindle speed.

Excessive chatter and tool wear were experienced during the finish boring cut of 0.015-in. depth. Tool wear was so severe that the tool had to be changed in the middle of the cut. Deflection of the steel bar made it difficult to match the cut with the second tool. The resulting surface irregularities required the hole to be honed to meet size and finish requirements.

Using the damped bar permitted the spindle speed to be increased from 30 to 90 rpm. At this faster speed but with the same feed of 0.017 ipr, two cuts, each 0.187 in. deep, were required to rough bore the forging. Finish boring was done in a single cut 0.015 in. deep at the same speed and feed as for rough boring. The damped bar eliminated chatter and provided a surface finish well within requirements, eliminating the honing operation.

Other Methods. Another method of overcoming vibration is by the use of a combination steel and carbide quill. Such a unit consists of a sintered carbide quill press-fitted into a steel mounting flange. On the end of the carbide is brazed a steel extension, which contains the cutting tool and damper. Where possible, the cutting tool is placed between the damper and the carbide quill.

Where it is not possible to use dampers in boring quills, oil or cutting fluid under pressure in the support bushing can act as a vibration damper. The liquid provides a film that will dissipate some of the vibrational energy.

Another method of damping vibration is to make a quill having the same diameter and length on both sides of the mounting flange. The end without the tool is damped. This design requires that the center portion of the mounting flange be relieved, to act as a diaphragm, and that the spindle of the

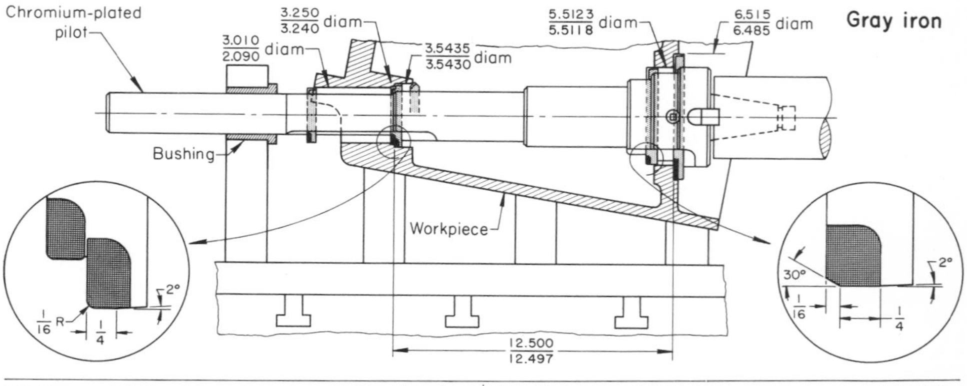

Finish specified	63 micro-in.
Finish obtained	30 to 35 micro-in.

Operating Conditions

Speed, roughing	120 rpm (94 to 204 sfm)
Speed, finishing	150 rpm (118 to 255 sfm)
Feed, roughing	0.020 ipr
Feed, finishing	0.012 ipr

Depth of roughing cut	0.250 in.
Depth of finishing cut	0.015 in.
Cutting fluid	None
Tool material	Carbide
Setup time	2 man-hr
Downtime for changing tools	6 min
Machining time per piece	27 min
Tool life per grind	50 pieces

Fig. 45. Two-pass rough and finish boring of five in-line holes, in which the use of specially designed finishing tools (insets) produced better-than-specified surfaces (Example 75)

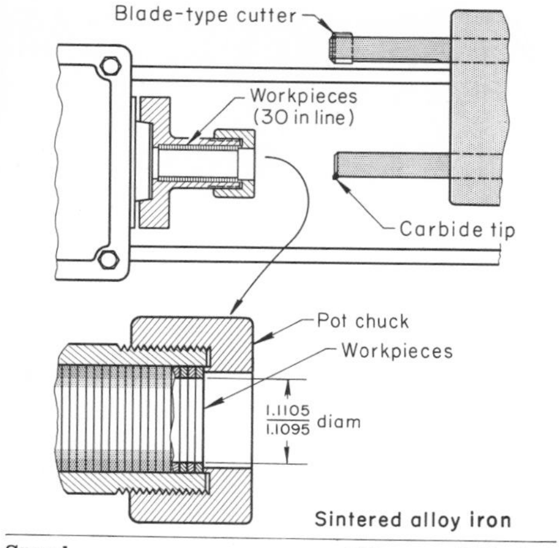

Speed	700 rpm (200 sfm)
Feed	0.012 ipr
Depth of roughing cut	0.035 in.
Depth of finishing cut	0.015 in.
Cutting fluid	None
Production rate	1600 pieces per hour
Tool life per grind	800 pieces

Fig. 46. Boring 30 piston rings at a time, using single-point carbide tool for roughing, and blade-type cutter for finishing to specified maximum surface roughness of 30 micro-in. (Example 76)

machine be hollow to accommodate the quill extension.

Design of the workpiece may promote vibration and chatter; for example, a long, small-diameter hub attached to a thin web or spokes radiating out to a rim makes a typical unstable arrangement. The change in direction of the cutting forces as the tool or the workpiece rotates can cause deflection and vibration in the hub. A heavy, ringlike weight properly clamped to the free end of the hub will damp the vibration and improve the finish of the bore.

Surface Finish

Aside from the inherent machining characteristics of the work material, factors that may singly or collectively affect surface finish are speed, feed, machine condition, tool design, tool support and cutting fluid. Rigid machines and tool supports are mandatory when low-micro-inch finishes must be achieved.

In many instances, finishes are improved by using higher speeds and lighter feeds — as indicated in many examples of precision boring operations presented in this article. In boring larger parts, finish often can be improved by decreasing feed without changing speed:

Example 74. Reduced Feed in Finish Boring to Attain Specified Surface (Fig. 44)

The setup shown in Fig. 44 was used for finish taper boring the workpiece illustrated, on a long-bed lathe equipped with a tracer attachment. A special boring bar heat treated to Rockwell C 46 to 49 was bolted to the face of the turret. The workpiece was made from 4330 steel tubing and heat treated to Rockwell C 39, and was previously rough bored, in two cuts, to 12-in. diameter.

The finish boring operation consisted of facing two ribs, boring a straight taper, and cutting two radii; two tools were used. The first tool faced the inside of the front rib, and opened the bore to finished diameter for about 2 in. The second tool bored the remainder of the taper and faced the rear rib.

As the data tabulated with Fig. 44 show, the bore was roughed at a speed of 69 rpm and a feed of 0.015 ipr; 0.030 in. of stock was left for removal in finishing. To meet the 100-micro-in. finish specified, it was found necessary to reduce the feed to 0.007 ipr in finish boring while retaining the 69-rpm spindle speed used in roughing.

Tool design is often a major factor in the control of finish, and on many parts finish can be improved by the use of specially designed tools. Sometimes, tool changes will improve productivity as well as finish, by permitting higher feed rate, increasing tool life, and decreasing downtime for changing tools. The two examples that follow deal with the effect of tool design on finish.

Example 75. Specially Designed Cutters for Low-Micro-Inch Finish (Fig. 45)

A horizontal boring mill was used for two-pass roughing and finishing of five in-line bores in gray iron machine-tool work heads as illustrated in Fig. 45. Maintenance of size control and concentricity dictated the use of a multiple-tool bar.

Achievement of the specified 63-micro-in. finish necessitated the development of specially designed finishing cutters (see insets in Fig. 45), which were inserted in the bar for the second pass. With these special tools, a better-than-specified finish of 30 to 35 micro-in. was obtained. Success resulted from the 30° lead chamfer on the 1/16-in.-radius lead, and from the 1/4-in.-long, circle-ground, 0°-back-taper land, which burnished the bearing bore as it passed through the cut.

Operating conditions for roughing and finishing are tabulated with Fig. 45.

Example 76. Tool-Design Change That Improved Productivity as Well as Finish (Fig. 46)

A special boring machine equipped with a rocking-type tool holder was used for rough and finish boring 30 sintered alloy iron piston rings at a time, using the setup and chucking method shown in Fig. 46. These rings, 1.385/1.380-in. OD, 1.1105/1.1095-in. ID, and 0.124/0.123 in. wide, were required to have a maximum surface roughness of 30 micro-in.

Originally, single-point tools had been used for both rough and finish boring. However, because of the tool configuration required for obtaining specified finish, the single-point finishing tool deflected excessively under pressure and adversely affected dimensional accuracy.

When a blade-type cutter was substituted as the finishing tool (Fig. 46), tool deflection was eliminated, accurate dimensions and acceptable finish were obtained, and downtime for changing tools was decreased to 2 min (from the 15 min formerly required). Changing from a single-point to a blade-type finishing tool also increased allowable feed rate, from 0.008 ipr to 0.012 ipr, and increased number of pieces per tool grind, from 400 to 800. Additional operating conditions are given in the table accompanying Fig. 46.

Cost

Cost is closely related to all other factors that determine the best procedure for a given boring operation. Stringent tolerance and finish requirements invariably increase cost and should always be carefully reviewed to determine whether or not concessions can be made to decrease the cost per piece.

Assuming that size, configuration, metal composition, tolerance and finish are all fixed, quantity is the major factor that determines cost. Sometimes, when relatively small quantities are to be produced, changes in machines or procedures can result in a substantial decrease in time per piece, thus resulting in lower cost. The three examples that follow illustrate the effect of production quantity on choice of equipment and techniques for achieving lowest over-all cost per piece produced.

Table 4. Effect of Quantity on Cost of Boring and Threading in an Engine Lathe, a Turret Lathe and a Single-Spindle Automatic (Example 77) (a)

Setup time, min	Production time per piece, min	Quantity of pieces produced	Total time per piece, min	Cost per piece
Engine Lathe ($7.50 per hr)(b)				
50	24.3	1	74.30	$9.288
		2	49.30	6.163
		3	40.96	5.120
		4	36.80	4.600
Turret Lathe ($8.40 per hr)(b)				
95	6.6	3	38.26	$5.356
		4	30.35	4.249
		300	6.92	0.969
		350	6.87	0.962
		400	6.84	0.958
Single-Spindle Automatic ($9.60 per hr)(b)				
180	5.5	300	6.10	$0.976
		350	6.01	0.962
		400	5.95	0.952

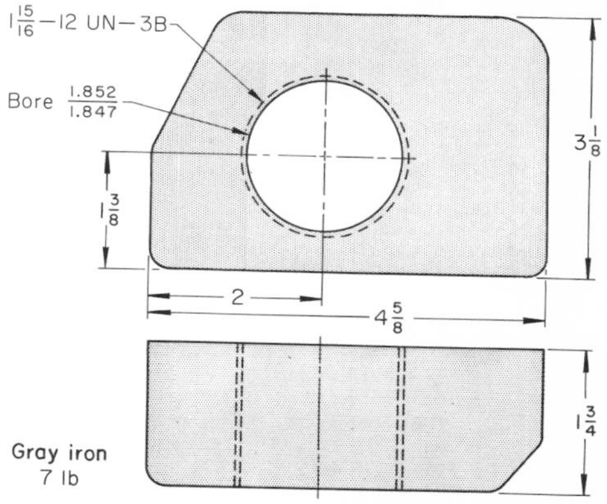

(a) Data are based on boring and internal threading of the cast adjusting-bracket block shown above. (b) Direct labor plus burden.

Example 77. Engine Lathe vs Turret Lathe and Single-Spindle Automatic (Table 4)

Gray iron adjusting-bracket blocks (sketch in Table 4) were bored and internally threaded on an engine lathe, a turret lathe, and a single-spindle automatic. The relationship of quantity, type of machine and cost per piece machined is shown in Table 4. It is evident from the cost figures given that for quantities of 1 to 3 pieces, the engine lathe was the most economical; for quantities of 4 to 350, the turret lathe; and for more than 350, the single-spindle automatic.

A single-point tool was used for producing the threads on the engine lathe. On the turret lathe, threads were produced by means of a piloted tap and lead screw. On the single-spindle automatic, a piloted tap with a gear-driven feed was used.

Example 78. Turret Lathe vs Double-End Boring Mill (Fig. 47)

In quantities of fewer than 20, the gray iron motor yoke illustrated in Fig. 47 was rough and finish bored, in two separate operations, on a turret lathe, as shown in Fig. 47(a). Because of the configuration of this part, these operations could readily be performed on a double-end horizontal boring mill, as shown in Fig. 47(b). However, although the boring mill produced 5.6 pieces per hour, as against only 3 pieces per hour on the turret lathe, the increased tooling and setup costs for the boring mill could not be justified for the production of fewer than 20 pieces. As quantities machined on the boring mill increased beyond the 20-piece break point, costs were further reduced, because longer runs lowered tooling cost per piece, and because two machines could be run by one operator.

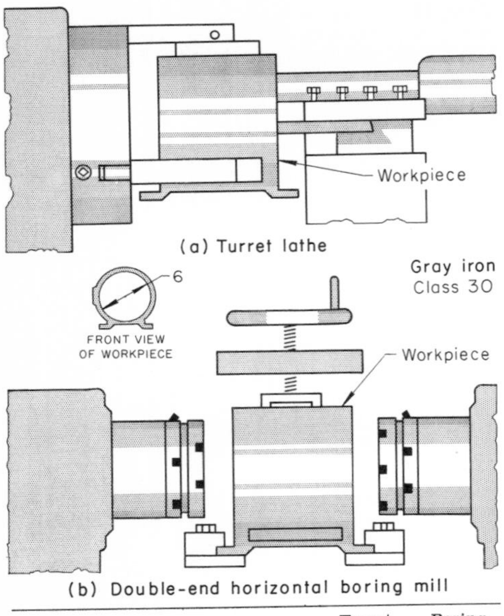

Operating condition	Turret lathe	Boring mill
Spindle speed, rpm:		
Roughing	160	127
Finishing	190	160
Surface speed, sfm:		
Roughing	250	200
Finishing	300	250
Feed, ipr:		
Roughing	0.0124	0.0118
Finishing	0.0124	0.0125
Tool material	Carbide	Carbide
Production, pieces per hour	3	5.6

Fig. 47. Two methods for boring a cast motor yoke. Turret lathe was more economical for production of fewer than 20 pieces. (Example 78)

Example 79. Single-Tool vs Multiple-Tool Boring Bars (Fig. 48)

A comparison of costs for rough and finish boring of gray iron valve bodies with multiple-tool boring bars (four tools per bar) and with single-tool bars is presented in Fig. 48. As the data there indicate, the higher setup cost for the multiple-tool method made it less costly to use single tools for machining these castings in quantities of up to six. For seven or more pieces, however, the considerably lower machining time per piece with multiple-tool bars made their use progressively more economical — until at 10,000 pieces the cost-per-piece difference leveled off at 50¢ for the multiple-tool method vs $4.06 for the single-tool method. Boring bars were all of a standard type readily available; hence, no design costs were involved.

Sometimes a change in tooling can lower costs, by reducing required tool inventory or by simplifying a subsequent operation, even though production rate is unaffected. One application in which this occurred is described in the following example:

Example 80. Cost Reduction by Change From Solid to Inserted Cutters (Fig. 49)

Although production rate remained the same (120 pieces per hour), changing from solid-carbide cutters to indexable, disposable carbide inserts in combination heads for rough and semifinish boring of centrifugally cast gray iron cylinder liners (Fig. 49) reduced over-all costs by 25%, effecting an annual saving of about $30,000.

The solid-carbide cutters had to be set out, adjusted and sharpened in the tool head. This required 80% of one tool-grinder's total time and also made it necessary to carry an inventory of 120 heads. In contrast, each disposable insert had four different cutting edges that could be used before the insert was discarded; downtime for changing tools was reduced by 60%.

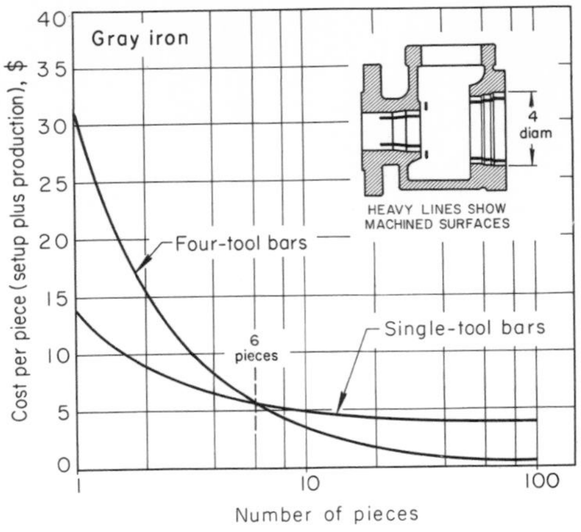

Item	Method(a) Single-tool bars(b)	Four-tool bars(c)
Setup time, hr	1.3	4.1
Setup cost(d)	$9.78	$30.83
Production time per piece, hr	0.54	0.067
Production cost per piece(d)	$4.06	$ 0.50

(a) For both methods, tools were used on a turret lathe with a 360°-indexing chuck, at a speed of 127 rpm (133 sfm max) and a feed of 0.011 ipr. (b) Two bars, each holding a single tool, were used, both in roughing and in finishing. (c) Roughing and finishing were each done with one bar holding four tools. (d) At $7.52 per hour ($2.35 for labor, plus $5.17 for overhead at a factor of 220%).

Fig. 48. Effect of quantity on cost per piece for use of single-tool vs four-tool bars for rough and finish boring and facing cast valve bodies (Example 79)

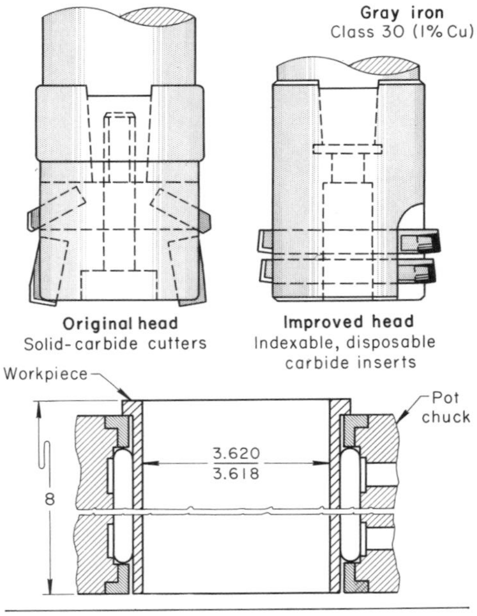

Operating Conditions(a)

Type of boring machine	Two-spindle vertical
Speed	270 rpm (256 sfm)
Feed	0.040 ipr
Depth of cut (total)	0.045 in.
Cutting fluid	Water-soluble oil
Tool life per grind or per edge	450 pieces
Production rate	120 pieces per hour
Downtime for changing tools:	
Solid-carbide cutters	5 min
Carbide-insert cutters	2 min

(a) Except for downtime for changing tools, the operating conditions were the same for both types of tooling.

Fig. 49. Change from solid-carbide cutters to indexable, disposable carbide inserts for 25% reduction in over-all cost of boring a cast cylinder liner (Example 80)

An additional saving resulted from the incorporation of a floating reamer as the semifinishing tool in the carbide-insert head. The free radial movement of the reamer (up to about 0.015 in.) enabled it to follow the bore axis established by the fixed-radius roughing tool and to maintain hole diameter. As a result, both hole roundness and size were closely controlled, and the amount of metal to be removed in secondary honing was reduced by 50%.

With both types of tools, the cylinder liners were held in a special pot chuck (Fig. 49) and bored on a two-spindle vertical boring machine. Additional operating conditions are tabulated with Fig. 49.

APPENDIX

Examples of the Use of Boring Equipment for Machining Operations Other Than Boring

Because of their rigidity, adaptability and accuracy, boring machines often are used for machining operations other than those that can be strictly classified as boring, in applications in which no boring, as such, is done. Three such applications are described in Examples 81, 82 and 83, which follow.

Example 81. Deep-Hole Drilling in a Precision Boring Machine (Fig. 50)

Because they are rigid and have easily adjusted feed controls, precision boring machines are well suited to driving gun-drilling tools. A single-end precision boring machine, fitted with a special type of gun-drilling tool (for combination drilling and boring), was used for simultaneously drilling from solid and boring a hole 14½ diameters long in a heat-resisting stainless steel workpiece (Fig. 50). The tool was a 14⅞-in.-long, single-flute steel shank with a brazed-on carbide cutting edge. Although in many gun-drilling operations the work is rotated while the drill is fed into it, in this application the workpiece was held in a fixture and the tool was rotated. As in all gun drilling, however, a cutting fluid was used to cool the tool and to flush chips out of the hole along the tool flute.

As shown in the tabulation of processing details that accompanies Fig. 50, this boring-drilling tool produced the hole to a diametral tolerance of ±0.00075 in. and to straightness within 0.0005 in. This type of tool, however, can drift as much as 0.001 in. per in., and

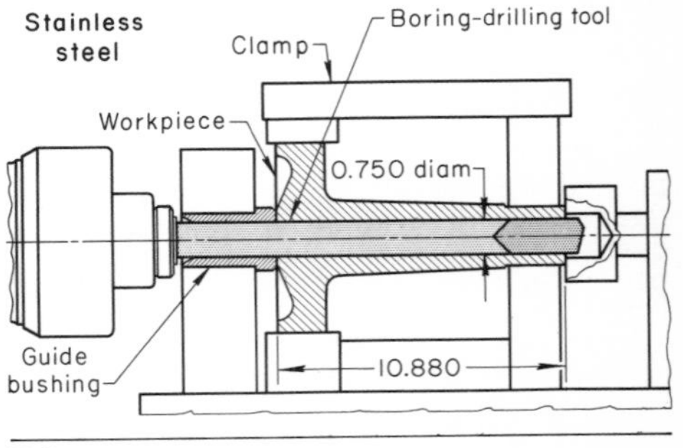

Tolerances:	
Diameter	±0.00075 in.
Straightness	Within 0.0005 in.
Finish specified	63 micro-in.

Operating Conditions

Speed	1150 rpm (225 sfm)
Feed	0.0005 ipr
Depth of cut	0.0375 in. per side
Cutting fluid	Oil
Tool material	Carbide tip, steel shank
Production rate	3.1 pieces per hour

The work material here was a heat-resisting stainless steel containing approximately 12 Cr, 1 Mn, 3 Mo, 0.25 C and 0.08 N.

Fig. 50. Use of a boring-drilling tool in a precision boring machine for simultaneously cutting from solid and finishing a long hole (Example 81)

therefore cannot be used to eliminate a separate boring operation when the tolerance on concentricity is extremely tight.

Example 82. Machining Pockets From Solid in a Contour Boring Machine

A special vertical contour boring machine was used for cutting contoured pockets in the solid walls of ring-shaped parts made from 1015 steel and stress relieved to 159 to 170 Bhn. The cutting tool used, a special two-flute end mill with one flute acting as a boring tool, removed ¾ in. of stock from the ring wall in a straight cut, then made a contour finishing cut of 0.005 to 0.031 in. (to specified tolerance of ±0.005 in. and finish of 20 to 25 micro-in.).

The carbide cutter, which was ground with 10° front clearance, 15° side clearance, and a negative rake angle of −2°, was operated at 500 sfm and 0.005 ipr; water-soluble oil was used as cutting fluid.

Workpieces were supported on an indexing fixture plate. Setup time was 2 hr, production rate was 16 pieces per hour, tools machined 80 pieces per grind, and downtime for changing tools was 6 min.

Example 83. Facing and Serrating in a Horizontal Boring Mill (Fig. 51)

A horizontal boring mill was used for seven facing or serrating operations on a 634-lb gate valve cast from CF-8 (type 304) stainless steel. The valve and the sequence of operations are shown in Fig. 51. The boring mill was equipped with a 4-ft-square, 360°-indexing table on a cross slide. Facing or turning capacity was 42 in. with 6-ft vertical travel. The workpiece was held on the machine bed with standard tie-down clamps. Facing and serrating were done with the same tool but at different feeds and speeds, as shown in the table of operating conditions that accompanies Fig. 51.

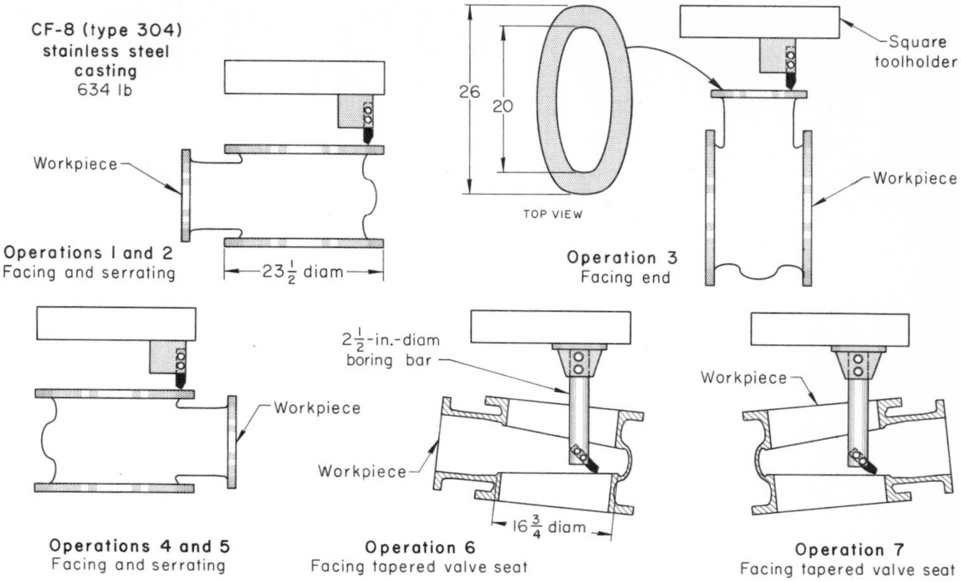

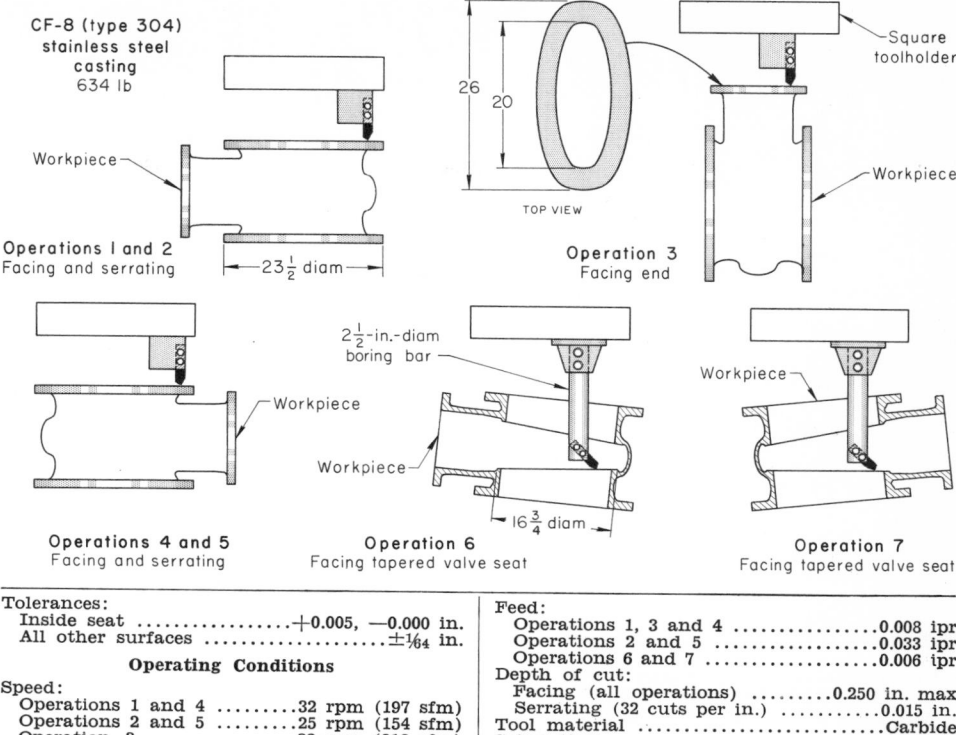

Tolerances:
- Inside seat ....+0.005, −0.000 in.
- All other surfaces ....±1/64 in.

Operating Conditions

Speed:
- Operations 1 and 4 ....32 rpm (197 sfm)
- Operations 2 and 5 ....25 rpm (154 sfm)
- Operation 3 ....32 rpm (218 sfm)
- Operations 6 and 7 ....25 rpm (110 sfm)

Feed:
- Operations 1, 3 and 4 ....0.008 ipr
- Operations 2 and 5 ....0.033 ipr
- Operations 6 and 7 ....0.006 ipr

Depth of cut:
- Facing (all operations) ....0.250 in. max
- Serrating (32 cuts per in.) ....0.015 in.

Tool material ....Carbide
Setup time ....3 hr
Total machining time ....12 hr

Fig. 51. Sequence of facing and serrating operations on a gate valve, using a horizontal boring mill with an indexing table (Example 83)

Other Examples of Boring in This Volume

Work material	Example number
Work Metals Compared in Boring	
Cast iron	644, 646, 661, 662, 663
Tool steel	687
Heat-resisting alloys	810
Aluminum	867, 872
Tool Design	
Stainless steel	745
Heat-resisting alloys	841, 842
Aluminum	877, 880
Beryllium	927
Magnesium	978, 987
Titanium	998

Work material	Example number
Methods	
Stainless steel	777
Heat-resisting alloys	841, 842
Aluminum	872, 877, 907
Beryllium	928
Magnesium	978
Titanium	998
Powder metallurgy parts	1008, 1009
Accuracy	
Stainless steel	759
Aluminum	876, 878, 879, 904, 906
Beryllium	927
Magnesium	987

Work material	Example number
Costs	
Cast iron	644, 646, 661, 662, 663, 665
Tool steel	687
Aluminum	872
Magnesium	978
Processes Compared	
Cast iron	664, 665
Aluminum	874
Multiple Operations	
Heat-resisting alloys	841, 842
Aluminum	906, 907

Trepanning

TREPANNING is a machining process for producing a circular hole or groove in, or a disk, cylinder or tube from, solid stock by the action of a tool containing one or more cutters (usually single-point) revolving around a center. The process is used in at least four distinct types of applications: the production of round disks, large shallow through holes, circular grooves, and deep holes.

Round Disks

One common use of trepanning is the production of round disks from flat stock. The process is particularly applicable when production quantities are too small to warrant the use of blanking dies and when flame-cutting equipment is unavailable. Hand-fed drill presses are the machines most used for this application of trepanning.

When a center hole is unobjectionable, the trepanning tool consists of an adjustable fly cutter mounted on a twist drill (Fig. 1); the drill serves as both driver and pilot, and the single-point tool can be positioned as desired to change the size of the circle cut. If a center hole cannot be permitted, a tool of the type shown in Fig. 1 can be used without a drill pilot. By this technique, however, rigidity is more difficult to maintain, and thus there is greater likelihood of tool chatter and loss of dimensional control.

There is no established maximum thickness or diameter of disks that can be cut by this method of trepanning. Because of the load imposed on the tool, however, the process is seldom used for cutting material more than about ¼ in. thick. Also, because rigidity decreases as diameter increases, disks cut by this method are usually less than 6 in. in diameter. Larger cuts by trepanning are not made if other methods can be used. Smaller trepanning cuts may compete with pressworking (if the means are available) and larger cuts may compete with other methods, such as flame cutting.

In this type of trepanning, slow speeds (ranging downward from about 35 sfm) ordinarily are used, feed is controlled manually, and cutting fluids are seldom employed.

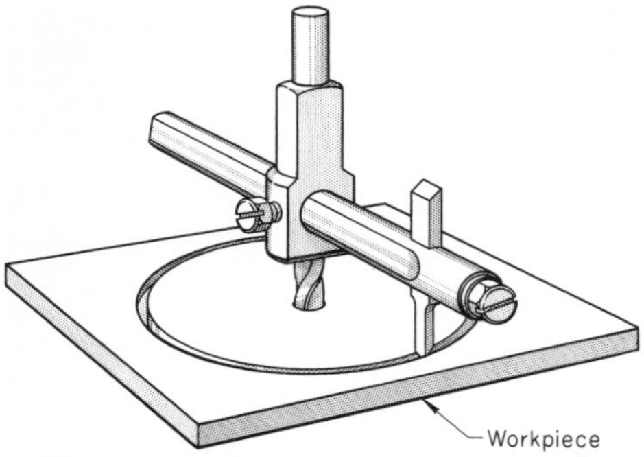

Fig. 1. Drill-mounted adjustable fly cutter used for trepanning various sizes of disks from flat stock, or grooves around centers

Large Shallow Through Holes

Round through holes having diameters that exceed depth by a factor of about five or more can often be efficiently and accurately produced by trepanning. The tools and techniques employed in one application are described in the following example, in which trepanning was preferred to drilling.

Example 84. Nine Shallow Holes in Web of a Steel Gear (Fig. 2)

Trepanning proved more practical than drilling for producing nine weight-reducing holes in the web section of an aircraft accessory drive gear made of 9310 steel (Fig. 2). Depending on the size of these gears, the holes ranged from ¾ to 1¼ in. in diameter, and web-section thickness ranged from 0.140 to 0.250 in.

Trepanning was done with carbide-insert single-point tools, at a speed of 300 sfm and a feed of 0.002 ipr. Originally, a top-brazed insert (bottom left in Fig. 2) was used, but tool life was only 30 holes per grind. By changing to side-brazed inserts (bottom right in Fig. 2), tool life was increased to 75 holes per grind. With either tool, maximum tool life was obtained when the tool was not allowed to cut completely through the web; a thin section was left to hold the plug, and this section was easily knocked out during indexing of the gear.

Configuration of the workpiece may influence the technique used in trepanning large-diameter shallow holes. Example 41, in the article "Boring", discusses the trepanning of 576 accurately positioned holes in a large thin-wall stainless steel drum. Because of the size of the drum (80½ in. in diameter and 80 in. deep) in relation to its wall thickness (⅜ in.), and because of the curvature of the surface being cut into, it was necessary to use special fixturing to obtain adequate rigidity.

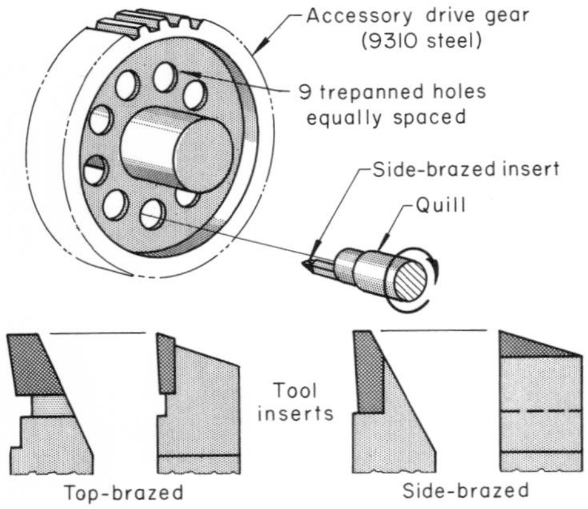

Fig. 2. Trepanning was more practical than drilling for producing shallow holes in aircraft gear shown at top left. Top-brazed carbide inserts cut only 40% as many holes per grind as side-brazed inserts. (Example 84)

Circular Grooves

The tools and techniques used for producing round disks or large shallow through holes (see the two preceding sections) can be used also to provide metal parts with circular grooves for accommodating O-rings or for other purposes. The only difference is that the cutter must be shaped so as to form the desired cross-sectional shape of the groove.

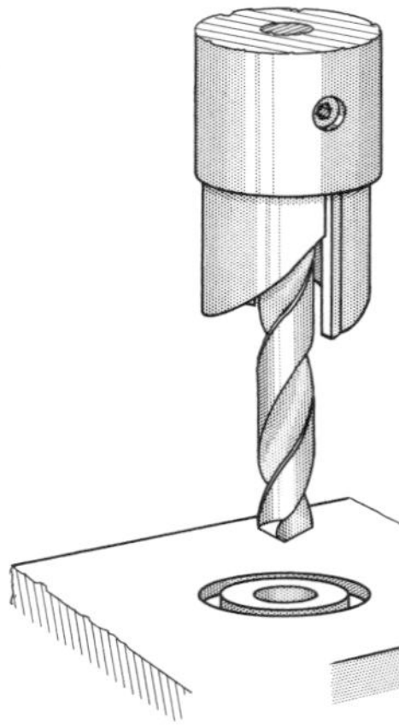

Fig. 3. Combination tool for producing a groove close to a concentric pilot hole

When a groove to be cut is only slightly larger in diameter than a concentric pilot hole, best results are obtained by the use of a combination drilling-and-trepanning tool that resembles a hollow mill (Fig. 3). With this tool, a twist drill is inserted into a hollow cutter and held by a setscrew. This type of trepanning cutter usually has two or more cutting edges to provide balance, which assists in maintaining dimensional control. Cutting edges have a back rake angle of about 20° for most applications.

Any machines normally used for drilling are suitable for driving combination tools of the type shown in Fig. 3. Speeds up to 100 sfm are ordinarily used, in conjunction with feeds of about 0.004 ipr. Soluble oils are usually satisfactory as cutting fluids, although sulfurized oils are preferred when tolerance and finish requirements are critical.

Example 173, in the article "Drilling", gives processing details and results for a combination drilling and trepanning operation using the tool shown in Fig. 3.

The example that follows describes an application in which trepanning was more efficient and economical than the use of single-point tools, for producing a circular face groove:

Example 85. Trepanning vs Single-Point Plunge Cutting (Fig. 4)

Originally, the 2⅞-in.-ID groove in the 4140 steel part shown in Fig. 4 was produced in roughing and finishing operations on a lathe, using single-point carbide-insert tools. Chip buildup and tool breakage were continual problems. Tool life per sharpening was only 25 pieces, and production time and cost per piece were 3.9 min and 49¢, respectively.

Tool breakage and chip buildup were eliminated (and grooving was reduced to a one-operation job) by substituting trepanning for the original method. The trepanning tool used had two carbide cutters mounted on an 1141 steel body; tool design is shown in Fig. 4. Trepanning also reduced time and cost per piece to 1.8 min and 22½¢, respectively (less than half, compared with the original method), and doubled tool life — to 50 pieces per sharpening.

Deep Holes*

Trepanning is often the most practical method for machining deep holes or tubes from the solid. Deep-hole trepanning is similar to gun drilling, in that both processes require a pressurized cutting-fluid system and employ self-piloting cutting action; the two main differences are: (*a*) trepanning is practical only for larger holes (more than about 2 in. in diameter); and (*b*) trepanning produces a solid core, whereas gun drilling forms only chips.

As a means for producing holes of 2-in. diameter or larger (especially holes whose depth is eight or more diameters), trepanning offers the following advantages over spade or twist drilling, with their allied operations:

1 Closer tolerances can be met on diameter and straightness.
2 Drilling of deeper holes is feasible.
3 Rate of metal removal is higher.
4 In machining costly work materials, cores are more valuable than chips.

The use of trepanning for producing a tube from a cylindrical billet is described in Example 928, in the article on Machining of Beryllium. The trepanning of a cylindrical core from the center of a solid cylinder of metal is not ordinarily done in regular mass production. But beryllium, of course, is a problem metal that needs special methods.

Misalignment is probably the most frequent single source of difficulty in deep-hole trepanning. The misalignment may be caused by insufficient rigidity in the tooling and setup. Accurate alignment and rigidity are essential for control of dimensions and finish, and for satisfactory tool life at high depth-to-diameter ratios.

*Much of the information on deep-hole trepanning in this article has been derived from the ASTME book "Gun Drilling and Trepanning" (Prentice-Hall, 1964).

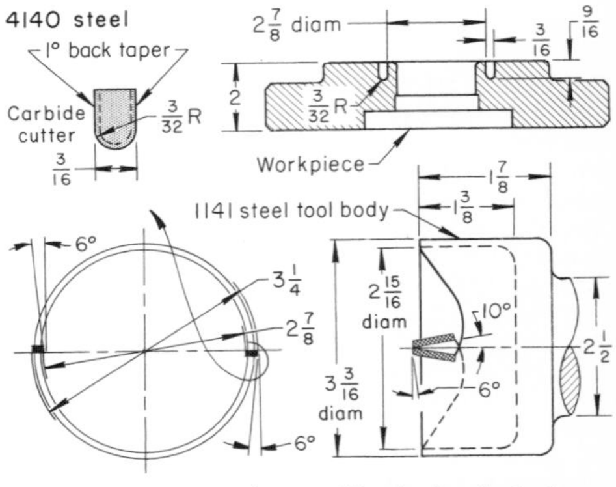

Fig. 4. Trepanning, with tool of design shown at top left and bottom, cost less than single-point plunge cutting for producing the groove in the part at top right. (Example 85)

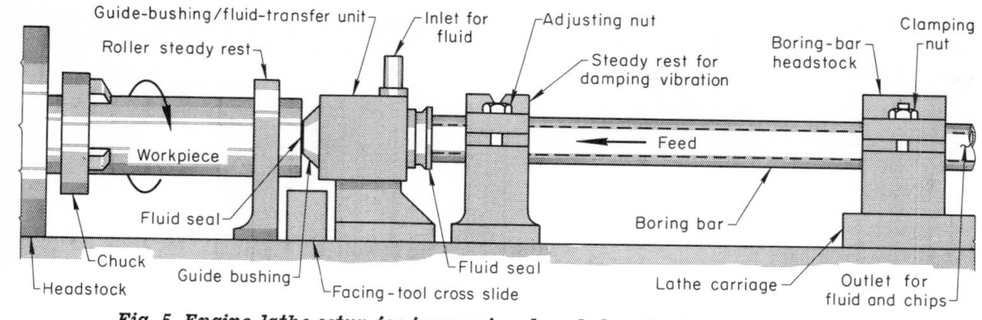

Fig. 5. Engine-lathe setup for trepanning deep holes. See text for discussion.

Machines for Deep-Hole Trepanning

For trepanning holes less than about five diameters deep, simple vertical drill presses are usually satisfactory. However, as the depth of the hole exceeds five times diameter, any type of vertical equipment becomes progressively more impractical. In addition, as depth-to-diameter ratio increases, accuracy is lost more rapidly in equipment where the tool is rotated and the work is held stationary. Hence, for trepanning deep holes, engine lathes, turret lathes or horizontal drilling machines are preferred. In all of these machines the workpiece is rotated while the tool remains stationary. This technique results in greater accuracy, other conditions being constant.

Regardless of the type of machine used, it must be rigid and capable of speeds up to 600 sfm to accommodate carbide tooling, and should have variable feed control.

Engine Lathes. Figure 5 shows a basic engine-lathe setup, in which a cylindrical workpiece is rotated, the tool is fed into it, and an inside-diameter-exhaust trepanning head (see section on tools, which follows) is used. Such a setup is used for holes about 2 to 4½ in. in diameter. One end of the workpiece is held in a three-jaw chuck, and the other end in a roller steady rest (rollers about 6 in. in diameter). A relatively long workpiece requires an additional steady rest midway between the chucking headstock and the roller steady rest.

The end of the workpiece next to the steady rest must be faced at right angles to the spindle centerline. The facing cut, made by a tool on a cross slide, provides a flat surface for the fluid seal on the guide bushing, and prevents runout that could make the fluid seal leak. The guide bushing should be mounted on ball bearings because they are the most economical means of support at the speeds involved.

Cutting fluid under pressure enters the leak-proof rotary joint behind the bushing and flows into the annular space around the hollow boring bar. The fluid then flows to the cut between the bushing and the periphery of the tool head, picks up the chips, and flushes them through the head between the cutter and the core, and out along the space between the core and the inner wall of the boring bar. An additional fluid seal is necessary at the rear of the guide-bushing/fluid-transfer unit.

The tailstock end of the boring bar is mounted in a headstock on the lathe carriage and rigidly clamped in position by means of a bearing cap and clamping nuts.

To serve as a vibration damper, a steady rest is located directly behind the guide-bushing/fluid-transfer unit. This damper is of the same construction as the boring-bar headstock, except that a two-piece bronze bushing is used to damp vibration and to allow the boring bar to slide.

Alignment is critical. The spindle, chuck, steady rests, guide bushing, and boring-bar headstock must be as nearly in line as possible. Also, the machine ways must be aligned and the boring bar must be ground to uniform diameter and straightness.

The bores in the guide-bushing/fluid-transfer unit, the vibration-damper unit, and the boring-bar headstock should be large enough to accommodate the boring bar for the largest-diameter hole to be trepanned on the machine. For smaller holes, smaller boring bars can be used with appropriate bushings.

For holes more than about 4½ in. in diameter, other setups are sometimes more economical and can be used with an outside-diameter-exhaust head (see the section on tools, which follows) for trepanning relatively deep holes. One of these adaptations is the use of a three-roll support on the bed of an engine lathe. A three-roll support used in conjunction with an outside-diameter-exhaust head effects a saving by eliminating the need for a starting or guide bushing.

Turret lathes are also suitable for trepanning relatively deep holes, as indicated in the next two examples:

Examples 86 and 87. Use of Turret Lathes for Trepanning

Example 86. On a saddle-type turret lathe, holes 5$^{13}/_{16}$ in. in diameter and 3½ in. deep were trepanned in 4340 steel workpieces at a hardness level of Rockwell C 34 to 36. A starting groove ½ in. deep was first plunge cut with a single-point tool ⅜ in. wide. The groove was cut at a speed of 146 sfm (at 96 rpm) and feed of 0.009 ipr. The same speed and feed were then used for trepanning through with an outside-diameter-exhaust tool, using 20 hp on the headstock. Water-soluble oil was pumped through the cutting area at a rate of 30 gal per min, through a 1½-in.-diam hose. The two-stage operation required a total of 12½ min, as opposed to a total of 48 min by the method that had previously been used, which consisted of center drilling, twist drilling, and boring.

Example 87. Holes 5 in. in diameter and 36 in. deep were trepanned in vacuum melted 4340 steel using an outside-diameter-exhaust trepanning head with a ¾-in.-wide carbide cutting tip. A turret lathe of 15-hp capacity was used to rotate the workpieces at 190 rpm (250 sfm). Water-soluble oil, under pressure of 40 psi, was pumped through the cutting area at 50 gal per min. At a feed rate of 0.007 ipr, two pieces per hour were produced.

Tools for Deep-Hole Trepanning

Boring bars for trepanning are hollow tubes that allow the workpiece core to enter with enough clearance for cutting fluid to flow to the cutter, or for fluid and chips to be forcibly exhausted from the cutter. The bar is usually made from 52100 or a similar steel. Wall thickness ranges upward from about $^5/_{16}$ in., depending on the length of the bar and the required resistance to torsional forces.

Trepanning heads are cylindrical and usually employ a single solid-carbide or carbide-tipped cutter. Multiple-cutter heads, despite their desirable chip-breaking action, are used to a lesser extent, because they pose problems in attaining balanced cutting action — without which hole accuracy may be sacrificed.

Single-cutter heads (Fig. 6) are self-piloting, being supported and guided by wear pads located about 90° and 180° behind the cutter. The head may fit onto the boring bar by means of a pilot diameter and be driven by three lugs. With this mating design, the head is locked to the bar screws. Some heads are secured to the bar by Acme threads around the inner circumference of the head, but high torsional forces can cause thread seizure. Ahead of the cutting edge on the outside diameter of the head is a relief for intake of cutting fluid or for exhaust of cutting fluid and chips.

One type of head (Fig. 6a), usually for holes up to 4½ in. in diameter and with depths of 12 to 15 diameters, accommodates cutting-fluid flow from the inside diameter of the bar and exhausts the fluid on the outside diameter. Recommended maximum depths for holes trepanned with outside-diameter-exhaust heads are as follows:

2 to 2½-in. diam	24 to 30 in. deep
2$^9/_{16}$ to 3½	30 to 42
3$^9/_{16}$ to 4½	42 to 70

For holes 4$^9/_{16}$ in. in diameter and larger, maximum depth is limited only by machine design.

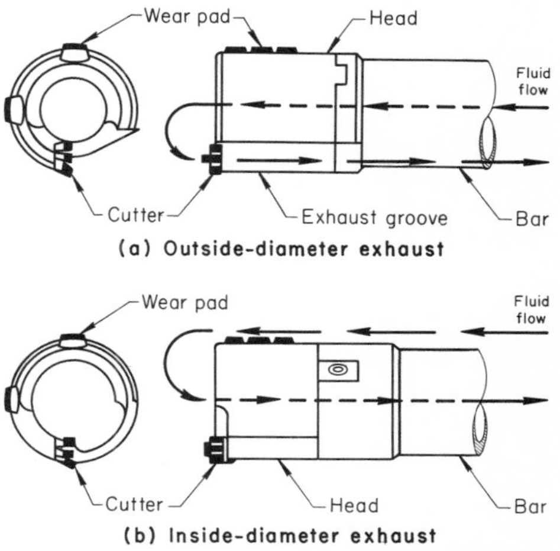

Fig. 6. Two types of single-cutter trepanning heads. See text for discussion.

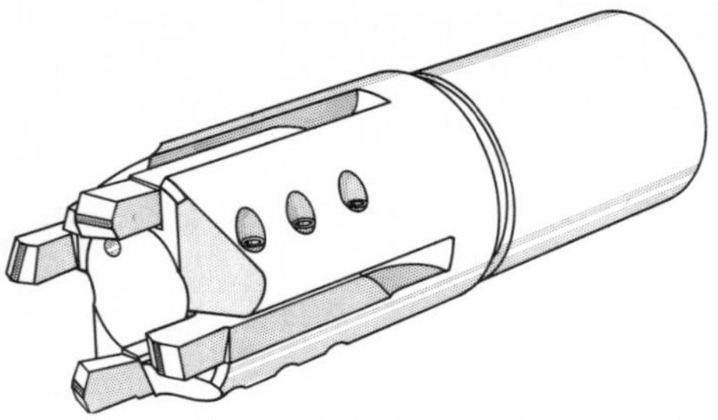

Fig. 7. Starting tool for trepanning (ASTME)

With this type of head, chips and fluid are exhausted along a longitudinal groove milled on the outside diameter of the head. The clearance between the core and the inside wall of the head must be controlled so that the volume of cutting fluid is restricted. As a result, there is a high-velocity centrifugal action that forces the chips away from the cutting edge.

In production trepanning, one plant found that a fluid-inlet area of 1 sq in. produces a pressure of about 50 psi on a 7-in.-diam head. This size of inlet area allows full pump flow through the head and provides sufficient velocity for chip disposal. As the hole size decreases and the inlet area remains constant, the pressure increases. Increased pressure is desirable as hole diameter decreases or as depth increases. For holes less than 4 in. in diameter, however, an inlet area of 1 sq in. is not possible; for these holes, the inlet area should be made as large as possible, to provide adequate volume without weakening the head.

The outside diameter of an outside-diameter-exhaust head is only 0.020 to 0.025 in. smaller than the diameter of the hole being cut, to prevent chips from escaping between the head and the wall of the hole. This lessens the possibility of a marred finish and helps channel the bulk of the fluid and chips through the exhaust groove.

To minimize the problem of chip disposal in holes more than about 15 diameters deep, an inside-diameter-exhaust head (Fig. 6b) is used. With this type of head, fluid under pressure flows to the cutting edge over the outside diameter of the bar and head, and is exhausted, with the chips, through the inside diameter of the boring bar.

Example 65, in the article "Boring", discusses the use of a standard single-cutter trepanning head in a converted gun-drilling machine to produce a hole seven diameters deep to a diametral accuracy of ±0.001 in.

Wear pads (Fig. 6) are essential components of single-cutter heads. Wear pads balance cutting force, control hole size, and provide a burnishing action that may improve finish.

Ordinarily, wear pads have steel bodies and brazed-on carbide wearing surfaces. The wear-pad body may have two angular sides that result in a dovetail fit in the head. The pads are circle ground so that when they are positioned in the head they will clear the bore wall by about 0.002 in. and project about 0.010 in. from the head.

One pad is located approximately 90° behind the cutting edge; this pad steadies the head against the bore and balances the cutting force. The other pad is about 180° behind the cutter, and automatically controls the size of the hole. If the cut is oversize, the bore is large and the pressure on this pad is immediately decreased. As a result, the head moves away from the surface being cut, reducing the bore size until equilibrium is again established. Similarly, if the cut is undersize, pressure on the pad is increased and the head moves toward the surface being cut.

Initial cutting action is controlled by a guide bushing (as in Fig. 5), by a counterbore, or by a starting tool that cuts a groove (Fig. 7). If a bushing is used, starting feeds are relatively light and characteristically produce stringy chips, which must be removed at intervals. The counterbored hole or starting groove should be deep enough to insure self-piloting by the trepanning head.

Conventional cutters (Fig. 8) have a carbide tip brazed on a tool steel body. (Because index positions are limited and chip flow is obstructed, disposable-insert tooling has not been widely used in trepanning.) The brazed cutter is designed so that the single edge has three steps to break the chip into three equal widths. Each step includes a parallel chip breaker. The cutter is commonly ¾ in. wide, but wider cutters have been used successfully for holes more than about 4 in. in diameter.

The radial position of the cutter when used in a stationary head is important. Viewed from the cutting end of the head, the cutter should be approximately at the 2 o'clock position, so that the cutting fluid will wash the chips away from the cutter through the relief on the outside diameter of the head, and so that the core, when cut, will fall away from the cutter.

Multiple-cutter heads are sometimes more appropriate than those with single cutters, particularly when hole starting is difficult or for minimizing shock on the bar or other components in the driving mechanism:

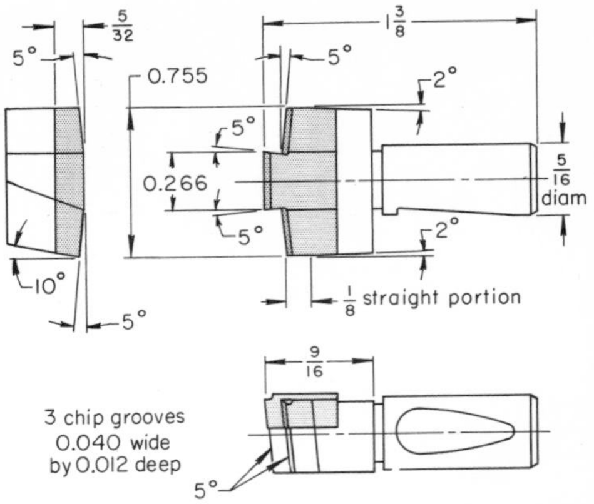

Fig. 8. Typical design of a trepanning cutter for producing deep holes (ASTME)

Example 88. Use of a Three-Cutter Head for Trepanning Transversely Through a Steel Cylinder (Fig. 9)

A 2½-in.-diam hole was trepanned through the 4-in. diameter of a solid cylinder of 8615 steel. A specially designed three-cutter head (Fig. 9) of 4140 steel was used, to minimize spindle shock. This head, of the outside-diameter-exhaust type, included three 6-in.-long bronze conventional wear strips, spaced 120° apart and 30° behind each cutter. To provide maximum stability and accuracy, an additional set of three cylindrical carbide wear strips (5⁄16 in. in diameter and 1¼ in. long) was incorporated. A guide bushing was used in conjunction with a modified drill press that provided 30 hp at the spindle. Cutting fluid (active mineral oil) was pumped through the bar at 50 psi and 100 gal per min.

Production rate can be increased, with only a slight increase in feed rate or chip thickness, by the use of a four-cutter head. The first pair of cutters produces a narrow groove; this is then widened to final dimensions by the second pair of cutters. Initial and

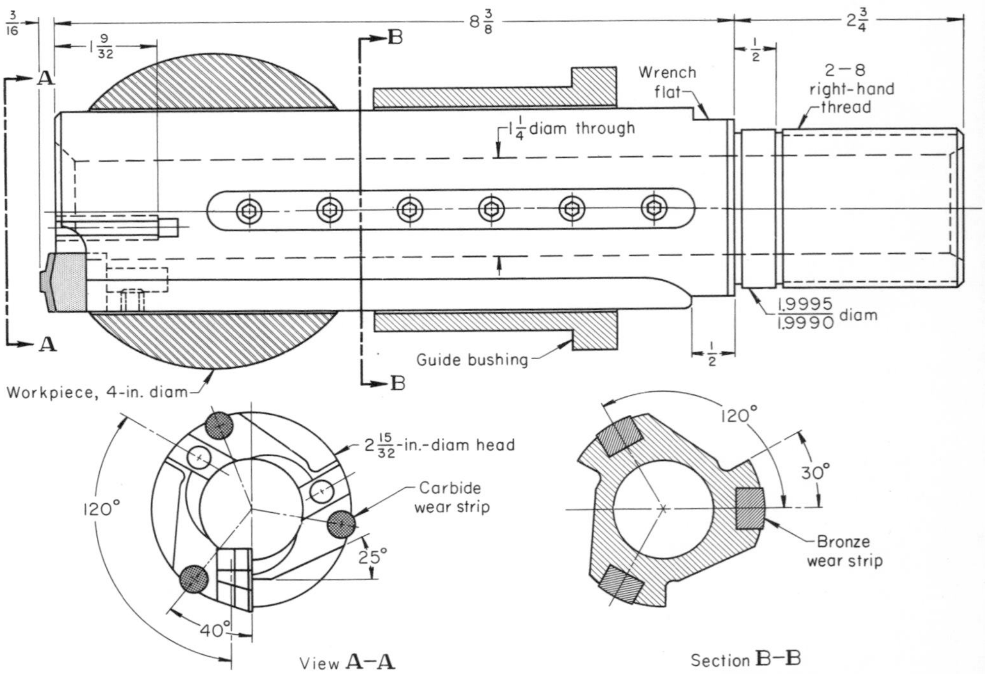

Fig. 9. Three-cutter trepanning head used for cutting a 2½-in.-diam hole through a solid cylinder of 8615 steel (Example 88) (ASTME)

maintenance costs, however, are greater for this type of tool than for a single-cutter head. The use of a four-cutter head is shown in the next example:

Example 89. Use of Two Staggered Pairs of Cutters on One Head for Trepanning

Holes 12 in. deep were trepanned in 94B17 steel, using a four-cutter head on a turret lathe with a 30-hp spindle. The first pair of cutters was narrower than the second pair and led the second pair by 0.006 in. The two cutters of each pair divided the cut equally, producing chips about half the inch-per-revolution feed rate in thickness. The first pair of cutters produced a 2³⁄₃₂-in.-OD annular groove 7⁄32 in. wide. The second pair widened the groove to 5⁄8 in. and enlarged the outside diameter to 2½ in.

Cutting speed was 360 sfm, and feed rate was 0.007 ipr. An emulsion-type cutting fluid, at 160 gal per min and 80 psi, was introduced through the wall of the boring bar to the cutting interface. From this point, the fluid and the chips were exhausted through the annular space between the bar and the hole wall.

Table 1. Nominal Speeds and Feeds for Deep-Hole Trepanning of Carbon and Low-Alloy Steels With High Speed Steel and Carbide Tools

Typical steel(a)	Brinell hardness	Speed, sfm HSS(b)	Speed, sfm Carbide(c)	Feed, ipr HSS(b)	Feed, ipr Carbide(c)
Carbon and Low-Alloy Steels (Except Free-Cutting Grades)					
1020, 1045, 4140, 7140 and 8620 at hardness ranges listed at right	85 to 125	110	600	0.008	0.008
	125 to 175	90	600	0.008	0.008
	175 to 225	75	600	0.007	0.007
	225 to 275	65	600	0.006	0.007
	275 to 325	55	550	0.006	0.007
	325 to 375	45	400	0.005	0.006
	375 to 425	30	350	0.004	0.005
Free-Cutting Carbon and Low-Alloy Steels					
1112 and 1117	100 to 150	120	600	0.008	0.008
	150 to 200	135	600	0.008	0.008
1137 and 12L14	100 to 150	125	600	0.008	0.008
	150 to 200	105	600	0.007	0.007
	200 to 250	90	600	0.007	0.007
	275 to 325	75	550	0.006	0.007
	325 to 375	45	400	0.006	0.007
	375 to 425	30	350	0.005	0.006
4140+S and 41L40	150 to 200	100	600	0.007	0.007
	200 to 250	80	600	0.006	0.006
	275 to 325	60	550	0.005	0.006
	325 to 375	45	400	0.005	0.006
	375 to 425	30	350	0.004	0.005

(a) Each steel listed is a frequently used grade in a group of similar steels. For a listing of the steels in the various groups, see Table 2, page 6. (b) High speed steels M2 and T5 for trepanning steels at hardness up to 225 Bhn; M2, T5 and T15 for steels at 225 to 375 Bhn, and T15, M41, M42, M43 and M44 for steels at hardnesses above 375 Bhn. (c) Carbide grade C-6. (Data are adapted from tables compiled by Metcut Research Associates, Inc.)

Speed and Feed in Deep-Hole Trepanning

Table 1 presents nominal speeds and feeds for trepanning deep holes in carbon and low-alloy steels. These values can serve as a starting point for selecting efficient and economical rates.

Processing conditions for a given application are best determined by production trials; the nature and amount of machining to be done, the size and shape of the part, the work material, and the equipment and tooling may necessitate substantial deviations from the nominal speed and feed. These deviations vary in much the same way as discussed in the article "Boring".

In deep-hole trepanning, the ability to use optimum speed and feed largely depends on the rigidity of the boring bar and on the effectiveness with which the cutting fluid cools, flushes away chips, and prevents chips from forcibly contacting the newly machined surface. The nominal values of Table 1 assume effective use of a suitable cutting fluid.

Cutting Fluids for Deep-Hole Trepanning

Cutting fluids used for trepanning of deep holes are essentially the same as those recommended for gun drilling — that is, straight oils. Mineral oils are often used, but sulfurized oils usually improve cutting action and result in a more efficient operation.

Water-oil emulsions are used less often than straight oils, although they have been satisfactory in some applications (see Examples 86, 87 and 89 in this article).

As in any deep-hole machining, the most important function of the cutting fluid used in trepanning deep holes is to flush away the chips. Therefore, the method of providing and controlling flow is more important than the composition of the fluid.

Planing

PLANING is a machining process for removing metal from surfaces in horizontal, vertical or angular planes, in which the workpiece is reciprocated in a linear motion against one or more single-point tools. Although planing is most widely used for producing flat, straight surfaces on large workpieces, the process can also be used to produce contours and a variety of irregular configurations (examples: deep slots in large rotors, helical grooves in large rolls, internal guide surfaces in large valves). Because it is often possible to produce one or two parts on a planer in less time than is required merely to set up for machining by an alternative method, planing is often used for machining parts to meet emergencies.

Process Capabilities

As the hardness of the workpiece increases above about Rockwell C 25, metal removal rate and tool life decrease. However, metals hardened to Rockwell C 46 or higher can be planed (for example, planing is often used to produce flat surfaces on large heat treated die blocks).

Size of workpiece that can be planed is limited only by the capacity of available equipment. Standard equipment is available that can make cuts as long as 50 ft, and still larger machines have been built to special order.

Although planing is most widely used for machining large areas, it is also used for machining smaller parts or areas — for example, jig-frame weldments may be squared and tooling-pad surfaces leveled on areas of less than 1 sq ft (see Example 95). However, 12 in. is about the minimum planing stroke.

Another common practice is tandem, or "gang", planing — that is, lining up a number of relatively small but identical workpieces on the table and planing all of them at the same time.

Tolerance and Finish. Despite the fact that the equipment used for planing is relatively large and rugged, under good conditions of maintenance and operation, planing is a precision process. For this reason, it is sometimes selected over competitive processes.

Flatness variations can be held within 0.0005 in. TIR on workpieces up to 4 sq ft in area or up to about 4 ft long.

Cast iron workpieces can be planed to a finish of about 63 micro-in. and steel workpieces to about 32 micro-in.

Planers

The planer develops cutting action from straight-line reciprocating motion between the tool and the workpiece. On a planer, the work is reciprocated longitudinally while the tools are fed sidewise into the work. The feed in planing is intermittent and represents width of cut. Planer tables are reciprocated by either mechanical or hydraulic drives. Most planers, however, are mechanically driven, by such means as variable-voltage, constant-torque drives.

The speed at which a mechanical-drive planer operates depends on the speed of the driving motor and on gear ratio. In hydraulic planers, table speed depends on the effective area of the piston and on the volume of oil pumped against the piston area per unit of time.

Regardless of whether the drive is mechanical or hydraulic, the efficiency of planers can be greatly increased by incorporating a means of increasing table speed on the return stroke, during which time no cutting is done. In the following example, efficiency was increased mainly because of increased speed on the return stroke.

Example 90. Belt Drive vs Hydraulic Drive (Fig. 1)

Press-brake bolsters (Fig. 1) of various lengths and widths were produced by planing from 3-in.-thick hot rolled steel. Lengths of the bolsters ranged from 4 to 14 ft, and widths from 5½ to 8½ in. All flat surfaces were planed sufficiently to "clean them up", and the dovetail configurations and slot were also produced by planing.

When a belt-driven planer with a table that moved at the same rate in both directions was used, the average production time was 33 hr per bolster (including setup). Replacement of this planer with a new hydraulic machine that had a rapid-return table resulted in a reduction in setup and planing time to an average of 24 hr per bolster. Some of the decrease in production time was attributed to the use of heavier cuts, as permitted by the new machine, because it was more ruggedly built and had no belts that could slip, as they sometimes did on the old planer. However, most of the saving in time was attributed to the rapid-return table.

Tools of a general-purpose high speed steel were used in both machines. Carbide tools were tried, but because they chipped excessively, their use was discontinued.

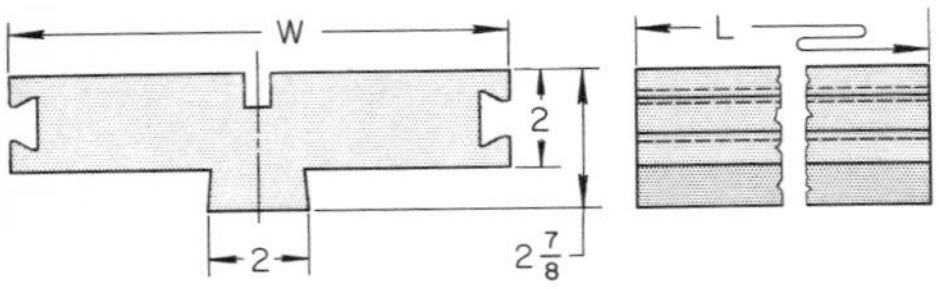

Fig. 1. Press-brake bolster planed from 3-in.-thick hot rolled steel (Example 90)

Double-housing planers (Fig. 2) incorporate two vertical uprights that support the crossrail.

Double-housing planers are more rigid than open-side planers (see below), but they are limited as to the width of workpiece they can accommodate.

Open-side planers differ from double-housing planers mainly in that they have only one upright column, from which the crossrail is cantilevered over the table. Open-side planers can accommodate wider workpieces than the double-housing machines, because workpieces can overhang from the side of the table without interfering with the planer mechanism. When the workpiece is considerably wider than the table, an outboard rolling table may be used to support the overhanging section of the workpiece.

The main disadvantage of open-side planers is that they are less rigid than double-housing planers. Open-side planers are also limited to three tool heads — two on the crossrail and one on the single upright column. However, an open-side planer can be converted to a double-housing planer by means of an outboard detachable housing. Outboard housings are available as optional equipment and can be mounted or dismounted in about an hour. This added support increases the rigidity of the machine and permits the use of an additional tool head.

Workpiece Capacity. Both double-housing and open-side planers are available in a wide range of sizes. Double-housing planers are rated by width, height and length, in that order. Width refers to the maximum width of workpiece that can pass between the upright housings. Height refers to the maximum height of workpiece that can pass under the crossrail when supported on the table. Length refers to maximum stroke. Thus, an 84-in. by 84-in. by 22-ft double-housing planer is capable of planing a workpiece 84 in. wide, 84 in. high and 22 ft long. Open-side planers are similarly rated as to size, except that width is table width and is not maximum workpiece width.

Tool Capacity. Although only three tool heads can be used on an open-side planer, and four on a double-housing planer, tool capacity can be increased by the use of special holders that accommodate more than one single-point tool. It is common practice to use a roughing tool and a finishing tool in the same head, thus completing a planing operation in one pass instead of two (usually with some sacrifice in surface finish).

For straight planing, the efficiency of the planer can be greatly increased by the use of double-cutting tools, in special holders on special heads, which permit planing on both the forward and return strokes of the planer. When these tools are used, the speed of the normally noncutting return stroke — which on most modern planers is several times greater than that of the forward stroke — is of course reduced.

Special accessories, such as automatic controls and tracer attachments, can be used to increase planer efficiency. Many planers are equipped for full control of speed and feed ranges from one suspended station, and for automatic rail positioning and leveling. Tracer attachments permit contour-planing of parts such as large propeller blades, steam chests, and rocker arms for bridge supports.

Duplex tables, which are split crosswise into two sections, also increase process efficiency. The two sections can be fastened together and used as one long table, or split for planing shorter workpieces. When split, one section of the table can be loaded and set up while work is being planed on the other section. This practice greatly increases the productivity of a planer, because in many applications setup time is greater than machining time. (A related productivity-increasing practice, the use of setup plates, is discussed in the section that follows.)

Workholding Methods and Devices

A planer is often difficult to set up, especially for tandem, or "gang", planing (in which a number of small or medium-size parts are arranged in line to be planed at one time), or when one large, irregularly shaped part is to be planed. When several workpieces in a row are being planed, their alignment is critical and each piece must be fixed securely to the table.

Workpieces such as bases for large presses or diesel engines are usually large rough castings, forgings or weldments produced one at a time, and often planing is the first operation in machining them. Setup of these pieces on a planer is extremely critical because the planed surfaces will be used as a means of locating for subsequent operations.

Planing is a rugged cutting operation during which the workpiece is subjected to such great force that it will be pushed from the table if not firmly secured. If the workpiece is allowed to move on the table, not only will it be damaged by a miscut, but serious damage to tools and the machine, as well as injury to operators, is likely to occur. To prevent such consequences, the number of stops, clamps, or other anchoring devices should be increased over the

Double-housing planer with a tool head on one of the two vertical support uprights in addition to the two tool heads on the crossrail. Another tool head can be supported on the other upright in some models. The two uprights are immovable and limit the width of workpiece that can be planed in this machine.

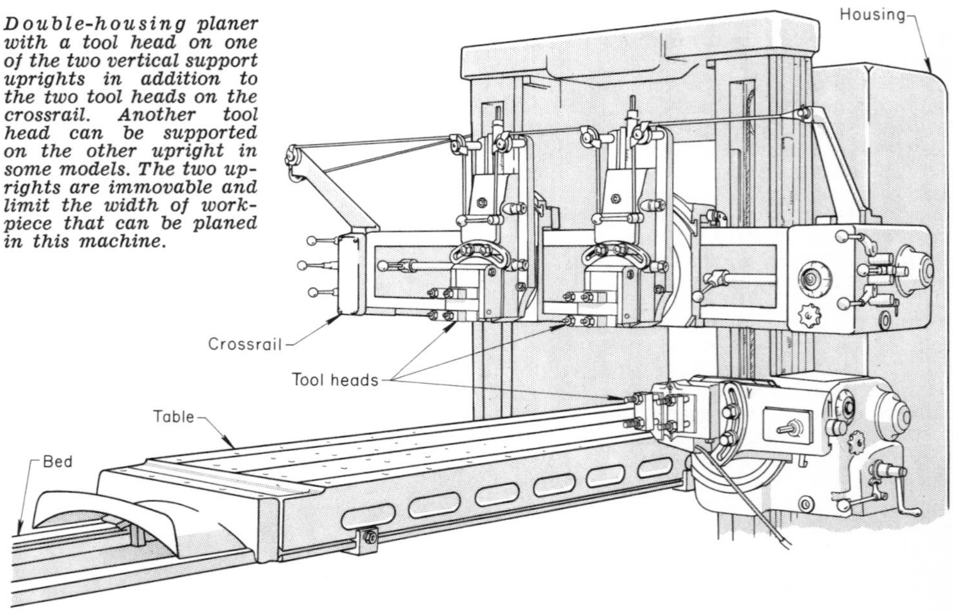

Fig. 2. Significant components of a double-housing planer

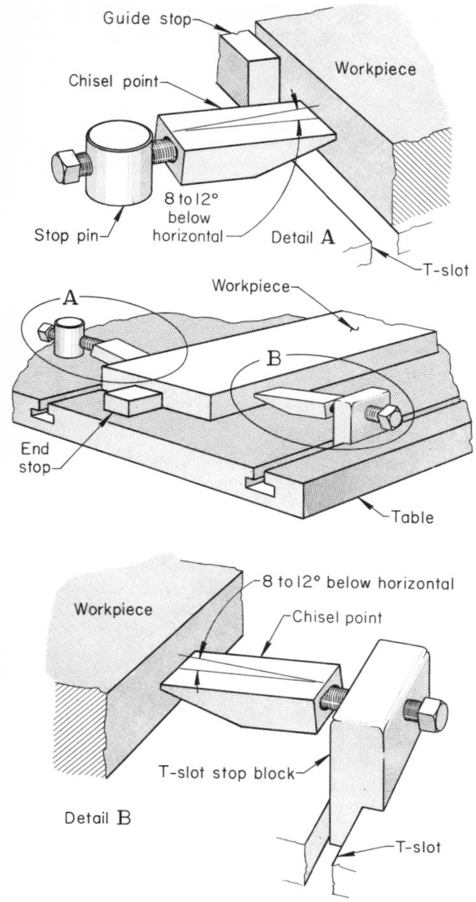

Fig. 3. A common method for securing a long flat plate to a planer table

minimum necessary for holding the workpiece rigidly in position.

Platelike Workpieces. Magnetic chucks are often used for holding cast iron or steel workpieces to planer tables. Magnetic chucking, however, is reliable only for holding workpieces that have a large table-contact area in relation to height. For this reason, holding by means of magnetic chucks is generally restricted to planing of platelike workpieces. To insure against movement of a workpiece held by magnetic chucking, an end stop should be placed against it counter to the cutting stroke (if double cutting is used, an end stop should be at each end of the work).

When magnetic chucks are not available, or when a platelike workpiece does not lend itself to this method of mounting, clamping devices of various kinds are used. Figure 3 illustrates a common method for securing a long flat plate to a planer table, using chisel points, T-slot stop blocks, stop pins, guide stops for initial alignment, and an end stop. In using this method, two precautions must be observed: (*a*) adjusting screws contacting the chisel points must not extend beyond the stop blocks or stop pins by more than the distances suggested in Fig. 3 (one or two diameters), or the screws may bend and allow the workpiece to loosen; and (*b*) chisel points must be set at an angle of 8° to 12° (Fig. 3).

Regardless of the holding method used for platelike parts, it is advisable to remove an equal or nearly equal amount from each side, to minimize unbalanced stresses and resulting warpage from planing. When it is not feasible to plane both sides, common practice is to rough plane to within 0.010 to 0.015 in. of final size for small workpieces and to within ⅛ in. of final size for very large workpieces; the workpieces are then stress relieved and finish planed to size.

Irregularly Shaped Workpieces. After a workpiece has been placed on the table, the first step is to ascertain that it rests solidly. If there is any wobble, shim jacking must be used. For large workpieces with relatively slender sections, such as some weldments, jacks or blocks should be used to damp vibrations. A strap or pin clamp should be used over each jack or block, to insure that the workpiece rests solidly.

A typical method of securing a large irregular casting to a planer table is illustrated in Fig. 4. This setup employs an angle bracket and an outboard support. If double-cutting practice were used, an angle bracket and two end stop pins would be used at each end of the workpiece. For workpieces of this type that are more than 4 or 5 ft long, the use of two outboard supports and screw jacks is recommended.

An ample supply of setup hardware in a wide variety of types and sizes, can greatly decrease the time required for setting up large and irregularly shaped workpieces, thus decreasing downtime. Inexpensive and seemingly inconsequential items of hardware can often reduce floor-to-floor time. For instance, special T-slot nuts are available that can be dropped into a 4-in.-long cleared section of the slot at the desired location and given a quarter turn, thus eliminating the necessity for clearing chips from the entire slot for loading another workpiece.

Cleaning chips from T-slots and stop-pin holes consumes operator time as well as machine time (in one instance, an operator spent 40 min planing a workpiece and 30 min picking chips from slots and pin holes before the next workpiece could be set up). This loss of time can be prevented by placing specially cut lengths of hardwood strips in the T-slots, and metal covers on the stop-pin holes. These protecting devices can be quickly removed to permit loading of the next workpiece.

Setup Plates. Planing efficiency can often be increased by the use of setup plates, regardless of whether the operation is used for planing a single workpiece or several workpieces in line (tandem planing).

A setup plate resembles a planer table in length and width, and has T-slots for mounting the work. In production planing, the work is secured to the plate away from the planer, and then the assembly is carried to the planer table and located on it by keys at each end of the setup plate that fit into the center T-slot in the table. When two setup plates are used, one load can be planed while another is being set up — a procedure comparable to the use of a duplex table.

Tandem (Gang) Planing. Specially designed fixtures that allow quick loading and unloading can greatly increase productivity in tandem planing. However, the cost of such fixtures can rarely be justified, except for continued production of identical or closely similar workpieces.

For tandem planing, the workpieces must either be tightly butted together (so that the tool cuts continuously for the entire stroke) or be separated by 6 to 8 in. (for a fully interrupted cut). If the workpieces are separated by only an inch or two, the tool is likely to break, because of deflection by chips lodged between the workpieces, or because the sudden release of pressure on the tool shank as the tool emerges from the cut will cause a vibration and allow the tool to enter the next workpiece before becoming fully seated.

Tool Materials

High speed steels, cast cobalt-chromium-tungsten alloys, and carbide are used as materials for planer tools.

High speed steels and cast alloys are often interchanged. In some heavy-duty planing applications, cast-alloy tools have proved superior to high speed steel tools. However, high speed steel tools are used more for planing.

Most planer tools have relatively large cross sections, because they are made for maximum rigidity (note the typical planer tool and mounting shown in Fig. 5). Because of the size of these tools, common practice is to make the shank from an alloy steel (such as 4140 or 4340) heat treated for high strength, and then to use inserts of high speed steel (brazed or mechanically secured).

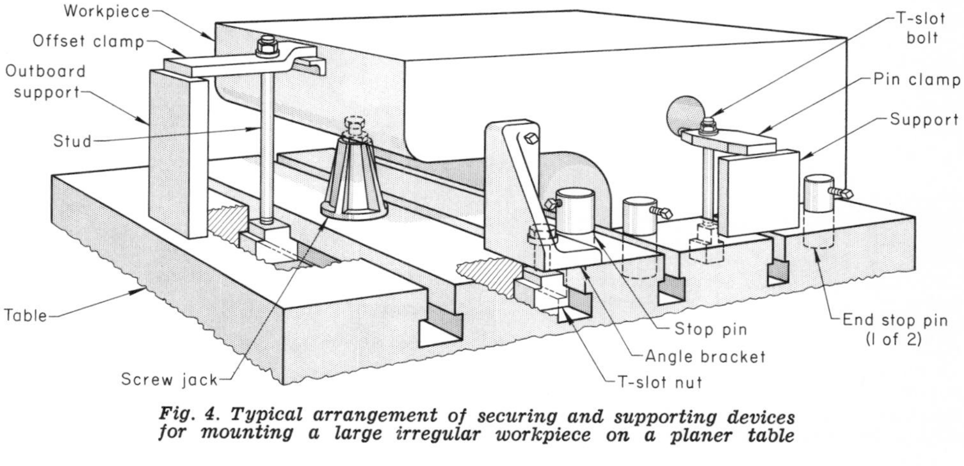

Fig. 4. Typical arrangement of securing and supporting devices for mounting a large irregular workpiece on a planer table

General-purpose high speed steels such as T1 and M2 have proved satisfactory for many planer tools or cutting edges. However, in applications involving hard work metals or heavy cuts, the cobalt types of high speed steel, such as T6, T15, M6 or M44, will give better tool life. These more highly alloyed high speed steels ordinarily are used as inserts.

Carbide. Under conditions of maximum rigidity of machine, tools and workpiece, carbide tools are more efficient than high speed steel or cast-alloy tools. Planing time often is reduced by 50% or more by using carbide instead of high speed steel cutting tools, as indicated in the following two examples:

Examples 91 and 92. High Speed Steel vs Carbide Tools

Example 91 — Planing Gray Iron. Originally, tools made of high speed steel were used on a rapid-return planer (300-sfm return stroke) for removing up to 3/4 in. of metal from a gray iron base 20 in. wide by 10 ft long. At a cutting-stroke speed of 40 sfm (the practical maximum) and a feed of 3/32 in. per stroke, planing time was 75 min.

By changing to carbide tools, it was possible to increase cutting-stroke speed to 200 sfm. With no change in other conditions, planing time was reduced to 30 min.

Example 92 — Planing Steel. Mild steel workpieces originally were planed with high speed steel tools on a rapid-return (300-sfm return stroke) planer. At a feed of 1/8 in. per stroke and with a 3/8-in. depth of cut, cutting-stroke speed was limited to 50 sfm. Under these conditions, planing time was 47 min.

When carbide tools were substituted for high speed steel, cutting-stroke speed was increased to 300 sfm, using the same feed, depth of cut, and return-stroke speed. The increase in speed resulted in a reduction of planing time to 17 min.

In choosing tool material for planing, however, over-all time is a more important consideration than machining time alone. In many applications, setup time is far greater than planing time — under which conditions, large reductions in planing time have a relatively small effect on total processing time.

Before considering the use of carbide tools for planing, it must be ascertained that the planer is rigid and in good condition, and is capable of the high speeds (up to 300 sfm) needed for successful use of carbide. The rail should be securely clamped to the housing or column, and the head should fit snugly to the rail. The tool box and apron should be free of spring and excessive wear, to permit the apron to seat in its clapper box. Also, the planer should be equipped with tool lifters, to prevent the carbide tools from dragging or bouncing on the return stroke. Sufficient horsepower must be available; in rough planing of steel with one carbide tool, as much as 90 hp is sometimes required.

A shock-resisting type of carbide must be used, regardless of whether it is a straight-tungsten grade for planing gray iron or a steel-cutting grade. Carbides suitable for planing usually contain up to about 16% cobalt.

Carbide planer tools should not be considered for the following:

1 Workpieces that limit tool runout to only a few inches (because the higher speeds used in carbide planing need a greater runout margin).
2 Workpieces that require the use of a longitudinal extension on the tool holder for reaching into blind areas (a practice called "poke planing").
3 Workpieces that require excessive tool overhang in a vertical plane. As the tool is lowered in the holder, rigidity decreases.
4 Weldments in which metal hardness at junctions may vary considerably. For this condition, high speed steel tools operated at slow speeds will generally give better results.
5 Planing of metals that are harder than about Rockwell C 40. These must be planed at slow speeds, with which the inherent advantages of carbide tools cannot be realized.

Tool Design

Recommended design details for the cutting portions of high speed steel planer tools are shown in Fig. 6. Tools are available in a variety of configurations suited to undercutting, slotting and straight planing of either horizontal or vertical surfaces. Tools having the small nose radii shown in Fig. 6

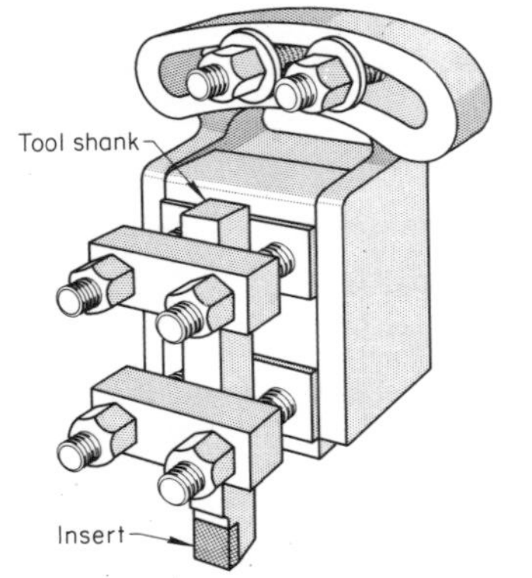

Fig. 5. Planer tool and method of holding for maximum rigidity

are preferred for roughing cuts; broad (often as wide as 1½ in.), flat-nosed tools are better for finishing of most metals.

Carbide Roughing Tools. Back rake angle for carbide planer tools ranges from 0° to −15°. As a general rule, the more difficult the work metal is to machine, the more negative is the back rake angle: a 0° back rake is used for soft metals; −3° to −5° for cast iron, mild steel, and medium-carbon steels; and −5° to −15° for difficult-to-machine steels (for example, 4340 at Rockwell C 40). Negative back rake is sometimes used also when planing "gummy" metals, because it aids chip flow and reduces face wear.

Side rake angles range from +3° to −15°, also depending on the machinability of the work metal. A side rake angle of +3° to 0° is usually suitable for free-cutting metals, 0° for medium-carbon steels, −3° for gummy metals, and up to −15° for difficult-to-machine steels. Excessive negative rake angles should be avoided, however, because they are likely to cause chatter.

Side rake, or the land of the tool, is the largest single factor in controlling chip flow. The use of optimum side rake eliminates the need for chip breakers, which is an advantage, because mechanical chip breakers are readily knocked off by the heavy chip produced in planing, and ground-in chip breakers weaken the cutting edge of the tool. Chip control is aided by grinding the land to a triangular shape, which causes the edge of the chip at the surface line of the cut to curl before the edge of the chip at the tool point, thereby flowing the chip toward the side of the tool and back onto the workpiece.

The lead, or side cutting-edge, angle directly controls chip thickness in relation to feed. A 45° lead angle will produce a thin chip, a 10° lead will produce a thicker chip, and a 0° lead will produce a chip equivalent in thickness to the feed used. The lead angle should be such that the chip produced is thick enough to take the initial shock away from the cutting edge and yet thin enough to curl properly. In planing mild steel, a lead angle less than 15° will cause excessive shock, and a lead angle greater than 35° will produce a long, straight chip. A lead angle of 23° to 25° is near optimum for many metals, allowing the chip to flow onto the workpiece or against the tool holder and break into small segments. To obtain an acceptable chip thickness in roughing, however, a lead angle of about 30° is most commonly used.

Carbide tools require a comparatively small nose radius, to prevent machining stress from focusing at the radial point of the radius and rupturing the carbide. A small radius permits heat and stress to flow straight through the tip and cause less chatter. A nose radius of 1/16 to 1/8 in. is suitable for cast iron, and a 1/32-in. radius for steel.

Relief (clearance) angles should vary with the type of material being planed. Side and end relief angles of 5° are usually suitable for cast iron. For the planing of most steels, it is advisable to strengthen the cutting tool as much as possible by reducing the side clearance angle, thereby providing a larger area of carbide for dissipating heat and absorbing shock.

Figure 7 shows a type of carbide-insert tool widely used for rough planing of cast iron and steel. When ground to the configuration shown in Fig. 7, the tool is best suited for planing cast iron, although tools of this design have been

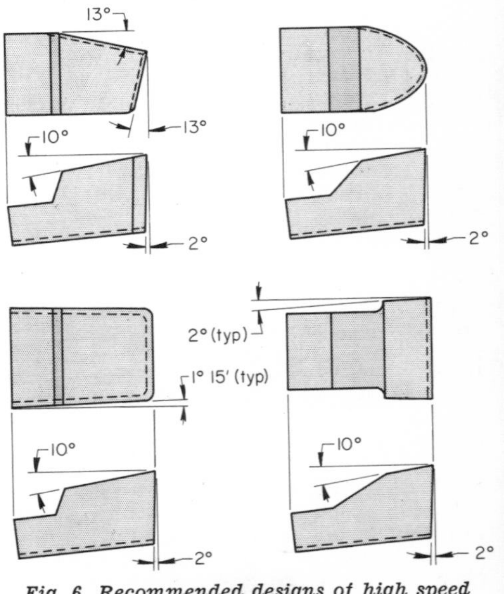

Fig. 6. Recommended designs of high speed steel planer tools

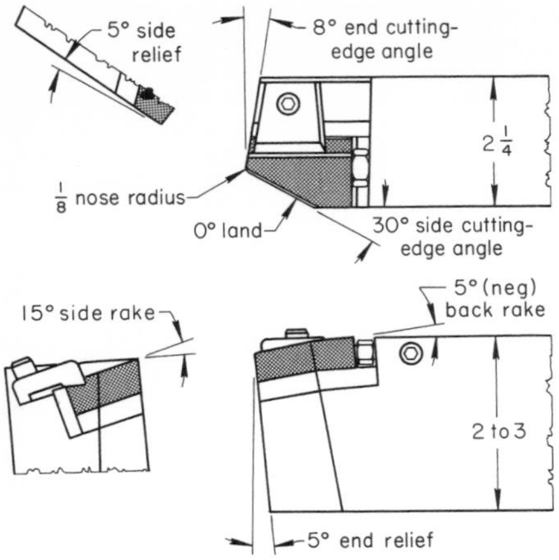

Fig. 7. Carbide-insert tool for rough planing of cast iron

successfully used on brass and aluminum. For planing carbon and alloy steels, the design of the tool should be modified in accordance with the recommendations in the preceding discussion.

Carbide inserts of the round or square button type also are used for rough planing. Between regrinds for sharpening, the inserts can be rotated to present new cutting edges, thus allowing greater total tool life. Square button inserts can be ground in position. Round button inserts 1 in. in diameter and ½ in. thick are suitable for depths of cut to ⅜ in.; for greater depths of cut, inserts 1¼ in. in diameter and ¾ in. thick should be used. For planing cast iron, 0° back and side rakes and a 6° side relief are satisfactory. For planing steel, a −5°, 1/32-in.-wide land on the cutting face has proved successful.

Finishing Tools. Figure 8 shows a typical broad-nose finishing tool that can also be used for slotting. Either a carbide or a high speed steel insert can be used in this type of tool. As Fig. 8 shows, the bottom of the insert is serrated lengthwise, and the top of the insert is serrated across the width. This design permits offsetting the insert to the left or right as needed and provides a rigid lock. The cross serration at the top prevents vertical movement of the insert.

The insert is held in place mechanically by a serrated clamp, which is secured by a socket screw. When the cutting edge becomes dull, a new insert can be installed without removing the shank from the tool holder.

Gooseneck-holder finishing tools (Fig. 9) are intended primarily for use on cast iron, but have been successfully used for finish planing of other metals. Gooseneck tools carry the cutting edge behind center so that the cutter is dragged in cutting. It does not dig in nor chatter so readily as a cutter that is ahead of center.

Inserts for gooseneck holders may be made of high speed steel or carbide, but greater accuracy is obtained with high speed steel. High speed steel inserts, which are available in widths up to 1¾ in., should be ground with a slight positive back rake; cutting edges should be honed with an oilstone to obtain maximum sharpness. With high speed steel inserts, it is possible to take cuts of less than 0.001 in. on cast iron, for surfaces that require extreme accuracy (as for fitting to template gages).

Carbide inserts, up to 1¼ in. wide, are also used in gooseneck holders for producing flat cuts. Edges of carbide inserts are not as keen as edges of high speed steel inserts, and therefore carbide inserts should not be used for depths of cut less than 0.002 in.

Double-Cutting Tools. Double-cut planing uses both strokes of the planer table for cutting, and requires special tool holders mounted to a spindle in the planer head (Fig. 10). This spindle oscillates 13° clockwise and places a tool in cutting position for the normal cutting stroke. At the completion of the normal cutting stroke, the spindle oscillates 13° counterclockwise and positions a second tool for cutting on the return stroke of the planer table (Fig. 10). In addition, a conventional finishing tool can be mounted in the clapper box of the head, to permit semifinishing a workpiece simultaneously with the roughing cut. This technique is known as triple planing.

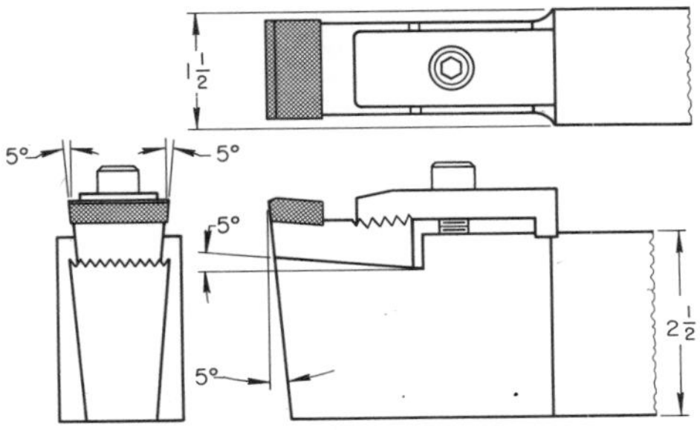

Fig. 8. Typical insert tool for semifinish and finish planing, or for slotting

Speed, Feed and Depth of Cut

Table 1 lists recommended speeds and feeds for various depths of cut in rough and finish planing of several different metals with high speed steel or carbide tools. The values shown in this table are not maximum, but are typical values that have proved consistent with optimum tool life and efficiency of metal removal.

Minor variables in work metal, tool design, or machine conditions often indicate the need for adjustments in speed or feed, or both. On new jobs, it is often necessary to inspect the tool after a few passes for the following conditions:

1. Edge wear, which indicates too much speed or not enough feed
2. Face wear, which indicates too much feed or not enough speed
3. Redness at the tool point, which may occur in extreme cases of interrupted cutting, and which should be kept to a minimum by adjusting speed or feed, or both.

In general, it is advisable to plane steel with as heavy a feed and as high a speed as possible, because this promotes good chip flow without the aid of mechanical or ground-in chip breakers. A heavy chip will curl and break into small segments better than a thin chip. Increased cutting speed is the best means to prevent overheating of the workpiece and the tool, by maximizing heating of the chip. Using carbide tools, thin plates have been more successfully planed by increasing the cutting speed from 225 to 300 sfm, thus transmitting more heat to the chips.

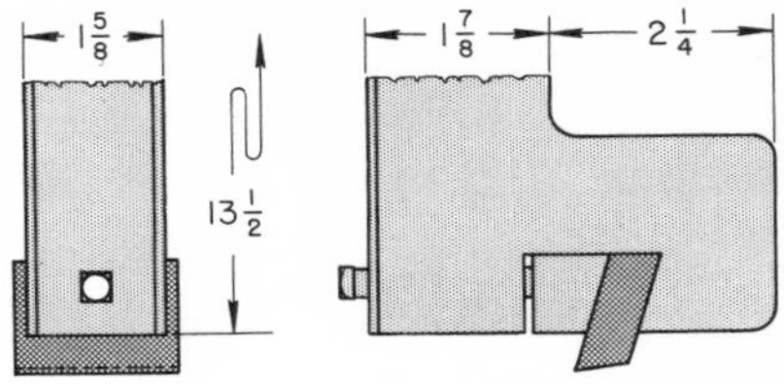

Fig. 9. Gooseneck-holder tool used for light cuts in finish planing

Uniform cutting speed and feed should be maintained throughout the entire stroke of the planer. It is not necessary to start the cut with a slow speed and a low feed, nor is it advantageous to preheat the tool before beginning a cut.

When carbide tools are used for planing medium grades of gray iron (approximately 200 Bhn), common practice is to operate at 150 to 175 sfm and 5/64 to 3/32-in. feed per stroke with a ½ to ¾-in. depth of cut. By decreasing the depth of cut to ⅜ in., speed can safely be increased to 180 to 200 sfm and feed can be increased to 3/32 to ⅛ in. per stroke.

Mild steel can be planed at higher speed than gray iron with carbide tools; 300 sfm and a feed of 3/32 to ⅛ in. per stroke with ⅜-in. depth of cut is common practice.

Medium-carbon low-alloy steel such as annealed 4130 can be planed at 175 to 200 sfm, 5/64-in. feed and ⅜-in. depth of cut. For higher-carbon higher-alloy steels like 4350 common practice is 100 to 150 sfm at 3/64-in. to 1/16-in. feed and ⅜-in. depth of cut. Die blocks at about Rockwell C 36 have been planed with carbide tools at 100 sfm, 3/64-in. feed per stroke and ½-in. depth of cut. Heat treated die blocks at Rockwell C 46 have been planed with carbide at 15 to 20 sfm, 1/32-in. feed per stroke and ¼-in. depth of cut.

A carbide tool may break because of side pressure as it makes the last pass or two on a workpiece. To minimize this possibility, on cuts of more than ¼ in. depth it is advisable to reduce the feed to 3/64 or 1/32 in. and to decrease the speed by 50% for four or five strokes before the tool emerges from a cut. This will often prevent breakage caused by pressure on the side clearance portion of the tool from the elastic behavior of the work metal. That is, too much feed will deflect the thin flange or remaining portion of the work at the cutting edge of the tool, thus

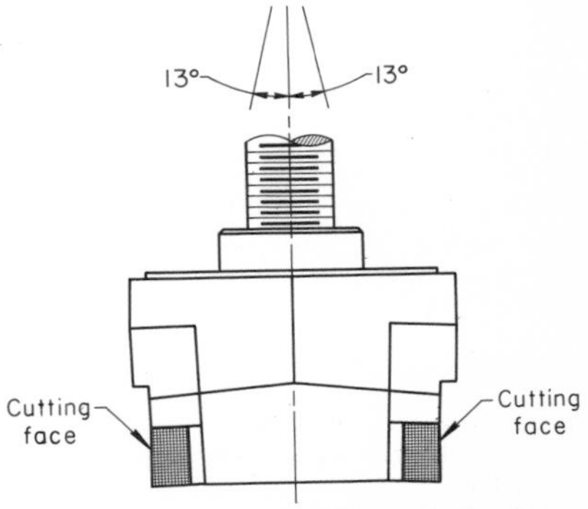

Fig. 10. Tool for double-cut planing

Table 1. Recommended Speeds and Feeds for Planing With High Speed Steel or Carbide Tools

Work metal	Hardness, Bhn	Roughing: Depth of cut, ⅛ in. Speed, sfm	Feed, in. per stroke	Depth of cut, ¼ in. Speed, sfm	Feed, in. per stroke	Depth of cut, ½ in. Speed, sfm	Feed, in. per stroke	Depth of cut, 1 in. Speed, sfm	Feed, in. per stroke	Finishing speed, sfm(a)
Planing With High Speed Steel Tools										
Cast iron	230	50	0.090 to 0.125	50	0.060 to 0.090	40	0.045 to 0.060	35	0.030 to 0.045	40
	175	70	0.090 to 0.125	60	0.060 to 0.090	50	0.045 to 0.060	40	0.045 to 0.060	60
Steel	270	35	0.060 to 0.090	30	0.060 to 0.090	25	0.045 to 0.060	20	0.045 to 0.060	20
	200	35	0.090 to 0.125	35	0.060 to 0.090	30	0.060 to 0.090	25	0.045 to 0.060	30
	130	60	0.090 to 0.125	50	0.090 to 0.125	40	0.060 to 0.090	30	0.045 to 0.060	50
Bronze	Hard	60	0.090 to 0.125	60	0.090 to 0.125	50	0.090 to 0.125	40	0.060 to 0.090	60
	Soft	140	0.156 to 0.188	120	0.125 to 0.156	100	0.125 to 0.156	100	0.090 to 0.125	140
Planing With Carbide Tools										
Cast iron	230	200	0.090 to 0.125	200	0.075 to 0.090	200	0.060 to 0.075	200	0.045 to 0.060	180
	175	300	0.100 to 0.125	300	0.090 to 0.100	300	0.075 to 0.090	300	0.060 to 0.075	220
Steel	270	250	0.060 to 0.075	250	0.060 to 0.075	250	0.045 to 0.060	...	....	250
	200	Max	0.060 to 0.090	Max	0.060 to 0.075	300	0.060 to 0.075	...	....	300
	130	Max	0.060 to 0.090	Max	0.060 to 0.090	Max	0.060 to 0.090	...	....	300
Bronze	Hard	Max	0.090 to 0.125	Max	0.090 to 0.125	Max	0.090 to 0.100	Max	0.060 to 0.090	Max
	Soft	Max	0.090 to 0.150	Max	0.090 to 0.125	Max	0.090 to 0.125	Max	0.090 to 0.100	Max

(a) For depth of cut ranging from 0.003 to 0.015 in. Finishing feeds at these speeds depend on the type of tool used: flat-nose tools are used for cast iron and bronze, at feeds of ½ to 1 in. per stroke; variations of flat-nose tools are used for steel, at feeds of ⅛ to ½ in. per stroke (although round-nose tools are sometimes used, at feeds of 0.045 to 0.060 in., depending on the nose radius and on the finish desired).

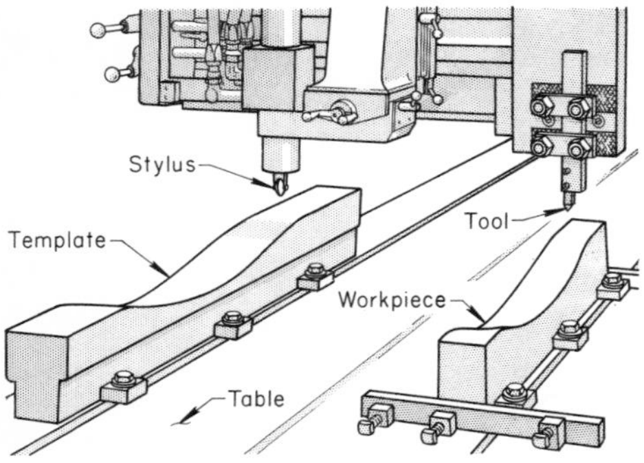

Fig. 11. Contour planing with a template

preventing the tool from removing the full amount of metal for which the feed is set. As the tool continues through the stroke, the metal flange, with the deflected amount of stock still intact, will spring back to its normal position and rub against the side clearance edge of the tool on the return stroke, thereby generating heat by friction. Even if this does not cause immediate tool failure, breakout of the steel may be caused when the tool, under automatic feed, overtakes the deflected metal and plows through an oversize flange equivalent to a double or triple feed. This will set up intense chatter and cause the tool to chip.

Special Applications

Planing is used primarily for removing metal in a straight line from flat surfaces. However, a variety of contour operations can be accomplished by template control such as illustrated in Fig. 11. An example of contouring by planing is the cutting of helical grooves in large rolls. For this operation, the roll is set up longitudinally on the planer table with special holding fixtures that include a drive mechanism to rotate the roll at a predetermined speed as it advances into the fixed cutting tool, thus cutting a helical groove.

Planing vs Alternative Processes

Although broaching, or even sawing, may be used as an alternative to planing, milling and grinding are most often the competitive processes. Selection of planing in preference to an alternative process usually is based on the following considerations:

1 The initial cost of a planer is about half that of a planer-type milling machine for performing the same job.
2 Because of the lower initial cost of the planer, burden rate is lower, regardless of whether the machine is used part time or full time.
3 Certain shapes are particularly suited to planing (examples: dovetails and V-sections).
4 For some parts, such as large machine-tool components, the dimensional accuracy required is obtainable only by planing.
5 Planing is preferred for bearing surfaces that must be finished by scraping, because the surface condition that results is more suitable than that produced by milling.
6 Because of its versatility, low tooling cost, and short tooling-up time, planing is more economical for low production.

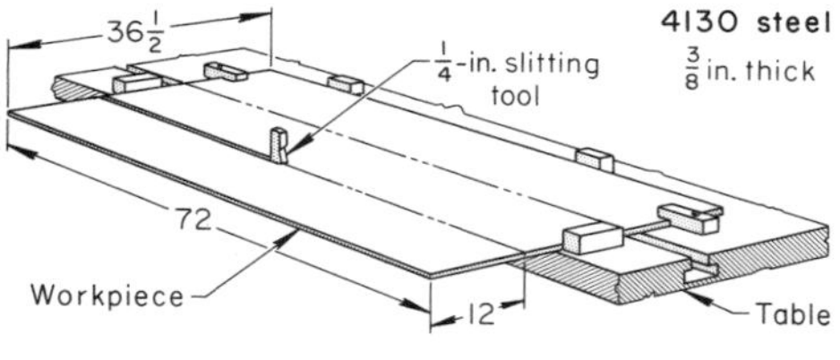

Item	Band sawing	Planing
Speed, sfm	125	60
Feed	¾ in. per min	0.005-in. chip load
Time and Cost per Strip Cut		
Time, min	11.2	1.8
Cost	$1.31	$0.22

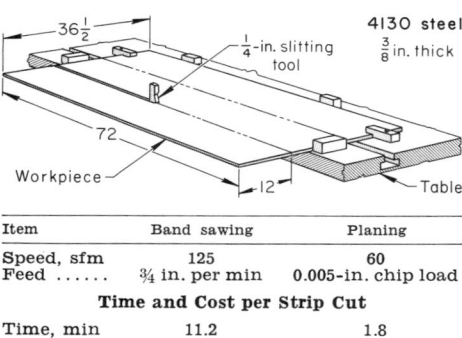

Fig. 12. Slitting steel plate by planing, and comparison with previous method, band sawing (Example 93)

Compared with milling on the basis of volume of metal removed per unit of time, planing is relatively inefficient; metal can be removed about twice as fast by milling as by the most efficient planing method (double-cut). However, the longer setup time required for milling, and the more expensive equipment and tooling (for one job, tooling for milling cost fifty times as much as tooling for planing), can be justified only when large quantities of similar parts are to be produced. For extremely large workpieces, production is usually low, and therefore planing is the less costly method.

In some applications, planing and band sawing are competitive operations. The following example describes an application where either planing or band sawing could have been used to obtain acceptable results, but planing was used because it was cheaper.

Example 93. Planing vs Gas Cutting vs Band Sawing for Slitting Steel Plate (Fig. 12)

Figure 12 shows the setup of a planer for slitting ⅜-in. alloy steel plates that were 36½ in. wide by 72 in. long into three 12-in.-wide strips. Strips were originally produced by band sawing, but this method was slow and costly. Gas cutting had been tried, but was rejected because an extra finishing operation was needed to smooth the cut edges. As shown in the table with Fig. 12, planing produced the strips at an 83% saving in time and cost, compared with band sawing.

Planing is often the most practical approach for machining several surfaces to a given absolute level, as in constructing jig-frame components. For such applications, milling would seldom be practical, mainly because only unit production is involved. A typical application is the following example.

Example 94. Planing in Jig Building (Fig. 13)

Figure 13 shows a typical setup used for planing of tooling pads for a jig-frame component. This practice was successful for machining pads to a common level for many frame sizes (as small as 1-sq-ft total area for all pads).

When a planer was used, all tooling pads could be made absolutely level, as determined by a waterline test. With all tooling pads in the same plane, locators were fabricated to an accurate height and erected on the jig frame by the "building-block" technique. Consequently, master or transfer gaging was not critical; locator positions were obtained by a transit and level. Furthermore, locators did not need to be as securely clamped in position as had been required formerly.

Former practice had been to construct jig-frame components with tooling pads welded to the main frame, without attempting to

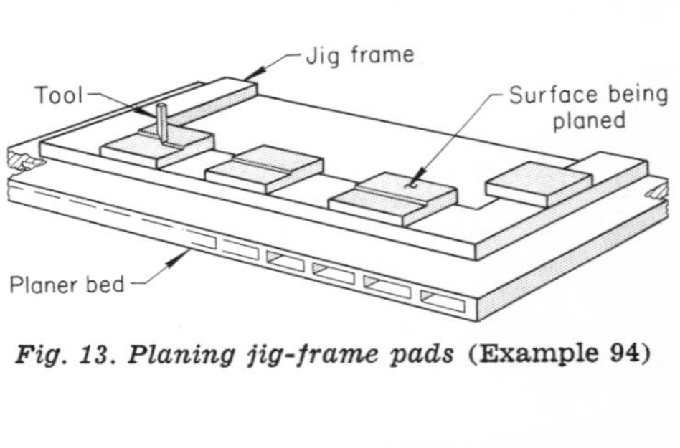

Fig. 13. Planing jig-frame pads (Example 94)

maintain tooling-pad accuracy to a given waterline. This practice required the use of master and transfer gages to hold the point of reference on the locator to be set. A low-melting alloy was used to fill gaps between the locator and tooling pads to obtain the required waterline accuracy.

By using a planer for preparing the locating pads, cost of setting a locator was reduced by 20%, cost of transfer gages was reduced by 60%, and time for jig erection (lead time) was reduced by 40%.

For some workpiece shapes, planing is the only practical machining process. A representative application is described in Example 95, which follows; the workpiece here was a large press frame machined on all four sides and in areas that would have been difficult to reach with milling cutters.

Example 95. Planing 27 Areas on a Press Frame in Two Setups (Fig. 14)

The casting shown in Fig. 14 was planed in two setups. Surfaces identified as 1 were planed in the first setup, and surfaces identified as 2 were planed in the second setup. Total time, including setup, planing and tool sharpening, averaged 140 hr per casting. The number of sand pockets and the amount of dross and scale varied from casting to casting, and this affected frequency of tool sharpening. Consequently, total machining time differed even for similar castings.

The amount of stock that had to be removed ranged from ¼ to ¾ in., varying on different surfaces of the same casting and on similar surfaces of different castings. As a result, the sequence of operations was not always the same. The usual sequence for planing outside surfaces was: rough; straighten; finish. However, when total stock to be removed was on the high side of the range (about ¾ in.), two roughing cuts had to be used. A straightening cut was necessary because of the different amounts of stock removed from any one surface and because surfaces had to be sufficiently flat for finishing. When an extremely heavy cut was taken in roughing, the cutting tool was deflected downward more than when a shallower cut was taken. After the straightening cut, 0.015 to 0.030 in. of stock remained for removal by the finishing cut.

Two roughing cuts were always used in planing the inside surfaces, because tools were held by extension arms and greater tool deflection resulted, compared with planing outside surfaces. Speed was also reduced when planing inside surfaces (see tabulation below Fig. 14).

Tools for planing outside surfaces were made from 1½-in.-square tool bits of cobalt-bearing high speed steel. The inside surfaces were planed with 1½-in.-square tools forged from general-purpose high speed steel.

The angles used on the tools for outside and inside cutting are shown at the bottom of Fig. 14; speeds and feeds for the two operations are tabulated with the illustration. All planing was done without a cutting fluid.

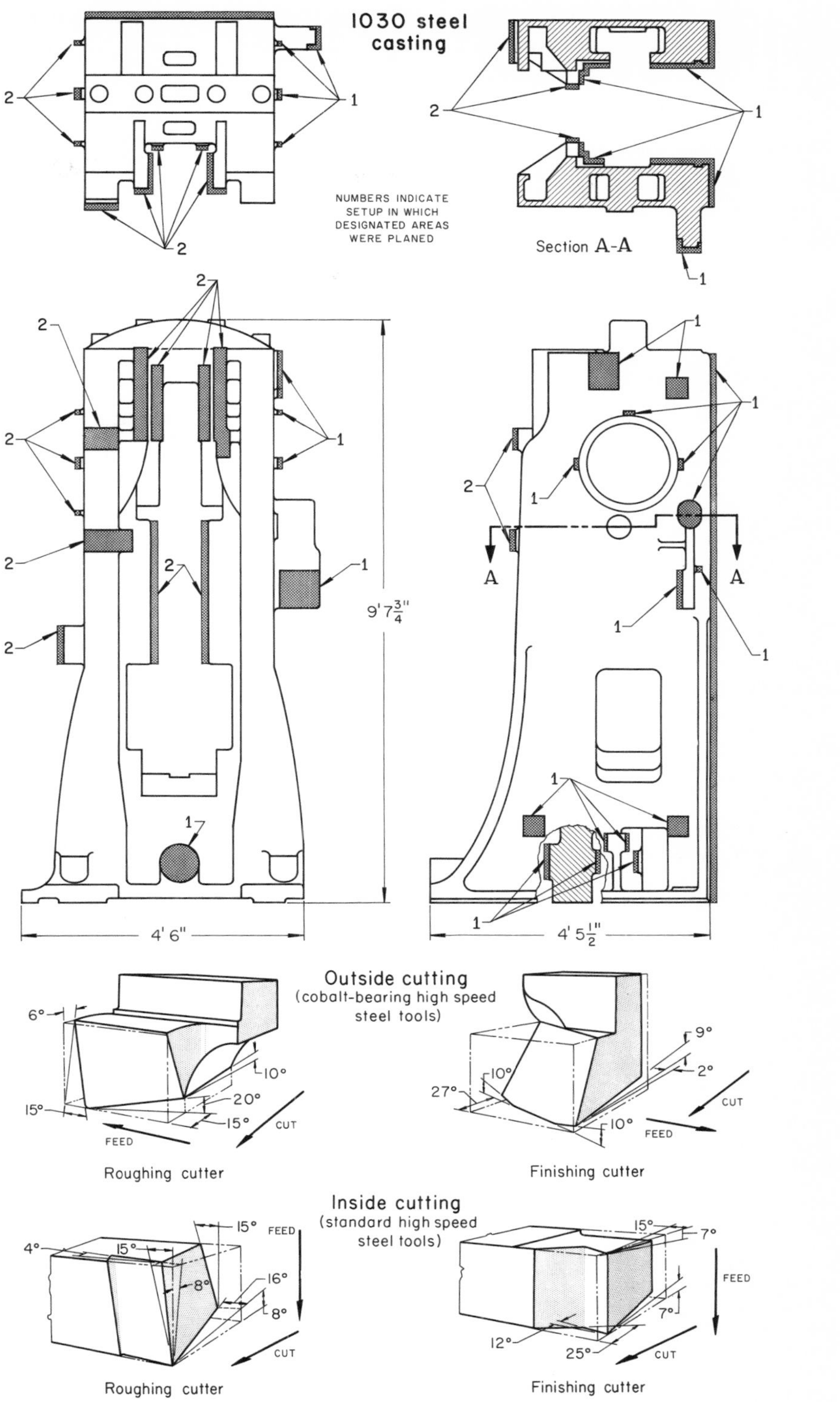

Type of cut	Outside cut: Speed, sfm	Outside cut: Feed, in. per stroke	Inside cut: Speed, sfm	Inside cut: Feed, in. per stroke
Roughing	20	0.375	15	0.375
Straightening	60	0.100	55	0.060
Finishing	50	0.060	45	0.040

Fig. 14. Casting (upper sketches) that was planed on 27 surfaces (shaded areas) in two setups on a planer table, with tools of the design shown in the lower sketches (Example 95)

Cutting Fluids

A flood of cutting fluid is seldom used for planing operations, because two of the three functions of cutting fluids (chip disposal and cooling) are less important than in operations such as turning. In most planing operations, chips are relatively thick and are thrown clear. Thus, they seldom interfere with successive cutting strokes. (As chips begin to pile up on the table or fixtures they should be brushed away. The use of compressed air is not recommended, because chips are likely to lodge in the mechanism.)

In planing the tool is seldom engaged more than 75% of the time. Therefore, cooling of tools and workpieces usually presents no problem. In some planing operations, however, cutting fluids will improve dimensional accuracy, finish and tool life, by minimizing the adherence of work metal to the tool. When cutting fluids are used, a common practice is to apply the fluid directly to the cutting area by means of a swab. Sometimes a spray mist of cutting oil diluted with a lower-viscosity oil such as mineral seal oil has proved advantageous. A film of oil mist aids cutting action and has a mild cooling effect on the tools in planing operations.

Shaping

SHAPING is a machining process for removing metal from surfaces in horizontal, vertical or angular planes, by the use of a single-point tool supported by a ram that reciprocates the tool in a linear motion against the workpiece. This article discusses the machines, tools and techniques employed in the process as defined above, or as modified to include the use of form tools or the shaping of contoured surfaces. High-production gear shaping, in which a rotating cutter is employed for generating gear teeth, is dealt with in the article beginning on page 194 of this volume.

Process Capabilities

Shaping, although a versatile process and one in which setup time is short and relatively inexpensive tools are used, is a comparatively inefficient means of metal removal. The cost per cubic inch of metal removed by shaping may be as much as five times that for removal by milling or broaching, in a given job. For this reason, the use of shaping generally is confined to unit or small-quantity production, as in toolrooms or model shops.

As the hardness of the workpiece increases above about Rockwell C 25, metal removal rate and tool life decrease. On the other hand, when the occasion demands, pieces much harder than that can be cut on a shaper. Steel hardened to Rockwell C 46, or even higher (heat treated die blocks, for example), have been successfully machined by shaping.

Size of workpiece that can be shaped is limited by the maximum length of stroke, which for standard shapers is about 36 in. When surfaces longer than 36 in. must be machined, planing or some other suitable process is used.

The usual range of cutting stroke is even less — from 6 to 24 in. Although machines with longer strokes could be built, they would be impractical for most purposes because, for any given machine, dimensional accuracy decreases as stroke length increases. On even the best-maintained shapers, deviation from dimensional accuracy is about 0.0005 in. per foot of ram travel.

Configuration of Workpiece. Although shaping is most commonly used for machining flat surfaces, the process may be used also for producing contours and a variety of irregular configurations. Shaping is sometimes used for machining contours because production quantities are too low to justify the expense of tooling required for producing the same configurations by milling or broaching. Also, some complex configurations are machined on a shaper because they would be difficult or impossible to produce by milling or broaching — for instance, deep internal slots and tortuous contours and configurations in blind holes.

Because of its versatility and short setup time, shaping is often used for emergency production of gears, splined shafts, racks or similar parts. It is often possible to produce one or two such parts in a shaper in less time than is required merely to set up for production on other, alternative equipment with a higher output rate.

Machines

Shaping machines develop cutting action from straight-line reciprocating motion between the tool and the work. The tool is driven forward and recovered by a sliding ram. The work is fed at right angles to the direction of the ram stroke in small increments. Most shapers have rams that drive the cutting tool in a horizontal direction, but there are a few shapers that have rams that drive the cutting tool in a vertical direction. In either type of shaper, the workpiece rests on a flat bed which advances it toward the cutting tool.

Horizontal shapers may either be crank driven or be operated hydraulically. A hydraulic shaper uses a piston and cylinder to operate the ram. However, because of the higher cost of a hydraulic unit, the comparatively low efficiency of the hydraulic drive, and the difficulty in obtaining stroke length accuracy with hydraulic shapers, most horizontal shapers are crank driven.

Figure 1 shows a sectional view of a crank-driven horizontal shaper and identifies its important working components. The rocker arm is reciprocated by a crankpin mounted on the crank gear. The crank mechanism is an application of a Whitworth quick-return mechanism.

For increased efficiency, shapers are built so that ram speed in the return stroke is greater than in the forward, or cutting, stroke (see velocity diagram in Fig. 2). This is accomplished as indicated in the rocker-arm cycle diagrammed in Fig. 2. As shown in this diagram, 220° of the circle is used for the cutting stroke and only 140° for the return stroke — a ratio of approximately 1.6 to 1. This ratio between forward and return strokes is not a fixed ratio; it varies among different designs of machines, and with the length of the stroke.

Horizontal shapers are furnished with either plain or universal tables. The universal table, in conjunction with a swivel vise, provides rotation on all three axes. Graduations on all three movements allow angular setups to be made quickly.

Horizontal shapers range in size from small bench models with a maximum stroke length of less than 6 in., to large, rugged machines with a maximum stroke of as much as 36 in. On a machine of any size, however, the length of stroke can be varied from its

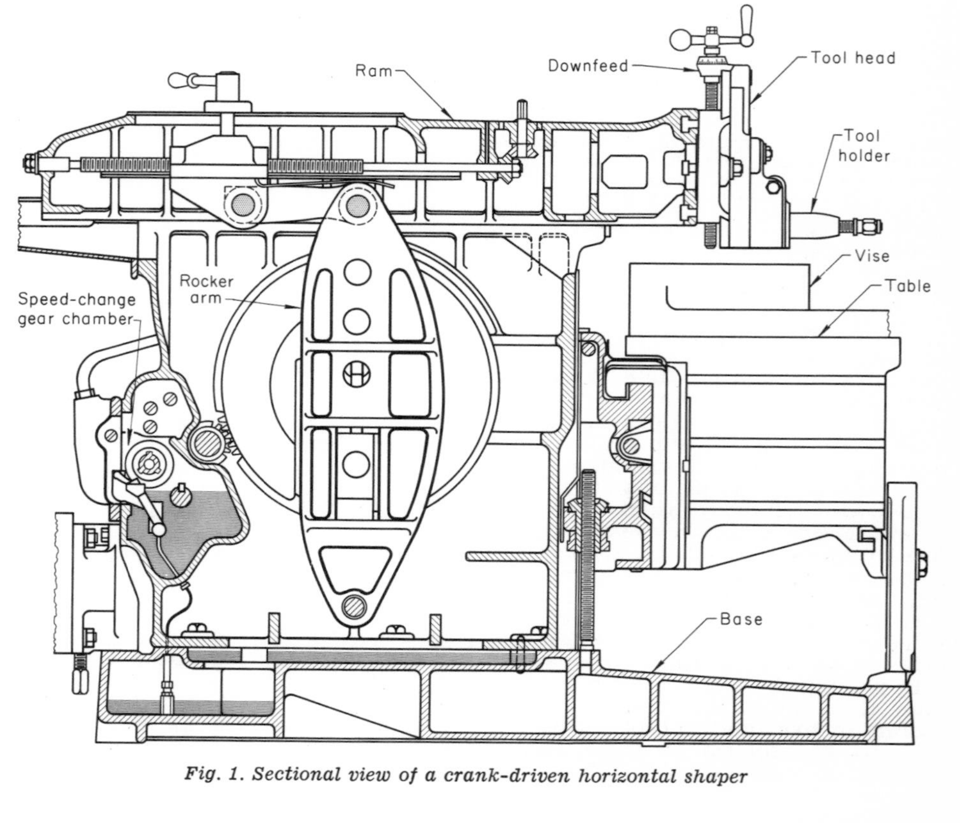

Fig. 1. Sectional view of a crank-driven horizontal shaper

Table 1. Surface Speeds in Shaping, as Related to Frequency and Length of Stroke

Strokes per min	Length of stroke, in.																											
	1	2	3	4	5	6	7	8	9	10	11	12	13	14	15	16	17	18	19	20	22	24	26	28	30	32	34	36
20-In. Standard Shaper (1–20); **16-In. Heavy-Duty Shaper** (1–14)																												
12	3	4	6	8	9	10	13	15	16	18	20	21	23	24	26	27	28	30	31	32	...	...	...	...	...	...	...	...
17	4	6	8	11	13	16	18	21	23	25	28	30	32	34	36	38	40	42	44	46	...	...	...	...	...	...	...	...
26	5	8	13	17	20	24	28	32	35	39	42	46	49	52	55	58	61	64	67	70	...	...	...	...	...	...	...	...
36	6	12	17	23	28	34	39	44	49	54	59	63	68	72	77	81	85	90	93	97	...	...	...	...	...	...	...	...
54	9	18	26	34	43	50	58	66	73	81	88	95	102	108	115	121	128	133	140	146	...	...	...	...	...	...	...	...
77	13	25	37	49	61	72	83	94	105	115	125	135	145	154	164	172	180	189	199	208	...	...	...	...	...	...	...	...
115	19	37	56	73	91	108	124	140	156	172	188	202	216	230	...	...	...	...	...	...	...	...	...	...	...	...	...	...
157	26	51	76	100	127	147	170	192	214	236	...	...	...	...	...	...	...	...	...	...	...	...	...	...	...	...	...	...
24-In. Standard Shaper (1–24); **20-In. Heavy-Duty Shaper** (1–20)																												
10	..	3	5	7	9	10	11	13	15	16	17	18	19	20	21	22	23	25	...	27	29	32	...	...	...	...	...	...
14	..	5	7	9	11	13	15	17	19	21	23	24	26	28	30	32	33	35	...	39	42	45	...	...	...	...	...	...
21	..	7	10	13	16	19	22	25	28	31	34	37	40	43	46	48	51	53	...	58	62	67	...	...	...	...	...	...
29	..	10	14	19	23	27	32	36	40	44	48	51	55	59	63	67	70	73	...	79	86	92	...	...	...	...	...	...
44	..	15	22	28	35	41	47	54	61	67	72	77	83	89	95	101	106	111	...	121	131	140	...	...	...	...	...	...
64	..	21	31	41	51	60	70	79	88	97	105	113	121	129	138	147	154	161	...	...	...	...	...	...	...	...	...	...
94	..	30	45	60	74	88	102	116	129	142	154	165	...	...	...	...	...	...	...	...	...	...	...	...	...	...	...	...
129	..	42	62	82	101	120	130	140	159	...	...	...	...	...	...	...	...	...	...	...	...	...	...	...	...	...	...	...
28-In. Heavy-Duty Shaper (1–28); **24-In. Heavy-Duty Shaper** (1–24)																												
9	..	3	4	5	7	8	9	11	12	13	15	16	17	18	...	21	...	23	...	25	27	29	31	33	...	...	...	...
13	..	5	7	8	10	12	14	16	18	20	21	23	25	27	...	30	...	34	...	37	40	43	46	49	...	...	...	...
20	..	7	10	13	16	19	22	25	28	31	33	36	39	42	...	47	...	52	...	57	61	66	70	74	...	...	...	...
27	..	9	13	17	21	25	29	33	37	41	45	48	52	56	...	61	...	69	...	77	83	89	95	101	...	...	...	...
41	..	13	20	26	32	38	44	50	56	62	68	73	79	84	...	94	...	105	...	115	125	135	144	152	...	...	...	...
59	..	19	28	37	46	55	64	73	82	90	98	106	114	122	...	138	...	152	...	116	...	...	...	...	...	...	...	...
87	..	28	41	54	67	80	95	106	119	132	144	156	168	...	...	...	...	...	...	...	...	...	...	...	...	...	...	...
119	..	39	57	75	93	111	129	147	165	...	...	...	...	...	...	...	...	...	...	...	...	...	...	...	...	...	...	...
36-In. Heavy-Duty Shaper (1–36); **32-In. Heavy-Duty Shaper** (1–32)																												
8	..	3	..	5	...	8	...	10	...	12	...	14	...	16	...	18	...	20	...	23	25	27	29	31	33	35	37	39
11	..	5	..	7	...	11	...	14	...	18	...	20	...	24	...	27	...	30	...	33	35	37	39	41	43	45	48	50
17	..	6	..	11	...	16	...	21	...	26	...	31	...	36	...	40	...	44	...	48	52	56	60	64	68	71	75	78
23	..	8	..	15	...	22	...	29	...	36	...	43	...	49	...	55	...	61	...	67	72	77	82	87	92	96	101	105
35	..	12	..	23	...	34	...	45	...	55	...	65	...	74	...	83	...	92	...	101	110	118	125	133	140	147	153	159
50	..	17	..	32	...	48	...	64	...	78	...	92	...	106	...	119	...	131	...	145	157	168	...	...	...	...	...	...
74	..	25	..	49	...	72	...	95	...	116	...	136	...	156	...	...	...	...	...	...	...	...	...	...	...	...	...	...
102	..	33	..	65	...	97	...	129	...	160	...	...	...	...	...	...	...	...	...	...	...	...	...	...	...	...	...	...

maximum, to slightly less than 1 in. for the largest machine, and to about ⅛ in. for the smallest.

Horizontal shapers are commonly provided with powered table feeds ranging from about 0.010 in. per stroke (for a machine with a 6-in. maximum stroke) to 0.200 in. per stroke (for a machine with a 36-in. maximum stroke). Over the same range of machine sizes, vertical power feeds on the tool head will range from about 0.005 to 0.100 in. per stroke.

Slotters and vertical shapers are very similar and are also much like the horizontal shaper except that the ram operates vertically, rather than horizontally, cutting on the downstroke. The slotter, as the name implies, was first developed for cutting slots or keyways. The vertical shaper is usually a much smaller version of this type of machine and was developed for toolroom work. Slotters may have ram strokes up to 72 in. long. Most vertical shapers have strokes of 6 to 12 in.

In these vertical machines, since the ram must be pulled against the force of gravity on its upward stroke, a counterweight is added to equalize the power requirements on the up and down strokes, and to enable a smoother action of the machine.

Most vertical shapers have means for adjusting the ram and its guides so that it can be set at an angle as great as 15° to the vertical. This permits the cutting of proper clearances in dies and similar work. Many slotters also have this ram adjustability.

Tables on vertical machines can be rotated, as well as moved longitudinally or transversely. With this much flexibility in direction of feed, a vertical machine can cut almost any type of groove, slot or keyway.

Vertical shaping machines have longitudinal and transverse power feeds ranging from about 0.002 to 0.100 in. per stroke for short-stroke machines, and up to 0.150 in. per stroke for a 36-in.-stroke machine. Rotary feeds usually range from 0.004 to 0.175 in. on a 20-in. circle.

Ram speeds of most shapers can be adjusted to provide incremental increases in surface speeds from about 5 to 300 sfm. Speeds are changed by positioning the range and speed levers. Typical shapers have four speeds available in each of four ranges; this permits adjustment so as to obtain 16 different speeds within the total speed range of a given machine. Cutting speed in surface feet per minute is a function both of length of stroke and of number of strokes per minute. This relation is shown quantitatively in Table 1.

Tool Capacity. Although most shaping is done with only one single-point tool, there are notable exceptions. For example, form tools are often used in shapers, for machining two or more surfaces simultaneously. In other applications, as in cutting closely spaced parallel grooves, a conventional box tool holder is mounted on the tool head, and two or three cutting tools are secured in the holder so that more than one cut can be made simultaneously. Seldom, however, are more than three single-point tools used, because this would exceed the power capacity of the machine.

Automatic Controls. Because shapers are seldom used for volume production, the degree of automation with which they are provided is generally less than that for other types of machines.

On the simplest type of shaper, the operator first sets controls for depth of cut, ram speed and stroke length, and then feeds the work sidewise into the tool by turning a handle that has a graduated dial; the work then is advanced into the tool at the end of each return stroke. Most shapers, however, are equipped with power feeds. Thus, a more common practice is to preset the controls for the desired feed per stroke. When the cut is finished, the operator stops the machine, returns the table to its starting position, resets the downfeed, and starts another cycle.

The degree of automation and process efficiency of shapers can be progressively increased by the addition of:

1 Power downfeed, operated either with or independently of the table feed
2 Various stops that control the end of a desired cycle
3 Complete controls that allow recycling according to a pre-established program
4 Automatic indexing devices for cutting slots or grooves according to an established spacing
5 Automatic duplicating equipment that guides the cutting tools by means of templates for shaping contours.

Workholding Devices

Shaper tables usually are provided with standard T-slots, which permit direct mounting of some workpieces by means of bolts, blocks, and clamp plates (Fig. 3a). However, most workpieces are placed in vises, which are secured to the table by T-bolt mounting. It is usually preferred that the direction of clamping in the vise be at right angles to the direction of tool travel. Clamping must be tight. If there is danger of marring the workpiece surfaces by clamping, shims made of soft metal (or, for more positive gripping, shims made of emery paper) can be used.

For workpieces that are too thin to be held firmly in a standard vise, a special clamping device having toe dogs and a stop may be used (Fig. 3b). In this arrangement, clamping forces are parallel with tool travel, the stop serving to prevent the workpiece from being forced out of the vise.

Outboard support by jacks is often utilized for obtaining rigidity in the shaping of irregular configurations such as angles (Fig. 3c).

In contouring and slotting operations, rugged vises (Fig. 3d) often must be used, both because workpieces usually are of irregular shape and because cutting forces are likely to vary during the operation. If special indexing fixtures are used, they must be designed for maximum rigidity.

Tool Heads

The principal components of a shaper tool-head assembly are illustrated in Fig. 4. The clapper box holds the tool rigidly on the forward (cutting) stroke and allows it freedom to tilt upward on the return stroke after force is removed from the tool face. Thus, on the return stroke only the weight of the tool bears on the work, which minimizes marring of the surface.

Another means of preventing the tool from marring the workpiece surface on the return stroke consists of keeping the tool in a vertical position and setting the clapper box at an angle away from the direction of feed. With this arrangement (view at right in Fig. 4), the tool will swing away from the work during the return stroke.

For applications where surface finish is so critical that tool drag against the work is unacceptable, devices are available that positively lift the tool clear of the work on the return stroke. Automatic tool lifters are always recommended when carbide cutting tools are used.

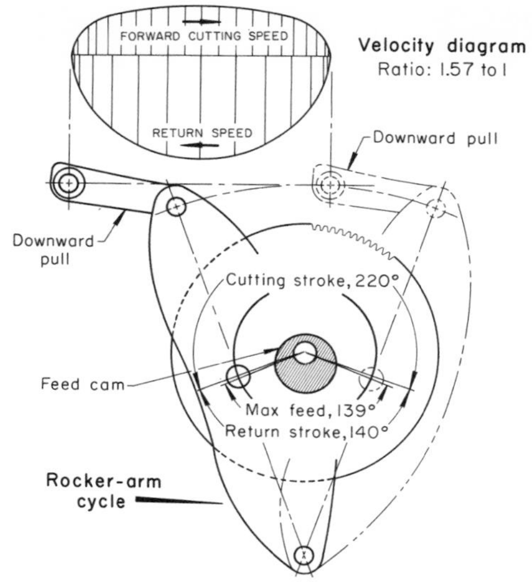

Fig. 2. Velocity diagram and rocker-arm cycle for a crank-driven horizontal shaper. See text for discussion.

Tool Material and Design

Cutting tools used for shaping may be made of high speed steel or carbide.

High speed steel tools are used for most shaping, mainly because:

1 Shaping generally is not a high-production operation, and thus the cutting speeds at which carbide functions best are not needed.
2 Shaping is an interrupted-cutting operation in which the cutting tool is subjected to impact forces at the beginning of each stroke, and hence one in which carbide is susceptible to chipping.

General-purpose types of high speed steel, such as M2 or T1, are satisfactory for most applications. For work made of highly abrasive materials (such as high-alloy tool steels or refractory metals), or for work of high hardness (more than about Rockwell C 35), one of the highly alloyed types of high speed steel, such as M6, M36 or T15, will result in longer tool life and usually in lower cost per unit volume of metal removed.

Carbide tools, of either the brazed or disposable-insert type, are used mainly: (*a*) in applications where maximum cutting speeds are being used and carbide has previously been satisfactory, (*b*) for making finishing cuts on workpieces such as die blocks (because carbide tools will result in better surface finish), and (*c*) for shaping of difficult-to-machine metals, such as heat-resisting alloys.

For any shaping operation in which carbide tools are used, two recommendations should be followed; (*a*) use a shock-resisting grade of carbide, and (*b*) use an automatic tool-lifter on the machine, to prevent the tool from dragging on the workpiece during the return stroke.

Design. Recommended designs of high speed steel tools for use on steel and cast iron in a variety of shaping operations are shown in Fig. 5. Figure 6 shows details of a carbide-tipped tool for use on heat-resisting alloys.

The use of lathe (single-point turning) tools for shaping is not recommended, because the angles used on lathe tools cause deflection and "digging in", ultimately resulting in chatter and dimensional inaccuracy. Grinding of shaper tools to a large nose radius is another common error. Tools having a nose radius of $\frac{1}{32}$ to $\frac{1}{16}$ in. usually perform best in shapers.

Ram Stroke and Clearance

It is common practice to set the ram stroke for a distance $\frac{5}{8}$ in. greater than the actual length of cut to be made, allowing about $\frac{1}{2}$ in. of this excess as clearance at the start of the stroke and $\frac{1}{8}$ in. at the end. Sometimes, however, allowing more than $\frac{1}{2}$ in. of clearance at the beginning of the stroke proves advantageous, as in the application described in the next example:

Example 96. Increase in Ram-Stroke Clearance for Improved Tool Life

A vertical shaper was used for cutting ten grooves $\frac{1}{4}$ in. wide, $\frac{3}{16}$ in. deep, and $1\frac{1}{2}$ in. long on the outer periphery of a cylindrical workpiece made of D2 tool steel at 270 Bhn (a difficult-to-machine metal).

Originally, the machine was adjusted for $\frac{1}{4}$-in. clearance at the beginning of the ram stroke. Life of the high speed steel cutting tools used was poor; resharpening often was required before one piece (ten grooves) could be completed. Varying speed from 40 to 10 sfm, and depth of cut from 0.025 to 0.005 in. per stroke, resulted in negligible improvement.

The problem was solved by increasing the clearance at the beginning of the stroke to $\frac{3}{4}$ in. With this change, one tool cut an average of ten pieces (100 grooves) before requiring resharpening. The improved tool life resulted largely because the increased clearance

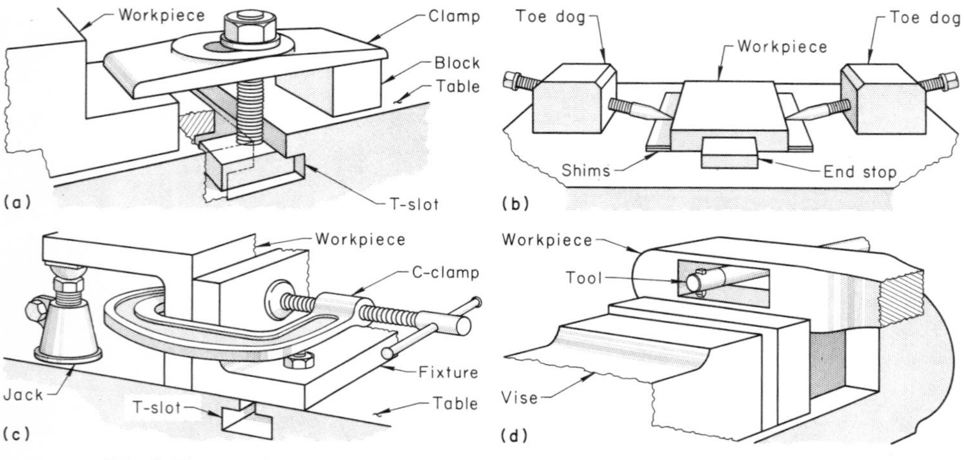

Fig. 3. Four working methods used in shaping. See text above for discussion.

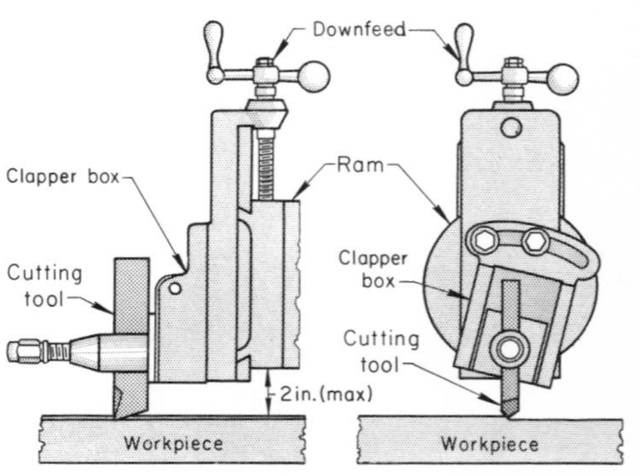

Side view (left) shows suggested maximum clearance between ram and workpiece. Front view (right) shows typical setting of clapper box for horizontal shaping.

Fig. 4. Shaper tool-head assembly, showing principal components

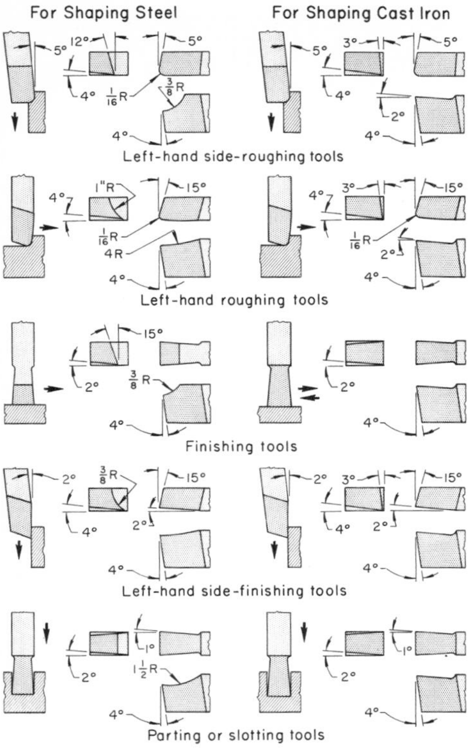

Fig. 5. Recommended designs of high speed steel tools for shaping steel and cast iron

gave the tool a "running start", so that it did not hesitate at the instant it contacted the work; however, the greater time allowed for the tool to cool also contributed, because no cutting fluid was used.

Clearance between ram and workpiece (see Fig. 4) should be kept to a minimum, not exceeding 2 in. whenever practicable. As the clearance between the front of the ram and the workpiece is increased, cutting action must be obtained either by lowering the tool post or by lengthening the cutting tool. In either case, rigidity is decreased as the distance increases, and chatter will occur, causing loss of accuracy and finish and a probable decrease in tool life.

Speed, Feed and Depth of Cut

Typical ram speeds used in rough and finish shaping are given in Table 2. As these data indicate, speeds are closely related to workpiece composition, microstructure and hardness, increasing or decreasing with the machinability of the work metal. (This relationship is further demonstrated in Examples 98 and 99.)

Feed per stroke in shaping also is influenced by the composition, microstructure and hardness of the work metal. However, ram speed, depth of cut, and required dimensional accuracy and finish also affect choice of feed.

Typical feed rates for shaping annealed carbon steel and gray iron are given in Table 3. These feed rates typify those used for roughing, to remove metal as fast as possible; note the relatively high metal removal rates.

Common practice in shaping is to make roughing (hogging) cuts at maximum feed but at slow speed, then to reverse this procedure for finishing cuts. Sometimes it is not practical to increase the speed for finishing, but lighter feeds are almost always used, as indicated in the following example:

Example 97. Feed-Rate Practice in Shaping Annealed 1045 Steel

A heavy-duty shaper with 24-in. maximum stroke was used to machine annealed 1045 steel.

For roughing, a feed rate of 0.030 in. per stroke was used with a speed of 23 strokes per minute and a 1-in. depth of cut.

For finishing, the speed was retained at 23 strokes per minute, but feed rate was reduced to 0.015 in. per stroke and depth of cut to 0.025 in.

By the above procedure, it was possible to retain flatness within 0.001 in. and to produce a finish of 20 to 30 micro-in. Properly ground tools are especially important in maintaining this accuracy and finish.

For almost all shaping operations, regardless of other conditions, there is a practical minimum feed rate. Feed rates that are too light do not allow the average tool to "bite" sufficiently, and will result in chatter. Feed rates less than 0.005 in. per stroke are seldom recommended.

Depth of cut usually is not less than about 0.015 in. Shallower cuts, like extremely light feeds, do not allow sufficient tool "bite", and result in chatter and glazing. Selection of depth of cut above this minimum is influenced by the following, singly or in combination:

Composition, microstructure and hardness of the workpiece metal
Amount of metal to be removed
Workpiece size
Workpiece configuration
Rigidity of the setup
Available power.

The workpiece configuration is often a factor affecting allowable depth of cut. For instance, a depth of cut as great as 1 in. is often used for machining a solid piece. For machining an intricately shaped workpiece, however, the maximum allowable depth of cut may be less than ⅛ in. because the forces for deeper cuts would deform the workpiece.

Rigidity of the setup and allowable depth of cut are directly related. Under conditions of insufficient rigidity, depth of cut must be reduced to avoid chatter.

Depths of cut employed at various speeds and feeds in shaping several metals are given in Tables 3, 4 and 5.

Cutting Fluids

A flood of cutting fluid is seldom used for shaping operations, because two of the three functions of cutting fluids (chip disposal and cooling) are not needed. In most operations, chips are thrown forward and seldom interfere with successive cutting strokes. (As chips begin to pile up on the table or fixtures, however, they should be brushed away by the operator. The use of compressed air for removal of chips is not recommended, because chips are likely to lodge in the shaper mechanism.) Because rate of metal removal in shaping is relatively low and the tool is seldom engaged in cutting more than about 60% of the time, cooling of tools and workpieces usually presents no problem.

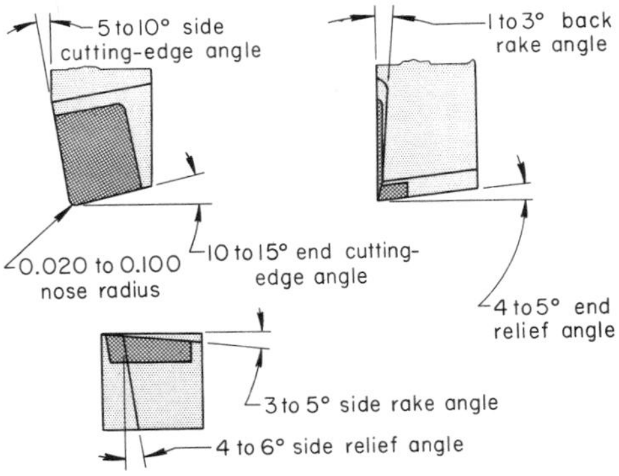

Fig. 6. Details of a carbide-tipped tool for shaping heat-resisting alloys

In many applications, however, the use of cutting fluids will result in improved dimensional accuracy, finish and tool life, by minimizing the adherence of work metal to the tool. When cutting fluids are used, the most common practice is to apply the undiluted fluid with a brush or swab. This practice was followed in Example 99, which describes an application in which a sulfur-free chlorinated oil was used as the cutting fluid in shaping heat-resisting alloys.

Sulfurized cutting oils are commonly used for steels. However, many nonferrous metals, such as copper-base alloys, are susceptible to staining from sulfurized oils; when a cutting fluid is needed for shaping these metals, kerosine with an addition of about 10% lard oil is recommended.

Flat Surfaces

Usually, shaping is selected as the method for machining flat surfaces when (*a*) required flatness is greater than can be obtained by other methods, (*b*) production quantity is too low to justify the cost of machines and tool-

Table 2. Typical Speeds Used in Shaping

Work metal	Speed, sfm Roughing	Speed, sfm Finishing
Aluminum	150	200
Brass and bronze ..	150	200
Gray iron	60	40 and 100(a)
Mild steel	50	35 and 80(a)
Tool steel	40	60
Heat-resisting alloys	10 to 15	20 to 30

(a) Lower speed is used for broad-nose finishing tools and higher speed for conventional or radius-nose tools.

Table 3. Typical Feeds, Depths of Cut, and Metal-Removal Rates for Shaping Steel and Gray Iron (a)

Feed, in. per stroke	Depth of cut, in.	Removal rate, cu in./min
1045 Steel (Annealed)		
At 21 cutting strokes per minute (about 44 sfm)		
0.062	0.187	3.3
0.075	0.187	4.0
0.050	0.250	3.5
At 15 cutting strokes per minute (about 32 sfm)		
0.075	0.250	3.8
Gray Iron		
At 30 cutting strokes per minute (about 65 sfm)		
0.037	0.500	7.5
0.050	0.500	10.0
0.025	0.750	7.6
0.037	0.750	11.3

(a) Data are based on use of a 13½-in. stroke on a 5-hp shaper having a maximum stroke length of 16 in.

Table 4. Shaping of W2 and D2 Tool Steel Die Sections (Example 98)

Tool Details for Both Steels	
Tool material	M3 high speed steel
Tool size	½ by ½ by 4 in.
Type of tool holder	Straight-shank (a)
Tool angles:	
Back rake	10°
Normal side rake	10°
End relief (on tool bit)	20°
Effective end relief (in holder) (a)	7°
Normal side relief	25°
End cutting edge	50°
Side cutting edge	30° (left-hand)
Nose radius	1/16 in.
Machining Conditions for W2(b)	
Ram speed, roughing and finishing	59 sfm
Feed, roughing	0.020 in. per stroke
Feed, finishing	0.010 in. per stroke
Depth of each cut, roughing	0.250 in.
Depth of cut, finishing	0.060 in.
Length of cut, rough and finish	8.000 in.
Cutting fluid	None
Metal-removal rate:	
Roughing	2.5 cu in. per min
Finishing	0.3 cu in. per min
Machining time per cut, roughing	2.3 min
Machining time per cut, finishing	4.4 min
Machining Conditions for D2(b)	
Ram speed, roughing and finishing	41 sfm
Feed, rough and finish	0.010 in. per stroke
Depth of each cut, roughing	0.250 in.
Depth of cut, finishing	0.060 in.
Length of cut, rough and finish	7.000 in.
Cutting fluid	None
Metal-removal rate:	
Roughing	0.77 cu in. per min
Finishing	0.18 cu in. per min
Machining time per cut:	
Roughing	6.1 min
Finishing	5.7 min

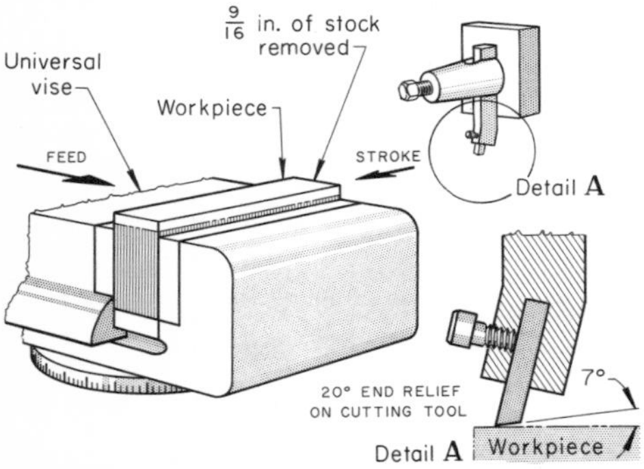

(a) Tool-holder angle was 13°. (b) Two roughing cuts, one finishing cut.

ing for milling or broaching, or (*c*) a few pieces are needed in an emergency and no production setup is available.

Dimensional Control. When workpieces such as dies, molds and fixtures must be matched, thus requiring the highest possible degree of flatness, shapers are preferred. Under good shop conditions (capable operator, machine in good repair, rigid setup), a heavy-duty shaper can machine a surface 18 in. square to a flatness within 0.001 in., and can hold variation in flatness among identical parts within 0.002 in. Under best conditions of control, including a highly skilled operator, flatness of an 18-in.-square surface can be held to within about 0.0005 in.

When shaping workpieces that are relatively thin compared with their length and width (for instance, a ½-in.-thick plate having 100 sq in. per side), warping is often a problem. If the two sides are flat and parallel, warping is best avoided by successively removing equal amounts of stock from the two sides, in both roughing and finishing; about 0.010 to 0.015 in. of material per side is left for the finishing cuts.

For thin workpieces from which all of the stock must be removed from one side, best practice is to rough machine to within about 0.015 in. of finished size, stress relieve, and then finish machine.

Examples. Tool details, techniques and operating conditions in applications involving the shaping of flat surfaces are discussed in the two examples that follow.

Example 98. W2 and D2 Tool Steel Die Sections (Table 4)

A heavy-duty 24-in. machine with 10-hp drive was used for rough and finish shaping of die sections made either of W2 hot rolled bar (202 Bhn max) or of D2 tool steel (255 Bhn). Before shaping, each section made of W2 measured 2½ by 6 by 8 in. and weighed 34 lb; each D2 section measured 2¼ by 6 by 7 in. and weighed 26.7 lb. Shaping reduced the 6-in. dimension on sections of both steels to 5 7/16 in., and the weight to 30.7 and 24.2 lb, respectively for the W2 and D2 sections. Tool details and machining conditions are listed in Table 4.

Each workpiece was clamped in the shaper vise with the longest dimension parallel to the ram stroke, as shown in the sketch contained in Table 4, after which it was machined with two ¼-in. roughing cuts and a 1/16-in. finishing cut. Tools were hand sharpened to the configuration detailed in Table 4.

A comparison of the data in Table 4 for the preceding example demonstrates the influence of machinability of workpiece metal on machining conditions employed and results obtained. For both the W2 and the D2 die sections, tools of the same design were used in identical machines for removing the same amounts of metal. For the more difficult-to-machine D2, however, speed had to be reduced by about 30% and feed by 50%, and metal removal rate in roughing (0.250-in. depth of cut) was only about one third that for W2.

Another group of difficult-to-machine materials are the nickel-base and cobalt-base heat-resisting alloys. As shown in Table 5, which accompanies the next example, even for shallower cuts, ram speed used in shaping these alloys must be much slower than that used for the highly alloyed D2 tool steel in Example 98.

Example 99. Shaping Hastelloy X, René 41 and HS-25 Alloys (Table 5)

Shaping, using high speed steel tools, proved to be an acceptable method for removing 0.065 to 0.130 in. of metal from between tabs on several types of aircraft fittings. These parts were made of three different heat-resisting alloys: Hastelloy X, at Rockwell C 20; René 41, at Rockwell C 28; and HS-25, at Rockwell C 25. Tool details and machining conditions for this application are listed in Table 5.

External or Internal Contours

The use of a shaper for cutting external or internal contours is usually limited to unit or low production. When identical workpieces must be produced in large quantities, cost per piece can be greatly reduced by milling or broaching these contours.

However, for cutting internal contours on workpieces like the one shown in Fig. 7, shaping is often the most satisfactory and economical method for producing up to medium quantities. The contour in this part could be produced in one cut with a broach, but a large and expensive machine would be required. In addition, a broach of this size would cost two thousand dollars or more. Such an investment could be justified only if the parts were to be produced in large quantities. In contour cutting of the workpiece shown in Fig. 7, the operation was manually controlled. However, contours can be cut by means of automatic duplicating equipment (Fig. 8), thus allowing repetitive production by operators with less skill than is necessary for manual control.

Table 5. Shaping of Heat-Resisting Alloys (Example 99)

(Hastelloy X, René 41 and HS-25)

Tool Details(a)	
Tool material	M30 or M34 high speed steel
Tool angles:	
Back rake	0° to 3°
Side rake	8°
End and side relief	4° to 6°
Nose radius	0.045 to 0.090 in.
Machining Conditions	
Ram speed	7 to 13 sfm
Feed, roughing	0.020 to 0.030 in. per stroke
Feed, finishing	0.010 to 0.015 in. per stroke
Depth of cut, roughing	0.050 to 0.100 in.
Depth of cut, finishing	0.015 to 0.030 in.
Cutting fluid	Sulfur-free chlorinated oil(b)

(a) Honing of cutting edges proved beneficial. Best cutting efficiency was obtained by keeping edge wear below 0.010-in. wear land. (b) Applied by a brush.

Automatic duplicating makes use of a template followed by a tracer that controls and directs the cutting path of the tool. Setup time is short, and tooling cost is low. The following example describes a typical application:

Example 100. Contour Shaping With Automatic Control (Fig. 9)

Figure 9 shows the setup used on a 36-in. shaper equipped with template control, for machining a variety of configurations in blanks made of pre-heat-treated (Rockwell C 25 to 30) 0.60% C steel that were later sawed to various lengths for use as bits for woodworking tools. These blanks were from 6 to 8 in. wide, and 20 to 30 in. long in the direction of the shaper-cut grooves.

The shaper was operated at 11 to 17 strokes per minute (45 to 70 sfm). Length of stroke varied from 24 in., for blanks 20 in. long, to 34 in., for the 30-in.-long blanks. Cutting tools were ground from ½-in.-square bars of high speed steel.

Templates were cut to the desired shape from sheet steel and placed in the template holder as shown in Fig. 9. The tool slide was set to cut ⅛ to 3/16 in. deep, with the follower stylus at the bottom of one of the grooves in the template. During roughing, the table was fed crosswise with a coarse feed (up to 0.030

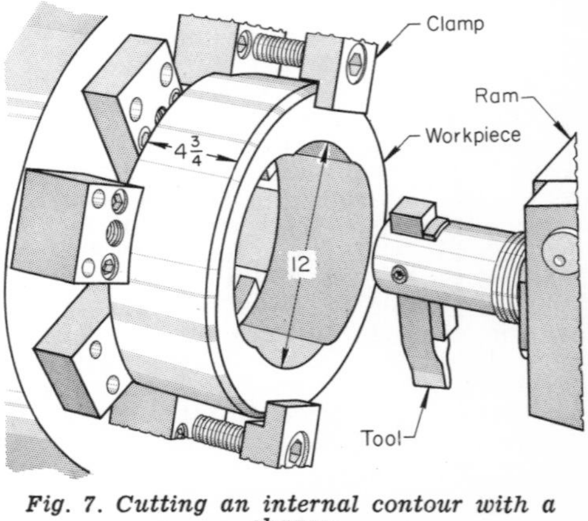

Fig. 7. Cutting an internal contour with a shaper

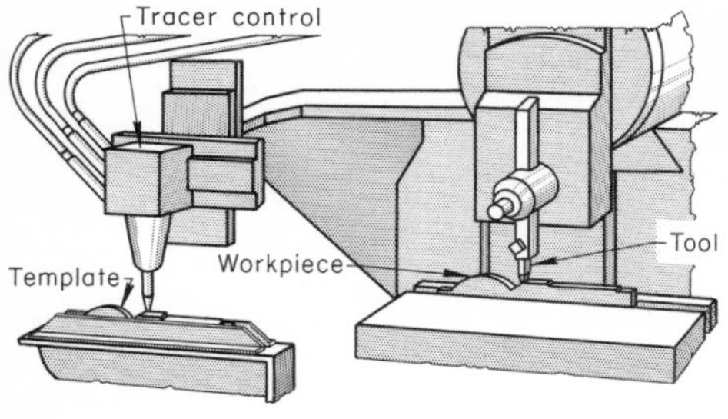

Fig. 8. Use of duplicating equipment on a shaper for cutting external contour of a trimming die

in. per stroke), to remove metal as rapidly as possible. For the final pass, crossfeed was automatically controlled to 0.005 in. per stroke. Workpieces were completed in a total of four passes — three roughing and one finishing. No cutting fluid was used.

Template-controlled shaping was the most economical method of machining these tool blanks, because no more than twelve of any given configuration were produced as a lot, and the shape cut could be altered simply by making a new template. These workpieces could have been produced by milling, but a cutter costing from $300 to $500 would have been required for each configuration — an expenditure unwarranted by the low quantity.

Form Cutting

In most form cutting on a shaper, the workpiece remains stationary while the form tool is advanced into the work by increasing the downfeed on each stroke. A typical form-cutting operation, that of cutting teeth in racks for emergency use, in unit or low-production quantities, is described in the following example:

Example 101. Form Cutting Heat Treated Tool Steel Racks (Fig. 10)

A 10-hp shaper having a 36-in. maximum stroke was used to form-cut teeth in 72-in.-long arbor-press racks made of 0.50% C, low-alloy tool steel and heat treated to a hardness of 300 to 320 Bhn. The setup is shown in Fig. 10.

The shaper was operated with an 8-in. stroke and at 41 strokes per minute (ram speed, 50 sfm). The form tool, which was ground from 1-in.-square high speed steel, was downfed at 0.020 in. per stroke. The workpiece was manually indexed and located for each succeeding tooth space with the aid of crossfeed, rapid-traverse and micrometer dials that were standard equipment on the shaper used. No cutting fluid was used.

Grooves, Slots and Keyways

Vertical machines usually are used in preference to horizontal shapers for cutting external or internal grooves.

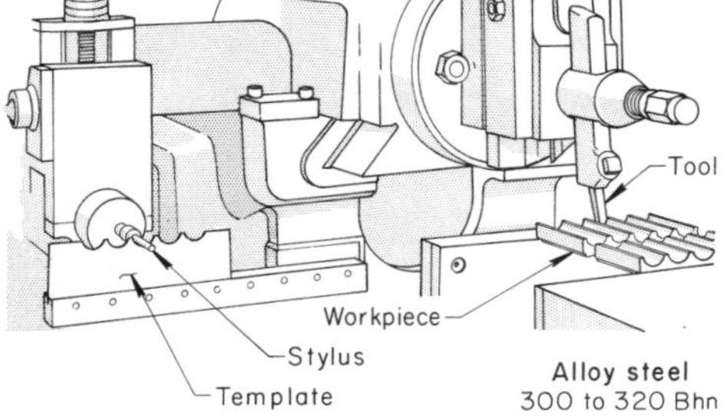

Fig. 9. Shaping woodworking-tool blanks by means of automatic template-follower control (Example 100)

This is particularly true when two or more grooves must be kept in a specific relationship to each other, because indexing for cutting in a vertical plane is usually simpler.

External grooves can be machined on shapers to about the same degree of dimensional accuracy as by milling. Holding close dimensions on external grooves cut on a shaper depends largely on the accuracy of the indexing fixture, because there is seldom any reason why rigid tools and tool mountings cannot be used. On most parts, two or more grooves can be held within 0.002 in. in relationship to each other.

Shapers are used for cutting external grooves when quantities are too low to justify the cost of tooling up for milling, or when workpiece configuration does not permit the use of a milling cutter. As an example of the latter

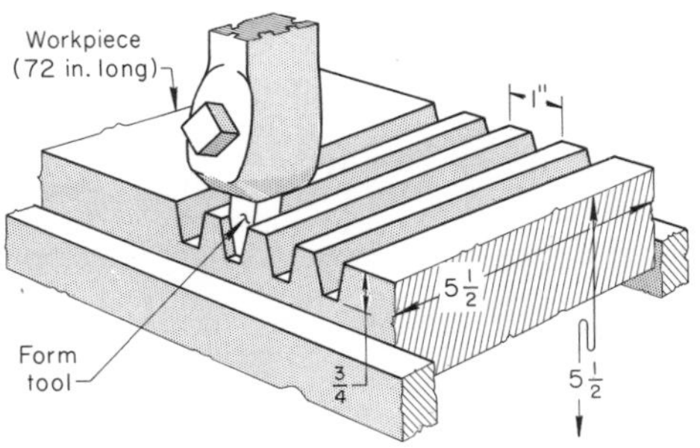

Fig. 10. Form shaping of teeth in arbor-press racks (Example 101)

condition, it is often required to cut grooves that terminate adjacent to a flange or other obstruction, thus precluding the use of a rotating cutter. By means of a shaper, it is usually possible to cut grooves or slots to within about ¼ in. of an enlarged section.

When it is feasible to use milling, and when production quantities warrant its use, external grooves are seldom cut by a shaper, because milling costs less under these conditions.

Internal grooves are machined on a shaper for the same reasons as noted above for external grooves — namely, low quantity and restrictive configuration. For internal grooves, however, broaching is the alternative process.

Shaping is generally used for cutting internal grooves or slots in tooling components such as dies for hot extrusion, not only because quantities usually are too low to warrant the cost of tooling for broaching, but also because the production of slots that are several times as deep as they are wide would be impractical for broaching.

The following example describes an application in which shaping was the only practical method for producing the required configuration:

Example 102. Deep, Narrow Slots in Extrusion Dies (Fig. 11)

After being drilled to permit the entry of a shaper tool, extrusion dies made of 0.60% C, alloy tool steel (hardness, 250 to 300 Bhn) were machined on a shaper to produce an internal configuration terminating in a deep narrow slot. The workpiece and machining setup are shown in Fig. 11.

A 15-hp shaper having a 36-in. maximum stroke was used, in conjunction with an extension tool holder long enough to reach through the 10-in.-thick die. Length of the cutting stroke was 12 in. Speeds ranged from 11 to 17 sfm, feeds from 0.010 to 0.020 in. per stroke, and depths of cut from 0.010 to 0.030 in. for the several tools used for machining the internal configuration. These values are less than normal, but accuracy was of the utmost importance in this application.

All surfaces were machined to dimensional accuracy within 0.003 in. and to a finish of 30 micro-in. max. The entire operation was manually controlled. Lard oil applied with a brush was used for best cutting conditions.

Hardness of the work material also can determine whether shaping or broaching is used for cutting intricately shaped internal grooves in dies. Heat treated tool steels as hard as Rockwell C 46 are commonly machined on a shaper, whereas broaching a steel of this hardness would be risky, because of the likelihood of broach breakage. Shaping also is virtually the only process by which grooves can be cut to about ¼ in. of the end of a blind hole.

The length of internal slots or grooves in relationship to their cross-sectional dimensions limits the use of a shaper. By using holders that extend the cutting tool out from the ram head (see Fig. 11), it is possible to remove metal from holes as small as about 1 in. in initial cross section. However, as the ratio of length to diameter (or to other cross sectional dimension) exceeds about 4 to 1, the decrease in accuracy is likely to become intolerable.

Gear Shaping

Gear shaping is more complex than general-purpose shaping. About the only thing the two operations have in common is reciprocating motion. Gear shaping is a form-generating operation; ordinary shaping is not. A gear shaping cutter is a conjugate of the workpiece and meshes with it; a shaping cutter is a single-point tool. Gear shaping usually requires motion of both cutter and work during the cut; shaping does not.

Other examples of shaping in this volume: Aluminum — Ex. 882; magnesium — Ex. 980.

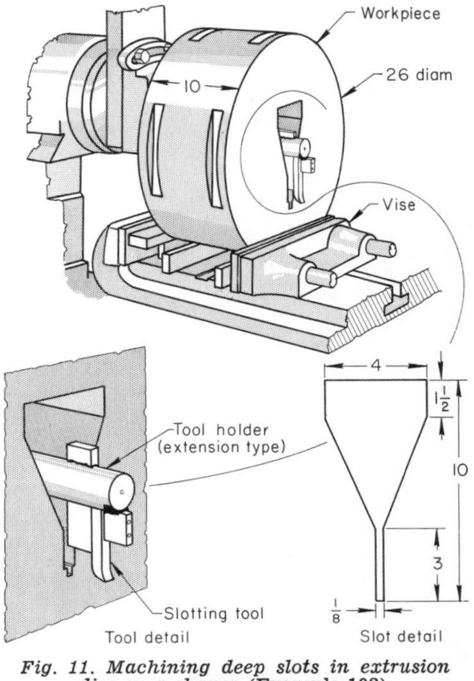

Fig. 11. Machining deep slots in extrusion dies on a shaper (Example 102)

Broaching

*By the ASM Committee on Broaching**

BROACHING is a machining process in which a cutting tool that has multiple transverse cutting edges is pushed or pulled through a hole or over a surface to remove metal by axial cutting. Because broaches are multitoothed cutting tools produced to close tolerances, they are expensive; consequently, the process usually is employed only for high production. Some part configurations, however, are practical to produce only by broaching; for parts of this type, the broaching of low production quantities may be warranted. Because several edges of a broach are cutting at once, forces are much greater than in other machining methods, and broaching is rated as the most severe of all machining operations.

Usually, a broach is a tapered bar into which teeth have been cut so as to produce a desired contour in a workpiece by a single pass of the tool. A typical broach for cutting a round hole is shown schematically in Fig. 1. Note that it has three basic sections of cutting teeth: roughing teeth, intermediate (semifinishing) teeth, and finishing teeth. The broach tapers from the first roughing tooth to the last intermediate tooth, the outside diameter of each tooth being slightly larger than the tooth that precedes it. Usually, the diametral differences of the roughing teeth are greater than for the intermediate teeth. Ordinarily, all finishing teeth are of the same diameter.

A workpiece to be internally broached must be provided with a starting hole through which the broach is pulled or pushed. This hole is just large enough to permit the front pilot section of the broach to enter freely. As the broach progresses through the part, cutting commences gradually, and as each succeeding tooth engages the work, it removes a small amount of metal. If the first finishing tooth becomes dull or nicked, the work metal is apt to be torn.

A broach is normally sharpened by grinding the cutting face. Each tool incorporates a backoff or relief angle (usually 1½°, except for finishing, where it may be as small as ¼°). Tooth diameter is changed only slightly when the broach is sharpened on the face, because only a small amount of metal is removed. Because the first finishing tooth does the work, only this tooth is ground at resharpening. As this tooth is decreased in size, the next tooth does the finish cutting; this continues until all finishing teeth have been reground to a point at which size tolerance can no longer be held.

Applicability

Broaching may be employed in a wide range of applications and, where applicable, offers several advantages over other machining processes. Because both roughing and finishing can be done in a single pass of the broach, broaching is rapid and efficient. Moreover, because close tolerances can be held and smooth surfaces provided, subsequent operations are seldom required. Almost any irregular shape can be broached if it is regular in the direction of broach travel. Large surfaces can be broached flat in one pass.

For many applications, broaching is selected because it is cheaper or faster, even though acceptable results could be obtained by other machining methods such as milling, boring, shaping or reaming (see the section in this article on Broaching vs Alternative Processes). For other applications, the required configuration is such that broaching is the only practicable method — for example, for fir-tree or dovetail slots in turbine wheels. Practice used for machining dovetail slots is described in the example that follows (also see Examples 117, 118 and 119, which describe broaching of similar configurations).

Example 103. Broaching of Dovetail Slots in a Compressor Wheel (Fig. 2)

The dovetail configuration shown in Fig. 2 was one of 33 slots broached in the periphery of a compressor wheel. The wheel, shown in section in Fig. 2, was made of 9310 steel (AMS 6260), Rockwell C 26 to 32.

Wheels were broached in a 15-ton machine with a 72-in. stroke; the broach was pulled through at 112 in. per min. Cutting fluid was a broaching oil having a viscosity of 155 SUS at 100 F, 2% fat content, 0.80% active sulfur, and 2.1% chlorine. The broach (T15 high speed steel, hardened to Rockwell C 66 to 68) was made up of nine sections — eight roughing sections for a total length of 49 in., and one 5-in.-long finishing section with 13 teeth. The first four teeth in the finishing section sized the throat area and the angle, the next four formed the bottom of the slot, and the last five sized and blended the radius with the angle and the bottom of the slot.

In general, the roughing section of the broach presented little or no difficulty, but the finishing section required close control, because dimensions of the finished shape had to be held to close tolerances. Broaches had an average life of 14.5 pieces (478 slots) per grind and five regrinds per tool. Average broach cost per piece, including regrinds and repair, was $17.31.

The limitations of broaching stem from the fundamental characteristics of the process. Except that it may be rotated (which permits broaching of helical teeth, either internal or external, on gear blanks), a broach always moves forward, and in a straight line. Consequently, all elements of broached surfaces must be parallel to the axis of travel. It is impossible to broach the entire surface of a tapered hole. A blind hole can be broached, but a recess must be provided larger in diameter than the broach, and deep enough to permit full travel of the broach. A series of push broaches is usually used for a blind hole. The techniques employed in the broaching of one such blind hole are described in the following example, which is another application where broaching is the only practical machining method.

Example 104. Broaching a Blind Hole in a Propeller Hub (Fig. 3)

Figure 3 shows an aircraft propeller blade that required an internal spline in the hub for pitch control. These propeller blades, fab-

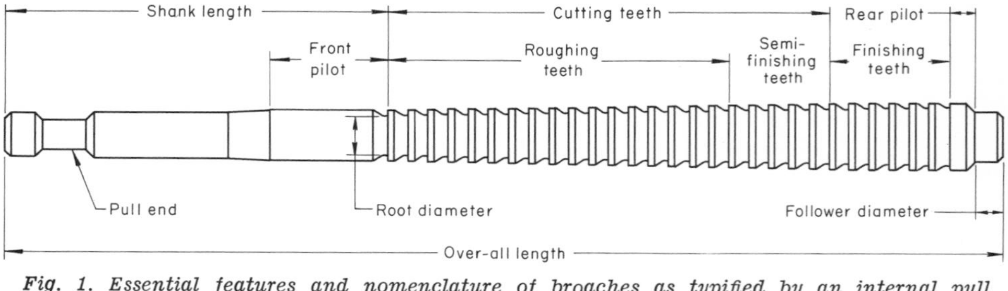

Fig. 1. Essential features and nomenclature of broaches as typified by an internal pull broach for cutting round holes

*T. A. FRISCHMAN, *Chairman*, Factory Manager, Eaton Axle Div., Eaton Yale & Towne, Inc.; CARL ANDERSON, Chief Tool Engineer, Atwood Vacuum Machine Co.; R. L. BEARSS, Manager, Manufacturing Engineering, Power Train Group, Chrysler Corp.

WILLIAM CAVALCANTI, Tool Engineer, Delco Products Rochester Operations, General Motors Corp.; GEORGE COMBS, Chief Industrial Engineer, Gardner-Denver Co.; J. J. DIPONIO, Manager, Manufacturing and Plant Engineering Office, Transmission and Chassis Div., Ford Motor Co.; R. L. HALEY, Mechanical Engineer, Memphis Works, International Harvester Co.; RONALD C. LESPERANCE, Engineering Dept., Detroit Broach & Machine Co.

FRANK W. MARTIN, Small Aircraft Engine Dept., General Electric Co.; W. P. MCDONALD, Engineering Supervisor, Special Machine Div., Cincinnati Milling Machine Co.; J. F. MONICAL, Supervisor, Tool Engineer, Aircraft Engine Operations, Allison Div., General Motors Corp.; JOSEPH A. PSENKA, Chief Field Engineer, Broach Div., National Broach & Machine Co.; P. F. ROSSBACH, Consultant, Eaton Axle Div., Eaton Yale & Towne, Inc.

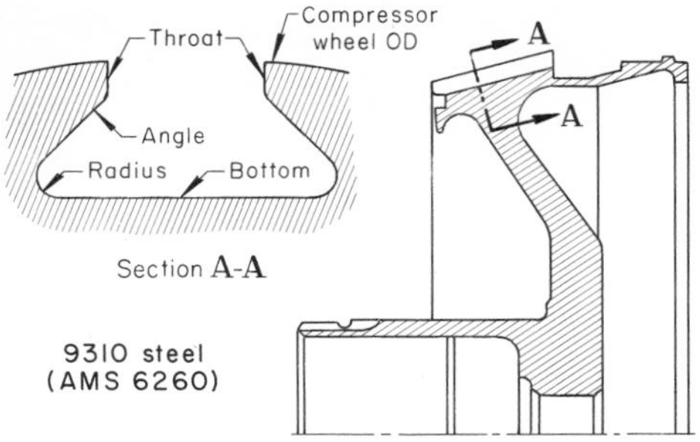

Fig. 2. Dovetail form broached in a compressor wheel (Example 103)

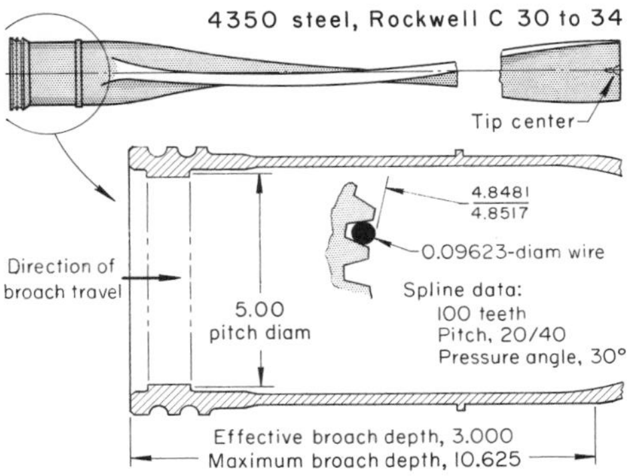

Broaches used for roughing, semifinishing and finishing were all of M2 high speed steel with a hardness of Rockwell C 63 to 64, and were 11⅛ in. in over-all length. All broaches had 5⁄16-in. pitch, ⅛-in. depth of flute, 3⁄32-in. tooth land, 15° face angle, and 2° cutting-relief back-off angle. Total tooth load of the roughing broach was 0.0062 in.; that of semifinishing and finishing broaches, 0.0099 in. each.

Fig. 3. Broaching a blind hole in a propeller hub (Example 104)

ricated from two pieces that were then welded together, were 77 in. long over-all and, as finished, weighed approximately 104 lb. The hub, a 4350 steel forging that weighed about 600 lb as forged, was rough machined before the camber sheet (the thin sheet-metal section) was welded in place. The assembly was then heat treated to Rockwell C 30 to 34 before being finish machined.

Because extreme accuracy was required in machining, the outside diameter of the hub was ground, piloting on the inside diameter. A tip center was incorporated in the blade end (see Fig. 3), and in all subsequent machining, the tip center and the ground outside of the hub were used as locating or chucking members to minimize eccentricity. Broaching the internal spline was a blind operation further complicated by the requirement that the spline be concentric with the outside diameter within 0.004 in. TIR.

Broaching was done in a special horizontal broaching machine capable of holding four broaches, although only three (one roughing, one semifinishing, and one finishing) were required for the operation. A through hole would have permitted incorporating these into one broach. The broaching machine held the broaches on a cross slide that moved; the workpiece was held rigid. Broaching speed was 4.25 ft per min; ram pressure was 600 lb. Production rate was 3.42 pieces per hour (17.5 min per piece).

Oil passages in the broaches permitted oil to flow through to assist in chip removal. Although the oil was not under enough pressure to cause it to jet from the holes, the pressure was sufficient to force oil from all of the holes in sufficient quantity to wash away the chips.

On external surfaces, it is impossible to broach to a shoulder that is perpendicular to the direction of broach movement. If the shoulder is parallel to the motion, however, broaching to the shoulder *is* possible, and often done.

It is also impractical to change the direction of travel of the broach (except for a spiral twist). Thus, surfaces having curves that lie in two or more planes cannot be broached in a single operation, although such surfaces are often machined by multiple broaching.

Because of the length of stroke and machine tonnage that would be required, broaching is seldom recommended for the removal of large amounts of metal. Where heavy stock must be removed, it generally is better

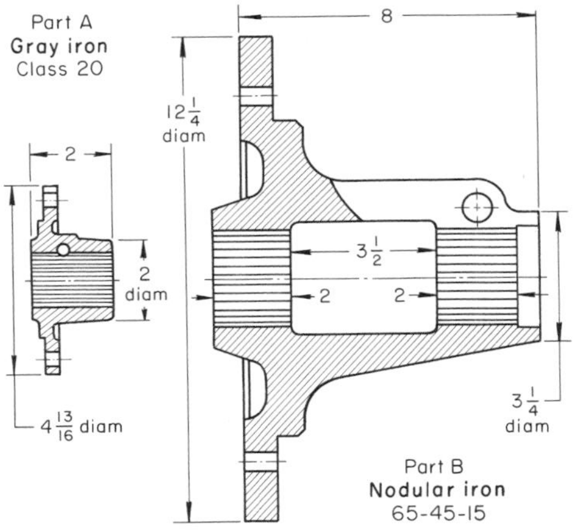

Item	Part A	Part B
Spline Data		
Number of involute teeth ..	21	19
Pressure angle	30°	30°
Pitch diameter, in.	1.3125	2.3750
Base diameter, in.	1.1367	2.0586
Circular tooth thickness, in.	0.1010	0.1995
Broach Details(a)		
Hardness, Rockwell C	64.5 to 66	65 to 66
Length, in.	26	57
Diameter, in.	1.3770	2.5009
Number of teeth	40	63
Size increase per tooth, in..	0.00397	0.00458
Broaching Conditions(b)		
Setup time, min	20	30
Production, pieces per hr ...	193	63
Tolerance required, in.	1.3770/ 1.3750	2.5009/ 2.4991
Number of parts per grind(c)	500	400
Tool life, number of regrinds	10	15

(a) Broaches used for both parts were pull broaches made of M2 high speed steel. (b) Parts were held singly during broaching; cutting fluid was an extreme-pressure cutting oil, chlorinated but having no active sulfur, with a viscosity of 160 SUS at 100 F. (c) Tools were reground when finish (80 micro-in. required) and size could no longer be maintained; regrinding took 2 hr, at $3.50 per hour. Downtime for changing tools was 10 min, for both parts.

Fig. 4. Parts of considerably different size in which internal splines were broached (Example 105)

to use a preliminary roughing operation other than broaching or to use two or more roughing broaching passes.

Where size is concerned, the size of the broach required, rather than the size of the workpiece, determines the applicability of the process. Broaching a hole 6 in. in diameter is commonplace. For a hole 12 in. in diameter, a much heavier broach is needed, and a much larger machine is required. Broaching of holes larger than 12 in. in diameter is seldom practical because of the size and cost of the broach.

The size of the workpiece has little influence on broaching conditions, provided the broach sections are similar in shape, workpiece sizes are in a range easily handled, and the materials are comparable in machinability. However, workpiece size does affect production rate per hour, as shown in the following example:

Example 105. Effect of Size in Broaching Similar Configurations (Fig. 4)

Figure 4 shows two machine components made of cast iron and having broached internal splines. Each spline is 2 in. long; the larger part has two splines with pitch diameters of 2.5009 in., and the smaller part has one spline with pitch diameter of 1.3770 in. Both parts were broached in a machine with a 56-in. stroke. Other pertinent processing details for each part are compared in the table accompanying Fig. 4.

Successful broaching is characterized by a close interdependence of all conditions of the process. The following example describes the revisions made to meet requirements at maximum efficiency of processing:

Example 106. Broaching of Internal Cams to Precise Dimensions (Fig. 5)

Figure 5 shows a cam spline produced from seamless tubing of modified 5060 steel that was hardened to Rockwell C 25 to 35 before being broached. This part required a high degree of accuracy in its manufacture; for example, the inside was required to be concentric with the outside within 0.002 in. TIR. In broaching, three conditions had to be met: (*a*) an axial line originating at point A had to be perpendicular to the face of the part within 0.003 in.; (*b*) within itself, each cam face had to be flat, axially, within 0.0005 in.; and (*c*) the surface roughness of each cam face could not exceed 130 micro-in. Three process or material revisions were required to bring this broaching operation to maximum efficiency, including a change in speed.

Broaching initially with a ram speed of 30 ft per min resulted in a production of approximately 550 pieces before surface roughness

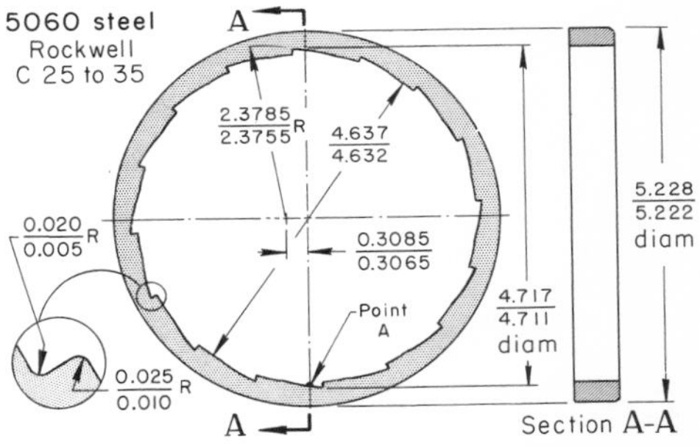

Workpiece Dimensions Before Machining

Outside diameter	5.228/5.222 in.
Inside diameter	4.576/4.582 in.
Thickness	0.605/0.603 in. (a)

Processing Details

Broaching machine(b)	30-ton vertical (pull-down type, 66-in. stroke)
Broach(c)	Pull type, 58 in. long, 4.636 in. in diameter; M3 (cl 2) high speed steel surface treated to Rockwell C 65 to 67
Fixture(d)	Diaphragm chuck, 2 pcs stacked
Ram speed	20 ft per min
Cutting fluid	High-fat, chlorinated, sulfurized mineral oil
Cycle time	0.42 min
Production rate	285 pieces per hour
Number of pieces per grind (avg)	1300(e)
Number of grinds per broach (avg)	24(f)

(a) Parallel within 0.0005 in. (b) Cost, installed, $38,235. (c) Cost, each, $3000. (d) Cost, $4000; includes diaphragm chuck, automatic shuttle tray, and hydraulic clamping.

(e) Broaches were reground when finish of 130 micro-in. could not be maintained. Regrind time was 6 hr. (f) Average number of pieces broached during total life of tool, 32,500.

Fig. 5. Cam spline that was broached as described in the tabulation above (Example 106)

exceeded the allowable 130 micro-in. Reducing the ram speed to 20 ft per min resulted in an increase to 685 pieces before regrinding was necessary. Changing the cutting fluid from a blend of sulfurized cutting oils to a special proprietary high-fat broaching oil increased average tool life to 1000 pieces per grind. The final improvement was to revise the broach material from M2 to M3 (class 2) high speed steel. This increased the broach life to 1300 pieces per grind — nearly 2½ times that obtained originally.

Broach details and pertinent processing data are given in the table accompanying Fig. 5.

For the production of die cavities, where the shape permits and where several similar cavities are required, broaching can provide a substantial saving. In the usual toolroom method of die production, labor costs per die are approximately the same whether one cavity or ten cavities are produced. In broaching, the major cost is that of the broach or broaches required, and this cost is reduced in proportion to the number of cavities produced. The five broaches required to produce each complete cavity in Example 107 cost $6400. If ten cavities had been required, the amortized cost of the broaches would have been $640. If, over the life of the part, 100 cavities had been required, the amortized broach cost would have been only $64 per cavity — considerably less than the cost per cavity of producing the cavities in a toolroom by the usual machining methods.

Example 107. Blanking Dies Broached in Five Operations (Fig. 6)

Figure 6 illustrates one cavity of a multiple-cavity blanking die made of tool steel and used to produce an intricate stamping for a cash register. For this die, five different broaches were required. A hole 1.152/1.150 in. in diameter was drilled through the die to permit starting the first broach. The progressive removal of metal by the five broaching operations is shown in Fig. 6.

Broaching Machines

In general, there are two types of broaching machines, horizontal and vertical, based on the direction of broach travel.

Horizontal machines are general-purpose machines and may be used for high or low production quantities. For machines incorporating extremely long strokes (more than about 80 in.), horizontal movement is the most practical.

Broaches of large girth (for example, a broach to cut the teeth of an internal gear with a 14-in. pitch diameter) would be excessively heavy and would require a more expensive machine for vertical than for horizontal operation. Therefore, a horizontal machine with accessories to assist in supporting the weight of the broach would be more practical. In addition, smaller work-handling equipment is required for lifting a heavy broach into position in a horizontal machine than in a vertical machine. Horizontal machines for internal broaching are further classified as "pull" or "push" machines, depending on how force is applied to the broach. Cutting fluid supply requires more attention in horizontal broaching:

Example 108. Horizontal Machine for Broaching Splines in a Long Tube

In a horizontal machine in one plant, a 3-in.-long internal spline with a 2¾-in.-pitch diameter was broached at one end of a long tubular part. It was necessary to broach with the spline end of the part against the backup plate of the machine. Because it was too difficult to force cutting fluid through the tubular section to the area being cut, grease was applied to the broach before each stroke. Had a vertical machine been available for this operation, a cutting fluid could have been pumped to the top end of the cavity to be broached and it would have flowed down to all areas being cut.

Vertical machines are more adaptable to high production, because the operator need not handle the broach; the machine automatically retrieves the broach before recycling. Vertical machines are more readily tooled to broach several pieces simultaneously, using multiple broaches (two, four, or six broaches may be used at one time). Vertical machines require less floor space (but more headroom) than comparable horizontal machines. They are more easily automated than horizontal machines, although horizontal machines can be automated and most of the ones used for external broaching are automated.

It is often easier to supply cutting fluid to the full length of cutting section of a vertically operated broach, especially of the pull-down type. However, supplying cutting fluid to the cutting areas sometimes requires considerable ingenuity.

Vertical broaching machines are further classified as "pull-up", "pull-down", or "push broach" machines, depending on the direction of movement when the broach is cutting.

Choice of Type. Some of the factors that determine whether a horizontal or a vertical machine is selected for a specific job are the length and weight of the broach required and the type of cut to be made. Many parts can be broached on either type of broaching machine, often with equal efficiency, as shown in the following example:

Example 109. Vertical Machine vs Horizontal Chain Machine for Broaching Connecting Rods and Caps (Fig. 7)

Figure 7 shows a connecting rod and a connecting rod cap on which similar broaching operations were performed but with different types of broaching equipment. For broaching the connecting rod, a vertical broaching machine was used; for the cap, a horizontal chain broaching machine. Both parts required two broaching operations. Broaching speed for all operations was 30 fpm.

Originally, both parts were broached in vertical machines, but in an attempt to reduce cost, chain broaching was tried for the cap. Because of the cost reduction effected by using the chain broach, if a retooling program were carried out, it would have included a change to the horizontal chain broach for machining the connecting rods also.

For the connecting rod (vertical machine), the first operation entailed broaching the shim face, broaching the half-round bearing seat, and chamfering the two corners at the junctions of the broached surfaces. The second broaching operation consisted of facing the bolt-head seats and the over-all width across the bolt bosses, and of chamfering the two corners, in order to control the over-all width dimension.

For the connecting-rod cap (horizontal chain machine), the first operation consisted of broaching the over-all width across the bolt bosses, and of facing the nut seats and the top of the weight-balancing lug. The second operation entailed broaching the shim face, broaching the half-round bearing seat, and final sizing of the over-all width across the bolt bosses.

A proprietary broaching oil was used for both operations. Pertinent production and cost data for both the first and second operations, for cap and rod, are given in the tabulation accompanying Fig. 7.

Chain broaches are horizontal machines (rarely vertical) capable of continuous operation. This type of machine utilizes an endless chain on sprockets actuated by a worm and a wheel reduction drive. Several workholding fixtures (usually 6 to 12) are mounted on this chain. Workpieces are placed in the fixtures, which are accurately guided through a rigid section of stationary tools where the broaching is done. Workpieces can be loaded or unloaded manually or automatically.

Chain broaching can be used for machining a variety of shapes and is adaptable to high-volume production. The principal limitation of chain broaching is workpiece shape. For continuous broaching, the workpiece must have one open side. Half rounds such as connecting-rod caps are notable examples of workpieces that are best adapted to chain broaching (see Example 109).

The chain broaching method is often used to reduce cost, as demonstrated in the following example:

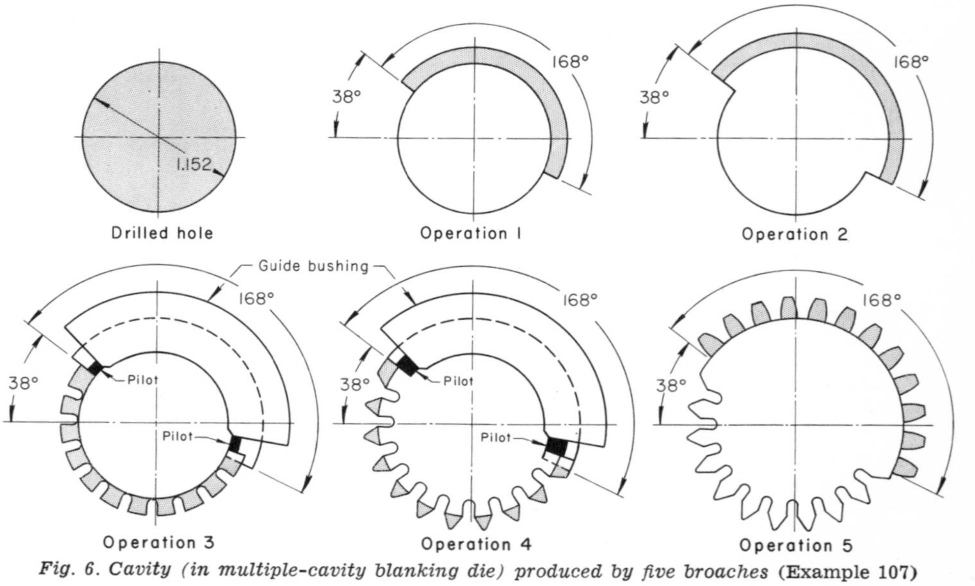

Fig. 6. Cavity (in multiple-cavity blanking die) produced by five broaches (Example 107)

Example 110. Vertical Machine vs Horizontal Chain Machine for Broaching Rotor Blades (Table 1)

For form broaching of Greek Ascoloy (AMS 5616) rotor blades at Rockwell C 32 to 38, changing from a vertical to a chain broaching machine resulted in improved tool life, increased production rate, and lower cost.

The broaching operation was originally done in a 66-in. dual-ram vertical machine. The broaching tool, made of T5 high speed steel, had a length of cut of 60 in. and was provided with 2° backoff and a face angle of 18°. Roughing broaches had full form.

In changing from a vertical to a chain broaching machine, it was necessary to alter broach design. The new broach contained inserts made of M3 (type 2) steel. Length of cut was extended to 96 in., and the broach was provided with 5° backoff and a reduced face angle of 15°. Instead of being full form, roughers were provided with graduated generating form. Broaching in both types of machines was done at 22 sfm; a cutting fluid composed of mineral oil with 1% active sulfur and chlorine, with synthetic additions, was used for both operations.

The improved performance obtained with this change of machine and broach is shown in Table 1, which gives comparative data for the two broaching operations. Production rate in chain broaching was four times that in vertical broaching; tool life (number of pieces per set of inserts) was 5½ times that in vertical broaching; and tool cost per piece was one sixth that in vertical broaching.

Titanium blades also were broached successfully in the chain broaching machine, using the improved tool design.

Other Classifications. Horizontal and vertical broaching machines are further classified according to the following:

1 **Method of drive**, which may be hydraulic, pneumatic, or mechanical. Mechanical drive may be supplied by means of bull gear and pinion (planer-type machines), screws (Acme thread or ball screw and nut), or chain and sprocket.
2 **Type of broaching operation** — that is, external (for surface broaching) or internal (for broaching a hole). External broaching machines are further classified as single-ram or dual-ram (indicating that a machine is capable of one or two broaching operations), and also on the basis of the flexibility of the work table (which may be fixed, receding, tilting or swinging).
3 **Special designs**, which include continuous horizontal or vertical surface broaching machines, and the vertical three-way machines used for pull-down internal and external broaching or for push-press applications. Utility presses tooled for broaching are designated as push-broaching machines.

Multiple-Operation Machines. Although broaching is most commonly done in a broaching machine, it is sometimes included in a sequence of several machining operations in single or multiple-spindle bar or chucking machines. Examples of this practice are given in the articles "Machining of Aluminum Alloys" and "Machining of Copper and Copper Alloys" (see Examples 885, 886 and 958).

Capacity. Broaching machines are available in a wide range of capacities. One manufacturer lists, as standard, machines having the following capacities and maximum stroke lengths:

Capacity, tons	Stroke, in.	Capacity, tons	Stroke, in.
1 or 2	30	10	54 to 66
3	30 to 48	25	48 to 66
5	42 to 48	30	72

Length of stroke of broaching machines is usually established to provide the maximum usefulness and flexibility of the machine. A machine with a 30-in. maximum stroke can be adjusted to use as much or as little of the stroke as is needed to satisfy requirements of a particular operation.

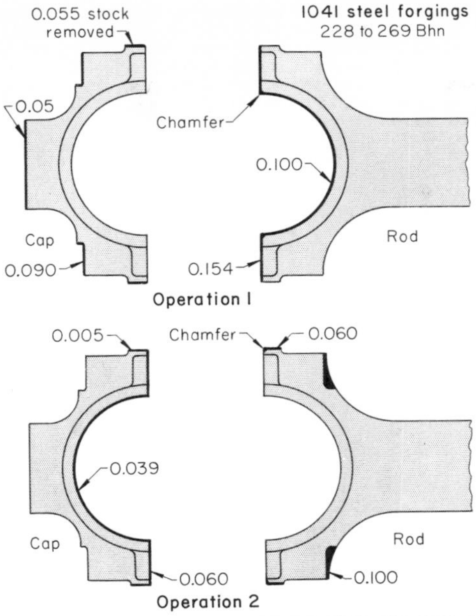

Item	Cap	Rod
Machine type	Horizontal	Vertical
First Operation		
Production, pcs/hr(a)	1474	648
Broach speed, sfm	30	30
Costs, per 1000 engines(b):		
Broach inserts	$15.73	$33.82
Regrinds(c)	$15.57	$15.10
Second Operation		
Production, pcs/hr(a)	1600	480
Broach speed, sfm	30	30
Costs, per 1000 engines(b):		
Broach inserts	$18.55	$22.72
Regrinds(c)	$15.20	$26.26

(a) Gross. (b) Eight pieces per engine. (c) Ten regrinds (average) per set of inserts.

Fig. 7. Connecting-rod cap and connecting rod on which similar two-stage broaching operations were performed in two different types of machines (Example 109)

Designations of broaching machines follow a simple letter-number code whereby the type and size (capacity and maximum length of stroke) of the machines are identified. Three examples of the use of this code are:

VPU-5-54 — Vertical pull-up machine, 5-ton capacity, 54-in. stroke
VPD-10-60 — Vertical pull-down machine, 10-ton capacity, 60-in. stroke
H-5-48 — Horizontal machine, 5-ton capacity, 48-in. stroke.

Determination of Power Requirements

Power requirements are influenced by the material to be broached, the axial length of the broached section, the perimeter of the cut to be taken, the amount of material to be removed, and the condition of the cutting edges of the broach.

To assist in evaluating the broachability of commonly encountered metals, the empirical constants given in Table 2 have been generally accepted. These constants are used in the following formulas to determine force required for broaching. In these computations, it is assumed that the broach is sharp and in good condition.

Table 1. Comparison of Vertical and Chain Broaching Machines in Form Broaching of Rotor Blades (Example 110)

Item	Machine(a) Vertical(b)	Chain(c)
Production pieces per hr	50	200
Cost per set of inserts	$1152	$1062
Number of pieces per set	2000	11,000
Tool cost per 1000 pieces	$576	$97

(a) In both types of machines, broaching was done at 22 sfm. (b) 66-in. dual-ram vertical machine. (c) 15L chain broach machine; broach had 96-in. length of cut.

Surface Broaching. The formula for determining the force in pounds, F, required for surface broaching is:

$$F = T \times R \times C$$

in which T is the total length, in inches, of all teeth engaged; R is rise per tooth, or chip thickness; and C is the broachability constant for the material being broached (Table 2). (T could be stated as $N \times L$, where N = number of teeth engaged and L = effective length of tooth or width of broach.) Use of the above formula is illustrated in the following example:

Example 111. Calculation of Force for Surface Broaching

Determine the force required for broaching the surface of a low-carbon steel part 4½ in. long by 2 in. wide, using a broach with a pitch of 0.75 in. and a rise per tooth of 0.0025 in. Effective tooth length of the broach is 2.07 in., because teeth are set at a 15° angle. Using the formula, we find that:

$$F = 6 \times 2.07 \times 0.0025 \times 450{,}000 = 14{,}000 \text{ lb}$$

Broaching Round Holes. The formula for determining the force required for broaching round holes is:

$$F = N \times \pi D \times R \times C$$

in which N is number of broach teeth engaged, D is hole diameter, R is rise per tooth and C is the broachability constant from Table 2.

Example 112. Calculation of Force for Broaching Round Holes

Determine the force required for broaching a 2-in. round hole in a cast iron hub 3¼ in. long, using a broach with a pitch of 0.625 in. and a rise per tooth of 0.003 in. According to the formula:

$$F = 6 \times 3.14 \times 2 \times 0.003 \times 350{,}000 = 39{,}600 \text{ lb}$$

Broaching Splined Holes. For broaching splined holes of which the inside diameter has been previously sized, the formula to determine force required is:

$$F = N \times S \times W \times R \times C$$

in which N is number of broach teeth engaged, S is number of splines, W is

Table 2. Constants for Broachability of Annealed Metals

Metal	Constant
Aluminum	50,000
Copper	250,000
Cast iron; bronze	350,000
Low-carbon steel; steel castings	450,000
Alloy steels 3115 to 4615	550,000
Alloy steels 5120 to 6195	600,000
Titanium and A-286 alloy	650,000

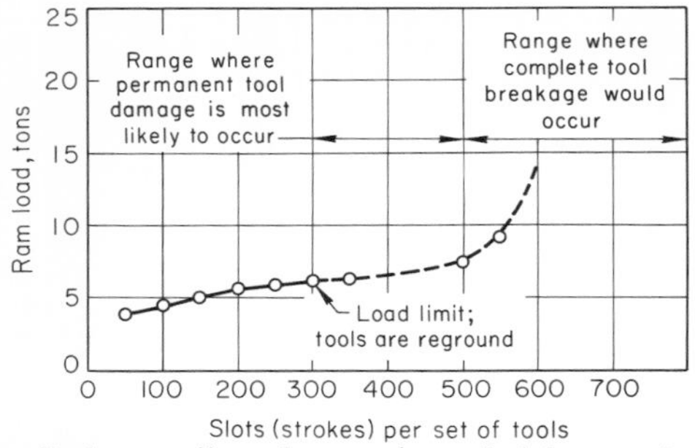

Broken portion of curve (compiled from early experience) shows how loads increased when dull tools were used beyond permissible wear limit.

Fig. 8. Load curve showing gradual increase in load as tools dull (Example 113)

width of spline, R is rise per tooth, and C is the broachability constant (Table 2). In applying this formula to a ten-spline hole (inside diameter previously sized) in 5140 steel 1.625 in. thick, with splines 0.25 in. wide, using a broach with rise per tooth of 0.0025 in. and a pitch of 0.5 in., the force for broaching the hole is calculated as 15,000 lb.

Operating Control by Load Meter. Because the load on a machine increases as tools become dull, the load meter described in the following example served as an accurate measure of wear progression, to indicate tool dulling, and to prevent tool breakage, damage to adjacent inserts, and damage to workpieces.

Example 113. Use of a Load Meter to Indicate Tool Wear (Fig. 8)

The meter described below was originally developed for use in broaching A-286, but was later utilized on René 41, V-57 and other heat-resisting alloys. The load meter recorded the increase in current required by constant-torque motors that actuated the ram of the broaching machine. The meter, which was calibrated in tons of force, indicated the magnitude of cutting force being developed on the tool faces.

Load data were first recorded for new tools on the initial run of a new material. Successive broaching forces were recorded as production continued. A range of working values was accumulated for each material, and a working average was established.

Loads increased as wear progressed, and limits were established for tool changes. Particular attention was given when load requirements began to increase at an accelerated rate, because such an increase was an indication of tool difficulty, a mechanical problem, or some other unusual circumstance.

When load meters were used, savings resulted from improved finish and fewer damaged parts or broken tools. Also, guessing on tool-edge wear was eliminated; the meter indicated the need for tool changes or setup check as trouble began to develop. Tools were ground on the basis of measured cutting performance, and a 25% gain in tool life was realized because of less grinding.

Figure 8 shows a typical load curve and illustrates the increase in load as tool wear progressed under normal conditions and beyond the permissible wear limit.

Types of Broaches

There are three general categories of broaches: solid, shell, and insert-type. Within these categories, broaches can be further classified by the type of cut (internal or external) they are designed to make, and by the method by which they are actuated (push or pull). Of the various types of broaches, the solid pull broach (Fig. 9) probably is the most commonly used.

Solid broaches are one-piece broaches produced from bar stock (Fig. 1 and 9). They can be provided with greater dimensional accuracy and concentricity than shell broaches. The chief disadvantages of solid broaches lie in the difficulty of repairing broken teeth, and in the cost of replacement when wear or abuse necessitates it.

Shell broaches consist of a main broach body (usually the roughing and intermediate broach sections), an arbor section over which a removable shell fits, and the removable shell that is the finishing section. A broach can have more than one removable shell. Shell broaches can be used for internal broaching or for some external operations such as broaching half bores. Shell broaches are superior to solid broaches in that worn or broken sections can be replaced without discarding other sections. The disadvantages of shell broaches are that some accuracy and concentricity are sacrificed as normal variations are multiplied by the number of pieces involved. A typical pull-down removable-shell broach is shown in Fig. 10.

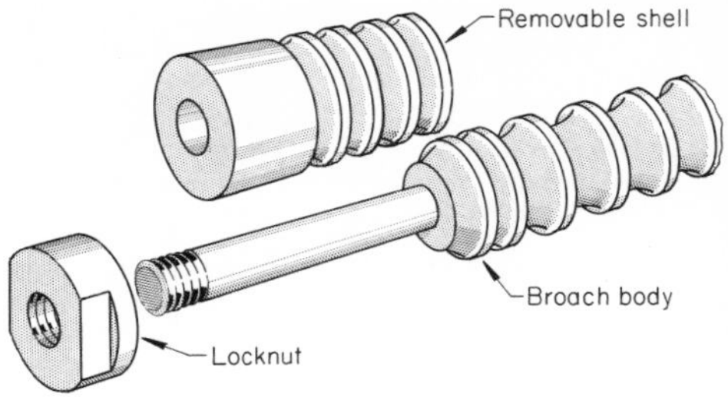

Fig. 10. Typical round internal shell broach

In some applications, shell broaches have proved superior to solid broaches because a shell broach is capable of floating, which is helpful in maintaining alignment. This and other advantages of shell broaches are demonstrated in the following example:

Example 114. Use of a Shell Broach for Making Splines (Fig. 11)

In broaching the internal splines in a coupling made of 4340 steel at Rockwell C 35 to 40, close dimensional and surface-finish requirements had to be met. At the same time, it was desirable to improve tool life by revising the design of the broaching tool. The splined coupling contained 16 equally spaced teeth 3½ in. long; slot width was 0.242 to 0.244 in. The entire spline had to be straight to within 0.0005 in. and entirely free of tears and drag lines.

Concentricity was difficult to maintain, because the broaching machine had to be in almost perfect alignment for the full 65-in. stroke of the broach.

The redesigned broaching tool incorporated a replaceable shell containing 12 side-cutting teeth with full-form backoff. Tooth size ahead of the shell was reduced to permit the shaving of a small amount of stock and the elimination of surface irregularities. By permitting the shell to float a maximum of 0.001 in., alignment could be maintained. Also, the new design allowed for removal and replacement of shells. The broach and replaceable shell, and the splined coupling, are shown in Fig. 11. The 16 splines were rough cut by a first-pass broach (not shown), leaving 0.020 in. of stock around the cut.

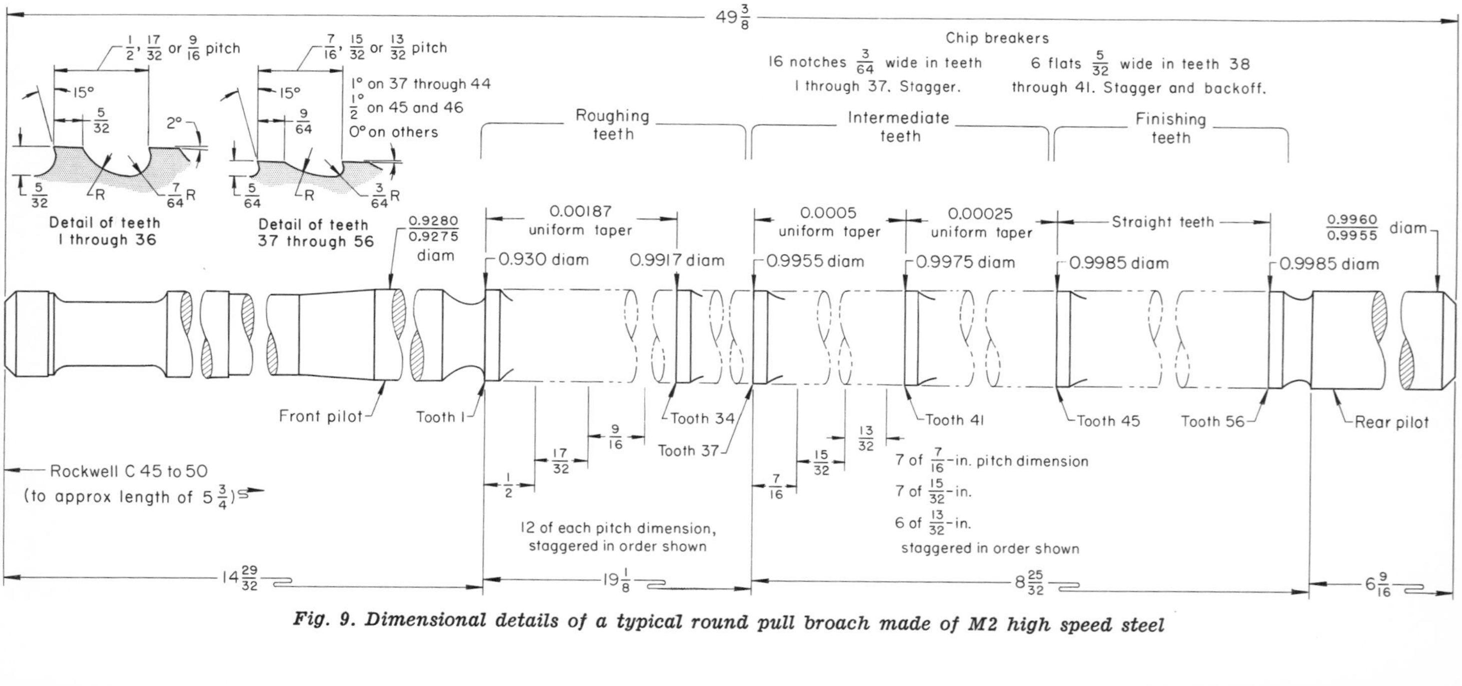

Fig. 9. Dimensional details of a typical round pull broach made of M2 high speed steel

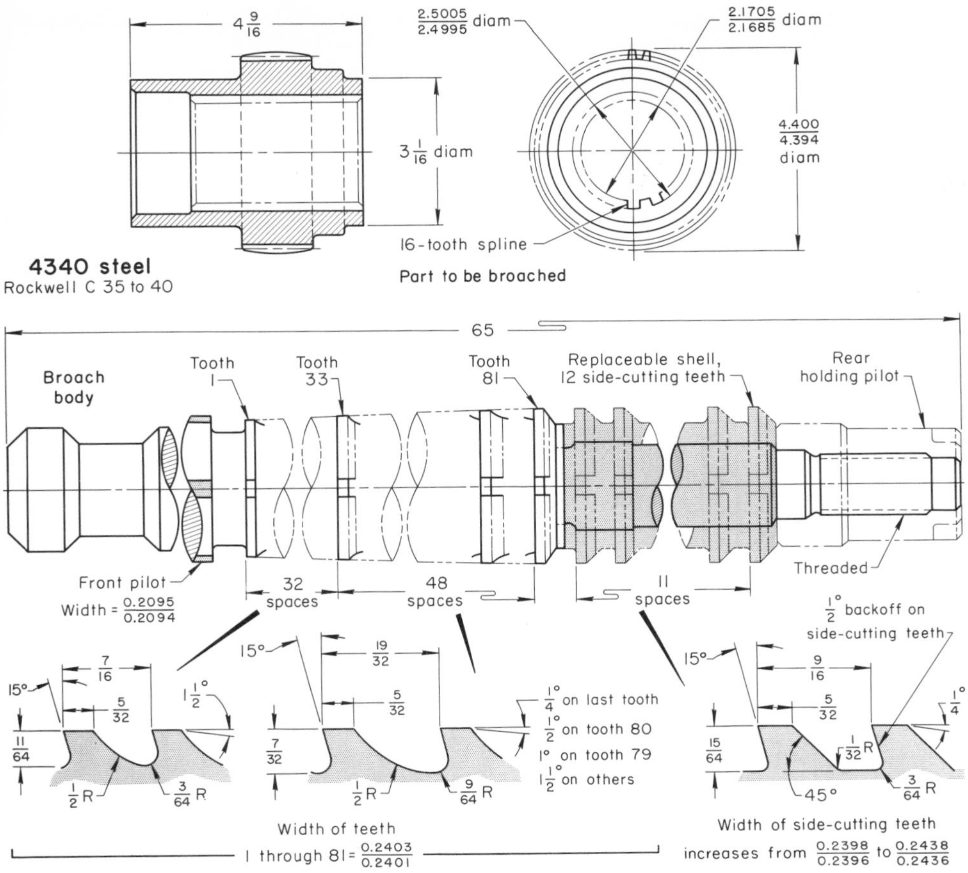

The replaceable shell proved effective in holding splines within tolerance, improved the maintenance of cutting edges, and provided increased tool life and savings in broach replacement.

Fig. 11. Splined coupling and details of broach used for finish cutting of internal splines (Example 114)

The use of removable shells improved the quality of the finished part, extended the life of broaches, and reduced the amount of time required for machine maintenance and tool resharpening. Replacement of undersized shells was far less costly than the former practice of replacing worn broaches.

Insert-type broaches are made up of a tool holder and inserts of high speed steel or carbide, which do the cutting. Although these broaches may be used for broaching contoured shapes, both internal and external, their main use is for broaching large flat surfaces, such as the machined faces of automotive engine blocks.

Carbide inserts can be brazed to the tool holder as shown in Fig. 12. However, the practice of using brazed inserts has been largely replaced by the use of disposable inserts for broaches of this type. Disposable inserts are either triangular or square, thus having six or eight cutting edges, respectively. A triangular insert secured to a holder is shown in Fig. 12. Instead of being sharpened, these inserts are discarded after the cutting edges have been used. The initial cost of a broach with disposable carbide inserts is about the same as that of a solid broaching tool.

Provided the holder is manufactured to close tolerances, particularly in those sections that determine the height of the cutting edge, gaging is not required when cutters are changed to present a new cutting edge. Disposable carbide cutters can be inserted in any position without removing the broach from the machine. To provide the required clearance behind the cutting edges, inserts must have a negative rake.

Inserts for contour cutting can be sharpened on the top and face, and shimmed to the correct position.

The considerable saving in tool cost that was made possible by a change from brazed carbide tools to disposable carbide inserts for the same broaching operation is described in the following example:

Example 115. Brazed vs Disposable Carbide Inserts for Surface Broaching (Fig. 12)

An automotive engine plant that had been broaching oil-pan mounting rails on cast iron cylinder blocks using brazed spike-tooth carbide tools realized a major cost saving by changing to disposable carbide inserts for the operation (see Fig. 12 and the comparison of cost data in the accompanying table).

The rails were broached as cast (170 to 229 Bhn) in a special horizontal machine at 120 to 135 sfm, without a cutting fluid; 0.059 in. of stock was removed. Length of cut was 26 in.; feed per tooth was 0.0033 in.; 126 tools were used per setup. By this technique, 90 to 100 cylinder blocks could be broached per hour at 80% efficiency.

Pull broaches, as the name implies, are pulled through or against the surface of the workpiece. Most internal broaching is done with pull broaches. Because there is no problem of bending, pull broaches can be longer than push broaches for the same size of hole, and they also can remove more stock in one pass. Although pull broaches can be made to long lengths, their cost usually limits solid pull broaches to a length of about 7 ft. Broaches longer than 7 ft usually are made up of sections similar to shell broaches, because the cost is less for replacing a damaged or worn section than for replacing the entire broach.

Push broaches, for internal broaching, are necessarily shorter than pull broaches, because of the problem of bending under load. Push broaches are used to broach blind holes (Example 104) or for multiple-station broaching machines wherein several short broaches, rather than a single long broach, are used, to reduce the time required for a given operation.

Broach Material

Hardened high speed steel is by far the most widely used material for solid broaches or for the cutting teeth of other types of broaches. The tools usually are ground to final dimensions after hardening. The grade of high speed steel is normally chosen on the basis of minimum over-all cost, balancing tool life and production rate against tool cost (material, heat treatment, fabrication and regrinding for re-use).

As can be seen from the examples in this article, general-purpose high speed steel M2 is the first choice for broach material, in the absence of special requirements (see Examples 104, 105, 120, 126, 134 and 142, and Fig. 9 and Table 5). As shown in Examples 106, 110, 126, 136 and 138, the more abrasion-resistant M3, which contains higher vanadium and carbon, is sometimes used in place of M2 when longer tool life is required. The material cost for M3 is 15 to 20% higher than for M2, and grinding cost is higher, because of the higher amount of extremely hard (2400 Knoop) vanadium carbide particles, thus partly offsetting the increase in tool life.

High speed steel T15, which has high vanadium and carbon contents and also

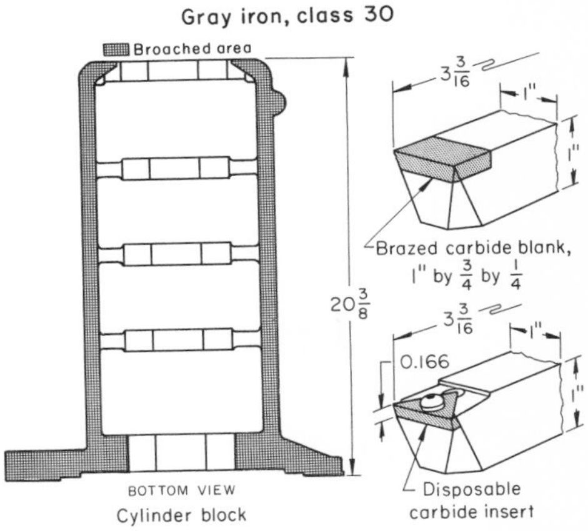

Item	Cost per 1000 engines: Brazed blanks	Disposable inserts
Tools	$21.76	$ 0.87
Grinding	23.07	0.00
Setup	5.93	0.72
Total	$50.76	$ 1.59
Saving, using disposable inserts		$49.17

Fig. 12. Cylinder block that was broached at lower cost with disposable carbide inserts than with brazed carbide tools (tools shown at right) (Example 115)

5% cobalt (to maintain high hardness at operating temperatures), is used when requirements are too severe for the general-purpose or intermediate grades. Material cost of T15 is more than double that of M2; grinding time and cost are also higher; and better support in the tool holder is needed, because T15 is more brittle than M2. The use of T15 in difficult broaching applications is described in Examples 103, 118, 119 and 123.

Other general-purpose and special grades of high speed steel are also used to a limited extent. Compositions, cost and properties of high speed steels are given in the article on High Speed Steel for Cutting Tools, beginning on page 311 in this volume.

Comparisons of high speed steels for broaches are presented in Example 749, in the article on Machining of Stainless Steel, and Example 822, in the article on Machining of Heat-Resisting Alloys.

To provide the optimum combination of abrasion resistance and toughness, broach cutting teeth are normally hardened to Rockwell C 64 to 66 for the general-purpose grade, ranging upward for the more highly alloyed grades to a maximum of Rockwell C 66 to 68 for T15. For longer tool life, surface treatments such as nitriding or oxidizing are sometimes employed. Nitriding increases superficial hardness, and both nitriding and oxidizing minimize sticking or welding of tool to work material. Chromium plating will also minimize sticking.

Carbide inserts or rings are used to a limited extent in internal broaching, chiefly on small parts made of free-machining materials such as gray iron, usually in applications requiring extremely close tolerances at high production rates. The use of carbide is illustrated in Example 115, which compares results with brazed and disposable inserts. Broaching of steel castings, in which a carbide tool can cut through local hard spots with less tool damage than high speed steel, is another application of carbide inserts.

Broach Design

Basic broach design is shown in Fig. 9, which presents dimensional details of a typical pull broach for producing a round hole. This broach has been used for production broaching of a hole 0.9985/0.9965 in. in diameter in a normalized forged steel steering knuckle. A starting hole $^{15}/_{16}$ in. in diameter was drilled through the forging, to accommodate the broach. As shown in Fig. 9, the first cutting tooth of this broach is 0.930 in. in diameter, and each tooth in the roughing section increases 0.00187 in. in diameter over the one preceding it (the first three or four teeth

Table 3. Approximate Tooth-Face Angles for Broaching Various Metals

Metal	Face angle
Aluminum; magnesium	10° to 15°
Brass; bronze	0° to 10°
Brass, leaded	−5° to +5°
Cast iron	6° to 8°
Steel, Rockwell C 12 to 22 ..	15° to 20°
Steel, Rockwell C 23 to 35 ..	8° to 12°
Stainless steels	12° to 18°

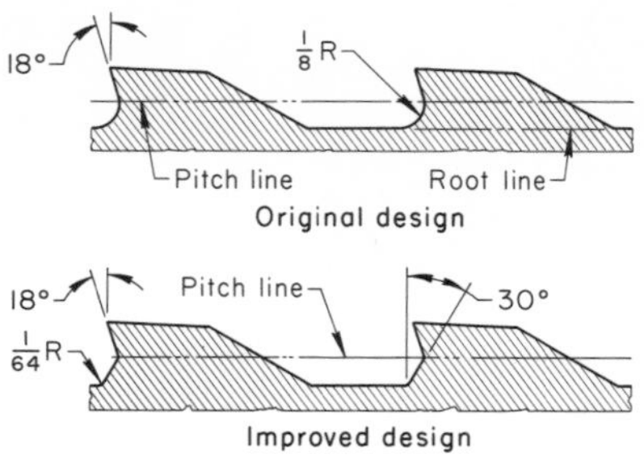

Fig. 13. Revision of gullet configuration to eliminate problems in broaching Incoloy 901 (Example 117)

may cut little or nothing, depending on the exact size of the drilled hole). Thus, as the broach is pulled through the workpiece, cutting commences gradually, and as each succeeding tooth engages the work, it removes a small amount of metal. The progressive increase in tooth diameter is usually greatest in the roughing section. In this broach, the increase is 0.00187 in. for the roughing teeth, 0.0005 in. for the first four teeth in the intermediate section, and 0.00025 in. for the remaining teeth in the intermediate section. In the finishing section, all teeth are 0.9985 in. in diameter — the maximum permissible diameter of the broached hole.

Tooth contours are shown in the upper left corner of Fig. 9. The greater depth of the gullet and the greater pitch for teeth 1 through 36 permit better chip accommodation. This is essential, because these teeth make the greatest advance and so remove the most metal. The pitch length (distance between teeth) in both the roughing and the intermediate sections is staggered to prevent chatter as the broach is pulled through the work.

Chip breakers (discussed in a subsequent section of this article) are incorporated in the roughing teeth and the first four intermediate teeth, as specified in the notes in Fig. 9. The chip breakers are staggered from tooth to tooth so that the ridges left in the workpiece surface by the discontinuities in any one tooth are removed by the tooth that follows. (Note that the last three intermediate teeth have no chip breakers, so that these teeth can remove all traces of irregularities left by chip-breakers on preceding teeth before the first finishing tooth starts cutting.)

The broach shown in Fig. 9 was produced from M2 high speed steel and heat treated to Rockwell C 64 to 66. The pull end was tempered to Rockwell C 45 to 50.

Face (hook) angles for broach teeth are selected on the basis of hardness and ductility of the work metal. Metals that yield brittle chips, such as cast iron or leaded brasses, usually are cut most efficiently by teeth with a narrow face angle. Ductile materials, such as annealed or normalized steels, usually respond better to wider face angles (but see Example 121). Face angles on broaches are similar to top rake on single-point tools. Recommended face angles for various metals are given in Table 3.

When broaching similar parts of different metals, a different face angle often must be used for each of the metals cut, as shown in the following example:

Example 116. Tooth-Face Angles for Broaching Steel and Cast Iron

A manufacturer of pulleys made from steel and from cast iron used broaching to produce drive-key slots. For steel pulleys, the broach teeth had a 15° face angle; broaches cut a minimum of 5000 key slots between grinds. When the same broaches were used on cast iron pulleys, fewer than 1000 slots could be broached per grind, and finish was unacceptable. When broaches with an 8° face angle were used, an average of 3600 key slots could be broached satisfactorily in cast iron pulleys, between grinds. (The difference in tool life — 5000 pieces for steel and 3600 for cast iron — was considered normal, and was attributed to the abrasiveness of the cast iron.)

Gullets. The shape of gullets (chip spaces) of broach teeth influences the efficiency of the broaching operation and has a marked effect on broach life. To obtain maximum efficiency, it may be necessary, when sharpening a broach, to deviate from conventional gullet shape, as was done in the example that follows:

Example 117. Gullet Redesign for Increased Broach Life (Fig. 13)

Figure 13 shows the original and revised designs of the gullet in teeth of a broach used for cutting fir-tree slots in a turbine wheel of Incoloy 901. The original full-radius design encouraged the packing of chips in the gullet so tightly that they were almost impossible to remove by wire brushing. The broach became overheated because of the transfer of heat from the packed-in chips. At times, the packing of chips in the gullet caused galling and tears in the broached surface of the workpiece.

When the gullet was ground to the two-angle configuration shown as the improved design in Fig. 13, broach life increased from one piece per grind to three pieces per grind, and galling and tearing of the broached surface were eliminated. The change of gullet had no effect on the number of resharpenings; broaches could still be reground seven or eight times.

Chamfered Edges. The sides of broach teeth used for forming configurations such as keyways or fir-tree slots are usually chamfered, the purpose being to prolong tool life. The need for chamfered teeth increases as the machinability of the work metal decreases.

The amount of chamfer may be restricted by the shape being broached, but even as little as 0.005 in. chamfer is helpful. The two examples that follow demonstrate the beneficial effect of tooth chamfer in broaching of heat-resisting alloys.

Examples 118 and 119. Broaching of Fir-Tree Slots

Example 118 — Addition of Chamfer (Fig. 14). A cross section of one of 102 fir-tree slots that were broached around the periphery of an aircraft-engine turbine wheel made of

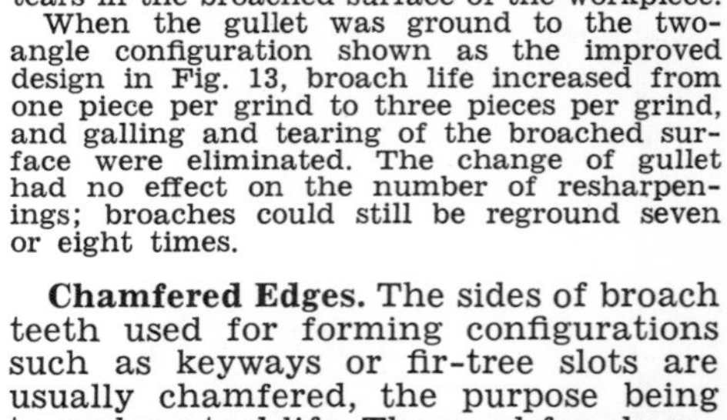

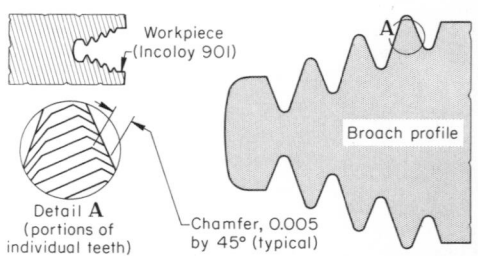

Fig. 14. Addition of chamfer to corners of broach teeth for increased tool life in broaching of fir-tree slots in turbine wheel (Example 118)

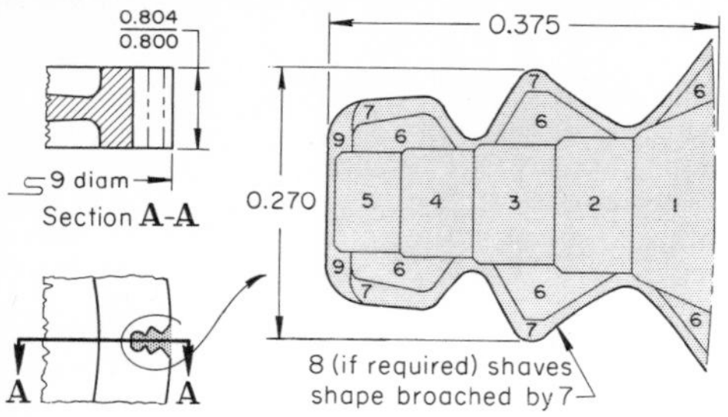

Tool Life and Cost Data

Cutter life per sharpening	600 in.(a)
Slots broached per sharpening	750(b)
Wheels broached per sharpening	10(c)
Regrinds per set of cutters	6 to 8
Cost per set of cutters	$1200
Cost of regrinding	$75
Cutter cost per wheel	$21.56(d)

(a) Total length of slots broached. (b) Through wheel rim 0.80 in. thick. (c) Each wheel had 75 slots. (d) Assuming an average of seven regrinds and a total of 80 wheels broached per set of cutters: ($1200 + 7 × $75) — 8 = $21.56.

	Cutter number(a)								
	1	2	3	4	5	6	7	8	9
Length, in.	8.750	11.250	11.250	10.312	11.250	14.875	22.000	2.250	3.125
Number of teeth	27	36	36	33	36	46	70	6	11
Pitch, in.	5/16	5/16	5/16	5/16	5/16	5/16	5/16	3/8	9/32
Rise per tooth, in.	0.0023	0.0023	0.0023	0.0023	0.0023	0.0016	0.0006–0.0017	0.004	0.005
Face angle	18°	18°	18°	18°	18°	—5°(b)	—3°(b)	—3°(b)	15°
Clearance angle	3°	3°	3°	3°	3°	3°	3°	2°	3°
Chip clearance depth, in.	0.125	0.125	0.125	0.125	0.125	0.035–0.070	0.030–0.120	0.120	0.109
Corner chamfer (45°), in.	....	0.023	0.015	0.015	0.015	....	....	....	....
Chamfer clearance angle	....	3°	3°	3°	3°	....	....	....	....
Chamfer rise per tooth, in.	....	0.0016	0.0016	0.0016	0.0017	....	....	....	....

(a) Cutters were made from T15 high speed steel and were heat treated to Rockwell C 66 to 68. As indicated in the figure, cutters 1 through 5 performed rough slotting; cutter 6, rough shaping; cutter 7, form finishing of sides; cutter 8, shaving of form cut by cutter 7 (if required); and cutter 9, form finishing of bottom radii.

(b) Face angle is 18°; negative angle was added to small area at cutting edge.

Fig. 15. Broaching a fir-tree slot in an A-286 alloy turbine wheel by a single pass of a broaching tool containing nine different cutters that sequentially cut the areas indicated. Cutter design is detailed in the large table, and tool life and cost are shown in the small table at upper right. (Example 119)

Incoloy 901 is shown in Fig. 14. The broach was made of T15 high speed steel and was heat treated to Rockwell C 66 to 68. The wheels were broached in an 85-ton vertical machine with a 90-in. stroke, at a speed of 120 in. per min. A broaching oil having a viscosity of 155 SUS at 100 F, 2% fat content, 0.8% active sulfur, and 2.1% chlorine was used.

Before a chamfer was added to the broach teeth (shown at the bottom in Fig. 14), broach life was 19.2 wheels, and an average of two wheels could be broached between sharpenings. The addition of this 0.005-in.-by-45° chamfer parallel to the broaching axis on the sharp corners of the teeth increased broach life to an average of 24.8 wheels and increased to three the number of wheels that could be broached between sharpenings. The improvement in broach life was assisted by improved grinding and resharpening procedures and by more careful handling of the broach.

Example 119 — Chamfer, Face Angle and Rise per Tooth (Fig. 15). Jet-engine turbine wheels 9 in. in diameter made of A-286 alloy required the broaching of 75 equally spaced fir-tree slots around their periphery. Hardness of these wheels before broaching was Rockwell C 28 to 38. Each slot (Fig. 15) was cut by means of a single pass of a broaching tool in which was mounted a series of nine cutters that sequentially removed metal to the configuration shown at the right in Fig. 15. Cutting speed was 16 ft per min; a sulfurized oil was used as cutting fluid.

As originally designed, the cutters could broach only three wheels (225 slots) before resharpening was required. The slots were of marginal quality, and cutter breakage was frequent. Broach efficiency and life were increased by the following design modifications: incorporation of a 45° chamfer on the corners of the teeth of cutters 2 to 5, and of negative face angles on the teeth of cutters 6 to 8; and establishment of chip loads (rise per tooth) of 0.0023 in. for cutters 1 to 5, 0.0016 in. for cutter 6, and 0.0006 to 0.0017 in. for cutter 7. These design revisions allowed the broaching of ten wheels (750 slots) between sharpenings, and reduced cutter cost per slot from $1.60 to less than 30¢ — an annual saving of more than $100,000. Tables accompanying Fig. 15 give tool-life and cost data and details of cutter shape after design revision.

Broach sections for this operation had an average cost of $4 per broach tooth, and an average sharpening cost of 25¢ per tooth. This compares favorably with the cost of single-point turning tools.

Effect of Tooth Design on Chatter. When chatter develops in broaching, loss of accuracy, poor surface finish on the workpiece, and excessive broach wear are probable results. With extreme chatter, the broach is likely to break. In broaching, cuts are often interrupted, depending on the length of the section to be broached and the distance between successive cutting teeth. In general, the likelihood of chatter increases as the severity of the interruptions in cutting increases.

Conventional broaches having circular teeth like those shown in Fig. 1 and 9 are more susceptible to chatter than are specially designed broaches, because there is a complete interruption after each cutting tooth. Either of two approaches is frequently used in broach design to minimize interrupted cutting and chatter: (*a*) In broaching flat surfaces or several internal splines spaced around a periphery, teeth staggered longitudinally provide a more uniform cutting action; (*b*) when broaching round holes, a broach having helical teeth is an effective means of eliminating chatter. Specially designed broaches are more expensive than conventional types, but the increased broach cost is often justified, as demonstrated in the following example:

Example 120. Broach Redesign to Eliminate Chatter (Fig. 16)

The pinion gear shown in Fig. 16, produced from 1024 hot rolled steel with a Brinell hardness of 140 to 165, required an accurately broached hole 0.871/0.870 in. in diameter. The thickness of the broached section was 0.906/0.849 in. After broaching, the gear teeth were cut, locating from the broached hole. The gear was then heat treated, and the shaft hole ground to 0.8755/0.8735 in. in diameter, locating from the pitch diameter of the gear teeth. Excessive eccentricity and poor broach life were problems, and broach chatter caused marks that were not removed in final grinding.

The gears were broached, four at a time, on a four-spindle, 10-ton, vertical hydraulic pull machine, using 16 in. of the 36-in. maximum stroke. Gears were loaded into the machine manually and unloaded automatically. Broaching speed was 17.5 ft per min; cutting fluid was soluble oil and water mixed in a ratio of 1 to 20.

As originally designed (Fig. 16), broaches had circular teeth. Broach chatter was caused by the shearing action of the teeth, and by the relatively short length of the broached section (which did not provide enough tooth contact to hold the broach rigid).

To eliminate the chatter, a full helical broach was tried, but the use of this tool gave rise to other problems. The broached hole had to be accurately located from the spherical radius, as shown in Fig. 16. Because the gear was permitted to float on the ground spherical radius during broaching, it was necessary that the broach start squarely. The helical lead prevented this.

A redesigned broach with 12 circular lead teeth followed by 23 helical teeth (Fig. 16) proved successful. The circular teeth aligned the hole properly with the spherical radius and correctly started the removal of metal. The helical section completed the metal removal with no evidence of chatter, because of the continuous contact of the teeth with the metal being cut.

Performance and cost for broaches of the original and final designs are compared in the table accompanying Fig. 16. Although initial and resharpening costs were greater for the redesigned broach than for the original design, and although the redesigned broach could be resharpened only about half as many times, the redesign lowered the over-all cost per piece by more than 85%, mainly because of the greater number of pieces that could be produced before tolerances could no longer be held.

Broaches of both designs were made of general-purpose high speed steel, hardened to

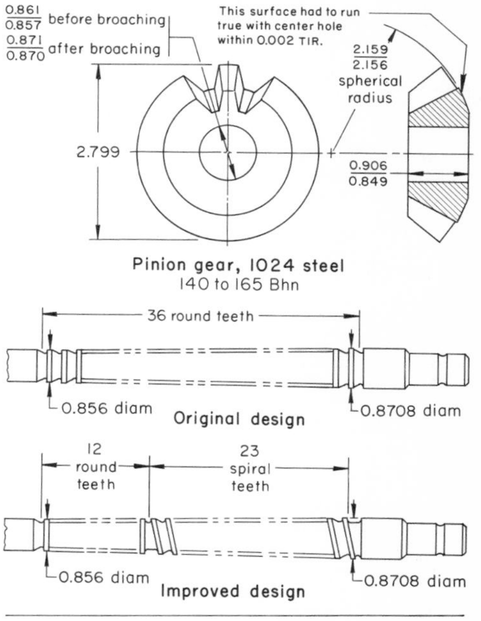

Item	Original design	Revised design
Initial cost per tool	$45	$53
Cost for regrinding	$3	$5
Number of regrinds	15	8
Pieces per grind	600	7,600
Pieces per tool	9600	68,400
Cost per piece(a)	$0.00938	$0.00136

(a) Initial cost per tool, plus cost for regrinding times number of regrinds, divided by number of pieces per tool.

Fig. 16. Pinion gear and original and revised designs of broach used to produce shaft hole (Example 120)

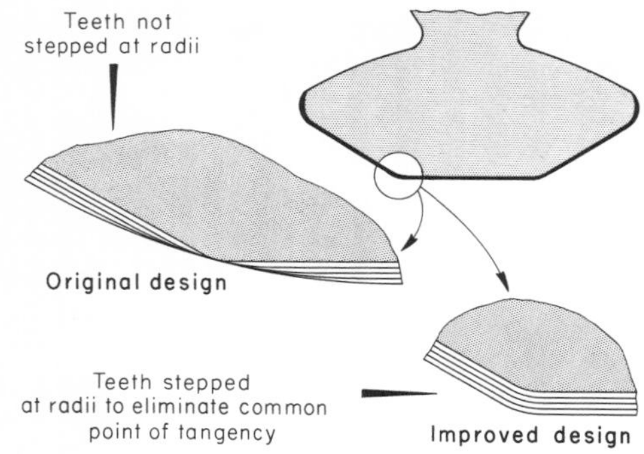

In the original design, teeth were not stepped, and cuts by successive teeth caused severe buildup of metal on teeth and galling of radii surfaces; tool wear was excessive. Improved design used full-form cutting at all radii of "rocking chair" dovetail form.

Fig. 17. Original and improved designs for broach used for dovetail slotting of compressor wheels made of type 410 stainless steel (Example 122)

Rockwell C 64 to 66; the shank portions were tempered to Rockwell C 45 to 50.

Other Examples of Broach Redesign. The example that follows describes an application in which improved results were obtained by reducing the face angle of broach teeth.

Example 121. Reduction in Face Angle for Greater Dimensional Accuracy and Improved Surface Finish

Broaching (following drilling) was selected as the most practical process for producing from 1½-in.-diam 1040 steel bar stock at approximately 190 Bhn a 3-in.-long tube that was required to have an inside diameter of 1.001/0.999 in. with a finish of 30 micro-in. maximum. The first parts broached, however, had wavy surfaces, and inside diameters were oversize. Stoning the broach to remove sharpening burrs before broaching eliminated surface waviness and permitted finish requirements to be met, but inside diameters still were oversize.

The broach then was reground to reduce the face angle of the teeth by 2° (the face angle formerly had been 20°). With this modification, broaches were able to produce tubes that met dimensional and finish requirements.

Other design features that markedly affect broach life, productivity, or quality of the work include radii, pitch, and amount of backoff. The two examples that follow illustrate the effects of these design features. A principle of broach design is developed in Example 122 that can be related to all problems involving radii — that is, the use of stepped radii. Very often design features become more critical when broaching hard metals (Example 123).

Example 122. Stepped Radii for Dovetail Forms (Fig. 17)

The broach initially designed for dovetail broaching of type 410 compressor wheels (Fig. 17) produced an unacceptable surface finish, torn radii, friction lines, and excessive buildup on teeth. Tool wear was excessive. All of these problems resulted from the fact that the radii of all inserts were ground in line (that is, straight, with no step), so that all teeth in a critical area had a common point of tangency.

Improved performance was obtained with the redesigned broach shown in Fig. 17. The revised design provided for six full-form, stepped teeth cutting a total of no more than 0.005 in. of stock. Each tooth was of a different size, progressing from the low to the high limit. Because all radii followed the same gradual progression also, there were no straight teeth, and each radius cut a full chip. The generation of radii was gradual and smooth-cutting. When stepless radii were used, the first few teeth of the broach formed each radius with an abrupt tearing action that damaged surface finish and accelerated tool wear. Radii of subsequent teeth did little but glaze over the torn surface.

The redesigned broach produced 90 to 100 pieces per grind, whereas the original produced only 8 to 15 pieces per grind. Breakdown on the original design was 0.025 to 0.030 in.; with the redesign, breakdown was only 0.005 to 0.010.

Example 123. Broach Material and Design for Machining Steel at Rockwell C 46 to 49 (Fig. 18)

Broached holes 1.125 in. in diameter were required in 3-in.-thick 4340 steel at Rockwell C 46 to 49 (tensile strength, 220,000 to 240,000 psi). Tolerance for these holes was −0.0000, +0.0005 in.; specified surface finish was 32 micro-in. Using a broach of conventional design, made of nitrided M2 tool steel, and a machine having a minimum speed of 20 sfm, it was not possible to produce parts to print specifications. On 22 pieces, surface finish ranged as high as 63 micro-in., and four sharpenings were required. Broaching with a machine of this speed was abandoned.

Use of the same broach design (Fig. 18) on a machine slowed to a speed of 8 sfm brought an improvement but, in general, failed to produce parts that met specifications. In further tests, conventional broaches of M2, M3, T15 and T6 tool steels were tried, with little difference evident; none was capable of broaching the part successfully.

When a broach of revised design (Fig. 18) was used, holes met specifications, and broach life was 10 to 12 sharpenings, with 186 to 208 holes being obtained per sharpening. This broach was installed on a machine slowed to a speed of 8 sfm. (The machine had capacity far in excess of the forces required and was used to eliminate hesitation at the slow speed of 8 sfm.) A high-viscosity, active sulfochlorinated oil with polar and wetting additives was used.

The revised broach was made of T15 tool steel, and this material seemed to offer the best combination of performance and tool life. However, in subsequent production runs, broaches of revised design made from nitrided M2 tool steel usually performed successfully under similar conditions.

With respect to tool materials, the following observations were made:

1. Because of their superior wear resistance, carbides were tried but edge chipping occurred, largely because of the slow speeds.
2. M3 tool steel was not satisfactory for broaching steel harder than Rockwell C 45, and attempts to improve tool life by incorporating special surface treatments were unsuccessful.
3. M2 tool steel was acceptable if nitrided and given an oxide treatment in a steam atmosphere.
4. T15 at a hardness of Rockwell C 65 to 67 gave the best results, if properly heat treated: three tempering treatments followed by an oxide-coating steam temper after grinding. The steam tempering relieved grinding stresses, and the oxide coating helped to minimize chip welding.

Twelve other applications in which improved results were obtained by redesign of broaches are described in Examples 811 through 821, in the article on Machining of Heat-Resisting Alloys.

Chip Breakers

Chip control is essential in all machining operations, but especially in broaching. In single-point machining such as lathe turning, the chip leaves the cutter as soon as it is formed. In broaching, however, the chip stays in the gullet, or chip space, behind each tooth until that tooth clears the workpiece. Chip space is limited by the pitch of the teeth, and in small broaches by the root diameter of the broach. Thus, it is seldom possible to provide plenty of space for chips, particularly in small-diameter broaches.

In broaching, therefore, chips must be controlled, to keep chip-space requirements to a minimum, and to facilitate chip removal. Broaches are provided with chip breakers, which are small grooves or notches that transversely break the cutting edge and land of each roughing and semifinishing tooth (see Fig. 9). These grooves break the continuity of the width of the chip. Thus, instead of one wide chip, several narrow chips are formed. These narrow chips are easily washed out by the cutting fluid or brushed out, or fall away when the gullet clears the workpiece.

Broaches that cut round holes especially require chip breakers. Without chip breakers, the chips would be continuous rings that would be difficult to remove from the broach. Also, the shape of the chips must permit them to drop into the chip space behind each tooth. Chip breakers accomplish this by making smaller chips.

Chip breakers are staggered from tooth to tooth, so that the ridge left by the chip breaker in one tooth is removed by the tooth immediately following. Generally, finishing teeth have no chip breakers, although some broaches require them in the first few teeth.

Fixtures

In broaching, as in other machining operations, fixturing of the workpiece is required. Broaching fixtures have several functions. They must locate the workpiece accurately, and hold it securely. For certain applications, such as broaching helical gears, the fixture must position the part accurately and firmly, yet permit the part to rotate as required. Fixtures may be used to carry workpieces in and out of the broaching position, or to carry them from one broaching position to another where more than one broach is required (as, for example, in broaching the propeller blade hub in Fig. 3). Fixtures may also be used to guide the broach when it moves over or through the workpiece.

Fixtures used in broaching must not obstruct the removal of chips. Broaching fixtures must provide more holding force and more rigidity and support than fixtures for most other machining operations, because more teeth are cutting at any one time than is normal for other operations.

Broaching fixtures may be manual, semiautomatic, or automatic. Cost considerations and the quantity of parts to be broached will largely determine

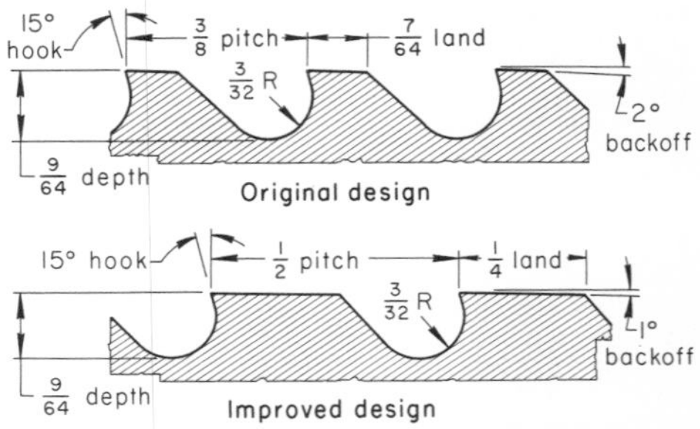

Fig. 18. Conventional and revised designs of broach used to cut 4340 steel at Rockwell C 46 to 49 (Example 123)

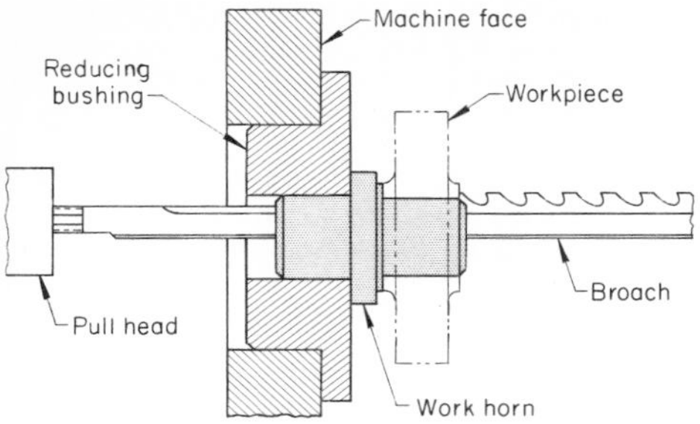

Fig. 19. Work horn that positions part and guides broach, during broaching of keyway. See text for discussion.

the type of fixture used. Semiautomatic and automatic fixtures may be operated pneumatically, hydraulically, or mechanically.

Types. The fixture employed may be as simple as a concave backup plate for positioning the piece. Such a plate was used with the pinion gear shown in Fig. 16; here, the pressure of the plate on the workpiece held it firmly as the broach was pulled through. A more elaborate, and more typical, workholding fixture is shown in Fig. 21.

A simple fixture known as a "work horn" is a special type of faceplate used when broaching keyways (see Fig. 19). A ground diameter on the back of the horn fits snugly into the machine platen or into a reducing bushing, depending on the size of the workpiece. A round pilot on the opposite end is ground about 0.001 in. smaller than the hole in the work for accurate positioning of the work. The horn is slotted to provide a guide for the broach. The depth of the slot in the horn and the height of the last tooth on the keyway broach determine the depth of the broached keyway. The horn is hardened and all functioning surfaces ground to size. All faces of the horn are accurately produced to hold the workpiece square and parallel to the axis of broach travel. The force that is applied to the workpiece by the broach as it is being pulled through the cut, holds the workpiece firmly in position.

An unusual method of "fixturing" a part during broaching is described in the following example:

Example 124. Fixturing by Means of Low-Melting Alloy (Fig. 20)

To position and hold a small vane for a jet-engine turbine wheel during broaching of a dovetail on the mounting end, a low-melting (about 375 F) bismuth alloy was cast around the blade end, leaving the mounting end exposed for broaching. The vane and holding method are shown in Fig. 20. After broaching, the vanes were freed from the holding metal by being placed, still embedded, in the melting pot used to heat the bismuth alloy for casting. Because the specific gravity of the holding metal was greater than that of the vanes, the vanes floated to the surface for retrieval when the holding metal melted away.

A special double fixture that was devised for use in the broaching of crankpins is described in Example 136 in this article.

Selection of Broach Length

Length of the broach usually is determined by three interrelated factors: (*a*) material to be broached, (*b*) type of cut, and (*c*) dimensions of the cut.

Material to be cut has a double influence on the required length of the broach or broach holder. In the broaching of hard metals, chips must be thinner to avoid damage to the broach teeth and to reduce power requirements; thus, more teeth are required to remove hard metal than to remove the same amount of a soft metal that permits deeper cuts.

The type of work metal determines the type of chip. Brass and cast iron produce chips that break up readily and can be packed into a smaller volume than chips from malleable iron, steel, aluminum and titanium, which produce continuous chips that coil and fill more space. Larger gullets (chip spaces) must be provided for the metals that form coiled chips. In some broaches, the gullet can be made deeper to accommodate the greater chip volume; in other broaches, however, deepening the gullet would make the broach too weak for service, and so the pitch of the teeth is increased, permitting a longer gullet and increasing the length of the broach and the stroke.

Type of cut — that is, whether the cut is internal or external, or whether it is a simple cut or one with a keyway, spline, or dovetail shape — influences the length of the broach. For example, if a dovetail form is to be broached, the broach must be almost twice as long as required for a keyway slot of comparable size, because the general procedure is first to broach a simple slot and then to follow with cutters that will shape and size the dovetail form.

Length and depth of cut may have the greatest influence on the length of the broach, particularly on internal cuts. Chips accumulate in the gullets of the teeth. As the cut increases in length, more chip capacity is required for the same amount of tooth advance. Adequate space must be provided to prevent damage to the broach or the surface being broached. It is desirable that chips be loose enough in the gullet so that they fall away (or can be washed away) from the broach when the gullet clears the work. Thus, for increased length of cut, the size of the gullet is increased or the amount of step per tooth is decreased, or both. For similar materials and the removal of similar amounts of metal, the broach must increase in length proportionately as the surface to be broached increases in length.

Table 4. Nominal Speeds and Feeds for Broaching Steel and Gray Iron With High Speed Steel Tools (a)

Work metal	Brinell hardness	Speed, sfm	Feed, ipt
Carbon and Low-Alloy Steels			
Non-free-cutting	85 to 125	30	0.004
	125 to 175	25	0.004
	175 to 225	20	0.004
	225 to 275	20	0.003
	275 to 325	15	0.003
	325 to 375	10	0.002
Free-cutting	100 to 200	30	0.004
	200 to 250	25	0.003
	275 to 325	20	0.003
	325 to 375	20	0.002
Gray Irons			
Classes 20 and 25	110 to 140	30	0.005
Class 30	150 to 190	30	0.004
Classes 35 and 40	190 to 220	25	0.003
Classes 45 and 50	220 to 260	20	0.003
Classes 55 and 60	250 to 320	15	0.002
Stainless Steels			
Ferritic	135 to 185	20	0.003
Austenitic	185 to 185	20	0.003
	225 to 275	15	0.003
Martensitic	140 to 225	25	0.004
	225 to 275	20	0.003
	275 to 325	15	0.002
	375 to 425	5	0.001
PH grades	150 to 200	15	0.002
	275 to 325	15	0.002
	325 to 375	8	0.002
	375 to 440	5	0.001

(a) For M2 high speed steel tools, except that M3, T5 or T15 tools are more suitable for broaching the harder or less machinable work metals. (Data are adapted from tables compiled by Metcut Research Associates, Inc.)

Selection of Speed of Stroke

The major consideration in the selection of optimum broaching speed is the need to operate at the lowest over-all cost. Related considerations are type and hardness of work metal, rigidity of the workpiece, and length of the cut.

Cost. Up to a point, increasing broach speed will increase the number of pieces that can be produced per hour. Beyond that point, however, as broach speed is increased, the number of parts that can be produced between sharpenings (and thus the total parts produced by a broach) will decrease. Maximum efficiency and minimum cost are achieved when that point is determined.

Initial broach cost, setup costs and broach maintenance costs are relatively high when compared to cost per man-hour of machining time. Therefore, the maximum number of acceptable pieces that can be produced between sharpenings has a greater influence on maximum efficiency and minimum cost than does the total number of pieces produced per hour.

Work Metal. In general, steels are broached at speeds of 10 to 30 sfm. The speed will vary with the hardness of the steel. Hard or tough steels are broached at lower speeds than the free-machining types. Some steels that are relatively soft are difficult to broach without galling or tearing, which results in unacceptable surface finish. Although this can often be corrected by a change in tooth angle or in cutting fluid, an increase in cutter speed will also provide a better finish. Nominal speeds and feeds per tooth for broaching carbon and alloy steels are given in Table 4.

Stainless steels are broached at speeds ranging from 5 sfm, for the harder types, to 25 sfm, for the free-machining types.

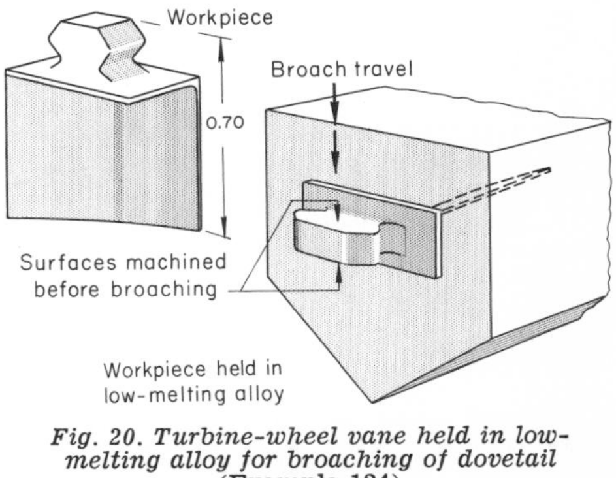

Fig. 20. Turbine-wheel vane held in low-melting alloy for broaching of dovetail (Example 124)

Cast iron and malleable iron are broached at speeds up to 30 sfm with high speed steel broaches, and at 120 sfm with carbide broaches.

Brass and bronze are broached at speeds of 25 to 30 sfm. Aluminum and magnesium usually can be broached at the highest speed of which a machine is capable. With tough alloys such as A-286, René 41 and AM-355, best broach life is obtained at speeds below 20 sfm, and sometimes as low as 5 sfm.

For additional information on speeds and feeds for broaching metals other than steel, see the broaching sections of articles dealing with the machining of cast iron, stainless steel, heat-resisting alloys, aluminum alloys, and other specific metals, in this volume.

Rigidity. The rigidity of the part and of the fixturing employed affects the most efficient cutting speed of the broach. Slight movement of the part, or vibration set up from cutter contact, can cause fracture of the cutting edge of the broach. High cutting speed usually increases the occurrence of fractured edges.

Length of Cut. All other factors being equal, surface speed must be decreased as the length of material to be broached increases. Broach life can be shortened if high speeds are employed in the cutting of long areas, because of the heat generated; trapped chips and restricted cutting fluid exposure (especially in horizontal broaching) usually generate more heat than in a similar operation with a shorter length to broach.

Cutting Fluids

Oils that are relatively high in viscosity and contain substantial amounts of fat, plus compounds of sulfur or chlorine or both, are most commonly used as cutting fluids for broaching steel, stainless steel, and cast iron. Sometimes these oils are used for broaching other metals. These specially prepared oil-base compounds are proprietary, but are readily available. They are frequently referred to as "broaching oils", although they are also used for other machining operations.

In Examples 103, 105, 106, 109, 110, 119, 123 and 126, oils belonging to this general class were used. Steels of several compositions and hardness levels, as well as cast iron and heat-resisting alloys, were the work metals included in these examples. One oil that is commonly used has a viscosity of approximately 155 sus and contains 2% fat, 0.8% active sulfur, and 2.1% chlorine (Examples 103 and 118).

Broaching oils are considered most effective in preventing adherence of work metal to the broach, thus producing the best finishes, dimensional accuracy, and broach life, other conditions being equal. Discriminating selection among the various proprietary broaching oils is usually based on experience with similar applications, and very often if tool life or finish on the part is poor, a change of broaching oil should be tried. For instance, in Example 106, broach life between regrinds was increased 50% by changing from a blend of sulfurized oils to a special high-fat oil (before broach material was changed for further increase).

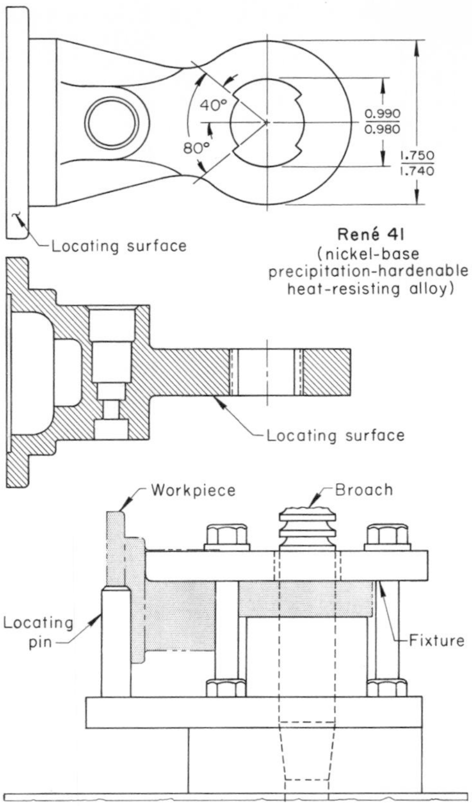

Broach Details

Over-all length	19 in.
Pitch	7/32 in.
Gullet depth	0.093 in.
Gullet radius	3/64 in.
Cutting-relief backoff angle	2°
Face angle	15°
Tooth land	0.062 in.
Tooth load	0.004 in.

Production, Tool Life and Costs

Minutes per piece	4.50
Pieces per hour	13.33
Broach speed	96 in. per min
Pieces per grind	9
Grinds per broach	6
Initial broach cost	$136.00
Cost per grind	$3.50
Broach cost per piece (incl. grinding)	$2.90

Frequent regrinds were required, and broach life was short, in broaching the René 41 cylinder end shown at top. Lower part of illustration shows method of fixturing.

Fig. 21. Broaching René 41 (Example 125)

Disadvantages of broaching oils are: (*a*) higher initial cost than for common cutting oils; (*b*) staining of some metals such as copper alloys; (*c*) necessity for 100% removal from heat-resisting alloys before they are heat treated or placed in high-temperature service; and (*d*) poorer ability to cool and remove chips than some other cutting fluids such as soluble-oil emulsions, because of their higher viscosity.

Water-soluble oils (1 part oil mixed with 15 to 20 parts water) are often used. They provide acceptable results in the broaching of steel, as well as other metals (Examples 120 and 136). Water-soluble oils are more effective for cooling and flushing chips away, but are far less effective for preventing adherence of the work metal to the broach than are the broaching oils. In Example 126, broach life between resharpenings was increased 50% when the cutting fluid was changed from soluble oil to a sulfurized oil.

Aluminum and some other soft nonferrous metals are sometimes broached without cutting fluid, although there are light oils that are especially prepared for broaching aluminum (Example 128). Copper alloys are susceptible to staining from oils containing sulfur and chlorine. When staining cannot be tolerated, kerosine containing 10 to 20% lard oil is often used.

Cast iron is sometimes broached without cutting fluid (Example 115). Whether or not a cutting fluid is used depends to a large extent on the need for cooling and chip removal, because cast iron is a free-cutting metal.

Regardless of which cutting fluid is used, it is of utmost importance to obtain an adequate supply at the cutting edges. This is more easily accomplished in vertical broaching than in horizontal broaching. In some horizontal broaching, the problem of supply at the critical areas can be solved only by coating the workpieces with an extremely viscous cutting fluid before broaching (Example 108). However, pumps supplied with the machines will usually force the cutting fluid into critical areas.

For additional information on cutting fluids, see the articles in this volume on machining of specific metals.

Effect of Work Metal and Hardness on Broach Life

Some metals are inherently difficult to broach and have a detrimental effect on broach life. The poor tool life obtained in broaching René 41, a typical difficult-to-broach alloy, is described in the example that follows:

Example 125. Short Broach Life With René 41 (Fig. 21)

In broaching the René 41 cylinder end shown at the top in Fig. 21, it was necessary to regrind the broach after every nine pieces, to maintain a satisfactory cutting edge. And, although only 0.004 to 0.006 in. of metal was removed from the broach at each sharpening, only six regrinds per broach were possible. For this operation, a 10-ton vertical machine was used. During broaching, the cylinder ends were fixtured as shown in the lower part of Fig. 21. Broach details and data on tool life and cost are given in the table accompanying Fig. 21.

Hardness. The effect of the hardness of the workpiece on broach life, and thus on broach cost per piece broached, is shown in Table 5, which compares results obtained in broaching internal shapes in four different production parts, each of a different steel and hardness. Although these data indicate that as workpiece hardness increased, total pieces per broach decreased and broach cost per piece increased, it should not be assumed that soft metals are always easily broached. Some metals (steels in particular) are too soft to be broached successfully, because they readily become welded to the cutting edges of the broach. This results in decreased production, shorter tool life, and increased operating costs. Welding may be minimized by the use of highly chlorinated or sulfurized cutting oils and by providing broach teeth with extremely high face and relief angles. High relief angles, however, reduce the num-

Table 5. Effect of Workpiece Hardness on Broach Life and Cost in Internal Broaching of Steel(a)

Steel and hardness	Length of cut, in.	Shape broached	Pieces broached per hour	Pieces per sharpening	Total pieces per broach	Broach cost per piece
1020, Rockwell C 3 to 16 ..	1.375	Square	50 to 70	2500	48,000	$0.004
1026, Rockwell C 16	0.605	Spline	90 to 120	4000	36,000	$0.006
8620, Rockwell C 25 to 30 .	1.50	Serrations	60 to 90	1500	28,500	$0.007
4140, Rockwell C 27 to 33 .	0.963	Spline	90 to 120	1000	24,000	$0.010

(a) For all operations, broaches were of M2 high speed steel, and cutting fluid was a chlorinated sulfur-base oil with lard oil added to obtain a suitable viscosity.

ber of regrinds possible before the broach loses its ability to hold dimensions. This reduces the effective life of the broach and can add substantially to over-all production cost. When practical, hardening of steel workpieces to Rockwell C 22 to 28 often is a better solution. Much of the welding will be eliminated.

Corrective measures that were taken against workpiece welding in one production application are described in the following example:

Example 126. Increase in Work-Metal Hardness to Increase Broach Life

In an over-running clutch plate of 1146 steel, eight cam splines were broached from the solid. This plate, which was 4½ in. in diameter and ¾ in. thick, was required to have high dimensional accuracy, and a finish of 80 to 100 micro-in. on the cam surfaces.

Originally, the plates were broached from fully annealed stock with a hardness of Rockwell B 86, using broaches made of M2 high speed steel at Rockwell C 64 to 66 and a water-soluble cutting fluid. Although 1146 steel offers some resistance to welding because of its high sulfur content, welding of the work metal to the broach was a problem. Moreover, tearing and distortion of the critical cam surfaces occurred, and only 500 pieces could be broached before the broach required sharpening.

When the cutting fluid was changed to a heavy sulfurized cutting oil, 750 to 1000 pieces could be broached between sharpenings. A heat treating operation was then incorporated, in which the parts were hardened to Rockwell C 28 to 32 before broaching. In this hardened condition, 1700 to 2000 pieces could be broached before broach sharpening was required. To obtain still greater efficiency, the broach material was revised to M3 high speed steel at Rockwell C 65.5 to 67. This permitted the broaching of 2500 pieces between sharpenings — five times the original broach life.

Effect of Carbon Content. Low-carbon steels (less than 0.25% carbon) in the annealed condition are often more difficult to broach than are medium-carbon steels, because low-carbon steels have a greater tendency to weld to the broach teeth. Heat treatment such as was used advantageously for broaching clutch plates in Example 126 is not always practical.

The example that follows describes an application where selection of a steel with a higher carbon content (with accompanying increase in hardness) improved results in broaching.

Example 127. Broaching 94B15 vs 8622 (Table 6)

Differential side gears weighing 7.06 lb before broaching and 6.5 lb after were originally made from 94B15 steel at 143 Bhn. To increase broach life and reduce cost of broaching the internal splines, the steel was changed to 8622 at 163 Bhn. Broach life and tool cost per piece broached from the two steels are compared in Table 6. Broaching procedure was the same for both steels, including speed of 25 sfm, and a broaching oil was used. The results were acceptable in both instances, including a surface finish no rougher than 125 micro-in. Additional manufacturing details are given in Table 6.

Dimensional Accuracy

Broaching is capable of providing and maintaining close tolerances during a long production run. This is inherent in the process for several reasons. Although broaching combines roughing and finishing cuts in a single broach, no single broach tooth performs both functions. Each successive tooth removes only a predetermined amount of metal and is in cutting contact only as long as it takes to pass over the work one time, and so a minimum amount of heat is developed. Also, the finishing teeth are shielded from the heavier cuts by both the roughing and the intermediate teeth, thus giving the finishing teeth maximum production life.

The broach-tooth shape permits repeated sharpening without loss of accuracy. Finishing teeth may have flat lands 0.005 to 0.030 in. in width on each tooth. Thus, a tooth may be sharpened without sacrificing any dimension. However, this land must be held to a practical minimum. A straight land increases friction, and the resulting heat may cause the broach to expand enough to cause galling of the broached surface, or even to exceed the tolerance.

It is unnecessary to sharpen all finishing teeth each time the tool is sharpened. Common practice is to sharpen only the first, or the first and second finishing teeth until they have become undersize. Then the second, or the third and fourth teeth are sharpened (depending on whether a single tooth or two teeth are sharpened each time) when the broach has again become dull. This practice permits the broach to hold tolerance for a long production run.

Table 6. Broach Life and Cost for Broaching Splines in Gears Made of 94B15 vs 8622 (Example 127)

Item	94B15 (143 Bhn)	8622 (163 Bhn)
Broach life (18 grinds):		
Parts per grind	418	507
Total per broach	7650	9126
Broach cost, per part	$0.055	$0.046

NOTE: Both steels were broached in a 30-ton vertical machine using a 58-in.-long broach with a uniform taper step-up; 40% of the broach teeth were used for the round hole and 60% for the splines.

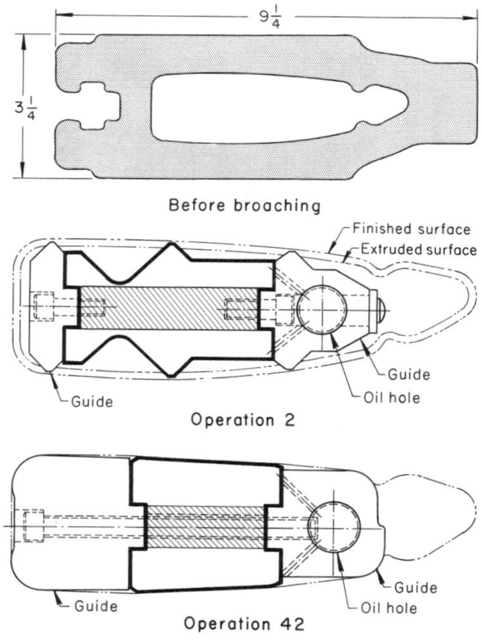

Fig. 22. Cross section of a 23-ft-long helicopter spar that was extruded from an aluminum alloy and broached the entire length of the inside contour using 42 different broaches (Example 128)

The following example illustrates the high degree of dimensional accuracy that is obtainable in broaching:

Example 128. Dimensional Accuracy in a 23-Ft-Long Spar (Fig. 22)

The 23-ft-long helicopter spar shown in cross section in Fig. 22 represents what is probably the maximum length that is practical to broach. Yet in the production of this part, which entailed the use of 42 separate broaches, dimensional specifications were satisfactorily met.

The spar was extruded from aluminum alloy 2014-T4, and approximately ⅛ in. of stock was provided on the inside for finishing. Broaching was done in a 15-ton horizontal machine with a 26-ft, 8-in. stroke. A special fixture at the front of the machine held the spar during broaching. Roughing was performed by 34 of the 42 broaches; eight broaches were used for finishing. Two men were required for operating the machine — one to load the broaches onto the puller, and one to unload the broaches at the exit end and place them on a conveyor for return to the loading end.

After the spar was positioned on the fixture, the long pull bar attached to the machine ram was fed through the spar. Then, successively, each of the 42 broaches was attached, pulled through the spar, removed, and conveyed to the loading end. The roughing broaches were pulled through at 80 ft per min; finishing broaches, at 20 ft per min. Total time to complete one spar was about 4 hr.

Cutting fluid was a special light oil mixture designed for use with aluminum. It was pumped at 100 psi through the pull bar into the broach holders or guides and on into the broaches. Holes in the broaches directed the oil to the cutting edges of the teeth, and also flushed away chips. Broach teeth were designed to produce short chips; this minimized the tendency of chips to pack and impede cutting, and thus to cause galling of the broached surface.

Despite the length of the spar and the complexity of the operation, a dimensional tolerance of +0.002, −0.000 in. on the cross section was maintained, and the internal contours were produced straight within 0.003 in. in any 3-ft length. A surface finish of 32 micro-in. or better was obtained.

Typical variations in dimensions obtained in three production applications of broaching are given in the examples that follow:

Examples 129, 130 and 131. Variations Found in Broaching Different Contours

Example 129 — Round Holes (Fig. 23). Dimensional variation obtained in broaching a hole 0.5624/0.5618 in. in diameter in a ball head forged from 1036 steel is plotted in Fig. 23. Broaching was done in a dual-ram vertical machine that was in good condition. Ram and table guides had clearance within the 0.002 in. that is considered maximum for "good" condition. During broaching, each part

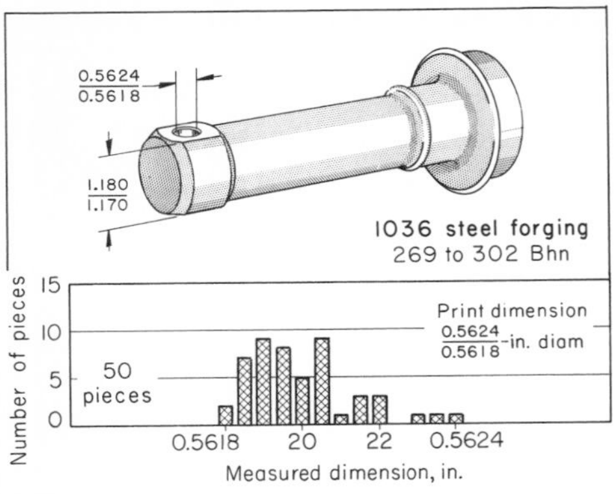

Fig. 23. Dimensional variations in broaching a round hole (Example 129)

was located by an indexing fixture; the floating broach holder was held in approximate position by a forked arm to the control rod, and the broach was centered by the lead angle on its pilot. The data in Fig. 23 are from measurements on 50 pieces — ten at random from each of five batches of 100.

Example 130 — Splines and Open-Side Areas (Fig. 24). Variations in dimensions of two areas that were broached in an axle-hub yoke of pearlitic malleable iron are plotted in Fig. 24. For broaching the inside faces to the 2.127/2.125-in. dimension, a dual-ram surface broaching machine was used. This machine had a capacity of 10 tons and a 54-in. stroke. A vertical 10-ton pull-down machine was used for broaching the 1.0628/1.0618-in. splined hole. Both machines were in good condition and had ram and table clearance of 0.002 in. The data on both dimensions in Fig. 24 are from measurements on 50 pieces — ten at random from each of five batches of 100.

Example 131 — Keyways (Fig. 25). The nodular iron casting shown in Fig. 25 required a keywayed through hole broached to the dimensions shown. Parts were broached at the rate of 152 per hour. Approximately 1000 pieces could be broached between regrinds, and the broaches usually could be reground eight times. Figure 25 plots keyway width at entrance and exit ends of every fifth piece in a 250-piece batch.

Because the part shown in Fig. 25 is a rigid casting, the difference in spread between the entering and the exiting dimensions (particularly for dimension B) points out a condition that must be considered in broaching parts with relatively thin walls. Broach-tooth shape and sharpness strongly influence the generated forces that tend to push the part walls outward. To maintain tolerances on some thin-wall parts, it may be necessary to revise the shape of the broach teeth or to increase the frequency of sharpening. Differences in depth of broached keyways at the entrance and exit ends are common. To compensate for the differences, the slot in the horn is often tapered.

Broaching vs Alternative Processes

Many parts can be produced by more than one process. Selecting the most efficient process requires consideration of available equipment, quantity to be produced, dimensional accuracy, surface finish and workpiece material.

Compared with reaming, broaching can hold a closer tolerance for a longer production run. The cutting edges of a reamer are constantly in contact with the work as long as the reamer is cutting; thus, the reamer travels many times around the circumference of the hole before the hole is complete. Although a reamer has a margin conforming to the circumference of the hole being reamed (comparable to the flat land on a broach tooth), which permits some sharpening of the reamer without loss of tolerance, considerably more grinding is done on a reamer than on a broach. This is because, in a reamer, fewer teeth are required to remove the same amount of metal as is removed by a greater number of teeth in a broach.

With respect to tolerance capabilities and tool life, milling also may suffer in comparison with broaching. Although a milling cutter usually has more cutting edges than a reamer, in milling as in reaming, each cutting tooth is required to do more work than is performed by any one tooth on a broach.

In Examples 132 through 139, broaching is compared with four alternative machining processes (gear shaping, reaming, milling and grinding) on the basis of costs, tool life, finish and tolerance capabilities, and other criteria of operating efficiency.

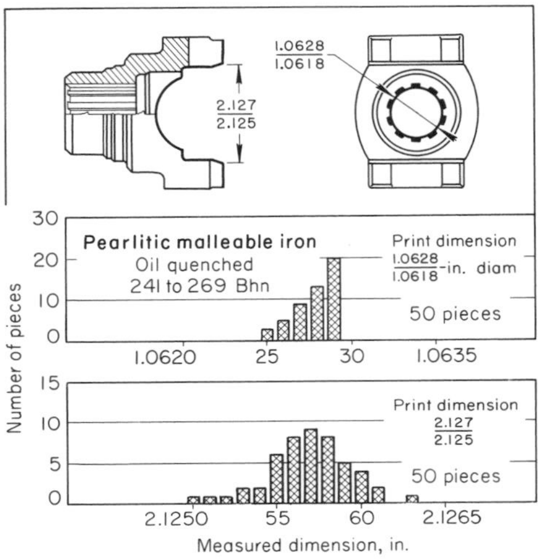

Fig. 24. Dimensional variations in broaching splines and open-side areas (Example 130)

Example 132. Broaching vs Gear Shaping (Fig. 26)

To reduce manufacturing costs, broaching was substituted for gear shaping as the method of producing the internal gear teeth in the part shown in Fig. 26. This part, a component of a planetary gear system, was made of 4140 steel, and was heat treated to Rockwell C 32 to 35 before machining. Production requirements were 6000 pieces per year, in lots of 1000.

The gear shaper used employed a 1-in.-diam shank-type cutter, which was operated at 250 strokes per minute and a feed of 0.0075 in. per stroke. The workpiece was held in place by an air-clamped fixture of the collet type. Total manufacturing cost per piece for gear shaping was $1.033.

Broaching was done in a horizontal machine of 6-ton capacity having a 48-in. stroke. A solid pull broach with a cutting section 12 in. long was used at a speed of 22 ft per min. The part was positioned by being nested in a ring adapter, and was held in place by the force of broaching. Total manufacturing cost per piece for broaching was $0.225 — a saving of nearly 80% in relation to the cost for gear shaping.

Gear data, together with a cost comparison of the two processes, are given in the table accompanying Fig. 26.

It should not be inferred from the comparison in Example 132 (Fig. 26) that all similar gear-shaping operations could be replaced at less expense by broaching. Broaches are expensive tools, and any revision in the design of a gear (such as a change in the number of teeth or the pitch diameter) would require a new broach. Furthermore, broaching costs are directly affected by the hardness of the material to be broached and by the tolerances applied to the broached shape. The flexibility of gear shapers minimizes these problems; the same shaping cutter can be used for gears having the same diametral pitch and pressure angle but having a different number of teeth and modified pitch diameters. Gear shapers also can be adjusted to compensate for cutter wear. (See "Machining of Gears", pages 194 to 213 in this volume.)

A study was made to determine the effect of three conditions of the availability of tooling on the cost of producing the internal gear on the part shown in Fig. 26 in various quantities by broaching or by shaping in a gear shaper. The three conditions studied were as follows:

1 Where no tooling is available
2 Where tooling is available for either process
3 Where tooling is available for shaping but must be purchased for broaching.

The results of the study are plotted in Fig. 27; tool cost is amortized for all quantities.

Examples 133 and 134. Broaching vs Reaming

Example 133 — Valve Guide (Fig. 28). The 0.344/0.343-in. diameter of the valve guide shown in Fig. 28 originally was reamed in a six-spindle bar machine. The reaming station was run at 800 rpm and a feed rate of 8 in. per min; production was 157 pieces per hour. To maintain a finish of 40 to 50 micro-in. on

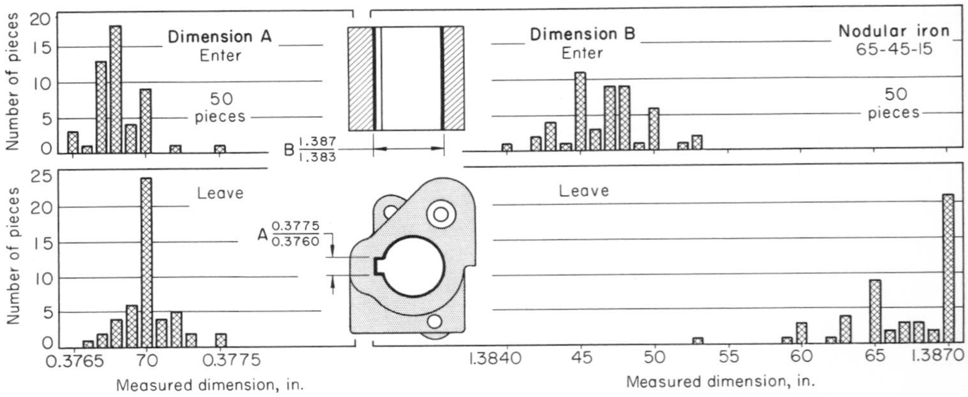

Fig. 25. Dimensional variations of a broached keyway, showing the difference in variation between the dimensions where the broach entered the part and where it left (Example 131)

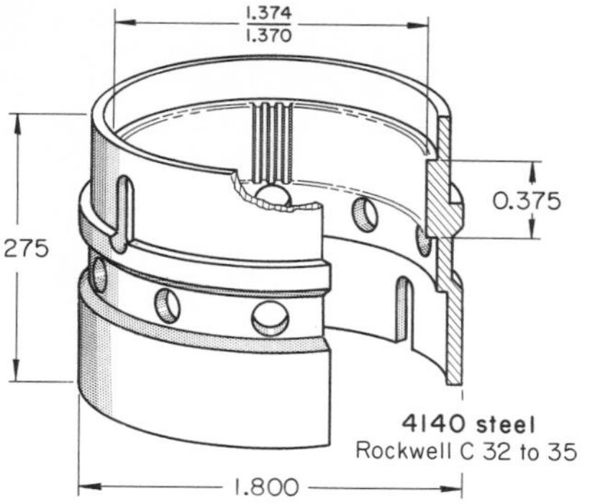

Gear Data

Number of teeth	56
Diametral pitch	40
Pressure angle	25°
Pitch diameter	1.400 in.
Tooth form	Full involute
Backlash allowance	None
Maximum circular tooth thickness	0.03927 in.
AGMA quality	Commercial class 2

Costs per Part Produced(a)

	Gear shaping	Broaching
Setup	$0.015(b)	$0.005(c)
Operation	0.738(d)	0.189(e)
Cutter (sharpening and replacement)	0.280(f)	0.031(g)
Total	$1.033	$0.225

(a) Costs are for producing parts in lots of 1000; the manufacturing cost of $8.10 per hour used in computing setup and operation costs is composed of direct labor and burden. (b) 1.87 hr × $8.10 ÷ 1000. (c) 0.65 hr × $8.10 ÷ 1000. (d) 0.091 hr × $8.10. (e) 0.0233 hr × $8.10. (f) Two shank cutters, at $110 each. (g) Two broaches, at $156 each.

Fig. 26. Part with internal gear teeth that were produced by gear shaping and by broaching (Example 132)

the workpiece, the four-flute carbide-tipped reamer had to be resharpened frequently. Had a finer reamed finish been required, it would have been necessary to use a feed rate of less than 8 in. per min.

By an improved method, guides that had been finish machined on the outside were pressed into cylinder heads (eight guides to a head). The eight guides were then simultaneously broached, at a speed of 15 ft per min. The operating broach length was 6 in.; hence, one cylinder head (eight guides) was broached every 2 min. The finish obtained by broaching these parts was 20 to 30 micro-in. Had finer finishes been required, burnishing buttons (see the Burnishing section on page 72) could have been added to the broaches.

Studies of tool life showed that a broach was capable of producing an average of 15,000 pieces before becoming undersize, whereas a reamer could produce only 11,000 pieces.

Example 134 — Long Thin-Wall Part (Fig. 29). The inside of a part formed from low-carbon steel sheet (top sections in Fig. 29) was originally reamed. Only 15 pieces could be produced per hour, and it was difficult to maintain the inside diameter within the assigned 1.1290/1.1265 in.

Although the combination of thin walls and 36⅞-in. length made this part borderline, broaching with a pull-type tool was substituted for reaming. Details of the M2 high speed steel broach employed are shown in Fig. 29. The first 11 teeth were serrated; this design was used to make the broach pull straight by approaching finish size rapidly and minimizing drift. From tooth 12 to the end of the broach, teeth were made round and stepped, so that they began cutting the high spots left by the serrated teeth until size was attained. With broaching, production rate was quadrupled, to 60 pieces per hour, and inside-diameter and finish requirements (125 micro-in. maximum) were readily met.

Examples 135 to 138. Broaching vs Milling

Example 135 — External Contours (Fig. 30). Changing from milling to broaching as the method of producing the external contours of the part shown in Fig. 30 resulted in a 58%

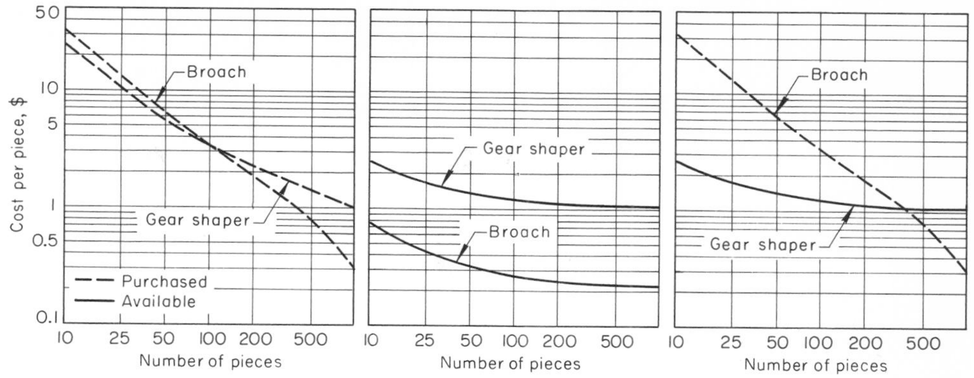

Fig. 27. Effect of availability of tooling and of quantity produced on cost per piece for cutting the internal gear teeth shown in Fig. 26, by gear shaping and by broaching. Cost of purchased tools is amortized for all quantities produced.

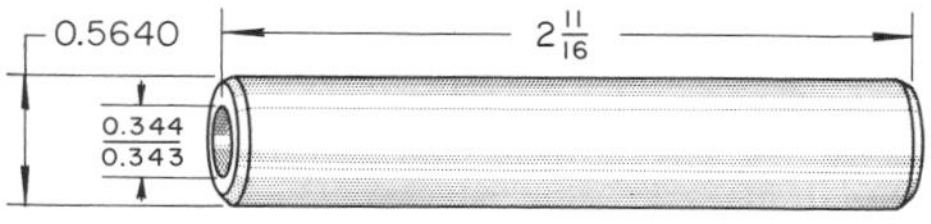

Fig. 28. Valve guide for which broaching was more satisfactory than reaming for finishing the hole (Example 133)

increase in production rate and a 100% increase in tool life. This part, a drive sprocket used in tractors and military tanks, was rough cut by torch before being machined. In producing the external contours, 3/32 in. of stock was removed. Production data for the two methods (milling and broaching) are given in the tabulation accompanying Fig. 30.

Because a single broach that could cut the shape from tooth tip to tooth tip would have been too difficult to manufacture and sharpen, broaches were designed that machined one side of one tooth and the opposite side of an adjacent tooth, broaching each space as one operation, but with each radius cut by a separate broach section.

The method of broaching employed introduced the problem of blending radii, but sharpening of the broach sections for this operation was fairly easy. A solid, full-contour broach could be sharpened on the cutting face only. However, on the broach for cutting a simple curve not extending more than 90° of a circle, the outer edge or land could be ground. The broach section was then accurately positioned by being shimmed inwardly by the amount that had been removed in grinding. During about every third or fourth sharpening, the cutting face of each tooth had to be ground to provide maximum sharpness over the life of the broach.

Example 136 — High Production of Flats (Fig. 31). The four flats on the crankpin shown in Fig. 31 were first produced by milling, but accuracy could not be maintained at the production rate required (1440 pieces per hour), partly because sufficiently rigid clamping for milling was difficult.

When broaching was chosen to replace milling, the crankpins (type 416 stainless steel at Rockwell B 86 to 100) were broached in a special two-station horizontal machine, hydraulically operated, with a capacity of 2½ tons and a 12-in. stroke. The M3 high speed steel surface broaches employed were 10 in. long and had 33 teeth; size increase per tooth was 0.0016 in. A 15-to-1 mixture of water and soluble oil was used as cutting fluid. Setup time was 10 to 12 hr; downtime for changing tools was 3 hr.

To meet production and tolerance requirements, a special double fixture was developed. This fixture was hydraulically operated and reciprocated horizontally. In operation, one side of the fixture clamped onto a part that was automatically fed to it from a hopper, pushed the part between a set of stationary broaches (which broached all four flats simultaneously), and released the part at the end of the stroke. During this time, the other side of the fixture returned to pick up the next part to be broached.

The clamp that held the crankpins during broaching was integral with the moving ram. The cradling half of the clamp was X-shaped and had a concave section to fit the crankpin and into which the pin was dropped auto-

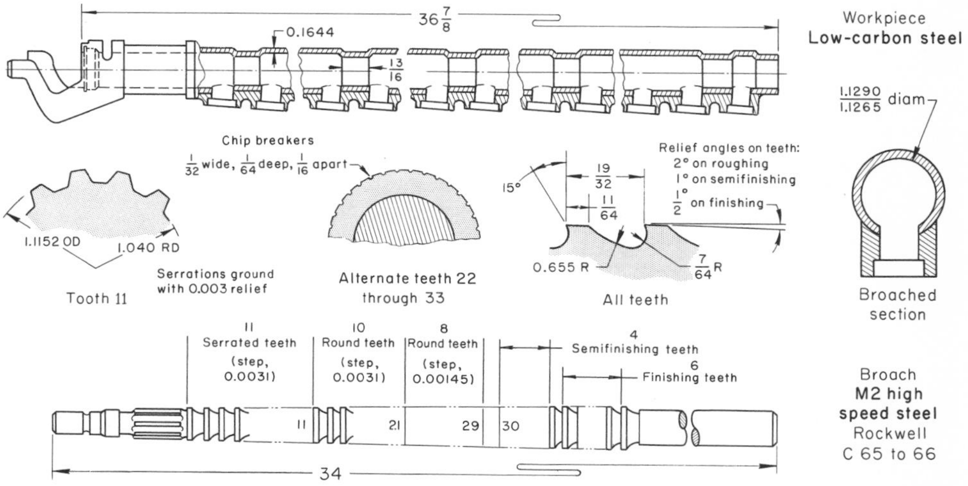

Parts were broached, one at a time, in a horizontal machine with a 56-in. stroke; cutting fluid was an extreme-pressure cutting oil, chlorinated but having no active sulfur, with a viscosity of 160 SUS at 100 F. Broaches (sketched in detail above) produced 300 pieces between sharpenings, and could be reground 15 times (total life, 4500 pieces). Downtime for changing tools was 15 min; regrinding required 1 hr and cost $3.50 per grind.

Fig. 29. Thin-wall part for which broaching of the inside diameter was more accurate and yielded higher production than reaming. Broach is shown below the part. (Example 134)

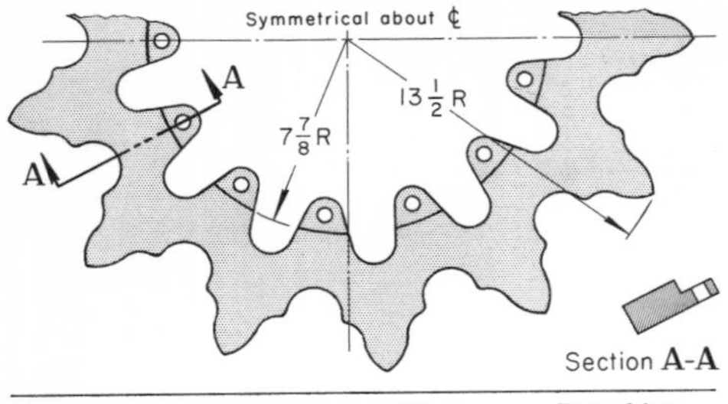

Item	Milling	Broaching
Type of machine	Rail, 56-72	Vertical, 10-66
Net weight, lb	35,110	18,080
Floor space, sq ft .	159½	43½
Weeks to build	49	37
Speed, ft per min ...	30 to 54	27
Horsepower required	23	25
Production, pcs/hr ..	6	9.5
Pieces per grind	250	600
Regrinds per cutter .	30	25
Pieces per cutter ...	7500	15,000

Fig. 30. External contours of drive sprocket for which broaching proved superior to milling (Example 135)

matically from the hopper. A cam-actuated, carbide-faced wedge moved across the part and, because of its wedge shape, applied sufficient force to the part to hold it rigidly in place during broaching. At the end of the broaching stroke, the broached crankpin dropped away from the fixture when the cam-actuated wedge was withdrawn. The clamp was then returned, automatically, to engage another crankpin and repeat the cycle.

Each slide made 720 strokes per hour (1440 pieces for the machine). At an over-all efficiency of 75%, in two 8-hr shifts an average of 17,280 pieces were produced that adequately met requirements. Broaches could produce 50,000 to 60,000 pieces between resharpenings. Cost data for broaching are given in the table below Fig. 31.

Example 137 — Slot and Radius (Fig. 32). On the basis of the cost comparison tabulated with Fig. 32, broaching was chosen in preference to milling for producing the configurations at the two ends of the part sketched in Fig. 32. The costs listed represent actual costs for broaching, and carefully estimated costs for milling. This part, an upset forging of 6150 steel, used as a push rod in a ratchet mechanism, was produced in lots of 3000; annual production was 12,000.

The parts were broached using a 10-ton, 60-in.-stroke vertical broaching machine, 10-in.-long broaching cutters mounted in subholders, and manually operated screw-clamp holding fixtures. The first operation consisted of cutting the 0.255/0.250-in. slot and finishing one face of the enlarged section to a 0.505/0.490-in. dimension. This was followed by broaching the radiused contour at the opposite end of the part. Broach speed was 29.3 ft per min.

Milling costs are computed on the basis of a speed of 50 sfm and a feed of 0.007 ipt.

Example 138 — Flats on Drive-Arm Shaft (Fig. 33). Straddle milling proved inefficient for producing the flats on the ends of the drive-arm shaft shown in Fig. 33.

The shaft was made from ½-in.-diam bar stock of 1113 or 1213 steel, and had a hardness of Rockwell B 87 to 94. In pilot production, flats were straddle milled at one end of two pieces at a time. At 100% efficiency, 1.1 hr was required for milling 100 pieces (91 pieces per hour). Thus, in two 8-hr shifts, 1456 pieces could be completely milled. To achieve the assigned production rate of 15,000 pieces per day, 11 milling machines and fixtures would have been required — obviously, not a practical production setup. Furthermore, milling was not consistently accurate in meeting the tolerances specified for the part (+0°30′, −0°0′ on angles; ±0.0005 in. on dimensions).

When broaching was substituted for straddle milling, the production rate was 0.09 hr per 100 pieces at 100% efficiency, or 17,776 pieces per day (two 8-hr shifts), which adequately met production requirements.

Fixtured shafts were broached, one at a time, in a continuous horizontal machine carrying 15 fixtures, and having a capacity of 10 hp or 5 tons, and a 42-in. stroke, and using surface broaches of M3 high speed steel. Roughing broaches were 15 in. long and had 46 teeth; size increase per tooth was 0.0027 in. Finishing broaches were 10¼ in. long and had 32 teeth; size increase per tooth was 0.001 in. Broach speed was 40 ft per min; soluble-oil cutting fluid was used. Setup time was 19.5 hr; downtime for changing tools, 5 to 6 hr. Each broach produced 80,000 to 85,000 pieces per grind. Yearly cost of broach maintenance (including replacement) was $5620.

Example 139. Broaching vs Grinding (Fig. 34)

A differential shaft was first produced with opposed flats along its entire length, as shown in the upper view of Fig. 34. To allow the shaft to be centerless ground, the flats were ground *after* the centerless grinding operation. This design was satisfactory for small lots, because the part could be manufactured on standard machinery, at low tool cost.

Increased volume requirements made automation practical. This necessitated a revision in design so that advantage could be taken of the most economical processes. The shaft was redesigned as shown in the lower view of Fig. 34, to allow production of the flats by broaching, *before* centerless grinding of the shaft. The parts were broached in an automatic, ten-station transfer machine. A comparison of the processing steps for both the original and the redesigned shaft, and a summary of broaching conditions, are presented with Fig. 34.

Combination Broaching and Boring. In many applications where holes to be machined are no larger than approximately 6 in. in diameter (boring is invariably more practical for larger holes), broaching and boring are alternative processes. When keyways or other internal forms are required, it is common practice to bore the hole and then broach the keyway. However, for production quantities, the hole can be broached with the key slot in one operation, using a broach of proper design, as shown in the following example:

Example 140. Broaching vs Separate Boring and Broaching (Table 7)

A keyed shaft drove a pump impeller that was made from a bronze casting. The shaft hole was bored in a turret lathe, and then the keyway was broached in a horizontal machine. When production had to be increased, a new tool was designed to broach the shaft hole and the key slot in the same stroke of the broach. The new method, using only the horizontal broaching machine, caused a large increase in production rate, as shown in Table 7.

Burnishing

Burnishing is often done in conjunction with broaching, for one or more of the following reasons: (*a*) to provide a smoother surface than can be obtained by broaching, (*b*) to provide greater accuracy in the diameter of a hole, or (*c*) to provide a hole with a better wearing surface. Burnishing is accomplished by the use either of a broach designed especially for burnishing (upper broach in Fig. 35), or of a broach in which burnishing buttons have been incorporated following the finishing teeth (lower broach in Fig. 35). Burnishing buttons do no cutting; they smooth and cold work the surface.

The next two examples describe the burnishing tools shown in Fig. 35:

Example 141. Burnishing a Hole in an Aluminum Pump Body (Fig. 35)

The upper broach shown in Fig. 35 is a burnishing pull broach of M3 high speed steel, heat treated to Rockwell C 66 to 67. It was used for burnishing a broached hole in an

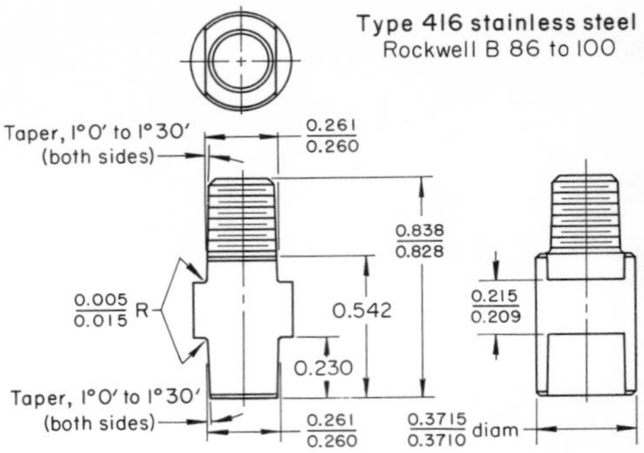

Broaching Cost Data

Amortization periods:	
Tools	1 year
Machine	10 years
Tool-maintenance cost per year(a)	$1000
Power cost per year(b)	$289
Labor costs per 100 pieces:	
Factory cost	$0.17
Total cost, including burden	$0.65
Cost of cutting fluid to load machine(c) ...	$4.43

(a) Includes purchase of new broaches. (b) For operation of one 7½-hp motor and one ½-hp motor. (c) 40 gal of cutting fluid consisting of 37½ gal of water and 2½ gal of lubricant (at $1.77 per gallon).

Fig. 31. Crankpin for which broaching replaced milling in the production of flats (Example 136)

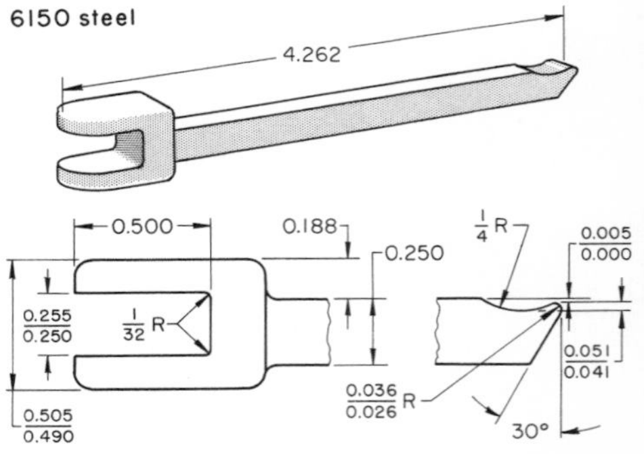

Item	Cost per piece(a) Milling	Broaching
Setup	$0.008(b)	$0.022 (c)
Operation	0.170(d)	0.140 (e)
Cutters(f)	0.056	0.034
Fixtures	0.009(g)	0.027(h)
Total	$0.243	$0.223

(a) Costs based on production in lots of 3000 (total, 12,000 per year). Manufacturing cost of $8.10 per hour used in computations consists of direct labor and burden. (b) 3 hr for entire lot × $8.10 ÷ 3000. (c) 8 hr for entire lot × $8.10 ÷ 3000. (d) 0.0210 hr per piece × $8.10. (e) 0.0173 hr per piece × $8.10. (f) Sharpening and replacement. (g) Initial cost, $535; 5-year amortization. (h) Includes cost of subholders, and represents 5-year amortization of $1635 initial cost of subholders and fixtures.

Fig. 32. Push rod for which broaching was more economical than milling for producing the configurations at both ends (Example 137)

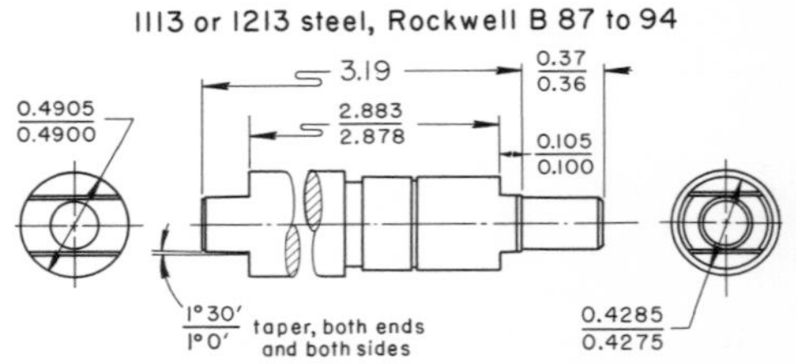

Fig. 33. Drive-arm shaft for which the production rate in broaching was superior to that in straddle milling for machining the flats at the ends of the part (Example 138)

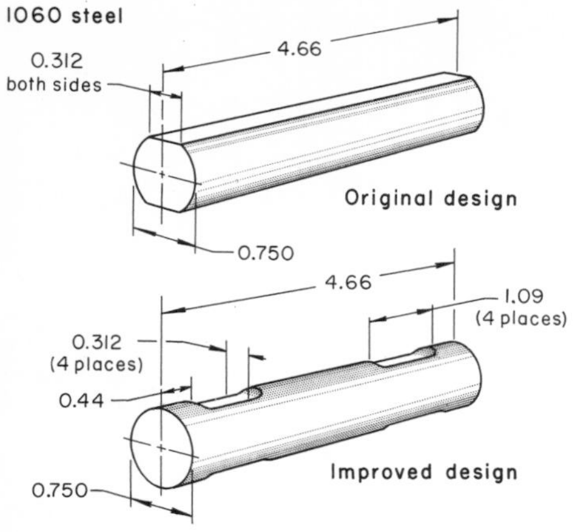

Process Before Redesign

A – Turn radius and cut off (bar machine)
B – Mill slot (hand mill)
C – Drill and countersink hole (drill press)
D – Rough grind outside (centerless grinder)
E – Heat treat
F – Finish grind outside (centerless grinder)
G – Grind flats
H – Phosphate coat; I – Inspect

Process After Redesign

A – Hopper load transfer machine
Station 1 – Grip bar
2 – Broach flats one side
3 – Broach flats other side
4 – Center vise; spot drill
5 – Center vise; drill
6 – Feed bar
7 – Saw and cut off
8 – Mill slot
9 – Cross transfer; form end radii
10 – Eject
B – Heat treat; C – Centerless grind; D – Phosphate coat; E – Inspect

Broach Data

Machine	Transfer, 10-station
Broach speed	40 sfm
Length of cut	1⅛ in.
Depth of cut	0.040 in.
Cycle time per piece	18 sec
Cutting fluid	Soluble-oil:water (1:5)
Broaches per setup	4
Initial cost of each broach	$28.50
Cost per regrind	$5.75
Number of regrinds	18
Total broach life	98,800 pieces
Tool cost per piece	$0.005344

Drilled and countersunk hole, milled slot, and radiused ends are not shown, to emphasize details of redesign to permit broaching of flats.

Fig. 34. Shaft redesigned so flats could be broached instead of ground (Example 139)

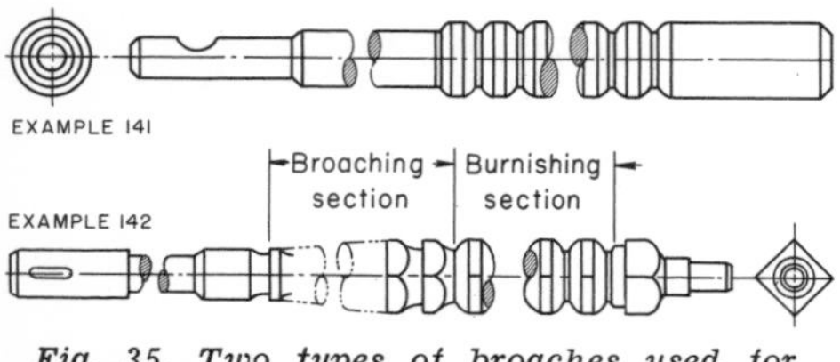

Fig. 35. Two types of broaches used for burnishing the walls of broached holes: upper broach for burnishing only (Example 141); *lower broach for cutting and burnishing* (Example 142)

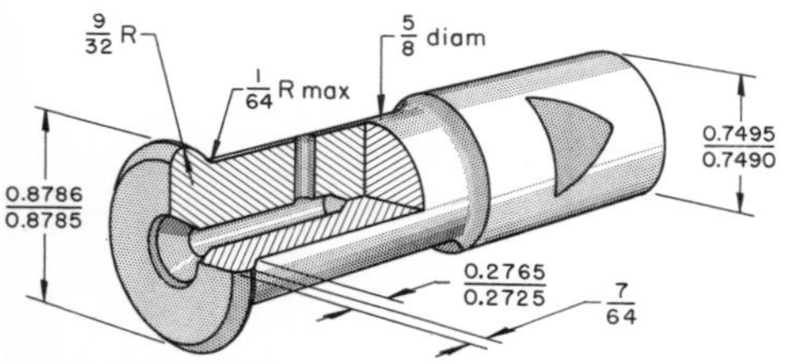

Fig. 36. Single-button burnishing tool used in a multiple-spindle automatic machine (Example 143)

aluminum pump body. A 3-ton, 36-in.-stroke horizontal broaching machine was used. The hole was burnished to obtain the 10-micro-in. finish required.

Example 142. Broaching and Burnishing a Square Hole in a Bronze Coupling (Fig. 35)

The lower tool shown in Fig. 35 was used to broach and burnish a square hole in a bronze coupling 3 in. long. A 10-ton, 48-in.-stroke horizontal broaching machine was used. The broach was made of M2 high speed steel. The broach started in a round hole, progressively changed it to a square hole, broached the square hole to size, and then burnished the sides of the hole to provide a smooth, accurate surface. The broach buttons were chromium plated. When worn, they were replated and ground to size. The cutting section of the broach could machine 2500 to 3000 pieces between grinds for sharpening, and could be reground 15 to 20 times before being discarded.

Although burnishing usually is done in a broaching machine, it may be done in conjunction with other machining operations in other machines. A burnishing operation similar to ball sizing can be incorporated as one of the stations of a multiple-spindle automatic machine. This operation differs from ball sizing in two important respects:

1 Ball sizing is a separate operation in which neither the ball nor the workpiece rotates, whereas in a multiple-operation machine, both the burnishing tool and the workpiece rotate.
2 In ball sizing, the ball is pressed through the workpiece, whereas in a multiple-operation machine, the burnishing tool is pressed into or through the workpiece and withdrawn. Thus, ball sizing is limited to through holes, but both through and blind holes can be finished by a burnishing tool.

Burnishing tools and techniques not involving broaching machines are described in three examples:

Example 143. Burnishing of Reamed Holes in Pinion Gears (Fig. 36)

Reaming followed by burnishing was chosen as the method for producing shaft holes in pinion gears. In addition to being less costly than the more usual method (broaching, heat treating, and grinding), which was employed for the gear in Example 120 (Fig. 16), the reaming-and-burnishing method provided a surface that reduced pinion seizure of the shaft after assembly.

The gear blank (1024 steel at 170 Bhn) was chucked in an eight-spindle automatic machine. The part was burnished in the final station. The burnishing tool (Fig. 36) was held in a special tool holder, which was attached to a machine slide. The workpiece rotated at 247 rpm; the burnishing tool advanced 0.014 in. per revolution of the workpiece. A mixture of soluble oil and water was used as cutting fluid.

The shaft hole was reamed to a tolerance of ±0.00075 in. Tolerance for burnishing was ±0.0005 in. The gross production rate was 130 pieces per hour. About 15,000 pieces could be burnished before the tool would no longer hold the tolerance; thus, at an initial cost of $9.10 each for the burnishing tools, tool cost per piece was only $0.000607.

Normally, the buttons on burnishing broaches are chromium plated to increase tool life, and when the chromium plating has worn away, the tools are replated. However, because the burnishing tool used here had only one burnishing button and was easily produced, it was more economical to discard the tool and use a new one, rather than to reclaim the used tool by replating.

Example 144. Burnishing Blind Holes (Fig. 37)

An idler-gear blank 0.257 in. thick and 0.514 in. in outside diameter, made of 6150 annealed steel, was produced in a six-spindle automatic bar machine. Burnishing was done

Table 7. Production of a Hole With a Keyway by Two Methods (Example 140)

Item	Bore and broach	Broach only
Tool cost for broach	$138	$298
Setups (machines)	2	1
Setup cost	$7.25	$2.50
Pieces per setup	5	25
Broaching speed, sfm	10	4.5
Production, pieces per hr	18	90

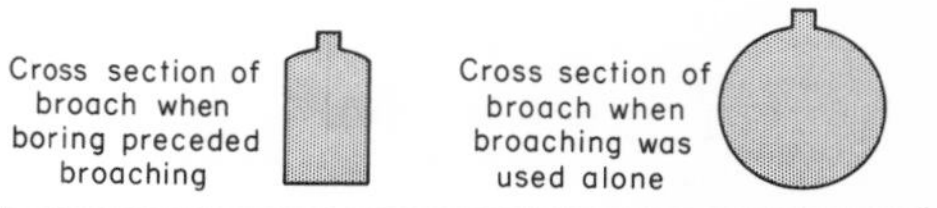

in the fifth station, using the tool shown in Fig. 37; cutoff was done in the sixth station.

The burnishing tool was mounted in a holder that permitted the tool to rotate within its housing. The housing was mounted in the regular tool-holding turret of the machine. The burnishing tool rotated on contact with the rotating workpiece and continued to rotate while it was being pushed through the hole by the advancing turret. The burnishing tool was provided with a vent hole to permit air and cutting fluid to escape when blind holes were burnished, and thus to prevent pressure from being built up by the advancing tool.

The hole in this gear blank was reamed to a diameter of 0.250/0.249 in. and burnished to 0.251/0.250 in. The total variation of the burnished hole was less than 0.0003 in. Surface finish obtained was 23 micro-in. or better.

Example 145. Combination Burnishing and Assembly Tool for Bushings (Fig. 38)

An unusual tool was devised that both inserted and burnished oil-impregnated bushings in an automotive crankshaft subassembly (see Fig. 38). For pilot production, before development of the tool, the bushings had been purchased with finish stock on the inside diameter. After a bushing had been pressed into place, the crankshaft was set up on V-blocks in a jig-type boring mill, and the inside diameter of the bushing was bored precisely to the required size. After machining, the bushing was hand lubricated.

For steady high production, employing the specially designed tool, bushings were purchased to close tolerances. A bushing was placed on the combination assembly-and-burnishing tool and pressed into place in the crankshaft. The press fit caused the bushings to compress and reduce in size. As the tool was withdrawn, the burnishing buttons on the end of the tool sized the inside diameter of the bushing, and a lubricating device automatically forced lubricant through holes provided in the tool.

To provide maximum tool life, the tools were chromium plated and ground to size. They were easily replated and reground when the chromium plate wore down. Each tool cost about $15, and tool life was indefinite.

Causes and Prevention of Broach Breakage

Broaches that are properly designed and well made seldom break in normal use. Broach breakage most often is the result of poor processing practices (such as failure to maintain tooth sharpness,

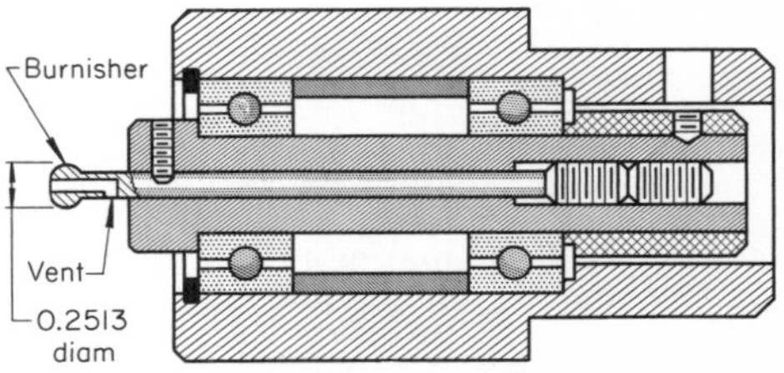

Fig. 37. Device used in the turret of a six-spindle automatic bar machine to perform an operation similar to ball burnishing, but in a blind hole (Example 144)

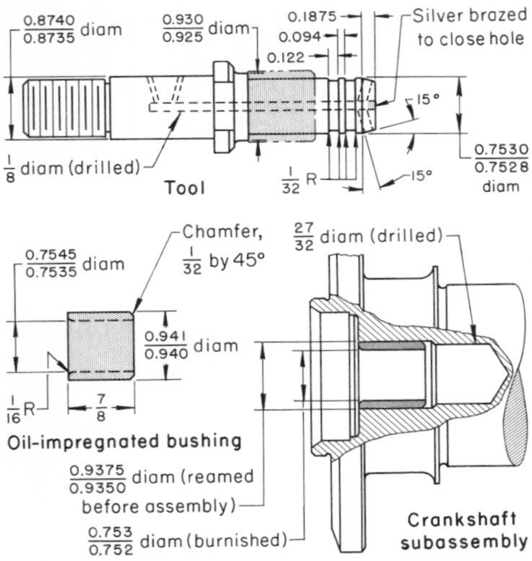

Fig. 38. Combination assembly-and-burnishing tool (top) that was used for pressing oil-impregnated bushing into automotive crankshaft subassembly (bottom). The inside diameter of the bushing was burnished when the tool was withdrawn. (Example 145)

overloading, or improper sharpening), careless handling of the broach, or improper preparation or excessive hardness of the workpiece.

Poor Processing Practices. More force is required for pulling a dull broach through the workpiece than is required for a sharp broach. If a broach is sufficiently dull, force requirements may be increased by as much as 50% (see Fig. 8). Overloading can cause an increase in tensile load that results in broach breakage. For example, a broach designed to machine one piece at each pass may fail if two or more pieces are stacked and broached simultaneously. Also, a broach designed to machine a soft, free-cutting material may break if the material is changed to one that is harder and tougher.

Sharpening in a manner that changes the type of chip may cause breakage if, after sharpening, the chips pack in the gullets so tightly that more force is required for moving the broach through the workpiece.

Careless Handling. Because broaches are extremely hard, and consequently brittle, they may break, rather than merely become nicked, if dropped.

Another cause of breakage is returning the broach through the completed workpiece. Because there is a small amount of springback of the metal surrounding a broached hole, movement of the broach back through the hole would be restricted.

Broaches also can be broken by being permitted to pass completely through the guide hole in the fixture. On the return stroke, the end of the broach can miss the guide hole, and can jam between the platen and the fixture — which usually causes the broach to buckle and break. The stroke length should be set so that the trailing end of the broach remains in the guide hole at the end of the stroke. Sometimes a rear pilot is incorporated to guide the broach at the end of the stroke.

Removing a stuck broach is emergency action that requires care to save the costly broach. Hand methods should be used, because the broach may be broken if the machine is reversed to pull out the broach. The broach and the work should be removed from the machine. Light hammer blows, carefully placed, may remove the work from the broach. If not, the workpiece can be cut with a hacksaw (which will not cut the hard broach if it touches it). A round workpiece with a stuck broach can be put in a lathe, and the work cut away from the broach by turning.

Improper Preparation of the Workpiece. Misalignment of piercing punches entering from opposite sides of a forging, misalignment of cores from opposite sides for a through hole in a casting, or a "bent" hole made by a drifting drill may result in overloading of the teeth on one side of the broach. If this overloading exceeds the strength of the tool, teeth can break off or the broach may break. In the simultaneous broaching of parallel holes, broach breakage can occur if the holes actually are not parallel or if their center-to-center distance is incorrect. Improper fixturing that establishes the centerline of a hole to be broached in a position that is not the centerline of broach travel will cause uneven loading of the broach, which may cause breakage.

Excessive workpiece hardness may cause broach breakage. This hardness may result from faulty heat treatment or from work hardening as a result of some previous processing operation.

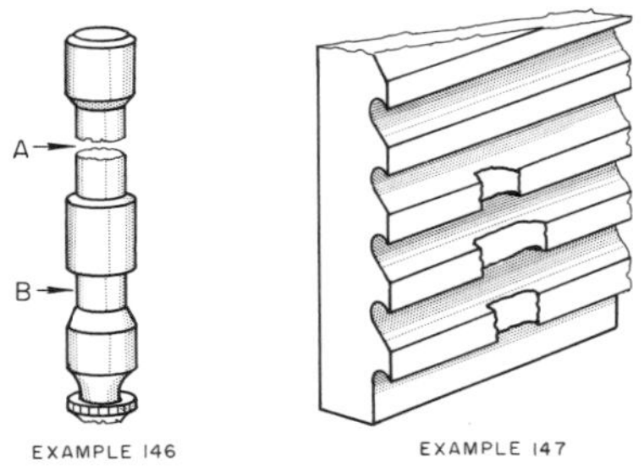

Fig. 39. Two broken broaches that were repaired by welding (Examples 146 and 147)

Machining operations such as drilling or boring, especially if the tools are dull, can increase the hardness of the part. Heat developed in poor grinding procedures can raise the hardness of some steels past the safe broaching range and result in broach breakage.

Broach Repair

Because of the high initial cost of broaches, and the amount of time required for producing them, it is often advisable (and is common practice) to repair a damaged broach rather than to replace it. Usually, before a broach is repaired, the cost of a new broach is weighed against the amount of life left in the old broach and the cost of repairing it. Generally, a broach can be repaired in less time than is required for producing a new one. This is an important consideration if production lines require minimum downtime to meet output schedules.

Repaired teeth usually last as long as the remaining original teeth. The repairs are made by building up the damaged section by welding, using the correct rod. Difficulty is seldom encountered after the sections are properly welded; however, some hazard exists that the broach will crack during welding.

Welding Methods. Broken broaches have been successfully welded by several different methods. The method selected depends largely on the type of break and the welding equipment available.

When a broach is broken into two pieces, butt welding or butt brazing (addition of filler metal) are commonly used after the surfaces to be joined have been faced. Often, a new section must be inserted, thus requiring two butt-welded or butt-brazed joints.

Broken teeth are usually repaired by arc welding. Gas welding has been used, but is generally less desirable than electric-arc welding, because the heat-affected areas are much larger in gas welding. Welding rods having a composition similar to high speed steel are available for electric-arc and gas welding. The weld metal hardens as it is deposited and cooled, so that heat treatment of the repaired broach is not required after welding.

Techniques used for repairing two different types of broaches are described in the following examples:

Example 146. Butt Brazing to Repair a Spline Broach (Fig. 39)

The shank of the spline-cutting pull broach shown in Fig. 39 broke at point A after about 25% of potential production had been obtained. Because this broach initially cost $350, repair was economical.

The shank was cut and faced at point B. A new shank was rough turned and butt brazed to the broach. The excess brazing metal was removed, and the new shank section was turned within 0.030 in. of finished size. At this point, the new shank was heat treated to Rockwell C 50 to 55 and then ground to size. The total cost of repair was $80; the broach was out of service ten days.

Example 147. Arc Welding to Repair a Surface Broach (Fig. 39)

Figure 39 shows a portion of a broach on which three teeth were broken. Because the initial cost of this broach had been $159 and considerable production life was still expected, it was decided to repair the broach rather than to replace it. The broken teeth were filled in by electric-arc welding using a tungsten-type welding rod. The repaired teeth were then reground, and the broach completely resharpened. Repairs cost $48; the broach was out of service seven days.

Other Examples of Broaching in This Volume

Work metal	Example number
Methods	
Cast iron	651, 653
Tool steel	687
Stainless steel	746, 750
Aluminum	883, 884, 885, 886
Copper	958
Magnesium	981
Unit Costs	
Cast iron	652
Stainless steel	750
Magnesium	981
Broach Design	
Stainless steel	748
Titanium	1000, 1001, 1002
Comparison of Broach Designs	
Stainless steel	747
Heat-resisting alloys	811, 812, 813, 814, 815, 816, 817, 818, 819, 820, 821, 823
Titanium	1000

Drilling

*By the ASM Committee on Drilling and Reaming**

A DRILL for cutting metal is a rotary end-cutting tool with one or more cutting lips, and usually one or more flutes for the passage of chips and the admission of cutting fluid. Drilling is usually the most efficient and economical method of cutting a hole in solid metal.

Drilling is often done in conjunction with other machining operations. This article discusses only those applications in which drilling is the sole or the major operation in a machining sequence. Additional information on drilling is presented in articles in this volume that describe the machining of specific metals (aluminum, copper, heat-resisting alloys, and others), and in the article on Multiple-Operation Machining in Bar or Chucking Machines, which begins on page 147.

Process Capabilities

Although most metals drilled are softer than Rockwell C 30, it is common practice to drill holes in metal as hard as Rockwell C 50, and steel at Rockwell C 60 has been drilled successfully (see pages 83 and 90 in this article).

Brittle material can be drilled by using backing material or special feed control (as in Example 929, in the article on Machining of Beryllium) to prevent damage at breakthrough.

Hole Size. Most drilled holes are ⅛ to 1½ in. in diameter. Drills are commercially available, however, for drilling holes as small as 0.001 in. in diameter (see the section "Small-Hole Drilling", page 91), and special drills are available as large as 6 in. in diameter.

Length-to-diameter ratio of holes that can be successfully drilled depends on the method of driving the drill and on straightness requirements. In the simplest form of drilling (feeding a rotating twist drill into a fixed workpiece), best results are obtained when hole length is less than three times diameter. As examples in this article show, however, by using special tools, equipment and techniques, straight holes can be drilled in which length is more than eight times diameter.

Machines

Almost every type of machine capable of rotating a tool or a workpiece has been used for drilling. When only a few parts are involved, when accuracy is not critical, or when workpieces are too large to be transported, hand drills are often used. (A comparison of hand versus automatic drilling is described in Example 890, in the article on Machining of Aluminum.) Engine lathes also are often used for drilling, particularly of large or long holes. In an engine lathe, the work is rotated and the drill is fed from the carriage or the tailstock.

The machines most used for production drilling, however, are hand-feed or power-feed drill presses, radial drilling machines, turret lathes, gang drilling machines, multiple-spindle drilling machines, turret-type drilling machines, horizontal drilling machines, and automatic drilling machines. The operating principles and the applicability of these machines are described in the sections that follow.

Hand-feed drill presses are among the simplest of drilling machines. Their essential components are: (*a*) a table to hold the workpiece; (*b*) a vertical, driven chuck to hold the drill; and (*c*) a mechanism that permits the chuck to be lowered manually, thus feeding the drill into the work at a rate controlled by the operator. These machines range in size from bench models to presses that can drill holes 1½ in. in diameter and larger.

Although the greatest use of hand-feed drill presses is for drilling only a few pieces at a time, they are often preferred regardless of the size of the production lot, because they take advantage of the operator's sense of feel. This sense is required in drilling holes in intricate cavities, and especially in drilling holes of very small diameter, so that the drill will be fed at the optimum rate. Typical applications of hand-feed drill presses are described in Examples 151 and 152.

Power-feed drill presses permit controlled feeding of the tool into the work. In most production operations, the vertical power-feed drill press produces more consistent results in dimensional accuracy, finish and tool life, than the hand-feed press. Power feeding also permits one operator to handle more than one machine spindle, and it reduces operator fatigue.

Radial Drilling Machines. In a radial drilling machine, the drilling head is attached to an arm that swings from a vertical column; the workpiece is secured in position, and the drilling head is moved to the required location. Radial machines therefore are used primarily to drill parts too large or heavy to move under a stationary spindle. Arm length is 2 to 12 ft or more.

Turret lathes are often used for drilling: (*a*) when drilling is included in a sequence with turning, facing or other machining operations; (*b*) for greater accuracy (particularly in drilling deep holes) than is provided by machines that rotate the tools instead of the work. The following example describes an application in which a turret lathe was chosen for both reasons:

Example 148. Accuracy in Deep-Hole Drilling (Fig. 1)

Because of the large length-to-diameter ratio (nearly 7 to 1) of the hole in the 6061-T6 aluminum alloy housing shown in Fig. 1, the preferred drilling practice was to rotate the work rather than the tool, to drill a straighter hole. Also, a concentricity of 0.004 in. TIR was required between the drilled hole and an internal thread.

These housings were machined in production lots of 500 to 2000. The sequence of operations (face, turn, drill, form radius, bore, recess, ream and cut off) also made the use of a turret lathe advisable. Details on tools and drilling procedure are given with Fig. 1.

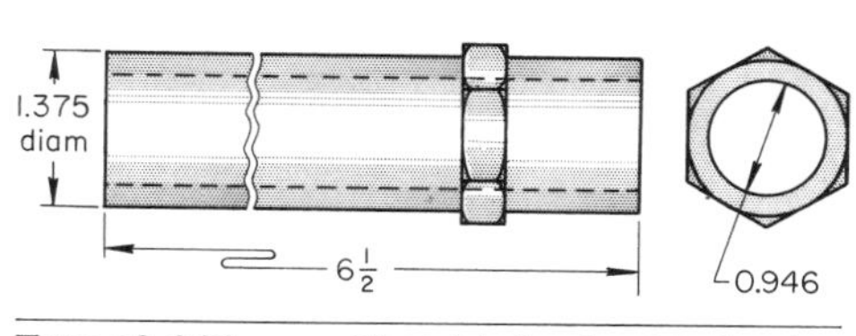

Type of drill	Straight-shank, chip-breaker
Number of flutes	2
Point angle (included)	118°
Lip relief angle	10°
Speed	1364 rpm (340 sfm)
Feed	0.012 ipr
Cutting fluid	Soluble-oil:water (1:20)

Fig. 1. Housing made in a turret lathe because of the number of machining operations, including drilling, to be performed, and because of the large length-to-diameter ratio (nearly 7 to 1) of the drilled hole (Example 148)

Another application in which a turret lathe was used because of a large length-to-diameter ratio of a drilled hole is described in Example 154.

Gang drilling machines operate on the same principle as the simple hand-feed or power-feed units, but they have two or more vertical drilling spindles in line on a common base and table. The spindles may be hand or power fed, and

*O. G. SAUNDERS, *Chairman*, Chief Metallurgist, Hobart Manufacturing Co.; GILBERT L. ALLEN, President, Chas. G. Allen Co.; RAYMOND BAIRD, JR., Staff Engineer, Industrial Engine Plant, Caterpillar Tractor Co.; HAROLD CLAUSE, Tool Engineer, Mack Trucks, Inc.

TRUMAN T. CRABTREE, Industrial Engineer, Ex-Cell-O Corp. (now with Manistee Iron Works Div., Michigan Tool Co.); G. V. HURLEY, Tool Section, Engine Manufacturing Engineering, Engine and Foundry Div., Ford Motor Co.; HAROLD KIM, Process Engineer, Pyle-National Co.; ROBERT KUNTZ, J. R. Kuntz Co.; LOUIS LUKER, Supervisor of Tool Design and Procurement, Evansville Div., Whirlpool Corp.

RICHARD NEWHOUSER, Automotive Div., Budd Co.; M. RICKS, Tool Engineer, General Dynamics/Pomona; R. A. SCHROEDER, Tool Engineer, Plumbing and Heating Div., American-Standard Corp. (now with Grival Co.); JOSEPH T. SUKAY, Advanced Manufacturing Engineering, Elliott Co. Div., Carrier Corp.; REX SUPERNAW, Chief Metallurgist, National Twist Drill and Tool Co.

they can be independently set for speed and depth. The number of spindles used depends on the number of different operations or tools required.

Gang drilling machines need not always do a sequence of operations (such as drilling, reaming and spotfacing). Power-feed gang machines can be used effectively for high-production drilling of identical parts (two or more at a time, depending on the number of spindles).

Multiple-Spindle Drilling Machines. Vertical machines of this type have two or more spindles operated by a common drive by means of universal joints and telescoping splined shafts. In some machines, the spindles feed down; in others, the table feeds up. Usually, the spindles can be arranged for various patterns of multiple drilling in one or more workpieces.

When drilling closely spaced holes, some of the spindles can be arranged to drill certain holes (say, every other one), after which the work is repositioned on the table and the remaining holes are drilled by another set of spindles. Similarly, holes can be drilled by one set of spindles and then reamed by the second set.

Turret-Type Drilling Machines. The vertical turret-type drilling machine, a modification of the single-spindle power-feed drill press, has a spindle mounted in each of as many as eight faces of an indexing turret. These spindles, which can be indexed manually or automatically, are not driven until they are in the drilling position (pointed down, above the workpiece). With various tools held in the turret spindles, this type of machine can be used to drill, ream, spotface, counterbore and trepan, in any sequence. Example 153 illustrates the use of a six-spindle turret-type drilling machine.

Horizontal drilling machines are available with various modifications. They usually have two or more drilling units on a common base, and may be arranged to drill two or more faces of the workpiece simultaneously. In many horizontal machines the work is rotated, but in some types (see Example 149) the drills are rotated.

Horizontal machines are commonly used for drilling holes three or more diameters deep (see Example 161). Modified horizontal machines are used also for gun drilling, for which they are well-suited, because of their long stroke and greater ease of chip removal (see Example 163). Another application is described in the following example:

Example 149. Seven Holes in Sequence (Fig. 2)

A 14-station horizontal drilling machine with an indexing table 48 in. in diameter was used for machining compressor rotors made of 8655 steel (see Fig. 2). The workpiece was automatically clamped and unclamped in holding fixtures, 14 of which (one for each station) were mounted on the indexing table.

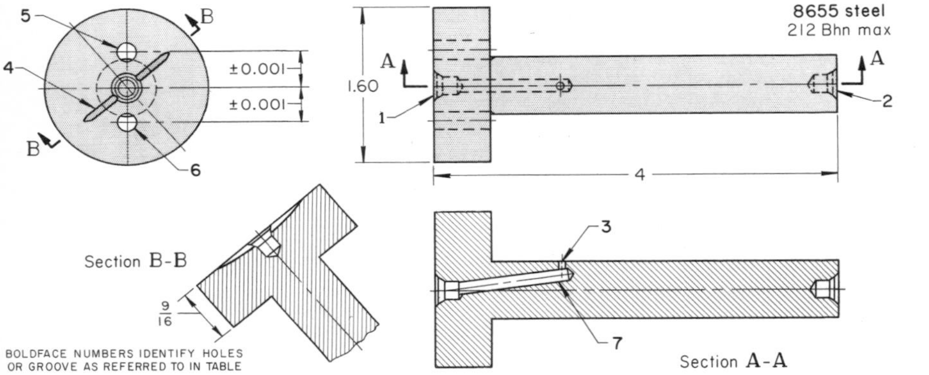

Machine station	Hole or groove	Operation(a)	Speed Rpm	Speed Sfm	Feed, ipr	Cycle time, sec(b)
1	..	Load and unload	....	...	....	...
2	1	Center drill head end of rotor(c)	1377	112	0.003	11.3
2R(d)	2	Center drill shaft end of rotor(c)	1377	112	0.003	11.3
2V(e)	3	Drill 1/16-in.-diam hole(f)	2431	39	0.0018	10.2
3	..	Idle	....	...	....	...
4(g)	4	Mill groove on head end of rotor(h)	37	58	0.052	9.2
5	1	Re-center head end of rotor(c)	1380	112	0.0026	10.7
6	5	Drill 13/64-in. diam, half depth(j)	1554	83	0.0034	10.8
7	5	Drill 13/64-in. diam, through(j)	1550	82	0.0035	11.5
8	6	Drill 13/64-in. diam, half depth(j)	1554	83	0.0034	10.8
9	6	Drill 13/64-in. diam, through(j)	1550	82	0.0035	11.5
10	7	Drill 0.147-in. diam, one-third depth(j)	1481	57	0.0031	11.3
11	7	Drill 0.147-in. diam, two-thirds depth(j)	1481	57	0.0031	11.3
12	7	Drill 0.147-in. diam, full 1 23/64-in. depth(j)	1481	57	0.0031	11.3
13	5	Ream 0.218-in. diam, through(k)	1119	64	0.0076	10.9
14	6	Ream 0.218-in. diam, through(k)	1119	64	0.0076	10.9

(a) For all operations, a 40 to 1 mixture of water and synthetic soluble oil was used as the cutting fluid. (b) Indexing time, 2.2 sec; tool-change time per 8-hr shift, 72 min; machine-maintenance time per 8-hr shift, 18 min; production rate, 185 pieces per hour. (c) With combination bell-type drill-and-countersink tool of high speed steel. (d) Station 2R was a single-spindle cam-driven unit mounted in the center of the table. (e) Station 2V, the only vertical unit, was mounted in a position to facilitate drilling of hole 3, and next to the operator's station for ease in changing the drill. (f) With high speed steel center drill. (g) Station 4 was a cam-driven unit with an attached auxiliary milling head. (h) With 50-tooth high speed steel metal-slitting saw 6 in. in diameter and 1/16 in. thick. Centerline of groove had to be within 0.005 in. of shaft center.

(j) With straight-shank jobber's-length drill of high speed steel. (k) With straight-shank, straight-flute reamer of high speed steel. Centerline of either 0.218-in.-diam hole had to be held within 0.006 in. of the plane established by centerline of the other 0.218-in.-diam hole and centerline of shaft center.

Fig. 2. Use of a 14-station horizontal drilling machine for machining of compressor rotors (Example 149)

All spindles of the machine had quick-locking, adjustable adapter assemblies with collet-type drill chucks for holding the tools, which the machine rotated. Each drilling and reaming station had a bushing bracket that slid into the holding fixture when needed. Other special features of the machine are noted in the table with Fig. 2, which summarizes tool details and operating conditions.

Loading and unloading, and starting and stopping the machine were hand operations. Frequent changing of tools was necessary.

Automatic drilling machines have a high initial cost; tooling and setup time also are costly. They usually are economical only for volume production.

These machines can be vertical or horizontal, or can combine vertical and horizontal operation. They use various methods of feeding, such as cam, screw, air or hydraulic. Some machines have a single spindle and a fixture for holding the hopper-fed workpiece, which is ejected automatically after being machined. More complex machines may have many units in angular, horizontal or vertical positions in various combinations on a special base; these machines can be equipped with an indexing table and workholding fixtures at each station. A machine so equipped was used for drilling, reaming, chamfering and milling shell-mold castings of gray iron in the following example:

Example 150. Twelve Holes, Eight Stations, 34 Operations (Fig. 3)

An eight-station vertical and horizontal center-column automatic drilling machine with a 54-in.-diam indexing table was used to machine shell-mold-cast gray iron compressor heads (187 to 223 Bhn) as diagramed in Fig. 3. The round base of this machine was designed with detachable base wings. Hydraulic vertical units were mounted on the center column; cam-driven horizontal units were mounted on the outboard base wings. All units except the milling unit at station 8 had bushing brackets that slid into the workholding fixture when needed. Spindles had quick-locking, adjustable adapter assemblies with collet-type drill chucks.

Both faces of the casting were ground parallel before it was drilled. The casting was located radially on the extended boss when placed in the first chucking side of the fixture (see table of operating data below Fig. 3), then clamped automatically by two jaws. After being drilled, the casting was transferred to the second chucking side of the fixture, where it was located radially by two holes drilled in the first chucking. Automatic swinging-arm clamps over the top of the casting held it in position. The only duty of the operator was to unload the casting in the second chucking, transfer it to the first chucking of the next station, and press the cycle-start button.

The four 3/32-in.-diam holes shown as No. 11 in Fig. 3, and the 1/8-in.-diam hole shown as No. 10, were originally drilled through the chilled surface in the cored sections of the casting. This caused considerable drill breakage. By predrilling the 1/4-in.-diam face for hole No. 10, and milling the 7/16-in.-diam face for holes No. 11, tool life of the smaller drills was increased by 50%. Except for chamfering of hole No. 9 (station 6 horizontal in Fig. 3), all drills had 118° points.

Tape (numerical) control, available for radial, turret or horizontal drilling machines, simplifies tooling, because a means of holding and positioning the work is the only additional requirement. Tape control also minimizes the possibility of operator error and assures repeatability of operation. The main disadvantages are the cost and complexity of equipment, and the time and skill required for preparing the tape.

The simplest type of numerically controlled machine has a two-position indexing table that automatically places the workpiece under a single vertical drill spindle. The movement of the drill spindle also can be numerically controlled, and this procedure, in conjunction with an automatic tool changer, can produce a completed part. The operator's principal function is to load and unload the workpiece.

Selection of Machine. Factors influencing the choice of machine for a specific application include: size and shape of workpiece; diameter and length of hole to be drilled; relation of drilling to other machining operations; quantity of pieces to be drilled per hour or per day, or over a longer period; and cost. The relation between machine selection and cost is discussed in greater detail under the heading "Selection of Machine for Economy of Production", on page 88. Examples in that section illustrate this relation with reference to specific applications.

Drills

Drills are available in a variety of types; eleven are shown in Fig. 4. Size ranges vary among the different types; some can be obtained as standard tools up to 3½ in. in diameter, and as special-order tools in even larger sizes. Type of shank (straight or taper) proportionate dimensions of flutes and shanks, and helix angle also vary widely.

Drills with helical flutes are called twist drills. Features of a typical twist drill are illustrated in Fig. 5.

Type of Shank. Taper-shank drills offer these advantages over straight-shank drills: (*a*) greater tool rigidity, (*b*) faster tool change, (*c*) closer control of concentricity, (*d*) closer spacing in gang drilling (because screw chucks are not used), and (*e*) drive without slip. For shallow holes, however, straight-shank drills should be considered, because they cost less. One disadvantage of straight shanks, particularly in drilling deep holes, is that they sometimes pull out of the chuck on the return stroke of the spindle. When this happens, the operation must be stopped to replace the drill. This pull-out is more likely in an operation in which the spindle retracts automatically at intervals to clear chips.

Drill Design. The included angle of the point on a conventional twist drill is 118°. The lip relief angle varies with drill diameter and the composition and condition of the work metal (Table 1).

Drill design for specific operations is indicated in numerous examples in the sections of this article that discuss applications of different types of drills. (See particularly the section "Applications of Drills With Modified Points",

Table 1. Lip Relief Angles for Twist Drills

Drill diameter	Lip relief angle: Cast iron or annealed steel	Hard or tough work metal	Soft or free-cutting metal
No. 80 to No. 61 ...	24°	20°	26°
No. 60 to No. 41 ...	21	18	24
No. 40 to No. 31 ...	18	16	22
No. 30 to 1/4 in.	16	14	20
F to 11/32 in.	14	12	18
S to 1/2 in.	12	10	16
33/64 to 3/4 in.	10	8	14
49/64 in. and larger..	8	7	12

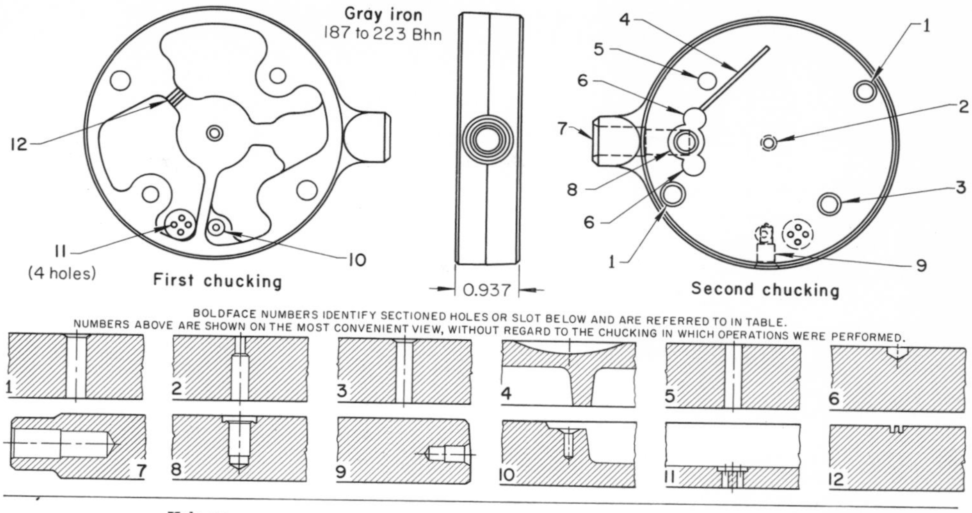

Chucking	Hole or slot(a)	Operation(b)	Speed: Rpm	Speed: Sfm	Feed, ipr
		Station 1			
....	....	Unload, transfer, load	....	...	......
		Station 2 Vertical (Cycle Time, 7.52 Sec)			
First	5	Drill 17/64-in. diam, 15/32 in. deep(c)	1441	100	0.0052
	1(d)	Drill 19/64-in. diam, 15/32 in. deep(c)	1290	100	0.0058
	2	Drill 15/64-in. diam, 11/32 in. deep(c)	1528	100	0.0049
	11	End mill 7/16-in. diam, 1/16 in. deep(e)	874	100	0.0085
Second	6	Drill 5/16-in. diam, 3/32 in. deep(c)	1222	100	0.0061
	1(d)	Chamfer, 23/64-in. diam by 118°(c)	874	100	0.0085
	3	Chamfer, 21/64-in. diam by 118°(c)	940	100	0.0079
		Station 3 Vertical (Cycle Time, 7.52 Sec)			
First	5	Drill 17/64-in. diam, through(c)	1441	100	0.0052
	1(d)	Drill 19/64-in. diam, through(c)	1290	100	0.0058
	2	Drill 1/4-in. diam, 45/64 in. deep(c)	1528	100	0.005
	11	End mill 7/16-in. diam, 1/16 in. deep(e)	874	100	0.0085
Second	11	Drill 3/32-in. diam, through(f)	4107	100	0.0018
	8	Drill 7/16-in. diam, 1/16 in. deep(c)	874	100	0.0085
		Station 3 Horizontal (Cycle Time, 8.5 Sec)			
First	7	Drill 13/32-in. diam, 11/16 in. deep(c)	941	100	0.008
Second	9	Drill 7/32-in. diam, 5/8 in. deep(c)	1752	100	0.0042
		Station 4 Vertical (Cycle Time, 8.53 Sec)			
First	2	Drill 5/32-in. diam, through(f)	2448	100	0.003
	3	Drill 17/64-in. diam, 1/2 in. deep(c)	1441	100	0.0052
	10	Drill 1/4-in. diam, 1/16 in. deep(c)	1528	100	0.0049
Second	11	Drill 3/32-in. diam, through(f)	4107	100	0.0018
	8	Drill 19/64-in. diam, 23/32 in. deep(c)	1290	100	0.0058
		Station 4 Horizontal (Cycle Time, 8.6 Sec)			
First	7	Drill 13/32-in. diam, 1 7/16 in. deep(c)	941	100	0.008
		Station 5 Vertical (Cycle Time, 8.53 Sec)			
First	10	Drill 1/8-in. diam, 7/16 in. deep(f)	3055	100	0.0024
	3	Drill 17/64-in. diam, through(c)	1441	100	0.0052
Second	11	Drill 3/32-in. diam, through(f)	4107	100	0.0018
	8	Ream 0.315/0.309-in. diam, 19/32 in. deep(g)	489	40	0.015
		Station 6 Vertical (Cycle Time, 8.18 Sec)			
Second	11	Drill 3/32-in. diam, through(f)	4107	100	0.0018
	6	Drill 5/16-in. diam, 3/32 in. deep(c)	1222	100	0.0085
		Station 6 Horizontal (Cycle Time, 8.3 Sec)			
First	7	Ream 0.428-in. diam, 3/4 in. deep; and chamfer(h)	350	40	0.035
Second	9	Chamfer, 3/32 in. deep by 60°(j)	631	62	0.019
		Station 7 Vertical (Cycle Time, 8.3 Sec)			
Second	8	Hollow mill 0.504-in. diam, 3/32 in. deep(k)	576	75	0.013
		Station 7 Horizontal (Cycle Time, 8.3 Sec)			
First	7	Ream 0.4375-in. diam, 3/4 in. deep(g)	350	40	0.036
	9	Ream 0.242-in. diam, 3/8 in. deep(g)	576	40	0.020
		Station 8 Vertical (Cycle Time, 8.4 Sec)			
First	12	Mill two slots 1/16 in. wide by 3/32 in. deep(m)	92	96	0.027
	4	Mill slot 1/16 in. wide by 3/16 in. deep(m)	92	96	0.027

(a) Tolerance on all holes was ±0.005 in. of location. (b) All operations were performed with no cutting fluid. (c) With straight-shank jobber's-length drill made of high speed steel. Diameter of drill is indicated in description of operation, except for chamfering in station 2. Here, 7/16-in. and 13/32-in. drills were used, respectively, for the 23/64-in. and 21/64-in. chamfers. (d) Both holes numbered "1" were machined as indicated, in this chucking. (e) With single-end, four-flute helical end mill of high speed steel. (f) With straight-shank taper-length drill made of high speed steel. (g) With straight-shank, straight-flute reamer made of high speed steel. (h) With special reaming-and-countersinking tool made of high speed steel. Chamfer was 1/16 in. deep by 30°. (j) With 3/8-in.-diam high speed steel drill (straight shank, jobber's length) having 60° included point angle. (k) With special hollow mill made of high speed steel. (m) With high speed steel slitting saw 4 in. in diameter by 1/16 in. wide.

Tool-change time per 8-hr shift	22 min	Production rate ....190 pieces per hour	
Machine maintenance per 8-hr shift ..	8 min	Labor cost per piece	$0.015

Fig. 3. Use of an eight-station vertical and horizontal automatic drilling machine for multiple-operation machining of shell-mold-cast compressor heads (Example 150)

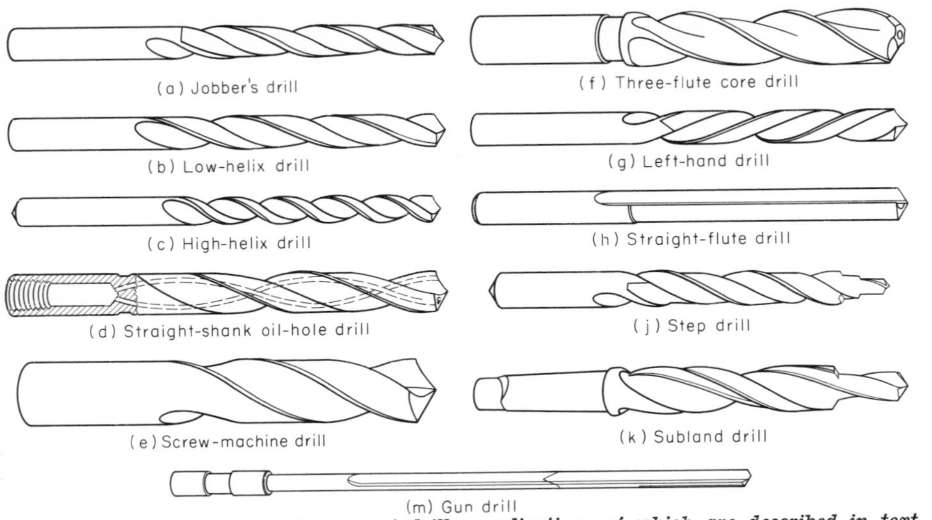

Fig. 4. Eleven commonly used types of drills, applications of which are described in text (see particularly Examples 151 through 166)

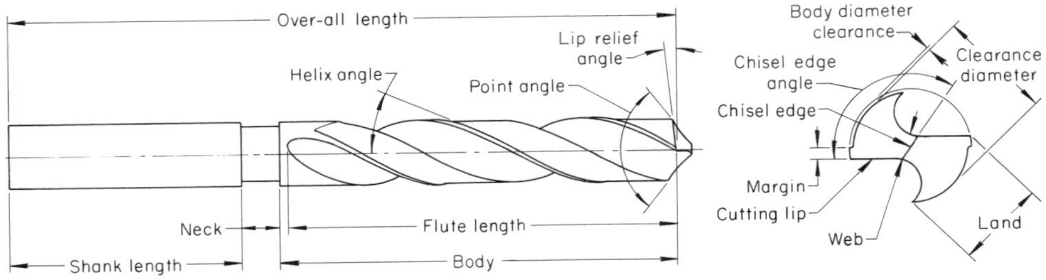

Fig. 5. Design features of a typical straight-shank twist drill

page 82.) Drill life can sometimes be greatly improved by the use of a design that varies from the standards of the drill manufacturer, as reported in Example 889, in the article on Machining of Aluminum. Drill design and rigidity of setup usually receive more attention than selection of drill material. This is because in most drilling, improvement of design and rigidity offers a greater potential for increasing drill life and reducing cost than does a change in drill material. Special means of clamping may be needed to insure rigidity of setup, as shown in Examples 836 and 837, in the article "Machining of Heat-Resisting Alloys".

Drill Materials. Most drills are made of common grades of high speed steel (M1, M2, M10 and, occasionally, T1). These grades provide, at comparatively low cost, strength, toughness and high-temperature hardness suitable for most drilling applications. For excessively hard or abrasive metals, drills may be made of higher-alloy high speed steels such as M3, M4, M6, M33 or T15; these steels, however, are used to make only a small percentage of drills produced.

Carbide-tipped drills are used for special applications — notably for drilling abrasive metals of low tensile strength (such as cast iron and castings of high-silicon aluminum alloys) or heat-resisting alloys (see page 82). Special carbide-tipped drills with longitudinal passages for conducting coolant to the drill tip are used on steel in gun drilling for which close tolerances on hole straightness, diameter and parallelism must be maintained. Another special application of carbide-tipped drills is the drilling of steel harder than Rockwell C 48 (see page 90). Solid-carbide drills (for example, spade drills) are used for extreme rigidity and drilling accuracy. However, the number of holes drilled in metal by carbide drills is comparatively small.

The factors that influence choice of drill material are discussed in Volume 1 of this Handbook (page 682). The influence of drill material on cost is shown in Examples 183, 184 and 185 in the present article.

Selection of Drills

The type of drill selected for a given application depends on:

1 Composition and hardness of work metal
2 Rigidity of the tooling setup
3 Dimensions of the hole to be drilled
4 Type of machine used to rotate the drill or the workpiece
5 Whether the drill is used for originating or enlarging holes
6 Tolerances on the hole to be drilled
7 Whether related operations, such as countersinking or spotfacing, must be performed with drilling
8 Cost.

Material drilled affects drill selection mainly because the need for a drill of rugged design increases with the hardness and strength of the work material. The need for rigidity in the setup also increases with work-metal hardness and strength.

Rigidity of Setup. In setups that are not rigid, drills with short flutes and tapered shanks are usually required.

Hole Dimensions. Diameter, length, and length-to-diameter ratio of holes to be drilled also influence selection of the drill. The shortest possible drill should be used, for maximum rigidity and minimum chatter. In drilling blind holes several times greater in length than in diameter, it may be necessary to use oil-hole drills or other special types of drills.

Type of machine to be used to drive (or hold) the drill is more likely to determine the design of the drill shank than of the fluted portion. However, some drills are designed for use with specific machines (such as screw-machine drills and left-hand drills).

Use of Drill. Whether a drill will be used for originating or enlarging holes also governs its selection. Holes can be enlarged more efficiently by drills designed for the purpose (core drills).

Tolerances. Although drilling is generally a roughing operation, with accurate surfaces depending on subsequent operations such as reaming or boring, tolerances do influence drill selection. Tolerances on roundness, diameter and straightness are often affected by the ability of the drill to remove chips.

Number of Operations. When other operations, such as countersinking or spotfacing, are to be done with drilling, the use of combination tools should be considered. Dual-purpose tools are available that can combine the following operations: drilling two different diameters, drilling and reaming, drilling and countersinking, drilling and spotfacing, and drilling and counterdrilling or counterboring.

Cost. Example 181 in this article describes the way in which a change of drill design in one application caused a two-thirds reduction in cost per piece produced.

Examples of selection are presented in the fourteen sections of this article that follow, which describe various types of drills and indicate their areas of applicability.

Applications of Jobber's Drills

Jobber's drills are of conventional two-flute design. Because of their versatility, low cost, and availability in a wide range of sizes, these drills are used for general-purpose drilling of cast iron, steel and nonferrous metals. They are suited to high production and can be operated under a variety of conditions. A typical jobber's drill is illustrated in Fig. 4(a). Jobber's drills are available only with a straight shank. Their short flutes and relatively short

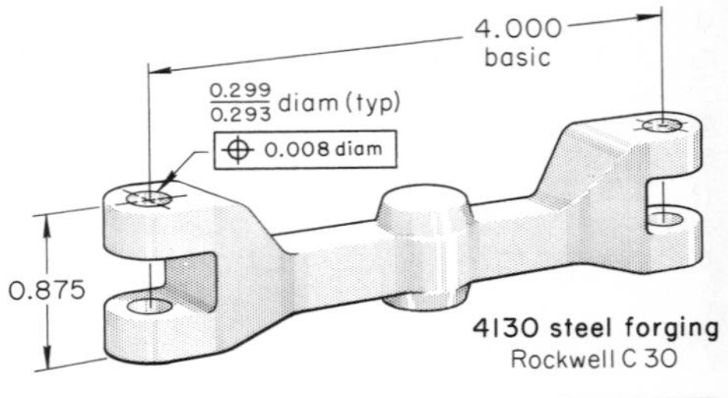

Speed	648 rpm (50 sfm)
Feed	0.003 ipr
Cutting fluid	Soluble-oil:water (1:20)
Setup time	15 min
Drilling time per pair of holes	3 min
Production rate	20 pieces per hour
Drill life per grind	150 pieces
Downtime for tool change	2 min

Fig. 6. Forging in which holes were drilled to in-line tolerance by the use of a jobber's drill under conditions given in table (Example 151)

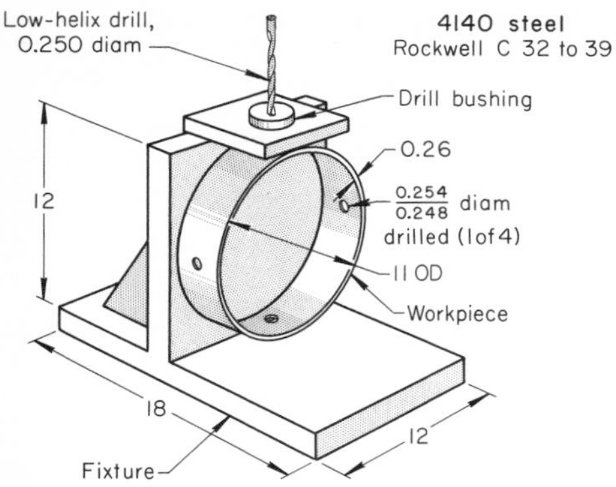

Speed	458 rpm (30 sfm)
Feed	0.005 ipr
Depth of through holes	0.260 in.
Cutting fluid	Soluble-oil:water(1:20)
Setup time	1 min
Drilling time per piece (4 holes)	3.5 min
Production rate	17 pieces per hour
Drill life per grind	112 pieces
Downtime for tool change	0.5 min

Fig. 7. *Use of low-helix drill for shallow holes* (Example 152)

length-to-diameter ratio aid in maintaining rigidity during drilling.

Example 151. In-Line Tolerance (Fig. 6)

A straight-shank, short-series jobber's drill (118° included point angle) made of M2 high speed steel was used for drilling the two pairs of 0.299/0.293-in.-diam in-line holes in the 4130 steel forging shown in Fig. 6. This component of an arm assembly was machined at a hardness of Rockwell C 30. The combination of a tough workpiece, shallow holes, and in-line tolerance on the holes made this application ideal for a short-series drill.

The forging was loaded manually into a drill jig equipped with renewable slip bushings. Drilling was done in a vertical hand-feed single-spindle drill press. Speed, feed and other operating conditions are given in the table accompanying Fig. 6.

Applications of Low-Helix Drills

Low-helix drills (Fig. 4b), known also as slow-spiral drills, have a comparatively thin web, which facilitates penetration of brass, plastics, and other soft materials and provides maximum space for chips. Low-helix drills are designed to break chips into small pieces, and are well-suited for applications in which a large volume of chips is generated. Straight-shank low-helix drills are more rigid than drills with a standard twist, and therefore permit greater torque. Low-helix drills also are less likely than standard-helix drills to grab the edge of a hole and "hang up" or pull through at drill breakthrough. Although developed primarily for drilling brass, these drills are often used successfully for drilling shallow holes in steel and in aluminum and magnesium alloys. A low-helix drill was selected in the following example mainly because of the shallow hole; chip removal was not a problem.

Example 152. Holes One Diameter Deep, in Formed Ring (Fig. 7)

A low-helix drill was used for drilling four 0.254/0.248-in.-diam holes in an 11-in.-OD ring formed from 0.260-in.-thick 4140 steel (hardness, Rockwell C 32 to 39). The workpiece, and the four-position indexing fixture (except for locating and clamping features), are shown in Fig. 7. The rings were drilled in a hand-feed single-spindle drill press with 11.2-in. travel. Speed, feed and other operating conditions are listed below Fig. 7.

Applications of High-Helix Drills

High-helix drills (Fig. 4c), known also as fast-spiral drills, are made with wide flutes and narrow lands. They are particularly recommended for drilling relatively deep holes in nonferrous metals. However, carbon, alloy and stainless steels have been drilled successfully with these drills. The wide flutes and high helix facilitate chip removal. The high helix also creates more land surface per linear inch of drill, thus increasing the bearing surface of the drill. In the example that follows, standard-helix drills were replaced by a high-helix drill mainly because a high-helix drill can remove chips from deep holes more efficiently than most other drills — especially at the relatively high feed rate used in this application:

Example 153. Elimination of Pilot Drilling (Fig. 8)

When standard-helix drills were used for the long hole in the 17-7 PH stainless steel inboard spar shown in Fig. 8, it was necessary

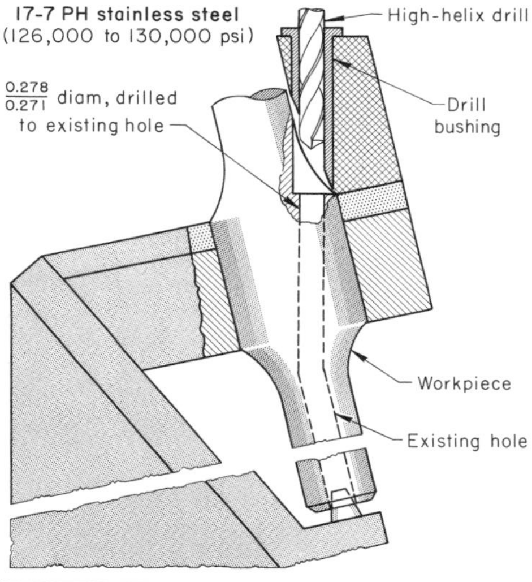

Speed	775 rpm (55 sfm)
Feed	0.004 ipr
Depth of hole	2 in.
Cutting fluid	Soluble-oil:water(1:20)
Setup time	1 hr
Production rate	30 pieces per hour
Drill life per grind	60 pieces

Change to high-helix drill eliminated pilot drilling, which was required for producing hole with standard-helix drills.

Fig. 8. *Use of high-helix drill for a hole 7½ diameters long* (Example 153)

to pilot drill undersize, then finish drill to size (two piloted operations). With a straight-shank high-helix drill, this hole was drilled in one operation, because the high feed rate, characteristic of high-helix drills, minimized drift from the hole centerline. As shown in Fig. 8, the hole was drilled at about 12° from the axis of the part. The point of the high-helix drill was ground to a 135° angle. A six-spindle turret-type drilling machine was used; operating conditions are given with Fig. 8.

Applications of Oil-Hole Drills

An oil-hole drill has one or more continuous holes through its body and shank to permit the passage of a cutting fluid under high pressure. The cutting fluid enters the shank, and upon emerging at the drill point assists in ejecting chips and dirt, which may clog or gall the hole being drilled. These drills may be used in a fixed position, as in a turret lathe or other type of multiple-operation machine, or they may be used with power drive in special sockets.

Straight-shank oil-hole drills (Fig. 4d) are well suited for drilling deep holes in hard metals. They are particularly useful when horizontal or inverted drilling is required, or when it is difficult to get cutting fluid to the work or to the cutting edges of the tool. An oil-hole drill provides the necessary fluid at the cutting edges, thereby permitting a greater feed rate, with a greater volume of chips.

Example 154. Avoiding Distortion in Drilling a Deep Blind Hole (Fig. 9)

When a standard twist drill was used for drilling the deep blind hole in the manifold liner shown in Fig. 9, chip disposal was a problem, and distortion occurred in the thin wall section as a result of the heat generated during drilling. These problems were solved by using a two-hole, two-flute, straight-shank oil-hole drill with a point modified as shown in Fig. 9. Drilling was done in a six-station automatic single-spindle vertical turret lathe. Processing conditions are listed below Fig. 9.

Taper-shank oil-hole drills have the following advantages over the straight-shank types: (*a*) they allow closer concentricity, (*b*) speed and feed can be higher, and (*c*) the tool is more rigid.

The following example describes an application for which a taper-shank oil-hole drill was selected in preference to a standard twist drill:

Example 155. Two Deep Holes (Fig. 10)

A taper-shank oil-hole drill was superior to a standard twist drill for drilling the two deep through-holes (length-to-diameter ratio, nearly 9 to 1) in the 4130 steel guide block shown in Fig. 10. The oil-hole drill not only maintained required straightness, but also eliminated a subsequent reaming operation, needed when using a standard twist drill.

Placed in a box-type drill jig, the guide block was drilled in a single-spindle drill press (¾-in. capacity, 17-in. swing). Speed, feed and other operating data are given with Fig. 10.

Applications of Screw-Machine Drills

Screw-machine drills (Fig. 4e), sometimes called stub drills, are made with short flutes and short over-all length, for maximum rigidity without loss of cutting ability. They are designed

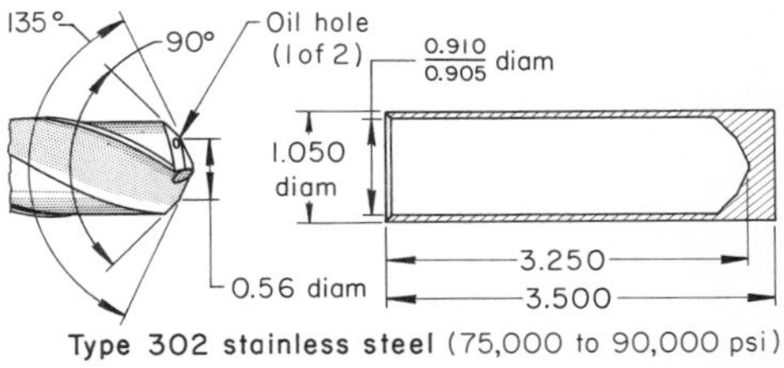

Speed	209 rpm (50 sfm)
Feed	0.004 ipr
Cutting fluid	Sulfurized oil
Setup time	2 hr
Production rate	15 pieces per hour
Drill life per grind	600 pieces
Downtime for tool change	10 min

Straight-shank, split-point oil-hole drill, ground as shown at left, eliminated distortion caused by heat buildup, which had occurred with standard twist drills, in drilling deep blind hole in the manifold liner shown at right.

Fig. 9. *Use of oil-hole drill* (Example 154)

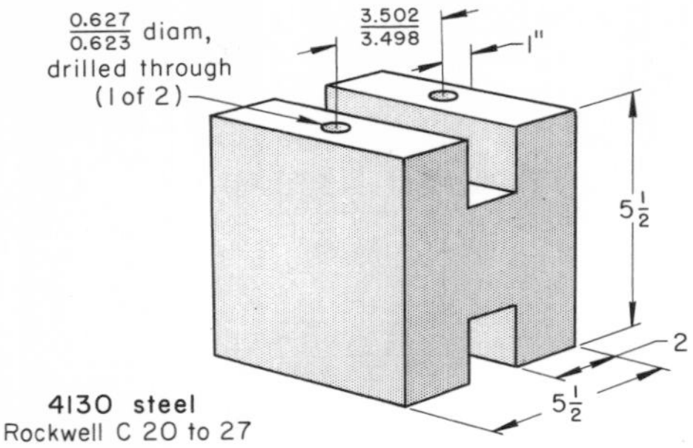

Speed	730 rpm (120 sfm)
Feed	0.006 ipr
Cutting fluid	Soluble-oil:water (1:20)
Setup time	30 min
Production rate	25 pieces (50 holes) per hour
Drill life per grind	125 pieces
Downtime for tool change	2 min

Oil-hole drill produced the deep through holes to specified finish without subsequent reaming, which was required when a standard twist drill was used.

Fig. 10. Guide block drilled with a taper-shank oil-hole drill under conditions in table (Example 155)

primarily for use in multiple-operation machines and in portable equipment, and are useful for drilling tough or hard materials. The short flute length (about half that of a standard-length twist drill) eliminates the excessive overhang of standard-length drills used without bushings. When an irregular, angled, or nonflat surface is drilled, excessive overhang causes walking or weaving of the drill, which results in oversize or tapered holes and in reduced tool life. The next example describes an application for which a screw-machine drill was particularly suitable:

Example 156. Nonrigid Setup (Fig. 11)

In drilling the 4130 steel assembly illustrated in Fig. 11, rigidity in the setup was difficult to maintain. The 16 holes in each of these assemblies had to be drilled to size from pilot holes in the heat treated steel (Rockwell C 38 to 42) after assembly. A cutting fluid could not be used, because chemical cleaning of the assembly could not be tolerated.

When standard-length twist drills were used, drill breakage was excessive because of high torque. The higher torque-to-drill-length ratio of the screw-machine drill made it more adaptable to this operation. The portable drilling machine used had a ¼-hp air motor. Spindle speed was constant, and the drill was fed manually. Processing details are listed below Fig. 11.

Applications in which drill life was increased by the use of shorter drills are described in Examples 824 and 825, in the article "Machining of Heat-Resisting Alloys".

Applications of Core Drills

Core drills, which have three to six flutes, are used for enlarging cored, forged, or previously drilled holes. Core drills are sometimes considered as roughing cutters when used primarily for heavy stock removal in holes that are finally sized by boring or reaming.

Three-flute core drills (Fig. 4f) are normally used for holes up to ½ in. in diameter. These drills are designed to allow greater chip clearance for heavy cuts. Four-flute core drills are more commonly used for holes larger than ½ in. in diameter. They are designed to combine maximum flute space with maximum rigidity.

Because of their greater number of cutting edges, core drills can be used at higher feed rates than other drills or boring tools without increasing chip load per cutting edge, as in the following example:

Example 157. Boring vs Core Drilling

Four-flute, straight-shank core drills were compared with single-point boring tools for enlarging 2¼-in.-diam holes in truck-wheel hubs made of 1035 steel (hardness, 170 to 210 Bhn) to a final diameter of 2½ in. Depth of these holes was 2 in. Both types of tools were used in an eight-spindle chucking machine at a speed of 100 rpm (65 sfm), and had a chip load of 0.010 in. per cutting edge. The four cutting edges of the core drill, however, allowed a 300% increase in feed rate, and a 75% reduction in cutting time, in comparison with the single-point boring tool:

	Boring tool	Core drill
Feed, ipr	0.010	0.040
Cutting time, min	2.0	0.5

Operations such as counterboring and chamfering are often combined with core drilling by step grinding the drill, as in the following example:

Example 158. Enlarging and Chamfering Tubing

A step-ground three-flute core drill with a standard helix was used for enlarging the 0.272-in. inside diameter of 1021 steel tubing (outside diameter, 0.438 in.), and for chamfering the end of the tubing. The core drill enlarged the inside diameter to 0.377/0.373 in. for a depth of 1½ in.

Applications of Left-Hand Drills

Left-hand drills (Fig. 4g) have the same flute length and over-all length as general-purpose jobber's drills. The principal use for left-hand drills is in multiple-operation machines when the spindle is rotated in the reverse of normal direction. This often occurs when tapping follows drilling, or when other machining operations are combined with drilling:

Example 159. Drilling, Reaming, Turning and Cutoff (Fig. 12)

The shroud shown in Fig. 12 was produced from 3⁄32-in.-diam stainless steel rod by drilling, reaming, turning and a cutoff operation in a single-spindle automatic bar machine. In this machine a left-hand drill was required.

The drill had a standard left-hand helix, but the point was ground to a 135° included angle and to a primary clearance angle of 10°. Web thinning of the drill was important, to reduce the rubbing action of the chisel edge and thereby avoid strain hardening of the work material. The drill was withdrawn three times in completing the operation. Processing details are given with Fig. 12.

Applications of Straight-Flute Drills

Straight-flute drills (Fig. 4h) are especially adapted for drilling brass and other soft materials and for drilling thin sheet of a wide variety of metals. Drills of this type do not run ahead or grab the work during drilling. The next example illustrates a typical application for a straight-flute drill.

Example 160. Deep Blind Holes (Fig. 13)

Figure 13 shows an electrical contact made from tellurium-nickel bronze rod ground to an outside diameter of 0.1245/0.1240 in. The seven-diameters-long blind hole in this contact was made by a drill with two straight flutes that was mounted in a bar machine with 7⁄16-in.-diam capacity. Drill details and operating conditions are given with Fig. 13.

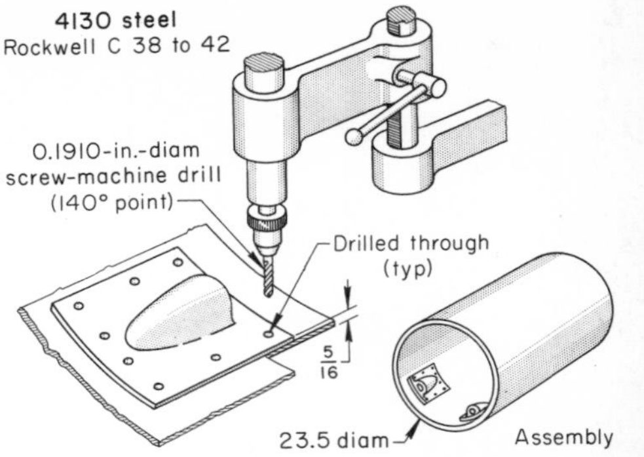

Speed	700 rpm (35 sfm)
Feed	0.004 ipr
Cutting fluid	None
Setup time	2 min
Drilling time per hole (approx)	1 min
Production per hour	4 assemblies (64 holes)
Drill life per grind	8 to 10 assemblies
Downtime for tool change	2 min

Because of the nonrigid setup, screw-machine drills were preferable to standard-length twist drills for the 16 holes in this assembly.

Fig. 11. Use of a screw-machine drill (Example 156)

The operation had to be completed using only one drill, with no withdrawals during drilling, and the hole required a surface finish of 32 micro-in. with total diametral tolerance of 0.003 in. With the straight-flute drill, all these requirements were met in production. It was determined that holes as deep as eight times diameter could be produced within tolerance with the straight-flute drill.

Past experience with the tellurium-nickel alloy indicated that a high-helix, thin-web, polished-flute high speed steel drill also could be used on tellurium-nickel bronze. However, because of the one-plunge requirement in this application, drill breakage was high when this type of drill was used, although it performed better than either standard-spiral or slow-spiral (low-helix) drills with thin webs and polished flutes. The high-helix (fast-spiral) drill functioned exceptionally well when maximum hole depth was no more than four times diameter; chips that formed were readily removed. But at greater depths, the chips powdered and packed, resulting in poor finish, ballooning of the part, and drill breakage.

Applications of Step Drills

Step drills (Fig. 4j) have two or more diameters, produced by grinding various steps on the diameter of the drill. The steps usually consist of a square or angular cutting edge. Step drills are used extensively in applications requiring multiple-diameter holes. They can

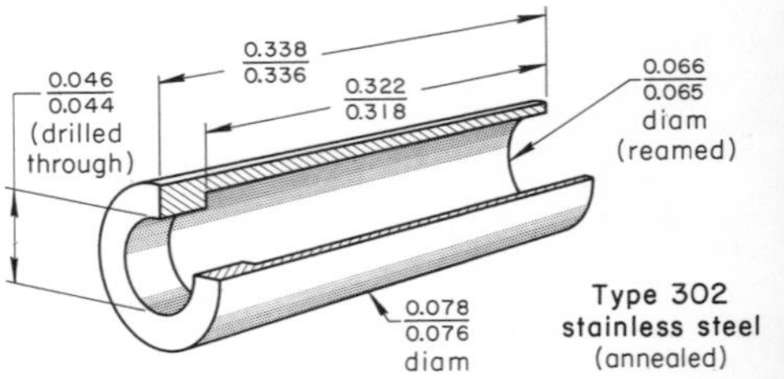

Speed	4500 rpm (53 sfm)
Feed	0.0008 ipr
Cutting fluid	Sulfurized oil
Production rate	75 pieces per hour
Drill life per grind	45 pieces
Downtime for tool change	1 min

Drilling, under conditions in table, was part of a multiple-operation sequence that included turning, reaming and cutoff, in an automatic bar machine.

Fig. 12. Shroud in which the 0.046/0.044-in.-diam through hole was made by a left-hand drill (Example 159)

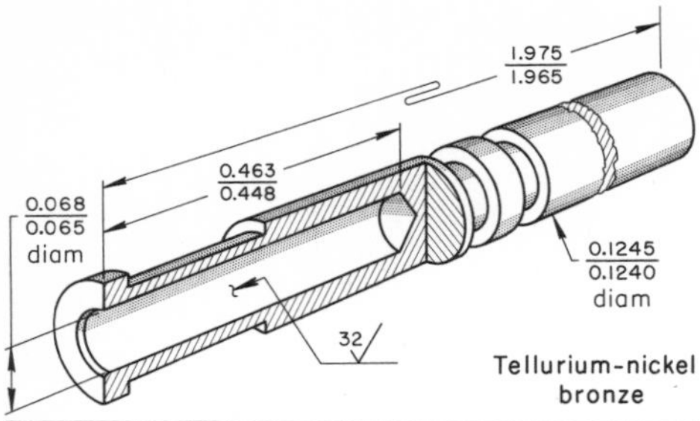

Drill Details

Number of flutes	2
Point angle (included)	118°
Lip relief angle	10°
Land width	0.010 in.

Drilling Conditions

Speed	3556 rpm (63 sfm)
Feed	0.0025 ipr
Cutting fluid	Sulfochlorinated oil
Drill life per grind	500 to 700 pieces
Downtime for tool change	1 min

Fig. 13. Electrical contact in which a deep blind hole was produced to tolerance and specified finish by use of a straight-flute drill (Example 160)

be made by grinding steps on common drills; usually, some thinning of the web is required. The simplest form of a step drill is a combination drilling and countersinking tool, such as was used in the following example:

Example 161. Combination Drilling and Countersinking (Fig. 14)

A short-length straight-shank step drill made of T15 high speed steel was used to drill and countersink the cross hole in the type 302 stainless steel detonator tube shown in Fig. 14. The drill had high-helix flutes, and an included point angle of 120°. Concentricity between the shank and the pointed end was held to ±0.0002 in. A special horizontal, opposed-spindle drilling machine was used. This machine was equipped with a multiple-station fixture and multiple-spindle drill heads for drilling four pieces at a time. Downtime was minimized by using preset tools and holders. Figure 14 gives processing details.

The use of a step drill for improved hand drilling of through holes is described in Example 888, in the article on Machining of Aluminum.

Applications of Subland Drills

Subland drills (Fig. 4k) are combination tools having separate lands or margins, which extend the full length of the flutes, for each of the two or more diameters.

Subland drills perform two or more operations in one pass of the tool. The different diameters or lands can be ground to permit drilling and countersinking for flathead screws, or drilling and counterboring for socket-head screws. Extensive use is made of subland drills in high-production work.

Subland drills with as many as four diameters have been used successfully. For best results, however, the largest diameter should be no greater than twice the smallest diameter, because of the variation in cutting speeds and feeds.

Because the lands or margins of subland drills are ground to the correct size the full length of the flute, each cutting edge can be sharpened separately and repeatedly without affecting the others. When correctly sharpened and operated, subland drills can readily produce accurate holes.

The following example describes the use of a subland drill in performing three operations:

Example 162. Drilling, Countersinking and Spotfacing (Fig. 15)

A two-land, two-flute subland drill made of M2 high speed steel was used to drill, countersink and spotface forged bicycle-pedal cranks (Fig. 15). Flutes and point were standard. A special drilling and tapping machine with an indexing table was used. Because of the difference in diameter between the drilling and spotfacing sections, drilling speed was less than optimum, but was satisfactory. Feed was 0.005 ipr, and at the end of the cycle the drill dwelled for spotfacing. Drills were changed about twice during each full shift of operation (8 hr) or when the point began to dull. Processing details are given with Fig. 15.

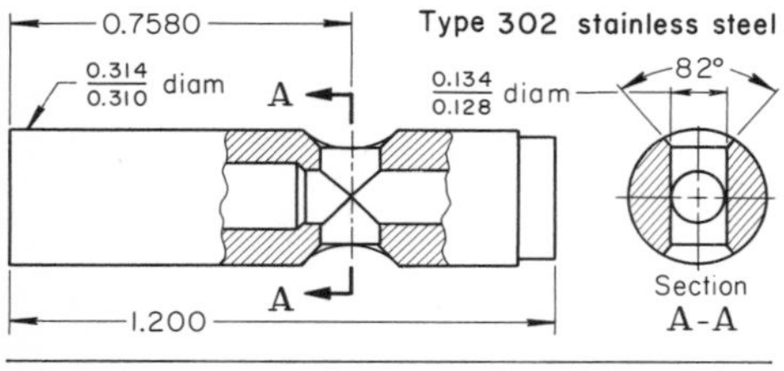

Speed	1000 rpm (34 sfm)
Feed	0.002 ipr
Cutting fluid	Soluble-oil:water(1:20)
Production rate	720 pieces per hour
Drill life per grind	400 pieces (800 holes)

Fig. 14. Detonator tube in which cross hole was drilled and countersunk by a step drill (Example 161)

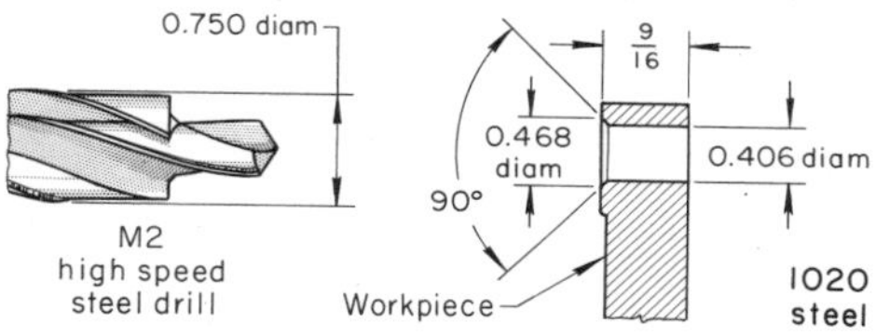

Spindle speed	350 rpm
Surface speed, drilling	37 sfm
Surface speed, spotfacing	70 sfm
Feed	0.005 ipr
Cutting fluid	Soluble-oil:water(1:30)
Production rate	220 holes per hour
Drill life per grind (approx)	880 holes

Two-land, two-flute subland drill (with standard flutes and point) shown at left was used for drilling, countersinking and spotfacing a bicycle-pedal crank as shown at right.

Fig. 15. Use of a subland drill (Example 162)

Applications of Gun Drills

Gun drills (Fig. 4m), which are used in horizontal machines, have a single V-shaped flute; the single cutting face is sharpened offset, to form two cutting angles. When drilling, these angles form two chips broken into short lengths for easier expulsion. The drill body is usually a steel tube through which a cutting fluid passes under pressure, and in sufficient volume to cool and lubricate the cutting area and flush out chips. To counter the unbalanced cutting force of the single cutting edge, wear pads (usually carbide) are provided in the drill opposite the cutting face, to keep the drill on center. Gun drills are used to drill soft as well as hard material.

For accurate holes, gun drills must be used in rigid equipment with a positive feed. With such equipment, gun drilling eliminates the need for subsequent rough and finish reaming. A properly started gun drill guided by a drill bushing will produce a hole that does not drift from the centerline more than 0.0005 in. in 2 in. of drill travel. A spotface or a precision center drill may be used for more accurate starting of a gun drill.

For maximum efficiency in gun drilling, the cutting fluid should provide a fluid film between wear pads and work material, prevent welding of chips to the cutting edge of the drill, cool the drill and the work, and dispose of chips by flushing out the hole. Advantages and uses of gun drills are indicated in the four examples that follow:

Example 163. Elimination of Bell Mouth (Fig. 16)

Gun drilling was used for producing the 0.363/0.358-in.-diam through hole in the 17-7 PH stainless steel spar shown in Fig. 16. A gun drill was selected in preference to a standard twist drill because the hole intersected a hole drilled in a previous operation. Gun drilling eliminated a bell mouth caused by the standard twist drill as it passed through the cross hole.

The gun drill used had a solid-carbide tip. The beveled point of the tip had an outside angle of 42°, and inside angle of 20°, apex distance of one fourth the drill diameter, primary clearance angle of 7°, and radial clearance angle of 15° extending to the 0.020-in.-wide primary cutting land. Drilling was done in a horizontal machine; each part was placed in a special fixture for drilling. Other operating conditions are given with Fig. 16.

Previously, this part had been made of 4130 steel at Rockwell C 38. This material also was gun drilled successfully with the same tooling and processing conditions.

Gun drilling is especially well suited to producing long holes to close tolerances. Hole straightness, roundness and size can be held within closer limits with a gun drill than with a twist drill, as shown in the following example:

Example 164. Twist Drill vs Gun Drill (Table 2)

A gun drill was compared with a standard twist drill for drilling ⅜-in.-diam through holes 5 in. deep in gray iron and type 304 stainless steel specimens. The twist drill was used in a general-purpose 2-hp vertical drill press; the gun drill, in a 5-hp modified boring machine with hydraulic feed. Processing details and results for each material drilled are shown in Table 2. As these data show, the gun drill not only produced markedly better finish and dimensional accuracy than the twist drill, but also drilled twice as many pieces per grind, under production conditions.

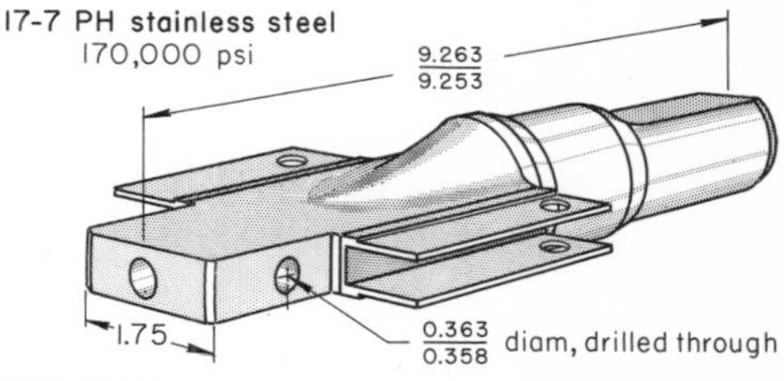

Speed	850 rpm (80 sfm)
Feed	0.0005 ipr
Cutting fluid	Sulfurized oil (at 800 psi)
Setup time	1 hr
Drilling/fixturing time per piece	5 min
Drill life per grind	50 to 60 pieces
Downtime for tool change	2 min

Gun drill produced 0.363/0.358-in.-diam through hole in this inboard spar without bell mouth at intersection with cross hole, which resulted when standard twist drills were used.

Fig. 16. Use of gun drilling (Example 163)

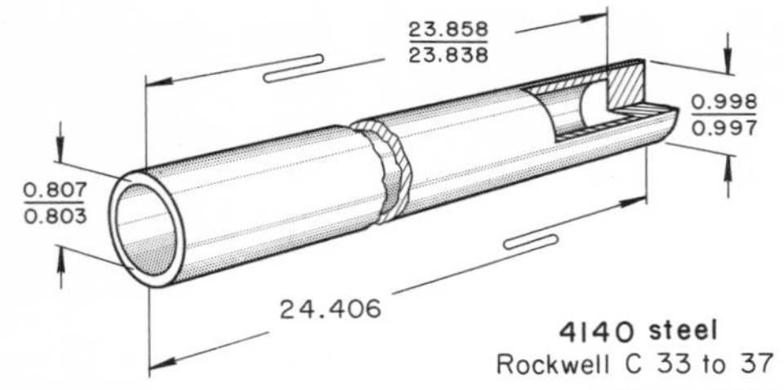

Speed	860 rpm (181 sfm)
Feed	0.0009 ipr
Cutting fluid	Sulfurized oil(a)
Setup time (2 spindles)	2 hr
Production rate	1.5 pieces per hour
Drill life per grind	2 pieces
Downtime for tool change	1.5 min per spindle

(a) At 700 psi; cooled in heat exchanger

Fig. 17. Part for which a gun drill, used under conditions in table, met concentricity tolerances on the blind hole 29½ diameters long (Example 165)

In the following example, gun drilling was the only practical way to drill a deep blind hole to concentricity tolerances:

Example 165. Close Tolerance on Deep Blind Holes (Fig. 17)

The blind hole in the part shown in Fig. 17 had to be concentric with the outside diameter within 0.003 in. for the first 4 in. of its length and within 0.007 in. TIR for the remainder. In spite of the steel hardness (Rockwell C 33 to 37) and the thin wall of the workpiece, a gun drill met these tolerances. A front grind on the tip of the drill to 20°/18° was necessary to overcome chipping of the cutting edge. This grind also aided in maintaining concentricity.

To avoid heat damage to the thin wall of the workpiece, three steps were taken: (*a*) Friction was reduced by shortening the carbide tip and wear pads to 2 in. or less; (*b*) cutting fluid flow was increased by enlarging the outlet to the drill tip to ⅛-in. diameter and raising pressure to 700 psi; and (*c*) cutting fluid was cooled with a heat exchanger. Process details are given with Fig. 17.

Because a gun drill can drill more accurately than a twist drill, gun drilling sometimes can eliminate a subsequent machining operation:

Example 166. Elimination of Boring (Fig. 18)

When a twist drill was used to produce the $5\frac{5}{16}$-in.-long hole in the 6145 steel casting shown in Fig. 18, a subsequent boring operation was required for achieving the specified 0.7505/0.7490-in. diameter. Changing to gun drilling produced the holes to size without subsequent boring.

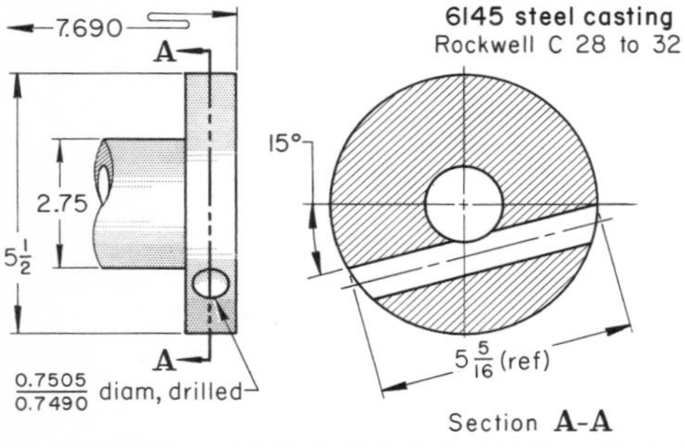

Speed	1100 rpm (216 sfm)
Feed	0.0009 ipr
Cutting fluid	Sulfurized oil (at 800 psi)
Setup time (one spindle)	2 hr
Production rate	7 pieces per hour
Drill life per grind	5 to 6 pieces
Downtime for tool change	2.25 min per spindle

Fig. 18. Cam-drive adapter in which gun drill produced the $5\frac{5}{16}$-in.-long hole to diametral tolerance without the subsequent boring operation that was required with a twist drill (Example 166)

The part was drilled in a precision boring machine, after being vertically mounted in a fixture, on a turned plug of the same material. The carbide-tipped drill entered through a drill bushing contoured to fit the 5½-in.-diam flange. With the plug in the center, the part was in effect a solid part, and there was no breakthrough of the drill.

For each part drilled, the plug was indexed 45°. After eight parts had been drilled using one end of the plug, the plug was reversed and the other end was used for eight additional parts. The point of exit was capped by a length of pipe, which was mounted on a swivel and contoured to fit the 5½-in.-diam flange. This cap over the exit maintained the cutting-fluid pressure and allowed the chips to be flushed back, even when the drill exited from the convex surface. Cutting fluid was forced through the drill body, chip return being along a flute in the body of the drill. Other processing details are given with Fig. 18.

Applications of Drills With Modified Points

The proper use of controlled drill-pointing, which consists of adjustments in the included point angle, cutting relief angle and clearance angle, can result in substantially lower drilling costs for a particular operation. The effect of drill-point design on drill efficiency is shown in the next example:

Example 167. Chisel vs Spiral vs Self-Centering Drill Points (Fig. 19)

Three different types of points on $\frac{15}{32}$-in. drills (see Fig. 19) were evaluated for endurance, power consumption and size retention. A tape-controlled drill press powered the drills as they cut through 2-in.-thick 1035 steel plate. Results are shown graphically in Fig. 19. As indicated, the spiral and self-centering points were nearly equal in endurance and power consumption, and both produced better results than the chisel points.

The proper point angle (the angle between the two cutting lips of the drill) depends on the material being drilled. An included point angle of 118° is usually satisfactory for drilling all carbon and alloy steels in the annealed or normalized condition. For drilling heat treated steels as hard as Rockwell C 40, or for drilling stainless steels, split-point drills are preferred, with the point angle increased to 125° to 135°. For drilling steels or other metals at Rockwell C 40 to 52, drills with split points of 140° to 150° are preferred.

For drilling cast iron to a depth up to three diameters, the standard 118° point is satisfactory; for deeper holes in cast iron, a point angle of 90° to 100° is preferred. Drills with point angles of 100° to 118° are generally used for drilling copper alloys and aluminum alloys. For more detailed information on drill points for drilling metals other than steel, see the sections on drilling in the articles in this volume on the machining of stainless steel, heat-resisting alloys and the various nonferrous metals (pages 375 to 512).

Production Examples. Drilling operations for which it was better to use drills with modified points are described in the four examples that follow.

Example 168. Large Holes in Plate (Fig. 20)

Standard-point twist drills were originally used to drill $2\frac{1}{16}$-in.-diam holes through 0.125-in. 1020 steel plate. Changing to a drill with a modified point resulted in better holes and a saving of 69% in drilling time. Figure 20 shows the two drill points and the drilled plate.

With the modified drill, the hole was drilled with less axial travel (0.262 in.) than with the standard drill (0.806 in.). This difference

Table 2. Gun Drill vs Standard Twist Drill for Through Holes in Gray Iron and Stainless Steel (Example 164) (a)

	Gray iron		304 stainless steel	
Condition or result	Gun drill(b)	Twist drill(c)	Gun drill(d)	Twist drill(e)
Operating Conditions				
Speed, rpm	2000	600	2000	500
Speed, sfm	200	60	200	50
Feed, ipr	0.001	0.006	0.0006	0.005
Feed, ipm	2	3.6	1.2	2.5
Cutting fluid	Cutting oil(f)	Soluble oil(g)	Cutting oil(f)	Soluble oil(g)
Results				
Surface finish, micro-in.	10 to 15	100 to 150	10 to 15	100
Hole straightness, in.	0.001	0.025	0.001	0.030 to 0.035
Out-of-roundness, in.	0.0002	0.002	0.0003	0.002
Diametral tolerance, in.	0.0005	0.002	0.001	0.003
Drill life per grind, pieces	160	80	50	25

(a) Specimens of both materials were ⅞ in. in diameter and 5 in. long. Through holes drilled were ⅜ in. in diameter and 5 in. deep. (b) Carbide-tipped center-cut drill, ⅜-in. diam. (c) Taper-length twist drill, ⅜-in. diam. (d) Solid-carbide center-cut drill, ⅜-in. diam. (e) Heavy-web jobber's drill, ⅜-in. diam. (f) Chlorinated mineral oil. (g) Mixed 1 part to 15 parts water.

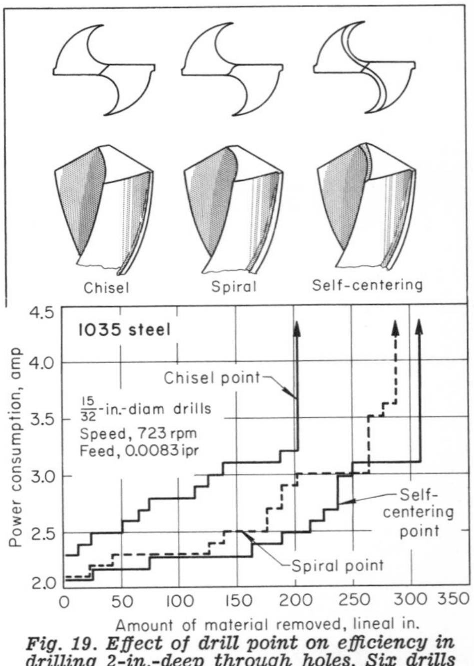

Fig. 19. Effect of drill point on efficiency in drilling 2-in.-deep through holes. Six drills of each type were tested. (Example 167)

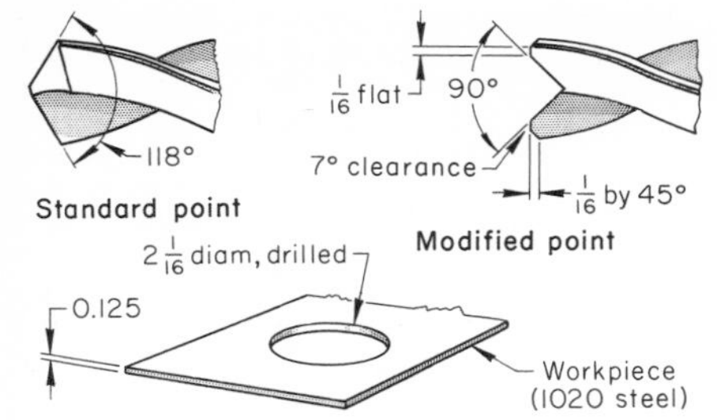

Fig. 20. Changing from standard to modified drill point improved results in drilling this steel plate. (Example 168)

accounts for the significant reduction in drilling time with the modified drill.

For holes of extremely high ratio of diameter to depth, as in the preceding example, quality is generally poor when a conventional 118°-point drill is used; as the center of the drill breaks through, it threads the work metal, resulting in rough finish or distortion, or both. With the modified drill point shown in Fig. 20, the hole can be drilled to full diameter for more of the cut, resulting in a more nearly round hole and better finish.

Example 169. Two In-Line Holes (Fig. 21)

The addition of a 90° angle to the 118° point of a standard two-flute drill (sketch at left in Fig. 21) permitted an increase in speed and also doubled drill life, in drilling the two in-line holes in the 1049 steel forging shown at the right in Fig. 21. Results for the conventional and modified drills are compared in the table with Fig. 21. The added 90° point angle improved results because it caused chips to break, thereby reducing wear and pressure at the drill margin.

Drills of split-point design are commonly used for drilling deep holes in crankshafts. One application is described in the following example:

Example 170. Angular Oil Holes in Crankshafts (Fig. 22)

A twist drill with a split point produced good results in drilling angular oil holes in forged steel crankshafts (Fig. 22). The heavy-duty drill for this operation had two flutes, right-hand helix, and an included point angle of 135°.

Because of the length-to-diameter ratio of these holes, a thicker web than standard was used to increase rigidity. The thickened web resulted in a wider chisel edge, which was modified by grinding the flanks as shown in Fig. 22. Without this clearance, the tool rubbed instead of cutting. A single-spindle gang-type reciprocating drill press was used. Processing details are given with Fig. 22.

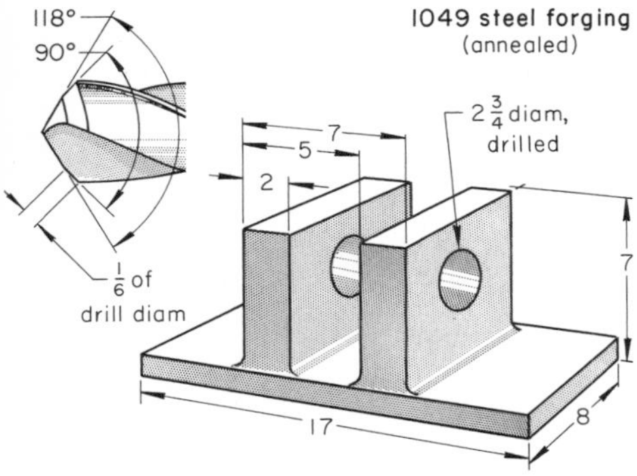

Condition or result(a)	Conventional point	Modified point
Speed, rpm	71	91
Speed, sfm	51	66
Production, pieces per hour	4.875	5.625
Drill life per grind, pieces	42	84

(a) Both types of drill were used in a radial drill press, at a feed of 0.013 ipr and with a 1-to-20 mixture of soluble oil and water as the cutting fluid.

Fig. 21. Addition of a 90° angle to the point of a standard two-flute drill (left) gave improved results in drilling the in-line holes in the forging shown at right. (Example 169)

Example 171. Forming Sharp Corners in Counterbores (Fig. 23)

The two sharp-cornered counterbores in the turbine-governor case shown at the left in Fig. 23 were produced with a specially ground piloted drill. This tool (sketch at right in Fig. 23) resembled a two-lip flat-bottom end mill, and had a primary relief of 8° to 10° and a secondary relief of 30° to 40°.

The complex hole in this part was produced as follows: (*a*) the part was drilled through with a 5⁄16-in.-diam standard twist drill; (*b*) the through hole was enlarged, for about 1⅝ in. from each end, with a 45⁄64-in.-diam standard two-lip taper-shank twist drill; (*c*) the specially ground drill (Fig. 23) removed the excess stock from the 45⁄64-in.-diam counterbores and formed the sharp corners; and (*d*) the counterbores were reamed to 0.720/0.716 in. in diameter.

These parts were drilled in a radial drill press, using a box jig and bushings to insure alignment of the cutting tools with the spindles. Processing details are given with Fig. 23.

Applications of Spade Drills

A spade drill is generally made up of a spade bit in a holder (Fig. 24a); this type of drill is most widely used for drilling holes 1 to 5 in. in diameter. (Solid spade drills, usually of carbide, are used for smaller holes.)

Spade-drill holders are made in various sizes with straight or tapered shanks. For deep-hole drilling, the holder has an axial hole through the shank to allow cutting fluid to be applied under pressure to the point of the drill.

Spade drills have heavier cross sections than comparable twist drills. The additional strength is concentrated along a direct line from the point to the shank of a spade drill. This gives a spade drill greater resistance to end thrust and greater ability to withstand torque. The increased strength minimizes vibration, chipping of cutting edges and drill breakage. Standard drills are likely to wear into a forward taper, which causes binding. Because the cutting edges of spade drills are shorter and have a greater back taper, binding is less likely.

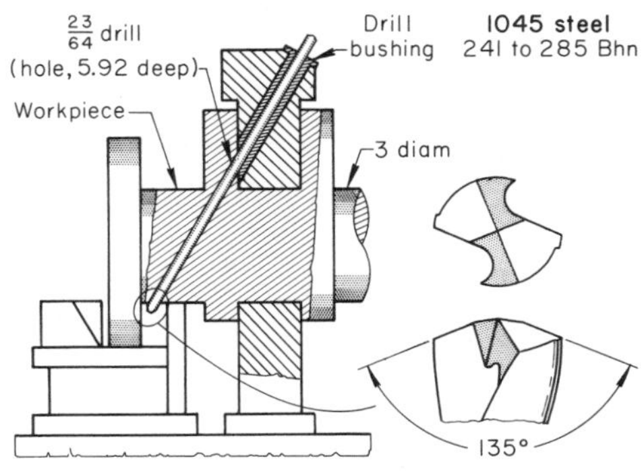

Speed	509 rpm (48 sfm)
Feed	0.003 ipr
Cutting fluid	Soluble-oil:water (1:20)
Production rate:	9¼ pieces per hr (6 holes each)
Drill life per grind (approx)	11 to 12 holes

Fig. 22. Oil hole in crankshaft (left) that was drilled with split-point drill of design shown at right (Example 170)

One advantage of the type of drill shown in Fig. 24(a) is that bits are replaceable. By having more than one for the holder, the operation can continue while others are being sharpened. Bits are relatively inexpensive.

Spade drills can be used in any machine in which feed and speed can be controlled. Example 182 compares the performance of spade and twist drills in terms of tool cost per hole.

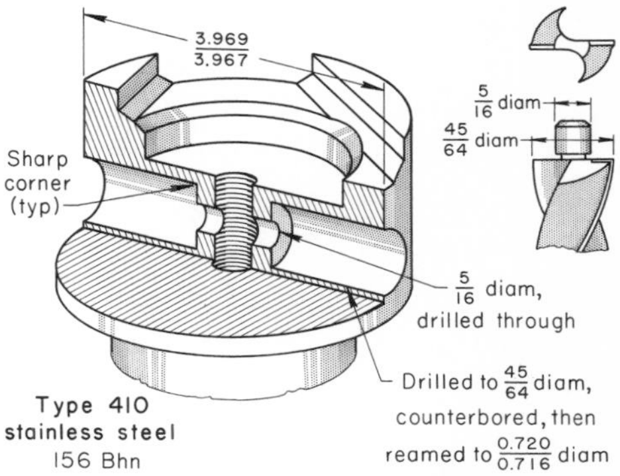

Speed	428 rpm (81 sfm)
Feed	0.005 ipr
Cutting fluid	Soluble-oil:water (1:20)
Production rate	4.2 min per piece
Drill life per grind (average)	80 pieces

Fig. 23. Sharp-cornered counterbores that were produced by piloted drill ground as shown at right (Example 171)

Applications of Special Drills for Hard Steel

Tool steels and other steels with hardness to Rockwell C 60 or higher can be drilled by a special type of drill (Fig. 24b). Blanks for these drills are cast from a heat-resisting alloy. They have a round shank (straight or tapered) and a triangular fluted section. The fluted end is ground to a three-sided-pyramid tip, and is then notched to provide chip clearance.

These drills work by heating the metal beneath the drill point by friction and then wiping out the softened metal as a chip. They are used in conventional drilling machines at speeds of 100 sfm, for ⅛-in.-diam drills, to 150 sfm, for 1-in.-diam drills.

Although these drills are sometimes used in production drilling, their greatest use is for salvaging parts when holes were accidentally omitted until after hardening, and for making changes in hardened dies.

In drilling case-hardened parts, these drills should be used only for penetrating the case. Standard drills should be used on the softer core of case-hardened parts.

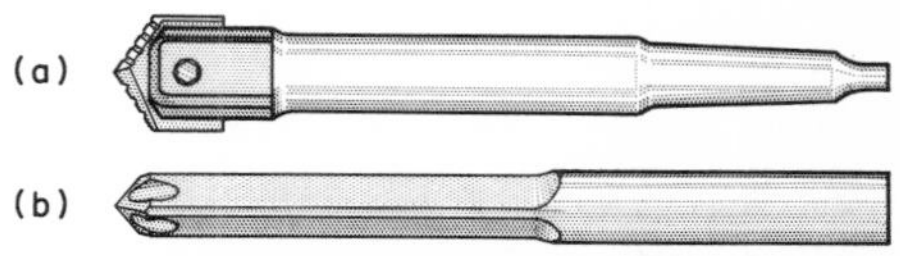

Fig. 24. (a) *Spade drill with interchangeable tip.* (b) *Special drill for hard steels. See text for discussion.*

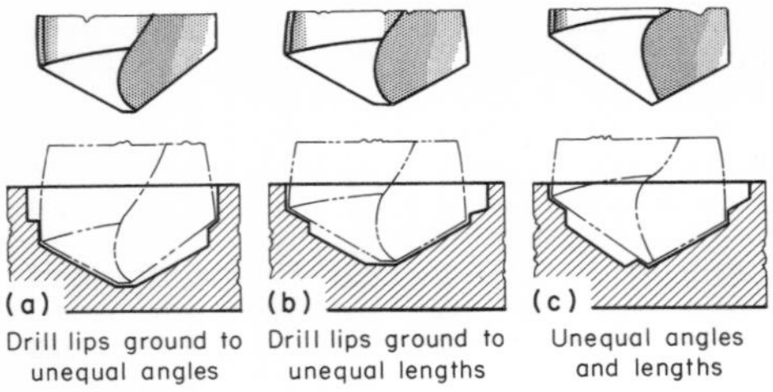

Fig. 25. Causes of oversize drilling

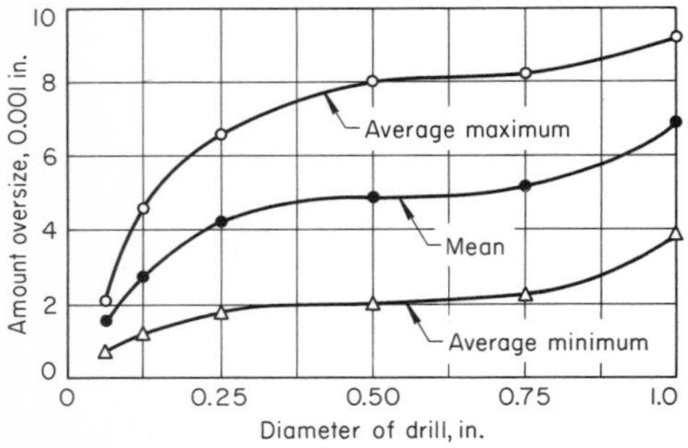

Data are based on drilling 468 holes with drills of each of six different diameters, in a series of tests conducted by several drill manufacturers. Drills were used without bushings.

Fig. 26. Hole oversize in drilling steel or cast iron with machine-sharpened drills

These drills are often used for drilling under water, which allows a 25% higher speed than in dry drilling. Wet drilling also minimizes workpiece distortion and maintains full hardness to the edge of the drilled hole.

The special drill shown in Fig. 24(b) can also be used for reaming. A minimum of 1/16 in. should be left on the hole diameter for reaming, and speed should be reduced to half that used for drilling. Hole diameters can then be reamed within a total tolerance of 0.003 to 0.005 in.

For additional information on drilling of hardened steel, see the section of this article "Drilling Steel at Rockwell C 48 to 55" (page 90).

Dimensional Accuracy of Holes

In most drilling operations, the drill is expected to cut oversize. Because a standard twist drill is primarily a roughing tool, some variation in hole size is expected even under the best conditions. When great accuracy is required (for example, meeting tolerances of less than 0.0005 in. on a ½-in.-diam hole), it is usually necessary to: (*a*) drill undersize and then ream to size, or (*b*) use a special drill or a special technique, or both.

Misalignment sometimes causes a drill to cut oversize. More often, imprecise sharpening is responsible:

1 If the drill is sharpened with unequal angles (Fig. 25a), the lip with the greater angle does most of the work, and the reaction forces the opposite margin into the wall of the hole.
2 If the drill is sharpened with unequal lip lengths (Fig. 25b), the two lips balance so that their reactions are equal, but the drill sweeps with one margin rubbing against the hole.

Sometimes both conditions exist (Fig. 25c), resulting in holes that vary widely in size and shape. This dual error is a typical result of sharpening drills by hand. Sharpening drills by machine is recommended. If a machine-sharpened drill does not cut within reasonable tolerance, the web may be off-center or flute spacing may be inaccurate. Small variations in web concentricity and flute spacing seldom have a significant effect on accuracy.

The amount of oversize cutting that can be expected from machine-sharpened drills has been determined from data compiled by several drill manufacturers. Results of drilling steel or cast iron with drills of six different diameters are shown graphically in Fig. 26. These results were obtained by drilling 468 holes with each size of drill. Although this drilling was done with normal good practice, no special equipment (such as bushings) or special technique was used.

As indicated in Fig. 26, for holes larger than ¾ in. in diameter, oversize increases rapidly with diameter. For close tolerance and uniformity, these holes must always be reamed.

When hole tolerances are closer than those shown in Fig. 26, it may be necessary to do one or more of the following:

1 Modify drill design, or use a different type of drill
2 Predrill with a center drill
3 Drill in steps
4 Use bushings
5 Rotate the work instead of the drill (this may require the use of a different drilling machine)
6 Change to special drills, such as oil-hole or gun drills
7 Use a precision drill collet or chuck to minimize drill runout.

Drill Design. Many holes can be drilled with more than one type of drill, but discriminating selection may allow closer tolerances. For instance, if a screw-machine drill can be used, somewhat closer tolerances can be met than with a longer drill, because of the decrease in drill overhang. In some applications a screw-machine drill has replaced a standard-length drill and eliminated the need for bushings. Modification of the drill point (Examples 167 to 171) often results in greater accuracy.

Predrilling with a center drill often improves accuracy, because the final drill has no chance to "walk" at the start. Walking causes out-of-line drilling, resulting in holes that are less accurate in size and roundness.

Drilling in steps can improve accuracy, although with some types of equipment it can also reduce productivity. In the following example, however, accuracy was improved and productivity was increased:

Example 172. Closer Tolerances and Increased Productivity (Fig. 27)

A through hole 2¾ in. deep and 0.752/0.748 in. in diameter was drilled in a passenger-car rear hub in four steps, in a multiple-spindle chucking machine. As shown in Fig. 27, the sequence entailed the use of progressively smaller twist drills in stations 1, 2 and 3 (the first drilling 1 in., the second 1 in. farther, and the third drilling through), and the use

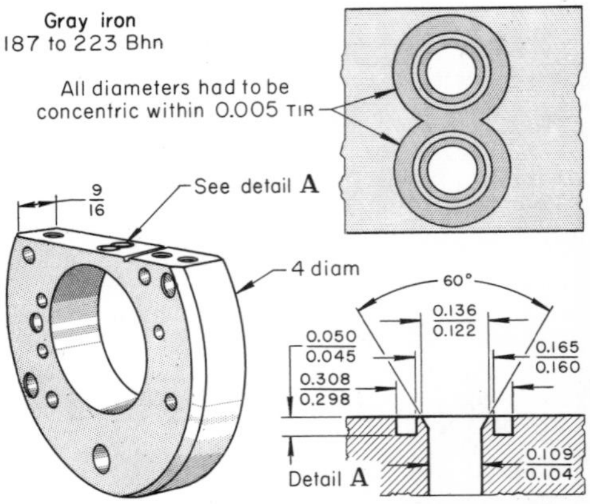

Spindle speed	3250 rpm
Surface speed, drill portion of tool	90 sfm
Surface speed, hollow-mill portion	255 sfm
Feed	0.0023 ipr
Cutting fluid	Soluble-oil:water(1:40)
Production rate	178 pieces per hour
Drill life	2500 pieces per tool

Fig. 28. Concentricity that was obtained by the use of a combination drill and hollow mill (see Fig. 3, page 42) made of T9 high speed steel (Example 173)

of a four-flute core drill in station 4 to complete the operation. The core drill acted as a rough reamer, thus producing greater accuracy.

Since all four drills operated simultaneously, one hole was completed every 0.357 min (see table of operating conditions with Fig. 27). Had the hole been finished completely with one drill in a single station, drilling time per hole would have been quadrupled.

Example 704, in the article "Machining of Tool Steel", describes a difficult application in which predrilling and drilling in steps were both necessary. Two small oil holes were drilled the length of a drill blank, in the production of an oil-hole drill.

Drill bushings in fixtures assure uniformly centered starts, which result in better alignment, and thus improve

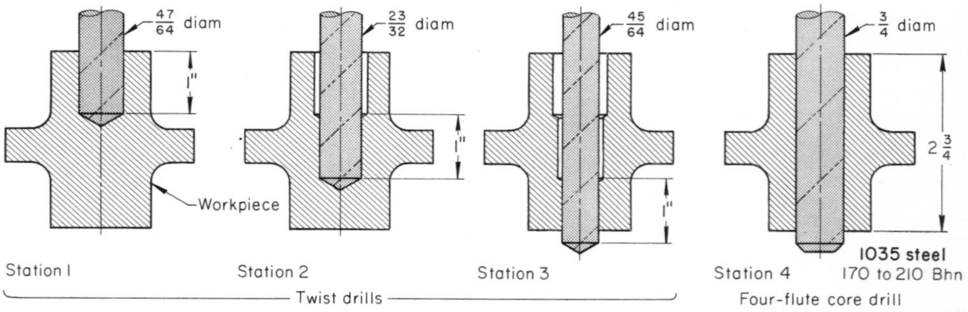

Machine	Multiple-spindle chucker	Cutting fluid	Soluble-oil:water(1:20)
Speed	350 rpm (68 sfm max)	Drilling time per hole	0.357 min
Feed	0.008 ipr	Drill life per grind	1600 pieces

Fig. 27. Step drilling that increased productivity and accuracy over that obtainable by drilling with a single drill (Example 172)

Table 3. Nominal Speeds and Feeds for Drilling of Carbon and Low-Alloy Steels With High Speed Steel Twist Drills (a)

Typical steel(b)	Brinell hardness	Speed sfm	Feed (ipr) for drill diameter of: ⅛ in.	¼ in.	½ in.	¾ in.	1 in.	1½ in.	2 in.
Carbon and Low-Alloy Steels (Except Free-Cutting Grades)									
1020, 1045, 4140, 7140 and 8620, at hardness ranges listed at right	85 to 125	90	0.003	0.005	0.010	0.015	0.018	0.020	0.025
	125 to 175	80	0.003	0.005	0.009	0.012	0.014	0.018	0.021
	175 to 225	70	0.002	0.004	0.007	0.010	0.012	0.015	0.018
	225 to 275	55	0.002	0.004	0.006	0.009	0.010	0.013	0.016
	275 to 325	45	0.002	0.003	0.005	0.008	0.009	0.011	0.013
	325 to 375	35	0.002	0.003	0.005	0.008	0.009	0.010	0.011
	375 to 425	25	0.002	0.003	0.005	0.007	0.009	0.010	0.010
	Rc 50 to 52 ...	15	0.0005	0.001	0.002	0.002	0.003	0.003	0.004
Free-Cutting Carbon and Low-Alloy Steels									
1112 and 12L14	100 to 150	110	0.003	0.005	0.010	0.015	0.018	0.020	0.025
	150 to 200	115	0.003	0.005	0.010	0.015	0.018	0.020	0.025
	200 to 250	75	0.003	0.005	0.010	0.015	0.018	0.020	0.025
1117 and 1137	100 to 150	90	0.003	0.005	0.010	0.015	0.018	0.020	0.023
	150 to 200	90	0.003	0.005	0.010	0.015	0.018	0.020	0.025
	200 to 250	90	0.003	0.005	0.010	0.015	0.018	0.020	0.023
	275 to 325	65	0.002	0.004	0.006	0.010	0.012	0.015	0.018
	325 to 375	40	0.002	0.003	0.006	0.008	0.009	0.010	0.011
	375 to 425	30	0.002	0.003	0.005	0.007	0.009	0.010	0.010
4140+S and 41L40	150 to 200	85	0.003	0.005	0.009	0.013	0.017	0.021	0.024
	200 to 250	75	0.003	0.004	0.007	0.010	0.012	0.015	0.018
	275 to 325	55	0.003	0.004	0.006	0.009	0.011	0.014	0.017
	375 to 425	25	0.002	0.003	0.005	0.007	0.009	0.010	0.010
	Rc 45 to 48 ...	20	0.0005	0.001	0.002	0.002	0.003	0.003	0.004

(a) High speed steels M1, M7 and M10, except M33 and T15 for hardness above 325 Bhn. (b) Each steel listed is a frequently used grade in a group of similar steels. For a listing of the steels in the various groups, see Table 2, page 6. (Data are adapted from tables compiled by Metcut Research Associates, Inc.)

hole roundness, straightness, and accuracy of location. The practical application of bushings is indicated in Examples 151, 152, 153 and 170.

Rotating the workpiece (provided its size and shape permit) will invariably result in more accurate drilling than rotating the drill while the work remains stationary. Machines in which the work is rotated include lathes, turret lathes, and horizontal multiple-station drilling machines. A turret lathe also makes it possible to drill a hole in steps, completing it with a core drill, and then to ream it for still greater accuracy.

Holding concentricity of two or more diameters is often a problem in close-tolerance drilling. One means of solving such a problem is described in the following example:

Example 173. Holding Concentricity and Eliminating Tool Failure (Fig. 28)

The shell-mold-cast gray iron compressor cylinder shown in Fig. 28 was drilled in a horizontal multiple-spindle drilling machine. The main problem was to hold the four diameters shown in "Detail A" in Fig. 28 concentric within 0.005 in. TIR.

Originally the machining sequence was:

1 Drill 0.109/0.104-in. diameter through.
2 Chamfer 0.136/0.122-in. diameter 60°.
3 Hollow mill 0.308/0.298-in. diameter 0.050/0.045 in. deep.

Tools used were guided in drill bushings in a sliding bushing bracket. The hollow mill was piloted by the drilled hole. This procedure posed two problems: the required concentricity could not be held, and the pilot of the hollow mill would gall in the drilled hole and break. A combination hollow mill and drill [shown as Fig. 3 in the article "Trepanning", page 42] was developed to overcome these problems.

The hollow mill was guided in a drill bushing, the drill being held in the hollow mill by a setscrew. This combination tool solved the earlier problems but introduced new ones. The spindle speed used (3250 rpm) was the right speed for drilling (90 sfm) but it was too fast for the hollow mill and overheated the tool, which was of general-purpose high speed steel. Use of carbide for the hollow mill solved the overheating problem and worked well for the first hole, but the carbide chipped in making the second hole because of the intermittent cut. The answer to the last problem was to make the hollow mill of a more heat-resisting type of high speed steel, T9. Chamfering was done by a chamfering tool mounted in a floating holder, at a separate station. Processing details are given with Fig. 28.

Speed and Feed

Optimum speed and feed for drilling depend on workpiece material, tool material, depth of hole, design of drill, rigidity of setup, tolerance, and cutting fluid. Consequently, it is impossible to recommend speeds and feeds applicable under all conditions. The nominal speeds and feeds in Table 3 are useful as starting points in selecting an optimum combination for a specific job.

In some of the production examples in this article, the speeds and feeds used are in reasonably close agreement with the nominal values in Table 3. In Example 151, for instance, 4130 steel at Rockwell C 30 was drilled with 0.295-in.-diam holes at a speed of 50 sfm and a feed of 0.003 ipr. For ¼-in.-diam holes in similar work metal (4140 group at 275 to 325 Bhn), Table 3 suggests a speed of 45 sfm at a feed of 0.003 ipr.

In other examples, the speeds and feeds used were considerably different from those in Table 3. The reason for the difference is usually apparent when all conditions are reviewed for any specific example. For instance, in Example 155, through holes nearly nine diameters long were drilled in 4130 steel (Rockwell C 20 to 27) at 120 sfm, which is more than twice the speed suggested in Table 3 (4140 group at 225 to 275 Bhn). But in Example 155 an oil-hole drill was used (which copiously supplied fluid to the cutting edges), and the part was fixtured (a practice permitting greater speed).

When unfavorable conditions prevail, such as less than normal rigidity or restrictions on the use of cutting fluid, slower speeds and lower feed rates than shown in Table 3 may be required. Oversize drilling (Fig. 25 and 26) increases as speed increases. Therefore, drill-grinding practice, drilling rigidity and drill design are closely related to the accuracy that can be obtained at any given speed. Feed rate must not exceed that at which chips can be flushed away. Clogging of chips decreases accuracy, and eventually leads to drill breakage.

Gun drills ordinarily have carbide tips, which can withstand greater speeds. The usual practice is to operate them at considerably higher speeds but lower feeds than those for high speed steel twist drills. This allows gun drills to form thin chips that are more readily flushed away by cutting fluid under pressure. The examples in the section "Applications of Gun Drills" represent typical gun-drilling practice. Nominal speeds and feeds for gun drilling of carbon and low-alloy steels with carbide-tipped drills are given in Table 4.

Cutting Fluids

Cutting fluids serve the same purposes in drilling as in other metal-cutting operations: to cool workpieces and tools, to flush away chips, and to minimize adherence of tool and work metal. Types of cutting fluids and principles of selection and use are described on page 19 in the article on Turning.

They are used in most drilling applications, except on such materials as cast iron (for which an air jet may be used instead), or when the use of fluids is incompatible with subsequent operations or the end use of the part (as in Example 156).

Table 4. Nominal Speeds and Feeds for Gun Drilling of Carbon and Low-Alloy Steels With Carbide-Tipped Drills (a)

Typical steel(b)	Brinell hardness	Speed, sfm(c)
Carbon and Low-Alloy Steels (Except Free-Cutting Grades)		
1020, 1045, 4140, 7140 and 8620, at hardness ranges listed at right	85 to 125	500
	125 to 175	425
	175 to 225	375
	225 to 275	300
	275 to 325	250
	325 to 375	200
	375 to 425	150
	Rc 45 to 48	100
	Rc 50 to 52	75
Free-Cutting Carbon and Low-Alloy Steels		
1112, 1117 and 12L14, at hardnesses at right	100 to 150	575
	150 to 200	605
	200 to 250	325
1137	175 to 225	400
	275 to 325	300
	325 to 375	200
	375 to 425	150
4140+S and 41L40	150 to 200	400
	200 to 250	325
	275 to 325	275
	325 to 375	200
	375 to 425	150
	Rc 45 to 48	100

(a) Carbide grade C-2. (b) Each steel listed is a frequently used grade in a group of similar steels. For a listing of the steels in the various groups, see Table 2, page 6. (c) At feeds determined by drill diameter and work-metal hardness, as follows:

Drill diameter, in.	Feed, ipr: To 425 Bhn	Rc 45 to 48	Rc 50 to 52
Under ¼	0.0004	0.0003	0.0002
¼ to ½	0.0006	0.0004	0.0003
½ to ¾	0.0008	0.0005	0.0004
¾ to 1	0.0010	0.0007	0.0005
1 to 2	0.0015	0.0009	0.0006

(Data are adapted from tables compiled by Metcut Research Associates, Inc.)

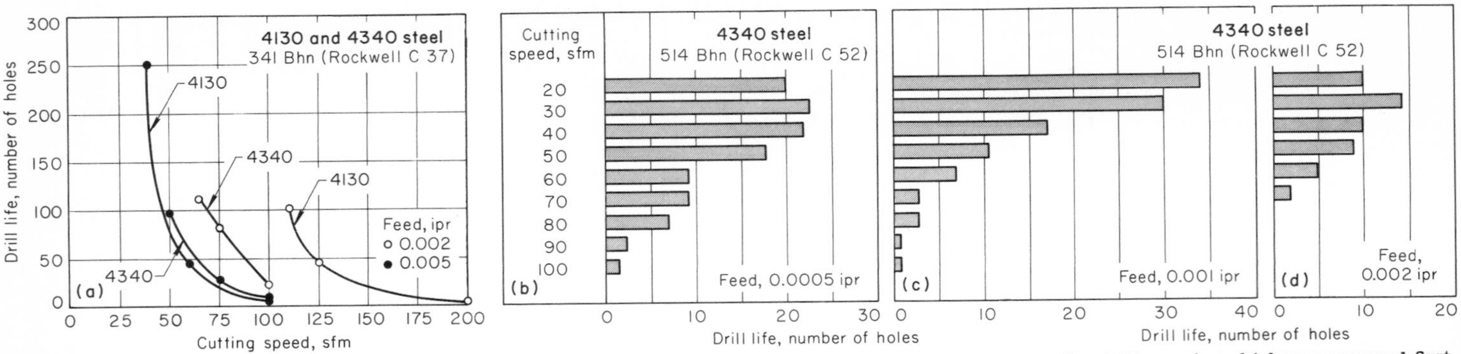

Holes for both series of tests were drilled through ½-in.-thick specimens 3 to 4 in. in diameter, with ¼-in.-diam drills (118° included point angle, 29° helix angle, 7° clearance), using a 1-to-1 mixture of thread-cutting oil and light machine oil as cutting fluid. Drills for data in (a) were 4 in. long and made of M2 high speed steel. Drills for data in (b), (c) and (d) were 2¾ in. long, of T15 high speed steel, and ground with crankshaft points. The end point of drill life was breakdown of the drill or a 0.015-in. wear land on the drill margin, whichever occurred first. Specimens were cut from round bars, and to remove any surface effect caused by heat treatment, 0.040 in. of metal was removed from the face of each specimen prior to drilling. All tests were conducted on a sliding-head box-column drilling machine equipped with variable-speed drive. A separate variable-speed drive was used to drive the feed mechanism, which could produce feed within the range of 0.0005 to 0.015 ipr.

Fig. 29. Effect of speed and feed on drill life

The use of sulfurized cutting oils is almost mandatory for gun drilling operations, because of the more accurate dimensions and smoother finishes that usually are required.

Variables That Affect Drill Life

Apart from drill design and material, and rigidity of the setup, the variables that most affect the life of drills are speed and feed, and hardness and composition of the work metal.

Speed and Feed. Figure 29 relates speed and feed to drill life. The curves of Fig. 29(a) for drilling 4130 and 4340 steels at 341 Bhn (Rockwell C 37) indicate that: (*a*) drill life decreased rapidly as cutting speed was increased; and (*b*) at a given cutting speed, drill life was shortened when feed rate was increased from 0.002 to 0.005 ipr.

Tests on 4340 steel at 514 Bhn (Rockwell C 52), as shown in the bar graphs of Fig. 29(b), (c) and (d), indicate trends somewhat different from those observed for the softer steels. Maximum drill life was found at the intermediate feed rate of 0.001 ipr, with shorter drill life observed at either a higher or a lower feed rate. Only at 0.001-ipr feed did drill life decrease progressively as speed was increased; at both the higher and the lower feed rates, maximum drill life was obtained at a cutting speed of 30 sfm. (These patterns of variation in drill life with speed and feed have been observed in machining tests on other metals; see Fig. 32 and 33, in the section "Determination of Optimum Speed and Feed", in this article.)

The use of a light feed reduces cutting temperature and cutting force. But if feed rate is reduced by half, the area of chip passing over the cutting edge is doubled. As a result, tool wear is likely to increase. Therefore, whether reducing the feed rate is advantageous or not depends on whether the lower cutting temperature and lighter cutting force offset the increased area of chip passing over the cutting edge. At high cutting speed, for which cutting temperature is a critical factor in drill life, reducing the feed is advantageous. At low cutting speed, for which cutting temperature is less critical, the longer chip and the increased rubbing over the cutting edge are likely to offset the advantages of lower feed, and drill life is likely to decrease.

The effect of speed on drill life is also discussed in Examples 834 and 835, in the article "Machining of Heat-Resisting Alloys". An application in which speed was reduced to prevent drill failure is described in Example 887, in the article on Machining of Aluminum.

Hardness and Composition of Work Metal. The effect of workpiece material on tool life in drilling carbon and low-alloy steels similar in composition and microstructure can be interpreted in terms of hardness. Results of one comparison of this type are given in Fig. 30. Although these results were affected to some degree by the use of a different tool material for drilling the softest steel, drill life (the amount of metal removed before the development of a predetermined wear land on the drill) was progressively shorter for increasing hardness of the steel being drilled.

The composition of carbon and low-alloy steels is usually of only secondary importance in its direct effects on drill life. Effects of practical significance include those of free-cutting additives, differences of 0.10% or more in carbon content, and substantial differences in the content of alloying elements. Some of these differences in composition also produce changes in hardness.

Composition is of primary importance when it is necessary to improve drill life by heat treatment or cold reduction of the work material, or by selection of a more suitable work material. (See pages 6 to 8 in the article "Turning" in this volume, and pages 302 to 316 in Volume 1 of this Handbook; see also pages 165 and 166 here.)

Effect of Workpiece Hardness on Cost

Hardness of the workpiece material exerts a major influence on drilling cost, and meaningful comparisons of the effect of hardness on drilling cost can be made for steels that are similar in composition and microstructure.

Drilling Cost. Figure 30, in addition to showing the effect of workpiece hardness on drill life, also shows its effect on drilling cost. Cost per cubic inch of metal removed has been computed by totaling the costs of new tools, tool setup, tool change, tool regrind, labor and overhead, for drilling ¼-in. and ½-in.-diam holes. Figure 30 indicates that drilling cost at Rockwell C 47 was 5 to 7 times greater than at Rockwell C 15, and at Rockwell C 52 was 8 to 17 times greater than at Rockwell C 15.

Although drilling cost almost always increases with increasing hardness in the range above Rockwell C 35 (330

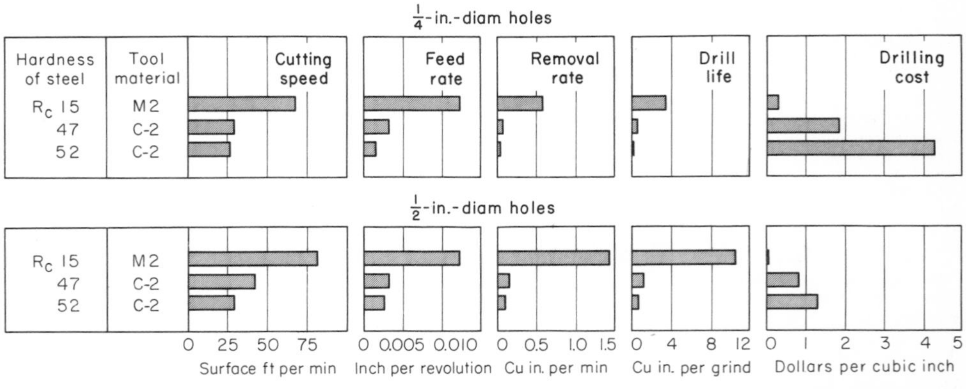

Comparative drilling tests were conducted on three similar steels, each at a different hardness. On each steel, the tools and machining conditions used had been previously determined to provide maximum economy in drilling that material. Drill life was based on the development of a predetermined amount of wear on the edge of the drill.

Fig. 30. Effect of workpiece hardness on drill life and drilling cost

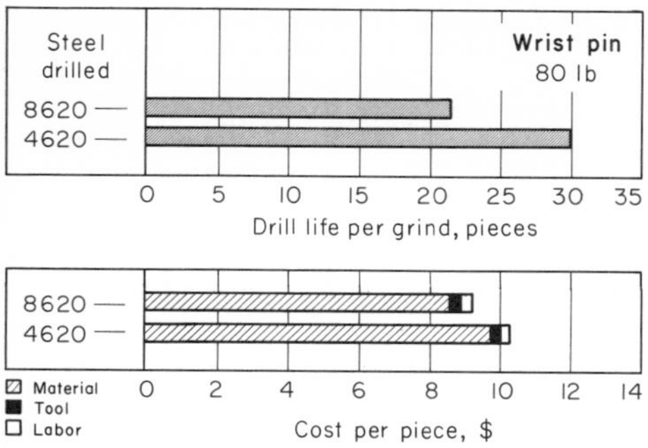

Item	4620	8620
Drilling Conditions		
Speed, sfm	70	70
Feed, ipr	0.006	0.005
Costs per Piece		
Tool	$ 0.23	$0.31
Labor	0.25	0.30
Material	9.83	8.67
Total	$10.31	$9.28
Saving		$1.03

Data are based on drilling of 200 pins, with a twist drill made of T1 high speed steel. All pins were carburized to a case depth of 0.080 to 0.100 in., with a case hardness of Rockwell C 23.

Fig. 31. Relation of material cost to machining cost (Example 175)

Bhn), the reverse effect is observed for low-carbon steel at lower hardness. For low-carbon steel, there is usually an optimum hardness range for lowest drilling cost; this range varies considerably according to composition. For some low-carbon steels a heat treating operation is warranted, to *increase* hardness before drilling—as in the following example:

Example 174. Higher Workpiece Hardness for Lower Cost

Gear blanks weighing 15 lb each, forged from 8617 steel, required a drilled hole 3 in. in diameter in the hub. This hole was drilled with a two-lip standard-helix drill with over-all length of 22 in. and flute length of 14 in.

When the gear blanks were drilled at a hardness of 149 to 156 Bhn, the drill burned and galled after only ten pieces were drilled. In addition, the holes were rough.

A process change was made: the blanks were heated to 1540 F and quenched in oil; resulting hardness was 217 to 241 Bhn. When the blanks were drilled at this hardness, drill life increased to 50 pieces before regrinding was required. Galling was reduced, chips were properly rolled and broken, and the surface finish of the drilled hole was improved. Production was at the rate of 20 pieces per hour in both the original and revised procedures. Tool cost for drilling the softer gear material was $0.092 per piece, compared with $0.018 per piece for the harder material.

Over-All Cost. In considering over-all economy of manufacture, cost-per-pound differences among mechanically equivalent steels should be evaluated along with the differences in cost of machining the steels. Even when machining costs for a grade of steel that is difficult to drill are much greater than for a similar grade that is not, the machining costs may be outweighed by the difference in cost per pound of the two steels. The heavier the part and the less machining done on it, the more important is material cost as a factor in total cost. In the following example, the saving in material cost for 8620 steel was nine times the increase in total cost of tools and labor incurred by the use of this grade of steel.

Example 175. 8620 vs 4620 (Fig. 31)

The graphs in Fig. 31 show drill life and cost per piece in drilling 80-lb wrist pins made of either 8620 or 4620 steel, both in the carburized condition (case hardness, Rockwell C 23). As these data indicate, although the 4620 could be drilled at higher feed and with longer tool life than the 8620, the lower cost of 8620 made this steel more economical for pins this heavy. Had the pins weighed less than 12 lb each, however, 4620 steel would have been the more economical material.

Additional examples of the relation of work-material cost to drilling cost are given in "The Selection of Steel for Economy in Machining", in Volume 1.

Determination of Optimum Speed and Feed

As numerous examples in this article indicate, a wide range of speeds and feeds can be employed to yield acceptable results in the drilling of most materials, particularly those that present no unusual difficulty in machining. For materials that are unusually hard, soft and gummy, abrasive, or otherwise difficult to machine, the range of economical operating conditions is narrow. For these materials, an optimum speed and feed can be determined by making drilling tests to establish the conditions for minimum cost per cubic inch of metal removed.

A systematic procedure for determining optimum speed and feed is described below and is illustrated in Fig. 32 and 33. Optimum drilling conditions were determined by changing one variable (speed or feed) while holding the other constant. The first step was to select a near-optimum feed; then speed was adjusted in increments, to find the most economical speed. Selection of the near-optimum feed was based on previ-

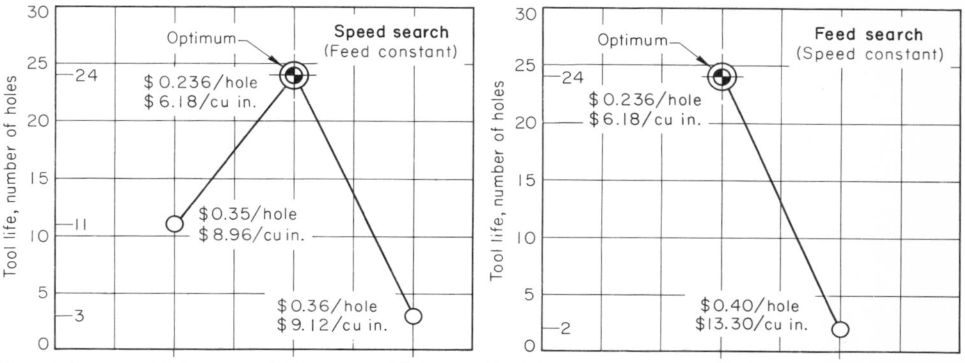

Speed, sfm	17.0	23.5	31.8
Speed, rpm	325	450	610
Feed, ipr	0.0015	0.0015	0.0015
Rate, holes/min	0.39	0.55	0.73
Rate, cu in./min	0.0152	0.021	0.0285

Feed, ipr	0.0015	0.003
Speed, sfm	23.5	23.5
Speed, rpm	450	450
Rate, holes/min	0.55	1.08
Rate, cu in./min	0.021	0.0327

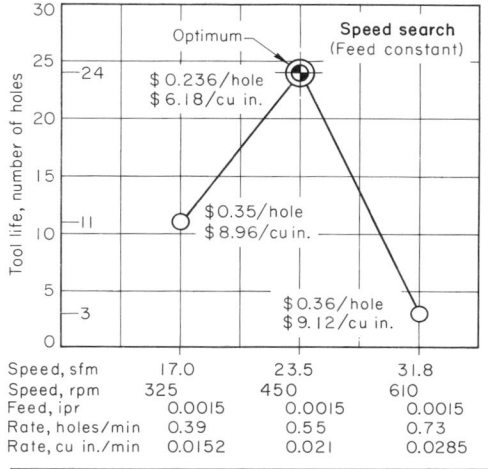

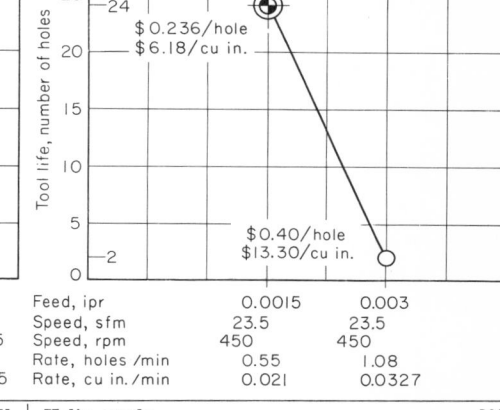

Machining Conditions: Vertical 4-spindle drill press; cutting fluid, 1-to-1 mixture of sulfurized oil and mineral oil, flow application; through holes, 1.25 in. deep.

Drill Details

Material	M10 high speed steel
Diameter	0.199 in.
Over-all length	4 in.
Number of flutes	2
Helix angle	30°
Point angle	135°
Lip relief angle	7°
Type of point	Split
Wear land	0.015 in.

Cost Factors

Tool use, per tool	$0.39
Tool change, per tool	0.20
Operating, per min	0.116

Fig. 32. Determination of speed and feed for drilling 0.199-in.-diam holes in A-286 alloy at minimum cost

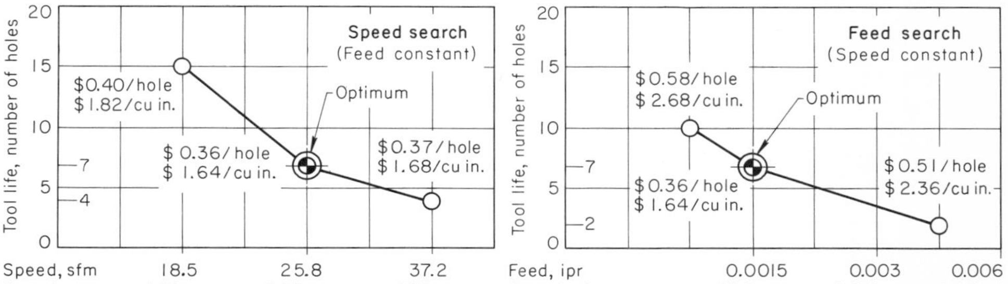

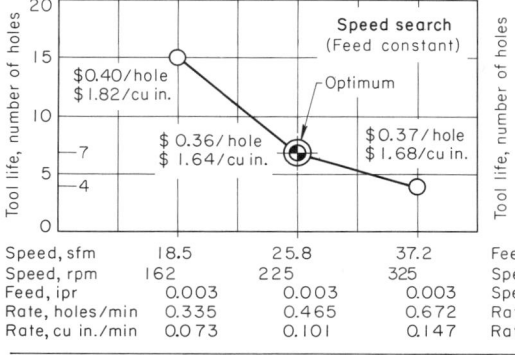

Speed, sfm	18.5	25.8	37.2
Speed, rpm	162	225	325
Feed, ipr	0.003	0.003	0.003
Rate, holes/min	0.335	0.465	0.672
Rate, cu in./min	0.073	0.101	0.147

Feed, ipr	0.0015	0.003	0.006
Speed, sfm	25.8	25.8	25.8
Speed, rpm	225	225	225
Rate, holes/min	0.232	0.465	0.931
Rate, cu in./min	0.050	0.101	0.202

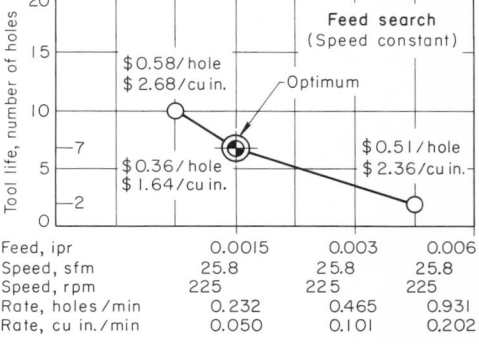

Machining Conditions: Vertical 4-station drill press; cutting-fluid, 1-to-1 mixture of sulfurized oil and mineral oil, flow application; through holes, 1.450 in. deep.

Drill Details

Material	M10 high speed steel
Diameter	0.4375 in.
Over-all length	5 in.
Number of flutes	2
Helix angle	29°
Point angle	135°
Lip relief angle	7°

Cost Factors

Tool use, per tool	$0.573
Tool change, per tool	0.20
Operating, per min	0.116

Fig. 33. Determination of speed and feed for drilling 0.4375-in.-diam holes in PH 15-7 Mo alloy at minimum cost

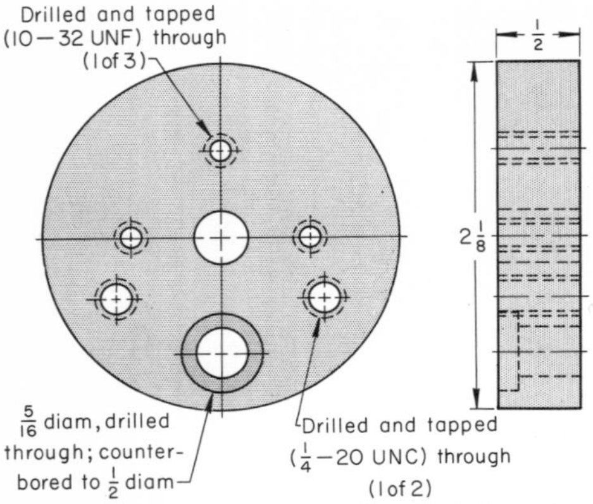

Fig. 34. Part that was produced at the rate of 25 per hour in hand-feed equipment, or at 480 per hour in automatic equipment (Example 176)

ous experience. After this first series of operations (the "speed search"), speed was held constant and feed was varied in increments, to verify or correct the initially selected feed rate (the "feed search").

The development of a predetermined wear land on the edge of the drill was the criterion for tool life. Different speeds and feeds caused wear at different rates. Attainment of the predetermined amount of wear, which was ascertained by the use of a hand microscope, marked the point at which each test was stopped.

Cost Factors. In this study, three factors were included in the determination of machining costs: tool-use cost, tool-change cost, and operating cost. Operating cost was based on a standard cost per minute for all operations. Tool-change cost was obtained by the use of a specific rate of tool changing that had been assigned to the operation. Tool-use cost included the cost of new tools and the cost of regrinding.

In the charts in Fig. 32 and 33, total cost per hole drilled for each test condition is the sum of the following:

1 Operating cost times number of minutes required to drill one hole
2 Tool-change cost divided by tool life in holes per tool
3 Tool-use cost divided by tool life in holes per tool.

Dividing this total by the volume of metal removed per hole gives the drilling cost in dollars per cubic inch of metal removed for each test condition.

Selection of Machine for Economy of Production

In selecting a machine, the following options should be considered for their suitability to the specific job:

1 Machine type: manual control, tape control; single spindle, or multiple spindle
2 Machine calibrations: speed and feed range, manual or automatic machine positioning, and automatic preselect
3 Tooling: complex or simple fixturing; high speed steel or carbide tools.

Once these have been decided on, a machine is selected for greatest economy on the basis of size of production lot. Small lots (fewer than 100 pieces) seldom justify large expenditures for jigs and fixtures, but numerically controlled machines are being used increasingly for low production quantities. Large production quantities may require more expensive tooling, and single-purpose machine tools often provide the greatest economy.

The four examples that follow demonstrate the relation between production requirements and the machine tool best suited for economical operation.

Example 176. Hand-Feed vs Automatic Machines (Fig. 34)

Production quantity determined the type of equipment used for drilling (and tapping or counterboring) the six holes in the part shown in Fig. 34.

When fewer than 100 pieces were required, a six-spindle, hand-feed gang drilling machine was used in conjunction with a simple box-type jig with slip bushings. Two spindles of this machine were equipped with tapping devices. With this equipment, it was necessary to drill one piece at a time by moving the fixture from spindle to spindle until all operations were completed. Production rate by this procedure was 25 pieces per hour.

For high production, a machine consisting of two automatic drilling units and one automatic tapping unit was selected. This machine had a four-station indexing table. The jig held and located two pieces at each station. The sequence of operations at the four stations was:

1 Load and unload two pieces.
2 Drill for counterbore, and tap drill three holes, in each piece, using an eight-spindle multiple-head unit.
3 Counterbore, and tap drill two holes, in each piece, using a six-spindle multiple-head unit.
4 Tap five holes in each piece, using a ten-spindle multiple-head unit.

Cycle time for these operations was: 0.170 min for machining, 0.050 min of idle time (advance and return), and 0.030 min for indexing; total, 0.250 min (480 pieces per hour).

Examples 177 and 178. Radial vs Multiple-Spindle Machines

Example 177 — Thirty Holes in Gray Iron Casting (Fig. 35). The influence of production quantity and cost per piece on selection of a radial versus a multiple-spindle machine for drilling gray iron radiator-tank bottoms is shown in Fig. 35. Each of these castings required 30 holes (see inset in Fig. 35). As the data in Fig. 35 indicate, radial drilling was the more economical method for producing up to about 60 pieces, but beyond this quantity multiple drilling gave progressively lower cost per piece.

The radial drill press had a 9-in. column and a 5-ft arm. Two fixtures were required, one to hold the piece for drilling the holes in the joint face, and one for drilling the holes in the pads.

The multiple drilling machine (24 by 40 in.), with 30 spindles, was used in conjunction with one fixture on a 360°-indexing table. With this machine the 24 joint-face holes were drilled simultaneously, after which the fixture containing the workpiece was indexed for drilling of the six pad holes in a second operation.

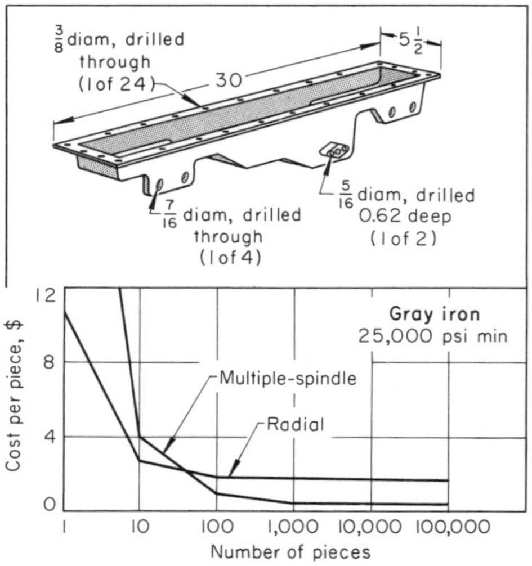

Fig. 35. Cost-quantity basis for selection of multiple-spindle or radial machine for drilling a gray iron radiator-tank bottom (Example 177)

Table 5. Radial vs Multiple-Spindle Drilling Machines (Example 178) (a)

Item	Type of machine(b) Radial	Multiple-spindle
Setup time, min	15	45
Time per piece, min:		
Drilling	3.00	0.30
Handling	1.65	0.65
Total	4.65	0.95
Total time (including setup), min:		
For 10 pieces	61.5	54.5
For 200 pieces	945	235

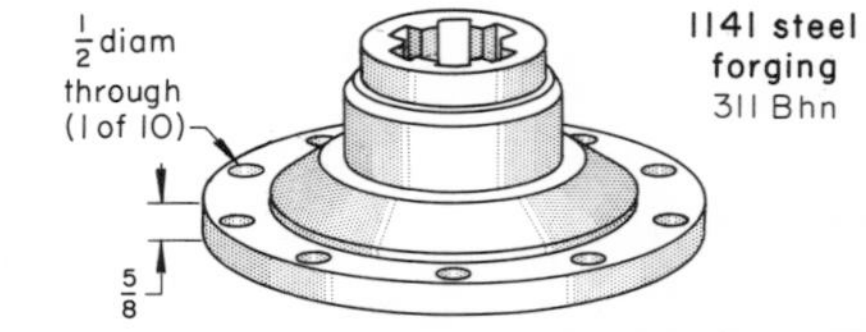

(a) Data are for drilling the ten ½-in.-diam equally spaced holes through the flange of the forging sketched above. (b) With both machines, speed was 458 rpm (60 sfm), feed was 0.006 ipr, and cutting fluid was a 33-to-1 mixture of water and a water-soluble semisynthetic.

Example 178 — Ten Holes in 1141 Steel Forging (Table 5). The drive flange shown in Table 5 was forged of 1141 steel and heat treated to 311 Bhn. The ten ½-in.-diam holes through the flange (⅝ in. deep), were made by drilling either with a radial machine, which drilled one hole at a time, or a multiple-spindle drilling machine, which drilled all ten holes at one time. The multiple machine had adjustable spindles. In both machines the workpiece was held in a "flopover" drill jig, and standard high speed steel drills were used.

Production data for the radial and multiple machines are compared in Table 5. These data demonstrate the increased production potential of the multiple drill. But machine availability, labor cost, amortization and overhead must be considered before selection of this type of machine can be justified.

Example 179. Tape-Controlled vs Radial Drill Presses (Table 6)

A 5-hp single-spindle tape-controlled drill press was compared with a 4-ft radial drill press for drilling annealed cast steel strainer-body covers in quantities of 2 to 50. As shown in Table 6, each of these parts required twelve ¾-in.-diam through holes, of two different depths.

Self-centering drills of high speed steel were used in both machines. The tape-controlled machine employed three locating pins and two clamps. The radial drill press employed two plate jigs and three clamps.

From the results of this comparison, presented in Table 6, it is evident that the slightly shorter drill life obtained with the tape-controlled machine was far outweighed by the superiority of the tape-controlled machine over the radial drill press in other respects — production rate was five times that with the radial drill press, and tooling cost was only one twelfth as great.

In high-production operations where changeovers are infrequent, it is often economical to combine drilling with other operations, as in the following example:

Example 180. Combination Drilling and Boring for Cost Reduction (Table 7)

The data in Table 7 show how combining drilling with boring in a chucking machine reduced labor cost by one third, in comparison with separate boring and drilling in a drill press. (The part was also turned in the chucking machine.)

The workpieces were wheel hubs made of 1035 at 170 to 210 Bhn. The operation involved drilling and boring of five holes 0.600 in. in diameter and 0.340 in. deep, and of one hole 1.25 in. in diameter and 0.140 in. deep, in each wheel hub. Production rate of the chucking machine was not reduced after the drilling operation was added, because the cycle time for drilling did not exceed the cycle time for boring and turning.

Table 6. Tape-Controlled vs Radial Drill Presses (Example 179) (a)

Item	Type of drilling machine(b): Tape-controlled(c)	Radial(d)
Number of setups	1	2
Setup time, min	3	25
Drilling time, min	5	15
Tool-change time, sec	10	10
Production, pieces per hr	7.5	1.5
Drill life per grind, pieces	25	30
Tooling cost per machine	$25	$300

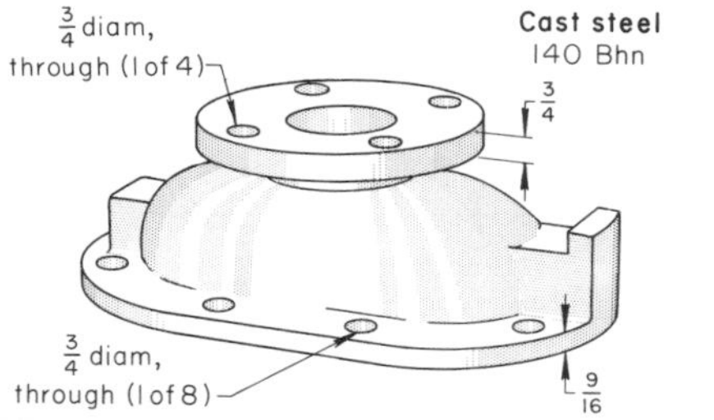

(a) Data are for drilling the twelve ¾-in.-diam through holes (two different depths) in the cast strainer-body cover sketched above, in production runs of 2 to 50 pieces. (b) With both machines, speed was 510 rpm (100 sfm), feed was 0.016 ipr, and cutting fluid was a high-sulfur-base liquid containing a lubricating additive. (c) 5-hp single-spindle machine. (d) 4-ft arm.

Effect of Drill Design and Material on Cost

Drill design and material can have a marked effect on drilling cost. This is demonstrated in Examples 181 through 185, which follow. (Additional information on drill material, drill design and drilling cost is given in the article entitled "The Selection of Material for Drills", pages 682 to 683 in Volume 1 of this Handbook.)

Examples 181 and 182. Drill Design

Example 181 — High-Helix vs Standard Twist Drills (Table 8). High-helix drills with thin webs and polished flutes increased production 25% over that obtained with standard twist drills. Also, by producing burr-free holes and thereby eliminating a separate deburring operation, the high-helix drills lowered cost per piece by 67%. The operation entailed drilling 0.032-in.-diam cross holes through bronze tubing (0.025-in. wall). Production and cost data for the two types of drills are compared in Table 8.

Example 182 — Spade vs Twist Drills (Fig. 36). A spade drill was selected in preference to a twist drill for drilling the relatively large holes in the 1017 steel part shown in Fig. 36. The selection was made on the basis of lower tool cost per hole for the spade drill, as indicated by the comparative data accompanying Fig. 36. These data were obtained in drilling 100 pieces (200 holes). (For greater quantities, the spade drill would have been less economical, because additional cutters would have been needed for it while the twist drill would have required only regrinding.)

The penetration rate was almost the same for both drills. Feed rates were approximately 25% higher for the twist drill, but this was offset by an increase in surface speed for the spade drill.

The importance of drill design as a factor in drill life is also illustrated in Examples 826, 827 and 828, in the article "Machining of Heat-Resisting Alloys".

Example 183, 184 and 185. Drill Material

Example 183 — Drill Life, M2 vs M4 (Table 9). A change in drill material, from M2 to M4 high speed steel, resulted in more economical production when 1030 steel was drilled with two-lip drills. The 1030 steel was soft, and the chips produced by drilling were stringy.

Drills made of M4 high speed steel produced 1200 pieces per grind, which represented the production output desired in one complete shift. Drills made of M2 high speed steel needed grinding after 700 pieces, thus requiring a change of tools during a shift, with consequent loss of production.

As indicated in Table 9, the change from M2 to M4 drills resulted in a reduction of about 45% in tool and setup costs per piece, in spite of a 13% higher initial cost for an M4 drill. The parts were drilled in a machine equipped with a drill head that contained a cluster of five individual drills.

Example 184 — Drilling Speed, Carbide vs High Speed Steel. A four-flute carbide core drill required less cutting time than one made of high speed steel for drilling holes $2\frac{13}{32}$ in. in diameter and $1\frac{1}{16}$ in. deep in normalized 4620 steel (175 Bhn). Drilling time per piece (excluding handling time) was 0.37 min for the high speed steel drill, and 0.15 min for the carbide drill. Speeds were 128 rpm (80 sfm) for the high speed steel and 280 rpm (176 sfm) for the carbide; feeds were 0.003 and 0.0035 ipr, respectively. A water-soluble cutting fluid was used for both carbide and high speed steel drills.

Example 185 — Cost Factors, Carbide vs High Speed Steel (Table 10). Operating conditions and cost factors for drilling forged H11 steel bars (Rockwell C 40) with carbide-tipped and with high speed steel drills are compared in Table 10.

Holes ½ in. in diameter were drilled through ½-in.-thick stock in about 15% less time with carbide than with high speed steel; holes ⅛ in. in diameter, in about 40% less time. Tool life of the carbide-tipped drills was 2½ to 3⅓ times that of the high speed steel drills. The initial cost of the carbide-tipped drills, however, was substantially higher than that of the high speed steel drills — nearly 2½ times as much in the ½-in. size and 6 times as much in the ⅛-in. size.

Testing to Evaluate Drilling Conditions

Laboratory tests are usually made to develop and evaluate drilling techniques and drill designs and materials, without concern for machines and fixtures. This requires close control over test conditions (especially rigidity) and the provision of adequate, smooth power to the drill. Production tests are used to evaluate drill performance in combination with drilling machines and fixtures. Accelerated tests may lead to erroneous conclusions because the wear or failure may be different in practice.

Variation Among Drills. There is considerable variation in performance among drills of the same type, and even on resharpening a single drill. Therefore, enough drills should be tested to allow for this variation, and drills should be sharpened often enough to represent shop practice. Sharpening should reproduce the original point of the drill, and should include removal of the part of the drill that has metal pickup on the margin or has reverse back taper. The web should be thinned to its original dimensions, and the resharpened drill should be free from burns and checks.

Criteria for Drill Life. Preliminary testing is often necessary to determine realistic criteria for drill life. Workpiece material, cutting fluid, and operating conditions influence the type of failure. Useful criteria include drill noise, drill wear, inability to cut, total failure of drill, inaccurate hole size, poor hole finish, burrs, drill breakage, and increase in the amount of torque required for a given drilling operation.

Interpretation of Results. Because of variation in drills, test conditions, and work material, a substantial number of tests usually must be made. As an illustration, differences of 30% or more between groups of identical drills can be detected reliably with about six drills of each type run through several sharpenings. Statistical analysis can indicate whether observed differences are significant.

Caution must be exercised in interpreting test results, because of the wide discrepancies shown by machining tests in general (see pages 302 and 303 in Volume 1 of this Handbook). For example, consider the data of Fig. 29(a). Results were essentially the same in drilling 4130 and 4340 steel at 0.005 ipr feed, but speed for a given drill life was 40 to 50% higher for 4130 at 0.002 ipr feed. It could validly be concluded from these results that this lot of 4130 could be drilled at higher speeds than 4340 at a feed of about 0.002 ipr. However, no

Table 7. Cost Reduction by Change of Machine to Combine Drilling With Boring (Example 180)

Item	Drill press: Boring	Drill press: Drilling	Chucking machine: Drilling plus boring
Production, pcs/hr	100	200	100
Labor cost/pc	$0.0372	$0.0186	$0.0372
Total labor cost/pc	$0.0558		$0.0372
Saving per piece			$0.0186

Table 8. Cost Reduction With High-Helix Drills (Example 181) (a)

Item	Standard twist drill	High-helix drill
Production, pieces per hour	1200	1500
Cost per piece:		
Drilling	$0.005	$0.004
Deburring inside	0.007	0.000(b)
Total	$0.012	$0.004

(a) Drilling 0.032-in.-diam cross holes through 0.025-in.-wall bronze tubing. Data are based on production of 3 million pieces per year. (b) Not required; drilled holes were burr-free.

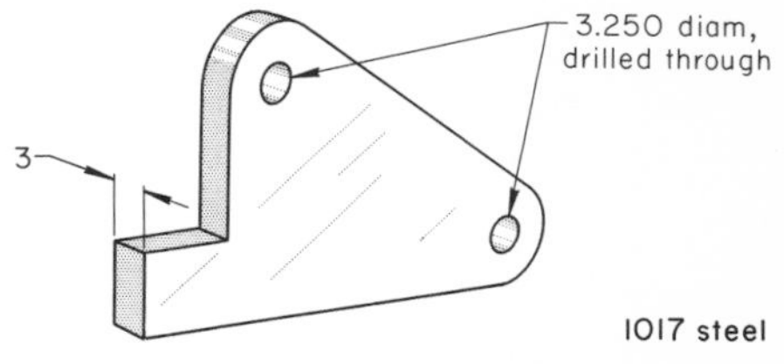

Item	Twist drill	Spade drill
Initial cost:		
Drill	$265	$14.25
Drill holder	...	77.50
Total	$265	$91.75
Drill cost per hole(a)	$1.33	$ 0.46

(a) For drilling 100 pieces (two holes each)

On the basis of the cost comparison given here, a spade drill was used instead of a twist drill for producing the two large holes in the part sketched above.

Fig. 36. Spade vs twist drills (Example 182)

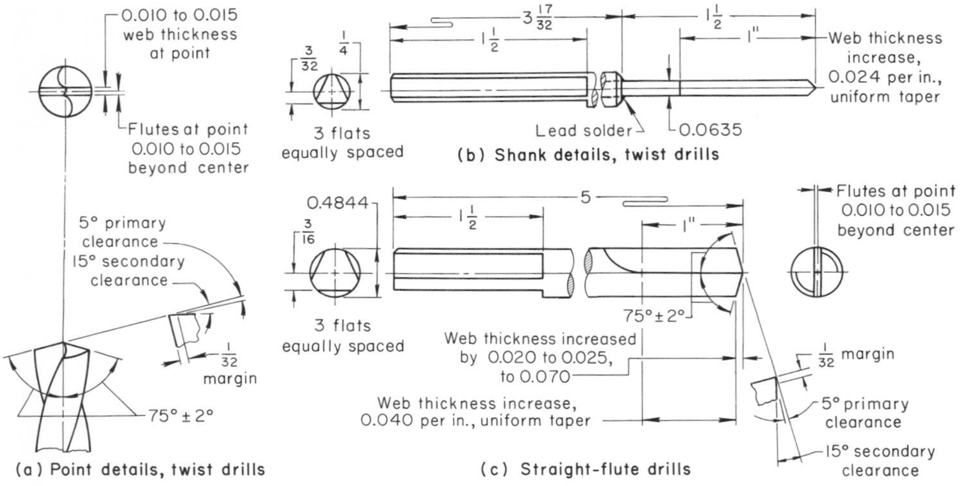

Fig. 37. Details of solid-carbide drills used successfully on H11 steel harder than Rockwell C 50. (a) *and* (b) *Twist drills, for holes less than 1/4 in. in diameter.* (c) *Straight-flute drills, for holes 1/4 in. in diameter or larger.* (Example 191)

conclusion could be drawn about 4130 and 4340 steels in general without additional testing.

Drilling Steel at Rockwell C 48 to 55

Successful drilling of steel that has been heat treated to a hardness of Rockwell C 48 to 55 depends mainly on the design of the drill, the rigidity of the machine setup, and the choice of tool material. As a rule, improvements in drill design and in machine and workpiece rigidity are of more direct benefit to drilling performance than is a change in tool material. A number of other conditions also may affect drill performance, and in certain circumstances they may become critical. Among these conditions are feed and speed, the efficiency and adaptability of power equipment (portable or stationary), and the accuracy of working surfaces of the drill. The next 11 examples illustrate the effects of operating variables in drilling hardened steel.

Examples 186 to 189. High Speed Steel Drills

Example 186 — Drill Redesign for Rigidity. In drilling 0.272-in.-diam blind holes (0.520 in. deep) in 4335 steel at Rockwell C 48 to 50, nitrided and oxide-treated high speed steel drills produced holes that were out-of-round (0.002 to 0.003 in.) and tapered (0.001 to 0.002 in.). Drill life was three to five holes per sharpening, using a radial-arm drill press and no cutting fluid.

To improve performance, drills of a different design were used. These were 4 1/8-in.-long heavy-duty drills ground from solid heat treated stock, with a 135° included point angle and a flat 1/32-in. primary lip relief angle of 5° to 7°. The flute length of these drills was shortened to 1 1/2 to 2 in., the web was thickened, the point was split, and a 3/4-in.-long bushing was used. The improved rigidity provided by these changes eliminated out-of-roundness and taper, and increased drill life to five to eight holes per sharpening.

Table 9. Cost Comparison, M2 vs M4 High Speed Steel for Drilling 1030 Steel (Example 183)

Cost factor	Drill steel M2	Drill steel M4
Initial cost of drill	$11.75	$13.25
Drill life, regrinds	12	15
Total cost of regrinds	$ 4.80	$ 6.00
Total cost, tool and regrinds	$16.55	$19.25
Drill life, pieces drilled	8400	18,000
Tool cost per piece:		
Per drill	$ 0.002	$ 0.0011
Total (5 drills)	$ 0.010	$ 0.0055
Number of setups per shift	2	1
Setup time for 5 drills, min	40	20
Setup cost per piece	$ 0.002	$ 0.001

Example 187 — Drill Design for Rockwell C 50. Two high-strength medium-alloy steels, 300M and X200, were satisfactorily drilled at Rockwell C 50 with high speed steel drills. Drill details were as follows:

Diameter	3/8 in.
Flute length	1 1/2 to 2 in.
Point angle	130°
Web thickness at tip	0.080 to 0.090 in. (split to zero)
Web taper	0.016 in. per in.
Axial rake in split portion	3° to 4° (pos)
Lip relief angle, 1/32 in. flat	5° to 7°

Both work materials were 0.093 in. thick. Best results were obtained with a speed of 20 sfm for the 300M steel and of 18 to 24 sfm for the X200. A mist of soluble-oil emulsion was used as a cutting fluid.

Example 188 — Effect of Nitriding on Drill Life. Blind holes, 0.272 in. in diameter and 0.620 in. deep, were drilled in 4335 steel hardened to Rockwell C 48 to 50. Drills had a life of only one to four holes per sharpening, and a breakage rate of one drill for every 16 to 20 holes. When the drills were nitrided, drill life was increased to 18 to 20 holes per sharpening, and drill breakage was reduced to one drill for every 50 to 60 holes.

All drills were standard heavy-duty drills ground from solid heat treated high speed steel. Each had a split point ground with a positive axial rake of 3° to 4° on the split portion, and included point angle of 135°, and a lip relief angle of 5° to 7°, ground flat 1/32 in.

Drilling was done in a radial-arm drill press with multiple speeds and automatic feed. Speed was 147 rpm (10.5 sfm), and feed was 0.002 ipr.

Example 189 — 4335 Steel at Rockwell C 48 to 51. Holes were drilled in 4335 steel at Rockwell C 48 to 51 with M2 high speed steel drills. These were heavy-duty drills, manufactured to NAS 907, type B, aircraft standards, with a point angle of 130° to 150°, a positive axial rake angle of 3° to 4°, and a split point. The drills were operated in a radial-arm drill press with variable speed and automatic feed.

In drilling 0.272-in.-diam holes completely through the 5/8-in.-thick hardened steel, best results were obtained with full-size drills; pilot drilling caused the material to harden. On the basis of test results of 15 to 20 holes per grind, the following speeds and feeds were selected:

Drill diameter, in.	Speed, sfm	Feed, ipr
1/8 and smaller	7 to 15	0.0005 to 0.001
3/16 to 1/4	7 to 15	0.001 to 0.002
0.272 to 1/2	7 to 15	0.002 to 0.004

Examples 190 and 191. High Speed Steel vs Carbide Drills

Example 190. Vanadium-containing 4335 steel at Rockwell C 48 to 50 was machined with high speed steel drills tipped with grade C-5 carbide (80% W, 1% Ta, 3% Ti, 6% C, 10% Co). To reduce excessive costs resulting from a high rate of drill breakage, heavy-duty high speed steel drills were substituted. (The quantity of work was too small to justify the purchase of equipment of sufficient rigidity to avoid breakage of the carbide-tipped drills.)

The new drills, 0.272 in. in diameter, were ground from solid heat treated stock and nitrided. They were provided with a split, or crankshaft, point having a positive axial rake angle of 3° to 4° on the split portion, an included point angle of 130°, and a lip relief angle of 5° to 7° ground flat 1/32 in. These drills were operated without coolant in an automatic drilling and tapping machine at a speed of 12 sfm and a feed of 0.002 to 0.004 ipr maximum.

When the hardness of the steel workpieces did not exceed Rockwell C 50, high speed steel drills had a life of 20 to 30 holes per sharpening. Above Rockwell C 50, however, tool life decreased to four to eight holes per sharpening, indicating that carbide-tipped drills should be considered for drilling the harder material.

Example 191 (Fig. 37). For H11 steel at Rockwell C 50 or below, M33, M34 and M36 high speed steel drills of heavy-duty construction gave good results. Positive-drive equipment was used, with drill speeds of 25 to 30 sfm and feeds of 0.0005 to 0.0007 ipr.

Material harder than Rockwell C 50 required solid-carbide drills with short flutes. Speeds of 40 to 50 sfm and feeds of 0.0005 to 0.001 ipr produced satisfactory results. The design of the solid-carbide twist drills used for holes of less than 1/4-in. diameter in this material is illustrated in Fig. 37(a) and (b); the design of straight-flute solid-carbide drills, for holes 1/4 in. in diameter or larger, is shown in Fig. 37(c).

Examples 192 to 196. Carbide Drills

Example 192 — Selection of Carbide Grade (Fig. 38). Three grades of carbide (C-1, C-2 and C-3) were tested to determine which was most suitable for drilling H11 steel sheet (5% Cr, 1.5% Mo) heat treated to Rockwell C 54. Two sheets of this material, each 0.083 in. thick, were drilled simultaneously with 0.250-in.-diam carbide-tipped drills, without a cutting fluid.

The softer 6% cobalt grade (C-1) failed because of abrasion, excessive burning, and chipping — all of which ultimately resulted in breakage. The hardest (and therefore most brittle) grade, C-3, which contained only 3%

Table 10. High Speed Steel vs Carbide-Tipped Drills (Example 185) (a)

(Drilling Forged H11 Steel at Rockwell C 40)

Item	HSS	Carbide
1/2-In.-Diam Holes		
Speed, rpm	250	600
Speed, sfm	33	78
Feed, ipr	0.0010	0.0005
Metal removed per min, cu in.	0.049	0.059
Drill life per grind, holes (b)	9	22
Initial cost per tool	$4.15	$10.30
1/8-In.-Diam Holes		
Speed, rpm	1050	2600
Speed, sfm	35	85
Feed, ipr	0.0005	0.0005
Metal removed per min, cu in.	0.0064	0.0160
Drill life per grind, holes (b)	27	90
Initial cost per tool	$1.20	$7.20

(a) Data are for drilling holes of both diameters through 1/2-in.-thick bars. High speed steel drills were of standard twist drill construction (118° included point angle) and had a hardness of Rockwell C 64.5. Carbide-tipped drills were made by brazing carbide tips of similar shape to standard high speed steel bodies. Cutting was interrupted, and the drill was withdrawn, after each successive penetration of 0.175 in. for the 1/2-in.-diam holes, and of 0.070 in. for the 1/8-in.-diam holes. Cutting fluid was soluble oil. (b) Average.

Table 11. Hardness, Thickness and Composition of Three Steels Drilled With Carbide Drills (Example 194)

Item	Steel 1	Steel 2	H11
Hardness, Rc	54 to 55	54 to 55	52
Thickness, in. ...	0.050	0.187	0.093
Composition, %			
Carbon	0.40-0.47	0.42-0.46	0.35
Chromium	0.80-1.05	0.70-0.90	5.00
Nickel	0.60-0.90	...	...
Molybdenum	0.45-0.60	...	1.50
Vanadium	0.01 min	0.01 min	0.40
Boron	0.005 min	...	...

cobalt, failed by excessive chipping and breaking during drilling. The C-3 also chipped and broke in handling.

The most satisfactory carbide was the harder of the two 6% cobalt grades, C-2, which showed only slight wear after testing; this grade was selected for machining on a production basis. (Although the C-1 and C-2 grades tested both contained 6% cobalt, the C-2 was harder because of its finer grain size, which decreased the size of the softer cobalt lakes between grains.)

The design of these drills is shown in the upper part of Fig. 38; the tool life for each grade of carbide is plotted in the lower part. Composition, hardness and grain size of the three grades of carbide were as follows:

Grade	Composition, % W	Ta	C	Co	Hardness, R_A	Grain size, microns
C-1	88.25	...	5.75	6.0	91.2	3
C-2	88.25	...	5.75	6.0	91.8	1 to 2
C-3	87.00	4.0	6.00	3.0	92.2	1 to 3

Example 193 — Point Angle for Rockwell C 54 to 55 (Fig. 39). The part shown in Fig. 39 was made of H11 steel (5% Cr, 1.5% Mo) heat treated to Rockwell C 54 to 55. In drilling the two in-line holes through the four sections, carbide-tipped drills with a 118° point angle were so weak at the web that the carbide point was crushed. Also, using these drills at a high feed force caused a surging breakthrough and overheated the part.

Short carbide tips having a flat silver-brazed joint close to the cutting action were unsuccessful in this operation because the heat generated weakened the brazed joint; the heavy torque loads ultimately twisted the carbide from the drill shank. With 118° point angle, neither a crankshaft grind nor a split-point grind provided acceptable drill life.

Design details of the drills that performed successfully are shown in Fig. 39. The 150° point angle strengthened the point, reduced the centering action that had caused an undersize hole, and eliminated crushing of the carbide at the intersection of the lips and outside surface.

Grade C-2 carbide (88.25% W, 5.75% C, 6.0% Co) gave much better tool life than did grades C-1, C-3 and C-5. (See the previous example for comparative drilling tests on C-1, C-2 and C-3 carbides.)

Example 194 — Speed and Feed for Three Alloy Steels (Table 11). Using solid-carbide drills, ⅜-in.-diam holes were successfully drilled in three alloy steels. The compositions and hardnesses of these steels, and the thicknesses of the workpieces, are shown in Table 11.

The most satisfactory drilling speeds were 45 to 50 sfm for steel 1, and 3 to 12 sfm for steel 2 and H11. Feed was constant for all three steels, and a soluble-oil emulsion mist was used as a coolant. All drills were of the same design: flute length, 1½ to 2 in.; point angle, 130°; web thickness at point, 0.080 to 0.090 in.; web taper, 0.016 in. per in.; and lip relief, 5° to 7°, ground flat 1/32 in.

Example 195 — Effect of Hole Diameter on Drilling Rate (Table 12). Conditions used for drilling holes 0.359 and 1.000 in. in diameter through ½-in.-thick forged H11 steel bars (Rockwell C 53 to 55) with carbide-tipped twist drills are compared in Table 12.

To obtain the same surface speed and feed per revolution for the two sizes of holes, the larger holes were drilled at about one-third the spindle speed and the feed rate per minute used for the smaller holes. For the larger holes, metal was removed 2½ times as fast, and total drilling time was 4½ times as long, as for the smaller holes. Cutting was interrupted, and the drill was withdrawn, after each successive penetration of 0.220 in. in the smaller holes, and of 0.261 in. in the larger.

Example 196 — Use of CO_2 Coolant vs Dry Drilling. On the basis of a series of tests, the use of a CO_2 coolant in drilling H11 steel sheet at Rockwell C 54 to 55 with carbide drills offered no advantage over dry drilling. On the contrary, the coolant resulted in increased costs and excessive drill maintenance. Because the use of CO_2 produced greater thermal shock at the cutting point, the carbide cutting edges frequently chipped. In dry drilling, normal drill wear, rather than chipping, was encountered. The tests in this series were conducted with ¼-in.-diam drills operated at 7200 rpm (470 sfm).

Small-Hole Drilling (Microdrilling)

The drilling of small holes (diameters of 0.001 in. to about ⅛ in.) requires machines, drills, techniques and operator skills different from those used in conventional drilling.

Machines used for drilling small holes are usually bench-mounted and resemble a jeweler's drill press. Alignment of spindle and table at any position should be within 0.0005 in. in 6 in., or at a radius equal to half the length of the table. Runout of the spindle should not exceed 0.0001 in. in any position. Spindle speeds are high, ranging from 3000 rpm, for drilling holes near 1/16 in. in diameter, to 20,000 rpm or higher for drilling holes 0.010 in. in diameter or smaller.

To minimize vibration, the machine is belt-driven by a balanced, vibration-damped motor mounted on a separate stand. The required sensitive feed is provided by a balanced crossarm or by a rack and pinion controlled by a knoblike wheel.

Larger machines for microdrilling have precision chucks or collets to hold the drill. However, for drills smaller than 0.015 in. in diameter, a one-piece spindle and drill that revolves in a jeweled V-block is used.

Drills larger than 0.008 to 0.010 in. in diameter may be of either the twist or the spade type (the latter are known also as pivot-type drills). Drills smaller than this usually are of the spade type, although twist drills have been made in diameters as small as 0.0039 in.

Drills smaller than 0.015 in. in diameter have their own mandrels. When drills are broken, mandrels are returned to the factory for insertion of new drills. By incorporating the drill in a mandrel, it is possible to grind the drill point concentric with the mandrel.

Drills are available in three classes of tolerance: +0.0000, −0.0001 in.; ±0.0001 in.; and ±0.0002 in.

An included point angle of 135° with an 8° clearance angle is usual for drilling steel; a 118° point angle with a 15° clearance angle is usual for drilling soft nonferrous metals. The point angle influences hole size, because small angles improve centering.

Carbon-tungsten special-purpose tool steels such as F2 or F3 are extensively used as materials for small-diameter drills; high speed steels are less used for these drills than for larger drills.

Techniques. To produce small holes that are accurate in size and finish, extreme care must be used in grinding the drill and in the drilling technique (centering and feeding), because:

1 Space for chip removal is limited by the greater ratio of web thickness to diameter of small-hole drills.
2 Pressure on end of drill is greater.

Table 12. Conditions for Drilling Holes of Two Diameters in H11 Steel at Rockwell C 53 to 55 (Example 195) (a)

Condition	Hole diam, in. 0.359	1.000
Speed, rpm	800	287
Speed, sfm	75	75
Feed, ipr	0.0005	0.0005
Feed, ipm	0.400	0.127
Depth per relief, in.	0.220	0.261
Metal removed per min, cu in.	0.041	0.104
Total drilling time, min	1.45	6.50

(a) Data are for drilling holes of both diameters through ½-in.-thick forged bars, with carbide-tipped twist drills, using a sulfurized, chlorinated cutting fluid. Drills were made by brazing carbide tips with a 118° point angle to high speed steel twist drill bodies, using a tapered shank for the 0.359-in.-diam drills.

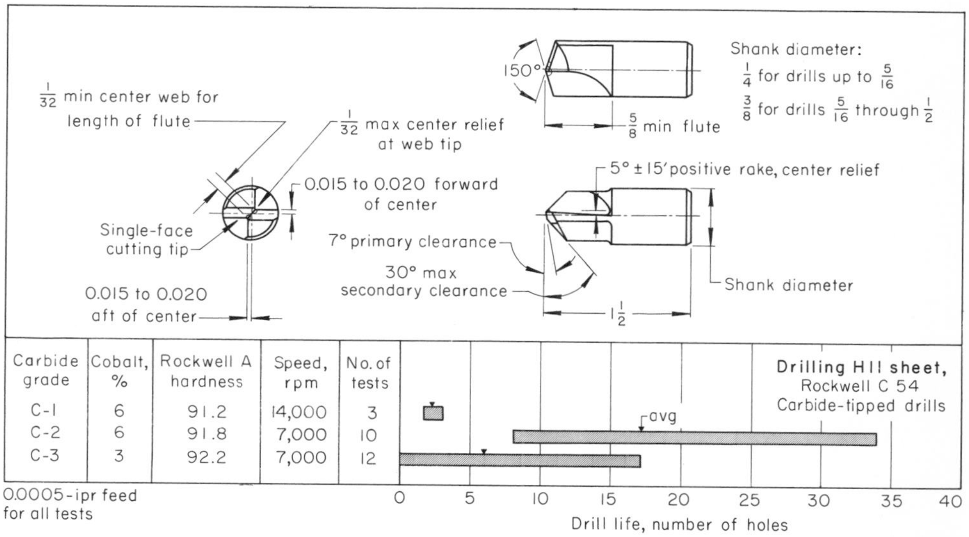

Fig. 38. (Top) *Design of carbide-tipped drills used to drill H11 steel sheet at Rockwell C 54.* (Bottom) *Comparison of tool life for the three grades of carbide tested on drills of the above design for performance in drilling 0.250-in.-diam holes through two 0.083-in.-thick sheets of this steel.* (Example 192)

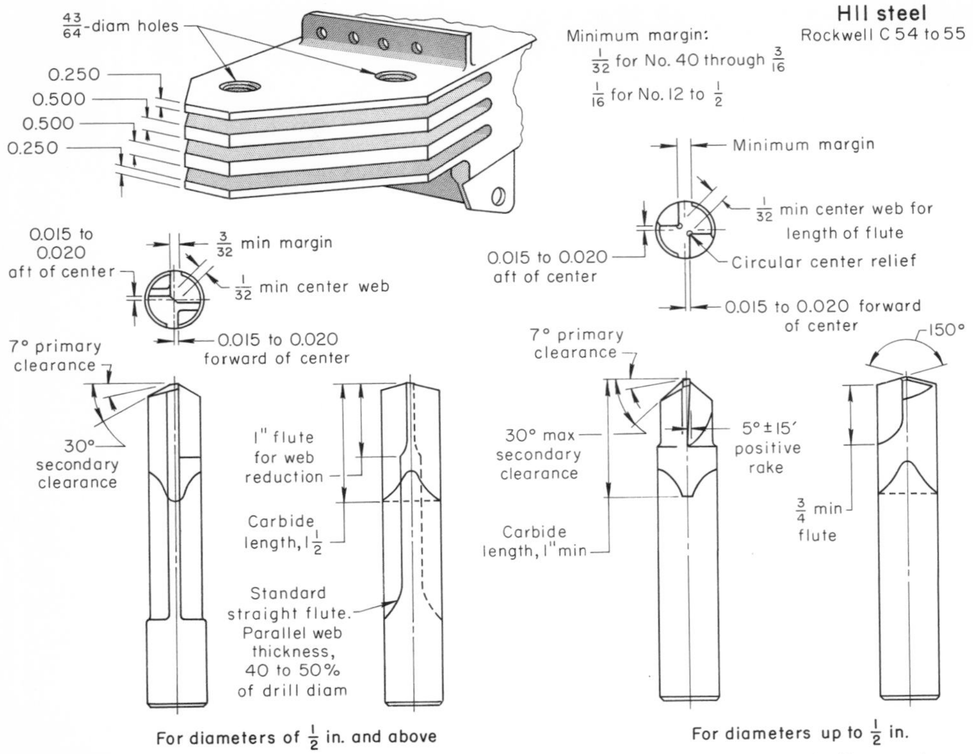

Carbide-tipped drills having 118° point angles were unsatisfactory for drilling the in-line holes in this part, because the carbide tip was twisted from the drill shank by high torque loads.

The dovetailing at the brazed joint of the 150°-point-angle drills shown here eliminated twist-off of the carbide point. For deep-hole drills (9/32 to 1 in. in diameter), the construction shown at the left (below sketch of part) was used, with modifications as follows: A 1/16-in. (minimum) land was used on all sizes; web minimum was increased to 1/8 in. for drills 9/32 to 1/2 in. in diameter, and to 3/16 in. for drills 1/2 to 1 in. in diameter.

Fig. 39. Details of 150°-point-angle drills used successfully for producing in-line holes through the four flanges of the H11 steel part shown in top left corner (Example 193)

3 Longitudinal and torsional deflections are greater because of the high ratio of length to diameter.

In small-hole drilling, the formation of metal powder rather than chips may result. This condition may lead to packing, causing the drills to break. Packing can be alleviated by frequent clearing of the hole by complete removal of the drill and application of a lubricant. One successful technique is the following: (*a*) the drill is withdrawn for chip clearance after the initial penetration has reached a depth no greater than three times the drill diameter (a lesser depth for initial penetration may be required for some materials), (*b*) another withdrawal is made after penetration has progressed for 1½ times the drill diameter beyond the first cut and, (*c*) the drill is again withdrawn following each succeeding cut to a depth of three-fourths the drill diameter.

Speed and Feed. Spindle speeds used for drilling of small holes are high in comparison to those used for ordinary drilling, but surface speeds, for holes down to about 0.008 to 0.010 in. in diameter, are not necessarily different. (See Examples 197 and 198, at the end of this section, in which spindle speeds of 7,875 and 20,000 rpm both produced a surface speed of 52 sfm.) The objective is a speed-and-feed combination that produces a true chip. If excessive speed is used, it becomes impossible to obtain a feed great enough to form a chip.

For drilling holes smaller than about 0.008 in. in diameter, the smaller the drill the lower the speed that is permitted. Applications have been reported where speeds as low as 50 rpm (0.01 to 0.02 sfm) were used for drills approaching 0.001 in. in diameter.

Feeds as great as 0.001 ipr (see Example 197) are often used. However, hand feeding is normal for drilling extremely small holes (see Example 198), and the rate of feed will vary widely among materials being drilled as well as among operators. Successful drilling of small holes requires considerable operator skill and "feel" for feeding the drill. In drilling extremely small holes, even an experienced operator will often break one or two drills when starting a work period before this "feel" is regained.

Cutting fluid requirements for drilling small holes differ somewhat from those for large holes, mainly because intermittent withdrawal of the drill disposes of chips and also cools the drill. Thus, in small-hole drilling, the main requirement of a cutting fluid is lubrication.

The usual practice is to coat the drill with lard oil (or a similar lubricant) at each withdrawal, either by hand brushing or with a lubricant dispenser.

Examples of procedure employed successfully in two applications of microdrilling follow:

Example 197. Hole Diameter, 0.025 In. (Fig. 40)

The small hole in the copper-nickel-tellurium alloy part shown in Fig. 40 was made with a standard twist drill 0.025 in. in diameter, with flute length of 5/16 in. The part was drilled in a multiple-operation machine. The drill was withdrawn six times to clear the chips. Drilling was more difficult than normal for this type of operation, because the hole depth and flute length were the same. This drilled hole represents about the maximum depth that a standard twist drill of 0.025-in. diameter can produce within the 0.003-in. total tolerance specified. Processing details are given with Fig. 40.

Example 198. Hole Diameter, 0.010 to 0.015 In.

In one plant, orifice holes in fuel-injection nozzles were drilled on a production basis. These through holes ranged in diameter from 0.010 to 0.015 in., and were about ten diameters deep. The nozzles were made of alloy steel as hard as 241 Bhn.

As many as 12 holes were drilled in each nozzle, evenly spaced around a cone surface. Spacing was maintained by placing the nozzles on a rigid indexing fixture. Drilling was done on a special machine (see foregoing section on machines for small-hole drilling) by skilled operators. Pivot or spade drills made of a carbon-tungsten tool steel, such as F3, were generally used.

Spindle speed usually was 20,000 rpm (52 sfm for a 0.010-in.-diam drill). Feed was entirely controlled by the operator. Twenty-five or more withdrawals were needed for completing one hole.

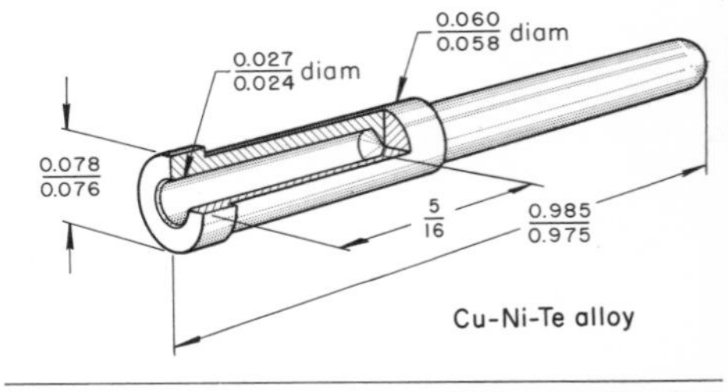

Speed	7875 rpm (52 sfm)
Feed	0.001 ipr
Cutting fluid	Sulfochlorinated oil (plus fat)
Drilling time per hole	18 sec
Drill life per grind	1200 pieces

Fig. 40. Ratio (12.5 to 1) of depth to diameter of hole in this part was maximum capability of the standard twist drill used. (Example 197)

Other Examples of Drilling Applications in This Volume

Work metal	Example number
Tool Design and Methods	
Cast iron	654, 657
Tool steel	681
Stainless steel	751, 752, 754, 755, 756, 757, 758, 759
Heat-resisting alloys	824, 825, 826, 827, 828, 834, 835, 836, 837
Aluminum	887, 888, 889, 890, 891, 892
Beryllium	929

Work metal	Example number
Copper	936, 937
Magnesium	982, 983
Work Metals Compared	
Cast iron	655, 656
Tool steel	687, 704
Tool Metals Compared	
Heat-resisting alloys	829, 830, 831, 832, 833

Work metal	Example number
Methods Compared	
Stainless steel	753
Aluminum	888, 890
Copper	938, 939
Gun Drills	
Stainless steel	760
Aluminum	893
Magnesium	984, 985

Reaming

*By the ASM Committee on Drilling and Reaming**

REAMING is a machining operation in which a rotary tool takes a light cut to improve the accuracy of a round hole, and to reduce the roughness of the hole surface. Most reamers have two or more flutes, either parallel to the tool axis or in a helix, which provide teeth for cutting and grooves for chips.

Reaming and boring are related processes, and sometimes their applications overlap. (There even are tools identified as reamers by some and as boring tools by others.) But hole diameter and length, or required straightness or tolerance, usually indicate whether reaming or boring is to be used.

Process Capabilities

Although steels that range in hardness from about Rockwell C 15 to 30 are the metals most often reamed, the process is widely used for finishing holes in cast iron and is also used for the softest nonferrous metals, as well as steels with a hardness of Rockwell C 52 or higher.

Hole Diameter. Most holes reamed are 1/8 to 1¼ in. in diameter. Reamers are commercially available for holes as small as 0.0135 in. in diameter, and specially designed reamers are obtainable for 0.005-in.-diam holes. Solid reamers are available for holes up to 2 in. in diameter, and are specially made for holes up to 3 in. in diameter. Reamers of other types are available for holes up to 6 in. in diameter.

Hole Length. The length of hole that can be successfully reamed depends on reamer diameter, method of holding and driving the reamer, and required dimensional accuracy.

Reamer diameter determines the maximum length of the reamer cutting edge, which affects the length of hole that can be reamed accurately. For example, the cutting edge of a 0.0135-in.-diam reamer may be as long as ¾ in. (a length-to-diameter ratio of 55 to 1), but that of a 6-in.-diam shell reamer usually is no longer than 6 in. In most applications with standard reamers, the length of the hole being reamed ranges from only slightly longer to considerably shorter than the cutting edge of the reamer. However, the length of the cutting edge does not necessarily limit the length of hole that can be reamed. Shank length can be extended to permit reaming of holes several times longer than the cutting edge of the reamer, but this makes it difficult to guide the reamer and to hold dimensional tolerances.

In horizontal reaming of holes several times longer than the cutting edge of the reamer, the difficulty of maintaining finish and dimensions is sometimes increased by misalignment in the machine. This can be minimized by the use of reamers with shorter cutting edges.

With special tools, such as gun reamers (see Example 207), accuracy can be attained in reaming holes many times longer than the cutting edge.

Stock Removal. Most reaming operations are not intended for the removal of large amounts of stock. This can usually be done more economically by other processes, such as drilling, boring or core drilling. When more than 0.020 in. on diameter must be removed from a hole less than 2 in. in diameter, special reaming methods or boring usually are considered. Special reaming methods may include the use of gun reamers (Example 207) or rough and finish reaming with different types of tools (Example 705, in the article "Machining of Tool Steel").

The practical minimum stock for reaming is greatly influenced by workpiece composition and hardness. Because reaming is a cutting operation, chip formation is required for efficient operation. If too little stock is being removed, the reamer will burnish the work, rather than cut it; this will result in damage to the reamer and to the work surface. For soft metals, the removal of 0.008 in. on diameter per pass is near the minimum — depending on hole length and tool rigidity. For harder metals, because of the difference in chip formation, this amount can be reduced to 0.005 in. For the removal of less than 0.005 in. of stock, another machining process, such as honing, is usually preferable.

Tolerances. Reamers are ground to size to eliminate tool adjustments during production runs. Tolerances of 0.001 to 0.003 in. on diameter are practical in production reaming. Tolerances of less than 0.001 in. can be maintained, but to do this requires closer than normal control of reamer dimensions, reaming feed and speed, and all other operating variables.

For reaming to extremely close tolerances, it is sometimes helpful to reduce the back taper of the reamer slightly, and to match the guide bushing with the reamer so as to obtain minimum clearance.

Finish of a reamed hole depends on workpiece hardness, condition of cutting edges, feed and speed. With best conditions it is possible to obtain finishes of 40 micro-in. or less. However, in production reaming of annealed steel, 100 to 125 micro-in. is more common. When extremely smooth surfaces are required, methods such as honing or burnishing should be considered.

Workpiece Material and Hardness

Hardness of carbon and low-alloy steels has a greater effect than composition on reamability.

The results of tests to determine the effect of workpiece hardness in reaming are shown in Fig. 1. Speed, feed, metal removal rate, reamer life, and reaming cost were compared for reaming holes of ¼-in. and ½-in. diameter in three similar low-alloy steels (4130, 4330 and 4340) at Rockwell C 15, 47 and 52, respectively. (Reamer and operating details are given with Fig. 1.) With

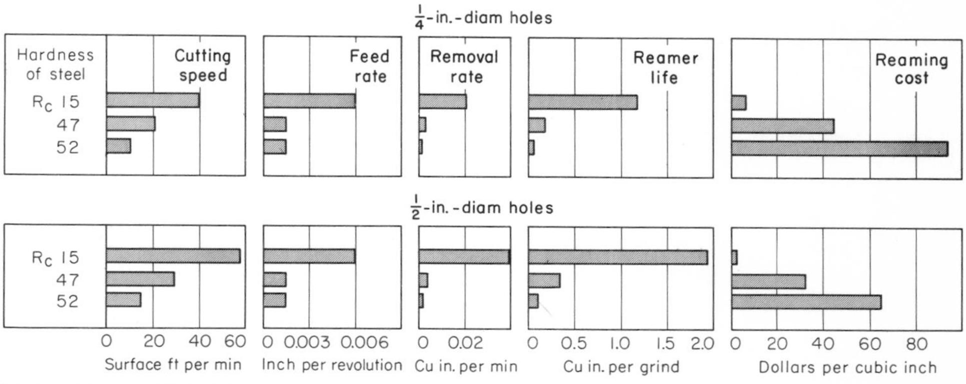

Reaming Conditions
(Holes of both diameters)

Type of machine	Vertical four-spindle
Depth of through holes	1¼ in.
Stock reamed, on diameter	1/64 in.
Cutting fluid	Sulfurized oil and mineral oil (1:1)
Criterion for tool life	Surface finish of 40 to 46 micro-in.

Reamer Details

	¼-in. holes	½-in. holes
Number of flutes	4	8
Land width, in.	0.007	0.009
Helix angle	0°	0°
Radial rake angle	3°	2°
Radial relief angle	17°	12°
Chamfer angle	42°	42°
Chamfer relief angle	6°	5° to 6°

Fig. 1. Effect of hardness of low-alloy steel workpiece on reaming conditions, reamer life (M10 high speed steel reamers), and reaming cost

*For committee list, see page 75.

increasing hardness of the steel workpiece, the metal removal rate was progressively lower, because of the reduced cutting speed and feed rate. Life of the M10 high speed steel reamers used also decreased progressively, in spite of the reduction in speed and feed. The combination of lower metal removal rate and shorter reamer life in reaming the harder steels resulted in greatly increased reaming cost. Reaming at Rockwell C 47 cost 6 to 11 times as much as reaming at Rockwell C 15; reaming at Rockwell C 52 cost 13 to 22 times as much.

Soft metals such as aluminum and brass can be reamed at speeds five to ten times greater than those for annealed steel. Free-cutting low-carbon steel, such as 1113, however, can be reamed to a smooth finish at nearly the highest speeds and lowest cost. On the other hand, low-carbon steel that does not contain additives for free cutting, such as 1015, produces stringier chips, thereby yielding a rougher finish and requiring slower speeds. As carbon content is increased, even in free-cutting steel, abrasiveness is increased, and this shortens tool life.

Machines

Probably every type of machine capable of rotating a tool or a workpiece has been used for reaming. Reamers sometimes are driven by hand-held air or electric motors, especially when only a few parts require reaming or when the equipment must be taken to the workpiece. Relatively large workpieces are rotated in an engine lathe and the reamers are fed from the compound rest or the tailstock of the lathe. Most production reaming, however, is done in drilling machines, or as one machining step in a turret lathe or other multiple-operation machine. Machines having automatic feed can hold close tolerances more consistently than hand-fed machines.

For a detailed description of the various machines used for production reaming, see the section on Machines, page 76 in the article "Drilling".

Selection. In many applications reaming is supplementary to, and performed in the same sequence with, other operations such as drilling. Under these conditions, the machine is selected mainly for the primary operation.

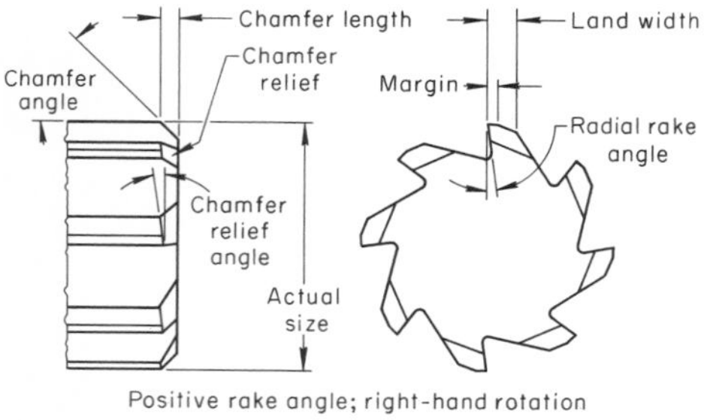

Margin	1/16 in.
Chamfer length	1/16 in.
Chamfer angle	45°
Chamfer relief angle	6° to 9°
Radial rake angle	7°

Details in table are for reamers ½ to 2 in. in diameter. "Actual size" in illustration refers to the actual measured diameter of a reamer, which usually is slightly greater than the nominal size to allow for wear.

Fig. 2. Typical design of a straight-flute solid reamer

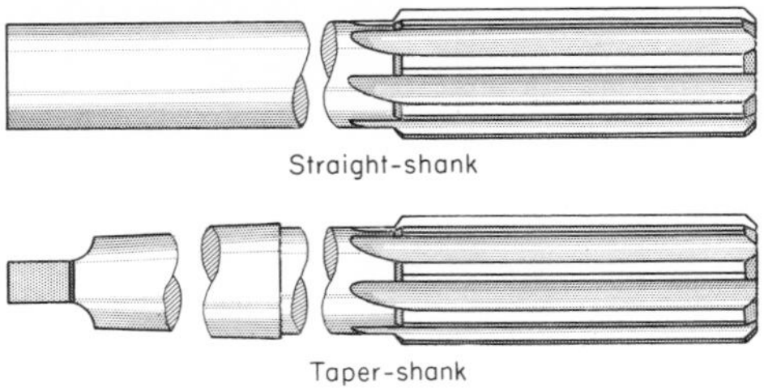

Fig. 3. Straight-flute chucking reamers

For production reaming of holes less than 1¼ in. in diameter, machines that rotate the tool and hold the workpiece stationary (drill presses, for example) are usually the most practical and economical. Guide bushings can be used in these machines to maintain tolerances of 0.003 in. or less for holes that are several diameters long.

For maximum accuracy, however, it is preferable, if size and shape of the workpiece permit, to rotate the work and hold the tool stationary. This also applies for reaming holes that are considerably larger than 1¼ in. in diameter, or for reaming holes that have a length-to-diameter ratio of more than about 8 to 1.

Size and shape of workpiece are often major factors in the choice of a machine for reaming, and for drilling or other operations that precede reaming. In many instances, although only relatively small holes are to be reamed, the workpiece is too large or heavy to be rotated in machines like turret lathes. In other instances, workpiece size or weight may allow rotation, but asymmetric shape makes rotation impractical. For either condition, the reamer must be rotated in machines such as drill presses or boring mills. Relatively small holes in extremely large workpieces often are reamed by portable, hand-operated machines.

Reamer Materials

Hand reamers are usually made of a carbon or low-alloy tool steel, such as W1 or O1, hardened to Rockwell C 62 or higher.

Reamers for machine operation are made either of high speed steel, or of a lower-alloy tool steel for the shank, and with carbide inserts for the cutting edges. High speed steels most used for reamers include T1, M2, M7 and M10. For reaming especially hard or abrasive metals, high speed steels with a higher content of vanadium, such as T3, T15, M3 or M4, are often used, because they give longer life than the lower-alloy steels.

Because the load imposed on the tool in reaming is usually far less than in drilling, reamers require less toughness than drills. Instead, reamers should be of maximum hardness (Rockwell C 65 or higher), to obtain best surface finish and tool life.

Many standard and special reamers are made of solid carbide or contain carbide inserts. Although more expensive than high speed steel, carbide will often outlast it ten times or more when reaming steel at near-optimum hardness (about Rockwell C 20). The longer life of carbide reamers makes them the usual choice for use on steel harder than Rockwell C 40.

For efficient use of carbide, maximum rigidity in the machine, reamer and workpiece is essential. Even with a machine in first-class condition, if the unguided or unsupported length of the reamer is more than six times its diameter, the use of carbide becomes questionable. If chatter develops, the life of carbide tools will be markedly shortened. If chatter is likely to occur, high speed steel reamers should be used (see Example 208).

Reamer Design

The design of a typical straight-flute solid reamer is shown in Fig. 2. The cutting angles and other tool details listed below Fig. 2 usually are not appreciably modified for reaming different work metals, except that chamfer relief angle generally is increased to 12° to 15° for soft metals like aluminum.

Sometimes, however, minor changes from the typical values shown in Fig. 2 can improve results. For example, the "normal" 45° chamfer angle at the lead end of a reamer is sometimes modified to obtain a better finish on the reamed surface (as in Example 202).

The eight flutes shown in Fig. 2 are typical of a 1-in.-diam reamer. Fewer flutes are used for smaller reamers, and more for larger ones (2-in.-diam reamers usually have 12 or more flutes).

If a reamer has too many flutes, it will not provide enough space for chips. If it has too few, it is likely to chatter — especially if it is a straight-flute reamer. Cutting efficiency has been improved by increasing the number of flutes to the practical maximum, as in the following example:

Example 199. Six vs Ten Flutes

Changing from a six-flute chucking reamer to one with ten flutes increased tool life by nearly 35% while effecting a 45% decrease in tool cost per piece reamed. Comparative results from 12 production runs with each type of reamer were as follows:

	Six-flute	Ten-flute
Pieces per grind (average)	1,052	1,417
Pieces per tool	12,624	17,004
Tool cost per piece	$0.002	$0.0011

Both types of reamers were operated at a speed of 100 sfm and a feed of 0.029 ipr.

An application in which a change from an eight-flute reamer to a single-flute reamer with wear pads provided greater accuracy in reaming a blind

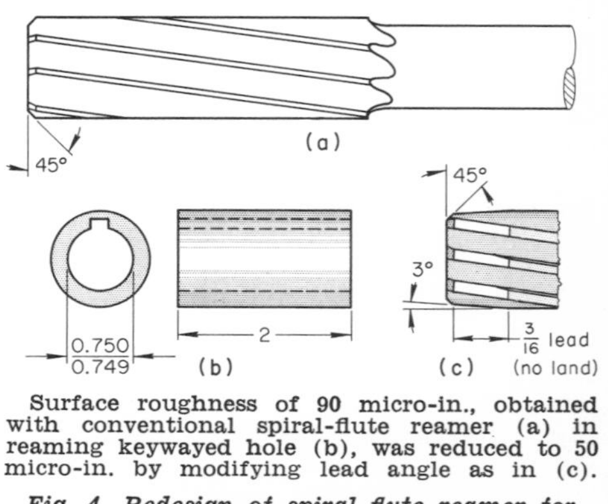

Surface roughness of 90 micro-in., obtained with conventional spiral-flute reamer (a) in reaming keywayed hole (b), was reduced to 50 micro-in. by modifying lead angle as in (c).

Fig. 4. Redesign of spiral-flute reamer for keywayed hole (Example 202)

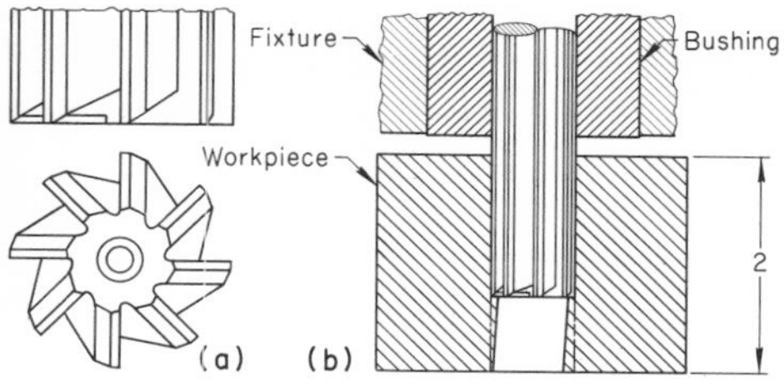

(a) A common type of end-cutting reamer, used for finishing blind holes. (b) When guided in a bushing, an end-cutting reamer can correct dimensional deviations in through holes.

Fig. 5. End-cutting reamers

hole is described in Example 940, in the article on Machining of Copper.

Selection of Reamer

Any reamer must of course be compatible with the machine in which it will be used. Apart from this, selection of reamer is governed mainly by one or more of the following:

1 Composition and hardness of workpiece
2 Hole diameter
3 Hole configuration
4 Hole length
5 Amount of stock removed
6 Type of fixturing, when used
7 Accuracy and finish requirements
8 Production quantity
9 Cost (initial and maintenance)
10 Salvage value.

When more than one type of reamer can produce acceptable results, the choice may depend on tool availability or established shop practice regarding the standardization of tools.

Composition and hardness of workpiece are more likely to affect choice of reamer material than type of reamer. However, there are notable exceptions; for example, shell reamers have been less satisfactory than solid reamers for reaming hard and tough metals.

Hole Diameter. For holes more than 2 in. in diameter, solid reamers made of high speed steel are seldom used, mainly because they would cost too much. Shell reamers are usually a better choice for holes of this size.

Hole Configuration. When holes to be reamed have keyways or other irregularities, spiral-flute reamers are preferred, because straight flutes may fail to bridge these irregularities and thus cause chatter.

Hole Length. When hole length is not more than two diameters, several types of reamers are suitable. However, as the length-to-diameter ratio increases, so does the problem of maintaining accuracy. Guide bushings and pilots often solve the problem, but when accuracy must be maintained in long holes, special reamers are required.

Amount of Stock Removed. When large amounts of stock are to be removed, a solid or a special reamer (see Example 207) is usually preferred. Shell reamers are not suited to the removal of large amounts of stock. In some heavy-removal applications, reaming is done in two stages, using a shell reamer for the second stage (see Example 705, in the article "Machining of Tool Steel").

Type of fixturing (when used) determines whether or not a piloted reamer is the best choice. (See the section "Bushings and Fixtures", later in this article.)

Accuracy and finish requirements are related to several other factors. For greater accuracy, the workpiece should be rotated, if possible. Thus, the reamer shank must fit the chosen machine. Accuracy depends on the rigidity of the setup and on the method of guiding the reamer. Self-guiding reamers are usually chosen for greater accuracy and finer finish in reaming long holes.

Production Quantity. For reaming a few pieces that can be produced with a single sharpening of the reamer, the simplest type is the logical choice. For long production runs, adjustable types should be considered, to minimize sharpening and downtime.

Cost. Reamer cost must be considered from three related standpoints: initial cost, maintenance cost, and salvage value. High initial cost often is warranted because of low maintenance cost; for example, reamers with inserted carbide blades cost more than solid steel reamers, but may finish ten times as many holes per grind. Also, the initial cost of large reamers made of solid high speed steel may seem excessive, but their salvage value is high.

Salvage Value. The amount realized from the sale of a worn-out high speed steel reamer (usually less than 30¢ a pound) is small compared to its original cost. It is common practice, therefore, to rework a worn-out solid reamer to a smaller size, rather than to sell it for scrap. The economy of reworking depends mainly on whether or not the necessary equipment is available; the advisability of buying such equipment depends on the amount of tool rework to be done. Worn-out reamers sometimes can be sold to tool shops where they will be reworked for resale. If this is done, the salvage value will be greater than if the reamers are sold for scrap.

The extent to which a reamer can be reworked is also governed by economy. A large reamer can be reworked progressively to smaller and smaller sizes, but this practice is limited by reamer design. The limit of decrease in reamer diameter by reworking is usually governed by depth of flute. When the diameter is so small that further decrease would require deepening of the flutes, the reamer is usually scrapped.

The two examples that follow describe cost savings realized by reworking of reamers to smaller sizes:

Examples 200 and 201. Cost of Reworked vs New Reamers

Example 200. A worn-out reamer 1.498 in. in diameter by 14½ in. long with ten flutes 8 in. long was reworked to a reamer 1.3855/1.3843 in. in diameter by 12¹³⁄₁₆ in. long with ten flutes 6⁵⁄₁₆ in. long. The procedure used for reworking consisted of seven operations:

1 Cut to length
2 Re-center by electrical discharge machining
3 Circle grind diameter and clean up taper
4 Grind 45° chamfer
5 Grind shank
6 Back taper the cutting portion
7 Assign new tool data.

The cost of this salvage operation was $15.60 (117 min at $8 per hr). A new reamer of the smaller size would have cost $39. Therefore, $23.40 was saved by salvaging. If the worn-out reamer had been sold for scrap, it would have brought only $1.09 (3.9 lb at 28¢ per lb).

Example 201. By the same procedure as in Example 200, three worn-out reamers 1.995 in. in diameter by 15¼ in. long with ten flutes 8½ in. long were reworked to reamers 1.8850/1.8848 in. in diameter by 13⅛ in. long with ten flutes 6⅜ in. long. Cost of salvaging these three reamers was $44.66 (335 min at $8 per hr). Three new reamers of the smaller size would have cost $235.50. Therefore, $190.84 was saved by salvaging ($235.50 less $44.66). The three reamers originally weighed 20.25 lb; their scrap value at 28¢ per lb would have been only $5.67.

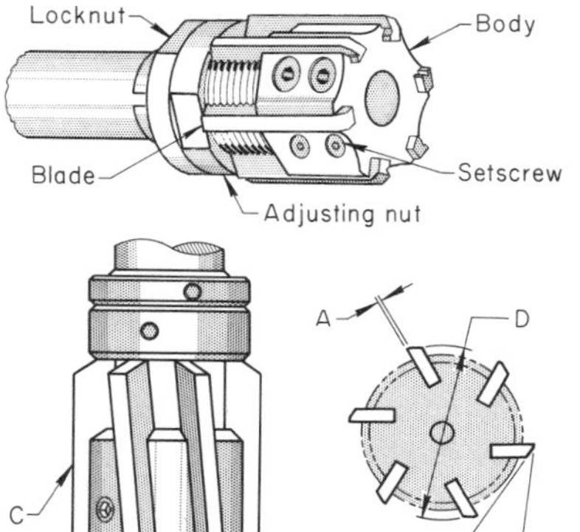

Fig. 6. Inserted-blade adjustable reamer, and typical details of design

Salvaging reamers by reworking them to smaller sizes requires a considerable amount of good equipment and operator skill. Accurate re-centering is important, because other operations depend on the centers.

Types of Reamers. Standard reamers include these principal types:

Straight-flute chucking reamers
Spiral-flute chucking reamers
End-cutting reamers
Adjustable reamers
Shell reamers (and expandable reamers)
Floating-blade reamers
Gun reamers.

There are also numerous types of reamers for special applications, including diemaker's reamers, taper reamers, bridge reamers, pipe reamers, drill-and-reamer combinations, and multiple-diameter reamers.

In the eight sections of this article that follow, the various types of reamers named above are described, and their areas of applicability are discussed. Many of these sections also cite examples of production applications for specific types of reamers.

Applications of Straight-Flute Chucking Reamers

Straight-flute chucking reamers are general-purpose solid reamers designed for use in various machines such as drill presses, turret lathes, and automatic bar or chucking machines. They are available with taper or straight shanks (Fig. 3), and thus may be held in collets or split bushings, or by setscrews. These reamers are most readily available in diameters of ³⁄₆₄ to 1½ in., in steps of ¹⁄₆₄ in.; they are seldom made in other sizes.

Straight-flute chucking reamers normally are pointed with a 45° chamfer, and are suited to reaming almost all metals. However, keyways or other irregularities in holes, tolerance requirements, blind holes, amount of stock that must be removed, or workpiece hardness may demand the use of reamers other than this general-purpose type (see the sections that follow, and Examples 202 to 207).

A "jobber's reamer" is a modified straight-flute chucking reamer. The chief difference between the two is that the flutes of the jobber's reamer are about twice as long in proportion to over-all length.

Applications of Spiral-Flute Chucking Reamers

Spiral-flute chucking reamers differ from straight-flute reamers only in that their flutes are milled in a helix. They are used in the same machines and are available (with straight or taper shanks) in the same sizes as straight-flute reamers. Spiral-flute reamers cut with a free reaming action and are used for the more difficult-to-ream materials. A typical spiral-flute chucking reamer is shown in Fig. 4(a).

Spiral-flute reamers are better than straight-flute reamers for reaming holes that have irregularities such as keyways (Fig. 4b). The spiral cutting edges bridge these irregularities, thus minimizing chatter, surface roughness and size variation, and prolonging reamer life. Sometimes, minor changes in reamer design produce other improvements in results, as in the following example:

Example 202. Holes With Keyways (Fig. 4)

Conventional spiral-flute reamers with a 45° lead (Fig. 4a) were used to ream $\frac{3}{4}$-in.-diam keywayed through-holes in 2-in.-long workpieces of low-carbon steel (Fig. 4b). Accuracy was within 0.001 in., and the specified maximum surface roughness of 90 micro-in. was obtained.

When specified finish was reduced to 50 micro-in., it was necessary to modify the reamer design by extending a 3° lead for $\frac{3}{16}$ in. back from the edge of the 45° chamfer, as shown in Fig. 4(c). At the speed (70 sfm) and feed (0.005 ipr) used for the conventional reamer, the modified reamer reduced surface roughness to the new specification.

Applications of End-Cutting Reamers

An end-cutting reamer, which may have either straight or spiral flutes, has no chamfer on the end for use as a lead; instead, the end has cutting edges at right angles to the reamer axis (Fig. 5a). In this respect, end-cutting reamers resemble end mills.

End-cutting reamers are used for finishing blind holes that must have little or no radius at the bottom. A more important application is the correction of deviations from parallelism in drilled through-holes. A reamer having a chamfered end for a lead usually will follow the hole already formed. An end-cutting reamer, when guided by a bushing (Fig. 5b), can correct several thousandths of an inch of out-of-parallelism.

The main disadvantage of end-cutting reamers is that they produce comparatively rough surfaces. When these reamers must be used (as for correcting hole deviations), they are usually used as roughing reamers, and a conventional reamer is used for finishing.

Applications of Adjustable Reamers

Although a number of different types of reamers are adjustable (including floating-blade reamers and expandable shell reamers, which are discussed in the next two sections of this article), the term "adjustable reamers" generally is used to refer only to a limited number of types. Two of the more common types are inserted-blade and expanding-pin adjustable reamers.

Inserted-blade reamers, which are made with and without adjustment for size, are tool holders in which slots are milled to receive inserted flat blades. In the adjustable type (Fig. 6), the blades are slid in angled slots by an adjusting nut to change cutting diameter. The adjusted blades are secured by a locknut and setscrews.

Inserted-blade reamers are available with either straight flutes (Fig. 6) or spiral flutes, in diameters of $\frac{5}{8}$ to 6 in. They are especially suited to high-volume applications in which variations in workpiece material or temperature, or in the stability of fixtures or machines, make it difficult to maintain hole size.

Between regrinds of the adjustable type of inserted-blade reamers, minor adjustments (0.0001 to 0.0002 in.) can be made to compensate for tool wear; greater adjustment between regrinds may result in eccentricity. Recommended major adjustments *before* regrinding vary with reamer diameter. For example, a $\frac{5}{8}$-in.-diam reamer should not be adjusted more than $\frac{1}{32}$ in., but a $3\frac{1}{2}$-in.-diam reamer can be adjusted $\frac{7}{16}$ in. These adjustments can be exceeded by inserting wider blades. This usually is inadvisable, because the added overhang can cause breakage and chatter. On the other hand, it is sometimes practical in low-volume production where maximum edge sharpness can be maintained through controlled tool changes.

The two examples that follow describe the procedures used and the results obtained in two high-production applications of reaming with inserted-blade adjustable reamers.

Example 203. Tolerance of 0.0015 In. on Bearing Bores (Fig. 7)

Bearing bores in passenger-car front-wheel hubs made of annealed 1035 steel (Fig. 7) were reamed in 10-in., 12-spindle vertical lathes. Boring with a single-point tool had left 0.010 to 0.012 in. on the inside diameter to be removed by reaming.

Inserted-blade adjustable reamers were used, ground to concentricity within 0.0002 in. TIR. Each reamer held six blades of M4 high speed steel, inserted to allow a 10° left-hand spiral. The blades were circle ground, backed off to 0.010-in. margin, and back tapered 0.002 in. per in. The bores were reamed to within 0.0015 in. Additional details are tabulated with Fig. 7.

Example 204. Stud Holes to Tolerance of ±0.001 In. (Fig. 8)

A 3-hp vertical drill press was used to ream six drilled stud holes in a truck-wheel hub made of annealed 1035 steel (Fig. 8). The hub was clamped in a six-station rotating fixture. The holes had been drilled to allow 0.008 to 0.010 in. of stock on the diameter for removal in reaming.

Inserted-blade adjustable reamers with straight flutes were used. Each reamer held six M2 high speed steel blades and was ground to a concentricity of 0.0002 in. TIR. Blades were circle ground, backed off to a margin of 0.008 in., and back tapered to 0.002 in. per in. The holes were reamed to ±0.001 in. Additional details are given in the table accompanying Fig. 8.

Expanding-pin reamers make use of a tapered, screw-type expanding pin to move blades and thus change reamer size (Fig. 9). These reamers are available with straight flutes only, and in diameters of $\frac{7}{16}$ to $2\frac{1}{2}$ in.

The maximum adjustment for expanding-pin reamers is $\frac{1}{32}$ in. for diameters of $\frac{7}{16}$ to $\frac{1}{4}$ in., and about $\frac{1}{4}$ in. for diameters of $1\frac{1}{4}$ to $2\frac{1}{2}$ in.

Advantages. In many high-production operations, inserted-blade and expanding-pin reamers are more economical than solid reamers, because blades can

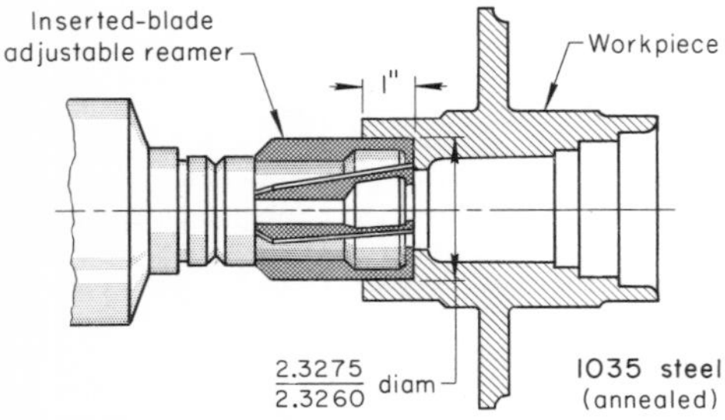

Reamer Details

Number of blade inserts	Six
Insert material	M4 high speed steel
Method of insertion	10° left-hand spiral
Margin width	0.010 in.
Back taper	0.002 in. per in.

Operating Conditions

Speed	74 rpm (45 sfm)
Feed	0.045 ipr
Stock reamed on diameter	0.010 to 0.012 in.
Cutting fluid	Soluble-oil:water (1:20)
Production rate	1200 pieces per hour
Reamer-blade life per grind	1200 pieces

Fig. 7. Reaming of bearing bore in wheel hub with spiral-flute inserted-blade adjustable reamer (Example 203)

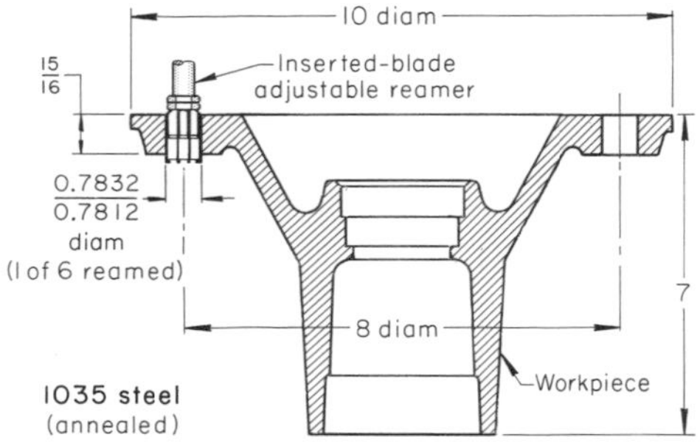

Reamer Details

Number of blade inserts	Six
Insert material	M2 high speed steel
Land width	0.008 in.
Back taper	0.002 in. per in.

Operating Conditions

Speed	146 rpm (30 sfm)
Feed	0.035 ipr
Stock reamed on diameter	0.008 to 0.010 in.
Cutting fluid	Soluble-oil:water (1:20)
Reaming time per hole	0.19 min
Reamer-blade life per grind	800 holes

Fig. 8. Reaming of six stud holes in wheel hub with straight-flute inserted-blade adjustable reamer (Example 204)

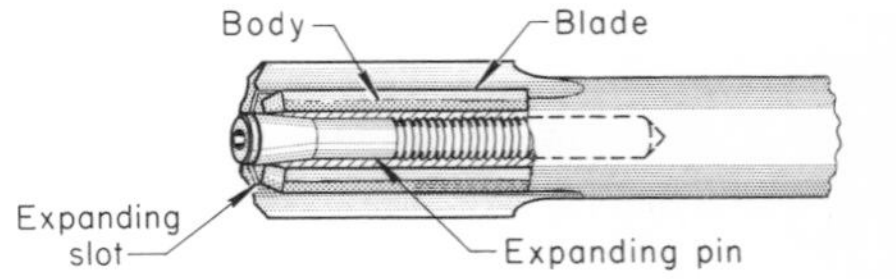

Fig. 9. Expanding-pin adjustable reamer

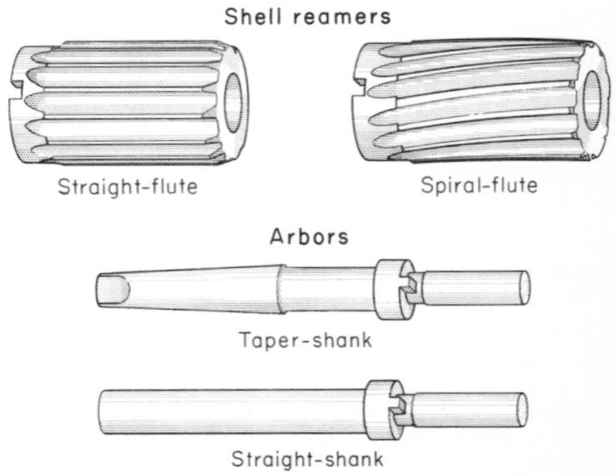

Fig. 10. Typical shell reamers and accommodating arbors

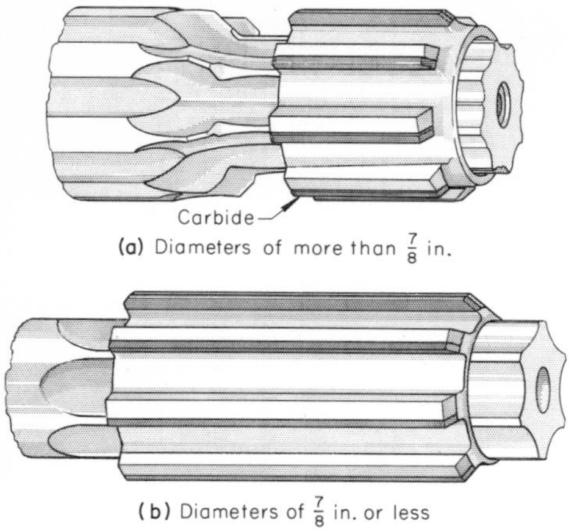

(a) Diameters of more than $\frac{7}{8}$ in.

(b) Diameters of $\frac{7}{8}$ in. or less

Fig. 11. Two types of expandable shell reamers

be reground many times before they need replacing (body life is unlimited). Also, the minor adjustments that can be made prolong reamer life between grinds.

The major adjustments that can be made are particularly useful in low-production operations, because the same reamer can be adjusted to ream holes of slightly different diameters, thus lowering tool inventory.

In addition to size adjustment, inserted-blade reamers have two other advantages over solid reamers:

1 Blade materials can be changed as required, using the same body.
2 In regrinding, tool design, including such details as angle of back taper, width of margins and lands, and radial clearance, is more easily modified for an inserted-blade reamer than for a solid reamer.

Applications of Shell Reamers

Shell reamers are used on arbors (taper or straight shank) with driving lugs and have either straight or spiral flutes (Fig. 10). The hole in a shell reamer is ground with a taper, to allow the reamer to be firmly seated on the tapered arbor. Usually, hole and arbor diameters are related so that there is enough space between the end of the reamer and the shoulder of the arbor to permit removal of the reamer with minimum danger of damage.

Shell reamers generally are used only when the tool remains stationary and the work rotates, as in a turret lathe. Sometimes, however, shell reamers are used in special machines in which both work and tools are rotated. Because shell reamers, being mounted on arbors, are two-piece assemblies, they are less rigid than solid reamers. Shell reamers are better suited for finishing operations than for removing larger amounts of stock.

Expandable Shell Reamers. As shown in Fig. 11, the shell portion of these reamers is a thin-wall fluted body with carbide cutting edges, and is forced on a hardened steel arbor that has a slight forward taper. The shell has a matching back taper so that it expands in outside diameter as it is forced farther onto the arbor. Expansion is achieved by striking, with a soft hammer, a soft metal sleeve that is inserted over the protruding end of the arbor.

Expandable shell reamers larger than ⅞ in. in diameter usually are of the type shown in Fig. 11(a). This reamer has a short cutting section followed by a hardened steel flute section (for guiding the cutting section). Reamers ⅞ in. in diameter or less are made with full-length flutes (Fig. 11b). There are also expandable shell reamers with special plugs flush with the end to permit reaming of blind holes.

Expandable shell reamers are not designed for adjustment to different hole sizes, but only for adjustment to compensate for tool wear. As the reamer wears out of tolerance, it is forced farther back on the arbor, until the limit of expansion is reached. Then the shell is removed and replaced with a new one.

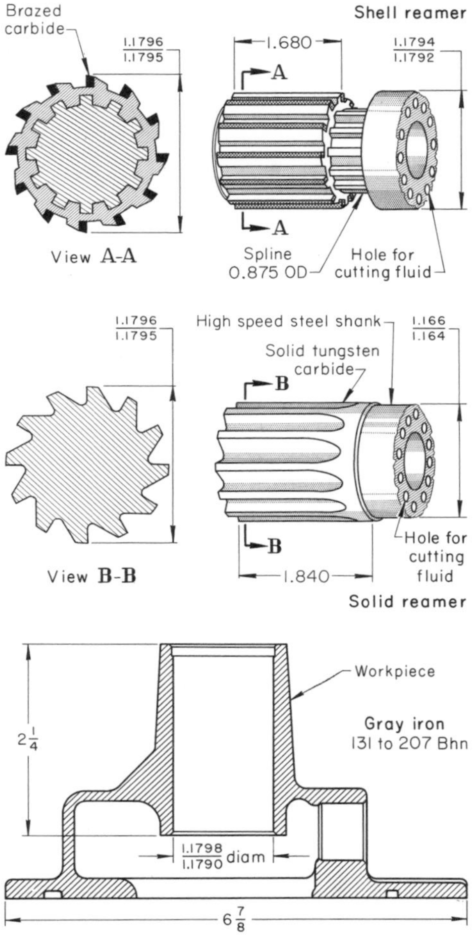

Operating Conditions for Both Reamers

Type of machine	Vertical two-spindle
Speed	875 rpm (270 sfm)
Feed	0.018 ipr
Depth of cut	0.019 in.
Reaming time per hole	13.7 sec
Setup time	5 min
Cutting fluid	Soluble-oil:water (1:20)

Comparison of Results

	Solid	Shell
Pieces per grind (average)	2,748	3,295
Number of runs	9	13
Number of regrinds	8	12
Regrinding time, min	30	28
Total pieces per tool	24,732	42,835
Total cost per piece	$0.006	$0.003

Shell reamer with brazed carbide cutting edges was superior to solid carbide reamer with high speed steel shank for reaming the shaft hole in this gray iron water-pump body.

Fig. 12. Shell vs solid reamers (Example 205)

The maximum amount a shell reamer can be expanded depends on diameter: approximately 0.007 in. for ½-in. diameter, 0.010 in. for 1-in., and 0.020 in. for 2-in. Shells expand evenly and need not be ground for roundness or straightness after each expansion.

Production Examples. The following example describes an application in which shell reamers were superior to solid reamers in tool life and tool cost per piece:

Example 205. Shell vs Solid Reamers for Gray Iron (Fig. 12)

In one plant, solid reamers were compared with shell reamers for reaming 1.1798/1.1790-in.-diam shaft holes in gray iron water-pump bodies (131 to 207 Bhn). Specifications called for maximum out-of-roundness of 0.0003 in., maximum taper of 0.0002 in., and finish of 60 micro-in. Figure 12 shows the workpiece and the two types of reamer used. The solid reamer had a 1.84-in.-long cutting tip of solid tungsten carbide on a shank of high speed steel, and the shell reamer had brazed carbide cutting edges.

Both types of reamer were used in a vertical two-spindle machine with the same operating conditions (see table accompanying Fig. 12). In each setup, a guide bushing was used, and cutting fluid was supplied under pressure to the tool.

The results obtained in 9 runs for the solid reamer and in 13 for the shell are tabulated with Fig. 12. As this comparison shows, tool life (number of pieces per grind) for the shell reamers was 20% greater than for the solid reamers, and tool cost per piece was 50% less. The shorter life of the solid reamer was due largely to the difference in the diameters of its shank and head. Because of this difference, the solid reamer was guided through the bushing for only a portion of the cut, whereas the shell reamer was guided during the entire cut.

An application in which tool life was increased by the use of expandable shell reamers for finish reaming is described in Example 705, in the article "Machining of Tool Steel".

Applications of Floating-Blade Reamers

Floating-blade reamers have replaceable and adjustable cutting edges (Fig. 13.) The blades, of either high speed steel or carbide, can be adjusted for wear (or, within small limits, for different hole sizes) by turning an adjusting screw in the blade assembly with a hexagonal wrench. The two-piece blade assembly is held in a slot in the bar (as shown in Fig. 13), in which it can float. The amount of float is controlled by the lockscrew and adjusting screw in the tool holder. By floating, the cutters can follow the surface of the bore being reamed, maintaining tolerances as close as 0.0005 in. Floating also permits compensation for machine or holder errors.

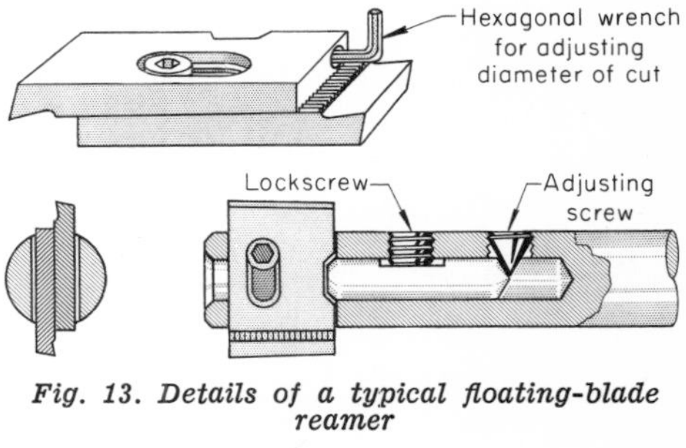

Fig. 13. Details of a typical floating-blade reamer

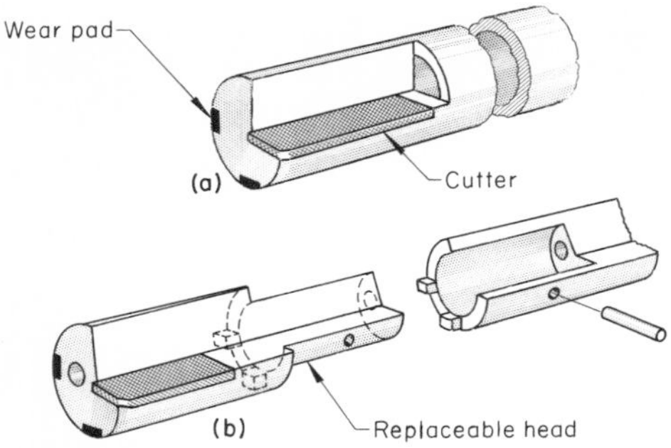

Fig. 14. Typical gun reamers for through holes: (a) *fixed-head (conventional) type;* (b) *replaceable-head type*

Floating-blade reamers provide liberal clearance for chips, and in special circumstances may cut faster than solid reamers. Other advantages of floating-blade reamers are: (*a*) cutters can be replaced, or removed for adjustment, without removing the holder from the machine; (*b*) the holder is not expendable, and can be used for many cutters; and (*c*) tool cost is usually less than that of comparable-size solid reamers (in one application, for example, the initial cost of a carbide-tipped floating-blade reamer for 1-in. holes was only about two thirds that of a solid straight-flute reamer with carbide cutting edges).

The use of floating-blade reamers usually is restricted to applications in which the workpiece is rotated, as in turret lathes. An application in which productivity was increased because higher speeds could be used for floating-blade carbide reamers than for solid high speed steel reamers is described in the following example:

Example 206. Floating-Blade Carbide vs Solid High Speed Steel Reamers (Table 1)

Holes 1.988 in. in diameter and 0.050 in. deep were reamed in gears made of 1118 steel (160 Bhn) to a total tolerance of 0.001 in. using eight-flute solid reamers made of high speed steel. As Table 1 shows, a change to floating-blade reamers (two carbide blades) allowed a 63% increase in speed at the same feed with a proportionate decrease in reaming time per piece. Reamer life between grinds was more than four times as long for the floating-blade reamer as for the solid reamer; total life was three times as long.

Some of the increased life for the floating-blade reamer was due to the decreased amount of stock on the hole diameter (0.006 in., as opposed to 0.012 in. for the solid reamer). Less stock was required because the increased accuracy obtainable with the floating-blade reamer permitted drilling closer to final size.

Table 1. Solid High Speed Steel Reamers vs Floating-Blade Carbide Reamers (Example 206)

Reaming condition or result	Type of reamer: Solid	Floating-blade
Speed, rpm	132	215
Speed, sfm	69	112
Feed, ipr	0.0092	0.0092
Stock reamed on diam, in.	0.012	0.006
Time per piece, min	0.46	0.21
Reamer life/grind, pieces	70	300
Total reamer life, pieces	1700	5500

Data are for reaming 1.988-in.-diam holes 0.050 in. deep in gears made of 1118 steel at 160 Bhn. Reaming was done in a turret lathe, using a 1-to-20 mixture of soluble oil and water as cutting fluid. Both types of reamers produced a 125-micro-in. finish.

Applications of Gun Reamers

Gun reamers consist of a hollow shank with a cutting edge (usually carbide) fastened to the end. Cutting fluid is fed through the stem under pressures of 25 to 100 psi to enhance cutting, cool the work and tools, and flush away chips. Gun reamers are used in machines in which the work is rotated and the tool remains stationary.

Blind-hole gun reamers have full-length flutes to permit backward ejection of chips. Through-hole gun reamers, with fixed or replaceable heads (Fig. 14), have a full round stem to the beginning of the cutter, and from this point have a cutaway portion to allow cutting fluid to flow.

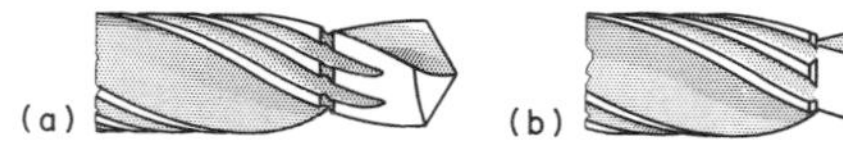

Fig. 16. Two types of drill-reamer combination tools; see text for discussion.

Fixed-head (conventional) gun reamers (Fig. 14a) are available in diameters of 1/8 to 2 in., and sometimes larger. Replaceable-head types (Fig. 14b) are available in diameters of 1 to 2 in.

A gun reamer resembles a gun drill in that it operates on the self-piloting principle and yields similar straightness, tolerance and finish. Speeds for gun reaming are usually about 200 sfm (about the same as for gun drilling), but feeds generally are 50 to 100% greater than those used in gun drilling. In gun reaming of soft metals, feeds as great as 0.010 ipr are often used. In reaming steel, the usual stock allowance is 0.010 to 0.040 in. on the diameter, depending on reamer size and workpiece hardness. In reaming softer metals, and sometimes in reaming annealed steel or cast iron, as much as 1/2 in. of stock can be removed from the diameter.

The following example illustrates a typical application of gun reaming:

Example 207. Accuracy and Finish in Reaming Holes Seven Diameters Long (Fig. 15)

Taper-cored through-holes in 17-in.-long hydraulic-press quills made of class 40 gray iron were gun reamed in a single pass in a turret lathe. During machining, the workpiece (Fig. 15) was held in a three-jaw face-plate fixture. Before reaming, a 2.250/2.248-in.-diam starting hole was bored to a depth of 1/2 in. The carbide-tip gun reamer (Fig. 15) was then fed into the workpiece, and removed stock ranging from about 3/16 in. on the diameter at the entrance end (beyond the starting hole) to about 3/8 in. at the exit end of the tapered hole.

Although specifications called for tolerance within 0.003 in. and a surface finish of 60 micro-in., the gun reamers held tolerance within 0.0014 in. and produced an average finish of 50 micro-in. For additional processing details, see the table with Fig. 15.

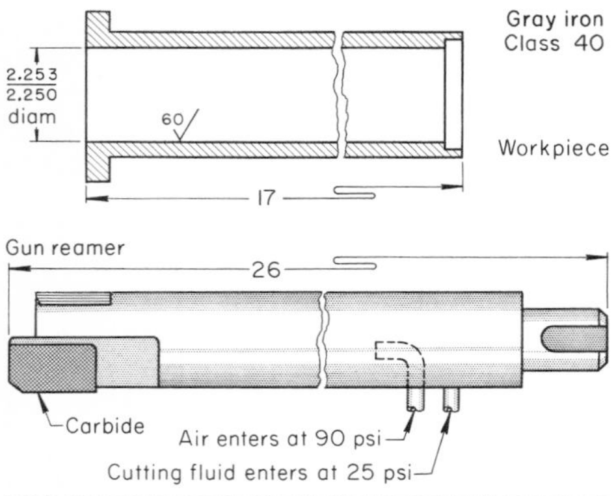

Reaming Conditions

Machine	Turret lathe
Speed	320 rpm (190 sfm)
Feed	0.004 ipr
Stock reamed on diameter	3/16 to 3/8 in.
Cutting fluid	Soluble-oil:water (1:15)(a)
Setup time	1 hr
Reamer life per grind	41 pieces
Maximum permissible runout	0.001 in. per ft

Results

Tolerance held on diameter	Within 0.0014 in.
Surface finish obtained	40 to 60 micro-in.

(a) Introduced with air at shank end of tool, as shown in illustration.

Fig. 15. Gun reaming of a taper-cored hole (Example 207)

Applications of Special-Purpose Reamers

Several types of reamers designed for special applications are readily available. Among these are oil-hole reamers, diemaker's reamers, taper reamers, bridge reamers, pipe reamers, drill-and-reamer combinations, and multiple-diameter reamers.

Oil-hole reamers have a hollow core through which cutting fluid is forced to flush the chips out through the flutes. They are available as solid reamers in diameters up to about 1½ in., or as inserted-blade reamers in larger sizes. Oil-hole reamers can produce good finish in horizontal reaming.

Diemaker's reamers have a high helix angle and left-hand high-spiral flutes, and are tapered about 0.013 in. per in. They are used for reaming dowel-pin holes in die parts.

Taper reamers produce tapered holes that receive taper shanks and taper pins.

Bridge reamers are used for reaming holes in products like ship plate and structural members. They are tapered at the end so they can enlarge an out-of-line hole until the entire body of the reamer can enter and enlarge the hole to the required size. They are not intended for reaming tapers. They are available with either spiral or straight flutes, and in diameters of 13/32 to 1½ in.

Pipe reamers are short, stubby tools used to taper-ream pipe fittings for tapping. They have a taper of 3/4 in. per ft and are of 1/8-in. to 2-in. pipe size.

Drill-and-Reamer Combinations. When producing shallow holes, it is sometimes possible to eliminate a second operation by using a combination drill and reamer. Two types are shown in Fig. 16. The tool shown in Fig. 16(a) is made by milling two spiral flutes the entire length of the tool. The drill section is slightly smaller in diameter than the reamer section, and the drill margins extend only the length of the drill section. The reamer section consists of one to three reamer flutes milled in each land left by the drill-flute milling cutter. This type of tool is subject to the same difficulties in regrinding as are encountered with step drills. These difficulties can be overcome by using the tool shown in Fig. 16(b), which is of subland construction. With this tool, the two drill flutes and cutting edges extend back through the reamer section; reamer cutting edges are in addition to these, and begin at a suitable distance from the drill point.

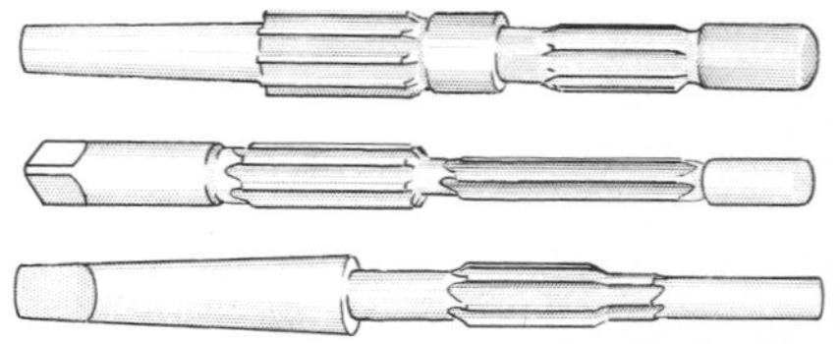

Fig. 17. Three types of multiple-diameter reamers

Multiple-Diameter Reamers. When two or more concentric holes of different diameters must be reamed, if a separate reamer is used for each hole several operations are necessary and it is difficult to keep the holes in line. The use of a multiple-diameter reamer (Fig. 17) permits the operations to be performed together and insures alignment of the holes.

In many multiple-diameter reamers, each reaming section is preceded by a pilot section to bear in the drilled holes or in bushings in the fixture. Generally, all reaming sections start to cut at the same time.

Speed and Feed

Nominal speeds and feeds for reaming of carbon and low-alloy steels at various hardnesses are given in Tables 2 and 3. The rates in Table 2 are for six-flute reamers made of high speed steel; those in Table 3 are for six-flute reamers with solid steel bodies and carbide cutting edges.

Speed. Because of their design, most reamers are more easily damaged than drills. Therefore, it is usual practice to ream a hole at about two thirds the speed at which it was drilled. A comparison of the nominal speeds in Table 2 with those for the same work metals in Table 3 in the article "Drilling" shows that, for high speed steel tools, reaming speeds are somewhat lower.

From Tables 2 and 3 it is evident that speed depends mainly on composition and hardness of the work metal, and on tool material. For reaming under similar conditions, recommended speeds for carbide reamers are three to four times those for high speed steel reamers.

Although composition of the steel being reamed has some effect on optimum speed, hardness has a much greater effect. The nominal speed in Table 2 for reaming steel at 400 Bhn is 20 sfm, and it is 55 to 80 sfm for steel at 160 Bhn — regardless of differences in composition. As Tables 2 and 3 show, greater differences in nominal speed are related to the differences in hardness of a steel in any of the groups.

Because other variables, such as reamer design, rigidity of the setup and depth of hole, influence optimum speed, the nominal speeds listed in Tables 2 and 3 can serve only as starting points in the selection of optimum speed for given conditions. Speeds used in Fig. 1 and in applications described in eight examples in this article are summarized in Table 4. Although some speeds shown in Table 4 agree closely with the nominal speed for the same work metal and hardness in Tables 2 and 3, there are several evident differences. But examination of all the details of the applications summarized in Table 4 usually explains the differences. Figure 1, for instance, shows that two reaming speeds (40 and 58 sfm) were used for reaming 4130 steel at Rockwell C 15. In Table 2, the nearest nominal speed is shown as 45 sfm (4140 group at 175 to 225 Bhn). But note that in Fig. 1 a four-flute reamer was used for the ¼-in.-diam holes and an eight-flute reamer for the ½-in.-diam holes, whereas the speeds in Table 2 are based on the use of six-flute reamers.

In Examples 203 and 204, annealed 1035 steel was reamed at 45 and 30 sfm, whereas Table 2 suggests 55 sfm for comparable steel (1045 at 125 to 175 Bhn). But in both examples, inserted-blade reamers were used (whereas the data in Table 2 are for solid reamers), and in Example 204 the shape of the workpiece suggests that less than normal rigidity prevailed.

In Example 206, the speed of 69 sfm used for reaming annealed 1118 steel at 160 Bhn with a high speed steel reamer is very near the 65-sfm speed Table 2 shows for the 1117 group at 150 to 200 Bhn, although the reamer used in Example 206 had eight flutes. But when a carbide reamer was substituted for this application, it was used at a speed of 112 sfm — less than half the 260 sfm suggested in Table 3. The carbide reamer, however, was a floating-blade type, and values in Table 3 are based on the use of solid reamers.

In Example 208, a hole in a stack of silicon steel laminations was reamed at 50 sfm. This speed is less than the 65-sfm speed shown in Table 2 for reaming 1020 in its softest condition. However, even though silicon steels are low in carbon content, the increased silicon content affects reamability. Also, in Example 208 no cutting fluid was used, whereas speeds listed in Table 2 are based on the use of cutting fluid.

Table 2. Nominal Speeds and Feeds for Reaming of Carbon and Low-Alloy Steels With High Speed Steel Reamers(a)

Typical steel(b)	Brinell hardness	Speed, sfm	Feed, ipr, for reamer diameter of: ⅛ in.	¼ in.	½ in.	1 in.	1½ in.	2 in.
Carbon and Low-Alloy Steels (Except Free-Cutting Grades)								
1020, 1045, 4140, 7140 and 8620, at hardness ranges listed at right	85 to 125	65	0.004	0.007	0.010	0.015	0.020	0.025
	125 to 175	55	0.003	0.005	0.010	0.015	0.020	0.025
	175 to 225	45	0.003	0.004	0.008	0.012	0.015	0.020
	225 to 275	40	0.0025	0.004	0.008	0.012	0.015	0.020
	275 to 325	30	0.0025	0.004	0.008	0.012	0.015	0.020
	325 to 375	25	0.002	0.003	0.005	0.009	0.012	0.015
	375 to 425	20	0.002	0.003	0.004	0.007	0.010	0.012
Free-Cutting Carbon and Low-Alloy Steels								
1112 and 12L14	100 to 150	75	0.004	0.006	0.010	0.015	0.020	0.025
	150 to 200	80	0.004	0.006	0.010	0.015	0.020	0.025
	200 to 250	50	0.002	0.004	0.008	0.012	0.015	0.020
1117 and 1137	100 to 150	70	0.004	0.006	0.010	0.015	0.020	0.025
	150 to 200	65	0.003	0.005	0.010	0.015	0.020	0.025
	275 to 325	45	0.002	0.004	0.008	0.012	0.015	0.020
	325 to 375	30	0.002	0.004	0.008	0.012	0.015	0.020
	375 to 425	20	0.002	0.003	0.004	0.007	0.010	0.012
4140+S and 41L40	150 to 200	60	0.004	0.006	0.010	0.015	0.020	0.025
	200 to 250	50	0.003	0.005	0.009	0.013	0.018	0.022
	275 to 325	35	0.002	0.004	0.008	0.012	0.015	0.020
	325 to 375	25	0.002	0.003	0.005	0.009	0.012	0.015
	375 to 425	20	0.002	0.003	0.004	0.007	0.010	0.012

(a) Based on removal of 0.015 to 0.020 in. from the hole diameter, with six-flute reamers made of high speed steels M1, M2 and M7, except T15 for hardness above 375 Bhn. All speeds and feeds are for use with ample cutting fluid. (b) Each steel listed is a frequently used grade in a group of similar steels. For a listing of the steels in the various groups, see Table 2, page 6. (Data are adapted from tables compiled by Metcut Research Associates, Inc.)

Table 3. Nominal Speeds and Feeds for Reaming of Carbon and Low-Alloy Steels With Carbide Reamers(a)

Typical steel(b)	Brinell hardness	Speed, sfm	Feed, ipr, for reamer diameter of: ⅛ in.	¼ in.	½ in.	1 in.	1½ in.	2 in.
Carbon and Low-Alloy Steels (Except Free-Cutting Grades)								
1020 and 1045, at hardness ranges listed at right	85 to 125	260	0.004	0.007	0.010	0.015	0.020	0.025
	125 to 175	250	0.004	0.007	0.010	0.015	0.020	0.025
	175 to 225	190	0.0025	0.004	0.008	0.012	0.015	0.020
	225 to 275	165	0.0025	0.004	0.008	0.012	0.015	0.020
	275 to 325	100	0.0025	0.004	0.008	0.012	0.015	0.020
	325 to 375	90	0.002	0.003	0.005	0.009	0.012	0.015
	375 to 425	60	0.002	0.003	0.004	0.007	0.010	0.012
4140, 7140 and 8620	125 to 175	200	0.003	0.005	0.010	0.015	0.020	0.025
	175 to 225	180	0.003	0.004	0.008	0.012	0.015	0.020
	225 to 275	160	0.003	0.004	0.008	0.012	0.015	0.020
	275 to 325	120	0.0025	0.004	0.008	0.012	0.015	0.020
	325 to 375	85	0.002	0.003	0.005	0.009	0.012	0.015
	375 to 425	60	0.002	0.003	0.004	0.007	0.010	0.012
	R_C 45 to 48	40	0.002	0.003	0.004	0.006	0.008	0.010
	R_C 50 to 52	20	0.002	0.003	0.004	0.006	0.008	0.010
Free-Cutting Carbon and Low-Alloy Steels								
1112 and 12L14	100 to 150	300	0.004	0.006	0.010	0.015	0.020	0.025
	150 to 200	335	0.004	0.006	0.010	0.015	0.020	0.025
	200 to 250	200	0.002	0.004	0.008	0.012	0.015	0.020
1117 and 1137	100 to 150	300	0.004	0.006	0.010	0.015	0.020	0.025
	150 to 200	260	0.003	0.005	0.010	0.015	0.020	0.025
	275 to 325	180	0.002	0.004	0.008	0.012	0.015	0.020
	325 to 375	100	0.002	0.004	0.008	0.012	0.015	0.020
	375 to 425	60	0.002	0.003	0.004	0.007	0.010	0.012
4140+S and 41L40	150 to 200	245	0.004	0.006	0.010	0.015	0.020	0.025
	200 to 250	205	0.003	0.005	0.008	0.012	0.015	0.020
	275 to 325	150	0.002	0.004	0.008	0.012	0.015	0.020
	325 to 375	95	0.002	0.003	0.005	0.009	0.012	0.015
	375 to 425	60	0.002	0.003	0.004	0.007	0.010	0.012
	R_C 45 to 48	40	0.002	0.003	0.004	0.006	0.008	0.010

(a) Based on removal of 0.015 to 0.020 in. from the hole diameter, with six-flute reamers made of grade C-2 carbide. All speeds and feeds are for use when cutting fluid is amply supplied to the cutting edges of the reamer. (b) Each steel listed is a frequently used grade in a group of similar steels. For a listing of the steels in the various groups, see Table 2, page 6. (Data are adapted from tables compiled by Metcut Research Associates, Inc.)

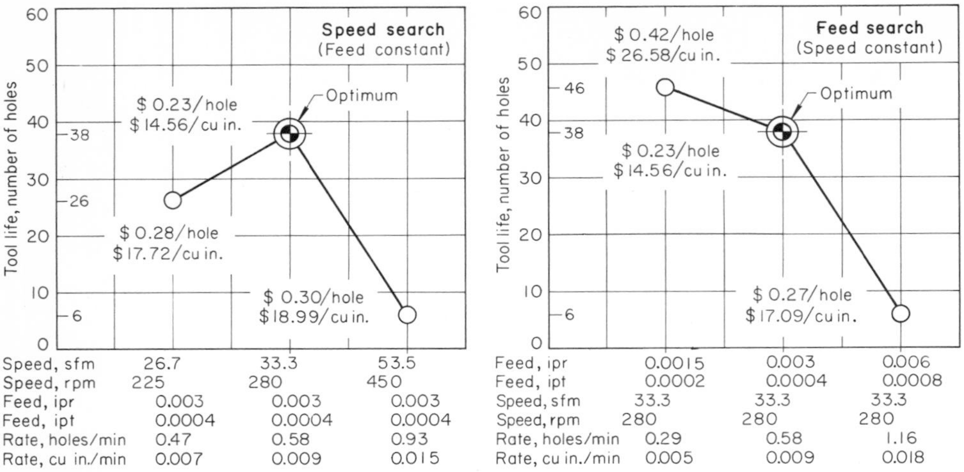

Reamer Details

Material	M10 high speed steel
Size	0.453-in. diam, 7.0 in. long
Number of flutes	8
Helix angle	0°
Flute type	Straight
Radial rake angle	3°
Radial relief angle	17°
Chamfer angle	42°
Chamfer relief angle	7°
Margin width	0.017 in.
Wear land	0.010 in.

Cost Factors

Tool use	$0.82
Tool change	0.20
Operating	0.116

Data are for reaming of through holes 1.25 in. deep. Reaming was done in a vertical four-spindle drill press; cutting fluid, a 1-to-1 mixture of sulfurized oil and mineral oil, was flow applied. Hardness of work was Rockwell C 35.

Fig. 18. Determination of speed and feed for reaming alloy A-286 at minimum cost

Feed is influenced not only by the variables that govern speed, but also by hole size and amount of metal being reamed (depth of cut). The nominal feed rates given in Tables 2 and 3 for six different hole diameters are based on the enlargement of all diameters 0.015 to 0.020 in.

Feed rates used in specific applications are likely to vary more from the nominal rates in Tables 2 and 3 than are speeds. A comparison of the feeds actually used in examples in this article (Table 4) with nominal feeds (Tables 2 and 3) shows that some agree closely and that others differ by a factor of three or more.

In Fig. 1, which involves reaming a total of $\frac{1}{64}$ in. from $\frac{1}{4}$ and $\frac{1}{2}$-in.-diam holes in 4130 steel at Rockwell C 15, a feed of 0.006 ipr was used for both sizes. Table 2 suggests 0.004 and 0.008 ipr for reaming $\frac{1}{4}$ and $\frac{1}{2}$-in.-diam holes under similar conditions (4140 group at 175 to 225 Bhn). In Example 202, the feed was only 0.005 ipr — less than half the rate suggested in Table 2. But in Example 202 the hole had a keyway, and surface finish was a major objective.

It is sometimes advisable to use a higher feed and slower speed. This is indicated in Example 204, where the speed was about 45% less than nominal (Table 2 for 1045 steel) and the feed was about 200% greater than nominal. Similar conditions, but with smaller percentage differences, prevailed in Example 203.

In Example 206, a feed rate of 0.0092 ipr was used for both a solid high speed steel reamer and a floating-blade carbide reamer. This is much less than the nominal 0.025 ipr in Tables 2 and 3 for a 2-in.-diam hole in 1117 steel.

Selection of Speed and Feed. Reaming speed and feed have important effects on results (mainly surface finish and tool life) and on cost. When setting up for a reaming operation without prior experience, it is advisable to use a conservative speed-and-feed combination first. For instance, in reaming holes of $\frac{1}{8}$-in. to 2-in. diameter in low-carbon steel, it would be well to start with a speed of 60 sfm and a feed of 0.004 to 0.025 ipr. Speed or feed, or both, can then be increased until the first signs of tool chatter appear. When this point has been determined, it is advisable to keep speeds and feeds below it for best finish and tool life; often a change in speed of 10% or less can cause or eliminate chatter.

For reaming soft brass, a speed of 250 sfm is a good starting point. About twice that, or 500 sfm, is right for a first setting in reaming aluminum. Much slower speeds must be used in steel harder than Rockwell C 20. As hardness increases, possible speed decreases. The maximum workable speed for steel at Rockwell C 52 is 15 sfm.

Detailed information and tables on reaming of metals other than steel are presented in the reaming sections of articles in this volume that deal with the machining of cast iron, stainless steel, heat-resisting alloys, aluminum, copper, and other specific metals.

Determination of Optimum Speed and Feed

Table 4 shows that a wide range of speeds and feeds can be used for reaming relatively easy-to-machine materials. But for best results in reaming difficult alloys, speed and feed must be carefully calculated. One method of calculation is detailed in the remainder of this section. It was used in a test program to determine optimum speed and feed for reaming through-holes in iron-base alloy A-286 that had been precipitation-hardened to Rockwell C 35. Conditions and results of the tests are given in Fig. 18.

The first step was a speed search: A near-optimum feed was selected, on the basis of experience, and speed was adjusted in increments until the most economical rate was found. In the next step, a feed search, the speed found to be optimum in the speed search was held constant and feed was varied in increments, to verify or correct the initially selected feed rate.

The development of a predetermined amount of wear on the edge of the reamer was the criterion for tool life. This amount of wear, observed with a hand microscope, marked the end of each test. Different speeds and feeds caused wear at different rates.

Cost Factors. As shown in Fig. 18, the determination of machining costs was based on tool-use cost, tool-change cost, and operating cost. Tool-use cost included the cost of new tools and the cost of regrinding. Tool-change cost was obtained by the use of a specific rate of tool changing that had been assigned to the operation. Operating cost was based on a standard cost per minute for all operations.

In the charts in Fig. 18, the total reaming cost per hole is the sum of:

1 Operating cost times number of minutes required to ream one hole
2 Tool-change cost divided by tool life in holes per tool
3 Tool-use cost divided by tool life in holes per tool.

Dividing this total by the volume of metal removed per hole gives the total reaming cost in dollars per cubic inch of metal removed.

Bushings and Fixtures

When a hole to be reamed must be an exact distance from some point or from another hole, reaming in jigs or fixtures is preferred. These hold the workpiece

Table 4. Speeds and Feeds Used in Examples in This Article

Example No.	Material reamed	Speed: Rpm	Speed: Sfm	Feed, ipr
[Fig. 1] (a)	4130 steel (R_C 15)	610, 450	40, 58	0.006
	4330 mod steel (R_C 47)	325, 225	21.3, 29.5	0.0015
	4340 steel (R_C 52)	160, 120	10.5, 15.7	0.0015
199	Low-carbon steel	. . .	100	0.029
202	Low-carbon steel	355	70	0.005
203	1035 steel, annealed	74	45	0.045
204	1035 steel, annealed	146	30	0.035
205	Gray iron (131 to 207 Bhn)	875	270	0.018
206 (b)	1118 steel (160 Bhn)	132, 215	69, 112	0.0092
207	Gray iron, class 40	320	190	0.004
208	Low-carbon steel	190	50	0.055

(a) Figure 1 deals with reaming of holes of two different diameters; first values listed in "speed" columns here were used for reaming $\frac{1}{4}$-in.-diam holes, second values for $\frac{1}{2}$-in.-diam holes. (b) Example 206 compares results from tools of different designs and materials; first values in "speed" columns here were used for conventional eight-flute reamer made of high speed steel; second values were used for a floating-blade reamer with two carbide blades.

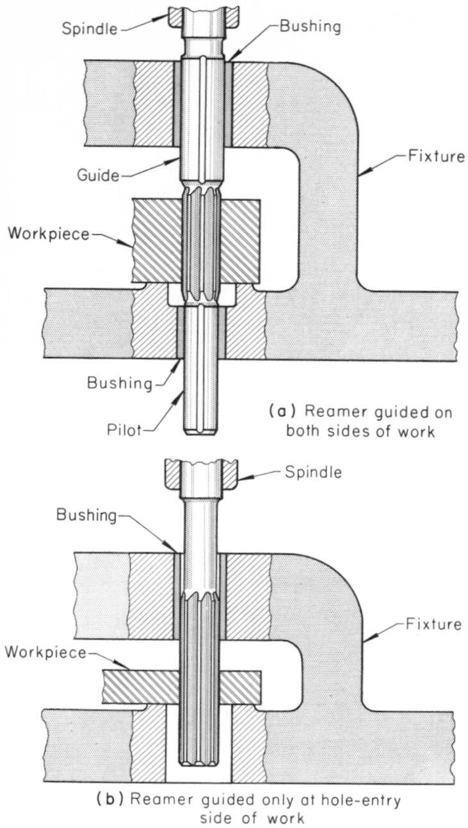

Fig. 19. Two setups employing fixtures and bushings for accurate guiding of reamers

securely, and the reamer is guided in bushings set in exact relation to locating points on the workpiece (Fig. 19).

If the hole is more than one diameter long, it is best to guide the reamer in bushings on both sides of the work, (Fig. 19a). For this, a special piloted reamer is required. Guide bushings should fit the pilots, but not so tightly that they seize and bind. Pilots should be grooved throughout their length. The grooves serve the double purpose of allowing cutting fluid to lubricate the pilots and of providing an escape for chips that could become wedged between the pilots and bushings.

If the hole is not more than one diameter long, the reamer may be guided only at the hole-entry side of the work, in a guide bushing made to fit the reamer (Fig. 19b).

When hardened bushings are used as guides, the machine spindle must be accurately aligned with the bushing. Otherwise, the reamer will hit the bushing and may be damaged. When using sliding fixtures in machines like gang drill presses, alignment is especially critical. Sometimes bronze or fiber caps are placed over the bushings to assist lead-in, but these caps will not completely protect the reamer if it is not aligned with the bushing.

For either setup shown in Fig. 19, a rigid drive (reamer shank held directly and rigidly in the machine spindle) is satisfactory, because any slight misalignment between the machine spindle and the work is corrected by the guide bushings. But if the reamer is to guide itself into a previously made hole, a rigid drive is *not* satisfactory, because any misalignment of the machine spindle with the work will result in reamed holes that are bell-mouthed, tapered, or out-of-round. Some type of floating drive or special reamer is used for these applications.

Floating drivers permit some limited angular misalignment of the reamer, some limited parallel misalignment, or both (Fig. 20). The ideal floating driver permits both kinds of float in amounts that can be adjusted for the greatest allowable misalignment in the setup.

Table 5. Cutting Fluids Used in Reaming Various Metals

Metal	Soluble oil	Sulfurized oil	Kerosine plus lard oil	Nonviscous neutral oil	Dry(a)
Steel	X	X	..	..	..
Stainless steel	X	X	..	..	..
Gray iron	..	..	..	..	X
Malleable or nodular iron	X	..	..	X	..
Aluminum	X	..	X	..	..
Copper	X	..	..	..	..
Brass	X	..	X	..	X

(a) When no cutting fluid is used, an air jet is advisable for cooling or chip removal.

Cutting Fluids

Cutting fluids used in reaming serve the same purposes as in other machining operations:

1 **Preventing temperature rise,** in the workpiece as well as the tool. Excessive temperature rise can adversely affect the dimensions of a reamed hole.
2 **Improving cutting action,** by minimizing the adherence of the tool to the surface of the workpiece. This adherence occurs most often when reaming soft, gummy metals. When no cutting fluid, or an ineffective one, is used, the finish obtained often is rougher by 10 to more than 20 micro-in.
3 **Flushing away chips.** In finish reaming, if chips are not continuously flushed away they may be picked up by the cutters and scratch or gouge the surface of the work.

The cutting fluids most widely used are noted in Table 5. In setups of borderline rigidity, chatter may be minimized or prevented by the use of mineral seal oil or kerosine containing 5 to 25% of lard oil or other buffers.

The *amount* of fluid used is often more important than the type. A copious supply maintains a nearly constant temperature and disperses chips.

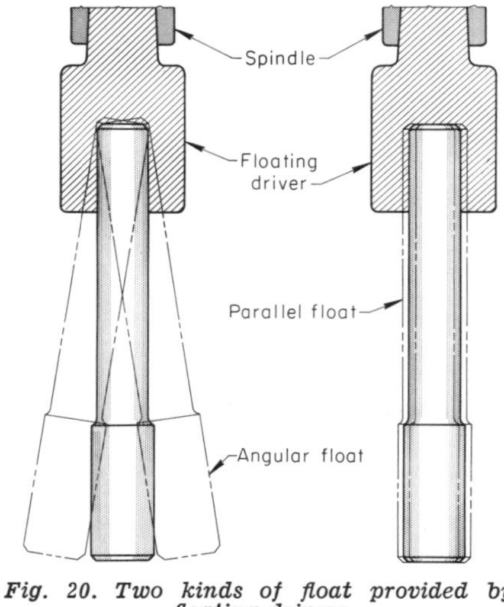

Fig. 20. Two kinds of float provided by floating drivers

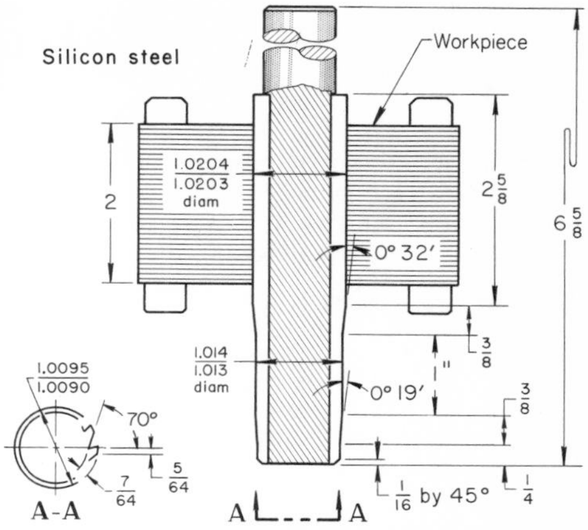

Reamer Details

Type	Spiral, ten-flute(a)
Material	M4 high speed steel
Margin width	0.002 in.
Back taper	0.0003 in. per in.
Radial hook angle in flutes	0°
Concentricity	0.0002 in. TIR

Operating Conditions

Machine	3-hp vertical drill press
Speed	190 rpm (50 sfm)
Feed	0.055 ipr
Cutting fluid	None
Tool life per grind	200 to 250 pieces

(a) 10° left-hand spiral; right-hand cut. Flute spacing was staggered, for elimination of chatter.

Fig. 21. Dry reaming of shaft hole in rotor (Example 208)

Dry Reaming. Although cutting fluids are beneficial in most reaming, some applications require no fluid. Gray iron usually is reamed dry. When no cutting fluid is used, it is advisable to direct an air jet on the work, for cooling and to assist in chip removal.

Sometimes the use of a cutting fluid is impractical because of workpiece design, as in the following example:

Example 208. Dry Reaming of Laminated Steel Rotors (Fig. 21)

In reaming shaft holes in rotors for fractional-horsepower electric motors (Fig. 21), cutting fluid was not used because it would have penetrated between the laminated flat stampings and have been nearly impossible to remove. The rotors were reamed with ten-flute spiral reamers (Fig. 21) made of M4 high speed steel. (High speed steel is preferred for reaming workpieces of this type, because they promote tool chatter.) The rotors were held on simple pins (to prevent them from rotating) in a two-station hand-indexing fixture; reamers were held in radial floating holders. Other details are tabulated with Fig. 21.

Other Examples of Reaming Applications in This Volume

Work metal	Example number
Work Metals Compared in Reaming	
Cast iron	661, 663
Method	
Cast iron	657, 666
Magnesium	986
Nickel	996, 997
Methods Compared	
Tool steel	705
Tool Design	
Copper	940
Magnesium	987
Combined Operations	
Stainless steel	752
Aluminum	892, 894, 895
Copper	948

Countersinking

IN COUNTERSINKING, a conical, reamerlike tool is used to cut a tapered enlargement at the opening of a hole, for receiving the head of a fastener, for receiving a center, or for deburring. The surface cut by the tool is concentric with the hole, and at an angle of less than 90° to it.

Machines used for drilling or reaming are used also for countersinking. For a description of the various types, see the article "Drilling", in this volume. Countersinking is often combined with drilling or other related operations.

Tools

Although countersinking tools are often ground from drills, tools designed expressly for countersinking are more rigid and produce holes with greater accuracy and better finish. Many standard types of these tools are available, in a variety of sizes and angles. Five common types of countersinking tools, or "countersinks", are shown in Fig. 1.

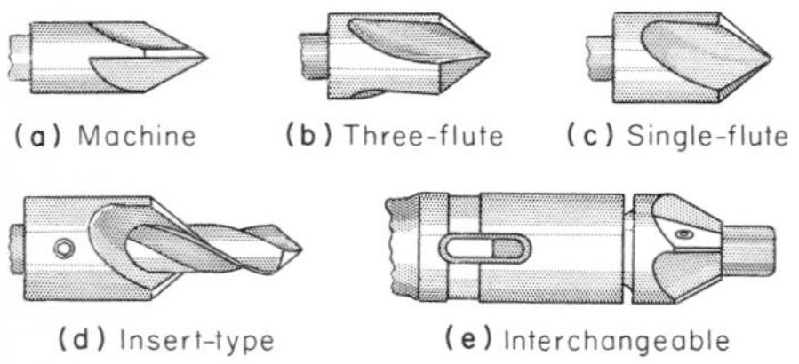

Fig. 1. Five common types of countersinking tools. See text for discussion.

Their design and application are discussed in the following paragraphs.

Machine countersinks (Fig. 1a) are made with a radial relief and have four flutes. They are most readily available in angles of 60° for centering, 82° for countersinking flathead screws, and 90° for chamfering or deburring — these being the most common applications. Other angles can be produced as needed.

Three-flute countersinks (Fig. 1b) are designed to minimize chatter in countersinking and deburring, and can be used in either fixed or portable equipment. They are especially suitable for use in portable equipment, because they can center readily in drilled holes. Three-flute countersinks are available in many angles and body diameters, and provide better tool life than single-flute countersinks.

Single-flute countersinks (Fig. 1c) are designed for use in machine countersinking and in light-duty countersinking with portable equipment. Much smaller holes can be countersunk with single-flute tools than with multiple-flute tools. However, the diameter of the drilled hole should be at least 10% of the diameter of the countersink. The single-flute tool should be chosen for applications in which multiple-flute tools chatter or when the drilled hole is too small for a multiple-flute tool.

Insert-type countersinks (Fig. 1d) are attached to the body of a drill and locked at the desired depth. The body of the drill serves as a pilot and provides rigidity. Near the bottom of the spindle stroke, the cutting edge of the insert engages the surface and countersinks the drilled hole.

An insert-type countersink can also be attached to a tap, but the countersink should then be spring-loaded instead of locked in place. This is required because the point at which the tap reverses is not accurately held, and because the lead of a tap is too coarse for a countersinking feed unless the countersink is spring-loaded.

Interchangeable countersinks, equipped with pilots and adapted to tool holders as shown in Fig. 1(e), are recommended for heavy-duty operations.

Combination tools, such as a reamer or a step drill combined with a countersink, are often used. Example 666, in the article "Machining of Cast Iron", shows the use of a reamer combined with a countersink. Multiple-flute subland drills (see page 81, in the article "Drilling") can also be adapted to countersinking, as in Example 162.

Spot drilling and countersinking are often combined, by the use of a drill of countersink diameter that has been ground at the point end to the countersink angle. The drill, guided by a drill bushing, first spot drills the fixtured workpiece, then countersinks to the desired depth. The hole is then drilled, with a drill of appropriate smaller diameter — usually through the same drill bushing and without removing the workpiece from the fixture.

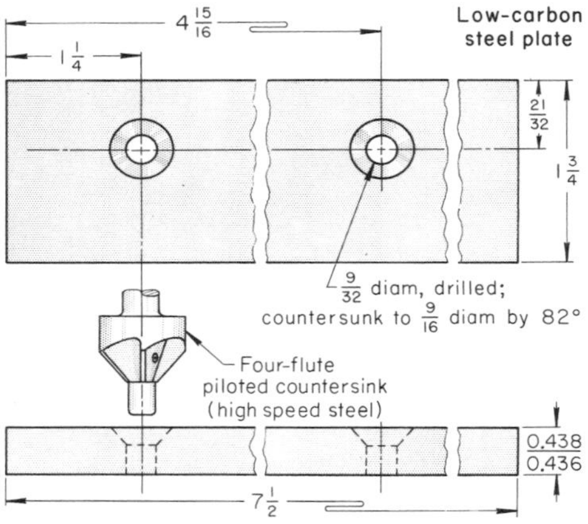

Speed	272 rpm (40 sfm)
Feed (manual)	0.004 ipr (approx)
Cutting fluid	Soluble-oil:water (1:20)
Setup time	0.3 hr
Production rate	160 pieces (320 holes) per hour
Tool life per grind (avg)	575 pieces (1150 holes)

Fig. 2. Workpiece drilled and countersunk (to seat flathead threaded fasteners) in two separate operations (Example 209)

Speed and Feed

Recommended speed for countersinking is normally one-half to two-thirds the speed used for drilling the same material. When drilling and countersinking are done with a single tool, drilling speed often is penalized as a result of the slower speed required for the countersinking operation.

Feed rates are governed largely by workpiece composition, and by the angle, diameter and depth of the countersink. For example, although a feed of 0.004 to 0.006 ipr is normal for countersinking a 90° angle in a 1-in.-diam drilled hole, the above factors may restrict feed to 0.002 ipr or may permit the use of feeds of 0.012 ipr or more.

Examples of Procedure

The two examples that follow typify countersinking practice. In the first example, countersinking was performed separately after a drill-jig operation; in the second, countersinking was done in sequence with drilling, on a three-spindle drill press.

Example 209. Countersinking in a Separate Operation (Fig. 2)

The two holes in the workpiece shown in Fig. 2 (low-carbon steel plate) were drilled and countersunk to accommodate flathead threaded fasteners. Drilling and countersinking were done separately, using a single-spindle vertical drill press with manual feed. Operating conditions are tabulated with Fig. 2.

In drilling, required accuracy was obtained by the use of a plate-type drill jig having pressed-in bushings. After the holes had been drilled, the workpiece was removed from the jig and positioned for countersinking in a sliding-jaw vise anchored under the spindle. The workpiece was not clamped; the vise was adjusted so as to allow the workpiece to slide through the jaws, utilizing the hole to hold position. The operator held the vise and workpiece with one hand while controlling feed with the other.

Example 210. Countersinking in Sequence With Drilling (Fig. 3)

Pins made of leaded 1050 steel and annealed required a ½-in.-diam through cross hole, positioned as shown in Fig. 3, countersunk on both ends at a 90° angle and to a diameter of 19/32 in. Drilling and countersinking were done on a three-spindle, power-feed drill press. The right and left spindles were used for drilling, and the center spindle for countersinking. Drilled parts coming from both left and right spindles were positioned in a V-block under the center spindle. A spiral-flute high speed steel drill with a 90° (included) point angle (Fig. 3) was used as the countersinking tool. Processing details are given with Fig. 3.

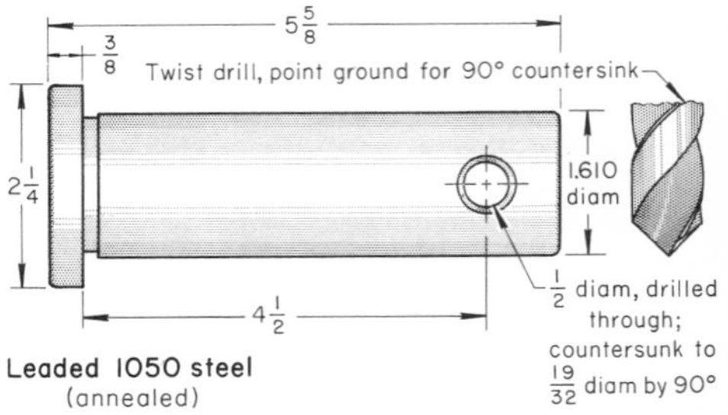

Speed	400 rpm (53 sfm)
Feed	0.004 ipr
Depth of cut	3/64 in.
Cutting fluid	Soluble-oil:water (1:20)
Setup time	1 hr
Production rate	70 pieces per hour
Countersink life per grind	500 pieces

Fig. 3. Pin that was drilled and countersunk (both ends) in sequence on a three-spindle drill press (Example 210)

Counterboring

COUNTERBORING is a machining process for enlarging a hole to a given depth. In most instances a shoulder is formed at the bottom of the enlarged hole. One of the most common applications of counterboring is the enlargement of holes to accommodate the socket heads of capscrews.

Counterboring is closely related to drilling, and the two operations are often done in sequence. Machines used for counterboring are the same as those used for drilling. These machines are described in the article "Drilling".

Tools

Most tools for counterboring are of either of two general types: (*a*) those that have pilots, and thus can use the predrilled hole to stabilize cutting action and minimize chatter; and (*b*) those that do not have pilots, and thus usually must be guided by drill bushings.

Pilots for counterbores either are integral with the cutter or are separate, interchangeable parts selected to fit the guide hole. A large counterbore should not be used with too small a pilot. The pilot diameter should be at least as large as the root diameter of the counterbore, so that chips will not be trapped between pilot and cutter. Chip packing can cause cutter breakage.

The pilot must not be too tight nor too loose in the guide hole. There should be enough clearance so that the pilot can enter the guide hole and rotate without binding. Too much clearance may cause chatter. Clearance of 0.001 in. on the diameter is enough for a pilot ⅛ in. in diameter; a pilot 3 in. in diameter requires clearance of 0.007 in. for comparable action. For greater accuracy, some guide holes are reamed to finish or semifinish size before counterboring.

Interchangeable-pilot counterbores (Fig. 1a) have three, four or five flutes, depending on the size of the counterbore. They are available in long or short lengths and with either straight or tapered shanks. Pilots of different diameters can be used with a counterbore of specific size. It is usually impractical to use a counterbore with an interchangeable pilot in holes smaller than ¼ in. in diameter.

Integral-pilot counterbores (Fig. 1b) are designed with two spiral flutes to produce holes for small fillister-head and flathead screws, and are used for holes up to ⅜ in. in diameter. The cutting action of integral-pilot counterbores produces accurate holes without causing chatter. These counterbores are available for fillister-head screws in sizes 0 through 12, and for flathead screws (82° angle) in sizes up to ⅜ in. and in some larger sizes.

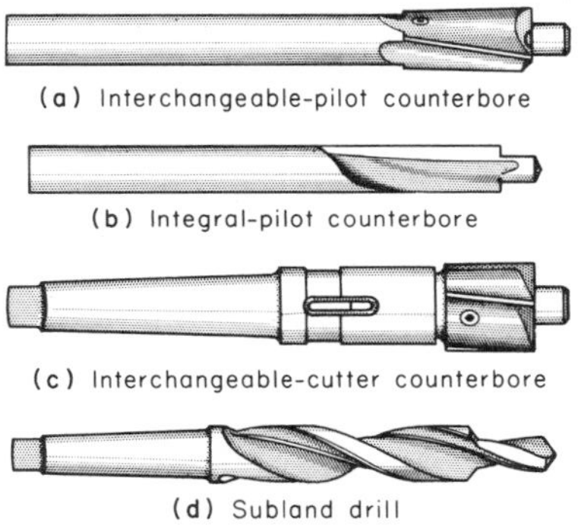

Fig. 1. Four types of tools used for counterboring

Interchangeable-cutter counterbores (Fig. 1c) are designed so that cutters of various diameters can be inserted interchangeably in a holder designated for a specific range. The inserted cutter is driven by a spline, a key or a pin. The short, rugged holders, which are available with straight or tapered shanks, make the tool especially well-suited for heavy-duty operations. The holder may have an integral or an interchangeable pilot.

Subland drills (Fig. 1d) can be used to produce counterbored holes in conjunction with drilling operations. These multiple-flute tools are of various designs for different applications. One type is discussed in Example 211 on the following page.

Combination tools other than subland drills are often used. Example 890, in the article on Machining of Aluminum, describes an application in which a single tool combined drilling, countersinking and counterboring.

Speed and Feed

Speed and feed for counterboring are influenced by the same factors as for drilling and show the same general relations (see page 85 in the article "Drilling"). Table 1 gives nominal speeds and feeds for counterboring carbon and low-alloy steels with high speed steel and carbide tools. These rates can serve as starting points for the selection of optimum machining conditions, based on a tool life of 1 to 2 hr.

Speeds are somewhat lower than for drilling, especially at low work-metal hardness, and feeds are lower in most applications. Speed is governed primarily by the tool material used and by

Table 1. Nominal Speeds and Feeds for Counterboring and Spotfacing of Carbon and Low-Alloy Steels With High Speed Steel and Carbide Tools

		High speed steel tools(b)	Feed, ipr, for tool diameter of:					Carbide tools(c)	Feed, ipr, for tool diameter of:						
Typical steel(a)	Brinell hardness	Speed, sfm	¼ in.	½ in.	1 in.	1½ in.	2 in.	3 in.	Speed, sfm	¼ in.	½ in.	1 in.	1½ in.	2 in.	3 in.
Carbon and Low-Alloy Steels (Except Free-Cutting Grades)															
1020, 1045,	85 to 125 ...	110	0.003	0.004	0.006	0.007	0.007	0.009	370	0.006	0.008	0.011	0.013	0.014	0.016
4140, 7140	125 to 175 ...	90	0.003	0.004	0.006	0.007	0.007	0.009	305	0.006	0.008	0.011	0.013	0.014	0.016
and 8620,	175 to 225 ...	70	0.003	0.0035	0.005	0.005	0.006	0.008	265	0.006	0.007	0.010	0.011	0.012	0.015
at hardness	225 to 275 ...	60	0.002	0.0025	0.003	0.004	0.004	0.006	250	0.004	0.006	0.008	0.009	0.010	0.012
ranges listed	275 to 325 ...	50	0.001	0.002	0.003	0.003	0.0035	0.004	215	0.003	0.004	0.006	0.007	0.007	0.008
at right	325 to 375 ...	45	0.001	0.002	0.003	0.003	0.0035	0.004	180	0.002	0.004	0.006	0.007	0.007	0.008
	375 to 425 ...	30	0.001	0.002	0.003	0.003	0.0035	0.004	140	0.002	0.004	0.006	0.007	0.007	0.008
Free-Cutting Carbon and Low-Alloy Steels															
1112, 1117	100 to 150 ...	120	0.004	0.005	0.007	0.008	0.009	0.011	440	0.008	0.010	0.012	0.014	0.015	0.020
and 12L14	150 to 200 ...	130	0.004	0.005	0.006	0.007	0.008	0.010	490	0.008	0.010	0.012	0.014	0.015	0.020
	200 to 250 ...	85	0.003	0.003	0.004	0.005	0.005	0.008	290	0.006	0.007	0.010	0.011	0.012	0.016
1137	175 to 225 ...	105	0.003	0.004	0.006	0.007	0.007	0.009	395	0.006	0.008	0.011	0.012	0.013	0.015
	275 to 325 ...	70	0.0015	0.002	0.003	0.003	0.004	0.005	270	0.003	0.004	0.006	0.007	0.008	0.010
	325 to 375 ...	45	0.001	0.002	0.003	0.003	0.0035	0.004	180	0.002	0.003	0.005	0.006	0.007	0.008
	375 to 425 ...	30	0.001	0.002	0.003	0.003	0.0035	0.004	140	0.002	0.003	0.005	0.006	0.007	0.008
4140+S	150 to 200 ...	90	0.004	0.005	0.006	0.007	0.008	0.010	320	0.008	0.010	0.012	0.014	0.016	0.020
	200 to 250 ...	70	0.003	0.0035	0.005	0.005	0.006	0.008	290	0.006	0.007	0.010	0.011	0.012	0.014
	275 to 325 ...	50	0.0015	0.002	0.003	0.003	0.004	0.005	225	0.003	0.004	0.006	0.007	0.008	0.010
	375 to 425 ...	30	0.001	0.002	0.003	0.003	0.0035	0.004	140	0.002	0.004	0.006	0.007	0.007	0.008
	R_C 50 to 52 ..	15	0.001	0.002	0.0025	0.0025	0.003	0.003	80	0.002	0.003	0.004	0.004	0.005	0.005
41L40	150 to 200 ...	125	0.004	0.005	0.007	0.008	0.009	0.011	440	0.008	0.010	0.012	0.014	0.016	0.020
	200 to 250 ...	85	0.003	0.003	0.004	0.005	0.005	0.008	290	0.006	0.007	0.010	0.011	0.012	0.016
	275 to 325 ...	60	0.0015	0.002	0.003	0.0035	0.004	0.005	240	0.003	0.004	0.006	0.007	0.008	0.010
	375 to 425 ...	30	0.001	0.002	0.003	0.003	0.0035	0.004	140	0.002	0.003	0.005	0.006	0.007	0.008
	R_C 50 to 52 ..	15	0.001	0.002	0.0025	0.003	0.003	0.003	80	0.002	0.003	0.004	0.004	0.005	0.005

(a) Each steel listed is a frequently used grade in a group of similar steels. For a listing of the steels in the various groups, see Table 2, page 6, in the article "Turning". (b) High speed steels M2 and T5 for carbon and low-alloy steels other than free-cutting grades at hardnesses to 225 Bhn, and for free-cutting grades to 275 Bhn; then high speed steels M2, T5 and T15 to 375 Bhn; above 375 Bhn, high speed steels T15, M41, M42, M43 and M44. (c) Carbide grade C-2. (Data are adapted from tables compiled by Metcut Research Associates, Inc.)

the hardness of the work metal; the presence of free-cutting additives in the work metal exerts a secondary effect. As indicated in Table 1, increasing work-metal hardness calls for the use of progressively lower speeds, except for certain free-cutting grades at hardness below 200 Bhn. Speeds for carbide tools are four to five times those for high speed steel tools in similar operations, and almost all counterboring of steels harder than Rockwell C 52 is done with carbide tools.

Feed is influenced by the same factors as speed, and also by tool diameter. Lower feeds are used on steels of higher hardness, and with tools of smaller diameter. Feeds for carbide tools are about twice those for high speed steel tools in similar operations.

When drilling and counterboring are done simultaneously with a combination tool (as with a subland drill), the diameter of the counterbore must be given primary consideration when selecting speed and feed. This often results in the use of subnormal speed and feed for the smaller-diameter drill portion of the combination tool.

Example of Procedure

The procedures employed in counterboring identical parts with two different types of tools are described in the example that follows. The two procedures used are typical of counterboring relatively small holes.

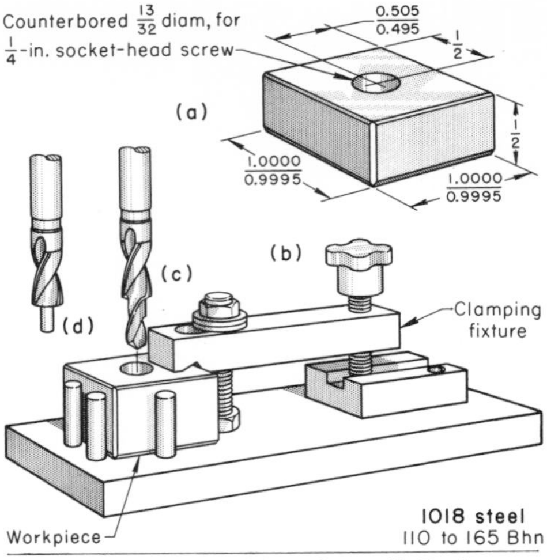

Operating Conditions for Both Tools

Speed	400 rpm (42 sfm)
Feed	0.004 ipr
Cutting fluid	Soluble-oil:water (1:20)
Tool life per grind	100 to 120 pieces

Production Rate per Hour

With combination tool	96 pieces
With separate tools	60 pieces

Workpiece (a), held as shown in (b), was drilled and counterbored in one operation with a subland drill (c), or in two operations with a drill and the piloted counterbore shown in (d).

Fig. 2. Counterboring with separate vs combination tools (Example 211)

Example 211. Combination vs Separate Tools (Fig. 2)

A three-spindle, floor-type vertical drill press with power feed was used for drilling and counterboring the small 1018 steel workpiece, shown in Fig. 2(a), to accommodate a ¼-in. socket-head screw (13⁄32-in. counterbore diameter). Two different procedures, employing different types of tools, were used.

In one procedure, the part was drilled and counterbored in a single operation, with a subland drill. After being centerpunched to locate the hole, the part was clamped to the table of the drill press as shown in Fig. 2(b). The point of the subland drill (Fig. 2c) was manually brought into contact with the part, and light pressure was applied to begin the cutting action — after which machine feeding was begun. A start or spot drill was not required. The baseplate of the clamping fixture was relieved to permit drill breakthrough.

In the other procedure, two tools were used, with quick-change chucks and the same machine and fixtures. The part was drilled with a standard twist drill and then was counterbored with a piloted drill. The counterboring tool was made from a standard drill by radial grinding of the flutes to form the pilot, and then recessing the portion of the pilot adjacent to the full diameter of the tool as shown in Fig. 2(d). Because of the tool changes involved, this procedure was more time-consuming than the single-operation, single-tool method, but it can be successfully used when special tools are not available.

Operating conditions and a comparison of production rates for the two procedures are given in the table accompanying Fig. 2.

Spotfacing

SPOTFACING is a machining operation for producing a flat seat for a bolt head, washer, nut or similar element at the opening of a drilled hole, concentric with the hole and at right angles to its longitudinal axis. Spotfacing usually follows drilling, either in combination with it in a single operation or as a separate operation. Sometimes, however, spotfacing precedes drilling, to provide a contoured workpiece with a flat surface so as to facilitate centering and starting of the drilled hole, which will then be at 90° to the spotface.

Spotfacing is similar to counterboring, except that the spotfaced surface is always at right angles to the axis of the hole, and depth of cut in spotfacing is shallower than in counterboring.

Machines used for spotfacing are the same as those used for drilling. These machines are described in the article "Drilling", page 75 in this volume.

Tools

Many tools used for spotfacing are the same as those used for counterboring (several are illustrated and described in the article "Counterboring", in this volume). There are, however, tools designed primarily for spotfacing and seldom used for counterboring. Examples are back spotfacers and double-end spotfacers (Fig. 1).

Back spotfacers (Fig. 1a) are used when the shape of the part makes it impractical to use the down stroke of the spindle (see Example 213). The tool driver is held in the spindle and inserted through the predrilled hole; then the spotfacer is loaded and locked on the driver shaft, and the spindle is rotated and fed upward into the workpiece.

Double-end spotfacers (Fig. 1b) permit spotfacing and back spotfacing to be done on two internal surfaces without removing the cutter.

Back or double-end spotfacers can be secured to the driver shaft by means of one or more setscrews. This makes it easy to reposition the spotfacer on the shaft. A disadvantage of this method is that setscrews are likely to loosen. At least two proprietary devices are available for securing spotfacers to driver shafts; one of these employs the principle of a locking pin, and the other is designed with a cam lock.

Speed and Feed

Speed and feed for spotfacing are the same as for counterboring. Nominal speeds and feeds are given in Table 1 on page 103, and the discussion of speed and feed in the article "Counterboring" applies also to spotfacing. Speed and feed for spotfacing, however, often are less critical than for counterboring, because depth of cut is less in spotfacing.

Cutting Fluids

Cutting fluids provide the same benefits in spotfacing as in drilling, counterboring and related operations. However, because depth of cut is relatively shallow in spotfacing, cutting fluids are less necessary than in related machining operations, and much spotfacing is done without cutting fluid.

Examples of Procedure

Most spotfacing operations are simple to perform. Problems sometimes arise with cylindrical or odd-shaped workpieces; likewise, access to a surface to be spotfaced may prove difficult.

Details of the equipment and techniques used in two such production applications of spotfacing are given in the examples that follow. See also Example

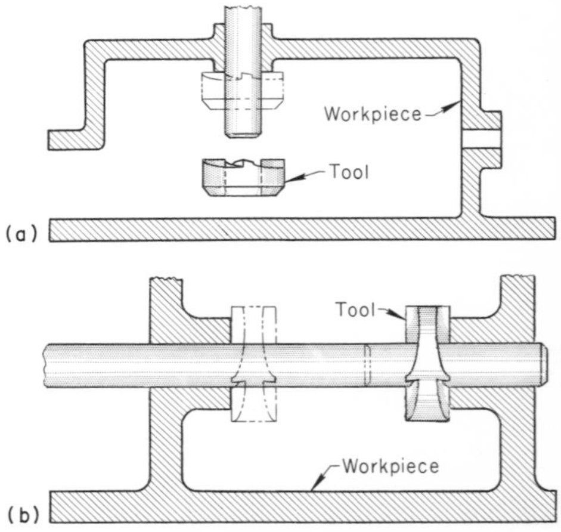

Fig. 1. Functions of (a) *back spotfacer, and* (b) *double-end spotfacer*

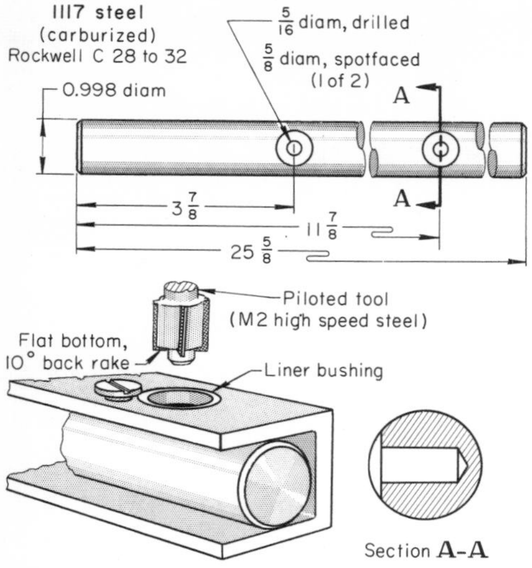

Speed	225 rpm (37 sfm)
Feed	0.007 ipr
Depth of spotface	⅛ in. max
Cutting fluid	Sulfurized oil
Tool life per grind	50 pieces (100 holes)
Production rate(a)	18 pieces per 50-min "hour"
Setup time	48 min
Spotfacing time per piece (2 holes)	0.15 min
Total time per piece(a)	2.75 min

(a) Drilling and spotfacing

Fig. 2. Spotfacing a round bar with a jig and a cutter piloted by a drilled hole (Example 212)

892 in the article that deals with machining of aluminum alloys.

Example 212. Spotfacing on a Small Diameter (Fig. 2)

A vertical hand-feed drill press was used for drilling and spotfacing the two holes in the 1117 steel bar shown in the upper half of Fig. 2, prior to tapping. For drilling and spotfacing, the bar was held in a jig constructed of 2-in. channel of U-shaped cross section, as shown in the lower half of Fig. 2. The jig was fitted with press-fit liner bushings. A slip renewable drill bushing was inserted in the liner bushing for the drilling operation, and was then removed to permit entry of the spotfacing tool. The spotfacing tool was piloted by the drilled hole. Additional details are given in the table accompanying Fig. 2.

Example 213. Back Spotfacing (Fig. 3)

A horizontal floor-type boring mill with a stationary floor plate was used to machine a base made of low-carbon steel (upper sketch, Fig. 3). The bottom surface of the base was milled, after which two jackscrew holes were drilled and tapped in each of four areas of the base (lower sketch in Fig. 3). One of each pair of holes was drilled to a diameter of 1 in., after which it was spotfaced to a diameter of 2 in. to provide a seat for a washer.

For conventional spotfacing, a tool of impractical length would have been required in order to reach the area to be spotfaced. Therefore, the most practical method was to back spotface, driving the cutting tool from the opposite side. A tool similar to the one shown in Fig. 1(a) was used. It was made of M2 high speed steel, and had a flat bottom and a 12° back rake angle. Operating conditions are tabulated with Fig. 3.

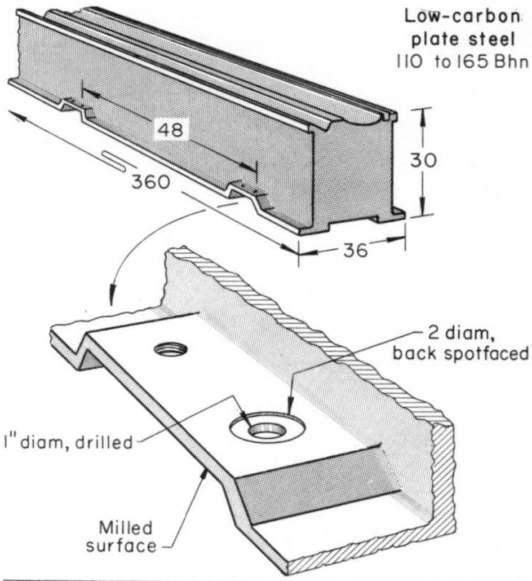

Speed	74 rpm (39 sfm)
Feed	0.008 ipr
Depth of spotface	⅛ in. max
Cutting fluid	None
Spotfacer life per grind	75 to 80 holes

Operation Times per Hole

Positioning spindle	0.50 min
Spotfacing	0.21
Inserting and removing tool	0.45
Total	1.16 min

Fig. 3. Machine base that was back spotfaced for seating of washers (Example 213)

Roller Burnishing

ROLLER BURNISHING is a method of improving finish and dimensional accuracy, and work hardening a surface, by pressure rolling without removing metal. By this process, hole diameters can be increased by 0.0005 to 0.002 in. (or even 0.005 in., for 5-in.-diam holes) without damage to the surface. Size increase, however, usually is a secondary objective, primary aims being improved accuracy and finish, and work-hardened surfaces.

In addition to the finishing of inside cylindrical surfaces, roller burnishing is applicable to the finishing of tapered holes and to outside cylindrical surfaces and circular flat surfaces.

Machines suited to roller burnishing include drill presses, lathes, boring machines and automatic bar or chucking machines.

Roller burnishing is sometimes used instead of reaming, but it is most often used to supplement reaming or boring. The process is applicable to metals softer than about Rockwell C 40. However, metals that work harden rapidly must be at lower hardness before roller burnishing than plain carbon steel or other steels that work harden slowly. Roller burnishing increases surface hardness to a depth of 0.005 to 0.030 in.

Workpiece Requirements

The workpiece must have wall thickness great enough to withstand the pressure exerted by the rollers; if the wall is too thin, the workpiece will expand, defeating the purpose of the process. Also, if thinwall parts vary significantly in wall thickness, roller burnishing may produce a wavy surface and taper or out-of-roundness.

Workpieces with walls as thin as 1/16 in. can be successfully roller burnished; but for walls this thin, supporting fixtures should be used and size increase should not exceed 0.0003 in. on the diameter.

For best results in roller burnishing, the hole must be round and straight; the burnishing tool will not correct deviations from roundness or straightness.

Stock Allowance. Recommended stock allowances for holes to be roller burnished are given in Table 1. Note that stock allowance depends on hole diameter, varying by a factor of five or more as hole diameter increases from 3/16 to about 2½ in.

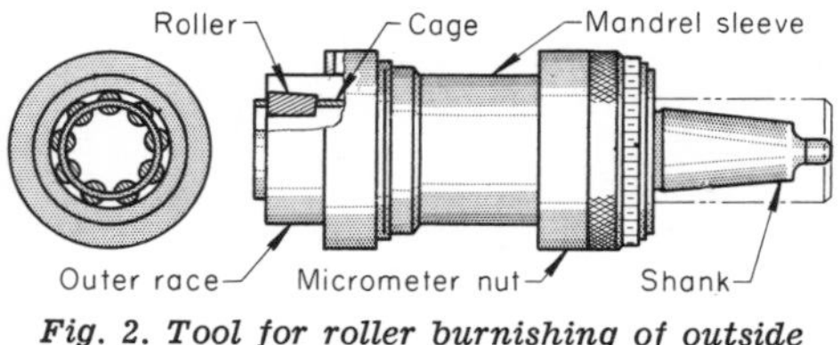

Fig. 2. Tool for roller burnishing of outside cylindrical surfaces

Tools

Tools for roller burnishing are illustrated in Fig. 1, 2, 3 and 4. The tool shown in Fig. 1, for roller burnishing of inside cylindrical surfaces, can be adjusted to accommodate a range of diameters, in increments as small as 0.0005 in. Outside cylindrical surfaces are roller burnished by means of a tool like the one shown in Fig. 2.

Tools of the types illustrated in Fig. 1 and 2 that are 0.468 in. or smaller in diameter can be adjusted to 0.003 in.

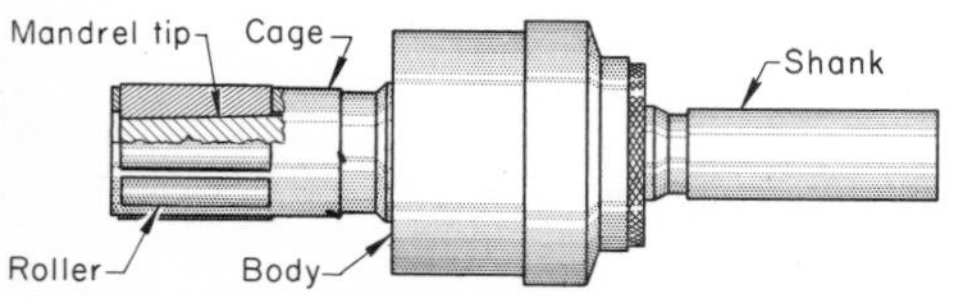

Fig. 1. Tool for roller burnishing of inside cylindrical surfaces

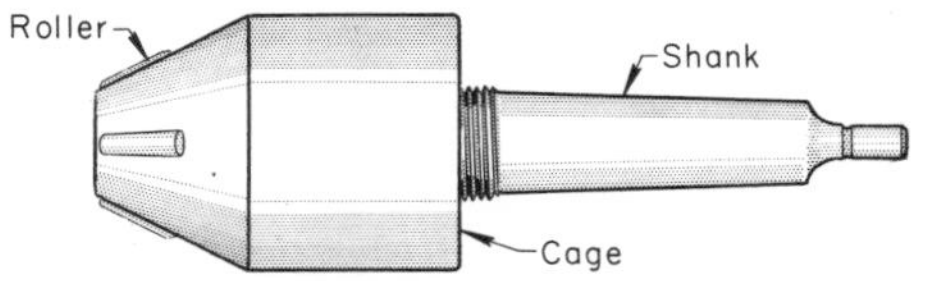

Fig. 3. Tool for roller burnishing of tapered holes

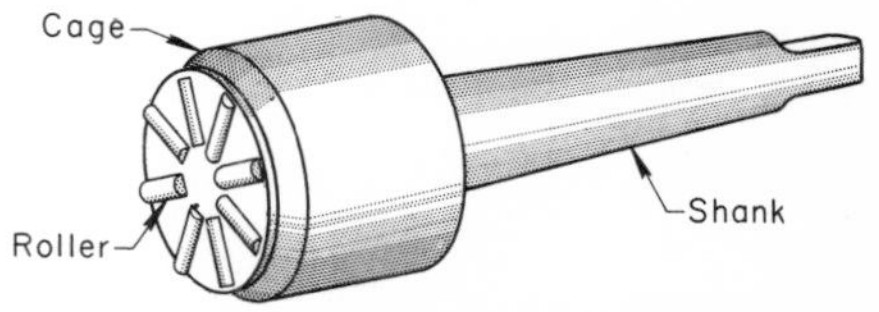

Fig. 4. Tool for roller burnishing of circular flat surfaces

above or 0.017 in. below each 1/64-in. size. Tools 0.500 in. or larger in diameter can be adjusted to 0.004 in. above or 0.037 in. below each 1/32-in. size.

The tool shown in Fig. 3 is used for roller burnishing of tapered holes. It is not adjustable or self-feeding, and pressure is exerted by the machine spindle.

To roller burnish circular flat surfaces as small as 3/8 in. in diameter, a tool like the one shown in Fig. 4 is used. This tool also is not adjustable, and pressure is exerted by the machine spindle.

Tolerance and Finish

Roller burnishing usually can work to tolerances with a total variation of 0.0005 in., and even closer tolerances may be obtained under closely controlled conditions.

Bores having an initial finish of 100 to 125 micro-in. have been roller burnished in a single pass to a finish of 2 to 15 micro-in., depending on the workpiece metal. Results obtained on specific metals are: 2 to 8 micro-in. on bronze and aluminum; 4 to 8 on steel; and 10 to 15 on cast iron. The finish typically obtained in boring or from an end-cutting reamer is preferred for roller burnishing.

Speed, Feed and Lubrication

Speed and feed for roller burnishing vary with the diameter being finished, but are not critical. Satisfactory results are obtained at speeds of 60 to 150 sfm and feeds of 0.005 ipr, for small diameters, to 0.200 ipr for large (up to 5 in.). Typical spindle speeds and feeds for various inside and outside diameters are given in Table 2.

Lubrication. Little heat is generated in roller burnishing. Enough lubrication is provided by applying a few drops (as from a squirt can) of a light spindle oil, or of a relatively rich soluble oil (mixed 1 to 10 with water), to each roller before the tool burnishes a hole.

Examples of Procedure

The two examples that follow describe techniques and conditions used in the roller burnishing of castings made of aluminum and magnesium alloys.

Example 214. In-Line Hole (Fig. 5)

Roller burnishing was used for sizing one of two in-line holes in a 356-T6 aluminum-alloy casting (Fig. 5). Both holes had been reamed to 0.625/0.624 in. in diameter. In a 2-hp single-spindle drill press, an adjustable burnishing tool was then used for sizing the top hole to 0.6255/0.6250 in. Burnishing was selected because it provided more accurate size control than reaming. Tool details and operating conditions are given with Fig. 5.

Example 215. Three 2.376-In.-Diam Cylinder Bores (Fig. 6)

Figure 6 shows a brake housing, cast from AZ92A magnesium alloy, in which the walls of three 2.376-in.-diam cylinder bores were roller burnished to a diametral tolerance of ±0.0008 in. and a 15-micro-in. finish. These bores had been machined undersize to a diametral tolerance of 0.001 to 0.0015 in. and a 60-micro-in. finish.

For roller burnishing, the housing was clamped, bore side up, to the fixture base with L-type clamps as shown in Fig. 6. The burnishing tool contained a series of hardened, tapered rollers that rode on a mandrel tapered inversely to the taper of the rollers. The tool had a No. 4 ASA tapered shank and was driven by a spindle of an automatic hydraulic turret-type drill press. Operating conditions are listed in the table below Fig. 6.

Table 1. Recommended Stock Allowances for Roller Burnishing

Hole diameter, in.	Stock allowance on diameter, in.
0.187 to 0.500	0.00067
0.531 to 0.968	0.001
1.000 to 1.750	0.0015
1.781 to 2.500	0.002
2.531 and larger	0.003 to 0.006

Table 2. Typical Speeds and Feeds for Roller Burnishing

Hole diameter, in.	Speed, rpm(a)	Feed, ipr
Inside Diameters		
0.187 to 0.500	1200 to 600	0.005 to 0.015
0.500 to 1.000	600 to 400	0.015 to 0.020
1.000 to 1.750	400 to 325	0.020 to 0.030
1.750 to 2.500	325 to 140	0.030 to 0.050
2.500 to 5.000	140 to 100	0.050 to 0.200
Outside Diameters		
0.125 to 0.500	450	0.005 to 0.025
0.500 to 1.000	400	0.025 to 0.040
1.000 to 2.000	250	0.040 to 0.060
2.000 to 3.000	200	0.060 to 0.080
3.000 to 4.000	150	0.080 to 0.100
4.000 to 5.000	100	0.100

(a) Speeds may be increased or decreased 30%.

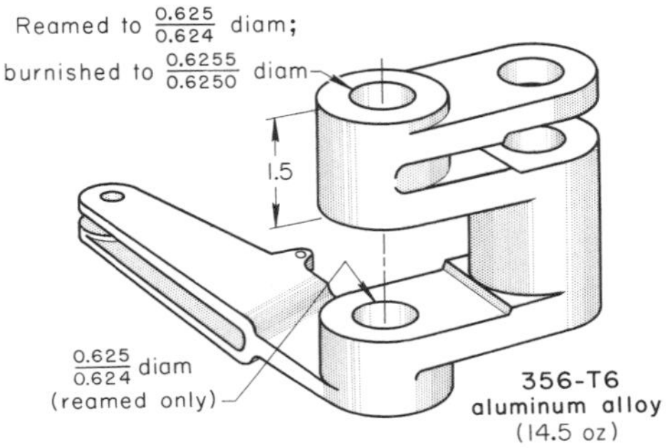

Details of Burnishing Tool

Number of rollers	5
Diameter of rollers	0.180 in.
Tool size	0.662/0.621 in.
Tool setting	0.6256 in.

Operating Conditions

Speed	420 rpm (69 sfm)
Feed	0.012 ipr
Cycle time	0.01 hr

Fig. 5. Casting in which an in-line hole was sized by roller burnishing (Example 214)

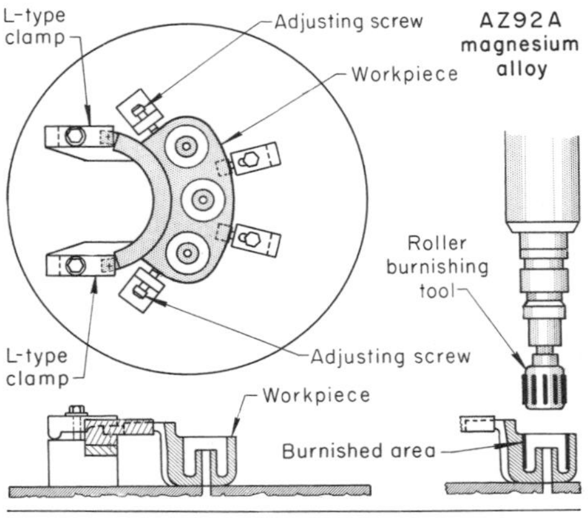

Speed	435 rpm (270 sfm)
Feed	0.100 ipr
Cutting fluid	SAE 20 oil:kerosine (1:1)
Downtime for changing tools	12 min
Tool life (average)	10,000 bores

Fig. 6. Roller burnishing cylinder bores in a magnesium brake housing (Example 215)

Fillet Rolling

Improved resistance to fatigue is the purpose of fillet rolling, a specialized operation that uses a narrow roller of required shape. The rolling and pressing cause combined rolling and sliding (lubrication is used). Forces are not large; for example, a fillet of 1/32-in. radius can usually be rolled with a force of 100 lb or less, in ten revolutions (passes) around the fillet. A plain roller of oil-hardening tool steel at Rockwell C 62 to 65 can roll fillets on several thousand pieces at low cost.

Simultaneous Burnishing and Peening

In a modification of roller burnishing known as bearingizing, metal surfaces are finished by combined rolling and peening action. In this process, hardened rollers rotating around and bearing on cams (Fig. 7) rise and fall rapidly, delivering as many as 200,000 blows per minute. This action produces a smooth surface, improves roundness and straightness, and increases surface hardness to a depth of 0.005 to 0.015 in. Inside surfaces of tubes 10 to 20 ft long have been successfully processed by this method. In most applications, however, bore length is relatively short (less than three times diameter).

Tools. Three basic styles of tools for finishing of bores are illustrated in Fig. 8. Choice of style depends on whether the hole is through or blind and, for blind holes, on how close to the bottom finishing is required. The bottoming tool shown in Fig. 8 can finish to 0.030 in. from the bottom of a blind hole. Two styles of cams are also available (Fig. 7); the steep-rise cam is used in thin-wall parts.

Taper-shank tools are available from stock in diameters of 3/16 to 1 in., in 1/32-in. increments. Over-all length and working length (distance from the leading end of the tool to the beginning of the taper shank) vary proportionately, from 2 15/16 in. for the 3/16-in.-diam tool, to 6 in. for the 1-in.-diam tool. Number and size of rollers also vary with diameter; for instance, the 3/16-in.-diam tool has six rollers, whereas the 1-in.-diam tool has 12.

Tools are available on special order in diameters up to 12 in. However, sizes larger than 8 in. in diameter are seldom used. A tool can be adjusted in a total range of about 0.004 in. by changing rollers. Rollers are available in increments of 0.0001 in. Because the rollers are diametrically opposed, the tool can be adjusted in increments of 0.0002 in.

Tolerance and Finish. Bores commonly are finished to tolerances of ±0.0001 in. per inch of diameter by the combined roller burnishing-peening process. Notable examples are piston-pin bores, which are finished to a total tolerance of 0.0002 in. However, such parts must be finished to close tolerances in a prior operation, because the total expansion for holes less than 1 in. in diameter is only about 0.0005 in. (except holes in thin-wall tubing, which

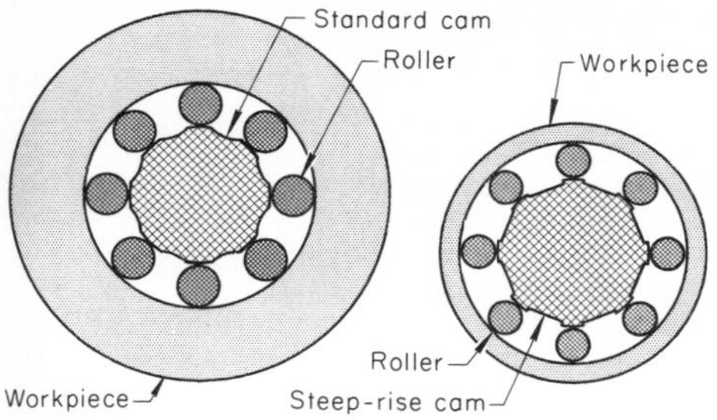

Fig. 7. Cross sections of roller burnishing-peening tools in workpieces, showing how rollers ride over cams

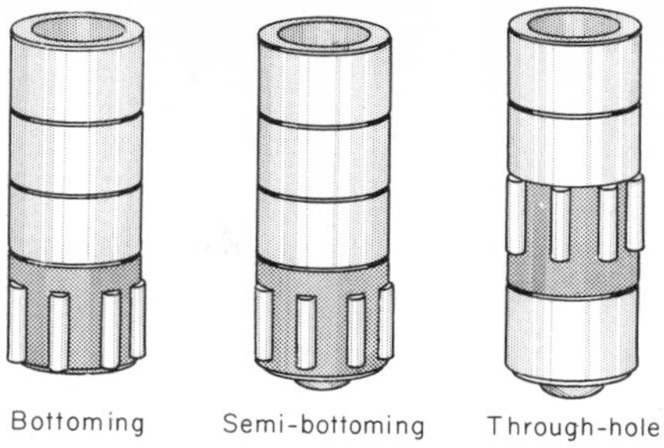

Fig. 8. Roller burnishing-peening tools for finishing through and blind holes

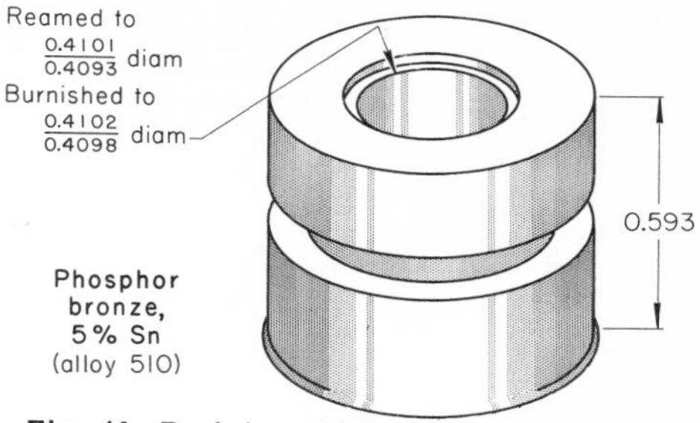

Fig. 10. Part in which hole was sized to close tolerance by roller burnishing-peening (Example 217)

can be expanded several thousandths of an inch). For holes larger than 1 in. in diameter, a total expansion of 0.001 in. is normal. Hole straightness depends largely on prior operations.

The preferred prior surface is one produced by a single-point tool (as in boring) to a roughness of 80 to 120 micro-in. Starting with this roughness, most metals can be finished to about 5 micro-in. For porous metals (such as sintered bronze), however, the resulting finish is likely to be nearer 12 micro-in.

Speed and Feed. Neither speed nor feed is critical. Speeds of 300 to 500 sfm have proved satisfactory. Because the operation is done in one quick pass, feed rate is difficult to measure, but 150 to 250 in. per min is normal.

Little time is required per hole; for example, a hole 3 in. deep is finished in slightly over 1 sec. Indexing of the workpiece usually requires more time than the actual operation.

Lubrication is seldom necessary, but tools should be cleaned frequently with a light oil having a viscosity of about 100 SUS (spindle oil is often used). Only

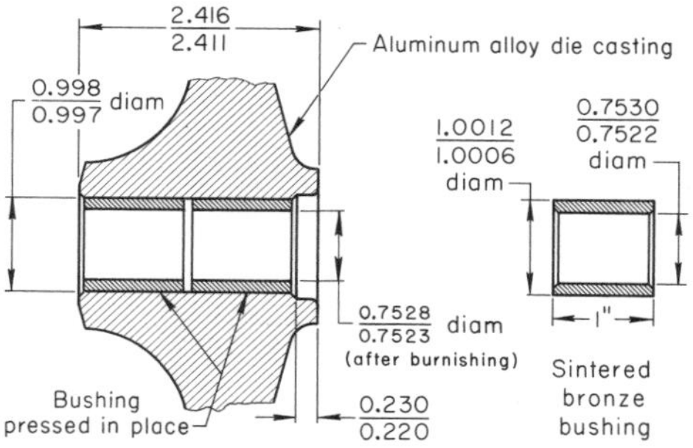

Fig. 9. Casting in which pressed-in bronze bushings were finished to +0.0005, −0.0000 in. by roller burnishing-peening (Example 216)

a few drops applied with a squirt can or a brush are necessary to get oil into the roller cage. Centrifugal force then washes out metal particles or dust.

Examples of Procedure. The two examples that follow describe typical practice as applied to copper-alloy parts. The roller burnishing-peening process is especially well-suited to copper alloys, because of their low hardness and high ductility.

Example 216. Sintered Bronze Bushings (Fig. 9)

Aluminum die castings were rough and finish bored to 0.998/0.997 in., for a length of about 2¼ in. Sintered bronze bushings were then pressed into both ends of the bore. These bushings, which served as bearings, were 1 in. long, thus allowing about ¼ in. between the bushings after assembly (Fig. 9). The bushings (bearings) were then subjected to the action of a roller burnishing-peening tool rotated at 1500 rpm (approximately 300 sfm). A through bore accurate within 0.0005 in. was obtained.

Example 217. Phosphor Bronze, 5% Sn (Fig. 10)

The 0.4102/0.4098-in.-diam through hole in the part shown in Fig. 10 was machined in four operations on a 1¼-in. six-spindle automatic bar machine at a spindle speed of 441 rpm (47 sfm max). The hole was drilled and then bored to maintain concentricity. Reaming the hole to the close-tolerance (±0.0002 in.) final size would have seriously curtailed tool life. Instead, the hole was reamed to 0.4101/0.4093-in. diameter with a reamer having a 20° lead angle, and was then finished with a roller burnishing-peening tool to the tolerance specified and an 8-micro-in. finish.

Tapping

*By the ASM Committee on Tapping and Threading**

TAPPING is a machining process for producing internal threads. A tap is a cylindrical or conical thread-cutting tool having threads of a desired form on the periphery. Combining rotary with axial motion, the tap cuts or forms the internal thread.

Most metals that can be machined with single-point tools can be tapped, but the cost of tapping usually rises sharply as the hardness of the work metal increases beyond Rockwell C 25. Although steel as hard as Rockwell C 52 can be tapped, efficiency is low and cost is high.

Threads as fine as 360 threads per inch in 0.0132-in.-diam holes, or as coarse as three per inch in 24-in.-diam pipe fittings are tapped routinely.

Machines

The machines most commonly used for tapping are drill presses, tapping machines, gang machines, manual or automatic turret lathes, and other multiple-operation machines.

Drill Presses. When no other machining operations are involved, drill presses are often used for tapping, because they are easily set up and simple to operate.

When a solid tap is used, the drill press must be provided with a tapping head, because the spindle cannot be stopped quickly or precisely enough to hold specified depth tolerance, and is not easily reversed to allow the tap to be removed from the workpiece. With a tapping head, movement of the feeding lever is stopped at a predetermined point; the tapping head then automatically stops the rotation of the tap. Upward movement of the control lever causes the tapping head to reverse and spin the tap out of the hole.

With a collapsible tap, a tapping head is not required. The tap penetrates the work to a predetermined point where it automatically collapses and retracts from the work, letting the spindle return without stopping or reversing.

*J. J. CLATT, *Chairman,* Superintendent – Hydraulic Factory, Joliet Works, Caterpillar Tractor Co.; ALLAN W. BATH, Vice President – Manufacturing, John Bath & Co.; EUGENE K. CHAPMAN, Chief Engineer, Hy-Pro Tool Co.

JOHN A. COOK, Chief Metallurgist, National Machine Products Co. Div., Standard Pressed Steel Co.; FOREST CROW, Supervisor, Manufacturing Engineering, Aro Corp.; D. R. EDWARDS, Manufacturing Engineer, Henry Vogt Machine Co., Inc.; GEORGE O. FREPAN (deceased), formerly with Propulsion Controls Processing, Bendix Products Aerospace Div., Bendix Corp.; WALTER KINNAL, Chief Engineer, Threading Tools Div., National Acme Co.

HAL MORTUS, Manufacturing Specialist, National Screw & Manufacturing Co.; H. N. MYERS, Assistant General Superintendent, Grinnel Corp.; CECIL SASHER, Chief Engineer, Cutting Tool Div., National Automatic Tool Co., Inc.; HAROLD J. SLAIGHT, Senior Engineer, Omaha Works, Western Electric Co., Inc.

Table 1. Processing Details for Example 218

Tap Details	
Material	High speed steel
Size	½–13 UNC–2B
Number of flutes	3
Helix angle	30° (right-hand helix)
Hook angle	5°
Type of chamfer	Plug
Number of lead threads	5
Operating Conditions	
Speed	150 rpm (20 sfm)
Feed	0.077 ipr
Cutting fluid	Sulfurized oil

Drill presses can be provided with lead-control devices (discussed at the end of this section), to regulate tap travel. However, when lead control is required, tapping machines ordinarily are used rather than drill presses.

Single-spindle tapping machines are operated by a foot control that allows the operator free use of both hands for loading and unloading work. The simpler models have no lead control but depend on the screw action of the tap in the hole to govern feed.

In a hydraulically driven machine without lead control, axially floated spindles or holders compensate for differences between the feed of the machine and the lead of the tap. An uncontrolled hydraulic feed will not maintain a stable feed rate, and might tear threads.

Multiple-spindle tapping machines are for high-volume production. All spindles (some machines have 25 or more) are rotated by a common power source. With these machines, holes of different sizes can be tapped simultaneously. Spindles having axial float can compensate for differences between the lead of the tap and the feed of the spindle. Thus, different thread pitches can be tapped simultaneously in the same machine.

Gang machines permit in-line drilling, reaming and tapping operations, much as in multiple-spindle drilling. Although gang machines are intended and used primarily for high production, their ease of setup often makes them practical for tapping small quantities.

Manual turret lathes are used for tapping small production lots. Turret lathes are generally more accurate than machines that rotate the tap instead of the workpiece. Moreover, in a turret lathe, tapping can be combined with other operations; thus, on the same machine the holes can be drilled, bored, reamed and tapped. This permits the use of higher tapping speed and results in longer tap life than is possible when the holes are less accurate.

A lead-control device is almost mandatory when tapping on a turret lathe, because the mass of the turret decreases the "feel" the operator needs for controlling feed by hand.

Automatic Turret Lathes and Bar or Chucking Machines. Tapping can often be included in a sequence of operations in an automatic turret lathe or in a single-spindle or multiple-spindle bar or chucking machine. However, because of the relatively long setup time required for these machines, they are usually efficient only for large production lots. Moreover, tapping efficiency may depend on the number of other operations that can be incorporated in the automatic sequence; some machines can perform 25 operations per piece.

All automatic turret lathes, bar machines and chucking machines use lead-control devices for regulating the feed.

Lead-control devices provide a positive axial movement of the tap into the hole at a rate that suits the pitch of the threads being tapped. This method of feeding the tap into the work produces less deformation of the threads than manual control.

A typical lead control is shown in Fig. 1. A driving pinion, keyed to the main drive shaft, drives a gear keyed to the lead-screw shaft. The lead screw passes through the lead-screw nut, which is fastened to the stationary housing. When the main drive shaft rotates, it turns the lead-screw shaft. The rotation of the lead screw within the lead-screw nut causes the assembly to travel up or down at a speed regulated by the lead screw. This controlled action, transmitted to the chuck, drives the tap into the workpiece at a controlled rate. At the end of the stroke, when the tap has penetrated the workpiece to the desired depth, the direction of shaft rotation is reversed, and the lead-control mechanism backs the tap out of the tapped hole.

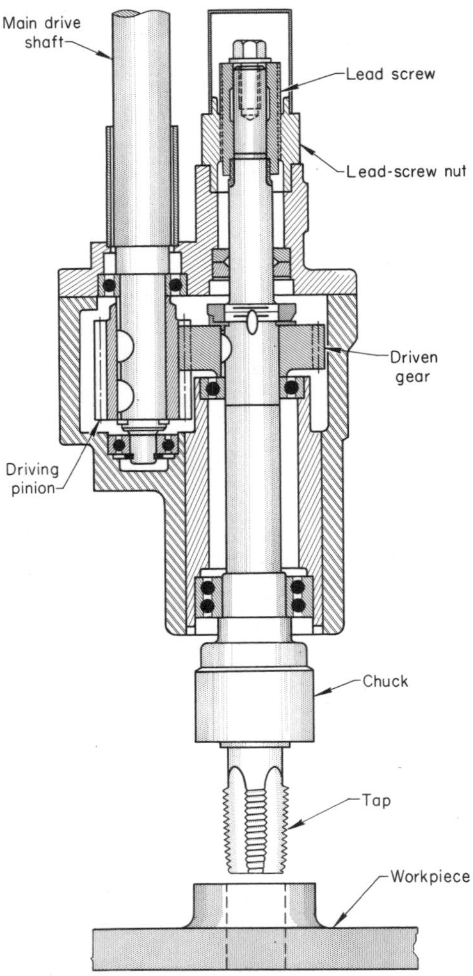

Fig. 1. Lead-screw mechanism for control of tap feed. See text for discussion.

Two disadvantages of lead control in tapping are:

1 The need to return to the starting point to begin each cycle, and to stop rotation between cycles, may lengthen the tapping cycle. (For example, when using a collapsible tap, it would be possible to retract the tap more rapidly from the workpiece without lead control.)
2 Changing taps for different thread sizes consumes more time when lead control is used, because the feed-controlling members in the mechanism must be changed also. The additional time required may increase cost in short-run tapping where changing of thread pitch is frequent.

Machine Selection

Selection of the appropriate machine for a tapping operation is based on:

1 Size of the workpiece
2 Shape of the workpiece
3 Production quantity
4 Tolerance
5 Specified finish
6 Number of related operations
7 Cost.

The four examples that follow describe applications in which machine selection (or reselection) was dictated by special requirements.

Examples 218 and 219. Use of Multiple-Spindle Machines for Simultaneous Tapping of Several Holes

Example 218 (Table 1). Because of high volume requirements, a multiple-spindle tapper was selected for tapping ½–13 UNC–2B threads in ten 1-in.-deep holes in the flange of a valve forged from 1030 steel. The machine was set up to tap the ten holes simultaneously. Tap details and operating conditions are given in Table 1.

Example 219 (Table 2). A 12-spindle tapper was selected for tapping class 2B threads in 12 holes simultaneously in rectangular bars of 1020 steel at a hardness between 160 and 190 Bhn. All holes had been drilled through the 0.375-in.-thick bars, but the tapped holes varied in depth and thread size: six holes were tapped to a depth of 0.300 in., two with 6–40 threads and four with 5–44 threads; the other six holes were tapped through (0.375-in. depth), with 5–44 threads. The

Table 2. Processing Details for Example 219

Tap Details	
Material	High speed steel
Size	6–40 and 5–44
Number of flutes	2
Flute-helix angle	0°
Hook angle	5°
Type of chamfer	Plug, with spiral point
Number of lead threads	4
Operating Conditions	
Speed, 6–40 taps	611 rpm (22 sfm)
Speed, 5–44 taps	611 rpm (20 sfm)
Feed, 6–40 taps	0.025 ipr
Feed, 5–44 taps	0.0227 ipr
Cutting fluid	Sulfurized oil
Production rate	72 pieces per hour

Table 3. Processing Details for Example 220

Tap Details	
Material	High speed steel
Size	10–24 UNC–2B
Number of flutes	2
Flute-helix angle	0°
Hook angle	5°
Type of chamfer	Plug, with spiral point
Number of lead threads	4
Operating Conditions	
Speed	1000 rpm (50 sfm)
Feed	0.0416 ipr
Cutting fluid	Sulfurized oil
Production rate	300 pieces per hour

different leads were possible because the spindles were mounted to float axially.

Special equipment included a work table fed by hydraulic power. Such a table minimizes shock during rapid cycling. Tool details and operating conditions are listed in Table 2.

Example 220. Effective Application of a Reversing-Spindle Tapper (Table 3)

Because collapsible taps are not practical for holes smaller than 1¼ in. in diameter, a single-spindle tapping machine with a reversing spindle was selected to through-tap 10–24 UNC–2B threads in a ¼-in.-thick part of cold-drawn 1144 steel. In this machine, the spindle was driven by one or the other of oppositely rotating friction clutches selected for quick response to a reversing signal. A limit switch automatically reversed clutch engagement for withdrawal when the spindle reached the desired bottom position. Tool details and operating conditions are given in Table 3.

Example 221. Multiple-Spindle Automatic vs Nonstandard Tapper

Originally, an old tapping machine was used for producing double left-hand threads (5⁄16–12, 60° stub) in the stems of bronze or stainless steel valves. Four-flute taps with 0° rake, thread relief, and a three-thread chamfer were used. However, this old machine required taps with nonstandard shanks and other special features that increased tool cost.

As the result of a job analysis, a much newer multiple-spindle machine was substituted for the old tapper. The new machine could use three-flute taps (15° spiral point, 4° hook) with standard shanks. The change reduced tool cost 20% and increased production rate from 300 to 720 pieces per hour.

Tap Classification

On the basis of their construction, taps are classified into seven categories:

1 Solid taps
2 Shell taps
3 Sectional taps
4 Expansion taps
5 Inserted-chaser taps
6 Adjustable taps
7 Collapsible taps.

The seven sections that follow describe the design and function of taps in these categories.

Solid Taps

Solid taps are one-piece taps, usually made of high speed steel but sometimes of carbon tool steel or of carbide. Solid taps are of two basic types, straight thread and taper thread. Straight thread taps make threads that do not vary in pitch diameter; taper-thread taps make threads with a uniform reduction in pitch diameter from thread to thread (pipe threads). Standard nomenclature for details of solid taps is given in Fig. 2. Most solid taps have flutes and chamfer.

Flutes. Taps have flutes for three reasons: to provide cutting edges, to provide chip clearance and a means of chip control and to conduct fluid to the cutting sections of the tap.

Taps may have straight flutes or spiral flutes, or a combination of both. Taps with straight flutes are the most commonly used, because they are more easily made and sharpened than spiral-flute taps, and because they perform satisfactorily under many conditions.

Chamfer. Solid taps have three types of chamfer:

Taper chamfer (7 to 9 threads)
Plug chamfer (3 to 5 threads)
Bottoming chamfer (1 to 1½ threads).

Taper chamfer (Fig. 3a) distributes the cutting load over the greatest number of threads and permits easiest starting of the tap into the workpiece. Thus, taper-chamfer taps are especially suited for tapping difficult-to-machine metals. However, taper-chamfer taps are seldom suitable for blind holes (too much of the hole is left unthreaded). They also require longer travel than other types to produce full threads in through holes.

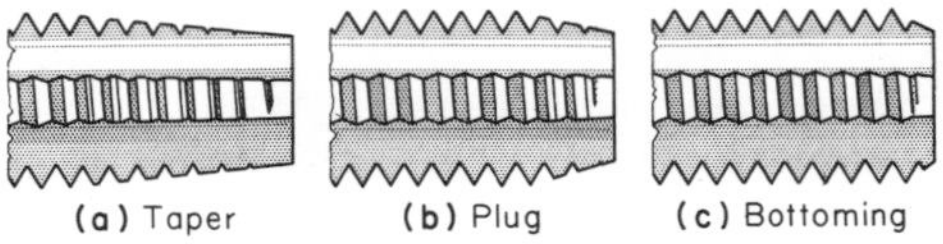

Fig. 3. Chamfers for solid taps

Plug chamfer (Fig. 3b) is the most commonly used type. Taps with plug chamfer are not required to penetrate a hole as deeply as taps with taper chamfer to produce a given length of thread; thus they produce at a slightly higher rate. Except in the difficult-to-machine metals, a plug-chamfer tap enters the hole with reasonable ease. If sufficient clearance can be provided, plug-chamfer taps are used successfully in blind-hole tapping.

Bottoming chamfer (Fig. 3c) usually is used only for blind holes. When tapping a blind hole in a difficult-to-machine metal, it is common practice to tap as deeply as possible with a taper-chamfer tap or a plug-chamfer tap (or sometimes with both, successively), and then to use a bottoming-chamfer tap to finish tapping to the required depth. This practice reduces the time that the 1 to 1½ cutting threads in a bottoming chamfer are under maximum stress.

Basic styles of solid taps generally in use are: standard hand taps, spiral-point taps and spiral-flute taps. Each style is described below:

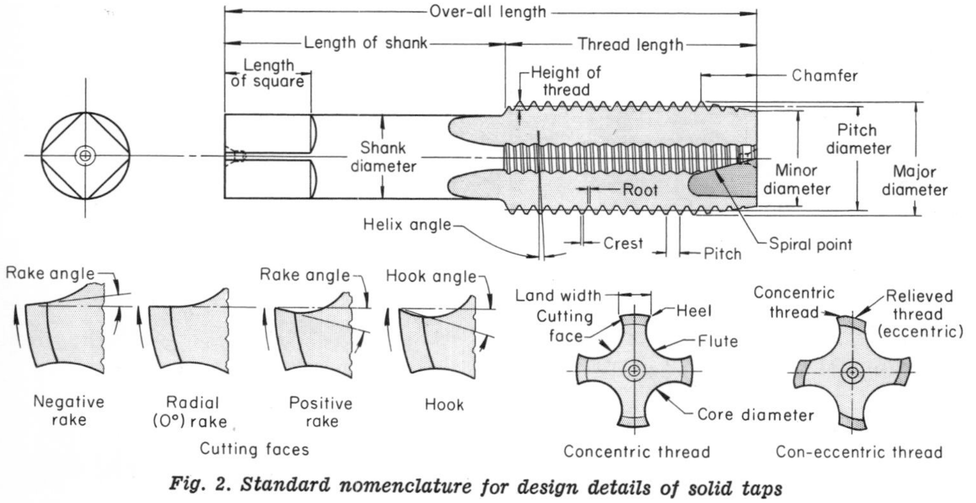

Fig. 2. Standard nomenclature for design details of solid taps

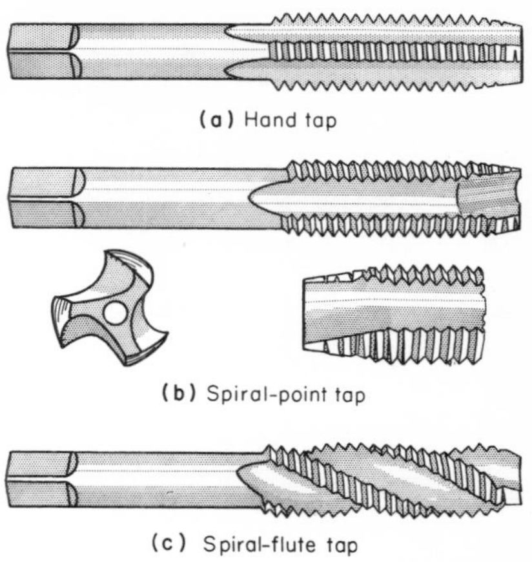

Fig. 4. Three basic styles of solid taps

Hand taps (Fig. 4a) are most commonly used. Originally, they were used for tapping by hand, and although most are now used in machines, the name has persisted.

Hand taps are produced with either straight or spiral flutes. Many have four flutes, but for tapping metals that produce soft, stringy chips, or for ease of chip removal in deep-hole tapping, three or even two flutes can be used.

Spiral-point taps (Fig. 4b) have straight flutes supplemented by left-hand angular flutes near the point. The purpose of the spiral point is to push the chips ahead of the tap as tapping progresses.

Spiral-point taps are best suited for through holes. However, spiral-point taps with plug chamfer can be used for blind holes, provided there is enough clearance beyond the tapped section to accommodate the chips.

Because the flutes in spiral-point taps are less needed for chip passage, they can be shallower than in standard hand taps, and the tap body can have a stronger cross section.

The angular cutting edges generated by the spiral points cut with a shearing action, producing a fine finish on the threads. Furthermore, with the flutes clear of chips, the cutting fluid can move more freely along the flutes to the cutting edges.

Spiral-flute taps (Fig. 4c) can have right-hand or left-hand flutes; right-hand are more common. The spiral produces a lifting action that forces the chips along the flute. The spiral of the flutes may be regular (about 25° to 35°) or fast (about 50° to 65°); a fast spiral accelerates chip removal.

Spiral-flute taps are also used to advantage when tapping holes with keyways or other interruptions. The cutting edges meet the interruption progressively, thus cutting more smoothly and being less subject to shock.

Taps cutting regular right-hand threads can be furnished with left-hand spirals. These spirals will push the chips ahead of the tap through the hole for disposal. Keeping the chips out of the flutes minimizes tap breakage and thread damage when the tap is reversed for removal.

The shearing action resulting from the angle of the cutting edge on spiral-flute taps produces a better thread finish on difficult-to-machine metals.

Modifications. Six of the many modifications of the three basic styles of solid taps are shown in Fig. 5.

Bent-shank tapper taps (Fig. 5a) are used for tapping nuts in an automatic tapping machine. The nuts are usually fed from a hopper and as they are tapped they pass over the shank and are ejected automatically over the bent end. Consequently, it is unnecessary to reverse the tap as it would be with a conventional tap.

Combination roughing-and-finishing taps (Fig. 5b) have two stages; the first cuts to rough dimensions, and the second cuts the finished thread. The main disadvantage of these taps is the distance they extend beyond the workpiece at the completion of tapping; this limits their use to through holes.

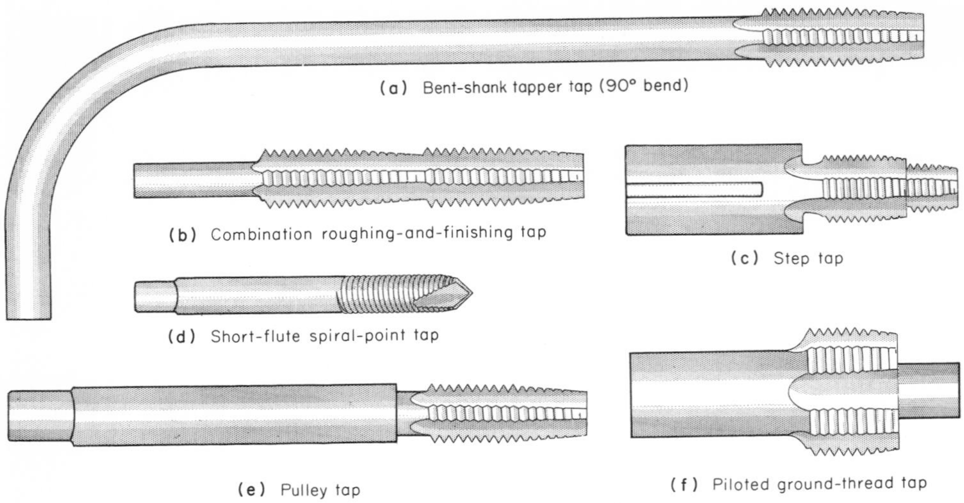

Fig. 5. Six modifications of solid taps

Step taps (Fig. 5c) are used for simultaneously cutting threads of the same pitch but of two different diameters.

Short-flute spiral-point taps (Fig. 5d) are designed for through holes in thin sections like webs and sheet metal. Because they are fluted only at the spiral point, these taps are durable. They are limited to tapped holes that are not deeper than one diameter.

Pulley taps (Fig. 5e) have the same thread dimensions as hand taps, but they have shanks as large in diameter as the major diameter of the tap thread, and much longer than the shanks of hand taps. When the taps thread holes for oil cups or setscrews in pulley hubs, the oversize shanks act as guides in the access holes in the pulley rims to keep the taps aligned.

Piloted ground-thread taps (Fig. 5f) are used to maintain concentricity of threads in workpiece holes. The pilot may be guided by the work hole, a special pilot hole, or a bushing. Piloted taps are specially made to order.

With solid taps, the relation of tap size to solid hole size is varied to meet specific conditions. For example, a tapped hole in a part to be electroplated must be oversize by a minimum of four times plate thickness to compensate for the electrodeposited metal. Another condition for which compensation is required is the outward force exerted by the tap when cutting. This force, particularly in thin-wall parts, may be sufficient to influence the final results because the part will expand during tapping and contract when the tap is removed. To meet these conditions, standard taps are ground oversize in established increments and coded for identification, as shown in Table 4.

Table 4. Tolerance on Pitch Diameter of Standard Taps Ground Oversize

Code(a)	Tolerance
Taps 1 In. or Less in Diameter	
GH1	Basic, to basic plus 0.0005 in.
GH2	Basic plus 0.0005 to 0.001 in.
GH3	Basic plus 0.001 to 0.0015 in.
GH4	Basic plus 0.0015 to 0.002 in.
GH5	Basic plus 0.002 to 0.0025 in.
GH6	Basic plus 0.0025 to 0.003 in.
GH7(b)	Basic plus 0.003 to 0.0035 in.
Taps Over 1 In., and Through 1½ In., in Diameter	
GH2	Basic, to basic plus 0.001 in.
GH4	Basic plus 0.001 to 0.002 in.
GH6	Basic plus 0.002 to 0.003 in.
GH8	Basic plus 0.003 to 0.004 in.

(a) GH = Ground high (oversize). (b) Nonstandard; for tapping workpieces susceptible to extreme distortion, or to which extremely heavy electrodeposits will be applied. Some manufacturers stock GH7 taps in a special series for tapping zinc die castings.

Standard taps ground undersize, identified as "GL" (ground low), are also available. These taps are used when the tapped hole will be retapped after some process such as heat treating has caused distortion. They are also used when the mating part is undersize. Tolerances for three GL taps are:

Code	Tolerance
GL1	Basic, to basic minus 0.0005 in.
GL2	Basic minus 0.0005 to 0.0010 in.
GL3	Basic minus 0.0010 to 0.0015 in.

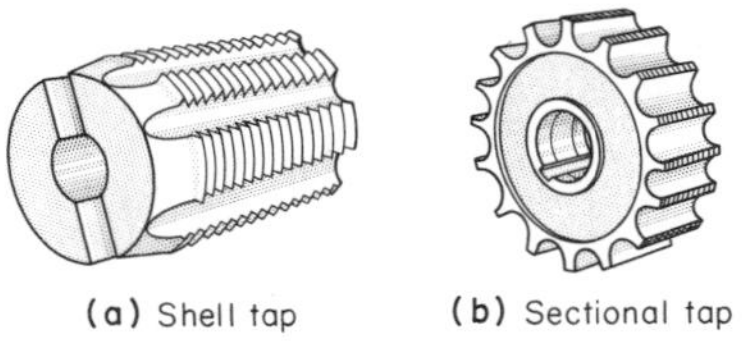

Fig. 6. Two styles of taps used with inserted shanks

Shell and Sectional Taps

Shell taps are generally made of high speed steel, without shanks, and are threaded to, or nearly to, their full length. As shown in Fig. 6(a) this type of tap has a full-length hole to accommodate an arbor or shank for driving purposes. The arbor hole is often made with a keyway for a positive drive. Other shell taps may have a tongue or groove across the middle of the back of the tap to fit a specific driver or shank.

Shell taps are made to order, usually 1 in. or larger in diameter and ½ in. or more in length. These taps are best suited for large-diameter holes where thread pitch is eight to the inch or finer, and where a short tap is required.

Shell taps may be resharpened in a gang by placing two or more on an arbor. In the large diameters they are sometimes cheaper than solid taps. However, shell taps of the smaller diameters are generally more expensive than their solid tap counterparts.

Sectional taps (Fig. 6b) are similar to shell taps in that they have inserted shanks. The cutting section is generally shorter for sectional than for shell taps. Like shell taps they can be resharpened in gang, two or more on an arbor.

Expansion Taps

Of the various kinds of expansion taps available, on special order, all have two features in common: (*a*) an axial hole is drilled from the front end to beyond the thread length of the tap; and (*b*) one or more radial slots or saw cuts are made from the surface of the tap to this hole between pairs of flutes. The slots, which extend the full working length of the tap, provide springiness to the threaded portion. Two types are illustrated in Fig. 7.

These taps are available in sizes ⅜ in. in diameter and larger. They are ordinarily used only for finishing work or for tapping free-machining metals. They are comparatively high in cost.

Inserted-Chaser Taps

The body of an inserted-chaser tap has slots that accept sets of four or more chasers held in place either by wedges, screws and grooves or by a combination of screws and serrations cut into the chaser body. A typical fixed-chaser type is shown in Fig. 8.

In one common inserted-chaser type, each chaser is wedge shaped — wider at the base than at the cutting surface. The ends of the chasers stop against a shoulder on the body of the tap and are held securely in position by hardened and ground wedges (Fig. 9). These taps, with a cut thread, are standard with some tap manufacturers and are available in sizes 1½ to 6 in. in diameter. The initial cost is relatively high, but for long production runs the replacement cost of a set of chasers is considerably lower than that of a solid tap. Ground-thread chasers for tapping taper pipe threads are also available but are special and designed to fit the user's tap bodies. Oversize holes can be tapped with inserted-chaser pipe taps by placing shims of uniform thickness under the bases of the blades.

Adjustable Taps. Another type of inserted-chaser tap is adjustable; that is, it can be made to cut smaller or larger. This tap uses ground-thread chasers with serrations on the backs. The chasers are held in position by locking cams, two for each chaser. The backs of the chasers stop against two hardened and ground nuts on the tap body. The taps are adjusted by loosening the locking cams and turning the nut nearer the chaser. The other nut locks the adjust-

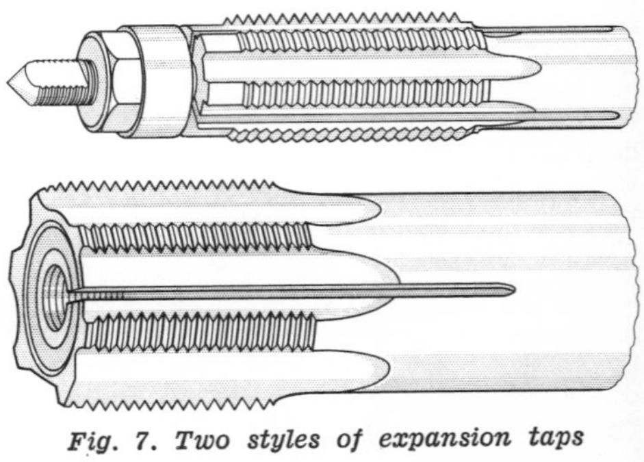

Fig. 7. Two styles of expansion taps

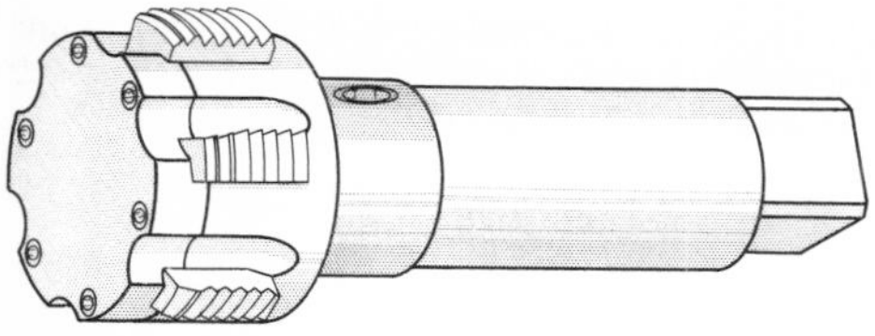

Fig. 8. Typical inserted-chaser tap

ing nut. The tap will cut larger when the chasers are pushed forward. A still larger cut can be made by removing the chasers from the body and replacing them one serration farther away from the axis of the tap. A smaller cut is made by placing the chasers one serration closer to the axis of the tap.

These taps are used almost exclusively as finishing taps where extreme accuracy is required. They are made only on special order and consequently the cost is relatively high.

Collapsible Taps

A collapsible tap has chasers that are set to retract radially after the thread is cut, so that the tap can be withdrawn without reverse rotation.

There are two basic types of collapsible taps: rotary and stationary. Rotary taps are used in machines in which the tool rotates, such as drill presses and tapping machines. Stationary taps are used in machines that rotate the workpiece, such as turret lathes. Both types are controlled by a yoke or ring arrangement that automatically withdraws the cutting edges when pressure is applied to the yoke. Stationary collapsible taps (Fig. 10) have a hand lever to reset the tap.

Collapsible taps can be used in the same equipment as solid taps, provided there is enough room to accommodate the collapsing head.

Collapsible taps are generally designed with flat or blade-type chasers, but for tapping large diameters, taps with circular chasers are frequently used. With a demountable nosepiece and blocks, either blade or circular chasers can be used in the same collapsible tap.

Taps with blade chasers are generally made for diameters of 1¼ to 4 in. Circular-chaser taps are made for 3½ to 5-in. diameters.

Advantages. Collapsible taps have two advantages over solid taps: (*a*) they can be adjusted, and (*b*) they can be removed from the workpiece without reversing the spindle.

The adjustability of collapsible taps is advantageous on first-run jobs where the reaction to the tapping forces is unknown, because it permits variation in the amount of compensation for distortion of the metal being tapped. Also, collapsible taps can be adjusted to allow for electroplated finishes or for growth resulting from heat treatment. Thus, collapsible taps are adaptable to both short runs and high production.

Collapsing the tap eliminates the wear that would be caused by friction between the cut threads and the tap when the tap is reversed for removal. In addition, a collapsible tap minimizes the danger of tap breakage or thread damage caused by trapped chips as the tap is removed from the tapped hole; this is of particular benefit when tapping metals that make stringy chips. An application in which better results were obtained when a solid tap was replaced by a collapsible tap is described in Example 895, in the article "Machining of Aluminum Alloys".

Disadvantages. In comparison with solid taps, collapsible taps have four disadvantages:

1 Because of the greater overhung inertia of a collapsible tap, a more sturdy machine is required than for a solid tap.
2 Because collapsible taps have a number of moving parts, they require more maintenance; worn or loose components cause excessive variation in tapped holes.
3 They can seldom be used for holes smaller than 1¼ in. in diameter.
4 Collapsible taps are expensive.

Tap Materials

Most taps are made of high speed steel. Carbide blades (chasers) are sometimes used in adjustable or inserted-chaser taps. However, the use of carbide is largely restricted to special applications, such as tapping of especially abrasive grades of cast iron or abrasive nonmetals such as fiberglass.

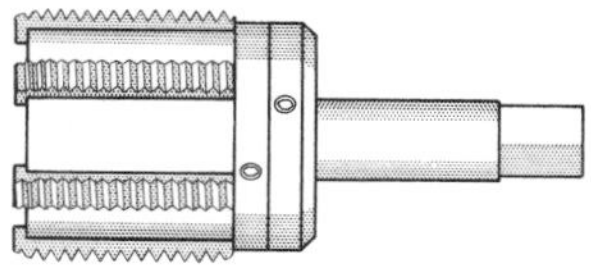

Fig. 9. Inserted-chaser tap in which chasers are held in place by wedges

General-purpose high speed steels, such as M1 and M2, are most widely used for taps and have proved satisfactory for the majority of applications. For tapping difficult-to-machine metals (such as heat-resisting alloys, or steels harder than about Rockwell C 35), taps made of one of the more highly alloyed high speed steels, such as M15 or T15, are often justified. However, taps made of the more highly alloyed high speed steels cost two to three times as much as similar taps made of the general-purpose types; the more highly alloyed types are more difficult to grind and more susceptible to grinding burn.

Cost. To the user, tap cost and tap expendability are directly related, especially in smaller sizes. Most users will sacrifice tap life rather than pay for maintenance and repair. A tap chipped along its chamfer or in the leading threads can be salvaged, but salvage is costly and replacement may be more economical. Also, cheaper taps, to be discarded after short runs, may be more economical than costly taps with a longer production life, depending on the cost of downtime for changing taps. In multiple-spindle setups where tap operating conditions are poor, a sacrifice in tap life may prove cheaper than a second tapping operation.

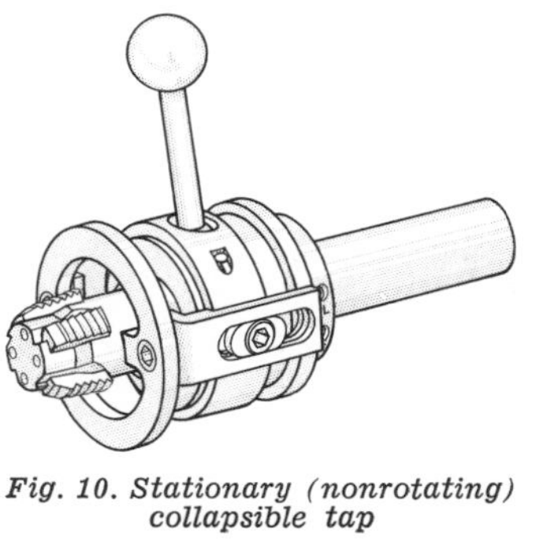

Fig. 10. Stationary (nonrotating) collapsible tap

Surface Treatment of Taps

Many taps are given one of the following surface treatments: nitriding, chromium plating, or oxidation (black oxide) by steam. The purpose of all these treatments is to increase tap life and improve thread finish by: (*a*) reducing adherence of the tap to the work metal, (*b*) reducing chip buildup on cutting edges, and (*c*) minimizing wear caused by erosion from chips (see Example 244). An application in which nitrided and chromium-plated taps had 40% longer life than untreated taps is described in Example 941.

Surface treatments can increase tap life by 500% or more. The greatest benefit of surface treatment is realized in metals that form stringy chips, or in hard metals such as heat treated steel. The relative merits of the three types of treatment are debatable; all have proved helpful. However, steam treated taps are not recommended for use in soft metals like brass, because they are likely to tap oversize (see Example 222).

The main disadvantages of surface treatments are cost and inconvenience. Regardless of the treatment used, the penetration (or buildup, in the case of plating) is so small that the taps must be re-treated each time they are ground. This is sometimes a great inconvenience, especially when the taps must be sent out for treatment.

Selection of Tap Features

The main influences on selection of tap design features are work-metal composition and hardness, class of thread required, and cost. The five examples that follow describe applications in which changes in the design of the tap proved beneficial (see also Example 244).

Example 222. Tap Redesign to Produce Acceptable Threads

Tapping 1–14 UNS threads in free-cutting brass was one of a sequence of operations in a multiple-spindle machine. The taps originally used were standard four-flute taps with a 12° positive rake and relatively wide lands, and had been subjected to a steam oxide surface treatment. These taps failed to pick up the lead, and consequently the threads were reamed to the extent that a no-go gage would enter the full length of the threads. In addition, the steam oxide treatment caused the taps to cut oversize, because the pitted surface from the oxide treatment, combined with the use of soluble oil as cutting fluid, caused the thread flanks to load.

The following revisions were made: (*a*) land width of the tap was reduced from 0.300 to 0.165 in., (*b*) the rake was reduced to 3°, (*c*) surface treatment of the taps was changed to nitriding, and (*d*) a light mineral oil (paraffin base) was substituted for the soluble oil. These changes produced acceptable parts. Tap life between grinds was 32,000 pieces. Each tap could be reground three times; thus, total tap life averaged 128,000 pieces.

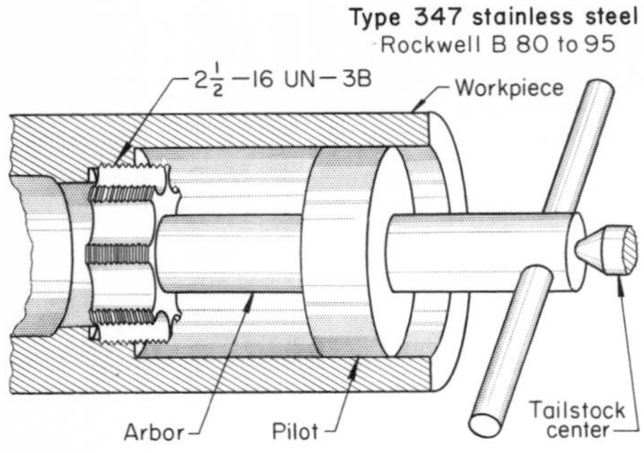

Length of tapped hole	0.440 in.
Length of threaded portion	0.320 in.
Cutting fluid	Chlorinated oil

Tap Details

Material	M44 high speed steel
Thread length	¾ in.
Number of flutes	8
Hook angle	12°
Chamfer diameter	2.438/2.433 in.
Number of chamfered threads	1½

Fig. 11. Use of shell tap on piloted arbor for hand tapping milled threads to finish size (Example 224)

Example 223. Straight-Flute vs Fast-Spiral Taps for Blind Holes

Aircraft engine parts of 1035 steel required blind holes with 4–40 threads, three diameters deep. Originally, straight-flute taps were used but, whether of three-flute or two-flute design, these broke after tapping only three or four holes, because of chip congestion.

The low productivity, high scrap rate and frequent repair were corrected by changing to a two-flute fast-spiral tap. Tap breakage was eliminated, and tap life per grind was 50 to 60 holes.

Example 224. Shell vs Collapsible Taps for Hand Tapping (Fig. 11)

Thread mills roughed out threads in 347 stainless steel. The threads were then finished to 2½–16 UN–3B by hand tapping with a collapsible tap. But misalignment of chasers after sharpening caused oversize threads, and rejections were excessive.

To overcome this problem, the collapsible tap was replaced with a shell tap; and to assure proper alignment, a pilot was pressed onto the tap arbor 3 in. behind the tap, as shown in Fig. 11. Tap details are given in the table accompanying Fig. 11.

Example 225. Combination Tap vs Serial Set

In a turret lathe, a serial set of four threaded-pilot, four-flute taps produced stem threads in a silicon bronze valve bonnet with 2–4 NA triple left-hand Acme threads. Tapping each part required 2.5 min.

To meet increased production requirements, the serial set of taps was replaced with a combination roughing and finishing Acme tap. This tap had six flutes, full eccentric thread relief, 5° negative rake, narrow lands and a nitrided surface. With the combination tap, at a speed of 30 sfm, the tapping time per piece was reduced to 0.58 min. Soluble oil was used as cutting fluid in both methods.

Selecting between three-flute and four-flute taps often involves a difficult decision; four-flute taps have less cutting load per tooth, but three-flute taps in the same size have greater strength and more chip room. Thread pitch sometimes influences the decision, as indicated in the following example:

Example 226. Three-Flute vs Four-Flute Taps (Fig. 12)

A four-flute spiral-point tap proved superior to one with three flutes for cutting ¾–16 UNF–2B threads in steel nuts, using an automatic nut tapper (Fig. 12). The greater number of cutting edges on the four-flute tap, together with the smaller chips it produced, resulted in smoother finish on the threads and longer tap life. Tap details and operating conditions are given with Fig. 12.

However, for tapping ¾–10 UNC–2B threads in these nuts, a three-flute tap was preferred, because of the greater strength in the tap and increased clearance to pass the larger chips.

An additional comparison of two-flute, three-flute and four-flute taps for a difficult operation is presented in Example 762, in the article "Machining of Stainless Steel".

Factors That Influence Procedures and Results

The principal factors that influence selection of equipment and procedure for tapping, and that affect thread quality, productivity and cost are:

1 Composition and hardness of the metal being tapped
2 Size and shape of the workpiece
3 Thread size and depth
4 Tolerance and finish specified
5 Whether blind or through holes are being tapped
6 Speed
7 Use or nonuse of lead control
8 Cutting fluid.

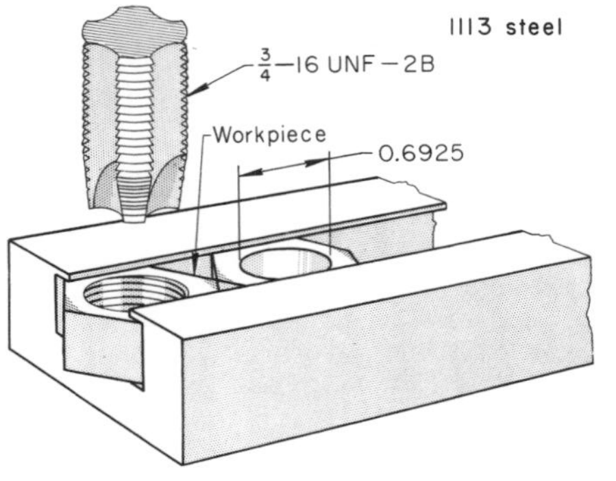

Tap Details

Material	M1 high speed steel
Surface treatment	Steam oxide
Hook angle	8°
Number of chamfered threads	6
Chamfer angle	5° 40′
Chamfer relief	0.009 to 0.0011 in.
Spiral-point angle	7° 45′
Spiral-point length	8 threads

Operating Conditions

Speed	407 rpm (80 sfm)
Cutting fluid	Sulfurized oil
Thread length	¾ in. (through)
Per cent of thread	71%
Tap life per grind	10,000 pieces
Production rate	500 pieces per hour

Fig. 12. Use of a four-flute spiral-point tap for threading nuts in an automatic nut tapper. A three-flute tap was preferred for ¾–10 UNC–2B threads in these nuts. (Example 226)

The sections that follow discuss the influence and control of these variables (except for lead control, which is discussed on page 108).

Metal Composition and Hardness

A metal is seldom selected for its machinability alone. However, a change of material may increase productivity and decrease cost without sacrifice in required properties. The simplest change is that from a specific alloy to a free-machining counterpart. Invariably, tapping of free-machining grades results in more accurate threads of better finish at higher production rates and lower cost than tapping of non-free-machining grades that are otherwise similar in composition and hardness. A typical comparison is presented in the following example.

Example 227. Result of Change to Free-Machining Steel (Table 5)

Two-flute spiral-point taps were used in a tapping machine to cut 8–32 UNC–2B threads in 0.250-in.-deep through holes in 1020 steel, using sulfurized oil as the cutting fluid. By changing to 1113 steel, but using the same machine, taps and cutting fluid, an increase in speed was made possible, and tap life was prolonged. Comparative data for the two steels are presented in Table 5.

The next seven examples show the influence of a variety of ferrous and nonferrous work metals on procedure, tap life, productivity and cost.

Example 228. 1113 Steel vs 304 Stainless Steel (Table 6)

A drill press, with a tapping-head attachment and standard 10–32 UNF–2B solid taps, was used for threading, to a depth of ¼ in., tap-drilled holes in two styles of fittings made, respectively, of 1113 steel and 304 stainless steel. Processing, tool-life and tool-cost data are compared in Table 6.

Fittings of the two materials were tapped at the same speed, but because of more frequent changing of taps for the stainless steel fittings, production rate per hour was 11% less than for the 1113 fittings. Also, even though less metal was removed in tapping the stainless steel fittings (because the tap-drilled hole was slightly larger), tap life was only one-third that of identical taps used for tapping the 1113 fittings. As a result, tool cost for tapping the stainless steel was nearly three times that for tapping 1113 steel.

Example 229. Brass vs Low-Carbon Steel vs 410 Stainless

The speeds used, and tool life and production rates obtained, in tapping 8–32 UNC–2B threads 0.125 in. through, in brass, low-

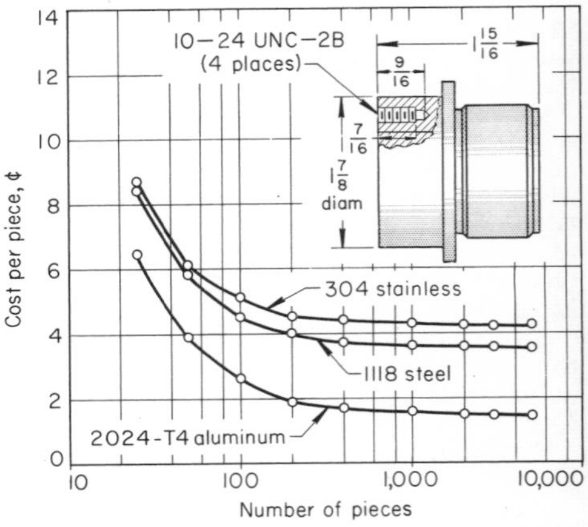

Item	1118 steel	304 stainless	2024-T4 aluminum
Tap Details(a)			
Number of flutes	3	3	4
Hook angle	15°	15°	10°
Operating Conditions(b)			
Speed, rpm	800	400	800
Speed, sfm	40	20	40
Cutting rate, cu in./min	0.003	0.0026	0.003
Tool life per grind:			
Holes tapped	165	90	250
Metal removed, cu in.	0.3795	0.207	0.575

(a) All taps had 10° chamfer and three lead threads. (b) For tapping all metals, soluble oil was used as the cutting fluid.

Fig. 13. Cost-quantity relations for tapping identical workpieces of three different metals (Example 231)

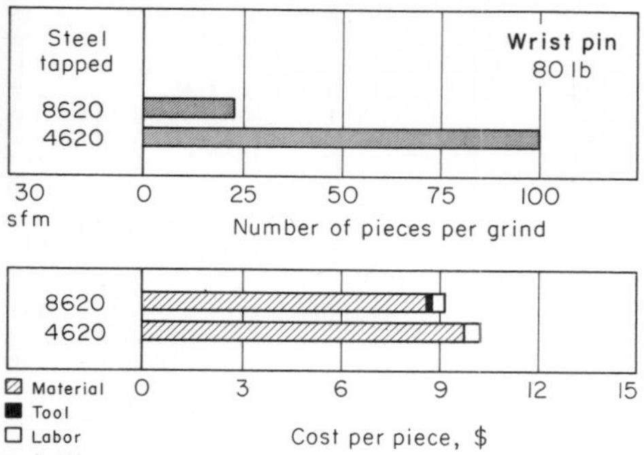

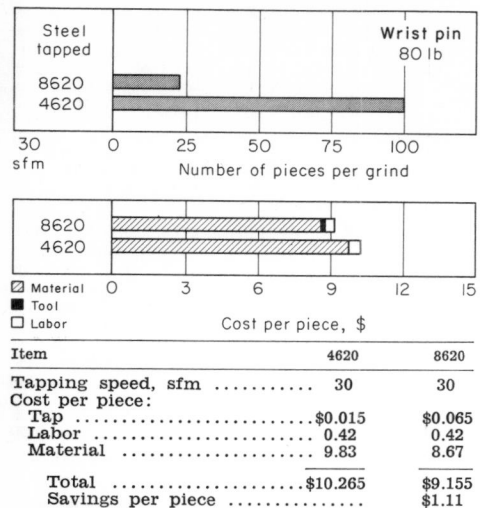

Item	4620	8620
Tapping speed, sfm	30	30
Cost per piece:		
Tap	$0.015	$0.065
Labor	0.42	0.42
Material	9.83	8.67
Total	$10.265	$9.155
Savings per piece		$1.11

Fig. 14. Results of tapping wrist pins from two carburizing steels (Example 233)

carbon steel and 410 stainless steel are compared in the table below. All three metals were tapped with 69% of full thread, in a single-spindle tapping machine using standard two-flute solid taps of high speed steel. For brass, taps had a 12° chamfer, and a lard-oil mixture was used as cutting fluid. For the two other metals, 15°-chamfer taps were used, with sulfurized oil.

Item	Brass (130 Bhn)	Low-carbon steel (140 Bhn)	410 stainless (185 Bhn)
Speed, rpm	3494	1396	698
Speed, sfm	150	60	30
Holes per hour	890	820	700
Tap life, holes	6700	6450	1850

As these data show, there was a relatively small difference in results between brass and low-carbon steel, compared with the difference (particularly in tap life) between brass or low-carbon steel and stainless steel. Tapping speeds, although widely different for the three metals, had a relatively small effect on production rate because of the large amount of time for loading and unloading.

Table 5. Improved Results Obtained by Change to Free-Machining Steel (Example 227) (a)

Item	1020 steel	Free-machining steel
Speed, rpm	1600	2300
Speed, sfm	70	100
Total tap life, holes	6800	8300
Production per hour, pieces	340	410
Cost per 1000 holes (b)	$38	$32

(a) Data are for tapping 8–32 UNC–2B threads in 0.136-in.-diam through holes 0.250 in. deep, using two-flute spiral-point taps. (b) Includes labor and burden.

Table 6. Effect of Workpiece Metal on Tap Life and Cost (Example 228) (a)

Item	1113 steel(b)	304 stainless(c)
Holes tapped per hour	169	150
Taps used for 300 holes	2	6
Total tap life, holes	150	50
Tap life per grind, holes	75	(d)
Number of regrinds	1	None
Cost per tap	$1.35	$1.35
Cost per regrind	$0.26	....
Total tool cost	$2.96	$8.10

(a) Data compared were obtained in tapping 10–32 UNF–2B threads to a depth of ¼ in. in blind holes 5⁄16-in. deep in 300 fittings made of each material. Both materials were tapped at the same speed. (b) Holes tapped were drilled to 0.1495-in. diam; cutting fluid was mineral oil. (c) Holes tapped were drilled to 0.1595-in. diam; cutting fluid was soluble oil. (d) Land wear was so great that tap was not worth regrinding.

Example 230. Low-Carbon Steel vs 302 Stainless vs Nickel Silver vs Phosphor Bronze (Table 7)

Table 7 compares workpiece, tap design and processing for four metals, all of which were tapped regularly. Although the tapped holes in the four metals were not identical, they were sufficiently similar that comparisons could be made.

An automatic multiple-spindle tapping machine was used for all the metals except stainless steel. Because of lower production of the stainless parts, they were tapped in a semiautomatic multiple-spindle machine.

Example 231. Aluminum vs Carbon Steel vs Stainless Steel (Fig. 13)

A tapping machine with a lead-screw attachment was used to produce 10–24 UNC–2B threads to a depth of 7⁄16 in. in workpieces with four equally spaced blind holes (Fig. 13). These workpieces were made of 1118 steel, 304 stainless steel or 2024-T4 aluminum alloy, as required.

Cost-quantity relations for tapping the three metals are shown graphically in Fig. 13. These data indicate that production quantity strongly influences cost, up to 200 parts. At that point, cost per piece begins to level off.

In these analyses, setup time was not considered; only direct-labor cost, tap cost, and tap-sharpening cost were included. Processing details and tap descriptions are given with Fig. 13.

Example 232. 1035 vs 1015 Steel (Table 8)

An automatic four-spindle tapping machine was used to produce 6–32 UNC–2B threads in 0.109-in.-diam perforated through holes, 0.090 in. deep, in a clamping die. These parts were originally made of 1035 steel (hardness, Rockwell B 65 to 70), but a change was made to 1015 steel (hardness, Rockwell B 55 to 60). Comparative data for the two steels are given in Table 8.

Taps for both steels were two-flute spiral-point taps made of high speed steel and chromium plated, with 8° hook angle and 12° chamfer. In tapping both steels, sulfurized oil was used as cutting fluid.

In the preceding example, the less costly material was also less costly to tap. More often, however, advantages and disadvantages offset each other. In the following example, the lower-cost steel was more expensive to tap, but because the difference in material cost far outweighed the increase in tapping cost, it was economical to keep the more costly tapping process.

Example 233. Carburized 4620 vs 8620 (Fig. 14)

Wrist pins weighing 80 lb and measuring 5½ in. in diameter, 12 in. long, each had 28 holes ⅝ by 11 in. deep to be tapped. Although 4620 gave much better tool life than 8620, the latter was less expensive initially and therefore more economical in the long run. Cost comparison is given with Fig. 14.

A difference in work-metal composition can affect requirements for hole preparation before tapping. For instance, when tapping aluminum, accuracy and thread finish can usually be improved by reaming after drilling, whereas in tapping carbon, alloy or stainless steel, reaming is seldom needed. The following example compares practices used for tapping identical threads in two metals differing greatly in chemical composition.

Table 8. Tapping 1035 vs 1015 Steel (Example 232)

Item	1035 steel	1015 steel
Speed, rpm	1520	2215
Speed, sfm	55	80
Total tap life (avg), holes	7950	9300
Tapping cost per 1000 holes	$5.60	$4.15 (a)

(a) Saving of $1.45 per 1000 holes amounted to a total saving of $7975 on annual production of 5½ million pieces. Tapping cost includes labor and burden.

Example 234. Aluminum Alloy vs Stainless Steel (Table 9)

A multiple-spindle tapping machine with an adjustable-torque tapping head was used for tapping parts for a jet-engine fuel system. Originally, these parts were cast aluminum alloy 355-T6 (AMS 4212), but an increase in severity of service necessitated changing to a type CA-15 stainless steel casting (similar to wrought alloy 410).

Tapped holes in the two materials were alike, except that the holes in the aluminum were tapped 1⁄32 in. deeper. However, to obtain acceptable results in tapping the aluminum, it was necessary to use a slightly larger drill and to ream between drilling and tapping (see Table 9).

Processing details for tapping the two metals are compared in Table 9. As these data show, tapping speed was reduced in changing from aluminum to stainless steel, and tap cost was increased by about 50%.

Except for low-carbon steels that do not contain free-cutting additives, and certain other soft metals that form gummy, adherent chips in machining, hard metals are less readily tapped than soft metals. Figure 15 illustrates the usual effect of differences in work metal hardness on the tapping of carbon and low-alloy steels. In this test on the tapping of ¼–28 and ½–20 through holes in similar low-alloy steels with M10 high speed steel tools, the cost for tapping at a hardness of Rockwell C 52 was about 30 times that at Rockwell C 15, and for tapping at a hardness of Rockwell C 47, about six times.

Under the conditions of this test, tap life increased with an increase in hole diameter, on the basis of volume of metal removed, but decreased on the basis of number of holes per grind. Tapping cost for the ¼-in.-diam holes was three times that for the ½-in.-diam

Table 7. Tapping UNC–2B Threads in Through Holes in Four Metals (Example 230) (a)

Item	Low-carbon steel (6–32 threads)	302 stainless (5–40 threads)	Nickel silver (6–32 threads)	Phosphor bronze (6–32 threads)
Workpiece Details				
Rockwell B hardness	60 to 75	90	90 to 95	94 to 98
Tensile strength, 1000 psi	48 to 60	75 to 90	90 to 110	97 to 110
Diameter of hole, in.	0.107 (b)	0.1015 (c)	0.113 (c)	0.106 (b)
Depth of through hole, in.	0.063	0.095	0.128	0.063
Processing Details				
Speed, sfm	65	30	55	45
Cutting fluid (type of oil)	Soluble	Sulfurized	Mineral	Mineral
Holes tapped per spindle per hour	2720	1250	2055	2152
Tap life, holes	13580	4150	8250	7650

(a) Taps for all materials were two-flute high speed steel taps with 12° chamfer angle and 5° hook angle, except taps for phosphor bronze, which had 8° hook angle. (b) Perforated. (c) Drilled.

Table 9. Tapping 10–24 UNC–2B Threads in Aluminum Alloy vs Stainless Steel Castings (Example 234)

Item	Aluminum (355-T6)	Stainless (CA-15)
Hole Dimensions		
Drilled hole diam, in. . .	0.154 (a)	0.152 (b)
Drilled hole depth, in. . .	9/16	9/16
Reamed hole diam, in. . .	0.157/0.154	(c)
Tapped depth, in.	15/32	7/16
Processing Details		
Tapping speed, rpm . .	300	150
Tapping speed, sfm . .	15	7.5
Tap life per grind, holes	200	100
Cost per tap	$2.14	$3.46

(a) No. 23 drill. (b) No. 24 drill. (c) Reaming of drilled hole not required.

holes, on the basis of volume of metal removed, but was only slightly greater on a per-hole basis. Machining and tool details are given with Fig. 15.

A tap manufacturer conducted a series of tests on eleven steels that ranged in hardness from Rockwell C 5 to 55, to determine the effect of hardness on tapping. Data obtained in these tests were used as the basis for the recommendations given in Table 10.

As indicated in Table 10, taps made of general-purpose high speed steels usually are the most economical when the hardness of the metal being tapped does not exceed Rockwell C 30 or 32; as workpiece hardness increases above this level, one of the more highly alloyed high speed steels usually is selected. Table 10 also indicates that tap design is more critical when high-hardness steels are being tapped; this is further demonstrated in the following example:

Example 235. Tapping H13 Tool Steel at Rockwell C 42 to 46 (Fig. 16)

A turret lathe was used for tapping blind holes in heat treated tool steel spindles, chucked as shown in Fig. 16. Because of the hardness of these spindles, specially designed four-flute taps made of M3 high speed steel and hardened to Rockwell C 67 were used. Details of tap design and operating conditions are given with Fig. 16.

The taps were strengthened by using a hook angle of 0° to 2° instead of the normal 8° angle. The taps also were provided with an eccentric relief of 0.0004 to 0.0008 in. per land, which reduced friction, for freer cutting. Although sulfurized and chlorinated oils ordinarily are used for tapping hard materials, soluble oil was used here because it removed chips more effectively.

Workpiece Size and Shape

Size and shape of the workpiece must be considered in establishing tapping procedures. For instance, a workpiece may be too large or too irregular in shape to be machined in a turret lathe, even though a turret lathe would otherwise be ideal. However, tapping problems are more likely to be encountered with workpieces that are too weak or flimsy to withstand normal tapping forces. This inability can result in loss of dimensional control, or even in damage to the workpiece. The example that follows describes procedures that have been successful for tapping tubular workpieces with a wall 15/64 in. thick.

Example 236. Tapping Seam-Welded Tubing (Fig. 17)

An eight-station vertical tapping machine and six-flute solid taps were used for cutting 2–11½ NPSC threads through 2⅛-in. lengths of seam-welded 1020 steel tubing (wall thickness, 15/64 in.), for use as steam-pipe couplings. As shown in Fig. 17, the workpieces were held in air chucks. After each piece had been tapped, it was automatically pushed up the long shank of the tap by the next piece, until the shank was filled — at which time the workpieces were unloaded. The eight stations were synchronized to permit one-man operation.

Solid taps were used in preference to collapsible taps because the variation from true roundness of the inside diameter, together with the seam, required that the tap provide some reaming action in addition to cutting the threads. Tap details and operating conditions are included with Fig. 17.

Techniques used in tapping thin-wall aluminum workpieces are discussed in Example 900, in the article "Machining of Aluminum Alloys".

Size, Pitch and Per Cent of Thread

Thread size and pitch, and per cent of full depth to which the threads are cut, determine the metal removed in any tapping operation and have a large effect on efficiency and tap life.

As the size of thread increases, the amount of metal removed increases in approximate proportion to the hole diameter (assuming that other factors remain constant). As the thread becomes coarser, the amount of metal removed in tapping increases for any thread diameter and per cent of thread.

Per cent of thread is half the difference between the basic major diameter and the actual minor diameter of an internal thread, divided by the basic thread height and expressed in per cent. As per cent of thread increases, the amount of metal removed will increase for any thread pitch and size.

The three examples that follow deal with the influence of thread size and per cent of thread on procedures and results. Example 897, in the article on Machining of Aluminum, shows how thread size affects tap life.

Example 237. Influence of Size and Per Cent of Thread on Productivity and Cost (Table 11)

Table 11 compares production rates, tap life and tap costs for cutting threads of different sizes and percentages of full depth in two stainless steel parts (inset sketches in Table 11). As these data show, tap cost per hole increased nearly fourfold, and productivity was substantially decreased, when per cent of thread was increased from 55% or 60%, to 70%. Also, as thread size increased (comparing part A with part B), tap cost per hole increased by a third to a half.

Example 238. Effect of Increase in Per Cent of Thread on Speed, Production Rate, and Tap Life

Two-flute spiral-point taps with a 15° chamfer were used in a two-spindle tapping machine for cutting 8–36 UNF–2B threads in through holes in low-carbon steel plate 0.112 in. thick. Speed, production rate and tap life for tapping these holes to 55% and to 78% of full thread depth were as follows:

	55%	78%
Speed, rpm	1863	1398
Speed, sfm	80	60
Holes tapped per hour	2195	1925
Tap life, holes	12500	9000

All taps were chromium plated, and sulfurized oil was used as the cutting fluid.

Example 239. Effect of Per Cent of Thread on Tapping of High-Hardness Steel (Fig. 18)

In a tapping test on H11 steel at Rockwell C 52, holes were tapped at 60, 70 and 75% of full thread. The conditions of the test

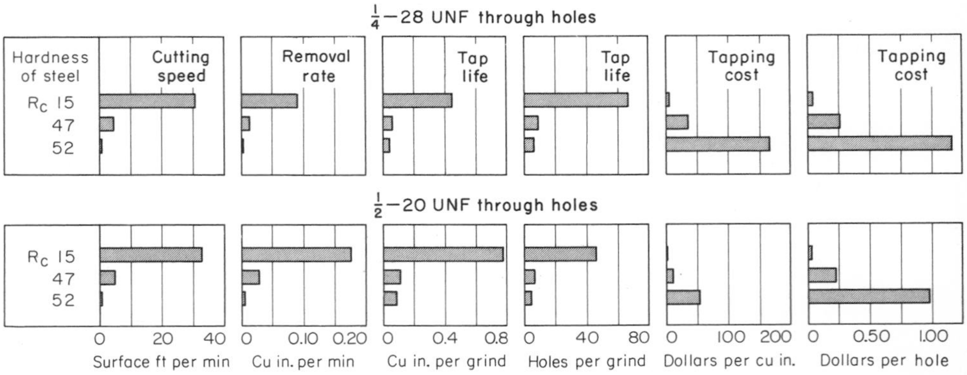

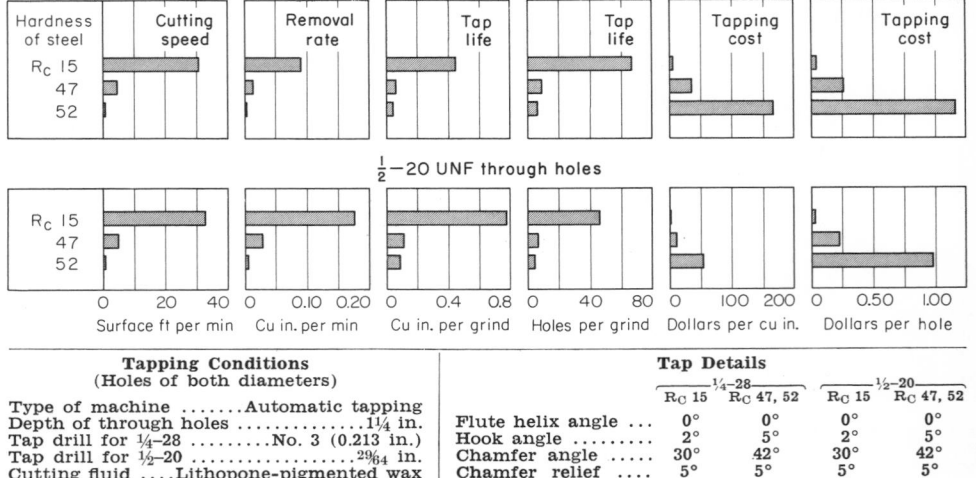

Tapping Conditions
(Holes of both diameters)

Type of machine	Automatic tapping
Depth of through holes	1¼ in.
Tap drill for ¼–28	No. 3 (0.213 in.)
Tap drill for ½–20	29/64 in.
Cutting fluid	Lithopone-pigmented wax and fatty ester in lard-mineral oil
Tap material	M10 high speed steel

Tap Details

	¼–28		½–20	
	R_C 15	R_C 47, 52	R_C 15	R_C 47, 52
Flute helix angle . . .	0°	0°	0°	0°
Hook angle	2°	5°	2°	5°
Chamfer angle	30°	42°	30°	42°
Chamfer relief	5°	5°	5°	5°
No. of lead threads	3	3	4	4
No. of flutes	4	4	3	3

Fig. 15. Effect of hardness on tapping of carbon and low-alloy steel

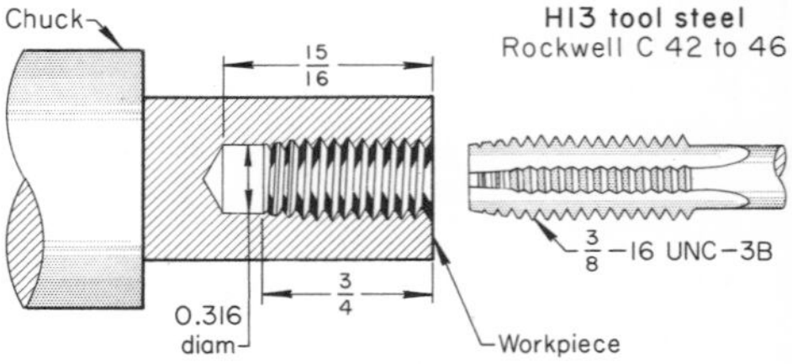

Tap Details

Material	M3 high speed steel
Hardness	Rockwell C 67
Hook angle	0° to 2°
Chamfer angle	11° 15′
Chamfer relief	0.005 to 0.007 in.
Number of threads in chamfer	3½
Eccentric relief per land	0.0004 to 0.0008 in.
Pitch diameter limit	GH3

Operating Conditions

Speed	55 rpm (5.4 sfm)
Cutting fluid	Soluble oil
Per cent of full thread	73%

Fig. 16. Use of specially designed four-flute tap for cutting threads in hardened steel spindles (Example 235)

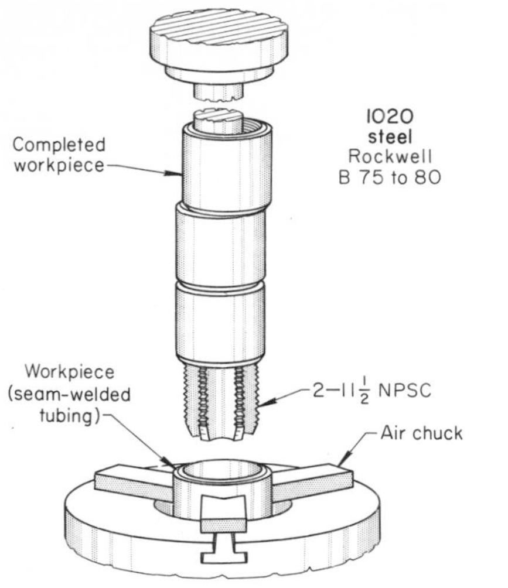

Tap Details

Material	M1 high speed steel
Number of flutes	6
Over-all length	15 in.
Chamfer length	15⁄64 in.
Chamfer angles (double)	10° 15′ and 4° 36′

Operating Conditions

Speed	80 rpm (50 sfm)
Cutting fluid	Sulfurized oil
Tap life per grind	1200 pieces
Production rate	80 pieces per hour

Fig. 17. Tapping seam-welded couplings (Example 236)

are listed with Fig. 18, which shows the results of the test. At 60% of full thread, the test was discontinued after 40 holes with the tap still cutting, but at 75% of full thread tool life was only 7 holes.

Accuracy and Finish

Conditions that cause dimensional variation in tapped threads also cause rough finish on the threads. Among these conditions are lack of concentricity between the tap holder and the spindle, worn taps, entrapment of chips in the tapped hole, and chip buildup on cutting edges and flanks of the threads.

Concentricity of Holder and Spindle. New taps are seldom responsible for poor threads. However, even a new tap is no more accurate than the combined eccentricity of the holder and rotating spindle. Eccentricity of these rotating members will cause the tapped holes to be oversize.

Condition of Taps. Worn taps are a major source of dimensional variation in tapped holes or of poor finish on threads, or both. As the cutting edges of a tap become dull, the chips produced are torn, rather than cut or shaved. Improperly sharpened taps, or taps with the wrong cutting-edge angles, will have a similar adverse effect on thread finish.

Chip Entrapment. Most taps have relief ground on the trailing part of the lands, which provides space between the heel of the tap and the cut threads. When the tap is backed out of the threaded hole, this space admits fine particles or chips between the tap and the workpiece, and they press against the thread flanks as the tap reverses — resulting in galled thread flanks or broken taps, or both.

Collapsible taps eliminate the entrapment of chips or particles, but they are impractical for threads smaller than 1¼-in. diameter and are sometimes unsatisfactory for other reasons (see Example 224). In through holes, damage from chips during reversal can be substantially reduced by running the tap far enough to clear all threads in the chamfer and then flushing cutting fluid through the flutes to wash out all the chips before reversing the tap for disengagement.

Blind holes, however, do not permit this through-flushing. Therefore, taps used for threading blind holes should be designed so that they either lift the chips out of the hole, by the action of the flutes, or (if enough clearance can be provided at the bottom of the hole) push the chips ahead of the tap. (See "Selection of Tap" in the section "Tapping Blind Holes", which follows.) When taps are used that lift chips out of the hole by the action of the flutes, it is sometimes helpful to direct a jet of cutting fluid down one flute at the end of the tapping cycle after the tap has stopped rotating. This forces the chips out the remaining flutes. However, when using taps that force the chips down into a clearance, this practice is not recommended. Another aid to chip removal when tapping blind holes is the insertion of a soft wax plug in the hole before tapping. As the tap progresses down the hole, the wax picks up chips and particles and carries them away as it is forced up the flutes of the tap. The wax also lubricates the tap.

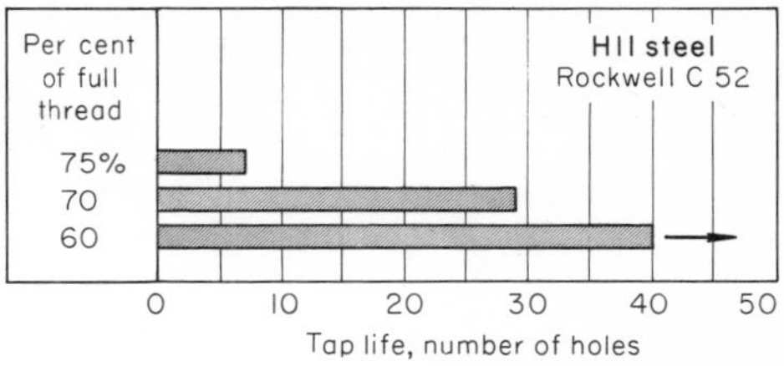

Tap	5⁄16–18 UNC, 4-flute taper
Tap material	M10 high speed steel
Surface treatment of tap	Cyanided
Cutting speed	5 sfm
Depth of through hole	0.500 in.
Cutting fluid	1 part highly chlorinated oil mixed with 3 parts inhibited trichloroethane
End point of test	Tap breakage(a)

(a) Test at 60% of full thread was discontinued at 40 holes, with tap still cutting.

Fig. 18. Effect of per cent of full thread on tap life in hardened steel (Example 239)

Chip buildup on the tap (adherence of work metal to the cutting edges) is a major cause of surface roughness. The buildup reduces the cutting efficiency of the tap and produces results similar to those obtained when tapping with a dull tap. Surface treatments of the tap (see page 111) greatly assist in the prevention of chip buildup. Buildup may also be prevented or minimized by a change in cutting fluid, or in the method of applying cutting fluid (see "Cutting Fluids", page 117).

Operating Procedure. Lead-control tapping (see page 108) usually produces greater accuracy in tapped holes

Table 10. Recommended Practice for Tapping Steels in Three Ranges of Hardness

Process variable	Rockwell C hardness of steel tapped: 5 to 30	30 to 40	40 to 55
Tap design	Standard	Modified standard, or special(a)	Special(a)
Tap material(b)	T1, M1, M7, M10	M2, M3	T15, M3, M33, M42
Tap hardness, minimum	Rockwell C 62	Rockwell C 64	Rockwell C 66
Surface treatment of tap	Steam oxide(c)	Nitride plus steam oxide	Nitride plus steam oxide
Per cent of full thread	75%	60%	55%
Speed, sfm	100 max	20 to 45	½ to 10
Cutting oil	Sulfurized	Sulfurized and chlorinated	Sulfurized and highly chlorinated

(a) Special tap should have four flutes, 3° (positive) hook angle, thread relief, and 3-to-4-thread chamfer. (b) High speed steels similar in total alloy content to steels listed may be substituted. (c) Or other oxidizing process; see the section "Surface Treatment of Taps", page 111.

Table 11. Effect of Size and Per Cent of Thread in Tapping Two Stainless Steel Parts (Example 237) (a)

Item	Part A (2–56 UNC–2B thread) 55%	Part A 70%	Part B (4–40 UNC–2B thread) 60%	Part B 70%
Diameter of tap drilled hole, in.	0.073	0.070	0.092	0.089
Production rate, holes per hr	240	168	200	150
Number of holes tapped	525	400	500	500
Holes per tap(b)	175	50	100	25
Number of taps used(b)	3	8	5	20
Cost per tap	$2.55	$2.55	$1.88	$1.88
Total tap cost	$7.65	$20.40	$9.40	$37.60
Tap cost per hole	$0.014	$0.051	$0.019	$0.075

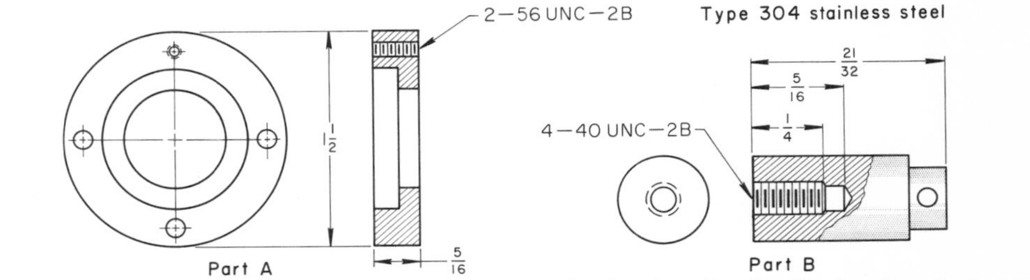

(a) Both parts were tapped in a drill press with a friction-type tapping head; mineral oil was used as cutting fluid. (b) Taps were discarded after they had become dull, because the added life after sharpening was not sufficient to warrant the cost of sharpening.

than manual control of the tap feed. Sometimes, however, the required control of dimensions or finish (or both) can be obtained only by special procedures (as in Example 898, in the article on Machining of Aluminum Alloys).

Tapping Blind Holes

In tapping blind holes, as the distance, or clearance, between the last full thread and the bottom of the hole decreases, the chamfer length of the tap used must be reduced. With shorter-chamfer taps, however, not only is the cutting load borne by fewer teeth, but the chips produced are larger and coarser, and consequently more difficult to expel. Moreover, as the clearance decreases, there is less room for chips that precede the tap. If more chips enter the clearance space than can be accommodated, they will be compressed by the advancing tap, which may cause tap breakage or hole damage, or both.

Selection of Tap. Standard hand taps with straight flutes are seldom used for blind-hole tapping. When there is enough clearance for the chips at the bottom of the hole, spiral-point straight-flute taps (see Fig. 4b), are commonly used, because they drive the chips ahead of the tap. When clearance at the bottom of the hole is insufficient for the chips, spiral-flute taps (see Fig. 4c), with a flute lead angle of 30° to 55°, are used.

Taper-chamfer taps (see Fig. 3a) are seldom used for complete tapping of blind holes, because of the large clearance required for their 7-to-9-thread chamfer. Plug-chamfer taps (Fig. 3b) are more commonly used, because they offer a compromise between the ideal load distribution of the taper chamfer and the high load concentration of bottoming-chamfer taps (Fig. 3c). The most common practice is to drill the hole deeper by a distance of at least five threads more than must be tapped, and then tap with a plug-chamfer tap.

Tapping to the bottom of a blind hole is slow and expensive, because it invariably entails some hand tapping. However, when blind holes *must* be threaded to the bottom (as, for example, when creating seals for pressures of 4000 psi or more), the practice most commonly employed is as follows:

1. Machine-tap as far as possible, using a plug-chamfer tap. (In many instances, it is more economical to start the hole with a taper-chamfer tap, thus minimizing the amount of metal that will later be removed by taps having shorter chamfers.)
2. Hand tap, using a standard bottoming-chamfer tap (which can produce threads within 1 to 1½ threads from the bottom).
3. If required, hand tap with a special minimum-chamfer (about 0.010 in.) tap, which can tap one thread or less from the bottom.

Examples of practice in two applications of blind-hole tapping are presented below (see also Example 761, in "Machining of Stainless Steel", and Example 899, in "Machining of Aluminum Alloys").

Example 240. Straight-Flute vs Spiral-Flute Taps for Deep Blind Holes

Blind holes, tap drilled to 0.089-in. diameter, 13⁄32-in. depth, in aircraft-engine parts made of 1035 steel were tapped with 4–40 threads to a depth of 0.336 in. (three times the major diameter of the No. 4 threads). Originally, straight-flute taps made of high speed steel were used. Both two-flute and three-flute taps broke after threading only three or four pieces, with resultant low productivity and high cost.

A change to two-flute taps with 30° flute lead solved the problem. With the spiral-flute taps, tool life was increased to 50 or 60 holes per grind, and tap breakage was almost eliminated. Machine and operating conditions were alike for both types of taps.

Example 241. Tapping to 3⁄32 In. From Bottom of Deep Blind Holes (Fig. 19)

Figure 19 shows the tap and setup used on a vertical tapping machine for cutting 3⁄8–24 UNF–2B threads within 3⁄32 in. of the bottom of deep blind holes (length-to-diameter ratio, about 2.8 to 1) in heat treated alloy steel workpieces. With the two-thread-chamfer tap, only about 0.010-in. chip clearance was provided at the bottom of these holes, making efficient chip removal mandatory.

Chips were removed by taps with three 18° right-hand-spiral flutes (Fig. 19). The taps were steam oxide treated, which helped to promote chip flow and to prevent edge buildup. During tapping, two streams of cutting fluid (under pressure) were directed into the hole, approximately parallel to the axis of the tap, to flush chips out of the hole.

Tap details and operating conditions are given with Fig. 19.

Speed

Table 12 lists nominal speeds for tapping carbon and low-alloy steels. It shows that work-metal hardness has a great effect on the speed used. Similar tables for tapping other metals will be found in separate articles in this volume that deal with machining of specific metals. The direction in which to modify tapping speed for various conditions is indicated in the list at the top of the next column.

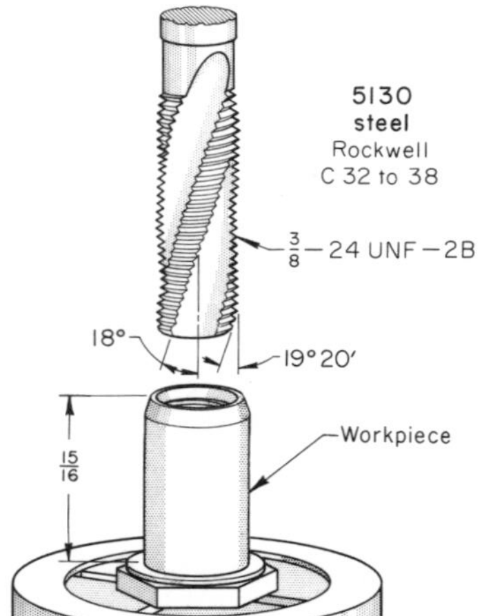

Tap Details

Material	M1 high speed steel
Surface treatment	Steam oxide
Number of flutes	3
Number of threads in chamfer	2
Hook angle	3°
Chamfer angle	19° 20′
Flute helix angle, right-hand	18°
Chamfer relief	0.0083 in.

Operating Conditions

Hole depth	15⁄16 in.
Length of threaded portion	27⁄32 in.
Per cent of full thread	71%
Speed	407 rpm (40 sfm)
Cutting fluid	Sulfurized oil
Tap life, holes	858

Fig. 19. Tapping a deep blind hole to 3⁄32 in. from the bottom in hardened steel (Example 241)

1. As hole length increases, speed must decrease because of chip accumulation.
2. In short holes, taps with long chamfers can run faster than taps with short chamfers.
3. Taps with bottoming chamfers must run slower than taps with plug chamfers.
4. As percentage of thread being tapped increases, speed must decrease.
5. As pitch becomes finer for a given hole size, tapping speed can increase.
6. With all other factors remaining equal, the cutting fluid, together with the amount used and the effectiveness of application, greatly influences optimum speed. (See Table 13, Example 243, and the section "Cutting Fluids", which follows.)

In tapping, feed is governed by the pitch of the thread being tapped; thus, only speed can be adjusted. Optimum tapping speed is usually based on minimum cost per hole, and is usually a compromise between maximum tap life and maximum productivity. Low speeds result in longer tap life (and consequently in lower tap cost) but productivity is low.

As indicated in the examples in this article, a wide range of speeds can be used successfully in tapping most metals. In tapping hard and otherwise difficult-to-machine alloys, however, it is especially important to select cutting speed carefully for optimum results, as the range of economical operating conditions is relatively narrow. The paragraphs that follow outline a method employed in determining optimum speeds for tapping through-holes in ferrous heat-resisting alloys.

Figure 20 illustrates the method by describing its application to the tapping of ¼–28 and ½–20 holes in PH 15-7 Mo, which had been precipitation hardened to Rockwell C 43. High speed steel tools were used, grade M1 for the smaller holes and grade M10 for the larger. Tool details and composition of cutting fluid are given with Fig. 20.

The first step was to select a workable starting speed on the basis of previous experience; then the speed was adjusted in increments to find the most economical value ("speed search"). Each tap was kept in use until it needed sharpening or replacement. Tool life was expressed in terms of volume of metal removed or number of holes tapped before the tap stopped performing satisfactorily. Three factors were included in the determination of machining cost: tool-use cost, tool-change cost, and operating cost.

In the graphs of Fig. 20, total tapping cost per hole is the sum of:

1. Operating cost per minute times number of minutes required to tap one hole
2. Tool-change cost divided by tap life in holes per tap.
3. Tool-use cost divided by tap life in holes per tap.

Dividing this total by the volume of metal removed per hole gives the total tapping cost in dollars per cubic inch of metal removed.

In both of the speed searches shown in Fig. 20, total tapping cost is at a minimum, and is nearly constant, over a limited range of speeds, but is substantially greater at higher cutting speeds.

The method for determining optimum speed just described is concerned with the relation between tapping speed

Table 12. Nominal Speeds for Tapping Carbon and Low-Alloy Steels With High Speed Steel Taps (a)

Typical steel(b)	Condi-tion(c)	Brinell hardness	Speed, sfm
1020	Ann	85 to 125	55
	Ann	125 to 175	45
	Ann	175 to 225	40
	Ann	225 to 275	30
1045	Ann	125 to 175	45
	Ann	175 to 225	40
	Ann	225 to 275	35
	Ann	275 to 325	25
	Q&T	325 to 375	20
	Q&T	375 to 425	10
1112	Ann	100 to 150	60
	CD	150 to 200	65
1117	Ann	100 to 150	50
	CD	150 to 200	55
1137	Ann	175 to 225	50
	Q&T	275 to 325	35
	Q&T	325 to 375	20
	Q&T	375 to 425	10
12L14	Ann	100 to 150	60
	Ann	150 to 200	55
	Ann	200 to 250	45
4140	Ann	175 to 225	35
	Q&T	275 to 325	25
	Q&T	325 to 375	15
	Q&T	375 to 425	10
4140+S	Ann	150 to 200	45
	Q&T	275 to 325	25
	Q&T	375 to 425	10
	Q&T	R_C 45 to 48	7
41L40	Ann	150 to 200	45
	Q&T	275 to 325	20
	Q&T	325 to 375	15
	Q&T	R_C 45 to 48	7
8620	Ann	125 to 175	45
	Ann	175 to 225	40
	CD	225 to 275	35
	CD	275 to 325	25
	Q&T	325 to 375	20
	Q&T	375 to 425	10

(a) M1, M7 and M10 high speed steel are suitable for tapping carbon and low-alloy steel no harder than 375 Bhn; M3 and M40, for steel of 375 Bhn and higher. (b) Each steel listed is a common grade in a group of similar steels. For a listing of the steels in the various groups, see Table 2, page 6. (c) Ann = Annealed; Q&T = Quenched and tempered; CD = Cold drawn. (Data are adapted from tables compiled by Metcut Research Associates, Inc.)

and cost. The two examples that follow demonstrate the relation of speed to other process variables.

Example 242. Effect of Speed on Productivity and Tap Life

To determine the effect of speed on tap life and production rate, three different speeds were used for tapping 4–40 threads in through holes, 3/32 in. deep and 0.089 in. in diameter, in 1015 and 1018 steels at 100 to 125 Bhn. The taps used at all speeds were straight two-flute taps made of general-purpose high speed steel, with 5° hook, 18° chamfer and 5° chamfer relief. Sulfurized mineral oil was used as the cutting fluid. Results were as follows:

Speed		Holes per hour	Tap life, holes
Rpm	Sfm		
4002	118	1200	7200
2728	80	1155	10800
1394	41	1080	9350

The greater tap life at 80 sfm than at 41 sfm may have resulted from slight variations in grinding the taps, or the slower speed of 41 sfm may have permitted chips to be trapped.

Example 243. Effect of Speed, Cutting Fluid and Workpiece Hardness on Tap Life (Table 13)

A series of tests was conducted to determine the speed, cutting fluid and material hardness that would result in optimum tool life in high-production tapping of 1041 steel nuts. Four different speeds, in combination with three different types of cutting fluid and three different ranges of workpiece hardness, were evaluated; test conditions and results are reported in Table 13. As these data indicate, the preferred hardness was Rockwell C 30 to 32, and nuts in this hardness range yielded the greatest tool life when tapped at 43 or 49 sfm and with a blend of sulfurized oil and lard oil as the cutting fluid.

Cutting Fluids

A cutting fluid is more important in tapping than in most other machining operations because tap teeth are more susceptible to damage from heat than are most other cutting-tool surfaces, and because chips are more likely to become congested in tapping than in operations in which the cutters are not surrounded by the work material. Cutting fluids are generally used in tapping all metals except cast iron.

For tapping holes longer than about twice the diameter, or blind holes, in cast iron, however, a cutting fluid or an air blast is recommended. A weak emulsion of soluble oil in water (1 part oil to 40 parts water) or plain water with a rust inhibitor have both been successful.

Cutting fluids most commonly used for tapping various metals are listed in Table 14. Regardless of the type of cutting fluid used, application (conveying the fluid to the cutting areas) is important and is usually more difficult than in operations such as turning or milling. To insure maximum effectiveness, the cutting fluid should be directed at the tap with pressure sufficient to force it down the flutes of the tap. Under extreme conditions, as in the tapping of deep blind holes, the cutting fluid should be directed at the tap in two streams, one on each side of the tap and as nearly parallel as possible to the axis of the tap.

Another important consideration is removal of fine metal particles from recirculated cutting fluid. This swarf, as it is called, is highly abrasive. Recirculated fluids should be screened or filtered.

Sulfurized or chlorinated oils, used individually or diluted with mineral oil, have proved satisfactory for a large proportion of tapping applications and are especially desirable for tapping most steels, including stainless steels, and difficult-to-machine metals like heat-resisting alloys. In a majority of the examples in this article, the cutting fluid is sulfurized oil. Sulfurized or chlorinated oil is usually lower in viscosity than a lard oil mixture. Thus, waste by carry-out is reduced. Another advantage of sulfurized or chlorinated cutting oil is adjustability — that is, the oil can be used straight (for full effectiveness) or diluted with mineral oil, to lower the viscosity and cost without sacrificing the desirable effects of the additive-containing oil. When prior experience in a similar application is not available, it is advisable to begin a tapping operation with straight sulfurized oil and then to dilute it gradually until results approach unacceptability in accuracy, finish, or tool life.

The main disadvantage in the use of sulfurized or chlorinated oil is that the fluid will stain some metals — for instance, many copper-base and nickel-base alloys. When staining is objectionable, a test should be made to determine compatibility of the cutting oil and work metal.

Soluble-oil emulsions are inexpensive and serve adequately for cooling and flushing away chips, but are less effective than straight oils for preventing adherence of tools to workpieces and preventing built-up edges. Soluble oil can be used without fear of staining metals like copper and aluminum. Most soluble oils contain an inhibitor to prevent rusting of steel workpieces.

Mineral oil blended with lard oil or other animal fats (usually 10 to 20%) is effective in preventing adherence of tool to work metal. Also, mineral oil can be used on all metals without causing staining or rusting. However, it is less effective for cooling and flushing away chips than are soluble oil emulsions. A marked disadvantage of mineral and lard oil mixtures is that, because of their relatively high viscosity

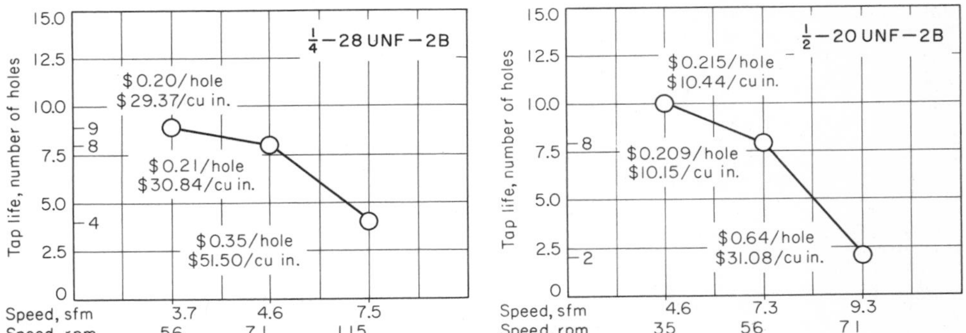

Item	Thread size(a) 1/4-28 UNF-2B	1/2-20 UNF-2B
Tap Details		
Material	M1 HSS	M10 HSS
Over-all length, in. ..	3	3 3/8
Number of flutes	4	3
Hook angle	2°	2°
Chamfer angle	30°	9°
Chamfer relief angle	5°	4°
Chamfered threads ..	3	3
Type of tap	Plug	Plug
Drilled holes diam, in.	0.213	0.453

Item	Thread size(a) 1/4-28 UNF-2B	1/2-20 UNF-2B
Cost Factors		
Tool use	$1.09	$0.99
Tool change	0.20	0.20
Operating	0.116	0.116

(a) Both sizes were tapped in an automatic machine; cutting fluid, brush applied, consisted of a lithopone-pigmented compound ground in a mixture of lard oil and mineral oil, containing additions of fatty ester.

Fig. 20. Determination of optimum speed for tapping of through holes in PH 15-7 Mo

Table 13. Tool Life in Tapping 1041 Steel Nuts as Influenced by Speed, Cutting Fluid, and Workpiece Hardness (Example 243) (a)

Speed Rpm	Speed Sfm	Nuts tapped per min	Average life of tap, nuts tapped at Rc hardness of: 30 to 32	32 to 34	34 to 36
Cutting Fluid 1(b)					
144	33	7.2	997	1002	728
162	37	8	1092	1037	830
186	43	9.3	1200	1148	1103
212	49	10.6	976	950	942
Cutting Fluid 2(c)					
144	33	7.2	1002	929	716
162	37	8	1285	1184	994
186	43	9.3	1426	1420	1167
212	49	10.6	1447	1382	1273
Cutting Fluid 3(d)					
144	33	7.2	580	623	514
162	37	8	968	796	644
186	43	9.3	1019	1000	979
212	49	10.6	1250	999	847

(a) Data are based on tapping, to 73% of full depth, ⅞–14 UNF–2B threads through 29/32-in.-thick hexagonal nuts that had been double chamfered and countersunk, in a 4.2-hp two-spindle horizontal automatic nut tapper. Taps used were straight four-flute taps made of M2 high speed steel (Rockwell C 65 to 66), and were nitrided and given a black oxide treatment. Taps had GH6 pitch-diameter limit, ten-thread chamfer, 30° chamfer angle, 5° chamfer relief, 3° rake, and thread relief of 0.0035 to 0.005 in. following a 1/32 in. concentric margin at the cutting edge. All cutting fluids were directed horizontally at the tap under 5-psi pressure and at 1⅓ gal per min.
(b) Brown-black sulfurized oil containing 2.92% total sulfur, 2.42% active sulfur, and 3.0% fat oils; viscosity at 100 F, 160 SUS. (c) Brown transparent blend of sulfurized and lard oils containing 1.25% total sulfur, 1.0% active sulfur, and 4.0% lard oil; viscosity at 100 F, 130 to 135 SUS. (d) Stable emulsion of 7 parts water and 1 part chalk-white petroleum-chemical concentrate mixed with highly chlorinated oils.

Table 14. Cutting Fluids Commonly Used in Tapping Various Metals

Metal	Sulfurized oil	Sulfurized and chlorinated oil	Soluble oil	Kerosine plus lard oil	Light mineral oil	Dry
Steel, Rc 5 to 30	X	...	...	...	...	...
Steel, Rc 30 to 40	...	X	...	...	...	...
Steel, Rc 40 to 55	...	X(a)	...	...	...	...
Stainless steel	X	X	...	...	...	...
Gray iron	...	...	X(b)	...	...	X(b)
Malleable or nodular iron	X	...	X	...	...	...
Aluminum and alloys	...	...	X	X	...	...
Copper and alloys	...	...	X	X	X	...
Heat-resisting alloys(c)	X(d)	X(d)	...	X(d)	...	...

(a) Highly chlorinated. (b) Dry tapping may cause chip congestion in deep or blind holes; for these, an air blast or a weak soluble-oil: water emulsion (1 part oil to 40 parts water) is recommended. (c) Nickel or cobalt base. (d) Some staining of the work may result from the use of sulfurized oils; when this is objectionable, kerosine plus lard oil can be used.

and wetting characteristics, they cling tenaciously to chips. Thus, waste by carry-out is higher than with less viscous fluids.

Examples. The two examples that follow describe applications in which cutting fluid was changed to increase tapping efficiency (see also Table 13).

Example 244. Effect of Cutting Fluid and Change of Tap on Tap Life

In tapping ¼–20 UNC–3B threads in mild steel T-nuts, tap life was increased more than threefold by changing from standard taps with no thread relief or surface treatment to nitrided taps provided with a thread relief and given a steam-oxide treatment. All taps were two-flute spiral-point taps with plug chamfers and GH3 pitch-diameter limit, cost $1.55 each, and were used in an automatic nut tapper with soluble oil as cutting fluid.

The original taps became loaded with metal on the thread flanks, and tapped oversize after 8000 holes (tool cost per 1000 holes, $0.19). With the nitrided, oxide-treated, thread-relieved taps, tool life was increased to 25,000 holes per tap, and tool cost per 1000 holes was reduced to $0.062.

Tool life with the reselected taps was further increased, to 40,000 holes per tap, by substituting sulfurized oil for soluble oil as the cutting fluid. This reduced tool cost per 1000 holes to $0.038.

Example 245. Reselection of EP Additive to Improve Tap Life

Annealed 1045 steel was tapped with ½–13 UNC–2B threads, ⅝ in. deep. A soluble oil with an EP (extreme pressure) additive was used for the cutting fluid; however, tap life was not satisfactory. A change was made in the cutting fluid to a more active EP lubricant. Tap life increased 80%, and surface finish showed a substantial improvement.

Another application in which a change in cutting fluid increased tool life is discussed in Example 896, in the article on Machining of Aluminum Alloys.

Torque for Tapping

Torque demand for tapping generally dictates the size of machine, rigidity of tool holder, and type of workholding devices. Some of the factors that determine torque demand are:

1 Workpiece material and hardness
2 Tap design
3 Surface speed
4 Per cent of full thread
5 Method of grinding the tap
6 Cutting fluid.

Workpiece Hardness and Composition. One company producing threaded nuts in large quantities conducted a series of tests to evaluate the effect of hardness of the steel workpiece on torque. The procedure and results are given in the following example:

Example 246. Effect of Hardness of Steel Workpiece on Torque (Fig. 21)

An automatic nut tapper was used to produce ⅞–14 UNF–2B threads, 73% of full depth, in pierced nuts of 1041 steel. The diameter of the pierced hole was 0.808/0.806 in. Nuts were sorted to obtain one lot that had hardness values of Rockwell C 20 or less and a second lot that was Rockwell C 25 or slightly less. Three additional lots were prepared by heat treating nuts to obtain ranges of Rockwell C 30 to 31, 34 to 35, and 43 to 45. All five lots of nuts were tapped in the same way. Torque was measured and recorded; results are plotted in Fig. 21.

Figures 22 to 25 show that work-metal composition also has a marked effect on torque. Gray iron shows the lowest torque for all conditions, and 1020 steel shows the highest of the three ferrous metals tested. This suggests that the more stringy chip characteristic of 1020 steel has a significant adverse effect on torque.

Tap Design. The data in Fig. 22 indicate only a small difference in torque between spiral-point and straight-flute taps for tapping O6 tool steel. However, when tapping 1020 steel, torque for the straight flute, plug-chamfer tap exceeds that for the spiral point by a factor of about three.

Figure 24 shows there is essentially no difference in torque between 4½° and 11° hook angles when tapping gray iron and only a small difference in tapping O6 tool steel. However, when 1020 steel is being tapped, the 11° hook angle shows less torque than the 4½° hook angle, by amounts varying from 10 to 50%, other factors remaining unchanged.

Surface speed has only a minor effect on torque for tapping any of the three materials, as indicated by the data shown in Fig. 22 and 23.

Per cent of full thread tapped has a marked influence on torque requirements (Fig. 24), because more metal is removed in producing full threads.

Grinding the Taps. Small differences in the grinding of tap chamfers have often proved to be a major variable causing large differences in tap life and other results. Three methods of grinding tap chamfers were included as part of the investigation of factors influencing torque. Results (Fig. 25) show that taps ground in an automatic chamfer grinder require less torque, regardless of the metal being tapped.

Cutting fluid influences torque, as indicated in Fig. 26. Even with cast iron, which is commonly tapped without a cutting fluid, it is apparent that torque is reduced a small amount by using an air blast and more by using liquids.

Rigidity of the tap was suspected of affecting torque, and gray iron was tapped using both full-floating and rigid types of tool holders. Results (Fig. 27) indicate that misalignment of the tap, which cannot be entirely avoided when a rigid holder is used, does increase tapping torque.

Cold Form Tapping

Cold forming taps produce internal threads by an action similar to thread rolling; metal is displaced rather than being removed. The thread form is produced by a tool like the one in Fig. 28. This tool has neither flutes nor cutting edges. It resembles a simple screw when viewed from the side (Fig. 28, left), but the end view (Fig. 28, right) shows that both the major and minor diameters have irregular contours that displace the work metal as either the tap or the workpiece is rotated.

Metals Tapped. Not all metals can be tapped by cold forming. Initially this process was successful only in soft, ductile metals such as copper and aluminum. (Cold form tapping of through

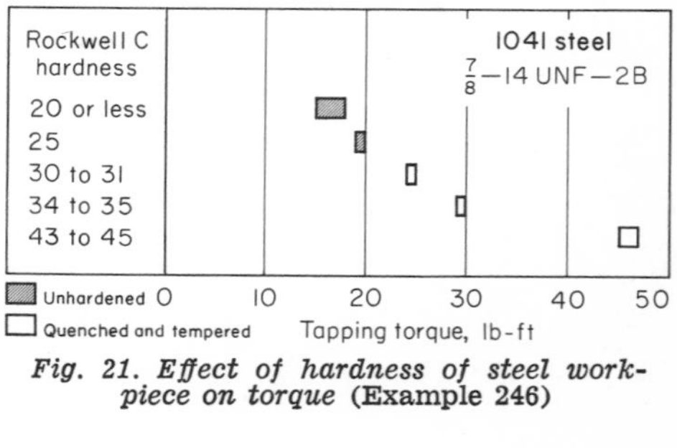

Fig. 21. Effect of hardness of steel workpiece on torque (Example 246)

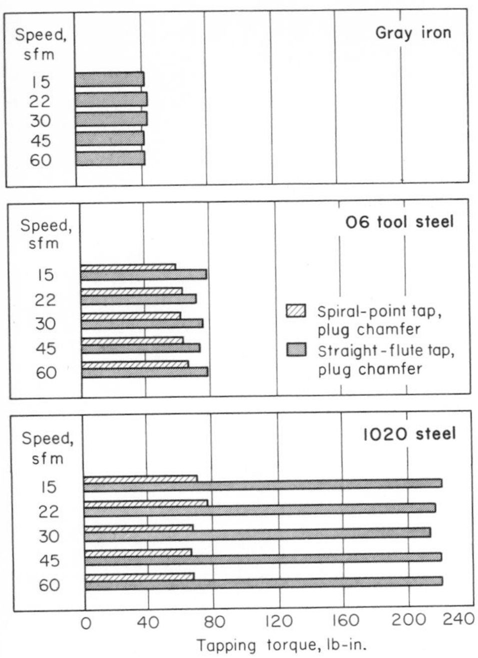

Data were obtained in cutting ⅜–16 UNC-2B threads, to 75% of full depth, through 9/16-in. stock, with high speed steel taps (hook angle, 4° 30′), using sulfurized oil as cutting fluid.

Fig. 22. Effect of work metal, tap design, and speed on torque

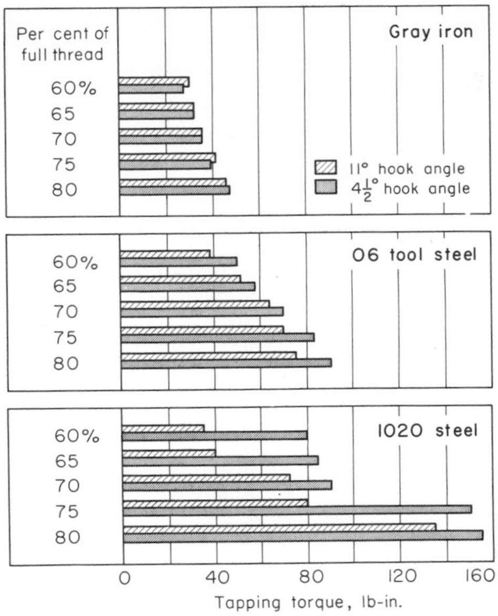

Fig. 24. Effect of work metal, hook angle of tap, and per cent of full thread on torque. Speed, 60 sfm; other conditions, same as for Fig. 22.

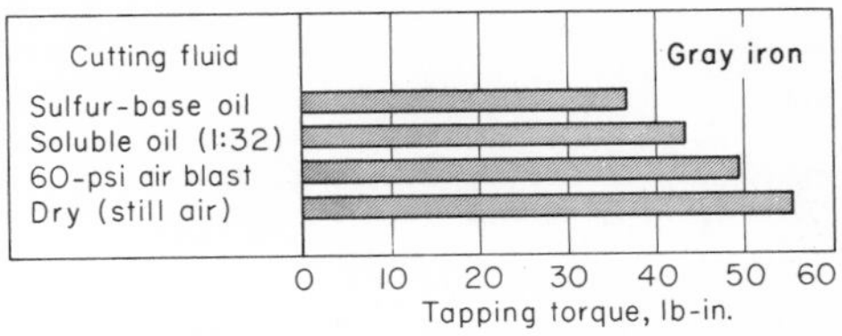

Fig. 26. Effect of type of cutting fluid on torque required for tapping gray iron. Speed, 60 sfm; other conditions, same as for Fig. 22.

holes in aluminum die castings is discussed in Example 901, in the article on Machining of Aluminum.) It has, however, been successful in some soft steels, precipitation-hardening stainless steels and iron-base powder metallurgy parts. Some metals that are difficult to tap by conventional tapping because they form stringy chips can be tapped more successfully by cold form tapping.

Because cold forming taps are used largely in nonferrous metals and in ductile low-carbon steels, they need not be so hard as cutting tools. Thus, M1, M2 and M10 high speed steels with lower-than-normal carbon content can be used for cold forming taps.

Advantages. The primary advantage of cold form tapping is that no chips are produced. Hence, cold form tapping is especially desirable for blind holes.

In one instance, during conventional tapping of aluminum, chips in the bottom of ½-in.-deep holes (4–40 UNC-2B threads to ⅜-in. depth) caused rejection of 30,000 pieces. A secondary operation was needed to remove the chips. Acceptable threads were obtained by cold form tapping of subsequent lots.

In another application, blind holes were being tapped in aluminum die castings, with a two-flute spiral-point tap. Removing the chips required 16 man-hours per 1000 parts. A change to cold forming eliminated the need for chip removal. In this operation, tool life averaged 9750 holes per tap.

(Cold form tapping of blind holes is also discussed in Example 943, in the article on Machining of Copper.)

Processing. Cold form tapping can be done in almost any machine used for conventional tapping; however, the power requirements are different. Tapping torque increases with tapping depth at a greater rate in cold form tapping than in conventional tapping. As a rule, where 75% or less of full thread is specified, the torque required for cold form tapping varies with the metal being tapped, from equal torque to twice as much as for conventional tapping. In cold form tapping stainless steel, however, the torque may be five times the torque for cutting threads.

Speed for cold form tapping is normally 2½ to 3 times as fast as for conventional tapping. However, high speed is not required; cold form tapping can be done successfully by hand in the simplest of methods.

Sulfurized and chlorinated oils are preferred for cold form tapping. Other fluids commonly used for metal cutting operations cause galling and tearing of the threads.

Because the metal is displaced as in thread rolling, tap drill holes must be larger than for conventional tapping.

Tapping of Taper Pipe Threads

Cutting taper pipe threads (Fig. 29) with taps does not differ greatly from tapping machine threads. However, because standard taper pipe threads (NPT) are designed to provide pressure-tight seals, they require closer control in tapping than do thread forms for which 75% of full thread is acceptable. Also, in tapping taper pipe threads, more teeth are cutting at one time than in tapping straight threads; consequently, pipe thread tapping requires more power than straight thread tapping, size for size. In one instance it was determined by tests that 1.93 hp was required to tap a ⅜–18 NPS straight thread, whereas to tap a ⅜–18 NPT taper pipe thread, 2.14 hp was required.

Machines used for cutting taper pipe threads are usually the same as those used for other types of tapping. Positive lead control is desirable for best results in taper thread tapping because all tap teeth are cutting at one time.

Tools. Solid taps for cutting taper pipe threads are of the same two general types as for tapping straight threads — nonadjustable and adjustable. Solid, nonadjustable taps are used for the smaller sizes where adjustable or collapsible taps would not be practical.

Adjustable solid taps have removable chasers that can be adjusted for pitch

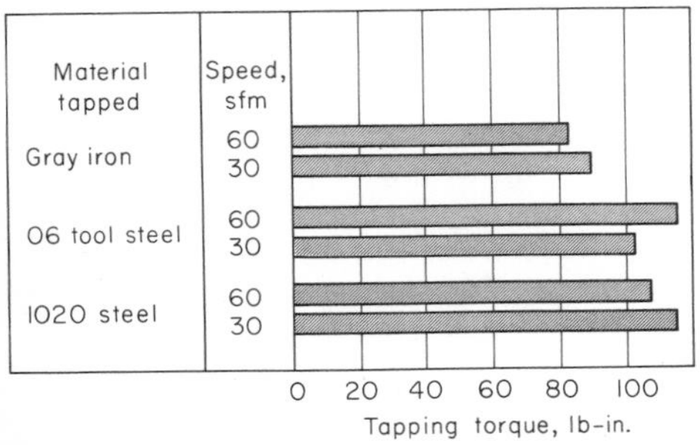

Data were obtained with ⅛–27 NPT high speed steel taps for cutting threads in 0.339-in.-deep straight reamed holes to gage line. Sulfurized oil was used as cutting fluid.

Fig. 23. Effect of work metal and speed on torque in taper tapping

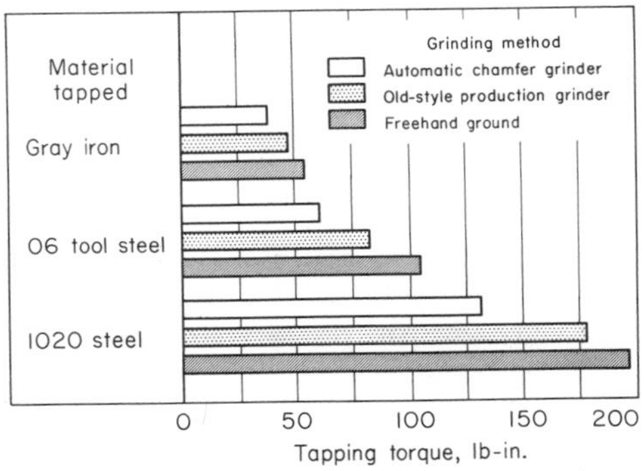

Fig. 25. Effect of method of grinding tap chamfer on torque for tapping workpieces of three different metals. Speed, 60 sfm; other conditions, same as for Fig. 22.

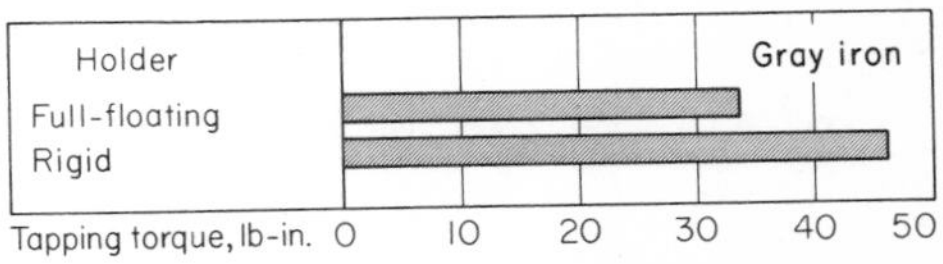

Fig. 27. Effect of method of holding tap on torque required for tapping gray iron. Speed, 60 sfm; no cutting fluid; other conditions, same as for Fig. 22.

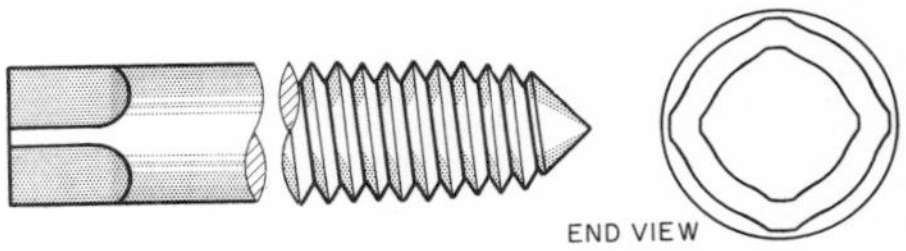

Fig. 28. Cold forming tap, showing the irregular contour whereby the tap displaces work metal when rotated

diameter and reground or separately replaced when worn. When close control of pitch line taper is required with heavy stock removal, the adjustable solid tap is preferred. Manufacturers of pipe fittings use adjustable solid taps to cut taper pipe threads in gray iron and malleable iron fittings without prior machining of the as-cast diameters.

Collapsible taps permit the individual cutting components to be retracted from the work automatically when the thread is completed and withdrawn without reversing the direction of rotation. Automatic collapsible taps permit shorter machine cycles by eliminating the backing-out time, and they also increase tool life because cutting edges are not dragged back over the previously cut threads. Disadvantages of collapsible taps in comparison with solid adjustable taps are: higher initial cost, greater susceptibility to fouling from swarf-contaminated cutting fluids, and increased maintenance.

Stop Lines. The prescribed taper in pipe threads is 1/16 in. in diameter for each inch of length (3/4 in. per foot). Thus, each successive tooth cuts a progressively larger diameter in the hole as the tap advances. Because each tooth is cutting at the instant of tap reversal, a stop line remains on the thread surface.

Some thread specifications do not permit stop lines. Also, when solid taps are used, cutting edges must be reversed over these stop lines, which create an abrasive action that causes excessive tap wear. The severity of stop lines can be reduced by increasing the number of flutes in the tap. However,

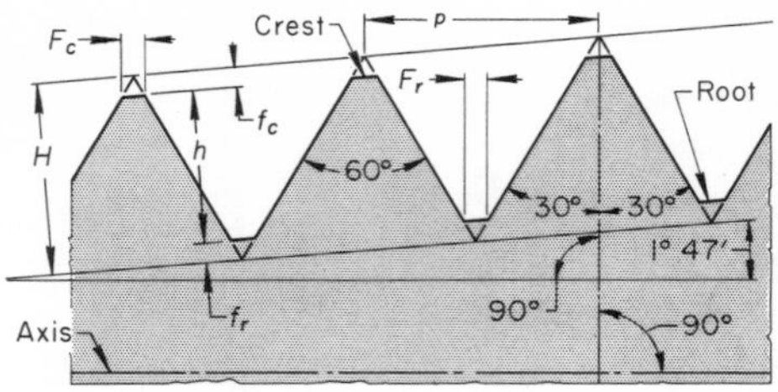

$H = 0.866025p$ = height of 60° sharp V thread
$h = 0.800000p$ = height of thread on product
$p = 1/n$ = pitch (measured parallel to axis)
n = number of threads per inch
f_c = depth of truncation at crest
f_r = depth of truncation at root
F_c = width of flat at crest
F_r = width of flat at root

Fig. 29. Basic form of American standard taper pipe threads

for complete elimination of stop lines, a collapsible tap is required.

In general, stop lines are more pronounced the more ductile the work metal. As stop lines increase in severity, problems of thread quality and tool damage also increase.

Speed, in surface feet per minute, is usually 20 to 30% lower for pipe tapping than for the cutting of machine threads, because more teeth are cutting during pipe tapping. However, in some shops little or no distinction is made between machine and pipe threads in determining tapping speed. Also, in some shops the same speed is used regardless of thread pitch. Figure 23 shows the influence of speed of tapping on torque.

Thread quality does not necessarily increase as speed is decreased. Rough and torn threads often result from speeds that are too slow. Excessive speeds always decrease tool life.

Cutting fluids recommended for pipe tapping are the same as those used for cutting of machine threads (Table 14).

A constant supply of fluid to the cutting area is generally more important in pipe threading than in cutting machine threads, because more cutting teeth are engaged at one time in pipe threading. In addition, because of the accuracy required in pipe threads and the greater amount of cutting that is being done at one time, susceptibility to thread damage from swarf-contaminated cutting fluids is greater in pipe threading. Damage from this source can be prevented by filtering the cutting fluid.

Other Examples of Tapping in This Volume

Work metal	Example number
Methods	
Cast iron	658, 659
Stainless steel	764
Heat-resisting alloys	839
Aluminum	896, 897, 898, 899, 900
Copper	942
Magnesium	989, 990, 991, 992
Methods Compared	
Stainless steel	763
Heat-resisting alloys	838, 340
Aluminum	901
Copper	943, 944, 945
Combined With Other Operations	
Copper	948
Nickel	997
Tap Design or Tap Material	
Stainless steel	761, 762, 765
Copper	941

Thread Milling

THREAD MILLING is a method of cutting screw threads with a milling cutter in a thread mill. Thread-milling cutters are either single-form or multiple-form and are used in either conventional or planetary thread mills. Screw threads cut by thread milling can have pitch diameters that are accurate within 0.001 in., surfaces smooth within 55 micro-in., leads accurate within 0.001 in. per foot, and spacing (of multiple-start threads) accurate within 0.0004 in.

Applications of thread milling are varied. A thread mill can cut internal or external threads and, in some work, can cut both internal and external threads at the same time. The workpiece may be fixed or rotating, so that thread mills compete with lathes and with machines that use taps and dies to cut threads.

The main reasons to prefer thread milling to other methods of cutting screw threads include: (*a*) thread milling makes a smoother and more accurate thread than a tap or a die, (*b*) thread milling is more efficient than cutting the thread with a single-point tool in a lathe, (*c*) the thread has too coarse a pitch for cutting with a die, and (*d*) the thread is near a shoulder or other interference so that thread milling is the most practical method.

Conventional thread mills are either universal or production machines. Universal thread mills have a lead screw and can cut all internal or external threads except square threads. Change gears permit the milling of threads with leads of 1/32 to 60 in. Pick-off gears in the cutter drive provide a wide range of speeds. The cutter head, on the cross slide, can be set at the angle for any right-hand or left-hand thread helix. A single-form cutter must be set at such an angle, and then must traverse the length of the thread.

A multiple-thread milling cutter is set with its axis parallel to the axis of the thread it cuts, and there is no traverse motion. With this method (the most efficient), the work rotates 1.1 turns.

Production thread mills are semiautomatic, using a master screw and stationary segment instead of a lead screw. The master screw and segment must be changed for each change in pitch or lead. A no-lead attachment is used in milling annular grooves.

Planetary thread mills are used to thread odd-shaped parts difficult to chuck, but are not used to thread long pieces such as lead screws. The work is clamped in a fixture. Only the cutter moves, rotating on its axis, which revolves around the work. Double heads can be used to cut both ends of a part. Internal and external threads can be cut at the same time.

Single-thread cutters are used for coarse pitches and for threads that are too long for a multiple cutter.

Multiple-thread cutters have annular rows of teeth of the right form and pitch but no lead. The cutters must be 2 to 3 pitches longer than the thread to be cut, or the work must be rotated more than the minimum 1.1 turns.

Most multiple-thread cutters are nontopping. They cut only the sides and the root of the thread, the top usually being machined by turning or boring. Topping cutters, not usually recommended, machine all diameters, usually removing not more than 0.010 in. from the diameter, for concentricity.

Speeds and feeds for thread milling of various steels are shown in Table 1.

Table 1. Nominal Speeds and Feeds for Thread Milling With High Speed Steel Tools

Work material	Hardness, Bhn	Speed, sfm	Feed, ipt
Plain carbon steels such as 1020	85-125	140	0.002
	125-175	120	0.002
	175-225	100	0.002
	225-275	80	0.0015
	275-325	70	0.001
Free-machining carbon steels such as 1112	100-150	170	0.002
	150-200	180	0.002
	200-250	125	0.002
	275-325	100	0.001
Alloy steels such as 4140	125-175	110	0.002
	175-225	90	0.002
	225-275	70	0.0015
	275-325	65	0.001
Free-machining alloy steels such as 41L40	150-200	160	0.002
	200-250	130	0.002
	275-325	80	0.001
Ferritic stainless	135-185	110	0.002
Austenitic stainless (304)	135-185	90	0.002
	225-275	80	0.0015
Free-machining austenitic (303)	135-185	100	0.002
	225-275	90	0.0015
Martensitic stainless such as 403	135-185	110	0.002
	185-225	100	0.002
	275-325	60	0.001
Free-machining martensitic such as 416	135-185	150	0.002
	185-240	135	0.002
	275-325	75	0.001
Precipitation-hardening stainless (17-4 PH)	150-200	70	0.002
	275-325	60	0.001
	325-375	45	0.001

Die Threading

*By the ASM Committee on Tapping and Threading**

DIE THREADING is a machining process for cutting external threads in cylindrical or tapered surfaces by the use of solid or self-opening dies. Die threading is a slower method of producing external threads than thread rolling, but it is faster than single-point threading in a lathe.

Hardness of the work metal limits the application of die threading. Attempting to die-thread metals harder than Rockwell C 36 usually causes excessive wear or breakage of tools. Single-point threading or thread grinding is recommended for metals harder than Rockwell C 36.

Size of workpiece seldom limits application of the process. Die threading has been used to cut 280 threads per inch in rods 0.017 in. in diameter. At the other extreme, three threads per inch have been die-cut into 24-in. pipe for the petroleum industry.

Machines

The machines most used for die threading are: drill presses, manual turret lathes, single-spindle and multiple-spindle automatic machines, and special threading machines.

Drill Presses. When workpiece shape permits, and if no other operations are involved, drill presses are often preferred for die threading, because they are easy to set up and simple to operate. A part that can be held in a fast-acting chuck or similar work-holding device can be threaded in a manually operated drill press at least as fast as in any other machine.

Lead-control devices (see page 108) can be incorporated in a drill press. However, if lead control is required, a more rigid type of machine, such as a lathe, is preferred.

*For committee list, see page 107.

Manual turret lathes are often used for threading small to medium quantities, particularly when threading is one of a sequence of required machining operations. When threading is the only operation, the productivity of a turret lathe is lower than that of a drill press, because manipulating a turret is slower than moving a drill-press spindle.

Turret lathes can be equipped to handle either bar stock or semifinished parts. They can also thread pieces that are too large for practical manipulation in a drill press.

Starting the die onto the workpiece by hand feeding is more difficult in a turret lathe than in a drill press, because the weight of the turret makes the operator less sensitive to the resistance of an improperly chased thread. For this reason, many turret lathes used for threading are equipped with lead-control devices (see page 108).

Automatic Machines. Because of the longer setup time and higher running cost involved, automatic machines (automatic turret lathes, single-spindle or multiple-spindle automatic bar or chucking machines, or other automatic equipment) are used only for medium or high production. On these machines, several other operations, in addition to threading, can be done in a cycle.

Special threading machines are available that perform only die threading, on either cylindrical or irregularly shaped parts. Workpieces can be loaded and unloaded by hand, or the machines can be hopper-fed and fully automatic. These machines usually incorporate lead-control devices (see page 108), and are capable of producing class 5 threads. Collet-type machines that can handle long workpieces are commonly used to thread rod, shafts and pipe.

Selection of the most appropriate machine is influenced by the same factors discussed on page 108 of "Tapping". Machines that can produce the various thread classes are selected according to class, as follows:

Class 1 and 2 Threads. Drill presses or turret lathes using manual feed

Class 3 Threads. Drill presses, turret lathes or threading machines equipped with lead control

Class 5 Threads. Precision threading machines equipped with devices for accurate lead control.

Solid Dies

Solid threading dies may be of one-piece construction, with integral cutting edges, or they may have replaceable cutting edges (chasers). One-piece solid dies can be either nonadjustable or adjustable; insert-type solid dies are adjustable. One-piece dies are usually discarded when worn out of tolerance; inserted chasers can be resharpened.

Nonadjustable one-piece dies have all cutting sections in rigidly fixed relationship (Fig. 1). They are available in standard sizes to fit various types of holders.

Adjustable one-piece dies are of two types. One type (Fig. 2) is similar to the nonadjustable type except that the body has been slotted, a spring (relief) hole added, and an adjusting screw incorporated. The adjusting screw permits a small amount of adjustment, to compensate for wear and to retain accuracy greater than is possible with the nonadjustable type.

The other type of adjustable one-piece die is the spring-type (Fig. 3). Adjustability is provided by the design of the body and the holder, which function like a collet chuck. As the outer nut on the holder is tightened, it applies pressure to the tapered section of the die, causing the jaws to be forced inward. The nut can be moved and locked in position as desired, permitting

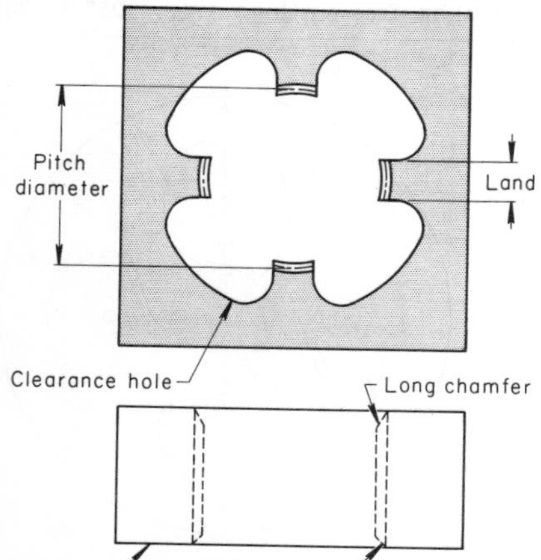

Fig. 1. Nonadjustable one-piece solid die for threading

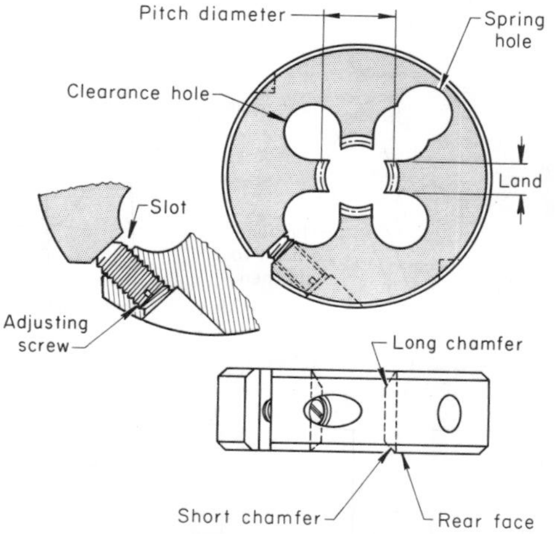

Fig. 2. Adjusting-screw type of solid die for threading

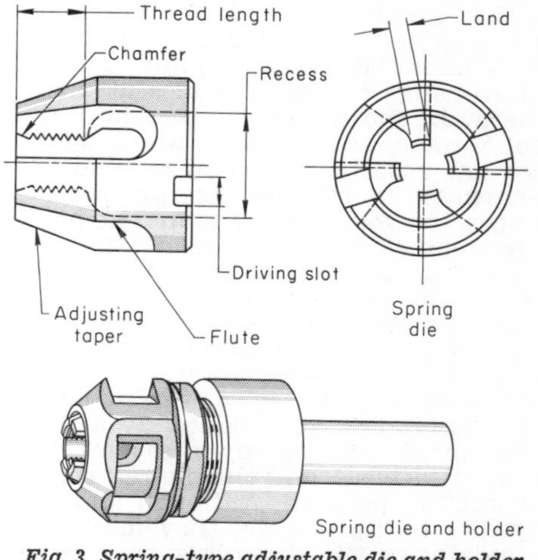

Fig. 3. Spring-type adjustable die and holder for threading

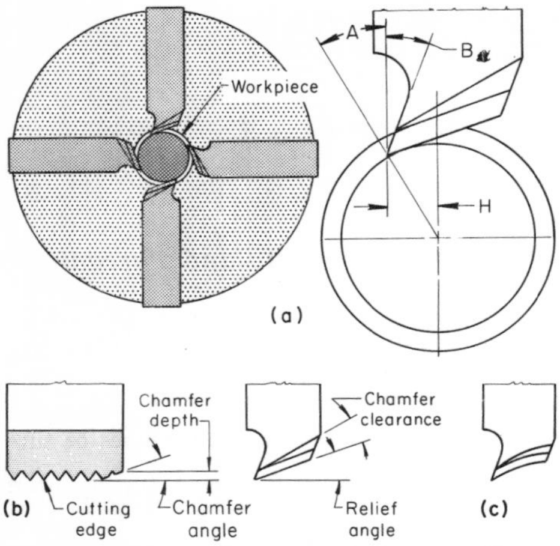

Fig. 4. Radial chasers and their positions in a self-opening die. See text for discussion.

adjustment of the cutting sections and greater accuracy than with nonadjustable dies.

Inserted-chaser solid dies consist of a holder and three or more inserted cutting edges (chasers). The inserts can be adjusted to compensate for wear, and can be removed for sharpening and replaced as required. Consequently, in long production runs, tool cost is lower than when one-piece dies are used.

Like one-piece dies, however, inserted-chaser solid dies can be removed from the work only by being backtracked over the threads cut. Moreover, size for size, they cost more than one-piece dies.

Circular chasers also are used in solid dies, in sets of four or five. With five chasers the die does less burnishing of the work in following the thread than it does using four chasers. The reduction in rubbing helps to make smoother threads and makes the die last longer. Besides, with five chasers the die cuts better with less torque. Example 768, in the article "Machining of Stainless Steel", shows the results of changing from a four-chaser die to one with five chasers.

Self-Opening Dies

There are two basic types of self-opening dies — revolving and stationary. The cutting elements of both types are called chasers, and each type is further identified by chaser design or position, or both. Chasers are designated as radial, tangential and circular.

Revolving self-opening dies are used where the workpiece is fixed and the tool rotates, as in a drill press. These dies are usually opened by a yoke arrangement in the die. As the die advances, the yoke meets a stop. The pressure against the yoke opens the die, retracting the chasers from the workpiece. The die can then return to its starting position for the next cycle.

Stationary self-opening dies are used where the workpiece rotates and the tool does not, as in a turret lathe. Stationary dies are opened at a predetermined point by any of several mechanical devices, and the die returns to its starting position. Although stationary dies do not rotate, they may feed in axially as the threading progresses, not remaining fixed.

Radial Chasers. Figure 4(a) shows the positions of four radial chasers in a self-opening die and the relation of each chaser to the workpiece. The true top rake angle of a radial chaser is determined by adding the visible rake angle B (if positive, as in Fig. 4a) to the point-height angle A. If angle B is negative, the true rake angle is determined by subtracting angle B from the point-height angle A.

Radial chasers are intended to operate at a specific distance from the centerline of the work being threaded. This distance (H, in Fig. 4a) is called the point height. It varies according to the diameter of the work, and is determined by point-height-angle constants supplied for specific models of dies. If distance H is reduced, the amount of bearing surface (chaser against workpiece) and top rake angle are also reduced.

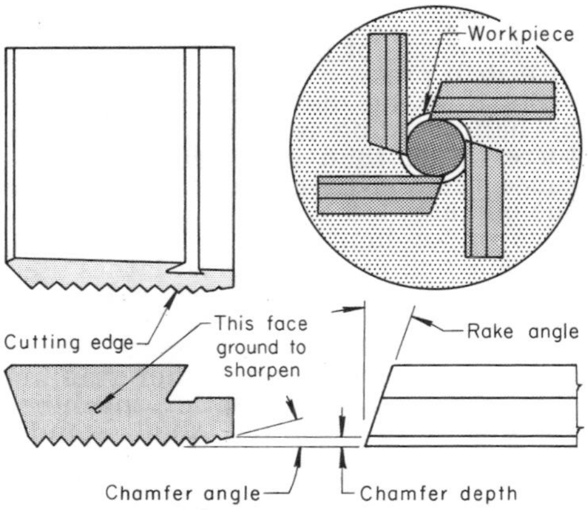

Fig. 5. Tangential chasers and their positions in a self-opening die

Two designs of cutting edge for radial chasers made of high speed steel are illustrated in Fig. 4(b) and (c). A straight cutting edge, as in Fig. 4(b), can be generated by a milling machine or shaper. A circular cutting edge, illustrated in Fig. 4(c), is generated by a rotary tool such as a hob.

Radial chasers can be effectively sharpened only on the chamfer; the removal of more than about 0.001 in. from the area of the rake angle will adversely affect the chaser-workpiece relationship (Fig. 4a). Consequently, the total life of radial chasers is relatively short, so their use is sometimes restricted to the threading of soft, easy-to-machine metals such as aluminum or free-cutting brass.

Tangential Chasers. The position of four tangential chasers in a self-opening die is shown in Fig. 5. These chasers are made in sets, with their cutting edges extending along one face as shown.

The chamfer angle is permanent for the life of the chaser and does not require regrinding. The chamfer section (including the first full tooth) not only cuts the initial thread form, but also removes excess material from oversize stock.

The rake angle of tangential chasers (Fig. 5) is varied according to machining characteristics of the work metal; typical values are given in Table 1.

Tangential chasers are especially suited to threading steel and other metals that are relatively hard, because of their long total life (including resharpenings). Repeated sharpening is permissible as long as a sufficient length of chaser remains to be held for sharpening or to be secured in the die.

Circular chasers, and their positions in the die, are shown in Fig. 6. Circular chasers are made in sets of four or five chasers with annular thread form. A single flute, cut axially across the chaser, provides the cutting edge. The bore of each chaser is serrated for positioning on a holder in the die.

Face and hook angles (Fig. 6) can be modified as required for different work metals. Face angle is usually about 1° 30′ to 2°; hook angle may vary from 5° negative, for threading soft free-cutting brass, to 20° positive, for metals that form stringy chips, such as mild steel or copper. Typical face and hook angles for ferrous metals are given in Table 2.

Circular chasers are used in high production for all metals that are threaded.

Table 1. Typical Rake Angles Used on Tangential Chasers

(All angles are positive.)

Work metal	Rake angle
Gray iron	15° to 25°
Malleable iron	18°
Steel, 160 to 200 Bhn	25°
Steel, 200 to 300 Bhn	18° to 22°
Steel, low-carbon:	
Free-cutting	15° to 25°
Other than free-cutting	25° to 35°

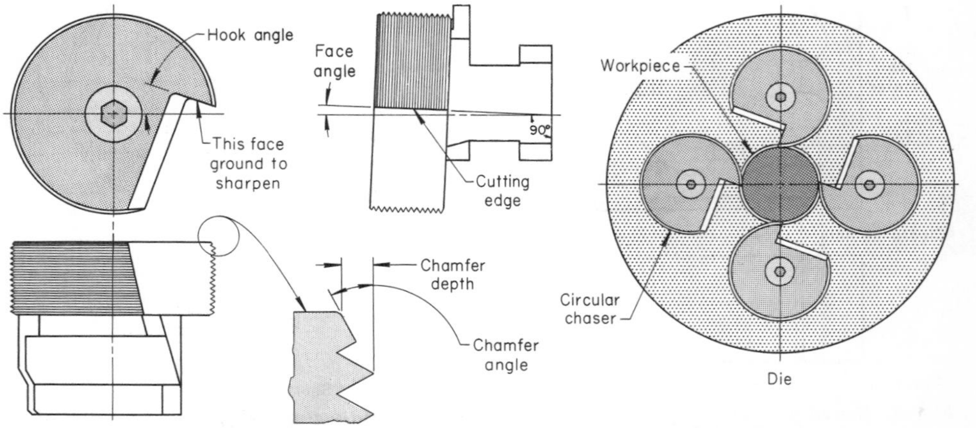

Fig. 6. Circular chasers and their positions in a self-opening die

Table 2. Typical Face and Hook Angles Used on Circular Chasers

Work metal	Face angle(a)	Hook angle
Gray iron	2°	10°
Malleable iron	1° 30′	10°
Steel	1° 30′	20°

(a) For fewer than three threads, double the angle. Decrease angle with higher-than-normal surface speeds, or if threads are excessively rough. Increase angle for subnormal speeds. In general, the larger the angle, the rougher the finish.

They have a long total life, because they can be resharpened as long as there is enough of the chaser remaining to retain the cutting edge and the serrated hole for mounting.

Solid vs Self-Opening Dies

The use of solid dies is generally restricted to small-quantity threading in manually operated machines, or to machines (such as multiple-spindle automatics) that provide insufficient space to permit a self-opening die to operate. The principal reason that solid dies are not preferred for high-production threading is that the spindle must be reversed for die removal after the threads are cut. Backing the die over the threads is time consuming and increases die wear; it can also trap chips between the threads, causing damaged threads or a broken die, or both.

Circumstances sometimes dictate the use of solid dies, despite these disadvantages. For example, when metal beyond the outside diameter of the thread must be removed in the threading operation, solid dies often are used because they are stronger than self-opening dies. A manufacturer of cast iron fittings used self-opening dies to increase production rate, but because excessive metal had to be removed, the dies frequently jammed and failed to open, thus breaking chasers. Breakage was eliminated by changing to solid dies.

Although self-opening dies cost more initially than one-piece solid dies, replacement (or sharpening) of the chasers costs much less than replacing a solid die, and therefore self-opening dies have a lower over-all cost. Also, because self-opening dies have a greater range of adjustability than solid dies, they can be used for threading to any degree of accuracy, in tolerance classes from 1 to 5. Other advantages of self-opening dies are: (*a*) They eliminate the necessity of reversing the spindle to remove the die from the workpiece; (*b*) chip clearance is more easily provided than in solid dies; and (*c*) stop lines can be eliminated.

Die Removal. Ease of removing the die from the workpiece is usually the most important advantage of self-opening dies. The use of a die that returns in the open position eliminates the need for stopping the spindle, regardless of whether the tool or the work is rotating. In some applications, this feature alone increases productivity by 50% or more. In addition to saving time, self-opening dies greatly reduce the possibility of damage to threads from entrapped chips. Furthermore, because the chasers make only one trip over the work, chaser wear is reduced and tool life is increased as shown in Example 247.

Example 247. Increase in Tool Life by Changing to a Self-Opening Die

Control arms for automobile knee-action mechanisms required 13/16–11 NS threads at both ends for a distance of 1¼ in. These arms had been forged from 1030 steel and were threaded in the annealed condition.

Originally, the forgings were threaded by a four-chaser solid die in a two-spindle horizontal threading machine equipped with a lead screw. Workpieces were located on pins and threaded two at a time at one end; then they were turned end for end and the opposite ends were threaded two at a time. Results were satisfactory, but only 600 pieces (1200 ends) could be threaded before the dies required sharpening.

When the solid dies were replaced with self-opening dies with five circular chasers (and with no other process changes), die life was increased to 1200 pieces (2400 ends) per grind.

For both types of dies, threading speed was 12 sfm and cutting fluid was sulfurized oil.

Chip clearance is a chronic problem in thread cutting. Adequate clearance must be provided, so that the chips can curl, break up, and drop away from the cutting edges. When the chip is forced into a pocket, or cannot clear the cutting edge, the threads being cut may be scored and the tool edge damaged.

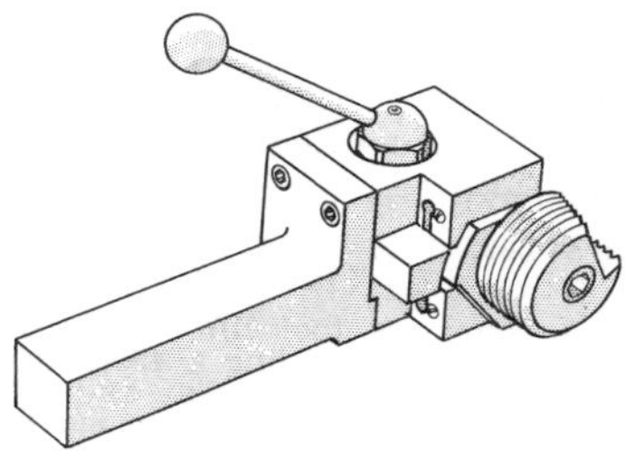

Fig. 7. Circular chaser mounted in a self-opening holder, for single-chaser threading

Solid dies made of expensive tool steel are produced only in small sizes. Practice in designing solid dies limits the length of threading fingers to an absolute minimum, to minimize chatter and premature die failure. This practice reduces the area available for chip clearance.

Although self-opening dies inherently provide more space for chips to enter and drop away from the work, available chip clearance in any die is influenced by the diameter of the threads being cut. As thread diameter decreases, the problem of chip congestion increases.

Stop lines are a problem in die-threaded pieces when solid dies are used. As the die advances on the workpiece, metal is removed by the cutting section. When the cutter stops at the end of the cycle, metal removal stops abruptly, and a stop line, or step, is left on the work at the farthest advance of the cutting edges. There is no practical way to avoid this line when solid dies are being used.

Self-opening dies can be opened just ahead of the point of full advance, causing the cutters to leave the work gradually with a forward rotating motion, thus avoiding cut marks.

Single-Chaser Threading

Thread chasers can be used singly, rather than arranged in groups in a die head. Cutting threads with a single chaser often is advantageous where a part is rotated on centers and a die or holder cannot surround the part, or where there is not enough tool space to permit the use of a multiple-chaser holder. The chaser can be held rigidly in a standard tool holder, or (as shown in Fig. 7) in a holder that opens and closes automatically by means of bumper stops on the machine.

Single-chaser threading often reduces threading time by 50%, compared with single-point threading, particularly if a relatively flat chamfer angle (10°, for example) can be used. A flat chamfer angle allows more threads to participate in the progressive removal of metal to the final thread form. It also increases tool life, although even with a normal chamfer angle of 15° to 20°, tool life of a single chaser is usually greater than that of a single-point tool.

Modification of Chasers

True thread forms are usually cut into the chaser for reproduction on the workpiece. Sometimes, however, the first three or four teeth on the chaser are modified to distribute the cutting forces over a larger area. This technique improves surface finish and prolongs chaser life when hard materials are being threaded.

Chasers are modified by grinding them so that the first thread is cut oversize and succeeding threads are progressively shaved to the correct size, as illustrated in the following example.

Example 248. Modified Chasers for Threading Monel (Fig. 8)

When chasers having true-form lead threads were used for cutting ¾–6 Acme threads in a Monel shaft, the threads were torn and rough along both flanks. The shafts were threaded with a four-chaser, self-opening die operated at 8 sfm and flooded with sulfurized oil.

To obtain a better finish when removing the relatively large amount of metal required by the Acme form, chasers were modified as shown in Fig. 8. The profiles of the 15° chamfered threads and of one or two full threads were changed by removing material as indicated by the black areas lettered A through L in Fig. 8. The sequence of reduc-

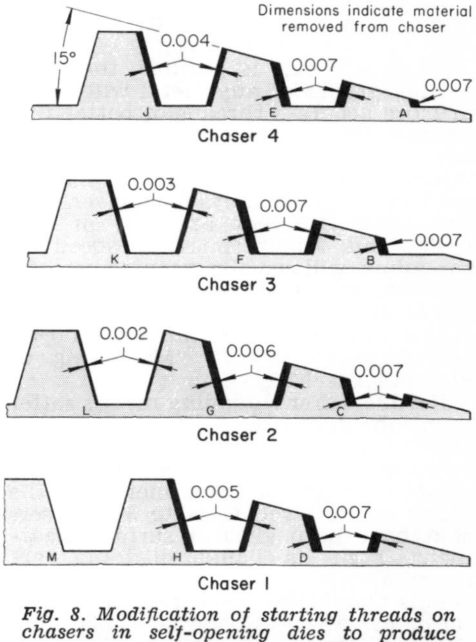

Fig. 8. Modification of starting threads on chasers in self-opening dies to produce acceptable thread finish on Monel shafts (Example 248)

Table 3. Tool Life and Cost in Die Threading Steel at 200 and 225 Bhn (Example 249)

Item	200 Bhn	225 Bhn
Chasers used, sets(a)	2	2
Grinds, total number(b) ...	3	5
Total tool cost for run(c) ..	$10.85	$11.55
Chaser life per set, pieces(d)	300	200
Production, pieces per hour	110	95

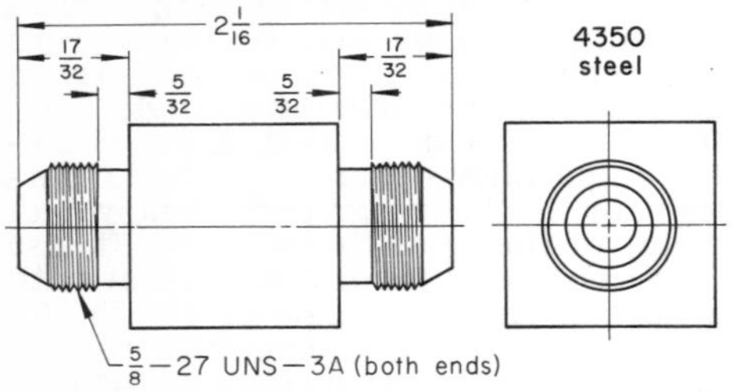

(a) Chasers cost $4.90 per set. (b) Cost for grinding, $0.35 per grind per set. (c) 350 pieces per run. (d) Second set of chasers not completely used during run.

tion in cutting width of the chamfered threads then was:

1 Surface A on chaser 4 was the starting point for a thread flank.
2 Surfaces B through F were consecutive steps along the thread flank progressively cut by each chaser.
3 At surface G, and continuing to surface M, each chaser tooth removed progressively smaller amounts of metal from the thread flanks until the desired thread form was finished by the unmodified chaser teeth.

Factors That Influence Output

The principal factors that influence thread quality, production rate and cost in die threading are:

1 Composition and hardness of work metal
2 Accuracy and finish
3 Thread size
4 Obstacles like shoulders or steps
5 Speed
6 Lead control
7 Cutting fluid.

These factors are usually related, and their relative importance varies greatly in different applications.

Composition and Hardness of Work Metal

When a choice is possible, the free-cutting grades of any metal will result in more accurate threads of better finish at higher production rate and lower cost than the non-free-cutting grades. When free-cutting metal cannot be used, comparable alloys for a given part will cause different amounts of tool wear, and the permissible speed of threading will usually vary somewhat. Typical differences between alternative alloys are illustrated in Example 871, in "Machining of Aluminum Alloys", and Example 766, in "Machining of Stainless Steel".

Hardness. For threading metals softer than about Rockwell C 24, standard chasers, made of general-purpose high speed steel and not surface treated, are usually satisfactory. For metals in the range of Rockwell C 24 to 31, chasers that have been given a surface treatment, such as liquid nitriding, are recommended.

It is possible to die-thread metals as hard as about Rockwell C 36, but chasers made from the more highly alloyed grades of high speed steel (such as M6, M36, M44 or T15) are necessary, and chaser life between grinds is short. Metals harder than Rockwell C 36 are usually threaded by a single-point tool or by grinding.

As work-metal hardness increases, more power is required and rigidity in machines and tools becomes more critical. Also, the advantages of lead control (see page 108) are more pronounced when harder metals are being threaded.

Soft metals, especially non-free-cutting grades, sometimes cause difficulty in die threading, because they form stringy chips that adhere to the chasers.

The hardness for best results in threading stainless steel and other austenitic steels is more critical than that for carbon or low-alloy steel. The preferred range for threading austenitic steels is 200 to 225 Bhn. When these metals are significantly softer than 200 Bhn, they are gummy and adhere to the chasers, causing dimensional variation and poor finish, and the chasers are likely to be damaged. When these metals are significantly harder than 225 Bhn, excessive chaser wear will result.

Examples 249 to 252, which follow, demonstrate the effect of hardness in die threading:

Example 249. 4350 Steel at 200 and 225 Bhn (Table 3)

Table 3 compares tool life, tool cost, and production rate in threading a 4350 steel part (shown in inset in Table 3) at two different hardnesses. The cost figures given represented actual outlay for the necessary chasers and grinding for the runs indicated; probable life remaining in the chasers was not considered. Despite higher tool cost and lower production rate, the harder steel was chosen because stringent finish requirements were more readily met on the harder metal.

Examples 250, 251 and 252. 4350 Steel vs Gray Iron vs Brass (Table 4)

Table 4 compares operating conditions and tool life for cutting ½–20 threads in alloy steel, gray iron and free-cutting brass parts (illustrated in the table), each at two different hardnesses. All threading was done in turret lathes using four-chaser dies having 30° chamfer angles.

As indicated, greater speed could be used for threading the softer alloy steel and brass parts, but the same speed was used for the gray iron part regardless of the hardness. For all three metals, however, tool life showed a substantial increase when the softer parts were threaded.

Accuracy and Finish

In die threading, dimensional accuracy and surface finish usually are closely related; excessive dimensional variation is commonly accompanied by rough surfaces on the threads.

In addition to the composition and hardness of the metal being threaded (see the preceding section), the major variables affecting accuracy and finish are the type and condition of the machine and tool used (see discussion below), and the type of cutting fluid used (see the section "Cutting Fluids" in this article, especially Example 258).

Machines. With other conditions constant, closer dimensional control is invariably obtained in a machine that rotates the workpiece rather than the tool. For example, better dimensional control can be obtained in a turret lathe than in a drill press.

Regardless of which type of machine is used, it must be maintained at maximum capability by adjustments that compensate for wear in bearings and other moving parts.

Tools. To obtain a condition of balance, thread-cutting dies contain a minimum of three chasers (or cutting lands, in solid dies). Increasing the number of chasers is helpful in maintaining close tolerances and good finish, because the greater the number of cutting edges, the lower the chip load per tooth. Five-chaser dies are often used for improving accuracy and finish, as indicated in Example 768, in the article "Machining of Stainless Steel".

Chasers with short chamfers (35° to 45° angles) may produce rough or substandard threads, especially on metals that are difficult to machine, because cutting forces on the leading teeth increase as chamfer length decreases. The relation between chamfer angle and the amount of metal removed in threading is tabulated with Fig. 9. These data show the desirability of using chasers having the longest possible chamfer, because as the length of chamfer increases, chips become thinner and chip load per tooth is reduced.

The cutting edges of chasers must be kept sharp by grinding or replacement, depending on the type of die. With self-opening dies, it is essential that all

Table 4. Effect of Hardness on Speed and Tool Life in Die Threading 4350 Steel, Gray Iron and Free-Cutting Brass (Examples 250, 251 and 252)

Item	Example 250 4350 steel		Example 251 Gray iron		Example 252 Free-cutting brass	
	200 Bhn	225 Bhn	174 Bhn	200 Bhn	½ hard	Full hard
Speed, rpm	190	155	535	535	690	460
Speed, sfm	25	20	70	70	90	60
Removal rate, cu in. per min	0.384	0.304	1.05	1.05	1.4	0.880
Cutting fluid	Sulfurized oil (both)		Soluble oil (both)		Mineral oil (both)	
Total tool life, cu in. of metal removed	4.0	3.2	6.4	5.2	16.0	11.2
Tool life per grind, pieces ..	250	200	400	325	1000	700

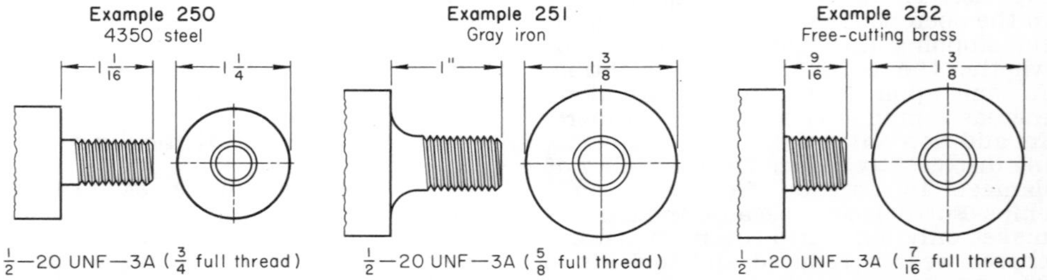

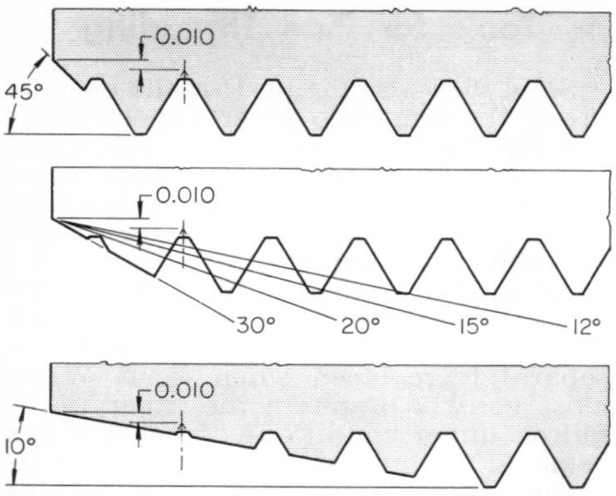

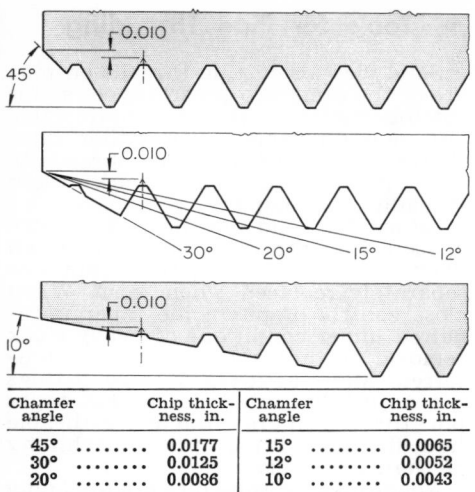

Chamfer angle	Chip thickness, in.	Chamfer angle	Chip thickness, in.
45°	0.0177	15°	0.0065
30°	0.0125	12°	0.0052
20°	0.0086	10°	0.0043

Fig. 9. Relation between chamfer angle and (in sketch) number of chamfered threads, or (in table) thickness of chip cut per thread, for 10-pitch UN threads

moving parts be hardened and that necessary compensation (by replacement if necessary) be made for wear. If dies having worn components are used, loss in accuracy will result.

Thread Size

Other factors being the same, diameter of the part being threaded has a significant effect on procedure, production rate and cost per piece threaded. In the following example, initial cost for chasers was the same for two different diameters but tool cost per piece threaded increased almost in proportion to diameter.

Example 253. Threading Two Sizes of Carbon Steel Tubing (Fig. 10)

The workpieces illustrated in Fig. 10 each required one inch of full thread as indicated. Each piece was threaded in a manually operated turret lathe of appropriate size, using self-opening dies. The workpieces, designated Part A and Part B in Fig. 10, were threaded at the same surface speed. As shown in the tabulation with Fig. 10, tool cost per piece threaded was significantly higher for the 2¾-in.-diam than for the ⅞-in.-diam thread, even though initial cost for chasers was the same.

Threading to a Shoulder

A workpiece to be threaded close to a shoulder should have a relief groove that is wide enough to admit the full chamfer of the chaser plus the first full thread, and to provide extra clearance for overtravel so as to allow the die to open without bumping the shoulder. Recommended minimum widths of relief grooves for chasers ranging in pitch from 32 to 4 and with four different chamfer angles are given in Table 5.

Workpiece design often limits the width of available relief. When possible, the relief width should be revised to allow the use of chasers having maximum length of chamfer, to provide maximum efficiency of operation (see Fig. 9, and the section "Accuracy and Finish", on the preceding page).

Aside from the danger of die breakage because of hitting the shoulder, the two main disadvantages of threading to a shoulder are: (*a*) increased tool cost because of shorter tool life, and (*b*) decreased productivity because of lower speeds and more downtime for changing tools. These are illustrated in the following example.

Example 254. Influence of Threading to a Shoulder on Productivity and Cost (Fig. 11)

1–20 UNEF–3A threads were cut in two different workpieces made of the same grade of steel. The comparison of chaser and operating details given with Fig. 11 is based on threading Ends 1 of Parts C and D. Part D was also threaded at the opposite end, but with a different thread (not shown). Shoulder interference complicated the threading of Part C, whereas there was no shoulder interference in threading End 1 of Part D.

In Part C the 3/32-in. clearance meets the minimum prescribed in Table 5 for chasers having a 30° chamfer. However, tool cost was higher in threading Part C than Part D because the 30° chasers required more frequent regrinding than did the 20° chasers used to thread Part D.

The difference in productivity in threading Parts C and D was attributed to the differences in threading speed and downtime for changing chasers.

Table 5. Recommended Minimum Widths of Relief Grooves for Cutting UN Threads Close to a Shoulder

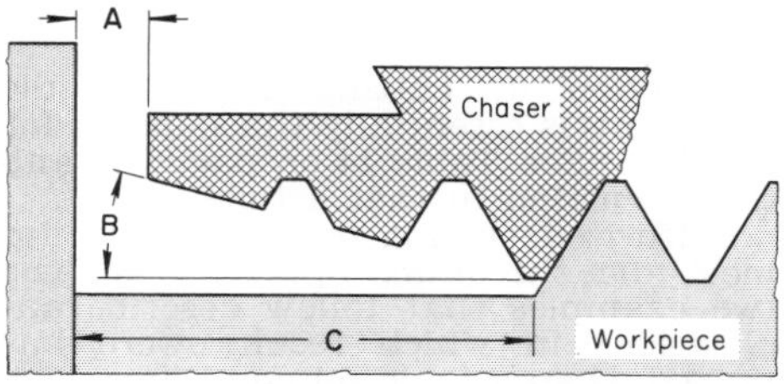

A = Extra clearance (for overtravel)
B = Chamfer angle (15° in sketch)
C = Total width required for relief

Pitch	Extra clearance (A in drawing), in.	Total width for relief (C in drawing), in., for chamfer angle (B in drawing) of: 45°	30°	20°	15°
32	1/32	1/16	1/16	3/32	7/64
28	1/32	1/16	5/64	3/32	1/8
24	1/32	1/16	5/64	7/64	9/64
20	1/32	5/64	3/32	1/8	5/32
18	1/32	5/64	3/32	1/8	11/64
16	1/32	5/64	7/64	9/64	3/16
14	1/32	5/64	7/64	5/32	13/64
13	3/64	3/32	9/64	3/16	15/64
12	3/64	3/32	9/64	13/64	1/4
11½	3/64	3/32	9/64	13/64	17/64
11	3/64	3/32	5/32	7/32	17/64
10	3/64	7/64	5/32	15/64	19/64
9	3/64	7/64	11/64	1/4	5/16
8	3/64	1/8	3/16	17/64	23/64
7	1/16	5/32	7/32	5/16	13/32
6	1/16	11/64	1/4	23/64	15/32
5	1/16	13/64	9/32	27/64	35/64
4½	1/16	7/32	5/16	29/64	39/64
4	1/16	15/64	11/32	1/2	43/64

Speed

Cuts that are made too slowly increase machining time and thus raise production costs. Slow cuts across keyways can also produce rough, irregular surfaces.

Cuts that are made too fast generate excessive heat and shorten tool life. Too high a speed can also affect thread accuracy, as in the next example:

Example 255. Influence of Speed on Class of Threads Obtained

Class 3 was specified for ½–13 threads in a copper alloy part. The machine speed, established for other operations, was 80 sfm for threading. The best thread that could be consistently produced at this speed (which could not be changed) was class 2, even though chaser design was modified, and cutting edges were kept sharp.

But higher-than-average speed can sometimes be a help in maintaining the accuracy of a cut. When cutting across keyways, holes, flats, parting lines or other irregularities, a threading die makes a better surface if it is cutting faster than otherwise would be considered normal for the conditions. Of course, tool life will suffer.

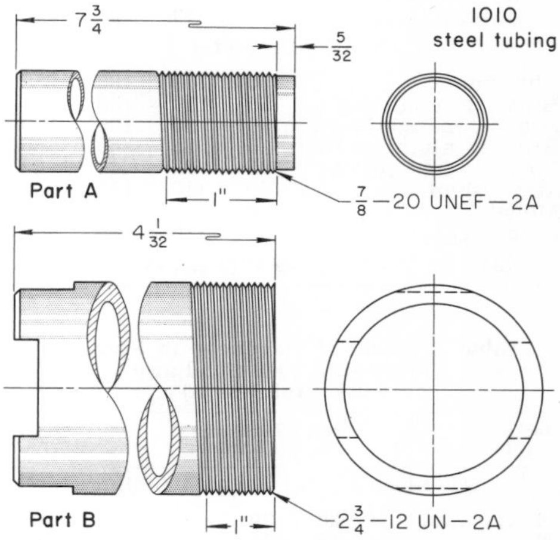

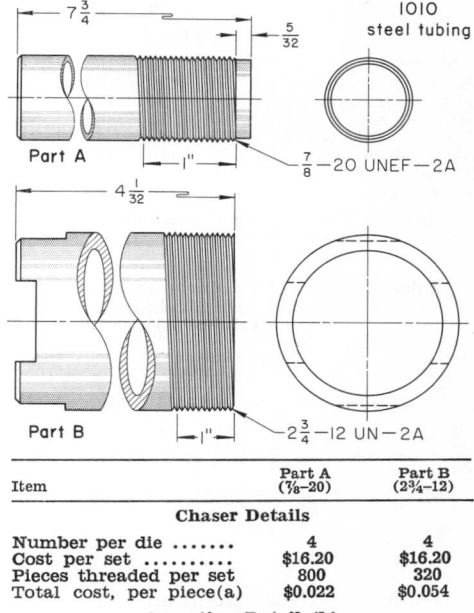

Item	Part A (⅞–20)	Part B (2¾–12)
Chaser Details		
Number per die	4	4
Cost per set	$16.20	$16.20
Pieces threaded per set	800	320
Total cost, per piece(a)	$0.022	$0.054
Operating Details(b)		
Speed, rpm	85 (20 sfm)	30 (20 sfm)
Production, pcs/hr	120	41
Tool life per grind, pcs	200	80

(a) Including grinding cost of $0.35 per grind. (b) Soluble-oil emulsion used for both parts.

Fig. 10. Influence of thread size on productivity and cost (Example 253)

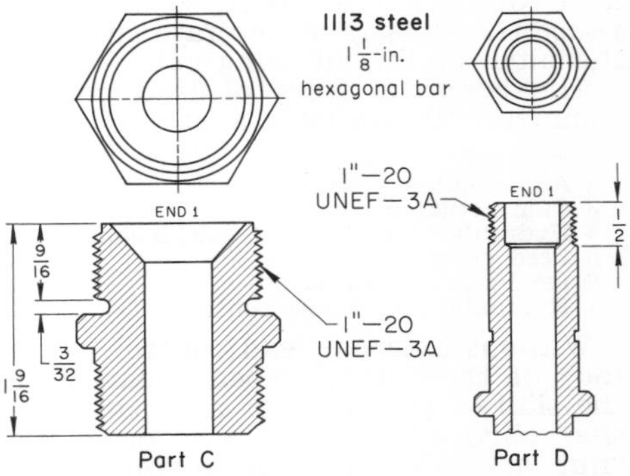

Item	Part C (End 1)	Part D (End 1)
Chaser Details		
Chamfer angle	30°	20°
Cost per set	$5.90	$5.90
Regrinds per 1000 ends threaded	5	3
Cost of regrinds	$1.75	$1.05
Tool cost per end threaded	$0.0077	$0.0070
Operating Details(a)		
Speed, rpm	155	190
Speed, sfm	40	50
Ends threaded per hour	261	293

(a) Soluble-oil emulsion was used as cutting fluid for both operations.

Fig. 11. Influence of shoulder interference on cost and productivity (Example 254)

Table 6. Nominal Speeds for Die Cutting of Screw Threads

Work metal	Speed, sfm, for pitch of: 7 or less	8 to 15	16 to 24	25 and up
Ferrous Metals				
Gray iron (class 30)	25	40	50	80
Malleable iron	20	30	40	50
Stainless steel:				
303, 410, 420F, 440F	10	15	20	25
416 and 430F	12	20	30	40
302, 304, 321	8	10	15	20
Steel, free-cutting	15	25	40	60
Steel other than free-cutting:				
Medium-carbon	8	10	15	20
Low-carbon	12	20	30	40
Nonferrous Metals				
Aluminum	50	110	180	250
Brass, free-cutting	50	110	180	250
Bronze, manganese	30	60	100	150
Bronze, aluminum (a)	15	25	40	60
Copper, free-cutting	15	25	40	60
Magnesium	50	110	180	250
Monel	8	10	15	20
Zinc	50	110	180	250

(a) Also nickel bronze or phosphor bronze

Table 7. Effect of Hardness on Speed in Threading 1040 Steel and 440A Stainless (a)

Rockwell C hardness	Speed, sfm	Rockwell C hardness	Speed, sfm
1040 Steel		**440A Stainless**	
6	20	20	10
20	15	30	8
30	10	40 (b)	5

(a) Data are based on cutting 8 to 15 threads per inch. (b) Harder than the limit recommended for die threading.

Table 6 gives nominal threading speeds for various materials. The effect of hardness on threading speed for two steels is shown in Table 7.

Lead Control

Lead control is control of the axial advance of the chasers in die threading. Lead screws or other devices used for lead control are adjusted so as to advance the chasers at the rate suited to the pitch of thread being cut.

The common types of lead control commercially available are:

1 Hydraulically actuated
2 Air-actuated
3 Cam-actuated
4 Hydraulic (or air) and cam combination
5 Feed gears
6 Lead screw and nut
7 Hydraulic lead-screw control.

Without external lead control, accuracy of the thread depends partly on the skill of the operator and partly on the ability of the chasers to develop a "nut action". This nut action is influenced by the weight of those machine components that drag on the chasers.

Manual control is usually satisfactory for threading diameters up to ¼ in., because the machine components that move with a threading die of this size are easily handled by the operator. As thread diameter or work metal hardness or both increase, the weight of the moving machine components is also increased, because heavier and more powerful equipment is required. Thus, accurate manual control becomes more difficult.

Under conditions of inadequate control, the leading threads will be poorly formed and the remaining threads will be shaved undersize. Too much force applied by the operator or too much drag from moving components will produce similar effects.

The following example describes how one manufacturer benefited by using lead control to correct difficulties in threading:

Example 256. Elimination of Chaser Damage by Lead Control

A 1–8 UNC–3A thread was machined at 10 sfm in a stainless steel workpiece. A finish of 63 micro-in. or better was required. The piece was threaded in a manual turret lathe without lead control. The chasers chipped and broke and produced unacceptable threads. Installation of lead control eliminated chaser damage and made it possible to produce acceptable threads.

Disadvantages of lead control are:

1 Initial cost of the lead-control unit
2 Susceptibility of the unit to wear, with consequent requirements for servicing and replacement
3 The need for continuing maintenance
4 The time required for resetting the unit to the starting point after each cycle, which usually lengthens total time for performing a threading operation.

Cutting Fluids

Selection of cutting fluid for die threading is essentially the same as for tapping. (See Table 14 on page 118 and the discussion in that article.)

Sulfurized cutting oil is effective for most die threading applications. The two examples that follow describe applications in which results were improved when soluble-oil emulsions were replaced by sulfurized oil.

Examples 257 and 258. Benefits From Change of Cutting Fluid

Example 257 — Improved Tool Life. A soluble-oil emulsion (1 part oil to 20 parts water) was used as cutting fluid for die threading fittings made of 1018 steel. Quality of the threads (3$^{3}/_{16}$–12) was acceptable, but chaser life was only 180 pieces per grind. Changing the cutting fluid to straight sulfurized oil increased chaser life per grind to 225 pieces.

Example 258 — Improved Accuracy and Finish. Class 3 fit and finish were required for 1½–12 threads on malleable iron castings die threaded at 30 sfm using a 1-to-20 mixture of soluble oil and water as a cutting fluid. Thread flanks were excessively rough, and some pieces did not meet class 3 requirements. When straight sulfurized cutting oil was substituted as the cutting fluid, all parts met class 3 and acceptable surface finish was maintained.

Taper Threading of Pipe

Practice for cutting taper pipe threads with dies does not differ greatly from that used for cutting standard screw threads. However, because standard taper pipe threads (NPT) are designed to provide pressure-tight seals, they require closer control in chasing than do thread forms for which 75% of full thread is acceptable. Also, in chasing taper pipe threads, more teeth are cutting at one time than in chasing standard screw threads; thus, taper pipe threading requires about 10% more power than screw threading, size for size. Machines used for threading pipe are usually the same as those used for other types of die threading. Positive lead control is essential in taper threading, because all chaser teeth are cutting at one time.

Tools for Pipe Threading

Solid dies for cutting threads on pipe are of the same two general types as for cutting machine threads — adjustable and nonadjustable. With either type, the die must back over the threads to be removed from the work when threading is complete.

Adjustable solid dies have removable chasers that can be adjusted for pitch diameter, and that can be reground or separately replaced when worn. When close control of pitch-line taper is required under conditions of heavy stock removal, the adjustable solid die is preferred. Manufacturers of pipe fittings use adjustable solid dies to cut taper pipe threads on gray iron and malleable iron fittings without prior machining of the as-cast diameters.

Nonadjustable solid dies are used only for hand operations or for low-production threading in a simple machine. They are seldom resharpened when worn, and cannot be adjusted for pitch diameter.

Self-opening dies permit the individual cutting components to be retracted from the work automatically when threading is complete, so that the die can be withdrawn without the need to reverse rotation. Self-opening dies permit shorter machine cycles than do solid dies, by eliminating the backing-off time. Self-opening dies also increase chaser life because cutting edges are not dragged back over the previously cut threads. Disadvantages of self-opening dies in comparison with adjustable solid dies are: higher initial and maintenance costs, and greater susceptibility to becoming fouled from swarf-contaminated cutting fluids.

Self-opening dies are used also to cut straight pipe threads. Straight pipe threads, the same size as taper pipe threads (at the large end of the taper) are needed for tank fittings and other places where nuts must be used along with standard taper pipe connections. Straight pipe threads are also known as locknut threads (pipe). Where a short pipe goes through a wall, as in tank fittings, a full-length straight pipe thread joins the taper pipe threads at the ends. A locknut, with matching internal straight pipe thread, screws onto the thread at the face of the wall, while fittings screw on at the ends.

Chasers. Radial, tangential and circular chasers are used for pipe threading, as for the production of screw threads (see the section "Self-Opening Dies", and Fig. 4, 5 and 6). For high-production pipe threading, standard (stock) chasers are not always the best choice, regardless of type. Specially designed chasers should be considered for long production runs. For instance in threading malleable iron pipe fittings that are threaded without prior machining, maximum rigidity is required because of the large and varying amount of stock removal. For such purposes a specific type of solid adjustable die equipped with tangential chasers has been designed. These chasers are ground with a 30° throat angle starting 0.010 in. below the root of the thread. Tungsten carbide chasers last long in this application if they do not break, but they are susceptible to breakage because some workpiece castings are not well annealed. In general, nitrided high speed steel chasers are the most practical for this application.

Stop Lines in Pipe Threading

The prescribed taper in pipe threads is 1/16-in. in diameter for each inch of length. Thus, each chaser tooth cuts a progressively smaller diameter on the workpiece as the die advances. Because each chaser tooth is cutting at the instant of die opening or reversal, a stop line remains on the thread surface. The same effect is caused in straight pipe threads. When solid dies are used, the reversal of the chasers over the stop lines creates an abrasive action that causes excessive wear of the cutting edges.

The kind of metal being threaded has a marked effect on the severity of stop lines. In general, stop lines become more pronounced as ductility of the work metal increases. With solid dies, the severity of stop lines can be reduced by increasing the number of chasers in the die. However, when specifications call for complete elimination of stop lines, a full-receding type of self-opening die is required, or else the piece must be threaded with a single-point tool.

In one plant where alloy steel pipe was being taper threaded with solid dies, stop lines were severe. When the dies were reversed for removal, fine chips were trapped between the cutting teeth and the threads, resulting in damage to both. Rejection rate because of scarred threads was excessive. Changing to a self-opening die, and frequent resharpening of the chaser teeth, solved the problem. The die was adjusted so that it tripped just prior to full advance of the spindle; chasers retracted smoothly and stop lines were eliminated.

Speed in Pipe Threading

Speed, in surface feet per minute, is usually 20 to 30% slower for pipe threading than for the cutting of screw threads (see Table 6), because more teeth are cutting during pipe threading. In some shops, however, little or no distinction is made between straight threads and taper threads in selecting threading speed. Also, in some shops the same threading speed is used regardless of thread pitch. For instance, one manufacturer taper threads malleable iron as-cast surfaces that range from 1/8-in. to 4-in. pipe size at the same surface speeds, using the same type of dies and cutting fluid. Straight pipe threads may be cut at faster speeds, equal to the speeds used in cutting unified threads of equal size.

Thread quality does not necessarily increase as threading speed decreases; rough and torn threads often result from threading speeds that are too low. Excessive speeds, however, always decrease tool life.

Cutting fluids used for pipe threading are the same as for the cutting of screw threads.

Flooding the cutting area is generally more important in pipe threading because, in pipe threading, more cutting teeth are engaged at one time.

In addition, because of the accuracy required in pipe threads and the amount of cutting that is being done at one time, susceptibility to thread damage from swarf-contaminated cutting fluids is greater in pipe threading. Damage from this source can be prevented by filtering the cutting fluid.

Other Examples of Die Threading in This Volume

Work metal	Example number	Subject
Stainless steel	766	Work metals compared
	767	Method
	768	Tool design
	769	Method
Aluminum	871	Work metals compared
	873	Work metals compared

Thread Grinding

*By the ASM Committee on Grinding**

THREADS are sometimes ground instead of being cut or rolled, for the following reasons:

1. If the work is harder than Rockwell C 36, grinding may be the only feasible production method.
2. If the work is softer than Rockwell C 17, grinding may give a better finish.
3. If a high degree of dimensional accuracy is required, grinding is almost invariably the method preferred.

Grinding Methods. Threads are ground by contact between a rotating workpiece and a rotating grinding wheel that has been shaped to the desired thread form. In addition to rotation, there is relative axial motion between the wheel and the workpiece to match the pitch of the thread being ground. Thread grinding can produce either external or internal threads.

Methods for grinding threads are: (*a*) cylindrical grinding, where the workpiece is held between centers or by means of a chuck; and (*b*) centerless grinding, where the workpiece is supported against the grinding wheel by a rest (work-support blade) and a regulating wheel. When workpiece shape permits and production quantities are large, centerless grinding is the best choice, because productivity is much greater than in cylindrical grinding.

Machines for thread grinding are distinguished by three features:

1. Means for imparting a precise axial motion between the wheel and the workpiece, to match the thread being ground. (The lead-screw principle is commonly used.)
2. Devices for truing or dressing of the grinding wheel to generate the required form in the workpiece.
3. Inclinable plane of rotation of the grinding wheel to cut the required helix.

*For committee list, see page 257.

Thread grinding machines differ in: (*a*) type of grinding wheel used (single ribbed or multiribbed); (*b*) method of supporting the workpiece; and (*c*) method of restoring the cutting contour of the grinding wheel (diamond dressing or truing, or crush truing).

Thread grinding machines are sometimes classified as external, internal, or universal; the universal type can grind external or internal threads.

Wheel Selection

Typical wheels for thread grinding of various metals are given in Table 1.

Selection of abrasive depends on work-metal composition and hardness, and number of threads per inch. With few exceptions, threads are ground with aluminum oxide wheels, designated by an A in the specification. Silicon carbide wheels, marked C, are used for grinding titanium, and diamond wheels for grinding sintered carbide and ceramic materials. Usually the semifriable varieties of aluminum oxide are preferred, but in some applications a friable type gives better results, and in a few cases, a tough variety is best. The variety of aluminum oxide is indicated by a subscript to the letter A in the designations in Table 1. (For more information on wheel classification and marking, see the section on Grinding Wheels in the article "Grinding".)

Grit size is determined primarily by the pitch of the thread being ground: the finer the thread, the finer the grit. Fine grit improves surface finish, but coarse grit removes metal faster.

Wheel grade depends mainly on the grit size: the finer the grit, the harder the wheel. The work metal also has an effect on grade selection (Table 1).

Either vitrified or resinoid bond is always used for thread grinding. Resinoid wheels remove stock more rapidly, but they are less rigid than vitrified wheels and deflect more readily. Therefore, resinoid wheels are usually used in high-production applications, whereas vitrified wheels are used where accuracy is the primary objective, as in grinding threads on gages. Vitrified wheels are used also for correcting lead error in precut threads. The more flexible resinoid wheels tend to follow lead error rather than to correct it.

Grinding Speed

Table 2 shows nominal speeds used for thread grinding of various metals, based on work-metal composition and hardness, and number of threads per inch.

Vitrified thread grinding wheels are run at considerably higher speeds than are normal in other operations with vitrified wheels. This is permissible under the safety code only when the

Table 1. Typical Grinding Wheels for Thread Grinding (a)

Work metal and hardness	Threads per inch: 4 to 13	14 to 28	29 to 64	65 to 80
Steels and cast irons, R_C 52 max (b)	A_s-90-R-B	A_s-120-S-B	A_s-180-T-B	A_s-220-U-B
Steels and cast irons, R_C 52 to 65 (c)	A_s-80-I-V	A_s-120-J-V	A_s-180-M-V	A_s-220-P-V
Tool steels, R_C 56 to 65 (d)	A_s-100-K-V	A_s-150-K-V	A_s-220-K-V	A_s-240-K-V
Titanium alloys, 110 to 440 Bhn (e)	C-100-K-V	C-150-K-V	C-240-J-V	C-280-K-V
Heat-resisting alloys, 200 to 400 Bhn (f)	A_s-90-S-B	A_s-100-T-B	A_s-180-T-B	A_s-280-T-B

(a) For explanation of wheel designations, see page 257. (b) Includes: all wrought and cast carbon, alloy and ultrahigh-strength steels in the normalized, annealed or quenched-and-tempered condition; nitriding steels at 200 to 350 Bhn; all tool steels at 150 to 285 Bhn; ACI casting alloys, both corrosion and heat-resisting types; all cast irons in the as-cast, normalized, annealed or quenched-and-tempered condition; all grades of stainless steel at 135 to 200 Bhn. (c) Includes: all wrought and cast carbon and alloy steels in the quenched-and-tempered condition; nitrided steels at Rockwell C 60 to 65; maraging steels; tool steels of the W, O, S, H, L and P groups, and also A2 to A6 and A8 and A10, all in the hardness range of Rockwell C 56 to 65. (d) Includes A7 and all members of the D, F, M and T groups in the hardness range of Rockwell C 56 to 65. (e) Includes all alloys in all conditions of treatment. (f) Includes all wrought and cast iron-base, nickel-base and cobalt-base alloys in all conditions of treatment.

Table 2. Nominal Wheel Speeds (Sfm) for Thread Grinding (a)

Work metal and hardness	Threads per inch: 4 to 13	14 to 28	29 to 64	65 to 80
Ferrous metals, R_C 52 max (b)	8500	9000	9500	10000
Ferrous metals, R_C 52 to 65 (c)	7000	7500	8500	9000
Titanium alloys, 110 to 440 Bhn (d)	7000	7500	8500	9000
Heat-resisting alloys, 200 to 400 Bhn (e)	9000	9000	9000	9000

(a) Work-rotation speed is 4 sfm for the softer ferrous metals, 6 sfm for the harder, except for the hardened high-alloy tool steels where it is 4 sfm for 4 to 28 threads per inch and 6 sfm for threads finer than 28 per inch; these latter work speeds apply also for titanium alloys. Work-rotation speed is 1.5 to 4 sfm for heat-resisting alloys; the lower speed is used for the coarser threads. (b) Includes all wrought and cast carbon and alloy steels, tool steels, cast irons, stainless steels, and ACI casting alloys in the normalized, annealed or quenched-and-tempered condition.

(c) Includes the same metals listed under footnote (b), but in the quenched-and-tempered (or age-hardened) condition. (d) Includes all alloys and all conditions of treatment. (e) Includes all wrought and cast alloys (iron-base, nickel-base and cobalt-base) and all conditions of treatment.

wheel has been tested by the wheel manufacturer for operation at such speeds and the machine is properly guarded to protect the operator against accidental wheel breakage. Although the maximum speed for vitrified wheels on a standard cylindrical grinder is 6500 sfm, speeds as high as 12,000 sfm can be used in thread grinding with vitrified wheels that have been certified by the manufacturer for that speed.

As shown in Table 2, in most thread grinding, the recommended wheel speed increases as the number of threads per inch increases. Grinding of heat-resisting alloys, however, is an exception; the recommended speed is the same regardless of thread pitch.

Grinding Fluids

Grinding oils are always used in thread grinding. Water-base fluids have never been successful, although many attempts have been made to replace oils with water-base fluids. Mineral-base sulfochlorinated grinding oils such as G1 or G2 (see Table 7 on page 428) are most widely used, especially when finish and accuracy of the threads are important. Such oils are generally satisfactory for all steels, as well as for other work metals, and many shops have standardized on them for all thread grinding. Other formulations prepared especially for thread grinding are available for specific applications where the conventional sulfochlorinated oils have proved unsatisfactory.

Cylindrical Grinding of Threads

Four different methods, identified by the design of the wheel, are employed for cylindrical thread grinding. Three of these methods use multiribbed wheels. Most cylindrical thread grinding, however, uses a single-ribbed or single-edged wheel. In this method, the edge of the wheel is trued to the form of the thread to be ground; the profile of the cutting edge works like that of a single-point metal tool for cutting threads on a lathe. Because the grinding wheel is frequently 18 to 20 in. in diameter, the arc of contact at full depth is appreciable. Thus, for accuracy, the wheel should be inclined to the helix angle; this adjustment is imperative for helices of 4° or more.

Multiribbed wheels have two or more parallel grooves or ribs around the periphery of the wheel. Each rib is trued to the form of the thread to be ground. The thread form is imparted to the wheel by diamond or crush truing.

If the grinding wheel is as thick as, or thicker than, the required length of the thread, Fig. 1(a), the thread can be completed in one revolution of the work plus a half revolution for feeding-in of the wheel.

In Fig. 1(b), the alternate or "skip-rib" type of truing is shown. The grinding wheel can be formed by crush or diamond truing. Diamond truing is used on resinoid wheels or to dress fine, accurate pitches. The ribs are spaced to grind every other turn of the thread during the first revolution of the work, the thread being completed on the second revolution. Consequently, about 2½ revolutions of the work are required for grinding a complete thread. Improved distribution of grinding oil makes possible higher-than-standard work speeds with this wheel.

Another variation of the multiribbed thread-grinding wheel is the three-ribbed wheel. This wheel, illustrated in Fig. 1(c), has a roughing rib, A, that removes about two thirds of the material, and an intermediate rib, B, that takes the remainder of the material except for about 0.005 in., which is left to be cleaned up by the finishing rib, C. If desired, the wheel can be dressed so that a flattened area, D, will finish grind the crest of the thread.

The three-ribbed wheel will produce threads as accurate as those produced by the single-ribbed wheel, or more accurate. If necessary, this type of wheel can be inclined to the helix angle, provided an allowance is made for the radius of curvature of the work. The three-ribbed wheel is designed to traverse the work rather than plunge cut.

Infeed. When a single-rib wheel is used, a roughing cut of 0.020 to 0.040 in. per pass can be made without burning the work metal. An infeed of 0.0015 to 0.004 in. per pass is used for close dimensional accuracy, whereas infeed for larger dimensional tolerances common to many commercial products, ranges from 0.004 to 0.010 in. per pass.

The work can be ground to final size in one cut when the depth of cut is less than 0.040 in. Work speed for finish grinding in one cut is slow — for example, a work speed of 1½ to 2 sfm is used for grinding 20 threads per inch with a thread depth of 0.032 in. For depths greater than 0.040 in., roughing cuts of 0.020 to 0.040 in. or more per pass at work speeds of 3 to 4 sfm are required. Work speed for the finish cut of 0.0015 to 0.004 in. is 6 to 8 sfm.

In multicut operations, infeed should be controlled so that the cutting edge of the grinding wheel will not break down before the finishing cut. For example, an infeed of 0.036 in. per pass for roughing and 0.018 in. per pass for finishing is satisfactory for grinding 20 screw threads per inch.

Centerless Grinding of Threads

Centerless grinding is the most productive method of grinding screw threads. This method is capable of grinding threads of classes 2A and 3A at high production rates; threads of class 5A are produced at slower rates.

Wheels for centerless thread grinding may also be either single-ribbed or multiribbed. Grain size ranges from 80 to 280, depending on the number of threads per inch, as shown in Table 1. Harder wheels are used in centerless thread grinding than for other centerless grinding operations on the same materials. Grade (hardness) ranges from M to R. Generally wheels of grade Q are used for products such as head-

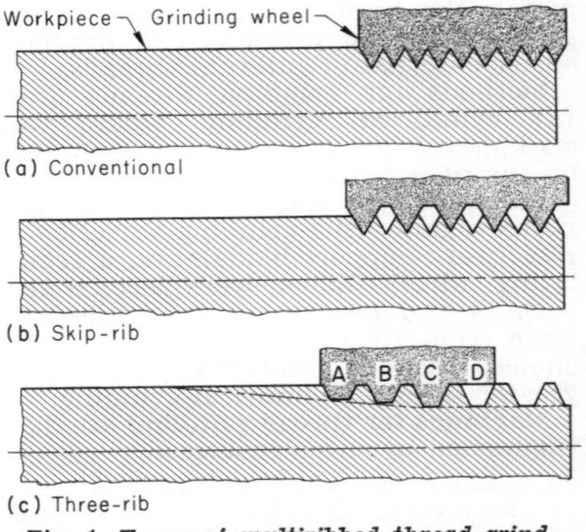

Fig. 1. Types of multiribbed thread-grinding wheels. Capital letters on the three-rib wheel identify ribs referred to in the text.

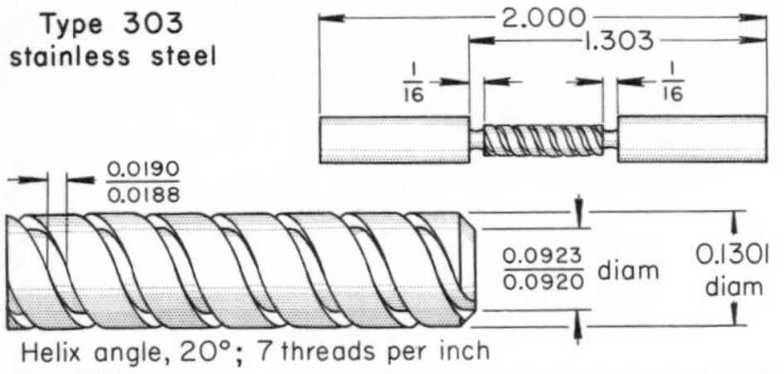

Wheel classification	A_t-100-T5-B
Wheel size	18 by ⅜ by 9 in.

Operating Conditions

Wheel speed	2100 rpm (9900 sfm)
Work-rotation speed	6 rpm (0.2 sfm)
Metal removed	0.019 in.
Grinding fluid	Grinding oil(a)
Production rate	15 pieces per hour
Setup time	3.5 hr
Wheel life per dressing(b)	10 pieces
Total wheel life	3000 pieces

Tolerances, Finish and Cost

Tolerance on root diameter	0.0004 in.
Thread concentricity with centers	Within 0.0003 in. TIR
Surface finish required	Commercial
Labor cost at $3.50 per hour	$0.23 per piece

(a) Inactive, free from fat, sulfur and chlorine; 300 SUS at 100 F. (b) Wheel was dressed with a single-point diamond tool.

Fig. 2. Stainless steel shaft in which right-hand spiral square threads were ground on an external thread grinder equipped with a resinoid wheel (Example 259)

less setscrews made of steel at Rockwell C 40. Wheel structure is usually fairly open, ranging from 8 to 11, depending on the wheel manufacturer.

Wheel life depends on the type and hardness of the material being ground, thread tolerance, and production rate. Because maximum wear occurs at the thread crests of the grinding wheel, the wheel must be dressed to maintain tolerance of the root of the product thread. Centerless thread grinding wheels are dressed by crushing.

Regulating wheels for centerless thread grinding are similar to those used for other centerless grinding operations. For precision thread grinding, however, regulating wheels of finer grain size are used.

Usually regulating wheels revolve in the same direction as the grinding wheel (down grinding). However, for coarse threads (1–8 or coarser) the regulating wheel rotates in the direction opposite to that of the grinding wheel (up grinding).

Regulating wheels are dressed with a single-point diamond dressing tool. The frequency of dressing depends on the depth of the grooves that develop in the wheel face during thread grinding. In general, the regulating wheel is dressed each time the grinding wheel is dressed; however, in some operations, the regulating wheel is dressed only once for every two or three dressings of the grinding wheel.

Production Practice

Pitches as fine as 80 threads per inch can be ground with conventional thread-grinding procedures. Special techniques have been developed for grinding threads as fine as 400 to the inch. Most threads ground in regular production are considerably coarser than 80 per inch.

Grinding is applicable to the production of various thread forms on workpieces that differ widely in shape and size, as evidenced by the two examples that follow.

Example 259. Square Threads on 0.13-In.-Diam Shaft (Fig. 2)

Square threads were ground in the center section of the small stainless steel shaft shown in Fig. 2. The thread grinder used for this operation was equipped with a resinoid aluminum oxide wheel, because high production speed was required. Processing details are given in the table accompanying Fig. 2.

Example 260. Tapered Threads on 13⅝-In. Diam Forged Section (Fig. 3)

Tapered threads on the hardened steel forging shown in Fig. 3 were produced on external thread grinders equipped with taper sine-bar attachments. Two machines were used. A resinoid grinding wheel removed 0.135 in. of metal from the workpiece surface during the grinding of five threads per inch. Processing details are shown in the table with Fig. 3.

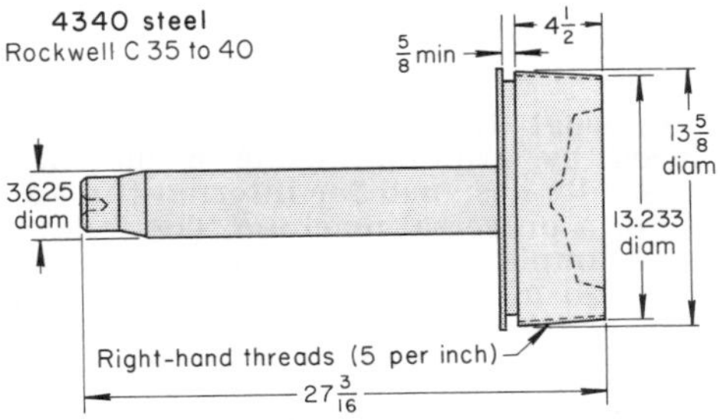

Wheel classification	A_t-100-T5-B
Wheel size	18 by ⅜ by 9 in.

Grinding Conditions

Wheel speed	1910 rpm (9000 sfm)
Work-rotation speed	1½ rpm (5.3 sfm)
Metal removed, roughing	0.010 in. per pass
Metal removed, finishing	0.002 in. per pass
Total metal removed from diameter	0.135 in.
Grinding fluid	Grinding oil
Production rate	12 hr per piece(a)
Setup time	8.0 hour

Tolerance, Finish and Cost

Tolerance on OD	−0.000, +0.003 in.
Tolerance on angle	±0° 10′
Tolerance on thread depth	−0.000, +0.001 in.
Surface finish required	Smooth, chatter-free
Labor cost at $3.50 per hour	$21.00 per piece

(a) Production rate for one machine

Fig. 3. Forging in which tapered threads were ground on an external thread grinder equipped with a taper sine-bar attachment (Example 260)

A hard thread can be obtained by thread grinding, because the workpiece can be ground after it has been fully hardened. This eliminates distortion, which is commonly found in workpieces threaded before heat treating, and, in addition, produces true thread forms with the lead and pitch diameter held to close tolerances. Limits of 0.0002 in. or less can be held on pitch diameter, and 0.0002 in. or less per inch on lead tolerances. The next example deals with the threading of a heat treated disk.

Example 261. Thread Grinding After Heat Treating (Fig. 4)

The workpiece shown in Fig. 4 was made of 4340 steel, heat treated to Rockwell C 39 to 43. The outer surface was threaded by an external thread grinder that removed 0.060 in. of metal in four passes while forming the 10¾–10 NS–3A threads. Other processing details are given with Fig. 4.

Thread grinding can be used on surfaces containing drilled holes, keyways or other irregularities. Shell-type parts are more amenable to thread grinding than to other methods of producing threads, in which pressure from the tool can cause distortion. Small worms can be roughed faster by thread grinding than by conventional thread milling.

Thread grinding is applicable to virtually all materials and all hardnesses. On the other hand, thread cutting is superior from the standpoint of material handling and production rate, especially when the thread tolerances are broad. But these advantages of thread cutting are quickly offset when close tolerances are required.

Example 262. Thread Grinding Compared With Single-Point Thread Cutting (Table 3)

The end section of the stainless steel part shown in Table 3 was threaded with ⅜–24 UNF–3A threads. The table compares processing details for threading the part by grinding and by cutting. The grinding procedure required 2 hr for setup and produced 7 pieces per hour, whereas setup time for cutting was 1½ hr and production rate was 23 pieces per hour. The part was held between centers during thread grinding and in chuck jaws during thread cutting.

When threads of fine finish and close tolerance are required, thread grinding has proved more economical than other methods. Example 263 compares costs for thread grinding and thread milling an aircraft landing gear component.

Example 263. Cost of Thread Grinding Compared With Cost of Thread Milling (Table 4)

An external grinder employing an aluminum oxide vitrified wheel was used to produce the 2.750–12 threads in an aircraft landing gear component made of 4330 steel and hardened to Rockwell C 46 to 48. Table 4 shows the processing details for thread grinding and compares several cost factors for thread milling to those for thread grinding.

The cost data in Table 4, which are based on a production lot of 25 pieces, show that thread grinding reduced setup time by 50% and threading time was 44%, and resulted in savings of 75% in threading-tool costs.

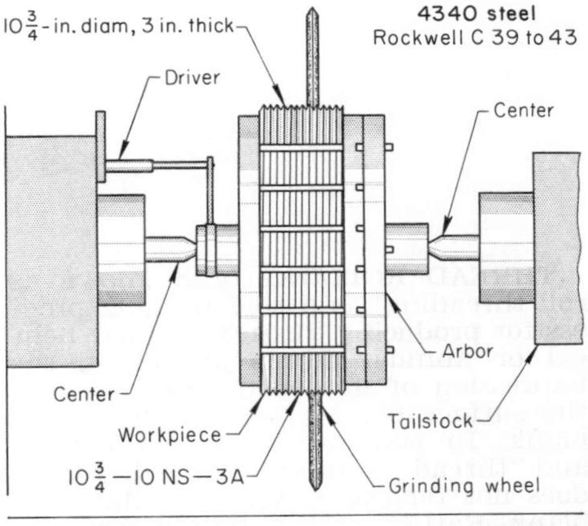

Wheel classification	A_t-100-V4-B
Wheel size	18 by ⅜ by 9 in.

Grinding Conditions

Wheel speed	2000 rpm (9440 sfm)
Work-rotation speed	⅝ rpm (1.7 sfm)
Metal removed	0.060 in. in four passes
Grinding fluid	Grinding oil
Production rate	43 min per piece
Setup time	1 hour
Wheel life per dressing(a)	1 pass

Tolerance and Finish

Tolerance	0.010 in.
Surface finish	63 micro-in.

(a) Wheel was dressed with a diamond tool.

Fig. 4. Part on which an external thread grinder was used to produce 10¾–10 NS–3A threads (Example 261)

Table 3. Comparison of Grinding and Cutting for Threading Annealed Stainless Steel (Example 262)

Item	Thread grinding	Thread cutting
Tool	Grinding wheel(a)	Single-point carbide
Wheel speed	2200 rpm (11,500 sfm)	....
Work-rotation speed	5.8 rpm (0.57 sfm)	878 rpm (86 sfm)
Grinding or cutting fluid	Sulfurized oil	Soluble oil (b)
Passes	4	14
Production rate	7 pieces per hour	23 pieces per hour
Setup time	2 hr	1.5 hr
Thread appearance	Excellent	Occasionally stringy; torn
Surface finish	12 to 20 micro-in.	32 micro-in., avg
Tolerance on threads	0.0029 in.	0.0029 in.
Tool life per dressing or sharpening	1 pass	25 pieces
Total tool life	3000 pieces	350 pieces
Tool cost per piece	$0.006	$0.008

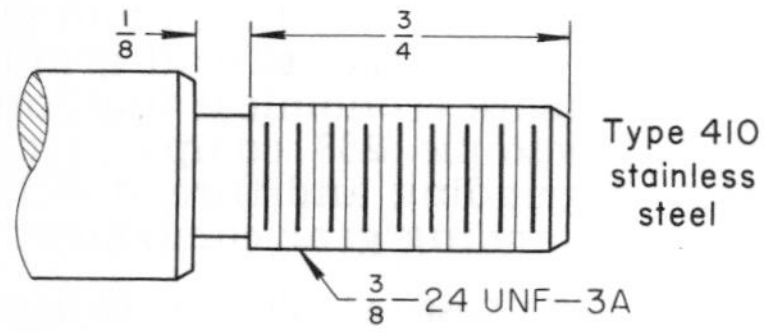

(a) A_s-120-T-B; 20 by 3/8 by 10 in. (b) Sulfurized oil is also suitable as the cutting fluid.

When workpiece design permits use of a multiribbed wheel, production rate in thread grinding can be greatly increased. For instance, in Example 262, on the previous page, it was estimated that using a multiribbed wheel would have increased production to 160 pieces per hour as against 7 pieces per hour by the grinding method described.

Table 4. Conditions for Thread Grinding an Aircraft Landing Gear Component of 4330 Steel and Comparison of Thread Grinding and Thread Milling (Example 263)

Wheel classification	A_s-100-B4-V
Wheel size	18 by 3/8 by 9 in.
Grinding Conditions	
Wheel speed	1800 rpm (8500 sfm)
Work-rotation speed	6 rpm (4.3 sfm)
Metal removed from diameter	0.108 in.
Grinding fluid	Grinding oil
Production rate	4 pieces per hour
Wheel life per dressing(a)	2 pieces
Tolerance and Finish	
Tolerance	0.005 in.
Surface finish	63 micro-in.

Thread Grinding vs Thread Milling	Thread grinding	Thread milling
Setup time, hr	1	2
Threading time/pc, min	14	25
Tool cost/pc(b)	$0.05	$0.20(c)

(a) Wheel dressed with a single-point diamond tool. (b) Cost based on 25 pieces. (c) Cost of regrinding milling cutters.

Internal threads also can be produced by grinding, using a machine especially designed for internal threading or a universal machine. The following example compares the time required to rough mill and finish grind internal threads to size with the time to produce the threads entirely by grinding.

Example 264. Internal Thread Grinding vs Milling and Grinding (Fig. 5)

Internal threads on the part shown in Fig. 5 were made originally by rough milling and then grinding to finished size. This double operation required 141 min for roughing and 160 min for finishing.

The part was made of 4330 steel and hardened to Rockwell C 32 to 39. Procedure was changed to threading by grinding only. A thread grinder equipped with an aluminum oxide wheel was used. Auxiliary equipment on the machine consisted of a faceplate center extension, a movable steady-rest base, and a steady rest that clamped and held the workpiece in position. All grinding was in one direction.

Elimination of the thread-milling operation reduced threading time by 61 min, or approximately 20%.

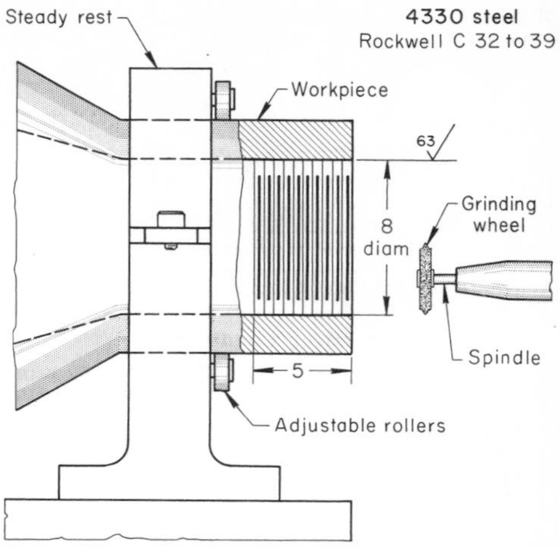

Wheel classification	A_s-80-K5-V
Wheel size	3¾ by 0.400 by 3/8 in.
Grinding Conditions	
Wheel speed	6000 rpm (6000 sfm)
Work-rotation speed	3½ rpm (7.3 sfm)
Metal removed	0.150 in. in 20 passes
Grinding fluid	Grinding oil
Production rate	4 hr per piece
Setup time	6 hr(a)
Wheel life	15 dressings per piece(b)
Total wheel life	3 pieces
Tolerance, Finish and Cost	
Tolerance on pitch diameter	0.010 in.
Surface finish	63 micro-in.
Cost of wheel	$0.43 per piece(c)

(a) Setup time includes forming of grinding wheel. (b) Wheel dressed with single-point diamond tool after each 0.010 in. of stock removal. (c) Based on cost of $1.28 per wheel.

Fig. 5. Part in which coarse internal threads (two per inch) were ground (Example 264)

Thread Rolling

*By the ASM Committee on Thread and Spline Rolling**

THREAD ROLLING (also known as roll threading) is a cold forming process for producing threads or other helical or annular forms by rolling the impression of hardened steel dies into the surface of a cylindrical or conical blank. In contrast to thread cutting and thread grinding, thread rolling does not remove metal from the work blank. Rather, thread rolling dies displace the surface metal of the blank to form the roots and crests of a thread.

Dies for thread rolling may be either flat or cylindrical (Fig. 1). Flat dies operate by a traversing motion. Methods that use cylindrical dies are classified as radial infeed, tangential feed, through feed, planetary, and internal. Each method is discussed in a separate section of this article.

Capabilities and Limitations

Most thread rolling is done on blanks having a hardness of Rockwell C 32 or less. However, threads on fasteners used for high-temperature service are rolled in metal as hard as Rockwell C 52. Some metal products such as gray iron castings and sintered metal pieces cannot be thread rolled because of their low ductility. These materials crumble rather than conform to the contour of the die.

All of the commonly used straight and tapered thread forms can be rolled. These include Unified, International Standard (the same as UNR), Whitworth, Acme, worm, buttress, screw shell, wood screw, tapping screw, lag screw, and drive screw. Thread diameters vary from less than 0.100 in., for instrument threads, to 9 in.; the larger threads can be as long as 20 ft.

Sixty-degree thread forms roll easily. In more blunt forms, metal flows with greater difficulty. Threads with fully rounded roots are more easily rolled than threads with wide, flat roots. Flank angles of less than 10° included angle and thread depths exceeding one

*FRANK ZUZICH, *Chairman*, Metallurgical Engineer, Hydra-Matic Div., General Motors Corp.; CLIFFORD T. APPLETON, Sterling Die Operation, Colt Industries, Inc.; R. B. BELFORD, Technical Advisor, Industrial Fasteners Institute; ERNEST V. BURKETT, Engineer, Indianapolis Works, Western Electric Co., Inc.

M. RICHARD CARPENTER, Advanced Manufacturing Engineer, Precision Fastener Div., Standard Pressed Steel Co.; HOWARD A. GREIS, President, Kinefac Corp.; W. R. HARVEY, Tool Superintendent, Lamson & Sessions Co.; WILLIAM HUGGINS, Indianapolis Plant, Ford Motor Co.

NORMAN KEGLER, Russell, Burdsall & Ward Bolt and Nut Co.; W. MCCARDELL, Chief Tool Designer, Michigan Tool Co.; WALTER SHELDON, Engineering Project Manager, Landis Machine Co.; FRANK G. WHEELER, JR., Vice President, Peen-Rite, Inc.; ELMER S. ZOOK, Chief Engineer, Reed Rolled Thread Die Co.

sixth of the major diameter should be avoided, except with the most ductile metals. For multiple threads, a thread depth of one fourth the major diameter for double and quadruple lead threads, and one fifth the major diameter for triple lead threads, is generally acceptable.

The rolling process can also accomplish many nonthreading operations such as the rolling of splines, helical and annular grooves, knurls, and involute teeth. (Spline rolling is discussed in a separate article beginning on page 145.) Rolling may be used also for burnishing and for displacing metal to form flanges and similar cylindrical shapes.

Surface Finish. When properly made, thread rolling dies impart smooth burnished roots and flanks to threads. Rolled threads are free of tears, chatter marks or cutting-tool marks common to cut threads. Such imperfections nucleate wear and can serve as starting points for fatigue failure. Surface roughness on rolled threads is usually from 8 to 24 micro-in., whereas on cut threads it is often 64 to 125 micro-in. with small ridges or unevenness along the flanks of the thread. However, because surface finish of thread flanks is extremely difficult to check, it is rarely specified on drawings.

In general, the coefficient of friction of a rolled thread surface in sliding contact is considerably lower than that of a comparable cut thread surface. Coefficient of friction between the thread and its mating nut determines how effectively a bolt can be tightened or a moving screw can transmit power. Therefore, the relatively low coefficient of friction of rolled thread surfaces provides for more uniform and consistent tightening of fasteners and for less loss of power in overcoming friction when a load is moved by a screw.

Strength of Rolled Threads. Thread rolling deforms the blank plastically as it is forced to flow along the contour imposed by the dies. The worked metal is appreciably harder and stronger than the blank prior to rolling. Thus, fasteners with rolled threads are harder and stronger than those with cut threads, as indicated by Table 1.

Heating thread rolled fasteners made of steel above the transformation range during a heat treating process completely relieves the favorable compressive stresses induced by rolling. Therefore, steel fasteners produced by thread rolling of blanks quenched and tempered to a given hardness usually have higher fatigue strength than fasteners quenched and tempered to the same hardness after thread rolling. Figure 2 shows this difference for the most common range of hardness. The different effects of hardness on fatigue strength of bolts that were roll threaded before and after heat treatment is illustrated in Fig. 3.

Evaluation of Metals for Thread Rolling

The three characteristics that are important in evaluating and selecting metals for thread rolling are: rollability, flaking, and seaming.

Table 1. Average Mechanical Properties of Hexagon-Head Capscrews With Rolled and Cut Threads(a)

Screw size and pitch	Type of thread	Core hardness, R_B(b) Shank	Core hardness, R_B(b) Thread area	Tensile strength, psi	Fatigue life, cycles to failure(c)
7/8–9	Rolled	82	92	91,550	71,800
	Cut	82	82	70,950	14,300
1–8	Rolled	91	94.5	98,350	51,800
	Cut	91	91	91,450	21,300
1 1/8–7	Rolled	91	96.5	103,100	68,500
	Cut	91	91	91,350	49,300

(a) Data are based on 15 pieces of each size and each threading method, made of 4027 steel. (b) Core hardness refers to the hardness at the area on the centerline of the thread below the pitch diameter. Converted from Knoop readings. (c) Fatigue test was tension-tension, at 60,000 psi, using a preload equal to 10% of maximum.

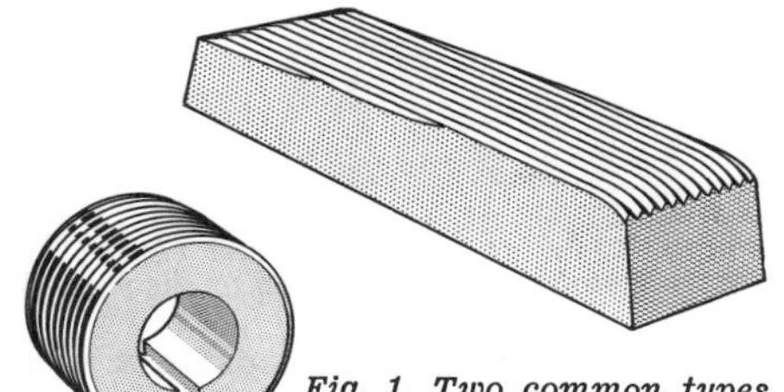

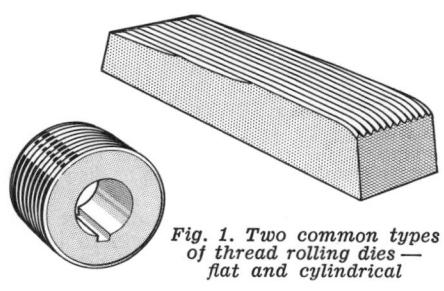

Fig. 1. Two common types of thread rolling dies — flat and cylindrical

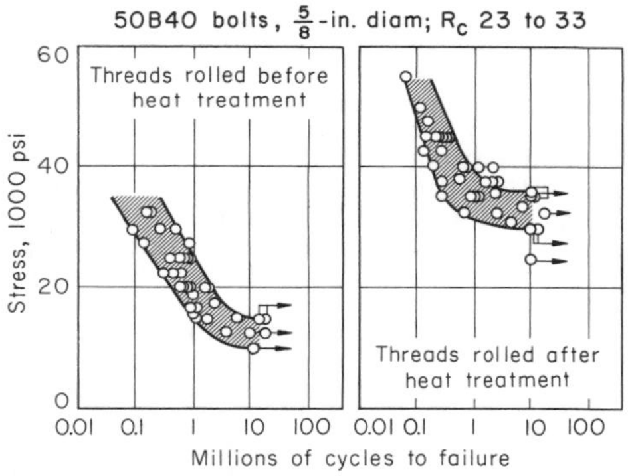

Curve at left is for four different lots of bolts tempered to an average hardness of Rockwell C 22.7, 26.6, 27.6 and 32.6. The curve on the right is for five different lots of bolts tempered to an average hardness of Rockwell C 23.3, 27.4, 29.6, 31.7 and 33. Harder bolts in each category had fatigue strength toward the high side of the ranges shown.

Fig. 2. Increased fatigue strength of steel bolts obtained when threads are rolled after heat treatment rather than before

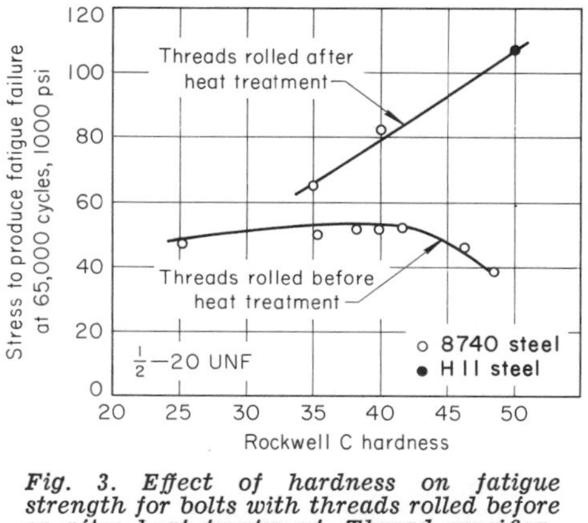

Fig. 3. Effect of hardness on fatigue strength for bolts with threads rolled before or after heat treatment. Thread specification was MIL-B-7838 for the 8740 steel and MIL-S-8879 for the H11 steel.

Rollability involves ductility and the resistance of a metal to flow when subjected to cold forming in thread rolling dies. Rollability indexes for 17 steels and for 6 nonferrous alloys commonly threaded are given in Table 2. The power required to form a given thread shape at a given rate in various metals is inversely proportional to the rollability indexes of the metals. If material in an operation is changed for one of lower rollability index, the production rate per horsepower for a rolled form in that operation decreases. For example, if a through-feed machine using its full 10-hp output produces 1/2–13 UNC–2A threads at a rate of 450 ipm in a solid bar of steel with an index of 1.00, the rate will be only 270 ipm when a steel of index 0.60 is threaded in the same machine under the same operating conditions.

The rollability index also provides a means of comparing radial die loads and expected die life in rolling two materials under identical operating conditions. The radial die loads required for roll threading various metals are approximately inversely proportional to the rollability indexes of the metals. Die life is approximately proportional to the third or fourth power of the indexes if final die failure is due to crumbling of thread crests of the die. Thus, if a die life of 100,000 ft of threaded rod is obtained when rolling steel having an index of 1.00, a die life of about 6000 to 12,000 ft can be expected when steel with an index of 0.5 is threaded under the same conditions.

Flaking is related to the shear strength of the metal being rolled. Lead and sulfur in brass and steel increase susceptibility to flaking during rolling. An increase in the carbon content of steel decreases susceptibility to flaking. In general, flaking increases directly with the amount of prior cold working of the blank material. This is true of almost all rollable metals, and especially of the work-hardening alloys such as series 300 stainless steel, copper, and some aluminum alloys. Annealing prior to rolling reduces flaking.

Work metals may be classified into four groups with respect to susceptibility to flaking:

- A – Little or no susceptibility, regardless of whether or not the material was previously cold worked, or regardless of the bluntness of form to be rolled
- B – Minor susceptibility
- C – Strong susceptibility
- D – Excessive susceptibility, which prevents the rolling of all but the most simple, shallow forms without flaking.

Table 2 indicates susceptibility to flaking for metals most commonly thread rolled. As indicated, all metals listed in Table 2 fall within the B or C class. Not many metals can be classified as A for susceptibility to flaking. Copper and some of the extremely ductile copper alloys when in the annealed condition are sometimes given the A rating. Metals that contain excessive amounts of free-machining additives, such as the specially prepared screw-machine steels, are likely to fall within the D class. Also some metals that work harden at an excessive rate (some of the stainless steels and the less ductile heat-resisting alloys) are likely to fall in the D class.

Seaming. If, during rolling, the work metal flows up the flanks of the die threads faster than it does at the center of the thread form, the displaced metal may fold together to form a seam as the metal fills the full crest of the thread form, as shown in Fig. 4. The formation of seams — or folds, as they are sometimes called — depends primarily on the metal being rolled, and secondarily on the shape of the thread form.

Open seams in the thread crests may occur when undersize blanks are rolled. The open seams can shorten the service life of the thread in a corrosive environment, although they are not usually detrimental in normal service, where corrosion is less important.

The softer, more ductile metals usually form deeper seams than the harder, less ductile metals. Figure 5 shows the types of metal flow associated with four degrees of seaming. Table 2 indicates susceptibility to seaming for specific alloys commonly used for thread rolling stock.

Preparation and Feeding of Work Blanks

The diameter of the blank to be threaded is intermediate between the major and minor diameters of the thread to be rolled, as shown in Fig. 6.

It is common practice to produce blanks for rolling Unified and American Standard threads having tolerances greater than 0.002 in. by extruding, by cold heading, or by shaving on automatic machines. Most of the class 3A threads in the sizes generally used have pitch diameter tolerances greater than 0.002 in. Therefore, they can be rolled on extruded, cold headed, or shaved blanks. Some of the smaller class 3A threads have tolerances closer than 0.002 in. Blanks for these threads should be ground.

To produce threads having a pitch diameter within a tolerance of 0.002 in., the tolerance of the blank diameter should be within 0.0005 in. Closer thread tolerances can increase the cost of blank preparation, sometimes far beyond the usual costs.

Blanks with close-tolerance diameters are ground. Blanks of material not suitable for extruding or cold heading, such as titanium and some stainless steels, are also ground.

Blank diameter must be within the tolerance required for the particular size and class of thread specified. It is not practical to roll threads to a close tolerance except on blanks held to appropriate diameter. Over-rolling an undersize blank to provide a screw of correct size will cause premature die failure. Maximum die life is obtained when the crest is not rolled full. When rolling a class 2A thread, for example, the most economical procedure is to use a blank of such diameter that the thread can be rolled to the mean class 2A pitch diameter (halfway between high and low limit of pitch diameter) and to maintain the major diameter of the thread just above the lower tolerance limit.

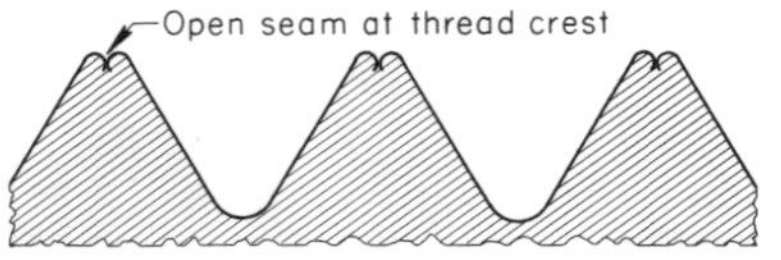

Fig. 4. Seam at crest of thread caused by faster metal flow along flanks of die thread

Table 2. Rollability of Alloys

Metal	Hardness, Bhn	Rollability index(a)	Flaking tendency (b)	Seaming tendency (c)
Carbon and Low-Alloy Steels				
1010	137	1.11	B	C
1018	148	1.08	B	C
1020	156	0.96	B	C
1095	260	0.47	B	B
1095	320	0.42	B	B
1112	198	1.00	C	C
1117	173	1.03	C	C
1144	225	0.78	B	C
4140	205	0.93	B	C
4140	234	0.57	B	C
4140	300	0.42	B	B
4340	235	0.45	B	B
8620	215	0.60	B	C
Stainless Steels				
303	174	0.46	C	B
316	150	0.45	B	B
416	221	0.58	C	B
430	225	0.56	C	B
Nonferrous Alloys				
Aluminum:				
2017, 2024	135	1.40	B	C
Brass:				
Cartridge	190	1.55	B	B
Naval	155	1.00	C	B
Phosphor bronze	130	1.28	C	B
Monel	235	0.93	B	B

(a) Index applies to metals rolled at room temperature. (b) B, minor susceptibility; C, strong susceptibility. (c) B, negligible susceptibility; C, moderate susceptibility. See Fig. 5, which also indicates the two extremes of seaming tendency (A and D).

Relation of Blank and Pitch Diameters. The thread form is said to be balanced when the volume of cavity below the pitch line (Fig. 7) is equal to the volume of metal above the pitch line. (Pitch line is defined as the location at which the widths of the thread ridge and the thread groove are equal.) In such threads, the correct blank diameter will be substantially the same as the pitch diameter. With metals that are commonly cold headed, the maximum blank diameter generally is equal to the mean pitch diameter. The optimum blank diameter varies with different work metals; some adjustment may be needed to get the desired crest formation. Additional dimensional allowance is necessary if subsequent plating is planned. If the form to be rolled is unbalanced (Fig. 7), the blank diameter is not the same as the pitch diameter.

Bevel on Blanks. Ground and extruded blanks are made with a bevel at the end or ends of the section to be threaded. This bevel ranges from 15° to 45°. Blanks for the majority of thread rolled products have a bevel angle of 30°. Thread rolling, however, increases the bevel by 15° to 30°. Therefore, the bevel angle on the blank must be less than the angle desired on the finished part. Figure 8 illustrates the different bevel angles used on blanks for rolling American Standard threads.

In addition to the bevel angle, some blanks have a bevel in the area that connects the section to be threaded with the section that will remain unthreaded. This bevel, sometimes called the extruding angle, is usually 30°.

Feeding. The various thread rolling methods employ three basic techniques for feeding the blank into the dies:

1. **Radial Infeed.** The die, usually cylindrical, moves in a radial line directly toward the axis of rotation of the workpiece.
2. **Tangential Feed.** The die, either cylindrical or flat, moves past the workpiece on a path that brings the pitch line of the thread form tangent to the work surface.
3. **End Feed or Through Feed.** The cylindrical die "tracks" on the workpiece causing it to move axially as it rotates.

Flat Die Rolling

Flat traversing dies are the type most commonly used for rolling threads in commercial fasteners and similar parts. One technique involves the use of two flat, rectangular dies; one is stationary and the other traverses in a plane parallel to the stationary die and separated from it by a distance equal to the minor diameter of the thread to be rolled. In another technique, both dies traverse the workpiece. Figure 9 shows the most common arrangement of dies and workpiece.

As the blank is forced into the space between the dies by a starting device, it is engaged by the forward motion of the traversing die and caused to roll between the threaded faces of the dies. This action forms the thread.

A thread is rolled on one blank at a time during the forward stroke of the

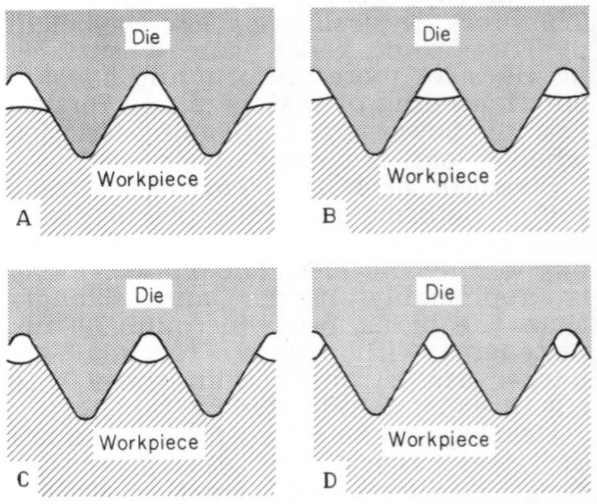

A – Negative susceptibility to form seams. Metal flow adjacent to the die surface is slower than in the middle of the roll form. This is characteristic of metals having a relatively high coefficient of friction with the die steel.
B – Negligible susceptibility to form seams. Metal flows up with an almost flat top during rolling in conventional thread forms.
C – Moderate susceptibility to form seams, typical of low-carbon steels.
D – Excessive susceptibility to form seams. Cavity is likely to be formed under crest of thread.

Fig. 5. Schematic illustration of four degrees of susceptibility to seaming during thread rolling

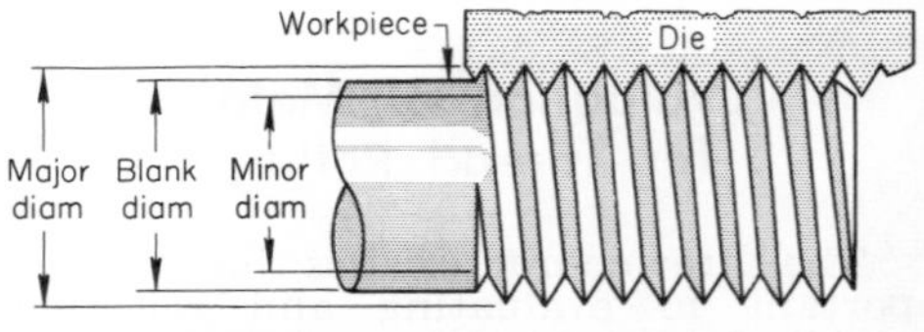

Fig. 6. Relation of blank diameter to major and minor diameters of threads

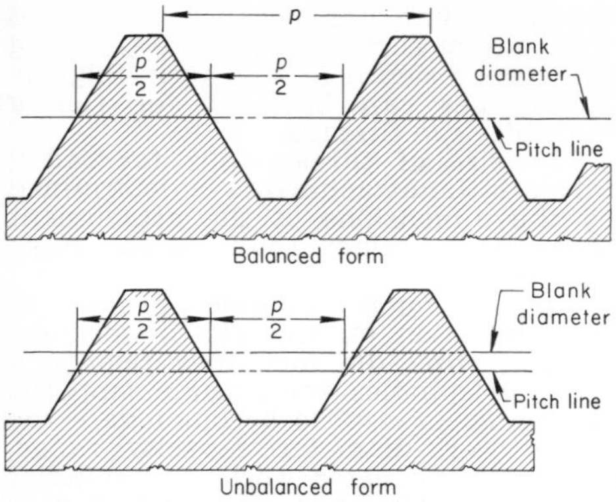

Fig. 7. Relation of blank diameter to pitch line for balanced and unbalanced thread forms

machine. There is no appreciable axial movement of the blank during rolling. The diameter of the finished thread is controlled by the diameter of the blank and the distance between the faces of the dies at the end of the stroke.

Machines. The generic term "flat die rollers" encompasses a large and varied family of machines that are made in a number of sizes, each for a limited diameter range and with a specified die length. Most flat die rollers have the dies in the side-by-side position shown in Fig. 9. Most of the newer machines also have dies that traverse in the horizontal plane, but with the faces of the dies at an angle to the vertical. The feed track is at an angle, thus permitting gravity feed down an incline into the inserting mechanism.

Specialized types of vertical and horizontal rolling machines also are available. One horizontal traversing unit has dies placed one above the other rather than in the usual side-by-side position. It is used to roll splines and related forms as well as threads. Another variation of the horizontal traversing machine uses an inclined feed chute at right angles to, rather than parallel with, the axis of traverse. This type of machine incorporates a different method of die alignment. Dies are adjusted longitudinally to match the threads of the two dies, rather than vertically by shims as in most other machines.

Dies used in flat die rollers consist of matching pairs of rectangular plates, with each of the opposed faces having a reverse image of the form to be produced on the part. Dies are made in various widths and are used to roll screws of any thread length up to the maximum die capacity.

The lead angle of flat dies can vary theoretically from 0° to 45°, but for producing most standard screw threads it is less than 5°. (Lead angle of the die is defined as the angle between the thread form and the longitudinal axis of the die.)

In flat die design, penetration rate is governed primarily by the length of the die. Best practice calls for complete penetration prior to the last revolution of the workpiece in the die. The last complete revolution of the workpiece should only iron out small irregularities. It is important that the die be long enough to prevent an excessive penetration rate.

The above principles can be used to roll more than one form on a part by use of a multiple stack of dies, which are inserted one atop the other in the machine and held together with a clamp. Thus, many combinations of forms that would be impossible to generate on a one-piece die can be easily produced on a multiple die with the proper arrangement.

In addition to the dies, secondary tooling is required for feeding, sorting, orienting, and inserting the parts between the dies.

Capabilities. The flat die process is commonly used for all types of straight and taper threaded commercial fasteners. Flat die rolling can produce more than one form in one operation, such as two entirely different types of threads at opposite ends of a part, knurling and a thread, or knurling and an annular groove on the same part.

Duplex face dies can be used for rolling straight threads. Such dies have threads on both the front and back sides so that they provide two rolling surfaces. When the screw length is less than half the die width, the die can be

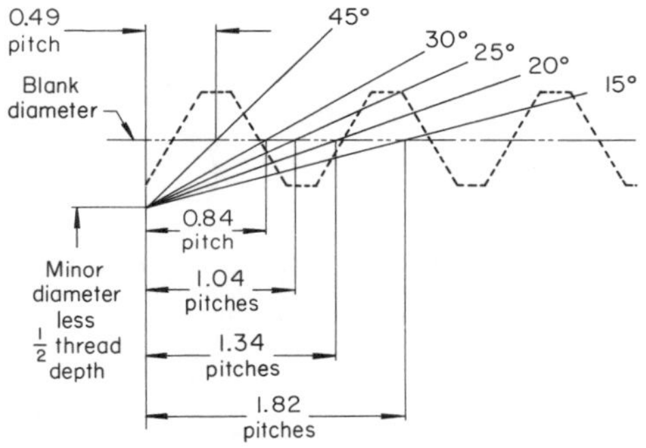

Fig. 8. Bevel angles on blanks for rolling American Standard threads. Length of incomplete thread is shown for each bevel angle, using pitch length as the unit.

reversed, top for bottom, so that four rolling edges are available for still greater economy.

Production rates vary widely and usually are inversely proportional to the size of the product. The small machines are capable of producing parts at a rate of 10,000 to 36,000 per hour. Larger units, producing a ⅜-in. or ½-in. bolt, can roll 3000 to 12,000 pieces per hour. Products such as 1¼-in.-diam bolts are thread rolled at much slower rates, ranging from 900 to 3000 pieces per hour.

Limitations. In general, flat dies are used for threading metals no harder than Rockwell C 32 before rolling, although steel as hard as Rockwell C 52 can be roll threaded. Thread diameters are commonly limited to 1 in., although a few machines can roll up to 1½-in.-diam threads. Thread lengths up to 10½ in. are rolled. These limitations — hardness, diameter and length — are interrelated, so that a workpiece having more than one or two of these measurements near maximum value may not be rollable.

The flat die method also is limited to parts of an over-all size that can be accommodated in the machine. Because of interference between the part and elements of the machine and die, part size as well as thread dimensions must be considered before the flat die method is selected for a specific piece.

Radial Infeed Rolling

Radial infeed thread rolling consists of moving a rotating cylindrical die or dies radially toward the center of the rotating workpiece. The operating principle of this method is shown in Fig. 10.

A minimum amount of axial movement between the dies and the workpiece occurs during the rolling cycle. This characteristic distinguishes infeed rolling from the through-feed method of cylindrical-die thread rolling. Axial movement is canceled by designing the die with an effective lead angle equal in magnitude but opposite in direction to that on the work. In rolling a 9⁄32–32 double-lead worm thread, movement would be as much as 3⁄16 in. during the rolling cycle if there were no compensating lead on the die. Axial movement does not affect thread quality, but it may restrict the ability to produce a full thread close to a shoulder and will reduce the amount of full thread that can be produced with a special die face.

The effective lead angle may vary slightly during die penetration so that some axial movement does occur. The amount of movement is usually insignificant when rolling standard threads but can be considerable when rolling blunt or very deep thread forms, or those with large lead angles.

Dies can be designed to give slight axial movement to the blank to increase die life, or to simplify regrinding of the dies. Movement of ⅛ to ¼ in. is common; movement of up to ½ in. has advantages in some applications.

When two or three dies are used, they must be matched to each other so that the helical path produced by one die is a continuation of that produced by the other die or dies; otherwise, there will be steps in the product thread (Fig. 11). Dies are matched by rotating one or more dies in relation to the others, or by moving one or more dies axially, to produce a continuous helix on the work.

Cylindrical-die machines capable of infeed thread rolling are equipped with either two or three dies (Fig. 10). Two-

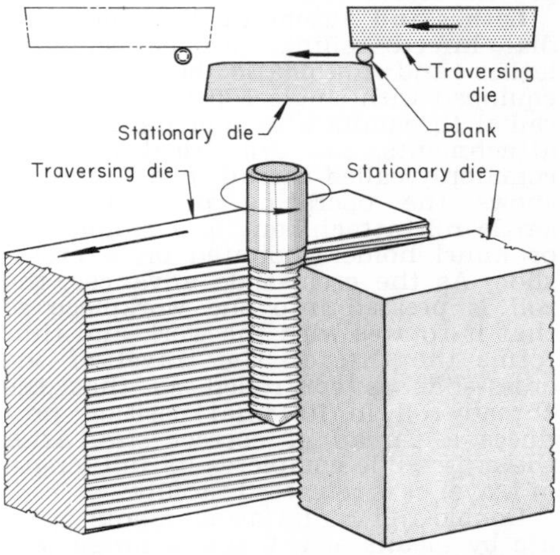

Fig. 9. Operating principle of flat traversing die thread rolling

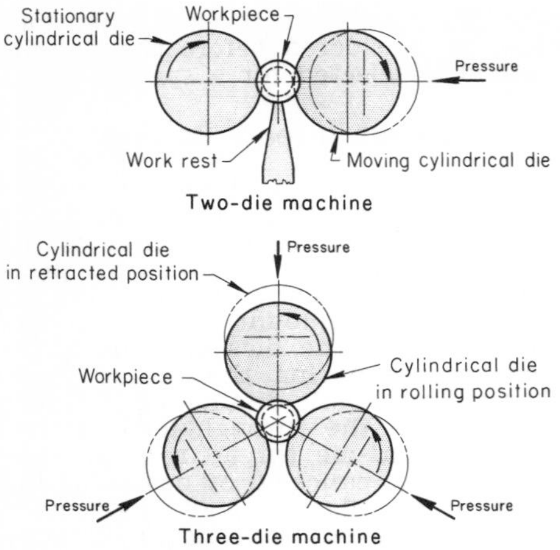

Fig. 10. Operating principle of radial infeed cylindrical-die thread rolling

die machines are usually of the horizontal type; that is, the workpiece is horizontal during rolling. Three-die machines are available in both horizontal and vertical models.

In two-die machines, either one or both dies can move radially. If one die does not move radially, the work must move radially during die penetration. If both dies move equally, the work can stay in place.

Most three-die machines provide equal radial movement of all dies so that the work position does not change during rolling. A few three-die machines have one or two dies stationary, and radial movement of the work must be allowed for.

Two-die machines require a work support, to position the centerline of the work in the same plane as the centerline of the dies. A work rest, as shown in the two-die machine of Fig. 10, can be used for short, manually loaded parts. Larger parts may require additional supports. In many instances, the parts can be inserted in a tube or bushing, or held between centers, to provide proper positioning for rolling. A spring-loaded work stop can be used for positioning the part in proper axial location.

The dies in a three-die machine serve to locate the part so that often the only fixture required for manual loading is a spring-loaded work stop to provide correct axial position.

Lathes and Automatic Machines. Radial infeed rolling can be done in lathes and automatic bar machines equipped with single-roll or double-roll radial threading attachments. In these attachments, the cylindrical dies are commonly called thread rolls. Figure 12 shows the operating principle. The single-roll attachment is a simple roll or knurl holder mounted on a cross-slide. As the cross-slide advances, the roll is pressed into the workpiece so that it rotates with the work and thus forms the thread. The travel of the cross-slide is controlled so that the thread roll in its final position produces a thread of correct size. After the cross-slide completes its full length of travel, it is retracted rapidly.

Double-roll radial attachments operate by means of a toggle arrangement that causes the rolls to close approximately radially to contact the rotating work, at which time the rolls begin to turn to form the thread. After reaching full depth, the rolls and attachment are retracted rapidly.

Dies (Rolls). A little axial movement occurs between the work and cylindrical dies, and it is necessary that the threaded length of the dies be about two to three threads per product lead longer than the length of the thread to be rolled. In practice, it is desirable to provide a bevel at each end of the die (Fig. 13); thus, the width of the die face must exceed the length of the thread to be rolled by twice the width of a bevel.

Long bevels with a small bevel angle increase die life by reducing breakage at the edge of the die. Usually 30° bevels are recommended, although workpiece requirements may necessitate 45°. For the harder workpieces bevel angles of less than 30° are desirable; they may need to be as small as 15° for the hardest rollable metals.

Die Size. For infeed rolling, the pitch diameter of the die must be a multiple of the pitch diameter of the finished workpiece. For single-lead threads, the number of thread starts is equal to the ratio of die-to-work pitch diameters. For rolling multiple-lead threads, the number of die thread starts equals the number of thread starts on the work multiplied by the ratio of die-to-work pitch diameters.

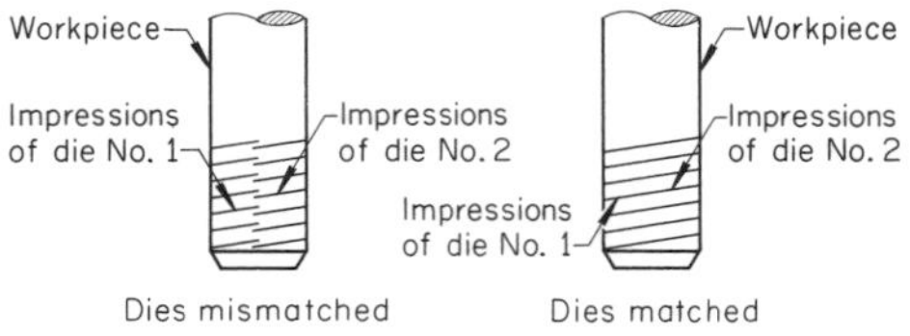

Fig. 11. Effect of mismatched and correctly matched dies on thread impression made by cylindrical dies

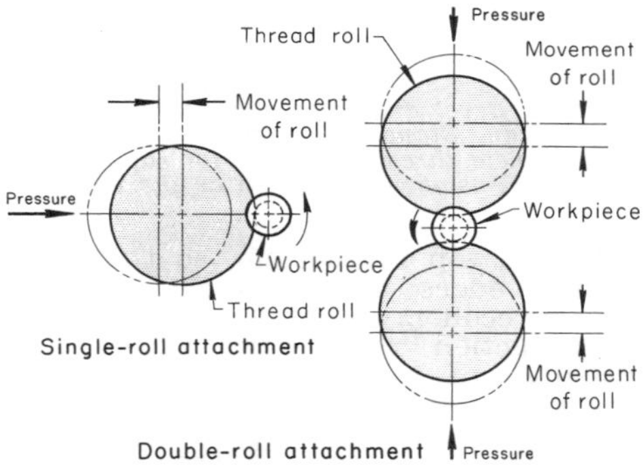

Fig. 12. Operating principle of two types of radial attachments for thread rolling on lathes and automatic bar machines

The diameter of dies for two-die machines is limited by the size of the machine and fixtures and is approximately constant regardless of work diameter. For instance, a typical two-die machine having capacity for 1/16 to 1½-in. workpieces uses dies that are 5 to 6 in. in diameter for all sizes of work. In general, but not necessarily, two-die machines use dies of larger diameter than three-die machines for threading the same size of workpiece.

Three-die machines generally cannot use dies larger than about five times the work diameter, because larger dies will contact each other before reaching full thread depth in the work. Slightly larger dies can be used for rolling multiple-lead threads.

The size of thread rolls for radial infeed lathe attachments is determined by the dimensions of the attachment being used, rather than by the work diameter.

Supports for Die Spindles. Because of the limitation on the die-to-work diameter, three-die machines require a series of spindles and spindle supports, graduated in size, to accommodate the entire work-diameter capacity range. For small-diameter work, the spindles are necessarily quite slender and may not be strong enough to roll hard alloys or long thread lengths, as indicated in the following example.

Example 265. Three Dies vs Two Dies for Rolling 4¾-In. Long Thread

A three-die cylindrical machine equipped with 5-in.-long dies was rolling ⅞–14 threads to a length of 4¾ in. on 0.40% carbon alloy steel blanks at Rockwell C 36 to 40. It was noticed that the pitch diameter was not a true cylinder but arched from one end of the thread to the other. This condition was caused by bowing of the spindles and dies. To roll acceptable threads, it was necessary to transfer the operation to a two-die cylindrical machine.

As a result of the difficulty with the three-die machine, the dies were altered to incorporate center supports, which for all practical purposes eliminated the bending previously encountered.

Capabilities. The minimum practical diameter of workpiece for rolling in two-die machines or attachments is 0.050 in. The maximum diameter is limited only by the capacity of available equipment. Two-die machines capable of rolling threads 6 in. in diameter and 12 in. long are in use.

Three-die machines roll threads from ¼ to 4½ in. in diameter and up to 5 in. long. They are seldom practical for rolling threads smaller than ¼ in. in diameter.

The rate of die penetration into the work is adjustable; thus metals of various hardnesses can be threaded. Most metals threaded by cylindrical dies or attachments are no harder than about Rockwell C 32. But work metals as hard as Rockwell C 52 have been thread rolled on cylindrical dies. Die life does deteriorate rapidly when material harder than Rockwell C 32 is rolled.

The versatility of the radial infeed method makes possible rolling of thin-wall parts, such as tubing or stampings, and some metals harder than Rockwell C 48 that would be difficult or impossible on other types of machine.

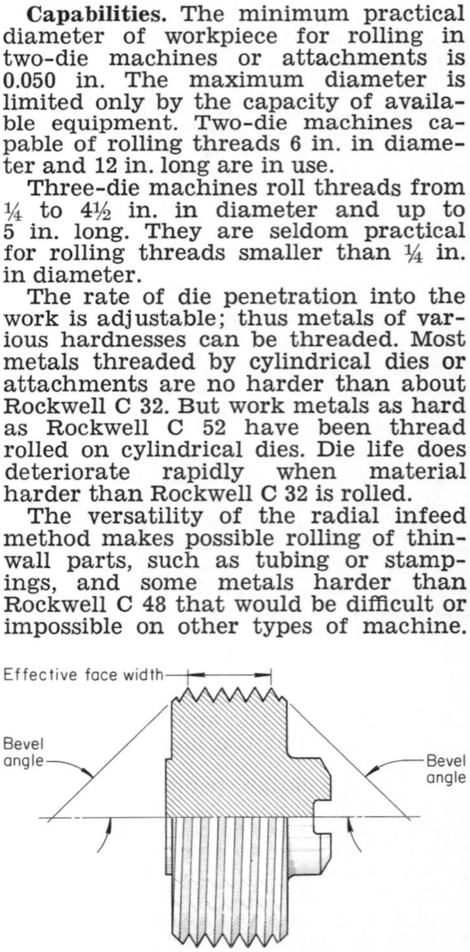

Fig. 13. Bevel on a cylindrical thread rolling die

Table 3. Typical Applications of Cylindrical-Die Thread Rolling

Product	Steel	Thread	Length, in.	Insertion	Die speed, rpm	Rate, pieces per min	Die life, pieces
Infeed Rolling							
Adjusting worm(a)	8620	9/16–10	1⅛	....	85	8 to 10	....
Armature shaft (worm)(b)	1045	0.065-in. pitch	¾	Manual	45	....	6000
Armature shaft (worm)(c)	1040	0.2805–32	....	Manual	....	6	....
Double-end stud	1018	1½–8 UN–3A	2	Manual	....	4(d)	....
Feed screw(e)	410	0.330–56 Acme	3¾	....	170	8 to 10	....
Feed screw(a)	410	⅜–33⅓ Acme LH	2 7/32	....	....	10	....
Worm	4140	Buttress(f)	....	Manual	85	8 to 10	....
Worm	8620	¾–5; 4 starts	1½	Manual	....	8 to 10	20,000
Through-Feed Rolling							
Threaded rod	1018	⅜–16 UNC	6 ft	Automatic	500	6	260,000
Jackscrew(g)	1018	½–10 Acme stub	8¼	Manual	260	....	25,000
Setscrew	(h)	⅜–19 BSP.F(h)	1.2	Hopper	....	300	....
Automatic Continuous Rolling							
Automotive stud	8115	½–20 UNF–2A	0.640	Hopper	....	125	500,000
Double-end stud	1335 or 1041(j)	5/16–24 UNF–3A(k)	(k)	Hopper	....	200(d)	....
Double-end stud	3135(j)	⅝–11 UNC(m)	(m)	Hopper	....	80(d)	....

(a) Pressure angle, 14½°. (b) Pressure angle, 20°. (c) Pressure angle, 25°; two leads on thread. (d) Both ends. (e) Pressure angle, 29°. (f) Modified buttress; 2 starts; 11½ threads per inch; flanks 10° and 30°. (g) Infeed and through-feed rolling. (h) British Standard Parallel Fastener; made of resulfurized screw stock. (j) Cold drawn, cut to length and ends extruded to blank diameter. (k) Thread length, 9/16 in. on each end of 4⅝-in.-long stud. (m) One end class 3A, 1⅛ in. long; the other end, class 5A, 1 in. long; total length of stud, 2¾ in.

Rolling of thin-wall parts is discussed in a subsequent section.

The radial infeed method permits rolling of threads close to shoulders, with a minimum of imperfect threads. Also, threads can be rolled between two sections of larger diameter as is common when rolling worms on large transmission shafts. Threading close to shoulders is considered in a subsequent section of this article (page 142).

The three-point support provided by three-die machines is advantageous for rolling parts with irregular or unbalanced overhangs, and for parts requiring a thread length considerably shorter than one diameter. Often such parts can be rolled while being supported only by the three dies, whereas cylindrical two-die machines or other types of threading equipment may require expensive or unwieldy fixturing.

Radial feeding single-roll or double-roll attachments are used to best advantage for rolling threads at the collet end of pieces being machined in a lathe or automatic bar machine (Fig. 14). Such threads are usually behind a shoulder so that radial infeed and tangential feed rolling (discussed below) are the only thread rolling methods practical.

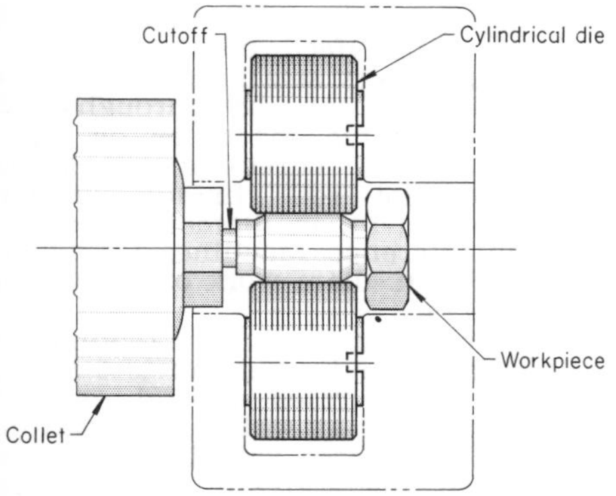

Fig. 14. Use of a double-roll attachment for thread rolling near the collet of an automatic bar machine

Because double-roll attachments exert a minimum of transverse pressure on the work, small diameters of considerable length can be rolled, and at a much greater distance from the collet than with the single-roll type of attachment. For example a double-roll attachment can roll a ½–20 UNF, ¾-in.-long thread on a ½-in.-diam bar at a distance of 1 in. from the collet to the first thread. With a single-roll attachment, maximum distance from the collet is ¼ in.

Production capabilities of cylindrical-die infeed machines vary according to the method and equipment for feeding the work and the type of work involved. In general, hand feeding is not practical at rates above 25 pieces per minute. Automatic feeding equipment can be installed on two-die or three-die machines to produce up to about 60 pieces per minute.

Typical applications of cylindrical-die infeed thread rolling are shown in Table 3.

Limitations. The axial travel caused by thread rolling machines when they are producing deep, blunt thread forms, or high lead angles is not objectionable except when it causes interference during rolling of a thread close to a shoulder. In single-roll or double-roll lathe attachments the work cannot move axially and roll movement is usually limited to approximately one third of the pitch so that rolls must be designed to cause a minimum of axial travel. The rolling of deep, blunt forms, or high lead angles requires careful attention to the roll design and also to the rate of penetration of the rolls, the accuracy of the setup, and the condition of the attachment.

The accuracy of threads rolled by single-roll infeed attachments depends on the accuracy of the cross-slide travel. Thread accuracy is limited also because of the bending action developed by the force of radial infeed rolling. In some applications, back-up rolls, bearing on a plain cylindrical surface outside the threaded area, can be used to reduce the bending. If a plain surface is not available or machine tooling does not permit the use of back-up rolls, single-roll attachments are restricted to thread rolling near the collet and to short thread lengths in the softer materials.

Tangential Rolling

Tangential thread rolling is similar to infeed rolling except that the dies (rolls) are fed past the blank on a path parallel to the radial path at a distance such that when the axis of the roll is opposite the axis of the blank, the pitchline of the thread form is tangent with the surface of the blank. Figure 15 shows the operating principle of this process. As the rolls advance, they reach maximum penetration when the centerline of the rolls is directly opposite the centerline of the work. The total depth of penetration is determined by the amount the rolls are offset in relation to the work. As in radial infeed rolling, only slight axial movement occurs between the rolls and work.

Machines. Tangential rolling is done in lathes or automatic bar machines equipped with one-roll or two-roll attachments mounted on a cross slide of the machine. The rolls are rotated by their contact with the rotating work. Two-roll attachments are the most common for tangential rolling. They are available in various sizes; each size has capacity for a range of work diameters. Capacity up to a work diameter of 2½ in. is commonly available, and larger sizes are obtainable for special applications.

Capabilities. Tangential feeding attachments have essentially the same capabilities as radial feeding attachments. Some advantage is gained with tangential attachments because the adjustments and control for a given size of work are made within the attachment rather than by the travel of the machine slide.

With a two-roll tangential attachment, no radial movement occurs between the roll spindles during rolling, and rolling pressures are greater than in radial infeed rolling.

Threads can be rolled at spindle speeds compatible with other machining operations; therefore, speed changes for threading are unnecessary. Two-roll tangential rolling produces bending loads somewhat higher than the two-roll radial-feeding attachment, but low enough to allow the rolling of threads on relatively hard work metals at a considerable distance from the collet. For instance, a ¾-in.-long ½–20 UNF thread can be rolled on a ½-in.-diam bar, hardened to Rockwell C 30, at a distance of ⅝ in. from the collet to the first thread.

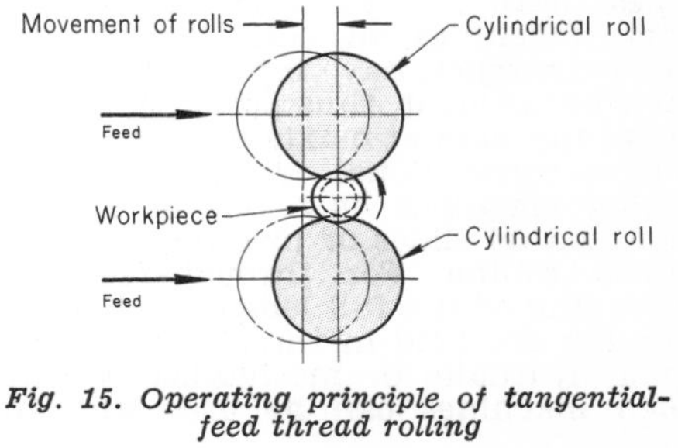

Fig. 15. Operating principle of tangential-feed thread rolling

Limitations. Thread rolling with a two-roll tangential attachment is limited primarily by the size and capacity of the equipment. Rolling threads with high lead angles or with deep, blunt forms can be troublesome because of axial travel. However, with proper attention to roll design and setup, and using only attachments in very good condition, the problem can usually be overcome.

Single-roll tangential rolling produces transverse loads capable of bending the workpiece. Therefore, this procedure is limited to rolling threads of short length near the collet in soft materials such as nonferrous alloys or soft steel (generally 197 max Bhn). In rolling a ½–20 UNF thread next to the collet on a ½-in.-diam bar of 1112 steel, the maximum practical thread length would be approximately ⅞ in. As with radial single-roll attachments, support rolls can sometimes be used to increase this capacity.

Through-Feed Rolling

In through-feed rolling, the work moves axially through the dies. Through-feed dies are designed with a lead angle generally different from that of the work, so that the part can feed. The dies are made with a starting taper, so that the thread is formed progressively as the blank feeds through the dies. The finish end of the dies also is tapered slightly so that rolling pressure is released gradually without marking the work.

Feed rate, in terms of feed per work revolution, is proportional to the ratio of the difference in lead angles of the dies to the lead angle of the work. The die lead angle can be either greater or less than that of the work and may be zero (annular form dies). Also, the die lead angle can be the same hand as the work (right-hand lead dies to produce right-hand threads).

Machines. Any cylindrical-die thread rolling machine is capable of through-feed rolling, but the capacity may be restricted. Vertical three-die machines, for example, can feed only short lengths because the gear box or other equipment located a short distance below the dies prevents passage of longer work. In three-die horizontal machines a passage through the gear box usually allows unlimited length, but restricts the diameter of long work. Obstructions behind the dies of some two-die machines limit the length or diameter of the work.

Machines having no provision for skewing the spindles are limited to parallel-axis through-feed rolling, for which the feed rates are low. Other machines, including many three-die types, have limited skew adjustment. Some machines, of both two-die and three-die types, have infinitely variable skew adjustment, thus permitting feeding of the work at maximum rate.

Most conventional cylindrical thread rolling machines have one or all dies mounted on slides or pivoting arms for infeed rolling. For through-feed roll threading of the full length of a blank, the dies are held in the closed position by a hydraulic or mechanical system. Such machines can be used also for rolling threads on only a portion of the blank, either by feeding through until the desired length has been threaded, and then opening the dies, or by inserting the work between the open dies to the correct position and then closing the dies so that the work feeds out of the dies. Some machines designed specifically for through-feed rolling of the entire workpiece are not equipped with die advance-retract mechanisms that permit partial-length rolling.

End-Feeding Attachments. Cylindrical through-feed rolling can be done with two-die and three-die end-feeding heads. Two-die heads are used for small work. The rolling heads can be mounted on the rotating headstock of a bolt-threading machine in which the blank is clamped to a slide that advances the work toward the head. When used in an automatic bar or chucking machine, the head is mounted on the tool slide, which advances it toward the rotating workpiece.

The dies are made with annular grooves, and the axes of the dies are set at an angle with the work axis equal to the required lead angle of the product thread. The rate of feed per revolution is equal to the lead of the thread being rolled. Some heads have interchangeable frontplate units that can accommodate a range of lead angles. In other heads, lead angles are varied by interchangeable bushings. End-feeding attachments are adjustable to produce correct thread size.

With the dies locked in the closed position, they engage the blank and roll the thread as they pass over the blank or the blank passes between the dies. When the desired length of thread has been rolled, the head opens and the work is withdrawn from the head. When used for continuous rolling, the head remains in the closed position at all times.

Dies for through-feed rolling are usually relieved at both ends. Through-feed dies for Acme, worm, or other wide threads often have a modified, pointed thread form at the starting end for efficient penetration into the blank.

The number of thread starts, which together with diameter of the die determines the lead angle, is different for through-feed rolling on cylindrical machines than for infeed rolling a similar size thread. Compared to infeed dies of similar diameter for a specific thread, the through-feed dies may have more or fewer starts for parallel-axis rolling or no thread starts (annular form) for skewed-axis rolling.

Capabilities. Through-feed rolling is applicable to threading the full length of a cylindrical part of uniform diameter and to threading one or more sections of the largest diameter of a multi-diameter cylindrical part. End-feeding heads are used for straight and tapered threads. Annular rings can be produced by through-feed rolling in skewed-axis dies or rolls. Typical examples of parts made by through-feed rolling are commercially threaded rod, high-strength studs, headless set screws, threaded mounting tubes for electrical fittings, pole line hardware, recirculating ball screws, and jackscrews of all types. Threads are through-feed rolled to partial length on parts such as compressor studs, large-diameter cap screws, clamp and jackscrews, finned heat-exchanger tubing, and reinforcing rods. Three specific applications of through-feed rolling are given in Table 3.

Most thread rolling machines and heads except the three-die vertical types are virtually unrestricted as to the length of bar that can be threaded. Mill length bars or tubes 10 to 16 ft long are commonly threaded. Heat exchanger tubing is through-feed rolled to produce integral fins in lengths up to 50 ft. Sometimes it is economical to through-feed parts of short length. For example, blanks for socket set screws and various types of studs are thread rolled at high production rates.

Rods or parts up to ¼ in. in diameter can be through-feed rolled at speeds up to 800 ipm depending on the type of machine, available horsepower, and hardness of the blanks. Larger sizes will feed slower; 12 ipm is a typical speed for 3-in.-diam steel parts at a hardness of Rockwell C 22.

In many applications, a larger thread can be rolled in a given machine by partial-length through-feed rolling than by infeed rolling.

Threads of very small diameter, such as 0–80 UNF, can be through-feed rolled on two-die machines or end-feeding heads. Three-die machines usually cannot roll threads smaller than about ¼-in. in diameter because of die interference. Machines are available for 4½-in.-diam work of length up to about 2 ft.

Standard end-feeding attachments are available for threads up to 9 in. in diameter. Feed rates depend on the maximum speed at which the head or work can be rotated with the available horsepower. Feed rates of 300 ipm are common for thread sizes up to ⅝ in. in diameter. Most standard heads have clearance holes through the center so that long thread lengths can be rolled. The maximum length depends on the ability of the equipment to grip the workpiece so as to prevent rotation or excessive torsional wind-up of the piece.

All of the common thread forms can be through-feed rolled, including blunt forms such as Acme and worm threads and ball-screw forms. Threads of very blunt form are produced with less difficulty by through-feed rolling than by infeed rolling.

Limitations. Like other types of cylindrical rolling, the process is limited primarily by the characteristics of the equipment being used.

Planetary Thread Rolling

Planetary thread rolling machines have one central rotating die on a fixed axis, and one or more stationary concave segment dies located near the outside of the rotary die, as shown in Fig. 16. One or several blanks may be rolled on a segment die at one time, depending on the gearing of the starting mechanism.

The starting end of the segment is adjusted so that the blank will contact both dies. As the rotary die revolves, the blank is rolled between the dies

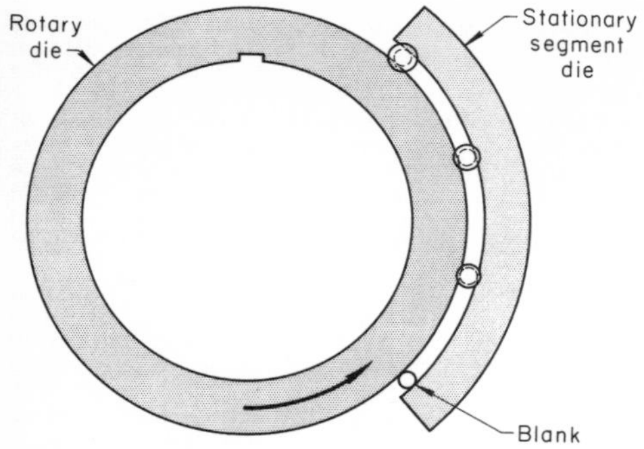

Fig. 16. Operating principle of planetary thread rolling. More than one segment die may be used.

until it traverses the full arc of the segment die, after which it drops out of the threading area.

For most applications, the finish end of the segment die is adjusted to produce the desired thread size. However, when rolling easily work-hardened parts, the dies may have to be adjusted so that the starting end of the die does most of the work and the finishing end does little, the part being completely formed by the time it is halfway through the die. Final thread size, however, does not depend entirely on correct adjustment of the die; hardness and size of the blank can cause variations. The effect of blank hardness is illustrated by the example that follows.

Example 266. Effect of Hardness of Blank on Thread Dimensions (Fig. 17)

The effect of blank hardness on thread dimensions (primarily pitch diameter and major diameter) was investigated in an effort to reduce the rejection rate of 4–40 UNC–2A machine screws. (Rejection was for undersize pitch diameter and major diameter.) The screws, which were made of 1038 steel cold heading wire, were produced in an automated planetary die threader. Blank diameter was 0.0925 to 0.0930 in. A rejection rate of not more than 0.1% was accepted.

Blanks of four different hardness levels were threaded: Rockwell B 60, B 95, C 28, and C 32. Blank diameter was held within specified limits and the same type of lubricant was used for all tests.

Results are shown in Fig. 17. Some endwise stretching in the softer blanks was observed, probably because the part was short and of small diameter. The harder blanks work hardened perceptibly, resulting in undersize thread dimensions and lower die life.

Other details of the threading operation are listed in the table that accompanies Fig. 17.

Machines. Planetary machines are made in several sizes, each having a different maximum rolling capacity. Although machines are usually rated on the basis of nominal work diameter, the blank hardness and length of thread rolled have considerable influence on the practical capacity of a machine.

The basic planetary machine is comparatively simple, consisting of a spindle for the rotary die, a mounting block for the segment die, which also provides size adjustment, and a starting mechanism for inserting the blanks. The starting finger is adjusted by means of gearing or an adjustable cam, so that the workpiece is inserted at the exact point on the rotary die where it is in match with the segment. There is one such match point for each thread start on the rotary die. The number of thread starts varies from 10 to over 100; however, it is seldom possible to feed a blank into the die at every thread start. Planetary machines usually can feed from 3 to 8 parts per die revolution, depending on size; five pieces per revolution is common for this mass-production process.

To make use of the high production capacity of planetary machines, automatic feeders are essential and are generally supplied as an integral part of the machine.

Dies. Lead angles are similar to those of radial infeed and flat dies; therefore, axial travel is at a minimum. Bevels are similar to those used on other types of dies.

Planetary dies vary in diameter from 4 to 14 in.; the most commonly used machines have dies approximately 7 in. in diameter. The segment die has an inside radius equal to or slightly greater than the sum of the rotary die radius and the minor diameter of the threaded part. The width of the dies can be the maximum accepted by the machine or can be much narrower when short-length threads are rolled. Dies for straight threads, such as those on machine screws, can be reversed so that both the upper and lower portions can be used for screws that have a thread length of less than half the die width.

The maximum length of the segment die is limited by the length of the pocket in which it is held. Shorter dies are used for small-diameter work so that the work receives the proper number of revolutions during rolling. Because the surface of the rotary die is longer than that of the segment die, the rotary die generally has greater life.

Planetary dies for gimlet-pointed screws, such as type A and AB sheet metal screws, are very similar to flat dies for the same screws. The length of the segment die is equivalent to one flat die and the circumference of the rotary die is usually equivalent to five segments and is capable of threading at least five pieces during each revolution of the die.

Capabilities. Planetary thread rolling machines can roll most of the smaller parts that can be rolled on flat die machines. Production rates of planetary rollers are higher than those of other types of thread-rolling equipment. Rates of 3000 pieces per minute can be reached on small pieces. The practical limit of production rate depends on the ability to feed the blanks rather than on speed of rolling. Planetary rollers lose their economic advantage over other equipment when it is necessary to reduce the production rate in order to feed difficult parts properly, or when quantities are too low (for instance, less than 1 million ¼-in. screws).

Because they are produced in large quantities and can be fed easily, headed parts comprise most of the production on planetary machines. Typical products are machine screws; types A, AB and B sheet metal screws; and drive screws. Size of product ranges in the popular machine sizes are No. 4 machine screws to ⅝-in.-diam screws, although machines with capacities up to 1⅛ in. have been built.

Limitations. The cost of rotary dies is in proportion to die size. Die cost per piece produced is generally competitive with other types of dies, but unless volume is high enough to use up the available die life, large inventories of dies will accumulate.

Continuous Rolling

Continuous rolling is a high-production method suited to cylindrical-die machines. The method uses two cam-type segmental dies, maintained at a predetermined center distance, as required for the desired pitch diameter.

Workpieces are fed from a hopper or magazine to a revolving cage-type workrest that indexes them into and away from the rolling position. Depending on the number of die segments, one, two or three workpieces are threaded for each revolution of the dies.

Continuous rolling in a two-roll cylindrical-die machine provides the highest rate of production for headed workpieces. This method is applicable to the threading of double-end studs and similar parts. Threads of different diameters, pitches and tolerances, as well as those of identical specifications, can be produced in a single pass. Parts can be rolled to produce threads on one end and knurling or splines on the other.

When thread rolling double-end studs, two sets of cam-type dies are used. Each spindle contains two dies maintained a fixed distance apart, depending on stud size. Both ends of the stud can be rolled simultaneously when thread diameters are the same. Except for studs larger than about ¾ in. in diameter, segmented dies can be used to roll different pitches on the two ends of a stud in one spindle revolution.

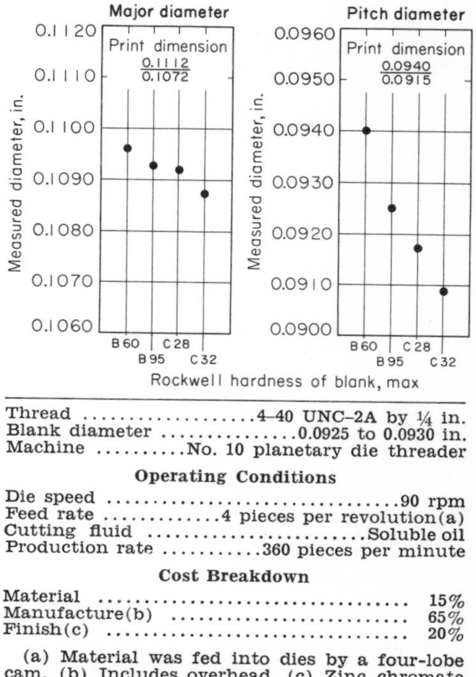

Thread	4–40 UNC–2A by ¼ in.
Blank diameter	0.0925 to 0.0930 in.
Machine	No. 10 planetary die threader

Operating Conditions

Die speed	90 rpm
Feed rate	4 pieces per revolution(a)
Cutting fluid	Soluble oil
Production rate	360 pieces per minute

Cost Breakdown

Material	15%
Manufacture(b)	65%
Finish(c)	20%

(a) Material was fed into dies by a four-lobe cam. (b) Includes overhead. (c) Zinc chromate finish by the barrel method.

Fig. 17. Effect of blank hardness on major and pitch diameters of machine screws made of 1038 steel (Example 266)

Studs and similar parts up to ¾ in. in diameter by 13½ in. long have been produced by this method. Production rate varies with size and shape of the part. Three applications of continuous rolling are shown in Table 3.

Threads on double-end studs 5/16 in. in diameter by 4¾ in. long can be produced at the rate of 240 complete parts per minute by this method.

Internal Thread Rolling

Rolling of internal threads requires dies of comparatively small diameter, which greatly limits die life and the load-carrying capabilities of die bearings and spindles. As a result, internal thread rolling is limited in its use. However, it has been used successfully for forming helical fins on the internal surfaces of heat-exchanger tubes, and internal threads in pipe couplings.

Internal threads can be rolled by impressing the inside surface of a workpiece shell of suitable wall thickness onto a close-fitting threaded mandrel, as shown in Fig. 18(a). Pressure is provided by three or four rotating plain external dies. The workpiece and mandrel may be clamped in a stationary position with the dies mounted in a rotating die head. Or the dies may be stationary while the work and mandrel rotate. It is necessary to unscrew the part from the mandrel after threading has been completed.

To be thread rolled internally, the workpiece must be made of highly ductile metal such as aluminum, brass or low-carbon steel. The wall must be thick enough to provide adequate material to fill the die thread, but not so thick that the external dies are prevented from creating sufficient load to cause the threaded mandrel to penetrate the workpiece.

Such parts have also been threaded internally by using a smaller, threaded mandrel or die, and a single plain external die or support roll, as shown in Fig. 18(b). In this procedure, the part will feed axially when a single-start thread is being rolled. Dies can roll a multiple-start thread with a minimum of axial movement.

Cold form tapping, discussed on page 118, in the article "Tapping", is another method of producing internal threads by metal displacement without the production of chips.

Selection of Rolling Method

Table 4 shows approximate ranges of production rate for different types of thread rolling equipment. Actual production rates depend on the condition of the machine, the work-handling equipment, type of workpiece, and the metal being rolled. Quantity of pieces to be rolled is an important factor in the selection of a machine.

In general, a low volume of identical parts (up to several thousand pieces) can be produced most economically on a hand-fed flat die machine. Hopper feeding is usually most economical for more than 10,000 pieces. Depending on the size of part, a production run of more than 100,000 pieces can often be produced most economically on a planetary-die machine.

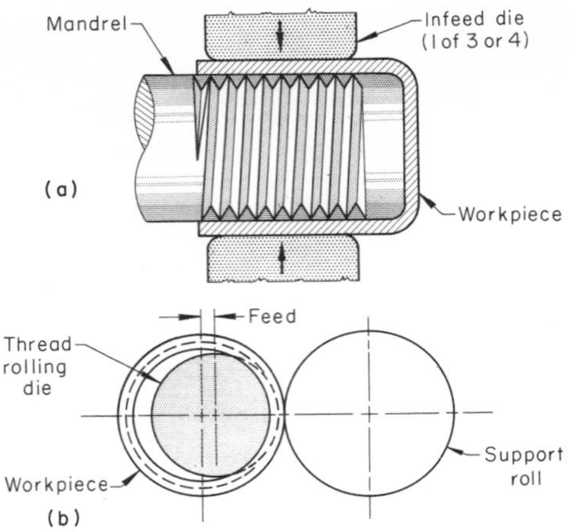

Fig. 18. Internal thread rolling with a close-fitting threaded mandrel (a) *or with a threading die* (b) *that is considerably smaller than the inside diameter being rolled*

In one operation involving standard hexagon-head screws ranging from ¼ to ⅜ in. in diameter, the optimum run for a hand-fed flat die machine was approximately 10,000 pieces. The hopper-fed flat die machine was best for quantities between 10,000 and 400,000 pieces, and the planetary-die machine for runs of more than 400,000 pieces.

The quantity of pieces economically producible on cylindrical-die machines is difficult to assess. These machines can roll special thread forms, and they can roll a greater range of diameters than either flat die or planetary-die machines.

Selection of a single machine that will be suitable for a variety of applications is discussed in the example that follows.

Example 267. Equipment for Varied Product Mix in Quantities from 50 to 1000 Pieces

Various products produced in one plant were threaded originally by cutting tools in secondary-operation equipment. Thread sizes ranged from ¼ to 1 in. diameter and from two diameters to 12 in. long. Production quantities ranged from 50 to 1000 pieces. Although thread cutting produced a quality product, the company decided to purchase thread rolling equipment capable of rolling class 2A and 3A threads and of handling the varied product mix. The various types of thread rolling equipment were considered and selection was based on the following factors:

Traversing Flat Die Machine. Die and setup costs for this equipment were favorable and a high production rate could have been obtained for most of the thread lengths involved. The limited diameter capacity, however, would have necessitated the purchase of more than one size machine in order to cover the range of thread diameters of the product mix, and this type of equipment would have been unsuitable for the long thread lengths required and the variety of workpiece configurations.

Planetary-Die Machine. The quantity of parts to be threaded was insufficient to warrant the purchase of this high-production type of equipment. Also, die cost per piece would have been excessive and the machine would have been unsuitable for the long thread lengths required.

Cylindrical-Die Machines. This type of equipment would have been satisfactory from the viewpoint of versatility in application to the product mix. Infeed rolling could have been used for the short thread lengths and through-feed rolling for the long thread lengths. Two-die and three-die machines were available and setup time would have been about the same as for other machines of similar capacity. However, because these machines rotate the workpiece, it was questionable whether the equipment could have been used for all sizes and shapes of product.

End-Feeding Heads. Thread-rolling machines equipped with end-feeding heads (thread rolls) could have rolled both short and long threads. Because each head could have rolled only a limited range of thread diameters, several sizes would have been required for the product mix involved. Setup of the machine and changing of the head would have been done easily and quickly. Cost of thread rolls was low because of their small size. Because end-feeding heads rotate around the workpiece, simple-work-holding fixtures could have been employed.

Selection. The equipment selected was a thread rolling machine equipped with end-feeding heads. Although a cylindrical-die machine would have been suitable for the work required in this plant, it was more expensive. Final selection of the machine with end-feeding heads was based on the low cost of heads and thread rolling dies and the simplicity of fixtures needed for holding the work.

Factors Affecting Die Life

The life of thread rolling dies is determined primarily by the rate of deterioration of the profile of the die threads. Rolling imposes severe stress on the dies from pressure, bending and sliding action.

Dies usually fail by spalling and crumbling of the thread crests, which roughens the minor diameter of the product thread and causes the screw thread to go out of tolerance. Failure is probably caused by fatigue from the stresses imposed in rolling. Best products and maximum die life can be obtained only when the dies are properly set up, and when the correct die speed and number of blank revolutions are used. The surface of the material being worked should be relatively free of oxide and scale.

Spalling or chipping may be the direct result of endwise extrusion or stretching of the blank during rolling, over-rolling, improper blank design, or

Table 4. Approximate Range of Production Rates of Thread Rolling Equipment

Thread diameter, in.	Infeed rolling, threads per minute: Flat-die traversing	Cylindrical die: Single revolution(a)	Cylindrical die: Multi-revolution	Rotary planetary	Through-feed or end-feed rolling, threads per minute: Parallel-axis dies	Skewed-axis dies
⅛	40 to 500	75 to 300	20 to 90	450 to 2000	20 to 40	140 to 280
¼	40 to 400	60 to 150	20 to 90	250 to 1200	20 to 40	200 to 450
½	25 to 90	50 to 100	15 to 70	100 to 400	25 to 55	110 to 300
¾	20 to 60	....	10 to 50	....	25 to 65	80 to 300
1	15 to 50	....	8 to 40	....	20 to 50	70 to 300
1½	....	....	6 to 30	....	15 to 30	50 to 200
2	....	....	4 to 25	....	10 to 20	30 to 140
2½	....	....	3 to 20	....	6 to 15	20 to 90
3	....	....	2 to 15	....	4 to 10	15 to 40
4	....	....	1 to 5	....	1 to 3	5 to 10
5	....	....	½ to 1	....	....	....
6	....	....	¼ to ½	....	....	....

(a) Two threads can be rolled on double-end studs in one die revolution in some machines.

Table 5. Nominal Die Life for Three Thread Rolling Methods

Thread diameter, in.	Die life: Flat dies, pieces	Die life: Cylindrical dies: Infeed, pieces	Die life: Cylindrical dies: Through-feed, ft
Threading Steel at Rockwell B 85 (80,000-Psi Tensile Strength)			
¼	700,000	350,000	70,000
½	625,000	315,000	63,000
1	450,000	245,000	50,000
1½	...	190,000	30,000
2½	...	125,000	17,500
3½	...	70,000	7,000
4½	...	18,000	...
Threading Steel at Rockwell C 30 (140,000-Psi Tensile Strength)			
¼	35,000	20,000	14,000
½	32,000	18,000	12,500
1	24,000	14,000	11,000
1½	...	11,000	6,000
2½	...	7,000	3,500
3½	...	4,000	1,400
4½	...	1,000	...

inferior design or quality of tools. When spalling occurs, relatively large pieces are broken out of the threads of the tools. This failure usually occurs near the edges of the tools or in the tool area where the ends of the blanks are rolled.

Spalling is frequently the result of improper bevels on the blanks and tools, or excessive tool hardness. Exces-

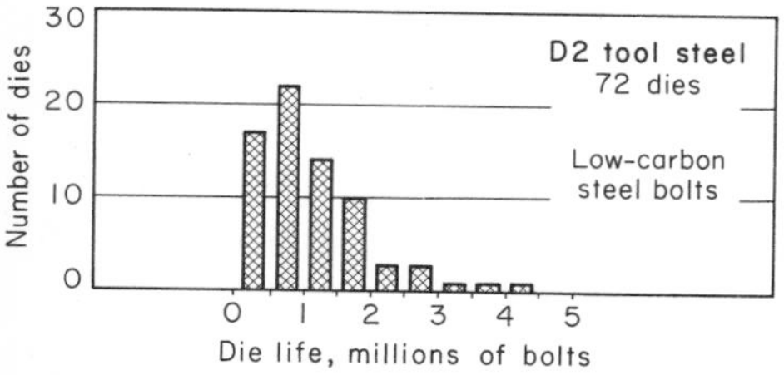

Fig. 19. Distribution of die life of 72 dies used for threading low-carbon steel bolts in a ½-in. boltmaker machine (Example 268)

sive variation or irregularity of blank diameter and hardness increases susceptibility to spalling, as does contact between the edge thread on the tools and the shoulders and fillets on the workpiece. Mismatching of the tools during rolling imposes transverse loading on the tool threads and causes spalling.

When crumbling takes place on the crests of die threads, failure usually starts in the more highly stressed rolling areas and spreads gradually over other portions of the die threads. Excessively sharp die crests are subject to greater initial crumbling action.

Useful tool life is greatly affected by the hardness and work hardening characteristics of the metal being rolled. Premature failures may be minimized by preventing over-rolling and by using clean blanks of correct, uniform size and hardness.

Wear of thread rolling dies seldom need be considered. When wear does occur, it is associated primarily with the abrasive action of scale or dirt on the surface of the blanks, or the use of contaminated coolant. Deep threads are generally subject to more rapid abrasive wear because of the greater amount of sliding action between workpiece thread and die thread. Rolling of deep threads of comparatively short length and small minor diameter may result in excessive extrusion of the blank, which causes permanent bending or chipping of the die thread profile at the end of the blank.

Die life ranges from millions of pieces for soft work metals to a few hundred pieces for hardened steels. Table 5 shows the approximate relationship between die life and method of rolling different thread sizes in steel at Rockwell B 85 and Rockwell C 30.

Even when production conditions are as nearly constant as feasible, die life varies greatly, as illustrated by the following example.

Example 268. Life of D2 Dies for ½-In. Bolts (Fig. 19)

Seventy-two identical thread rolling dies, made of D2 steel by hobbing before hardening, failed with die life distribution as shown in Fig. 19. These data for dies of the same design and tool steel, all used for rolling the same threads on the same blank material, represented about the narrowest variation of factors affecting die life possible in normal production. Although the average die life was about 1 million, the longest life observed was 4.5 million and the shortest was 100,000.

Fine Threads. Dies for rolling 40 or more threads per inch, especially with class 3A fits, require greater precision than dies for rolling coarse threads, but they impose less cold work on the blanks during rolling and have longer life. Fasteners with the closest tolerances and finest pitches require grinding of dies after hardening to achieve required accuracy.

Die Life vs Hardness of Blank. Increasing hardness of the blanks being rolled shortens die life. Figure 20(a) shows the approximate average life of a number of flat dies made of D2 tool steel in rolling ¼–20 threads on 1022 steel blanks of various hardnesses.

Some of the tests were run on hardened blanks, including the two hardest specimens plotted. On blanks harder than Rockwell B 94, die life was low and inconsistent. The shaded portion of the curve indicates this spread and inconsistency in die life. A blank hardness of about Rockwell C 32 is the limit for normal thread rolling.

Figure 20(b) shows minimum and maximum die life versus hardness of the screw blank for a large number of circular dies made of A2 tool steel. These dies were used mainly in rolling fine-pitch threads on parts made mostly from free-cutting brass and aluminum alloys. The data include some high-production runs where conditions of setup and blank material were nearly ideal. Therefore, the average life of cylindrical dies would be less than the mean between the two curves shown.

Table 6. Specifications for High-Quality Rolled Threads on Ground and Extruded Blanks

Thread size	p (pitch), in.	0.25p (min), in.	R (min runout radius), in.	T (min root radius), in.(a)
10–32	0.03125	0.008	0.012	0.003
¼–28	0.03571	0.009	0.013	0.004
5/16–24	0.04167	0.010	0.015	0.005
⅜–24	0.04167	0.010	0.015	0.005
7/16–20	0.05000	0.012	0.018	0.006
½–20	0.05000	0.012	0.018	0.006
9/16–18	0.05556	0.014	0.020	0.006
⅝–18	0.05556	0.014	0.020	0.006
¾–16	0.06250	0.016	0.023	0.007

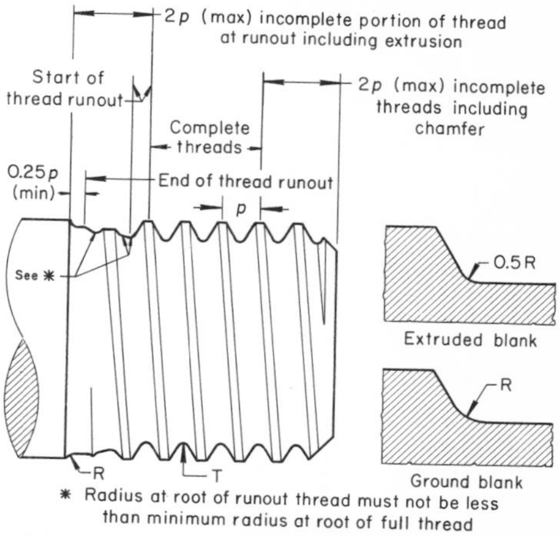

(a) Maximum root radius is limited by requirement that threads accept a "go" thread gage.

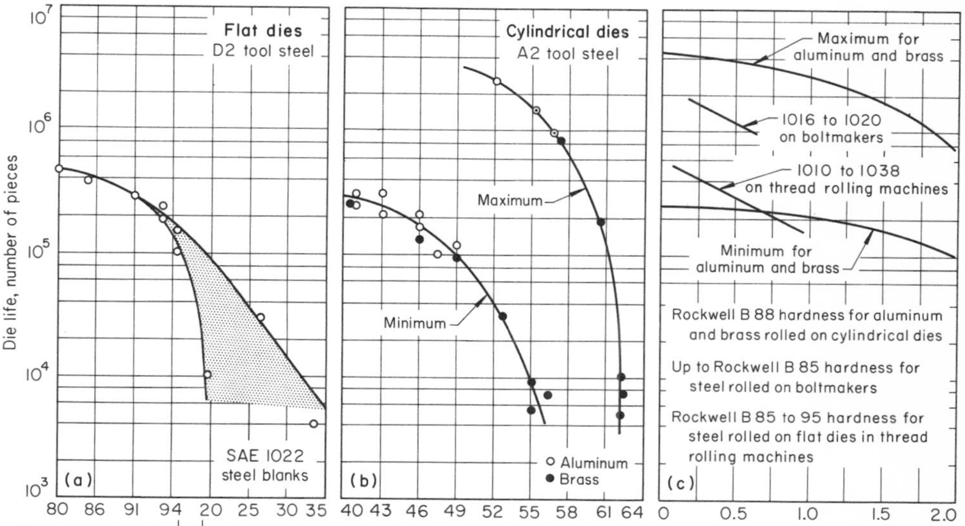

(a) Die life vs hardness of blanks of 1022 steel threaded with flat dies of D2 tool steel. (b) Die life vs hardness of blanks of aluminum or brass threaded with cylindrical dies of A2 tool steel. (c) Die life vs diameter of steel blanks threaded with standard flat dies or with special-contour dies in boltmakers, and of aluminum and brass blanks threaded with cylindrical dies.

Fig. 20. Relation of die life to hardness and diameter of blank

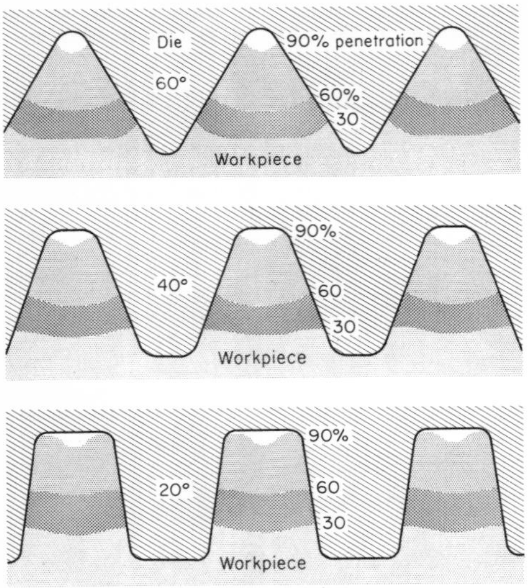

Fig. 21. Effect of three different thread forms on seam formation at thread crest, and the rolled shape of the workpiece at three levels of die penetration (30%, 60%, and 90%)

Also, dies that roll fine threads on small parts have longer average life than those that roll coarser threads on larger parts.

Figure 20(c) shows the relation between die life and diameter of threads rolled on aluminum and brass with circular dies and on steel with flat dies. The upper and lower curves relate to A2 circular dies, most of which were ground after hardening and used primarily for rolling fine-pitch threads, the majority of them special threads. The original data indicated no detectable difference in die life between aluminum and brass at a hardness of about Rockwell B 88.

The curve relating to 1016 and 1020 steel gives the average life in a single setting of several hundred D2 dies with special contour on entering threads and used as hardened after machining.

The other curve gives similar data for 1010 to 1038 steels on machines of the traversing type.

Unusual variables can alter die life considerably. For example, rolling ⅝-in.-diam hot rolled 1040 steel blanks that were nonuniform in diameter, scaled, and unannealed, on a thread rolling machine, has reduced die life to only 45,000 pieces.

Effect of Thread Form on Processing

The form of the thread affects the radial die load, seam formation, surface finish, and thread dimensions.

Radial Die Load. Greater loads are required as the form becomes more blunt. For example, if a radial load of 10,000 lb is required to produce a ½–13 UNC thread 2 in. long, a radial load 40 to 70% greater would be required to roll a ½–10 Acme thread under the same conditions. The amount of increase in load is determined by the blend radii on the crest of the die thread and by the degree of fullness of thread required.

Seam formation at the crest of the thread is affected greatly by the shape of the thread form, as indicated in Fig. 21. Sharp crests on the dies cause sharper seams than those produced when a wider form is being rolled more deeply.

Surface Finish. In general, surface finish is independent of the form for 60° threads. However, as the thread form becomes more blunt or if it has sharp root corners, the normal, smooth flow pattern of the metal being rolled is altered. Restriction of metal flow may cause localized subsurface shear failures. During subsequent die contacts, these shear failures form small flakes, which downgrade the surface finish.

Thread Dimensions. Table 6 shows proper specifications for thread rolling high-quality threads in ground and extruded blanks. Note that no specification for chamfer angle on the end thread is required. In addition to the dimensional details tabulated and shown in the inset illustration, principal dimensions such as the major and minor diameters should, of course, be specified.

Changes in the thread form affect the relation between pitch diameter and outside diameter of thread. Figure 22 shows that if a standard 60° thread form with a typical sharp thread crest is not quite fully rolled, an additional die penetration of 0.001 in. on the diameter with a commensurate reduction in the pitch diameter results in an increase of 0.003 in. in the outside diameter until the thread form is filled.

For the more blunt Acme thread, the outside diameter increases at only about 1½ times the rate of decrease of the pitch diameter until the material fills the form through the crest radii.

The class of thread affects the size of the blank diameter and the major and minor diameters for a given thread. Class 1A, 2A, and 3A threads of the same size and pitch in the American Standard series can be rolled with the same die. However, a different die may be required for rolling a given thread of a class other than 1A, 2A, or 3A. The following example illustrates a production operation for rolling class 2A and class 5HF threads.

Example 269. Effect of Thread Class in Rolling Same-Size Threads (Table 7)

A change in design required the use of double-end studs instead of ¾–10 UNC–2A screws. One end of the stud had a ¾–10 NC–5 HF interference-fit thread, whereas a ¾–16 UNF–2A thread was to be rolled on the other end. Screws and studs were made from 4140 steel at Rockwell C 28 to 32 and all were threaded by the flat die method in the same machine. The threaded section of the ¾–10 UNC–2A screws and one end of the studs was 1¾ in. long. The section of the studs having ¾–16 UNF–2A threads was 1¼ in. long. The dies used for the screws, however, could not be used to roll the ¾–10 NC–5HF threads on one end of the stud. New dies were required because of differences in thread and blank diameters. Because of the close tolerances required for the interference-fit threads, the blanks were centerless ground. Table 7 shows the blank and thread diameters for the screws and studs. Die life was approximately 15,000 pieces for both threads.

Rated motor horsepower of flat die and cylindrical-die infeed thread rolling machines is not a direct measure of peak power consumption on specific jobs. The motor horsepower of these intermittently loaded machines is supplemented by the stored energy of the drive system momentum. Motor horsepower of through-feed machines can be related more directly, because power is applied continuously. Each unit of power delivered to the through-feed die rolls threads in material with a rollability index of 1.00 at approximately the rates shown in Table 8.

In addition to the power used for threading the workpiece, the rolling process develops various power losses. Because of these losses, power available for actual threading ranges from 30 to 90% of rated power of the machine.

Energy delivered to the thread rolling dies is dissipated in forming the metal and in friction between the work and the die. On shallow threads, die friction accounts for about 10% of the energy delivered. For deep threads, losses due to die friction may be as much as 25% of the energy delivered; the remainder is used to flow the metal.

Surface Speed

Permissible surface speeds for thread rolling are governed by the mechanical power limitations of the threading equipment and, when the workpiece is rotated, by the speed (rpm) of the workpiece or of the holding equipment used with end-feeding heads.

Table 9 compares die surface speeds in modern thread rolling equipment with the surface speeds of thread-cutting tools. Table 10 shows the approximate thread rolling time for different spindle speeds used with tangential infeed double-roll attachments.

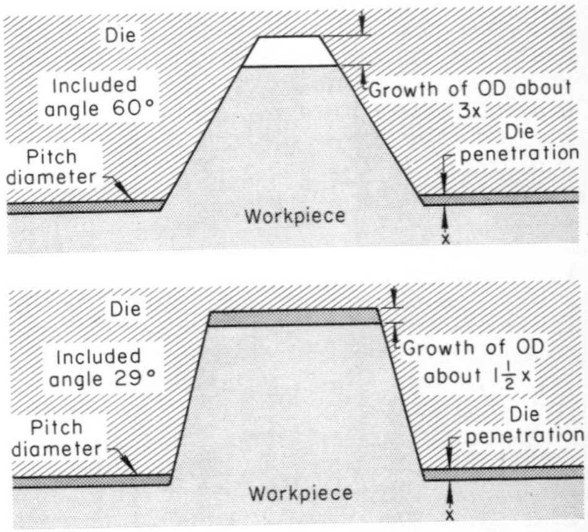

Fig. 22. Effect of thread form and die penetration on the relation between pitch diameter and outside diameter of the thread

Table 7. Blank and Thread Diameters for Rolling Same-Size Class 2A and 5HF Threads (Example 269)

Workpiece diameter	Range of diameter, in.: Screw threads ¾–10 UNC–2A	Threads on double-end stud: ¾–10 NC–5HF	Threads on double-end stud: ¾–16 UNF–2A
Blank diameter	0.6773 to 0.6827	0.6937 to 0.6945	0.7029 to 0.7074
Major diameter	0.7353 to 0.7482	0.7270 to 0.7360	0.7391 to 0.7485
Pitch diameter	0.6773 to 0.6832	0.6910 to 0.6955	0.7029 to 0.7079

Table 8. Approximate Rates of Through-Feed Thread Rolling for Metals With a Rollability Index of 1.00(a)

Thread diam, in.	Threads per inch	Rolling rate, in./min/hp(b)	Thread diam, in.	Threads per inch	Rolling rate, in./min/hp(b)
1/4	28	174	9/16 ...	12	39
	20	166	5/8	18	40
5/16	24	156		11	35
	18	121	3/4	16	34
7/16 ...	20	64		10	28
	14	61	7/8	14	26
1/2	20	47		9	22
	13	44	1	14	18
9/16 ...	18	43		8	16

(a) To determine the through-feed rate for a metal of different rollability index, multiply the rolling rate by the rollability index. (b) Horsepower is actual power delivered to the dies.

Table 9. Operating Speeds of Thread Rolling and Thread Cutting Tools

Tool	Surface speed, sfm
Thread Rolling Tools	
Flat traversing die	100 to 325
Cylindrical die	70 to 600
Lathe attachments	70 to 300
Thread Cutting Tools	
High speed steel tools	10 to 150(a)
Carbide tools	250

(a) Speed range for threading aluminum, copper, steel and Monel.

Penetration Rate and Load Requirements

The total die penetration per revolution of the blank varies with different machines, the kind of work, and the type and hardness of metal being rolled. Low penetration rates are necessary for hard metals, hollow workpieces, and workpieces of nonrigid cross section. Higher penetration rates are used for rolling metals that work harden at an excessive rate.

The rate of die penetration is limited normally by the rigidity of the workpiece and the machine, and by the hardness of the metal being rolled. Penetration rates for infeed rolling range from 0.0005 to 0.0060 in. per revolution of the workpiece. Penetration rates for through-feed and end-feed rolling are governed by the lead and pitch of the thread and the length of the entrance threads on the dies.

If the pitch and other rolling variables are held constant and only the diameter of the work is increased, the rolling load will increase about one third as much as the increase in diameter. For example, if a load of 3800 lb is required to roll a 1-in. length of 1/4–20 thread, the initial die load for rolling a 1/2–20 thread under the same conditions would be about 5000 lb. However, because the thread pitch normally increases proportionally with the diameter, a proportional change in the rolling conditions causes the die load to increase about half to three-fourths as much as the increase in the workpiece diameter.

Many rolling machines have insufficient power to provide proportionately rapid penetration rates on larger work; thus an increase in workpiece size presents a problem when rolling threads of large diameter in a metal that work hardens rapidly. In such applications, inability of the equipment to produce adequate absolute penetration rates increases the number of die contacts necessary and causes too rapid an increase in the hardness of the work metal. As a result, disproportionately large radial die loads are required to complete the thread form. This is hard on machines and dies. More powerful machinery must be used if work hardening of the metal being rolled causes this kind of load escalation.

Warm Rolling

Low-strength materials, such as aluminum, brass and low-carbon steel, are always thread rolled at room temperature. Because of their relatively low yield strength, these metals are easily penetrated by the threading die. However, some metals such as high-strength steels and heat-resisting alloys offer considerable resistance to die penetration. To facilitate thread rolling, blanks of these materials are often heated and rolled while warm.

For example, warm rolling is used to thread fasteners made of 5% Cr-Mo-V steel (H11) that has been quenched and tempered. The H11 steel is induction heated to about 900 F immediately before threading. Heating temporarily decreases the yield strength so that threads can be formed without great difficulty. However, for optimum life, the dies should not be allowed to reach too high a temperature. An ideal ambient die temperature is 200 F. Dies can be cooled by spraying as needed with a conventional die-cooling oil or a soluble-oil emulsion.

Workpieces that have been heated under controlled conditions and warm rolled on dies with a positive lead have a tensile strength equal to, and a fatigue strength greater than, similar parts rolled cold. In addition, die life in warm rolling is greater than in cold rolling of high-strength materials, as illustrated by the following example.

Example 270. Thread Rolling High-Strength Steel at 700 F

An aircraft parts manufacturer was thread rolling 1/4-28 bolts from blanks made of alloy steel with a tensile strength of 160,000 to 180,000 psi (Rockwell C 32 to 36). The bolts were rolled with flat dies. Subsequently, specifications for the material were changed to call for a tensile strength of 200,000 to 220,000 psi (Rockwell C 42 to 46). This increase in properties resulted in a die life of only about 15 to 20% of that obtained when rolling the softer work metal. It also lowered the production rate and thus caused a marked increase in both the manufacturing and tool costs.

To reduce these increased costs, the blanks were heated to 700 F immediately before thread rolling. Warm rolling increased die life, improved fatigue life and quality of the threaded area, and reduced manufacturing and tool costs.

Threading of Thin-Wall Parts

Three-die machines and end-feeding heads are better suited to the threading of hollow work than are two-die machines, because the application of rolling forces at three points on the circumference has much less tendency to collapse the work.

Table 11 shows the minimum wall thickness for thread rolling tubular workpieces on three-die machines. For satisfactory thread rolling of tubular workpieces in a two-die machine, a minimum wall thickness of twice the thickness shown in Table 11 for any given set of conditions is the recommended practice.

When the wall thickness of the tubular blank is too thin to be rolled as a finished part, solid metal or heavy-wall tubular stock is used for the thread rolling operation and the threaded workpiece is then drilled or bored to the desired wall thickness in a secondary operation.

Threading of Work-Hardening Materials

The crests of threads rolled in metals such as austenitic stainless steel that work harden rapidly usually have a more pronounced seam or fold (Fig. 4) than metals that work harden at lower rates. Although seams do not affect thread strength significantly and are not detrimental for most applications, some thread specifications do not permit seams. One of the main objections to seams at the crest of threads, particularly in stainless steel, is that they are likely to become focal points for corrosive attack of the material. To avoid them, either the use of a metal that does not behave this way is required, or specially constructed dies that minimize seams must be used.

Other factors that can lead to difficulty when rolling threads in metal

Table 11. Preferred Minimum Wall Thickness for Thread Rolling Tubular Sections

Threads per inch	Minimum wall thickness (in.) for thread pitch diameter (in.) of: Up to 1/2	1/2 to 1	1 to 2	2 to 3	3 to 4	4 to 5
32	0.040	0.050	0.070	0.095	0.110	0.130
24	0.055	0.070	0.095	0.120	0.150	0.175
20	0.065	0.080	0.115	0.145	0.180	0.210
18	0.070	0.090	0.130	0.160	0.195	0.230
16	0.080	0.100	0.140	0.180	0.220	0.265
14	0.095	0.115	0.165	0.210	0.250	0.300
12	0.110	0.135	0.190	0.240	0.300	0.350
10	...	0.160	0.230	0.290	0.360	0.420
8	...	0.285	0.360	0.450	0.530	

Data apply to a thread length of one diameter or less, and are based on 1010 steel in the soft condition, rolled in a three-die machine. For rolling the same threads in a two-die machine, minimum wall thicknesses twice those shown here are recommended.

Table 10. Thread Rolling Time for Tangential Infeed Double-Roll Attachments

Threads per inch	Approximate work revolutions(a)	Thread rolling time (sec) for spindle speed (rpm) of: 500	1000	1500	2500	5000
32	11 to 27	1.3 to 3.2	0.7 to 1.6	0.4 to 1.1	0.3 to 0.6	0.1 to 0.3
24	14 to 31	1.7 to 3.7	0.8 to 1.9	0.6 to 1.2	0.3 to 0.7	0.2 to 0.4
18	17 to 35	2.0 to 4.2	1.0 to 2.1	0.7 to 1.4	0.4 to 0.8	0.2 to 0.4
14	20 to 39	2.4 to 4.7	1.2 to 2.3	0.8 to 1.6	0.5 to 0.9	0.2 to 0.5
10	23 to 43	2.8 to 5.2	1.4 to 2.6	0.9 to 1.7	0.6 to 1.0	0.3 to 0.5
8	26 to 47	3.1 to 5.6	1.6 to 2.8	1.0 to 1.9	0.6 to 1.1	0.3 to 0.6

(a) The actual number of work revolutions used within the ranges shown depends on the material rolled and the size of the thread rolling attachment.

that has a high rate of work hardening are as follows:

1 Lead contraction
2 Out-of-round threads
3 Rough surface finish
4 Increased power requirement
5 Reduced production rate
6 Decreased die life.

All of these effects are undesirable; some may be tolerable; most can be minimized by combining high penetration rates, heavy-duty equipment, and special extra-hard dies with expanded leads. Dies as hard as Rockwell C 68 are available for thread rolling of work-hardening metals.

Too many revolutions of the blank can work harden some materials, resulting in reduced die life and failure of the threads to meet dimensional tolerances, as in the example that follows:

Example 271. Die Setting and Blank Diameter for Threading 1038 Carbon Steel (Fig. 23)

The available planetary-die equipment in one plant could not produce machine screws of 1038 steel to the required dimensions when blanks of standard diameter were used. The screws were out of tolerance because the length of the segment die required too many revolutions of the blank. This problem was not encountered with similar parts made on flat dies of shorter length. The use of the planetary-die machine, however, was necessary, because of the large volume of screws to be made and the high production rate required.

Satisfactory screws were made by experimentally adjusting the blank size and by setting the dies so that the thread was nearly all formed in the first few revolutions of the blank, after which the threaded blank dwelled in the remaining portion of the die. This procedure produced adequate die life (about 1,500,000 pieces per grind) and the required production rate (20,000 pieces per hour).

Figure 23 shows the variation of major and pitch diameters obtained with the standard and oversize blanks. A variation in blank diameter of about 1% resulted in loss of control over these dimensions.

Two characteristic types of thread rolling phenomena were observed when too large a blank diameter was used. A large number of "roll-ups" occurred. (A roll-up is a part that rides up in the dies as it rotates, resulting in no helix angle but merely a number of disconnected annular rings.) Also, oversize blanks caused overloading of the dies, and when the parts were released from the dies, considerable expansion occurred; some pieces "exploded" upon being released, resulting in hollow parts.

Rolling Threads Close to Shoulders

The minimum dimension between a rolled thread and a shoulder depends on the rolling method, the type and size of thread, the diameter of the shoulder in relation to the thread diameter, and the metal being rolled.

Infeed rolling dies usually are beveled, as shown in Fig. 13. The most common bevel angle is 30°. When unified threads are being rolled with a die of this type, a distance of 1½ threads from the shoulder to the root of the first full thread usually allows sufficient clearance between the edge of the die and the shoulder. When longer bevels are required on the dies, the distance from the shoulder to the root of the first full thread should be increased proportionately. For infeed dies, the distance from the shoulder to the root of the first full thread usually runs from 1½ to 2 threads per lead.

The rolls of end-feeding heads have imperfect starting threads similar to those on the throats of die chasers. In general, the length of imperfect thread on heads with nonreversible rolls for rolling unified threads is 1½ threads. For heads with reversible rolls, the length of the imperfect starting threads varies from about 1½ to 2½ threads. In addition to the length of the imperfect starting threads, the distance from the shoulder to the root of the first full thread varies with the lead angle of the thread and the clearance from the shoulder required to trip and open the head for withdrawal at the end of the rolling cycle. Therefore, depending on the design of the head, the approximate distance for rolling threads close to a shoulder using end-feeding heads ranges from 2 to 3 threads per lead. Specially designed rolls can thread closer.

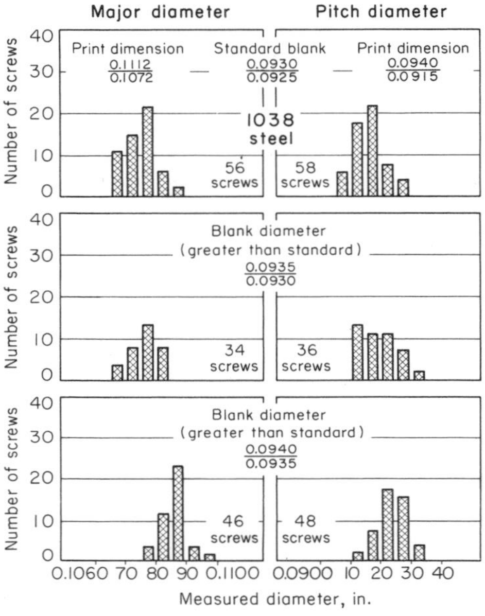

Fig. 23. Effect of blank size on the major and pitch diameters of 1038 steel screws with thread length of ¼ in. See the table accompanying Fig. 17 for screw details and threading conditions. (Example 271)

Threads can also be rolled fairly close to a shoulder in cylindrical-die machines with the through-feed rolling method. Because of the longer imperfect starting threads on dies used in through-feed rolling, they can roll threads no closer to an obstruction than 5 or 10 threads, depending on the type of equipment.

The length of starting thread discussed in the preceding paragraphs is applicable to rolling threads in soft and medium hard materials. These distances must be increased by 1 to 2 threads when threads are being rolled close to a shoulder in steel harder than about Rockwell C 25.

Blank Preparation. Four different blanks that involve rolling threads close to a shoulder are shown in Fig. 24. The blank shown in Fig. 24(a) is a type used extensively for cap screws and bolts. The 30° bevel at the junction of the large and small diameters matches the bevel on the thread rolling die, thus allowing a thread to be rolled close to the bevel. After rolling a blank of this proportion, the large diameter shown and the major diameter of the rolled thread are usually the same.

A blank like that shown in Fig. 24(b) is used when the thread runs out on the blank without relation to the shoulder.

Use of an undercut as illustrated in Fig. 24(c) is the most practical approach for threading to a shoulder. Under these conditions the blank can be threaded to within 1½ threads of the shoulder; the unthreaded portion is undercut so that a nut can be tightened against the shoulder.

There is likely to be end movement of the blank between the dies; thus, rolling between two shoulders as in Fig. 24(d) requires a wider undercut, as shown. Under these conditions rolling to within four threads of the shoulder is about as close as is practical. Worm threads are often rolled on the type of blank illustrated in Fig. 24(d).

Dies Without Bevels. Sometimes it is necessary to roll a full thread closer to a shoulder than can be done with a beveled die. In such applications, a die is used that has no bevel on the leading end. Although the omission of bevel shortens the life of the die, it eliminates the imperfect threads and permits forming of a full thread closer to a shoulder, as illustrated by the following example.

Example 272. Use of an Infeed Die Without a Bevel

One end of a 1020 steel workpiece required a ⅝–11 UNC–2A full thread within 0.120 in. of a shoulder 1¼ in. in diameter.

Because thread cutting could not produce a full thread at the required distance from the shoulder, the piece was threaded by rolling with an infeed attachment mounted on the cross slide of an automatic bar machine. It was necessary to remove the bevel from the end of the die and to modify the shape of the edge thread.

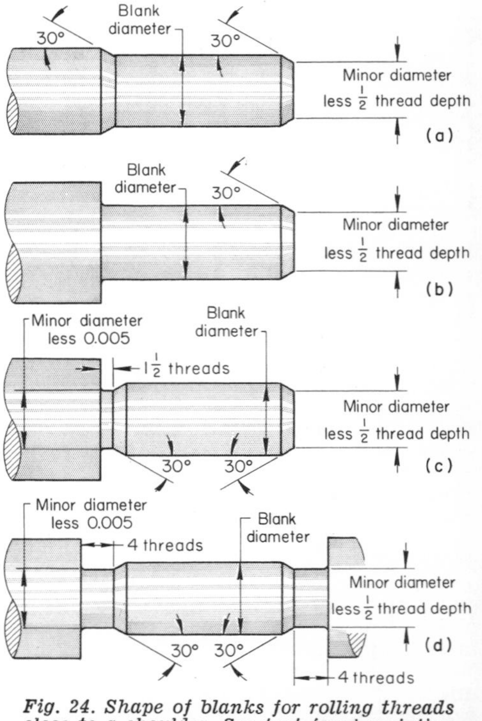

Fig. 24. Shape of blanks for rolling threads close to a shoulder. See text for description of each type and its application.

Normally a beveled infeed threading die cannot produce a full thread closer than 1½ threads from a shoulder. The width of a ⅝–11 thread is 0.0909 in. Therefore, a beveled die for this application would have formed the first full thread at a distance of about 0.136 in. from the shoulder.

Fluids for Thread Rolling

There are two reasons for using fluids in thread rolling: to cool the dies and the work, and to improve finish on the rolled products.

Low-carbon steel or nonferrous screws under ¼ in. in diameter are often rolled dry on flat dies at rates as high as 24,000 pieces per hour. This is especially true when rolling pointed screws on which the lubrication supplied by even a low-concentration soluble-oil emulsion may cause detrimental slippage. Soft steel or nonferrous metal screws have been rolled in larger sizes (½ in. in diameter) without fluid, but only at speeds no greater than 300 pieces per hour.

At higher production rates a fluid is required, to control temperature. For cooling only, a low-concentration of soluble oil in water (as weak as 1 part oil to 40 parts water) is satisfactory. However, as surface finish requirements become more stringent a fluid with better lubricating qualities is required. In many applications more concentrated mixtures of soluble oil in water (1 part oil to 8 parts water) will suffice, but for best results lubricating oil (mineral oil) is recommended. A wide variety of oils have been successfully used. Sometimes, for extremely severe rolling (deep threads or hard work metal, or both) EP lubricants are used. However, for most applications a low-viscosity mineral oil is sufficient. Any oil selected, in addition to having good lubricating properties, must be nontoxic and free from additives that will stain the work metal.

Cylindrical dies are more susceptible to heat buildup than are flat dies; therefore, some type of fluid is usually used for rolling in cylindrical dies. Soluble oils are preferred for maximum die life and optimum machine performance, but some high-tensile fasteners, and other high-quality threads require the use of lubricating oil to provide the quality of finish required. Many three-die machines use the same oil on the work and dies as is used for lubrication of the rolling spindles.

Lubricating oils do not dissipate heat as readily as the soluble-oil emulsions. thus, in high-production rolling in cylindrical die machines, it is often necessary to provide an oil cooler to control temperatures. Generally, such cooling equipment is required only in the most extreme applications when using soluble oil emulsions.

Thread Rolling vs Alternative Processes

For commercial products, the types of equipment available, size and shape of workpiece, number of pieces to be made, and the accuracy required are the principal considerations in determining the method that will be used for producing threads to the required specifications.

Rolling vs Cutting. As production quantity decreases, it becomes more economical to cut the thread rather than to roll it. For instance, 500 ¾-in. screws 6 in. long with 2-in. threaded length could be made more economically by die threading at about 300 per hour than by setting up a roller that could produce 3000 screws per hour. Thread rolling would be worthwhile, however, for 7500 or more such screws.

Production quantity is not a criterion for determining the method of threading when special products are involved. For example, manufacturers of aircraft products have employed thread rolling for a single piece in order to obtain a product that would meet service requirements.

Table 12 shows comparative costs of tooling for one size of capscrew. Lower tooling costs for thread rolling also were obtained in an operation involving the threading of an automotive part, as discussed in the following example.

Table 12. Comparative Tooling Costs for Producing Capscrews ½–13 by 6 in.(a)

Item	Thread cutting	Thread rolling
Production rate per hour	300	4000
Die cost per set	$20	$62.50
Die life, pieces (avg)....	20,000(b)	110,000
Die cost per 1000 pieces..	$1.00	$0.57

(a) Screws made of 1038 steel. (b) Thread cutting dies required 14 regrinds during life of set.

Example 273. Thread Rolling vs Thread Cutting of a Sector Shaft

A ¾–16 UNF–2 thread, 1 in. long, was machined on one end of a forged sector shaft used in an automotive steering gear assembly. The shaft was made of 4620 steel.

Originally the thread was cut on a semiautomatic threading machine equipped with four die heads. This setup made possible threading of four shafts simultaneously. The method of threading was changed to thread rolling on a horizontal flat die machine, with comparative results as follows:

Item	Thread cutting	Thread rolling
Production rate, pieces per hr..	345	517
Tool cost, per 1000 pieces	$5.48	$1.56

Production was at 80% efficiency. Life of a duplex die was 110,000 pieces. Savings in tooling cost as a result of the change to thread rolling were $955 per month, based on monthly production of 250,000 pieces. Thread rolling also improved the quality of the thread.

Thread milling, another method of cutting threads, is more expensive than thread rolling or die threading. Thread milling is seldom used except when extreme accuracy is needed or the workpiece is of such a size or shape that roll or die threading is impractical. In thread milling, threads can be produced with pitch diameter held within 0.001 in. and lead error held to 0.001 in. per foot.

Rolling vs Grinding. Thread grinding is much more expensive than rolling and is used in preference to rolling only when: (*a*) work metal is too hard to be rolled or cut; (*b*) work metal is extremely soft, under which condition grinding may be the only way to hold required dimensions; or (*c*) a high degree of dimensional accuracy is required. Before selecting thread grinding over rolling, however, the various cutting procedures should be considered.

APPENDIX

Materials for Thread Rolling Dies

*By the ASM Committee on Thread Rolling Dies**

The tool steels most commonly used in the manufacture of thread rolling dies are A2, D2 and M2. Of the high-carbon high-chromium tool steels, D2 is used more frequently than any of the other steels of this type. Both the high-carbon high-chromium steels and the medium-alloy A2 are widely used for general work. In addition to the standard M2, some manufacturers of high speed steel thread rolling dies prefer to use M2 with 0.75% carbon (about 0.05% less than the typical carbon content for this steel). The slightly modified carbon content is intended to provide greater toughness with adequate hardness.

In most applications, performance of D2 and M2 is about the same, and the life of A2 dies is about 10% less than that of D2 or M2.

Tool Steel Composition. A2 tool steel is an air-hardening grade containing 1% C, 5% Cr and 1% Mo. D2, with a base price almost twice that of A2, is one of the three popular grades of high-carbon high-chromium tool steel, and contains 1.5% C, 12% Cr and 1% Mo. M2, with a base price almost three times that of A2, is the most readily available grade of molybdenum high speed steel, and contains 0.85% C, 6% W, 5% Mo, 4% Cr and 2% V.

Die Hardness. Recommended hardnesses for various types of thread rolling dies are given in Table 13. In both flat and circular dies, too soft a die can fail by upsetting, sinking or flattening of thread crests, and too hard a die can fail by cracking of die threads at the base.

Hardness of Rockwell C 57 to 59 yields freedom from spalling and chipping, with less sensitivity to grinding cracks or to failure by cracking at the base of the thread on the die, and little or no evidence of increased wear from abrasion. When abrasive wear is the prime consideration, a harder die may be justified. In notable instances, dies two points harder on the Rockwell C scale than recommended in Table 13 have operated successfully. However, die hardness should be increased only when past experience with a similar application has proved that the harder die is safe.

Hardness indicated in Table 13 should be obtained by double tempering after quenching. Early failure is more likely if the die is tempered only once to obtain recommended hardness.

Flat Dies. Dies to roll special threads in quantities up to 500,000 parts may be made of die materials shown in the first column of Table 14. For rolling standard fasteners, die steels listed in the second column are recommended.

*John J. Hoffer, *Chairman*, Metallurgist, Apparatus & Optical Div., Eastman Kodak Co.; Freeman G. Anderson, Metallurgist, National Lock Co.; R. N. Needham, President, Aeroll Engineering Corp.; Emerson D. Spengler, Tool Engineer, Lebanon Plant, Bethlehem Steel Co.; Carl H. Gerlach, *Secretary*. This Appendix is adapted from the article on pages 727 to 730 in Volume 1 of this Handbook.

Table 13. Recommended Rockwell C Hardness Ranges for Thread Rolling Dies

Type of die	A2	D2	M2
For Rolling Aluminum and Copper Alloys, and Soft Steel			
Flat	57 to 60	60 to 62	58 to 60
Cylindrical	56 to 58	58 to 60	58 to 60
For Rolling Ferritic Steel Harder Than Rockwell B 95, and Austenitic Stainless			
Flat	57 to 59	59 to 61	59 to 61
Cylindrical	56 to 58	58 to 60	58 to 60

Dies for rolling standard fasteners are made either by machining or grinding before hardening, or by hardening first and then grinding. All grades of tool steel can be ground before hardening, but generally it is done with D2 to avoid grinding hardened dies, since a small percentage of such dies develop grinding cracks and must be reground. However, beyond this, there is no apparent advantage in die life whether the dies are ground before hardening or after hardening.

Cylindrical Dies. Table 15 shows tool steels recommended for cylindrical dies to roll threads on special and tubular parts in automatic bar machines or by some other method. Cylindrical dies are usually ground after hardening; this accounts for the increased use of A2 steel, which is less expensive than D2 and M2 and cracks less frequently in grinding than D2.

Tooling Conditions

With intermediate fits and pitches, where least dimensional change in dies during normal heat treating is required and accurate machining or grinding of die threads is desirable, A2 should be selected. For long production runs of up to 3 million small ½-in.-diam parts made of nonferrous alloys of Rockwell B 85 or less, or for about 1 million such parts of ferrous or nonferrous alloys with hardness to Rockwell B 95, A2 should also be selected. D2 and M2 should be selected for dies to roll larger parts, coarser threads and harder or less rollable alloys.

Fasteners with the finest fits and pitches require grinding of dies after hardening in order to achieve the required accuracy.

Tolerances. Dies for rolling of workpieces that have close tolerances on diameter and on accumulated lead but that still can be ground or machined before hardening must be made from steels that change dimensions least during normal heat treating. The recommended steels for these applications, given in descending order of preference, and their average distortion during the accepted heat treating practice to obtain recommended hardness are as follows: A2, about 0.0004 in. per in. distortion; D2, about 0.0005 in. per in.; and M2, about 0.0011 in. per in. The most demanding tolerances are closer than these distortions and require that the dies be ground after hardening.

Alloy Rolled. Die materials for rolling the common ferrous and nonferrous alloys are given in Tables 14 and 15. Alloys such as aluminum bronze and silicon bronze are highly abrasive and require die materials of the same class

Table 14. Recommended Tool Steels for Flat Thread Rolling Dies

Alloy to be rolled	Quantity of parts 500,000	1,000,000
Class 2 Threads; Pitch Coarser Than 40 per Inch		
Aluminum and copper alloys and soft steel	A2	D2(a)
Ferritic steel over R_B 95, and austenitic stainless steel..	D2(a)	D2(a)
Class 3 Threads; Pitch Finer Than 40 per Inch(b)		
Aluminum and copper alloys and soft steel	A2	A2
Ferritic steel over R_B 95, and austenitic stainless steel..	D2, M2	D2, M2

(a) D2 is the preferable selection when the die is ground or machined before hardening. About 10% of all D2 dies ground after hardening are likely to have grinding cracks, even with the best grinding practice. For dies that are to be ground after hardening, M2 may be used.

(b) D2 and M2 dies to produce class 3 threads will usually be ground after hardening, for dimensional accuracy. The economy of D2 over M2 is largely offset by the need to regrind D2 dies that develop cracks during grinding.

Table 15. Recommended Tool Steels for Cylindrical Thread Rolling Dies

Alloy to be rolled	Quantity of parts 500,000	1,000,000
Class 2 Threads; Pitch Coarser Than 40 per Inch		
Aluminum and copper alloys and soft steel	A2	A2, M2, D2(a)
Ferritic steel over R_B 95, and austenitic stainless steel ..	A2	M2 D2(a)
Class 3 Threads; Pitch Finer Than 40 per Inch(b)		
Aluminum and copper alloys and soft steel	A2	A2
Ferritic steel over R_B 95, and austenitic stainless steel ..	A2	M2

(a) D2 dies are ground or machined before hardening. A small percentage of D2 dies ground after hardening will develop grinding cracks and will have to be reground, making D2 less economical than M2. (b) All dies are ground after hardening, for required accuracy; this eliminates D2 from the recommendations.

Table 16. Recommended Materials for Knurling Dies 1 In. in Diameter

Alloy to be knurled	Quantity of parts 10,000	100,000	1,000,000
Aluminum and copper alloys and steel up to R_B 85	A2	A2	A2
Aluminum and copper alloys and steel from R_B 85 to 95	A2	A2	D2, M2
Ferritic steel over R_B 95, and austenitic stainless steel	A2	D2, M2	....

as those shown in the tables for austenitic stainless steel. Ferritic stainless steel can be rolled with dies of the same steel as that selected for dies to roll carbon and alloy steels of the same hardness.

Alloys such as free-machining leaded brass and free-machining aluminum, which are processed primarily in automatic bar machines, require high unit pressure to flow them to the required form and may cause early failure of thread rolling dies made from A2, D2 or M2. In one instance that involved the rolling of free-cutting aluminum, where excessive early die failure could not be otherwise avoided, die life was increased by using S1 tool steel for the dies.

Cost of Tooling. Figure 25 shows the relative cost of A2, D2 and M2 flat dies and cylindrical dies. Two processing conditions are dealt with: one where the dies are machined, hardened, tempered and used with no further preparation; the other where the dies are hardened before the threads are finish ground.

For flat dies, the cost shown is for one die of the pair, as illustrated in Fig. 1. The cost of any scrap incurred because of grinding cracks is not included in the cost figures.

In flat dies, the cost of D2 and M2 dies is more than for A2 dies, but if setup and other costs are included, the steel with the longest die life will be the most economical on production runs that equal the die life.

For cylindrical dies, the cost of tool steel is low and selection is based on performance and processing cost, as shown in Fig. 25.

Knurling Dies

Satisfactory materials for knurling dies are given in Table 16. Steels such as W1, O1 and O2 (not shown in the table) are only slightly less costly than A2 in small dies such as these. Because of the small cost difference, the use of those steels is recommended only where A2 is not readily available.

Quantity and hardness are the important variables. However, the diameter to be knurled and the knurling speed can vary over a wide range and can thus affect die life. Knurling dies to be used on various jobs successively until worn out should be made of D2 if they are ground before hardening,

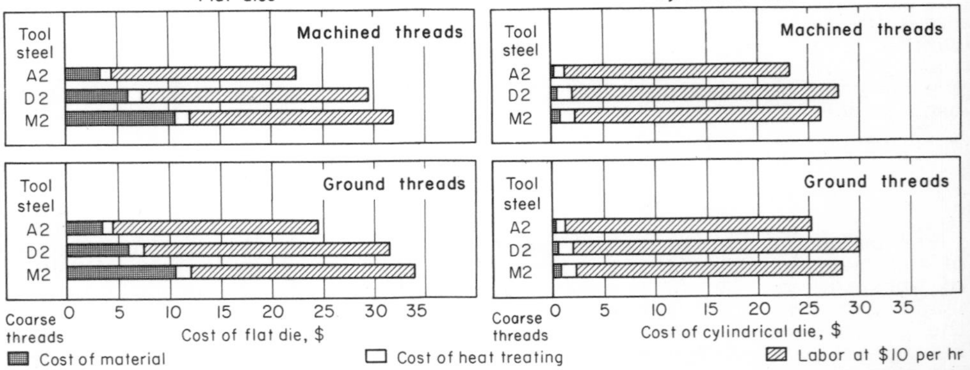

Fig. 25. Cost of dies for thread rolling ½-in.-diam capscrews with coarse threads. Weight of flat die was 7.3 lb; weight of cylindrical die was 0.54 lb.

but M2 is preferable if the knurl pattern is to be machined into the die.

Selected References

William T. Taylor, Rolled Threads — Materials and Blank Diameter Calculations, *Metals & Alloys*, **21**, 1643 to 1647 (June 1945). How to calculate blank diameter, and the importance of pitch diameter in this calculation. Problems in producing taps with rolled threads; equations for calculating diameters of blanks for threading high speed steel. Three tables give constants and tolerances to be used in calculations for different types of threads.

Roger W. Bolz, Thread and Form Rolling, *Machine Design*, **19**, 145 to 150 (Aug 1947). Illustrates and discusses parts made on flat and cylindrical dies, describing blank preparation and tolerances.

J. W. Batchelder, Thread Rolling — Theory and Practice, *Iron Age*, **158**, 58 to 64 (Dec 19, 1946); **158**, 55 to 61 (Dec 26, 1946); **159**, 52 to 57 (Jan 9, 1947). Problems in thread rolling, including prevention of ropy threads, detection and prevention of noncircularity of blanks. Optimum rate of penetration of die; rolling speeds. Selection of die steel, stresses imposed on dies, die life tests, grinding die threads, and tungsten carbide dies are discussed in the second part. In the third part, finishing of thread rolling dies by grinding, lapping and abrasive blasting are considered, along with the toeing of dies and setting them parallel, universal thread matching, and die thread angles.

W. G. Patton, Screw Machine Attachment Rolls Accurate Threads, *Iron Age*, **176**, 74 and 75 (Dec 22, 1955). Manufacture of rocker-arm valve studs on automatic bar machine by Pontiac Motor Div.

C. T. Appleton, Thread and Form Rolling, *Mechanical Engineering*, **77**, 866 to 871 (Oct 1955). Advantages of the process, dies and thread rolls, equipment, production rates. 24 figures, 1 table.

C. T. Appleton, Thread Rolling Improves Part Quality and Cuts Production Costs, *Tool Engineer*, **38**, 87 to 92 (May 1957). General discussion of thread rolling methods and machines, characteristics of rolled threads, blank preparation.

Raymond H. Spietta, Thread Rolling May Be for You, *Machinery*, **64**, 181 to 197 (Nov 1957). Equipment and design of blank. Tables of production rates with various machines, blank diameters and tolerances.

How to Design for Thread Rolling, *Machine Design*, **29**, 102 to 112 (Dec 26, 1957). Discusses nomenclature, applications and advantages of thread rolling. Six tables and 24 figures assist in explaining blank specifications and design recommendations. Examples include pipe threads and oil-groove threads.

P. R. Brierley, Small Screws — Their Standardization, Production and Measurement, *Machinery (London)*, **91**, 374 to 377 (Aug 16, 1957); also in *Fasteners*, **13**, 3 to 6 (Summer 1958). Comparison of screw-thread designations by ten different systems (British, American, German, French and Swiss) presented in tabular form. How small (watch) screws are rolled and cut. Inspection procedures for small screws.

D. H. Seymour and F. M. Lomas, Thread and Form Rolling, *Machinery (London)*, **93**, 673 to 677 (Sept 17, 1958). General description tells how to determine blank diameter and effect of roll diameter. Illustrations of threads and worms that were rolled. Use of thread rolling equipment for burnishing and straightening. Description of planetary thread rolling machines and multiple-operation machines.

B. Sullivan, Trouble Shooting Thread Rolling Operations, *Machinery*, **65**, 105 to 109 (March 1959). Problems discussed are: lead error, correcting pitch diameter that is not within tolerance, difficulties with tapered threads, workpiece out of round, "drunken" threads, poor surface finish, scuffed crests, axial seams and crest seams, rolling external threads on hollow work.

A. C. Ellsworth, Thread Rolling Feeders Improve Output, *Tool Engineer*, **43**, 70 and 71 (Dec 1959). Screw nails are made to high-production requirements by use of automatic feeder that is described and illustrated. Design of the die used.

Charles H. Wick, "Chipless Machining", Industrial Press, New York, 1960; 502 pages. Chapter 4, Thread Rolling (pages 72 to 114), contains a general description of advantages, limitations, attachments, rolling internal threads, machines, dies, tools and designing for thread rolling. 27 figures, 4 tables.

E. C. Hanna, How to Design Rolled Worm, *Am Machinist/Metalworking Manuf*, **105**, 108 to 113 (Feb 20, 1961). Eight worm gears that are produced by infeed and through-feed rolling are described. Production data, including dimensions and production rate. Maximum thread depth-to-diameter ratios (Fig. 1). Straightness of worm as affected by number of starts (Fig. 2). How a worm thread is formed (Fig. 3). Importance of pressure angle (Fig. 4). Root and crest corner radii, die edges and starts, blank design, and thread blank chamfers. Choosing work material.

R. H. Bell, Roll Threading of Fasteners, *Wire & Wire Products*, **36**, 1014 to 1016, 1069 (Aug 1961). Includes table of tensile strength of rolled threads on 1020, 1021, 1045 and 1060 steels, and table of material saved by thread rolling as compared to thread cutting.

D. F. Griffin, Thread Rolling at 1000 F, *Am Machinist/Metalworking Manuf*, **106**, 84 and 85 (March 5, 1962). High-strength fasteners were rolled at 1000 F, with increase in die life (no data given). Table on properties of 4340 and H11, comparing high-temperature rolling and rolling in ausformed condition.

Peter Leckie-Ewing, How to Reduce Failure of Thread Rolling Dies, *Steel*, **151**, 66 and 67 (July 2, 1962). Need for wear resistance and good fatigue resistance in die steels. Selection of die steel. Control of grinding procedures for dies.

New Machine Speeds Part Orientation, *Tool & Manufacturing Engineer*, **49**, 70 and 71 (Oct 1962). Machine senses small differences in diameter of studs that are to be threaded on both ends and that have different diameters on the ends, so that they may be fed correctly.

Thread Rolling up to Date, *Machinery*, **69**, 104 to 108 (Jan 1963). Examples of application of thread rolling to set screws (3/8-in. BSP.F, 1/2 in. long), speedometer worm shafts, bar lengths 3 ft long roll formed by through-feed, helical gear, studs, transmission shafts, turbine studs. Steels used were 1117, 8640, 8620.

Spline Rolling

*By the ASM Committee on Thread and Spline Rolling**

STRAIGHT, fine-pitch spur and helical splines and other forms such as serrations can be rolled on cylindrical thread rolling machines, or on rack rolling machines, which use flat dies that are commonly called racks.

For rolling splines and similar forms, the workpiece is held between centers or in a fixture. Tools for rolling helical and straight splines are similar. Because of the close fit required in assembly of the splined workpiece with its mating component, the blank diameter of the splined area must be made to a relatively close dimensional tolerance. When major-diameter fit of a spline is critical, the major diameter can be rolled oversize and ground to final size after heat treatment. Grinding also can be used to correct the somewhat oval configuration sometimes observed in the splined section as rolled. Sides of the spline teeth are controlled within dimensional tolerances, and the product is used as rolled in the side-fit assemblies that comprise the majority of spline applications.

Limitations. The process of spline rolling is limited primarily by the hardness, tensile strength, compressive strength, and homogeneity of the work metal, and by the type and depth of the spline that is being rolled.

*For committee list, see page 130.

Spur splines of 16/32 diametral pitch or finer and with 15 to 19 teeth as a minimum can be produced by cylindrical rolling. Spur involute splines with a pressure angle between 30° and 45° are formed by through-feed rolling. Helical splines, which provide sufficient helical angle overlap to effect continuity of contact, can be rolled with 8 or 10 teeth, and are not subject to the same limitations as spur splines. Helix angles can vary from 6° to 85°.

Properties of Rolled Splines. Cold rolling of splines prestresses the workpiece in the spline area. The rolling increases surface hardness and strength. Rolled splines in the as-rolled condition (no heat treatment) are about 15 to 35% stronger than cut splines. Heat treatment after spline rolling completely relieves the beneficial compressive stresses induced by cold rolling. However, the service performance of heat treated rolled splines is better than that of cut splines, because the finish is more fatigue-resistant.

Cold rolled splines that are not stress relieved also have greater fatigue resistance than cut splines. For example, changing from spline cutting to spline rolling enabled one manufacturer to increase the power input to a shaft by 10%. Also, spline rolling made possible an increase in the number of reversing cycles before failure from a range of 40,000 to 60,000, as required by the original specification, to 175,000. In another application, rolling a spline with a runout of spherical radius increased life expectancy by more than 750,000 cycles, which was a fifteenfold improvement.

Materials for Spline Rolling

Splines and serrations can be rolled in plain carbon, low-alloy and stainless steels, pearlitic malleable iron, brass, and some aluminum alloys.

Steel. Although some free-cutting steels have been rolled successfully, it is generally recommended to avoid the use of free-cutting alloys for spline rolling. Sulfur or lead in steel lowers the ductility and increases the susceptibility to flaking, especially in the root area of the form being rolled. The type and depth of spline determine the amount of sulfur, lead or other free-cutting additive that can be tolerated. This can be established only by trial for each spline design and application.

Cold extruded steel can be used for spline rolling; however, the amount of forming that is feasible is usually less than for hot rolled steel, because of the increased yield strength and decreased ductility that are characteristic of cold extruded steel.

The maximum yield strength and hardness of steel in which splines can be rolled economically depend on the pressure angle of the spline to be rolled, as well as on the pitch and number of teeth. Steel of low yield strength should be used for rolling splines of low pressure angle, as shown in Table 1.

Table 1. Relation of Pressure Angle of Spline to Maximum Yield Strength and Hardness of Steel to Be Spline Rolled

Pressure angle	Maximum yield strength, psi	Corresponding hardness, Bhn
30° (a)	75,000	220
30° (b)	90,000	265
37.5°	120,000	340
45°	130,000	365

(a) Dies not shot peened. (b) Dies shot peened.

Pearlitic Malleable Iron. Compared with steel, only a small amount of pearlitic malleable iron has been proc-

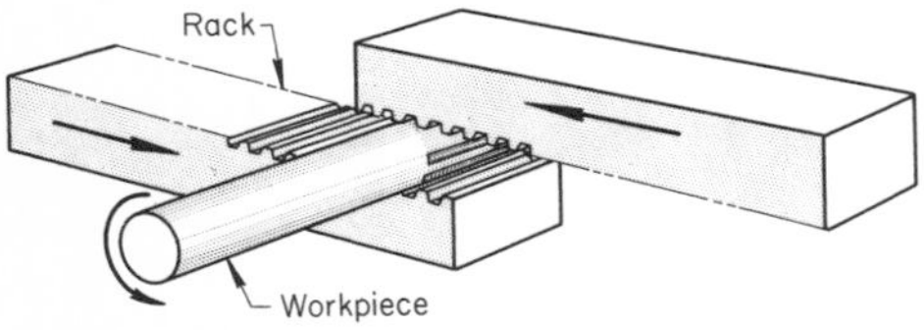

Fig. 1. Operating principle of rack rolling of splines

essed by spline rolling. Normal practice for rolling splines and thread forms in pearlitic malleable iron is to follow initial processing details similar to those for steel, and to make adjustments when difficulties are encountered.

Thread or spline rolling work hardens pearlitic malleable iron appreciably. Fatigue life increases in about the same percentage as it does for steel. Surface finish and accuracy of the rolled form are excellent. Compared with steel, pearlitic malleable iron causes greater tool wear and shorter tool life, as indicated in the subsequent section on Die Life in this article.

Rack Rolling

In the rack rolling of splines, a pair of linear forming racks with teeth of the required shape traverse the workpiece simultaneously in opposite directions. As the racks traverse, they rotate the workpiece and their teeth penetrate progressively deeper into the surface. Penetration causes backward extrusion of the metal to form the addendums of the spline teeth. The operating principle of rack rolling is illustrated in Fig. 1.

Machines and Racks. Machines for rack rolling are available (1967) in three standard sizes, accommodating racks up to 24, 36 and 48 in. long, respectively. Each machine is equipped with one set of rolling racks and one set of synchronizing racks.

Rack teeth are made with straight flanks and generate standard involute profiles. Spline teeth as fine as 16/32 diametral pitch can be formed. For a given application, the minimum length of rack depends on the diameter and the diametral pitch of the spline to be formed.

The rate of penetration by the rack teeth varies according to the pitch of the spline teeth and the hardness of the workpiece; it is about 0.003 in. for each successive tooth penetration.

Capabilities and Limitations. Spur splines can be formed in steel by rack rolling, provided the minimum number of teeth is about 15 to 19, and provided the pitch diameter is not greater than about 3 in. Forming of helical splines is not restricted as to minimum number of teeth, because helical overlap provides the necessary continuity of contact between racks and workpiece.

Another application of rack rolling is the forming of splines on a part that must be assembled only in one orientation with the mating part. Figure 2 shows a shaft of this type. To obtain the foolproofing blocked space at the entry end of the splined section of this shaft, the teeth that normally would penetrate this area are removed from the rack by grinding.

For assembly, the internally splined part that mates with this part must have a section of its teeth removed. A

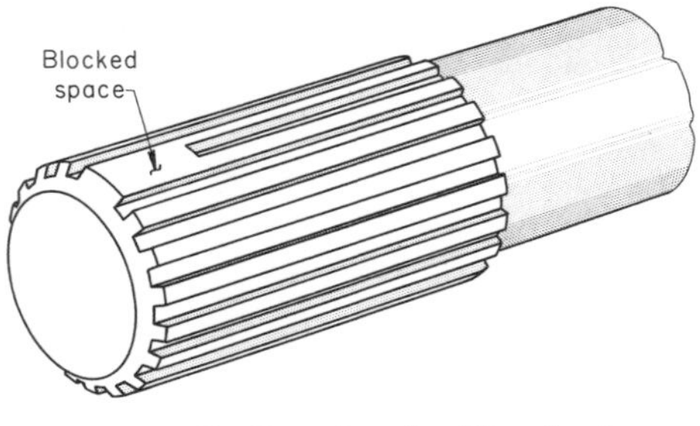

Fig. 2. Application of rack rolling for forming splines, and a blocked space for a one-orientation assembly

broach usually does this job while it cuts the internal spline.

Serrations can be rolled on a taper end of a shaft in order to prevent angular movement when the shaft is assembled with the mating component. A standard taper of ¾ in. per ft is common.

The involute contours of splines produced by rack rolling are more accurate than those made by most other rolling methods. Rack rolling can be used to form threads and splines on adjacent diameters, as shown in Fig. 3. The threads and splines are not formed simultaneously on the same piece, but they can be produced on the same machine in separate, successive operations.

Rack rolling is used in the manufacture of automotive parts such as axle shafts, rear-axle drive pinions, transmission shafts, speedometer and governor worms, drive shafts, steering shafts, drive-line components, torsion bars, and starter shafts.

Die Life

Spline rolling develops bending stresses in the forming dies, and the magnitude of these stresses increases as the pressure angle decreases. Therefore, for best die life, work metal of lower yield strength must be used for the lower pressure angles (Table 1). Otherwise, excessive bending stresses will cause premature die failure by fatigue. As shown in Table 1, if the work metal has a yield strength as high as 130,000 psi, the pressure angle must be 45° or rolling will be impractical.

Spline rolling of cold extruded metals, particularly those of low ductility and high yield strength, decreases die life, especially when forming splines requiring a pressure angle of 30° or less.

Die life in rolling pearlitic malleable iron is considerably less than that when the same form is rolled in steel. For example, rolling of two sets of splines in a pearlitic malleable iron transmission shaft resulted in a die life of about a quarter to a half that obtained when rolling low or medium-carbon steel. The splines in this shaft consisted of 25 teeth with a diametral pitch of 24 and a pressure angle of 30°; the splines were ½ in. long in one set and 1 in. long in the other.

Die life can be improved by shot peening the dies. This increases the fatigue strength of the dies, which can then roll splines in steel of higher yield strength. For example, steel of 75,000-psi yield strength can be rolled to produce a spline with a 30° pressure angle, but if a shot-peened tool is used, steel of about 90,000-psi yield strength can be spline rolled with the same pressure angle.

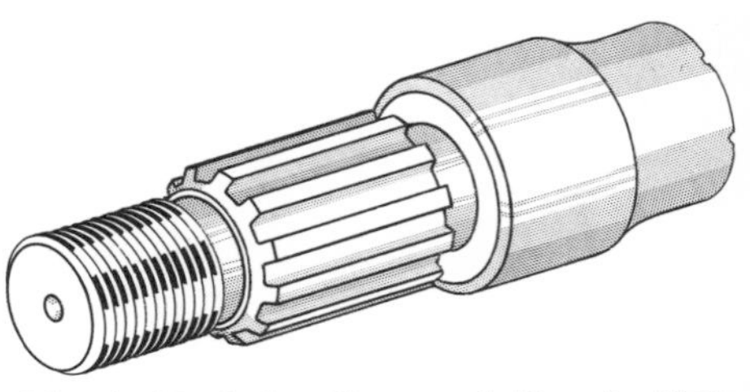

Fig. 3. Typical splines and threads that can be rolled between racks on the same machine by two different sets of tooling, but not simultaneously

Selected References

Harry Pelphrey, Rolled Flow Forming of Toothed Parts, paper presented at the 23rd Annual Meeting of the American Society of Tool Engineers, Los Angeles, Calif., March 14 to 18, 1955, 10 pages. Describes method. Micrographs of formed teeth in 6061 aluminum, 410 stainless steel, 18-8 stainless steel, and 1040 steel. 24 figures.

Charles H. Wick, Buick Cold Forms Serrations on Hardened Shafts, *Machinery*, 62, 177 to 180 (Jan 1956). How serrations are cold formed on rear-axle shaft.

How to Design for Form Rolling of Knurls, Splines and Serrations, *Machine Design*, 30, 105 to 112 (Jan 9, 1958). Nomenclature for knurls, splines and serrations. Data on circular pitches for knurling, blank diameters, minimum knurled diameters, outside-diameter tolerances, and diametral pitch. Diameters and teeth for splines and serrations, tooth-fillet radius, minimum number of teeth. 9 tables, 6 figures.

Charles H. Wick, "Chipless Machining", Industrial Press, New York, 1960, 502 pages. Chapter 5, Rolling of Serrations, Splines, and Gears, p 115 to 144. Several processes are discussed; examples of rolling of rear-axle and propeller shafts. 25 figures, 1 table.

C. T. Appleton, Thread Rolling — but not Always Threads, *Am Machinist/Metalworking Manuf*, 104, 116 to 117 (March 1960). Thread rolling used for knurling, splines, serrations, grooving, burnishing, nonuniform leads, threading stampings, and hollow parts. Sizes range from 0.060 to 4½ in. in diameter and 2 to 80 threads.

Niles Etzel and C. E. Kopp, Splines Formed Ten Times Faster by Cold Rolling, *Machining*, 63, 165 to 167 (Aug 1957). How splines are rolled on propeller shafts of 410 stainless steel.

D. Clark, Job-Lot Rolling of Splines and Threads on Mass-Production Equipment, *Machinery*, 70, 119 to 121 (March 1964). Producing 50 different designs a month on two machines. Racks used, spline data for 11 different parts.

Multiple-Operation Machining in Bar or Chucking Machines (Screw Machines or Turret Lathes)

*By the ASM Committee on Multiple-Operation Machining**

MACHINING operations discussed in this article utilize various machine tools designed to perform a number of operations consecutively or simultaneously, or both. With this equipment, many parts are completely machined from bars, tubes, forgings, castings or extrusions, in an uninterrupted sequence. For some parts, however, the time required for completing a specific operation in the sequence is too great to be compatible with the time required for the other operations, resulting in an inefficient machining cycle. Under these conditions, completion of the workpiece by secondary operations, performed after the multiple-operation sequence, may be more practical and economical.

Process Capabilities

It is seldom practical to use multiple-operation equipment and methods for workpieces that can be machined with fewer than three tools, or for production runs of fewer than 10 or 15 identical pieces. For only a few operations or a few workpieces, or both, the use of an engine lathe, a drill press or some other type of less complex machine may be more practical.

Size of workpiece that can be machined by a multiple-operation process is limited only by the capacity of available equipment. Parts such as instrument components weighing only a fraction of an ounce are frequently machined on multiple-operation machines. At the opposite extreme, machines are available that can handle bars or tubes 8 in. or more in diameter, or castings or forgings weighing several hundred pounds. Most multiple-operation machining, however, is done on bars ranging from about ¼ to 2 in. in diameter, or on castings or forgings weighing less than 10 lb each.

Work-Metal Composition. All metals from which parts are made on a repetitive basis can be machined by multiple-operation methods. This article presents examples describing the techniques employed or results obtained in multiple-operation machining of carbon and low-alloy steels, stainless steel, and cast iron (gray, nodular and malleable). The table that follows lists ten examples in other articles in this volume that compare procedures used or results obtained for two or more work metals in various multiple-operation machining setups:

Example	Alloys compared
661	Gray iron, ferritic malleable
662	1141 steel, pearlitic malleable
663	Class 35, class 25 gray iron
687	A2, A7, D2, M1 tool steel
867	2017-T4, 2011-T3 aluminum
868	2017-T4, 2011-T3 aluminum
869	2017-T451, 2024-T351 aluminum
871	356, 355 aluminum
933	Naval brass with and without Pb
934	Phosphorized Cu with and without S

Variety of operations that can be performed in multiple-operation equipment is almost unlimited. Most conventional operations can be performed on basic equipment, and numerous special attachments and modifications are available that can extend the range of equipment capability to include almost any machining operation. All the operations listed below are performed in multiple-operation sequences:

More Frequent	
Turning (single-point)	Counterboring
Form turning	Countersinking
Facing	Knurling
Chamfering	Cutting off
Boring	**Less Frequent**
Drilling (longitudinal)	Milling
Reaming	Drilling (cross)
Shaving	Trepanning
Tapping	Roller burnishing
Threading	Broaching

Although it is unlikely that all of these operations would be performed on a single workpiece, in many applications nine or ten different ones are, and some are performed more than once. For example, one tool may perform two or more facing operations simultaneously or consecutively, or one tool may be used to produce several counterbores.

Types of Machines

All machines utilized for multiple operations as described in this article are modifications of the basic engine lathe; some have undergone several stages of evolution. The first multiple-operation machine was built by replacing the tailstock of an engine lathe with an indexing turret that contained several tools, thus permitting a sequence of operations to be completed without removing the workpiece from the rotating chuck. The need for duplication of repeated motions led to the addition of cams, levers and other powered devices; the machine that resulted was a single-spindle automatic. This development was followed by the appearance of the multiple-spindle automatic machine, to satisfy the need for greater productivity.

Terminology for different machines used for essentially the same purposes varies among different manufacturers. Some terms that have been extensively used are inaccurate, misleading or inadequate. The term "screw machine", for example, has become inappropriate, because nearly all screws are now made by other methods. In this article, more generally descriptive terms are used.

Although multiple-operation machines are of an almost unlimited variety, they can be classified as either chucking machines or bar machines. Machines in either category are further classified as:

- Manual turret lathes
- Automatic turret lathes (single-spindle automatics)
- Multiple-spindle automatics.

Bar machines are made only as horizontal models. Chucking machines are either horizontal or vertical, although the use of vertical models is generally confined to workpieces that are too large to be conveniently placed in horizontal chucks.

Aside from the number of spindles, the principal differences among the various machines are: (*a*) method of loading, holding or feeding the work material; and (*b*) method of holding and moving the cutting tools into and out of position.

When forgings, castings, extrusions or bar slugs are being machined, they are loaded into chucks at the front face of the headstock. When bars or tubes are being machined, hollow headstocks and collets are needed to permit bringing the work material through from the rear of the machine.

There are three basic methods of bringing tools into and out of position: (*a*) a revolving turret that can hold one or more tools on each of its index positions, (*b*) cross slides that feed tools to workpieces at right angles to the machine spindles, and (*c*) tool carriers that advance or move back on a main slide parallel to the machine spindle. Single-spindle bar or chucking ma-

*Elliot S. Nachtman, *Chairman,* Director of Research and Development, LaSalle Steel Co.; J. R. Barnard, Plant Superintendent, Lundberg Screw Products Co.; Francis V. Daniels, Screw Machine Layout Engineer, Westclox Div., General Time Corp.; Roger M. Dillon, Senior Methods Engineer, John Deere Des Moines Works.

T. M. Garvey, Chief Staff Engineer, Bar, Rod and Semifinished Products, Applied Research Laboratory, U. S. Steel Corp.; Elbert A. Hoffman, Chief Products Engineer, LaSalle Steel Co.; W. H. Leinbach, President, Hudson Metal Products, Inc.; Leroy G. Pankrac, Screw Machine Engineer, Supreme Products Corp.; Delbert E. Peterson, Tool Engineer, AC Spark Plug Div., General Motors Corp.

Gilbert N. Sippel, Automatic Screw Machine Engineer, Union Drawn Div., Republic Steel Corp.; Ralph E. Smart, Foreman, Screwmaking Dept. No. 1, National Cash Register Co.; Robert M. Sprinkle, Tool Engineer, Kokomo Plant, Chrysler Corp.; G. E. Tubaugh, Project Manager, General Products Div., International Business Machines Corp.

chines use turrets and cross slides for moving tools. In multiple-spindle bar or chucking machines, tools are moved by cross slides and a sliding tool carrier.

Manual Turret Lathes

Essential components and operating principles of a horizontal turret lathe are illustrated schematically in Fig. 1. The workpiece shown could be either a short-length part (such as a casting or a forging) held by a chuck, or a long bar or tube fed through a hollow headstock from the rear and held by a collet.

The turret, mounted on a ram or a saddle, advances to the workpiece in an axial direction on the latheways. The turret shown in Fig. 1 has six tool-holding faces or index positions, and hence is called a six-station turret.

A smaller turret on the cross slide may have four tool-indexing positions, obtained by clockwise rotation. The turret and cross slide are supported on a saddle and thus can be moved axially to perform operations such as turning. This turret can also move on the cross slide at right angles to the longitudinal axis of the workpiece, to perform operations like form turning, facing or grooving.

The number of stations that can be used in the main turret of a machine of this type is governed primarily by the tool clearance needed for a given job. If tools extend only a short distance from the turret, or if the workpiece is small in diameter compared with the size of the turret, more stations can be used than when the above conditions are reversed. Also, the workpiece must clear the tools extending from stations next to the one from which the operating tools extend. Turrets having as many as nine stations have been built and used, but turrets with four, five or six stations are more usual.

A difference in construction of the main turret unit separates turret lathes into two general classes: ram-type and saddle-type.

Ram-Type Turret Lathes. In this type of machine, the main turret is mounted on a separate slide, or ram, which moves along the lathe axis on a saddle supported by the ways. During setup, the saddle containing the ram and turret is positioned along the ways as close as possible to the workpiece, to provide maximum support for the ram and turret, which in operation will move axially on the saddle. When the setup is completed, the saddle is locked in position and remains fixed during machining.

The main advantage of the ram type over the saddle type is that the operator has less mass to move during operation, which results in easier and faster handling. The main disadvantage of the ram-type machine is that as the turret and ram move forward, overhang of the ram from the saddle increases, and some sag of the turret is inevitable. This sag causes tools to cut tapers — to the extent that the use of a ram-type machine may be precluded for making long turning or boring cuts, particularly when the cutting tools are in a vertical position.

Saddle-Type Turret Lathes. In this type of machine, the turret is mounted directly on the saddle, which moves axially during operation. This type of construction provides greater rigidity than that of the ram-type machine, because it overcomes the problem of ram overhang and turret sag.

The main disadvantage of the saddle type is that greater operator effort is required than with the ram type, but this can be overcome by adding a power attachment for moving the turret-and-saddle unit.

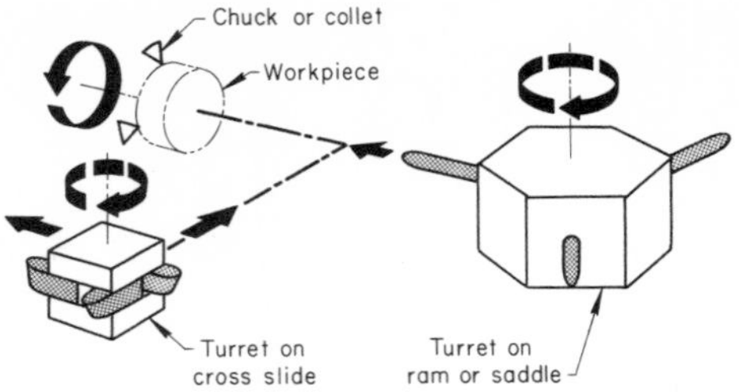

Fig. 1. Rudiments of a horizontal turret lathe

Manually operated turret lathes are normally used for producing parts in small to medium production runs for which an engine lathe is too slow and an automatic machine is unwarranted by production demands. "Manually operated" means that an operator must be in attendance during the entire machining cycle; but the exact duties of an operator may vary, depending on how the machine is equipped.

When the operation is entirely manual, the operator loads the workpiece in the chuck, starts the machine, and then manually performs all operations — including starting and stopping the headstock, indexing the turret, advancing the turret, moving and retracting the cross slide, and unloading the workpiece. This procedure generally is applicable only when fewer than about a dozen identical parts are being made and when highly skilled operators are available.

Accessories. The productivity and versatility of a manual turret lathe can be greatly increased, and the need for operator skill decreased, by the addition of one or more of the following accessories:

1 Automatically controlled headstock
2 Power feed on turret slide (axial)
3 Power feed on cross slide
4 Cross-slide turret
5 Automatic turret indexing.

Automatic headstock control permits starting, stopping, speed changing and reversing of the spindle by indexing and axial movement of the turret. It can substantially increase productivity, especially where handling time constitutes half or more of the floor-to-floor time or where a number of changes of spindle speed or direction, or both, are required during a short machining cycle. In many instances when the machine is equipped with headstock control, the operator can complete cycles by handling only the turret.

Power feed on the turret reduces operator fatigue and often saves enough operator time to permit an additional machine to be tended by one man. Also, a powered turret results in greater accuracy in some machining operations, especially tapping or die threading.

Power Feed on the Cross Slide. In simple operations, a power-fed cross slide is seldom worthwhile, but in operations like facing of large areas, the power feed can be used to increase efficiency and produce more uniform results.

The cross-slide turret, with its ability to feed in four directions, adds greatly to the versatility of the manual turret lathe. This unit is available as standard equipment, but its use is generally restricted to large turret lathes having saddle-type construction.

A cross-slide turret is especially advantageous for machining small lots of workpieces, because it often permits machining of several surfaces (such as inside diameters) with the same tool. A graduated dial for cross motion allows the use of the turret for turning different diameters on parts in low-quantity production, for which the cost and setup time for more elaborate tooling would be impractical.

In addition to its advantages for low-quantity production, the cross-slide turret is often advantageous for machining the following types of work:

1 *Large bores,* which can be machined more easily using standard boring bars, because cutter overhang is less than on a fixed-center machine.
2 *Deep internal faces and recesses*
3 *Large-diameter work,* which limits or prohibits use of a conventional turret.

Automatic turret indexing can be applied to virtually any type of manual turret lathe. This feature, as well as the other accessories described here, increases setup time, but will also increase productivity and decrease operator effort. Total quantity to be produced, and parts required per unit of time, usually determine whether automatic turret indexing and other accessories should be considered.

The use of one or more of these accessories often makes it possible for one operator to attend more than one machine — provided they are properly grouped. In some plants, manual turret lathes that have thus been made partly automatic are preferred for large-quantity production, mainly because of their versatility. Hand-operated machines are compared with automatic machines in Examples 291, 292, 293, 298 and 299 in this article, and are compared with semiautomatic machines in Examples 664 and 665 in the article "Machining of Cast Iron", and in Examples 771 and 772, in the article "Machining of Stainless Steel".

Automatic Turret Lathes

The terms automatic turret lathe and single-spindle automatic bar or chucking machine are frequently synonymous. In operating an automatic turret lathe for chucking applications, the operator loads the workpiece and pushes the start button. All machining operations are then conducted automatically by a pre-established sequence, after which the machine stops automatically and is unloaded by the operator. If the workpiece is a bar or a tube, automatic stock feeding can be incorporated, thus permitting continuously repeated cycles.

Automatic turret lathes do not vary greatly from manual turret lathes equipped with the accessories discussed in the preceding section. The main difference between a manual turret lathe with added accessories and one designed and built for automatic operation is that the latter usually has both back and front cross slides, thus increasing its tooling capacity.

Automatic turret lathes are most often used where production requirements are too high for efficient production on manually operated machines but too low to warrant the use of multiple-spindle equipment. The setup time is lower, and less elaborate tooling is needed, for automatic turret lathes than for multiple-spindle machines.

Automatic turret lathes are generally of two types: (*a*) the type on which the turret rotates in a horizontal plane and is attached to a saddle that slides axially on the latheways, and (*b*) the type on which the turret indexes by rotating around an axis parallel with the machine spindle, and is supported by a main slide, or "turret bar".

Essential components and operating principles of the first of these types are shown in Fig. 1 and discussed in the preceding section, "Manual Turret Lathes". Machines incorporating these principles are available as chucking or bar machines, and in a wide range of sizes. Maximum diameter of workpiece that can be machined is usually 12 in.

The essential components and operating principles of the second type indicated above are shown schematically in Fig. 2. This type is available only as a chucking machine and cannot be used for producing parts directly from random lengths of bar or tube. It is made in sizes large enough to accommodate workpieces somewhat greater than 12 in. in diameter. As indicated by arrows in Fig. 2, tools are advanced to the workpiece from three directions and three sources. All axial cutting operations are performed by tools mounted in the turret. The turret is rigidly supported by, and moves axially on, a main slide, and can be indexed to any of its operating positions (usually five, as indicated in Fig. 2) by rotating in a counterclockwise direction. When the tool is in operating position, its centerline coincides with the centerline of the workpiece, as indicated. Turret tools are secured in standard adapters, which are fastened into the turret by dovetails. Machines of this type are equipped with one front and one rear cross slide. Tools from the cross slides move only in directions at right angles to the axis of spindle rotation. Consequently, cross-slide tools are restricted to operations such as facing, form turning, grooving or knurling. (The use of a single-spindle chucking machine is described in Examples 279, 292, 295, 305 and 306 in this article, and in Example 660 in the article "Machining of Cast Iron". Example 838, in the article "Machining of Heat-Resisting Alloys", compares a drill press with a chucking machine for equal results.)

Multiple-Spindle Chucking Machines

Essential components and operating principles of a multiple-spindle chucking machine are illustrated schematically in Fig. 3. These machines are available in models that can accommodate chuck sizes up to 12 in. and that have four, five, six or eight spindles. These spindles, which rotate the chucks that hold the workpieces, are arranged radially around a main slide.

Tools are brought into position from: (*a*) cross slides (usually, one for each spindle, although only four cross slides for six spindles are indicated in Fig. 3), and (*b*) the tool carriage (sometimes called the "end slide"), which moves axially on the main slide. This tool carriage does not rotate; indexing is accomplished by rotation of the entire spindle carrier, as indicated in Fig. 3.

The spindle carrier is supported by, and indexes in, the frame of the headstock. The carrier is rotated by the index arm from the main camshaft, and by the index plate, which is geared to the carrier.

Cutting tools are secured in adapters, which are fastened to the cross slides or to the tool carriage by means of T-slots. In some machines the tool carriage is actuated by means of a drum cam on the main camshaft, so that all tools moving axially are controlled

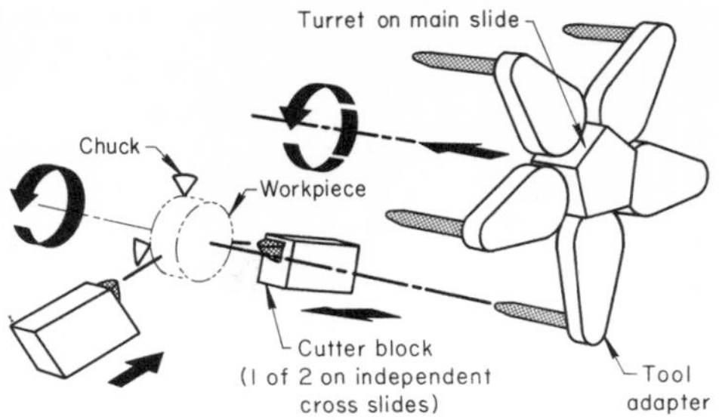

Fig. 2. Rudiments of a single-spindle automatic chucking machine (one type of automatic turret lathe)

simultaneously. Other types of machines have independent slides for each axial tool, controlled by individual cams. This permits greater versatility for tools working from the carriage.

Multiple-spindle chucking machines are equipped with devices that permit some spindles to be stopped while machining continues on others. Stopping specific spindles allows loading and unloading as well as operations such as cross-drilling, milling or broaching.

Loading and unloading are usually done manually, but if production quan-

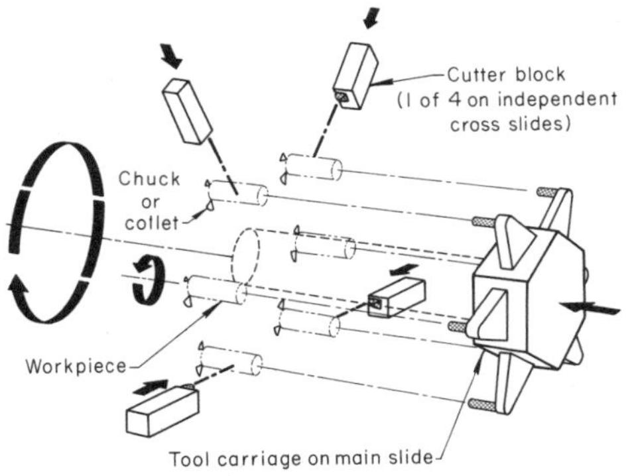

Fig. 3. Rudiments of a multiple-spindle automatic chucking or bar machine

tity justifies the cost, special equipment can be designed for magazine-loading many kinds of workpieces.

Multiple-spindle chucking machines are intended to accomplish the same machining operations as single-spindle machines (automatic turret lathes). The main advantage of the multiple-spindle over the single-spindle machine is a reduction in machining time per piece. In contrast to the single-spindle machine, in which tools from only one turret position are working at one time, the multiple-spindle machine can be set up so that all tools

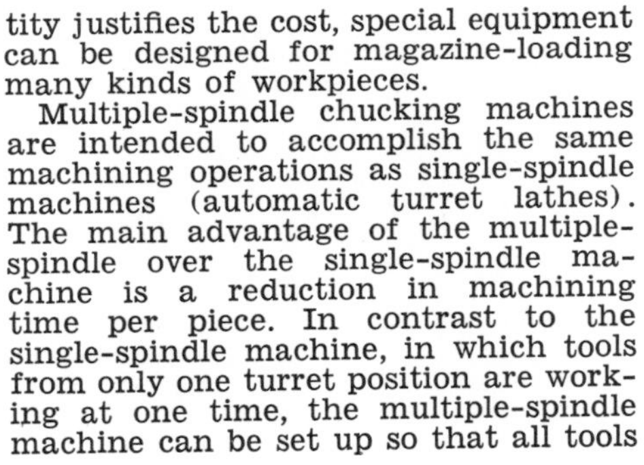

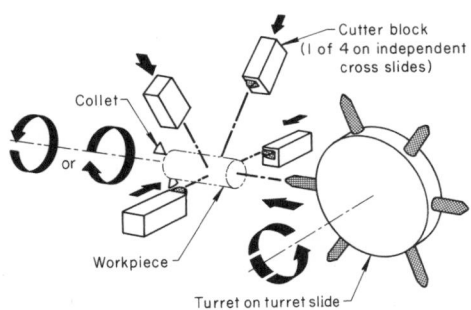

Fig. 4. Rudiments of one type of single-spindle automatic bar machine

are working at one time. In the single-spindle machine, the time required for completing one piece is the sum of the times required for the individual turret operations (not considering cross-slide operations that may be conducted simultaneously with turret operations). In multiple-spindle operation, the time required for completing one piece is usually that required for the most time-consuming single operation. (A multiple-spindle chucking machine is compared with a hand-operated turret lathe for the same result in Example 293 in this article, and in Example 954 in the article on Machining of Copper.)

Disadvantages of multiple-spindle chucking machines are high initial cost, increased setup time and increased cost of tooling. Thus, they are intended for long production runs.

Single-Spindle Bar Machines

Manually operated single-spindle bar machines are counterparts of manually operated turret lathes, discussed in a preceding section and illustrated schematically in Fig. 1. Manual turret lathes for machining bars are sometimes called "hand screw machines". Their essential difference from the chucking type of turret lathe is construction of the headstock end. To accommodate bars, this portion of the machine must be constructed so as to permit the bars to be fed through from the rear and to be held by collets rather than chucks.

Special attachments (see "Accessories" in the section "Manual Turret Lathes") can also be incorporated on bar machines to increase productivity or decrease operator effort, or both. Machines that can handle bars up to about 8 in. in diameter are available, but it is seldom economical to use this type of machine for solid bars this large, because of the time needed for cutoff.

Single-spindle automatic bar machines ("single-spindle automatic screw machines" is a term that still persists) are bar-machine counterparts of automatic turret lathes, insofar as operations performed are concerned.

There are several different types of single-spindle automatic that produce parts directly from lengths of bar or tube, but all types utilize cross slides and some form of turret to manipulate the tools. Some types are constructed so as to operate by the principles of a horizontal turret lathe, illustrated schematically in Fig. 1.

Essential components and operating principles of another type of single-spindle automatic bar machine are illustrated schematically in Fig. 4. In this type of machine, the turret indexes by revolving on a horizontal axis at right angles to the longitudinal axis of the machine spindle and workpiece. The turret, which may have up to eight index stations, advances to the workpiece on a turret slide supported by the ways. All axial operations are performed by tools mounted in the turret. Tools mounted on the four cross slides may perform, consecutively or simultaneously, operations such as facing, form turning, grooving or knurling.

For any of these machines, work metal is supplied from a bar (or tube) held firmly in the spindle by a spring collet. After each piece has been completed, the bar is repositioned for machining of the next piece by being automatically moved forward and butted against an established stop. Some means must be provided for supporting the bar section extending out the rear of the headstock, to minimize whipping action. Whipping will cause excessive vibration in the machine.

Bars of less than 2-in. diameter comprise the majority of those machined in this type of equipment. However, machines that can handle bars up to about 8 in. in diameter are in use.

(Comparisons of manual turret lathes with single-spindle automatic bar machines for equal results are presented in Examples 298 and 299 in this article, in Example 773 in the article "Machining of Stainless Steel", and in Examples 944, 945, 946, 947, 952 and 953 in the article "Machining of Copper and Copper Alloys".)

Multiple-Spindle Bar Machines

With respect to indexing of the spindles and tool-positioning methods, multiple-spindle automatic bar machines operate on principles essentially the same as those described in the preceding section "Multiple-Spindle Chucking Machines" and illustrated schematically in Fig. 3. However, the construction of bar machines is entirely different from that of chucking machines in regard to spindles and related devices for holding and feeding the work metal. In multiple-spindle bar machines, the bars are supported in a stock reel attached to the rear of the machine. The bars are moved automatically from the stock reel through hollow spindles and spring collets by means of feed fingers.

Six-spindle machines are the most common, although these machines are also available with four, five or eight spindles. Some models can handle bars up to 8 in. in diameter, but few are used to machine bars larger than 5 in. in diameter — mainly because the cutoff operation consumes too much time to be compatible with other operations.

(Six-spindle automatic bar machines are compared with manual turret lathes in Example 299 in this article, and in Example 951 in the article "Machining of Copper and Copper Alloys".)

Tools

Most cutting tools used in multiple-operation machining are similar to those used for the same operations conducted individually. For instance, a drill made of the same material and having the same cutting angles will ordinarily be used for drilling a given work metal regardless of whether the drilling is done as a single operation in a drill press or as one of several operations in a sequence on a multiple-spindle automatic machine. The same is usually true for reamers, taps, threading dies, boring tools and single-point turning tools.

There are sometimes exceptions for the tools listed above. In a sequence of operations in multiple-operation machining, one tool may be unavoidably abused in order to obtain better efficiency from other tools that operate in sequence. Under these circumstances, tools such as drills or reamers are often made from a more highly alloyed high speed steel, such as M33 or T15, than they would be otherwise. (Tool materials are compared in Examples 743 and 774 in the article on Machining of Stainless Steel, and Example 950 in the article on Machining of Copper.)

Tool design is sometimes modified from that normally used for single-operation machining when experience with a specific application indicates the need. (Redesign of a carbide tool that resulted in improved tool life and better surface finish is described in Example 744 in the article on Machining of Stainless Steel.)

Information on tool material and design for specific operations will be found in this volume in articles dealing with specific machining processes such as lathe turning, boring, drilling and reaming. Features of cutting tools that are unique to machining of specific metals are also covered in this volume, in the articles on machining of the various metals.

Radial vs Tangential Turning. Some multiple-operation machines (notably turret lathes) have a saddle-type positively driven tool carrier supported on the ways. With this type of equipment, turning tools are mounted on the carrier, thus permitting turning of the workpiece by the same procedures used with an engine lathe (see the article "Turning", page 1).

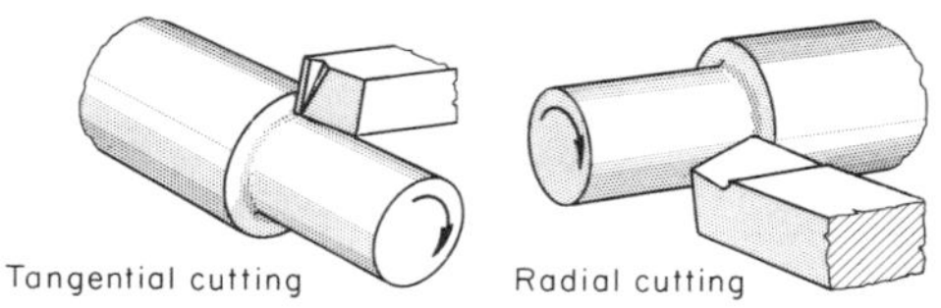

Fig. 5. Positions of tool and workpiece for tangential and radial cutting

When using machines that do not have a saddle-type tool carrier, turning must be done from the turret or the tool carriage supported by a main slide (depending on the type of machine). Under these circumstances more elaborate tool holders are needed, to maintain rigidity in the tools and sometimes to prevent bending of the workpiece (see "Tool Adapters and Mountings" on the next page).

However, mounting of tools for turning from turrets or tool carriages does permit greater flexibility in locating the tools radially at various positions than when such tools are mounted on a carrier supported by the ways.

In tangential cutting, the turning tool is set so that the bottom of the side cutting edge is on the vertical center line of the work (Fig. 5). In radial cutting, the top of the side cutting edge is set on the horizontal center line (Fig. 5). In many instances, the choice between tangential and radial cutting (where it is convenient to use either one) is arbitrary. Tangential cutting is often preferred for finish turning, particularly of brass and aluminum.

Tool material, design and rigidity are all major influences on productivity, tool life, tolerance and finish.

Experience with specific applications often indicates that changes in tool material or design, or both, will improve results (see Examples 303 through 308 in this article).

Although composition of the metal being machined is usually the most important factor affecting selection of tool material and design, rigidity of equipment and specific conditions of the workpiece also must be considered. For instance, carbide tools are not recommended for applications in which chatter is likely to develop, or for workpieces requiring interrupted cutting.

Lack of rigidity in tool holders can erase all benefit gained from careful selection of tool material and design. Vibration allows chatter, and chatter results in dimensional inaccuracy and poor finish, as well as in subnormal tool life. For drills, reamers, boring bars or other shank-mounted tools, the ratio of the unsupported length of the tool to its diameter is the main factor influencing rigidity. For holding tolerances of ± 0.001 in., an unsupported length 3½ times the tool diameter is about the limit that can be machined. Sometimes this ratio is exceeded — as in Example 280, where the unsupported length was about 6.80 times diameter. In this application, however, tolerances were not close and all cutting tools were made of high speed steel (it is unlikely that carbide cutters would survive this lack of rigidity). Sometimes, when a high length-to-diameter ratio is mandatory for a specific application, solid carbide tools or boring bars are used, because carbide has a modulus of elasticity about three times that of steel. Methods of holding and supporting tools are discussed in the section "Tool Adapters and Mountings" (next page).

Form Tools

Tools used for form turning are more important in multiple-operation machining than in engine-lathe work. In more than half the applications described in examples presented later in this article, form tools were used, for turning a wide variety of tapers, grooves, and special shapes — often, several simultaneously.

Although there is no limit to the complexity of shape that can be incorporated in form tools and transferred to the workpiece, there is a limit to the total width of forming cut that is practical in a machine of a given horsepower. Form tools are moved in at right angles to the axis of the workpiece, thus making plunge cuts. Hence, forming cuts are seldom wider than 3¼ in., and most are less than 2½ in. wide — mainly because of the power that would be required for forcing wider tools into the work.

Design. Relief and back-rake angles for form tools are essentially the same as for single-point tools, which vary with the metal being machined (see the article "Turning", page 1, and the articles that deal with machining of specific metals). A major difference between form tools and single-point tools, however, is that single-point tools usually are ground with a side rake angle, whereas form tools are not. Because form tools are used for plunge cutting, by movement of the cross slide, the cutting edge is kept parallel to the longitudinal axis of the workpiece, and no side rake is used. This simplifies sharpening of form tools, because only the top of the cutting edge need be ground, so that the established back rake angle is retained.

Regardless of size or design, form tools are of two general types: flat and circular (Fig. 6). Each has advantages and disadvantages over the other, as noted in the discussion that follows.

Flat form tools are most commonly of the dovetail type (which refers to the method of mounting), shown in Fig. 6(a), although simple flat form tools for mounting on standard tool posts also are available. Rigidity is especially difficult to maintain in form turning, and the dovetail method of mounting the cutting tool in the holder or adapter is preferred because it provides greater rigidity than tool-post mounting.

Most flat form tools are made from high speed steel, mainly because high speed steel is less sensitive than carbide to lack of rigidity. Some tools have an alloy steel body and inserted cutting edges of high speed steel. The inserting practice is most often used for larger tools, or in applications where the general-purpose types of high speed steel have proved inadequate and special grades like T15, M4 or M44 are required. It is seldom practical to make the entire form tool from these more highly alloyed grades of high speed steel, because they cost two or three times as much as the general-purpose types. In addition, the highly alloyed grades are extremely difficult to machine, which further increases cost.

Carbide inserts also are used for flat form tools, and are satisfactory if the setup is sufficiently rigid. Carbide cutting edges are especially well-adapted to form turning of soft metals like aluminum and brass at high speeds (often up to 600 sfm).

Rigidity is the main advantage of flat form tools of the dovetail type over circular form tools. The main disadvantage of flat form tools is higher cost. Flat form tools (particularly of the dovetail type) are more expensive to produce, because of the numerous machining operations involved. In addition, the total life of a flat form tool is usually less than that of a circular tool, because a flat tool cannot be ground as many times.

Circular form tools (Fig. 6b) are simpler to make than flat tools, because the required contour can be produced by turning. After turning, only a milling operation is needed to provide the cutting edges. As indicated in Fig. 6(b), the tool is often locked in the adapter by means of serrations on one face that engage matching serrations in the adapter.

Circular form tools are seldom made with inserts, because this would destroy their two main advantages over flat form tools — simplicity of production and longer tool life. When made from solid material, circular form tools have extremely long life, because they can be reground repeatedly as long as there is enough metal remaining for mounting. Most solid circular form tools are made from a general-purpose high speed steel, such as M2, although one of the more highly alloyed grades may be used when necessary. Some circular form tools are made of solid carbide.

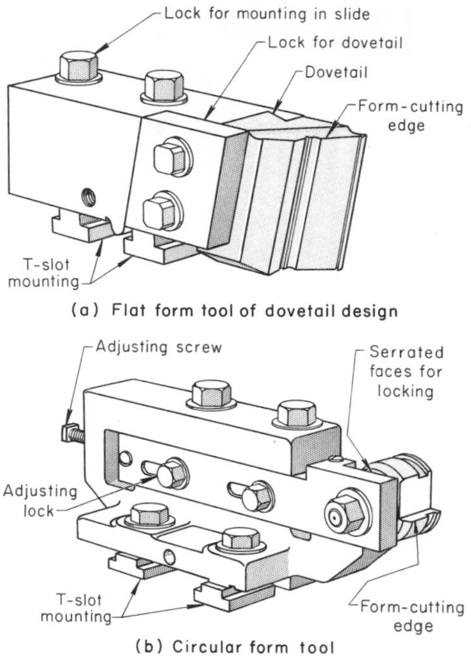

Fig. 6. Two principal types of form tool, shown in adapters for mounting on cross slide

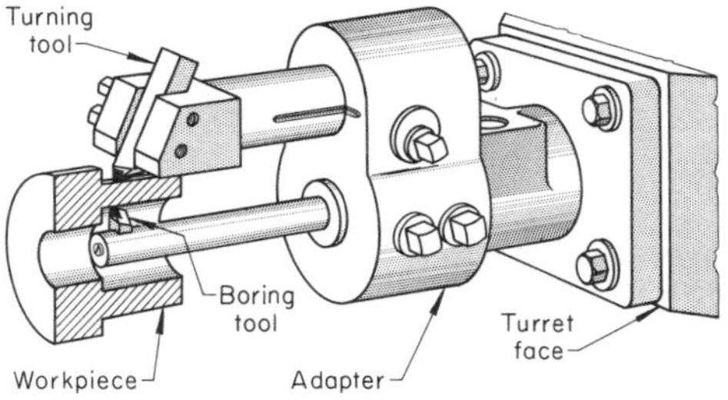

Fig. 7. Method of mounting tools to the face of the main turret on a horizontal turret lathe

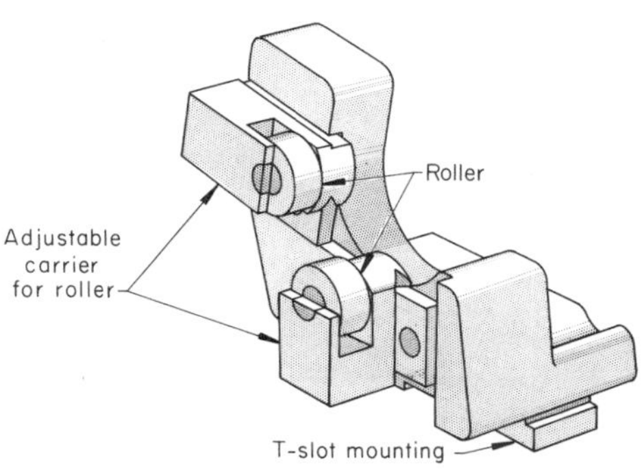

Fig. 8. Roller support used to prevent workpiece from bending during machining

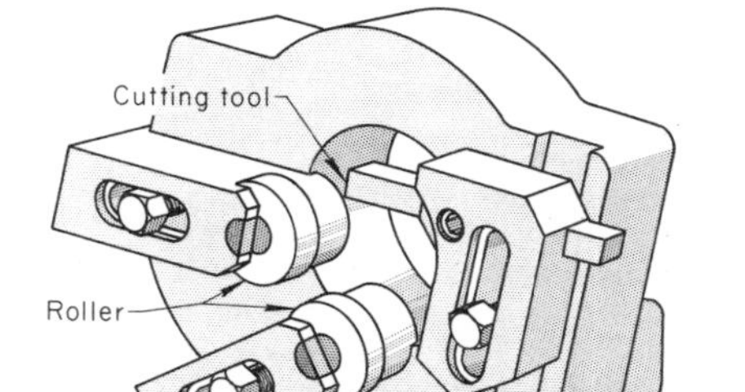

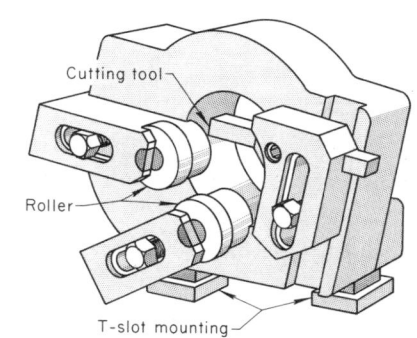

Fig. 9. "Box tool", incorporating rollers for support of workpiece during axial turning

The chief disadvantage of circular form tools is the difficulty of mounting to obtain the same degree of rigidity as with dovetail tools.

Tool Adapters and Mountings

The T-slot principle of mounting, shown on the two form-tool adapters in Fig. 6, is used for most tools that operate from cross slides, regardless of how the adapter is designed. T-slot mounting is used also for securing tool adapters to carriers that move axially on main slides of multiple-spindle machines (Fig. 3). The tees used for mounting are similar to those used for cross-slide mounting (Fig. 6), except that they are parallel with the axial cutting direction of the tool instead of being at right angles to the direction of cutting.

Turret tools are usually mounted by one of three methods, depending on the type of turret.

The most common method of mounting tools on the main turret of a conventional horizontal turret lathe (Fig. 1) is the use of a standard type of adapter that is fastened directly to the turret face by means of four bolts (Fig. 7). For single shank-type tools such as drills or reamers, the adapter can be a simple holder that is modified for various sizes of tool shanks by means of bushings. The adapter shown in Fig. 7 is of a more complex design that holds one turning tool and one boring tool, thus enabling two operations to be performed at one position of the turret. Special adapters are available that hold three or four tools for performing three or four operations simultaneously, particularly when the turret is capable of moving horizontally in two directions.

Turrets that rotate on a horizontal axis parallel with that of the workpiece (Fig. 2) require a rugged mounting between the turret and the tool, to maintain rigidity. Consequently, the tool adapters (indicated in Fig. 2) are secured to the turret by means of dovetails. Coarse adjustment of the tool is obtained by loosening the entire adapter and sliding it along the dovetail slot in the turret. Finer adjustment is obtained by moving the tool within the adapter.

Turrets that rotate on a horizontal axis at right angles to the axis of the workpiece (Fig. 4) have bored holes in which tool shanks can be inserted directly, if of the same diameter as the holes, or (more usually) in which round shanks of standard tool adapters are inserted and locked.

Workpiece Supports

One feature of construction common to all types of machines dealt with in this article is the absence of a tailstock. Consequently, workpiece overhang can become a problem. As unsupported length increases, difficulty in controlling dimensions increases, and so does the possibility that the workpiece will climb on the tool — which often has been responsible for a costly wreck. The amount of unsupported length that can be tolerated depends greatly on the operations being performed. For cross-slide operations such as form turning, an unsupported length of about 3½ times the diameter usually is the recommended maximum.

Natural Support. Sometimes, a sequence of operations to be performed can be planned in such a way that the workpiece is provided with natural support from the tools. For instance, it may be possible to perform simultaneous operations with axially and radially mounted tools — as in Example 281 (Fig. 17), wherein it is seen that the drill provided a measure of support while form turning was accomplished from the cross slide. Cutting simultaneously from two or more cross slides is another method by which sufficient support is achieved by natural means.

Usually, however, where unsupported workpiece length is equal to several diameters, some special means of support must be provided when the outside diameter of the workpiece is machined.

Roller supports (Fig. 8) are frequently used where workpiece overhang is excessive (see Examples 275, 281, 283 and 284, and accompanying illustrations).

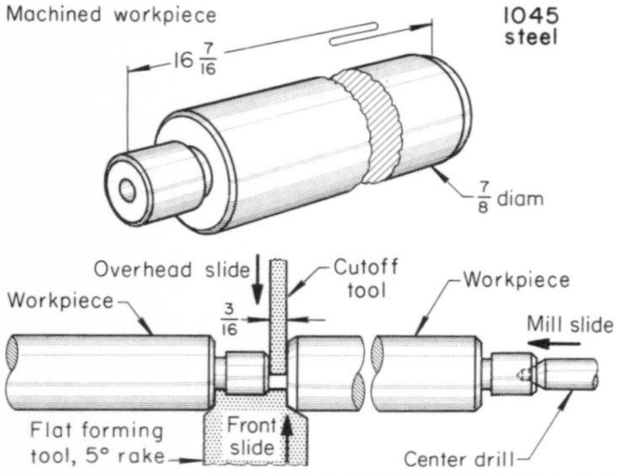

Speed	421 rpm (96 sfm max)
Feed, center drilling	0.0065 ipr
Feed, form turning	0.0013 ipr
Feed, cutting off	0.0014 ipr
Cutting fluid	Proprietary cutting oil
Tool material	High speed steel
Setup time	1.57 hr
Production rate	34 pieces per hour

Fig. 10. Machining a long, slender shaft without roller support (Example 274)

Usual practice is to mount such a device on a cross slide opposite to the direction of the cutting forces, to prevent bending of the workpiece during machining. As seen in Fig. 8, the rollers can be adjusted to accommodate a range of workpiece diameters. Supports similar to the type shown in Fig. 8, but in which the work is supported in a vee instead of by rollers, have also been successfully used, but supports that utilize rollers are preferred.

Box Tools. Roller (or vee) support can also be utilized for axial turning, as from a turret. Tools used for this procedure combine support with one or more cutting tools. Tools that incorporate both support and cutters are often called "box tools", and are made in a variety of designs and sizes. A box tool that incorporates two supporting rollers and one cutting edge is illustrated in Fig. 9.

In turning with this type of tool, the rotating workpiece passes between the rollers and the cutter. The cutter is set slightly ahead of the rollers (usually about 1/32 in.), which allows the rollers to

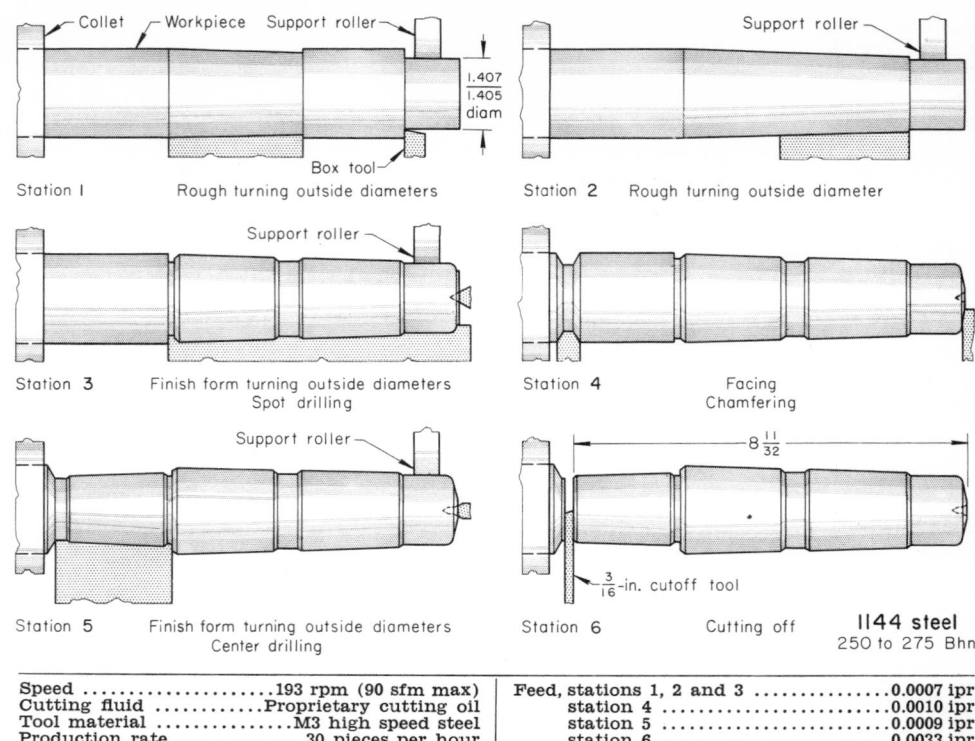

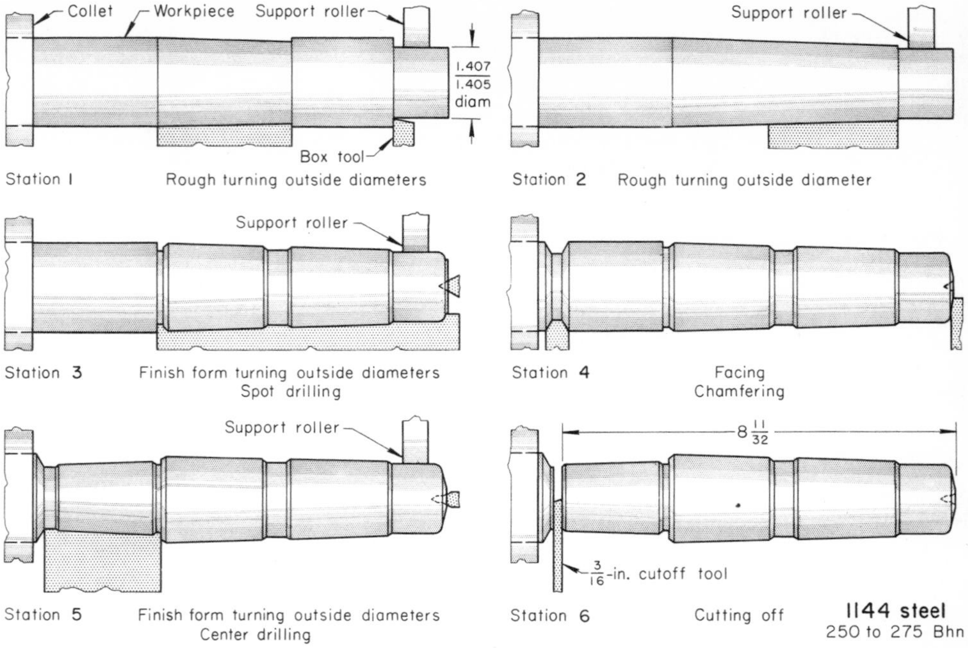

Speed	193 rpm (90 sfm max)	Feed, stations 1, 2 and 3	0.0007 ipr
Cutting fluid	Proprietary cutting oil	station 4	0.0010 ipr
Tool material	M3 high speed steel	station 5	0.0009 ipr
Production rate	30 pieces per hour	station 6	0.0033 ipr

Fig. 11. Use of box tool and separate roller supports to prevent bending of a long workpiece during turning (Example 275)

begin their function of providing support as turning progresses.

As indicated in Fig. 9, both the rollers and the cutter can be adjusted, permitting considerable size variation (commonly about 100%) for any given tool.

Die-Head Support. The use of adjustable die heads is another means of providing support for workpieces while

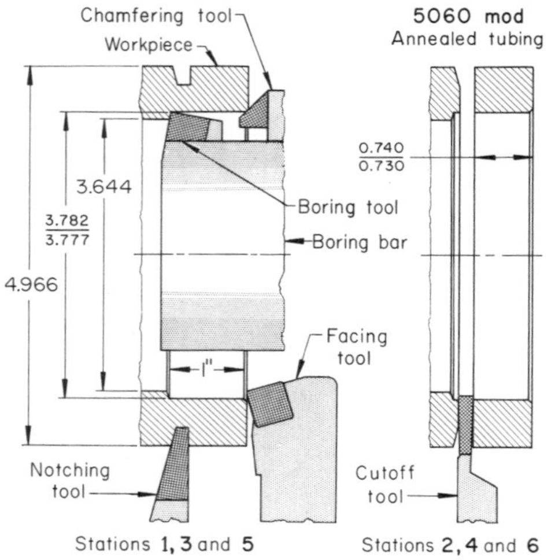

Speed	222 rpm (290 sfm max)
Feed, boring or chamfering	0.0051 ipr
Feed, facing	0.0046 ipr
Feed, notching or cutting off	0.0025 ipr
Tool material	Carbide
Cutting fluid	Soluble oil
Cycle time per part	59.6 sec
Production rate	174 parts per hour
Tool life per grind, pieces:	
Boring	400
Facing	115
Chamfering	529
Notching	83
Cutting off	73

Fig. 12. Machining cam blanks from steel tubing in a six-spindle bar machine (Example 276)

performing axial cutting. Die heads used for this purpose are similar in construction to those used for die threading (see article "Die Threading", page 121), and can be mounted on the face of a turret or to a sliding tool carriage. The die head serves as a holder for four identical cutting tools. The cutting tools can be used for plain turning, contour turning, taper turning, turning of multiple diameters, and some types of form turning. The four tools are mounted in the die head 90° apart; thus, each tool is directly opposite another tool and the cutting forces during operation are balanced.

End Support. In some instances, particularly for extremely small workpieces, end support is more practical than side support. Either male or female supports can be mounted in a turret or a tool carrier that slides axially. In effect, this type of support serves the same purpose as a tailstock on an engine lathe. Examples 283 and 296 indicate effective use of end supports.

Selection of Equipment and Procedure

In choosing the most appropriate machine for processing a given workpiece at lowest cost, one or more of the following factors must be considered:

Workpiece shape or product form
Workpiece size
Type and number of operations required
Production quantity
Production rate
Special requirements
Cost.

The next seven sections of this article discuss the influence of these factors, and present examples that describe equipment and techniques selected for specific production applications.

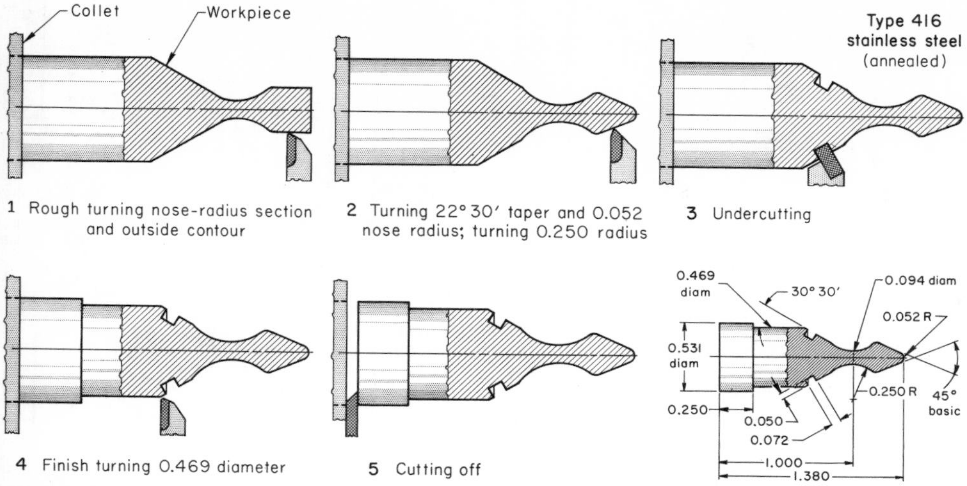

Speed .... 900 rpm (125 sfm max)	Feed, undercutting .... 0.0003 ipr
Feed, rough turning .... 0.001 ipr	turning 0.469-in. diam .... 0.0012 ipr
generating 30° 30′ angle .... 0.0005 ipr	cutting off .... 0.0004 ipr
generating 22° 30′ taper .... 0.0006 ipr	Cutting fluid .... Proprietary cutting oil
generating radius form .... 0.0006 ipr	Time per piece .... 4.2 min

Fig. 13. Production of a complex part in five operations in a Swiss-type single-spindle automatic bar machine **(Example 277)**

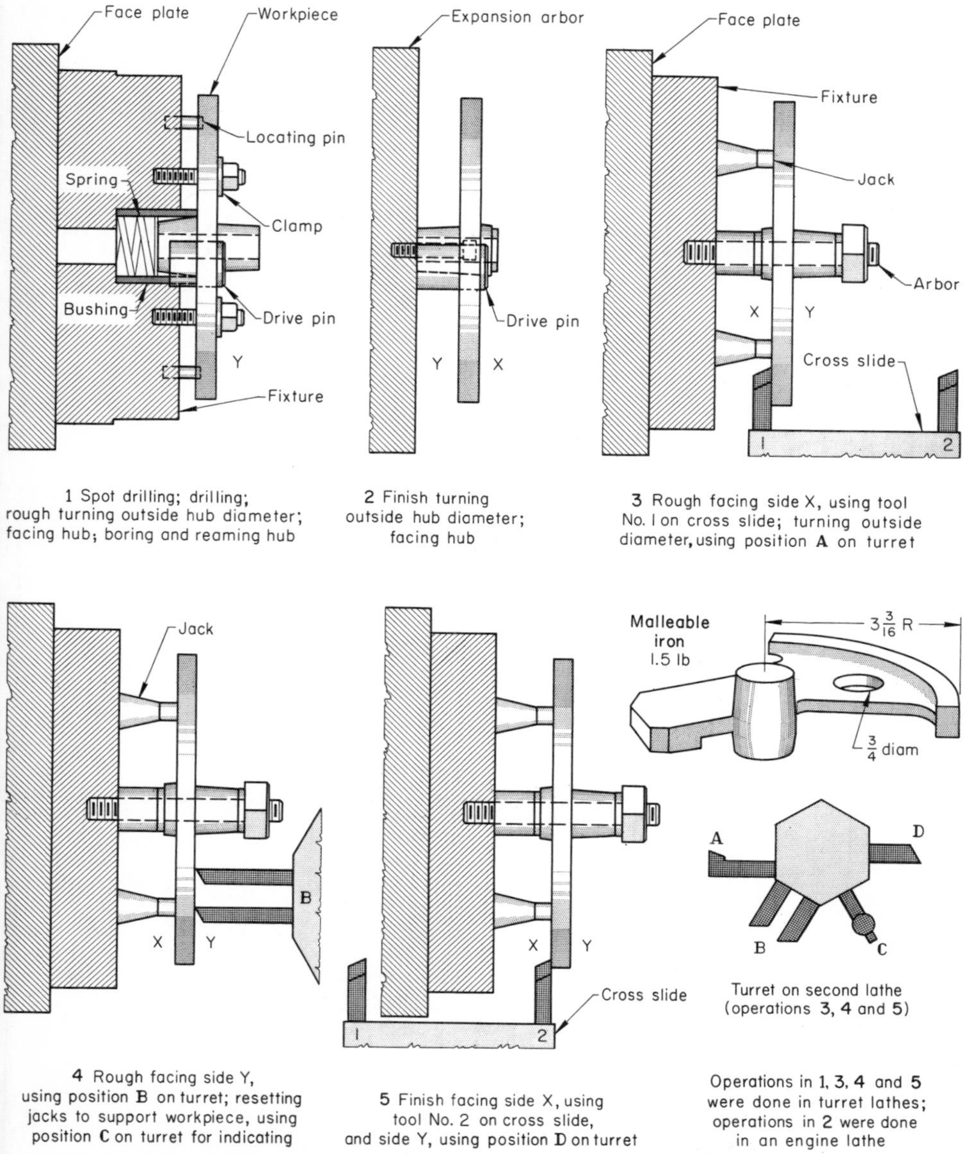

Fig. 14. Machining an unsymmetrical, nonrigid casting **(Example 278)**

Workpiece Shape and Product Form

In most instances, the product form of the work material is known prior to the selection of machine and procedure, so that the choice between a bar machine and a chucking machine is established. It is common practice to cut bars into slugs for processing in a chucking machine — particularly when the bars are large and the time required for the cutoff operation on a bar machine would impair the efficiency of the operation sequence.

The shape of a casting or a forging may determine whether a single-spindle or a multiple-spindle chucking machine is the better choice. Workpieces that are symmetrical and can be placed directly in a two-jaw or three-jaw chuck present less of a problem than irregularly shaped workpieces that require special holders. Work holders add substantially to the cost of tooling, and, to justify the cost of tooling multiple spindles, total production quantities of parts requiring work holders must be larger than for parts that can be chucked directly. Large irregularly shaped parts that must be fastened to a face plate are invariably machined on a single-spindle machine.

Because none of the multiple-operation machines under discussion here utilizes a tailstock, the amount of overhang of the workpiece (or its length-to-diameter ratio) may affect the selection of machine and procedure, as indicated in the two examples that follow.

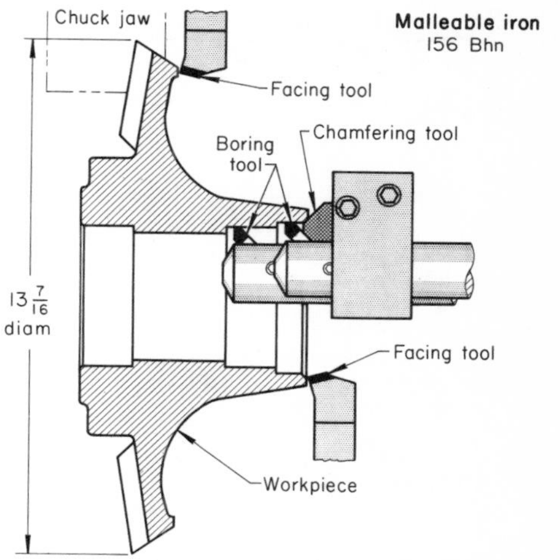

Operation(a)	Speed, Rpm	Speed, Sfm	Feed, ipr	Depth of cut, in.	Cycle time, min(b)
Face rim(c)	72	250	0.0085	0.125	0.77
Face hub(d)	228	280	0.0085	0.125	0.39
Rough bore:					
Large ID	228	234	0.0067	0.120	0.84
Small ID	228	220	0.0067	0.120	0.52
Finish bore:					
Large ID	228	234	0.0067	0.005	0.84
Small ID	228	220	0.0067	0.005	0.52
Chamfer	228	220	0.0067	0.047	...

(a) For all operations, carbide tools were used, and cutting fluid was soluble oil. Facing tools had negative rake; boring and chamfering tools, positive rake. (b) Floor-to-floor time per piece was 9.506 min (production rate per machine, 6.2 pieces per hour); setup time was 1.51 hr. (c) Tool life, 20 pieces per grind. (d) Tool life, 38 pieces per grind.

Fig. 15. Sixty-pound wheel casting machined in a single-spindle chucking machine **(Example 279)**

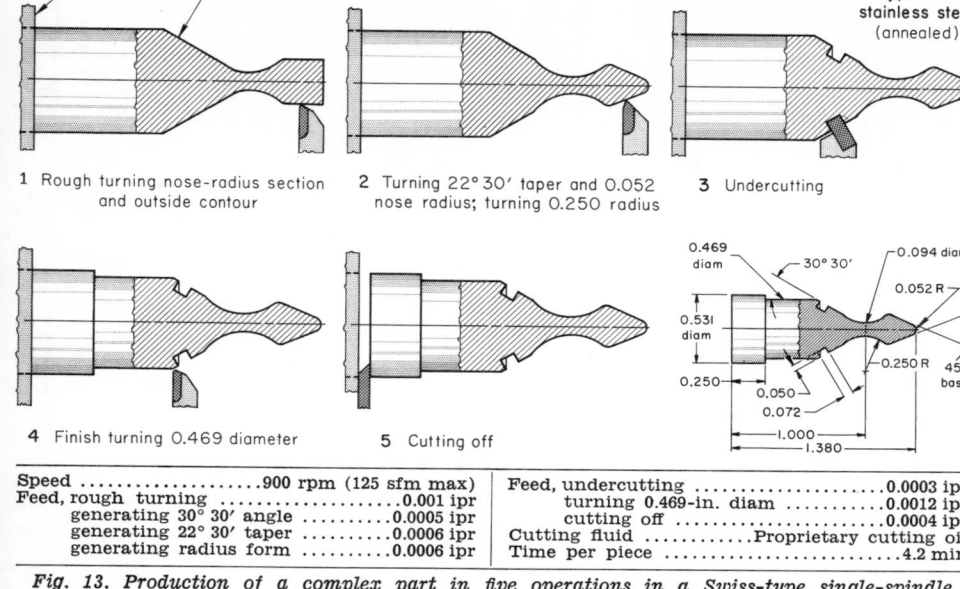

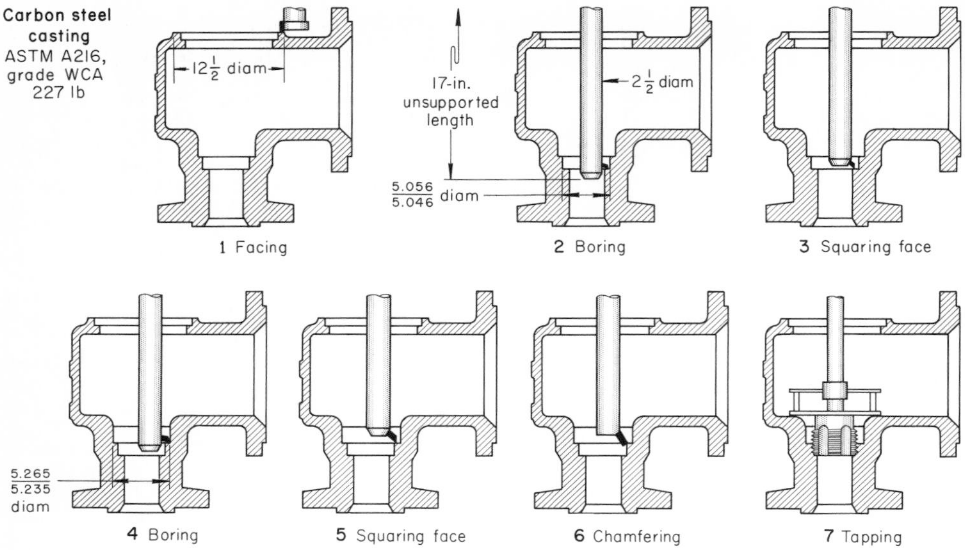

Operation(a)	1	2	3	4	5	6	7
Speed, rpm	140	140	140	140	140	140	30
Speed, sfm	470	187	187	200	200	187	39
Feed, ipr	0.011	0.011	Hand	0.011	Hand	Hand	Hand

(a) All machining was done dry, using high speed steel tools. Tool life was approximately seven pieces per grind, and production rate was one piece per hour.

Fig. 16. Seven-operation machining of a large, heavy steel casting in a vertical turret lathe **(Example 280)**

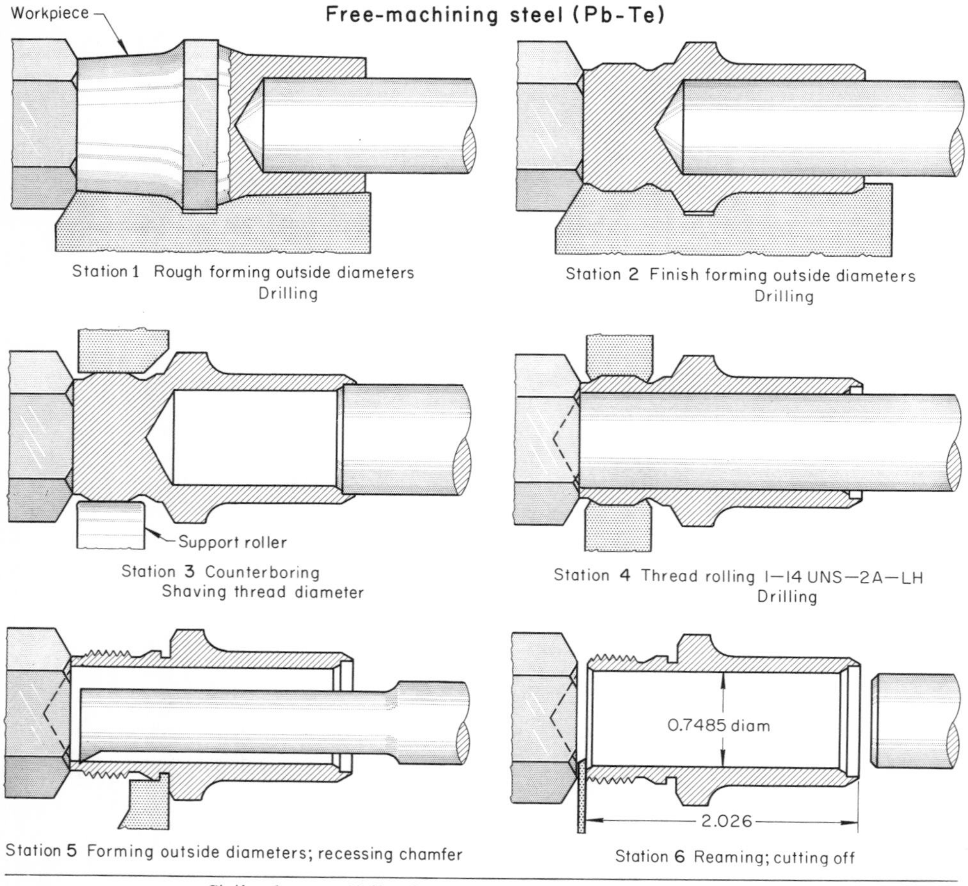

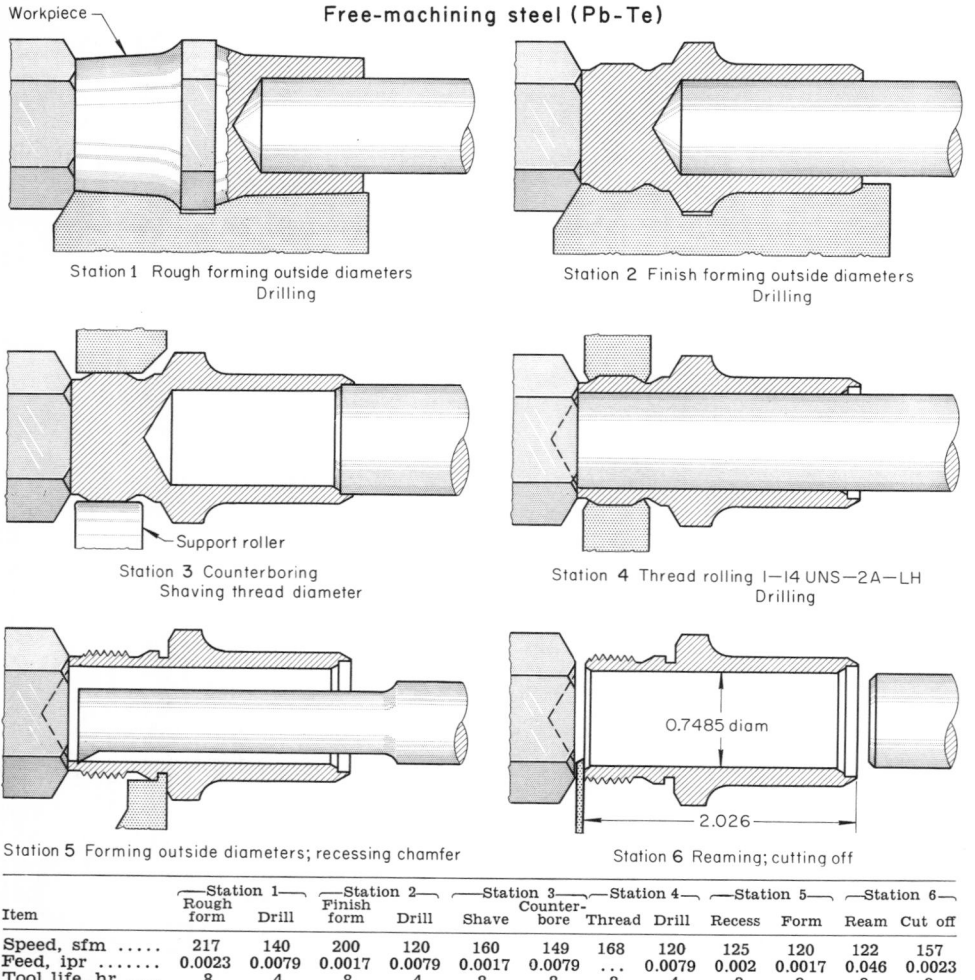

Item	Station 1 Rough form	Station 1 Drill	Station 2 Finish form	Station 2 Drill	Station 3 Shave	Station 3 Counter-bore	Station 4 Thread	Station 4 Drill	Station 5 Recess	Station 5 Form	Station 6 Ream	Station 6 Cut off
Speed, sfm	217	140	200	120	160	149	168	120	125	120	122	157
Feed, ipr	0.0023	0.0079	0.0017	0.0079	0.0017	0.0079	...	0.0079	0.002	0.0017	0.046	0.0023
Tool life, hr	8	4	8	4	8	8	8	4	8	8	8	8

For all operations, high speed steel tools and sulfurized cutting oil were used.

Fig. 17. Twelve-operation complete machining of special nuts in a six-spindle automatic bar machine **(Example 281)**

Example 274. Machining Long, Slender Shafts Without Added Support (Fig. 10)

Shafts of the shape shown in Fig. 10 and weighing 3.07 lb each were machined (center drilled, form turned, cut off) from cold drawn, stress-relieved bars in a 1½-in. single-spindle automatic bar machine. The long slender workpiece was formed to ¾-in. diameter for threading with thread relief and chamfers. Processing details are given in the caption for Fig. 10.

Although most long, slender workpieces require some type of added support, on these shafts the only operation performed from the turret was center drilling (first operation); no axial turning was required. Consequently, it was possible to design a form tool that simultaneously turned and chamfered the back of one workpiece and the front of the next from the front cross slide. Even before forming was finished, the cutoff operation was started (Fig. 10). By this procedure, operations that exerted force on the side of the workpiece were performed close to the machine collet, where overhang was not significant.

Center drilling was accomplished by the use of a mill slide or flat bed slide with T-slots, for box tools and end-working tool holders. The center drill holder was equipped with support rollers.

The nearly 20-to-1 ratio of length to diameter of these shafts was too great for machining in a multiple-spindle bar machine, regardless of production requirements. Adapting a multiple-spindle machine for the production of these shafts would have required a special feed-out mechanism costing about $5000.

Example 275. Use of Support Rollers in Machining Long Double-Taper Arbors (Fig. 11)

Figure 11 shows the sequence of operations in producing double-taper arbors from 1[13]/16-in.-diam 1144 steel bar stock, on a 2⅝-in. six-spindle bar machine. Length-to-diameter ratio of the stock being machined was about 6 to 1. To provide the required support for the wide rough turning cuts taken in station 1, the 1.407/1.405-in. diameter was turned with a box tool, operating from the tool carriage, that incorporated a support roller in addition to the cutter. This turned diameter was then used for roller support from the tool carriage during machining in stations 2, 3 and 5,

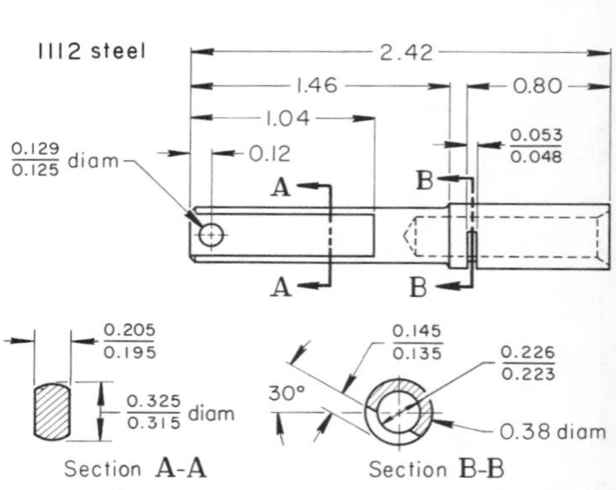

Operation(a)	Speed Rpm	Speed Sfm	Feed, ipr	Tool life per grind, pieces
Form	1540	152	0.0025	2500
Spot drill	1540	75	0.0045	6000
Drill	1540	75	0.0045	1700
Face, chamfer	1540	152	0.0045	3600
Cross drill	2372	78	0.0035	1700
Mill slot	204	108	0.0005(b)	2000
Mill flats	162	105	0.0021(b)	3000
Ream	980	55	0.0081	1700
Cutoff	1540	152	0.0025	3400

(a) For all operations, tools were made of M2 high speed steel, and water-soluble oil was used as the cutting fluid. Form tools had 8° front clearance and 7° top rake; drills were of standard design, with 118° point angles; milling cutters were ground with standard angles and clearances. (b) Feed in inch per tooth.

Fig. 18. Control-cable adapter produced in a six-spindle bar machine, in sequence of operations for which data are given in the table above, and which are described in **Example 282**

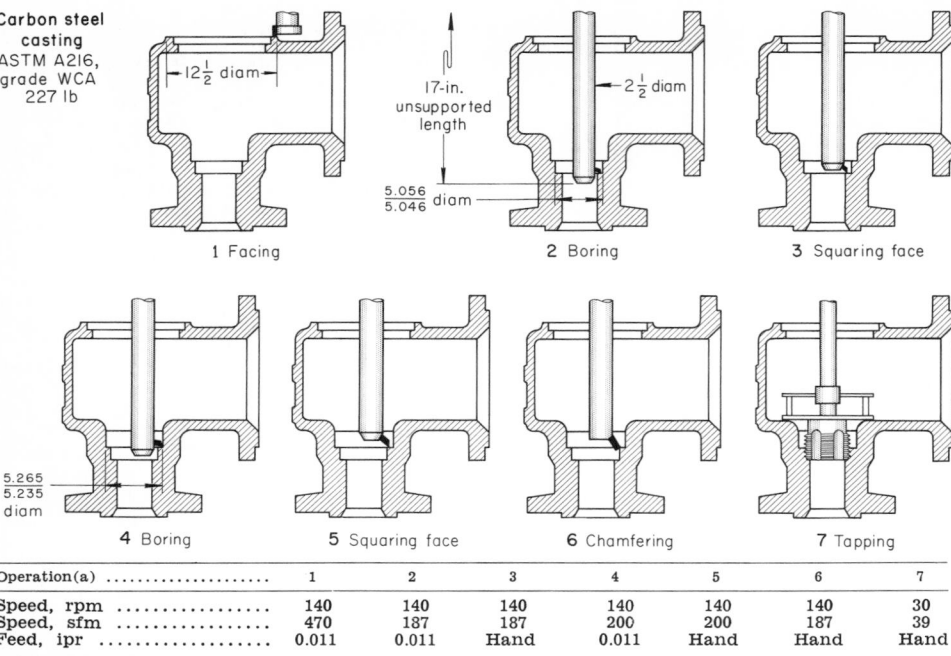

which consisted principally of wide form turning by tools mounted on cross slides. Processing details are given with Fig. 11.

The workpiece in the example that follows, in contrast to the long, slender parts in Examples 274 and 275, was almost seven times greater in diameter than in length. This ringlike part represents a borderline case in choice of product form. Although an ideal part for machining from tubing on a bar machine (as described in the example), production quantities must be sufficient to warrant the large capital investment required for this equipment. Under other conditions, machining these parts from forgings on a chucking machine might be more economical.

Example 276. Producing Ringlike Parts From Tubing (Fig. 12)

A six-spindle, 6-in.-capacity bar machine was used for producing cam blanks from annealed alloy steel tubes received scale-free and in random lengths of 7 to 14 ft. As shown in Fig. 12, boring, chamfering, facing, and notching for cutoff were done in one station, and cutoff was completed in a second station. Performing complete cutoff with one tool proved to be impractical because of the time required and short tool life. Even with the two-step procedure used, the life of the notching and cutoff tools was low (see processing details accompanying Fig. 12). Because each part was completed on two spindles of the six-spindle machine, three parts were produced per cycle.

For quantities ranging from 25,000 to 100,000 pieces, these operations could have been performed more economically on a single-spindle machine, but the production requirements of 500,000 justified the use of a multiple-spindle unit.

The following example describes an instance where a special machine was selected because of workpiece shape:

Example 277. Use of Swiss-Type Machine for Generating Radii (Fig. 13)

The radii specified for the workpiece shown in Fig. 13 would have been difficult to generate on a conventional single-spindle bar machine. A Swiss-type machine (a single-spindle automatic bar machine with five radial tool slides in the same plane) was used.

As shown in Fig. 13, the part was machined in five operations. In the first operation, a cam-controlled tool rough turned the section for the nose radius and generated the contour shown. In a second operation, the taper and nose radius were completed. Another tool then advanced and generated the undercut, in a third operation. The outside diameter was finish turned in a fourth operation, and the bar was cut off in a fifth, as indicated in Fig. 13. (Not shown is a corner-breaking tool that overlapped the action of the cutoff tool in the fifth operation.) Processing details are given with Fig. 13.

Some workpieces are so complex, fragile or unsymmetrical (or all three) that they are not well suited to machining on any of the conventional multiple-operation machines. One alternative is to machine small quantities of such parts on an engine lathe and large quantities on machines specially built for the specific application. Another alternative is to use a combination of machines, as in the following example, where both an engine lathe and turret lathes were utilized:

Example 278. Use of Turret and Engine Lathes for Machining a Complex, Nonrigid Casting (Fig. 14)

The malleable iron casting shown in Fig. 14 presented problems in machining because (*a*) lack of rigidity resulted from the thin web connecting the hub and the rim, and (*b*) the unsymmetrical shape caused severely interrupted cutting. All lathe operations on these parts were done in three separate steps: two in manually operated turret lathes and one in an engine lathe.

As shown in Fig. 14 (see operation 1), each casting was first located in the chuck of a turret lathe by means of specially designed spring-loaded bushings. Two clamps held the workpiece rigidly against the locating pins. Driving was accomplished by means of a pin that extended through the ¾-in.-diam hole in the web. After being drilled, turned, faced, bored and reamed, the workpiece was transferred to an engine lathe, where it was mounted in a reverse position on an expansion arbor and again driven by means of a pin extending through the ¾-in.-diam hole, for machining as indicated in operation 2 in Fig. 14.

The workpiece then was reversed again, mounted on a face plate, and chucked in a second turret lathe. The short side of the hub (side "X" in Fig. 14) was held against a shoulder on a threaded arbor, and two jacks were set in position against the web section to keep the part from springing while it was being machined. With this setup, lathe operations were completed, in three stages, utilizing the cross-slide and turret tools as indicated in operations 3, 4 and 5 in Fig. 14. The cross-slide tools (1 and 2) were spaced far enough apart to straddle the face plate as it revolved.

As Fig. 14 indicates, only four of the six positions on the main turret were used in operations 3, 4 and 5, and only three of these were used for cutting — position C on the turret being used for indicating to reset the supporting jacks.

All operations were done without cutting fluid at a spindle speed of 255 rpm. Feeds were manually controlled (0.0035 ipr). Cutting tools were made from high speed steel.

This casting, which weighed 1.5 lb, was not large or heavy enough to require counterbalancing while being rotated, but workpieces of similar shape that weighed more than 3 lb would require counterbalanced chucks.

Table 1. Guide Used in One Plant for Selection of Chucking Machine on the Basis of Workpiece Weight and Production Quantity

Lot size, pieces	Machine for processing forgings or castings weighing: 5 to 25 lb	25 to 50 lb	Over 50 lb
Up to 10	Horizontal turret lathe, or engine lathe	Vertical turret lathe	Vertical turret lathe
10 to 100	Horizontal automatic lathe	Vertical turret lathe (automatic or with tape control)	Vertical turret lathe (automatic or with tape control)
100 to 1000	Horizontal multiple-spindle automatic	Vertical multiple-spindle automatic	Vertical automatic turret lathe
1000 to 100,000	Horizontal multiple-spindle automatic (possibly with automatic loading)	Vertical multiple-spindle automatic	1 or 2 double-spindle vertical automatic turret lathes
Continuous high production	Horizontal multiple-spindle automatic; automatic loading	Vertical multiple-spindle automatic; automatic loading	Special machine for particular part and operation

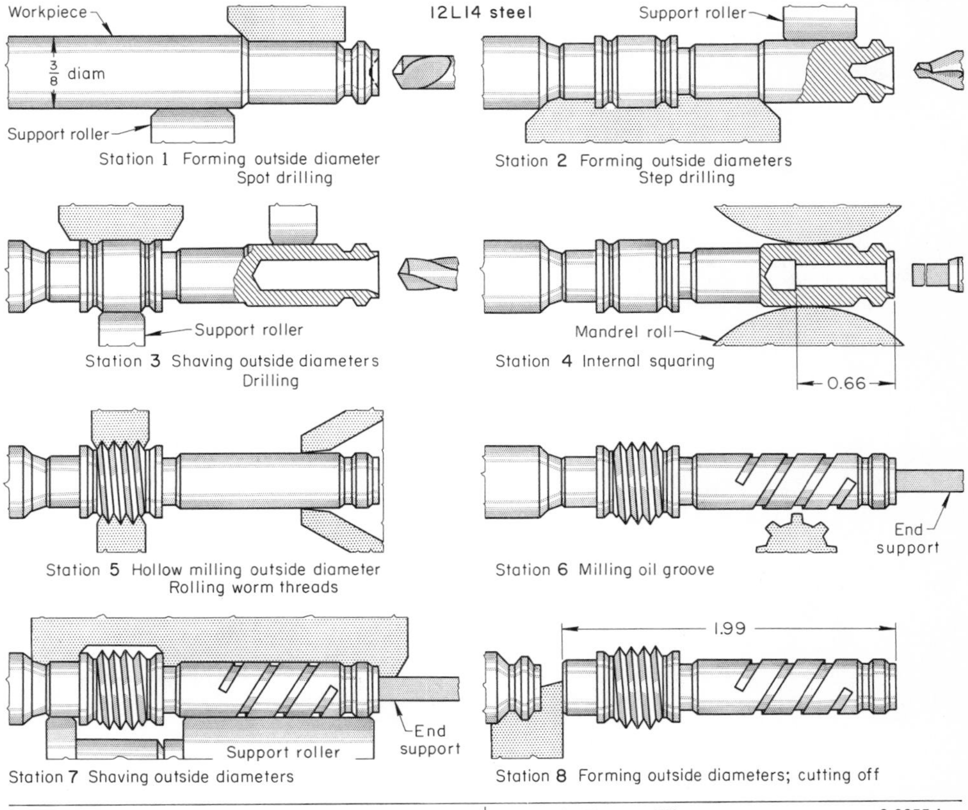

Speed	2000 rpm (200 sfm)
Feed, spot drilling	0.0055 ipr
forming, station 1	0.0015 ipr
step drilling	0.0055 ipr
forming, station 2	0.001 ipr
drilling	0.0055 ipr
shaving, stations 3 and 7	0.001 ipr
Feed, hollow milling	0.0055 ipr
forming, cutting off	0.0015 ipr
Tool material	M3 high speed steel
Cutting fluid	Mineral oil
Setup time	24 hr
Production rate	600 pieces per hour
Tool life per grind (approx)	20,000 pieces

Fig. 19. Machining sequence and processing details for production of worm-drive component in an eight-spindle bar machine (Example 283)

Workpiece Size

Workpiece size, alone or in conjunction with shape, sometimes restricts the choice of machine that would be suitable. Some plants have developed guides to the selection of machines on the basis of workpiece size or weight and other variables. Table 1, for example, was developed in one plant to be used in selecting chucking machines for processing forgings and castings, on the basis of weight and quantity of workpieces. Although useful as guides, tables of this kind are often deficient because they do not consider all the factors by which machine selection is determined. For instance, in Table 1 a multiple-spindle machine is recommended for machining workpieces weighing from 5 to 25 lb in lots of 1000 to 100,000. This recommendation does not take into account that some workpieces are of such shape that a multiple-spindle machine could not be used, or that some requirement such as special tolerances might preclude the consideration of multiple-spindle equipment.

Although most bar machines (particularly multiple-spindle bar machines) are built for handling bars or tubes less than about 3 in. in diameter, single-spindle machines, and multiple-spindle machines with up to four spindles, are available that can handle bars up to 8 in. in diameter. The maximum diameter of work material that can be handled in machines having more than four spindles decreases as the number of spindles increases.

Parts are seldom machined from solid bar stock larger than about 3 in. in diameter, because: (*a*) the cutoff operation consumes too much time to be compatible with other operations, and (*b*) the initial cost of large multiple-spindle machines often becomes prohibitive, because the high burden rate is reflected in cost of the finished part. Consequently, when making parts from the larger sizes of bars, it is usually more practical to saw or otherwise cut them into slugs in a preliminary operation, and then use a chucking machine. This practice, however, has a disadvantage when the metal enclosed by the chuck also requires machining. Under these conditions, either a preliminary or a secondary operation is required (see Example 286, in which bars cut into slugs were turned on an engine lathe before being machined in a six-spindle chucking machine).

Size of workpiece alone seldom influences a choice between a hand-operated and an automatic machine, but workpiece size is likely to influence the choice between single-spindle and multiple-spindle machines. This is particularly true for chucking machines. For instance, some workpieces are of such shape that they can be held in relatively small chucks, but other portions would require clearance between workpieces that would be out of proportion to the chuck size, thus precluding the use of a multiple-spindle machine. An example of such a workpiece is a wheel-like part having a relatively small hub that can be used for chucking.

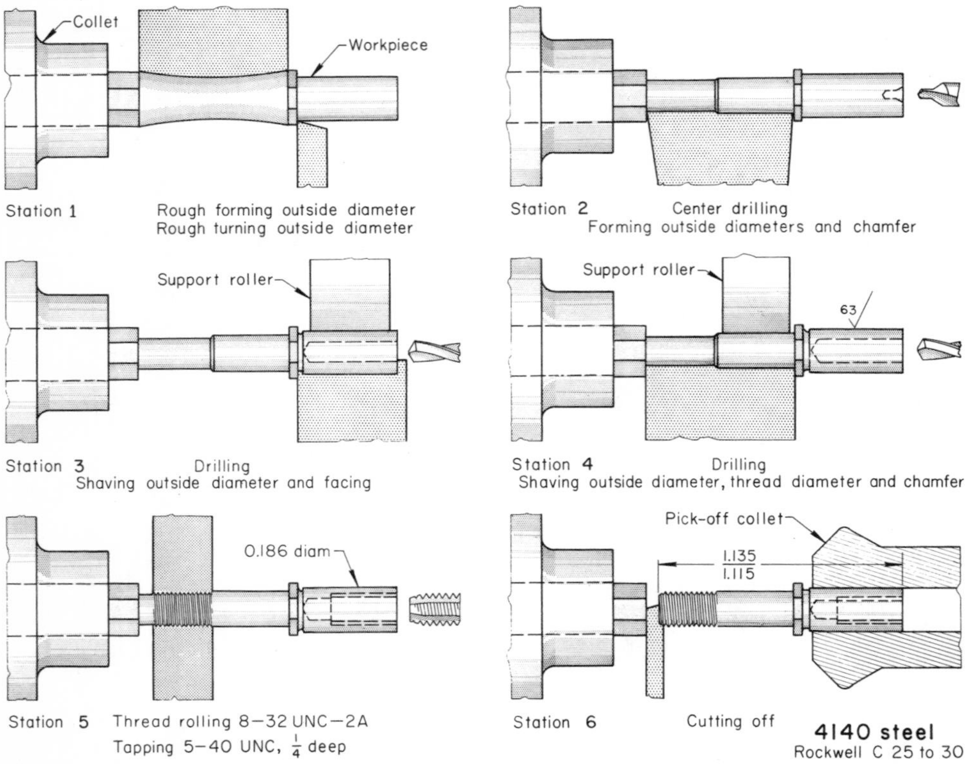

Speed .... 1035 rpm (78 sfm, max)	Cutting fluid .... Thread-cutting oil(a)
Feed, rough turning .... 0.0022 ipr	Machining time per piece .... 16 sec
Feed, forming, shaving, cutoff .... 0.0075 ipr	Production rate .... 225 pieces per hour

(a) Diluted 3-to-1 with mineral oil having a viscosity of 100 SUS

Fig. 20. Sequence of operations for producing a small part in a six-spindle automatic bar machine. Parts required secondary chucking when produced in single-spindle machines, which nearly doubled manufacturing cost. (Example 284)

In other applications, the chucks required for a given size of workpiece are too large for practical consideration of multiple-spindle equipment. For instance, if a multiple-spindle machine were to be used for machining the large castings described in the following example, the spindles would necessarily be located on a 40-in.-diam circle (minimum) and would require a work space at least 5 ft in diameter. Although such a large machine could be obtained, the large capital investment could not be justified unless quantity requirements were extremely high, because the versatility of such large equipment is low.

Example 279. Facing, Boring and Chamfering 60-Lb Wheel Castings (Fig. 15)

A 15-hp single-spindle chucking machine was used for facing, boring and chamfering 60-lb malleable iron castings (Fig. 15). To permit machining of the inside diameter of the hub, it was necessary to chuck each casting on the outside, using an 18-in. chuck.

As indicated in Fig. 15, both facing operations were performed by tools held in opposing cross slides, and boring and chamfering were done with tools attached to a boring bar operated from the longitudinal slide. Processing details for these operations are included with Fig. 15. Subsequent operations included facing, boring, chamfering, drilling and tapping from the opposite side.

For large and heavy workpieces, the problems of securing and supporting that accompany the use of a horizontal machine are minimized by the use of a vertical machine, as in the following example:

Example 280. Machining Large Castings in a Vertical Machine (Fig. 16)

A 36-in. vertical turret lathe proved to be the best choice for machining 227-lb carbon steel castings in seven operations as shown in Fig. 16. Workpieces were secured to the revolving table with standard clamps. Castings of this size and weight sometimes are difficult to secure in a horizontal chuck. Note that the boring bar has an unsupported length of 17 in. Even though this bar is 2½ in. in diameter, close tolerances could not be expected with this unsupported length and high ratio of length to diameter. However, the relatively loose tolerances assigned to the bored diameter of these castings (see Fig. 16) were maintained without difficulty. Processing details are given with Fig. 16.

Type and Number of Operations

Number of operations frequently refers to the number of dimensions obtained on a workpiece by machining. This number may differ from the number of tools, because in many applications one tool is utilized to perform two or more operations. Seldom should any type of turret lathe or automatic machine be considered for parts that can be machined with fewer than three different tools.

Because of the way they are constructed, turret lathes generally have less tool capacity than machines having a sliding tool carriage. (For example, although turret lathes having as many as nine turret stations have been used in production for performing as many as 25 operations, most turret lathes have no more than six turret stations and a cross slide.) The tool clearance usually limits the number of turret stations. Therefore, when more than eight or nine tools are required, machines having cross and longitudinal slides should be considered.

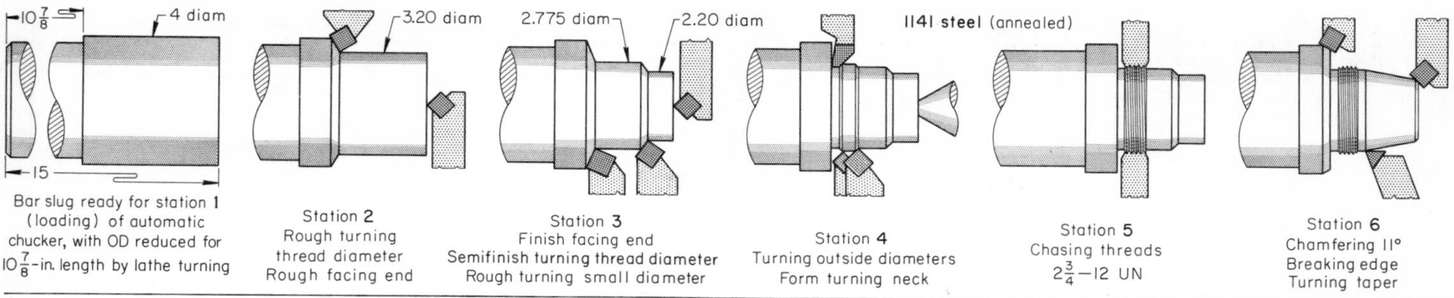

Station	Operation(a)	Speed, sfm	Feed, ipr	Depth of cut, in.
1	Loading	...	....	....
2	Rough turn thread diameter	236	0.0050	0.1685
	Rough face end	106	0.0045	....
3	Finish face end	106	0.0045	....
	Semifinish turn thread diameter	146	0.0050	0.2125
	Rough turn small diameter	184	0.0050	0.2875
4	Turn outside diameters	211	0.0050	0.4585
	Form turn neck	182	0.0045	0.0511
5	Chase threads	...	....	....
6	Chamfer	236	0.0050	0.0255
	Break edge	130	0.0050	0.3341
	Turn taper	152	....	0.6682

(a) Threading tool was of high speed steel; all other tools were of carbide. All cutting tools (other than threading) had negative rake, except for forming tool (station 4), which had a 4° positive rake. Soluble oil used for all operations. Cycle time was 1.05 min per piece.

Fig. 21. Twelve-operation machining of one end of lathe-turned bar slugs in a six-spindle automatic chucking machine (Example 286)

Although it is possible to mount as many different axial tools in a single-spindle machine as in a multiple-spindle machine, there are limitations on the number that can be cross-slide-mounted in single-spindle machines. Thus, when some of the tools are not adaptable to turret mounting, a single-spindle machine will have less capacity than a multiple-spindle machine. Some tools (for example, thread-rolling tools) must be mounted accurately in relation to other tools, under which conditions turret mounting is inadequate. Consequently, there are many parts for which the types of operations or the number of operations, or both, indicate the most practical machine and procedure. The following example describes a typical application for which a multiple-spindle machine was preferable:

Table 2. Single-Spindle vs Six-Spindle Bar Machines (Example 285)

(For production of the part shown below)

Sequence of Operations(a)	
Single-Spindle Machine	**Six-Spindle Machine**
Turret tools:	*Longitudinal tools:*
1 Turn OD	1 Spot drill; rough turn OD
2 Spot drill	2 Tap drill; rough turn OD
3 Tap drill	3 Step drill
4 Step drill	4 Undercut
5 Undercut	5 Tap
6 Tap	6 Step ream
Cross-slide tools:	*Cross-slide tools:*
1 Radius corners	1 Radius back corner
2 Cut off	2 Finish form OD
Secondary operations:	3 Radius front corner
Step ream	4 Stamp letters
Stamp	5 Knurl
Knurl	6 Cut off

Results(a)	Single-spindle	Six-spindle
Setup time, hr	4	14
Tool life per grind, pieces ..	100	208
Production, pieces per hour ..	12(b)	35

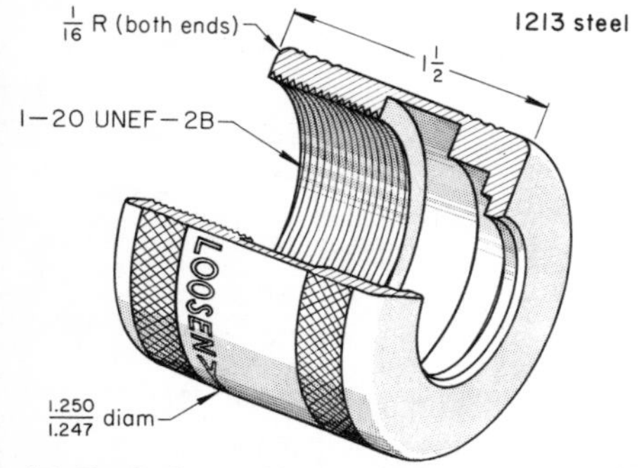

(a) For both machines, spindle speed was 645 rpm (210 sfm max), feed was 0.0031 ipr, carbide tools were used, and cutting fluid was a blend of lard and sulfurized oils mixed 4-to-1 with mineral oil having a viscosity of 100 SUS. (b) Parts still required secondary machining operations, which had been completed on the six-spindle machine.

Example 281. Producing Special Nuts in Six Stations With 12 Tools (Fig. 17)

Special nuts for cotton pickers were completely machined from hexagonal bar stock of free-machining steel (Pb-Te) in 12 operations on a 30-hp six-spindle automatic bar machine. These workpieces could have been produced on a single-spindle machine, but because 12 tools were used and the operations were such that two operations could be performed simultaneously on each spindle (Fig. 17), the six-spindle machine was more efficient. Production rate was 175 pieces per hour, or about six times as many pieces as could have been produced per hour on a single-spindle machine. The free-cutting steel, together with the use of a sulfurized cutting oil, permitted unusually high speeds and feeds, as indicated in the tabular data presented with Fig. 17.

In making some parts, spindle rotation must be stopped to permit cross-machining operations. In multiple-spindle machines, one or more spindles can be stopped while the others continue working. Consequently, for applications in which operations such as cross drilling or milling are incorporated in the sequence, a multiple-spindle machine is usually the most practical — as in the next example:

Example 282. Cross Drilling and Milling in a Bar Machine (Fig. 18)

A six-spindle automatic bar machine was used for complete machining of ⅝-oz control-cable adapters (Fig. 18) from 12-to-14-ft random lengths of cold finished 1112 steel bars, at a rate of 391 pieces per hour. This machine was selected mainly because it was equipped with clutches that could be cammed to stop spindles in three stations for cross drilling and milling. The sequence of operations, which made use of a near-maximum of work slides, was as follows:

Station 1. Part was rough formed from the cross slide and spot drilled from the end tool slide; a two-roll support was used to offset the pressure of the form tool.

Station 2. Part was finish formed from the cross slide and drilled to required depth from the end slide. Part was then faced and chamfered by means of a roller turner from the end slide.

Station 3. The spindle was stopped, and the cross slide operated a special angular cross-drilling attachment; a special V-support mounted on the end tool slide was used to offset cross-drilling pressure.

Station 4. The spindle remained stopped, and a specially designed slotting attachment was utilized to mill the slot from the cross slide; a special V-support on the end slide was used to offset milling pressure.

Station 5. Spindle remained stopped, and a specially designed cross-milling attachment with two cutters was used to straddle-mill the two flats with relation to the cross-drilled hole and milled slot; this attachment was mounted in the cross slide. A live auxiliary reamer spindle mounted on the end tool slide was used to ream the end-drilled hole to 0.226/0.223-in. diam. A special V-support was again used, mounted on the end tool slide, to offset milling pressure.

Station 6. Part was picked up by a standard rotating pick-off attachment and held while being cut off by the cross slide.

All special attachments were driven from the main gearbox by separate sliding splined drive shafts and universal joint, to allow for the movement of the work slides. Additional processing details are given with Fig. 18.

For some parts, it is impractical to complete all operations on a single-spindle machine because of insufficient cross-slide capacity, and it is necessary to utilize secondary operations or to change to multiple-spindle machines. The following four examples describe applications for which multiple-spindle machines were preferred because they could, for reasons given in each example, produce parts more efficiently than single-spindle machines:

Example 283. Producing Worm-Drive Components in an Eight-Spindle Bar Machine (Fig. 19)

An eight-spindle bar machine of 1¼-in.-diam capacity was used for producing worm-drive components from ⅜-in. bar stock of 12L14 steel, in the sequence of operations illustrated in Fig. 19. The internal squaring done in station 4 is an example of a machining operation seldom incorporated in a multiple-operation sequence. In this operation, the drilled hole was changed to square shape by insertion of a spring-loaded mandrel that rotated at the same speed as the workpiece and was inserted into the hole from the tool carriage. The mandrel was surrounded by four rolls, equally spaced, which swaged the work metal inwardly against the mandrel. After squaring, the mandrel and rolls were retracted by the tool carriage.

In this sequence of operations, nearly maximum use was made of the eight spindles, even to the extent of combining the cutoff operation with forming the end of the next piece (station 8). Workpieces of this shape pose problems because they bend if not supported. Note in Fig. 19 that where natural support was not available (stations 1, 2, 3, 6 and 7), roller supports or end supports were used. Processing details for the machining of this part are given with Fig. 19.

Example 284. Change to Multiple-Spindle Machine That Eliminated Secondary Chucking (Fig. 20)

Originally, the small internally and externally threaded shaft shown in Fig. 20 had been produced in single-spindle bar and chucking machines, from ¼-in. hexagonal bars of 4140 steel that were not heat treated as purchased. After operations had been completed on the internally threaded end in a bar machine, the workpiece was heat treated to Rockwell C 25 to 30, then chucked on the machined end, from a magazine loader, in an automatic chucking machine for completion of the opposite end.

To eliminate heat treating and the secondary operation, the bar stock was purchased in the heat treated condition, and was machined in a six-spindle automatic bar machine in the sequence of operations shown in Fig. 20. The shaving operation (station 3) produced an acceptable finish of 63 micro-in. max, thus eliminating the need for grinding. The pick-off collet (station 6) permitted a clean cutoff without burrs.

This change in procedure also eliminated the need for the magazine loader for the secondary operation in the original, single-spindle method, and reduced the manufacturing cost of the part by about 50%. Operating conditions for the multiple-spindle method of machining are given with Fig. 20.

Example 285. Single-Spindle vs Six-Spindle Bar Machines (Table 2)

Table 2 compares procedures and results for using a single-spindle and a six-spindle bar machine for producing the small part shown in the inset sketch, from 1¼-in.-diam 1213 steel bar stock. As noted, with the single-spindle machine, it was necessary to stamp, knurl and step ream in secondary operations, because of inadequate cross-slide capacity; whereas with the six-spindle machine it was possible to produce complete parts, and at a rate three times as fast as the single-spindle machine could produce parts that still required three operations.

Example 286. Use of Engine Lathe Followed by Six-Spindle Chucker for 12-Operation Machining of Bar Slugs (Fig. 21)

Figure 21 shows the tooling setups in a six-spindle automatic chucking machine for completion of parts produced from 15-in.-long slugs of 4-in.-diam 1141 steel bar stock. As indicated, the first station was used only for loading. Because of the time that would be required for cutting off bar stock of this diameter as part of a machining sequence, it proved more economical to cut the bars into slugs rather than to machine parts from long bars. As shown in Fig. 21, the outside diameter of each slug was reduced for a distance of 10⅞ in. from one end in a prior operation on an engine lathe.

Because of the number of operations and the sequence required for the most economical production, a multiple-spindle machine was chosen in preference to one with only a single spindle. Machining sequence and other processing details are given with Fig. 21.

It is often necessary to rechuck the workpiece between two series of operations. A procedure for completing such parts in a chucking machine is described in the following example:

Example 287. Complete Machining of Castings in Two Chuckings (Fig. 22)

Figure 22 shows a nodular iron casting that was completely machined in two chuckings in a six-spindle machine. The sequence of operations in each chucking, and the speeds and feeds used, are listed in the table below Fig. 22. As shown in the illustration, the shorter-hub end of the casting was machined first; hardened steel chuck jaws held the longer-hub end. The casting was then rechucked, being held in the chuck by soft steel jaws to avoid marring the finished surface, for the second sequence of operations.

Because of the number and type of operations, as well as quantity requirements, a multiple-spindle chucking machine was used. Although a six-spindle machine was used because of availability, a five-spindle machine could have been used because one spindle remained idle in both machining sequences.

When workpiece shape is such that all surfaces being machined can be indexed around a common center, a box

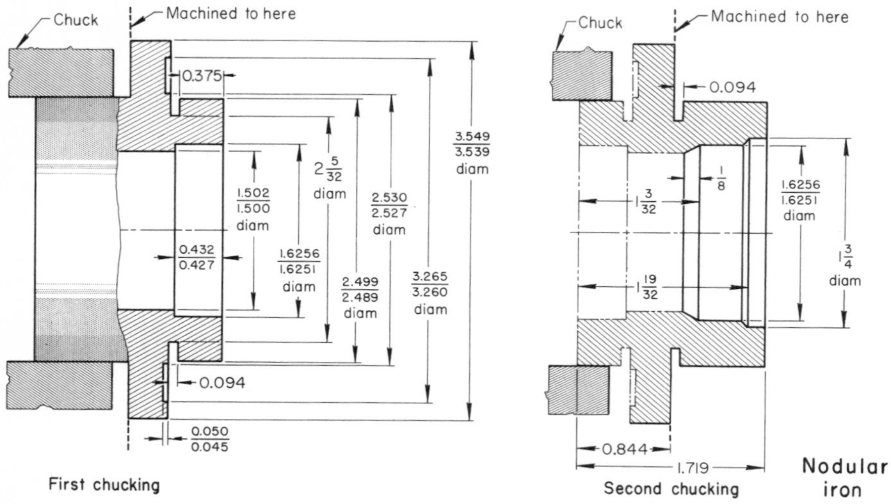

Station	First chucking	Second chucking
Sequence of Operations		
1	Rough bore; rough counterbore; turn OD; turn hub; face hub	Rough face hub; rough bore; rough counterbore; rough turn hub
2	Bore; counterbore; face flange and form groove; face hub	Face flange; form groove; face hub
3	Turn OD; turn hub	Turn hub
4	Form groove	Counterbore
6 (Sta. 5 idle)	Break corners (OD, hub, bore, c'bore)	Break corners; form angle

Machining Conditions(a)

Station	Speed, Rpm	Speed, Sfm(b)	Feed, ipr	Speed, Rpm	Speed, Sfm(b)	Feed, ipr
1	200	188	0.0065(c)	200	131	0.0105
2	200	188	0.0065	200	188	0.0061
3	389	333	0.0105	389	254	0.0105
4	200	170	0.0065	389	178	0.0105
6 (Sta. 5 idle)..	389	333	0.0154	389	333	0.0105

(a) For all operations, carbide tools were used and averaged 100 pieces per grind; water-soluble oil was used as cutting fluid. Setup time was 6 hr; production rate was 15 pieces per hour. (b) Maximum. (c) For all operations in first station except rough boring, for which feed was 0.0154 ipr.

Fig. 22. Machining of a casting in two chuckings in a six-spindle machine (Example 287)

Table 3. Quantity-Cost Relations for Producing the Same Part From Bar Stock in Three Types of Machine (Example 291) (a)

Item	Six-spindle automatics(b)	Manual turret lathe	Engine lathe
Conditions for Any Quantity			
Machine cost(c)	$41,000(d)	$22,000	$10,000
Tooling cost	$1200	$250	$50
Time per piece, minutes	0.715	5.08	66
Production rate, pieces per hour	168	11.8	0.91
Labor cost per piece(e)	$0.015(f)	$0.212	$2.75
Setup time, hr	10	3	0.5
Setup cost(e)	$25.00	$7.50	$1.25
Labor Plus Setup Costs, Based on Annual Quantity			
9722 pieces per year:			
Cost per piece	$0.0253(g)	$0.215(g)	$2.75
Cost per year	$245.96	$2090.23	(h)
1504 pieces per year:			
Cost per piece	$0.0316	$0.217	$2.75
Cost per year	$47.53	$326.37	$4137.25
275 pieces per year:			
Cost per piece	$0.106	$0.239	$2.754
Cost per year	$29.15	$65.73	$757.35
3 pieces per year:			
Cost per piece	Not practical	$2.71	$3.17
Cost per year		$8.14	$9.50

(a) Quantity-cost comparison is based on the production of the idler-gear blank illustrated in the sketch at right. (b) Two-machine battery. (c) Includes standard collets, tool holders and other equipment normally furnished with machines. (d) Each machine.

(e) At $2.50 per hour. (f) One operator manned both machines. (g) Four setups per year for this quantity. (h) Completely impractical for this quantity; cost per year would be $26,735.50, and two engine lathes would be required for meeting schedule.

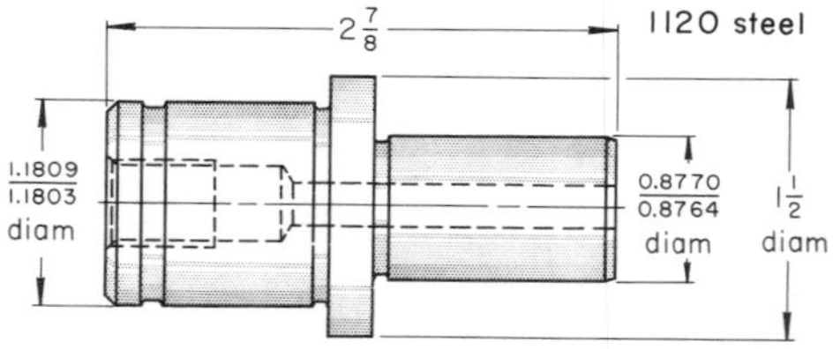

chuck can be used, thus extending the number of possible operations. One such part is described in the next example:

Example 288. Thirteen Operations in a Turret Lathe (Fig. 23)

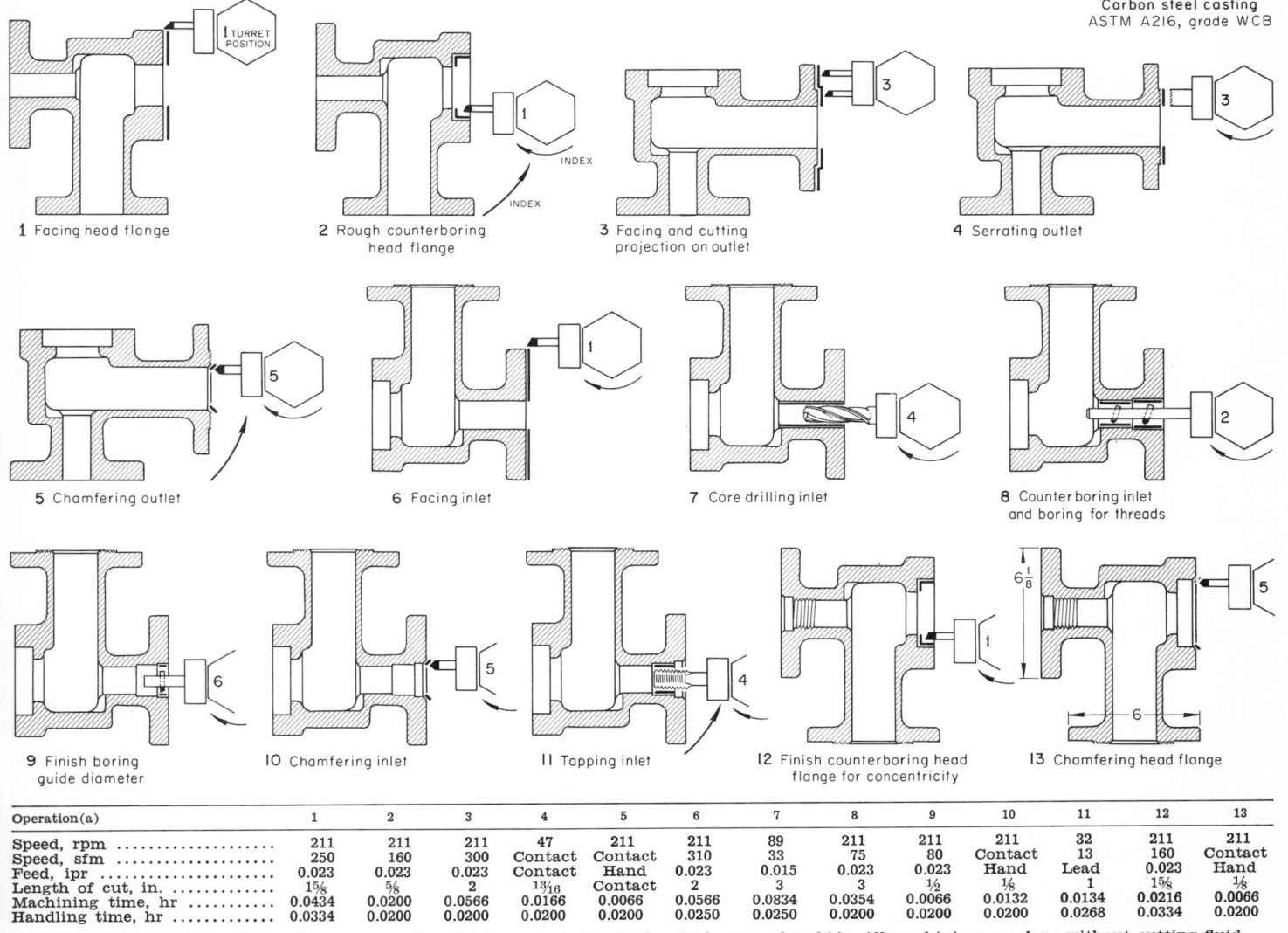

A horizontal turret lathe was used to perform 13 operations on carbon steel castings as shown in Fig. 23. The shape of these castings made it possible for all machined surfaces to be indexed around a common center, and hence they were held in a box chuck that could be indexed through 360° around a vertical axis.

Referring to Fig. 23, it is seen that from the first index position of the box chuck, two operations were performed using one turret position. In the second index position of the workpiece, two turret positions were utilized to perform three operations. Position 3 of the turret was equipped with a multiple tool holder, which held the facing tools used in operation 3 as well as the serrating tool used in operation 4.

Six operations were performed in a third index position of the workpiece, utilizing five turret positions and six tools. Turret position 4 was equipped with taper holders that allow quick changes of shank-type tools (operations 7 and 11). The workpiece was then returned to the same index position used for performing operations 1 and 2. In this final position of the workpiece, two more operations were performed from two different positions of the turret. Additional processing details are included with Fig. 23.

In many instances, where quantities are low, this same general type of part is machined on *vertical* turret lathes; however, production quantities of the part in Example 288 were sufficient to warrant the cost of fixtures and tooling, which resulted in lower processing cost and improved reproducibility.

Production Quantity

For lots of fewer than about 12 pieces, none of the machines dealt with in this article is economical. Regardless of the operations required, a lower-cost machine is more practical for machining a few pieces. Manual turret lathes are the most logical choice for lots of about 12 to 200 pieces, and are sometimes used for much larger quantities.

When lot size exceeds about 200 pieces, an automatic turret lathe (single-spindle chucking or bar machine) should be considered, especially if repeat orders for the same or similar parts are expected. Labor is markedly reduced by the use of automatic machines, because: (*a*) machining time per part is reduced to a fraction of that required on a hand-operated machine, and (*b*) even though the automatics are manually loaded and unloaded, one operator can handle two or more machines if they are ganged (placed for efficiency). Manual machines require one operator for each machine.

The lot size that warrants selection of multiple-spindle machines is often influenced more by required rate of production than by total quantity requirements, because parts can usually be produced on multiple-spindle machines two to five times as fast as on single-spindle machines. Some plants use a minimum of 100,000 parts (total) as the production quantity for which the use of multiple-spindle machines is warranted. In other plants, however, it has been found that multiple-spindle machines are justified for lot sizes of fewer than 50,000 pieces, and in some instances (see Examples 299 to 301), for even fewer than 5000 pieces.

In the following two examples, selection of machine was based on quantity.

Example 289. Multiple-Spindle Machine Warranted for 600-Piece Lots (Fig. 24)

A four-spindle automatic chucking machine was selected for the seven operations on gray iron castings shown in Fig. 24. These castings could have been machined in simpler equipment, but quantity requirements (600-piece

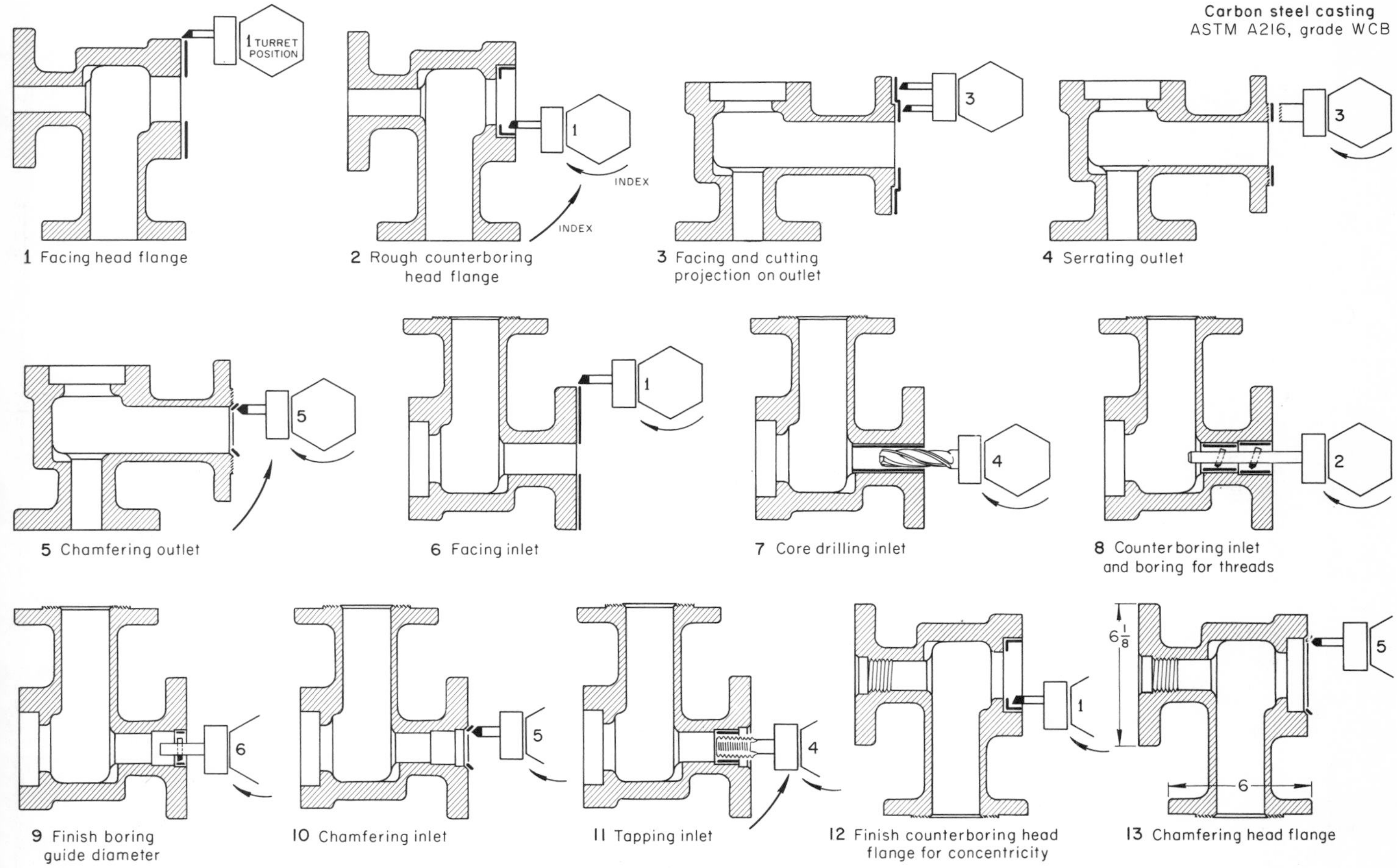

Operation(a)	1	2	3	4	5	6	7	8	9	10	11	12	13
Speed, rpm	211	211	211	47	211	211	89	211	211	211	32	211	211
Speed, sfm	250	160	300	Contact	Contact	310	33	75	80	Contact	13	160	Contact
Feed, ipr	0.023	0.023	0.023	Contact	Hand	0.023	0.015	0.023	0.023	Hand	Lead	0.023	Hand
Length of cut, in.	1⅝	⅝	2	1³⁄₁₆	Contact	2	3	3	½	⅛	1	1⅝	⅛
Machining time, hr	0.0434	0.0200	0.0566	0.0166	0.0066	0.0566	0.0834	0.0354	0.0066	0.0132	0.0134	0.0216	0.0066
Handling time, hr	0.0334	0.0200	0.0200	0.0200	0.0200	0.0250	0.0250	0.0200	0.0200	0.0200	0.0268	0.0334	0.0200

(a) Serrating tool, core drill and tap were made of high speed steel; all other tools were of carbide. All machining was done without cutting fluid.

Fig. 23. Sequence of operations for machining steel castings, held and indexed in a box chuck, in a horizontal turret lathe (Example 288)

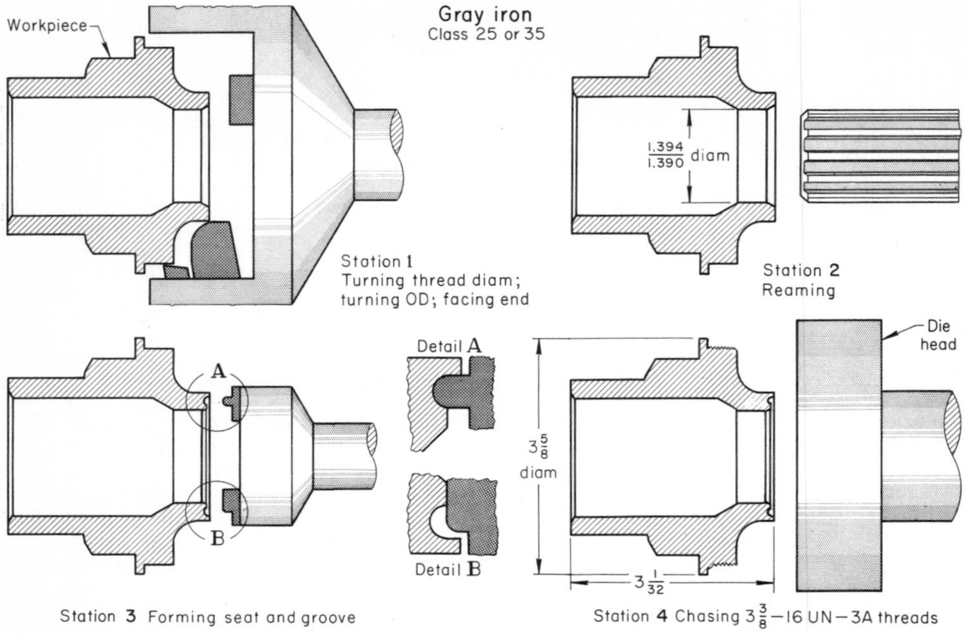

Spindle speed	105 rpm	Cutting fluid	Soluble oil
Cutting speed	38 to 93 sfm	Tool material	High speed steel
Feed	0.015 ipr	Production rate	72 pieces per hour

Fig. 24. Seven-operation machining of a gray iron casting in 600-piece lots in a four-spindle automatic chucking machine (Example 289)

lots) warranted the higher capital investment and greater setup time for the automatic machine. Electromechanical chucks with specially designed adapters were utilized for the seven cutting operations in the four stations. Processing details are included with Fig. 24.

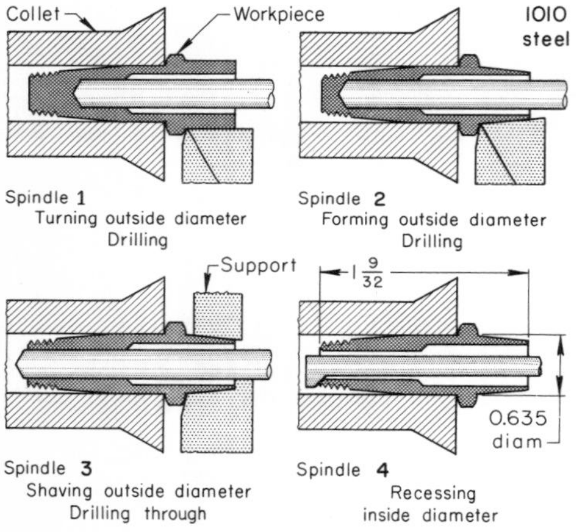

Operation(a)	Speed Rpm	Speed Sfm	Feed, ipr	Depth of cut, in.	Tool life per grind, pieces
Turning(b)	900	135	0.0011	0.015	20,000
Drilling, spindle 1	450	37	0.0034	0.250	10,000
Forming(b)	900	135	0.0011	0.030	20,000
Drilling, spindle 2	450	37	0.0034	0.218	10,000
Shaving(c)	900	135	0.0058	0.005	30,000
Drilling through	450	37	0.0027	0.170	10,000
Recessing	900	43	0.0010	0.030	10,000

(a) Spindle 5 was used for loading and unloading. Cutting fluid for all operations was mineral oil. Setup time was 8 hr; cycle time per piece was 2.8 sec. (b) Tool had 3° front and side clearance, and 25° rake on both cutting edges. (c) Tool had 10° front clearance.

Fig. 25. Use of a five-spindle automatic chucking machine for seven-operation finish machining of cold extrusions, to obtain a production rate of 1285 pieces per hour required for continuous high-quantity machining (Example 290)

Example 290. Continuous High-Quantity Machining of Cold Extrusions (Fig. 25)

To maintain the production rate necessary for continuous high-quantity machining, a five-spindle automatic chucker was used for seven-operation finish machining of cold extruded adapters, as shown in Fig. 25. Threads (¼–18 NPTF) on these parts were rolled in a prior operation.

Because the 1010 steel from which these adapters were extruded is inherently soft and "gummy", special attention was given to tools and cutting fluid, to obtain acceptable dimensional accuracy and surface finish. All tools were made of T15 high speed steel and kept extremely sharp; tools for turning, forming and shaving were specially ground as noted in the data accompanying Fig. 25. Mineral oil was used instead of soluble oil as the cutting fluid.

The following example presents the results of a study of the relation between production quantity and cost for machining the same part on three different types of machines:

Example 291. Quantity vs Cost (Table 3)
(Multiple-spindle automatics compared with turret lathe and engine lathe)

Fifteen operations were required for machining from 1½-in. bar the idler-gear blank shown in Table 3. When required in a quantity of 9722 pieces per year, these parts were produced in a battery of two six-spindle automatic bar machines manned by one operator. Because of an engineering change, annual requirement dropped first to 1504 pieces and subsequently still lower. A study was made of cost-quantity relations to determine which type of machine and method would produce these parts at the lowest cost for the reduced quantities required. The resulting data, presented in Table 3, compare cost of producing four different quantities on three types of machines — the multiple-spindle automatics, a bar-stock manual turret lathe, and an engine lathe.

The turret lathe is more economical than the engine lathe for quantities of only three parts; thus, an engine lathe would be practical only for occasional, emergency production. It was also surprising to find that for quantities as low as 275 pieces the six-spindle automatics yielded lower labor and setup costs per piece than did the turret lathe. However, the cost figures in Table 3 do not reflect machine burden; thus, availability of machine time and tooling would determine the economic advisability of using the six-spindle automatics for such a low production quantity.

Production Rate

Quantity and productivity are often of equal importance in the selection of methods for machining (see Example 290). In many applications, however, the rate at which a given part must be produced has a greater influence on selection of machine and method than total quantity requirements. For instance, assuming a total lot size of 100,000 specific pieces, if only 1000 per day were needed and a manual turret lathe were available, it might well be advisable to utilize existing equipment. On the other hand, if 5000 pieces per day were needed and could not be produced on existing equipment, single-spindle automatic chucking or bar machines (as required by product form) would be considered; and for higher productivity, multiple-spindle machines would be the logical choice.

In some plants the availability of floor space is a major factor, thus emphasizing the selection of equipment that can produce the greatest number of parts in the least space. Sometimes

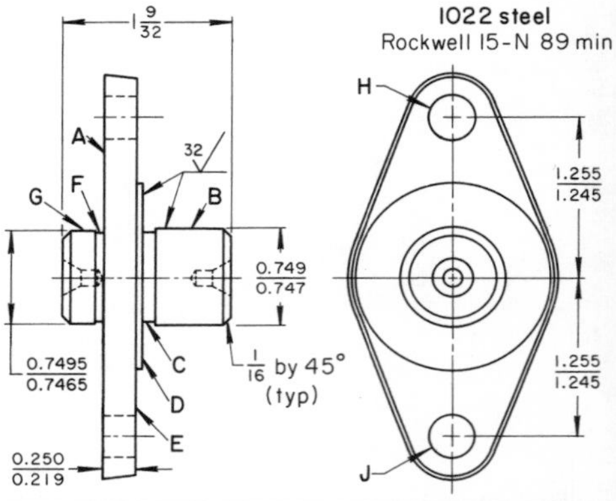

Manual turret lathe(a)	Automatic turret lathes(b)
Sequence of Operations(c)	
First Chucking:	*First Chucking:*
Rough face A	Face E
Rough turn, chamfer G	Rough turn, chamfer B
Turn groove F	Face D
Finish face A	Finish turn B
Center drill H	Burnish B and D
Second Chucking:	*Second Chucking:*
Face E	Rough face A
Rough turn, chamfer B	Rough turn, chamfer G
Face D	Finish turn G
Turn groove C	Finish face A
Finish turn B	Drill H and J
Center drill J	
Secondary Operations:	*Secondary Operations:*
Drill H and J	NONE. Center drilling not required. Grooves not cut because grinding was replaced by burnishing, finish turning.
Grind G	
Grind B and D	
Production Rate	
11.5 pieces per hour(d)	27.7 pieces per hour(e)

(a) One machine manned by one operator. (b) Two machines manned by one operator. (c) On both machines, a 20-to-1 mixture of water and soluble oil was used as the cutting fluid. Tool life per grind was as follows: rough facing, 45 pieces; finish facing, 70 pieces; turning, 100 pieces. (d) Parts still required deburring and grinding, which added 3.78 min per piece. (e) Completely machined.

Fig. 26. Change from manual turret lathe to two automatic turret lathes more than doubled production rate for this forging and eliminated secondary operations. (Example 292)

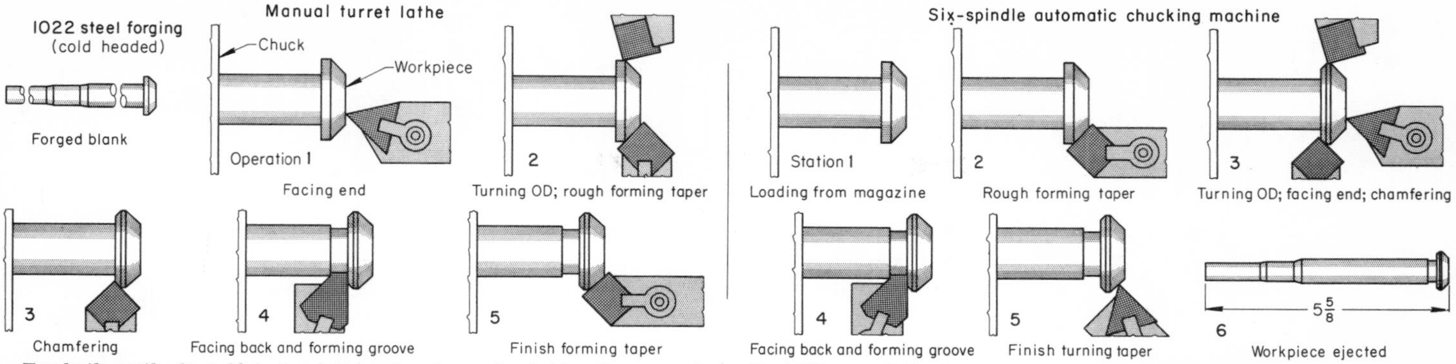

For both methods, a 20-to-1 mixture of water and soluble oil was used as cutting fluid, and tools had indexable, disposable carbide inserts. Tool life was 1200 pieces per edge. Labor cost per piece machined on the turret lathe was $1.67; on the six-spindle chucking machine, $0.33.

Fig. 27. Production rate was increased, from 83 to 970 pieces per hour, by changing from a manual turret lathe (upper sequence) to a six-spindle automatic chucking machine (lower sequence) for seven-operation machining of cold headed steel spindles. (Example 293)

productivity requirements are based directly on shipments, or on other manufacturing operations, which are often interdependent.

The following two examples describe applications in which equipment and machining procedures were changed to increase productivity (see also Example 285 and Table 2).

Example 292. Change From Manual to Automatic Turret Lathes (Fig. 26)

When bearing studs forged from 1022 steel were machined in two chuckings in a manual turret lathe to the size and shape shown in Fig. 26, three secondary operations were required for complete machining. As the comparison tabulated below Fig. 26 shows, a change to the use of two single-spindle automatic turret lathes not only increased production rate, but also allowed complete machining of these forgings in two chuckings without the need for secondary operations. To accomplish this, the procedure was altered to incorporate roller burnishing and finish turning, which eliminated the need for secondary grinding operations (and made it unnecessary to turn relief grooves for grinding). Also, a special drill head permitted through drilling of the flange holes in the second chucking (replacing the former practice of center drilling and subsequent through drilling).

Production requirements warranted the use of two automatic machines, and by the revised sequence of operations, one man could operate two machines. In addition to increasing productivity, the change of machines also reduced the tool inventory and material handling.

Example 293. Change From Manual Turret Lathe to Multiple-Spindle Chucker (Fig. 27)

Originally, a manual turret lathe was used for the seven operations with six cutting tools on cold headed steel spindles shown in the sequence at left in Fig. 27. As production requirements increased, the job was moved to a six-spindle automatic chucking machine (sequence at right in Fig. 27). The change in method increased productivity nearly twelvefold, from 83 to 970 pieces per hour, although it produced no significant cost savings in tooling or tool life.

The increase in productivity resulted not only because of the increase in number of spindles, but also because the multiple-spindle machine was equipped with an automatic handling mechanism, which in itself resulted in a saving of 0.199 min per piece. When the turret lathe was used, much of the gaging and work handling was necessarily done while the machine was idle. With the multiple-spindle machine, some of this work was done by the operator during the cycle.

Special Requirements

Special requirements or unique workpieces often govern the selection of a specific type of machine. For instance, for 6-ft-long tubular parts that require several identical machining operations on each end, a bar machine is a logical choice because the workpiece can be loaded through the back of the headstock and machined on one end, then reversed and machined on the opposite end — a two-stage operation.

The obvious economies made possible by this type of procedure are often important enough to warrant the designing (or redesigning) of parts to be compatible with such processing.

Required dimensional accuracy often influences the choice between a single-spindle and a multiple-spindle bar or chucking machine. Machine condition and other factors being equal, closer tolerances can be held in a single-spindle machine because it is inherently more rigid. This results mainly from the absence of a spindle carrier, which is a source of inaccuracy in the multiple-spindle machines. In multiple-spindle bar machines, moreover, the weight of heavy bar stock fed into the spindles can be an additional source of inaccuracy.

Special tooling, together with careful choice of machines and procedures, often makes possible the production of special shapes or machining to unusual dimensional accuracy, or both, as in the following example:

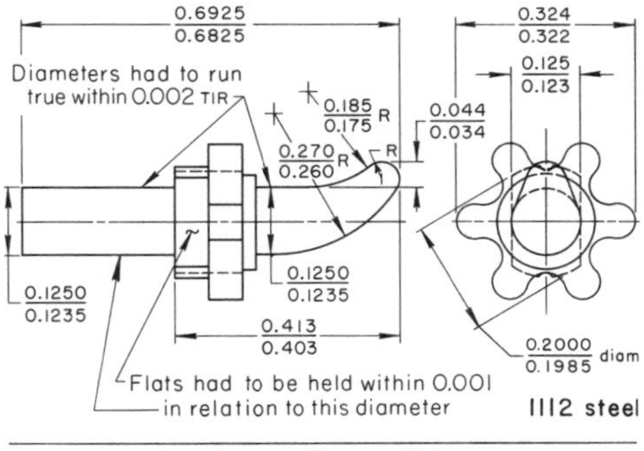

Sequence of Operations

1 Feed stock	5 Bend end
2 Rough turn	6 Mill flats
3 Rough point	7 Form
4 Finish point	8 Cut off

Processing Details

Speed	2260 rpm (192 sfm)
Feed	0.001 ipr
Cutting fluid	Thread-grinding oil(a)
Production rate	65 pieces per hour

(a) One part heavy thread-grinding oil (75% fat, 15% sulfur), mixed with four parts mineral oil having a viscosity of 100 SUS.

Fig. 28. Complex part machined to close tolerances from profile stock in a single-spindle automatic bar machine (Example 294)

Example 294. Milling and Bending in an Automatic Bar Machine (Fig. 28)

The workpiece illustrated in Fig. 28 was completely machined from profile stock on a single-spindle automatic bar machine, in the sequence of operations tabulated with the illustration.

It was found that the close tolerances specified for this part were easier to hold by completing the operations on one machine than by the use of separate machines for turning, milling and bending.

To produce this part on an automatic bar machine, three special devices were required:

1. A spindle-stopping device to locate and hold the part in the collet in definite relation to the centerline of the gear teeth (profile-stock shape)
2. A special bending tool, on the turret, to reshape the tapered end after turning
3. One open cross-slide position on which to mount a special milling attachment that must clear all turret tools.

A special spindle-stopping attachment was developed that utilized the longitudinal "gear teeth" of the profile stock to position the stock in the collet and to stop spindle rotation in a specific position with reference to the gear teeth.

The bending fixture was a two-piece forming die that had taper on the outer edges. Forward movement of the die halves was provided by the turret cam. As the dies moved forward, they were forced inward as they moved along the taper on their outer edges, thus forming the end section of the part.

For the milling operation, an air cylinder was linked with the rear slide holding a special milling attachment. The cylinder provided the necessary movement to retract the milling attachment far enough to clear all turret tools. Because both cross slides were occupied for milling and forming, cutoff was done by a tool attached to the vertical slide.

A choice between a manual and an automatic machine usually is influenced by considerations other than the type of operations each can perform. There are, however, applications in which one type of machine is preferable to the other because it is better suited to a specific operation. For instance, automatic turret lathes are preferable for workpieces that require taper boring. Although taper boring attachments can be obtained for manual turret lathes, they are seldom available with standard tooling, whereas on a single-spindle automatic tapers can be formed with a quill-mounted single-point boring tool:

Example 295. Boring Tapers in a Single-Spindle Automatic (Fig. 29)

Figure 29 shows the sequence of operations and gives processing details for machining a 12⅞-lb gray iron fan-drive sheave in a single-

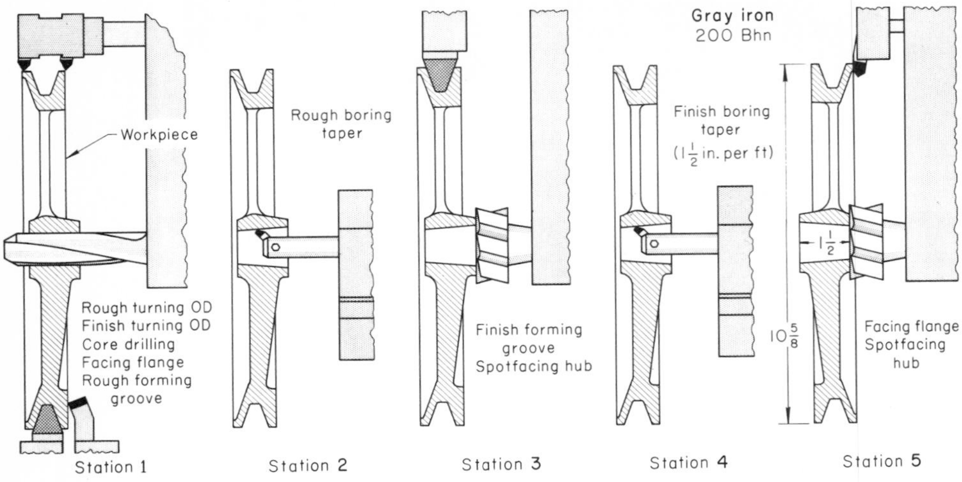

Station(a)	1	2	3	4	5
Speed, rpm	90	496	54	496	54
Speed, sfm	250 (turning) 44 (drilling)	225	150 (turning) 25 (spotfacing)	225	150 (turning) 25 (spotfacing)
Feed, ipr	0.009	0.006	0.009	0.006	0.009

(a) Tools in all stations were of carbide, except high speed steel core drill and spotfacers. Soluble oil was used as cutting fluid. With cycle time of 9.076 min, production rate was 6.6 pieces per hour. Setup time was 6 hr.

Fig. 29. Use of a single-spindle automatic chucking machine for machining of fan-drive sheaves in 11 operations, including taper boring (Example 295)

spindle automatic chucker. As shown, a total of 11 tools were used — eight from the five-station turret and three from cross slides — and the workpiece was rechucked after station 4, to permit two final facing operations from turret tools.

Rough and finish boring of the taper (stations 2 and 4) were the most difficult of the operations performed. The use of a taper reamer resulted in unacceptable results in terms of tolerance, concentricity and finish. Satisfactory results were obtained with quill-mounted single-point tools (Fig. 29).

Machining to close tolerances or to obtain close relations between dimensions may require careful selection of machine and the use of special procedures, as in Examples 904 and 905, in the article on Machining of Aluminum. [Other applications in which required accuracy determined machine selection are Example 773 in the article on Machining of Stainless Steel (a turret lathe was chosen over a single-spindle automatic) and Example 959 in the article on Machining of Copper (a single-spindle automatic was used).]

For machining of small parts that require concentricity of two or more diameters (as in the two examples that follow), a single-spindle machine is usually preferred to a multiple-spindle machine regardless of quantity to be produced, because of the inaccuracies that inherently result from performing successive operations at different index positions of the spindles.

Examples 296 and 297. Single-Spindle Machines for Concentricity

Example 296 (Fig. 30). A single-spindle bar machine was selected for producing small shafts in the operations illustrated and detailed in Fig. 30, mainly because of its ability to maintain specified concentricity of 0.004 in. TIR in turning (see inset between operations 2 and 3 in Fig. 30). As an aid in maintaining this concentricity, the spindle was adjusted to within 0.0002-in. runout while cold.

As Fig. 30 also shows, two methods were used to prevent the shaft from bending because of excessive overhang: (*a*) the stock was fed out from the collet in two steps (operations 1 and 5), and (*b*) a V-support was used in operation 2, support rollers were used in operation 4 and carbide female end supports were used in operations 7 and 8.

Example 297 (Fig. 31). Because of the need to maintain concentricity within 0.003 in. TIR between diameters of the shaft illustrated in Fig. 31, a single-spindle bar machine was used. As an aid in maintaining concentricity, the machine spindle was adjusted to within 0.0002-in. runout while cold.

The sequence of operations used for machining these workpieces is illustrated in Fig. 31, and processing details are given with the illustration. When required to hold concentricities on two or more diameters of small parts such as illustrated in Fig. 31, it is almost mandatory to form them simultaneously in one feed (operations 1 and 4). Referring to Fig. 31, it is seen that operations 1 and 2 were completed before the bar was fed into position, thus taking advantage of the greater rigidity for forming and knurling the end. Carbide bushings were used for workpiece support during other operations, as indicated; high speed steel bushings were not satisfactory because they galled.

(The use of a turret lathe for machining to close concentricity is described in Example 906, in the article on Machining of Aluminum Alloys.)

Cost

When two or more types of machines can produce acceptable parts, cost per piece usually determines the final choice. Machining cost per piece is influenced most by cost of setup, cost of labor, and burden (amortization) of machine and tools. High-production machines always cost more to set up than simpler machines, but for long runs the cost of setup is rapidly absorbed. As the number of pieces required increases, the cost per piece decreases. Also, labor costs are lower when one operator can attend two or more machines.

As production capabilities of machines increase, however, so do the initial cost of the machines and the cost of tooling. Thus, prior calculations that indicate that specific parts can be produced at lower cost on expensive, high-

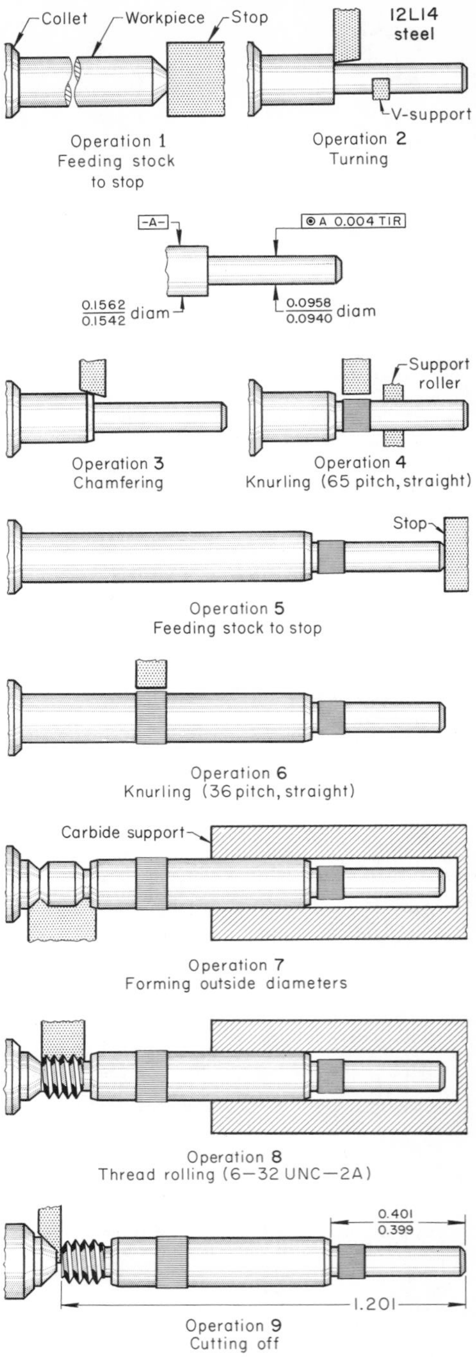

Speed	6100 rpm (245 sfm max)
Feed:	
Operation 2	0.003 ipr
Operation 3	0.001 ipr
Operation 4 and 6	0.001 ipr
Operation 7	0.0012 ipr
Operation 8	0.006 ipr
Operation 9	0.0015 ipr
Cutting fluid	Lard oil
Setup time	5.2 hr
Cycle time per piece	7 sec
Production rate	514 pieces per hour
Tool life, pieces per grind(a):	
Turning (box tool)	16,000 to 20,000
Chamfering	20,000 to 25,000
Knurling	100,000 to 150,000
Forming	7,000 to 10,000
Thread rolling	125,000 to 175,000
Cutting off	5,000 to 7,000

(a) All tools were made of high speed steel except the box tool used for turning, which had a carbide-tipped blade.

Fig. 30. Use of a single-spindle automatic bar machine for producing shafts requiring close concentricity of two diameters (Example 296)

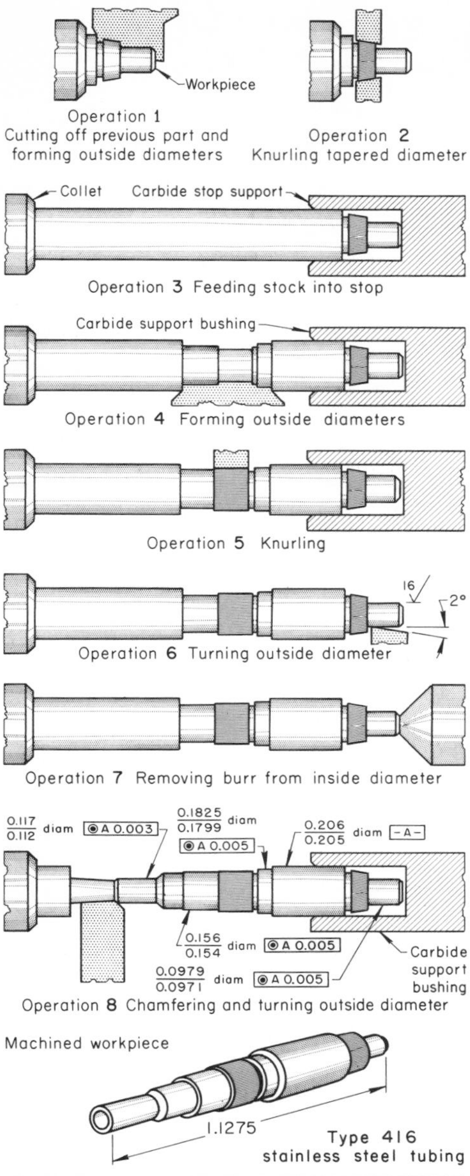

Speed	3600 rpm (203 sfm)
Feed, ipr:	
Cutoff and form (operation 1)	0.0006
Knurl (operation 2):	
On feed	0.0040
Off feed	0.0080
Forming ODs (operation 4)	0.0004
Turning ODs (operation 6)	0.0020
Countersink hole (operation 7)	0.0010
Slide tool (operation 8)	0.0005
Lead cam (operation 8)	0.0020
Cutting fluid	Lard oil
Setup time	8 hr
Cycle time per piece	29 sec
Production rate	124 pieces per hour
Tool life, pieces per grind(a):	
Cutoff, forming (operation 1)	1400 to 1600
Knurling:	
Operation 2(b)	4500 to 5000
Operation 5(c)	12,000 to 15,000
Forming (operation 4)	1200 to 1400
Turning (operation 6)	7000 to 10,000
Chamfering, turning (operation 8)	2500 to 3000

(a) Forming and cutoff tools were made of solid carbide, and had 5° top rake. Turning tools were carbide tipped. Knurling tools: straight knurl, 50 to 60 pitch. Support tools were bushed with carbide. (b) Done with straddle knurls in a fixed position moving axially into the piece; lead edge of knurls took brunt of work load. (c) Plunge cut from vertical-slide tool operating radially with full width of knurl contacting the workpiece.

Fig. 31. Machining to close concentricities in a single-spindle automatic bar machine (Example 297)

production equipment may prove erroneous unless machine burden is taken into account. This is most likely to occur when the quantity of one specific part available for a run at one time is borderline and more frequent setups are required, thus involving more setup time and downtime of the machine. Full value of highly automatic multiple-operation machines can be realized only when they are operating for a major portion of the time.

Cost studies are often made to determine break points that indicate which of two or more machines and procedures will prove the most economical for specific lot sizes. Results of one cost study are reported in Example 291 and Table 3 (page 158); other cost studies are detailed in the five examples that follow. Note, however, that all these examples compare only setup and labor costs for the use of different types of machines for specific parts; in none is machine amortization considered.

Example 298. Manual Turret Lathe vs Single-Spindle Automatic (Fig. 32)

An analysis was made in one plant to determine the quantity break point above which it would be more economical to use a single-spindle automatic bar machine instead of a manual turret lathe for producing valve-disk holders from 304 stainless steel bar stock. Results are plotted in Fig. 32. This comparison, which is based on setup and labor costs for the two machines, shows the turret lathe to be more economical for machining fewer than 56 pieces. Above this quantity, the single-spindle automatic becomes progressively more economical, until at 10,000 pieces the cost-per-piece levels off at 34¢ for the automatic machine vs 80¢ for the turret lathe.

Example 299. Manual Turret Lathe vs Single-Spindle Automatic vs Six-Spindle Automatic (Table 4)

Table 4 presents cost and other data comparing the use of three machines for producing small yoke hubs from ⅜-in. cold drawn bar stock of leaded 1112 steel.

Although it cost $7.50 more to set up the single-spindle automatic than the manual turret lathe, parts produced on the automatic cost $1.176 less per hundred than on the lathe. By dividing $7.50 by $1.176 and multiplying the result (6.38) by 100, it is seen that for lot sizes of fewer than 638 of these parts, the manual turret lathe was more economical than the single-spindle automatic.

Similarly, although it cost $6.60 more to set up the six-spindle automatic than the single-spindle machine, the six-spindle machine produced parts at $0.135 less per 100 than the single-spindle machine. Dividing $6.60 by $0.135 and multiplying the result by 100

Table 4. Comparison of Costs of Producing the Same Part in Three Different Types of Machine (Example 299) (a)

Item	Manual turret lathe	Single-spindle automatic	Six-spindle automatic
Machines per operator	1	5	3
Pieces machined per hour	125	232	1125
Setup time, hr	1.2	3.7	5.9
Setup cost(b)	$3.60	$11.10	$17.70
Cost per 100 pieces(c)	$1.40	$0.224	$0.089

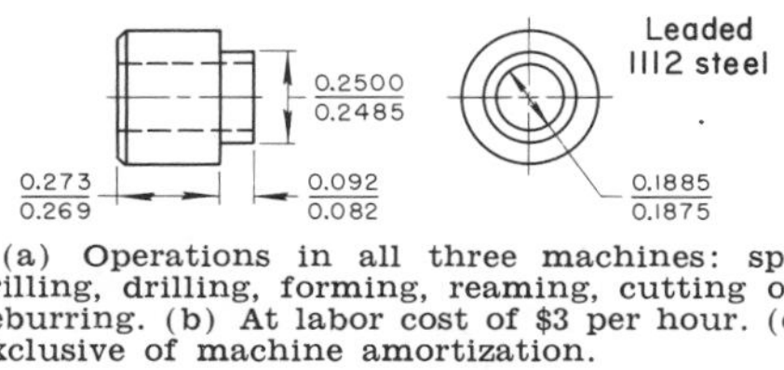

(a) Operations in all three machines: spot drilling, drilling, forming, reaming, cutting off, deburring. (b) At labor cost of $3 per hour. (c) Exclusive of machine amortization.

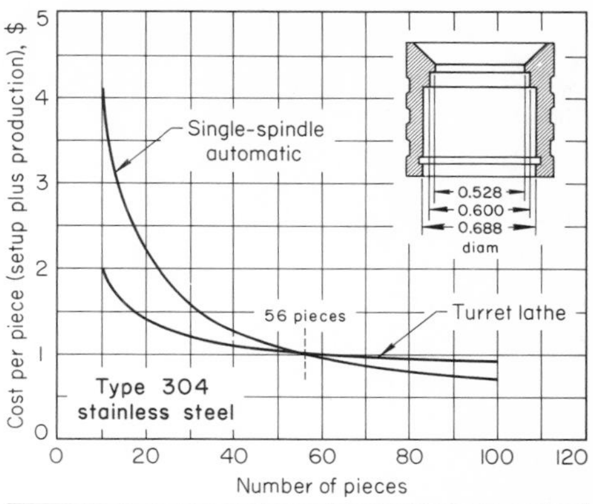

Item	Turret lathe	Single-spindle automatic
Setup time, hr	1.6	5
Setup cost(a)	$12.03	$37.60
Production time per piece, hr	0.106	0.045
Production cost per piece(a)(b)	$0.797	$0.338

(a) At $7.52 per hour ($2.35 per hour for labor, plus $5.17 per hour for overhead at factor of 220%). (b) For 10,000 pieces.

Although done in slightly different sequences, operations on both machines included turning, facing, drilling, boring the three diameters dimensioned in sketch above, forming the internal groove and the grooves on the outside diameter, and cutting off.

Fig. 32. Effect of quantity on cost per piece for machining valve-disk holders in a manual turret lathe and a single-spindle automatic bar machine (Example 298)

shows that the single-spindle machine was more economical than the six-spindle machine for lot sizes of fewer than about 4900 parts.

From these calculations based on the data in Table 4, it is evident that the manual turret lathe was the most economical for producing this part in quantities below about 650, the single-spindle automatic for 650 to about 5000, and the six-spindle automatic for 5000 or more.

Examples 300, 301 and 302. Single-Spindle vs Six-Spindle Automatics (Table 5)

Manufacturing and cost data are compared in Table 5 for single-spindle and six-spindle automatic machines producing each of the three parts shown in the inset illustration. From the differences between setup costs and costs per 100 pieces for the two types of machines in each of these examples, and using the method of calculation detailed in Example 299, it is seen that economic break points are:

Example 300	3350 pieces
Example 301	4600
Example 302	9900

These points represent the quantities below which a single-spindle machine, and above which a six-spindle machine, would produce the respective parts more economically.

Tool Material and Design

In multiple-operation machining, changes are often made in tool material or design that improve tool life, workpiece finish, dimensional accuracy, or productivity. When operations are done in a sequence, it is common for one tool to be abused by being run at excessive speed or feed, or both, in order to obtain greater efficiency from other tools that operate in the sequence.

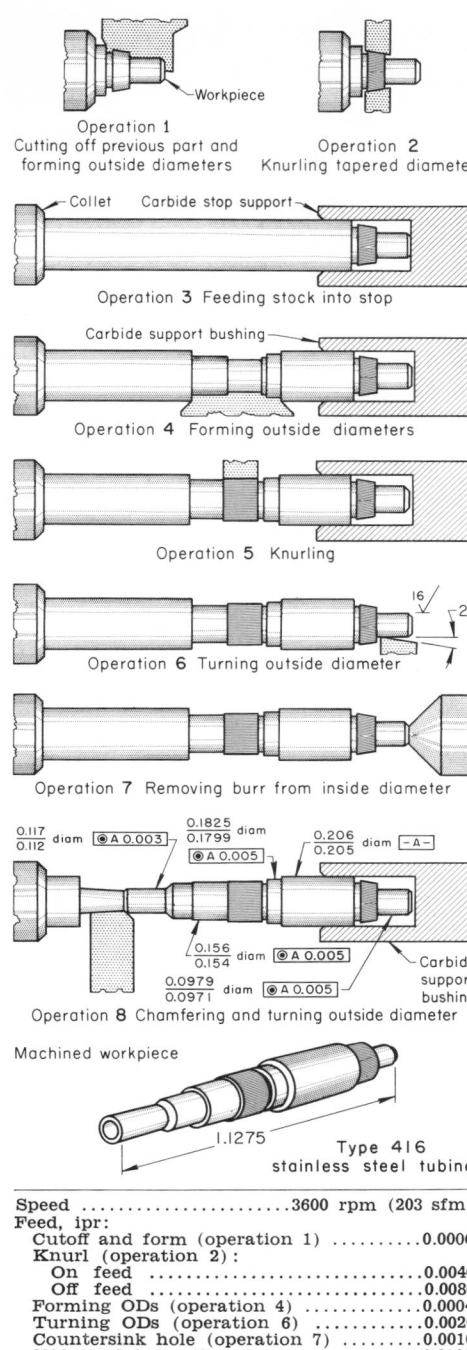

Because form tools usually are subjected to rigorous service, they are often made from some material that is more highly alloyed than a general-purpose type of high speed steel. In some plants, the established practice is to use general-purpose types of high speed steel

Table 5. Costs of Using Single-Spindle vs Six-Spindle Automatic for Producing Three Different Parts (Examples 300, 301 and 302)

Item	Example 300		Example 301		Example 302	
	Single-spindle(a)	Six-spindle(b)	Single-spindle(c)	Six-spindle(b)	Single-spindle(a)	Six-spindle(b)
Speed, rpm	1150	1293	745	717	1135	1160
Speed, sfm	188(d)	211(e)	102	98	223	228
Production per hour, pieces	90	450	60	170	172	450
Setup time, hr	5.5	9.8	4.2	9.1	5.0	8.5
Setup cost(f)	$16.50	$29.40	$12.60	$27.30	$15.00	$25.50
Cost per 100 pieces(g)	$ 0.58	$ 0.195	$ 0.85	$ 0.53	$ 0.301	$ 0.195

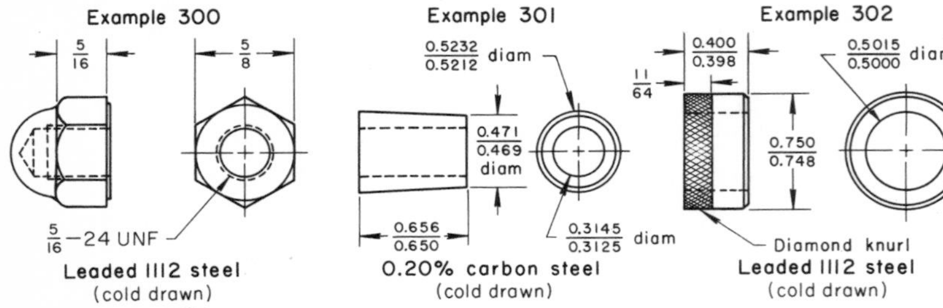

(a) Machine cost $11,500. (b) Machine cost $16,800. (c) Machine cost $7835. (d) On outside diameter. Speed in tapping was 94 sfm. (e) On outside diameter. Speed in tapping was 106 sfm. (f) At labor cost of $3 per hr. (g) Exclusive of machine amortization.

for form tools, changing to a cobalt-containing grade only when specific experience indicates the necessity. Metal being machined is a major factor in selecting form-tool material. For cutting difficult-to-machine metals, such as stainless steels, form tools made from the more highly alloyed types of high speed steel are nearly always superior, as in the following example:

Example 303. M3 vs M30 High Speed Steel for Form Turning (Fig. 33)

Circular form tools made of M30 high speed steel had 100% greater life in roughing, and about 50% greater life in finishing, than M3 circular form tools, in producing the stainless steel part shown in Fig. 33 from 1$\frac{3}{16}$-in. diameter stock. Pieces machined per grind were as follows:

	M3	M30
Roughing	22	44
Finishing	15	22

Tools of both materials were operated under identical conditions.

The following example describes an application in which it proved advantageous to replace cast cobalt-base alloy tools with highly alloyed high speed steel tools, despite higher initial cost.

Example 304. Cobalt-Base Alloy vs T15 High Speed Steel for Form Tools (Fig. 34)

Production of the push rod illustrated in Fig. 34 from 1144 steel bar stock (hardness, 30 to 35 Rc) entailed the use of 2-in.-wide form tools in the area indicated. An eight-spindle bar machine was used; cycle time was 14 sec. At 165 sfm and 0.0014-ipr feed, excessive wear (not burning) of the cast Co-Cr-W alloy form tools originally used (cost, $40 each) resulted in poor tool life (600 pieces per grind), and low production efficiency (69.9%) because of downtime for tool changes.

Changing to form tools made of T15 high speed steel (cost, $50 each), operated at the same speed and feed, resulted in a tool-life increase of 300% (2400 pieces per grind), and, because of the decrease in tool-change downtime, increased production efficiency to 83.3%.

Carbide is used for cutting edges on many tools for multiple-operation machining. Sometimes, reselection of carbide grade has a significant effect on results, as in the following example:

Example 305. Surface Finish Improved by Changing Grades of Carbide (Fig. 35)

The 0.749/0.747-in. diameter of the 1022 steel forging illustrated in Fig. 35 required a turned finish that could be burnished to a maximum roughness of 32 micro-in. Turning was done in a single-spindle chucker using triangular indexable carbide inserts.

Inserts made from a conventional grade of tungsten carbide formed built-up edges, resulting in score marks that made it impossible to meet surface-finish requirements. Changing to inserts made from titanium carbide corrected this difficulty. Both types of inserts were used under identical conditions, as detailed in the tabulation with Fig. 35, except for the difference in nose radius. However, both $\frac{1}{32}$ and $\frac{1}{64}$-in. nose radii were tried with the conventional carbide, but finish was unsatisfactory.

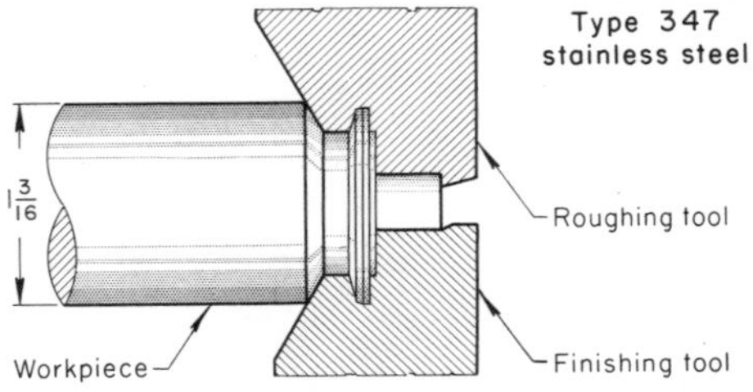

Fig. 33. Forming operation in which tool life was increased by changing from M3 to M30 high speed steel tools (Example 303)

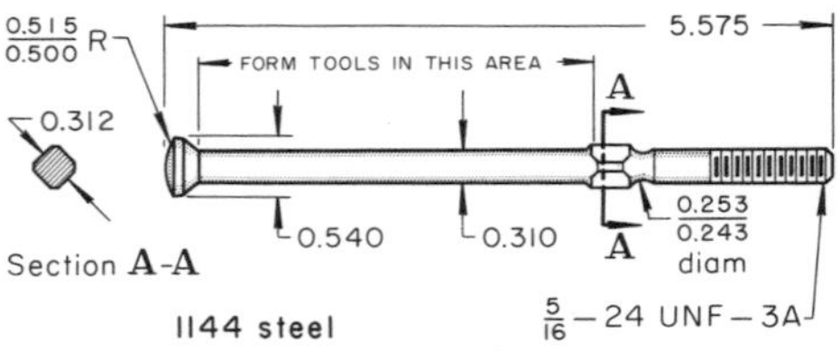

Fig. 34. Push rod for which change from cast-alloy to T15 high speed steel form tools resulted in increased tool life and production efficiency (Example 304)

Changing the design and the method of mounting carbide tools often results in increased productivity or increased tool life, as demonstrated in the two examples that follow:

Examples 306 and 307. Positive-Rake Brazed, vs Negative-Rake Indexable Insert, Carbide Tools

Example 306 (Fig. 36). A change was made from positive-rake brazed carbide tools to negative-rake indexable throwaway carbide inserts, for turning and facing 1.2-lb forged 1045 steel gear blanks (200 to 220 Bhn) in an 8-in., 5-hp single-spindle automatic turret lathe (Fig. 36). As shown in the comparison of tool and processing details tabulated below Fig. 36, the change resulted in about a 75% reduction in machining time per piece. This was made possible because with the insert tools higher speeds could be used and downtime for tool change was decreased.

Example 307 (Fig. 37). Bevel-gear blanks cold headed from 1022 steel (180 to 200 Bhn) and weighing 0.28 lb were grooved and back faced as shown in Fig. 37, in a six-spindle automatic chucking machine. The tool originally used was made by brazing a carbide tip to a holder and had a 5° positive rake (see Fig. 37). Changing to indexable triangular disposable inserts of the same grade of carbide but with a 3° negative rake (see Fig. 37) resulted in greatly increased tool life, and also decreased tool cost and downtime for tool change. Comparative data for the two types of tools are presented in the table accompanying Fig. 37.

Soft non-free-machining steels like 1008 or 1010 are not preferred for high-production, multiple-operation machining, because they are susceptible to tearing, and excessive amounts of burr are probable. When it is necessary to machine these steels, special attention must be paid to the design of the cutting tools used (see Example 290 and Fig. 25, page 160). Often, minor changes in tool design are effective, as shown in the following example:

Example 308. Redesign of Form Tool (Fig. 38)

Form cutting on a 25-hp multiple-spindle chucker with the tool shown in Fig. 38(a) produced an excessive amount of burr on the hexagonal portion of a 1010 steel workpiece. Redesigning the tool to provide it with a 25° hook angle, as shown in Fig. 38(b), eliminated the burr problem. Changing the tool material from high speed steel to carbide increased tool life at the same speed and feed by 400%.

Machinability and Physical Condition of Work Metal

Metals are usually selected because of required mechanical properties rather than for their machinability. In many applications, however, minor changes

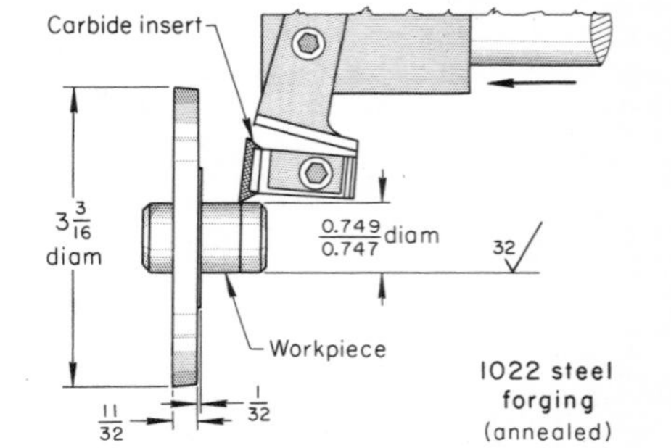

Insert Material(a)

Original	Conventional tungsten carbide
Revised	Special titanium carbide

Processing Details
(For inserts of both materials)

Speed	1564 rpm (307 sfm)
Feed	0.006 ipr
Cutting fluid	Soluble-oil:water (1:20)
Production rate	27.6 pieces per hour
Tool life per edge	100 pieces

(a) Inserts of both materials were triangular ($\frac{1}{4}$-in. IC), with negative rake. Original insert had $\frac{1}{32}$-in. nose radius; revised insert, $\frac{1}{64}$ in. $\frac{1}{64}$-in. nose radius was tried with original insert also, but finish was unsatisfactory.

Fig. 35. Turning operation in which score marks were eliminated by changing from a tungsten carbide to a titanium carbide insert (Example 305)

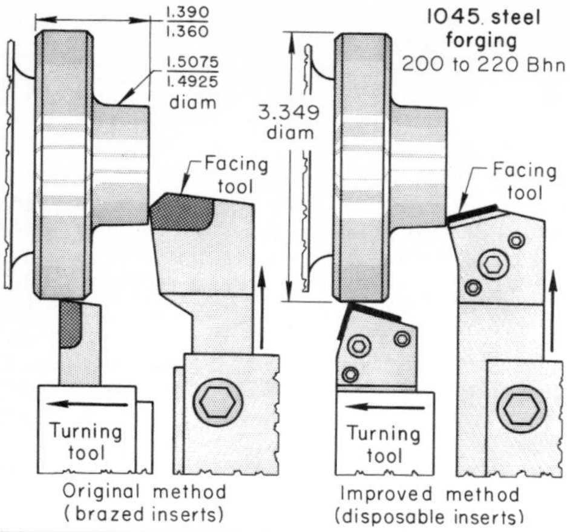

Item	Brazed inserts Turning	Brazed inserts Facing	Disposable inserts Turning	Disposable inserts Facing
Tool Details(a)				
Rake angle	6°	5°	−5°	−5°
Lead angle	8°	45°	15°	15°
Nose radius, in. ..	1/16	1/16	3/64	3/64
Processing Details(b)				
Speed, rpm	366	504	818	818
Speed, sfm	322	200	750	325
Feed, ipr	0.007	0.0045	0.006	0.006
Depth of cut, in. ..	0.076	0.063	0.076	0.063
Tool life per grind or edge, pieces ..	50	50	95	150
Downtime for tool change, min	5	5	1	1
Cycle time, min ..	0.29	0.51	0.22	0.15

(a) Both types of tools were made from the same grade of carbide. (b) Soluble oil (in 20-to-1 mixture with water) was used as cutting fluid with both types of tools.

Fig. 36. Change in tool design and method of mounting that increased productivity (Example 306)

can be made in metal selection that will favorably affect machinability without impairing service performance.

Free-Machining Metals. Many steels and some nonferrous metals are available as free-machining grades. These are similar in composition to the non-free-machining grades except that they contain small, measured additions of sulfur, phosphorus, lead, tellurium, selenium or bismuth, singly or in combination. The purpose of these additions is to promote better chip breakage and to minimize friction between tools and work metal, thereby permitting the use of higher speeds and contributing to improved tool life, better surface finish and greater control of dimensions.

The free-machining grades are especially desirable in multiple-operation machining, because of the numerous tools involved. In most instances, each type of tool has its own optimum speed, but, when several operations are performed simultaneously, some tools are operated at excessive speeds while others are operated too slowly for efficient performance. Free-machining work metals contribute markedly to minimizing the sensitivity of tools to higher cutting speeds.

Free-machining metals cost more than their non-free-machining counterparts (for steel, the extra cost for free-machining grades is usually $0.75 to $1.50 per hundred pounds), and because cost per part is significant, it is essential to balance the added cost of the metal against the decreased cost of machining before deciding to use a free-machining grade. In many applications, the amount of machining to be done (number of operations or weight of metal removed, or both) has a large influence on whether or not the higher cost for free-machining grades is warranted. For instance, if only two or three operations were utilized to reduce the volume of a steel bar by 10% in producing a finished part, the extra cost for a free-machining steel probably would not be warranted. On the other hand, if ten or more operations were utilized to reduce the volume of a bar by 50% in producing a finished part, a free-machining grade probably *would* be warranted. Thus, each workpiece design requires individual consideration, even when there are no specific restrictions on the use of free-machining grades. Metal cost, machining cost and machine capacity must all be considered simultaneously.

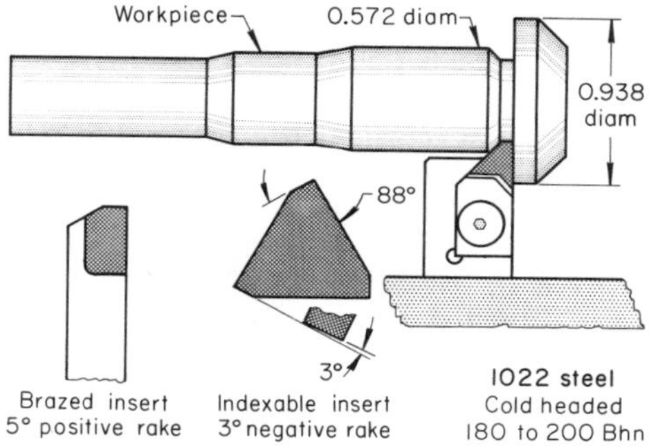

Conditions for Both Tools

Speed ....2630 rpm (640 sfm)
Feed ....0.0033 ipr
Depth of cut ....1/32 in. max
Cutting fluid ....Soluble-oil:water (1:20)
Production rate ....970 pieces per hour

Comparison	Brazed insert	Indexable insert
Tool life, pieces	300(a)	1200(b)
Tool-change time, min ..	5	1.012
Tool cost per piece	$0.0005	$0.0001

(a) Per grind. (b) Per edge; total, 3600 pieces per tool.

Fig. 37. Change from brazed carbide tool to indexable-insert carbide tool for grooving and back facing cold headed blank to obtain improvements noted in table (Example 307)

Maximum return on the large investment that a multiple-operation machine represents can be realized only by keeping the machine in operation at or near its full capacity. For this reason, in most plants, the addition of new machines lags behind demand for machine time. Under conditions of peak demand, it is therefore most important to operate machines at maximum speed. As a result, demand for machine time is often an impetus to the selection of a free-machining work metal.

Paying a higher price for a steel having better machinability may result in lower manufacturing cost solely on the basis of increased tool life. This is most often true when the machine is already being operated at maximum speed; under these circumstances cycle time per part cannot be decreased, regardless of work-metal machinability. However, longer tool life results in lower tool cost and usually in some increase in productivity, because downtime for changing tools is decreased.

For many applications, a choice can be made among two or more free-machining grades of work metal that vary in both cost and machinability. The six examples that follow describe six different applications involving comparisons between two grades of free-machining steel:

Example 309. 1117 vs 1215 Steel (Table 6)

Table 6 compares operating conditions and production rates for making pivot bushings (inset sketch in Table 6) from two different types of free-machining steel — 1117 and 1215 — in seven operations on a six-spindle automatic bar machine. The 4-to-1 ratio of unmachined to machined weight of the workpiece (indicating a large amount of machining) strongly influenced the decision to change to a more free-machining steel.

The increase in speed and feed permitted by the use of the 1215 steel resulted in an increase in productivity of almost 100% (Table 6). This increase justified the higher cost for the 1215 ($7 more per ton), not only because of a saving in labor cost (30% reduction) but also because it increased the capacity of a machine that carried a high burden rate.

Example 310. 1215 vs Lead-Tellurium Steel (Table 7)

Table 7 compares operating conditions and productivity for making the same part from two different grades of free-machining steel — 1215 at 137 Bhn and a lead-tellurium steel at 121 Bhn. A sketch of the workpiece (a spindle collar), which was made in seven operations on a six-spindle automatic bar machine, appears in Table 7.

The higher speed at which it was possible to machine the lead-tellurium steel resulted in greatly increased productivity. This increase in productivity justified the higher cost of the lead-tellurium steel ($30 more per ton than 1215) because it increased the capacity of a machine that carried a high burden rate.

The 4-to-1 difference between the unmachined and the machined weight of the workpiece was a significant influence on the decision to change to the more free-machining

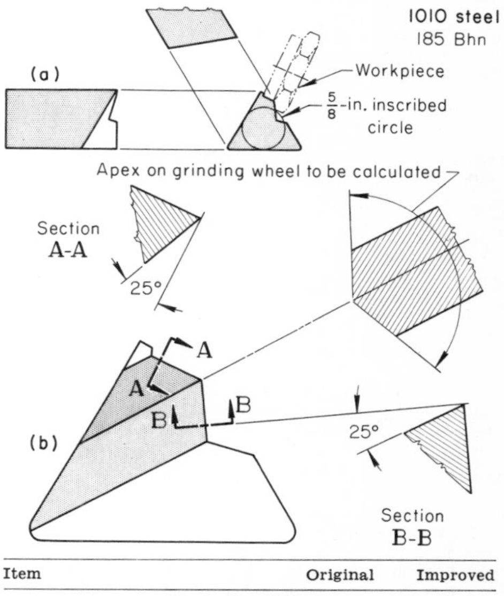

Item	Original	Improved
Tool Conditions		
Tool material	HSS	Carbide
Tool life per grind, pcs ...	1500	7500

Other Conditions
(The same for both tools)

Speed ....1500 rpm (350 sfm)
Feed ....0.0015 ipr
Depth of cut ....0.090 in.
Cutting fluid ....Fine mineral oil
Production rate ....700 pieces per hour

Fig. 38. Change in design of solid dovetail form tool from (a) *to* (b) *for burr-free forming of soft steel adapter* (Example 308)

Table 6. 1117 vs 1215 Steel (Example 309) (a)

Item	1117 (143 Bhn)	1215 (137 Bhn)
Speed, sfm	125	225
Feed, ipr:		
Drilling	0.006	0.008
Forming	0.0015	0.0025
Production per hour, pcs	91	179

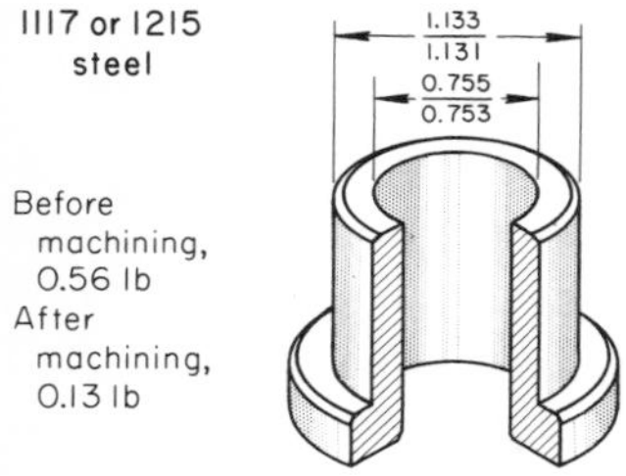

(a) Workpiece shown, a pivot bushing, was produced from each steel in seven operations in a six-spindle automatic bar machine. For both steels, tools were made of M2 high speed steel (except carbide cutoff tool), and sulfurized oil was used as the cutting fluid.

steel. However, the more costly steel could not have been justified in this instance by the decrease in labor cost alone (15%).

Example 311. 12L14 vs 12L14 With Tellurium (Table 8)

Operating conditions and productivity for making retainers from two different grades of 12L14 free-machining steel are compared in Table 8. A sketch of the workpiece, which was machined on a 1¼-in. six-spindle automatic bar machine, is included in Table 8; note the close tolerances on two angles.

Because these parts could be produced at lower cost by cold forming than by machining from 12L14, the process was changed from machining to cold forming. However, because of the 4-to-1 difference between unmachined and machined weight, a steel that could be machined at higher speed (12L14 plus tellurium) was tried. Although this steel cost $15 more per ton than the 12L14, productivity was increased (cycle time decreased) enough so that the cost of producing the parts by machining was lower than for cold forming, and the method was therefore changed back to machining.

Example 312. 12L14 vs 12L14 With Bismuth (Table 9)

Table 9 compares speeds, feeds and cycle times for making the part shown in the inset sketch from two different free-machining steels — conventional 12L14 and 12L14 with added bismuth — in a six-spindle automatic bar machine. As indicated, changing to the bismuth-containing steel permitted an increase in both feed and speed, which resulted in a 21% decrease in cycle time. The increase in machine capacity effected by the shorter cycle time justified the higher cost ($15 more per ton) of the bismuth steel.

Examples 313 and 314. 1213 vs 12L14 With Bismuth (Table 10)

Example 313 — Decreased Cycle Time. The part shown in the left-hand sketch in Table 10 was produced from 1-in.-diam cold drawn bar stock in a single-spindle automatic bar machine; operations included turning, forming, threading, and cutting off. As shown by the comparison of operating data in Table 10, changing from 1213 steel to a leaded and resulfurized steel containing bismuth permitted an increase in speed and feed, and a consequent decrease in cycle time. The reduction in machining time per piece increased machine capacity sufficiently to justify the higher cost ($30 more per ton) of the bismuth-containing steel.

Example 314 — Increased Tool Life. The small roller shown in the right-hand sketch in Table 10 was originally produced from 1-in.-diam 1213 steel cold drawn bar stock, in a single-spindle automatic bar machine that was operated at high speed (approximately 570 sfm). Because this speed was maximum for the machine, changing to a freer-cutting steel could not decrease cycle time. However, with the bismuth-containing steel, tool life was increased by more than 200% (Table 10).

Physical Conditions. Workpiece variations other than composition that affect productivity, dimensional accuracy, surface finish, machine wear, tool life, and cost are:

1 Dimensions of cross sections (bars, tubes or extrusions)
2 Surface finish
3 Straightness (bars, tubes or extrusions)
4 Length (bars, tubes or extrusions)
5 Symmetry (castings or forgings).

Dimensions of Cross Sections. Cold drawn products are usually preferred for multiple-operation machining, mainly because of their close dimensional tolerance and smooth finish. Hot rolled and pickled bars are sometimes used because they cost less than their cold drawn counterparts, but not all machines will operate successfully with hot rolled bars because of dimensional variation. Thus, the capability of the feeding mechanism to be used must be considered and the tolerance of the hot rolled bars must be known (and, if possible, the bars tried out on location), before a decision is made to substitute hot rolled and pickled bars for cold drawn bars.

Table 7. 1215 vs 12L14 With Tellurium (Example 310) (a)

Item	1215 (137 Bhn)	12L14+Te (121 Bhn)
Speed, sfm	225	400
Feed, ipr	0.0015	0.0025
Production per hour, pcs	620	1175

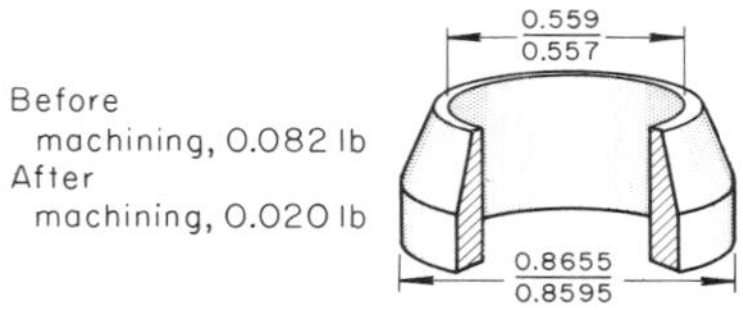

(a) Data are for seven-operation machining of part shown above, in a six-spindle automatic bar machine. For parts made from both steels, high speed steel tools were used (except for carbide cutoff tool), and sulfurized oil was used as the cutting fluid.

Table 8. 12L14 vs 12L14 With Tellurium (Example 311) (a)

Item	12L14	12L14+Te
Speed, sfm	250	407
Feed, ipr:		
Forming	0.0032	0.0040
Taper drilling	0.0068	0.0084
Taper reaming	0.0020	0.0025
Cycle time per piece, sec	5.5	3.8
Production per hour, pcs	653	954

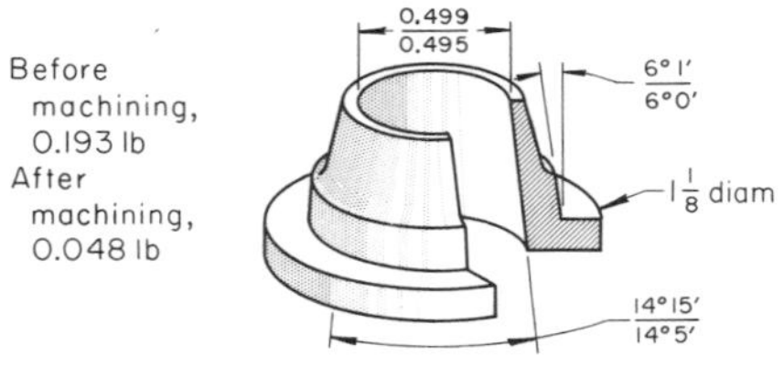

(a) Data are based on producing part shown above in a six-spindle automatic bar machine; hardness of both steels was Rockwell B 70 to 80. Form tools for both steels were made of M3 high speed steel, and tools for rough forming had an average life of 8 hr per grind; other tools were made of general-purpose high speed steel and ran 16 hr between grinds. Thread-cutting oil was used as the cutting fluid.

Not only do significant variations in cross section (including out-of-roundness) affect feeding mechanisms, but they also affect tool life. Dimensional variations cause nonuniform amounts of stock removal on initial cuts, which may damage tools.

Some automatic machines are so sensitive to dimensional variations of the work material that they may require adjustment for different shipments of material purchased to the same specifications. Consequently, for machines that are extremely sensitive, it is best practice to separate shipments from different suppliers, or to use some method for sorting the stock.

Surface Finish. Bars or tubes that have mill scale are often unsuitable for processing in an automatic machine, because the abrasive scale impairs the action of the feeding mechanism. Also, taking initial cuts on scaly surfaces damages tools and shortens their life. If hot rolled bars or tubes are processed, it is usually necessary that they be descaled, by pickling or blasting, before being machined.

Straightness. Regardless of whether cold or hot finished bars or tubes are used, they must be machine straightened. Bars or tubes that have been straightened to commercial limits are straight enough for operation in most machines. Extra straightness can be obtained at a premium price, but is seldom needed.

Bars or tubes that are not commercially straight develop whip in the stock reels, which causes abnormal vibration throughout the machine. This eventually results in excessive wear on machine parts and tools, tool chatter, and loss of dimensional control.

Length. For single-spindle machines, uniform length in bars or tubes seldom provides any benefit, except for ease of handling and storage. In a multiple-spindle machine, however, extreme nonuniformity of stock length decreases productivity, because as shorter lengths are fed through, some tools will be idle until the longest bar or tube is consumed. Also, significant differences in length of large, heavy bars, because of the variation in weight, can adversely affect the action of the stock reel. Usually, random-length bars are segregated as they are loaded into stock reels, so that the bars in a reel at any one time do not vary in length by more than a few inches.

Table 9. 12L14 vs 12L14 With Bismuth (Example 312) (a)

Item	12L14	12L14+Bi
Speed, sfm	290	334
Feed, ipr:		
Drilling	0.006	0.007
Cutting off	0.0022	0.0026
Cycle time per piece, sec	7.0	5.5

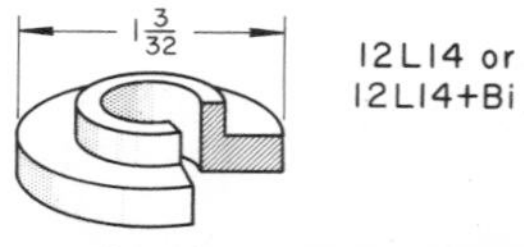

(a) Data are based on producing part shown above in a six-spindle automatic bar machine, using high speed steel tools and a sulfurized-oil cutting fluid. Tool life was the same for parts made of both steels.

Dimensional Control

Quality control by statistical methods can help to establish practical limits within which dimensional variations may be permitted to differ before the process should be corrected. The dimensions of the majority of pieces produced in any given operation usually are in an average group or cluster close to the nominal, but "fliers" (pieces departing to an unusual degree from the nominal) frequently are observed. Statistical quality control determines the trend of the average or majority group in relation to specifications or tolerances.

The three examples that follow illustrate typical variations in dimensions obtained with single-spindle or multiple-spindle machines. Other typical variations will be found in Example 903, in the article on Machining of Aluminum, and in Example 959, in the article on Machining of Copper.

Example 315. Variation in Length of 33 Consecutive Parts (Fig. 39)

Figure 39 plots measurements made of the over-all length of thirty-three 12L14 steel parts produced consecutively in a six-spindle automatic bar machine. The cutoff tool used had not been sharpened for 7 hr before the parts measured were produced.

The range of dimensional variation (0.006 in.) shows that the machine was producing well within the allowable tolerance of ±0.010 in. However, the irregular distribution of dimensions indicates that the machine was not functioning properly, probably requiring adjustment of the bearings in one or more of the spindles to decrease end play.

Example 316. Diameter and Eccentricity of Eccentric Screws Produced in a Single-Spindle Automatic (Fig. 40)

The charts in Fig. 40 show the variations in the diameter of the eccentric and in the amount of eccentricity of eccentric screws (top sketch in Fig. 40) produced from 7/16-in. hexagonal bars of leaded 1112 steel in a single-spindle automatic machine. The data plotted were obtained by measuring the two dimensions on 100 parts selected in 20 groups of five from a production run of 4000, beginning with parts 1401 to 1405 and (with the groups being selected at intervals of 125 parts) ending with parts 3871 to 3875.

As shown in the upper chart in Fig. 40, the diameter of the eccentric was well within the ±0.001-in. tolerance, and the distribution of the variations was considered acceptable.

In the lower chart of Fig. 40 (variation of eccentricity), note that there was one "flier". For no reason that could be established, eccentricity on the 65th piece measured (the 2965th in the run) was minus 0.008 in. from the nominal 0.040 in. However, because all other pieces were well within allowable limits, no corrective action was taken.

Although the patterns of distribution show the major portion of both measurements to be on the high side of the allowable ranges, this was not regarded as being sufficiently out of proportion to warrant machine adjustment.

Example 317. Diameter and Length of Worms Produced in an Eight-Spindle Automatic (Fig. 41)

Variations in the bearing diameter and the cutoff length of worms produced from 12L14 steel bar stock in an eight-spindle automatic machine are shown in Fig. 41. These data represent measurements made on 25 consecutively produced worms taken as a sample from a continuous production run using four machines. The bearing diameter was form turned, hollow milled, and shaved. When the sample was taken, the shaving tool had been operated for 5 hr, and the other tools (including the cutoff tool) for 7 hr, since being sharpened.

The spread of dimensions for the bearing diameter (upper chart in Fig. 41) was within allowable tolerance, but the location of the spread with reference to the nominal dimension indicates that slight adjustment of the tools or stops would bring the average dimension closer to nominal. This condition is more pronounced for the cutoff length (lower chart in Fig. 41); two parts were under the minimum, and corrective action was needed.

Table 10. 1213 vs 12L14 With Bismuth (Examples 313 and 314)

Item	1213	12L14+Bi
Example 313(a)		
Speed, sfm	200	260
Feed (forming), ipr	0.002	0.003
Tool life (forming), pieces per grind	2850	9600
Cycle time per piece, sec	18.5	10.5
Example 314(b)		
Tool life, pieces per grind	185(c)	600(d)

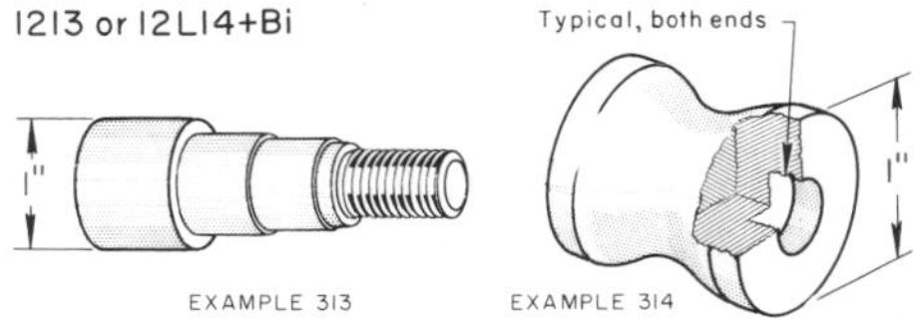

(a) Data are for machining part shown at left, above, in a single-spindle automatic bar machine. For parts made of either steel, tools were made of high speed steel, and sulfurized oil was used as cutting fluid. (b) Data on tool life were obtained in machining part shown at right, above, in a single-spindle automatic bar machine. For parts made of either steel, tools were made of high speed steel and were operated at 570 sfm and identical feed rates (not reported); sulfurized oil was used as cutting fluid. (c) Tools burned. (d) Tools did not burn.

Control of Machine Adjustment. Parts cannot be produced on any multiple-operation machine to tolerances closer than variations existing in the machine. Loose bearings and poorly adjusted slides or stops are the most common conditions that influence dimensional variation. Among other conditions are broken collet-lockup pins, worn cams, and broken connectors in slide-linkage mechanisms.

Periodic checking of the machine and a method for controlling its condition are mandatory for maintaining close and uniform tolerances. In many plants, methods of statistical quality control have been successfully applied to monitor the condition of multiple-spindle automatics. The use of these methods involves the following terms:

R. The spread between the high and low reading on a round, or of consecutive pieces from a spindle, as the case may be.

R_{ar}. The average range of four consecutive rounds. (The symbol $\bar{R}$ is widely used instead of R_{ar}.

Round. One piece from each spindle, in succession.

Spindle round. Four pieces, in succession, from a given spindle.

Spindle average. The average dimensional reading of consecutive pieces from a given spindle.

It is first required to have a table of established constants of R and R_{ar}. Typical values that serve as a guide to expected tolerance capabilities of automatic bar machines with four, six or eight spindles are given in Table 11.

A typical procedure used for practical application of quality control principles to the checking of machine condition is described in the following example. As this example demonstrates, data from a simple study can be utilized to keep machines adjusted and to rectify difficulties before unacceptable parts are produced.

Example 318. R_{ar} Study of a Six-Spindle Bar Machine (Fig. 42; Table 12)

The 1113 steel part shown in Fig. 42 was produced on a six-spindle automatic bar machine. Maintaining the 1.512/1.508-in. dimension within the 0.004-in. tolerance range was a chronic problem, and statistical quality control methods were applied to try to solve it.

Experience proved that for an R_{ar} study, data for four rounds, kept separate by round and spindle, would provide adequate information on the operating condition of the machine. The procedure used was as follows:

1 The operation-range limit R, 0.0028 in., was determined from the data for six-spindle machines in Table 11, using the 0.004-in. tolerance allowed by specifications.
2 The machine-study range limit R_{ar}, 0.0014 in., also was determined from Table 11.
3 Daily checks were made to the operational R (one round).
4 Weekly checks were made to R_{ar}.

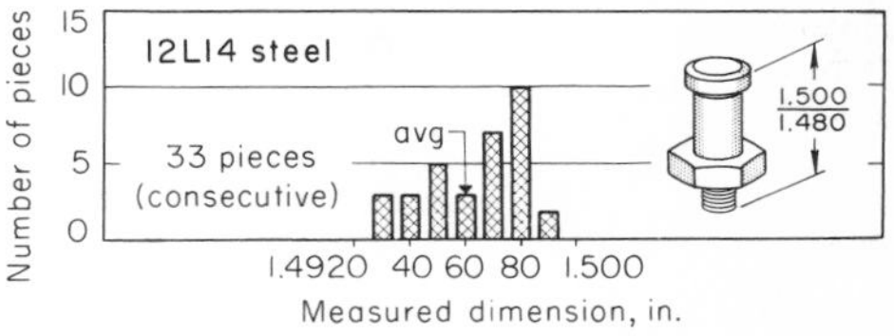

Fig. 39. Variation in length produced by cutoff tool in a six-spindle automatic bar machine (Example 315)

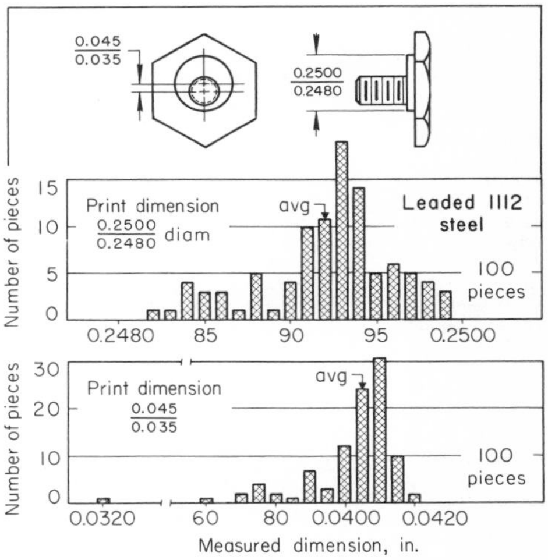

Fig. 40. Variation in dimensions on eccentric screws produced in a single-spindle automatic bar machine (Example 316)

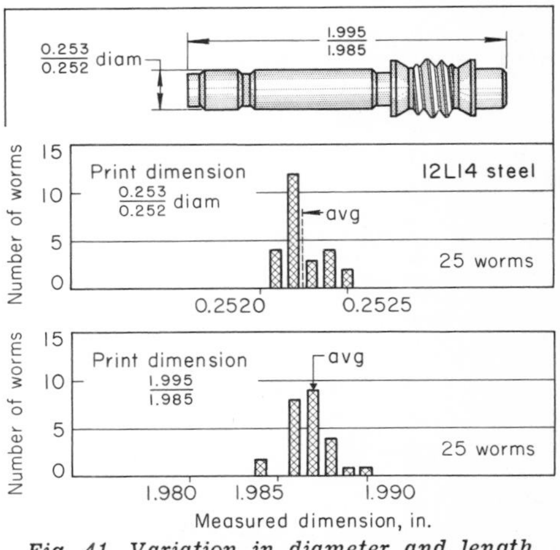

Fig. 41. Variation in diameter and length of worms consecutively machined in an eight-spindle automatic (Example 317)

Table 11. Typical Tolerance Capabilities for Multiple-Spindle Automatic Bar Machines (a)

Tolerance, in.	R, in.	R_{ar}, in.
Four-Spindle Machines		
0.002	0.001	0.0004
0.003	0.0015	0.0006
0.004	0.002	0.0008
0.005	0.0025	0.0011
0.010	0.005	0.0022
0.015	0.0075	0.0033
0.020	0.010	0.0044
0.030	0.015	0.0066
Six-Spindle Machines		
0.002	0.0014	0.0007
0.003	0.0021	0.00105
0.004	0.0028	0.0014
0.005	0.0035	0.0017
0.010	0.007	0.0035
0.015	0.0105	0.0052
0.020	0.014	0.007
0.030	0.021	0.0104
Eight-Spindle Machines		
0.002	0.0016	0.0008
0.003	0.0024	0.0012
0.004	0.0032	0.00165
0.005	0.0039	0.0021
0.010	0.0078	0.0042
0.015	0.0117	0.0063
0.020	0.0156	0.0084
0.030	0.0234	0.0126

(a) R is the spread between high and low ratings on pieces produced in a "round" (one piece from each spindle, in succession), or on consecutive pieces from a spindle; R_{ar} is the average range of four consecutive rounds. See Table 12 for actual dimensional data that illustrate these definitions for a particular part.

5 If, on the daily check, R was out of limits, an immediate study was made to determine the cause and to correct it.

Details of one R_{ar} study are given in Table 12 and summarized in the histogram of Fig. 42. These readings show that, although no out-of-tolerance pieces were found, the machine was operating at an R_{ar} of 0.00225 in. — well outside the 0.0014-in. R_{ar} limit. The "Spindle average" column in Table 12 shows that spindle 3 was cutting 0.0015 in. longer than the next-longest-cutting spindle. The end play of spindle 3 was reduced to nominal by adjustment of the bearings, and the average length of the dimension produced by spindle 3 was thus reduced to 1.5095 in.

Loading the machine before it is set up is best practice, because accuracy of the machine may be affected by setting up an almost empty machine and then filling it with heavy bars.

Bar weight increases rapidly with diameter (for example, ten 10-ft-long steel bars 1 in. in diameter weigh about 265 lb, whereas ten 5-in.-diam steel bars of the same length weigh about 6670 lb), and when the total weight in the stock reel is too great for the equipment, shorter bars must be used.

Speed and Feed

Speeds used in multiple-operation machining are not necessarily different from those recommended and used for specific single operations (see the articles in this volume that deal with drilling, turning, reaming, boring and other specific operations involved in multiple-operation machining).

Table 12. Measurements of 1.512/1.508-In. Dimension on Part Shown in Fig. 42 (Example 318)
(Data from quality control R_{ar} study of a six-spindle automatic bar machine)

Item	Round 1	Round 2	Round 3	Round 4	Sum of readings	Spindle average	Spindle R
Spindle 1	1.509	1.509	1.510	1.5105	6.0385	1.5096	0.0015
Spindle 2	1.5095	1.5095	1.5095	1.509	6.0375	1.5094	0.0005
Spindle 3	1.5115	1.512	1.511	1.510	6.0445	1.5111	0.002
Spindle 4	1.5095	1.509	1.510	1.509	6.0375	1.5094	0.001
Spindle 5	1.510	1.5095	1.509	1.510	6.0385	1.5096	0.001
Spindle 6	1.510	1.509	1.5095	1.509	6.0375	1.5094	0.001
High	1.5115	1.512	1.511	1.5105	...	...	...
Low	1.509	1.509	1.509	1.509	...	...	...
Range R	0.0025	0.003	0.002	0.0015		R_{ar} = 0.00225	

In the examples in this article that describe process techniques and conditions, speeds ranged from about 40 to 640 sfm (although in most, 300 sfm was maximum).

Feeds used in multiple-operation machining are essentially the same as those used in the specific operations when performed singly (see the articles in this volume on specific machining operations).

Processing examples presented in this article show the use of feeds ranging from 0.0004 ipr, for forming cuts on 416 stainless steel (Example 297), to as high as 0.023 ipr, for machining a carbon steel casting (Example 288).

Cutting Fluids

In about 90% of the examples in this article that present processing details, some type of cutting fluid was used. Frequency of use of the various types of fluids was as follows:

Soluble oil	38%
Sulfurized oil	24
Proprietary cutting oils (probably sulfurized)	10
Straight mineral oil	7
Special oils or mixtures	14
	93%

The main factors influencing choice of cutting fluid are specified finish and tolerance, composition of the work metal, and the specific type of operations to be performed.

Soluble oil is the most widely used cutting fluid, because it costs the least and is equal to, if not better than, any other fluid for cooling and for flushing away chips.

Straight mineral oils are often used where soluble oils do not meet requirements, particularly when the work metal is non-free-machining or where better surface finishes are necessary. In Example 290, mineral oil proved necessary to obtain acceptable finishes and tool life when low-carbon steel extrusions were being machined. In Example 283, mineral oil was used even though the work metal was a free-cutting grade of steel; the types of operations required oil to obtain acceptable results.

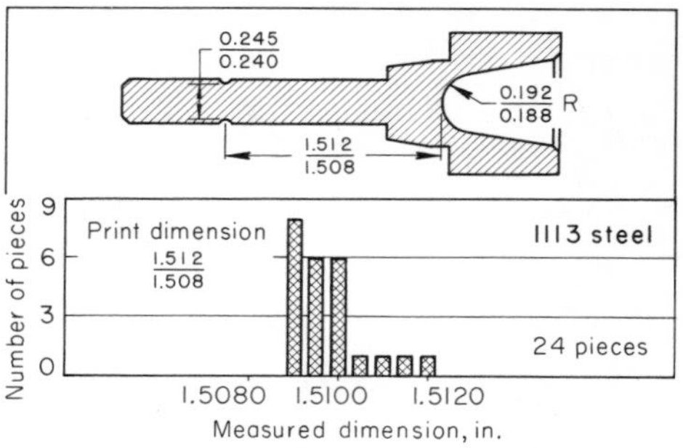

Fig. 42. Distribution of dimensions, although all are within tolerance, indicated that six-spindle bar machine used for producing this part was outside R_{ar} limit. See Table 12 and Example 318.

Proprietary cutting oils were used for the applications described in Examples 274 and 275. In both of these, the unsupported length of the workpiece was abnormal; in addition, the steel (1045) machined in Example 274 is non-free-machining. Proprietary cutting oils are more effective than soluble-oil emulsions for preventing chatter under abnormal conditions of unsupported length or vibration. Similar conditions prevailed in Example 277.

Special Oils and Mixtures. Special cutting fluids are often prepared for unusual applications. They are especially desirable for use in tapping operations (Examples 284 and 285).

Lard oil is often used in small single-spindle machines for such special purposes (Examples 296 and 297). Thread-cutting or lard oils are often mixed with mineral oils (Examples 285 and 294) to improve viscosity.

Dry Cutting. In 7% of the examples in this article no fluid was used. For instance, Example 278 describes the machining of a nonrigid malleable iron casting in three setups, using manual feed control without cutting fluid. In Example 280, a large steel casting was machined without a cutting fluid.

Other Examples of Multiple-Operation Machining in This Volume

Work metal	Example number
Work Metals Compared	
Cast iron	661, 662, 663
Tool steel	687
Stainless steel	776
Aluminum	867, 868, 869, 871, 872, 873, 874, 905
Copper	933, 934
Tool Materials Compared	
Stainless steel	774
Copper	950

Work metal	Example number
Methods	
Cast iron	660
Heat-resisting alloys	841, 842, 843
Refractory alloys	861
Aluminum	875, 892, 895, 905, 907, 908, 909
Copper	937, 948, 949, 955, 957, 958
Magnesium	978
Nickel	995, 996, 997

Work metal	Example number
Methods Compared	
Cast iron	664, 665, 666
Stainless steel	771, 772, 773, 775, 777, 778
Heat-resisting alloys	838
Copper	944, 945, 946, 947, 951, 952, 953, 954
Accuracy	
Aluminum	903, 904, 906
Copper	959

Milling

*By the ASM Committee on Milling**

MILLING is a machining process in which metal is removed by a rotating multiple-tooth cutter, each tooth removing a small amount of metal with each revolution of the spindle. Because both workpiece and cutter can be moved in more than one direction at the same time, surfaces having almost any orientation can be machined.

The principal differences between milling and other machining processes are: (*a*) the interruptions in cutting that occur as the teeth of the milling cutter alternately engage and leave the workpiece, (*b*) the relatively small size of chips in milling, and (*c*) the variation in thickness within each chip. Chip thickness varies during the cut of any individual tooth, because feed is measured in the direction of table motion (workpiece moving into cutter) whereas chip thickness is measured along the radius of the cutter.

Milling is most efficient when the work is no harder than Rockwell C 25. However, steel at Rockwell C 35 is commonly milled, and steel as hard as Rockwell C 56 has been successfully milled. (The effect of high hardness of work metal on cutter design, cutter life and machining cost is discussed in later sections, on pages 189 to 192.)

Milling Machines

Most milling is done in machines designed primarily for milling. But milling has been done in almost every type of machine that can rigidly hold and rotate a cutter while allowing a workpiece to be fed into the cutter, or vice versa. For instance, milling can be done in single-spindle or multiple-spindle bar and chucking machines in sequence with other machining operations. Conversely, some specially designed milling machines include facilities for other machining operations.

Machines used for production milling should incorporate:

1. A means of changing speed and feed to accommodate a variety of cutters and work metals
2. Automatic backlash eliminators on table feed (especially for climb milling)
3. A built-in spindle flywheel for smoother rotation — particularly desirable when carbide cutters are used
4. A vibration damper to minimize chatter
5. Automatic lubrication
6. Tapered gibs for all slides, which permit adjustments to compensate for normal wear, thus preventing long periods of downtime
7. A trip mechanism for the table, to eliminate manual setting
8. Positive kick-outs on all handwheels and cranks, for safety
9. A quick-change spindle-nose adapter for saving time in changing tools, particularly on knee-and-column machines.

Spindle orientation is one means of classifying milling machines. Machines that drive cutters with horizontal spindles are the most common, although vertical spindles also are widely used. Some special-purpose machines have horizontal, vertical and angular spindles that operate consecutively or simultaneously, or both.

Type of construction is the basis for classifying machines as: (*a*) knee-and-column, (*b*) bed-type, or (*c*) special. The first two types are available in a wide range of capacities and with many modifications and accessories. Special machines are individually designed and constructed for specific requirements.

Knee-and-Column Machines

Knee-and-column machines (Fig. 1) consist of six basic components: (*a*) the base, which supports the other components; (*b*) the column, which contains the spindle and its driving mechanism; (*c*) the overarm, which provides support for arbor-mounted cutters; (*d*) the knee, a separate section attached to the column and movable vertically on the column; (*e*) the saddle, which is supported by and moves horizontally (in and out) on the knee; and (*f*) the table, which supports the workpiece and can move horizontally at right angles to the saddle movement.

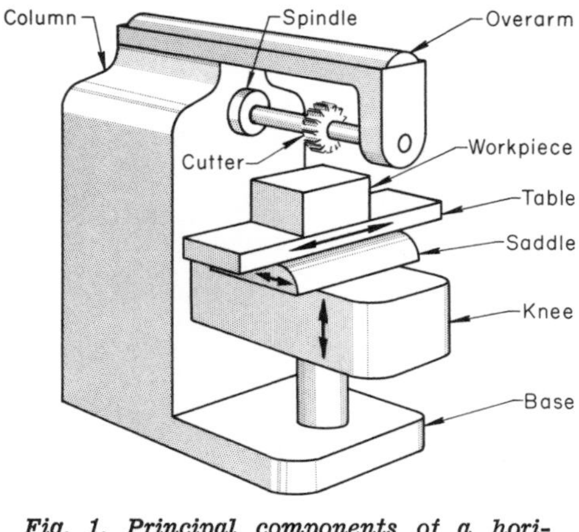

Fig. 1. Principal components of a horizontal-spindle knee-and-column milling machine

The plain knee-and-column machine permits three-dimensional movement of the workpiece by up-and-down motion of the knee and by two-direction horizontal motion of the saddle and table.

The universal knee-and-column machine has a two-piece saddle that permits swiveling of the machine table for milling radial cuts. The machine is equipped with a dividing head and a special driving mechanism.

Most knee-and-column machines have a removable head that is attached to the column and converts the machine into a vertical-spindle machine. Some of these heads can be swiveled 180°.

Vertical-spindle knee-and-column machines also are available. Large vertical-spindle machines have the spindle and driving mechanism mounted on a ram attached to an overhang on the column. On small machines, the vertical spindle and driving components are attached to a horizontal slide at the top of the column.

The usual power range available for knee-and-column machines is 1 to 50 hp. These machines are rated also by the size of workpiece they can handle. A numbering system is used to designate milling machines in accordance with the largest workpiece that can be milled — the higher the number, the larger the maximum workpiece size. For example, a No. 3 machine has maximum table, saddle and knee movements of 34, 12 and 20 in., respectively. The largest knee-and-column machine has a table travel of 60 in., cross travel of 18 in., and vertical travel of 20 in.

The method of operating knee-and-column machines varies from manual control of all movements to power control of all movements. Also, by the use of stops and other control devices the machine can be adapted for automatic cycles. Because of their versatility in machining workpieces of different sizes and shapes, these machines are widely used for low-production milling.

The main disadvantage of the knee-and-column machine is its inherent lack of rigidity. The machine has three

*J. D. ROBINSON, *Chairman,* Manager of Metallurgical Operations, Bendix Products Aerospace Div., Bendix Corp.; H. A. BIRK, Division Superintendent, Ewart Plant, Link-Belt Co.; RICHARD W. COLBURN, Supervisor, Development Unit, AOD, Springfield Armory; R. V. DOUGLAS, Chief Manufacturing Engineer, Ordnance Div., FMC Corp.

MYRON P. DZIADIK, Technical Assistant, Data Systems Div., International Business Machines Corp.; WILLIAM J. GAMBLE, Director of Manufacturing Development, Carrier Air Conditioning Co.; KARL B. KAISER, Director of Engineering, Ingersoll Milling Machine Co.; D. F. NERSWICK, Assistant Manager, Engineering Service Dept., Milling Machine Div., Cincinnati Milling and Grinding Machines, Inc.; ROLLO G. RICE, Bendix Products Aerospace Div., Bendix Corp.

SIDNEY SCHNEIDER, Manufacturing Research Group Engineer, Metallics Section, Republic Aviation Corp.; R. E. SNIDER, formerly with Columbus Division, North American Aviation Inc.; E. A. SODERLUND, Supervisor, Machine Tool Engineering Section, Facilities Engineering Dept., Grumman Aircraft Engineering Corp.; JOHN P. WALKER, General Foreman, Machine Shop, Evansville Div., Whirlpool Corp.

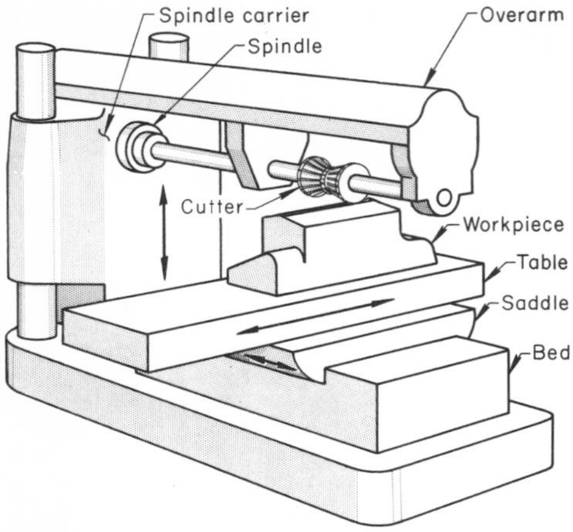

Fig. 2. Principal components of a horizontal-spindle bed-type milling machine

or four joints with sliding fits, each requiring a minimum of 0.002 in. clearance. The joint between the knee and the column bears the combined weight of the knee, saddle, table, fixture and workpiece. Deflection is therefore inevitable under milling stress. To add some rigidity, and reduce deflection, an outboard support may be placed between the overarm and the knee. To prevent chatter, limitations must be imposed on feed, speed, and depth of cut in milling. Chatter will cause a decrease in dimensional accuracy, unacceptable surface finish, and reduced cutter life.

Bed-Type Machines

Principal components of a bed-type machine are shown in Fig. 2. These machines are almost as versatile as knee-and-column machines, and have at least 50% greater rigidity. In a bed-type machine, the table and saddle are mounted on a bed of fixed vertical position and vertical movement is obtained from the spindle carrier. Consequently, less weight is moved on guide ways, which are about 50% longer for any given size of machine, compared with movement of the knee. In addition, spindle overhang is reduced as much as 75%, because the cutter can be located closer to the vertical way.

Vertical-spindle bed-type machines also are available, with a rigid headstock on which the entire spindle carrier can slide up and down as required.

Specific advantages of the bed-type machine in comparison with the knee-and-column machine are: (*a*) greater rigidity, permitting heavier cuts and closer dimensional control; (*b*) a constant reloading level of the table; (*c*) controls at a uniform level; (*d*) a greater range of vertical movement; and (*e*) versatility that can be increased by providing a longer saddle and outboard support.

The main disadvantage of the bed-type milling machine is its high initial cost.

Manufacturing-type machines (Fig. 3) are large bed-type machines used for milling of high production quantities. They are available as standard models with up to 300 hp, and can be modified or equipped as needed for mass production. On some, the spindle carrier is a ram slide mounted on a vertical column.

The machine illustrated in Fig. 3 is a simplex model (one spindle carrier). Duplex models have a spindle carrier on each side of the bed, enabling simultaneous operation of opposing cutters, thereby doubling productivity with a relatively low (about 30%) increase in investment. (An application in which increased productivity and accuracy resulted from replacing a knee-and-column machine with a duplex mill is discussed in Example 667 in the article "Machining of Cast Iron". The ease of maintaining accurate parallelism by the two-spindle setup in a duplex machine is described in Example 914 in the article "Machining of Aluminum Alloys".)

Manufacturing-type machines permit manual adjustment of all slides. Most of these machines have automatic table control, some are equipped for automatic cycling of the spindle carriers, and a few have automatic control of the table *and* the spindle carriers.

Planer-type machines (Fig. 4) are so called because of their structural resemblance to a planer. Known also as adjustable-rail machines, they can provide almost any combination of vertical,

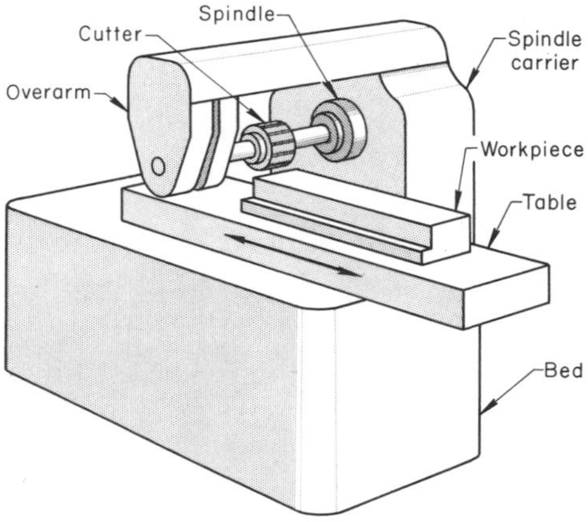

Fig. 3. Principal components of a manufacturing-type milling machine with one spindle carrier

horizontal or angular spindles for driving milling cutters as well as boring bars. They also can do several milling and boring operations simultaneously.

The machine illustrated schematically in Fig. 4 is a triplex model (three spindle carriers). On a triplex machine, workpieces are secured to the table, which carries them back and forth between the two vertical columns and under the crossrail. Two horizontal spindle carriers move vertically on the columns, and a vertical spindle carrier moves horizontally on the crossrail. The crossrail can move vertically on the two columns.

Planer-type machines are large and represent a major capital investment. Therefore, their use is generally restricted to removing large amounts of metal from massive workpieces like mill or power-plant components, or to mass-production milling in which identical workpieces are arranged in a row to be milled together.

Diesinkers are machines originally designed for unit or low-production work in tool and die shops. A diesinker is similar to a small vertical bed-type machine because it has a sliding table mounted on a rigid bed and a vertical spindle carrier mounted on a column. A diesinker can be equipped with automatic depth control for roughing out die impressions, and with a mechanism for 360° profiling for finish machining of dies. (When a diesinker is equipped with a profiling mechanism, it is often called a profile milling machine.) With the ease of operation provided by a servo system, diesinkers are used for milling of production workpieces that require miscellaneous complex cuts and contours, such as aerospace components.

Automatic feed can be applied to any or all slides on simplex, duplex or triplex manufacturing machines. The most critical feeding device on manufacturing machines is the one that drives the table. Four drives are in common use: (*a*) lead screw and nut box, (*b*) hydraulic cylinder, (*c*) half nut and screw, and (*d*) rack and pinion.

The lead-screw drive is suited only to short table feeds, because of "play" in the components. A backlash eliminator is needed for climb milling when a lead-screw drive is used.

Hydraulic-cylinder drives are usually limited to a table feed of about 10 ft because of compressibility in a long column of oil. Hydraulic-cylinder drives are not suitable for climb milling.

The half-nut-and-screw or rack-and-pinion drives are both suitable for long table feeds. These drives also eliminate backlash, permit variable speed for workpieces on which the amount of stock removal varies, and can be used with a tracer roller for contour milling.

Special-Purpose Machines

Innumerable special-purpose milling machines have been designed and built, sometimes for use on special workpiece configurations, but more often for high-volume production of a specific part. Most special-purpose machines are combinations of two or more of the basic machines described earlier.

The cost of special-purpose milling machines can be justified only for continuous high production of identical workpieces or if several operations can be combined in one handling to reduce manufacturing cost.

Specially designed machines usually are more readily adapted to automatic control than are standard machines, although standard machines can be automated to various degrees.

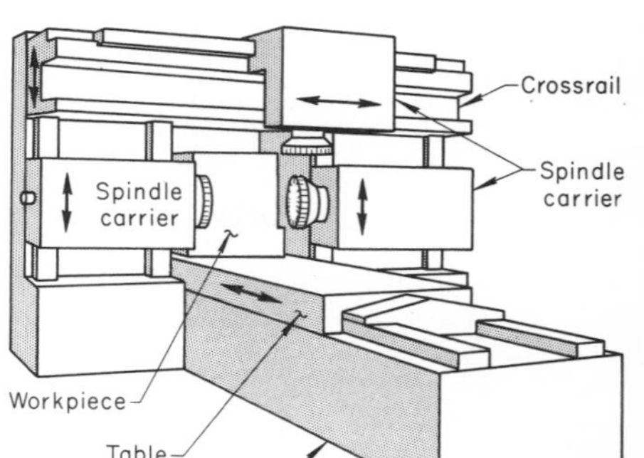

Fig. 4. Principal components of a triplex planer-type milling machine

Automatic Controls

Four types of automatic controls that are used on milling machines are: mechanical-electric, mechanical-hydraulic, mechanical-electric-hydraulic, and numerical.

Mechanical-electric controls operate by means of limit switches that actuate solenoids to engage or disengage mechanical components of the machine. Controls of this type are used only for single-cycle operations that involve few variations.

Mechanical-hydraulic controls are actuated by means of a trip plunger having radial and axial movement for positioning a hydraulic valve. Mechanical components of the machine are engaged or disengaged by oil emerging under pressure from ports in the hydraulic valve. These controls are used only for single-cycle operations involving few variations. The addition of a sequence valve and a cycle selector will provide control for many variables. The cycle selectors are arranged with variable-depth cams that depress plungers in a valve block to select the direction of all slides, to start and stop the spindle, and to control indexing and reloading operations.

Mechanical-electric-hydraulic controls are an improvement over the types described above for controlling complex machine cycles. These controls utilize an electric stepping switch and connectors or on-and-off switches. By this means an automatic cycle is changed by repositioning the connectors or resetting the switches. Because this system lacks automatic positioning, the operator must set stops for length of traverse for each sliding component.

When connectors are used, the tool designer can punch out the cycle in advance on plastic sheets. This punched sheet is then forwarded to the shop with the fixture and tooling, and the operator has only to insert the connectors in the punched-out spaces to control the operation automatically. A typical application is described in Example 345.

Numerical Control. The ultimate in equipment for production milling is a machine with numerical control and an automatic tool changer. A punched tape or card establishes the programming, selects the cutter for the tool changer and determines milling speed and feed. The machine operator inserts the tape (or card) in the control, positions the workpiece on the table with reference to the starting point, and then starts the cycle. All operations are performed automatically with one handling of the workpiece.

Advantages of numerical control are usually related closely to cost reduction or better reproducibility, or both. The more important advantages are:

1 A multiplicity of cuts are possible with one handling of the workpiece.
2 All cuts are taken from the same location points.
3 Feed and speed are computed, rather than being dependent on operator judgment.
4 Results are more consistent, because operator variables are eliminated.
5 Changes in the machining cycle can be made without detailed instructions to the operator.
6 Operator duties are decreased, thus allowing more time for "housekeeping" around the machine.
7 Closer control of operations permits more accurate cost estimates for milling of similar workpieces.

Numerically controlled machines were used in the milling operations described in Examples 347 and 348 in this article, and in Example 912 in the article on Machining of Aluminum.

Adapters and Attachments

Longitudinal T-slots are standard on milling machine tables. Thus, many workpieces can be secured directly to the table by means of simple clamps. Workpieces that cannot be fastened directly to the table are held in standard vises or specially designed work holders secured to the table by means of T-bolts.

All standard milling machines are supplied with an American Standard taper hole in each spindle. Standard tool holders have this taper, and are available in at least eight different designs to accommodate all common types of cutters.

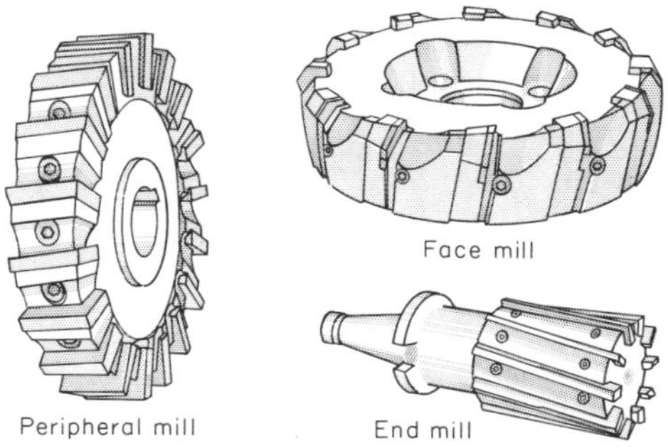

Fig. 5. Three types of milling cutters

Attachments. The number of special attachments that can extend the use of a milling machine is almost unlimited. Three widely used ones are:

1 Rotary tables, which are fixtures designed to rotate the workpiece accurately through angles for graduating, indexing or milling helixes. Rotary tables can be operated manually or by power.
2 Independent or dependent overhead spindles that have as many as eight speeds. These attachments can be applied to any machine having a slide in the top of the column.
3 Dividing heads, for accurate indexing to the desired angle. These are usually secured directly to the machine table.

Milling Cutters

Milling cutters vary widely in type and size and are broadly classified as: peripheral mills, face mills, end mills and special mills. Cutters may be machined from the solid, thus having integral teeth, or may have inserted cutting edges (blades) that are held in place by brazing or by mechanical fasteners.

Peripheral mills (Fig. 5) are so named because cutting is done mainly by teeth on the periphery to produce the finished surface. A peripheral mill is usually mounted on an arbor with axis parallel to the surface being milled. Peripheral mills are further classified as slab mills, slotting cutters, half-side mills, angle cutters and form cutters. Circular saws also are a form of peripheral mill (see Example 333).

Peripheral mills are available in a wide range of diameters, widths and width-to-diameter ratios, and with straight or spiral cutting edges. The most widely available range of diameters for peripheral mills is from about 4 to 18 in.

Slotting cutters as thin as 3/16 in. can be obtained in diameters up to about 5 in. The minimum available width increases as diameter increases. For instance, in a 12-in.-diam cutter minimum thickness is usually 7/16 in. Slab mills represent the opposite extreme in width-to-diameter ratio and are often four or five diameters wide.

Thin slotting cutters or complicated form cutters are usually of the solid type, regardless of diameter. Plain peripheral milling cutters less than about 3 in. in diameter are usually of the solid type; larger ones have inserted blades.

Most peripheral cutters have zero to positive radial rake, with either positive or negative axial rake.

Face mills (Fig. 5) are so named because the workpiece surface is produced by the face of the cutter, although the outside-diameter or bevel cutting edge removes most of the stock. The cutter is driven by a spindle on an axis perpendicular to the surface being milled.

Face mills can be made to almost any size, but usually range in diameter from 2¾ to 20 in. Face mills smaller than 2¾ in. are seldom needed, and machine power and rigidity restricts the use of cutters larger than 20 in. Face mills less than 3 in. in diameter are usually machined from solid; larger face mills characteristically have inserted blades.

Tooth design on face mills is usually one of the following:

1 Double positive (positive axial rake and positive radial rake)
2 Double negative (negative axial rake and negative radial rake)
3 Negative radial rake, positive axial rake and a corner angle.

End mills (Fig. 5) have cutting edges on both the face end and the periphery; thus they may be used for facing cuts or for peripheral cuts, or both. As peripheral cutters, they can be used to form either plane or irregular surfaces on the workpiece.

End mills are generally available in diameters of 3/16 to 4 in., although larger ones have been used. End mills less than 2 in. in diameter are usually made of solid tool steel; those larger than 2 in. have inserted blades, of either tool steel or carbide.

End mills normally have zero to positive radial rake, and positive axial rake. Axial rake angles in the form of true spiral or helix angles will produce smoother surfaces. For a combination of end and peripheral cutting, a cutter with a right-hand cut and a right-hand helix is used. For peripheral milling only, most cutters have a right-hand cut and a left-hand helix.

Special milling cutters can be made to almost any design. For instance, the teeth may be of either the profile-sharpened or the form-relieved type, and may be integral with the body or inserted. The cutter may be designed for mounting on an arbor or directly

Table 1. Angles of Carbide Cutters for Milling Steel

Type of steel work material	Axial rake	Radial rake	True rake	Corner angle	Incli-nation
Peripheral Milling					
Low-carbon and annealed alloy	5°	− 5°	− 5°	..	..
Hardened alloy	10°	−10°	−10°	..	..
Slotting and Sawing					
Low-carbon and annealed alloy	0°	− 5°	− 5°	..	..
Hardened alloy	0°	−10°	−10°	..	..
Face Milling					
Low-carbon and annealed alloy	5°	−12°	− 5°	45°	12°
Hardened alloy	5°	−18°	−10°	45°	16°

on the spindle nose, or may have a shank integral with the body. Special cutters may be used singly, or they may be made in sections and combined to mill the desired contour. Material and angle considerations that apply to standard cutters generally apply also to the special designs. The higher cost of special cutters can often be justified by combining operations, thus reducing machine time and machining cost.

(Performance of a special form cutter is compared with standard milling methods in Example 332 in this article, and in Example 916 in the article on Machining of Aluminum.)

Nomenclature of milling cutters is illustrated in Fig. 6 and defined in the following list. These terms apply primarily to plain milling cutters.

1 **Outside diameter** is the diameter of a circle passing around the peripheral cutting edges and is used to calculate surface speed from spindle speed.
2 **Root diameter** is the diameter of a circle tangent to the roots of the teeth fillets.
3 **The tooth** is the part of the cutter starting at the body and ending with the peripheral cutting edge. Inserted teeth are called blades.
4 **Tooth face** is the surface of the tooth between the fillet and the cutting edge, where the chip slides during cutting.
5 **Land** is the area behind the cutting edge on the tooth that is relieved to avoid interference.
6 **Flute** is the space for chip flow between the teeth.
7 **Fillet** is the radius at the bottom of the flute to promote chip flow and curling.

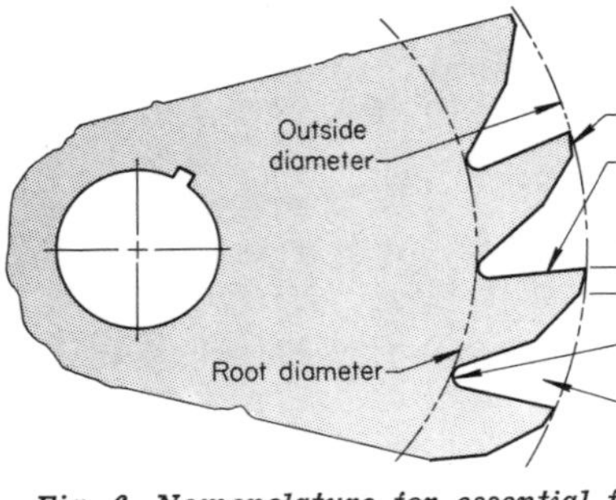

Fig. 6. Nomenclature for essential features of milling cutters

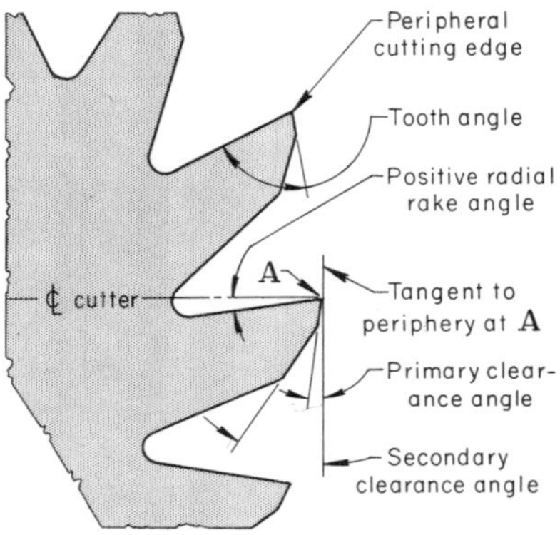

Fig. 7. Nomenclature of tooth design of milling cutters

The following terms refer to tooth design (Fig. 7):

1 **Peripheral cutting edge** is the edge aligned principally in the direction of the cutter axis. In peripheral milling it is the edge that removes metal.
2 **Face cutting edge** (not shown in Fig. 7) is the metal-removing edge on a face mill that travels in a plane perpendicular to the axis. It is the edge that sweeps the milled surface in normal face milling.
3 **Tooth angle** is the angle included between the face and the land of the cutter tooth. This angle should be as large as possible to provide maximum tooth strength and better dissipation of heat.
4 **Radial rake angle** (shown as positive in Fig. 7) is the angle between the tooth face and a radial line passing through the cutting edge in a plane perpendicular to the cutter axis.
5 **Clearance angle** is the angle included between the land on the back or flank of the milling cutter tooth, and the tangent to the periphery of the cutter at the cutting edge. Clearance angles are always positive and are usually divided into primary and secondary angles (see Fig. 7).
6 **Axial rake angle** (not shown in Fig. 7) is measured between the peripheral cutting edge and the axis of the cutter, when looking radially at the point of intersection. For a cutter with helical teeth, the axial rake angle equals the helix angle.
7 **Blade setting angle**, or cone angle (not shown in Fig. 7) is the nominal angle with the cutter axis, along which the blades are moved for adjustment.

Cutter angle combinations that have been satisfactory for milling steel with carbide cutters are listed in Table 1.

Material for Milling Cutters

High speed steel is widely used as a tool material for all types of milling cutters. With high speed steel, the cutter body and teeth can be integral. The required shapes are machined from annealed high speed steel and then hardened and ground to a finished cutter. Many large cutters of simple design consist of high speed steel blades inserted in bodies made of heat treated alloy steel. But as cutter shape increases in complexity, the use of separate blades becomes more difficult. Consequently, complex cutters are often made from solid high speed steel, regardless of size.

Cutters made from the more highly alloyed grades of high speed steel (especially those containing cobalt) have higher hot hardness than the general-purpose grades. The higher hot hardness permits faster cutting speeds. As noted in Fig. 8(a), in end milling 4340 steel quenched and tempered to Rockwell C 49, the cutting speed for a tool life of 50 in. of workpiece machined was approximately 45 sfm for M7 high speed steel and 70 sfm for T15 high speed steel, an increase of more than 50%.

The life of milling cutters of T1, M1 and M10 high speed steels shortens quickly as the hardness of the workpiece rises beyond Rockwell C 35. The tool life of four high speed steels in end mills cutting H11 steel at Rockwell C 41 is compared in Example 369 in this article. Performance of five grades of high speed steel is compared in end milling René 41 at Rockwell C 41 in Example 846 in the article "Machining of Heat-Resisting Alloys", and nine grades of high speed steel are compared in Example 847 in that article.

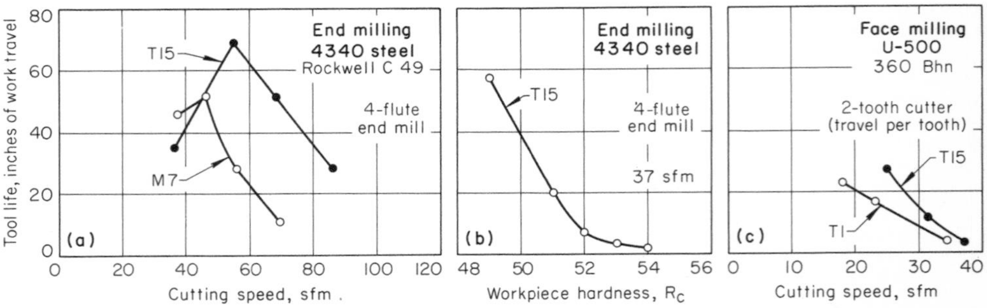

Chart	Cutter diameter, in.	Feed, ipt	Depth of cut, in.	Width of cut, in.	Ratio of soluble oil to water	Wear land, in.
Milling Conditions						
(a)	¾	0.0010	¼	¾	1 to 20	0.016
(b)	¾	0.0005	¼	¾	1 to 20	0.016
(c)	4	0.0050	0.060	2	1 to 20	0.016

Chart	Helix angle	Radial rake	Corner angle	Side clearance	End clearance
Cutter Angles					
(a)	35° rh, rh cut	15°	45°, 0.060 in. wide	5° pr, 10° sec	5° pr, 20° sec
(b)	35° rh, rh cut	15°	45°, 0.060 in. wide	5° pr, 10° sec	5° pr, 20° sec
(c) (Note 1)	....	10°	45°	....	....

Note 1. For chart (c), other cutter angles were: axial rake, 10°; true rake, 14°; inclination, 0°; end cutting-edge angle, 5°; peripheral clearance, 10°.

Fig. 8. Comparative tool life of milling cutters made of different grades of high speed steel, when used under the conditions shown

The more highly alloyed high speed steels can be used to cut work at Rockwell C 35 to 50. Performance of three grades of high speed steel in end milling PH 15-7 Mo stainless steel at Rockwell C 45 is compared in Example 782 in the article "Machining of Stainless Steel". For work that is harder than Rockwell C 50, cutters of high speed steel would not last long, as shown in Fig. 8(b).

Carbide cutters are used for work that is harder than Rockwell C 50. Carbide cutters are better, in general, because they are used at cutting speeds three to six times those for high speed steel. Performance of carbide is compared with that of high speed steel in Examples 360, 370, 371 and 372 in this article, in Example 672 in the article "Machining of Cast Iron", and in Examples 697 and 699 in the article "Machining of Tool Steel". Examples 358 and 362 in the present article compare performance of several carbides.

Carbide blades, inserted in alloy steel bodies, and brazed carbide tips are extensively used in milling cutters. The smallest cutters (especially end mills) are sometimes made of solid carbide; but high cost and high susceptibility to breakage limit the use of solid carbide to specialized applications.

Inserted blades may be of the grind type or of the indexable type. In the grind type, the blades are sharpened while assembled in the cutter body. In the indexable type, the removable blades have several cutting edges. When one edge becomes worn, the blade is indexed to another edge. When all edges have been used, the blade is discarded.

On many of the nickel or cobalt-base high-temperature alloys, such as U-500 and HS-25, carbide milling cutters are not recommended. Tool life is usually poor in milling these alloys with carbide, because of edge chipping. Cutters made of cast cobalt-chromium-tungsten alloys have also been unsatisfactory for milling of nickel or cobalt high-temperature alloys. A combination of low cutting speed and a cobalt high speed steel cutter is required for milling these alloys. The chart in Fig. 8(c) indicates the advantage of T15 over T1 high speed steel, and the effect of cutting speed on life of both tool materials, in face milling U-500.

Other factors to be considered in selecting the tool material for milling cutters are: (*a*) rigidity of setup, (*b*) available horsepower, and (*c*) cutter-sharpening facilities.

Rigidity of setup is particularly important when carbide milling cutters are used. Looseness in the bearings or slides of the machine can result in vibrations that lead to poor cutter life. If the setup cannot be made rigid, high speed steel cutters should be used.

Carbide cutters give best results when used at higher speeds. As speed is increased, more power is required. Therefore, when considering the use of carbide cutters it should be made certain that enough power is available.

Carbide cutters are more difficult to sharpen than high speed steel cutters. Diamond wheels are commonly used, although there are grinding machines that use silicon carbide wheels for grinding carbide cutters.

Geometrical Relation of Cutter to Work

Axial rake, radial rake, and corner angle in face milling are respectively equivalent to back rake, side rake, and side cutting-edge angle in turning. These are the angles by which the relationship of cutting edge to work is usually defined. (See page 3, in the article "Turning", for identification of the basic elements and nomenclature of a single-point tool.)

The most significant angle in any machining operation is the "true rake" angle. True rake angle directly affects the shear angle in the chip-forming process, and therefore greatly affects tool force, power requirement and temperature. The larger the positive value of the true rake angle, the lower the force. It is limited in magnitude, however, by the strength required of the tool for a given machining operation.

In milling, the true rake angle is the resultant of the axial rake, radial rake, and corner angle.

Figure 9 shows the geometrical arrangement of the various rake angles. Each rake angle is measured with respect to a reference plane which, in milling, passes through the axis of cutter rotation and the point of the tool. True rake (by definition) is measured in a plane perpendicular to the projection of cutting edge on reference plane.

The angle of next importance in machining is *inclination*. This is the angle that the cutting edge makes with the reference plane, which, by definition, is perpendicular to the direction of tool travel. Inclination determines the direction of chip curling. When the inclination is zero, chip flow is virtually in the plane of true rake.

Many combinations of axial rake, radial rake and corner angle other than those listed in Table 1 have been successfully used in practice. The require-

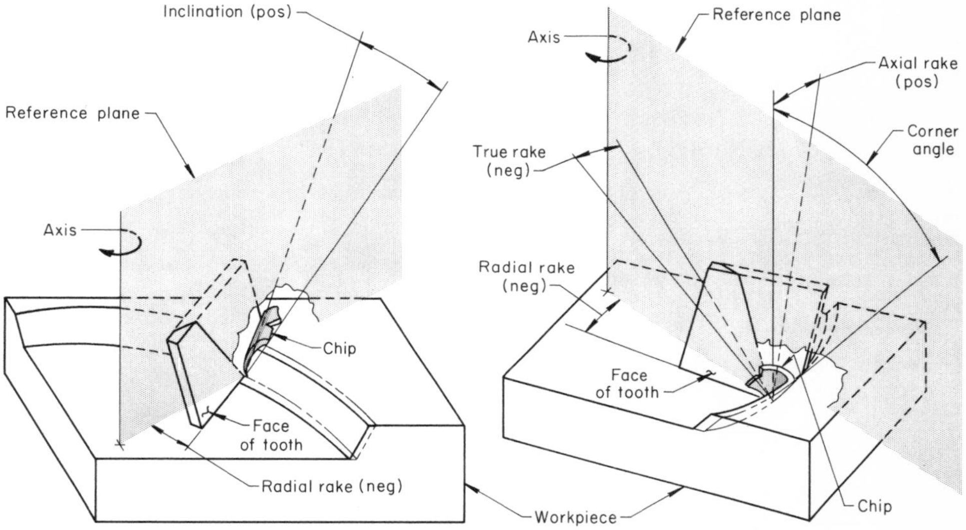

Fig. 9. Geometrical relations of tool angles and reference plane

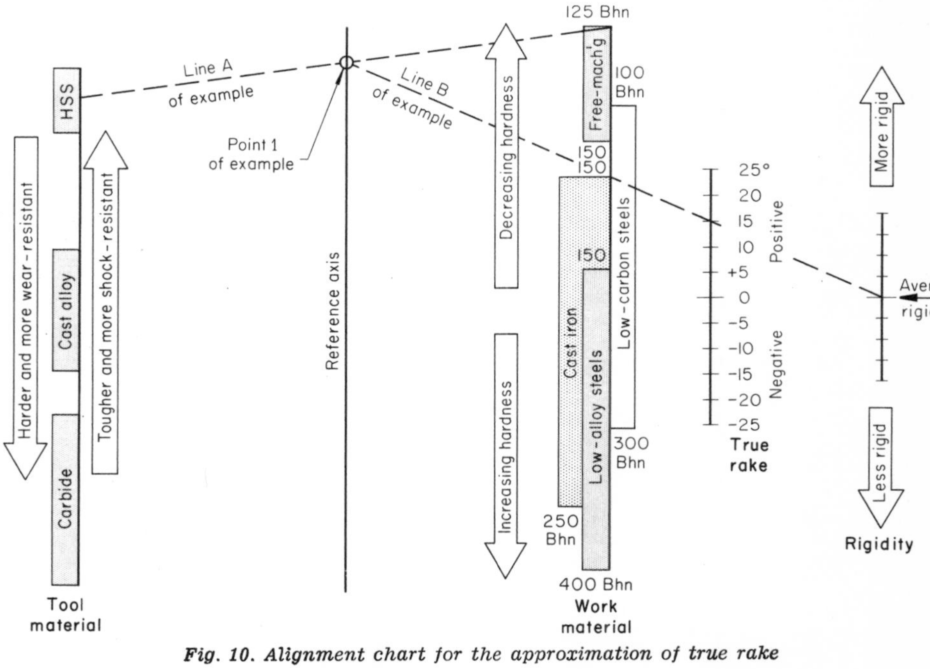

Fig. 10. Alignment chart for the approximation of true rake

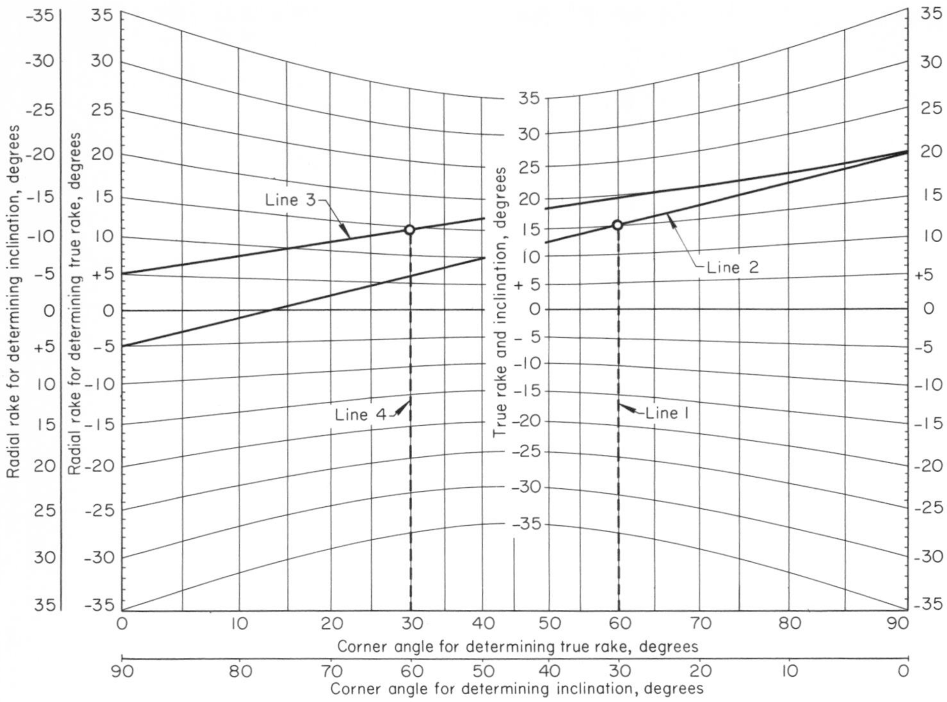

Fig. 11. Chart for determining true rake components and inclination of teeth for milling

ments are: first, to select a true rake large enough for the particular cutting conditions to provide effective chip formation, yet leaving an included angle for the tool large enough to provide the required strength and heat conduction; second, to select an inclination for the cutting edge that will provide the desired direction of chip flow. In face milling, positive inclination directs the chip outward and negative inclination directs the chip toward the center of the cutter. A positive inclination is therefore generally desired.

The alignment chart of Fig. 10 is a semiquantitative guide for the selection of true rake angles for various combinations of tool materials and common ferrous metals. The rigidity scale is a qualitative modifier of tool-work combination to allow for various degrees of rigidity in work, fixture or machine. Increased rigidity permits a positive increase in true rake.

After the suggested initial value for true rake has been selected from Fig. 10, it may be resolved into a tentative combination of rake and corner angles by means of the chart in Fig. 11. The inclination provided by this combination may then be checked on the same chart.

Use of the charts in Fig. 10 and 11 is illustrated by the following example:

Assume a face milling operation on free-machining 1112 steel with a high speed steel cutter and a setup and machine of average rigidity. On the alignment chart, Fig. 10, connect the high speed steel index with the upper end of the free-machining steel block as indicated by line A, and mark its intersection with the reference axis at point 1. Then connect point 1 with the "average rigidity" point by the line B and note its intersection on the true rake line at the recommended value of +15°.

Next, consult Fig. 11. Usually one may begin with a desired or assumed value of corner angle say 60° in this example. (For long tool life and maximum production, the corner angle should be as large as possible. If chatter or heavy scale is encountered, the corner angle should be decreased.) Note the intersection of the true rake corner angle line 1 for 60° and the true rake line for +15°. Through this point draw line 2 connecting some tentative value for axial rake (say +20°) with the radial rake scale, and read the value (−5°) for radial rake.

Next check this combination to find the corresponding inclination. Connect the +20° axial rake point with the −5° inclination point by the line 3. (Note that the scale for radial rake is inverted for determining inclination.) Read inclination (−14°) at the intersection of this line with the vertical line 4 for 60° corner angle. If some other value of inclination is desired (so as to provide a different direction of chip flow), a different orientation of the line 2 through the +15° true rake line must be tried.

Many different combinations of axial and radial rake angles will provide a given true rake with a given corner angle; however, only one combination will provide both a given true rake and a given inclination with a given corner angle.

Effect of Cutter Design on Efficiency

The angular relations of the cutting edge greatly affect cutting efficiency. The important elements in these relations, and their effects, are as follows:

1 **Radial rake** has a major effect on power efficiency of metal removal and on cutter life. Generally, zero to positive radial rakes are used on high speed steel cutters and negative radial rakes on carbide cutters. Negative rakes are less efficient, but usually are necessary for good life of carbide cutters because carbide edges are brittle.

2 **Axial rake** controls chip flow, thrust force of cut, and strength of the cutting edges. The axial rake of high speed steel cutters usually is positive, except for end mills that cut only on the periphery — which often have negative axial rake to transfer cutter thrust back against the spindle bearings. Carbide cutters may have either positive or negative axial rake, depending on the workpiece material and hardness and on the type of cutter.

3 **Corner Angle.** Cutters may have a corner angle of 90°, to cut a square shoulder, or (as in many face mills) may have a corner angle ranging from 30° to 60°, to reduce chip thickness and to ease the blades into the cut with less shock.

4 **Clearance.** A clearance angle is necessary behind all cutting edges, to prevent the cutter teeth from dragging or rubbing across the workpiece. Primary clearance angle (see Fig. 7) usually ranges from 3° to 7°, depending on the type of cut and the workpiece material.

Number of Teeth. A milling cutter should have enough teeth to insure uninterrupted contact with the work metal, and yet not so many as to provide too little space between teeth for chip disposal. Figure 12(a) shows cutter teeth so close together that chip interference is likely. This will increase power consumption and may cause damage to the cutter or the workpiece, or both. Figure 12(b) shows cutter teeth that are too far apart; one tooth will leave the work before the next is engaged. This will cause vibration and chatter, resulting in poor finish, dimensional inaccuracy and excessive tool wear. A nearly optimum compromise is shown in Fig. 12(c).

Characteristics of the metal being milled also influence the number of teeth in a milling cutter. Tooth spacing as shown in Fig. 12(a) would be satisfactory for milling a brittle metal like cast iron, because chips are fine and therefore less likely to interfere. The same tooth spacing would cause chip problems in milling of steel or other metals that yield stringy chips.

When other cutting conditions are constant, an increase in the number of teeth causes a finer feed per tooth, resulting in higher specific energy of metal removal and causing greater rubbing on the land. This condition requires that the cutter be ground to closer tolerances, to insure uniform chip size. On the other hand, surface finish is better with finer feeds. Coarser feed per tooth results in a rougher finish and a higher force on each tooth; however, specific energy of metal removal is lower.

There must be chip space between teeth on the cutter, although excessively large flutes between closely spaced teeth will weaken the teeth. Obtaining adequate chip space does not depend entirely on the number of teeth in the cutter. Other design features can also contribute. For instance, in peripheral milling it is often possible to use a helical-tooth cutter when a minimum number of teeth are needed for chip space. Helical teeth allow a longer period of contact, thus avoiding the condition that would occur when using a straight-tooth cutter as shown in Fig. 12(b). Lower peak forces on the teeth of helical cutters reduce vibration and susceptibility to chatter.

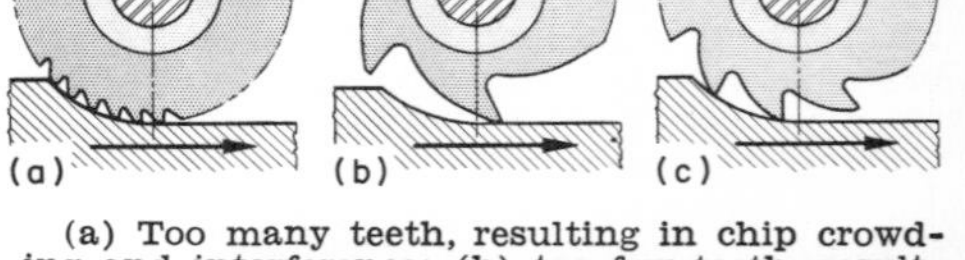

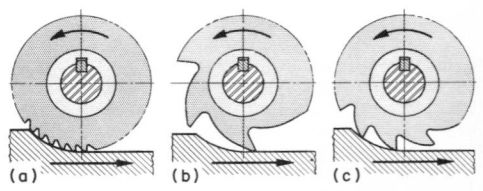

(a) Too many teeth, resulting in chip crowding and interference; (b) too few teeth, resulting in intermittent contact; (c) compromise for satisfactory milling.

Fig. 12. Effect of number of teeth on a milling cutter

Limitations in power and table speed also affect the number of teeth on the cutter. Doubling the number of teeth on the cutter requires that the table speed also be doubled, to maintain a constant feed per tooth. This doubles metal removal rate and power consumption. But if power is available and chips can be disposed of, increasing the number of teeth in the cutter is one means of increasing productivity.

In face milling, the tooth-contact arc is usually longer than in peripheral milling; thus, fewer teeth can be used successfully in face milling when chip space is a problem or when available power is limited.

Spindle speed is established for the most economic operation for each cutter diameter and workpiece and cutter material. The number of chips per minute can be varied only by changing the number of teeth on the cutter. The product of feed per tooth and chips per minute (number of teeth times spindle revolutions per minute) is the table speed. Thus, to keep within specific power limitations when milling at high speed, the number of teeth on the cutter may be reduced. This reduces the number of chips per minute, which in turn reduces table speed.

Power Requirements

The power required for a milling operation is usually computed from the metal removal rate, as follows:

$$P_n = uvdw$$

where P_n = power required at the cutter; u = specific energy, horsepower per cu in. per min; v = table speed, ipm; d = depth of cut, in.; and w = width of cut, in.

If the metal removal factor is known, divide vdw by the factor to find the power required. The above equation gives the average power consumption. The instantaneous rate of doing work will vary with the chip thickness and may be considerably higher than the value calculated from the equation. However, the rotating parts of the machine and the cutter act like a flywheel to smooth out power drawn from the motor. Thus, metal removal rates for milling can be safely based on calculations of average power consumption.

Climb Milling vs Conventional Milling

The relations between cutter rotation and feed direction in climb milling and in conventional milling are shown in Fig. 13. In climb milling, as implied by the name, the milling cutter attempts to "climb" the workpiece. Climb milling is also called "down milling". Conventional milling is often referred to as "up milling".

In climb milling, chips are cut to maximum thickness at initial engagement of cutter teeth with the work, and decrease to zero thickness at the end of engagement. In conventional milling, the reverse occurs: the chips start with no thickness and increase in size as the teeth progress through the cut.

The climb technique can be used for most milling applications. Its widespread use has been prevented by the lack of rigid machines with backlash eliminators, which are essential for climb milling. With such equipment, climb milling has several advantages over conventional milling:

1. Fixtures and holding devices are simpler and less costly, because climb milling exerts a downward force on the workpiece.
2. Cutters with higher rake angles can be used, decreasing power requirements.
3. Chips are less likely to be carried by the tooth, reducing the possibility of marring the machined surface.
4. Chip disposal is easier, because chips pile up behind the cutter rather than in front of it.
5. Cutter wear is less, because chip thickness is maximum at the start of the cut.

The main advantage of conventional milling is in the lower impact encountered at initial tooth-workpiece engagement (zero chip thickness). Furthermore, the direction of milling force compensates for the backlash of the feed mechanism. Conventional milling is preferred over climb milling in: (*a*) milling of surfaces on which depth of cut varies excessively (say by 20%), or (*b*) milling of castings or forgings with very rough surfaces due to sand or scale.

Rigidity of Setup

Optimum results in milling depend greatly on good rigidity of the tooling-and-workpiece setup. Tool deflection and chatter resulting from lack of rigidity cause excessive tool wear and breakage, damage to workpieces, dimensional inaccuracy and unacceptable surface finish. Rigid setups minimize or eliminate these adverse conditions, thereby increasing production and lowering production cost. The selection of more efficient cutting tools and the increased feed and speed possible with a rigid setup further increase production rates. Several methods of increasing the rigidity of a tool setup or of providing greater support for workpieces are discussed in the seven examples that follow. (See also Example 912, in the article on Machining of Aluminum, which discusses an application in which a special arbor was needed for rigidity in milling with an end mill on a long unsupported holder.)

Example 319. Change to More Rigid Arbor That Eliminated Chipping of Cutter Teeth

Deflection of a 2-in.-diam arbor caused excessive chipping of the carbide teeth of a 12-in.-diam slotting cutter used in finish milling slots 1.25 in. wide by 3.25 in. deep in 4340 steel bars at Rockwell C 50 to 52. Prior to heat treatment, the slots had been rough milled to 0.750-in. width and 3-in. depth.

The slotting cutter was redesigned to permit the use of a 2½-in.-diam arbor. This increase in arbor rigidity eliminated cutter damage.

Example 320. Added Arbor Support and Staggering of Cutters for Improved Rigidity (Fig. 14)

In machining a compressor-case assembly made of type 410 stainless steel, it was required that the tops of nine bosses be milled simultaneously. To accomplish this, the heat treated material (Rockwell C 26 to 32) was climb milled on a No. 3 horizontal machine, using a gang-type tool that contained nine high speed steel (inserted-blade) slotting cutters. In the original setup, all nine cutters made contact with the workpiece simultaneously, resulting in a force that deflected the mill arbor and caused excessive cutter breakage. (At least one cutter failed for every two or three assemblies milled.)

Providing the arbor with an added support, as shown in Fig. 14, appreciably reduced arbor deflection, but did not eliminate it; the arbor was still overloaded by the force produced by the simultaneous engagement of all nine cutters with the work.

With the arbor receiving maximum support, a solution to the overloading was found in staggering the cutters to provide sequential, rather than simultaneous, engagement with the workpiece. This stepped arrangement was accomplished by cutting keyway slots in all cutters in progressive increments of 3° from cutter to cutter, thus providing the total assembly of cutters with a spiral-like pattern of cutting edges. This arrangement of cutters served to minimize the load on the arbor and resulted in virtually complete elimination of arbor deflection.

The combination of arbor support and improved cutter arrangement resulted in the extension of cutter life from an average of 3 to an average of 125 pieces per grind. Without changing other operating conditions, cutter breakage was completely eliminated, and a previously rough machined surface was consistently milled to a 32-micro-in. finish.

Example 321. Added Support Between Gang Cutters for Increased Rigidity (Fig. 15)

In milling landing-gear main inner cylinders made of 300M steel at Rockwell C 46 to 49, the use of only one arbor support contributed to a low production rate and an erratic surface finish. Milling speed was only 12 rpm and feed was only 0.250 ipm. Surface finish varied from 125 to 200 micro-in.

Placing a second arbor support midway between the six cutters, as shown in Fig. 15, permitted cutting speed to be increased to 22 rpm and feed to 0.875 ipm. A uniform finish of less than 125 micro-in. was consistently obtained, and cutter life was increased 65%.

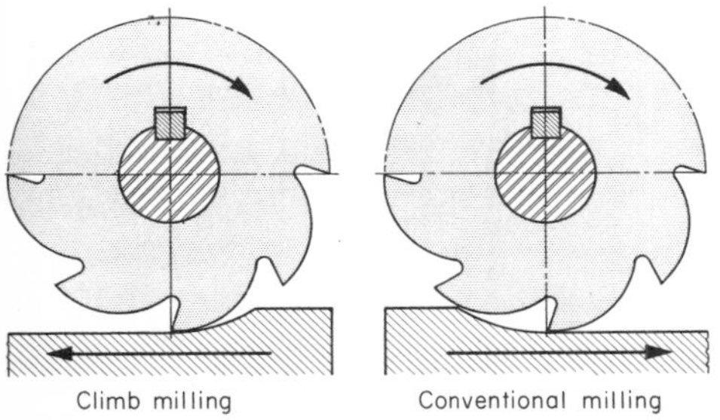

Fig. 13. Cutter rotation and feed direction in climb milling and conventional milling

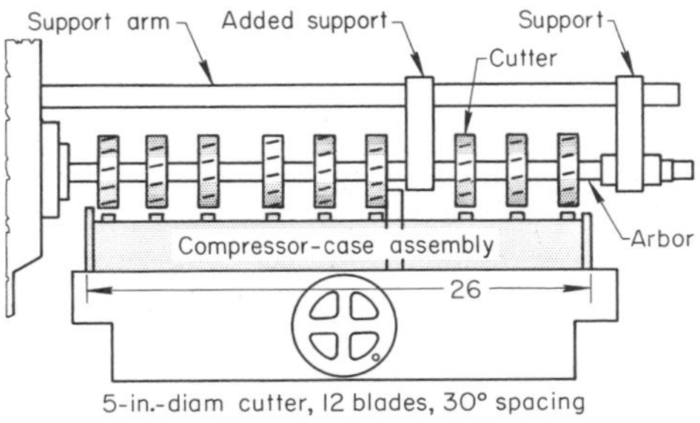

Fig. 14. Added arbor support that improved rigidity in milling setup (Example 320)

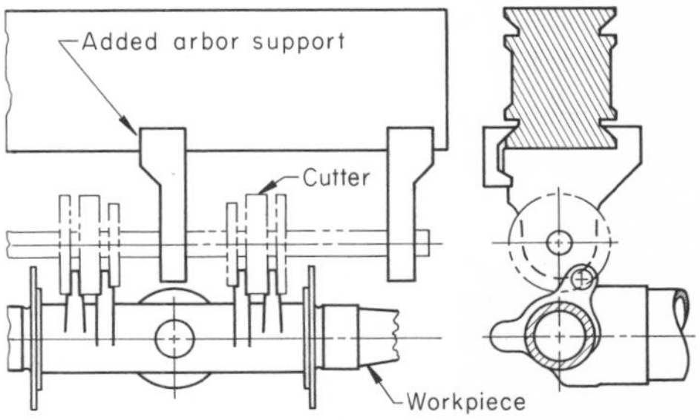

Fig. 15. Added arbor support that increased rigidity of gang-milling setup (Example 321)

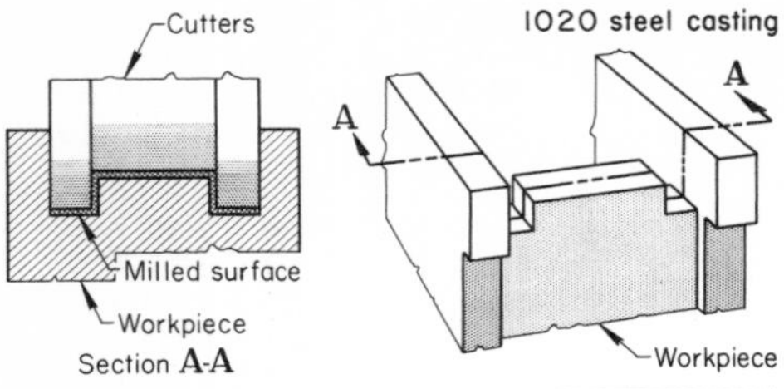

Item	Original method	Improved method
Work-holding method	Standard vise	Special fixture
Cutter material	HSS	Carbide
Improvements Resulting From Changes		
Speed, rpm	140	510
Feed, ipm	1	8⅞
Production, pcs/hr	8.6	28.5
Cutter life per grind:		
Machining time, hr	4	16
Pieces machined	35	450

Fig. 16. Straddle milling operation for which more rigid fixturing permitted the use of carbide cutters, which resulted in the improvements detailed in the table (Example 322)

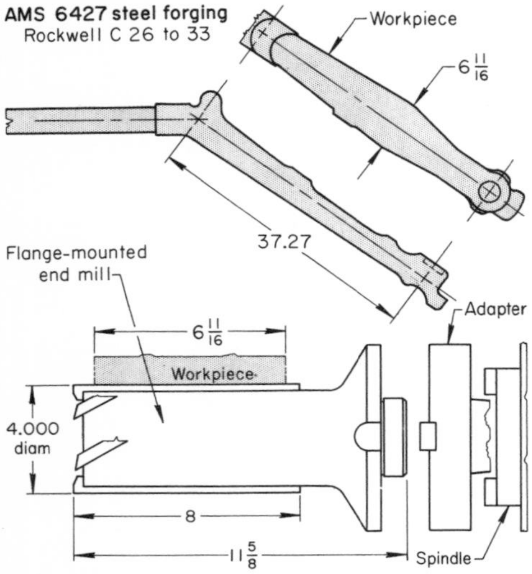

Cutter Details

Type	Flange-mounted end mill
Diameter	4 in. (nominal)
Flute length	8 in.
Number of teeth	6
Number of blades per tooth	4
Primary land	5°
Helix angle	30° (left-hand)
Material	M3 (class 2) high speed steel

Machining Conditions

Speed	48 rpm (50 sfm)
Feed	0.007 to 0.009 ipt
Depths of cut, approx	1/32 to ½ in.
Cutting fluid	Soluble oil
Finish obtained	200 micro-in. max
Setup time	3 hr
Machining time per piece	3 hr
Cutter life per grind:	
Length machined	444 in.
Pieces machined	3
Downtime for changing tools	20 min(a)

(a) Including time for change of control tape when changing to different diameter of cutter

Fig. 17. Use of a flange-mounted end mill for increased rigidity in continuous-pass profile milling of a piston (Example 323)

Example 322. More Rigid Fixturing That Permitted Change in Tooling for Higher Production (Fig. 16)

The straddle milling operation illustrated in Fig. 16 (milling two slots and a central pad on 1020 steel castings) was performed on a 10-hp horizontal machine. Originally, high speed steel cutters were used, and the workpiece was held between the jaws of a standard vise — which did not provide adequate rigidity. The results obtained were unacceptable: tolerances could not be held, milled surfaces did not meet finish specifications, and tool life and production rate were low.

Changing to the use of a specially designed fixture for holding the workpiece resulted in an increase in rigidity that permitted the use of carbide-tipped cutters. As shown by the comparison in the table with Fig. 16, the improved method permitted an increase in speed and feed, produced a 1200% increase in tool life (which considerably decreased downtime for changing tools), and more than tripled production rate. Also, with the improved method, the castings were milled to specified tolerance and finish.

Example 323. Flange-Mounted End Mill for Profile Milling a Complex Forging (Fig. 17)

A 20-hp tape-controlled horizontal profiler was used in rough milling the irregular contour of the forged steel piston shown in Fig. 17. This machine had a No. 50 taper spindle, but to obtain the cutter rigidity required for the 149-in.-long continuous-pass cut (four times 37.27 in.) and for the amount of stock removal entailed, an adapter was used that permitted the flanged end mill to be bolted directly to the spindle (lower sketch in Fig. 17). This method of tool mounting, together with careful selection and correlation of speed and feed (see table of processing details accompanying Fig. 17), resulted in acceptable tool life and virtually eliminated chatter and tapered cuts. Conventional rather than climb milling was used, because the forgings were heavily scaled and because of the wide variation in depth of cut.

Example 324. Use of Low-Melting Alloy for Fixturing Thin-Wall Parts (Fig. 18)

A simple clamp arrangement was initially used to anchor a thin-wall turbine vane during peripheral milling. The vane was made of AMS 5382 (a heat-resisting alloy comparable to X-40 and HS-31) and was machined at a hardness of Rockwell C 36 to 40. Because of its thin cross section, the vane was deflected by the tool; this deflection resulted in chatter and chipping of the carbide cutting edges. The operation was performed on a No. 4 vertical machine with a 12-tooth inserted-blade shell end mill (5° axial rake and 15° radial rake).

To provide improved anchorage that would eliminate chatter, the part was pinned to the supporting shuttle, as shown in Fig. 18. Attachment was accomplished by drilling eight ⅜-in.-diam holes in the vane, locating the vane on the shuttle, and pouring a low-melting-point (about 180 F) alloy into the spaces between the cross members of the vane, the eight holes, and the T-slots of the shuttle. Upon freezing, the alloy firmly anchored the part to the shuttle. Using this technique it was possible to locate shuttles on both sides of the upright fixture, thus permitting two parts to be milled at the same time.

The fixture was positioned at an angle of 60°, to accommodate a compound-angle cut that was milled at one end of each part. As a result of improved rigidity, cutter life was increased from 4 to 125 pieces per grind.

Example 325. Use of Expanding Arbor for Support of a Thin-Wall Part (Fig. 19)

A thin-wall part with two sets of ears on its outside diameter required rigid support during milling to prevent taper and to obtain acceptable surface finish. The part was made of 300M steel and heat treated to Rockwell C 53 to 56.

The expanding arbor shown in Fig. 19 had two shoes that were forced outward as the tapered center shaft advanced. This arrangement not only provided the support needed for eliminating taper and obtaining acceptable surface finish, but also resulted in a 70% increase in tool life.

Methods

The principal methods of milling are classified as peripheral, face and end. These terms refer to the type of cutter used (Fig. 5) and to the relationship of

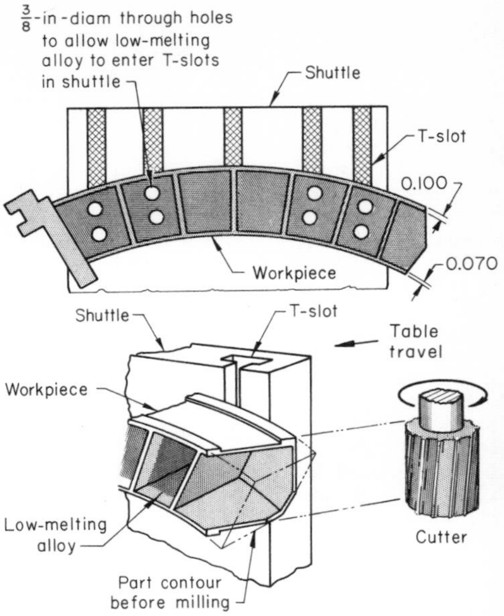

Fig. 18. Use of low-melting alloy for holding a thin-wall turbine vane during peripheral milling (Example 324)

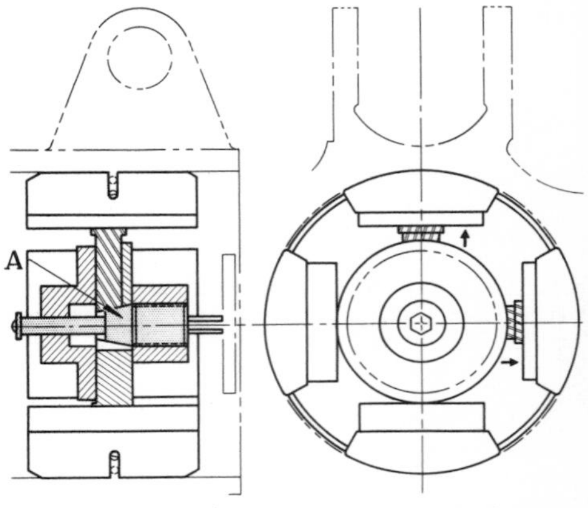

Tapered shaft A forces out two support shoes

Fig. 19. Expanding arbor (A) *that provided rigid support during milling of a thin-wall part* (Example 325)

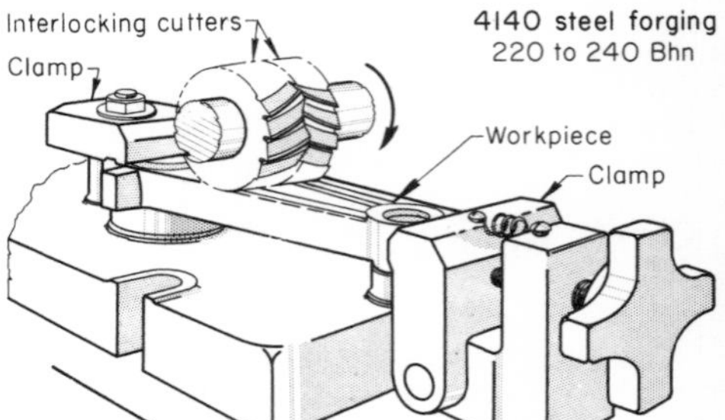

Cutter Details

Type	Plain peripheral (two, interlocking)
Size	3-in. diam, 1⅞ in. wide, 1¼ in. bore
Number of teeth	16
Helix angle	18°
Rake angle	20° (positive)
Material	T5 high speed steel

Machining Conditions

Speed	133 rpm (104 sfm)
Feed	0.0044 ipt
Cutting fluid	Soluble oil
Finish obtained	125 micro-in. max
Setup time	30 min
Production rate	40 pieces per hr (both sides)

Fig. 20. Peripheral milling of channel sides of a connecting rod (Example 326)

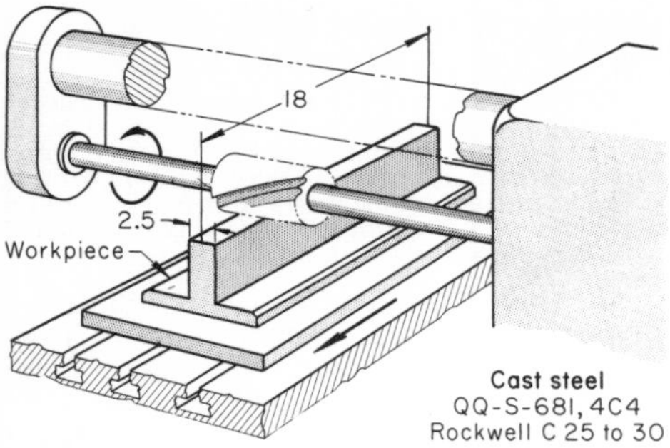

Cutter Details

Type	Peripheral, 45° left-hand helix
Size	4-in. diam, 6 in. wide
Number of teeth	8
Material	High speed steel

Machining Conditions

Speed	78 rpm (82 sfm)
Feed	0.014 ipt (8.75 ipm)
Depth of cut	$\frac{1}{4}$ in.
Cutting fluid	Chemical-base soluble oil
Production rate	20 pieces per hour

Fig. 21. Peripheral milling of a sand casting (Example 327)

the spindle to the surface being milled. In some instances, the differences between the three methods are clearly defined, but more often a given milling operation is a combination of two methods. This is particularly true of end milling, which is almost invariably a combination of peripheral and face milling.

The method of milling selected for a specific application depends largely on the amount of metal to be removed, workpiece size and shape, and the configuration to be milled. Total quantity to be produced, production rate (quantity per unit of time), work-metal hardness, and cost are more likely to influence modifications of procedure within a given method than to determine selection of the method itself.

Details of 25 specific milling applications are given in examples in the three sections that follow. These descriptions of practice are presented under headings of peripheral, face or end milling, although many of the examples represent modifications of these broad classifications.

Peripheral Milling

Peripheral milling is a method of generating a machined surface by cutting with the teeth on the periphery of a cutter whose axis is parallel to the milled surface. The operation is usually performed on horizontal milling machines in which one or more cutters are mounted by means of keys on arbors with outboard support.

In the simplest type of peripheral milling, cutting is done only by teeth on the periphery of the cutter (as in Examples 326 and 327). However, many applications, such as slotting, require cutting action from both the periphery and the sides (as in Examples 330 and 331). Some side cutting action is often needed for gang, slab and straddle milling applications (as in Examples 333 to 336), and for other specific applications (as in Examples 337 and 338).

Capabilities. Peripheral milling can be used for removing metal from simple flat surfaces, for cutting keyways and deep slots, and for milling contoured surfaces and surfaces having two or more angles or complex forms.

Long keyways can be milled faster by peripheral milling with a keyway cutter or a slotting cutter than by end milling. In addition, the width of the keyway is maintained more accurately, because in peripheral milling cutter wear is distributed over a larger number of teeth than in end milling (see Example 330).

Deep slots, including T-slots (see Fig. 27), are usually generated by peripheral milling, because greater rigidity can be maintained than in end milling. Staggered-tooth slotting cutters are generally used for peripheral milling of deep slots.

Some configurations of contoured surfaces can be produced by peripheral milling, cutter direction being controlled by rise-and-fall templates and tracers. Forms that can be milled in a single direction by the peripheral method are limited only by cutter design. Several flat and angular surfaces can be produced simultaneously by combining peripheral and face milling (see Example 337).

Limitations. In terms of metal removed per unit of time, peripheral milling is less efficient than face milling for producing simple flat surfaces. Other considerations, however, sometimes make peripheral milling the preferable method (see Examples 326 and 327).

Peripheral milling is more limited than end milling for cutting complex configurations; therefore, pockets and intricate recesses are usually cut by end milling.

Peripheral vs Face Milling. In many applications, either peripheral milling or face milling may be used for machining a specific area of the workpiece. Selection of the milling method will then be based on the surface finish required, rigidity of setup, length of feed stroke, and simplicity of fixturing. Production applications that exemplify the advantages of peripheral over face milling for specific applications are described in the following four examples:

Examples 326 to 329. Peripheral Over Face Milling

Example 326 — Higher Production and Simpler Fixturing (Fig. 20). Connecting rods for racing cars required machining on both channel sides, to obtain the degree of balance necessary for high-speed operation. Peripheral milling, utilizing the setup illustrated in Fig. 20, was used in preference to face milling, because in peripheral milling: (*a*) feed stroke was 50% shorter, which resulted in increased production; and (*b*) simpler fixturing could be used because cutting forces imposed on the workpiece are all in one direction (in contrast to face milling, in which cutting forces are variable and would have caused deflection and twisting of the workpiece, thus requiring more complex fixturing to hold tolerances).

This operation was performed using a 5-hp plain automatic bed-type machine with rise-and-fall spindle motion. The 12-in.-wide table had a 2-ft length of travel. Additional details are tabulated with Fig. 20.

Example 327 — Greater Rigidity (Fig. 21). Peripheral milling was used rather than face milling for machining the top face of T-section sand castings as shown in Fig. 21. Face milling could have been used, but chatter would have been likely because the section being milled was not rigid enough to withstand the multidirectional forces of a face mill.

In this operation, a conventional cut was used because a climb cut (cutting directly into the as-cast surface) would have caused the

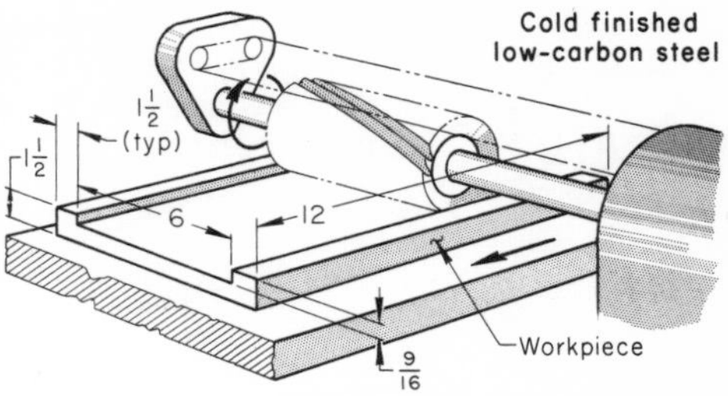

Cutter Details

Type	Peripheral, 45° helix
Size	4-in. diam, 6 in. wide
Number of teeth	8
Relief hollow ground on both ends of each tooth	2°
Material	High speed steel

Machining Conditions

Speed	112 rpm (117 sfm)
Feed	0.011 ipt
Depth of cut	$\frac{9}{16}$ in.
Cutting fluid	Chemical-base soluble oil
Production rate	16 pieces per hour

Fig. 22. Peripheral milling of a channel in bar stock (Example 328)

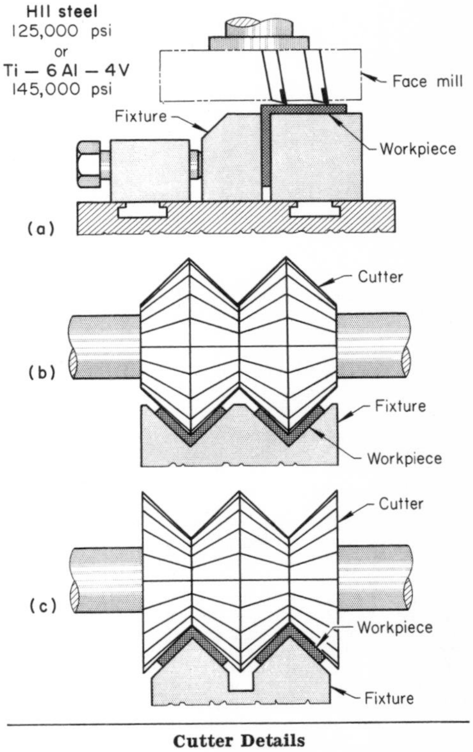

Cutter Details

Type	45°-angle peripheral (matched sets of 4)
Size	6-in. diam
Number of teeth	20
Material	M3 high speed steel

Machining Conditions

Speed	22 rpm (35 sfm)
Feed	0.0035 ipt (1.5 ipm)
Depth of cut	0.100 in.
Cutting fluid	Sulfurized oil
Finish obtained, approx	125 micro-in.
Production rate, approx	1 piece per hour
Cutter life per grind	75 to 100 linear ft

Extrusions were 8 ft long; each leg of L was 2 in. long and (before being milled) $\frac{5}{16}$ in. thick.

(a) In original method, each surface was milled separately — outside surfaces by face milling, as shown, and inside surfaces by peripheral milling.

(b) and (c) Improved method, in which two pairs of peripheral cutters milled both inside or outside surfaces of two extrusions simultaneously (details in table).

Fig. 23. Original and improved methods of milling angle extrusions (Example 329)

cutter to wear excessively. The 6-in.-wide cutter was more economical than one nearer the 2½-in. width of the section being milled, because successive workpieces could be positioned at different locations on the table, and the entire cutter surface used, before it was necessary to stop the operation to change cutters. Cutter and machining details are given with Fig. 21.

Example 328 — Better Finish on Bottom Surface (Fig. 22). Peripheral milling in a horizontal machine was used for cutting wide, shallow channels in cold finished low-carbon steel bars, as illustrated and detailed in Fig. 22. Peripheral milling was selected instead of face milling because surface finish specified for the bottom of the channel (125 micro-in. max) was more critical than that for the sides (250 micro-in.). Had the reverse been true, however, face milling (preferably in a vertical machine) would have been used. By both methods, tool maintenance (because, as shown in the data table with Fig. 22, the ends of the teeth on the peripheral cutter were ground with a relief, to decrease drag in the climb cut) and production rate would have been closely similar.

Example 329 — Increased Accuracy and Efficiency (Fig. 23). In milling both sides of each leg of right-angle extrusions of H11 steel (annealed) and titanium alloy (solution treated), deformed extrusions with unacceptable surface finish were being produced at low production rates. Originally, complicated fixturing and clamping were required to face mill the outside surfaces (as shown in Fig. 23a) and then to peripheral mill the inside surfaces, one at a time.

In the revised method, two pairs of 45°-angle peripheral cutters were used to mill the inside surfaces of two extrusions, as shown in Fig. 23(b). Cutters were reversed for milling the outside surfaces as shown in Fig. 23(c). The cutters were made in matched sets of four to assure that all diameters were equal and that keyways aligned the teeth in correct relation.

In addition to doubling production rates, the revised method produced straighter extrusions; the accurate positioning possible with the simplified fixtures equalized cutter forces, minimizing vibration, and thus improved surface finish. Cutter details and machining conditions are tabulated with Fig. 23.

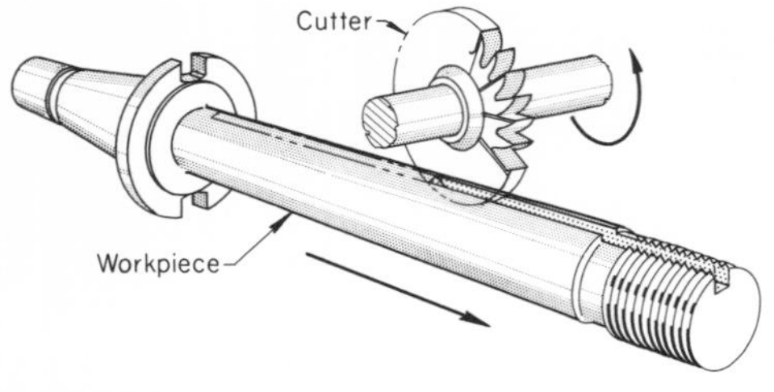

Fig. 24. Peripheral milling (climb cut) of a long keyway in a machine arbor

Milling of Keyways. The greater accuracy possible with peripheral milling makes it preferable to end milling in the machining of keyways — particularly of long keyways, such as are found on machine arbors (Fig. 24).

The following example describes the different equipment and techniques used in one plant for milling long keyways in progressively larger production quantities.

Example 330. Effect of Production Quantity on Method of Peripheral Milling of Long Keyways

In a plant having a heavy schedule of keyway milling operations, quantity requirements strongly influenced tooling setups, fixturing, clamping requirements, and machine selection.

In milling quantities of 10 pieces or less, a vise mounted on the table of a small knee-and-column milling machine held the workpieces. The commercial, staggered-tooth, peripheral slotting cutter was positioned by hand; conservative speed and feed were used to maintain tolerances.

For lots of 10 to 100 pieces, a small bed-type milling machine was used, with simple fixturing and dog setting to control the length of cut. Increased production, because of higher speed and heavier feed possible in the heavier, more rigid machine, justified the selection of this machine in preference to a knee-and-column machine.

Production lots of 100 to 1000 pieces were machined on a production-type automatic milling machine. Higher equipment costs were offset by production increases at lower operator and machining costs. Rise and fall of the spindle carrier cleared the cut on the rapid return stroke, extending cutter life. The use of two fixtures with the reciprocating machining cycle eliminated loading and unloading time. A 20° positive rake angle on the cutter in this setup permitted high speed and heavy feed.

For quantities greater than 1000 pieces, two special fixtures, each holding three workpieces for simultaneous milling, were used on a large automatic milling machine. To permit uninterrupted machining cycles, a hydraulic clamping attachment on the fixtures expedited loading and unloading of the large volume of work processed with this setup.

Slotting. The accuracy and efficiency of peripheral slotting cutters (which essentially are circular saws) make them preferable to power saws for the machining of slots. A simple slotting operation is shown in Fig. 24. More complex operations and techniques are described in the two examples that follow:

Example 331. Milling of Multiple Slots (Fig. 25)

Cutter and processing details are given with Fig. 25 for a milling operation in which simultaneous slotting of opposite ends of two 5145 steel parts by sets of peripheral cutters at two stations produced the equivalent of one complete piece per machining cycle. At the end of each cycle, completed parts were unloaded; parts slotted on one end in the first station were turned and positioned in the second station, and unmachined parts loaded at the first station. As shown in Fig. 25, an additional support between the sets of cutters minimized arbor deflection and permitted adherence to tolerances on slot dimensions and spacing. Climb milling was used rather than conventional milling because: (*a*) less clamping pressure was required; (*b*) cutter life was longer; and (*c*) burrs were left in an area easily accessible for subsequent removal.

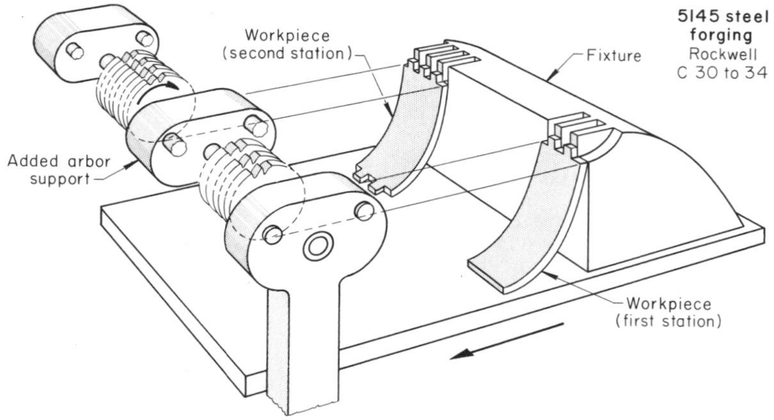

Cutter Details

Type	Staggered-tooth	Number of teeth	28
Size	9-in. diam, 0.562 in. wide	Material	High speed steel

Machining Conditions

Speed	37 rpm (87 sfm)	Tolerances:	
Feed	0.0014 ipt (1.42 ipm)	Slot depth	$+\frac{1}{32}$ in.
Cutting fluid	Sulfurized oil	Slot width	0.556 to 0.566 in.
Finish obtained	250 micro-in.	Spacing	0.610 to 0.620 in.
Setup time	1½ hr	Production rate	24 pieces per hour
Downtime for tool change	¾ hr	Cutter life per grind of gang	160 pieces

Fig. 25. Use of cutters in gangs of three and four for slotting both ends of a steel part (Example 331)

Example 332. Cutter Redesign and Electronic Feed Control in Slotting (Fig. 26)

The gun component of 4340 steel (220 to 250 Bhn) shown in Fig. 26 required two slots 0.125 in. wide by 0.125 in. deep, with edges chamfered 0.030 in. by 45°. Part configuration

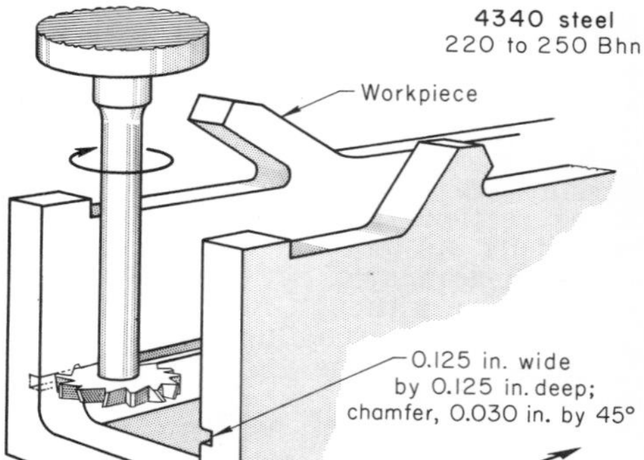

Cutter Details

Type	Staggered-tooth slotting cutter with chamfer, arbor-type shank
Size	1.165-in. diam
Number of teeth	12
Material	M2 or M7 high speed steel

Machining Conditions

Speed	375 rpm (114 sfm)
Feed	0.0015 ipt
Cutting fluid	Sulfurized and chlorinated mineral oil
Tolerances:	
Slot depth	±0.002 in.
Slot width	+0.002 in.
Chamfers	+0.010 in.
Finish obtained	50 to 60 micro-in.
Setup time....1 hr (includes first piece milled)	
Downtime for tool change	8 min
Production rate	7.68 pieces per hour
Cutter life per grind	50 pieces
Total cutter life, approx	350 pieces

Fig. 26. Milling slots in a gun component (Example 332)

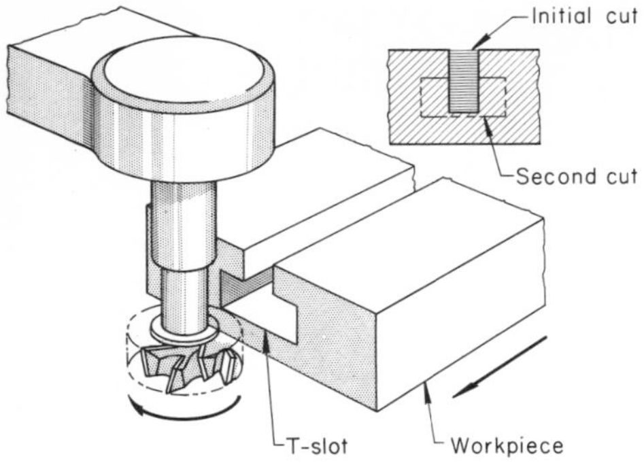

Fig. 27. Typical setup for milling T-slots

required $3\frac{5}{8}$ in. of unsupported tool overhang and a maximum allowable shank diameter of $\frac{13}{16}$ in., to eliminate interference between the spindle and workpiece.

Originally, these parts were slotted on a vertical dial-type milling machine in two operations, using standard T-slot cutters and chamfer cutters. Finished parts did not meet tolerances and specified finish, and tool breakage was excessive.

The operation was changed to a 5-hp automatic profile milling machine with electronic feed control. A specially designed cutter incorporating a chamfer was mounted on an arbor-type shank with maximum diameter at the cutter end and minimum runout at the spindle end. With precision feed control and more rigid tooling, susceptibility to chatter was minimized and acceptable parts were produced in one operation, with extended tool life. Cutter and processing details are given with Fig. 26.

T-slots are produced in two separate milling operations, as shown in Fig. 27. Removal of the largest possible amount of metal, commensurate with slot dimensions, is accomplished in an initial cut with a peripheral mill or an end mill. A second cut is then made, using a staggered-tooth T-slotting cutter (solid or tipped) at a constant feed rate. To prevent damage to the cutter or the workpiece, cutting fluids (or air blasts in dry milling) are used copiously to flush chips out of the slot.

Gang milling refers to milling with two or more peripheral cutters mounted on the same arbor. The cutters may be of the same size or of different sizes, and the surfaces being milled may be adjacent or separated. Gang milling is commonly used to produce simultaneously several different steps in a workpiece or to produce sections of the same thickness from bars or extrusions. Typical applications of gang milling are described in the five examples that follow:

Example 333. Gang Milling vs Power Sawing for Cutting Off (Fig. 28)

Figure 28 shows the gang milling method selected over power sawing for cutting slugs from 4140 steel extrusions for subsequent disk grinding to close tolerances. Although sawed parts were produced at greater speeds, milled parts were more uniform in thickness and required less deburring, thus reducing grinding costs. The milling was done on a $7\frac{1}{2}$-hp bed-type milling machine with reciprocating cycling. Cutter details and machining conditions and results are given in the tabulation accompanying Fig. 28.

Example 334. Close-Tolerance Milling at High Production Rates by Six-Cutter Gang (Fig. 29)

The 1018 steel workpiece shown in Fig. 29 was milled before heat treatment and grinding to close tolerances. For small quantities, milling was done in several operations, using single cutters. When production requirements were increased, the operation was changed to a 10-hp horizontal milling machine, using the six-cutter gang setup illustrated and detailed in Fig. 29. Machine stability and close-tolerance grinding of the cutters on a special arbor provided milling accuracy that minimized finish grinding costs.

Speed and feed established were correlated to: (*a*) maintain production quotas; (*b*) minimize peak-to-valley cutter marks on surfaces subsequently ground; and (*c*) maintain acceptable tool life.

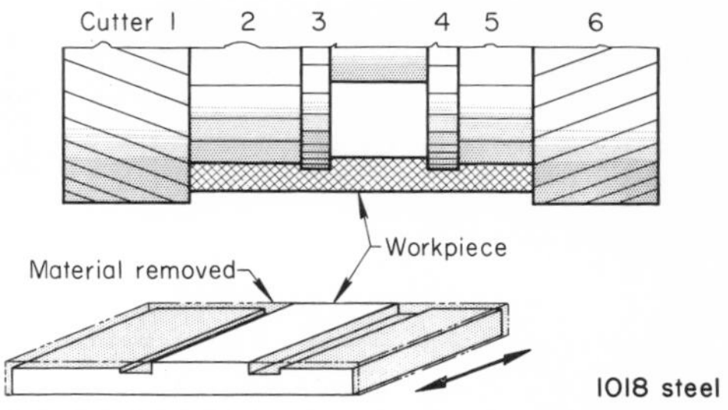

Cutter diameter:	
Cutters 1 and 6	$4\frac{1}{2}$ in.
Cutters 2 and 5	$3\frac{3}{4}$ in.
Cutters 3 and 4	$3\frac{7}{8}$ in.
Number of teeth:	
Cutters 1 and 6	14
Cutters 2, 3, 4 and 5	20
Speed	140 rpm (165 sfm max)
Feed	7 ipm

Fig. 29. Gang milling of several surfaces simultaneously (Example 334)

Example 335. Simultaneous Slab and Side Milling (Fig. 30)

Inserted-blade slab mills with side teeth were used to mill the 4130 steel forging shown in the setup in Fig. 30. The inserts incorporated chip-breaking grooves to attain acceptable finish and to distribute the cutting load. Close tolerances on the width of the protruding lug were maintained by using a micrometer spacing collar between the two mills. Milling was done on a 15-hp bed-type milling machine equipped with a reciprocating cycle cam and hydraulic feed. Conventional rather than climb milling was used for two reasons: (*a*) the only machine available at the time did not have sufficient power for climb milling; and (*b*) from previous experience it was assumed that better tool life would be obtained using conventional milling because of scale on the surfaces of the forgings. For cutter and machining details, see Fig. 30.

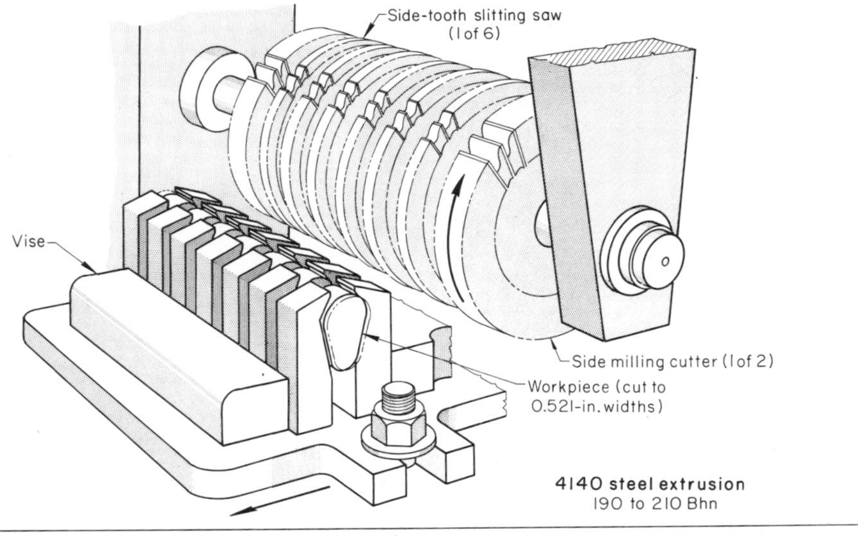

Details of Side-Tooth Slitting Saws

Size	5-in.-diam, $\frac{3}{16}$ in. wide; 1-in.-diam arbor bore
Number of teeth	40
Number of cutters	6
Material	M2 or M7 high speed steel

Details of Side Milling Cutters

Size	5-in.-diam, $\frac{1}{2}$ in. wide; 1-in.-diam arbor bore
Number of teeth	40
Number of cutters	2
Material	M2 or M7 high speed steel

Machining Conditions and Results for Gang Milling

Speed	60 rpm (79 sfm)
Feed	0.0007 ipt
Cutting fluid	Sulfurized and chlorinated mineral oil
Tolerance on widths cut	−0.005 in.
Finish obtained	125 micro-in.
Setup time	1 hr (includes first load milled)
Downtime for tool change	45 min
Production rate	120 pieces per hour
Cutter life per grind of gang	1100 pieces

Fig. 28. Eight-cutter gang used in cutting off (Example 333)

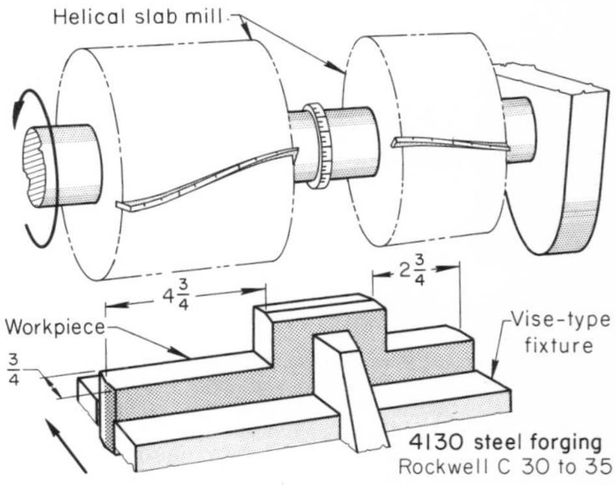

Cutter Details

Type	Plain peripheral with side teeth, inserted blades
Size	7-in. diam, 3 and 5-in. widths, 2-in.-diam arbor bore
Number of teeth	12
Insert material	M2 or M7 high speed steel

Machining Conditions

Speed	28 rpm (51 sfm)
Feed	0.0044 ipt (1.48 ipm)
Depth of cut	0.040 to 0.090 in.
Cutting fluid	Sulfurized and chlorinated mineral oil
Tolerances: Depth	−0.010 in.
Coplanarity	Within 0.005 in.
Finish obtained	125 micro-in.
Setup time	1.5 hr (includes first piece milled)
Downtime for tool change	45 min
Production rate	11 pieces per hour
Cutter life per grind	450 pieces

Fig. 30. Simultaneous slab and side milling of coplanar surfaces (Example 335)

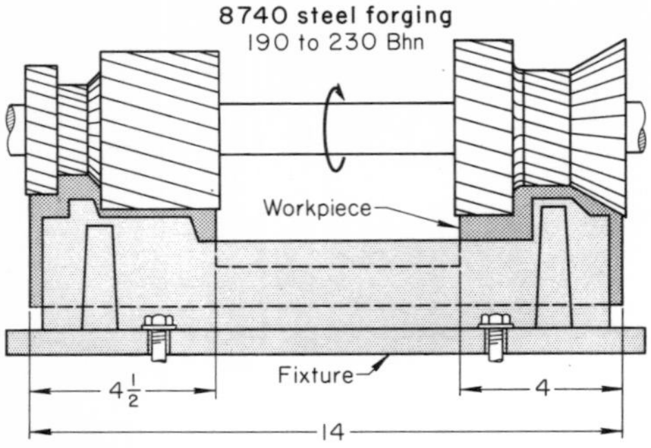

Cutter Details

Type	8-cutter gang; slab, angle, interlocking form and side mills
Diameters	4 to 5 in.
Widths	0.300 to 3¼ in.
Arbor-bore diameter	1 in.
Number of teeth	20 to 26
Material	M2 or M7 high speed steel

Machining Conditions

Speed	78 rpm (102 sfm max)
Feed	2 13/16 ipm
Cutting fluid	Sulfurized and chlorinated mineral oil
Finish obtained	80 to 125 micro-in.
Tolerances: Angles	±1°
Depths	−0.004 in.
Lengths	±0.005 in.
Setup time	30 min (cutter gang preset)
Production rate	19 pieces per hour
Cutter life per grind	300 pieces
Downtime for tool change	20 min

Fig. 31. Gang milling of eight surfaces on a complex forging (Example 336)

Example 336. Gang Milling Eight Surfaces Simultaneously (Fig. 31)

An eight-cutter gang was used to mill eight surfaces simultaneously on an 8740 steel forging in a single setup, as illustrated in Fig. 31. It had been estimated that two setups might be required to mill this workpiece. However, by concentrating the slab mill portion of the cut near the machine column and by using two overarm arbor supports (not shown in Fig. 31), the total 8½-in. width was conventionally milled to dimensions within tolerances. This method was used for milling a total of 5000 pieces in job lots of 200 to 300. Milling was used in preference to broaching because quantity requirements did not warrant the cost of broaching tools and because available broaching machines did not have sufficient capacity to machine the entire width in one pass. Cutter and machining details are tabulated under Fig. 31.

Example 337. Milling Two Parallel Surfaces and a Slot Simultaneously (Fig. 32)

Steel castings of the configuration shown in Fig. 32 were clamped to a special fixture to permit simultaneous milling of two bolting surfaces and a slot. The slot was milled with a slitting saw having side chip clearance. The two outboard cutters were conventional side mills secured to the same arbor. Cutter and machining details are included with Fig. 32.

Form Milling. The number of parallel surfaces and their angular relationships to each other that can be machined by peripheral milling is limited almost solely by cutter design. Form cutters are expensive, but often there is no other satisfactory means of producing complex contours such as the one discussed in the following example:

Example 338. Form Milling Six Surfaces With One Cutter (Fig. 33)

For small job lots, a knee-and-column horizontal milling machine with a special form cutter was used in milling a six-surface contour in 1117 steel shafts, as illustrated and detailed in Fig. 33. A vise mounted on the machine table held the workpiece, and the cutter was positioned manually.

For production lots of more than 1000 pieces, the cutter was used on a bed-type machine with rise and fall of the spindle, and fixtures with air-clamping attachments.

Face Milling

Face milling is used for machining flat surfaces by means of cutters having teeth on their peripheral faces and driven by spindles whose axes are perpendicular to the surface being milled. In face milling, the tooth path is generated by a combined action of the tooth similar to actions obtained in climb and conventional milling with peripheral cutters. The chip thickness is minimum at the points where the tooth enters and leaves the work, and maximum at the transition point between climb and conventional milling.

Face milling cuts are deep radially and narrow axially, whereas peripheral cuts are shallow radially and wide axially; therefore, face milling removes a given amount of metal with less power than peripheral milling.

Capabilities. In addition to being a more efficient method of removing metal, other advantages of face milling over peripheral milling are:

1 The cutter has greater rigidity, because it is attached directly to the spindle nose.
2 Large areas can be milled with little protrusion of the spindle.
3 Outboard bearings are not required, which allows greater flexibility in workpiece size.
4 Cutting forces are more evenly distributed.
5 Less time is needed for tool changes.
6 Cutter grinding costs are less than for peripheral cutters of comparable size.

The efficiency of face milling in removing large amounts of metal and in milling to close tolerances is described in the example that follows. (See also Example 914, in the article on Machining of Aluminum Alloys.)

Example 339. Face Milling 12-In.-Wide Plates in One Pass per Side (Fig. 34)

Face milling was selected for machining both sides of the 12-in.-wide steel plates shown in Fig. 34, mainly because it was more efficient than peripheral milling. The operation was performed on a fixed-rail bed-type milling machine. The plates were secured horizontally by means of a magnetic table, and the vertical spindle was driven by a 100-hp head.

Had this operation been performed on a slab miller (peripheral milling), a helical cutter at least 6 in. in diameter and having about ten rows of inserted blades would have been required. Using carbide-tipped blades for a peripheral cutter of this size would have been prohibitively expensive; thus, high speed steel inserts would have been used. Allowable feed and speed for peripheral milling with high speed steel would have resulted in a metal removal rate of only 12 cu in. per min, compared with 122 cu in. per min by face milling with carbide cutters. Cutter and machining details are tabulated with Fig. 34.

Limitations of face milling compared with peripheral milling are listed in the first column on the next page:

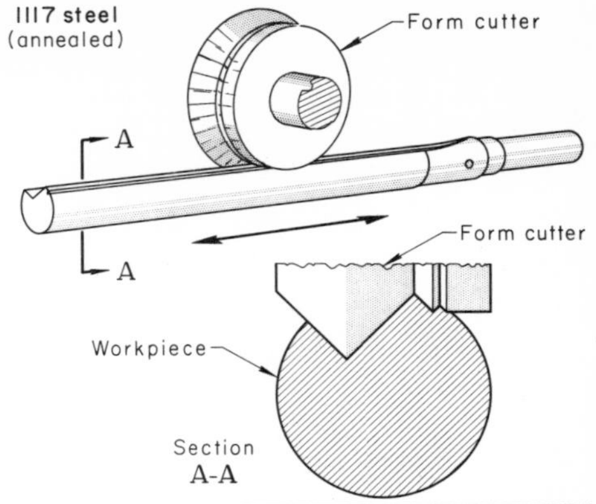

Cutter Details

Type	Special form
Size	3½-in. diam max
Number of teeth	12
Material	High speed steel

Machining Conditions

Speed	225 rpm (206 sfm max)
Feed	0.0022 ipt (5.94 ipm)
Depth of cut	¼ in. max

Fig. 33. Use of a special form milling cutter for producing a six-surface contour (Example 338)

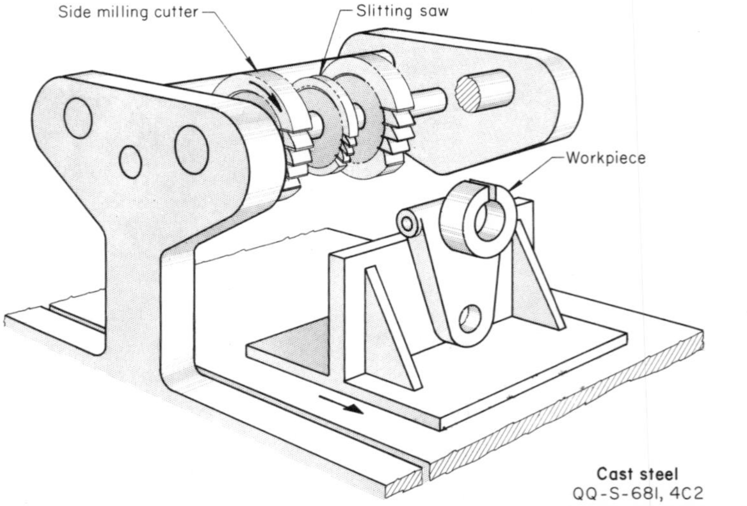

Cutter Details

Type	Two side milling cutters; one slitting saw
Size: Mills	5-in. diam
Saw	3-in. diam
Number of teeth	28
Material	High speed steel

Machining Conditions

Speed: Mills	145 rpm (190 sfm)
Saw	145 rpm (115 sfm)
Feed	0.750 ipm
Cutting fluid	Chemical-base water-soluble
Production rate	25 pieces per hour
Cutter life per grind	230 pieces

Fig. 32. Simultaneous side milling and slotting of a steel casting (Example 337)

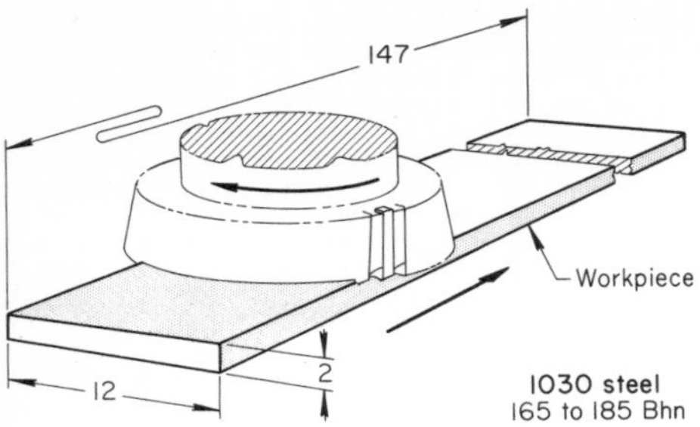

Cutter Details

Type	Face mill, inserted blade
Size	16-in. diam, 3¾ in. thick
Number of teeth	32
Material	Carbide-tipped blades

Machining Conditions

Speed	72 rpm (302 sfm)
Feed	0.027 ipt (62 ipm)
Depth of cut	⅛ in.
Cutting fluid	None
Tolerances:	
Parallelism error	0.003 in. max
Depth of cutter marks	0.003 in. max
Power required	95 hp
Metal removal rate	122 cu in. per minute
Cutter life per grind, approx	30,000 sq in.

Fig. 34. Face milling of a steel plate in one pass per side (Example 339)

1 Face milling is restricted to machining of flat surfaces.
2 As the width of the cut increases in relation to the diameter of the face mill, the larger number of teeth engaged in cutting exerts a greater force at right angles to the direction of feed. Thus, more rugged fixturing and clamping of the workpiece are required, particularly if the part configuration is sensitive to tangential forces imposed by the cutter (see Examples 326 and 327).

End Milling

As shown in Fig. 5, end mills have cutting edges on the face end as well as on the periphery. Thus, cuts that vary widely in configuration can be made with an end mill by using the side and end consecutively or simultaneously. End milling is usually differentiated from peripheral milling or face milling by application rather than by definition.

End milling is less efficient than other milling methods in removing metal because the end of the cutter is not supported and the length-to-diameter ratio is usually high. Consequently, heavy cuts are not feasible. But despite its low efficiency in removing metal, end milling is often preferred for facing, profiling, slotting, recessing, and (as in the next example) box milling.

Example 340. Stepless Seating Surface on a Box Cover (Fig. 35)

End milling was used to produce rectangular seating surfaces on gray iron covers, in the setup shown in Fig. 35. End milling was preferred for this application mainly because the entire surface could be milled in one setup, thus eliminating steps in the milled area.

The covers were milled in a plain automatic bed-type machine having rise-and-fall feed to the spindle carrier. High speed steel cutters, because of their capacity for a larger number of teeth, were superior to carbide-tipped cutters. The greater number of teeth at a higher rake angle and steeper helix allowed a decrease of cutting force, resulting in better flatness. Cutter and machining details are tabulated with Fig. 35.

Unsupported Length. End milling is characterized by unsupported length of the cutter or its driving member, or

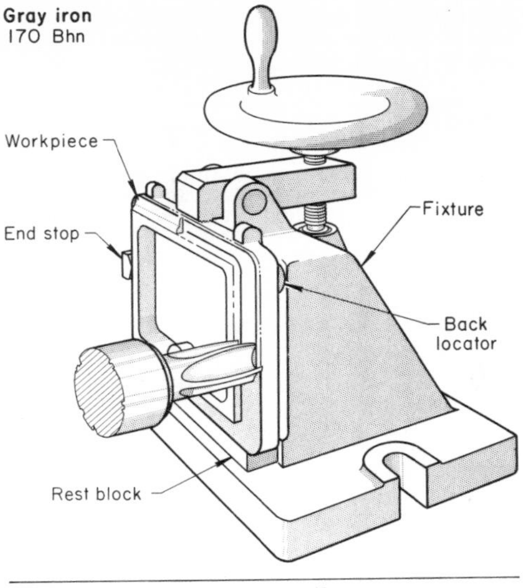

Cutter Details

Type	End mill
Size	1¼-in. diam
Number of teeth	6
Material	High speed steel

Machining Conditions

Speed	350 rpm (115 sfm)
Feed	0.005 ipt
Depth of cut	¼ in. max
Cutting fluid	None
Tolerances:	
Dimensional	±0.002 in.
Flatness	±0.001 in.
Finish obtained	125 micro-in.
Setup time	30 min
Production rate	21 pieces per 50-min hour

Fig. 35. End milling a joint face on a gray iron box cover (Example 340)

both. As this unsupported length increases, the difficulty in maintaining dimensional accuracy also increases, because of cutter deflection. The length-to-diameter ratio that can be tolerated depends largely on dimensional accuracy required, method of advancing the cutter (manual or automatic), work-metal hardness and rate of cutter feed. Excessive unsupported length can sometimes be tolerated when soft metals are being milled with light feeds. For most applications, however, an unsupported length greater than about five diameters is excessive (assuming the shank and cutter body are made of steel).

When workpiece shape or other conditions demand that milling be done with cutters having excessive unsupported length, cutter deflection can be minimized by the use of solid carbide cutters (for greater modulus of rigidity), electronically controlled feed, extremely light cuts, and collet-type adapters for securing the end mill. Also, the exact amount of runout for each specific off-the-shelf cutter should be determined by an indicator. When the runout is known, it can be corrected before the cutter is used. Minimizing runout will invariably prolong cutter life and is usually helpful in producing a better surface finish.

The three examples that follow deal with solutions to problems involving excessive unsupported cutter length, and the means used to provide workable rigidity in cutting. (See also Example 912, in the article on Machining of Aluminum Alloys, for another solution, involving a tapered adapter.)

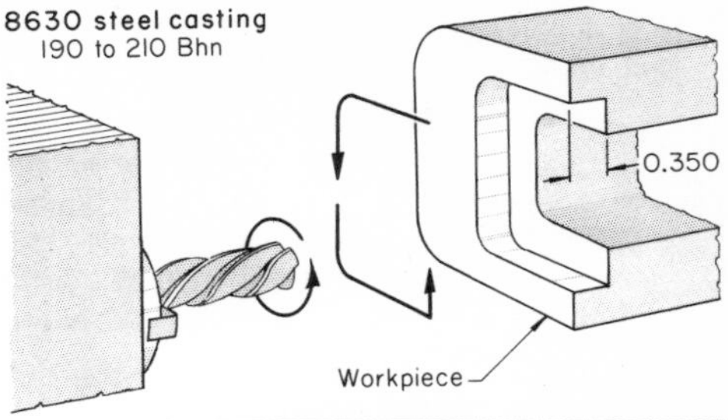

Cutter Details

Type	End mill, left-hand rotation
Size	0.375-in. diam
Number of teeth	4
Material	Tungsten carbide

Machining Conditions

Speed	1200 rpm (118 sfm)
Feed	0.0006 ipt
Depth of cut	0.006 to 0.020 in.
Cutting fluid	Soluble-oil:water (1:15)
Tolerances:	
Locating	−0.004 in.
Depth	+0.020 in.
Width	+0.005 in.
Length	+0.005 in.
Finish obtained	60 to 80 micro-in.
Setup time, approx	55 min
Downtime for tool change	6 min
Production rate	13 pieces per hour
Cutter life per grind	60 pieces
Total cutter life	240 to 250 pieces

Fig. 36. End milling with an electronically controlled carbide cutter (Example 341)

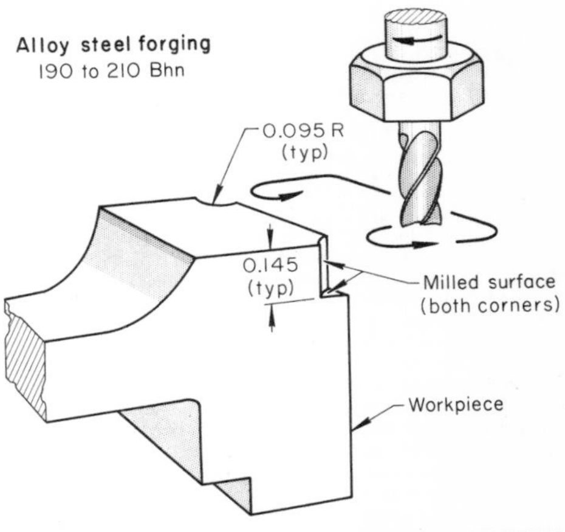

Cutter Details

Type	End mill
Size	0.125-in. diam
Number of teeth	4
Material	M2 or M7 high speed steel

Machining Conditions

Speed	1400 rpm (46 sfm)
Feed	0.0003 ipt
Cutting fluid	Sulfurized and chlorinated mineral oil
Tolerance	±0.0025 in.
Finish obtained	40 to 50 micro-in.
Setup time, approx	42 min
Downtime for tool change	7 min
Production rate	23.5 pieces per hour(a)
Cutter life per grind	150 pieces

(a) One man operating two machines produced 47 pieces per hour.

Fig. 37. End milling of radiused contours with electronic feed control (Example 342)

Example 341. Change to Solid Carbide Cutter and Electronic Control That Solved Problem of Unsupported Length (Fig. 36)

U-shaped steel castings required three milled surfaces as shown in Fig. 36. Fixturing prevented the spindle from being brought close to the work, and as a result cutters with excessive unsupported length had to be used. When high speed steel end mills were used in a cycle cam machine, cutter deflection caused

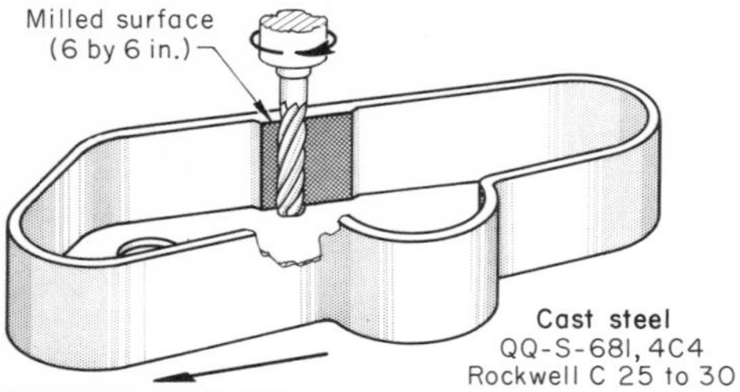

Cutter Details

Type	End mill
Size	1½-in. diam, 8-in. flute length
Number of teeth	6
Material	High speed steel

Machining Conditions

Speed	210 rpm (82 sfm)
Feed	0.0035 ipt (4.4 ipm)
Cutting fluid	Chemical-base water-soluble
Tolerance	±0.005 in.
Finish obtained	125 micro-in.
Setup time	30 min
Downtime for tool change	5 min
Production rate	18 pieces per hour
Cutter life per grind	120 pieces
Total cutter life	30 regrinds

Fig. 38. Vertical end milling of an internal profile (Example 343)

unacceptable dimensional variation, and cutters often broke during pocketing and change of direction.

Changing to solid carbide end mills eliminated cutter deflection, because the modulus of rigidity of carbide is nearly three times that of steel. Also, the use of electronic control on the machine eliminated the cutter breakage that had previously occurred. Cutter and machining details for the improved method are tabulated with Fig. 36.

Example 342. Use of Uniform Feed to Compensate for Unsupported Cutter (Fig. 37)

In profile milling the configuration illustrated in Fig. 37, the necessary fixturing required protrusion of the end milling cutter from the adapter to about the maximum distance that could be permitted. Because of liberal tolerances, achieving the required dimensional accuracy was not difficult. However, milling to an acceptable finish in one pass required uniform feed, which was obtained by electronic control on a 5-hp machine.

Collet-type adapters and correction of runout for each individual cutter also aided in obtaining acceptable finish, and helped to prolong cutter life. Cutter details and machining conditions are given with Fig. 37.

Example 343. Profile Milling With Unsupported Cutter Length of 5⅓ Diameters (Fig. 38)

An end mill 1½ in. in diameter with 8-in.-long flutes was used for profile milling a 6-in.-square internal pad of a steel casting (Fig. 38). Despite the high ratio of unsupported cutter length to cutter diameter (5⅓ to 1), an end mill was used because the surface to be milled was not accessible to a peripheral cutter. The unsupported cutter length was reduced as the end mill was reground.

A vertical milling machine was used rather than a horizontal machine, because the castings were easier to secure for vertical milling and because better visibility was afforded the machine operator. Cutter and machining details are given below Fig. 38.

Complex contours are regularly machined by end milling, although some type of automatic control is almost mandatory to achieve good tool life, dimensional control, surface finish, reproducibility, and efficiency of metal removal. End milling with automatic control has been particularly effective in machining complex configurations for aircraft and aerospace vehicles and in machining of small complex components of firearms or instruments. The five examples that follow describe applications of end milling with automatic control. (See also Example 1004, in the article on Machining of Titanium.)

Example 344. Change From Manual to Tracer Control That Increased Production Rate and Cutter Life (Fig. 39)

Originally, a 2-hp manually operated profile milling machine was used for end milling wedge-shaped pockets in steel forgings as illustrated in Fig. 39. Average production rate was only 3.3 pieces per hour, average cutter life was only 3.8 pieces, and cutters broke frequently. These results were unacceptable, because about 1000 pieces, produced in runs of 300 to 400, were required.

Changing from manual operation to tracer control eliminated cutter breakage and increased cutter life to 65 pieces. Production was increased to 27 pieces per hour.

Pockets were milled in one pass by both the original and the improved methods. Cutter details and machining conditions are listed in the table with Fig. 39.

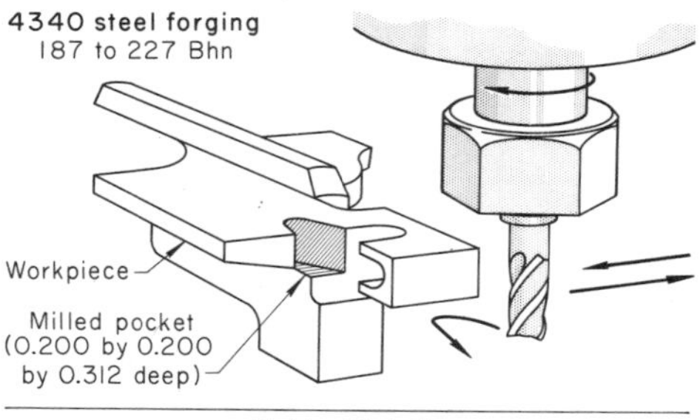

Cutter Details

Type	End mill, fast spiral
Size	0.125-in. diam
Number of teeth	4
Material	M2 high speed steel

Machining Conditions

Speed	2400 rpm (78 sfm)
Feed	0.00013 ipt
Cutting fluid	Sulfurized and chlorinated oil
Tolerances:	
Locating	+0.003 in.
Depth	+0.003 in.
Radius	−0.010 in.
Angles	±0° 15′
Finish obtained	80 to 90 micro-in.
Setup time, approx	1 hr
Downtime for tool change	7 min
Production rate	27 pieces per hour
Cutter life (no regrinds permitted)	65 pieces

Fig. 39. End milling a wedge-shaped pocket. Production rate and cutter life listed in table were obtained with tracer control. (Example 344)

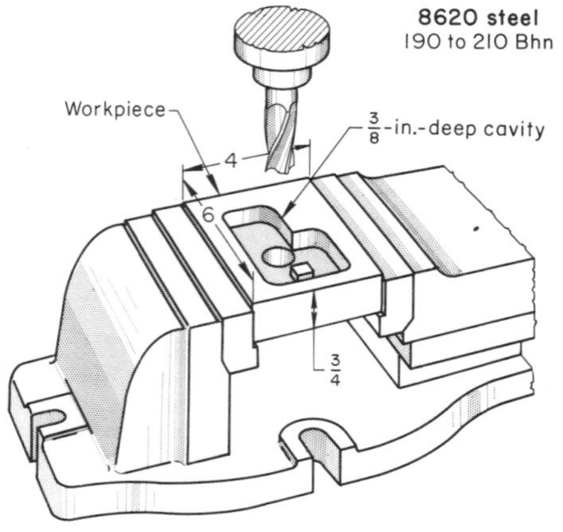

Cutter Details

Type	End mill
Size	¾-in. diam
Number of teeth	4
Material	High speed steel

Machining Conditions

Speed	400 rpm (79 sfm)
Feed per tooth	0.0025 in.
Cutting fluid	Soluble oil
Tolerances:	
Horizontal cuts	±0.002 in.
Vertical cuts	±0.001 in.
Finish obtained	125 micro-in.
Setup time(a)	30 min
Cutter life per grind, approx	10 pieces

(a) Using prepared plastic control sheet

Fig. 40. Milling of a complex cavity with a single cutter under three-axis control (Example 345)

Example 345. Use of Automatic Control for Producing a Complex Cavity With One End Mill (Fig. 40)

The need for consistent reproduction of the L-shaped cavity in the 8620 steel part shown in Fig. 40 justified the use of a vertical-spindle milling machine equipped with automatic controls for positioning the end milling cutter along the x, y and z axes.

The workpiece was secured in a vise having step jaws. Starting at a predrilled hole, the cutter was moved by automatic control (punched plastic sheet) to form the cavity, leaving a square island. Then the spindle was raised, and the island was milled to the required height. Cutter and machining details are presented with Fig. 40.

Example 346. Profile Milling a Two-Step Contour With Tracer Control (Fig. 41)

The most practical method for machining the profile illustrated in Fig. 41 was by means of two 5-hp single-spindle automatic profilers.

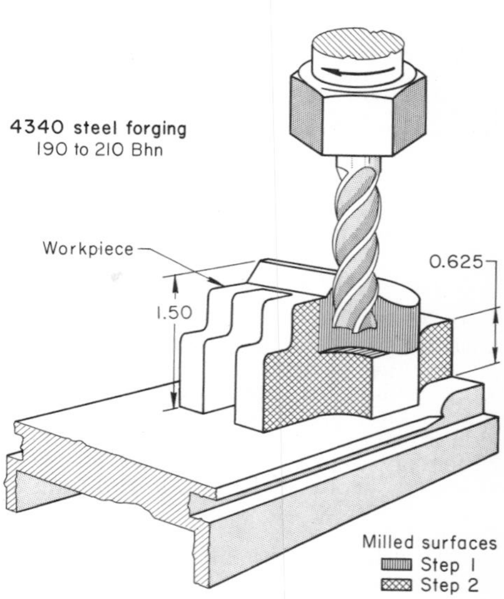

Cutter Details

Type	End mill, special length
Size	0.4375-in. diam
Number of teeth	4
Corner radius	0.060 in.
Material	M2 or M7 high speed steel

Machining Conditions

Speed	500 rpm (57 sfm)
Feed:	
Roughing, step 1	0.001 ipt (2 ipm)
step 2	0.00037 ipt (¾ ipm)
Finishing	0.00125 ipt (2½ ipm)
Depth of cut:	
Roughing	0.005 to 0.180 in.
Finishing	0.007 to 0.009 in.
Cutting fluid	Sulfurized and chlorinated oil
Tolerances:	
Step 1(a)	−0.005 in.
Step 2	−0.003 in.
Locating	Within 0.002 in.
Finish obtained:	
Roughing	125 micro-in.
Finishing	63 micro-in.
Setup time, approx	1¼ hr
Downtime for tool change	4 min
Production rate	5.9 pieces per hour
Cutter life per grind	18 pieces

(a) No mismatch permitted at blend points of steps 1 and 2

Fig. 41. Profile milling of a forged steel gun part (Example 346)

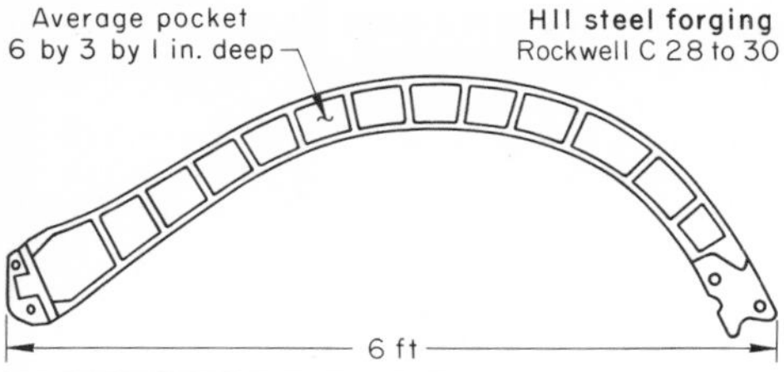

Item	Operation: Pockets, Roughing	Pockets, Finishing	Moldline, Roughing	Moldline, Finishing
Cutter Details(a)				
Diameter, in.	2	1	1¼	1½
No. of teeth	4	4	4	6
Speeds and Feeds				
Speed, rpm	250	413	250	250
Speed, sfm	130	108	82	100
Feed, ipt	0.002	0.0025	0.002	0.0035
Feed, ipm	2	4	2	5

Other Machining Conditions

Cutting fluid ....Soluble oil:water (1:20)
Tolerance ....±0.005 in.
Finish obtained ....125 micro-in.
Production rate, approx ....1 piece per 8-hr day
Cutter life per grind, approx ......200 linear in.

(a) End mills of T15 high speed steel

Fig. 42. Aircraft structural member end milled to reduce weight (Example 347)

Each machine was equipped with tracer control. Rough milling was done on the first machine and finish milling on the second. It was previously determined that tolerances (see data in the table accompanying Fig. 41) could not be met by manually controlled profiling machines.

Rough and finish profiling were each completed in two operations, denoted as steps 1 and 2 in Fig. 41. In the first operation the area indicated as step 1 (and its counterpart on the opposite side of the workpiece) was rough milled. This was followed by a second operation in which the larger area (indicated as step 2) was rough milled. Workpieces were then transferred to a second machine for finish milling in two similar operations. This method was used for producing up to 1000 pieces in lots of 300 to 400. Cutter details, machining conditions, and tolerances and finish are tabulated with Fig. 41.

Example 347. Profile Milling of Curved-Wall Pockets (Fig. 42)

A horizontal spindle numerically controlled (punch card) profiler was used to end mill the pockets and curved sides of the H11 steel forging shown in Fig. 42. This workpiece was complex in that the two curved sides were a moldline contour. The adjoining sides of the pockets were also machined to the moldline contour to maintain a constant thickness of the stand-up webs. Description of the four cutters used and machining details are given with Fig. 42.

Example 348. Milling a Complex Aircraft Component on a Numerically Controlled Profiler (Fig. 43)

Originally, the part shown in Fig. 43 was machined on a tracer-controlled hydraulic milling machine, requiring a variety of fixtures and templates. Changing to a tape-controlled vertical bridge profiler made possible closer adherence to tolerances and specified finish. In addition, machining time was reduced 25%, with no reduction in cutter life. Machining opposite sides of two parts positioned on the project plate resulted in the equivalent of one complete part being machined in each setup.

Of prime importance in maintaining tolerances was the placement of the locating hole in each end of the part. After rough milling, parts were quenched and tempered to Rockwell C 43 to 46. Precision bushings were inserted in the locating holes, assuring proper positioning on the project plate for finishing operations. Three clamps at edge points on each part prevented any shifting of the part during machining; clamps were moved to clear cutter paths. A subsequent machining operation removed the locating holes, as shown in lower portion of Fig. 43.

The final cuts of approximately 0.005 in. in operations 3, 4 and 5, which minimized the adverse effects of cutter deflection, were made by using the same program tape and cutters as for the preceding cuts [footnote (c), Fig. 43]. Sequence of operations, cutter details, and machining data are given with Fig. 43.

Combination Processes

For production quantities ranging from 1000 to 10,000, or for steady high production, specially designed equipment for machining several surfaces consecutively or simultaneously is sometimes economical. With this equipment, two or more methods of milling are often combined with other machining operations as described in the two examples that follow.

Example 349. Milling of Eight Surfaces With Ten Cutters in Three Machine Stations (Fig. 44)

Figure 44 shows a cross section of a gray iron cylinder block on which eight surfaces were milled or otherwise machined in three stations of a special-purpose machine with automatic transfer between stations. With this machine, tolerances were more easily maintained than when a low-production machine and setup had been used.

The sequence of operations, the tools used, and machining conditions are listed in the table with Fig. 44. Three face milling cutters were used in station 1 because the cast block had weak wall sections on the surfaces being milled. The two outside cutters were placed so as to cut tangentially, thus directing the principal cutting force along the length of the casting rather than across the weak wall. This resulted in less deflection and prevented chatter, and reduced chip thickness at the high feed rate (89 ipm). The center cutter was placed so as to clean up the remaining material. The force of this cutter was cross-

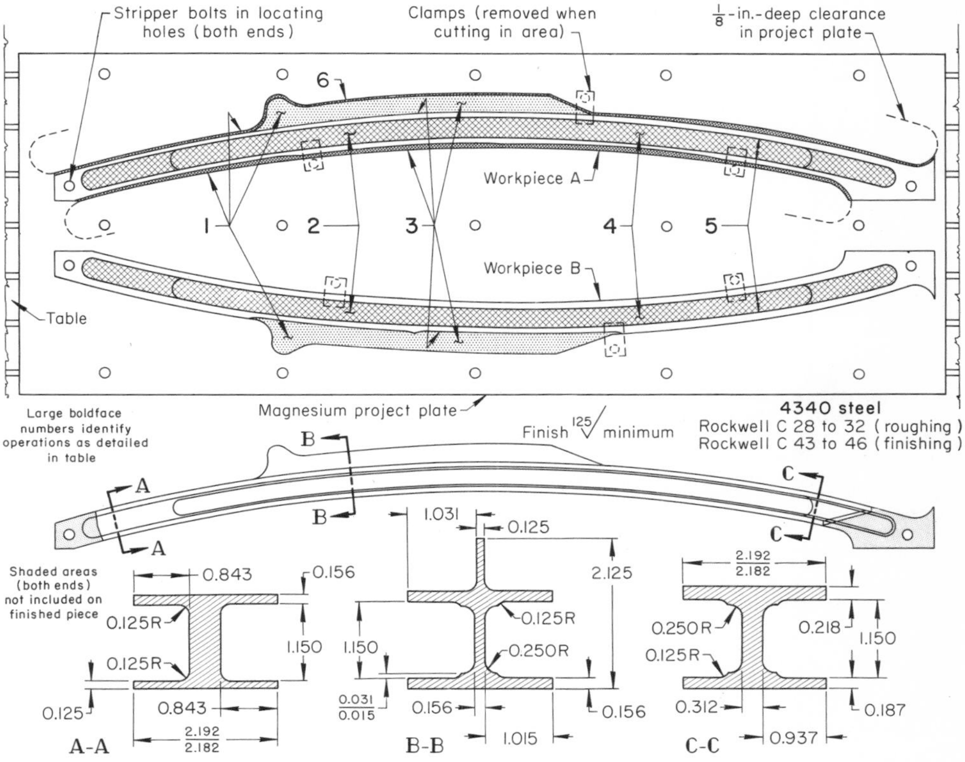

Item	1 Roughing periphery and top of ear	2 Roughing slot, Cutter No. 1	2 Roughing slot, Cutter No. 2	3 Finishing periphery and top of ear	4 Finishing bottom of slot	5 Finishing wall of slot	6 Finishing periphery of ear
Cutter Details(a)							
Diameter, in.	2.000	0.875	0.875	2.000	0.875	1.000	0.750
Number of teeth	4	2	4	6	4	4	4
Corner radius, in.	0.125	0.250	0.250	0.125	0.250	0.125	None
Cutting length, in.	3	1½	1½	3	1½	1½	1⅝
Over-all length in.	5½	3¾	4⅛	5½	4⅛	4½	3⅞
Machining Conditions							
Speed, rpm	97	210	210	80	210	176	255
Speed, sfm	52	49	49	42	49	46	50
Depth of cut, in.	¼ to ⅜	⅜	(b)	1/16(c)	1/16(c)	1/16(c)	1/16
Width of cut, in.	2⅜(d)	⅞	⅞	2⅜(e)	⅞	1	⅛

Feed, avg ....0.0035 ipt
Cutting fluid ....Sulfurized oil
Tolerance, roughing ....±1/32 in.
Tolerance, finishing ....±0.005 in.
Setup time ....15 min(f)
Downtime for tool change ....2 min(g)
Production rate ....13 hr per piece
Cutter life per grind ....1 piece

(a) All cutters were end mills of high speed steel; off-the-shelf cutters were modified by grinding to the dimensions given. (b) Section A-A in the above drawing was cut to depth of 0.775 in.; B-B to 1.082 in.; C-C to 0.870 in. (c) 1/16-in. cuts were followed by one additional pass of approximately 0.005-in. depth of cut (see text). (d) 1⅛-in. depth of cut at ear. (e) 1 1/16-in. depth of cut at ear. (f) Five minutes required for four bolts at the locating holes in two parts; 10 min required for bolting three clamps on each of two parts. Initially, 3 hr was required for installing project plate on machine table, using T-nuts and stripper bolts. (g) One minute each for cutters and adapters.

Fig. 43. Setup and processing details for profile milling of slat tracks for aircraft wing flaps (Example 348)

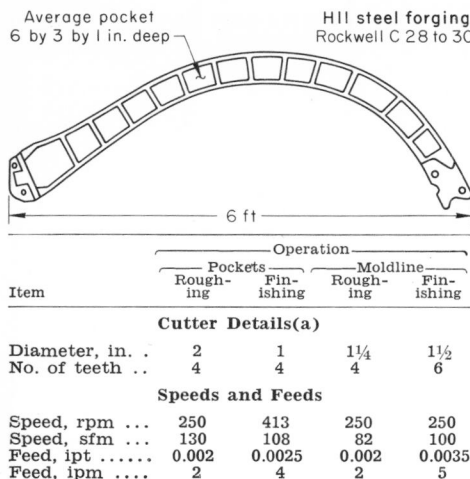

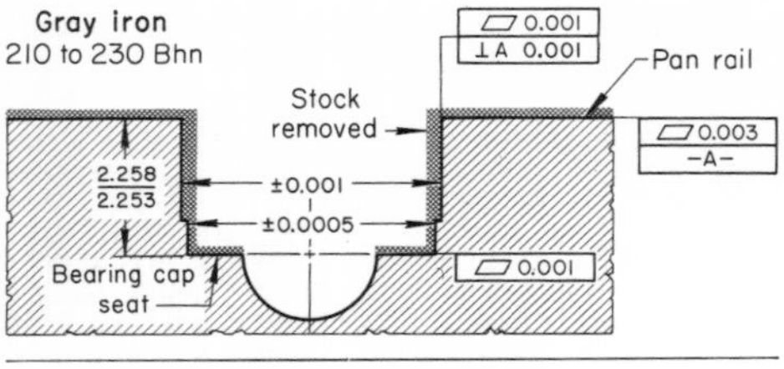

Sequence of Operations

Station 1 ....Rough mill pan rail
Station 2 ....Rough mill bearing channel
Station 3 ......Finish mill pan rail and bearing channel; shave or broach cap seat

Cutters

Station 1 ....Three 10-in.-diam face mills
Station 2 ....Two 7½-in.-diam side mills, one 4-in.-diam end mill
Station 3 ....Two 9-in.-diam face mills, two 4½-in.-diam end mills, shaving tool or broach

Speeds

Station 1 .... 88 rpm (230 sfm)
Station 2, 7½-in. cutter .....178 rpm (350 sfm)
Station 2, 4-in. cutter ....267 rpm (280 sfm)
Station 3 ....272 to 327 sfm

Other Machining Conditions

Feed, all stations ....89 ipm
Cutting fluid ....None
Cycle time per piece ....0.7 min
Production rate ....85 pieces per hour
Cutter life per grind ....3000 blocks

Fig. 44. Cylinder block surfaces milled with ten carbide-tipped cutters in three stations on a special-purpose machine (Example 349)

wise of the cylinder block — again in the direction of greatest workpiece strength, across the end walls. The use of three cutters also distributed the cutting among a greater number of blades, thus increasing cutter life.

Example 350. Sixteen-Operation Milling of Slots in Large Rotors (Fig. 45)

Thirty-two taper form slots 6¼ in. deep and 168 in. long were milled in a large forged steel rotor in 16 operations as illustrated and detailed in Fig. 45. Milling was done in a special machine of rugged construction to withstand the cutting force required for removing the large volume of steel.

Two vertical spindles and 14 horizontal spindles on each side of the machine made it possible to cut two opposed slots simultaneously and, by taking successive cuts, to complete each pair of slots in only three passes. Carbide-tipped slotting cutters in the vertical spindles removed most of the stock from the slots, thereby minimizing adverse effects in subsequent end milling with cutters of high length-to-diameter ratio.

Speed, Feed and Depth of Cut

Nominal speeds for milling carbon and low-alloy steels are given in Table 2 for peripheral milling, Table 3 for face milling, and Tables 4 and 5 for end milling. The speeds in these tables reflect differences in cutter material and depth of cut, but not in rigidity of setup, surface finish required and some other variables. For this reason, speeds used in practice are likely to differ considerably from the nominal speeds given in the tables.

Speeds as low as 20 sfm are used in milling some difficult-to-machine metals with cutters made of high speed steel. At the other extreme, speeds as high as 16,000 sfm have been used to mill aluminum or magnesium with carbide cutters.

When rigidity of the setup permits, carbide-tipped cutters can usually be operated 3 to 10 times faster than high speed steel cutters for a given application. Rigidity of setup has a marked effect on the maximum speed that will not cause chatter. Chatter is a condition in which the cutter and the workpiece vibrate in resonance at a frequency usually determined by the natural frequency of one or more elements of the machine. Chatter adversely affects tolerance, finish and tool life. Carbide tools are especially susceptible to chatter and usually fail by chipping when chatter occurs. When it is impossible to increase rigidity, lower speeds and high speed steel cutters must be used.

Speed is influenced also by feed rate. If the established feed rate is high, it is often necessary to lower speed because of inadequate power. Conversely, if a high speed is established, it may be necessary to decrease feed per tooth or to use a cutter having fewer teeth, to stay within the limits of available power.

The speed used for a specific application is ordinarily a compromise between a high speed that will yield a high rate of metal removal and produce the best finish and a low speed that will result in desirable tool life.

Feed is expressed as the rate at which the work moves past the cutter (or vice versa) in inches per minute (ipm) or in inches per tooth (ipt). Feed per tooth is the linear distance of tooth advance for each revolution of the cutter; thus, feed per revolution of the cutter is the product of feed per tooth and the number of teeth on the cutter. Feed in inches per minute (ipm) can be converted to feed per tooth by dividing ipm

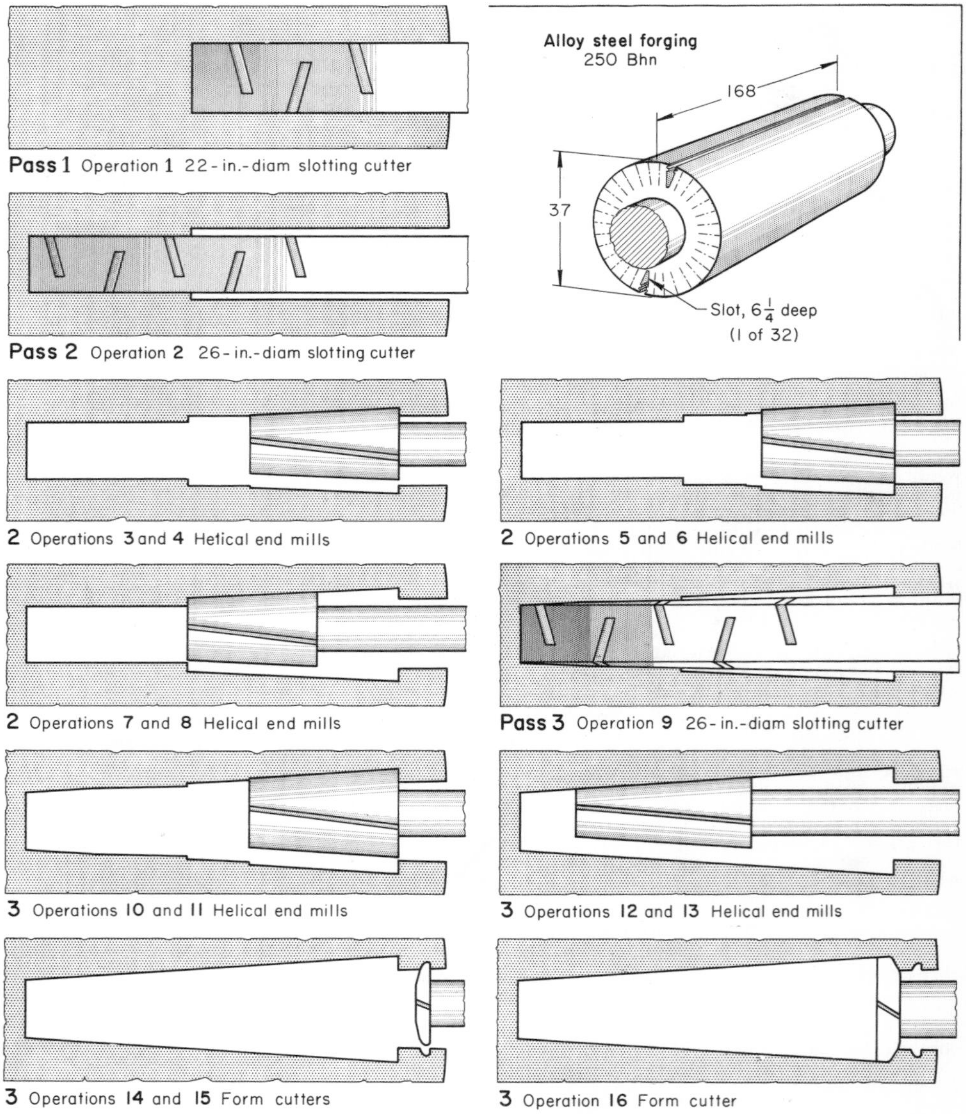

Pass	Operation(a)	Speed, sfm	Feed, ipr
1 ...	1, slotting	275	7½
2 ...	2, slotting	275	5
	3 through 8, end milling	60	5
3 ...	9, slotting	200	10
	10 through 13, end milling	100	10
	10 through 16, form cutting	100	10

(a) Slotting cutters, carbide tipped; end mills and form tools, solid high speed steel

Other Machining Conditions

Cutting fluid ..Soluble-oil:water (1:20), air mist
Setup time, approx ....4 hr
Downtime for tool change .....Slotting cutters, ½ hr; end mills, 5 min
Production rate ....65 hr per rotor
Cutter life per grind:
Slotting cutters ....100 linear ft (approx)
End mills, roughing ....75 linear ft
End mills, finishing ....125 linear ft

Fig. 45. Sequence and conditions for milling tapered slots in a large rotor in 16 operations on a special machine (Example 350)

by the product of the cutter revolutions per minute (rpm) and the number of teeth in the cutter.

For highest efficiency of metal removal and least susceptibility to chatter, the feed per tooth should be as high as possible in any milling operation. However, several factors influence or limit the rate of feed: type of cutter, number of teeth, cutter material, work-metal composition and hardness, depth of cut, width of cut, speed, rigidity of the setup, and available power.

Nominal feed rates for peripheral, face and end milling of carbon and low-alloy steels are shown in Tables 2, 3, 4 and 5. Because these tables do not reflect all the pertinent variables, feeds used in practice may differ from the nominal rates by a factor of 20 or more.

Typical feed rates based on variation in type of cutter and cutter material for 19 different classes of work metal are given in Table 6 on page 193. When depth of cut or amount of unsupported spindle length is abnormal, the values shown in Table 6 must be reduced.

Determination of Optimum Speed and Feed. As indicated in the examples in this article, a wide range of speeds and feeds can be used successfully. But for optimum results in milling hard or otherwise difficult-to-machine alloys, speed and feed must be carefully selected, because the range of workable and economical operating conditions is relatively narrow. This section outlines a method used to arrive at optimum conditions for milling an iron-base heat-resisting alloy:

Procedure. Figures 46, 47 and 48 illustrate the application of the method to face milling, peripheral (slab) milling and end milling of A-286 alloy that had been precipitation hardened to Rockwell C 35 (tensile strength, 163,500 psi). Cutter details and machining conditions are given below each of the illustrations.

First, a workable starting feed was selected on the basis of previous experience; then speed was adjusted in increments of about 20% to find the most economical value ("speed search"). After the speed search was completed, feed rate was varied in increments of about 20% while speed was held constant at the optimum value found, to verify or correct the initially selected feed rate ("feed search").

The development of a wear land of predetermined dimensions on the teeth of the cutters, as observed by examination with a hand microscope, served as the criterion for tool life, and tools were reground or discarded at this point. Tool life was expressed in cubic inches of metal removed.

Cost factors included in the determination of machining costs were: tool-use cost, tool-change cost, and operating cost. Operating cost was based on a standard cost rate per minute for all operations. Tool-change cost was obtained by the use of a specific rate of tool changing that had been assigned to the operation. Tool-use cost included the cost of new tools and the cost of regrinding.

Calculation. In the charts in Fig. 46, 47 and 48, total cost per cubic inch of metal removed is the sum of:

1 Operating cost times number of minutes required for removing 1 cu in. of metal
2 Tool-change cost divided by tool life in cubic inches
3 Tool-use cost divided by tool life in cubic inches.

Results. As shown in Fig. 46, 47 and 48, milling cost was more responsive to changes in feed than to changes in speed. Cost was increased 10 to 20% by each change in speed from optimum, except that in end milling cost was doubled by the increase in speed. The feed search showed that cost for face milling was increased 10 to 20% by changes from optimum feed. However, peripheral and end milling cost was raised 30 to 50% by the decreases from optimum feed shown, and 150% by the increases from optimum feed. In

Table 2. Nominal Speeds and Feeds for Peripheral (Slab) Milling of Carbon and Low-Alloy Steels With High Speed Steel Cutters(a)

Typical steel(b)	Brinell hardness	Roughing (0.150-in. cut)(c) Speed, sfm	Roughing Feed, ipt	Finishing (0.025-in. cut)(c) Speed, sfm	Finishing Feed, ipt
Carbon and Low-Alloy Steels (Except Free-Cutting Grades)					
1020, 1045, 4140 and 8620, at hardness ranges listed at right	85 to 125	170	0.010	225	0.008
	125 to 175	135	0.010	185	0.008
	175 to 225	110	0.010	155	0.008
	225 to 275	90	0.008	130	0.007
	275 to 325	80	0.007	105	0.005
	325 to 375	70	0.006	85	0.004
	375 to 425	50	0.004	65	0.003
	Rc 48 to 50	30	0.003	45	0.002
7140	200 to 250	80	0.008	100	0.006
	300 to 350	60	0.005	75	0.004
Free-Cutting Carbon and Low-Alloy Steels					
1112, 1117, 1137 and 12L14, at hardness ranges listed at right	100 to 150	185	0.010	245	0.008
	150 to 200	205	0.010	275	0.008
	200 to 250	130	0.010	180	0.008
	275 to 325	110	0.008	140	0.006
	325 to 375	70	0.008	85	0.006
	375 to 425	50	0.004	70	0.003
4140+S and 41L40	150 to 200	145	0.010	195	0.008
	200 to 250	125	0.010	170	0.008
	275 to 325	85	0.008	110	0.006
	375 to 425	50	0.004	65	0.003
	Rc 45 to 48	40	0.003	50	0.002

(a) High speed steels M2 and M7, except T15 and M33 for hardness above 375 Bhn. (b) Each steel listed is a frequently used grade in a group of similar steels. For a listing of steels in the various groups, see Table 2, page 6. (c) Depth of cut measured parallel to axis of cutter. (Data are adapted from tables compiled by Metcut Research Associates, Inc.)

Table 3. Nominal Speeds and Feeds for Face Milling of Carbon and Low-Alloy Steels With High Speed Steel and Carbide Cutters

Typical steel(a)	Brinell hardness	Roughing (0.150-in. cut)(b) Speed, sfm HSS(d)	Roughing Speed, sfm Carbide(c) Brazed	Roughing Speed, sfm Carbide(c) Disposable	Roughing Feed, ipt HSS(d)	Roughing Feed, ipt Carbide(c)	Finishing (0.025-in. cut)(b) Speed, sfm HSS(d)	Finishing Speed, sfm Carbide(c) Brazed	Finishing Speed, sfm Carbide(c) Disposable	Finishing Feed, ipt HSS	Finishing Feed, ipt Carbide(c)
Carbon and Low-Alloy Steels (Except Free-Cutting Grades)											
1020, 1045, 4140 and 8620, at hardness ranges listed at right	85 to 125	165	565	625	0.012	0.014	220	755	830	0.010	0.012
	125 to 175	145	465	510	0.012	0.014	190	620	680	0.010	0.012
	175 to 225	130	385	425	0.012	0.014	170	545	600	0.010	0.012
	225 to 275	100	360	400	0.009	0.012	135	480	525	0.007	0.010
	275 to 325	85	285	315	0.009	0.010	105	380	420	0.007	0.008
	325 to 375	65	225	250	0.008	0.007	85	300	330	0.006	0.006
	375 to 425	50	175	195	0.004	0.006	65	230	255	0.003	0.005
	Rc 48 to 50	30	125	140	0.003	0.005	40	165	180	0.002	0.004
	Rc 54 to 56	...	90	100	...	0.005	...	120	130	...	0.004
7140	200 to 250	85	275	305	0.006	0.007	110	365	400	0.005	0.006
	300 to 350	65	250	275	0.006	0.007	85	330	365	0.005	0.006
Free-Cutting Carbon and Low-Alloy Steels											
1112, 1117, and 12L14	100 to 150	210	575	630	0.012	0.014	280	765	840	0.010	0.012
	150 to 200	195	500	550	0.012	0.014	260	665	730	0.010	0.012
	200 to 250	125	450	495	0.012	0.014	165	600	660	0.010	0.012
1137	175 to 225	160	425	470	0.012	0.014	215	565	620	0.010	0.012
	275 to 325	110	375	415	0.009	0.012	150	500	550	0.007	0.010
	325 to 375	65	250	275	0.008	0.010	90	335	370	0.006	0.008
	375 to 425	50	175	195	0.004	0.008	70	230	255	0.003	0.007
4140+S and 41L40	150 to 200	160	475	520	0.012	0.014	225	630	695	0.010	0.012
	200 to 250	125	385	425	0.012	0.014	160	515	570	0.010	0.012
	275 to 325	90	300	330	0.009	0.010	115	400	440	0.007	0.008
	375 to 425	50	175	195	0.004	0.006	65	235	260	0.003	0.005
	Rc 45 to 48	35	150	165	0.004	0.005	45	200	220	0.003	0.004

(a) Each steel listed is a frequently used grade in a group of similar steels. For a listing of steels in the various groups, see Table 2, page 6. (b) Depth of cut measured parallel to axis of cutter. (c) Carbide grade C-6 for roughing and C-7 for finishing, except C-2 for both depths of cut at hardness above Rockwell C 54. (d) High speed steels M2 and M7, except T15 and M33 for hardness above 375 Bhn. (SOURCE: same as for Table 2)

Table 4. Nominal Speeds and Feeds for End Milling of Carbon and Low-Alloy Steels With High Speed Steel Cutters(a)

Typical steel(b)	Brinell hardness	Roughing (0.050-in. cut) Speed, sfm	Roughing Feed, ipt, for cutter diameter of: ¼ in.	½ in.	¾ in.	1 to 2 in.	Finishing (0.015-in. cut) Speed, sfm	Finishing Feed, ipt, for cutter diameter of: ¼ in.	½ in.	¾ in.	1 to 2 in.
Carbon and Low-Alloy Steels (Except Free-Cutting Grades)											
1020, 1045, 4140 and 8620, at hardness ranges listed at right	85 to 125	140	0.002	0.003	0.005	0.006	180	0.001	0.002	0.004	0.005
	125 to 175	115	0.002	0.003	0.005	0.006	150	0.001	0.002	0.004	0.005
	175 to 225	90	0.002	0.003	0.004	0.005	120	0.001	0.002	0.003	0.004
	225 to 275	75	0.002	0.003	0.004	0.005	100	0.001	0.002	0.003	0.004
	275 to 325	60	0.001	0.002	0.004	0.005	80	0.0007	0.0015	0.003	0.004
	325 to 375	50	0.0005	0.0015	0.003	0.004	65	0.0005	0.0015	0.003	0.004
	375 to 425	45	0.0005	0.001	0.002	0.003	60	0.0005	0.0007	0.001	0.002
	Rc 48 to 50	35	...	0.0005	0.0005	0.0015	45	0.0005	0.0005	0.0005	0.001
	Rc 50 to 52	30	...	0.0005	0.0005	0.0015	40	0.0005	0.0005	0.0005	0.001
7140	200 to 250	80	0.002	0.003	0.004	0.005	105	0.001	0.002	0.003	0.004
	300 to 350	50	0.0005	0.001	0.002	0.003	65	0.0005	0.0007	0.001	0.002
Free-Cutting Carbon and Low-Alloy Steels											
1112, 1117 and 12L14	100 to 150	190	0.002	0.003	0.005	0.006	245	0.001	0.002	0.004	0.005
	150 to 200	160	0.002	0.003	0.005	0.006	215	0.001	0.002	0.004	0.005
	200 to 250	135	0.002	0.003	0.005	0.006	175	0.001	0.002	0.004	0.005
1137, 4140+S and 41L40	150 to 200	140	0.002	0.003	0.005	0.006	180	0.001	0.002	0.004	0.005
	200 to 250	115	0.002	0.003	0.005	0.006	150	0.001	0.002	0.004	0.005
	275 to 325	80	0.001	0.003	0.005	0.005	105	0.0007	0.002	0.004	0.005
	325 to 375	50	0.0005	0.0015	0.004	0.005	65	0.0005	0.0015	0.003	0.004
	375 to 425	45	0.0005	0.001	0.002	0.003	60	0.0005	0.0007	0.001	0.002
	Rc 45 to 48	40	...	0.0005	0.001	0.002	50	0.0005	0.0005	0.001	0.001
	Rc 48 to 50	35	...	0.0005	0.0005	0.0015	45	0.0005	0.0005	0.0005	0.001

(a) High speed steels M2 and M7, except T15, M33, M41, M42, M43 and M44 for hardness above 375 Bhn. (b) Each steel listed is a frequently used grade in a group of similar steels. For a listing of steels in the various groups, see Table 2, page 6. (SOURCE: same as for Table 5)

Table 5. Nominal Speeds and Feeds for End Milling of Carbon and Low-Alloy Steels With Carbide Cutters(a)

Typical steel(b)	Brinell hardness	Roughing (0.050-in. cut) Speed, sfm	Roughing Feed, ipt, for cutter diameter of: ¼ in.	½ in.	¾ in.	1 to 2 in.	Finishing (0.015-in. cut) Speed, sfm	Finishing Feed, ipt, for cutter diameter of: ¼ in.	½ in.	¾ in.	1 to 2 in.
Carbon and Low-Alloy Steels (Except Free-Cutting Grades)											
1020, 1045, 4140 and 8620, at hardness ranges listed at right	85 to 125	425	0.0025	0.004	0.006	0.008	550	0.0015	0.0035	0.006	0.007
	125 to 175	400	0.0025	0.004	0.006	0.008	520	0.0015	0.0035	0.005	0.007
	175 to 225	360	0.0025	0.004	0.006	0.007	470	0.0015	0.003	0.005	0.006
	225 to 275	335	0.002	0.003	0.005	0.007	435	0.001	0.002	0.004	0.005
	275 to 325	255	0.002	0.0025	0.004	0.006	335	0.001	0.002	0.004	0.005
	325 to 375	200	0.001	0.003	0.005	0.006	260	0.001	0.003	0.005	0.006
	375 to 425	150	0.001	0.002	0.003	0.004	195	0.001	0.001	0.002	0.003
	Rc 48 to 50	85	...	0.0005	0.002	0.002	110	0.0005	0.0005	0.001	0.001
	Rc 54 to 56	40	...	0.0005	0.002	0.002	50	0.0005	0.0005	0.001	0.001
7140	200 to 250	300	0.0025	0.004	0.006	0.007	390	0.0015	0.003	0.005	0.006
	300 to 350	225	0.001	0.002	0.003	0.004	290	0.001	0.001	0.002	0.003
Free-Cutting Carbon and Low-Alloy Steels											
1112, 1117 and 12L14	100 to 150	500	0.0025	0.004	0.006	0.008	650	0.0015	0.003	0.005	0.007
	150 to 200	475	0.0025	0.004	0.006	0.008	615	0.0015	0.003	0.005	0.007
	200 to 250	425	0.0025	0.004	0.006	0.008	550	0.0015	0.003	0.005	0.007
1137, 4140+S and 41L40	150 to 200	425	0.0025	0.004	0.006	0.008	550	0.0015	0.003	0.005	0.007
	200 to 250	385	0.0025	0.004	0.006	0.008	500	0.0015	0.003	0.005	0.007
	275 to 325	310	0.0025	0.004	0.006	0.008	405	0.0015	0.002	0.004	0.006
	325 to 375	200	0.001	0.003	0.005	0.006	260	0.001	0.0015	0.003	0.005
	375 to 425	150	0.001	0.002	0.003	0.004	195	0.001	0.001	0.002	0.003
	Rc 45 to 48	125	...	0.0005	0.002	0.002	160	0.0005	0.0005	0.001	0.0015
	Rc 48 to 50	85	...	0.0005	0.002	0.002	110	0.0005	0.0005	0.001	0.001

(a) Carbide grade C-2. (b) Each steel listed is a frequently used grade in a group of similar steels. For a listing of steels in the various groups, see Table 2, page 6. (Data are adapted from tables compiled by Metcut Research Associates, Inc.)

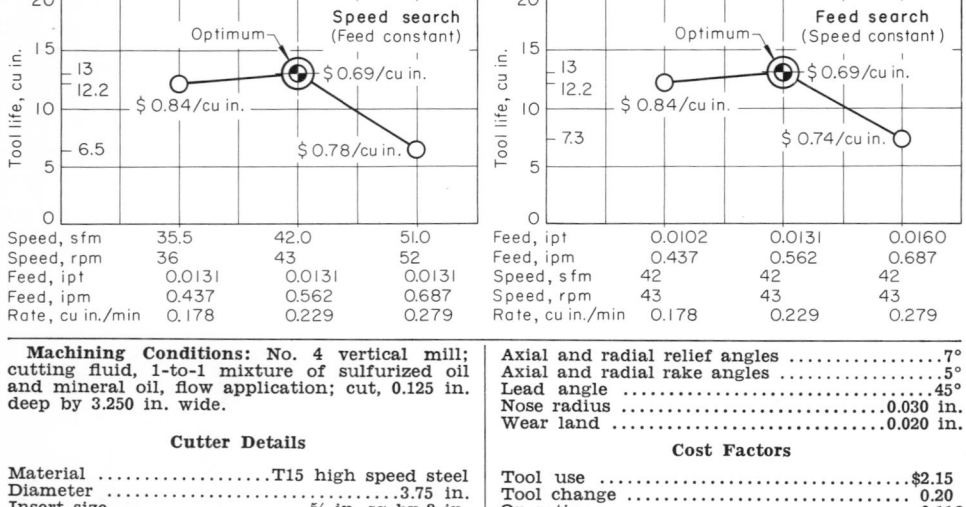

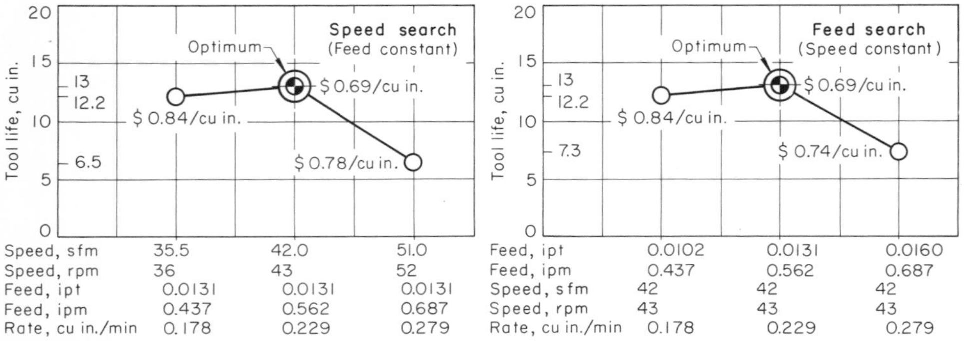

Machining Conditions: No. 4 vertical mill; cutting fluid, 1-to-1 mixture of sulfurized oil and mineral oil, flow application; cut, 0.125 in. deep by 3.250 in. wide.

Cutter Details

Material ....T15 high speed steel
Diameter ....3.75 in.
Insert size ....⅝ in. sq by 3 in.
Axial and radial relief angles ....7°
Axial and radial rake angles ....5°
Lead angle ....45°
Nose radius ....0.030 in.
Wear land ....0.020 in.

Cost Factors

Tool use $2.15
Tool change 0.20
Operating 0.116

Fig. 46. Optimum speed and feed for face milling of A-286 alloy at Rockwell C 35

addition, the feed search in end milling failed to confirm the initial feed rate of 0.0022 ipt; the final optimum value was 0.0037 ipt.

Depth of cut in rough milling is usually ⅛ in. or more. In finish milling, depth of cut may vary from a few thousandths of an inch to 1⁄16 in. For best surface finish (particularly when using high speed steel cutters) roughing cuts followed by finishing cuts are generally required. When using carbide-tipped cutters, it is often possible to attain the required surface finish in a single cut.

Surface Finish

The surface finish obtainable by milling depends on work-metal composition and condition, speed, feed, tool material, tool design and cutting fluid. Peripheral and face milling produce different types of surfaces, because of the different relations of cutter rotation to the workpiece in the two methods.

Peripheral milling produces a surface characterized by lines approximately parallel to the cutter axis. Sometimes these lines lie parallel and normal to the helix angle of the cutter teeth, and are spaced at a distance equal to the feed per tooth. Finish in peripheral milling is also affected as follows:

1 A high or low tooth produces a mark on the surface.
2 A bent arbor results in surface waviness.
3 An arbor too small in diameter causes chatter, resulting in a rough surface.
4 Uneven spacing of the cutter teeth causes vibrations that result in rough surfaces.
5 Climb milling produces a different surface texture than conventional milling, because in climb milling maximum chip thickness occurs at the beginning of the cut, whereas in conventional milling maximum chip thickness occurs at the end of the cut. Tooth and revolution marks usually are less noticeable than in climb milling.

Face Milling. The surface texture produced by face milling is characterized by a series of arcs when the heel or following edge of the cutter is slightly elevated during milling. If the work surface is parallel to the cutter face, a lattice-type texture is produced.

Practical Limits. A finish of 125 micro-in. can usually be obtained with either carbide or high speed steel cutters without stringent control of process variables. Finishes of 63 micro-in. or less are often obtained in milling with carbide tools. Under good conditions — which include the use of carbide cutters operated at high speed, a free-cutting grade of work metal, and a sulfurized (or sulfurized and chlorinated) cutting fluid — a finish of 32 micro-in. can be achieved. With special cutters used under closely controlled conditions, 20-micro-in. finishes and steam-tight joint surfaces have been obtained by milling.

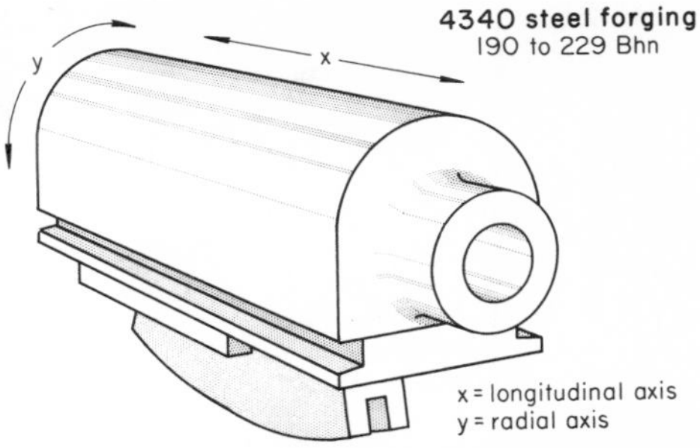

Fig. 49. Forged breech block that required spheroidization for acceptable finish in milling (Example 351)

Improvement of surface finish has been obtained by altering the heat treated structure of the work metal, by modifying cutter design, and by increasing cutting speed, as described in the four examples that follow.

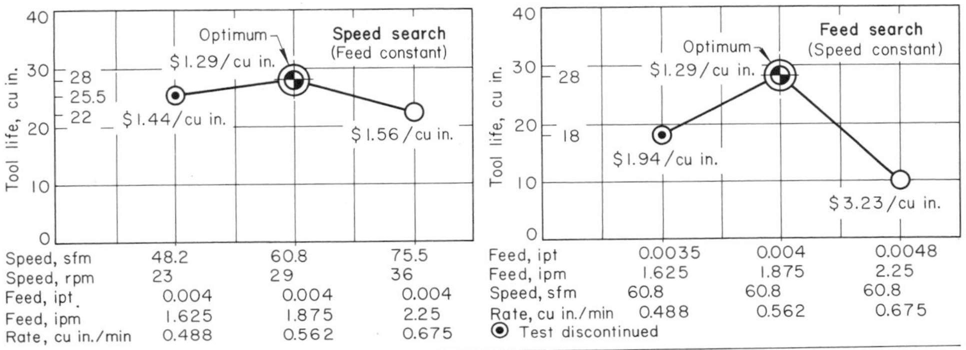

Machining Conditions: No. 4 horizontal mill; cutting fluid, 1-to-1 mixture of sulfurized oil and mineral oil, flow application; cut, 0.150 in. deep by 1.00 in. wide; conventional (up) cutting.

Cutter Details

Material	M10 high speed steel
Diameter	8.0 in.
Number of teeth	16 per side
Size	⅜ by 1½ by 1¼ in.
Axial rake angle	30°
Axial relief angle	6°
Radial rake angle	18°
Radial relief angle	10°
Nose radius	0.120 in.
Arbor diameter	1.5 in.
Wear land	0.020 in.

Cost Factors

Tool use	$27.10
Tool change	3.48
Operating	0.116

Fig. 47. Determination of optimum speed and feed for peripheral (slab) milling of A-286 alloy at Rockwell C 35

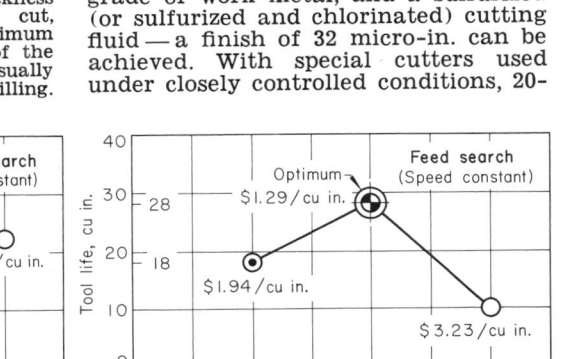

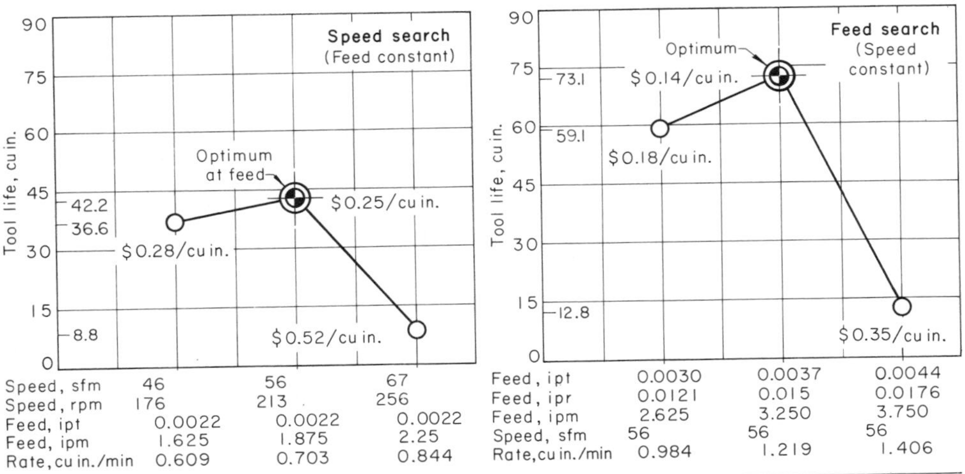

Machining Conditions: No. 4 vertical mill; cutting fluid, 1-to-1 mixture of sulfurized oil and mineral oil, flow application; cut, 1.00 in. deep by 0.375 in. wide; material 1.200 in. thick; climb cutting.

Cutter Details

Material	M10 high speed steel
Diameter	1.000 in.
Over-all length	4.5 in.
Flute length (4 flutes)	2.0 in.
Helix angle	30°
Axial relief angle	3°
Radial rake angle	3°
Radial relief angle	10°
Corner radius	0.120 in.
Wear land	0.025 in.

Cost Factors

Tool use	$3.17
Tool change	0.20
Operating	0.116

Fig. 48. Determination of optimum speed and feed for end milling of A-286 alloy at Rockwell C 35

Examples 351 to 354. Methods for Improving Finish

Example 351 — Spheroidizing of Work Metal (Fig. 49). A 7½-hp bed-type milling machine with a 180°-arc concave form cutter of M2 or M7 high speed steel was used for producing a radius on breech blocks for machine guns. Milling these 4340 steel forgings with a predominance of lamellar pearlite in the microstructure produced unacceptable surface finish of 120 micro-in. on the *y*-axis of the part (Fig. 49). Readings of 45 micro-in. on the *x*-axis met requirements. A change in the method of heat treatment to effect nearly complete spheroidization (with no significant change in hardness) resulted in a milled surface that registered acceptable finish of 40 to 45 micro-in. in both directions.

Example 352 — Modification of Cutter Design. Tests were made to determine surface finish obtainable, using two 12-in.-diam face mills, in making cuts ¼ in. deep and 10 in. wide in 1141 steel at 220 Bhn. Machining was at speeds of 475 to 500 sfm and feed of 12 ipm.

A commercial face mill of standard design produced unacceptable chip formation and surface finish (200 to 250 micro-in.). When the cutter was redesigned to incorporate an axial rake of +10°, radial rake of −11° 40′, and a corner angle of 60°, chip formation improved and an acceptable finish of 70 to 80 micro-in. was obtained.

In further tests, the feed of the redesigned cutter was increased from 12 to 19 ipm; chip formation and the finish produced (80 to 90 micro-in.) remained satisfactory.

Example 353 — Change to Different Design of Cutter With More Blades. A finish of 125 micro-in. was specified in milling hot rolled 1015 steel plates, using 14-in.-diam face mills in an adjustable-rail milling machine. The cutters originally used produced acceptable finish at a feed of 20 ipm, but when scheduling required that feed be increased to 40 ipm, chips clogged and were carried under the cutter face, resulting in a finish of 200 to 300 micro-in. A 14-in.-diam cutter with more blades and of different design produced the specified finish at the 40-ipm feed. Differences in three principal angles of the original and improved cutters were as follows:

	Original	Improved
Number of blades	18	28
Axial rake	+10°	+15°
Radial rake	+10°	− 5°
Corner angle	90°	45°

Example 354 — Increase in Speed. A surface of 63 micro-in. was required in finish milling of pads and joint areas of mild steel weldments, using a 16-in.-diam face mill with carbide blades. At a speed of 500 sfm and feed of 40 ipm, tearing of the work metal resulted in an unacceptable finish of 125 micro-in. When speed was increased to 850 sfm at the same feed, tearing was minimized and a finish smoother than the specified 63 micro-in. was obtained. An increase in feed, to 72 ipm, did not impair the surface finish obtained at the increased cutting speed.

Cutting Fluids

Some type of cutting fluid is ordinarily used with high speed steel cutters in milling steel, stainless steel, copper-base alloys and heat-resisting alloys. Aluminum and magnesium alloys and gray iron are usually milled dry. Cutting fluid is used more for malleable and nodular iron than for gray iron.

Regardless of the work metal, cutting fluids are used less often with carbide-tipped cutters than with high speed steel cutters, because carbide withstands higher temperature and is less susceptible to buildup at the cutting edges. With carbide-tipped cutters, the functions of the cutting fluid are to maintain low tool-workpiece temperature, thereby reducing the possibility of cracking in the carbide tips, and to flush away chips.

When heavy roughing cuts are taken on annealed steel (high rate of metal removal), cooling of the tools and flushing away of chips are important, and finish (influenced largely by built-up edges) is of lesser importance. Conversely, in light finishing cuts (low rate of metal removal), surface finish may be far more important than cooling and flushing away chips. When milling difficult-to-machine metals, cooling is the most important function of the cutting fluid; chip disposal is less important because the rate of metal removal is low.

In climb milling, chip disposal is less of a problem than in conventional milling, because the chips are forced out behind the cutter in climb milling but ahead of the cutter in conventional milling.

Characteristics of the three principal types of cutting fluid are discussed in the following paragraphs:

Soluble oils have superior cooling and flushing ability, but are not effective in preventing adhesion of the tool to the workpiece. When surface finish is critical, it may be necessary to sacrifice some cooling and flushing and select a cutting fluid more effective in preventing adhesion.

Cutting oils prevent tool-workpiece adhesion, thereby allowing closer dimensional control and better finish. Many cutting oils are dark in color, thus making it difficult for operators to observe the operation. Viscosity of cutting oils should be kept below 100 SUS at 100 F, to prevent excessive amounts being carried away with the chips.

Compressed air, supplied through jets, is often used in place of a cutting fluid and is effective as a coolant and in keeping chips cleared from the cutter path. Air is used when milling cast iron or for operations where the use of liquids is not practical.

Methods of Application. In milling, cutting fluids are usually distributed by nozzles to the cutter and workpiece. A pressure of 5 psi or less is usually sufficient. Higher pressure results in loss of fluid by splashing and serves no useful purpose.

Nozzles vary in shape from a plain round tube to a manifold type, depending mainly on the width of the milling cut. Width of the nozzle should approach the width of the cut, to maintain uniform distribution of the fluid.

In peripheral milling, the nozzle should be at the outgoing side of the cutter, so that the stream of cutting fluid hits the outgoing teeth and outer surface of the chip. A nozzle in this position allows the most effective use of the cutting fluid because, as a tooth leaves the work after cutting a chip, it will be wetted and cooled by the cutting fluid. Thus, a tooth will carry a film of fluid as it revolves and begins another cut.

In addition to directing cutting fluid less effectively, a nozzle at the ingoing side can be dragged under the cutter, damaging the equipment and the work. Also, the cutting fluid may wash small chips under the ingoing teeth, resulting in gouging of the workpiece surface.

In face milling, best results are obtained by applying the cutting fluid on the side where the cutting is done rather than on the idle side.

Another effective method of application consists of spraying the fluid with compressed air and directing the jets of vapor at the area being milled. Soluble-

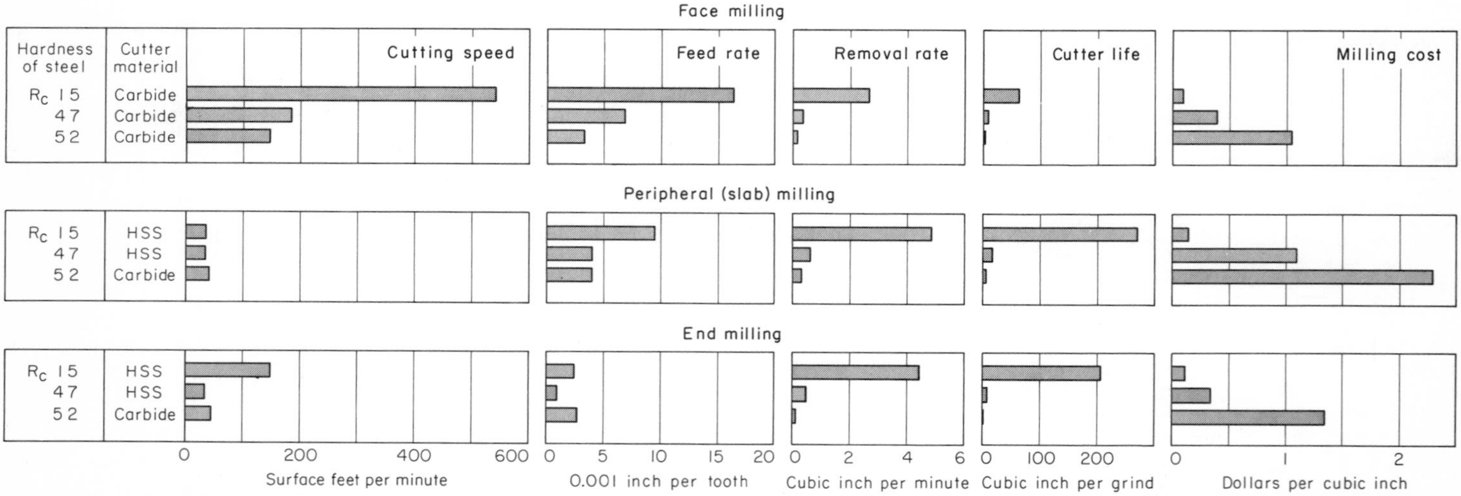

Item	Face milling(a) R_C 15	Face milling(a) R_C 47	Face milling(a) R_C 52	Peripheral (slab) milling(b) R_C 15	Peripheral (slab) milling(b) R_C 47	Peripheral (slab) milling(b) R_C 52	End milling(c) R_C 15	End milling(c) R_C 47	End milling(c) R_C 52
Machining Conditions									
Speed, rpm	344	117	94	19	17	17	527	137	180
Speed, sfm	543	185	148	37.8	35.6	42	150	36	47
Feed, ipm	5.623	0.875	0.3125	3.25	0.8125	0.8125	5.25	0.5625	0.75
Feed, ipt	0.0163	0.0068	0.0033	0.0095	0.004	0.004	0.0025	0.001	0.0028
Depth of cut, in.	0.125	0.125	0.125	1.0	1.0	1.0	0.970	0.970	0.100
Width of cut, in.	4.0	4.0	4.0	0.75	0.4	0.2	0.850	0.850	1.75
Cutter Details									
Material(d)	Carbide	Carbide	Carbide	T15 HSS	T15 HSS	Carbide	M10 HSS	M10 HSS	Carbide
Diameter, in.	6	6	6	8	8	8	1.0	1.0	1.750
Axial rake angle	—7°	—7°	—7°	10°	10°	10°	30°(e)	30°(e)	3° 30′(e)
Radial rake angle	—7°	—7°	—7°	10°	10°	10°	6°	6°	—1° 30′
Axial relief angle	7°	7°	7°	5°	5°	2°	3°	3°	+3° 30′
Radial relief angle	7°	7°	7°	5°	5°	7°	10°	10°	+1° 30′
Corner radius, in.	0.030	0.030	0.030	0.070	0.070	...	0.120	0.120	0.030

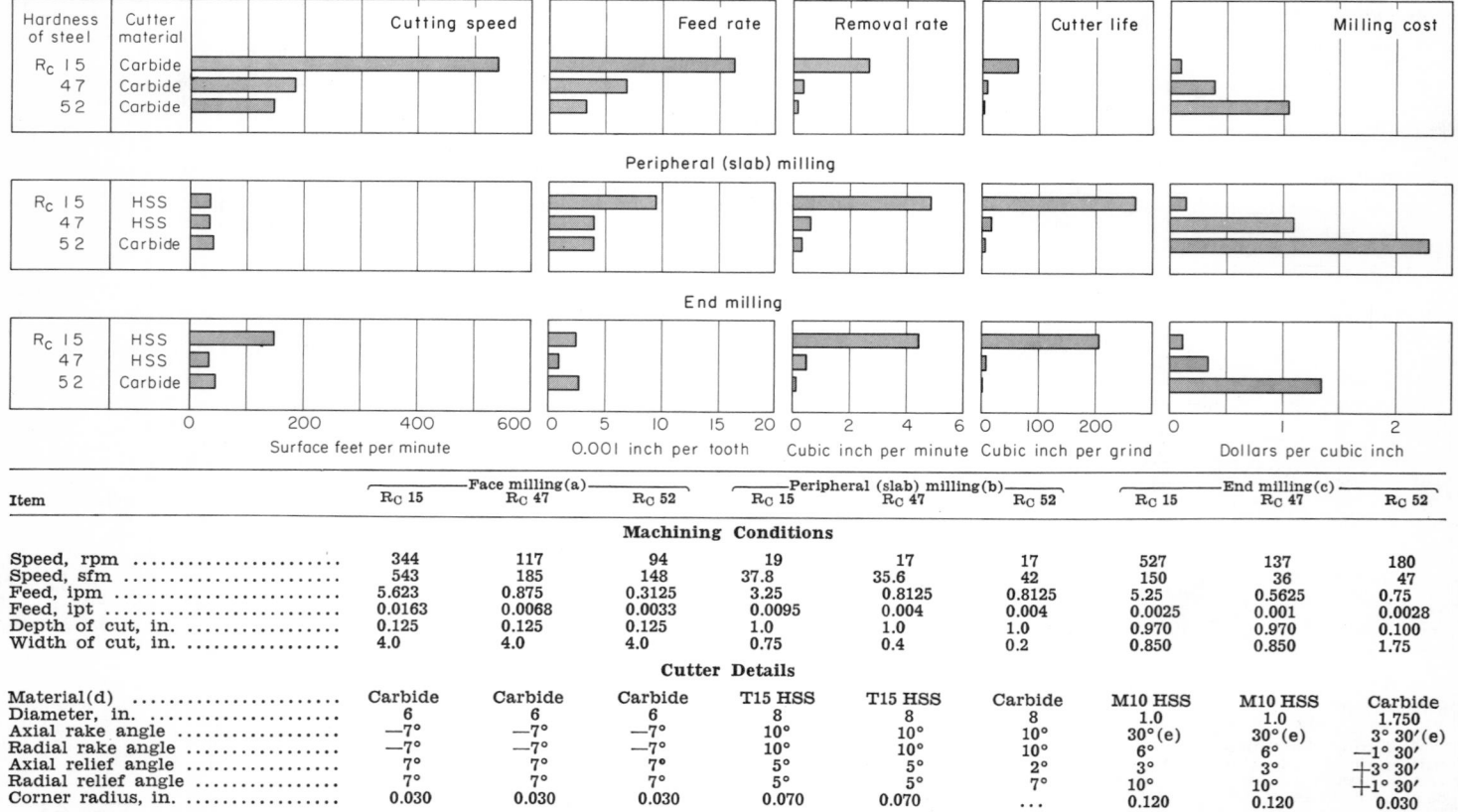

(a) Steels were milled in a vertical No. 5 machine, using climb cut, and with no cutting fluid. Single-blade cutter (inserts, ¾ by ¾ by 3⁄16 in.) had 45° lead angle. Cutter life was based on development of 0.018-in. wear land. (b) Steels were milled in a vertical No. 4 machine, using conventional cut, and with a 1-to-1 mixture of sulfurized oil and mineral oil as cutting fluid. Cutters had 1½-in.-diam arbor holes and 16 teeth (for steels at Rockwell C 15 and 47) or 18 teeth (for Rockwell C 52). Cutter life was based on development of 0.020-in. wear land. (c) Steels were milled in a horizontal No. 4 machine, with a 1-to-1 mixture of sulfurized oil and mineral oil as cutting fluid. Cutters were 4½ in. long, with four flutes (for steels at Rockwell C 15 and 47) or three flutes (for Rockwell C 52). Cutter life was based on development of 0.015-in. wear land. (d) Approximate composition of carbide used was 67.5 W, 6.0 Ti, 10.5 Ta, 7.5 C, 8.5 Co (grade C-5). (e) Helix angle.

Fig. 50. Effect of work-metal hardness on machining conditions, metal removal rate, cutter life, and cost in milling low-alloy steels

oil or proprietary chemical emulsions are readily sprayed. The use of this method is especially effective in large milling installations in which it is otherwise difficult to supply liquid to, and collect it from, the cutting area.

Effect of Workpiece Hardness

Production milling of steel at hardnesses of Rockwell C 40 to 55 is not unusual. But the difficulty of milling increases as hardness increases and is manifested mainly in reduced tool life (Fig. 8b), even at the reduced speeds and feeds necessary. Speed, feed, cutter material and design, rigidity and cutting fluid all require more careful consideration as workpiece hardness increases. Control of these variables will influence the magnitude of reduction in tool life, but even under the best conditions cycle time will increase and tool life will decrease as hardness increases. The net result is increased machining cost, particularly for roughing operations.

Figure 50 summarizes the results of tests made to determine the influence of hardness on conditions, results and costs in rough milling. In these tests, three similar low-alloy steels (4130, 4330 and 4340) at Rockwell C 15, 47 and 52, respectively, were machined by face, peripheral and end milling under the conditions given in the table below Fig. 50. The steels were milled under average shop conditions, and in sufficient quantity to assure that the data obtained would approximate production practice. Tests were stopped when cutter edges developed a predetermined wear land.

As shown in Fig. 50, as work-metal hardness increased, it was necessary to use lower speed and feed or (for peripheral and end milling) to change from high speed steel to carbide tools. The product of depth times width of cut was also lower for milling the harder materials, except in face milling. Metal removal rate was much lower in milling at the higher hardnesses, and — in spite of the changes in feed, speed and tool material — so was cutter life. Milling the steel at Rockwell C 47 cost three to seven times as much as milling at Rockwell C 15, and the cost of milling at Rockwell C 52 was ten to fifteen times that at Rockwell C 15. The largest increases in cost were for peripheral milling. Peripheral milling was also more costly than face or end milling in dollars per cubic inch of metal removed.

Cutter Design and Material for Milling Steel Harder Than Rockwell C 40

Strength of milling cutters is more critical when high-hardness, high-strength steel is being milled.

The number of cutter teeth affects strength, feed rate, and elapsed time per cut. A design that incorporates the maximum number of teeth (short of interfering with necessary chip clearance, or exceeding power capacity) is most economical. Other operating factors, however, may require that the number of cutting teeth be reduced (to as few as one, under certain extreme conditions).

Cutter design must permit maximum conduction of heat away from the heat-sensitive edges of cutting teeth. Inadequate heat conduction will inevitably shorten tool life. The effects of high cutting temperature can be offset to some extent by using a more heat-resistant material for the cutter.

Tooth angles must insure adequate and properly directed chip flow. When chips are accommodated adequately, there is no crowding or jamming in the spaces between teeth. The direction of chip flow is determined by the inclination angle of the cutting edge — a combination of axial rake, radial rake, and corner angles.

Proper relief angles minimize built-up edge and rubbing action between cutter surfaces and the workpiece. This rubbing action, in addition to accelerating tool wear, produces work hardening in many of the heat-resistant alloys. Work hardening reduces cutting efficiency and adversely affects surface finish.

Cutter design and material have major effects on cutter life and productivity. These factors are usually interrelated with speed and feed. The twelve examples that follow deal with effects of cutter design and material on results in milling steel at high hardness.

Example 355. Face Milling 4335 Steel at Rockwell C 48 to 52

In face milling 4335 steel at Rockwell C 48 to 52 on a vertical milling machine, the necessity for increasing production and metal-removal rates by 30% required an increase in the number of cutter teeth and changes in tooth angles. Cutter diameter (8 in.) and carbide material (77 W, 6.5 Ti, 6.5 C, 10 Co; grade C-6) were unchanged. Details of the original and revised cutters were as follows:

	Original	Revised
Number of teeth	12	16
Axial rake	—10°	30°
Radial rake	—10°	— 5°
Primary clearance	..	5°
Chamfer, in. (by 45°)	1/16	1/2

The effective rake angle of the revised cutter (measured in the plane of chip flow) was +19°, and was the result of the 45° chamfer, 30° axial rake and —5° radial rake.

Operating conditions also were revised, as appropriate for the changes in tool angles, to achieve a higher rate of metal removal. Cutter speed was decreased from 96 to 63 rpm and depth of cut was increased from 0.200 to 0.500 in. Chip load was increased from 0.0038 to 0.0075 in. No cutting fluid was used.

Example 356. Slotting 4335 Steel at Rockwell C 54

A cutter 5 in. in diameter and ½ in. wide used for slotting 4335 steel at Rockwell C 54 was designed as follows:

Number of teeth	8
Axial rake	—10° (trihelix)
Primary clearance	5°
Chamfer	45° by 1/32 in.

The cutter was made of carbide (80 W, 1 Ta, 3 Ti, 6 C, 10 Co; grade C-5) and was operated at a speed of 97 rpm in a No. 4 horizontal milling machine. The operation, performed without a cutting fluid, yielded a surface finish of 125 micro-in.

This slotting cutter removed about 14 cu in. of metal before requiring resharpening. With alternative methods (climb milling and the use of staggered and specially ground cutters), less than half this tool life was obtained.

Both the cutter and the setup must be as rigid as possible. Body sections and tool sections must be able to support the cutting load without chatter or excessive vibration. Arbor holes should be as large as possible, and the workpiece must be firmly seated and anchored.

Example 357. Face Milling 4340 Steel at Rockwell C 54, 41 to 42, and 39 (Test Results)

Rockwell C 54. In face milling 4340 steel at Rockwell C 54, eight-tooth, triangular ceramic (aluminum oxide) inserts produced an erratic surface finish and failed because of chipping of the cutting edges. The cutter containing these inserts was operated at 875 sfm and a chip load of 0.0017 in., in making a facing cut 1/16 in. deep and 12 in. long.

The ceramic-insert cutter was replaced by a 16-tooth cutter tipped with carbide (77 W, 7 C, 8 Ti, 8 Co; grade C-6). The carbide-tipped cutter, operated at a slower speed (50 sfm), and with a much heavier chip load (0.008 in.), had a life of 216 linear inches. In facing to a depth of 0.100 in. (12-in. length of cut), no chipping or other difficulties occurred. The cutter produced a surface finish of 125 micro-in.

Rockwell C 41 to 42. In face milling 4340 steel at Rockwell C 41 to 42, an 8-in.-diam cutter containing grade C-6 carbide inserts produced a surface finish of 150 micro-in. at a cutting speed of 200 sfm and a feed of 6 ipm. The cutter had ten teeth and required 2.5 min in facing a 6-in. length to a depth of 0.187 in. These conditions reduced machining

Carbide tested (a)	No. of tests	Axial rake, degrees	Radial rake, degrees	Speed, sfm	Feed, ipm
A	1	-3	-3	150	2.87
B	10	-3, -10	-3, -10	100, 150	1.87, 2.87
C	8	-3, -10	-3, -10	100, 150	1.87, 2.87
D	8	-5, -10	-3, -10	100, 150	1.87, 2.87
E	2	-5	-5	100, 150	1.87, 2.87
E	2	-10	-5	100, 150	1.87, 2.87
E	3	-10	-10	100, 150	1.87, 2.87

(a) 0.005-in. chip load per tooth

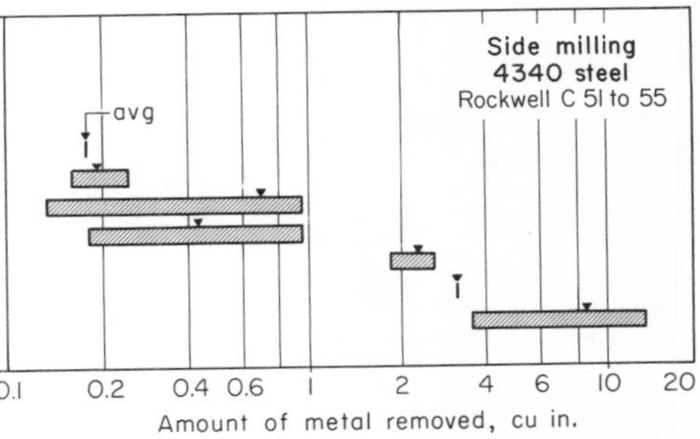

Carbide tested	Composition, % W	Ti	Ta	Cb	Co	C	Rockwell A hardness	Density, g per cu cm
A	65	11.0	5.8	1.8	8.8	7.6	91.5	11.10
B	69	6.7	5.4	1.6	10.7	6.7	91.0	11.90
C	71	9.6	3.75	...	8.0	7.3	92.0	11.80
D	72	4.9	7.0	2.3	6.7	6.8	92.0	12.45
E	75	3.2	5.2	1.6	8.5	6.2	91.5	12.90

In the one test resulting in a removal of 14 cu in., a diamond-lapped tool was used, but the additional cost for lapping could not be justified. Carbide E (used with —10° axial rake, —10° radial rake, 2 to 3° primary relief, and 0.02-in. corner radius; and at 150-sfm speed and 2.87-ipm feed) removed 9.3 cu in. of metal and was recommended as most efficient. A wear land of 1/32 in. was obtained with carbide E, and some carbide C, cutters. All other cutters failed because of chatter, chipping or edge erosion.

Fig. 51. Effect of composition and design of carbide cutters on amount of metal removed in milling 4340 steel at Rockwell C 51 to 55 (Example 358)

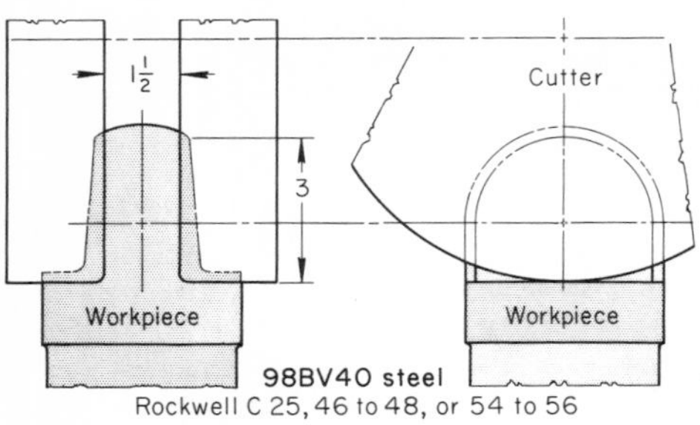

Item	Workpiece hardness, R_C 25	46 to 48	54 to 56
Cutter Details			
Diameter, in.	10	10	10
Width, in. ..	2	2	3
No. of teeth .	20(a)	32	14(a)
Material	M3 HSS	M3 HSS(b)	C-2 carbide
Speeds and Feeds(c)			
Speed, rpm .	32.5	25	38
Speed, sfm .	85	65	100
Feed, ipt ...	0.0025	0.002	0.0004

(a) Inserts. (b) Solid cutter heat treated to Rockwell C 65 to 67 and nitrided. (c) Soluble oil was used as cutting fluid.

Fig. 52. Effect of workpiece hardness on cutter material and design, and on speed and feed, in straddle milling (Example 360)

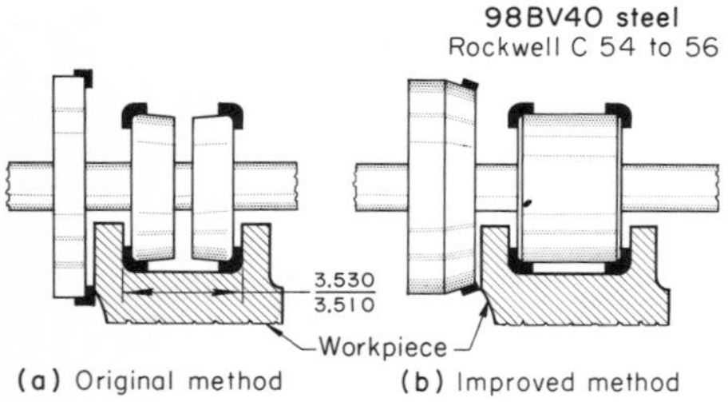

Item	Original method: Two side mills (rh and lh)	Original method: One side mill	Improved method: One solid mill	Improved method: One side mill
Cutter Details(a)				
Diameter, in. ...	8	10	8	10
Width, in.	1¼	1½	3.520	3
Number of inserts	12(b)	14	24(c)	14
Rake angles(d) ..	−8°	−8°	−7°	−7°
Machining Conditions(e)				
Speed, rpm	35		38	
Speed, sfm (max)	92		99	
Feed, ipt	0.0006		0.0008	
Finish, micro-in.	100		60	
Setup time, hr ..	3		2	
Tool-change time, hr	1		½	
Production, pcs/hr	1		2	
Cutter life/grind, pcs	4		15	

(a) All cutters had carbide inserts, brazed in original method, disposable in improved method. (b) Each cutter. (c) 12 each side. (d) Axial and radial. (e) Depth of cut in both methods, 0.090 in. No cutting fluid was used in either method, to avoid flaking of the carbide.

Fig. 53. Original and improved cutter design and machining conditions for milling high-hardness steel (Example 361)

cost 37½%, compared with the cost of face milling 4340 steel of the same hardness with a 6-in.-diam eight-tooth cutter operated at 200 sfm and a feed of 3¾ ipm.

Rockwell C 39. An increase in feed rate from 2¹⁄₁₆ to 5¼ ipm (cutting speed: 180 sfm) resulted in a 60% cost reduction in face milling 4340 steel at Rockwell C 39. The cutter, operated without cutting fluid, was 6 in. in diameter and had eight inserts of grade C-6 carbide. It produced a 12-in. cut (0.100 in. deep) in 4 min. The same cut had required 10 min to produce at the lower feed rate.

Successful results were also obtained with 8-in.-diam cutters of C-6 carbide that were operated at speeds and feeds of 250 sfm and 9 ipm, and of 300 sfm and 11 ipm, although differences were observed in depths and lengths of cut and in surface finishes. The cutter that was operated at the lower speed and feed contained 12 teeth, whereas the cutter that was operated at the higher speed and feed contained 16 teeth.

Example 358. Side Milling 4340 Steel at Rockwell C 51 to 55 (Fig. 51)

A series of tests was conducted to select the carbide grade and tool angles for a 10-in.-diam cutter to be used for production side milling of 4340 steel at a hardness of Rockwell C 51 to 55. The composition, hardness and density of each of the five grades of carbide tested are given in the table with Fig. 51.

Detailed results of this investigation, plotted in Fig. 51, indicate that, of the five carbides tested, only carbide E (listed as grade C-5 or C-6 on most grade-reference charts) is likely to be efficient at a high production rate. In the first and third series of tests with carbide E, the lower speed (100 sfm) and feed (1.87 ipm) removed the least amount of metal. When speed and feed were increased to 150 sfm and 2.87 ipm, respectively, and 10° negative rake angles were employed, carbide E removed 9.3 cu in. of metal.

Example 359. Side Milling Alloy Steel at Rockwell C 55

In side milling a Cr-Ni-Mo-V alloy steel forging (0.42% C) heat treated to Rockwell C 55, cutter life was increased by increasing negative rake angles and decreasing the corner angle. A right-and-left-hand cutter (8-in. diam) having seven teeth tipped with carbide (80 W, 1 Ta, 3 Ti, 6 C, 10 Co; grade C-7), was used to remove 0.090 in. of stock from each of two 4-in.-long lugs. Water-soluble oil was used as a cutting fluid.

With an axial rake of −4°, a radial rake of −2°, and a corner angle of 45°, cutter life was limited to one part per cutter. Changing to a −5° axial rake, a −5° radial rake, and a 15° corner angle extended the life of each cutter to five to eight pieces, and improved surface finish by eliminating chipping.

Example 360. Straddle Milling 98BV40 Steel at Three Hardness Levels (Fig. 52)

In straddle milling the 98BV40 steel workpiece shown in Fig. 52, cutter design and material, as well as operating conditions, had to be varied to obtain acceptable results at three levels of work-metal hardness. The operation was performed on a 50-hp horizontal milling machine.

Details of cutter design, material and operation for the three different work-metal hardnesses are given with Fig. 52. Here it is seen that an M3 high speed steel cutter was used for milling at Rockwell C 25. The same cutter material was used for milling the steel at Rockwell C 46 to 48, but the cutter was nitrided and had 32 instead of 20 teeth. Concurrently, both speed and feed were reduced.

For milling at Rockwell C 54 to 56, a 3-in.-wide cutter was used to obtain greater strength. Carbide inserts were used and the number of teeth was reduced to 14. Speed was increased and feed per tooth was decreased to about ⅕ of that used for milling the lower-hardness work with high speed steel tools.

Example 361. Improvement in Milling 98BV40 Steel at Rockwell C 54 to 56 (Fig. 53)

In milling torque lugs on 98BV40 steel pistons at Rockwell C 54 to 56 with the tooling setup shown in Fig. 53(a), cutter life was unacceptably low. Milling was done in a 50-hp machine with special fixturing. Cutter rigidity was increased by changes in cutters as shown in Fig. 53(b) and detailed in the table below the illustration. As a result, increased speed and feed were possible, a better finish was obtained, and tool life was almost quadrupled.

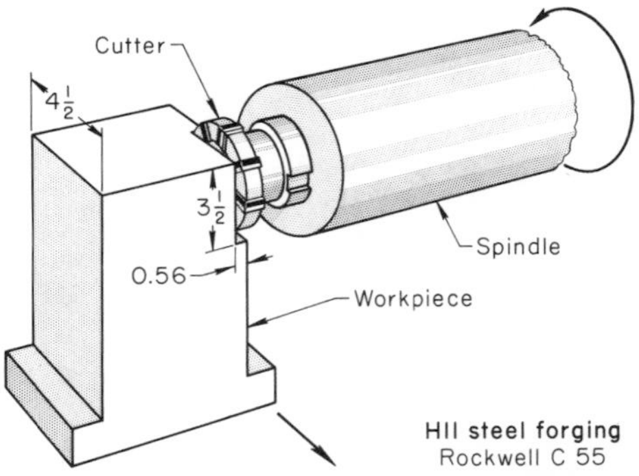

Item	Cutter(a) 1	2	3
Cutter Details			
Axial rake	+7°	−5°	+5°
Radial rake	−7°	−5°	−5°
Corner radius, in.	0.375	0.500	0.125
Results(b)			
Edge wear, 0.001 in.	2 to 5	30 to 40	None
Number of teeth chipped	5	5	None

Machining Conditions for All Cutters

Speed	49 rpm (64 sfm)
Feed	0.002 ipt (0.8 ipm)
Depth of cut	0.07 in. max
Cutting fluid	Sulfurized oil
Stock removed per pass	1.025 cu in.
Time per pass	10.6 min

(a) Five-inch-diameter shell mills with eight carbide blades. (b) Obtained in 13 passes with cutter 1, three passes with cutter 2, and eight passes with cutter 3.

Fig. 55. Effect of cutter design on results in shell milling of H11 steel at high hardness (Example 363)

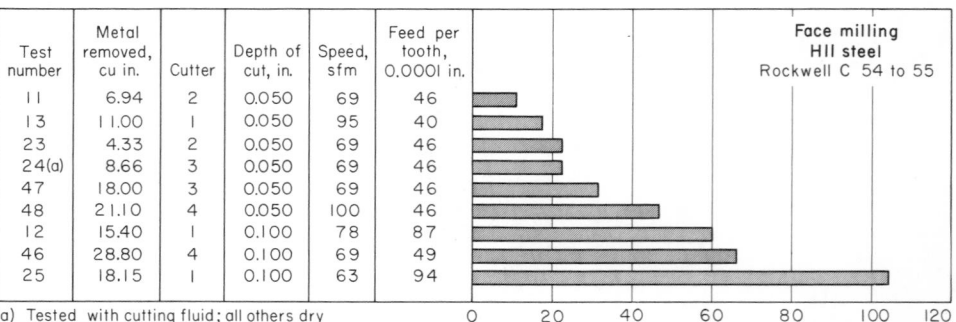

Test number	Metal removed, cu in.	Cutter	Depth of cut, in.	Speed, sfm	Feed per tooth, 0.0001 in.
11	6.94	2	0.050	69	46
13	11.00	1	0.050	95	40
23	4.33	2	0.050	69	46
24(a)	8.66	3	0.050	69	46
47	18.00	3	0.050	69	46
48	21.10	4	0.050	100	46
12	15.40	1	0.100	78	87
46	28.80	4	0.100	69	49
25	18.15	1	0.100	63	94

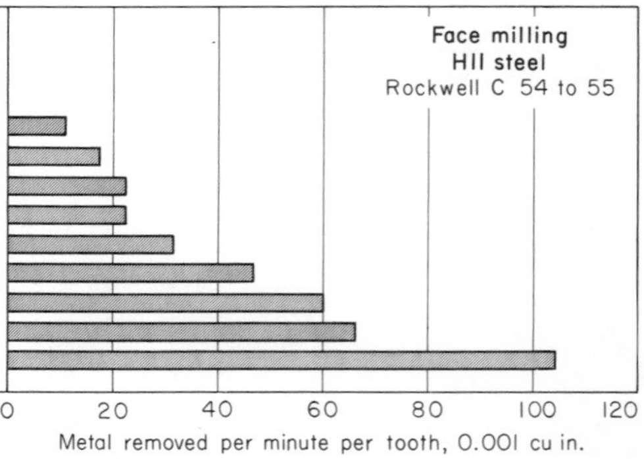

(a) Tested with cutting fluid; all others dry

Cutter	Diameter, in.	Number of inserts	Axial rake	Radial rake	Corner	Carbide designation
1	6	6	−10°	−10°	⅛ in. by 45°	80 W, 1 Ta, 3 Ti, 6 C, 10 Co (grade C-5)
2	8	12	− 7°	− 7°	¹⁄₃₂-in. radius	Same as cutter 1
3	8	12	− 7°	− 7°	⅛ in. by 45°	Same as cutter 1
4	8	16	+ 5°	−10°	¹⁄₃₂ in. by 45°	88 W, 6 C, 6 Co (grade C-2)

Fig. 54. Rate of metal removal as influenced by different speeds and feeds of cutters of different design and material (Example 362)

Example 362. Face Milling H11 Steel at Rockwell C 54 to 55 (Fig. 54)

In 48 tests, four types of carbide-tipped face mills were evaluated for machining performance in face milling H11 steel at a hardness of Rockwell C 54 to 55 on a No. 2 vertical milling machine. The work consisted of bars of three different widths. After heat treatment, the bars were machined 1/8 in. all over to insure uniform surface conditions and hardness. Details of the four milling cutters are given below Fig. 54.

Every effort was made to maintain constant test conditions. All carbide tips were diamond-honed (approximately 0.002 in. by 45°) to remove feather edges caused by tool grinding. Cutters were never stopped in the cut, moved over the machined surface, or allowed to dwell in one spot while rotating. All cuts were made with the feed in the same direction, and the positioning of the cutter relative to the workpiece was controlled so that entry and exit angles were approximately the same.

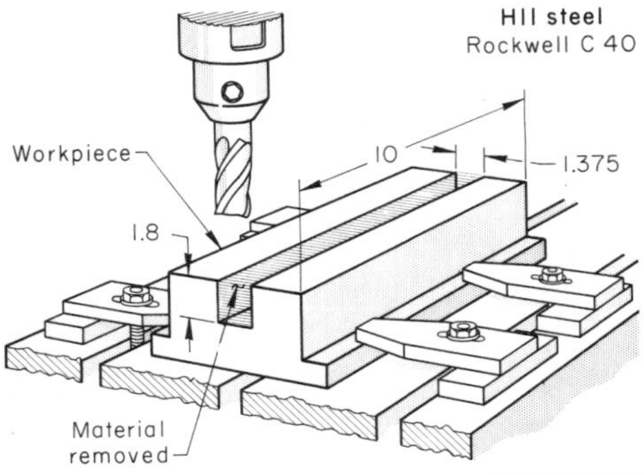

Cutter Details

Type	Four-flute end mill
Size	1.375-in. diam, 4-in. flute length
Corner radius	0.250 in.
Material	Carbide-tipped

Machining Conditions

Speed	729 rpm (260 sfm)
Feed	0.0018 ipt (5.21 ipm)
Depth of cut	0.300 in. max
Cutting fluid	None
Number of passes	6
Stock removed per pass	4.125 cu in.
Total stock removed	24.75 cu in.
Stock removal per minute	2.145 cu in.
Cutter life per grind	24.125 cu in. removed

Fig. 56. End milling of slots in H11 steel at Rockwell C 40 (Example 364)

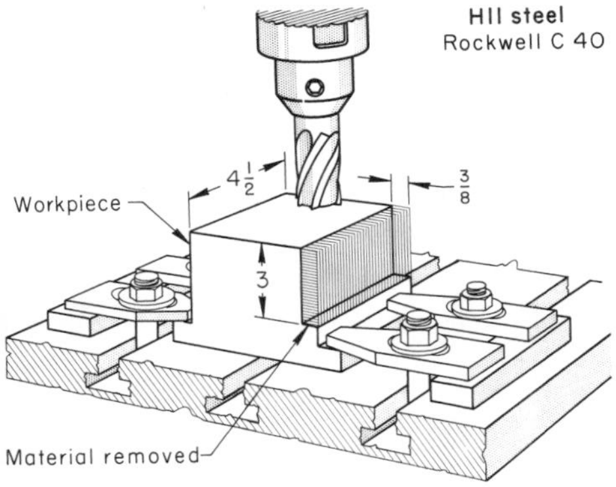

Machining Conditions(a)

Speed	280 rpm (100 sfm)
Feed	0.0005 ipt (0.56 ipm)
Depth of cut	0.060 in.
Cutting fluid	Sulfurized oil
Number of passes	6
Stock removed per pass	0.81 cu in.
Stock removed per minute	0.10 cu in.
Total stock removed	4.86 cu in.
Cutter life per grind	5 cu in. removed

(a) Cutters were of the same design as in Example 364 (Fig. 56).

Fig. 57. End milling H11 steel slabs at Rockwell C 40 (Example 365)

From the 48 tests, results of the nine combinations of cutter design and material that resulted in the highest metal removal rates are plotted in Fig. 54. As shown, a removal rate of 0.103 cu in. per min per tooth was obtained in test 25, in which a six-tooth cutter 6 in. in diameter and 2¾ in. wide was used. In test 46, a 35% reduction in metal removal rate resulted when a 16-tooth cutter 8 in. in diameter and 4 in. wide was used.

For these tests, tool life was determined by the development of 1/32-in. wear land or by severe chipping that terminated in complete breakdown, whichever occurred first. Tool life for cutters with a 1/32-in.-by-45° corner angle was 72 in., compared with 2 in. for cutters with a 1/32-in. corner radius.

Example 363. Milling H11 Steel at Rockwell C 55 With Shell Mills of Three Different Designs (Fig. 55)

Three variations in the design of carbide-blade shell mills were tested in milling the H11 steel forging shown in Fig. 55 at a hardness of Rockwell C 55. Simple bolt clamping was used to secure workpieces to the table of a horizontal milling machine for climb milling. Cutter details, machining conditions, and results of the tests are tabulated below Fig. 55.

Examples 364 and 365. End Milling H11 Steel at Rockwell C 40

Example 364 — Milling of Slots (Fig. 56). In a vertical milling machine, using the setup shown in Fig. 56, slots were milled in H11 steel at Rockwell C 40. Cutter details and machining conditions are given in the table with Fig. 56. The cutter had a low (3-to-1) ratio of unsupported length to diameter and was designed with chip breakers in the form of interruptions in the cutting edge at ¾-in. intervals.

Example 365 — Milling of Slabs (Fig. 57). The setup used for milling slabs of H11 steel at Rockwell C 40 is shown in Fig. 57. The machine and cutters were of the same type as in Example 364, above. Machining conditions are listed in the table with Fig. 57.

Example 366. Stub Arbor for Rigidity in Vertical Slotting of H11 Steel at Rockwell C 54 (Fig. 58)

Mounting the slotting cutter on a stub arbor provided sufficient rigidity for vertical milling of two slots in one end of a curved H11 steel forging at Rockwell C 54. As shown in Fig. 58, the forging was laid on its side and secured to the mill table with simple fixturing. Had horizontal milling been used, a massive fixture would have been required for supporting the forging, and the slot area would have been about two feet above the mill table. Cutter details and machining conditions are given with Fig. 58.

Cutter Life and Machining Cost in Milling Steel Harder Than Rockwell C 40

Variations in machining conditions (speed, feed and depth of cut) and in cutter material can have marked effects on cutter life and cost in milling steel at high hardness. The influence of these interrelated conditions is described in the six examples that follow.

Examples 367, 368 and 369. Effect of Process Variables on Cutter Life in Milling H11 Steel at Rockwell C 41 to 46

Example 367 — Speed and Feed in Face Milling (Fig. 59). As speed was increased at constant feed and depth of cut in face milling H11 steel at Rockwell C 46, the life of single-tooth C-6 carbide cutters decreased more than proportionately (Fig. 59a).

As feed was increased at constant speed and depth of cut, cutter life rose to a maximum and then declined (Fig. 59b). Milling was done without a cutting fluid. Cutter details are given with Fig. 59.

Example 368 — Feed, Speed, and Depth of Cut in End Milling (Fig. 60). The effect of these three operating variables on cutter life in milling H11 steel at Rockwell C 41 was evaluated for four-flute end mills 1 in. in diameter, made of high speed steel. Results of the evaluations are plotted in the graphs in Fig. 60 (next page).

As shown in Fig. 60(a), cutters of two different high speed steels (T15 and M3), operated at a constant speed and depth of cut, had increased life as feed was increased from 0.0034 to 0.0096 ipt.

Figure 60(b) shows that an M4 cutter operated at speeds of 35, 43 and 65 sfm (at constant feed and depth of cut) had maximum life at 43 sfm.

In Fig. 60(c) it is seen that the life of an M3 high speed steel cutter operated at constant speed and feed decreased by more than 60% when depth of cut was increased from 0.100 to 0.300 in. But 7.2 cu in. of steel was

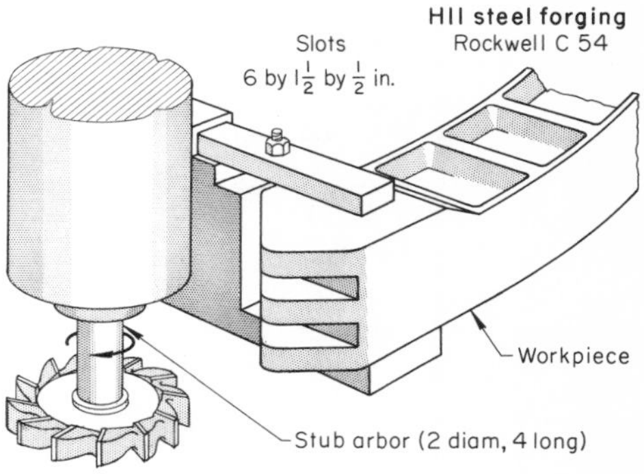

Cutter Details

Type	Slotting cutter
Size	8-in. diam, 1/2 in. wide
Number of teeth	12
Blade material	Carbide

Machining Conditions

Speed	27 rpm (56 sfm)
Feed	0.0017 ipt (0.562 ipm)
Depth of cut	1/32 in. each side
Cutting fluid	Soluble oil
Tool life per grind	2 slots

Fig. 58. Use of stub arbor for rigidity in vertical milling of slots in H11 steel (Example 366)

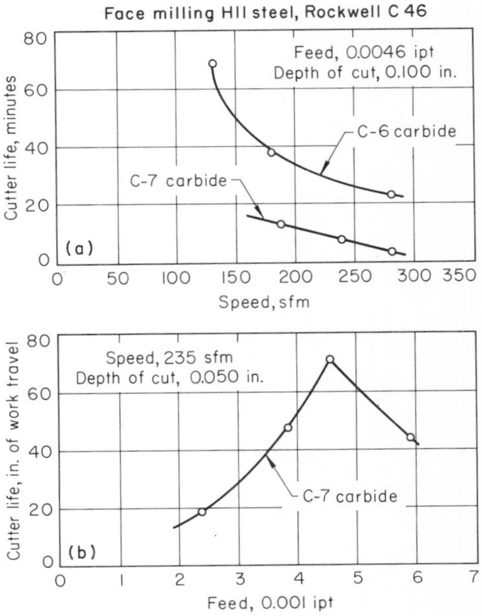

Cutters were 6 in. in diameter and 2 in. wide. Axial rake, radial rake, clearance and end cutting-edge angles were all −5°; corner angle was 45°. Cutter life was based on attainment of 0.015-in. wear land.

Fig. 59. Effect of speed and feed on life of single-tooth carbide cutters in face milling H11 steel at Rockwell C 46 (Example 367)

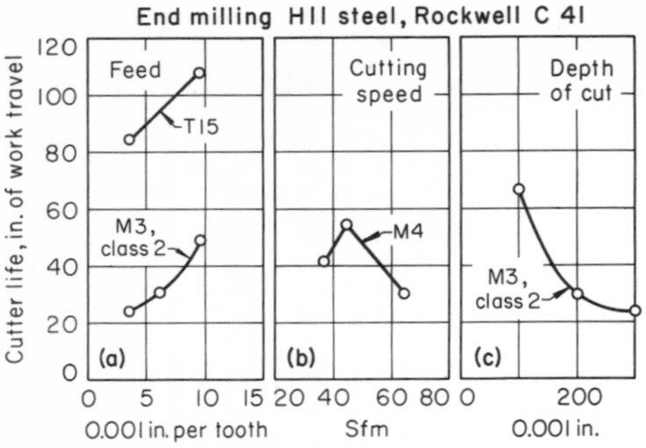

Results were obtained with four-flute end mills of 1-in. diameter. Cutter life was based on attainment of 0.010-in. wear land. (a) Speed was 43 sfm and depth of cut 0.100 in. (b) Feed was 0.0034 ipt and depth of cut 0.100 in. (c) Speed was 43 sfm and feed 0.0034 ipt.

Fig. 60. Effect of operating variables on cutter life (Example 368)

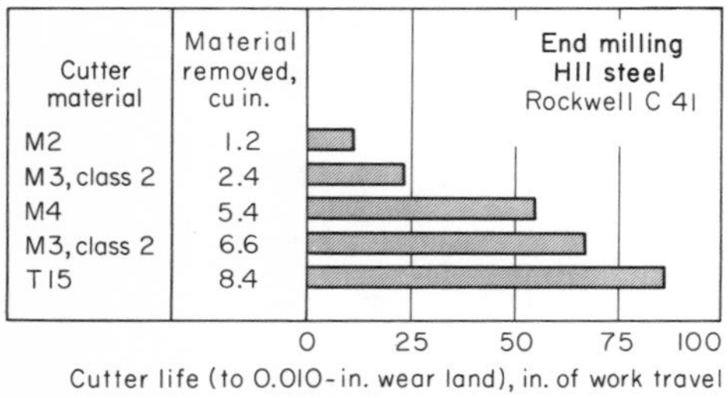

Each bar represents one cutter. All cutters were four-flute end mills 1 in. in diameter, with helix angle of 30° to 35° and primary clearance of 5° to 6°, and were operated at a speed of 43 sfm and a feed of 0.0034 ipt.

Fig. 61. Effect of cutter material on cutter life (Example 369)

removed in 10.6 min with the 0.300-in. cut, and only 6.6 cu in. was removed in 29 min with the 0.100-in. cut.

Example 369 — End Mills of Four Different High Speed Steels (Fig. 61). Tool life obtained in end milling H11 steel at Rockwell C 41 with 1-in.-diam cutters made of M2, M3 (class 2), M4 and T15 high speed steels is compared in Fig. 61. Each bar in the graph represents a single cutter. All cutters were used under the same conditions (Fig. 61).

As demonstrated in the three examples that follow, the use of disposable-insert carbide blades instead of resharpenable high speed steel blades can lower milling costs by:

1 Eliminating tool regrinding
2 Reducing tool-change time
3 Reducing tool-maintenance costs (for example, damaged teeth can be replaced more easily and quickly)
4 Providing an increase in tool life (because of the lower residual stress characteristic of mechanically inserted carbide)
5 Allowing the use of higher speeds.

Examples 370, 371 and 372. High Speed Steel Inserts vs Disposable Carbide Inserts

(Straddle Milling 4340 Steel at High Hardness)

In straddle milling of three different 4340 steel parts at hardnesses between Rockwell C 34 and 45, the substitution of disposable carbide blades for blades of T15 high speed steel greatly reduced milling costs. All milling was done on a horizontal machine. Details, presented in the examples here and in Fig. 62, 63 and 64, are summarized in Table 7.

Example 370 (Fig. 62). In the setup shown in Fig. 62, 100 fittings of 4340 steel at Rockwell C 40 to 45 were straddle milled with disposable blades of carbide (74 WC, 11 Co, 9 Ti, 6 Ta; grade C-5) and with T15 high speed steel blades, inserted in 8-in.-diam cutters for climb milling. Results, tabulated below Fig. 62, show that with the carbide blades production rate was nearly tripled and cost per piece was reduced more than 90%.

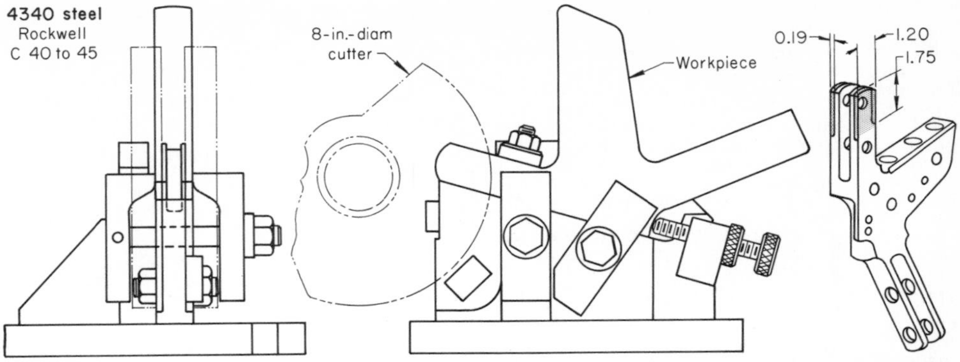

Item	Type of blade: T15 high speed steel	Type of blade: Disposable C-5 carbide
Machining Conditions		
Number of cutter teeth	18	12
Speed, rpm	17	96
Speed, sfm	36	200
Feed, ipt	0.0024	0.0055
Production per hour, pieces	27.6	78.6
Cutter life, pieces	20	160

Item	Type of blade: T15 high speed steel	Type of blade: Disposable C-5 carbide
Costs per Piece(a)		
Tool use	$1.700	$0.034
Tool change	0.174	0.016
Operating	0.256	0.089
Total machining cost	$2.130	$0.139
Saving per 100 pieces(b)		$199.10

(a) Based on tool life. (b) Size of production lot.

Fig. 62. Straddle milling of high-hardness steel in which change from high speed steel blades to disposable carbide blades reduced machining costs (Example 370)

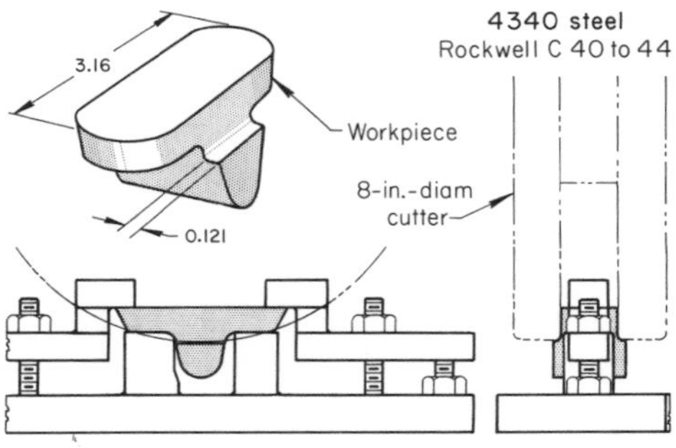

Item	Type of blade: T15 high speed steel	Type of blade: Disposable C-6 carbide
Machining Conditions		
Number of cutter teeth	16	12
Speed, rpm	27	153
Speed, sfm	57	320
Feed, ipt	0.0035	0.0033
Production per hour, pieces	18.6	74.4
Cutter life, pieces	30	256
Costs per Piece(a)		
Tool use	$0.903	$ 0.023
Tool change	0.116	0.007
Operating	0.369	0.094
Total machining cost	$1.388	$ 0.124
Saving on 805 pieces(b)		$1017.52

(a) Based on tool life. (b) Size of production lot.

Fig. 63. Straddle milling of high-hardness steel in which change from high speed steel blades to disposable carbide blades reduced machining costs (Example 371)

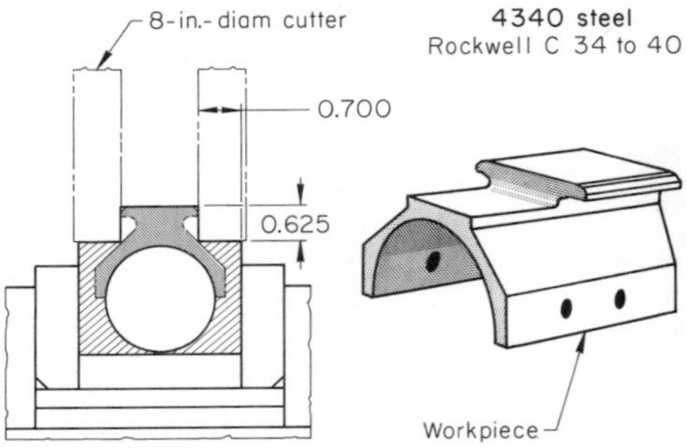

Item	Type of blade: T15 high speed steel	Type of blade: Disposable C-5 carbide
Machining Conditions		
Number of cutter teeth	16	12
Speed, rpm	29	148
Speed, sfm	61	310
Feed, ipt	0.0024	0.0042
Production per hour, pieces	6.6	43.8
Cutter life, pieces	3	48
Costs per Piece(a)		
Tool use	$ 9.033	$ 0.125
Tool change	1.160	0.041
Operating	1.036	0.163
Total machining cost	$11.229	$ 0.329
Saving on 54 pieces(b)		$588.60

(a) Based on tool life. (b) Size of production lot.

Fig. 64. Straddle milling of high-hardness steel in which change from high speed steel blades to disposable carbide blades reduced machining costs (Example 372)

Example 371 (Fig. 63). In conventional straddle milling of 805 backup blocks made of 4340 steel at Rockwell C 40 to 44 (Fig. 63), disposable-insert blades of carbide (82 WC, 10 Co, 8 Ti; grade C-6) were substituted for T15 high speed steel blades in 8-in.-diam cutters. The carbide permitted spindle speed nearly six times that for the T15, quadrupled production rate, and extended cutter life more than eightfold. (See also Table 7.)

Example 372 (Fig. 64). Total machining costs were reduced more than 90% in straddle milling the part shown in Fig. 64 by substituting blades of carbide (74 WC, 11 Co, 9 Ti, 6 Ta; grade C-5) for T15 high speed steel blades in an 8-in.-diam cutter for climb milling. The part, a launch-gear snubber, was made of 4340 steel at Rockwell C 34 to 40. With the carbide, production and tool life were increased, also (see Fig. 64 and Table 7).

Milling Compared With Alternative Processes

Broaching is discussed in Example 336 in this article. Examples 135 to 138 in the article on Broaching show applications in which broaching was superior to milling.

Planing or Shaping. The initial cost of a milling machine is considerably greater than that of a planer or a

Table 6. Typical Feeds for Milling Ferrous and Nonferrous Metals With Six Types of High Speed Steel and Carbide Cutters

Work metal	Face mills	Helical mills	Slotting and side mills	End mills	Form-relieved cutters	Circular saws
	Feed, in. per tooth					
High Speed Steel Cutters						
Aluminum and magnesium	0.022	0.018	0.013	0.011	0.007	0.005
Free-cutting copper alloys	0.022	0.018	0.013	0.011	0.007	0.005
Medium-hard copper alloys	0.014	0.011	0.008	0.007	0.004	0.003
Hard copper alloys	0.009	0.007	0.006	0.005	0.003	0.002
Copper	0.012	0.010	0.007	0.006	0.004	0.003
Gray iron, 150 to 180 Bhn	0.016	0.013	0.009	0.008	0.005	0.004
Gray iron, 180 to 220 Bhn	0.013	0.010	0.007	0.007	0.004	0.003
Gray iron, 220 to 300 Bhn	0.011	0.008	0.006	0.006	0.003	0.003
Malleable iron	0.012	0.010	0.007	0.006	0.004	0.003
Cast steel	0.012	0.010	0.007	0.006	0.004	0.003
Free-cutting low-carbon steel	0.012	0.010	0.007	0.006	0.004	0.003
Low-carbon steel	0.010	0.008	0.006	0.005	0.003	0.003
Medium-carbon steel	0.010	0.008	0.006	0.005	0.003	0.003
Alloy steel, 180 to 220 Bhn	0.008	0.007	0.005	0.004	0.003	0.002
Alloy steel, 220 to 300 Bhn	0.006	0.005	0.004	0.003	0.002	0.002
Alloy steel, 300 to 400 Bhn	0.004	0.003	0.003	0.002	0.002	0.001
Free-cutting stainless steel	0.010	0.008	0.006	0.005	0.003	0.002
Stainless steel	0.006	0.005	0.004	0.003	0.002	0.002
Nickel-copper alloys	0.008	0.007	0.005	0.004	0.003	0.002
Carbide Cutters						
Aluminum and magnesium	0.020	0.016	0.012	0.010	0.006	0.005
Free-cutting copper alloys	0.020	0.016	0.012	0.010	0.006	0.005
Medium-hard copper alloys	0.012	0.010	0.007	0.006	0.004	0.003
Hard copper alloys	0.010	0.008	0.006	0.005	0.003	0.003
Copper	0.012	0.009	0.007	0.006	0.004	0.003
Gray iron, 150 to 180 Bhn	0.020	0.016	0.012	0.010	0.006	0.005
Gray iron, 180 to 220 Bhn	0.016	0.013	0.010	0.008	0.005	0.004
Gray iron, 220 to 300 Bhn	0.012	0.010	0.007	0.006	0.004	0.003
Malleable iron	0.014	0.011	0.008	0.007	0.004	0.004
Cast steel	0.014	0.011	0.008	0.007	0.005	0.004
Free-cutting low-carbon steel	0.016	0.013	0.009	0.008	0.005	0.004
Low-carbon steel	0.014	0.011	0.008	0.007	0.004	0.004
Medium-carbon steel	0.014	0.011	0.008	0.007	0.004	0.004
Alloy steel, 180 to 220 Bhn	0.014	0.011	0.008	0.007	0.004	0.004
Alloy steel, 220 to 300 Bhn	0.012	0.010	0.007	0.006	0.004	0.003
Alloy steel, 300 to 400 Bhn	0.010	0.008	0.006	0.005	0.003	0.003
Free-cutting stainless steel	0.014	0.011	0.008	0.007	0.004	0.004
Stainless steel	0.010	0.008	0.006	0.005	0.003	0.003
Nickel-copper alloys	0.010	0.008	0.006	0.005	0.003	0.003

shaper that can machine workpieces of similar size. Also, the tooling for milling usually costs up to 50 times as much, and setup time is usually longer. However, milling is far more efficient than planing or shaping in removing metal within a given time.

Grinding is often preferred to milling when the amount of metal to be removed is small and dimensional accuracy and surface finish are critical. Milling and grinding are frequently used in combination, but when grinding can perform the entire machining operation, the time and expense of an extra setup are avoided. Examples 470, 472 and 525 in the article "Grinding" describe applications in which machining costs were reduced by removing all stock by grinding.

Other processes may be more efficient and economical than end milling for machining pockets and complex shapes, as in the following example.

Example 373. End Milling vs Electrical Discharge Machining and Electrochemical Machining (Fig. 65)

Three methods of machining two 3⁄16-in.-wide cam wells in breech blocks for machine guns were compared for cost. Results are shown below Fig. 65.

In the first method, the basic shape of the cam well was generated by boring a series of holes on a jig boring machine, advancing the centerline of the machine quill in 0.015-in. increments along the coordinate path. The resultant scalloped effect was then removed, and slots were brought to final size, by end milling in a duplicating machine, utilizing a template. The tool overhang required because of the 1½-in.-high protruding member immediately adjacent to the area being end milled (Fig. 65) resulted in excessive deflection of the 3⁄16-in.-diam end mill, making it difficult to meet tolerance. By this method, four days was required for producing three sets of wells, making the cost unacceptable.

In electrical discharge machining of a development lot of 50 pieces, these cam wells were produced at a significant reduction in cost. For production lots of 300 and 1500 pieces, the cost of EDM was further reduced.

Table 7. Production and Cost Improvements Obtained With Carbide Cutters in Examples 370, 371 and 372(a)

Item	Example 370 (Fig. 62)	Example 371 (Fig. 63)	Example 372 (Fig. 64)	Average
Production and Tool-Life Increases, %				
Production rate	185	300	563	349
Tool life	700	753	1500	984
Reduction in Costs per Piece, %				
Tool use	98.0	97.4	98.6	98.0
Tool change	90.8	93.9	96.5	93.7
Operating	65.2	74.5	84.3	74.7
Total mach'g.	93.4	91.1	97.9	94.1

(a) Data are based on change from cutters with T15 high speed steel inserts to cutters with disposable carbide inserts.

Of the three methods compared, however, electrochemical machining was the most satisfactory. Using a dual filter and two nonreroding electrodes, this method produced slots at the rate of one pair every 4 min, and was selected for continuous high production.

Selected Reference

"A Treatise on Milling and Milling Machines", 3rd Edition, Cincinnati Milling Machine Co., Cincinnati, Ohio, 1951; 910 pages. A comprehensive work dealing with machines, tools, conditions and practice for a variety of milling methods and applications.

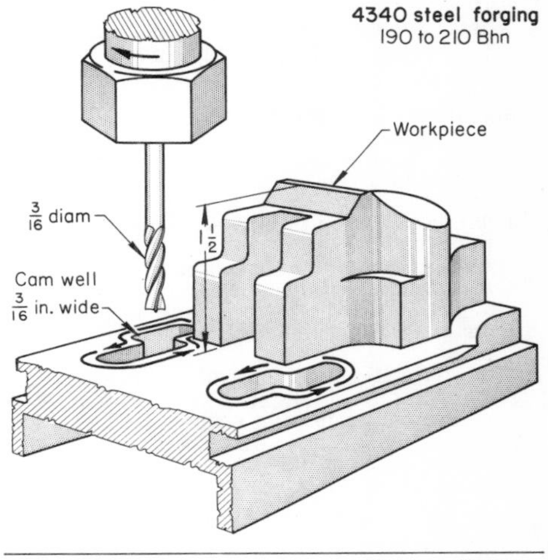

Method	Quantity	Time required (a)	Cost per piece
End milling	35(b)	11 hr	$88.00
EDM(c)	50(d)	...	16.00
EDM	300(e)	...	12.00
EDM	1500(e)	1½ hr	9.50
ECM(f)	400	4 min	0.98

(a) Total time for machining one piece (two slots). (b) Performed in toolroom. (c) Electrical discharge machining. (d) Development lot. (e) Production lot. (f) Electrochemical machining.

Fig. 65. End milling of small complex slots, and cost comparison with two alternative methods (Example 373)

Other Examples of Milling Applications in This Volume

Work metal	Example number
Methods, Face Milling	
Cast iron	669
Tool steel	677, 688
Stainless steel	779
Refractory metals	863
Aluminum	913, 914
Beryllium	930
Magnesium	994
Methods, Straddle or Gang Milling	
Tool steel	678
Stainless steel	785
Aluminum	911, 916
Copper	962, 963
Copper (slitting cutters)	960, 961
Other Methods	
Tool steel	680, 685, 694, 697, 700, 703, 708, 710, 711, 712
Stainless steel	783, 784
Aluminum	912, 919
Comparison of Methods or Tool Design	
Cast iron	667, 668
Stainless steel	780, 781
Heat-resisting alloys	844, 845
Work Metals Compared in Milling	
Cast iron	671
Tool steel	695, 696, 698, 701, 702
Aluminum	910
Cutter Materials Compared in Milling	
Cast iron	672
Tool steel	699
Stainless steel	782
Heat-resisting alloys	846, 847, 848
Tracer or Numerical Control	
Tool steel	679
Aluminum	917, 918
Titanium	1003, 1004
Rotary Table	
Cast iron	670
Magnesium	993

Machining of Gears

*By the ASM Committee on Machining of Gears**

THIS ARTICLE deals exclusively with procedures for machining the teeth of steel gears. Machining operations used for preparing the gear blanks are no less important than those used for machining the teeth. However, these processes — chiefly turning, broaching, drilling, and reaming — are fundamentally the same for gear blanks as for other workpieces, and are dealt with in separate articles in this volume.

Shaving, as applied to the finishing of gear teeth, is included in this article. Finishing gear teeth by grinding is covered in the article "Grinding of Gears" (page 213). Honing of gear teeth is covered in the article "Honing" (page 288), and lapping of gear teeth is described in the article "Lapping" (page 298).

Terminology. Several terms commonly used in describing gears are defined as follows:

addendum. Height of tooth above pitch circle.
circular pitch. Length of arc of the pitch circle between corresponding points on adjacent teeth.
dedendum. Depth of a tooth space below the pitch circle.
diametral pitch. Ratio of number of teeth to the number of inches of pitch diameter.
pitch circle. A circle of radius equal to the distance from the gear axis to the pitch point.
pitch diameter. Diameter of the pitch circle.
pitch point. The tangency point of the pitch circles of two mating gears.
pressure angle. The angle between a tooth profile and a radial line at its pitch point.

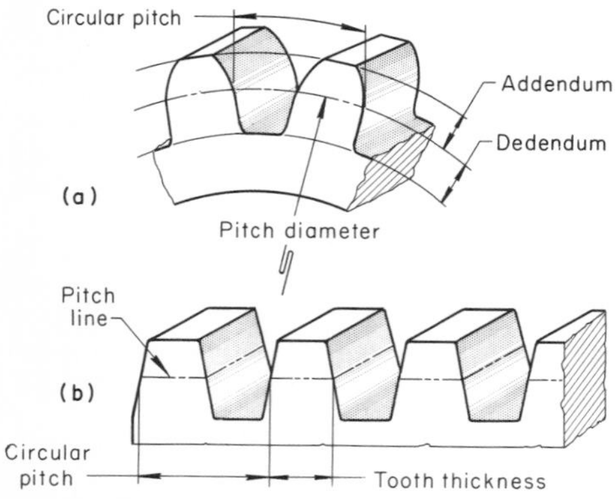

Fig. 1. Sections of (a) *a spur gear, and* (b) *a spur rack*

Types of Gears

The types of gears for which machining information is given in this article are described in this section.

Spur gears (Fig. 1a), the most common of all types, are used to transmit power or motion between parallel shafts or between a shaft and a rack. Spur gears have radial teeth uniformly spaced around the outer periphery of their circular shapes, and parallel to the shafts on which they are mounted. Tooth contact between mating spur gears is in a straight line tangent to the pitch circles.

Helical gears (Fig. 2a) are used to transmit motion between parallel or crossed shafts, or between a shaft and a rack by meshing teeth that lie along a helix at an angle to the shaft. Because of this angle, mating of the teeth occurs in such a way that more than one tooth of each gear is always in mesh. This condition permits smoother action than with spur gears. However, unlike spur gears, some end thrust is inevitable in helical gears, causing loss of power and requiring thrust bearings.

Herringbone gears (Fig. 3), sometimes called double helical gears, are used to transmit motion between parallel shafts. Herringbone gears combine the principal advantages of spur and helical gears because their tooth engagement is progressive, with two or more teeth sharing the load at the same time. Because they have equal right-hand and left-hand helixes, end thrust is eliminated. Herringbone gears can be operated at higher pitch-line velocities than spur gears.

Crossed-axes helical gears operate with shafts that are nonparallel and nonintersecting (Fig. 4). The action between mating teeth has a wedging effect, which results in sliding on tooth flanks. These gears have low load-carrying capacity, but they are useful where shafts must rotate at an angle to each other.

Worm-gear sets are usually right-angle drives consisting of a worm gear (or worm wheel) and a worm. A double-enveloping worm-gear set is shown in Fig. 5. Worm-gear sets are used where the ratio of the speed of the driving member to the speed of the driven member is large, and for a compact right-angle drive.

Internal gears are used to transmit motion between parallel shafts. Their tooth forms are similar to those of spur and helical gears except that the teeth point inward toward the center of the gear. Common applications for internal gears include rear drives for heavy vehicles, planetary gears, and speed-reducing devices. Internal gears are sometimes used in compact designs, because the center distance between the internal gear and its mating pinion is much smaller than that required for two external gears. A typical relation between an internal gear and a mating pinion is shown in Fig. 6.

Racks. A rack is a gear having a pitch circle of infinite radius. Its teeth lie along a straight line on a plane. The teeth may be at right angles to the edge of the rack and mesh with a spur gear (Fig. 1b), or the teeth on the rack may be at some other angle and engage a helical gear (Fig. 2b).

Bevel gears transmit rotary motion between two nonparallel shafts. These shafts are usually at 90° to each other.

Straight bevel gears (Fig. 7a) have straight teeth which, if extended inward, would intersect at the axis of the gear. Thus, the action between mating teeth resembles that of two cones rolling on each other (see Fig. 8 for angles and terminology). The use of straight bevel gears is generally limited to drives that operate at low speeds and where noise is not important.

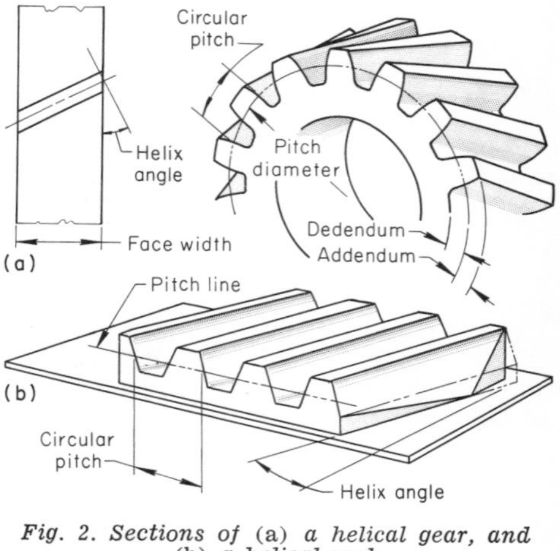

Fig. 2. Sections of (a) *a helical gear, and* (b) *a helical rack*

*D. W. HEMPHILL, *Chairman,* Chief Metallurgist, Fort Wayne Div., Dana Corp.; ROBERT H. BUNKER, Methods Gear Engineer, Barber-Colman Co.; MARTIN J. COFFEY, Manager, Manufacturing Engineering Dept., Mack Trucks, Inc.; EUGENE W. GOLOMB, Manufacturing Engineer, Gleason Works; DONALD J. KEIL, Senior Process Engineer, Manufacturing Engineering, Transmission and Chassis Div., Ford Motor Co.

ROBERT S. KISNER, Assistant Plant Superintendent, Ingersoll-Rand Co.; JOHN KOINIS, Resident Engineer, Detroit Universal Div., Chrysler Corp.; JOHN MACINNES, Senior Engineer, Westinghouse Electric Corp.; STEVEN MANDREGER, Gear Cutting Tool Engineer, Transmission Div., Clark Equipment Co.; RAYMOND C. MELVIN, Gear Engineer, Harnischfeger Corp.; HARRY T. MORTON, Superintendent, Quality Engineering, Buick Motor Div., General Motors Corp.; ARNOLD PAPROCKI, Supervisor, Gear Dept., Kearney & Trecker Corp.; GEORGE W. REBECK, Superintendent, Tool Steel Gear and Pinion Co.

ALOIS SEIDL, Shop Gear Engineer, Transmission and Axle Div., Rockwell-Standard Corp.; H. A. SQUIRES, Chief Manufacturing Engineer, Bucyrus-Erie Co.; ARTHUR STOUGHTON, Production Engineering, Allison Div., General Motors Corp.; CLARENCE G. THYBERG, Analyst, Advanced Methods Engineering, Small Aircraft Engine Dept., General Electric Co.

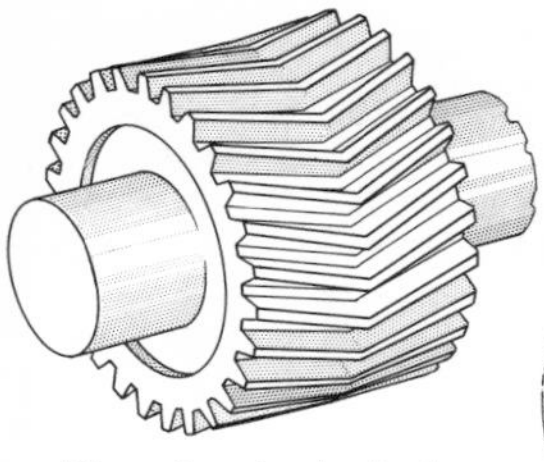

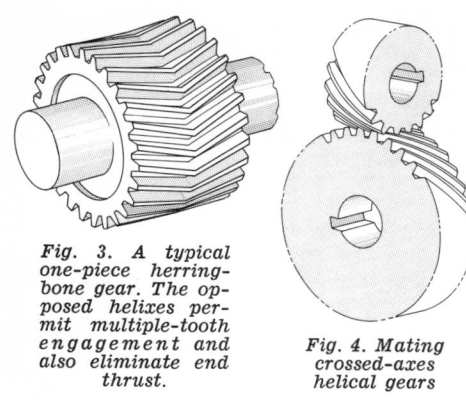

Fig. 3. A typical one-piece herringbone gear. The opposed helixes permit multiple-tooth engagement and also eliminate end thrust.

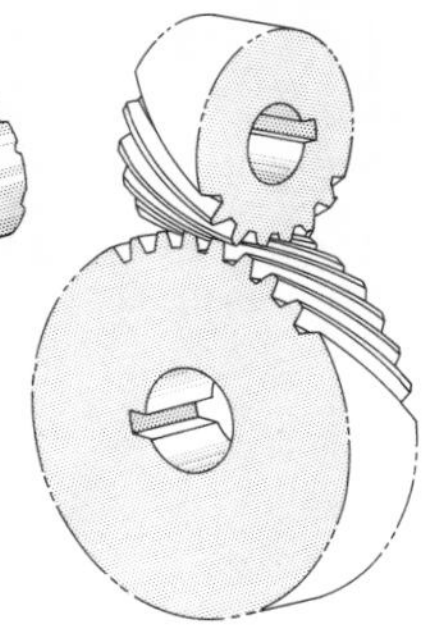

Fig. 4. Mating crossed-axes helical gears

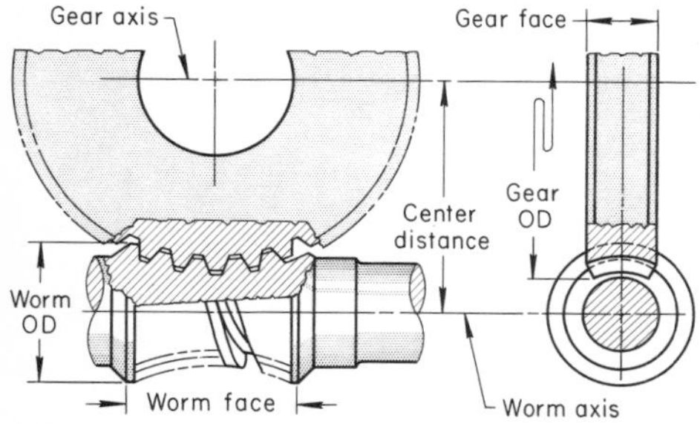

Fig. 5. Mating of worm gear (worm wheel) and worm in a double-enveloping worm-gear set

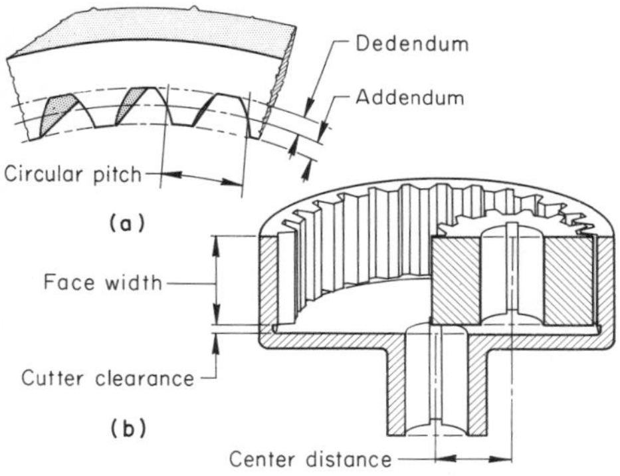

Fig. 6. (a) *Section of a spur-type internal gear, and* (b) *relation of internal gear with mating pinion*

Spiral bevel gears (Fig. 7b) have teeth that are curved and oblique. The inclination of the teeth results in gradual engagement and continuous line contact or overlapping action; that is, more than one tooth will be in contact at all times. Because of this continuous engagement, the load is transmitted more smoothly from the driving to the driven gear than with straight bevel gears. Spiral bevel gears also have greater load-carrying capacity than their straight bevel counterparts. Spiral bevel gears are usually preferred to straight bevel gears when speeds are greater than 1000 sfm, and particularly for very small gears.

Zerol bevel gears (Fig. 7c) are curved-tooth bevel gears with zero spiral angle. They differ from spiral bevel gears in that the teeth are not oblique. They are used in the same way as spiral bevel gears, and they have somewhat greater tooth strength than straight bevel gears.

Hypoid gears (Fig. 7d) are similar to spiral bevel gears in general appearance. The important difference is that the pinion axis of the hypoid pair of gears is offset somewhat from the gear axis. This feature provides many design advantages. In operation, hypoid gears run even more smoothly and quietly than spiral bevel gears, and are somewhat stronger.

Spiral bevel, Zerol and hypoid gears are of two types — generated and nongenerated. In appearance, the two types are nearly identical, the only difference being a slight variation in the profile shape of the teeth. In a generated pair, the teeth of both the gear and pinion are cut on a generating-type machine, whereas in a nongenerated pair, only the pinion member is generated, the teeth of the gear being straight-sided. In generating a pinion to operate with a nongenerated gear, the tooth profile is modified to compensate for the lack of profile curvature in the gear tooth. For reasons of tooth design, nongenerated gears are usually limited to ratios of at least 2.5 to 1.

Nongenerated gears are used primarily for economy. Because no generating roll is required when cutting the gear member, machining is several times faster than for a generated counterpart. For this reason nongenerated bevel gears are widely used when mass production is required.

Machining Processes for Gears Other Than Bevel Gears

The methods used to cut the teeth of gears other than bevel gears are milling, broaching, shear cutting, hobbing, shaping, and rack cutting. In any method, a fixture must hold the gear blank in correct relation to the cutter, and the setup must be rigid.

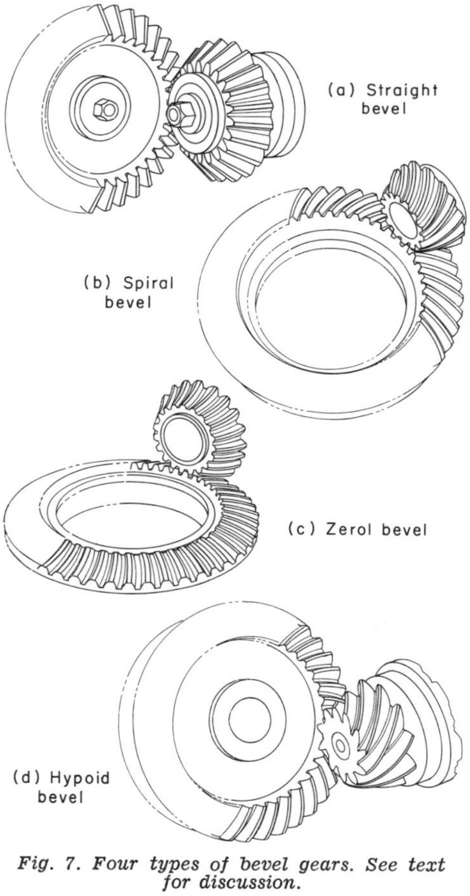

Fig. 7. Four types of bevel gears. See text for discussion.

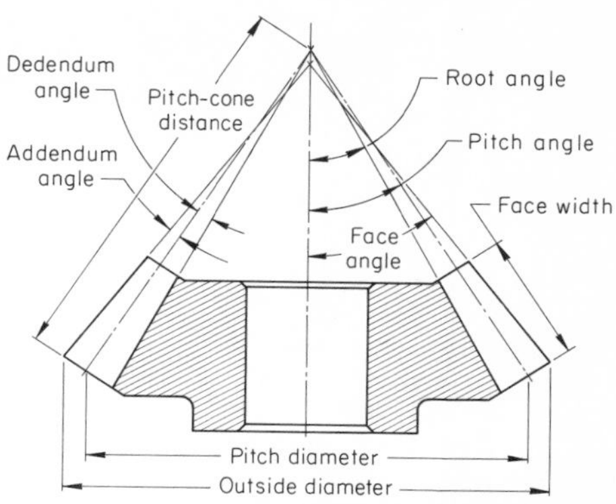

Fig. 8. Angles and terminology for straight bevel gears

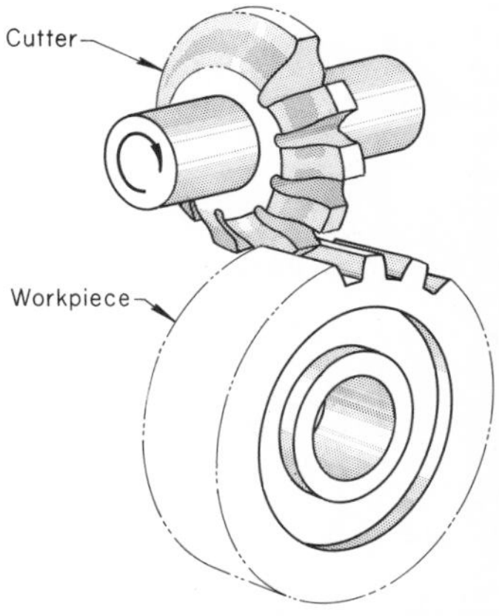

Fig. 9. Relation of cutter and workpiece when milling teeth in a spur gear

Milling produces gear teeth by means of a form cutter. The usual practice is to mill one tooth space at a time. After each space is milled the gear blank is indexed to the next cutting position.

Peripheral milling can be used for roughing of teeth in spur and helical gears. Figure 9 shows teeth in a spur gear being cut by peripheral milling with a form cutter. End milling can also be used for cutting teeth in spur or helical gears and is often used for cutting coarse-pitch teeth in herringbone gears (see Example 390).

In practice, gear milling is usually confined to replacement gears or to small-lot production, roughing and finishing coarse-pitch gears, and finish milling fine-pitch gears of special tooth forms. Although high-quality gears can be produced by milling, the accuracy of tooth spacing is limited by the inherent inaccuracy of the indexing mechanism. Most indexing techniques do not produce spacing accuracy comparable with that of hobbing.

Broaching. Both external and internal gear teeth, spur or helical, can be broached, but conventional broaching is usually confined to cutting teeth in internal gears. Figure 10 shows progressive broach steps in cutting an internal spur gear. The form of the space between broached gear teeth corresponds to the form of the broach teeth. The cutting action of any single broach tooth is similar to that of a single form tool. Each cross section of the broach

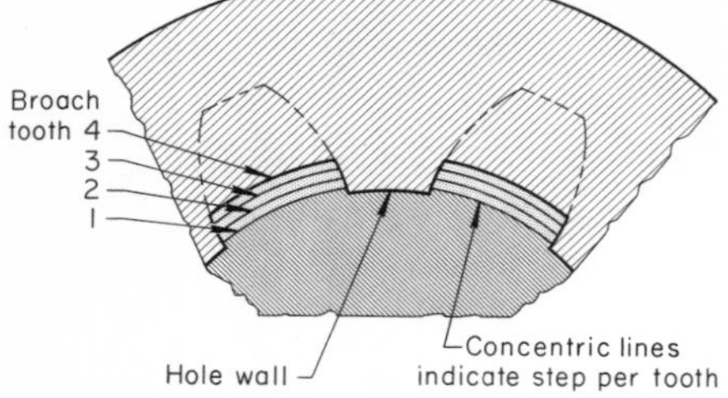

Fig. 10. Progressive action of broach teeth in cutting teeth of an internal spur gear

has as many teeth as there are tooth spaces on the gear. The diameter of each section increases progressively to the major diameter that completes the tooth form on the workpiece. Broaching is fast and accurate, but the cost of tooling is high. Therefore, broaching of gear teeth is best suited to large production runs.

Shear cutting is a high-production method for producing teeth in external spur gears. This process is not applicable to helical gears. In shear cutting, as in broaching, all tooth spaces are cut simultaneously and progressively (Fig. 11). Cutting speeds in shear cutting are similar to those for broaching the same work metal. Machines are available for cutting gears up to 20 in. in diameter, with face width up to 6 in.

The shear-cutting head is mounted in a fixed position, and the gear blanks are pushed through the head. Cutting tools are fed radially into the head, a predetermined amount for each stroke, until the required depth of tooth space is reached. In shear cutting, some space is required for overtravel, although most workpieces with integral shoulders or flanges (such as cluster gears) do have enough clearance between sections to allow shear cutting to be used. Tooling cost for shear cutting is high. Therefore, this process is best suited to large production runs.

Hobbing is a practical method for cutting teeth in spur gears, helical gears, worms, worm gears and many special forms. Conventional hobbing machines are not applicable to cutting bevel and internal gears. Tooling costs for hobbing are lower than for broaching or shear cutting. Therefore, hobbing is used in low-quantity production or even for a few pieces (see Example 375). On the other hand, hobbing is a fast and accurate method — compared with milling, for instance — and is therefore suitable for medium and high production quantities.

Hobbing is a generating process in which both the cutting tool and the workpiece revolve in a constant relation as the hob is being fed across the face width of the gear blank. The hob is a fluted worm with form-relieved teeth that cut into the gear blank in succession, each in a slightly different position. Instead of being formed in one profile cut, as in milling, the gear teeth are generated progressively by a series of cuts (Fig. 12). The hobbing of a spur gear is shown in Fig. 13.

Gear shaping is the most versatile of all gear-cutting processes. Although shaping is most commonly used for cutting teeth in spur and helical gears, this process is also applicable to cutting herringbone teeth, internal gear teeth (or splines), chain sprockets, ratchets, elliptical gears, face gears, worm gears, and racks. Shaping cannot be used to cut teeth in bevel gears. Because tooling costs are relatively low, shaping is practical for any quantity of production. Frequently workpiece design prevents the use of milling cutters or hobs (notably, for cluster gears; see Example 378) and shaping is the most practical method for cutting the teeth.

Gear shaping is a generating process that uses a toothed disk cutter mounted on a spindle that moves in axial strokes as it rotates. The workpiece is carried on a second spindle. The work-

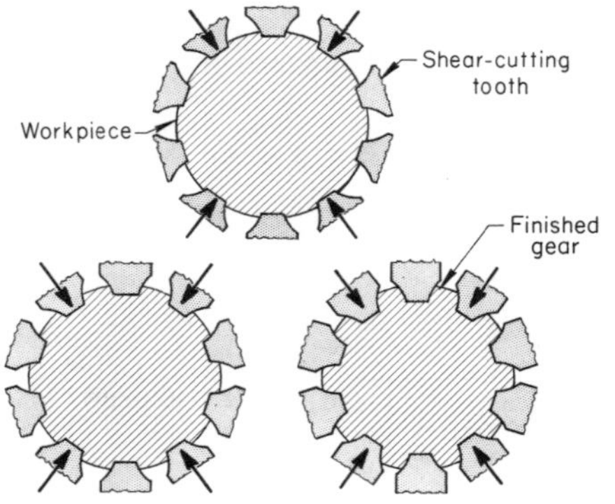

Fig. 11. Progressive action in shear cutting teeth of an external spur gear

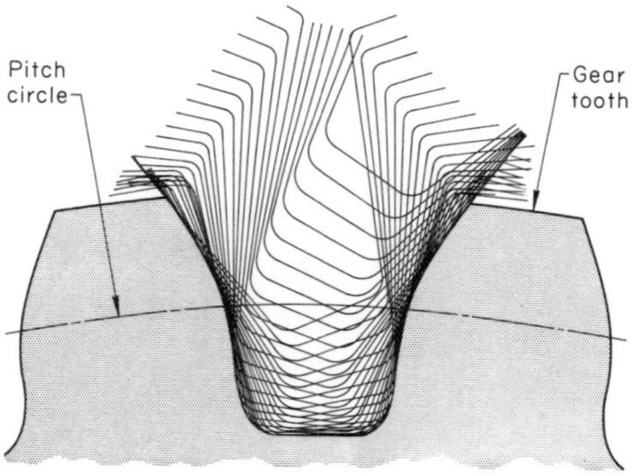

Fig. 12. Hobbing action as a gear tooth is generated progressively by hob teeth

piece spindle is synchronized with the cutter spindle and rotates as the tool cuts while it is being fed gradually into the work. The action between a shaping cutter and a gear blank is illustrated in Fig. 14. Shaping applied to the cutting of a worm (Fig. 15) involves no axial stroke of the cutter spindle.

Rack cutting is done with a cutter in the form of a rack with straight teeth (usually three to five). This cutter reciprocates parallel to the gear axis when cutting spur gears and parallel to the helix angle when cutting helical gears. Metal is removed by a shaper-like stroke similar to the cutting action in gear shaping. In addition to the reciprocating action of the rack cutter, there is synchronized rotation of the gear blank with each stroke of the cutter, with a corresponding advance of the cutter as in the meshing of a gear and rack. By these combined actions, the true involute curve of the gear tooth is developed. Several gear-cutting machines use this principle. Rack cutters are less expensive than hobs (see Example 404). Rack cutting is especially adapted to the cutting of large gears or gears of coarse pitch, or both. Gears with diametral pitch as coarse as ⅜ are commonly cut by the rack method.

Machining Processes for Bevel Gears

The machining of bevel gears is treated as a separate subject because most bevel gears are cut in special machines with special cutters. However, the action of these cutters bears a close resemblance to one or more of the basic processes — milling, broaching or shaping. Both generating and nongenerating processes are discussed in the paragraphs that follow.

Milling is not widely used for cutting bevel gears, because of accuracy limits of indexing devices and because the operation is time-consuming (as many as five cuts around the gear may be required for completing one gear). Sometimes straight bevel gears are roughed by milling and then finished by another method. This two-operation procedure is more common when availability of special gear-cutting machines is limited.

Template machining is a low-production, nongenerating method used to cut the tooth profiles of large bevel gears using a bevel gear planer (Fig. 16). Because the setup can be made with a minimum of tooling, template machining is useful when a wide variety of coarse pitch gears are required. Template machining uses a simple, single-point cutting tool, guided by a template several times as large as the gear tooth to be cut. Under these conditions high accuracy in tooth form is possible. The necessary equipment is special. The setup utilizes two templates; one for each side of the gear tooth. In theory, a pair of templates would be required for each gear ratio, but in practice a pair is designed for a small range of ratios. A set of 25 pairs of templates encompasses all 90° shaft angle ratios from 1:1 to 8:1, for either 14½° or 20° pressure angles. This system of templates is based on the use of equal-addendum tooth proportions for all ratios. The tooth bearing localiza-

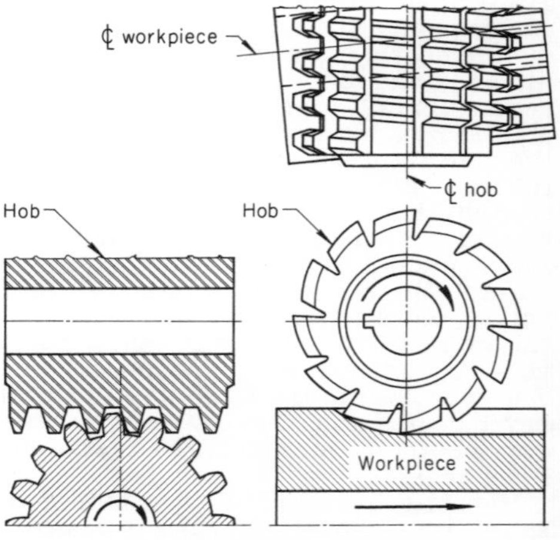

Fig. 13. Hobbing a spur gear

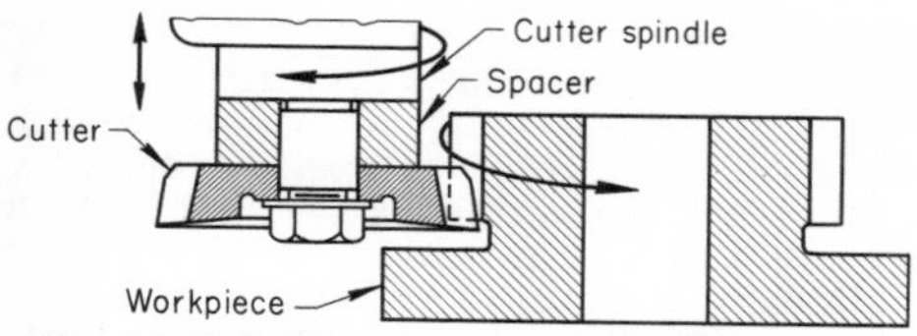

Fig. 14. Relation of cutter and workpiece in shaping gear teeth

tion is produced by a slight motion of the tool arm as the cutting tool moves along the tooth. The length and position of the cut can be controlled by the machine operator. To produce a finished gear five or six cutting operations are required. The first is a roughing operation, made by feeding a slotting tool or a corrugated V-tool to full depth. If the first cut is made with a slotting tool, a second cut is required with a V-tool or a corrugated V-tool. Cuts are made with the template follower resting on a straight guide. After roughing, the templates are set up and the teeth are finished by making two cuts on each side. Slotting tools are specified by point width and depth of cut; corrugated roughing tools, by point width, depth of cut, and pressure angle; finishing tools, by point width only. To set up a straight bevel gear planer for template machining, the operator need know only the tooth proportions of the gear to be cut, plus the template list and the index gear list furnished with the machine.

Formate cutting is a nongenerating method for cutting spiral bevel and hypoid gears when nongenerated gears are acceptable (usually when the gear-to-pinion ratio is 2.5 to 1 or greater). The Formate method is applicable for both roughing and single-cycle finishing of gears with pitch diameters up to 33 in. Sometimes roughing and finishing are both done by one cutter in the same machine. More often, for greater efficiency, roughing and finishing operations are done in different machines.

By the Formate single-cycle finishing method one tooth space is finish cut in one revolution of the cutter. Stock removal is accomplished by cutting blades mounted in a circular cutter that resembles a face-milling cutter. Each blade in the cutter is slightly longer and wider than the preceding blade; thus, the cutting action is, in effect, that of a circular broach. A gap between the first and last cutting blades permits indexing the workpiece as each tooth space is completed. Relative positions of cutter and gear during Formate single-cycle cutting are illustrated in Fig. 17.

Helixform cutting, another nongenerating method of cutting spiral bevel and hypoid gears, is generally similar to Formate cutting, although there is one significant difference in the method and likewise in the finishing operation for the gear member.

One turn of the Helixform cutter finishes both sides of a tooth space. The cutter has both rotational and reciprocating motion, and this combination makes the path of the cutter-blade tips tangent to the root plane of the gear. Because the cutting edge is a straight line, the surface cut by a Helixform gear cutter is a true helical surface. The principal advantage of Helixform cutting compared with Formate cutting is that the gear produced by Helixform is conjugate to the mating pinion and the resulting contact pattern has little or no bias.

The Cyclex method is also a nongenerating method, and the result is the same as for the Formate method. The Cyclex method was developed for rough and finish cutting of gears in one operation and is particularly suitable when production quantities are not great enough to warrant separate Formate roughing and finishing machines for the gear member. Cyclex machines of the generator type can cut a wide range of gear sizes and can be used for cutting both gears and pinions. When cutting by the Cyclex method, the gear is roughed and finished in one chucking from the solid blank. The finishing

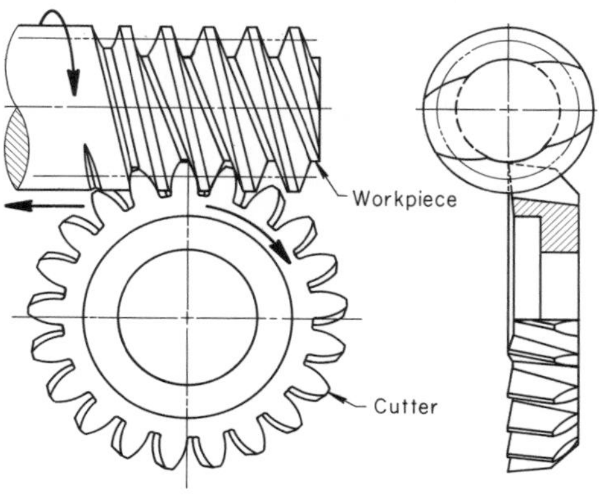

Fig. 15. Relation of cutter and workpiece in generating a worm by shaping

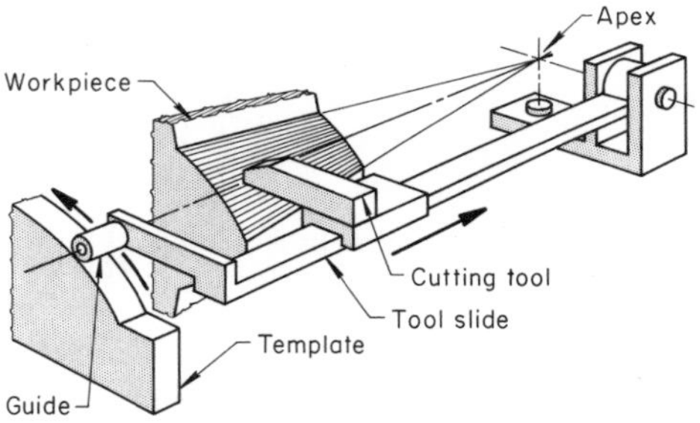

Fig. 16. Cutting teeth in a large straight bevel gear by template machining in a bevel gear planer

blades of the cutter are set below the roughing blades and do not touch the work during the roughing cycle. Several revolutions of the cutter may be required for roughing, the number required depending on the pitch of the gear. In the final revolution, after the last roughing blade has passed through the cut, the work is rapidly advanced, permitting the finishing blades to make contact and finish the tooth space to size. After the finishing blades have passed through the cut, the work is rapidly withdrawn and indexed, and the cycle is repeated until all teeth are completed.

Face-mill cutting machines are used to finish cut teeth in spiral bevel, Zerol and hypoid gears. Machines and cutters are available for cutting gears ranging from small instrument gears up to about 35 in. in diameter.

The three types of face-mill cutters are identified by the design of their cutting blades: integral, segmental and inserted. All of these can be used for both roughing and finishing. Solid or integral-blade cutters are made from a single piece of tool steel and are usually less than 6 in. in diameter. They are used for fine pitch gears. Segmental cutters are made up of sections, each having two or more blades. The segments are bolted to the cutter head around the periphery. Inserted-blade cutters have individual blades bolted to slotted heads. They usually have parallels for changing diameter, and adjusting wedges for truing individual blades. For finishing, each of the three types of cutters can be furnished with all outside blades, all inside blades, or alternate outside and inside blades. Roughing cutters may have either alternate inside and outside blades or may have end-cutting or bottom-cutting blades alternately spaced with inside and outside blades.

There are four basic cutting methods — spread-blade, single-side, fixed-setting, and single-setting. The rotating cutting edges of a face-mill cutter generate an imaginary gear surface. The spread-blade method is the generation of the part by a circular face-mill cutter with alternate inside and outside blades that cut the tooth surfaces on both sides of a tooth space at the same time.

In the single-side method, the part is finished by a circular face-mill cutter with alternate inside and outside blades that cut the tooth surface on each side of a tooth space in separate operations with independent machine settings.

In the fixed-setting method the part is finished by two circular face-mill cutters; one with inside blades only for cutting the convex side of the tooth, the other with outside blades only, for cutting the concave side. The two sides of the tooth are produced separately in two entirely different machine setups. For large production runs a pair of machines is used, one for cutting one side of the tooth, the other for the other side of the tooth.

The single-setting method is a variation of the spread-blade method and is used when the available cutters have point widths too small for spread-blade cutting. Both sides are cut with the same machine settings, and the blank is rotated on its axis to remove the amount of stock necessary to produce the correct tooth thickness. After the first cut, only one side of the cutter is

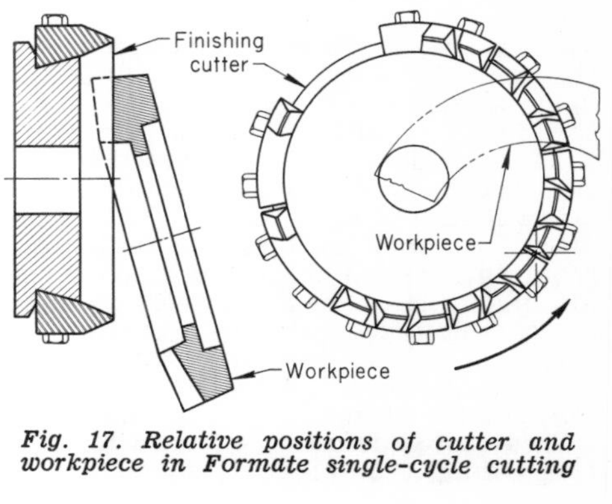

Fig. 17. Relative positions of cutter and workpiece in Formate single-cycle cutting

cutting in the tooth slot. Figure 18 illustrates the action of a face mill when generating pinion teeth by the fixed-setting method (inside blades).

Interlocking cutters, known also as completing generators, generate the teeth on straight bevel gears or pinions from a solid blank in one operation.

Two interlocking disk-type cutters rotate on axes inclined to the face of the mounting cradle, and both cut in the same tooth space (Fig. 19). The cutting edges present a concave cutting surface that removes more metal at the ends of the teeth, giving localized tooth contact. The gear blank is held in a work spindle that rotates in timed relation with the cradle on which the cutters are mounted. A feed-cam cycle commences with the workhead and blank moving into position for rough cutting, without generating roll, and cutting proceeds until the cut is just short of full depth. After a rough generating roll the work is fed in to full depth, and a fast up-roll finish generates the tooth sides. At the top of the roll, the work backs out, and the cradle and work spindle roll down again into roughing position. During this short down-roll, the blank is indexed.

Revacycle is a generating process used for cutting straight bevel gears up to about 10-in. pitch diameter in large production runs. This is the fastest method for producing straight bevel gears of commercial quality. Initial tooling cost is greater for the Revacycle process than for other processes for cutting straight bevel gears, but the high production rate results in the lowest cost for mass production.

Most gears produced by the Revacycle method are completed in one operation, using cutters 16, 18, 21 or 25 in. in diameter that rotate in a horizontal plane at a uniform speed (Fig. 20). The cutter blades, which extend radially outward from the cutter head, have concave edges that produce convex profiles on the gear teeth. During cutting, the workpiece is held motionless while the cutter is moved by means of a cam in a straight line across the face of the gear and parallel to its root line. This motion produces a straight tooth bottom while the desired tooth shape is being produced by the combined effect of the motion of the cutter and the shapes of the cutter blades.

Feed is obtained by making cutter blades progressively longer, rather than by moving the entire cutter into the work. The completing cutter contains three kinds of blades: roughing, semifinishing and finishing. One revolution of the cutter completes each tooth space, and the work is indexed in the gap between the last finishing blade and the first roughing blade. For the small amount of Revacycle work that is too deep to be completed in one cut, separate roughing and finishing operations are used. Under these conditions separate cutters and setups are required for each operation. The cutters and machine cycles are similar to those for completing cutters, except that the roughing cutters have no semifinishing or finishing blades. A second cutter has only semifinishing and finishing blades.

Two-tool generators are used for cutting straight bevel gears by means of two reciprocating tools that cut on opposite sides of a tooth (Fig. 21). Tooling cost is low for two-tool generators, but production rates are lower than with other straight bevel generators such as interlocking cutters and Revacycle machines.

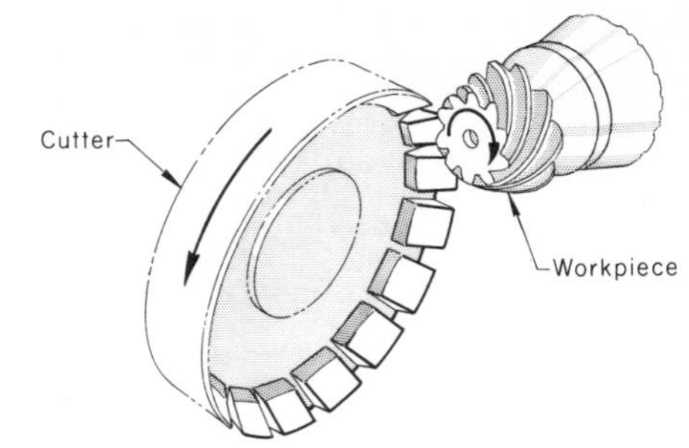

Fig. 18. Face-mill cutter shown in position to generate a pinion by the fixed-setting method (see text for explanation)

Two-tool generators are usually employed: (*a*) when the gears are beyond the practical size range (larger than about 10-in. pitch diameter) of other types of generators; (*b*) when gears have integral hubs or flanges that project above the root line, thus preventing the use of other generators; or (*c*) when a small production quantity or a variety of gear sizes cannot be accommodated by other types of machines used for cutting straight bevel gears.

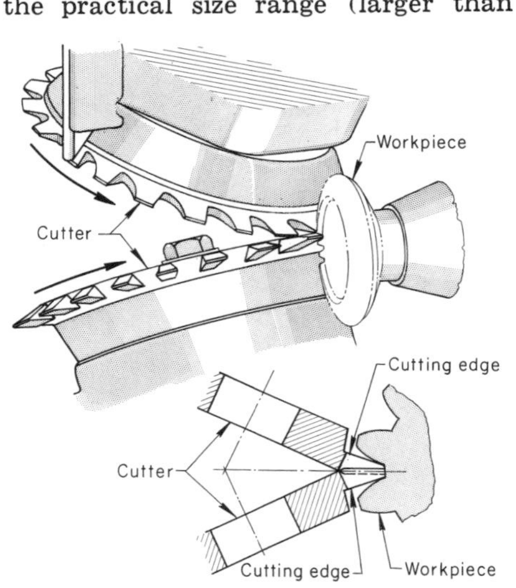

Fig. 19. Relation of interlocking cutters (completing generators) with the bevel gear being cut

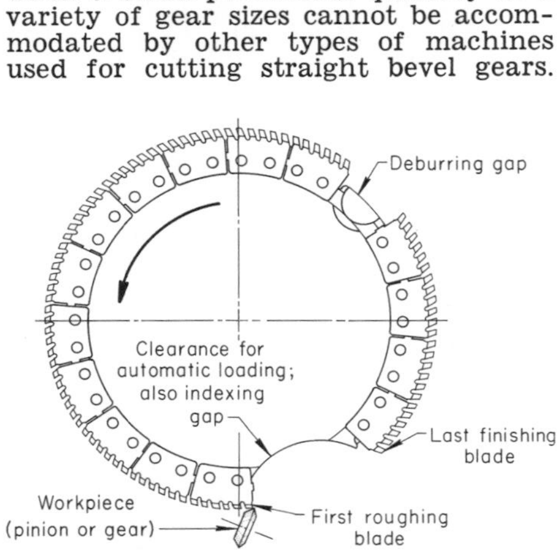

Fig. 20. Revacycle cutter in position to cut a bevel gear

Two-tool generators are used for both rough and finish cutting. When warranted by production quantities, roughing is done in separate machines, which are the same as the generators except that the machines used only for roughing have no generating roll. For small production quantities both roughing and finishing cuts are made in the generators, the roughing cut being made without generating roll.

To make the machine setup for producing a gear that will operate at right angles to its mating gear, the operator must have the gear specifications and one calculated machine setting called the tooth angle (Fig. 21). The remaining setup data are taken from tables furnished with the machine. When the shaft angle of the two gears is not a right angle, the ratio of roll, and the data required for checking the roll, must be calculated.

Most two-tool generators can produce straight bevel gears with teeth crowned lengthwise to localize tooth contact. Crowned teeth are produced by means of two angularly adjustable guides on the back of each slide. The guides ride on a pair of fixed rollers (Fig. 22). When the guides are in line with each other the tool stroke is a straight line, and when they are out of line the tool is stroked along a curved path. The amount of curvature is controlled by setting the two guides. A table with each machine lists the guide settings for making the tooth contact approximately one half the face width. The machine settings can be varied to shorten or lengthen the tooth contact.

Planing generators are unique because they can cut both straight-tooth and curved-tooth bevel gears. However, the use of planing generators is ordinarily restricted to cutting gears about 35 in. in diameter or larger, or to diametral pitch coarser than 1½. Standard machines can generate straight, Zerol and spiral bevel gears. Special heads can be added to standard machines to permit the cutting of hypoid gears.

Tools have straight cutting edges and are mounted on a reciprocating slide that is carried on the face of the cradle and connected to a rotating crank by a connecting rod (Fig. 23). Tooth profiles are made by rolling the work with the generating gear. The lengthwise shape of the teeth is formed by a combination of three motions: (*a*) stroke of the tool; (*b*) continuous uniform rotation of the work; and (*c*) an angular oscillation of the work produced by the eccentric shown in Fig. 23. The eccentric motion modifies the effect that the first two motions have on the shape of the teeth. The eccentric is timed for the correct tooth relief.

The spiral angle of the teeth is controlled by the angular offset of the tool slide from the angle of the cradle axis. Continuous rotation of the work is principally for indexing. In effect, the tool makes a cut on all teeth in succession in one generating position, and then the cradle and the work roll together a slight distance before another cut is taken on all teeth in the new generating position. Actually, however, rolling is continuous and occurs gradually until all teeth are completely generated in the last pass around the gear.

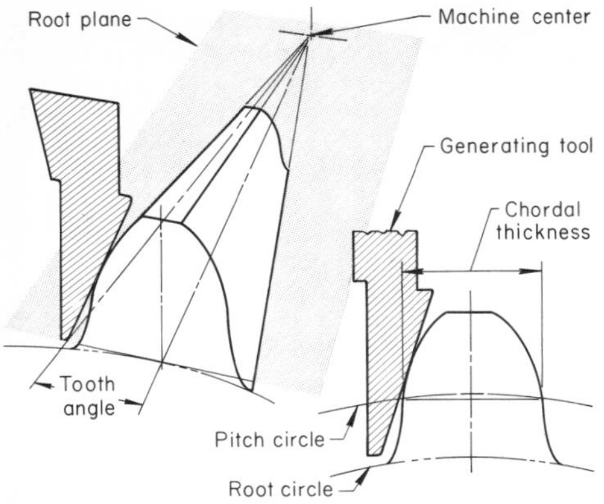

Fig. 21. Angle of straight bevel gear tooth and sections of tools used for two-tool generating

Several passes are required to complete a gear, the number depending on tooth depth and shape. Flat gear blanks are usually roughed without a roll, first using a corrugated tool and then using a single cut with a V-roughing tool. This is followed by at least two side-cutting operations on each side of the tooth, including generating cuts with roll. A similar sequence is used for cutting pinions except that roughing is done with roll.

Tools for use in planing generators are simple and inexpensive. Corrugated tools are furnished with a 14½° pressure angle, regardless of the pressure angle of the gear being cut, but point width and depth of cut must be specified when the tools are ordered. The operator must know the specifications for the gear being cut. A table of settings for specific requirements is supplied with the machine.

Selection of Machining Process

Each gear-cutting process discussed in the preceding sections has a field of application to which it is best adapted. These fields overlap, however, so that many gears can be produced satisfactorily by two or more processes. In such instances, availability of equipment often determines which machining process will be used.

The type of gear being machined (spur, helical, bevel or other) is usually the major factor in the selection of machining process, although one or more of the following factors must usually be considered in the final choice of method: (*a*) size of the gear; (*b*) configuration of integral sections (flanges or other); (*c*) quantity requirements; (*d*) accuracy requirements; (*e*) gear-to-pinion ratio; and (*f*) cost.

The following eight sections consider the type of gear as the major variable and discuss the machining methods best suited for specific conditions.

Machining of Spur Gears

Milling, shear cutting, hobbing and shaping are the methods most commonly used for cutting teeth in spur gears.

Form milling, with the cutter ground to the desired shape of the tooth space (Fig. 9), is a simple means of cutting teeth in spur gears. Tooling cost is low; the process requires only a conventional milling machine, a form cutter, and an indexing mechanism. Except for low-quantity production, milling is seldom used for cutting spur gears. The main disadvantage in form milling of spur gears is the lack of accuracy in tooth spacing, which depends on the accuracy of the indexing mechanism. Also, form milling is much slower than shear cutting or hobbing.

One milling cutter is not universal for all numbers of teeth, as are hobs and shaper cutters. To produce theoretically correct gear teeth, the tooth form of the cutter must be designed for the exact number of teeth. However, if a small departure in tooth form is acceptable, cutters have been standardized for a range of teeth, the form being correct for the lowest number of teeth in that particular range. Thus, all teeth within the range are provided with sufficient tip relief. The same form is produced in all tooth spaces within that range. For reasonably accurate gear cutting, eight different cutters are required to cut all sizes of gears of a given pitch. A No. 1 cutter will cut all gears with 135 or more teeth; a No. 2 cutter, gears with 55 to 134 teeth; No. 3, from 35 to 54 teeth; No. 4, from 26 to 34 teeth; No. 5, from 21 to 25 teeth; No. 6, from 17 to 20

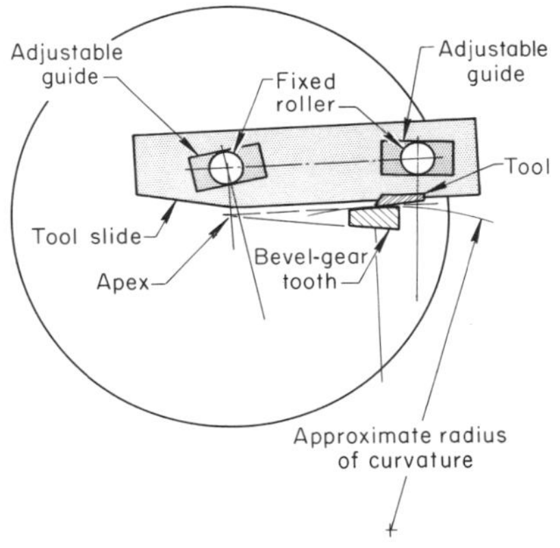

Fig. 22. Provision for crowning gear teeth by means of adjustable guides in two-tool generators

teeth; No. 7, from 14 to 16 teeth; and No. 8 will cut gears with 12 or 13 teeth. If more accurate tooth form is desired for gears near the higher part of the ranges, seven half-number cutters can be obtained. A No. 1½ cutter, for example, will cut gears with 80 to 134 teeth; and No. 2½ cutter, 42 to 54 teeth. For still greater accuracy, cutters of the proper shape for an exact number of teeth can be furnished by most tool manufacturers on short notice.

The tooth form of a single cutter is centered with the gear axis so that a symmetrical tooth space is produced. By the use of gang cutters, portions of adjacent tooth spaces can be rough machined simultaneously. Normally, a roughing and a finishing cutter are ganged, the finishing cutter being centered with the gear axis. Gang cutters and multiple-tooth cutters are specially designed for the specific application.

Shear cutting (see description of the process on page 196 in this article) is faster and more accurate than milling for cutting teeth of almost any involute modification in spur gears. Total cutting time is often less than one minute for gears up to about 6 in. in diameter. However, tooling cost is high, and shear cutting is therefore practical only for large-scale production.

Hobbing is the process most widely used for cutting teeth in spur gears, usually for one or more of the following reasons:

1 High accuracy in a wide range of gear sizes
2 Flexibility in quantity production
3 Low cost
4 Adaptability to work metals having higher than normal hardness.

Shape of the workpiece sometimes limits the use of hobbing — for instance, if the teeth to be cut are close to another portion of the workpiece having a diameter larger than the root diameter of the gear. The axial distance between the two sections must be large enough to allow for hob overtravel at the end of the cut. This overtravel is about half the hob diameter. The clearance required between the gear being cut and any flange or other projecting portion of the workpiece is, therefore, about half the hob diameter plus additional clearance to allow for the hob thread angle.

In the two examples that follow, quantity is very different. In the first example, production quantities were large; in the second, the quantity was two gears.

Example 374. Small Pinions Hobbed to Class 3 Requirements at 130 per Hour (Table 1)

Small pinions (see illustration with Table 1) were hobbed to tolerance and finish requirements of AGMA commercial class 3 in continuous production, in a ½-hp, 1-in.-by-1-in., semiautomatic hobbing machine. This machine was magazine-fed, permitting one operator to handle more than one machine, or to perform other duties while a magazine load (50 gears) was being hobbed. Hobs for this operation were purchased in lots of 24, which resulted in tool cost of less than $0.002 per piece hobbed. Production rate was 130 pieces per hour. Manufacturing details are listed in Table 1.

Pinion blanks were prepared by turning, drilling, reaming, and chamfering in an automatic bar machine. Holes of the blanks were ball burnished, after which the blanks were hobbed, hardened and finally ground on their faces prior to stocking. This pinion could have been manufactured by milling or shaping the teeth, but these methods could not compete with hobbing in productivity. Teeth are often formed by wire drawing to make small "pinion stock", but pinion stock could not be used for this application because of problems in maintaining the required concentricity between the bore and the pitch line.

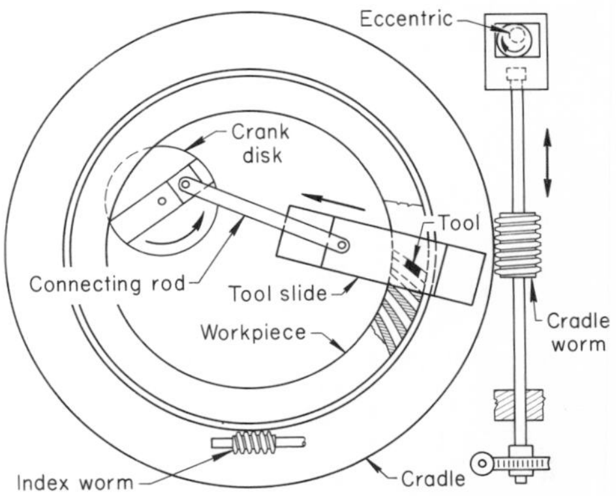

Fig. 23. Components of a planing generator

Example 375. Hobbing Two Heat Treated 4340 Gears to Close Tolerances (Fig. 24)

Two spur gears of the shape shown in Fig. 24 were required for almost immediate delivery. There was not sufficient time to purchase special cutters or grinding wheels, although specifications permitted teeth to be either shaped or ground. Shaping and shaving equipment of the required size was not available.

Hobbing equipment was available, and through extreme care in setting up, it was possible to produce the two gears to tolerance and finish requirements (see tabulation with Fig. 24). However, the established limits on both tolerance and finish represent a borderline application for hobbing; more stringent requirements would have required grinding.

Table 1. Hobbing of Fine-Pitch Spur Pinions (Example 374) (a)

Cutter Details	
Type	Shell hob
Size	¾-in. OD, ½-in. face, 0.315-in. bore
Class	A
Number of flutes	10
Material	M2 high speed steel
Operating Conditions	
Hob speed	758 rpm
Effective cutting speed	150 sfm
Feed, per revolution of workpiece	0.0105 in.
Cutting fluid	Sulfurized oil
Hob life per grind	1040 pieces
Total hob life	18,720 pieces
Production rate	130 pieces per hour

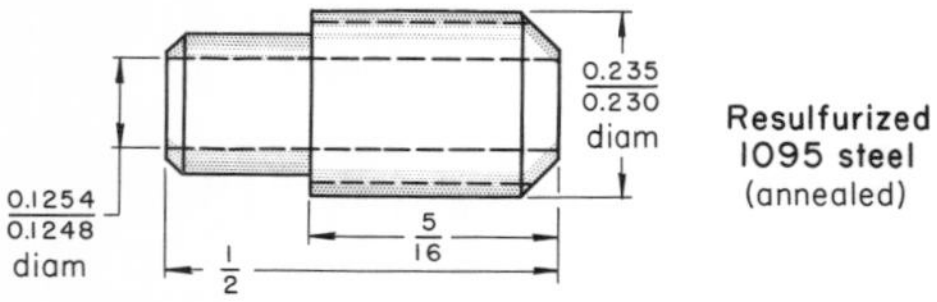

(a) Pinion (gear), illustrated above, had 16 teeth, diametral pitch of 64, pitch diameter of 0.2031 in., addendum of 0.0156 in. and pressure angle of 20°, and was produced to tolerance and finish of commercial class 3 (AGMA).

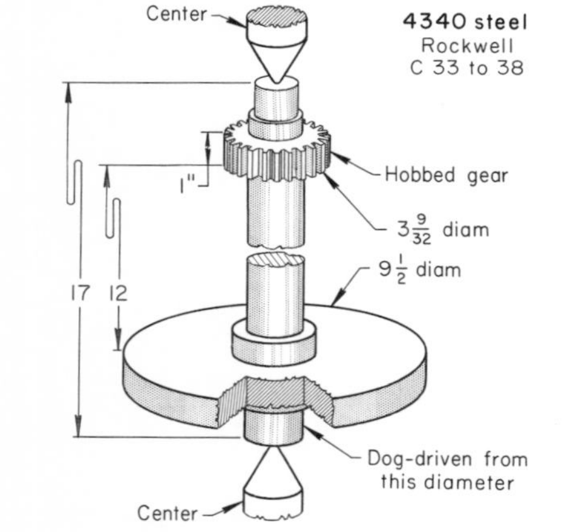

Gear Details	
Number of teeth	30
Diametral pitch	10
Pressure angle	20°
Tolerances:	
Involute	True within 0.0005 in.
Tooth-to-tooth spacing	0.0003 to 0.0007 in.(a)
Helix	Within 0.0005 in., full length
Specified finish:	
Active face	63 micro-in., max
Root fillet	125 micro-in., max
Hob Details	
Type	Single-thread
Size	2.50-in. diam
Class	A
Material	High speed steel
Operating Conditions	
Hob speed	200 rpm
Effective speed	115 sfm
Axial feed, per revolution of work	0.015 in.
Cutting fluid	Sulfurized oil

(a) Between any three adjacent teeth

Fig. 24. Hobbing teeth to close tolerances in heat treated spur gears (Example 375)

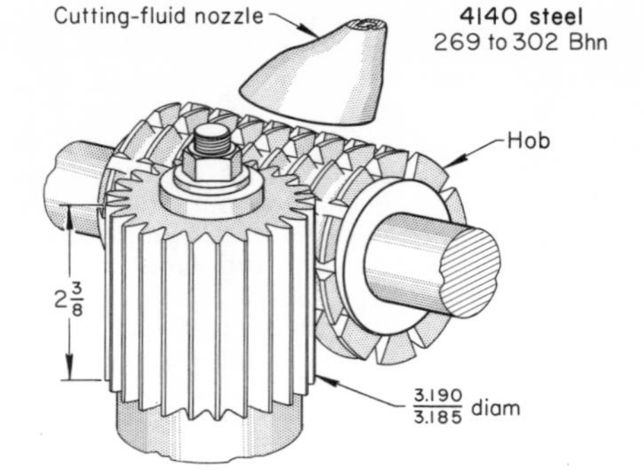

Gear Details	
Number of teeth	23
Diametral pitch	8
Pressure angle	20°
Addendum	0.157 in.
Tolerance	Class 3
Hob Details	
Size	3-in. diam, 3 in. long
Class	A
Number of flutes	10
Material	High speed steel
Operating Conditions	
Hob speed	66 rpm
Effective speed	52 sfm
Feed, per revolution of workpiece:	
Roughing	0.060 in.
Finishing	0.040 in.
Cutting fluid	Cutting oil
Hob life per grind	30 pieces
Total hob life	1000 pieces
Time per piece, floor to floor	50½ min

Fig. 25. Hobbing of heat treated spur pinions (Example 376)

In many instances, it is necessary to cut teeth on heat treated gear blanks to avoid the difficulties caused by distortion in heat treating. Hobbing is especially suitable for cutting gear teeth in hardened steel (sometimes as hard as Rockwell C 48; see Examples 375, 384, 385 and 386). Although hob wear increases rapidly as workpiece hardness increases, normal practice should produce an acceptable number of parts per hob sharpening. Success in hobbing gears at high hardness depends greatly on maintaining minimum backlash in the machine and on rigid mounting of both the hob and the workpiece.

The following example deals with the hobbing of heat treated steel.

Example 376. Hobbing 4140 Pinions at 269 to 302 Bhn (Fig. 25)

Motor pinions (Fig. 25) made of 4140 steel and heat treated to 269 to 302 Bhn were hobbed to class 3 requirements in a 10-hp, 36-in. hobbing machine. Because of the relatively high hardness and the tolerance requirements for class 3, slower speeds and lighter feeds were used than those permissible for class 1 or 2. Processing details are tabulated below Fig. 25.

Hob life between grinds was prolonged by shifting the hob axially along the drive shaft. This technique distributed the wear evenly along the hob. It was possible to hob ten gears in each of three hob positions. Thus, 30 pieces were made before the hob was removed for sharpening. From 0.010 to a maximum of 0.020 in. of metal was removed from the hob during each sharpening. Each hob could be sharpened 30 to 40 times before being discarded, thus giving an average total life of about 1000 pieces.

The ability to cut teeth in two or more identical spur gears in one setup can also justify use of the hobbing method. Inexpensive fixturing is often utilized for cutting two or more gears at one time when the ratio of face width to pitch diameter is small. A typical case of increasing productivity in hobbing spur gears is described in the following example:

Example 377. Fixturing To Permit Hobbing of Two Gears in One Setup (Fig. 26)

The 9.567-in.-diam spur gears shown in Fig. 26 were successfully hobbed in pairs by means of the fixturing arrangement shown. The setup included a center ring to separate the two gears and to increase rigidity by preventing abutment of the gear hubs. The two gears were keyed to the arbor and were forced together by the securing nut (see setup illustrated in Fig. 26).

A standard 14-in. hobbing machine was used for this operation. Climb hobbing (cutter entering at the outside diameter instead of at the root as it would for conventional hobbing) was selected because it gave better surface finish in this application. When surface finish is critical it is common practice to try both climb and conventional techniques to determine which is better. Additional gear details and operating conditions are given in the tabulation accompanying Fig. 26.

Shaping (see description on page 196 in this article) can produce high accuracy in cutting spur gears because shaping is a generating process. Although seldom as fast as hobbing, shaping is used for a wide range of production quantities. Many types of gears can be produced to requirements by either shaping or hobbing, and availability of equipment determines which of the two processes is used. However, if the workpiece configuration cannot be hobbed, shaping is often the only practical method. In the two

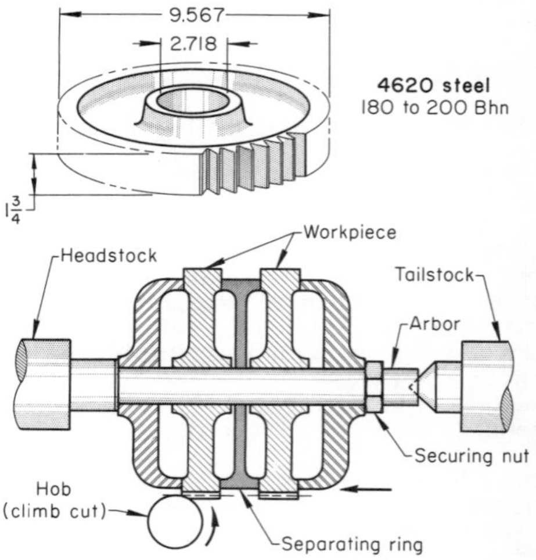

Gear Details	
Number of teeth	47
Pressure angle	20°
Tolerances:	
Involute composite error, max	0.0012 in.
Parallelism	Within 0.0009 in.
Pitch variation, max	0.0007 in.
Preshave diam (over pins)	9.702 to 9.706 in.
Surface finish	To be shaved
Hob Details	
Size	4-in. diam, 4 in. wide
Class	C
Material	High speed steel
Operating Conditions	
Hob speed	232 sfm
Feed, per revolution of hob	0.050 in.
Cutting fluid	Sulfurized oil
Hob life per grind	30 pieces
Time, total for two gears	9.45 min

Fig. 26. Hobbing of two spur gears in one setup (Example 377)

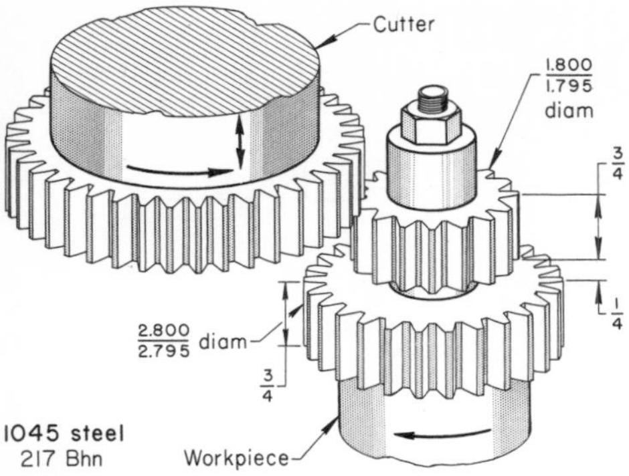

Gear Details

Number of teeth on large gear	26
Number of teeth on small gear	16
Diametral pitch	10
Pressure angle (both gears)	20°
Addendum (both gears)	0.100 in.
Tolerance, relation between gears	0.001 in.
Specified finish	125 micro-in., max

Cutter Details

Type	Disk, involute
Size	4.235-in. OD, 1¼-in. bore
Number of teeth	40
Material	High speed steel
Cutting face (total regrind life)	½ in.

Operating Conditions

Cutter strokes per minute	450
Cutter strokes per revolution	1440
Infeed	60 strokes(a)
Cutting fluid	Sulfurized oil
Cutter life per grind	35 pieces(b)
Time per piece (both gears)	6¾ min(c)

(a) Number of strokes required for cutter to go from outside diameter to full depth (0.225 in.). (b) For both gears, based on 55 large or 83 small gears per sharpening, removing 0.015 in. maximum stock per sharpening. (c) Based on 3¾ min each for the large gears and 3 min each for the small gears.

Fig. 27. Cutting teeth in cluster gears (Example 378)

examples that follow, shaping was the best means of cutting the gear teeth because of workpiece configuration.

Example 378. Shaping of Two-Gear Clusters in a Single Setup (Fig. 27)

Teeth were cut in both members of the cluster gear shown in Fig. 27 in one setup with one cutter in a 1½-hp gear shaper. Final size and finish were obtained in a subsequent shaving operation, thus permitting higher shaping speeds than if shaping had been the final operation. For processing details, see Fig. 27.

Shaping was the only practical method for cutting teeth in the smaller gear because of its close proximity (¼ in.) to the larger gear. Hobbing was feasible for the larger gear, but would have required two setups (one for hobbing and one for shaping), which would have been more costly than shaping both gears in a single setup.

Example 379. Shaping of a Small Spur Gear at Rockwell C 33 to 38 (Fig. 28)

Teeth in the 1⅜-in.-diam gear illustrated in Fig. 28 were finish cut in a 1½-hp gear shaper equipped with an overhead center attachment to increase rigidity. Hobbing and grinding could not be used to finish the teeth on the small gear, because it was too near the large gear (Fig. 28). Workpiece shape did not preclude shaving, but acceptable accuracy could be obtained in small-lot production (25 per month) without shaving, a most desirable condition because shaving cutters are expensive and have short life when machining steel at Rockwell C 33 to 38.

Previous operations included carburizing and quenching the entire workpiece, with the small gear section protected from carburizing by copper plating. Thus, shaping was done on the material at its core hardness (Rockwell C 33 to 38). This hardness is near the practical maximum for gear shaping.

The copper plating was not always completely effective in preventing carburization. Consequently, small areas would frequently be much harder (Rockwell C 58 to 63). A combination of high general hardness and spots that were still harder resulted in poor and erratic cutter life. However, because of the low production, cutter life was of no great concern, especially as this method produced acceptable parts without shaving. Manufacturing details are tabulated with Fig. 28.

Cutting teeth in cluster gears that must meet close tolerances is sometimes a problem, because the method used must frequently be restricted to shaping and shaving. The same quality requirements cannot be met by shaping and shaving as by hobbing and grinding. Sometimes when tolerances for cluster gears are closer than can be met by shaping and shaving, a corrective procedure must be employed. In the following example, separating a cluster gear permitted hobbing it to greater precision.

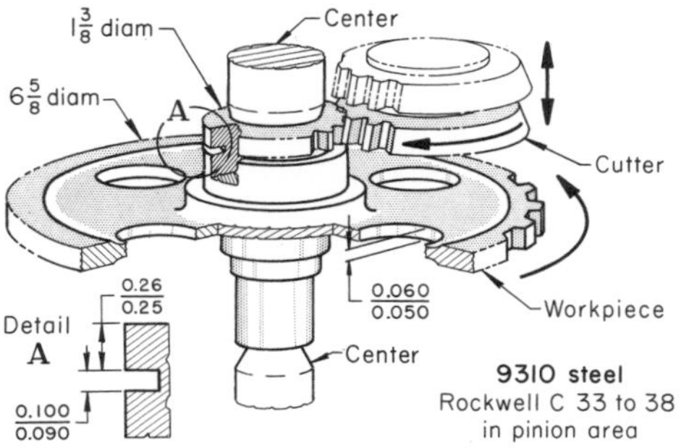

Gear Details

Number of teeth	16
Diametral pitch	20
Pressure angle	20°
Tolerances:	
Involute	Within 0.0005 in.
Tooth-to-tooth spacing:	
Between adjacent teeth	0.0003 in.
Between three consecutive teeth	0.0006 in.
Specified finish:	
Working surface	63 micro-in., max
Root fillet area	125 micro-in., max

Cutter Details

Type	Disk-type precision
Size	3-in. diam
Number of teeth	60
Material	M3 high speed steel

Operating Conditions

Cutter strokes per minute	200
Cutting speed (for ⅜-in. stroke)	75 sfm
Feed	0.0016 in. per stroke
Cutting fluid	Sulfurized oil
Time per piece	20 min

Fig. 28. Shaping of a small involute spur pinion adjacent to a large gear (Example 379)

Example 380. Shaping and Shaving vs Hobbing and Grinding of Cluster Gears (Fig. 29)

Teeth in the two-section spur gear cluster (8 diametral pitch) illustrated in Fig. 29(a) were originally machined by shaping and shaving. Hobbing and grinding was not possible, not only because the two gear sections were close together, but also because they were of so nearly the same diameter. The blanks were shaped and shaved at relatively low hardness (180 to 230 Bhn), after which the teeth were induction hardened to Rockwell C 55 to 58. Because of the distortion caused by induction hardening, the desired accuracy could not be consistently maintained.

Separating the cluster so that it became a two-part assembly (Fig. 29b) solved the problem. This procedure permitted the separate gear sections to be hobbed in the soft condition, induction hardened, and then ground to ultraprecision quality (AGMA 14), whereas it was not feasible to produce a quality better than AGMA 11 (precision range) by shaping. However, the increase in quality from the new procedure was accompanied by a machining time and cost increase of more than 100% (see data with Fig. 29).

Machining of Helical Gears

Milling, hobbing, shaping and rack cutting are the methods most used for producing teeth in helical gears. Rack cutting is most often used for large gears (see Examples 403 and 404). Identical machining methods are applicable to conventional helical and crossed-axes helical gears.

Milling is used less than any other method, because of the difficulty in obtaining accuracy and productivity. However, for some low production requirements, milling is the most satisfactory method, because the tooling cost is low. Sometimes, in low-volume production, milling is used for roughing only, and the gear is finished by hobbing or shaping.

Milling of helical gears usually requires cutters specially designed for the specific gear. In milling helical teeth, the cutter travels along the helix angle of the gear. At this setting, the cutter axis of rotation is in the normal plane through the center of the gear tooth space. Under these conditions, only one point on the finished profile is produced in this normal plane. All the others are produced in different planes. Therefore, the form of the cutter teeth is not reproduced in the gear. In addition to the setting angle, the diameter of the cutter affects the gear tooth form and must be considered in designing the cutter.

Hobbing is used extensively for generating the teeth of helical gears for any production volume. With the exception mentioned below, procedures for hobbing helical gears are the same as for spur gears: When hobbing spur gears with a single-thread hob, the blank rotates one tooth space for each rotation of the hob, the rotation being

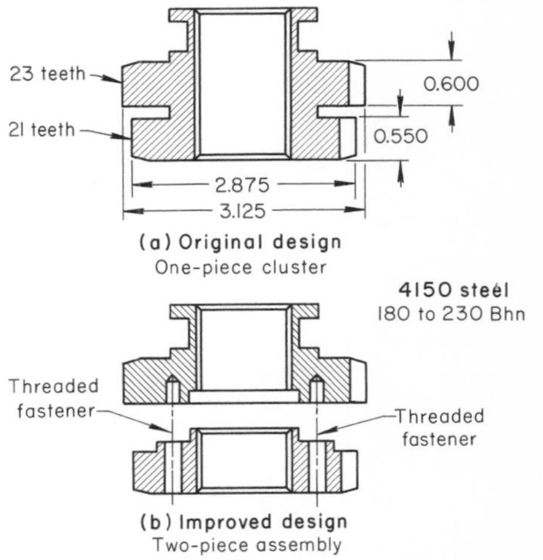

Item	Shaping and shaving (original design)	Hobbing and grinding (improved design)
Time per gear(a)	1.05 hr	2.22 hr
Cost per gear(a)	$10.12	$21.40
AGMA quality	No. 11	No. 14

(a) Machining; for both portions of cluster

Fig. 29. Change in design of two-diameter spur gear to obtain improved quality, but at an increase in time and cost (Example 380)

synchronized by means of change gears. When hobbing helical gears, the rotation of the work is retarded or advanced in relation to the rotation of the hob, and the feed is also held in definite relation to the work and the hob. Whether the workpiece rotation is retarded or advanced depends mainly on whether the hob is a single-thread or multiple-thread type. The amount by which the workpiece is retarded or advanced depends on the helix angle.

In medium to high production, it is common to use fixtures that allow hobbing of two or more identical gears in one loading of the machine. The following two examples deal with procedures for hobbing two or more gears in one machine load.

Example 381. Hobbing Two 6.30-In.-Diam Gears per Machine Load (Fig. 30)

Using the setup shown in Fig. 30, it was possible to cut helical teeth in two gear blanks per machine load. More than two gears could not be hobbed at one time because opposite faces had to be abutted. A 10-hp hobbing machine equipped with a hydraulic clamping device was used. Processing details are given below Fig. 30.

When gears are hobbed butted together on an arbor, close tolerances must be held on faces and bores, because these tolerances have a direct effect on the runout, lead and involute form of the gear teeth. The faces of these gears were turned so as to be parallel with each other within 0.001 in., and at right angles to the bore within 0.002 in. TIR. The bore was formed by first drilling and then broaching to within 2.489 to 2.490 in. The keyway was broached in a separate operation.

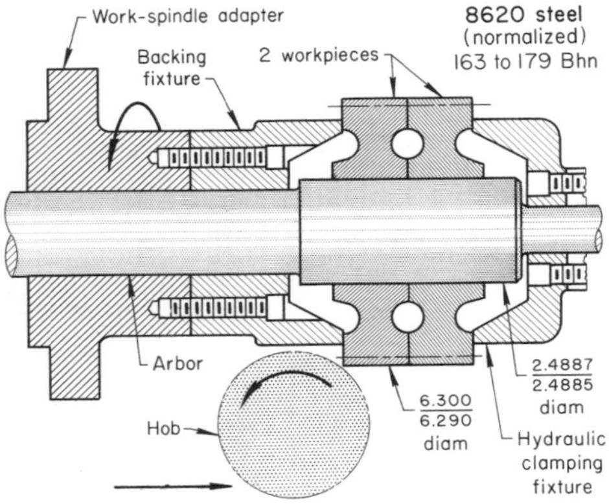

Gear Details

Number of teeth	36
Diametral pitch (normal)	6.5199
Pitch diameter	5.967 in.
Helix angle	23° 2′ 9″
Pressure angle	18° 31′ 5″
Tolerances:	
Preshave size	6.400/6.398 in.(a)
Eccentricity, max	0.002 in.

Hob Details

Type	Single-thread, RH, preshave, semitopping
Size	3½-in. OD, 4 in. long, 1¼-in. bore
Class	Accurate, unground
Material	M2 high speed steel

Operating Conditions(b)

Hob spindle speed	224 rpm
Effective cutting speed	205 sfm
Feed, per revolution of workpiece	0.075 in.
Cutting fluid	(c)
Hob life per grind (est)	50 pieces
Total hob life (est)	937 pieces
Production rate	12 pieces per hour

(a) Measured over 0.250-in.-diam balls. (b) Preshave, single-cut climb hobbing. (c) Sulfurized and chlorinated cutting oil (3.43% total sulfur content, and 0.65% chlorine) mixed with 5% lard oil; viscosity, 110 SUS at 100 F.

Fig. 30. Hobbing of two right-hand helical gears per machine load (Example 381)

After being hobbed, gears were shaved to a diameter of 6.389/6.387 in. (measured over 0.250-in.-diam balls).

Example 382. Hobbing Three 3.222-In.-Diam Gears per Machine Load (Fig. 31)

With the setup illustrated in Fig. 31, three helical gears were hobbed in each machine load in a 10-hp hobbing machine equipped with a nut-type arbor for clamping the workpieces. Processing details are tabulated below Fig. 31. Prior to hobbing, the gear blanks were turned so that sides were parallel within 0.001 in., and at right angles to the bore within 0.002 in. TIR. The bore was produced by first rough drilling and then broaching to a tolerance range of 2.143 to 2.144 in. These dimensions were required to obtain acceptable results when three parts were clamped together on an arbor for hobbing. After being hobbed, the gears were shaved to a diameter of 3.372/3.370 in. (measured over 0.250-in.-diam balls).

Gears with integral shanks can usually be hobbed without difficulty. The shanks may assist in fixturing and handling for loading and unloading.

Table 2. Hobbing of Integral-Shank Helical Gears in an Automatic Machine (Example 383) (a)

Cutter Details

Type	Shell hob
Size	2-in. OD, 1¾ in. long, ¾-in. bore
Class	A
Number of flutes	13
Material	M2 high speed steel

Operating Conditions

Hob speed	480 rpm
Effective cutting speed	241 sfm
Feed, per revolution of workpiece	0.025 in.
Cutting fluid	Sulfurized oil
Allowable tool wear	0.010 in.
Hob life per grind	1530 pieces
Total hob life (306 hr)	27,360 pieces
Production rate	90 pieces per hour

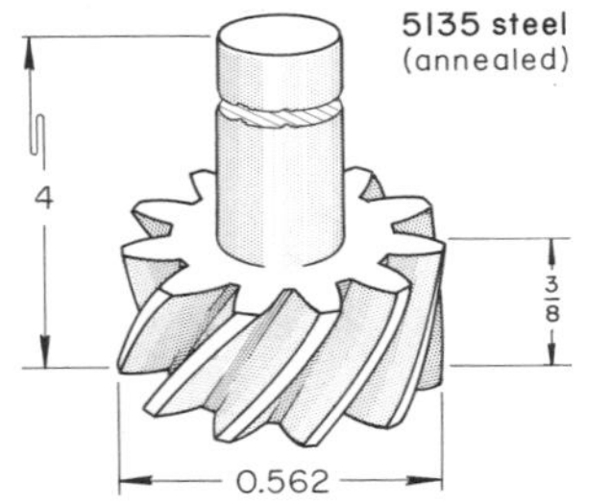

(a) Data are for hobbing the gear illustrated above, which had 12 teeth, diametral pitch of 33.867 (0.75 module), helix angle of 45° and pressure angle of 14.5°. Tolerance and finish requirements were commercial class 3 (AGMA).

When warranted by high-volume production, hobbing can be done in automatic machines:

Example 383. Helical Gears Hobbed to Class 3 Requirements at 90 per Hour (Table 2)

Hobbing was used to cut 45° helical teeth in the gear portion of the integral gear and shank (sketch with Table 2). The operation was performed in a 2-hp fully automatic machine with a specially long bed. Workpieces were magazine-fed into the work holder, which consisted of a serrated driver and hydraulically clamped center. Automatic features permitted operation of several machines by one man. By purchasing twelve hobs at one time, the hob cost per gear was $0.0033. Additional details are given in Table 2.

Although hob life decreases as workpiece hardness increases, helical gears of hardness as high as Rockwell C 48 are sometimes hobbed. When hardnesses of Rockwell C 48 or lower can be tolerated, the sequence of rough hob-

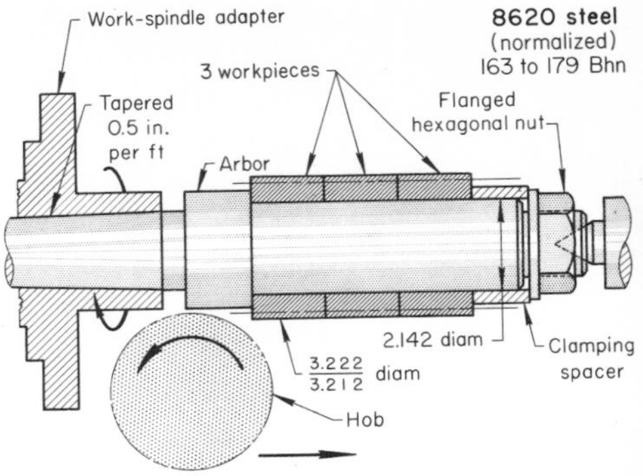

Gear Details

Number of teeth	21
Diametral pitch (normal)	7.6168
Pitch diameter	3.00 in.
Helix angle	23° 12′ 57″
Pressure angle	18° 22′
Tolerances:	
Preshave size	3.378/3.376 in.(a)
Eccentricity, max	0.002 in.

Hob Details

Type:	Double-thread, LH, preshave, semitopping
Size	3½-in. OD, 4 in. long, 1¼-in. bore
Class	Accurate, unground
Material	M2 high speed steel

Operating Conditions(b)

Hob spindle speed	224 rpm
Effective cutting speed	205 sfm
Feed, per revolution of work gear	0.075 in.
Cutting fluid	(c)
Hob life per grind (est)	144 pieces
Total hob life (est)	2390 pieces
Production rate	28 pieces per hour

(a) Measured over 0.250-in.-diam balls. (b) Preshave, single-cut, climb hobbing. (c) Sulfurized and chlorinated cutting oil (3.43% total sulfur content, and 0.65% chlorine) mixed with 5% lard oil; viscosity, 110 SUS at 100 F.

Fig. 31. Hobbing of three left-hand helical gears per machine load (Example 382)

bing, heat treating, and finish hobbing is likely to cost less than grinding after heat treatment:

Examples 384, 385 and 386. Finish Hobbing Heat Treated Drive Worm and Pinions (Table 3)

Table 3 lists specifications and machining details for a drive worm and two pinions that were finish hobbed after being heat treated to Rockwell C 42 to 48.

Shaping is a practical process for generating teeth of helical gears having helix angles up to 45°. The only difference between shaping helical gears and spur gears is that the machines used for cutting helical gears must impart additional rotary motion to the cutter spindle as it reciprocates. The amount of rotation per stroke is controlled by a helix guide. The lead of the guide must be the same as the lead of the cutter.

Workpiece configuration is often the main factor in selection of shaping as a process for cutting helical gears. For the application described in the following example, rotary cutters such as hobs could not be used, because the teeth being cut were too close to the flange.

Example 387. Shaping Gear Teeth Adjacent to a Large Flange (Fig. 32)

Teeth in the gear section that was an integral part of the workpiece illustrated in Fig. 32 were cut in a gear shaper because the gear section was too close to the 10-in.-diam flange to permit use of a rotary cutter. Workpiece, tool and processing details are listed in the table that accompanies Fig. 32.

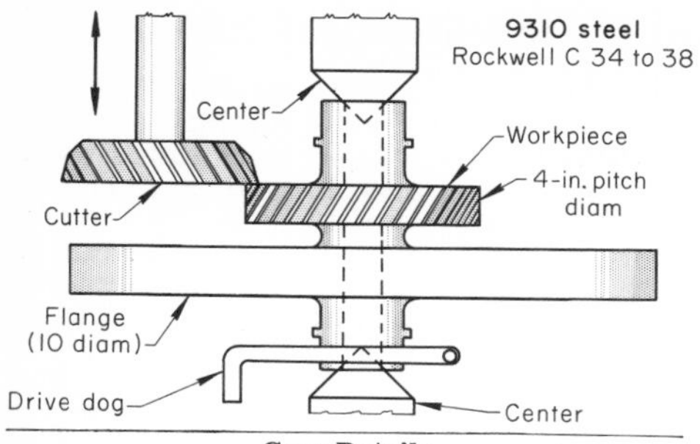

Gear Details

Number of teeth	40
Diametral pitch	10
Helix angle	30°
Tolerances:	
True involute	+0.0005 in.
Arc tooth thickness	0.157 +0.000, −0.002 in.
Specified finish on teeth	63 micro-in., max

Cutter Details

Type	Disk
Pitch diameter	3 in.
Number of teeth	30 (10 diametral pitch)
Material	M3 high speed steel

Operating Conditions

Cutter speed	¼ rpm; 180 strokes per min
Effective cutting speed	60 sfm
Cutter life per grind	40 pieces
Total cutter life	800 pieces
Production rate	3 pieces per hour

Fig. 32. Use of a gear shaper for cutting helical gear teeth near a large flange (Example 387)

Machining of Herringbone Gears

Milling, hobbing and shaping are the methods most often used for cutting herringbone gears. Selection of method depends largely on whether the gear is designed with a gap between the two helixes or whether the herringbone is continuous (see sketches in Table 4).

Rotary cutters such as form milling cutters and hobs can be used to cut herringbone teeth only when there is a gap wide enough to permit cutter run-out between the right-hand and left-hand helixes. Hobbing machines have been built that can cut herringbone teeth in gears up to 220 in. in diameter (see the section "Machining of Large Gears", page 206).

Details of practice for hobbing a herringbone gear having a wide center slot are given in Example 389 (Table 4).

End milling can also be used for machining teeth in herringbone gears, regardless of whether the gears have center slots. The end mills for cutting herringbone gears are used in special machines. Many large-diameter herringbone gears are cut by end milling (see Example 390 and Table 4).

Shaping is also a suitable method for cutting teeth on herringbone gears; those designed with a center slot as well as the continuous herringbone can be shaped. The type of shaper used for cutting herringbone gears is similar in principle to the type used for helical gears, except that for herringbone gears two cutters, one for each helix, are operated simultaneously. Both cutters reciprocate, one cutting in one direction to the center of the gear blank and the other cutting to the same point from the opposite direction when the motion is reversed. The cutters not only reciprocate, but also rotate. Both the gear blank and the cutters turn slowly, thus generating the teeth the same way as in a conventional shaper.

Examples of Practice. The three examples that follow permit a side-by-side comparison of the most common methods of cutting herringbone gears:

Examples 388, 389 and 390. Shaping, Hobbing and End Milling of Teeth in Herringbone Gears (Table 4)

Specifications for three different herringbone gears are listed in Table 4; sketches showing sizes and shapes are included with the table. Of the three gears shown, only the one having the 4½-in.-wide center slot could be hobbed (Example 389). The two other gears (Examples 388 and 390) had continuous herringbone teeth that precluded hobbing; only end milling or shaping was suitable. For operating details, see Table 4.

Machining of Internal Gears

Broaching, shear cutting and shaping are the methods most frequently used for cutting internal gears. Milling

Table 3. Finish Hobbing of a Drive Worm and Two Pinions Heat Treated to Rockwell C 42 to 48 (Examples 384 to 386)

Item	Example 384 Drive worm(a)	Example 385 Pinion	Example 386 Pinion
Gear Details			
Steel	Leaded 4140	Leaded 4140	4615
Hardness, Rockwell C(b)	42 to 45	42 to 45	45 to 48
Pitch diameter, in.	1.17	1.525	2.15
Face width, in.	2	2⅛	7-3/16
Number of teeth	8	24	17
Diametral pitch	6.88	16	8
Helix angle (LH)	61° 7′	10°	18°
Pressure angle	26° 50′	14° 30′	20°
Circular pitch, in.	0.4584	....	....
Tolerance on lead, in.	0.002(c)	0.0005(c)	0.0004(d)
Tolerance on profile, in.	0.0007	0.0003	0.0003
Hob Details(e)			
Diameter, in.	4½	3	4
Class	AA	A (nontopping)	AA
Number of threads	1 LH (topping)	1 RH	1 RH
Number of flutes	16	14	....
Operating Conditions			
Hob speed, rpm	60	99	64
Effective cutting speed, sfm	70.5	78	67
Workpiece feed, ipr	0.005	0.030	0.040
Type of cut	Conventional	Conventional	Climb
Hob wear allowed, in.	0.005 to 0.007	0.005 to 0.007	0.005

(a) Drive worm was rough hobbed with an unground hob 3¾ in. in diameter with one left-hand thread and 11 flutes. Hob speed was 139 rpm (effective cutting speed, 136 sfm); workpiece feed, 0.010 ipr; conventional cut; hob wear allowed, 0.005 to 0.007 in. (b) Rough hobbing was at Rc 28 to 32. (c) Full width of face. (d) Per inch of face. (e) Hobs: M3 high speed steel.

Table 4. Use of Shaping, Hobbing and End Milling for Cutting Teeth in Three Different Herringbone Gears (Examples 388 to 390)

Item	Example 388 Shaping	Example 389 Hobbing	Example 390 End milling
Machine	Shaper-generator (a)	Gear hobber (b)	Pinion hobber (c)
Gear Details			
Steel	4617	4617	2325
Hardness, Rockwell C	22 to 24	22 to 24	22 to 25
Outside diameter, in.	9	15	33
Number of teeth	22	43	31
Diametral pitch	2.5	3	1
Helix angle	45°	15°	30°
Pressure angle	20°	20°	20°
Addendum, in.	0.490	0.333	0.800
Cutter Details(d)			
Type	(e)	Hob	End mill
Size	6.875-in. OD	4¾-in. OD, 6-in. face	3.5-in. OD, 12 in. long
Number of flutes	15	9	4
Operating Conditions(f)			
Speed, sfm	50 and 25 (g)	117 (95 rpm)	85 (100 rpm)
Feed	0.0015 in./stroke	0.056 ipr	1.120 ipm
Tolerance (backlash), in.	0.012 to 0.016	0.009 to 0.012	0.032 to 0.037 (h)
Type of cut	4, 1, 1 (j)	Rough and finish	Rough and finish
Allowable tool wear, in.	0.002	0.002	0.005 and 0.002 (g)
Cutter life, grinds per pc	0.25	2	2
Cutter life, grinds	50 to 75	100	1 (k)

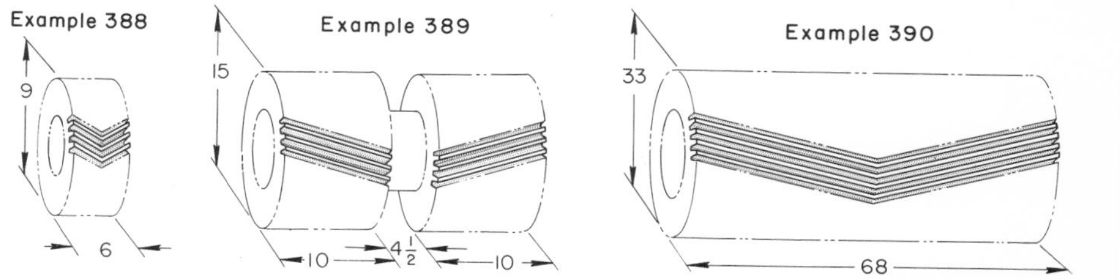

(a) 10 hp, 60 in. (b) 10 hp, 42 in. (c) 30 hp, 57-in. OD, 157 in. (d) All cutters were of M2 high speed steel. (e) Two matched sets of left-hand and right-hand cutters. (f) For all methods, sulfurized oil was used as the cutting fluid, and surface finish specified was 60 to 90 micro-in. (g) Roughing and finishing, respectively. (h) Maximum accumulated error, 0.003 in. (j) Four roughing, one semifinishing and one finishing. (k) Re-formed after each gear.

is seldom used, except for some very large gears.

Broaching of internal spur gear teeth is restricted to workpieces having configurations that permit the broach to pass completely through the piece. The action of a broach in cutting internal gear teeth is shown in Fig. 10. Broaching of gear teeth, which is similar to other types of broaching, is discussed on page 195 in this article. Broaching is an extremely fast and accurate means of machining internal gear teeth, but tooling cost is high; therefore broaching is practical only for high-volume production.

Shear cutting (discussed on page 196) is applicable to internal gear teeth. The principle involved is essentially the same as illustrated in Fig. 11 for cutting external spur gears, except that the cutting edges and direction of radial feed are reversed. Unlike broaching, shear cutting is not restricted to parts where the tool must pass completely through the piece. Shear cutting can be used with no more than a ⅛-in. relief groove between the end of the cut and a shoulder. Because tooling cost is high for shear cutting, the process is practical only for high-volume production.

Shaping is applicable to cutting internal gear teeth. Tooling cost is lower than for broaching and shear cutting and so shaping is applicable to low-volume production. Shaping is less restricted to specific configurations than is broaching, because gear teeth can be cut to within ⅛ in. of a shoulder; however, for adequate chip clearance and to avoid danger of striking the shoulder, it is better to have ample clearance. Shaping is often the only practical method for cutting teeth in large internal gears, because the cost of large broaches or shear cutting tools is prohibitive.

The example that follows illustrates conditions under which shaping was the process best suited for cutting internal gear teeth.

Example 391. Shaping Internal Teeth Close to a Shoulder (Fig. 33)

Internal teeth were cut in the spur gear illustrated in Fig. 33 by means of a standard vertical gear shaper (generating). Cutter and operating details are tabulated below Fig. 33. This shape could not be broached. Shear cutting could have been used, but volume requirements were insufficient to warrant a ten-fold increase in tooling costs. However, shear cutting could produce these parts about ten times faster than gear shaping.

Accuracy of internal teeth cut by a gear shaper depends greatly on rigid fixturing. Note in Fig. 33 how the workpiece was located by means of its splined bore and then held securely against a mounting pad by a clamping ring.

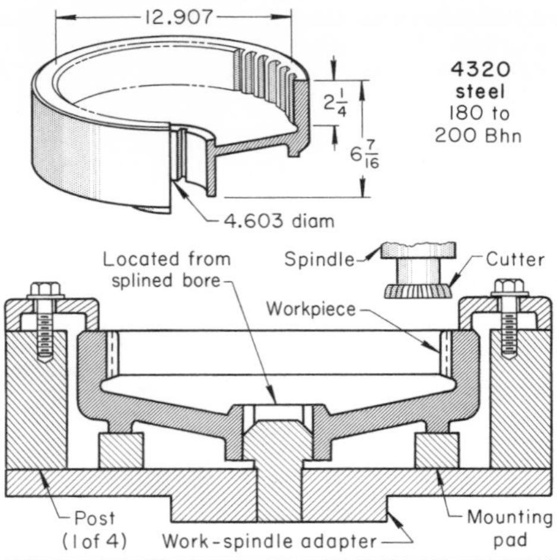

Gear Details

Number of teeth	52
Diametral pitch	4
Tolerances:	
Involute composite error, max	0.0020 in.
Parallelism, composite error, max	0.0014 in.
Pitch variation, max	0.0010 in.
Diameter (under 2 pins)	12.768 to 12.761 in.

Cutter Details

Type	Disk
Number of teeth	20
Diametral pitch	4
Class of grind	Commercial
Material	High speed steel

Operating Conditions

Cutter speed	138 strokes per min
Effective speed	65 sfm
Strokes to complete one revolution	1688
Feed	0.011 in. per stroke
Cutting fluid	Sulfurized oil
Cutter life per grind (approx)	10 pieces
Time per gear cut	31.8 min

Fig. 33. Use of a gear shaper for cutting internal spur gear teeth near a shoulder (Example 391)

Machining of Worms

Several types of worms are used for power transmission, among them the double-enveloping type (Fig. 5), also known as the "hour-glass worm" because of its shape. Milling, hobbing, and shaping are used to machine the various types of worms.

Milling. For double-thread worms of low lead angle and commercial accuracy, a duplex cutter can be used. Each milling cutter is specially designed for cutting a specific worm. Another technique for machining worms utilizes the multiple-thread cutter. The cutter is set with its axis parallel to the work axis and is fed to depth. The work then makes one revolution for completion. The infeed can be made automatic and, because no indexing is required, this method is adaptable to volume production.

Hobbing produces the highest-grade worm at the lowest machining cost but hobbing can be used only when production quantities are large enough to justify the tooling cost.

Because of the large helix angle at which most worm hobs operate, the teeth at the entering end are chamfered to reduce the cutting load. Hobs for cutting worms are made to the same tolerance standards as those for cutting spur gears. When it is necessary to increase the hob diameter to provide more flutes, the tolerances are increased proportionately. The reason for increasing the number of flutes in a worm hob is to improve surface finish, because the greater the number of flutes, the smaller the feed marks. (See Example 384 for typical practice used in hobbing a drive worm.)

Shaping. Worms can also be generated by a shaper cutter. In this technique a helical gear cutter is used in a special machine similar to a hobber. Both the work and the cutter rotate and, in addition, the cutter is rolled axially along the worm, providing true generating action (Fig. 15).

Machining of Racks

Milling and shaping are used to cut teeth in spur and helical racks.

Milling can be used to produce teeth in both spur and helical racks. The milling cutter must have the exact tooth space form. Racks may be cut in any standard milling machine; requirements are essentially the same as for a conventional milling operation and the rack to be cut must be rigidly clamped. Either manual or automatic indexing mechanisms are used. Special rack-cutting machines are available for milling all sizes of racks in high-volume production.

Shaping of spur and helical racks involves rolling action of the operating pitch circle of the generating shaper cutter along the corresponding pitch line of the rack. In cutting racks on a gear shaper, the machine is equipped with a special fixture to hold the work. Several arrangements are used for imparting a transverse indexing movement to the member carrying the rack. One method employs a face gear secured on the work spindle that meshes with a pinion. The latter, by means of change gears, drives a lead screw, which operates the slide carrying the rack. Another method is to attach a pinion to the work spindle, which meshes with a master rack attached directly to the slide carrying the rack being cut. The first method is necessary when high ratios are involved in the drive; the second method needs only the regular work change gears.

Machining of Bevel Gears

Milling, template machining, Formate cutting, Helixform cutting, the Cyclex method, face-mill cutting, interlocking cutters, Revacycle, two-tool generators, and planing generators are used to cut teeth in straight and spiral bevel gears. Fundamentals of these processes are discussed on pages 196 to 199, in this article. Choice of method depends mainly on the type of gear being cut (straight or spiral bevel), size, configuration, accuracy requirements and production quantities.

Milling is sometimes used for cutting straight bevel gears when production requirements are low and accuracy is not critical. Template machining and planing in a gear generator are more often used for cutting teeth in gears larger than 32-in. OD. (Techniques for machining large gears are discussed separately in this article, beginning on page 206.)

Straight Bevel Gears. The two-tool generator is widely used for cutting straight bevel gears and is especially well-adapted to the cutting of gears in a wide range of sizes (up to about 35-in. OD) in low to medium production quantities, because tool cost is low. Two-tool generating is also adaptable to cutting of gears that have protruding portions such as front hubs which preclude the use of some processes.

Interlocking cutters provide a means of completing straight bevel gears in one operation. The interlocking-cutter method is faster than two-tool generating, but more costly. Gears without front hubs and less than 16-in. OD are

Table 5. Processing Details for Cutting Teeth in Straight Bevel Gears of Six Different Sizes and Designs (Examples 392 to 397)

Item	Example 392	Example 393	Example 394	Example 395	Example 396	Example 397
Gear Details						
Steel	303 stainless	4620	Leaded 8620	4620	1019	4620
Hardness, Bhn (a)	140 to 170	160 to 190	160 to 190	160 to 190	126 to 145	160 to 190
Outside diameter, in.	0.500	1.857	3.110	3.200	6.500	9.000
Face width, in.	0.090	0.781	0.625	0.625	1.000	1.500
Number of teeth	16	10	18	16	32	27
Diametral pitch	32	5	6	5	5.1	3
Whole depth, in.	0.070	0.400	0.280	0.440	0.438	0.730
Tooth-to-tooth tolerance, in.	0.0002	0.0005	0.0004	0.0005	0.0004	0.0006
Specified finish, micro-in.	80 to 100	90 to 110	70 to 90	80 to 100	80 to 100	80 to 100
Cutter Details(b)						
Type	Interlocking disk cutters	Circular broach (c)	Interlocking disk cutters	Reciprocating straight (d)	Reciprocating straight (d)	Interlocking disk cutters
Size, in.	4.5 OD	16 OD	9 OD	5 long	5 long	15 OD
Blades cutting per side	20	63, 29 (e)	20	1	1	24
Operating Conditions(f)						
Cutter speed, rpm	105	33	77	....	....	37
Cutter speed, sfm	124	139	183	40, 50 (e)	50	145
Feed	0.003 ipr	0.006 ipr	0.004 ipr	34.0, 24.6 ipm (e)	24.6 ipm	0.004 ipr
Allowable tool wear, in.	0.005 to 0.010	0.015	0.009	0.012, 0.009 (e)	0.009	0.015
Cutter life per grind, pieces	200	4500 (g)	600	40, 55 (e)	250	45
Total cutter life, pieces	4000	67,500 (g)	21,000	11,600, 22,000 (e)	12,500	1800
Cutting time per tooth, sec	5.8	1.8	5.4	....	30	31
Production, pieces per hour (h)	33.3	166	33.5	3.7 (j)	2.2	4.2

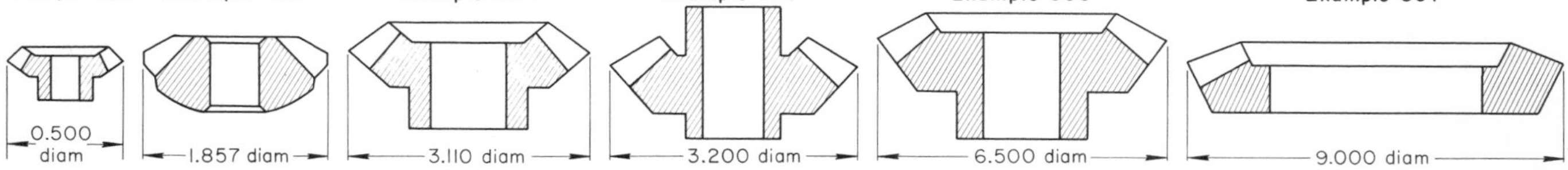

(a) Type 303 stainless in annealed condition; all other steels were normalized. (b) All cutters were of M2 high speed steel, made to precision class and with straight-angle cutting portion. (c) Revacycle machine. (d) Two-tool generator. (e) For roughing and finishing, respectively. (f) For all operations, cutting fluid was mineral oil (viscosity, 180 to 220 SUS at 100 F). (g) For roughing; cutter life was doubled in finishing. (h) At 100% efficiency. (j) Total number of pieces per hour, for roughing and finishing.

best adapted to machining with interlocking cutters.

The Revacycle process is the fastest method for cutting straight bevel gears. Gear teeth are often completed at the rate of 1.8 sec per tooth. This method was designed primarily for cutting gears having up to 10-in. pitch diameter at 4-to-1 ratio with the pinion, and having face width of 1⅛ in. maximum. In the Revacycle method, the cutter must have an uninterrupted path; thus, the process cannot cut gears that have front hubs. Because of the high tooling cost, Revacycle cutting is economical only for high-volume production.

The six processing examples that follow illustrate the appropriate use of three different processes for cutting gears up to 9-in. OD.

Examples 392 to 397. Cutting Teeth in Six Different Straight Bevel Gears

Example 392 (Table 5). Small straight bevel gears (sketch in Table 5) were produced in one cut from solid blanks in a small generator by two interlocking cutters. The generator used for this application could cut straight bevel gears as large as 4½-in. OD, face width to 7⁄16 in., and 16 diametral pitch or finer. Manufacturing details are given in Table 5.

Example 393 (Table 5). Differential gears (sketch in Table 5) were machined from the solid in one cut by the Revacycle method, the fastest process for cutting straight bevel gears. In this application, volume production warranted the high cost of tooling. Both productivity and tool life were high (Table 5), thus indicating low cost for high-volume production. Equipment included automatic loading and transfer devices. The generator in this application was capable of cutting straight bevel gears as large as 10-in. pitch diameter and face width up to 1⅛ in.

Example 394 (Table 5). The interlocking-cutter method was used to cut the 3.110-in.-OD straight bevel gears in one cut from solid blanks (sketch in Table 5). Details of the operation are listed in the table. The generator used for this application was capable of cutting gears up to 8½-in. OD and 1⅜-in. face width, and as coarse as 3 diametral pitch.

Example 395 (Table 5). Because of the front hub on the 3.200-in. OD gear (sketch in Table 5) the use of interlocking cutters or Revacycle was precluded. A two-tool generator (reciprocating tools) was used to cut the teeth in one roughing and one finishing operation. Manufacturing details are given in Table 5. Productivity was low in comparison with methods that employ rotating cutters.

Example 396 (Table 5). The 6.500-in.-OD straight bevel gears (sketch in Table 5) were completed in a two-tool generator in two operations — roughing and finishing. Manufacturing details, with the exception of operating details for the roughing operation, are given in Table 5. These gears could have been machined by either the interlocking-cutter or the Revacycle method, but volume requirements were too low to warrant the higher cost for tooling these high-production methods.

Example 397 (Table 5). The 9.000-in.-OD straight bevel gears (sketch in Table 5) were completed in one cut from solid blanks by the interlocking-cutter method. Manufacturing details are listed in Table 5. The machine used for this application was capable of cutting gears up to 16-in. OD, 2¼-in. face width and diametral pitch as coarse as 2½.

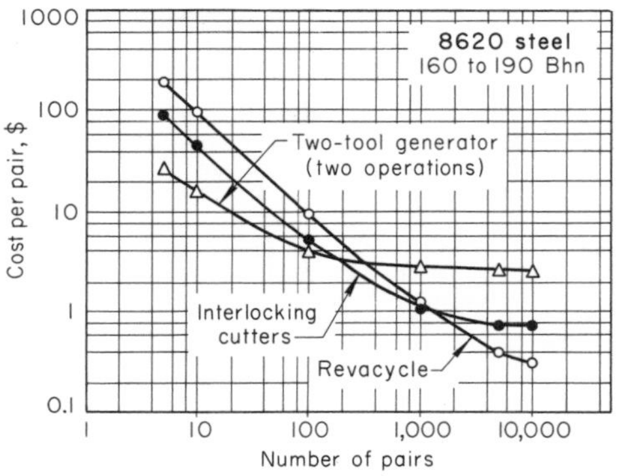

Fig. 34. Relation of cost (machine burden and initial tool cost) and quantity for cutting straight bevel gears by three methods

Cost vs Quantity (Straight Bevel Gears). Data presented in Fig. 34 compare unit cost versus quantity for cutting straight bevel gears by the three most widely used methods. These data include machine burden and initial tool cost only; cost of labor and tool maintenance are excluded. Hydraulic chucking and automatic machine cycles were used in all cases. The pairs of gears cut were differential gears having a 10-to-16 ratio, 5 diametral pitch and whole depth of 0.410 in.

The two-tool generator, because it has the lowest tooling cost, is the most economical method for producing up to approximately 150 pairs, at which point the two-tool generator and interlocking-cutter methods are equivalent. For large production runs the two-tool generating method becomes prohibitively expensive. The Revacycle and interlocking-cutter methods are equivalent in cost at about 1200 pairs, beyond which the Revacycle method is cheaper.

Spiral Bevel Gears. Spiral, Zerol and hypoid bevel gears (see Fig. 7) — of which the hypoid are by far the most numerous, being used in quantities that exceed those of the spiral and Zerol gears combined — are cut in the same type of equipment and by the same general procedures.

Pinions are generally cut by some type of generator (the face-mill type is commonly used). Gears may or may not be cut in generators. When the gear-to-pinion ratio is greater than about 2.5

Table 6. Processing Details for Cutting Spiral or Hypoid Bevel Gears of Four Different Sizes and Designs (Examples 398 to 401)

Item	Example 398	Example 399	Example 400	Example 401
	Gear Details			
Type	Hypoid pinion	Spiral bevel	Helixform hypoid	Formate hypoid
Steel	4027	4620	4028	8822
Hardness, Bhn(a)	160 to 190	160 to 190	160 to 190	179 to 202
Outside diameter, in.	3.920	5.750	8.375	16.500
Face width, in.	1.240	1.000	1.318	2.250
Number of teeth	11	40	37	49
Diametral pitch	5.0	7.0	4.55	3.0
Helix	50°	30°	25°	10°
Type of tooth	Octoid	Octoid	Conjugate	Formate
Whole depth, in.	0.450	0.290	0.441	0.667
Tooth-to-tooth tolerance, in.	0.00035	0.0004	0.0005	0.0005
Tooth-to-tooth eccentricity, in.	0.001	....	0.0025	....
	Cutter Details(b)			
Type	Face mill	Face mill	Face mill	Face mill
Outside diameter, in.	9	6	7.5	16
Blades cutting per side	20	10	4	6
Type of cut	Fixed setting	Completing-generated	Broach	Milling
	Operating Conditions(c)			
Cutter speed, rpm	64	95	20	55
Cutter speed, sfm	150	150	38.7	172
Feed per blade, in.	0.020(d)	0.003	0.0015	0.006
Allowable tool wear, in.	0.008 to 0.010	0.010 to 0.012	0.020	0.010 to 0.015
Cutter life per grind, pieces	500	35	400	20
Total cutter life, pieces	25,000	1000	20,000	1600 to 2000
Cutting time per tooth, sec	19.3	21	3.8	27.6
Production, pieces per hour(e)	15.8(f)	4.2	22.3(g)	3.0

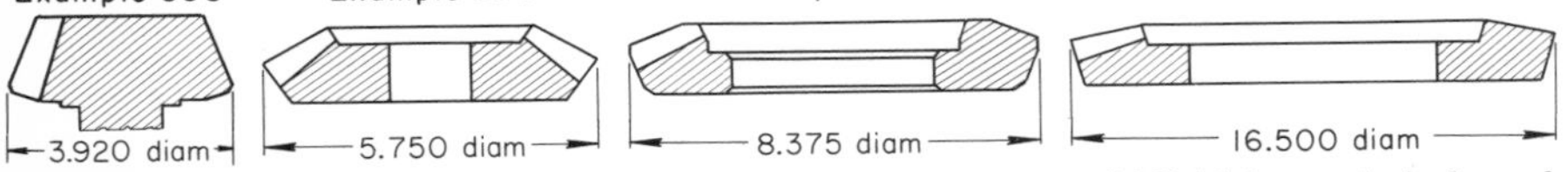

(a) All steels were in normalized condition. (b) All cutters were of M2 high speed steel, made to precision class and with straight-angle cutting portion. (c) For all operations, cutting fluid was mineral oil (viscosity, 180 and 220 SUS at 100 F). (d) Rolling feed. (e) At 100% efficiency. (f) One side. (g) Finishing.

to 1, it is common practice to cut the gears without generating roll. Thus, the Formate single-cycle, Helixform and Cyclex methods are used extensively for cutting spiral bevel gears having a ratio of 2.5 to 1 or greater.

Nongenerated gears are cheaper than their generated counterparts, although there is a smaller difference in cost between the various methods for cutting spiral bevel gears (of less than 32-in. OD) than between the various methods for cutting straight bevel gears (compare the cost-quantity relationships plotted in Fig. 34 and 35). Cutting of large bevel gears is dealt with separately, on the next page (see particularly Examples 405 and 406).

The four examples that follow present details of practice used for both generating and nongenerating methods.

Examples 398 to 401. Manufacturing Practice for Cutting Teeth in Four Different Spiral Bevel Gears

Example 398 (Table 6). The 3.920-in.-OD hypoid pinions (sketch in Table 6) were cut by generating in a face-mill machine. Manufacturing details are given in Table 6. The machines used to cut these pinions were specially designed for high-volume production. First, they were equipped with special cams with which the rate of roll could be varied so that the cutting blades removed stock equally throughout the generating roll, resulting in increased production. High-volume production warranted the use of separate machines to cut the drive and coast sides of the work pinions. When this two-stage operation is employed, machines are equipped to cut only on the up-roll or on the down-roll, depending on which side of the pinion is being cut.

Example 399 (Table 6). The 5.750-in.-OD spiral bevel gear (sketch in Table 6) was cut in a face-mill generator using a solid blade. Manufacturing details are listed in Table 6. The machine used for this application could be used for roughing without generating roll, for uniform roll cutting, or for variable roll cutting of gears up to 8½-in. OD with face widths up to 1¼-in. and diametral pitch as coarse as 4.

Example 400 (Table 6). The 8.375-in.-OD hypoid gear (sketch in Table 6) was finish cut by the Helixform method (nongenerating) in a single-purpose machine (Helixform finisher). Rough cutting was done in a previous operation. The operating details given in Table 6 refer to finishing only. This type of machine is capable of finish cutting ring gears up to 10½-in. OD at 10-to-1 ratio and diametral pitch as coarse as 2½.

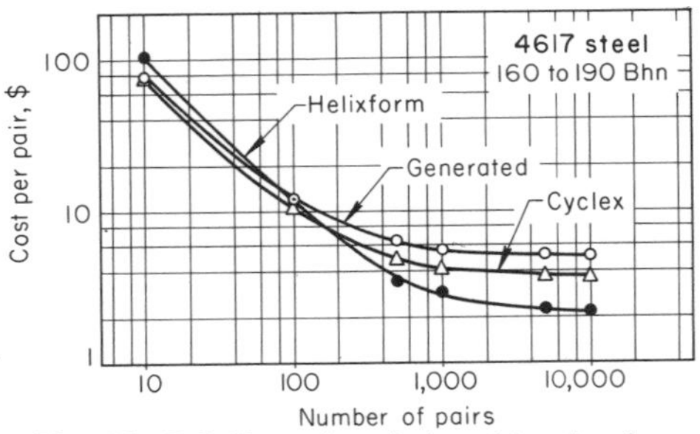

Fig. 35. Relation of cost (machine burden and initial tool cost) and quantity in cutting hypoid gears by three methods

Table 7. Tool Cost and Production Rate for Cutting Gears by Formate Single-Cycle and Helixform Methods (Example 402)

Item	Formate single-cycle	Helixform
Cost per set of inserts	$265.00	$265.00
Gears cut per set	10,000	18,000
Cutter cost per gear	$0.0265	$0.0147
Production, pieces per hr	15	23

Based on cutting 40-tooth spiral bevel gears (8-in. OD) made of 4620 steel at 160 to 190 Bhn.

Example 401 (Table 6). The 16.50-in.-OD hypoid gear (sketch in Table 6) was completely cut from a solid blank by the Formate single-cycle method (nongenerating). Manufacturing details are listed in Table 6. The machine used for this application was capable of cutting both gears and pinions having a ratio of 3 to 1 or higher. The pinion was cut by conventional single-roll generating.

Cost vs Quantity (Spiral Bevel Gears). Data presented in Fig. 35 show cost versus quantity for cutting hypoid gears having a ratio of 10 to 40 and diametral pitch of 6. These data include machine burden and initial tool cost only; cost of labor and tool repair are omitted. Hydraulic chucking was used with automatic machine cycles.

The data in Fig. 35 show that the cost of cutting 100 pairs of gears is about the same for the two nongenerating (Helixform and Cyclex) and the generating methods. As quantity increases the nongenerated gears show a distinct cost advantage.

Formate Single-Cycle vs Helixform Method. Although the Formate single-cycle method is widely used to cut spiral bevel gears, the Helixform method results in gears that are closer to true mathematical conjugacy (see description of both methods on page 197 in this article). In addition, the Helixform method is usually capable of machining gears in less time and at lower tool cost per gear machined, as described in the example that follows.

Example 402. Formate vs Helixform — Tool Cost and Productivity (Table 7)

Spiral bevel gears having 40 teeth and 8.00-in. OD were cut by both the Formate single-cycle and Helixform methods. Initial cost of cutters was approximately the same for both methods, but because of the longer cutter life in the Helixform method, tool cost per gear was reduced by about 50% (Table 7). In addition to the lower tool cost per gear, Helixform cutting increased productivity by 50% (Table 7).

Machining of Large Gears

There is no one dimension that defines a "large" or a "small" gear. As various sizes are reached, some methods of manufacture become impractical, and other methods must be used. The gears discussed in the examples in this section range from 32.74-in. to 100-in. outside diameter.

Herringbone gears of large size are discussed in the section on page 203.

Spur and Helical Gears. Milling, hobbing and rack cutting are the methods most commonly used for cutting large spur and helical gears. Milling is the least expensive, and the least accurate, of these three methods; therefore, the accuracy required in the gear will determine whether or not milling can be used.

Hobbing is more costly than milling, but produces more accurate gears than milling. Hobs are available for cutting gears well over 100-in. OD, provided the diametral pitch is finer than 1. Because of the size of hob required, and limitations of hobbing machines, it is difficult to hob gears of 1 diametral pitch and coarser.

Once it has been decided that hobbing will be used, it must be determined whether a hardened and ground hob will be required or whether an unground hob will provide the required degree of accuracy. The two types vary greatly in price. However, if a ground hob is selected, extreme care must be used in resharpening or the original accuracy will not be maintained and errors may occur in the gear tooth form.

For machining large gears that have large teeth (coarser than 1 diametral pitch), rack cutting is usually the most practical method. Rack cutting may be cheaper than hobbing, even when teeth are finer than 1 diametral pitch (see Example 404).

The two examples that follow describe practice for hobbing and rack cutting of large helical gears and pinions.

Table 8. Cutting Teeth in Large Helical Gears and Pinions (Example 403)

Item	Gear	Pinion
Workpiece Details(a)		
Steel	Low-alloy	4340
Product form	Casting	Forging
Hardness, Bhn	330	369
Pitch diam, in.	100	13
No. of teeth	100	13
Diametral pitch	1	1
Face width, in.	15	17
Cutter Details		
Type	Rack	Hob
Size	3-tooth	10¾-in. diam
Material	T1 HSS	M3 HSS
Operating Conditions(b)		
Speed, sfm	25, 45(c)	21
Feed, ipr	...	0.030(d)
No. of cuts	4, 1, 1(e)	1, 1(f)
Time/pc, hr(g)	47	33

(a) Both gear and pinion had 14.1375° helix angle and 25° pressure angle. (b) Cutting oil was used in both operations. (c) Number of strokes per minute; roughing and finishing, respectively. (d) Per revolution of workpiece. (e) Roughing, semifinishing and finishing, respectively. (f) Roughing and finishing. (g) Floor to floor.

Table 9. Processing Details and Tool Cost for Hobbing vs Rack Cutting of Large Gears (Example 404) (a)

Item	Hobbing	Rack cutting
Machine Details		
Type	Gear hobber	Rack cutter
Size, in. (max)	98	197
Horsepower	10	20
Cutter Details		
Type	Hob	Rack
Size, in.	8 diam, 9 face	4 wide, 12 long
Class	B	....
Number of edges	9 flutes	5 teeth
Cost	$1500	$150
Operating Conditions(b)		
Cutter speed	55 rpm	20(c)
Cutting speed, sfm	112	42, 33(d)
Feed, in.	0.050, 0.030(e)	0.012(f)
Cutter life:		
Grinds per piece	3	2
No. of grinds	50	20
Time per gear, hr	53.2	40.2

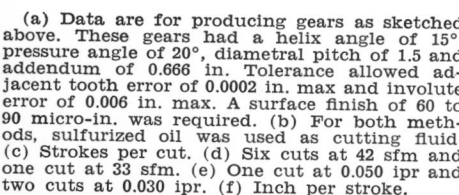

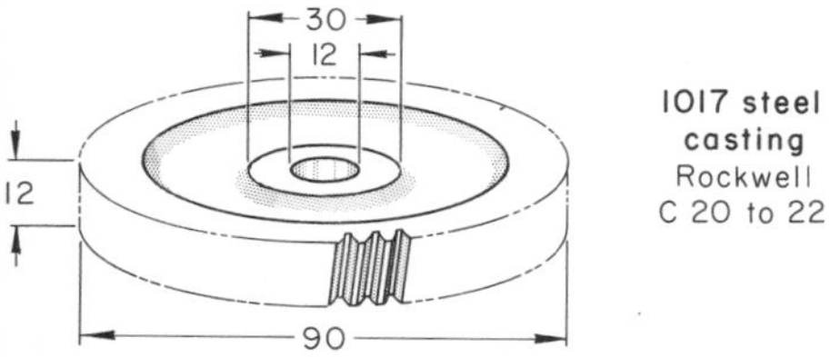

(a) Data are for producing gears as sketched above. These gears had a helix angle of 15°, pressure angle of 20°, diametral pitch of 1.5 and addendum of 0.666 in. Tolerance allowed adjacent tooth error of 0.0002 in. max and involute error of 0.006 in. max. A surface finish of 60 to 90 micro-in. was required. (b) For both methods, sulfurized oil was used as cutting fluid. (c) Strokes per cut. (d) Six cuts at 42 sfm and one cut at 33 sfm. (e) One cut at 0.050 ipr and two cuts at 0.030 ipr. (f) Inch per stroke.

Example 403. Cutting 100-In. Helical Gears and 13-In. Mating Pinions (Table 8)

Details of practice that proved successful for cutting coarse teeth (1 diametral pitch) in helical gears of 100-in. pitch diameter and mating pinions of 13-in. pitch diameter are given in Table 8. Large gears having teeth as coarse as 1 diametral pitch are borderline for hobbing. Thus, for this gear and pinion combination, rack cutting was used for the gear and hobbing for the pinion. The cutting speeds shown in Table 8 are low, but they prolonged cutter life and avoided the difficulties involved in changing tools during operation and in matching the cuts.

Example 404. Hobbing vs Rack Cutting for 90-In. Helical Gears (Table 9)

The 90-in.-OD helical gears (see illustration in Table 9) were equally satisfactory for service when cut by hobbing or by rack cutting. The time required for cutting one gear was nearly the same for both methods, despite the fact that in rack cutting half the teeth on one gear could be cut per tool grind, compared with one third of the teeth in hobbing (see details in Table 9). However, as shown in Table 9, initial cost for the hob exceeded the cost of the rack cutter by a factor of 10. This difference was partially offset by the fact that the hob had a total life of 50 grinds, compared with 20 for the rack cutter. Thus, actual tool cost of a hob was only about four times greater than for the rack cutter.

Bevel Gears. Milling, template machining, two-tool generating and planing generating are the methods most commonly used for cutting large straight and spiral bevel gears.

Large bevel gears are seldom cut by milling, because the accuracy obtained by milling is seldom acceptable. Template machining in a bevel gear planer produces accurate results with low-cost tools, but template machining is slow. Two-tool generators offer a practical means for cutting straight bevel gears having diameters up to about 35 in., face widths up to 6 in., and teeth as coarse as 1 diametral pitch. Tooling cost for the two-tool generating method is also low.

Planing generators can be used for cutting straight bevel gears, but they are most widely used for cutting spiral bevel gears ranging from 35 to 72 in. in outside diameter, with up to 10-in. face width, and teeth as coarse as ¾ diametral pitch.

The two examples that follow give details of typical practice for cutting large straight and spiral bevel gears.

Example 405. Use of Two-Tool Generator for Cutting 32.74-In. Straight Bevel Gears (Table 10)

The 32.74-in.-OD, 5-in.-face-width straight bevel gear illustrated by the sketch in Table 10 was cut on a two-tool generator arranged for roughing without generating roll and then finished on the same machine with generating roll. Manufacturing details are listed in Table 10.

Example 406. Use of Planing Generator for Cutting 40-In. Spiral Bevel Gears (Table 10)

The 40-in.-OD by 6.25-in.-face-width spiral bevel gear illustrated by the sketch in Table 10 was cut in a planing generator using a single reciprocating tool. The tooth profile was generated by the relative motion of the gear blank and the cradle carrying the tool slide. Indexing of the work was continuous, timed in relation to the stroke of the tool in such a way that the tool was cutting on a different tooth at each stroke.

Rough and finish cutting was done in the same machine, but with different tools. Roughing was followed by a semifinish cut and a finish cut on each side of the tooth. Manufacturing details are given in Table 10.

Shaving of Spur and Helical Gears

Gear shaving is a finishing operation that removes small amounts of metal from the flanks of gear teeth. It is not intended to salvage gears that have

Table 10. Cutting 32.74-In. Straight-Bevel and 40-In. Spiral Bevel Gears (Examples 405 and 406)

Item	Example 405 Straight bevel	Example 406 Spiral bevel
Gear Details		
Steel	Mo alloy	4140
Condition	Normalized	Quenched and tempered
Hardness, Bhn	225 to 250	269 to 302
Number of teeth(a)	40	48
Diametral pitch	1.25	2.10
Whole depth, in.	1.750	0.900
Face width, in.	5	6.25
Helix angle	....	15°
Tolerance	0.002-in. tooth to tooth	0.0035-in. pitch error
Specified finish, micro-in.	90 to 110	125 to 150
Machine and Cutter Details(b)		
Machine type	Two-tool generator(c)	Planing generator(d)
Horsepower	7.5	25; variable speed
Cutter size, in.	1.25	1$\frac{15}{16}$
Operating Conditions(e)		
Effective cutting speed, sfm	50	25 roughing, 35 finishing
Cutter life, pieces	7 per grind, 350 total	1-2 per grind, 75-100 total
Time per piece, hr	3.3	9.3

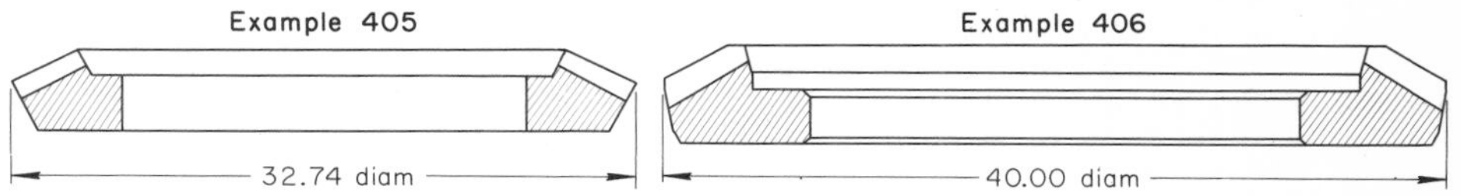

(a) Both gears had octoid teeth. (b) Cutters were pressure angled, with one blade per cutting side and straight-angle cutting portion, were of precision class and were made of modified M2 high speed steel. (c) Capable of roughing and double roll finishing. (d) Capable of cutting straight and spiral bevels. (e) Both gears were generated. The straight bevel gear was completed in two cuts, the spiral bevel gear in four cuts.

been carelessly cut, although it may correct small errors in tooth spacing, helix angle, tooth profile, and concentricity. Shaving improves the finish on tooth surfaces and can eliminate tooth-end load concentration, reduce gear noise and increase load-carrying capacity. Shaving has been successfully used in finishing gears of diametral pitches from 180 to 2. Standard machines and cutters are available for shaving gears that range in size from ¼-in. to 220-in. pitch diameter.

Leaving excessive stock for shaving will impair the final quality of the shaved gear. For maximum accuracy in the shaved gear and maximum cutter life, a minimum of stock should be allowed for removal by shaving; the amount depends largely on pitch. As little as 0.0003 to 0.001 in. of stock should be left on gears having diametral pitch as fine as 48; 0.003 to 0.005 in. is allowable for gears having diametral pitch of 2.

Operating Principles. The shaving operation is done with cutter and gear at crossed axes; helical cutters are used for spur gears, and vice versa. The action between gear and cutter is a combination of rolling and sliding. Vertical serrations in the cutter teeth take fine cuts from the profiles of the gear teeth.

During operation the tip of the shaving cutter must not touch the root fillet, or uncontrolled, inaccurate involute profiles will result. For gears to be shaved, protuberance-type hobs that provide a small undercut at the flank of the tooth may be preferred. This type of hob avoids initial tip loading of the shaving cutter.

Shaving Cutters. A typical rotary gear-shaving cutter is shown in Fig. 36(b). This cutter is serrated on the profile to form the cutting edges. The depth of the serrations governs total cutter life, in terms of the number of sharpenings permitted. A shaving cutter is sharpened by regrinding the tooth profiles, thus reducing the tooth thickness. This causes a reduction in operating center distance for the same backlash and, in turn, changes the operating pressure angle. These changes are compensated for by a change in addendum after resharpening. Tolerance is an important consideration in original purchase and resharpening. Shaving cutters are manufactured to standardized tolerances, not unlike those of master gears. For example, cumulative tooth spacing error can be held to 0.0003 in. and profile to 0.000025 in. Because the engineering and facilities necessary to produce such accuracy are not available in most gear manufacturing plants, cutters are ordinarily returned to a tool manufacturer for resharpening.

Shaving Methods. Shaving is done by two basic methods — rack and rotary. In rack shaving, the rack is reciprocated under the gear and infeed takes place at the end of each stroke. Because racks longer than 20 in. are impractical, 6 in. is the maximum diameter of gear that can be shaved by the rack method.

Rotary Shaving. The several applications of rotary shaving include underpass, modified underpass, transverse,

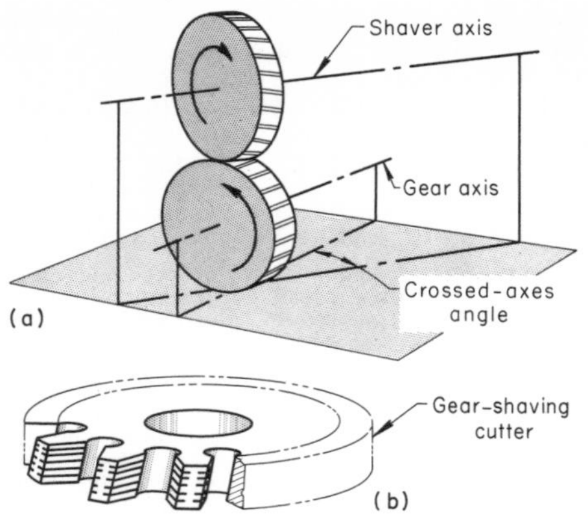

Fig. 36. (a) *Work gear in mesh with shaving cutter.* (b) *Serrated gear-shaving cutter.*

axial traverse and angular traverse. Crown shaving can be incorporated in all of these modifications.

In rotary shaving the cutter has the approximate form of a gear (Fig. 36b). The size of gear that can be shaved is limited by the machine rather than by the cutter. Rotary shaving can be any of three types: underpass, modified underpass, and transverse.

Underpass shaving is used on cluster gears or gears with shoulders. To avoid interference with the adjacent gear or shoulder, the cross-axes angle is usually 4° to 6°. The face of the tool must be wider than the face of the shaved gear. Because underpass shaving is a one-cycle, short-stroke process, it is the fastest method of shaving. Disadvantages include relatively short tool life and light stock removal, thus requiring precise size control of the preshaved gear.

Modified underpass shaving is the most widely used method because it is a rapid one-cycle process. Tool cost is moderate, because the cutter need be no wider than the gear and may be narrower. The high cross-axes angle of

Table 11. Nominal Speeds and Feeds for Shaving of Carbon and Low-Alloy Steel Gears With High Speed Steel Tools (a)

Typical steel (b)	Brinell hardness	Speed, sfm (c)
Carbon and Low-Alloy Steels (Except Free-Cutting Grades)		
1020, 1045, 4140,	85 to 125	525
7140 and 8620, at	125 to 175	500
hardness ranges	175 to 225	450
listed at right	225 to 275	375
	275 to 325	325
	325 to 375	275
Free-Cutting Carbon and Low-Alloy Steels		
1112	100 to 150	650
	150 to 200	730
1117	100 to 150	580
	150 to 200	620
1137, 12L14,	100 to 150	550
4140+S and	150 to 200	525
41L40, at	200 to 250	475
hardness ranges	275 to 325	350
listed at right	325 to 375	275

(a) High speed steels M2 and M7. (b) Each steel listed is a frequently used grade in a group of similar steels. For a listing of the steels in the various groups, see Table 2, page 6. (c) Feed rate for shaving steel gears is determined by pitch, as follows:

	Diametral pitch			
	1 to 4	5 to 10	11 to 19	20
Feed, in./stroke...	0.012	0.008	0.005	0.003

Feeds given above are for rigid machinery; for less rigid equipment, use lower feeds. (Source of data: same as for Table 13)

30° to 60° promotes rapid stock removal and smoother surface finish.

Transverse shaving is the slowest shaving method because multiple passes are required. Because it is a method of handling gears much wider than the cutter, cutter cost is moderate for gears with wide faces.

Crown shaving is used to relieve load concentration at the ends of gear teeth caused by misalignment of axes in operation. Crowning is a modification of the tooth profile in both the radial and axial planes. Figure 37 shows a gear tooth crowned in the axial direction. In the axial traverse method of shaping, crowning is done by rocking the work table as it is reciprocated. In the higher-production angular traverse method, the cutter is modified to provide crowning. The amount of crown varies, but usually 0.0003 to 0.0005 in. per inch of face width is sufficient.

Speed and Feed. Although cutting speeds are always high, optimum speed of rotation for gear shaving varies considerably with work metal hardness and composition. Speeds and feeds for several steels and hardness ranges are given in Table 11.

Details of specific gear shaving operations that produced crowned teeth are described in the next two examples.

Example 407. Shaving Helical Gears by the Angular Traverse Method (Fig. 37)

Helical gears, as illustrated in Fig. 37, were shaved by the angular traverse method, using cutters specially ground to provide the 0.0008-in. horizontal tooth crown shown. Shaving was done in a standard gear-shaving machine. Gears were shaved one at a time, using the method of fixturing shown in Fig. 37. Manufacturing details are tabulated below the illustration. Accuracy required for this gear could have been obtained by honing after hobbing. However, because of the end use, crowned teeth were desired, and shaving was chosen as the method for finishing.

Example 408. Shaving Helical Gears by the Rotary Transverse Method (Fig. 38)

Figure 38 shows the method of holding and the relative motions of a helical gear and shaving cutter during rotary transverse shaving. The rocking method was used to obtain a crown of 0.0007 to 0.001 in. on the gear teeth. The operation was completed in three cycles (six strokes) of a standard rotary gear-shaving machine. The last two strokes were idle strokes for improving tooth finish. Manufacturing details are tabulated below the illustration in Fig. 38.

Grinding, Honing and Lapping of Gears

Gear grinding, a major process, is dealt with in a separate article in this volume, beginning on page 213.

The teeth of hardened steel gears are sometimes honed to remove nicks and burrs, to improve finish, and to make minor corrections in tooth shape. For a discussion of this process, see the article "Honing" (page 288 in this volume).

Lapping is sometimes required for sets of hardened steel gears that must run quietly. This process is discussed on page 298, in the article "Lapping".

Cutter Material and Construction

High speed steel is used almost exclusively as the material for cutting edges of gear cutting tools. The steels most widely used are the general-purpose grades such as M2 or M7. Grade M3 (higher in carbon and vanadium than general-purpose grades) is also used in many gear-cutting applications and is often preferred to M2 or M7 for cutting quenched and tempered alloy steels. The more highly alloyed grades of high speed steel such as T15 or M30 are recommended only for conditions where greater red hardness is necessary. Such conditions include hard work metal, inadequate supply of cutting fluid, or high cutting speeds. Cutters are made from these highly alloyed grades only when one of the general-purpose grades (or M3) have proved inadequate.

Carbide cutters have been tried for a variety of gear-cutting applications, but they have proved uneconomical in all but a few applications.

Construction. Most reciprocating tools such as those used in gear shaping and planing operations are made of solid high speed steel.

Rotary cutters (hobs and milling cutters) for spur and helical gears can be either solid or inserted blade. Economy is the governing factor; the two methods of construction are equally satisfactory in terms of producing acceptable gears. Cutters less than about 3 in. in diameter are invariably solid. As cutters increase in size the practice of using high speed steel cutting edges (blades) as inserts in alloy steel bodies is usually more economical. Inserts are normally held by mechanical fasteners.

Rotary cutters (face mill, rotary broach and other) for bevel gears are usually designed to use inserts.

In rotary cutters, feed rate is a direct function of the number of cutting faces. Thus it is desirable to have as many cutting edges as possible, to increase the amount of metal removed during each revolution. However, tooth strength and chip clearance must be considered when selecting the number of blades (cutting edges). Despite the limitations imposed by chip clearance and tooth strength, gear cutters are often redesigned for greater efficiency. One such instance and the influence on results is described in the next example:

Example 409. Redesign of Cutter for Increased Efficiency in Cutting 10-Tooth Pinions (Table 12)

Spiral bevel automotive pinions with ten teeth were cut in a face-mill machine with a standard face-mill cutter having 16 cutting edges. A complete redesign of this cutter allowed 20 cutting edges, which resulted in a higher production rate and lower cutter cost per pinion. Results are summarized in Table 12.

Speed and Feed

In addition to the type of gear being machined and the method of cutting, other factors that influence the choice of cutting speed are: work metal composition and hardness, diametral pitch of the work gear, rigidity of the setup, tolerance and finish requirements, and cutting fluid used.

Hobbing Speed. Nominal speeds and feeds for gear hobbing that take into account several of the above variables are listed in Table 13. As carbon content, alloy content and hardness of the steel workpiece increase, recommended cutter speed decreases; for any given work metal, cutting speed increases as diametral pitch becomes finer. Numerical values given in Table 13, as well as in other speed and feed tables in this section, assume that an additive-type cutting fluid will be used. The processing examples presented in the sections of this article dealing with cutting of spur and helical gears show hobbing speeds of 25 to 241 sfm. The reason for this wide range is the existence of other variables in addition to those considered in Table 13. For instance, a speed of only 25 sfm is shown in Table 8 of Example 403, but this operation involves hobbing a 100-in.-diam. helical gear at 330 Bhn; the low cutting speed prolonged tool life and avoided the difficulties involved in changing tools and matching the cuts. In contrast, small fine-pitch gears were successfully hobbed at 241 sfm in an automatic machine, in Example 383 (Table 2).

In Example 376 tolerance requirement was the reason for using a hob speed of only 52 sfm on heat treated 4140 spur gears having a diametral pitch of 8. For hobbing gears of this material, hardness and pitch, Table 13 suggests a speed of 145 sfm, but in Example 376 a slow speed was required, in order to meet class 3 requirements.

In many instances speeds shown in Table 13 are conservative for the conditions shown. For instance, in Examples 381 and 382 normalized alloy steels are hobbed at 205 sfm. In Table 13, a speed of 130 sfm is suggested for the same conditions. However, in both Examples 381 and 382 hobbing was followed by shaving; thus, hobbing tolerances were less critical and higher speed was permissible.

Shaping speed is influenced by variables similar to those that affect hobbing speeds, with the exception of diametral pitch. Nominal speeds and feeds for gear shaping under a variety of conditions are given in Table 14. Cutter speed varies with composition and hardness of work metal but not with diametral pitch. The speeds listed in Table 14 are generally conservative, and most of the shaping examples in this article show speeds close to those

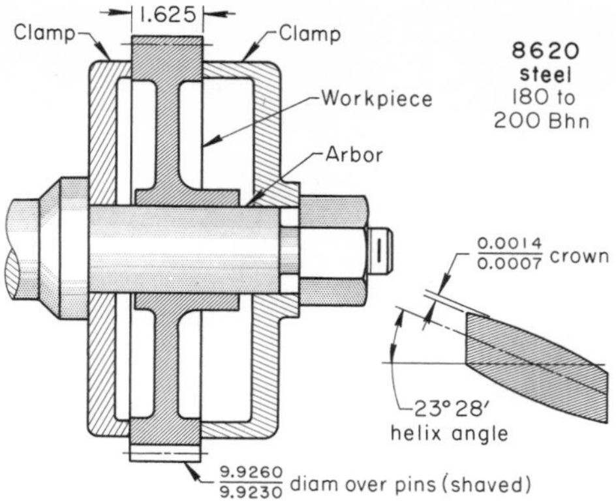

Gear Details

Number of teeth	43
Diametral pitch	5.0112
Pitch diameter	9.3818
Whole depth	0.4215 in.
Tolerances:	
Diameter over pins:	
Hobbed	9.9350/9.9310 in.
Shaved	9.9260/9.9230 in.
Involute composite error, max:	
Hobbed	±0.0015 in.
Shaved	+0.0011, −0.0007 in.
Lead composite error, max:	
Hobbed	+0.0022, −0.0002 in.
Shaved	+0.0011, −0.0007 in.

Cutter Details

Type	Circular serrated
Pitch diameter	8.2383 in.
Number of teeth	41
Helix angle	12° RH
Pressure angle	22° 30′

Operating Conditions

Speed	422 sfm
Feed	3.20 ipm
Number of strokes	2 (one cycle)
Cutting fluid	Sulfurized oil
Time per piece	1.6 min

Fig. 37. Method of fixturing a helical gear for angular traverse shaving, and plan view of sectioned gear tooth showing crown at pitch line (Example 407)

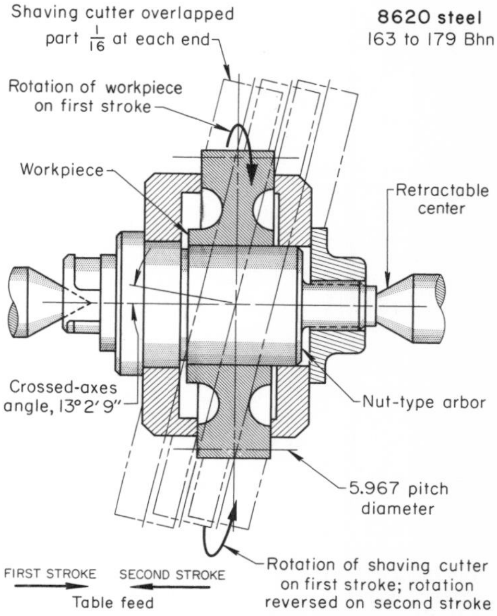

Gear Details

Number of teeth	36
Diametral pitch	6.5199
Pitch diameter	5.967 in.
Whole depth	0.400-in. full root radius
Tolerances:	
Preshave size	6.400/6.398 in.(a)
Shave size	6.389/6.387 in.(a)
Eccentricity, max	0.002 in.
Crown	0.0007 to 0.001 in.

Cutter Details

Type	Rotary transverse
Size, in.	9⅜ OD, 2½ hole, 1¼ wide
Number of teeth	57
Helix angle	10° LH
Pressure angle	18° 31′ 5″

Operating Conditions

Cutter speed	219 rpm (537 sfm)
Feed	2.9 ipm
Number of strokes	6 (3 cycles)
Cutting fluid	(b)
Cutter life per grind (est)	1800 pieces
Total cutter life (est)	10,800 pieces
Production rate	15.8 pieces per hour

(a) Measured over 0.250-in.-diam balls. (b) Sulfurized and chlorinated cutting oil (3.43% total sulfur content, and 0.65% chlorine) mixed with 5% lard oil; viscosity, 110 SUS at 100 F.

Fig. 38. Rotary transverse shaving of helical gears (Example 408)

Table 12. Improved Results Obtained With Redesigned Cutter for Producing Spiral Bevel Pinions (Example 409)

Item	Cutter: Original, 16-blade	Cutter: Improved, 20-blade
Pinions produced per hr	14.6	23
Cost per set of blades	$165	$210
Pinions per set of blades	6000	20,000
Cutter cost per pinion	$0.0275	$0.0105

Table 13. Nominal Speeds and Feeds for Hobbing of Carbon and Low-Alloy Steel Gears With High Speed Steel Tools(a)

		Operating conditions(c) for diametral pitch of:									
		1 to 4		5 to 10		11 to 19		20 to 48		Over 48	
Typical steel(b)	Brinell hardness	Speed, sfm	Feed, ipr(d)	Speed, sfm	Feed, ipr(d)	Speed, sfm	Feed, ipr(d)	Speed, sfm	Feed, ipr(d)	Speed, sfm	Feed, ipr(d)
Carbon and Low-Alloy Steels (Except Free-Cutting Grades)											
1020, 1045, 4140 and 8620, at hardnesses listed at right	85 to 125	165	0.060	195	0.050	210	0.030	225	0.015	240	0.008
	125 to 175	130	0.060	145	0.050	165	0.030	180	0.015	195	0.008
	175 to 225	110	0.060	125	0.050	145	0.030	160	0.015	175	0.008
	225 to 275	95	0.060	115	0.050	125	0.030	140	0.015	155	0.008
	275 to 325	80	0.035	95	0.029	110	0.020	120	0.010	135	0.008
	325 to 375	60	0.032	70	0.027	85	0.019	90	0.008	100	0.008
7140	200 to 250	85	0.060	100	0.050	110	0.030	115	0.015	125	0.008
	300 to 350	65	0.035	80	0.029	90	0.020	95	0.010	105	0.008
Free-Cutting Carbon and Low-Alloy Steels											
1112 and 1117	100 to 150	170	0.060	195	0.050	230	0.030	240	0.015	270	0.008
	150 to 200	190	0.060	215	0.050	250	0.030	260	0.015	290	0.008
1137	175 to 225	140	0.060	160	0.050	170	0.030	185	0.015	200	0.008
	275 to 325	90	0.035	110	0.029	130	0.020	135	0.010	150	0.008
	325 to 375	70	0.035	90	0.029	110	0.020	115	0.010	130	0.008
12L14 and 4140+S	100 to 150	210	0.060	240	0.050	270	0.030	280	0.015	310	0.008
	150 to 200	180	0.060	200	0.050	230	0.030	245	0.015	270	0.008
	200 to 250	135	0.060	160	0.050	185	0.030	200	0.015	225	0.008
	275 to 325	125	0.035	145	0.029	165	0.020	185	0.010	205	0.008
	325 to 375	65	0.035	75	0.029	95	0.020	100	0.010	135	0.008
41L40	150 to 200	130	0.060	140	0.050	160	0.030	165	0.015	200	0.008
	200 to 250	110	0.060	120	0.050	140	0.030	145	0.015	180	0.008
	275 to 325	80	0.035	90	0.029	110	0.020	115	0.010	150	0.008
	325 to 375	65	0.035	75	0.029	95	0.020	100	0.010	135	0.008

(a) High speed steels M2 and M7. (b) Each steel listed is a frequently used grade in a group of similar steels. For a listing of steels in the various groups, see Table 2, page 6. (c) Type of cut; climb, except conventional for diametral pitch of 1 to 4. (d) For hobbing gears to be finished by grinding; 50% of indicated feed for hobbing gears to be finished by shaving. (Data are adapted from tables compiled by Metcut Research Associates, Inc.)

suggested in Table 14. For instance, 65 sfm was used for cutting the internal gear of Example 391, and the same speed is suggested in Table 14 for the same conditions.

Speeds for Interlocking and Face-Mill Cutters. Nominal speeds for cutting straight and spiral bevel gears with two common types of cutters are given in Table 15. As in shaping, speed is not varied with diametral pitch when other conditions are the same. For both the interlocking cutters and the face-mill cutters, speeds are increased for finishing when roughing and finishing are done separately. In Examples 392 to 401, the speeds used for cutting straight and spiral bevel gears with rotating cutters are close to those suggested in Table 15. When straight bevel gears are being cut with reciprocating cutters, much lower speeds are used (see Examples 395 and 396).

Feeds. Nominal feeds for hobbing of steel gears are included in Table 13. Values are given in inches per revolution (ipr) of the gear being hobbed and are based on the assumption that the gears will be ground after hobbing. As noted in Table 13, hobbing feeds should be decreased when gears are to be finished by shaving. As also shown in Table 13, hobbing feeds are sensitive to differences in diametral pitch, but feeds are not ordinarily changed for differences in the composition or hardness of the gear steel when diametral pitch is the same, except for the coarser-pitch heat treated gears.

Nominal feeds for cutting gears by shaping are given in Table 14. These values are based on the assumption that the gears will be finished by grinding; a reduction in speed as noted in Table 14 is recommended when gears are to be finished by shaving. As shown in Table 14, feeds for shaping vary with diametral pitch and comparatively little with work metal composition and hardness. Conditions for a specific operation may require feeds higher or lower than those shown in Table 14.

Feeds for cutting straight and spiral bevel gears by rotary cutters are suggested in Table 15. The specific feed is obtained by teeth that are progressively longer in a given cutter, rather than by advancing a cutter with uniform teeth, as in milling. As indicated by the feeds suggested in Table 15, the optimum feed is influenced greatly by diametral pitch; work metal composition and hardness have a minor influence on feed. The same rates of feed are commonly used for both roughing and finishing, although the cutting edges of the teeth are altered for finishing as shown in Table 15.

Cutting Fluids

Cutting fluids are recommended for all gear cutting, although for some applications (notably cutting of large gears) the use of a cutting fluid is impractical.

The three cutting fluids most commonly used for gear cutting are:

1 Mineral oil (without additives) having a viscosity of 140 to 220 SUS at 100 F
2 Cutting oil, sulfurized or chlorinated (or both), usually diluted with mineral oil to a viscosity of 180 to 220 SUS at 100 F
3 Motor oil (SAE 20 grade) of either the detergent or the nondetergent type.

Water-soluble oils, which are widely used in many metal cutting operations, are used to a lesser extent for gear cutting, because the oils referred to above are more effective for producing the surface finishes desired on gear teeth and for prolonging cutter life. Nevertheless, soluble oils are sometimes used in gear cutting. One notable application for soluble oil (20 parts water to 1 part oil) is in finish broaching of fine-pitch gears.

The relative advantages and disadvantages of the three oils mentioned above are matters of opinion among different plants producing steel gears. The speeds and feeds in Tables 13, 14 and 15 are based on the use of cutting oils with additives (No. 2 in the list above). However, in some plants mineral oils (including motor oils) are used, when records have proved that the use of these oils resulted in longer cutter life than when prepared cutting oils were used.

In some plants additive cutting oils are used for roughing operations and mineral oils for finishing when the operations are done separately in different machines.

Having an adequate supply (a flood) of fluid under slight pressure (about 5 psi) at the cutting area is extremely important; usually more important than the composition of the oil.

Comparison of Steels for Gear Cutting

End use is the main factor in the selection of steel for a specific gear. However, two or more steels will often serve equally well. Under these condi-

Table 14. Nominal Speeds and Feeds for Shaping of Carbon and Low-Alloy Steel Gears With High Speed Steel Tools(a)

Typical steel(b)	Brinell hardness	Speed, sfm	Feed(c), in. per stroke, for diametral pitch of: 1 to 4	5 to 10	11 to 19	20 to 48
Carbon and Low-Alloy Steels (Except Free-Cutting Grades)						
1020, 1045, 4140 and 8620, at hardness ranges listed at right	85 to 125	90	0.018	0.012	0.010	0.008
	125 to 175	75	0.018	0.012	0.010	0.008
	175 to 225	65	0.018	0.012	0.010	0.008
	225 to 275	55	0.016	0.012	0.010	0.008
	275 to 325	45	0.016	0.012	0.010	0.008
	325 to 375	40	0.012	0.010	0.008	0.008
7140	200 to 250	40	0.016	0.012	0.010	0.008
	300 to 350	25	0.012	0.012	0.010	0.008
Free-Cutting Carbon and Low-Alloy Steels						
1112 and 1117	100 to 150	85	0.022	0.016	0.011	0.008
	150 to 200	90	0.022	0.016	0.011	0.008
1137, 12L14, 4140+S and 41L40, at hardness ranges listed at right	100 to 150	100	0.022	0.016	0.011	0.008
	150 to 200	80	0.022	0.016	0.011	0.008
	200 to 250	70	0.022	0.016	0.011	0.008
	275 to 325	55	0.018	0.012	0.010	0.008
	325 to 375	40	0.012	0.010	0.008	0.008

(a) High speed steels M2 and M7. (b) Each steel listed is a frequently used grade in a group of similar steels. For a listing of the steels in the various groups, see Table 2, page 6. (c) For shaping gears to be finished by grinding; 50% of indicated feed for shaping gears to be finished by shaving. Three cuts for diametral pitch of 1 to 4; two cuts for higher diametral pitch. (Data are adapted from tables compiled by Metcut Research Associates, Inc.)

Table 15. Nominal Speeds and Feeds for Cutting Steel Bevel Gears With High Speed Steel Tools

Grade of steel(a)	Brinell hardness(b)	Diametral pitch	Straight bevel gears(c) — Roughing — Speed, sfm	Straight — Roughing — Feed, ipt	Straight — Finishing — Speed, sfm	Straight — Finishing — Flat width, in.(e)	Spiral bevel gears(d) — Roughing — Speed, sfm	Spiral — Roughing — Feed, ipt	Spiral — Finishing — Speed, sfm	Spiral — Finishing — Flat width, in.(e)
1213	150 to 200	1 to 3	225	0.006	250	0.018	225	0.009	250	0.008
		4 to 6	225	0.005	250	0.010	225	0.007	250	0.006
		7 to 16	225	0.004	250	0.007	225	0.006	250	0.005
		17 to 24	225	0.003	250	0.003	225	0.004	250	0.003
		25 to 32	225	0.002	250	0.001	225	0.003	250	0.002
1141	175 to 225	1 to 3	150	0.005	175	0.016	150	0.008	180	0.007
		4 to 6	150	0.004	175	0.008	150	0.006	180	0.006
		7 to 16	150	0.003	175	0.005	150	0.005	180	0.004
		17 to 24	150	0.002	175	0.002	150	0.003	180	0.003
		25 to 32	150	0.001	175	0.001	150	0.001	180	0.002
1020	175 to 225	1 to 3	130	0.006	155	0.018	130	0.008	160	0.007
		4 to 6	130	0.005	155	0.010	130	0.006	160	0.006
		7 to 16	130	0.0045	155	0.007	130	0.005	160	0.004
		17 to 24	130	0.004	155	0.003	130	0.003	160	0.003
		25 to 32	130	0.003	155	0.001	130	0.002	160	0.002
1040	175 to 225	1 to 3	130	0.006	155	0.018	130	0.010	155	0.008
		4 to 6	130	0.005	155	0.010	130	0.007	155	0.006
		7 to 16	130	0.004	155	0.007	130	0.006	155	0.005
		17 to 24	130	0.003	155	0.003	130	0.004	155	0.003
		25 to 32	130	0.002	155	0.001	130	0.003	155	0.002
8620	175 to 225	1 to 3	125	0.006	145	0.018	125	0.008	145	0.007
		4 to 6	125	0.005	145	0.010	125	0.006	145	0.006
		7 to 16	125	0.0045	145	0.007	125	0.005	145	0.004
		17 to 24	125	0.004	145	0.003	125	0.003	145	0.003
		25 to 32	125	0.003	145	0.001	125	0.002	145	0.002
4140	200 to 250	1 to 3	150	0.005	180	0.016	135	0.007	185	0.008
		4 to 6	150	0.004	180	0.008	135	0.005	185	0.006
		7 to 16	150	0.003	180	0.005	135	0.004	185	0.005
		17 to 24	150	0.002	180	0.002	135	0.003	185	0.004
		25 to 32	150	0.001	180	0.001	135	0.002	185	0.002
	275 to 325	1 to 3	120	0.005	150	0.016	120	0.007	150	0.008
		4 to 6	120	0.004	150	0.008	120	0.005	150	0.006
		7 to 16	120	0.003	150	0.005	120	0.004	150	0.005
		17 to 24	120	0.002	150	0.002	120	0.003	150	0.004
		25 to 32	120	0.001	150	0.001	120	0.002	150	0.002
	325 to 375	1 to 3	75	0.005	110	0.015	95	0.007	110	0.006
		4 to 6	75	0.004	110	0.007	95	0.005	110	0.005
		7 to 16	75	0.003	110	0.004	95	0.003	110	0.004
		17 to 24	75	0.002	110	0.002	95	0.002	110	0.002
		25 to 32	75	0.001	110	0.001	95	0.001	110	0.001

(a) Each steel represents a family of steels similar in composition. (b) All values below 250 Bhn are for the steel in the hot rolled, normalized, annealed or cold drawn condition; values above 250 Bhn are for quenched and tempered steel. (c) Using interlocking-cutter or similar method. (d) Using face-mill-type generator. (e) Width of flat on cutting edge of tool.

tions the cost of the steel and the cost of processing it are significant factors in making a final selection, and in all selections both these factors must be considered. In several examples in this section, the cost of machining standard steels is compared with the cost of free-machining counterparts. Such changes can often be made without affecting end use and, almost without exception, the use of a free-machining grade will result in lower machining costs. However, when changing from one standard grade of a given steel to its free-machining counterpart, additional cost (up to one cent a pound) of the free-machining grade must be considered in the cost comparison.

In Examples 410 to 424, which follow, all except the last one deal with changes in steel composition that resulted in cost reduction because of decreased machining time or increased tool life. The last example describes an application where the composition of the gear remained the same but a change in microstructure resulted in increased cutter life.

In the example that follows, a change in grade of steel was made because of a difference in price, and the difference in machinability was discovered after the change had been made.

Example 410. Cutting Bevel Gears From 1024 vs Modified 1027 (Table 16)

The 3.62-in.-diam straight bevel gear illustrated with Table 16 was originally made from 1024 steel in the normalized condition at 156 to 187 Bhn. The material was changed to modified 1027 at 143 to 174 Bhn in the normalized condition. The modified grade was used in preference to the standard grade because the former was 45¢ per 100 lb cheaper than the latter and 70¢ per 100 lb cheaper than 1024 (see details in Table 16). In addition to the saving in cost of steel, modified 1027 proved to be easier to machine than 1024, as shown by the 5.7% increase in cutter life (Table 16). These gears were machined in a Revacycle process with a 21.4-in.-diam segmented circular broach. One tooth was roughed and finished per revolution of the cutter. Total time for cutting 16 teeth was 0.86 min. Mineral oil with a viscosity of 140 to 160 SUS at 100 F was used as cutting fluid.

Table 16. Cutter Life in Cutting Bevel Gears From 1024 and Modified 1027 Steels (Example 410) (a)

Cutter life	1024	Mod 1027(b)
Pieces per grind	977	1064
Pieces per cutter	19,554	20,669

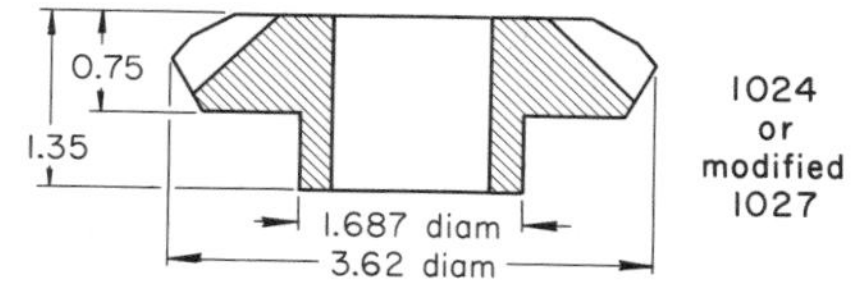

(a) The bevel gear, illustrated above, had 16 teeth, diametral pitch of 4.569, whole depth of 0.451 in., working depth of 0.405 in., face angle of 62° 37′, pitch angle of 55° 29′, and root angle of 44° 25′.
(b) Modified 1027 differs from standard 1027 in allowable manganese range (1.10 to 1.40% for the modified and 1.20 to 1.50% for the standard grade); 1024 contains 1.35 to 1.65% manganese. Modified 1027 was 45¢ per 100 lb cheaper than the standard grade. By allowing a silicon range of 0.15 to 0.30% with a maximum of 0.29% carbon, an additional 25¢ per 100 lb was saved: thus, the total saving on steel was 70¢ per 100 lb by changing the grade.

When changes in steel composition that result in lower machining costs require changes in the method of heat treating, the cost of heat treating must also be considered. The five examples that follow deal with applications in which substantial changes in composition were permitted.

Examples 411 and 412. Costs in Hobbing Spur Gears of 5145 vs 8620 (Table 17)

The first two examples in Table 17 compare machining time and cost for hobbing spur gears from 5145 and 8620. In Example 411, the production rate was increased by about 50% when changing from 5145 to 8620, this increase being shown in lower machining cost. Similar conditions prevailed for hobbing the larger gears (10.583-in. PD) from the same two steels (Example 412). The time and cost differential was more than 100% for the larger gears. Details for both gears are given in Table 17.

Example 413. Steel 8620 vs 4320 for Zerol Gears (Table 18)

In the cutting of Zerol gears in the cycle annealed condition (156 to 163 Bhn), 8620 steel showed a cost advantage over 4320 steel (Table 18). At the same feed and speed as for the 4320 steel, the less expensive 8620 steel also machined with less tool wear.

Example 414. Steel 8620 vs 4422 for Hypoid Bevel Gears (Fig. 39)

Hypoid bevel gears were machined from 8620 and 4422 steel at 149 and 137 Bhn, re-

Table 17. Effect of Steel Composition on Production Rate and Cost of Hobbing Spur Gears (Examples 411, 412, 416, 417 and 418)

Item	Original	Improved
Example 411 (24-tooth gear, 4-in. PD, ¾-in. face)		
Steel	5145	8620
Production, pieces per hr	16.153	24.51
Machining cost per gear .	$0.20	$0.12
Example 412 (64-tooth gear, 10.583-in. PD, 15⁄16-in. face)		
Steel	5145	8620
Production, pieces per hr	4.2	8.5
Machining cost per gear .	$0.69	$0.34
Example 416 (13-tooth gear, 0.2031-in. PD, 5⁄16-in. face)		
Steel	1095	1095+S
Production, pieces per hr	68.965	78.62
Machining cost per gear .	$0.1074	$0.0942
Example 417 (13-tooth gear, 0.2031-in. PD, 5⁄16-in. face)		
Steel	4140	41L40
Production, pieces per hr	62.896	78.62
Machining cost per gear .	$0.1130	$0.0942
Example 418 (45-tooth gear, 5.666-in. PD, 1¼-in. face)		
Steel	4140	41L40
Production, pieces per hr	6	7
Machining cost per gear .	$1.235	$1.058

Table 18. Cutting Zerol Gears From 8620 and 4320 Steels (Example 413) (a)

Item	8620	4320
Hardness, Bhn (b) ..	156 to 163	156 to 163
Cutting speed, sfm ..	131	131
Feed, sec per tooth .	42	42
Cost per gear:		
Tool	$0.173	$0.241
Steel (extra)	0.48	0.815
Total	$0.653	$1.056
Saving	$0.403	....

(a) Machine was a 15-in. generator using 9-in. spiral-bevel cutters of molybdenum high speed steel. (b) Cycle annealed.

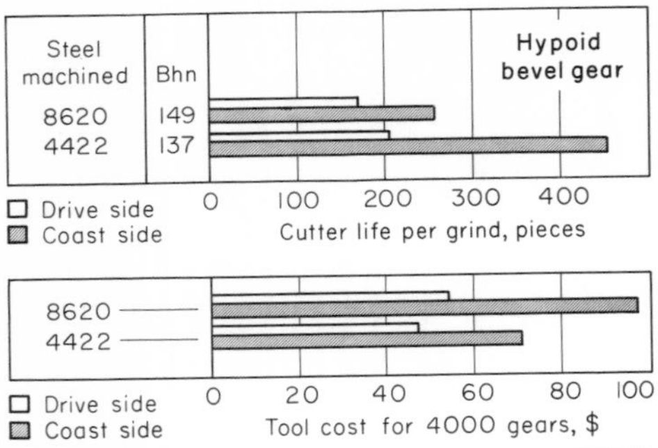

Item	8620	4422
Hardness, Bhn	149	137
Cutting speed, sfm	174	174
Feed, sec per tooth	22	22
Tool costs for 4000 gears:		
Drive side	$54.80	$47.20
Coast side	41.84	23.84
Total	$96.64	$71.04
Saving		$25.60

The machine was a 12-in. gear generator using cutters of molybdenum high speed steel. Gears had 13 teeth, 1½-in. face and 0.414-in. depth of cut. 4422 cost $0.40 per 100 lb less than 8620.

Fig. 39. Cutting hypoid bevel gears from 8620 and 4422 steels (Example 414)

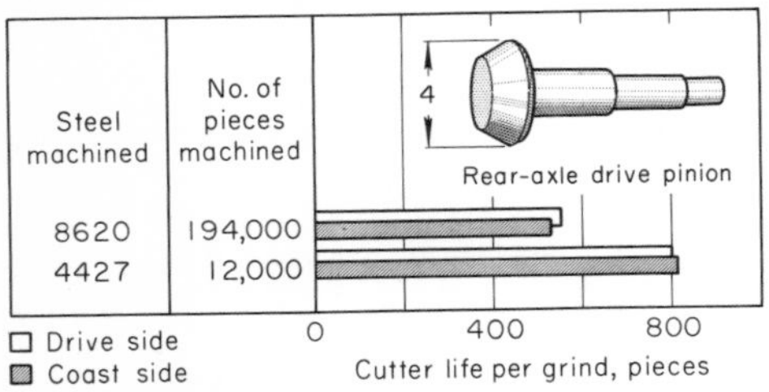

Fig. 40. Cutting rear-axle drive pinions from 8620 and 4427 steels (Example 415)

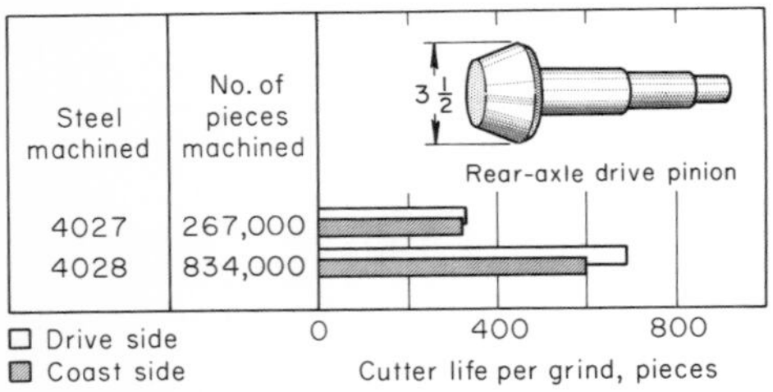

Fig. 41. Cutting rear-axle drive pinions from 4027 and 4028 steels (Example 420)

spectively. The less costly 4422 steel gave the added advantage of longer tool wear, at the same speed and feed, than 8620 steel (Fig. 39).

Example 415. Steel 8620 vs 4427 for Pinions (Fig. 40)

Rear-axle drive pinions machined from 4427 steel showed a definite advantage in tool life over those machined from 8620. Data are given with Fig. 40.

The eight examples that follow present comparisons of machining time, machining cost or cutter life when hobbing or shaping spur gears made from conventional grades and from free-cutting counterparts. The difference between conventional and free-cutting grades is often more pronounced as the hardness of the work increases, as shown in Example 422.

Examples 416 to 418. Costs in Hobbing Spur Gears From Conventional and Free-Cutting Steels (Table 17)

The three last examples in Table 17 compare time and cost for hobbing three different spur gears from conventional grades of steel and from free-cutting counterparts. The sulfur and the lead additions both permitted an increase in production rate, which decreased hobbing cost.

In all three examples, the improved results were obtained by the increase in hob speed, gained without sacrifice in hob life, when free-cutting steel was used. For instance, in hobbing the small spur gears (Examples 416 and 417), hob speed was increased from 157 to 224 rpm and feed was increased from 0.0625 to 0.085 in. per revolution of the workpiece.

Example 419. Change From 8620 to Leaded 8620 for Improved Hob Life

Three different spur gears with pitch diameters of 1.56, 2.25 and 2.625 in. were originally hobbed from annealed 8620 blanks. Changing to leaded 8620 for all three sizes resulted in a 10% increase in hob life. No changes were made in hobbing speed; consequently the number of parts produced per unit of time remained the same, except for the fact that tools could be run an average of 10% longer before changing. This increased the production rate correspondingly, because of decreased downtime. In addition to improved hob life, surface finish on the gear teeth was much better with the leaded steel than with the standard alloy.

Example 420. Cutting 4027 and 4028 Steels (Fig. 41)

The tool life obtained with 4027 molybdenum steel was markedly improved by resulfurizing to 0.035 to 0.050% S (grade 4028). Data are plotted in Fig. 41.

Example 421. Standard vs Leaded 8620 for Pinions (Table 19)

The machining properties of 8620 steel were considerably improved by a lead addition. This resulted in an increased production rate and an increase in tool life. Details of a gear-cutting operation, showing the effects of the additive, are given in Table 19.

Example 422. Effect of Free-Cutting Additives on Cutter Life in Cutting Spur Gears in a Shaper

Internal spur gears having a pitch diameter of 9.111 in. and 82 teeth were machined from quenched and tempered 4150 steel at 388 Bhn. Results were unacceptable in terms of gears per cutter sharpening, and an excessive amount of stock removal was required in sharpening the reciprocating 25-tooth cutters. Three different free-cutting grades of 4150 were tried; although some differences in results were observed among the three, each showed marked improvement compared with 4150 having no additive. Tool life and stock removal required for sharpening the cutters for machining the 4150 and its three modifications were as follows:

Grade	Pieces per sharpening	Stock removal to sharpen, in.
4150	1	0.050
Leaded	4	0.020
Resulfurized	5	0.015
Sulfate-treated	6	0.023

Example 423. Leaded vs Resulfurized 4140 for Ring Gears (Fig. 42)

Internal ring gears were manufactured from leaded 4140 and resulfurized 4140 steel. Details of the tool life and tool costs for the two forms are given with Fig. 42. They show a decided advantage in favor of the resulfurized steel. The gears were machined from rough forgings (quenched and tempered). The resulfurized forgings were considerably harder than the leaded material.

As shown by the data with Fig. 42, the largest component of cost was in cutting gear teeth. Six gears were cut from each steel before regrinding was required but the tools used for the resulfurized steel required less stock removal in resharpening.

Sometimes a change in microstructure, independent of steel composition, has a significant effect on tool life or surface finish, or both. The following

Table 19. Standard vs Leaded 8620 Steel for Pinions (Example 421)

Item	8620	86L20
Turning		
Speed, rpm	149	298
Feed, ipr	0.0035	0.0070
Time per piece, min	0.069	0.034
Gear Cutting		
Speed, sfm	128	186
Feed, sec per tooth	2.65	1.82
Extra Costs per Piece		
Material	....	$0.0175
Labor, turning	$0.0051	....
Labor, gear cutting	0.0028	....
Overhead	0.0190	....
Total (extra)	$0.0269	$0.0175
Saving per piece		$0.0094
Saving on 400,000 pieces		$3760

Pinions were automotive differential pinions machined from hot rolled, pickled bar stock. The bar was turned, faced, bored, chamfered and cut off in an automatic bar machine. Gears were cut with a Revacycle gear cutter. Note that the greatest potential in savings arises from savings in overhead.

example deals with an operation where altering the heat treatment to produce a more machinable microstructure resulted in increased cutter life.

Example 424. Elimination of Acicular Ferrite for Increased Cutter Life

Drive pinion forgings of 4027 steel were originally machined in the normalized condition at 156 to 186 Bhn; microstructure consisted of normal ferrite, pearlite and varying amounts of acicular ferrite. A change from normalizing to isothermal annealing eliminated the acicular ferrite and resulted in a hardness range of 143 to 163 Bhn. This change in microstructure did not affect the life of roughing cutters, but the life of finishing cutters was increased from an average of 366 pieces per grind in cutting normalized blanks to 477 pieces per grind for the blanks that were isothermally annealed.

Rolling of Gears

Spur and helical gears are roll formed like splines. See the article on Spline Rolling, page 145. Rolling produces gears 50 times as fast as gear cutting, and with surfaces as smooth as 4 micro-in. Not only does rolling usually need no finish operation, but rolling refines the microstructure of the workpiece.

Production setup usually takes only a set of rolling dies and the proper fixture to equip the rolling machine. By either the infeed (plunge) method or the throughfeed method (explained in the article on Spline Rolling) the rolling dies drive the workpiece between them, forming the teeth by pressure.

Limits. Spur gears can be rolled if they have 18 teeth or more. Fewer teeth cause the work to roll poorly. Helical gears can be rolled with fewer teeth if the helix angle is great enough.

It is usually impractical to roll teeth with pressure angle less than 20°. Lower angles have wide flats at root and crest that need more pressure in rolling, and hinder metal flow. Although 0.005-in.-radius fillets can be rolled, 0.010 in. is a better minimum. For greater accuracy, gear blanks are ground before rolling. Chamfers should be 30° or less.

Steels for gear rolling should not have more than 0.13% sulfur, and, preferably, no lead. (See the article on Spline Rolling, page 145.) Blanks should not be harder than Rockwell C 28.

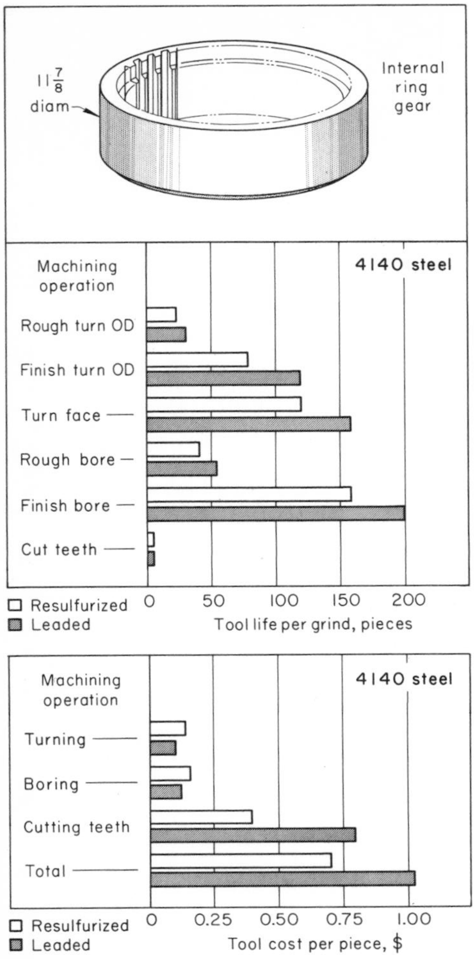

Item	Leaded 4140	Resulfurized 4140
Hardness, Bhn	285-293	321-341
Turning		
Roughing speed, sfm .	180	180
Finishing speed, sfm .	250	250
Facing feed, ipr	0.013	0.013
Turning feed, ipr	0.020	0.020
Boring		
Roughing speed, sfm .	225	225
Finishing speed, sfm .	300	300
Roughing feed, ipr ...	0.0124	0.0124
Finishing feed, ipr ...	0.0167	0.0167
Gear Cutting		
Speed, sfm	14	14
Feed, in. per stroke ..	0.027	0.027
Material and Tool Costs per Piece		
Material (extra)	$0.32	...
Turning	0.104	$0.140
Boring	0.125	0.165
Gear cutting	0.812	0.401
Total	$1.361	$0.706
Saving per piece		$0.655

The internal ring gear was machined from a 42½-lb forging. Dimensional data: 52 teeth, 5/6 pitch, 11⅞-in. OD by 3½ in. wide, 10.105/10.100-in. ID; counterbore on one side, 10.460/10.450-in. diam by 11/16 in. deep. All forgings were hardened and tempered to the hardness indicated. Costs were based on a lot of 500 pieces of each steel.

Gear blanks were turned in a turret lathe, with disposable-insert tools. Carbide tools were used for boring. Gear cutting was done in a 36-in. gear shaper, using a 25-tooth cutter made of T15 high speed steel. In gear cutting, although six pieces were cut for each steel before regrinding the tool, a cost difference was involved since 0.025 in. of stock was removed from the tool in order to sharpen it properly for cutting the leaded steel, and only 0.012 in. stock removal from the tool was required for proper cutting of the resulfurized steel.

Fig. 42. Leaded vs resulfurized 4140 steel for ring gears (Example 423)

Grinding of Gears

*By the ASM Committee on Machining of Gears and the ASM Committee on Grinding**

GEAR TEETH can be produced entirely by grinding, entirely by cutting, or by first cutting and then grinding to the required dimensions. Usually, gear grinding removes only a few thousandths of an inch of metal from precut gears to make accurate teeth for critical applications. Teeth made entirely by grinding are usually only those of fine pitch, for which the total amount of metal removed is small. Grinding of fine-pitch gear teeth from uncut blanks may be less costly than the two-step procedure if there is not much metal to be removed.

The two basic methods for grinding of gear teeth are form grinding (nongenerating) and generation grinding. Either method can be used for spur or helical gears, but the generating method is always used for spiral bevel and hypoid gears. Many varieties of machines have been built especially to grind gears and pinions.

Advantages and Disadvantages. A gear is ground when it is so hard that it cannot be finished by other methods, or when the required accuracy is greater than can be obtained by other methods. If the hardness of the gear does not exceed Rockwell C 40, and its size is within the capacity of the machine, shaving will produce teeth of an accuracy close to that produced by grinding. Gears made of steel harder than Rockwell C 40 are finished by grinding when dimensional accuracy, or correction beyond that feasible by honing, is required.

The major disadvantage of grinding gears is the cost. Usually it is more expensive to grind gears than to cut them, because material is removed in smaller increments in grinding. Ground gears usually are subjected to more inspection than that given cut gears. Magnetic particle inspection of the finished teeth detects fine cracks, and macro-etching with dilute nitric acid detects grinding burn. Both inspection procedures are advised in gear grinding.

A carbide network in carburized steels, or the presence of sufficient retained austenite or of hydrogen in any hardened steel, can increase the susceptibility of the steel to grinding cracks. Therefore, it is necessary to keep these conditions under control. Reducing the heat generated in grinding, by decreasing the rate of stock removal, or by the use of a grinding fluid, can help to eliminate both cracking and burning of the ground surface.

Stock Allowance. When workpieces are prepared for grinding by cutting, the least possible stock should be left to be removed by grinding. This stock should be evenly distributed; otherwise, additional wheel dressings and operating adjustments will be needed, to maintain wheel contour.

In general, it is not practical to remove more than 0.006 in. of stock from each face of the teeth of spur gears up to 7 in. in diameter or 0.008 in. from gears between 7 and 10 in. in diameter. Usually these amounts of stock can be removed in three to five passes. However, the number of passes depends on number of teeth, pressure angle, and required finish. Sometimes nine or ten passes are needed.

Recommended stock allowance for grinding straight bevel teeth is 0.003 in. at the root of the tooth and 0.003 to 0.005 in. on the face of each tooth. Grinding time depends on the amount of stock to be removed. For example, removing 0.0030 to 0.0035 in. of stock from a gear of 4 diametral pitch and 32 teeth takes 30 sec per tooth; a gear of 10 diametral pitch and 32 teeth takes about 20 sec per tooth.

Grinding stock allowance per tooth side for spiral bevel and hypoid gears should be 0.004 to 0.005 in. for gears coarser than 10 diametral pitch, and 0.003 to 0.004 in. for gears of 10 to 20 diametral pitch. Stock allowance at the root of the tooth should be about 0.003 in. for gears up to 20 diametral pitch.

Multiple-Piece Loads. Because gear grinding is an expensive operation, it is important to control the amount of metal to be removed by grinding, to reduce runout and spacing errors, and to try to grind multiple-piece loads.

Multiple-start hobs can cause enough spacing error to make extra grinding passes necessary. Therefore, when a hobbed gear is to be ground, it is better to use a single-thread hob. The multiple-start hob will not save enough to pay for the extra grinding passes. Single-thread hobs are available with nonground class-C tooth forms.

Wheel Specifications. Aluminum oxide wheels are preferred for grinding of teeth in through-hardened and case-hardened steel gears. For nitrided gears, silicon carbide wheels are sometimes used. Grit size, which depends mainly on the type of grinding and the pitch of the gear, ranges from 46 to 100, although somewhat finer grits may be used for form grinding. A grit size of 60 is generally recommended for diametral pitch in the range of 1 to 10; 80 for the range of 8 to 12; and 100 for gears of pitch finer than 14. With crush-formed wheels, grit sizes as small as 400 are used in grinding gears of diametral pitch as fine as 200. For grade (hardness), a range of H to M is generally recommended.

Vitrified-bond wheels are used for most gear-grinding operations because of their rigidity and ability to be diamond dressed with a minimum of diamond wear. Wheel rigidity is particularly important for dish-shaped wheels of the large sizes used in generation grinding. Resinoid-bond cup wheels are satisfactory for generating bevel gear teeth.

Only vitrified-bond wheels are used for forming. They are generally crush trued. The vitrified bond is friable and is rigid enough to support the force of crush truing without deflection.

* For committee lists, see pages 194 and 257.

For a discussion of wheel classification and factors in selection, see the section on Grinding Wheels, pages 257 and 258, in the article "Grinding".

Speed. Most gears are ground with wheel surface speeds of 5500 to 6500 sfm. When very small amounts of stock are being removed, speeds higher than 6500 sfm may be used. When grinding gears with cup-shaped or dish-shaped wheels, slower speeds (450 sfm or less) are common.

Infeed. Pitch of the gear being ground is the main factor influencing optimum infeed. For instance, in plunge grinding of case-hardened or hardened-and-tempered steels (Rockwell C 50 to 62), an infeed of 0.0015 in. per pass is recommended for gears having diametral pitches of 1 to 4. Infeed is reduced to 0.0012 in. per pass for pitches of 5 to 8, and to 0.0005 in. per pass for pitches finer than 8.

Correcting for Distortion in Heat Treating

Most steel gears are heat treated. Because some dimensional change occurs during heat treatment, gear teeth are cut prior to heat treating and ground to finish dimensions after heat treating. The magnitude of the dimensional change depends on the type of heat treatment and the shape of the part. Distortion is greatest when the entire part is heated and quenched. Induction hardening and flame hardening cause small changes, because only the tooth area of the part is heated and quenched.

Usually, nitrided gears do not need to be ground to correct for distortion. When gears are properly nitrided, dimensional change is so small that any correction required can be accomplished by honing or lapping.

When the entire gear is heat treated, dimensional change is less in gears of nearly uniform cross section than in those of intricate design or large variation in cross section. For example, short, stubby pinions are least likely to lose accuracy because of unequal cooling rates during quenching, whereas thin-web gears with heavy-section teeth or heavy rims change the most. The thin-web gears described in the following example are typical of those susceptible to excessive distortion in heat treatment.

Example 425. Grinding Thin-Web Gears to Close Tolerances (Fig. 1)

A standard gear grinder was used to finish the teeth of a helical gear in the setup shown in Fig. 1. Excessive distortion resulted during heat treating, because of the heaviness of the rim in proportion to the web thickness. Close tolerances made grinding mandatory.

The clamping arrangement shown in Fig. 1 adequately supported the rim during grinding. More information on the gear, grinding wheel and grinding operation is given in the table accompanying Fig. 1.

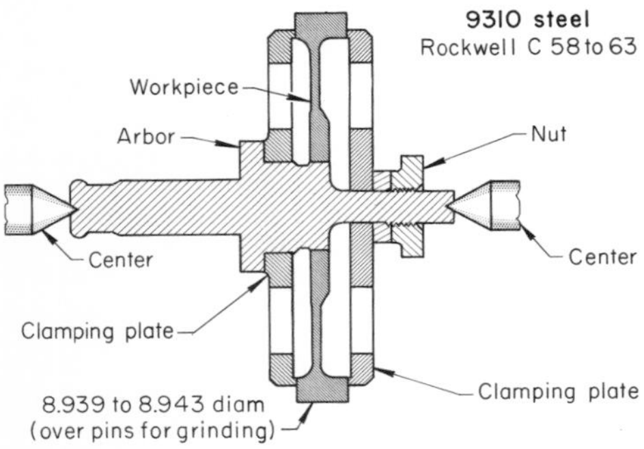

Gear Details

Type	Helical
Number of teeth	66
Pitch diameter	8.6373 in.
Diametral pitch	9.8539
Helix angle	39° 9′ 9″
Pressure angle	14° 30′
Tolerances:	
Involute error	0.0007 in.
Lead error	0.0007 in.
Pitch variation	Within 0.0003 in.
Index error	0.0015 in.

Grinding Wheel

Classification	A-150-L9-V
Size	13¾-in. OD, 6.3-in. ID, 3⁵⁄₁₆-in. width

Operating Conditions

Speed	1650 rpm (6000 sfm)
Depth of feed per pass	0.0016 in.
Axial feed	0.060 to 0.020 in.
Grinding fluid	General-purpose grinding oil
Time per piece	17.04 min

Fig. 1. Setup for grinding a thin-web gear. Special clamping supported the heavy rim during grinding. (Example 425)

The use of a heat treating procedure that allows maximum dimensional control, such as placing the heated part in a fixture for quenching, helps reduce the amount of grinding, and sometimes has eliminated the need for grinding. However, some dimensional changes occur during heat treatment regardless of special techniques. The following example is typical of a gear that required grinding even though it had been quenched in a die to control distortion.

Example 426. Grinding Die-Quenched Gears (Fig. 2)

The gear teeth for the part illustrated in Fig. 2 were cut by hobbing, after which they were carburized and quenched in a die to minimize distortion. However, this practice did not prevent distortion beyond tolerance, and lightening holes caused a scalloping of the pitch line by approximately 0.004 in. TIR. Therefore, grinding was necessary. No grinding burns or cracks could be accepted.

Conditions of the grinding operation are given in the table with Fig. 2. Damper plates prevented excessive vibration of the gear during grinding, thereby reducing the likelihood of both burns and cracks.

Form Grinding

Usually, form grinding consists of passing a formed wheel through a tooth space to grind to root depth the left side of one tooth and the right side of the next tooth at the same time (see modifications in Fig. 3). When straight teeth are ground, as in spur gears, the workpiece is held in a fixed radial position during a pass. For helical gears, however, the workpiece must be rotated so that the helix will be followed as the wheel passes through the tooth space. A lead bar having the same lead as the helix controls rotation during grinding.

When the wheel pass through a tooth space is completed, the workpiece is indexed to the next position and the procedure is repeated. The indexing mechanism usually consists of an index plate with the same number of spaces as the workpiece. Control of tooth spacing errors depends primarily on the accuracy of this plate.

Spur gears are ground with (*a*) a single straight wheel with a periphery that has been formed to produce the space between teeth, (*b*) a single wheel with several ribs that grind more than one tooth space during each wheel pass, or (*c*) two single-ribbed wheels (see Fig. 3). Helical gears are ground with a formed, single straight wheel. Bevel gears are form ground with a cup-shaped wheel.

Form grinding can be used also to finish grind precut threads of worms:

Example 427. Worms Finished by Form Grinding (Table 1)

A thread grinder with a formed wheel was used to grind the worm shown in Table 1. The worm was cut and the workpiece was heat treated to the required hardness. The worm was then ground to produce final form and tolerance requirements. A vitrified-bond aluminum oxide wheel was used. Worm details and operating conditions are given in Table 1.

Wheels for form grinding are usually less than 6 in. in diameter; wheel thickness depends on the size of the teeth to be ground. Wheels of larger diameter may be used, but the smaller wheels are more common because they need less clearance in finishing a gear that is close to a larger gear or to a shoulder. Also, smaller wheels are better for grinding internal gears.

Standard gear grinding machines are available for form grinding spur gears ranging from a minimum root diameter of ¾ in. to an outside diameter of

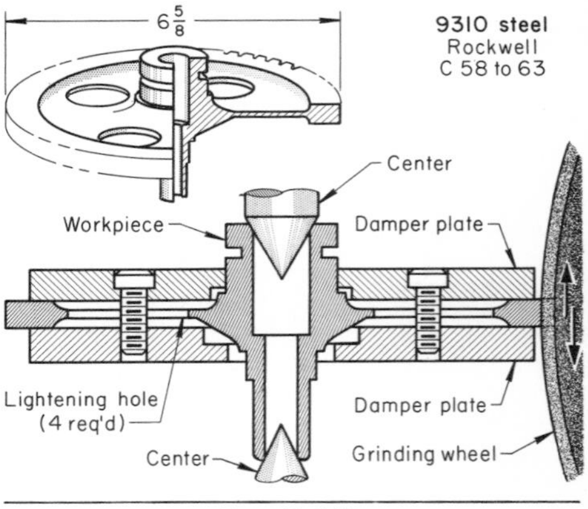

Gear Details

Type	Involute spur
Number of teeth	63
Diametral pitch	12
Pressure angle	20°
Tolerance:	
Involute error	0.0002 in.
Tooth-to-tooth spacing	Within 0.0002 in.
Spacing between any three adjacent teeth	Within 0.0005 in.
Finish required, involute sides and root fillet	32 micro-in. max

Grinding Wheel

Classification	As-180-H9-V
Size	13¾-in. OD
Form	Diamond dressed

Operating Conditions

Machine	Gear grinding, rack-type
Speed	1850 rpm (6650 sfm)
Infeed per pass:	
Roughing	0.0012 in.
Finishing	0.0008 in.
Axial feed:	
Roughing	0.035 in.
Finishing	0.016 in.
Grinding fluid	Sulfurized grinding oil
Time per piece	12 min

Fig. 2. Setup for grinding a thin-web gear. Damper plates prevent excessive vibration. (Example 426)

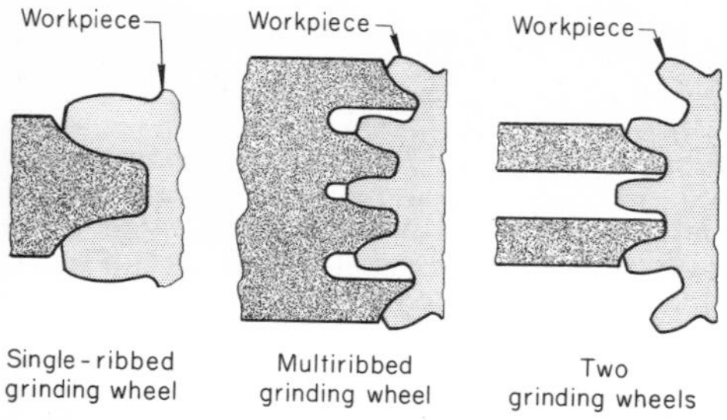

Fig. 3. Relations of wheel and workpiece in form grinding of spur gears (top views)

36 in. Special machines have been built to grind spur gears 8 ft in diameter. Machines are available that are capable of form grinding external helical gears up to 18 in. in diameter.

Generation Grinding

There are four methods of generating gear teeth by grinding. Each method is identified by the type of wheel used: Straight, cup-shaped, dish-shaped, and rack-tooth worm wheels.

Straight Wheels. In this method, a straight wheel beveled on both sides reciprocates across the periphery of the workpiece as the workpiece rolls under it in a direction perpendicular to its reciprocating motion. The reciprocating action of the wheel is similar to that of a reciprocating gear cutter. This grinding method can be used to generate the teeth of spur gears.

Cup-Shaped Wheels. In this method, the gear tooth is rolled against a cup-shaped wheel, the sides of which are beveled to an angle equal to the pressure angle required on the teeth. During grinding, the wheel moves in a straight line along the length of the tooth. The sides of the wheel simultaneously grind adjacent sides of two teeth.

A master gear and rack control the generating motion and indexing of the workpiece. The master gear may have the same pitch and number of teeth as the workpiece. However, in many instances, especially for gears of smaller size, the master gear will have more teeth than the work gear. The ratio between the number of teeth in master and work gears must be a multiple of two; that is, the master gear will have two, four or six times as many teeth as the work gear. In the setup, the master gear is marked for the tooth spacing in the work gear and indexed accordingly.

Teeth can be generated by grinding with a cup-shaped wheel on spur and helical gears up to 18 in. in pitch diameter. However, when helical gears are being ground, the master gear and rack must match the pitch in the plane of rotation of the gear to be ground. With this grinding method, it is impractical to generate tip and root reliefs.

Dish-Shaped Wheels. This method uses two dish-shaped grinding wheels, which may be inclined 15° or 20°, or may be parallel in a vertical position (0°), as shown in Table 2.

Sometimes, the generating motion is controlled by steel bands that are fastened to a pitch block of the same diameter as the pitch circle of the workpiece minus the thickness of the rolling bands. Modification of the shape of the tip and root of the teeth can be made by using a cam to change the normal generating motion.

Usually an index plate similar to that used in form grinding indexes the workpiece if a pitch block is used. Large machines use worm gearing for indexing. Gears are ground dry, and machines incorporate a device depending on a feeler diamond to compensate for wheel wear. Machines are available for grinding spur and helical gears ranging from 1 to 142 in. in diameter with diametral pitch 2 to 17 by this method.

When the wheels are in the 15° or 20° position, as in sketch (a) in Table 2, their active faces rotate in planes forming an acute angle. In this position, the wheels simulate the tooth flanks of a rack that the workpiece engages during the rolling-generating motion. The inclination of the grinding wheels to the vertical in the pitch plane generally equals the pressure angle of the gear to be ground (usually 15° or 20°). Under these conditions, the generating circle coincides with the pitch circle of the gear. This method produces a criss-cross pattern of grooves (lay of surface roughness) and has been widely used because machine settings are simple and the desired pressure angle is accurately and simply set by adjusting the inclination angles of the wheels.

The 15° or 20° wheel position is not suitable for making longitudinal modifications. Although the two simultaneous points of contact between the grinding wheels and the respective tooth flanks move along the tooth-form involutes during each transverse rolling-generating motion, the locations of these points relative to each other change constantly.

For helical gears this differential position applies not only along the involutes, but also to the position in the longitudinal tooth direction. Therefore, it would be impractical to try to coordinate modification impulses of the grinding wheel and the generating or feed motion to make longitudinal modifications.

In a newer method, the angle between the two wheels is 0°, as shown in sketch (b) in Table 2. The active surfaces of the wheels are parallel and face each other. Because the grinding pressure angle is 0° and corresponds to the pressure angle on the base circle,

Table 1. Finishing a Worm by Form Grinding (Example 427)

Worm Details	
Class	Commercial, type 3
Lead angle, left hand	43° 34′
Normal pitch	0.0813 in.
Addendum	0.0259 in.
Center distance	0.9904 in.
Whole depth	0.0589 in.
Number of threads	9
Linear pitch	0.1122 in.
Lead	1.0098 in.
Theoretical pitch diameter	0.338 in.
Actual pitch diameter	0.3352 in.
Outside diameter	0.3848 to 0.3868 in.
Width of flat at bottom	0.0165 in.
Wire diameter	0.0444 in.
Three-wire diameter	0.3967 to 0.3947 in.
Pressure angle in normal plane	20°
Index error	0.001 in.
Tolerance on pitch diameter	0.002 in.
Grinding Wheel	
Classification	A_s-100-K-V
Size	18-in. OD, 9-in. ID, ⅝-in. width
Operating Conditions	
Wheel speed	2000 rpm (9432 sfm)
Work-rotation speed	4 rpm
Total metal removed	0.122 in.
Surface finish of tooth contact area	16 micro-in.
Grinding fluid	Thread grinding oil
Wheel life per dressing (a)	3 pieces
Production rate	25 pieces per hour
Labor cost at \$3.50 per hour	\$0.14 per piece

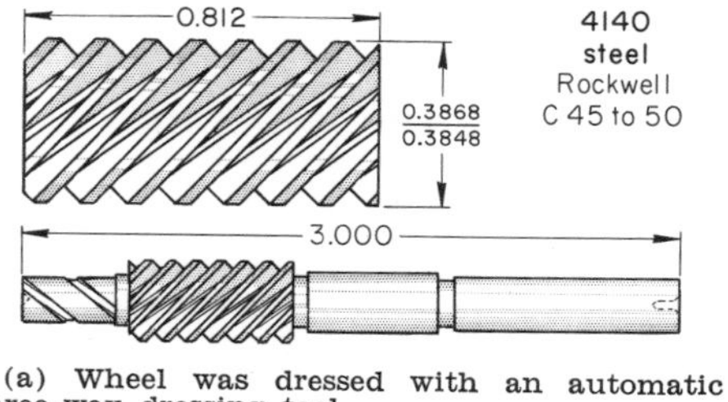

(a) Wheel was dressed with an automatic three-way dressing tool.

Table 2. Grinding of Gears With Dish-Shaped Wheels in the 0° Position
(Details for seven different spur and helical gears that had been carburized and hardened)

Gear Details							
Diametral pitch	10	5	4	3	5	3	2.75
Module	2.5	5	6	8	5	8	9.5
Number of teeth	23	44	80	80	120	100	379
Face width, in.	2.2	2.4	4.7	4.7	11.8	7.1	16.5
Tip diameter, in.	2.8	9.2	19.8	25.7	24.8	32.6	132
Pressure angle	15°	20°	20°	20°	20°	15°	15°
Helix angle	26°	20°	10°	10°	15°	0°	7°
Grinding allowance per flank, in.	0.006	0.007	0.008	0.009	0.007	0.009	0.010
Gearing quality	S20	S30	S20	S20	S10	S30	S20
Grinding Time per Piece							
Roughing time, hr	0.17	0.77	4.3	6.6	21.9	32.6	475
Finishing time, hr	0.14	0.35	1.8	2.5	9.6	3.4	56
Total time, hr	0.31	1.12	6.1	9.1	31.5	36.0	531

SOURCE OF DATA: Maag Gear Book, Maag, Zurich (1963)

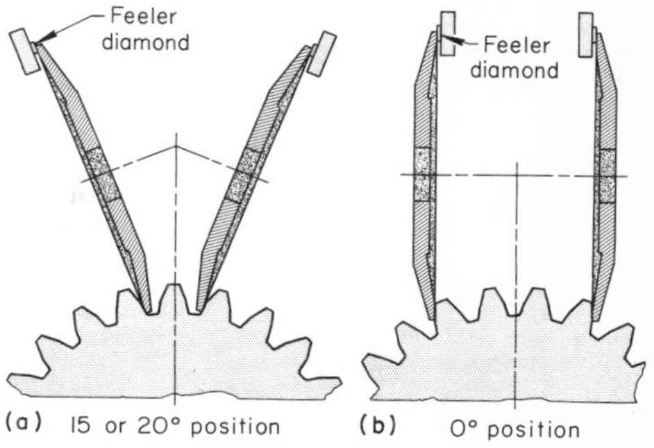

the generating motion is obtained by rolling on the base circle.

Advantages of grinding gears in the 0° position over the 15° or 20° position are: (*a*) greater production without sacrifice in quality, and (*b*) ability to grind more exacting flank profiles and make longitudinal modifications. The main disadvantage is the lack of uniform transition between the flank and the tooth root, which is objectionable in some gearing applications. Approximate times required for grinding of teeth in seven different spur gears, using dish-shaped wheels in the 0° position are given in Table 2.

Rack-Tooth Worm Wheels. The wheel used in this method of generating gear teeth is crush trued into the shape of a rack-tooth worm. Grinding a gear by this method is illustrated in Fig. 4.

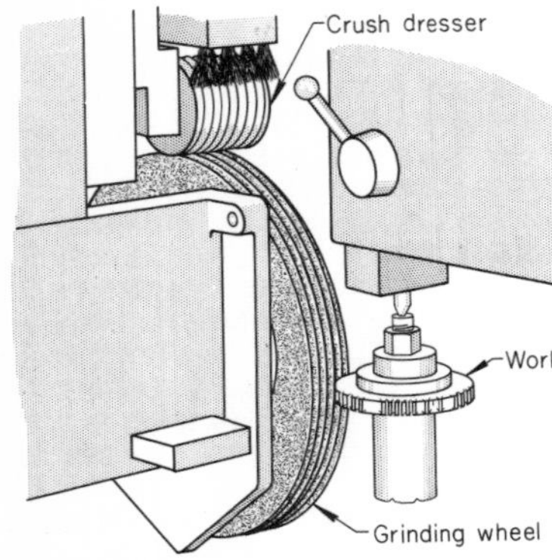

Fig. 4. Generation grinding with a rack-tooth worm wheel

The workpiece is mounted vertically on an arbor or in a fixture that fits between the centers of the machine. For grinding helical gears, the work-holding slide of the machine is set at an angle equal to the helix angle required on the gear. The workpiece is rotated by a motor that is synchronized with the wheel motor.

The gear may be ground with a small portion of the length of the grinding worm wheel. Generation takes place as a result of rotating the worm wheel and gear in mesh as the wheel is traversed axially across the gear face.

In general, a soft wheel is used to prevent burning the hardened teeth, but this results in greater wheel breakdown and loss of correct tooth profile. To continue using a fresh unbroken part of the wheel, the work is fed in a direction parallel to the axis of the worm. This type of wheel was used in one application to grind the teeth of a high-speed pinion, as indicated in the following example.

Example 428. Rack-Tooth Worm Wheel Grinding of Aircraft Pinions (Fig. 5)

The gear shown in Fig. 5 is a high-speed aircraft pinion. It was ground after nitriding (0.010 to 0.015-in. case depth). A soft wheel was used to prevent burning the hardened teeth. More information on this operation is tabulated below Fig. 5. Grinding worm wheel and the workpiece were driven by synchronized motors. Diamonds for dressing were of special design and dressed the wheel in a manner similar to cutting a thread with a single-point tool. The operation was performed in a gear grinding machine having a capacity range of 6 to 48 diametral pitch.

Usually nitrided teeth are not ground because, if properly done, the nitriding process causes only a small dimensional change. Also, grinding may remove most of the beneficial effect of nitriding. In this application, however, the required high degree of accuracy necessitated grinding after nitriding.

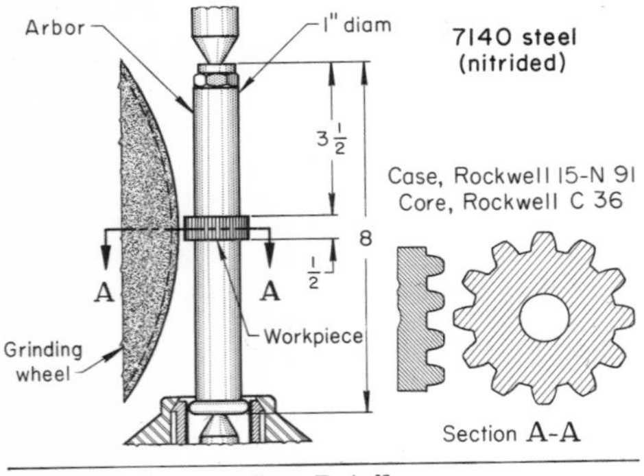

Gear Details

Type	Spur
Number of teeth	12
Diametral pitch	16
Pressure angle	20°
Tolerance:	
Outside diam	1.1723 to 1.1753 in. over wires
Involute error	0.0002 in.
Composite error (tooth-to-tooth)	0.0004 in.
Composite error (total)	0.001 in.
Surface finish	16 micro-in.

Grinding Wheel

Classification	A_s-120-L9-V
Size	13¾-in. OD, 6.3-in. ID, 2 7/16-in. width

Operating Conditions

Wheel speed	1800 rpm (6480 sfm) (a)
Work-rotation speed	152 rpm (45 sfm)
Infeed of wheel	0.0015 in. per pass(b)
Total metal removed	0.015 to 0.018 in.(c)
Grinding fluid	Soluble oil
Setup time	4 hr(d)
Wheel life per dressing	45 pieces
Production rate	10.52 pieces per hour
Wheel cost per gear	$0.0013
Dressing cost per gear	$0.0025

(a) Dressed at 60 rpm. (b) A pass is a complete revolution of the gear, plus its width. The wheel passed through the gear at a rate of 0.054 in. per revolution of the gear arbor. (c) Measured over wires. (d) Includes changing wheels.

Fig. 5. Grinding an aircraft pinion by the worm wheel method (Example 428)

Success in gear grinding with a grinding worm wheel depends greatly on careful dressing of the wheel to the required contour and on synchronization of the workpiece rotation with the rotation of the worm wheel. Special diamond wheel dressers are required. The accuracy of the diamond and of the dressing operation determine to a great extent the quality of gear teeth produced.

Wheels are about 2 in. wide, and they can be rough formed by crushing and finished to the proper pressure angle by diamond dressing. Some machines use wheels that have been finish dressed by crushing only. Because a considerable amount of time is required to crush true a new wheel, it is advisable to stock wheels for each pitch and pressure angle required. In diamond dressing, two diamonds are needed to dress both sides of the thread at the same time. Modifications in the gear tooth design can be made easily by lapping the tip of the dressing diamond.

Spur gears and helical gears up to 20 in. in diameter can be ground in machines using a threaded wheel. Although gears of fine pitch can be ground from a solid gear blank, gear teeth with diametral pitch of 24 or coarser should be cut prior to grinding.

The advantages of gear grinding with a threaded wheel are accuracy, speed, and ease of incorporating changes in tooth design. Machines also are available that crown the gear teeth during grinding. However, this type of grinder is complicated and sensitive, and a considerable amount of skill by the operator is required.

Gear grinding with a threaded wheel is 6 to 30 times as fast as the other methods discussed in this article. The next two examples compare speed of grinding of gear teeth by generating with a worm wheel and by form grinding with a single straight wheel.

Examples 429 and 430. Generating vs Form Grinding of Spur Gears

Example 429 (Table 3). Intermediate spur gears, cut from blanks of hot rolled 1118 steel bar 6 in. in diameter, were case hardened to Rockwell C 56 to 62 and finish ground in a machine using a single straight wheel for form grinding each tooth. When the method of grinding was changed to generation of the tooth contour by the use of a worm wheel, production rate was tripled and costs were reduced by 63%.

The machine for generation grinding had a capacity of 11 in. OD, and was equipped with a diamond lapper, a wheel balancer, and dressers for the profile, top and root contours of the grinding wheel. Operating and cost details for grinding two pieces per load by each method, gear specifications, and processing conditions are shown in Table 3.

Example 430 (Table 4). Spur gears cut from forged 4145 steel were hardened to Rockwell C 50 to 55 prior to grinding. Originally the parts were form ground. Subsequently, the method was changed to generating the tooth contour with a worm grinding wheel. This resulted in a higher production rate and a cost reduction of 64%.

Generation grinding was done in the same equipment used for the spur gears discussed in Example 429. Details comparing the generating and the form grinding are given in Table 4. Processing conditions for both methods were

Table 3. Generation vs Form Grinding of Intermediate Spur Gears (Example 429)

Gear Details

Type	Intermediate spur
Steel	1118, at Rockwell C 56 to 62
Number of teeth	46
Diametral pitch	8
Pressure angle	20°
Size	6-in. OD, ¾-in. width
Pin measurements:	
After cutting	6.0781 to 6.0818 in.
After grinding	6.0533 to 6.0570 in.
Tolerances:	
Runout error	0.001 in.
Pitch variation	0.0003 in.
Profile error	0.0004 in.
Accumulated errors	0.001 in.
Surface finish	25 micro-in. max

Grinding Comparison

	Generation grinding	Form grinding
Setup time, hr	2.30(a)	1.30
Time per piece, hr	0.185	0.600
Production, pieces/hr(b)	5½	1⅔
Cost per piece	$0.92(c)	$2.50(c)

Processing Details

Wheel classification	A-180-K6-V
Wheel size	13¾-in. OD, 2 7/16-in. width
Wheel speed	1800 rpm (6500 sfm)
Total metal removed	0.005 in.(d)
Grinding fluid	Oil
Wheel life	4525 loads(e)
Wheel cost per piece	$0.011(f)

(a) Includes prorated use of all auxiliary equipment. (b) Based on grinding two pieces per load. (c) Based on amortizing setup time over 50 pieces and on standard cost of $4 per hour. (d) Stock removed per tooth side. (e) Number of two-piece loads based on average grinding time of 25 min per load. (f) Based on wheel cost of $95, actual grinding time of 22.20 min per load, and wheel life of 1675 hr.

Table 4. Generation vs Form Grinding of Alloy Steel Spur Gears (Example 430)

Gear Details

Type	Spur
Steel	4145, at Rockwell C 50 to 55
Number of teeth	58
Diametral pitch	10
Pressure angle	20°
Size	6-in. OD, ¾-in. width
Pin measurements:	
After cutting	6.0688 to 6.0725 in.
After grinding	6.0433 to 6.0470 in.
Tolerances:	
Runout error	0.001 in.
Pitch variation	0.0003 in.
Profile error	0.0004 in.
Accumulated errors	0.001 in.
Surface finish	25 micro-in. max

Grinding Comparison

	Generation grinding	Form grinding
Setup time, hr	2.30(a)	1.30
Time per piece, hr	0.230	0.750
Production, pieces/hr(b)	4⅓	1⅓
Cost per piece	$1.11(c)	$3.10(c)

(a) Includes prorated use of all auxiliary equipment. (b) Based on grinding of two pieces per load. (c) Based on amortizing setup time over 50 pieces and standard cost of $4 per hour.

the same as those shown in Table 3, except that useful wheel life for the generated worm was 2080 hr of production based on a grinding time of 27.60 min for each load of two pieces.

Grinding of Bevel Gears

When accuracy is required, grinding is the most economical method for finishing teeth as coarse as 1.5 diametral pitch on straight bevel, spiral bevel, and hypoid gears. With good grinding practice, by the methods already described, bevel and hypoid gears can be finished with a tooth-to-tooth spacing accurate within 0.0002 in., eccentricity with bore or shaft within 0.00025 in., as little backlash as 0.001 to 0.002 in., and a surface finish of 15 to 30 micro-in.

In general, any bevel or hypoid gear that is cut with a circular cutter can be ground with a wheel of similar shape and grinding action, except nongenerated gears that are cut with a face mill.

Nongenerated (Formed) Gears. The gear teeth are ground by a cup-shaped wheel that simultaneously grinds the facing sides and root of adjacent teeth. There is no generating motion, and the wheel produces a curved tooth whose sides have a straight profile. Three or four revolutions of the workpiece are required for the complete finish grinding of a bevel gear. A predetermined amount of stock is removed with each revolution of the workpiece. The grinding wheel makes line contact with the tooth being ground.

An A_s-46-J-V wheel commonly is used to grind gears ranging from 2 to 10 diametral pitch. Wheel speed ranges from 3800 to 4500 sfm. The wheel is dressed automatically at predetermined intervals between grinds.

This method is applicable for finishing hypoid and spiral gears, and special spiral gears that have a 0° mean spiral angle.

Generated Gears. Spiral bevel and hypoid gears are ground with a cup-shaped wheel. The grinding wheel is dressed to produce a smooth blend of flank and root profile. The curved profile of the tooth is generated by relative rolling motion between the grinding wheel and the workpiece.

Vitrified-bond and resinoid-bond aluminum oxide cup-shaped wheels are used for spiral bevel and hypoid gears. Typical wheel classifications are A_s-60-J-V and A_t-60-M-B. Wheel speed ranges from 3800 to 4500 sfm.

Generating gear teeth with a cup-shaped wheel produces spiral bevel gears with highly accurate tooth spacing, concentricity and profile shape. Following is an example of a typical application of this grinding method.

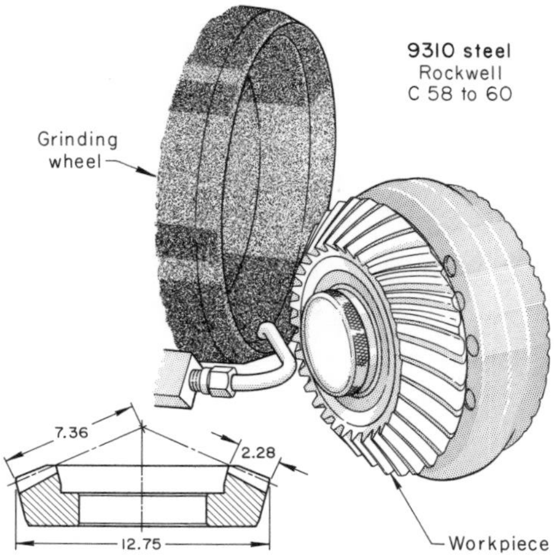

Gear Details

Type	Spiral bevel (octoid)
Number of teeth	51
Diametral pitch	4
Helix angle	30°
Whole depth	0.475 in.
Tolerance, tooth-to-tooth	0.0003 in.
Surface finish	25 to 30 micro-in.

Grinding Wheel

Type	Cup(a)
Classification	A_s-54-J8-V
Size	12-in. OD

Operating Conditions

Wheel speed	1200 rpm (3770 sfm)
Feed	3.2 sec per tooth(b)
Grinding fluid	Straight mineral oil (no active sulfur)
Production rate	1.7 pieces per hour(c)

(a) Straight-angled grinding area. (b) Twelve passes per tooth. (c) At 100% efficiency.

Fig. 6. Grinding a spiral bevel gear (Example 431)

Example 431. Grinding Spiral Bevel Gears With a Cup-Shaped Wheel (Fig. 6)

The spiral bevel gear illustrated in Fig. 6 was carburized, hardened and tempered before being ground by the generation method with a cup-shaped wheel. An automatic wet-type 5-hp machine designed for grinding spiral bevel, Zerol and hypoid gears was used for this application. Additional manufacturing information is given in the table with Fig. 6.

Grinding Fluids

Use of a grinding fluid is generally recommended for grinding of steel gears. A grinding fluid prolongs wheel life between dressings, flushes away chips, and improves gear tooth finish. Flooding the work surface minimizes the possibility of burning the surfaces of gear teeth. Complete absence of grinding burn is essential for high-quality gears. Virtually all of the grinding fluids listed on pages 258 and 259 in the article "Grinding" have been used successfully for grinding of gears.

In many critical gear-grinding applications, mineral-base sulfochlorinated or sulfurized oils are used (Examples 426 and 432 in this article). Plain soluble-oil emulsions have proved satisfactory for many gear-grinding applications (Example 428). Chemical solutions have also been satisfactory.

Surface Finish

Grinding produces a finish unlike that produced by any other process. Whether this finish is more desirable than some other depends on the service requirements of the gear. In some applications, a gear with a ground finish operates more quietly, even though grinding has not improved dimensional accuracy of the product. The effect of a ground finish, in comparison with other finishes, on lubrication of gears has not been precisely evaluated.

The surface finish of ground gears usually ranges from 15 to 32 micro-in. Under conditions of unusually good control, a surface finish of 10 micro-in. or better can be produced. Sometimes surface finish becomes the major consideration in determining whether a gear shall be ground. In the following example, grinding had the dual purpose of correcting dimensional change from heat treating and of producing a fine surface finish.

Example 432. Grinding to Produce a Finish of 10 Micro-In. (Fig. 7)

The gear shown in Fig. 7 was form ground to fall within stringent dimensional tolerances and to gain a required surface finish of 10 micro-in. An acceptable product could not be made by any other method. Data on gear design and processing are given in the table accompanying Fig. 7.

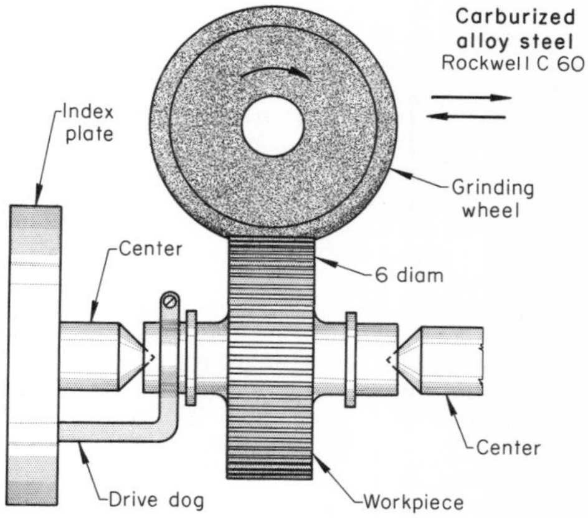

Gear Details

Type	Modified involute spur (−0.0012 in. at tip; + 0.0002 in. at pitch diam)
Number of teeth	60
Diametral pitch	10
Addendum	0.1 in. +0.0000, −0.0025 in.
Arc tooth thickness	0.157 in. +0.000, −0.002 in.
Finish required on teeth	12 micro-in. max

Grinding Wheel

Classification	A_s-60-I12-V
Size	6-in. OD, ½-in. width
Form	Diamond dressed to modified involute

Operating Conditions

Speed	200 rpm (3142 sfm)
Feed (down)	0.002 in. per revolution of gear(a)
Grinding fluid	Gear-grinding oil
Time per piece	12 min

(a) Wheel was allowed to spark out on final feed. It was dresed before the final feed.

Fig. 7. Grinding a spur gear to 10-micro-in. finish (Example 432)

Contour Band Sawing

*By the ASM Committee on Band Sawing**

CONTOUR band sawing is a process for cutting metal and other materials by means of a power-driven saw band, to produce workpieces of desired contour. The process employs a machine with a C-shaped, open-yoke frame and a continuous saw band that moves vertically in cutting. Although this equipment can do cutoff operations, it is seldom used for this purpose. Cutoff band saws are usually horizontal (see "Cutoff Band Sawing", page 224).

Capabilities and Limitations

Because contour sawing requires an open-yoke frame, clearance between workpiece and frame imposes a size limitation. Workpiece height or thickness can be as much as 55 in., which is the maximum capacity between the guides of standard machines. However, special machines have been built with yoke height up to 120 in.

The saw band must be thin enough to bend over the driving wheel and idler wheel, and yet have enough thickness and beam strength to withstand the pressures that are exerted during cutting. In all types of band sawing, the horsepower rating of the machine places a limit on the cutting rate and on the thickness and hardness of metal that can be cut.

Convex radii of less than 1/16 in. can be cut in a single pass using commercially available bands, thus making it possible to produce complex contours in one straightforward machining operation. To produce internal contours, the ends of the saw band are welded together after the band has been inserted through a hole provided in the workpiece for this purpose.

Dimensional tolerances that can be maintained in contour band sawing depend greatly on the dexterity of the operator. Other factors that affect dimensional accuracy are the suitability of the setup, tooling and machining conditions, and the availability of accessories, such as servo controls, intended to promote speed and accuracy. A servo-controlled contour sawing attachment maintains a constant feed force and, by lessening the effort required of the operator, permits him to concentrate more fully on following the line to be cut, thus increasing over-all accuracy. Under the best conditions, a skillful operator with the aid of a magnifying glass can follow a contour to within ±0.010 or ±0.015 in. A tolerance of ±1/32 in. is more nearly typical of production work. When using a power table for ordinary work thicknesses, flatness of the cut surface can be held to 0.004 in. per inch of work thickness or per inch of cut length.

Surface finish also varies with operator skill, equipment and operating conditions. A surface roughness of 200 to 300 micro-in. results under ordinary production conditions. With the use of a fine-pitch blade, high band speed, and low feed force, a finish of 60 to 200 micro-in. can be produced, and a surface roughness as low as 25 micro-in. has been obtained under specially controlled conditions.

Applications. The two examples that follow illustrate the types of contours that can be cut in contour sawing and compare dimensional tolerances and production rates with those obtained when other machining processes were employed to produce identical parts (see Examples 443 to 446 also). Another large shape, which was contour band sawed from an aluminum alloy billet, is described in Example 922, in the article on Machining of Aluminum Alloys.

Example 433. Four-Inch-Thick Low-Alloy Steel (Fig. 1)

The part shown at the top in Fig. 1 was machined from a square block of 4340 steel (230 to 250 Bhn) that measured 24 by 24 by 4 in. and weighed approximately 700 lb. Originally, the shape was produced by making 26 cuts with a cutoff band saw to rough the contour and then smoothing the sawed surfaces in a milling machine. By this method, 15 hr of machining time was required to complete one part. A contour band saw, cutting at a rate of 2.5 sq in. per min, machined the same contour in 3 hr and 20 min. Total cutting area was 500 sq in.

The contour sawing was done with a high speed steel band (regular tooth form, raker set, 6-pitch, 1 in. wide, 0.042 in. thick), using a heavy-duty soluble-oil cutting fluid. The dimensional tolerance maintained by milling was ±0.005 in.; by contour sawing, ±1/32 in.

Example 434. Four-Inch-Thick 1040 Steel Blocks (Fig. 1)

Carbon steel (1040) drop-hammer blocks and tooling plates, such as that shown at the bottom in Fig. 1, were rough milled in approximately 12 hr. These parts were machined from slabs measuring 50 by 6 by 4 in. and weighing 360 lb. Similar blocks were produced by conventional contour band sawing in 8 hr, using standard equipment. However, a radial-arm contour band saw completed the machining operation in 46 min. The total area cut was 280 sq in.

In both types of contour sawing equipment, a high speed steel band (hook tooth form, 4-pitch, 1 in. wide) was used. Cutting fluid was an emulsion of soluble oil and water.

Types of Machines

Contour band sawing is done on vertical machines that are available in a wide range of sizes and modifications. There are three general types: fixed-table, power-feed-table, and radial-arm.

Fixed-Table and Power-Table Machines. With a fixed-table machine, work must be fed by hand. Power-table machines, usually heavier than fixed-table machines, are equipped with a worktable that pushes the work into the saw band, thus relieving the operator of pushing or manual feeding. These machines have enough power to use high speed steel bands, whereas fixed-table machines usually employ a lower cutting rate and bands of carbon steel.

Radial-arm machines are designed for handling large, heavy workpieces. The articulated structure of the equipment provides capability for unlimited cutting within a crescent-shaped area. The machine shown in Fig. 2 has a cutting crescent area of 99 sq ft and consists of three major members, of which two are capable of movement and the third is stationary. The two moving members, an intermediate arm and a cutting yoke, permit the cutting edge of the saw frame to move anywhere within the prescribed area, while the workpiece — mounted on a worktable that can be raised or lowered — remains stationary. The longest straight cuts that can be made on this particular machine are 209 in. across the crescent and 59 in. to the depth of the crescent, as shown by the shaded portion of the cutting-area diagram in Fig. 2.

Fixtures and Attachments

Much of the work done on contour band saws requires a device to hold or guide the workpiece. Because the downward cutting force of the saw band assists in holding the workpiece to the table, simple, standard attachments are usually adequate. When they are not, special fixtures must be employed.

A work-squaring bar is a simple attachment that serves as a guide in making straight-line cuts. It consists of a movable workstop that is held securely to a backup bar by means of a cam lock. The backup bar acts as prime

*KENNETH F. PACKER, *Chairman*, Packer Consulting Associates; C. C. BRUMFIELD, General Foreman of Machine Shops, ACF Industries, Inc.; GEORGE J. DANIS, Chief Metallurgist, Peninsular Steel Corp.; MARVIN R. ELENBAAS, President and General Manager, Tannewitz Works, Inc.

SALVATORE FIORILLO, Machine Tool Engineer, Grumman Aircraft Engineering Corp.; G. M. HESS, Vice-President, Armstrong-Blum Mfg. Co.; GEORGE KEYES, Metal Band Saw Product Manager, Simonds Saw and Steel Co.; GEORGE W. LYMAN, Chief Engineer, Henry G. Thompson & Son Co.; ROY MOISAN, Building and Equipment Manager, C. A. Roberts Co.; GEORGE RIENERTH, Products Manager, National Acme Co.

G. SCHISSLER, Industrial Engineer, Robbins & Myers, Inc.; CHARLES C. SCHOMP, Supervisor Toolmaker, Apprentice School, Picatinny Arsenal; GEORGE H. SHEPPARD, Director, Demonstration-Test Center, DoAll Co.; ARNE B. THOMPSON, Mfg. Engineering Manager, Eaton Yale & Towne, Inc.; GRANVILLE WARD, Materials Superintendent, Halliburton Co.

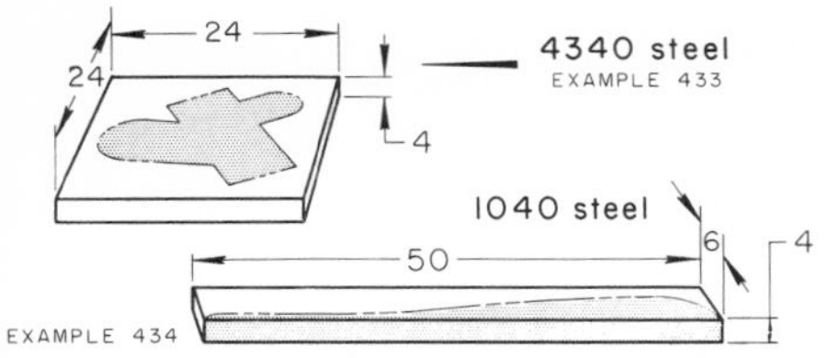

Fig. 1. Shapes that represent the capabilities of contour band sawing for production machining (Examples 433 and 434)

locator and is attached to T-slots in the worktable by means of T-nuts and socket-head screws. The movable workstop slides along the calibrated backup bar and can be clamped to it at any point with the cam-locking lever.

Contour sawing attachments provide additional capability for holding and rotating the work and for work or table feed.

Heavy workpieces are usually handled with table feed and, to minimize friction, are supported on ball transfer strips on the movable table (Fig. 3). The sprocket is mounted on an extension arm that is clamped to the movable table, and the roller chain feeds the workpiece into the saw band. Servo control on the hydraulic feed system maintains feed force constant at the value selected for the job, regardless of variation in radius of cut, work thickness, work hardness, or other factors. Turning the hand control wheel rotates the sprocket and pulls the chain to rotate the workpiece as needed to follow the contour of the cut. Three positions of a foot switch give forward or reverse feed or stop.

Light workpieces rest directly on the table and can be manipulated and fed without the use of table feed. Instead, the workpiece is fed into the saw band by a roller chain partly wrapped around the workpiece (or around a workholding jaw containing the workpiece). In this arrangement, the table-feed piston is disconnected from the table and exerts the feed force against a movable extension arm that holds the sprocket. Servo control of hydraulic feed pressure can be used, as described above, but it is needed less often than for cutting heavy workpieces. Turning the hand control wheel rotates the workpiece as desired. On fixed-table machines, the feed force can be supplied by weights attached to the chain or by other means, and the workholding jaw can be rotated manually by handles attached to each end.

Examples 437 through 441 show improvements in production time resulting from the use of servo-controlled feed mechanisms.

Welders. Most contour band sawing machines are equipped with built-in resistance-type butt welders, to make possible the cutting of internal contours. The saw band is cut to length, threaded through a hole drilled in the workpiece for this purpose, and welded into a continuous band. The weld is annealed and ground, and the band is placed on the machine.

To obtain optimum cutting performance and maximum life from a saw band, the weld area should be identical in strength and flexibility to the remainder of the band. Welds in carbon steel bands approach this ideal more closely than those in high speed steel or intermediate-alloy tool steel bands, because welds in the latter two materials are somewhat brittle, as a result of the short welding and annealing cycle used.

Band Construction and Materials

Bands are made of carbon steel, high speed tool steel, and intermediate-alloy tool steel. Composite types are also used; these are made with high speed steel cutting edges electron-beam welded to a carbon steel back, or tungsten carbide inserts brazed or welded to a carbon steel back.

Carbon steel bands are the type most widely used for the contour band sawing of metals. Fixed-table machines seldom have adequate power, feed mechanism, and cutting-fluid distribution system for other types of bands. Satisfactory cutting rates and tool life are obtained in sawing carbon and low-alloy steels, some grades of tool steel,

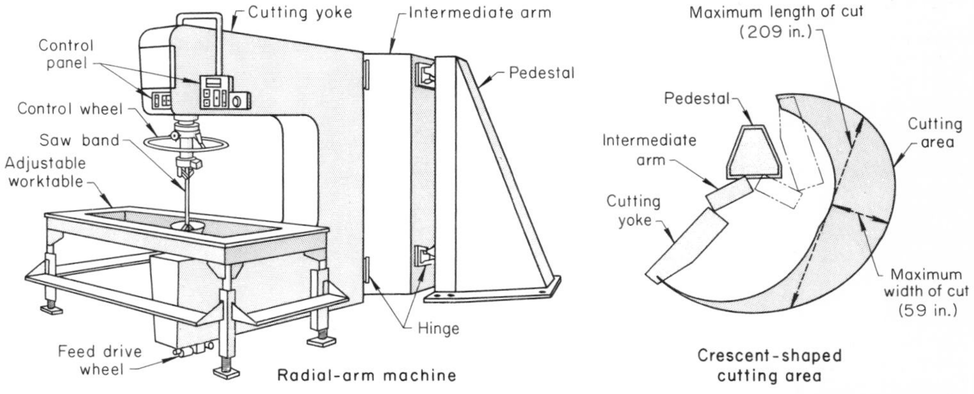

Fig. 2. Radial-arm contour band sawing machine and shaded crescent showing the total area within which the cutting yoke can move. The workpiece, mounted on the adjustable worktable, remains stationary.

and the more readily machinable nonferrous alloys. A typical nominal composition for carbon steel bands is 1.3% C, 0.3% Mn, 0.2% Si, and 0.2% Cr.

High speed steel bands are second in usage. They are used on heavy-duty machines equipped with systems for circulating cutting fluid. These are usually power-table machines rated at 1½ hp or more and designed for continuous, high-volume production.

High speed steel bands give higher cutting rates and longer tool life than carbon steel bands in cutting the same materials, and are required for contour sawing more-difficult-to-cut metals such as stainless steels, heat-resisting alloys, the more highly alloyed tool steels, and some nonferrous alloys. These bands are usually made of M2 high speed steel and are sometimes nitrided for difficult applications.

Intermediate-alloy tool steel bands are used to some extent in the same applications as high speed steel bands. They are usually operated at the same speeds and feed forces, but give shorter tool life. In general, they are intermediate in tool life and cost between high speed steel and carbon steel bands. They are sometimes preferred for applications in which tool life is limited by factors other than normal tooth wear.

A typical composition for intermediate-alloy tool steel bands is 0.9% C, 0.25% Mn, 0.25% Si, 4.0% Cr, 2.25% V, 1.0% W and 2.0% Mo.

High speed steel composite bands are used in the same applications and under the same operating conditions as the single-material high speed steel bands. High speed steel cutting edges are electron-beam welded to a carbon steel back, and the composite material is then given a single-temperature heat treatment.

Carbide Inserts. Bands with tungsten carbide cutting edges brazed or welded to a carbon steel back are used for cutting the most-difficult-to-machine alloys, such as nickel-base and cobalt-base heat-resisting alloys, and for sawing sections thicker than about 6 in. of common metals. Compared to high speed steel, these blades have relatively low shock resistance, but they provide maximum hot hardness and wear resistance.

Band Material Selection Example. The effect of band material on production rate and cost is illustrated by the following example:

Example 435. Cost Comparison With Different Types of Bands (Table 1)

Tool cost, cutting rate, and tool life for making straight cuts in 5-in.-thick 1020 steel (160 to 175 Bhn) were determined for three different band materials: carbon steel, high speed steel, and high speed steel cutting edge on a carbon steel band. Operating conditions and results of the comparison are given in Table 1.

Actual cutting time (exclusive of workhandling and indexing time) and total band costs are given for sawing a 24,000-sq-in. cross section with a contour band saw. Cutting time with the two types of high speed steel bands was considerably less than that required with

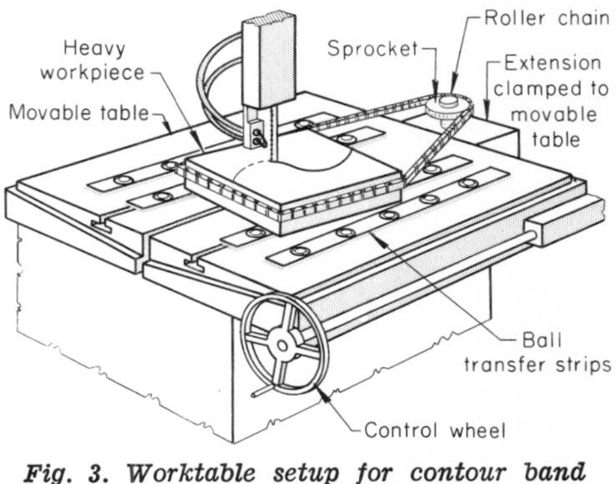

Fig. 3. Worktable setup for contour band sawing of heavy workpieces

Table 1. Comparison of Cutting Rate, Tool Life, and Machining Cost With Three Types of Saw Steel (Example 435) (a)

Item	Carbon steel bands	High speed steel bands	HSS composite
Band speed, sfm	150	240	240
Cutting rate, sq in. per min	2	12	16
Total cutting time, hr (b) (c)	200	33	25
Blade life, sq in. cut	1000	8000	12,000
Blade cost:			
Per blade	$ 5.40	$ 20.33	$ 22.05
Total (b)	130.00	61.00	44.00
Labor plus overhead cost (b) (c) (d)	2000.00	330.00	250.00
Total cost	$2130.00	$391.00	$294.00

(a) Saw bands: 12 ft long, 1 in. wide, 0.035 in. thick, regular tooth form, 6-pitch, raker set (set dimension, 0.058 in.). Work material: 1020 steel, 5 in. thick, at 160 to 175 Bhn. Data are for straight cuts. (b) For a production run of 24,000-sq-in. cross section of cut. (c) Does not include work-handling and indexing of machine. (d) Based on $10 per hr for labor and overhead.

carbon steel bands. Total band cost was only a third to a half as much as with the carbon steel bands (even though the cost of the individual high speed steel band was about four times as much as a carbon steel band), because of the much greater productivity and longer life of high speed steel bands. Use of high speed steel bands reduced operating cost to 14 to 18% of that when carbon steel bands were used, chiefly because of the increased rate with the high speed steel bands.

Hardening of Bands. Heat treating procedures vary with band material and manufacturer. Hardness of the teeth after tempering is usually Rockwell C 58 to 65 for carbon steel bands and Rockwell C 63 to 65 for intermediate-alloy tool steel and high speed steel bands.

To improve life and cutting performance, special procedures are employed to impart hardness and abrasion resistance to the cutting edges and flexibility and strength to the body of the band. These treatments usually bring the entire band to a hardness of Rockwell C 44 to 46 (although other values are sometimes specified for special purposes), after which the teeth are flame hardened or induction hardened to Rockwell C 63 to 65.

The components of composite high speed steel bands are selected so that optimum properties for the teeth and the back of the band are developed in a single-temperature heat treatment. The composite bands combine the welding characteristics of carbon steel with the heat resistance and wear resistance of high speed steel.

Tooth Form

As shown in Fig. 4, steel bands are available in three tooth forms — regular, skip and hook — and bands with carbide inserts, in a special form. Individual manufacturers of saw bands have referred to the tooth shapes by various names; the terminology followed in this article is based on "Simplified Practice Recommendation R214-55" (U. S. Department of Commerce).

The regular form is the only form available for saws that are finer than 6-pitch. For 6-pitch and coarser, the hook form affords the best tool life and fastest cutting rate. For best surface finish, either a regular or a skip tooth form is usually recommended.

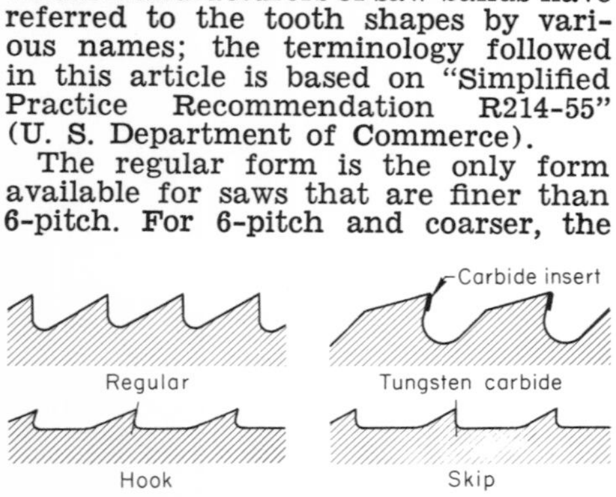

Fig. 4. Standard tooth forms for steel and carbide-tipped band saw blades

The regular tooth form is most frequently used in contour band sawing. It has a deep gullet with a smooth radius at the bottom. The rake angle is 0°, and the back clearance angle is about 30°. (See Fig. 5 for an explanation of the nomenclature applied to blade angles.) This tooth form produces fine-finish cuts accurately and has ample chip capacity for most sawing operations. The largest selection of widths is available in this form.

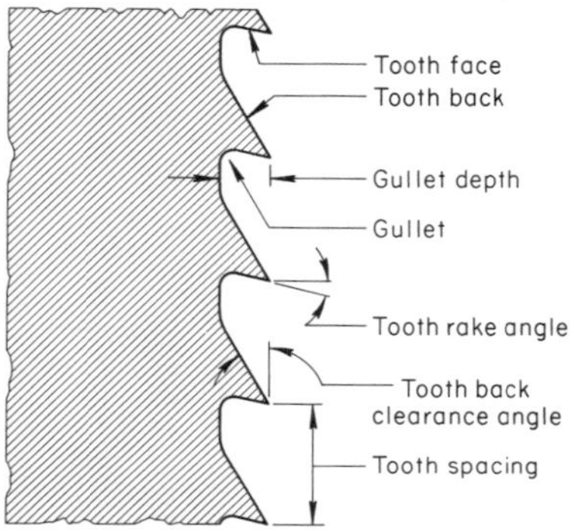

Fig. 5. Standard nomenclature for saw blade teeth

The skip tooth form is similar to the regular tooth form, except that the teeth are more widely spaced to provide greater chip clearance. It has a special gullet design, but rake angle and back clearance angle are the same as those of the regular tooth form. Because of its shallow gullet, the skip tooth form may have a coarser pitch on a narrow band. This tooth form is recommended for making deep cuts in soft metals.

The hook tooth form has a positive rake angle that permits faster cutting rates, reduced feeding pressures, and longer tool life. The back clearance angle is slightly less than that of the regular and skip tooth forms, and the wide gullet is of a special design.

Blade Design

Pitch, width and thickness of the blade, and type of set and set dimension, are important factors in selection of a blade for a particular application.

Pitch of a saw blade is the number of teeth per inch of blade. Each of the tooth forms previously discussed is available in various numbers of teeth per inch. The pitch of a blade is selected primarily on the basis of thickness and shape of the cross section to be cut; the type of material to be cut is of minor importance. Thus, a given cross-sectional thickness of aluminum, mild steel, or tool steel would be cut with blades with identical pitch, although speed and feed would vary.

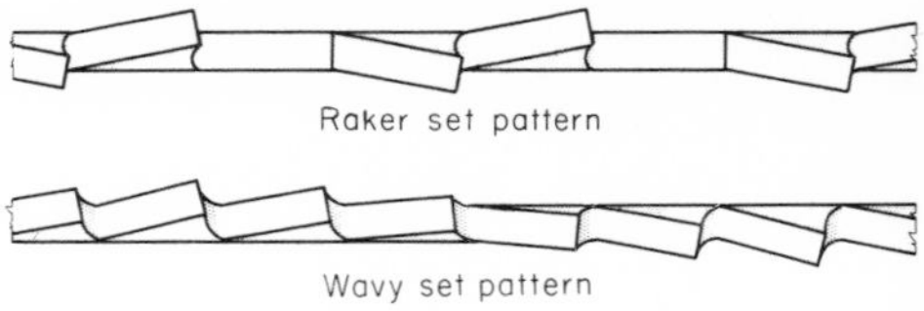

Fig. 6. Set patterns for saw blades

It is essential that at least two teeth remain in contact with the workpiece at all times; it is preferable to have a larger number of teeth in constant contact, thereby reducing proportionately the load on each tooth and increasing tool life. Thus, thin sections are usually sawed with a blade of 10-pitch or finer, whereas heavier sections employ a coarser pitch. The use of a pitch as coarse as 3 or 4 is limited to very heavy sections; blades with coarse pitch usually employ the hook or skip tooth form.

Aside from the basic relationship of tooth pitch and thickness of workpiece to be cut, a tooth that is too small for a given application will cut at a slow rate, and will bind and load up. If a tooth is too large for the application, tooth breakage and stripping are likely.

Blade Width. To maintain accuracy of cutting and a high cutting rate, the widest blade capable of cutting the desired radius should be used (Table 2). Beam strength increases in proportion to the cube of the blade width, thus permitting the use of higher feed force. Also, accuracy of cutting along a straight line is greater for wider blades. Instead of increasing blade width when greater beam strength is needed for difficult straight cuts, the band is sometimes supported by a carbide-faced backup plate of the same thickness.

The thickness (or gage) of a saw blade is usually not open to choice; it has been standardized. Thus, blades that are ½ in. or less in width are generally 0.025 in. thick, ⅝ and ¾-in. widths are generally 0.032 in. thick, and a 1-in. width is 0.035 in. thick. Beam strength increases linearly with an increase in thickness.

In general, a blade of standard gage is adequate for all applications except those involving large workpieces and requiring extreme accuracy. For these applications, a heavier gage is recommended, because it will offer increased resistance to side displacement. Similarly, in cutting the more-difficult-to-

Table 2. Recommended Band Width for Contour Sawing Various Radii

Radius to be cut, in.	Band width, in.	Radius to be cut, in.	Band width, in.
Less than 1/16	1/16	3 3/4	5/8
1/16	3/32	5 7/16	3/4
1/8	1/8	7 1/4	1
5/16	3/16	12	1 1/4
5/8	1/4	21	1 1/2
1 7/16	3/8	28	2
2 1/2	1/2		

machine alloys, a thicker blade will cut more efficiently up to the full capacity of the machine.

Set. The teeth of a saw band are intentionally offset to provide clearance for the back of the band and to permit the cutting of contours. The distance from the extreme corner of one tooth to the extreme corner of the tooth set to the opposite direction is the set dimension. The maneuverability of the band increases as band width decreases (see Table 2) and as the set dimension increases.

Both the raker and wavy set patterns (Fig. 6) are used for sawing metals. The raker pattern is developed by a series of three consecutive teeth: one set to the left, one on center, and one to the right. This pattern is repeated for each successive group of three teeth. In contrast, the wavy pattern consists of series of teeth that are gradually offset, first to the right and then to the left, to form a pattern similar to a wave.

Raker set blades are recommended for all sawing applications except those involving workpieces with marked changes in cross section, such as tubing, pipe and structural shapes, or in thin cross sections. The wavy set operates better than the raker set in thin cross sections, because the wave cuts into the work more gradually and uniformly, thus minimizing shock loading of the cutting teeth.

Special Saw Blades. In addition to the types of blades already described, three special types — spiral-tooth, diamond-edge, and aluminum-oxide-edge — are also available. The spiral-tooth blade is capable of cutting accurate contours to a minimum radius of 0.010 in. Because it has an effective cutting edge of 360°, it is well adapted to cutting intricate patterns in light-gage metal. Diamond-edge and aluminum-oxide-edge blades may be used to cut metals that are extremely tough, such as nickel-base and cobalt-base heat-resisting alloys (see also Example 864), as well as steel that has been heat treated to high hardness. Both types of blade generate a great deal of heat, and use of a cutting fluid is mandatory.

Sawing Variables

Metal composition, hardness (or tensile strength), structural homogeneity, and work-hardening potential are the most important metallurgical factors affecting machinability. (See Tables 2 and 3 on page 225, in the article "Cutoff Band Sawing", and Examples 849 and 850 in the article "Machining of Heat-Resisting Alloys".)

Speed and Feed. Tables 3 to 8 list nominal speeds for contour band sawing of various metals in different ranges of thickness. These tables cover the frequently used alloys and the tempers most commonly machined. Band material, tooth form and pitch are those most commonly used for the particular metal and thickness. These data are intended to serve as starting points for the selection of optimum sawing conditions for specific applications.

Feed rate is given in the footnotes of Tables 3 to 8 only in a general way — as minimum, average or maximum feed force. Feed rate is usually controlled by adjusting feed force (between 2 and 8

Table 3. Speeds for Contour Band Sawing of Carbon and Low-Alloy Steels(a)

Steel being cut	Brinell hardness	Speed (sfm) for stock thickness (in.) of: Carbon steel bands ¼ to ½(b)	1 to 3(c)	6 to 12(d)	High speed steel bands ¼ to ½(e)	1 to 3(c)	6 to 12(d)
1008 to 1013	150 to 175	200	150	125	350	265	175
1015 to 1035	160 to 175	225	175	125	350	280	200
1036 to 1064	160 to 180	150	100	75	250	180	120
1065 to 1095	180 to 205	150	100	65	225	160	100
1108 to 1132	125 to 175	260	210	135	425	310	200
1137 to 1151	155 to 180	225	175	110	320	230	150
1212 to 1213	150 to 175	275	225	145	450	320	200
1330 to 1345	200 to 220	150	100	70	245	180	125
4023 to 4047	170 to 220	150	125	90	345	250	150
4130 to 4140	190 to 215	125	75	50	320	220	125
4320 to 4340	200 to 250	120	65	50	275	190	110
4815 to 4820	220 to 240	125	75	50	240	170	100
5046	170 to 190	125	75	50	300	230	150
5140 to 5160	200 to 220	120	80	50	280	200	125
50100 to 52100	210 to 230	150	100	50	210	135	70
6118 to 6150	180 to 220	125	75	50	260	175	95
8615 to 8645	160 to 220	110	65	50	285	170	105
8720 to 8740	180 to 215	110	65	50	280	160	100
9310	210 to 240	100	50	50	225	150	90

(a) Based on use of a suitable cutting fluid. (b) Regular tooth form; 14-pitch; minimum feed force. (c) Regular tooth form; 6 to 8-pitch; average feed force. (d) Hook tooth form; 3-pitch; maximum feed force. (e) Regular tooth form; 10-pitch; minimum feed force. (Data are adapted from tables in "Fundamentals of Band Machining", Wilkie Brothers Foundation, 1964.)

Table 4. Speeds for Contour Band Sawing of Tool Steels(a)

Steel being cut	Brinell hardness	Speed (sfm) for stock thickness (in.) of: Carbon steel bands ¼ to ½(b)	1 to 3(c)	6 to 12(d)	High speed steel bands ¼ to ½(e)	1 to 3(f)	6 to 12(d)
W1	155 to 195	150	100	50	270	180	100
S2, S5	175 to 230	80	50	50	190	120	60
O1, O2	185 to 205	150	100	50	260	180	100
A2	215 to 240	170	100	65	250	175	100
D2*, D3*	215 to 240	100	60	50	150	100	50
D7*	230 to 255	80	50	50	110	70	50
H12, H13, H21	205 to 230	100	60	50	240	160	90
T6*, T8*	220 to 295	90	55	50	125	80	50
M4*, M10*, M15*	215 to 240	90	50	50	110	70	50
L6	190 to 230	100	65	50	230	160	90

*Operating conditions for these tool steels differ slightly from those for the other tool steels; differences are indicated in footnotes (b), (c), (e) and (f).

(a) Based on use of a suitable cutting fluid, except for D2, D3 and D7, which are sawed dry. (b) Regular tooth form; 14-pitch; minimum feed force, except average feed force for steels that are starred. (c) Regular tooth form; 6 to 8-pitch; average feed force, except maximum feed force for steels that are starred. (d) Hook tooth form; 3-pitch; maximum feed force. (e) Regular tooth form; 10-pitch; minimum feed force, except average feed force for steels that are starred. (f) Regular tooth form; 6-pitch; average feed force, except maximum feed force for steels that are starred. (Data are adapted from tables in "Fundamentals of Band Machining", Wilkie Brothers Foundation, 1964.)

Table 5. Speeds for Contour Band Sawing of Cast Iron (125 to 250 Bhn) With High Speed Steel and Carbon Steel Saw Bands(a)

Work metal (ASTM grade)	Speed (sfm) for stock thickness (in.) of: ¼ to ½(b)	1 to 3(c)	6 to 12(d)
High Speed Steel Bands			
Gray Iron			
Class 30	250	185	110
Class 35; Class 40	200	145	165
Nodular Iron			
60-45-10; 65-45-12	400	300	200
80-60-03; 80-55-06	240	180	110
100-70-03	200	145	160
Malleable Iron			
32510; 35018	350	250	160
53004; 60003	230	160	160
Carbon Steel Bands(e)			
Nodular Iron			
60-45-10; 65-45-12	250	200	NR
Malleable Iron			
32510; 35018	210	NR	NR

(a) All cast irons are sawed dry. (b) Regular tooth form; 10-pitch for high speed steel bands, 14-pitch for carbon steel bands; minimum feed force. (c) Regular tooth form; 6-pitch for high speed steel bands, 8-pitch for carbon steel; average feed force. (d) Hook tooth form for class 30 gray iron, 60-45-10 and 80-60-03 nodular, and 32510 malleable, and carbide tooth form for the other cast irons; 2.5 to 3-pitch; maximum feed force.

(e) Use of carbon steel bands is recommended only for the cast irons and conditions shown; NR = Not Recommended. (Data are adapted from tables in "Fundamentals of Band Machining", Wilkie Brothers Foundation, 1964.)

Table 6. Speeds for Contour Band Sawing of Stainless Steels With High Speed Steel Saw Bands(a)

Steel being cut	Brinell hardness	Speed (sfm) for stock thickness (in.) of: ¼ to ½(b)	1 to 3(c)	6 to 12(d)
201, 202, 302, 304	130 to 190 ...	150	100	70
303, 303F	150 to 200 ...	160	130	100
308*, 309*, 310*, 330*	160 to 220 ...	110	80	50
314*, 316*, 317*	160 to 220 ...	95	60	40
321, 347	165 to 200 ...	150	100	70
410, 420, 420F	140 to 185 ...	175	110	85
416, 430F	155 to 195 ...	230	160	80
430, 446	170 to 215 ...	140	90	70
440 A*, B*, C*	160 to 190 ...	110	90	50
440F, 443	175 to 215 ...	140	115	60
17-7 PH*, 17-4 PH*	150 to 360 ...	110	70	50

*Operating conditions for these stainless steels are slightly different from those for the others, as defined in footnotes (b) and (c).

(a) Based on use of suitable cutting fluid. Cutting fluids, listed in order of increasing effectiveness, include straight mineral oils, soluble-oil emulsions, and chemical solutions, as discussed on pages 222 and 223.

(b) Regular tooth form; 10-pitch; minimum feed force, except average force for steels that are starred. (c) Regular tooth form; 6-pitch; average feed force, except maximum force for steels that are starred. (d) Hook tooth form; 3-pitch; maximum feed force. (Data are adapted from tables in "Fundamentals of Band Machining", Wilkie Brothers Foundation, 1964.)

Table 7. Speeds for Contour Band Sawing of Heat-Resisting Alloys With High Speed Steel Saw Bands(a)

Work metal	Brinell hardness	Speed (sfm) for stock thickness (in.) of: ¼ to ½(b)	1 to 3(c)	6 to 12(d)
A-286	....	75	50	50
Discaloy	....	80	65	65
Hastelloy A	210 to 260 ...	80	55	50
Hastelloy B	230 to 270 ...	90	60	55
Hastelloy C	185 to 250 ...	80	55	50
Inconel	150 to 200 ...	100	65	50
Inconel 700	....	80	55	50
Inconel X-750	....	60	50	50
Waspaloy	....	80	55	50
U-500	....	90	55	50
René 41	....	80	55	50
Refractaloy 26	....	55	35	45

(a) Based on the use of a suitable cutting fluid. (b) Regular tooth form; 8-pitch; average feed force. (c) Regular tooth form; 4 to 6-pitch; maximum feed force. (d) Carbide tooth form; 2.5-pitch; maximum feed force. (Data are adapted from tables in "Fundamentals of Band Machining", Wilkie Brothers Foundation, 1964.)

Table 10. Effect of Hardness of Steel Cut on Band Speed for Contour Band Sawing(a)

Typical steel(b)	Brinell hardness	Speed, sfm
Carbon and Low-Alloy Steels (Except Free-Cutting Steels)		
1020, 1045, 4140, 7140 and 8620, at hardness ranges listed at right	85 to 125	280
	125 to 175	270
	175 to 225	230
	225 to 275	160
	275 to 325	130
	325 to 375	100
Free-Cutting Steels		
1112 and 1117	100 to 150	285
	150 to 200	295
1137, 12L14, 4140+S and 41L40, at hardness ranges listed at right	100 to 150	320
	150 to 200	280
	200 to 250	225
	275 to 325	155
	325 to 375	100

(a) For work up to 3 in. thick, with M2 bands. (b) Each steel represents a group of similar steels; for definition of groups, see Table 2, page 6. (Data are adapted from tables compiled by Metcut Research Associates, Inc.)

lb per tooth) to obtain the proper cutting action, as gaged by the formation of a clean, tightly curled chip or by obtaining a cutting rate determined by experience to be optimum for the work material, stock thickness, equipment and saw band.

A brief summary of linear cutting rates is given in Table 9.

Work-Metal Composition and Hardness. The general effects of work-metal composition and hardness are reflected in Tables 3 to 8. These tables apply directly only to the hardness ranges shown, which represent the conditions in which the metals listed are most frequently sawed (as rolled or annealed). Speed and feed should be adjusted when metals in other ranges of hardness are sawed. Lower band speed (and feed force) is usually required for the higher hardnesses of a given work metal (see data for carbon and low-alloy steels in Table 10). There are, however, exceptions in which the reverse is true; for example, *higher* speeds are required for sawing free-cutting steels similar to 1112 to 1117 in the hardness range of 150 to 200 Bhn than in the range of 100 to 150 Bhn, as shown in Table 10.

Effect of Work Thickness. As shown by Tables 3 to 8, band speed varies inversely with the thickness of metal being sawed. The number of teeth per inch of band (the pitch) must be greater for thin material. The recommended tooth form may be different when thickness exceeds about 3 in. For example, in contour sawing 1015 steel with a high speed steel band, a section thickness of 1 in. indicates the use of a 6-pitch band with regular tooth form and a band speed of 280 sfm. However, a 7-in. section calls for a 3-pitch, hook-tooth band, and a band speed of 200 sfm. In cutting 316 stainless steel of the same thickness, blade requirements remain unchanged, but cutting speed is markedly reduced.

When sawing irregular shapes, blade selection and band speed should be based on the *thinnest* section to be cut in traversing the workpiece.

Effect of Stacking. When sheet materials are stacked for contour band sawing, selection of saw band should not be based on the total thickness to be cut, but more nearly on the thickness of an individual sheet. Thus, if a 10-pitch blade would normally be required to cut a single sheet, this would be slightly modified when cutting a stack of sheets, to an 8-pitch blade. Band speed should be reduced to that called for by the total thickness of the stack.

Cutting Fluids

Cutting fluids are used to prevent overheating of the saw band and the workpiece. Depending on the original tempering treatment to which it was

Table 8. Speeds for Contour Band Sawing of Nonferrous Alloys(a)

Work metal	¼ to ½ in. thick: Tooth form(b)	Pitch	Speed, sfm(c)	1 to 3 in. thick: Tooth form(b)	Pitch	Speed, sfm(d)	6 to 12 in. thick: Tooth form(b)	Pitch	Speed, sfm(e)
Aluminum Alloys									
1100, 2011, 2017, 3003, 3004	R	10	7000	R	6	5000	H	3	4000
2014, 2018, 2025, 6053, 7075	R	14	2800	R	2	2400	H	3	2000
2024, 5052	R	14	8500	R	6	6500	H	3	5000
4032, 6151	R	14	1500	R	6	800	H	3	300
6061, 6063	R	14	5000	R	6	3500	H	3	2500
13, 43, 85	R	14	1500	R	6	800	H	3	300
108, A108, A132	R	14	1000	R	6	600	H	3	200
113, 152, B214, 312, 333 ..	R	14	1400	R	6	900	H	3	300
122, 214, 218, 220	R	14	5000	R	6	4000	H	3	3000
138, B195, 212, 355, 356 ..	R	14	1400	R	6	900	H	3	300
142, 195, 750	R	14	2800	R	6	2400	H	3	2000
360, 380	R	14	1400	R	6	900	H	3	300
Copper Alloys									
102, oxygen-free copper..	R	10	300*	R	6	200*	S	3	100*
170, beryllium copper ...	R	10	275	R	6	325*	S	3	200*
220, com'l bronze, 90% .	R	14	400	R	6	400*	S	3	200*
240, low brass, 80%	R	10	500*	R	6	360*	S	3	200*
314, leaded com'l bronze	R	14	2500	S	3	1500	H	3	500
360, free-cutting brass ..	R	14	3400	R	6	2000	S	3	1000
544, phosphor bronze B-2	R	14	2000	R	6	1200	S	3	400
694, silicon red brass	R	14	600	R	6	325*	C	2.5	250
757, nickel silver 65-12 ..	R	10	500*	R	6	360*	S	3	200*
614, aluminum bronze D.	R	14	200	R	6	225*	C	2.5	135
Other Nonferrous Metals and Alloys									
Magnesium	R	8	4500	H	4	3500	H	3	3000
AM100A, AZ63A, AZ80A, AZ91A, AZ92A, M1A ..	R	10	3500	H	3	2500	H	3	2000
AZ31B, AZ61A	R	6	5000	H	3	4000	H	3	2000
Monel 400, Monel K-500.	R	8	65*	R	4	50*	C	2.5	50
Monel 501, Monel R-405.	R	8	105*	R	4	65*	C	2.5	55
Titanium, 99%	R	10	120*	R	6	90*	C	2.5	100
Ti-6 Al-4 V	R	10	80*	R	6	65*	C	2.5	50
Ti-4 Al-4 Mn; Ti-2 Fe-2 Cr-2 Mo	R	10	110*	R	6	75*	C	2.5	70
Zircaloy-2; Zirconium (2.5 Hf)	R	10	100*	R	4	90*	C	2.5	100

*Band material for this speed and metal is high speed steel (see footnote a).

(a) Based on the use of a suitable cutting fluid, except for copper alloys 314, 360 and 544, which are sawed dry; based on sawing with carbon steel bands, except for tooth forms marked C, where carbide is used, and except for starred speed entries, where high speed steel bands are used. (b) Tooth form codes: R = regular; S = skip; H = hook; C = carbide tooth form. (c) Minimum feed force. (d) Average feed force, except maximum feed force for starred speed entries under "Other Nonferrous Metals and Alloys". (e) Maximum feed force. (Data are adapted from tables in "Fundamentals of Band Machining", Wilkie Brothers Foundation, 1964.)

Table 9. Linear Cutting Rates for Contour Band Sawing

Work metal	Cutting rate (ipm) for stock thickness (in.) of: Carbon steel bands ¼	½	1	1½	2	3	4	6	8	High speed steel bands ¼	½	1	1½	3	6	Carbide 3	6	12
Carbon and low-alloy steels (low-carbon)	9.00	4.00	1.75	1.62	0.87	0.50	0.44	0.29	0.22	21.00	10.80	8.00	6.00	3.00	1.50	4.50	2.50	1.50
Alloy steel (high-carbon)	2.25	1.00	0.50	0.37	0.25	0.17	0.12	0.08	0.06	7.20	4.72	2.62	1.62	0.66	0.30	0.75	0.50	0.30
Gray iron	16.00	7.50	3.25	2.12	1.62	1.00	0.81	0.50	0.40	32.00	16.00	10.00	8.00	4.00	2.00	5.50	3.10	2.00
Tool steel	4.50	2.12	1.00	0.62	0.50	0.31	0.25	0.16	0.12	11.75	6.06	3.12	1.92	0.82	0.39	1.20	0.80	0.50
Titanium	..	..	..	..	..	..	..	..	..	2.30	1.50	0.60	0.30	0.20	0.15	0.35	0.25	0.15

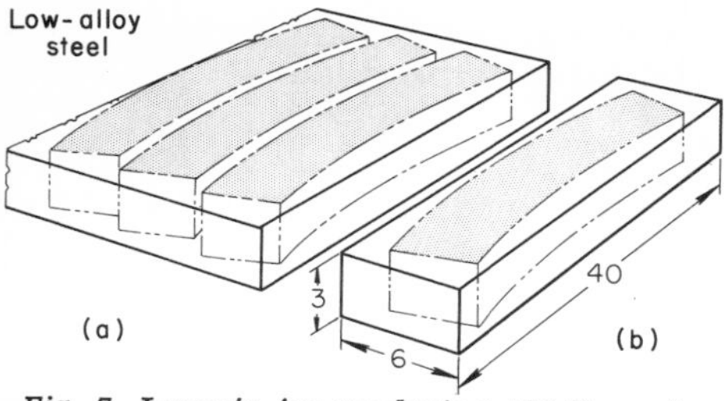

Fig. 7. Layouts for producing 220-lb parts (a) by contour band sawing several from a single billet, and (b) by milling each piece from an individual block (Example 436)

subjected, a carbon steel band can be expected to soften somewhat at temperatures above about 400 F; an intermediate-alloy tool steel band will tolerate somewhat higher temperatures; a high speed steel band can withstand temperatures up to about 1000 F without softening. An oily cutting fluid lubricates the saw guides, thus preventing scoring of the guides and subsequent damage to the band.

Dry Sawing. Fluids are seldom required when cutting at low band speeds or when sawing cast iron. The use of fluids can be harmful in sawing certain work-hardening alloys if the fluid interferes with the cutting action and creates a rubbing action instead.

Types of Cutting Fluid. Three general types of cutting fluid are used in contour band sawing: mineral oils that contain no water, emulsions of soluble oil and water, and chemical solutions.

Straight mineral oils provide maximum lubricity and are particularly useful on difficult-to-machine alloys that are cut at low band speeds (175 sfm or less), where lubricity is more important than cooling power. These oils cannot be used at high cutting rates, because they overheat and smoke. They also have the disadvantage of leaving an oily film on the workpiece, which requires thorough cleaning for removal. Copper, brass and bronze will tarnish if exposed to straight mineral oil containing sulfur additives.

Soluble-oil emulsions are suited to both the free-machining and difficult-to-machine materials, and cover the operating speed range from 150 to 300 sfm. The ratio of soluble oil to water varies with specific job requirements. Thus, a concentrated mixture (1-to-3 to 1-to-5) is selected for maximum lubricity, whereas a dilute mixture (1-to-10 to 1-to-15) is selected for maximum cooling capacity.

Chemical solutions, usually nitrite solutions containing wetting agents, are formulated to provide excellent cooling qualities and are employed at speeds above 250 sfm.

Production Examples and Cost

The examples presented in this section give information on productivity and cost for various applications of contour band sawing, and compare contour band sawing with milling and shaping.

Example 436. Saving in Material by Contour Band Sawing Instead of Milling (Fig. 7)

Figure 7 shows layouts for two methods of producing 220-lb parts from low-alloy (chromium-molybdenum) steel — by contour band sawing from billets (Fig. 7a) and milling from individual blocks (Fig. 7b). Because contour band sawing permitted nesting of the parts, 44 lb less steel was required for each part than in milling. This resulted in a saving of $22 per part produced.

Sawing was done on a radial-arm band saw, which permitted following the contour by guiding the saw band at a fixed feed without moving the billet. Cutting rate was 2.5 sq in. per min, and the area of the cut was 240 sq in. Total time for sawing each piece was 96 min.

The use of a servo-feed attachment, as described in the section "Contour sawing attachments" (page 219), greatly facilitates the handling of heavy work. Easier and more accurate work-handling and avoidance of underfeed or overfeed increase productivity, as illustrated in the next five examples.

Example 437. Sawing 1112 Steel Disks 1⅜ In. Thick (Fig. 8)

Disks, 4¼-in. diam by 1⅜ in. thick, were cut from square plates of 1112 steel at 125 to 150 Bhn (Fig. 8). When the disks were cut on a band saw with servo-feed attachment, cutting rate was 3.68 sq in. per min. Total machining time for cutting an area of 18.42 sq in. was 5 min. The same cut with manual feed took 15 min. A high speed steel saw band, ⅜ in. wide by 0.035 in. thick, with 0.062-in. set, was used at a speed of 300 sfm.

Example 438. Sawing 1112 Steel Disks 1 In. Thick

Using the same tooling as for Example 437, disks measuring 4¼-in. diam by 1 in. thick were cut from 1112 steel (125 to 150 Bhn) in 4 min — 20% less time than required for the 1⅜-in.-thick disks in Example 437. A total area of 13.35 sq in. was cut at a rate of 3.3 sq in. per min, using a band speed of 325 sfm, for a cutting time of 4 min per disk.

Example 439. Sawing 4340 Steel Blocks 4½ In. Thick (Fig. 8)

The contour shown in Fig. 8 was sawed from a 4-in.-square by 4½-in.-thick block of 4340 steel (Rockwell C 40), using the same tooling as in the two preceding examples. Use of a servo-feed attachment reduced machining time to 12 to 15 min, as compared with 45 min when feeding was manual. A total area of 13.5 sq in. was cut at a rate of approximately 1 sq in. per min with the servo feed, using a band speed of 200 sfm.

Example 440. Sawing 4340 Steel Blocks 2 In. Thick (Fig. 8)

A part was sawed from a block of 4340 steel (Rockwell C 40) measuring 5½ by 8½ by 2 in. thick (Fig. 8), using the same tooling as in the preceding examples. An area of 27 sq in. was cut at rates of 3 and 4 sq in. per min, requiring total machining times of 9 and 6¾ min, respectively. Band speed was 220 sfm. When this part was fed manually, total machining time was 1 hr.

Example 441. Sawing 4340 Steel Blocks 1 In. Thick (Fig. 8)

The part shown in Fig. 8 was sawed from a block of 4340 steel (Rockwell C 40) measuring 7 in. square and 1 in. thick, using the same tooling as in the preceding examples. The total area of 11 sq in. was cut at a rate of 4 sq in. per min, requiring a sawing time of 3 min when using servo feed and a band speed of about 240 sfm. In contrast, sawing time with manual feed was 45 min.

In the following example, hydraulically controlled feed produced a better surface finish than manual feed.

Example 442. Sawing Aluminum Honeycomb Sections

In contour band sawing aluminum "hobe" blanks (unexpanded honeycomb sections) to obtain a surface finish of 110 to 150 micro-in., best results were obtained with the following tooling and operating conditions: an 8-pitch, regular-form blade, a band speed of 3000 sfm, and a constant, hydraulically controlled feed of 3 sq in. per min (for a 2-in. section thickness). These conditions provided a surface finish of 130 to 160 micro-in.; surfaces obtained by manual feeding were poor.

Practices successfully employed in four band sawing applications are presented in the examples that follow, which compare contour band sawing with milling and shaping (also see Examples 433, 434 and 436).

Example 443. Cutting Relief Grooves (Fig. 9)

Machining of two grinding reliefs in the hot rolled 1035 steel slide base shown in Fig. 9 originally was done on a milling machine. A change to a contour band saw resulted in a reduction in setup time from 30 to 10 min, and an increase of 100% in production rate. The 1/16-in. reliefs were sawed with a ¾-in.-wide, 6-pitch, high speed steel saw band at a speed of 200 sfm.

Example 444. Cutting of Slots (Fig. 9)

Over-all cost of producing the ⅛-in. slot in the gray iron finger holder shown in Fig. 9 in lots of 200 to 300 pieces was substantially

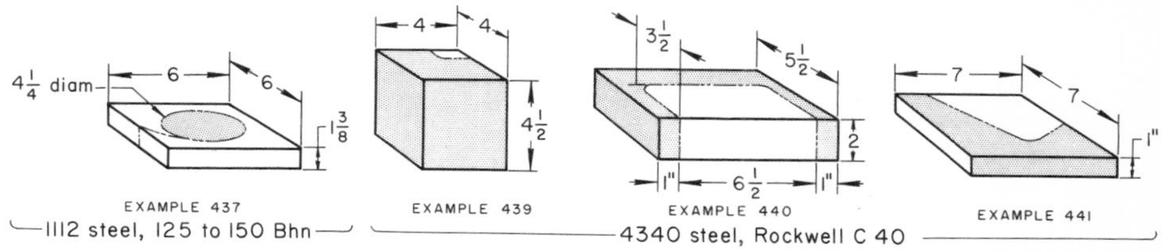

Fig. 8. Shapes produced on a contour band saw with the aid of a servo-feed mechanism (Examples 437, 439, 440 and 441)

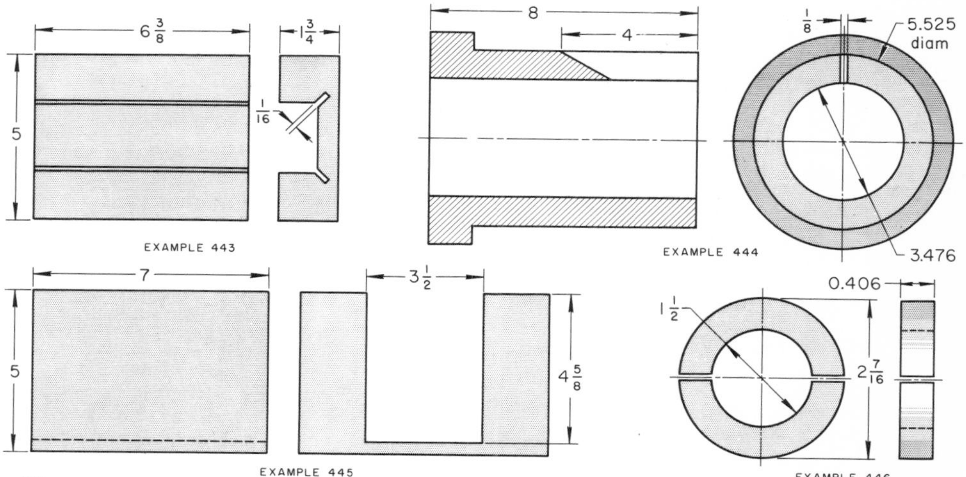

Fig. 9. Production parts that were produced more economically by contour band sawing than by other machining processes (Examples 443 to 446)

reduced by changing from a milling machine to a contour band saw. The milling operation required special fixtures and a large-diameter slitting saw. Setup time was 45 min, and machining time was 6.8 min per piece. No special fixtures were required on the contour band saw; setup time was 20 min, and a standard high speed steel band sawed the slot in 2.5 min, a reduction of 64% in machining time. The slot area was sawed with a 6-pitch ¾-in.-wide saw band at a speed of 275 sfm. No cutting fluid was used.

Example 445. Contour Band Sawing vs Shaping of 1020 Steel (Fig. 9)

Lever brackets of 1020 steel (Rockwell C 20), one size of which is shown in Fig. 9, were machined on a shaper in quantities of three to five in a series of sizes. Setup time for special tooling and holding fixtures was 30 min; production rate was 180 min per piece.

Substantial savings resulted from switching the operation to a contour band saw; setup time was essentially zero, operator costs were lower, and machining time was reduced to from 180 min per piece to 58 min per piece. The piece was sawed at a rate of 1.7 sq in. per min, using a 6-pitch, ¾-in.-wide high speed steel saw band at a speed of 250 sfm. Total area of the cut surface was 99 sq. in.

Example 446. Contour Band Sawing vs Milling of 1020 Steel Nuts (Fig. 9)

A productivity increase of 300%, in addition to a reduction in setup time from 45 to 10 min, was realized in changing from a milling operation to contour band sawing in making large quantities of the hot rolled 1020 steel split nut shown in Fig. 9. The cuts of ⅜-sq-in. total area were made at a band speed of 275 sfm, using an 8-pitch, ¾-in.-wide, regular-tooth, high speed steel band.

Safety

Several important safety features have been incorporated in the design of standard contour band saws, particularly the more recent models. Older machines may or may not be similarly equipped; however, older machines can usually be modified to include many of the latest safety features.

Machine Safety Features. Because the saw band is frequently required to travel at high speed, a most important safety feature is an automatic wheel brake that instantaneously stops the drive wheel when a saw band breaks, thus minimizing damage that might be caused by the broken band. Another important device is the safety interlock; this should be installed on all doors, hatches and drawers that permit access to compartments containing moving parts, such as belts, wheels and gears. All corner surfaces of the machine — inside or outside — should be rounded to avoid snagging. Safety guards should always be in place and should be kept operable at all times. Limit switches and automatic devices should also be kept in good operating condition and should be inspected periodically.

Dust and Fire Hazards. The sawing of beryllium and magnesium is potentially hazardous. The dust and fumes generated by the sawing of beryllium are extremely toxic. To guard against this hazard, the operator should wear respiratory protective equipment and the band saw should be equipped with an effective exhaust system.

The sawing of magnesium presents a fire hazard. Therefore, band saws that are to be used for cutting magnesium should be identified by a bright color and should not be used for sawing other materials, because of the possibility of spark generation. Band saws used to cut magnesium should be cleaned before starting and after completing the operation. Pumps and cutting fluid lines should be inspected before and during operation. When in operation, the machine should not be left unattended. The area in which the band saw is located should be equipped with fire-control implements intended for magnesium fires, such as a dispenser for graphite-base powder.

Cutoff Band Sawing

*By the ASM Committee on Band Sawing**

IN CONTRAST with the contour band saw, the cutoff band saw is usually a horizontal machine. It cuts a kerf of about 1/16 in., as compared to ⅛ and ¼ in., respectively, for the power hacksaw and the circular saw, thereby wasting less metal in the form of chips. Because the saw band is thinner than other types of cutoff tools, less power is required to drive it through the workpiece; because it is continuous, it provides uninterrupted cutting action and wears evenly over its entire length. Other advantages of the cutoff band saw include dimensional accuracy and a high cutting rate (up to 30 sq in. per min in soft low-carbon steel when a high speed steel band is used).

Because the cutting edge of a band saw is longer than for other cutoff saws, blades are changed less frequently. Because the blade is narrower, binding in the kerf is less likely.

Surface Finish and Dimensional Accuracy. As with contour band sawing, surface finish and dimensional accuracy vary with operator skill, equipment and operating conditions. The surface roughness usually ranges between 200 and 300 micro-in. A surface of 100 to 200 micro-in. can be produced by using a fine-pitch blade, high band speed, and low feed force. Cutting accuracy (straightness of cut) usually is within 0.002 in. per inch.

Setup time varies greatly, depending on accessibility of new bands, proficiency of the operator or setup man, type of band guides, and stock-handling equipment. Generally, it requires from 2½ to 5 min to remove and install a saw band, including all adjustments. In normal production, this is not done for each job: Standard shop practice is to change a saw band only when it is worn out and needs to be replaced. The following example compares cutoff band sawing with other cutoff sawing methods and illustrates the effect of blade-changing procedures on machining time for short production runs.

Example 447. Machining Time for Different Methods of Sawing (Table 1)

Hot rolled 1020 steel bars 3 in. in diameter were cut off by power hacksawing, circular sawing, and horizontal band sawing, to determine cutting rate in short runs. The highest cutting rate was obtained with the band saw, using high speed steel bands (Table 1); cutting rate for the 2-in. bands was 50% higher than for the 1-in. bands.

Machining time for short runs completed without changing blades (fourth column in Table 1) varied inversely with the cutting rate. Because the usual shop practice is to provide several machines of varying capabilities and to change blades only when they are worn out, this comparison is applicable to most production situations.

The effect of changing blades before each run is shown in the remainder of Table 1. Machining time was highest for single pieces, for which production time was increased 87 to 700% by blade-changing time. The effect of blade-changing time dropped off rapidly for longer runs, the increase in production time being only 5 to 36% for 20 pieces.

Equipment

The cutoff band saw cuts horizontally or vertically, but in a straight line only; cutting angle, however, is adjustable. The cutting tool is a flexible saw blade that has been welded into a band to revolve around two wheels, a drive wheel and an idler wheel, similar to those used in contour band sawing machines. In a cutoff band sawing machine, the band is twisted through

Table 1. Machining Time for Short-Run Cutoff Sawing (Example 447) (a)

Type of machine	Type of blade or band	Cutting rate, sq. in. per min	Total machining time, min per piece: Without blade change (b)	Blade changed before each run of(c): (3½ min for blade change) 1 pc	2	5	20	(8 min for blade change) 1 pc	2	5	20
Power hacksaw..	Carbon steel(d)	2	4.0	7.5	5.8	4.7	4.2	12.0	8.0	5.6	4.4
	High speed steel	3	2.8	6.3	5.6	3.5	3.0	10.8	6.8	4.4	3.2
Circular saw	High speed steel	6	1.7	5.2	3.5	2.4	1.9	9.7	5.7	3.3	2.1
Band saw	Carbon steel	4	2.3	5.8	4.1	3.0	2.5	10.3	6.3	3.9	2.7
	High speed steel:										
	1 in. wide	8	1.4	4.9	3.2	2.2	1.6	9.4	5.4	3.0	1.8
	2 in. wide	12	1.1	4.6	2.9	1.8	1.3	9.1	5.1	2.7	1.5

(a) For cutoff of 3-in.-diam 1020 steel bars. (b) All runs, from 1 to 20 pieces. (c) Blade change time of 3½ min is within the usual range, but change time of 8 min is unusually long, indicating inefficient operation or special circumstances. (d) Not commercially available.

*For committee list, see page 218.

guides to bring the blade perpendicular to the surface of the worktable.

Cutoff band saws range from machines used for light, intermittent toolroom work to automatic production machines of high capacity. There are also machines for angular cutoff. Unlike contour band sawing machines, cutoff machines have no welders; prewelded bands are used (no internal sawing is done).

Vises and Nesting Fixtures. Workpieces must be held securely during the cutoff operation. Work is clamped in either a vise or a nesting fixture, depending on shape, size and quantity of pieces to be held. Rectangular and square bars can be readily stacked and held firmly in a vise; small and medium-size rounds can also be clamped two abreast and held firmly in a vise. However, holding a larger number of stacked rounds requires the use of a nesting fixture such as that shown in Fig. 1. This type of fixture is widely used for stacking pipe and structural shapes. Stack sawing with the aid of a nesting fixture is most effective when the total area to be sawed is roughly half the capacity of the nesting vise and when the nest is higher than it is wide. Special precautions must be taken in stack sawing of round pieces to insure positive clamping of all pieces, as the rotation of a piece during cutting can cause premature band failure. Instead of being stacked as in Fig. 1, a number of round, hexagonal or irregularly shaped bars can be held by special jaws in standard vises.

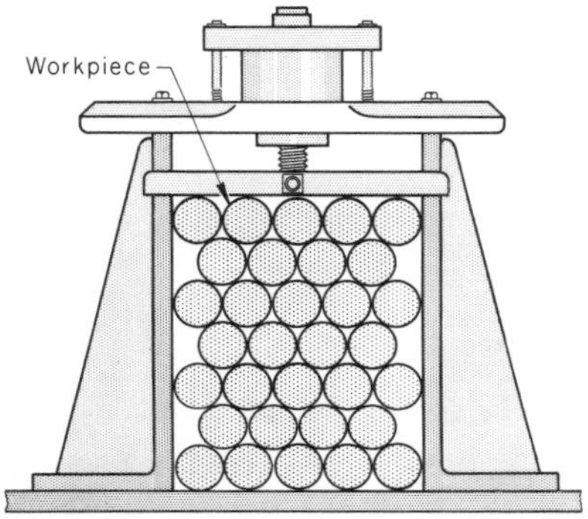

Fig. 1. Nesting fixture used with a standard vise in cutoff band sawing

Worktables. The cutoff band saw is usually equipped with at least two worktables — a stack feeding table on which are mounted one or more vises for gripping and indexing the work to be cut, and a discharge table that provides continuous support for the workpiece and the stack from which it is cut. These tables are made in various lengths to suit operating requirements, and additional tables may be added to accommodate the longest stack length that is being handled.

Cutting fluid systems are essential to the effective performance of cutoff band saws. They consist of a reservoir and pump, a screening system for chips, draining elements, and a chip drawer or automatic chip remover. When changing from one type of cutting fluid to another, or when replacing contaminated fluid, the system must be drained and cleaned.

Table 2. Nominal Speed, Cutting Rate, and Band Life for Cutoff Band Sawing of Steel Bars(a)

Steel being cut	Brinell hardness	Band speed, sfm	Cutting rate, sq in. per min	Band life, sq in. cut(b)
Carbon and Low-Alloy Steels				
1008 to 1013	150 to 175	325 to 275	14 to 10	6700
1015 to 1035	160 to 175	350 to 300	15 to 11	7500
1036 to 1064	160 to 180	225 to 190	9 to 7	4200
1065 to 1095	180 to 205	170 to 145	8 to 6	3000
1108 to 1132	125 to 175	350 to 275	15 to 12	8000
1137 to 1151	155 to 180	260 to 225	10 to 8	5400
1212 to 1213	150 to 175	350 to 300	15 to 12	8500
1330 to 1345	200 to 220	210 to 190	8 to 6	3500
4023 to 4047	170 to 220	260 to 230	8 to 6	3700
4130 to 4140	190 to 215	250 to 220	9 to 7	3300
4320 to 4340	200 to 250	230 to 180	7 to 5	3000
4815 to 4820	220 to 240	190 to 175	6 to 4.5	2500
5046	170 to 190	250 to 220	9 to 7	3300
5140 to 5160	200 to 220	230 to 200	6.5 to 5	2500
50100 to 52100	210 to 230	170 to 120	6 to 4	2500
6118 to 6150	180 to 220	225 to 150	7.5 to 4	2600
8615 to 8645	160 to 220	230 to 175	7 to 5	3800
8720 to 8740	180 to 215	225 to 175	7 to 5	3200
9310	210 to 240	175 to 150	4 to 3	2000
Tool Steels				
W1	155 to 195	220 to 180	6 to 5	3000
S2, S5	175 to 230	150 to 110	4 to 3	1500
O1, O2	190 to 205	210 to 180	6 to 4	2500
A2	215 to 240	200 to 170	4 to 3	2300
D2, D3	215 to 240	120 to 90	3 to 2	1500
D7	230 to 255	90 to 60	2 to 1	850
H12, H13, H21	205 to 230	190 to 160	5 to 4	2000
T1, T2	215 to 250	130 to 100	3.5 to 2	1700
T6, T8	220 to 295	100 to 70	2.5 to 1	1200
T15	230 to 255	75 to 50	2 to 1	1000
M1	215 to 230	150 to 120	5 to 3	1700
M2, M3	215 to 240	110 to 80	4 to 2	1500
M4, M10, M15	215 to 230	90 to 60	2.5 to 1	1200
L6	190 to 230	180 to 160	6 to 4	2500
Stainless Steels				
201, 202, 302, 304	130 to 190	120 to 80	4 to 2	3000
303, 303F	150 to 200	130 to 90	5 to 2	3300
308, 309, 310, 330	160 to 220	80 to 60	2 to 1	1300
314, 316, 317	160 to 220	75 to 50	2 to 1	1200
321, 347	165 to 200	120 to 90	4 to 2	2400
410, 420, 420F	140 to 185	140 to 100	4 to 2	1500
416, 430F	155 to 195	180 to 140	7 to 5	2500
430, 446	170 to 215	90 to 60	4 to 3	1700
440A, B, C	160 to 190	110 to 70	4 to 2	1500
440F, 443	175 to 215	130 to 100	4 to 2	1300
17-7 PH, 17-4 PH	150 to 360	90 to 50	4 to 2	1700

(a) Based on the use of a 1-in.-wide high speed steel band, regular tooth form (except hook tooth form for metal thicker than about 10 in.), raker set, to cut scale-free, solid bar stock up to 18 in. thick; based on the use of a cutting fluid, except for D2, D3 and D7 tool steels, which are cut dry. (b) For 10-ft band; proportionate life for other band lengths.

Table 3. Nominal Speed, Cutting Rate, and Band Life for Cutoff Band Sawing of Nonferrous Alloys(a)

Work metal	Brinell hardness	Band speed, sfm	Cutting rate, sq in. per min	Band life, sq in. cut(b)
Copper Alloys				
170, beryllium copper	100 to 120	275 to 200	8 to 6	3800
	220 to 250	225 to 175	6 to 4	2700
	310 to 340	140 to 90	3 to 2	1700
510, phosphor bronze 5% A	60 to 100	300 to 250	10 to 8	5800
	180 to 210	175 to 125	5 to 3	2500
614, aluminum bronze D	70 to 90	350 to 300	14 to 10	6700
	190 to 220	175 to 125	5 to 3	2500
656, high-silicon bronze	70 to 100	325 to 275	15 to 12	7500
	180 to 210	175 to 125	6 to 3	2500
675, manganese bronze A	95 to 120	325 to 275	15 to 12	7500
	180 to 190	200 to 150	6 to 4	2700
Nickel Alloys				
Inconel	150 to 200	100 to 60	3 to 2	650
Inconel X-750	200 to 300	80 to 60	1.5 to 0.5	400
Monel 400	125 to 200	100 to 60	3 to 1	850
Monel R-405	145 to 180	150 to 75	4 to 2	1000
Monel K-500	160 to 210	80 to 60	2 to 0.5	500
Monel 501	160 to 210	100 to 60	3 to 1	850
Hastelloy A	210 to 260	120 to 75	3 to 1.5	1000
Hastelloy B	230 to 270	100 to 75	2.5 to 1	850
Hastelloy C	185 to 250	90 to 60	1.5 to 0.7	600
Titanium Alloys				
Ti; Ti – 1.5 Fe – 2.5 Cr	270 to 350	90 to 60	1 to 0.3	400
Ti – 4 Al – 4 Mn; Ti – 6 Al – 4 V	290 to 360	110 to 70	2 to 0.5	600
Ti – 2 Fe – 2 Cr – 2 Mo	300 to 330	90 to 60	1.5 to 0.5	750

(a) Based on the use of a 1-in.-wide high speed steel band, regular tooth form (except hook tooth form for metal thicker than about 10 in.), raker set, to cut scale-free, solid bar stock up to 18 in. thick; based on the use of a suitable cutting fluid.
(b) For 10-ft-long band; for other band lengths, proportionate life will apply.

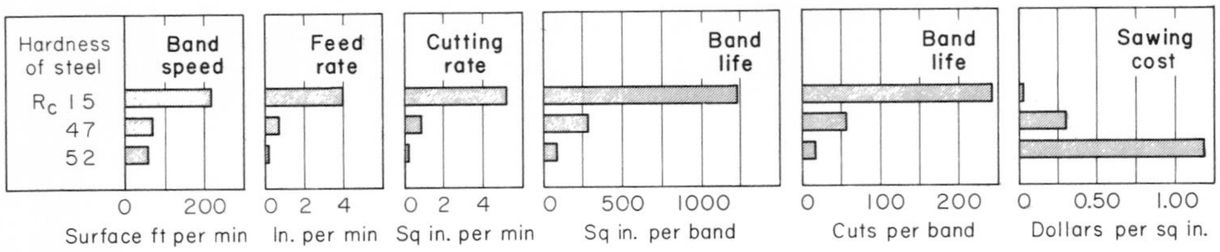

Steels were sawed with high speed steel bands (1 in. wide by 0.035 in. thick, 4-pitch for the steels at Rockwell C 15 and 47 and 6-pitch for the steel at Rockwell C 52, regular tooth form, raker set). Cutting fluid was a 1-to-1 mixture of sulfurized oil and mineral oil. Criterion for band life was the development of a wear land of 0.030 in. on cutting edges of the saw teeth.

Fig. 2. Effect of workpiece hardness in cutoff band sawing of low-alloy steel

Band Selection

In general, materials of construction, types of bands, tooth forms, and principles of selection of bands are the same as those described on page 219 in "Contour Band Sawing". However, high speed steel bands are used in cutoff applications to a greater extent than all other types combined, because of their high cutting rates and long life in sawing nearly all types of metals. Also, wider bands are used, because only straight-line cuts are made in cutoff machines. The wider bands provide greater beam strength and permit higher loading. Consequently, bands 1 in. or more in width are preferred in cutoff sawing. The following table is a general guide to band selection:

Thickness of work, in.	Band width, in.	Pitch	Tooth form
To 5/8	1	10	Regular
5/8 to 1	1	8	Regular
1 to 4	1	6	Regular
4 to 10	1 to 1¼	4	Regular
10 to 18	1 to 2	3	Hook

Machining Variables

The effects of speed, feed, thickness of work, and other machining variables on cutoff band sawing operations are similar to those in contour sawing.

Nominal speed, cutting rate, and band life for cutoff band sawing of various metals are given in Tables 2 and 3. These tables are based on the cutting of scale-free rounds, 3 to 5 in. in diameter, with 1-in.-wide high speed steel bands, and are applicable to solid bar stock up to 18 in. thick. Substantial amounts of scale on the work will require the use of lower band speed and cutting rate, and will shorten band life, particularly in cutting thin material.

Band life values shown in Tables 2 and 3 are for bands 10 ft long; a proportionate figure can be assumed for a saw band of different length.

As discussed on page 222 in "Contour Band Sawing", a cutting fluid should be used (except for the sawing of certain work-hardening alloys), with the selection of fluid based primarily on band speed.

Cutting of Hollow Shapes. Optimum cutting rates are obtained in sawing solid materials, because many teeth are uniformly loaded at all times. In sawing pipe, tubing and structural sections, only a fraction of the total cross section through which the saw band must pass is metal, and cutting rate must therefore be lower to keep the feed force per tooth at an acceptable level.

The following factors, which depend on minimum wall thickness to be cut, should be applied to the cutting rates of Tables 2 and 3 to estimate rates for sawing pipe, tubing and structural shapes.

Minimum wall thickness, in.	Factor
Less than 3/16	0.4
3/16 to 3/8	0.5
3/8 to 5/8	0.6
More than 5/8	0.7

Pitch of saw band should be selected on the basis of the minimum wall thickness to be sawed.

Effects of composition and hardness of work metal on sawing conditions and results are similar to those described for contour band sawing, as can be seen from Tables 2 and 3. Figure 2 shows the effect of hardness of quenched-and-tempered low-alloy steel on cutoff sawing with a 1-in.-wide high speed steel band. Band speed, feed rate, band life, and machining cost are shown for cutting 1¼-by-4-in. bar stock of 4130, 4330 and 4340 steels at Rockwell C 15, 47 and 52, respectively. Speed, feed, cutting rate, and band life were all considerably lower at the higher hardnesses, resulting in a substantial decrease in productivity and an increase in cost.

In band sawing the steel at Rockwell C 47, it was necessary to employ heavy feed pressure and high band tension, to prevent the saw teeth from riding over the work without cutting. Satisfactory rough band sawing of the steel at Rockwell C 52 was achieved by reducing both speed and feed. Machining details are given with Fig. 2.

A similar effect of hardness is observed with the copper alloys listed in Table 3, comparing band speed, cutting rate, and band life for a given alloy at different hardnesses. Table 10 in the article "Contour Band Sawing" shows this same relation to exist for carbon and low-alloy steels in general, with the exception of certain free-machining alloys in the hardness range of approximately 100 to 200 Bhn.

In comparing alloys that are not closely similar in chemical composition or microstructure, large differences in other properties (such as work-hardening rate) can be more significant than differences in hardness. This is illustrated by Examples 849 and 850, in "Machining of Heat-Resisting Alloys".

Cutting Rate vs Cost. The relative importance of the various elements in machining cost must be considered in arriving at an optimum manufacturing method in an individual application. In Example 447, productivity was greatly increased by using high speed steel blades. Another cost analysis was made in Example 435 in the article "Contour Band Sawing", where lower tool cost, higher productivity, and lower over-all cost were obtained by substituting more expensive high speed steel and composite high speed steel bands for carbon steel bands. Labor cost is usually a major item in band sawing; the following example describes a reduction in cost by sawing at a higher speed.

Table 4. Band Speed, Tool Life, Productivity and Cost in Cutoff Band Sawing of 5-In.-Diam 1020 Steel Bars (Example 448) (a)

Item	Method A	Method B
Band speed, sfm	200	325
Cutting rate, sq in. per min	5	12
Cycle time per piece, min	5	2.08
Band life, sq in. cut	14,000	10,000
Band life, cuts	560	400
Cost per cut:		
Labor plus overhead (b)	$0.83	$0.35
Saw band	0.04	0.05
Total	$0.87	$0.40

(a) High speed steel band, 1 in. wide by 0.035 in. thick, 4-pitch, regular tooth form, raker set. (b) Labor-plus-overhead rate, $10 per hour.

Example 448. Sacrificing Tool Life for Increased Production Rate and Lower Cost (Table 4)

A high speed steel band was used at a cutting rate of 5 sq in. per minute for the cutoff sawing of 5-in.-diam bars of 1020 cold rolled steel. Band life was excellent — 14,000 sq in. per band. Increasing the cutting rate to 12 sq in. per minute reduced band life to 10,000 sq in., but reduced the cycle time per piece and over-all cost to less than half the former values. Production and tool details are summarized in Table 4.

Friction Band Sawing

In friction band sawing, the work metal is softened (or melted) just ahead of the saw band by frictional heat from dry cutting at high band speeds (6,000 to 15,000 sfm), and the saw teeth remove the softened metal. These band speeds are about 50 to 100 times those for conventional band sawing of the same metals with a cutting fluid. The saw band is not overheated because only a small part of the rapidly moving band is in the work, and heat is dissipated readily from the rest.

Applicability. The method is used chiefly on ferrous metals that are harder than Rockwell C 42 or that work harden rapidly. It is used also for distortion-free cutting of thin material, and can produce complex contours as well as straight cuts. It gives high cutting rates, long band life and low machining cost on material up to 1 in. thick. Most steels can be cut efficiently because of their low thermal conductivity and wide softening range; alloys of copper or aluminum, and most cast irons, are not suitable for friction sawing. In comparison with thermal conductivity, hardness of the work metal is of minor importance.

Saw bands for friction sawing are made of carbon steel. They are thicker than standard bands and have wider set; the teeth are designed for heavy shear loads, and the gullets are shaped for plastic flow of chips. Sharp teeth are not required; saw bands are used until they break from flexing. Standard saw bands can also be used.

Other Examples of Band Sawing in This Book

Tool steels .... Examples 682, 686
Heat-resisting alloys .... Examples 849, 850
Aluminum alloys .... Examples 922, 923

Electrical Discharge Machining (EDM)

By John F. Kahles*

ELECTRICAL DISCHARGE MACHINING (EDM) is a method for producing holes, slots or other cavities in electrically conductive material by means of the controlled removal of material through melting or vaporization by high-frequency electrical sparks. The spark discharge is produced by controlled pulsing of direct current between the workpiece (which is usually anodic or positively charged) and the tool, or electrode (which is usually the cathode or negative electrode). The end of the electrode and the workpiece are separated by a spark gap of 0.0005 to 0.020 in. and are immersed in or flooded by a dielectric fluid. The dielectric in the gap is partially ionized under the pulsed application of a high voltage, thus enabling a spark discharge to pass between tool and workpiece. Each spark produces enough heat to melt or vaporize a small quantity of the workpiece, leaving a tiny pit or crater in the surface of the work.

Applicability of EDM depends on many factors, including workpiece material, shape to be produced, accuracy required, and amount of material to be removed. Table 1 lists conditions that favor the selection of EDM over chip-removal processes.

The widest use of EDM is for the machining of dies and molds, either before or after hardening, as these applications usually combine poor machinability, complex shape and close tolerances with other factors that favor the use of EDM. The process is used also for machining carbide, tungsten, honeycomb structures and other fragile materials, small deep holes or odd-shaped holes, slots as narrow as 0.001 in., and other work difficult or impossible to machine by other methods.

Holes 20 or more diameters deep can be made by EDM with virtually no drifting or bending. For extreme accuracy of roundness or taper, or for low-micro-inch finishes, EDM is often combined with reaming or honing. The method is also applicable to small, intricate or precision parts.

Because of low tool life and the high cost of accurate tools, ordinary EDM techniques are seldom competitive for parts that are readily produced by mechanical machining methods. However, "no-wear" EDM roughing with graphite electrodes, as described on page 230, often has a cost advantage in the sinking of large contoured cavities in hardened tool steel dies for forging, casting or plastic molding, and in related parts.

Setup. Figure 1 shows a diagram of a typical setup for electrical discharge machining. The electric current usually is 0.5 to 400 amp at 40 to 400 volts dc, pulsing at 180 to 260,000 cps, and using 0.0004 to 400 mfd of capacitance. The dielectric fluid is pumped through the tool at a pressure of 50 psi or less. In some applications, the fluid is circulated in the reverse direction by the use of a vacuum.

Table 1. Factors That Favor the Selection of EDM Over Chip-Removal Processes

Work Material
High hardness, high tensile strength, poor machinability.
Type of Workpiece
Complex or irregular shape, fragile structure, small holes, holes of large depth-to-diameter ratio, narrow and odd-shaped slots, acute-angle holes or slots, large numbers of holes or slots.
Manufacturing Considerations
Need for freedom from burrs, requirement for mating of a punch and die.

The tool, or electrode, may be made of graphite or of such metals as copper, brass, aluminum, steel, zinc-tin alloy, or tungsten alloyed with copper or with silver. Odd shapes can be machined by using an electrode in the form of a mirror image of the shape wanted; an actual part can be used as the electrode in making some types of dies, such as forging and trimming dies. Because of wear during machining, electrodes are sometimes replaced several times in making a single cut; hence, for some work, quantities of interchangeable electrodes must be available. Electrodes must be attached accurately in repeatable position.

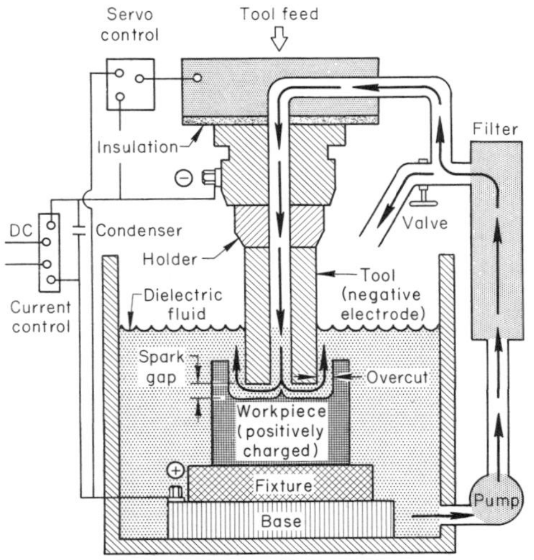

Fig. 1. Typical setup for electrical discharge machining

Electrodes are used at negative polarity for most EDM operations. Exceptions include steel or aluminum alloy electrodes, copper-tungsten electrodes when machining steel, and graphite electrodes when used for roughing — all of these are used at positive, or "reverse", polarity (see Table 3 and later section on Electrodes).

Machines. Most machines for EDM are ram-type, in which the workhead is moved by a hydraulic cylinder. Quill-type machines are used mostly for smaller work. For equivalent capacity, they are slightly lower in cost than ram-type machines. The quill usually is driven by a hydraulic motor with bevel gears and a lead screw, or by a hydraulic cylinder.

Both ram and quill machines have servo control for tool advance, to keep the spark gap constant. The servo gets its input signal from the difference between a selected reference voltage and the actual voltage across the gap. The signal is amplified and the tool is advanced by hydraulic control. A short circuit across the gap causes the servo to reverse the motion of the tool until proper control is restored.

Dielectric fluid is flushed through the spark gap, supplied either through a hollow tool or from external jets, or both. It may also be supplied through holes in the workpiece. It serves as a spark conductor and coolant, and as a flushing medium for disposal of the small particles of material removed from the workpiece. The fluid must have a suitable dielectric constant and must ionize readily at applied potentials of 40 to 400 volts to conduct the spark discharge. It must also quench the melted or vaporized metal produced by the spark and remove it from the gap. The fluid is continuously filtered through such mediums as wound-cotton-yarn cartridges or diatomaceous earth, to remove foreign material and solid products of machining; or solids are removed by centrifuging or settling. Complete removal of suspended solids is not always necessary; in making roughing cuts at large gap spacing, such suspended material sometimes enables the passage of a larger current without increasing the voltage.

The most widely used type of fluid is hydrocarbon (petroleum) oil having a viscosity of about 40 SUS at 100 F. Other types of fluids used, for special applications, include kerosine, silicone oils, deionized water, and polar liquids such as aqueous solutions of ethylene glycols. Desirable properties of fluids include

*Vice President, Metcut Research Associates Inc. This article includes contributions from: E. L. Anderson, Corning Glass Works; P. D. Bivens, Bendix Corp.; A. L. Galgano, Grumman Aircraft Engineering Corp.; J. Karr, Electromac, Inc.; Edward Krabacher, Cincinnati Milling Machine Co.; A. L. Pickrell, Boeing Co.; K. Shelton, Elox Corp.; R. K. Springborn, editor, "Non-Traditional Machining Processes", ASTME; H. N. Tiemann, Pratt & Whitney Aircraft Div., United Aircraft Corp. See also literature references cited in Table 2 and Example 449(a).

known dielectric strength in a suitable range (170 volts per 0.001 in. is typical for the oils used), low viscosity, high flash point, and low cost. They should also be nonhazardous to operators, and noncorrosive to equipment.

Power-Supply Circuit. The resistance-capacitance, or "R-C", circuit (basically a relaxation oscillator) shown in Fig. 2(a) is a simple, reliable, low-cost power source that is ordinarily used with copper or brass electrodes. When R-C circuits are used, machining rate is slow, because the time required to charge the capacitors prevents the use of high frequencies. Figure 2(b) illustrates a vacuum tube pulse circuit, in which charging takes only a small portion of the cycle. This type of circuit makes possible improved control at high frequencies, high metal removal rates, and lower electrode wear, as compared to the simpler R-C circuit.

The limitations of the basic pulse circuit are that large numbers of vacuum tubes are required to obtain high currents and that design problems arise from the basic incompatibility of vacuum tube characteristics (high voltage, low current) and spark gap characteristics (low voltage, high current). These limitations are offset by the following modifications of power supply circuits:

1 Augmenting the output of a tube-type power supply with an auxiliary power supply (rectifier shown as optional in Fig. 2b)
2 Using a small number of vacuum tubes at high voltage and low current on the primary side of a transformer, and connecting the spark gap to the secondary side for low voltage and high current
3 Using a transistor type of pulse generator that functions efficiently at low voltage and high current.

In all types of circuits, inductance is kept as low as possible for maximum efficiency of metal removal.

Control. For a given machine, electrode and dielectric fluid, the machining process is controlled by regulating current, duration of discharge ("duty cycle"), pulse frequency, and spark gap.

When current begins to flow across the gap at the initiation of a pulse, the current path is very small and the current density is correspondingly high, producing temperatures of several thousand degrees Centigrade. As the discharge continues, the current path gradually broadens, and the current density decreases. Each spark melts or vaporizes a small quantity of metal from the workpiece, leaving a small crater in the surface. (A similar but lesser cratering effect occurs on the negatively charged metal electrode or tool; with a graphite electrode, cratering of the electrode is very slight.)

Metal removal rate depends on the volume of metal removed by each

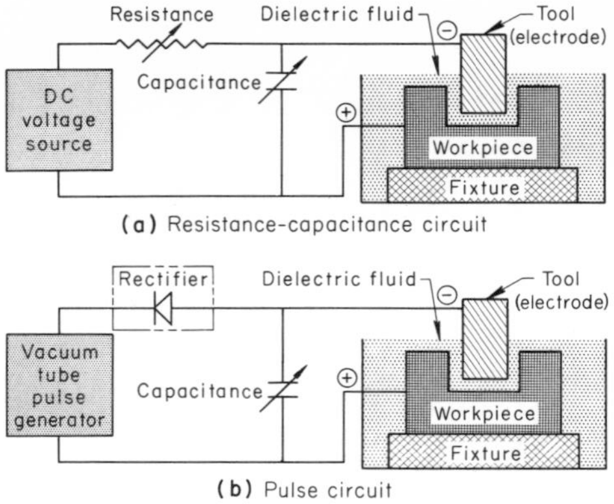

Rectifier is not included in the basic pulse circuit (b); it may be added to obtain a high gap current with a small number of tubes.

Fig. 2. Two types of circuits for electrical discharge machining

Table 2. Typical Operating Conditions and Size of Crater Produced on Workpiece and Electrode for Different Metal Removal Rates

Pulse frequency, kc	Current, amp	Surface roughness, micro-in.	Crater size, mils: Workpiece Depth	Workpiece Width	Electrode Depth	Electrode Width	Removal rate, cu in./hr
5	1 to 20	200 to 500	1.9 to 4.0	5.3	1.2	1.3	1.7
10	5 to 17	150 to 200	1.5 to 1.9	2.4	0.57	0.58	0.5
20	4 to 12	100 to 150	1.0 to 1.5	2.0	0.45	0.46	0.25
450	3 to 9	50 to 75	0.5 to 0.6	0.65	0.18	0.2	0.1
1000	0.5 to 3	25 to 10	0.1	0.15	0.03	0.04	0.005 to 0.0005

Work material was high-carbon high-chromium die steel at Rockwell C 62 to 64. Copper electrodes were used. Source of data: A. Bonales (Western Electric Co.), The Spark That Carves, *Product Engineering,* Sept 27, 1965, p 53-57.

Table 3. Advantages and Disadvantages of Various Materials for EDM Electrodes (Tools)

Electrode material	Advantages	Disadvantages
Graphite (reverse polarity in roughing)	Easily machined. Easily attached to punch or holder, with conductive adhesives. Can be ground together with hardened tool or holder. Very good rate of metal removal. Best wear ratio. Can be used with suitable current source for "no-wear" roughing.	Must be machined completely to shape, because it cannot be etched. Needs very good flow of dielectric fluid, or vibration, or periodic withdrawal. Dangerous arcing can occur in machining carbides. Dielectric fluid soaks the graphite so that it cannot be cemented again for re-use. Small pieces difficult to attach firmly enough to be ground. Cannot machine smoother than 40 micro-in. without rotation.
Copper-tungsten alloys (reverse polarity in machining steel)	Can be attached by brazing. Good resistance to breakdown of edge. Can readily produce surfaces smoother than 40 micro-in.	Brazing can soften the punch; grinding may be needed to restore the hardness. Costs more than graphite. Can machine steel only with reverse polarity.
Steel (reverse polarity)	Good for short-run dies. Small punches can be machined readily. Can be used to mate punch to punch holder. One-piece electrode and holder (no tipping).	Wear ratio is satisfactory only for certain combinations of steels. Machining time is about five times that with graphite electrode. Work metal is disturbed to greater depth than by graphite electrode.
Zinc-base die-casting alloys(a)	Best wear ratio of any zinc alloy. High production of electrodes.	Costly die-casting die. Additional flow holes may be needed for the dielectric.
50-50 zinc-tin alloy	Easily coined to accurate dimensions. Permits accurate machining of complex shapes. Low melting temperature (about 650 F), and easy to cast. Can be remelted indefinitely for re-use. Costs less than most machined electrodes.	Will not produce fine detail. Has rapid corner wear. Poorer wear ratio than 70-30 zinc-tin alloy.
70-30 zinc-tin alloy	Better wear ratio than 50-50 zinc-tin. Current can be as much as 150 amp.	Accuracy of casting decreases with drop in tin content. Greater coining pressures needed than for 50-50 zinc-tin.
Aluminum alloys (reverse polarity)	Current can be as much as 270 amp, permitting removal of up to 15 cu in./hr. Wear ratios are like those for 70-30 zinc-tin.	High melting temperature (about 1220 F); shrinkage is 5 to 7%. Not suitable for use with capacitance-type pulse circuits.
Copper	Low cost. Easily machined (especially free-cutting grades) Higher wear ratios than brass. Produces extremely smooth finishes on work.	Lower wear ratio than graphite. Free-machining grades not readily available in all sizes.
Brass	Available in small tubing and shim stock. Machines almost any material.	Wear ratio as poor as 1 to 6 for small electrodes, and for machining tungsten. Loads grinding wheels.
Silver-tungsten alloys; silver-tungsten carbide alloys	Good wear ratios; makes accurate cuts. Good resistance to tool-edge breakdown. Thin portions resist vibration in use. Silver-tungsten carbide needs no dielectric flow for shallow cuts.	Initial cost is high. Difficult to machine. Nonmagnetic.

(a) Alloys AG40A and AC41A

Table 4. Applicability of Various Materials for EDM Electrodes (Tools)

Electrode material	Form of electrode material	Circuit(a) Pulse	Circuit(a) R-C	Wear ratio(b) End, in roughing	Wear ratio(b) Corner, in finishing	Relative Cost	Machinability(a)	Recommended uses Work metal	Recommended uses Application	Uses not recommended
Graphite	Blocks, rod, tube, bar	A	D	100:1	5:1	Low	A	Steel	Tooling	Carbide
Copper-tungsten	Short bars, flats, shim stock, rod, wire, tube	A	A	8:1	3:1	Medium	C	All	Carbide slots, thin slots	Large areas
Brass	Bar, rod, tube, forgings, sheet, wire, stampings	A	C	1:1	0.7:1	Low	B	All	Holes	High accuracy; deep slots
Copper	Same as brass	B	A	2:1	1:1	Low	B	All	Holes	Same as brass
Silver-tungsten	Sintered and infiltrated	A	A	12:1	8:1	High	C	All	Small slots or holes	Large areas
Tungsten	Wire, rods, ribbon	B	B	10:1	5:1	Medium	D	All(c)	Small slots or holes	Irregular holes
Tungsten carbide	Sintered rod	B	B	10:1	6:1	High	D	All(c)	Small slots or holes	Irregular holes
Steel	All forms	B	D	4:1	4:1	Low	A	Nonferrous	Through holes	Carbide
		C	D	1.5:1	1:1	Low	A	Steel	Stamping dies	Carbide
Zinc alloys(d)	Die castings, cast shapes	C	D	2:1	(e)	Low	B	Steel	Forging dies(f)	Holes(g)
Aluminum	Cast or forged shapes	C	D	5:1	0.5:1	Low	B	Steel	Forging dies(f)	......
Molybdenum	Rods, wire, tubes	B	A	8:1	3:1	High	D	Refractory	Holes	......
Nickel	Plated shapes	A	A	8:1	5:1	High	C	All	Intricate detail(f)	......

(a) A = Excellent; B = Good; C = Fair; D = Poor. (b) See Fig. 3. (c) Especially refractory metals. (d) Zinc-tin alloys, and die-casting alloys AG40A and AC41A. (e) Ratio is 0.7:1 for zinc-tin alloys and 5:1 for AG40A and AC41A. (f) Cavities only. (g) Zinc-tin alloys only.

spark and on the frequency of discharge, and is thus directly related to the current and the duty cycle. Surface roughness is determined by the size of the individual craters; it varies directly with current and duty cycle, and inversely with frequency. The usual conditions for roughing and finishing are:

Operation	Current	Capacitance	Duty cycle	Pulse frequency
Roughing	High	High(a)	Long	Low
Finishing	Low	Low	Short	High

(a) Except for "no-wear" EDM with graphite electrodes; see page 230.

Typical operating conditions and cratering produced on die steel and a copper electrode at different machining rates are shown in Table 2.

Depending on the type of equipment and on the charge-discharge cycle, overcut is determined either by the initiating voltage or by the current; overcut is increased by an increase in either of these factors. The spark gap is regulated by servo control of electrode feed.

Electrodes (Tools)

The productivity, results and cost of electrical discharge machining depend greatly on the material used for the electrode, or tool. Improved performance of electrode materials has been the primary reason for development of improvements in power supplies; a further benefit has been to extend the range of materials that can be used as electrodes. Table 3 lists advantages and disadvantages, and Table 4 lists areas of applicability for electrode materials.

Low electrode wear (high "wear ratio"; see data presented in Table 4) is associated with high melting point. Graphite has the highest melting point of any known material (6300 F) and is low in cost and readily fabricated. Tungsten (melting point, 6100 F) and tungsten alloys are next in melting temperature, followed by molybdenum (4700 F), but these metals are expensive and difficult to fabricate. It is often possible to produce accurately dimensioned parts by using, consecutively, several electrodes made from inexpensive, easily fabricated materials (Table 4); the relative importance of wear ratio and electrode cost depends largely on the quantity of workpieces to be processed and the accuracy required.

Conventional machining methods and casting are widely used to make electrodes for EDM; metal spraying, press forming, and electroplating techniques are also used. Electrode dimensions must be closely controlled, particularly on finishing electrodes.

Machined electrodes are made from copper, brass, copper-tungsten alloys, silver-tungsten alloys, and graphite, using standard machining methods.

Graphite electrodes are used more often than metal electrodes (except when the machined surface of the work must be smoother than 40 micro-in.). Graphite generally costs less than metal; it wears exceptionally well and is easy to machine. It is also used under the special conditions of "no-wear" EDM for roughing operations, as described on page 230, in this article.

Graphite electrodes are machined and ground by standard methods, and then are hand finished. A dust-collecting system should be used to carry off graphite dust during machining and grinding. Except with adhesive-bonded electrodes, the dust can be minimized by soaking the graphite in kerosine.

For some applications, a steel punch can be tipped with graphite. The graphite tip may be machined along with the punch after being attached to it. Tips may be attached to punches by mechanical means, by soldering, or (most commonly) by conductive epoxy cements. Quick-setting, high-strength "nonconductive" adhesives (such as cyanoacrylate contact cements) are used in some applications. These materials do not interfere with the passage of current in the thin films produced by pressure bonding. Mechanical attachment gives the lowest electrical resistance. Solder or adhesive is used when there is no room for the pins and screws required for mechanical attachment. A graphite tip to be soldered must first be plated with copper.

Cast Electrodes. Electrodes are often die cast from standard zinc-base die-casting alloys (AG40A and AC41A), from zinc-tin alloys (80-20 to 50-50), and from aluminum alloys. Such electrodes can be remelted for re-use.

Properties and applicability of cast electrodes are described in Tables 3 and 4. Aluminum alloy electrodes have better corner-wear characteristics than those cast from zinc-containing alloys, but are more difficult to fabricate because of their higher melting temperature (1220 F) and higher shrinkage (5 to 7%). Zinc-tin and aluminum alloy electrodes have enough ductility to permit cold coining for greater accuracy.

Flow holes for the dielectric fluid usually must be provided through the electrode. For roughing cuts, the holes should be as large as practical, to allow high flow rates at low pressure. The position of the flow holes is sometimes made to vary slightly in a set of electrodes, so that an electrode can remove cores left by the previous one.

Etching. Electrodes are sometimes etched to remove small amounts of metal, either by immersion or by local application of a suitable etchant. (See the article "Chemical Machining", on page 240.) Aqueous solutions for etching some electrode materials are described in Table 5. These solutions must be agitated once a minute during etching, to remove trapped gases. The rate of etching will decrease as the solution is depleted of chemicals during use. Changes in temperature will also affect the etching rate. Lacquer or other protection can be used for masking any portion not to be etched. After etching, the exposed surfaces of the electrode should be neutralized.

Wear ratio, a measure of electrode life, is important in EDM because electrodes are often expensive. In addition, rapid consumption of electrodes increases the difficulty and cost of producing the accurate dimensions and the sharp corners needed in many

Table 5. Aqueous Solutions for Etching EDM Electrodes (Tools)

Electrode material	Component	Concentration	Temperature, F	Etching rate per side, in. per min
Brass	70% HNO_3	20% by volume	115	0.0002
Brass	70% HNO_3	30% by volume	85	0.0002
Steel	37% HCl	80% by volume	135	0.0001
Tungsten and alloys(a)(b)	70% HNO_3, 50% HF	20-25% by volume, 80-75% by volume	85	0.0001(c)
50-50 zinc-tin alloy(a)	93% H_2SO_4, 70% HNO_3	10% by volume, 20% by volume	85	0.0002

(a) Etching solution is a mixture of acids shown. (b) Because gas is evolved, including fluorine, tungsten must be etched under an exhaust hood. (c) Estimated.

kinds of workpieces, such as dies.

Wear ratio is expressed in terms of end wear, side wear, corner wear, and volume wear, as shown in Fig. 3. Wear is always greatest at the corners (generally about double the end wear). When accuracy is important, corner wear controls the choice of electrode material and the number of electrodes, and therefore controls electrode cost.

Unless indicated otherwise for a specific application, "wear ratio" of an electrode refers to either (*a*) the ratio of the volume of work material removed to the volume of electrode consumed in the process, or (*b*) the ratio of depth of cut to the length of electrode consumed in making the cut. Wear ratios for different electrode materials are listed in Table 4.

"No-Wear" EDM

"No-wear" EDM roughing uses graphite electrodes at reverse (positive) polarity, high current density and low pulse frequency. Maximum metal removal rate is 10 to 20% lower than for ordinary EDM roughing with graphite electrodes. No-wear EDM requires a power source and equipment capable of maintaining the following conditions:

1 One-direction discharge, positive or "reverse" polarity for the tool
2 Frequencies in the range of 400 to 20,000 cps, generally about 2000 cps
3 Variable control of pulse timing to set the pulse for at least 90% on to 10% off
4 Temperature of dielectric not above 120 F
5 Graphite electrodes
6 Voltage never more than 80 volts
7 No capacitance across the spark gap, and no inductance in series with it
8 Low-pressure flow of the dielectric fluid
9 Smooth servo control
10 Dielectric flow must not trap particles.

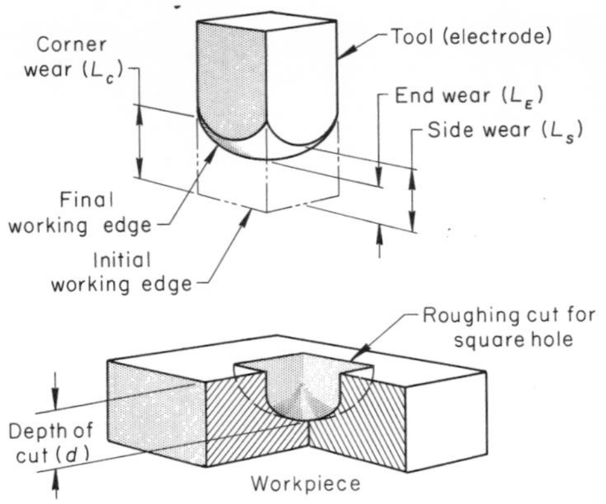

End wear ratio $= d/L_E$
Side wear ratio $= d/L_S$
Corner wear ratio $= d/L_C$

$$\text{Volume wear ratio} = \frac{\text{Vol of workpiece removed}}{\text{Vol of electrode consumed}}$$

Drawing shows final contours of electrode after long use in making roughing cuts, as illustrated, for square holes. Radii in holes can be reduced to a few thousandths of an inch by making additional cuts with electrodes having progressively sharper radii.

Fig. 3. Wear of electrodes in EDM

When using this technique, some of the molten or vaporized work metal solidifies on the electrode in a thin, adherent film, which may have to be removed if it becomes thick enough to alter processing conditions significantly.

Because it does not produce low-micro-inch surfaces, no-wear EDM is not used for finishing. However, the absence of machining wear on tools eliminates or greatly reduces the need for redressing or replacement of tools, and no-wear EDM is often used in roughing applications that require the removal of large amounts of metal.

Table 6 shows the effect on manufacturing costs of using no-wear roughing in making die cavities for forging shoes to be used on tracked vehicles. Costs are compared for three manufacturing procedures: (*a*) ordinary EDM for both roughing and finishing, (*b*) no-wear EDM for roughing and ordinary EDM for finishing, and (*c*) conventional diesinking. Operating conditions for EDM also are listed.

As shown in Table 6, for three or more dies, ordinary EDM is slightly less expensive than conventional diesinking, and the use of no-wear EDM for roughing the cavities results in a substantially lower cost.

One half of the die is pictured in the illustration accompanying Table 6; the other die-half, although different in shape, required the same maximum depth of cut. The dies were made from low-alloy, prehardened 6G steel at Rockwell C 42 to 46 (for composition of 6G, see Table 1, page 354). The 400-amp EDM machine had a maximum removal rate of 12 to 15 cu in. of steel per hour, and was designed for both no-wear and ordinary EDM. Roughing electrodes were 0.020 to 0.025 in. smaller per side than finishing electrodes. Surface finish of the completed die sets averaged 125 micro-in.

Table 6. Comparative Costs for Making the Cavities in Dies for Forging Track Links by Ordinary EDM, "No-Wear" EDM, and Conventional Diesinking, and Operating Conditions for EDM(a)

Cost items	One die: Ordinary EDM	One die: No-wear EDM	Three dies: Ordinary EDM	Three dies: No-wear EDM	Six dies: Ordinary EDM	Six dies: No-wear EDM
Electrode cost:						
Number of electrodes(b)	6	4	6	4	6	4
Total cost(c)	$1453	$1007	$1453	$1007	$1453	$1007
Cost for redressing electrodes:						
Number of redressings	.....	.....	8	.....	20	2
Total cost(d)	.....	.....	$1400	.....	$3500	$ 350
Machining cost (EDM methods):						
Setup	$ 45	$ 45	$ 135	$ 135	$ 270	$ 270
Machining	300	300	900	900	1800	1800
Total	$ 345	$ 345	$1035	$1035	$2070	$2070
Manufacturing cost, total:						
EDM methods	$1798	$1352	$3888	$2042	$7023	$3427
Conventional diesinking(e)	$1350		$4050		$8100	

Condition	Roughing: Ordinary EDM	Roughing: No-wear EDM	Finishing
Operating Conditions for EDM Methods			
Tool polarity	Reverse (+)	Reverse (+)	Normal (−)
Pulse frequency, kc	2	2	32
Current, amp	200 max(f)	200 max(f)	30
Machining time(g)	6.5	6.5	3.75
Removal rate, cu in. per hr(h)	6 max	6 max	1 to 1.5
End wear ratio(j)	50:1 (average)	No wear	8:1 (average)
Overcut per side, in.	0.008 max	0.012 max	0.003
Dielectric pressure, psi	5	5	30

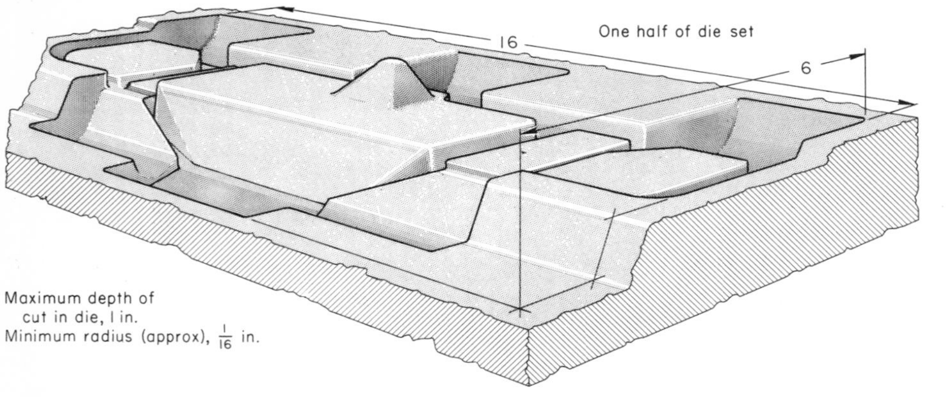

(a) No-wear technique used for roughing only — all finishing by ordinary EDM. Electrodes, graphite; dielectric, hydrocarbon (petroleum) oil with viscosity of about 40 SUS at 100 F, at a pressure of 5 psi for roughing and 30 psi for finishing; costs other than for electrodes based on $15 per hour for labor plus overhead. (b) Ordinary EDM: two electrodes for roughing, one for finishing, per die half; no-wear EDM: one for roughing, one for finishing, per die half. (c) Includes $48 material cost and $175 fabrication cost per electrode, plus $115 for manifold for mounting and positioning electrodes. (d) At $175 per redressing. (e) Machining time was 90 hr per die. (f) Initial current, 30 amp; gradually increased to 200 amp in 4½ hr; decreased to final 80 amp in next 2 hr. (g) Cutting time only. (h) Average of 2.85 cu in. per hr, based on total time for roughing and finishing. (j) See Fig. 3 for definition of wear ratios.

Examples of Application

The following list identifies by number nine examples dealing with production applications of electrical discharge machining that will be found in sections of this volume covering other processes.

Example	Application
373	Cost comparison of end milling, EDM and ECM for making complex slots in 4340 steel
461	Time and cost comparison of EDM and ECM in producing square holes in hardened tool steel
462	Time and cost comparison of EDM and ECM in producing six parallel holes in U-700 turbine blades
683	Production of stamping dies from W2, A2 and S1 tool steels by EDM
706	Production of punching dies from T15 and A2 tool steels by EDM

851....Machining an outside contour and a hole in A-286 turbine rotor buckets by EDM
864....Cutting flat test specimens from 0.50-in. tungsten plate by EDM
865....Trepanning ⅝-in.-diam cylindrical test specimens from tungsten forgings by EDM
1005....Drilling ten holes simultaneously in titanium alloy sheet assemblies by EDM.

The examples that follow (449a to 449j) present details of ten applications of EDM that involved slots and holes. Table 7 presents data taken from typical production applications to show results obtained from fifteen combinations of electrodes and work metals. Table 8 presents similar data obtained from research work on nineteen combinations of electrodes and work metals, showing both roughing and finishing data where available.

Example 449 (a). Slots in a Low-Carbon Steel Mold (Fig. 4)

Five parallel slots were produced by EDM in the bottom of a low-carbon steel mold for plastics, shown in Fig. 4(a). Total stock removed was 0.085 cu in. Overcut was 0.0007 ±0.0005 in. on each side. Tolerance was ±0.001 in. on slot dimensions and ±0.002 in. on total taper. The roughness of the machined surface was 50 micro-in. Processing conditions and cost data are given with Fig. 4.

The graphite electrode, which consisted of two matching halves cemented together (Fig. 4b), was held in a slotted holder with a built-in manifold. The manifold connected automatically with the slots in the electrode to supply the dielectric oil. The tip of the electrode was reground three times in the machining of one slot. After regrinding, the electrode was reversed in the holder, to eliminate core tips left from the previous cut.

To make the slots by mechanical machining, the mold would have been made in several pieces. The cost of making the slots by mechanical machining was estimated at $350 per mold, more than three times the cost by EDM. [SOURCE: S. Ratmansky (Electrical Machining Specialists, Inc.), "EDM? ECM? How Do They Fit In???", ASTME technical paper No. SP 64-87, 1964]

Example 449 (b). Slots in Three 52100 Steel Valve Components at Rockwell C 60

Material 0.030 In. Thick. A slot 0.024 by 0.060 in. was machined through 0.030-in.-thick 52100 steel in a valve component. The electrode was made of a copper-tungsten alloy. At a removal rate of 0.00063 cu in. per hr, 4 min was required for completing the slot. Overcut was 0.001 in. per side, with current of 1 amp, capacitance of 0.6 mfd, and pulse frequency of 32 kc.

Material 0.045 In. Thick. A slot 0.030 by 0.092 in. was machined through 0.045-in.-thick 52100 steel in a valve component, using an electrode made of silver-tungsten alloy. This slot was produced in a roughing cut to a depth of 0.035 in., followed by a finishing cut for the remaining 0.010-in. thickness. Cutting time was 6 min, at a removal rate of 0.00123 cu in. per hr for both cuts, with 0.001-in. overcut per side. The roughing cut was made at 2 amp, 4 mfd and 16 kc; the finishing cut at 0.5 amp, 0.75 mfd and 65 kc.

Material 0.055 In. Thick. A slot 0.060 by 0.086 in. was machined through 0.055-in-thick 52100 steel in a valve component, using an electrode of silver-tungsten alloy. A roughing cut was made 0.045 in. deep, then a finishing cut was made for the remaining 0.010-in. thickness. Cutting time was 3.5 min, at a removal rate of 0.0048 cu in. per hr for both cuts, with overcut of 0.001 in. per side. The roughing cut used 5 amp, 5 mfd and 65 kc. The finishing cut used 0.5 amp, 0.5 mfd and 130 kc.

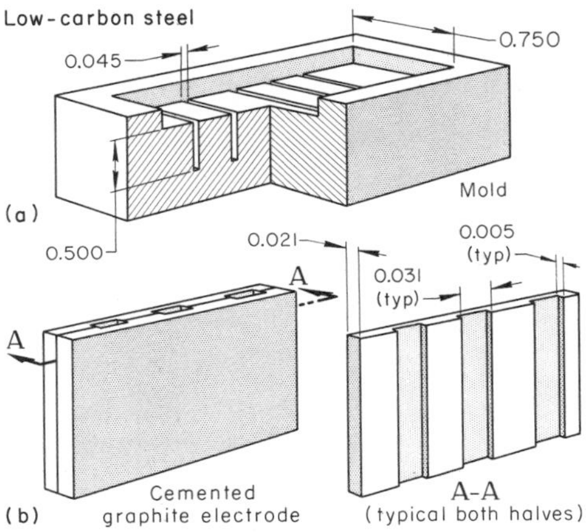

Process Details

Current	2 amp
Capacitance	0.25 mfd
Gap voltage	40 volts
Spark gap	0.001 in.
Dielectric (oil) pressure	10 psi
Removal rate	0.030 cu in. per hr
Machining time	4 hr
Time required to make electrode	4 hr
Setup time	2 hr
Total time	10 hr

Cost per Mold

Electrode material	$ 2.30	
Electrode machining	28.00	
Total		$ 30.30
Electrode holder	$15.00	
Setup	5.00	
Total		20.00
Machining		40.00
Bench work		17.50
Inspection		3.50
Total		$111.30

Fig. 4. Mold in which five slots were produced by electrical discharge machining with graphite electrodes (Example 449a)

Example 449 (c). Round Holes in 8620 Steel

Holes 0.0082 in. in diameter were machined through 0.031-in.-thick 8620 steel, using a tungsten wire 0.0068 in. in diameter as the electrode. At a penetration rate of 0.074 in. per min, machining time per hole was 25 sec. Current was 0.33 amp, capacitance was 0.26 mfd, and pulse frequency ranged from 70 to 100 kc.

The dielectric was mineral seal oil, and was used without flushing pressure. Volume wear ratio was 5.1 to 1. Overcut per side and hole taper were both 0.0007 in.

Only 0.0005-in. overcut, with no measurable taper, resulted for the same operation at a slower penetration rate (0.012 in. per min). Wear ratio also dropped, to 3.1 to 1. Machining time per hole was 2.5 min, using 0.1 amp, 0.01 mfd and the same varying frequencies.

Example 449 (d). Holes in 302 Stainless Steel

Round holes 0.004 in. in diameter were machined through the 0.041-in. thickness of 302 stainless steel, using a tungsten wire 0.003 in. in diameter as the electrode. Machining time per hole was 1 min, 55 sec, at a penetration rate of 0.021 in. per min. Current was 0.1 amp, capacitance was 0.9 mfd, and pulse frequency varied from 70 to 100 kc. The dielectric was mineral seal oil, and was used with no flushing pressure. Volume wear ratio was 3.1 to 1. Overcut was 0.0005 in. per side, with total taper of 0.0002 in.

Fluted holes with major and minor diameters of 0.007 and 0.004 in. were machined through 0.031-in.-thick 302 stainless steel, using a fluted tungsten wire with major and minor diameters of 0.006 and 0.003 in. as the electrode.

It took 1 min, 50 sec to machine through, at a penetration rate of 0.017 in. per min. Wear ratio, overcut, taper and dielectric were the same as for drilling the round hole.

Example 449 (e). Slots in 440C Stainless Steel

Slots 0.034 by 0.508 in. were machined through 0.050-in.-thick 440C stainless steel in a valve component. The hardness of the workpiece was Rockwell C 60. The electrode was made of silver-tungsten alloy. Roughing, to a depth of 0.040 in., took 1.5 min, at a removal rate of 0.028 cu in. per hr, using 3 amp, 8 mfd and 32 kc. Finishing, through the remaining 0.010-in. thickness, took 14 min, at a removal rate of 0.00074 cu in. per hr, using 5 amp, 0.5 mfd and 130 kc. Overcut was 0.001 in. per side for both cuts.

Example 449 (f). Square Holes in Ta – 10 W

Holes ½ in. square were machined through a thickness of 0.125 in. of Ta – 10 W, using a carbon electrode, in a dielectric of transformer oil at 10 psi. At 10 amp, 14 mfd and

Table 7. Conditions and Results in Typical Production Applications of Electrical Discharge Machining

Work material (Footnotes describe shape machined)	Electrode material	Operating conditions(a) Current, amp	Capacitance, mfd	Pulse frequency, kc	Results Removal rate, cu in./hr	Overcut, in. per side	Wear ratio (E = end, V = vol)	Penetration, in./min	Roughness, micro-in.
302 stainless(b)	Tungsten(c)	1.0	0.9	70-100	....	0.0005	V 5.1:1	0.006	....
440C stainless(d)	Cu-W alloy	1.0	0.6	32	0.007	0.001	....	0.009	....
440C stainless(e)	Cu-W alloy	1.8	0.75	16	0.037	0.0015	....	0.021	....
Ta – 10 W(f)	Brass	23	32	16	0.108	.....	V 0.6:1	0.007	185
Ta – 10 W(g)	Graphite	3	0.9	65	0.042	.....	V 1.0:1	0.005	150
FS-85(f)	Brass	28	32	16	0.180	.....	V 0.75:1	0.012	200
FS-85(g)	Graphite	3	0.9	65	0.072	.....	V 1.3:1	0.0086	150
Ti – 6 Al – 4 V(h)	Brass	3	1	130	0.040	.....	E 1.37:1	0.0034	65-75
	Brass	20	14	36	0.534	.....	E 3.92:1	0.045	350-400
	Copper	20	14	36	0.132	.....	E 2.40:1	0.011	175-200
TD nickel(j)	Brass	28	32	16	0.162	.....	V 1.4:1	0.010	225
TD nickel(k)	Graphite	3	0.9	65	0.060	.....	V 1.2:1	0.0071	150
Tungsten carbide(m)	Tungsten(n)	0.2	0.9	70-100	....	0.0007	V 10.1:1	0.022	....
7079-T6 Al alloy(p)	Graphite	15	14	65	....	.....	V 10.0:1	....	....
	Graphite	3	0.9	65	....	.....	V 10.0:1	....	125

(a) Dielectric: mineral seal oil for 302 stainless steel and tungsten carbide; transformer oil for remaining applications. Pressure: 10 psi. (b) Rectangular hole 0.013 by 0.021 in., through material 0.031 in. thick. (c) Rectangular wire, 0.012 by 0.020 in. (d) Rectangular hole 0.035 by 0.378 in., through 0.040-in.-thick material at Rockwell C 60. (e) Hole 0.197 in. in diameter through 0.081-in.-thick material at Rockwell C 60. (f) Hole ½ in. square, through material ⅛ in. thick. (g) Hole ½ in. square (at ⅜-in.-diam through hole), through material ⅛ in. thick. (h) Hole ½ in. in diameter, in material at Rockwell B 71. (j) Hole ½ in. square, through material 0.090 in. thick. (k) Hole ½ in. square (at ⅜-in.-diam predrilled hole), through material 0.090 in. thick. (m) Hole 0.0095 in. in diameter, through material ⅛ in. thick. (n) Wire 0.0081 in. in diameter. (p) Data on first line are for roughing; on second line, for finishing (in a weight reduction cut).

Table 8. Results Obtained in Research and Development Work on EDM Applications

(Where two lines of data are given for a single application, the first describes roughing and the second describes finishing.)

Work material (Footnotes describe shapes machined)	Electrode material	Operating conditions: Type of dielectric fluid(a)	Current, amp	Capacitance, mfd	Pulse frequency, kc	Results: Removal rate, cu in. per hr	Overcut, in. per side	Tool wear, cu in. per hr	Wear ratio: End	Side	Volume	Penetration, in. per min	Roughness, micro-in.
1018 steel(b)	Graphite	Oil	40	108	2.0	1.26	0.0025	....	8.9:1	1.7:1	.....	0.006	400-450
		Oil	10	1.75	130	0.081	0.0015	....	2.8:1	2.0:1	.....	0.0012	140-190
	F-C brass	Oil	25	4	130	0.30	0.002	0.154	1.98:1	0.8:1	1.95:1	0.0031	170-185
	(alloy 360)	Oil	5	1.5	130	0.036	0.002	0.028	1.26:1	1.0:1	1.27:1	0.00054	90-100
	ETP copper	Oil	47	84	2.0	0.50	0.0045	0.249	2.45:1	0.4:1	2.0:1	0.0029	300-400
	(alloy 110)	Oil	15	1.75	130	0.083	0.002	0.016	6.13:1	1.0:1	5.19:1	0.0027	110-130
	Zinc	Oil	20	108	2.0	0.42	0.0045	0.176	2.62:1	0.33:1	2.4:1	0.0038	230-270
		Oil	4	1.5	130	0.041	0.0015	0.042	0.98:1	0.44:1	0.99:1	0.00043	110-120
4340 steel, Rockwell C 40(c)	Yellow brass	Polar	19	12	4	0.60	0.004	....	.....	.....	2.81:1	0.017	400
	(alloy 270)	Polar	5	6	130	0.08	0.001	....	.....	.....	1.40:1	0.002	120
O1 tool steel, Rockwell A 81(d)	Graphite	Oil	40	56	36	1.64	0.004	....	6.6:1	.....	.....	0.19	....
		Oil	5	2.4	36	0.19	0.0013	....	3.5:1	.....	.....	0.02	90
H13 tool steel, Rockwell A 76(d)	Graphite	Oil	40	56	36	1.84	0.0048	....	6.5:1	.....	.....	0.20	....
		Oil	5	2.4	36	0.19	0.0014	....	3.4:1	.....	.....	0.02	....
405 stainless, Rockwell A 60(d)	Graphite	Oil	40	56	36	1.90	0.0034	....	6.3:1	.....	.....	0.20	....
		Oil	5	2.4	36	0.17	0.0017	....	3.2:1	.....	.....	0.02	....
420 stainless(e)	Graphite	Oil	25	24	16	0.40	0.002	....	5.45:1	1.96:1	.....	0.0037	210-270
	Brass	Oil	25	24	16	0.34	0.003	0.16	2.08:1	0.67:1	2.12:1	0.0033	170-210
	Copper	Oil	25	24	16	0.38	0.0024	0.10	3.55:1	0.85:1	3.77:1	0.0025	210-240
	Zinc	Oil	15	16	16	0.21	0.0034	0.05	6.45:1	0.50:1	3.95:1	0.0011	200-230
17-7 PH, Rockwell C 38(c)	Graphite	Polar	17.5	24	14	2.28	0.004	....	.....	.....	7.3:1	0.063	550
		Polar	4.5	2	130	0.25	0.001	....	.....	.....	3.34:1	0.007	132
René 41, Rockwell C 36(c)	Yellow brass	Polar	17.5	42	8	0.73	0.003	....	.....	.....	5.82:1	0.020	400
		Polar	4	6	130	0.08	0.001	....	.....	.....	1.75:1	0.002	110
René 41, Rockwell A 70(d)	Graphite	Oil	40	56	36	1.87	0.0046	....	8.3:1	.....	.....	0.196	....
		Oil	5	2.4	36	0.22	0.0015	....	4.4:1	.....	.....	0.026	....
HS-25, Rockwell C 19(c)	Graphite	Polar	15	12	4	1.29	0.004	....	.....	.....	4.22:1	0.035	475
		Polar	6	3	38	0.17	0.002	....	.....	.....	2.32:1	0.0047	118
HS-31, Rockwell A 63(d)	Graphite	Oil	38	56	20	1.51	0.0046	....	6.4:1	.....	.....	0.17	....
		Oil	5	2.4	20	0.22	0.0022	....	4.1:1	.....	.....	0.024	....
Tungsten sheet, 99% density(f)	Brass	Oil	30	...	...	0.9	.....	....	.....	.....	0.5:1	0.009	....
Tungsten forging, 100% density(g)	Brass(h)	Oil	40	...	...	0.9	.....	....	.....	.....	0.5:1	0.0125	....

(a) "Oil" denotes a hydrocarbon (petroleum) oil, viscosity of about 40 sus at 100 F; "Polar" denotes a polar liquid, such as an aqueous solution of an ethylene glycol. (b) 1¼-in.-diam holes through material ¼ in. thick. (c) Blind hole in shape of right triangle with sides 1.35 and 0.90 in. at right angle. (d) ½-in.-square hole through material ⅜ in. thick, with ⅜-in.-diam predrilled hole. (e) ¼ in. thick. (f) Tensile specimen trepanned from sheet 0.050 in. thick. (g) Hole ⅝ in. diam by 3 in. long trepanned 1½ in. from each side. (h) Tubes of ⅝-in. ID, rotating.

16 kc, machining time was 2.9 min per hole, for a removal rate of 0.64 cu in. per hr. Wear ratio was 1.2 to 1; surface roughness, 250 micro-in.

Surface roughness was reduced to 100 micro-in. when ½-in.-square holes were machined with a brass electrode. In this operation, a hole ⅜ in. in diameter was drilled through the 0.125-in. thickness before making the square hole that had the same axis. The current for the second machining step was 3 amp, capacitance was 0.9 mfd, and pulse frequency was 65 kc. Machining time for the second step was 43.5 min, for a removal rate of 0.024 cu in. per hr.

Example 449 (g). Square Holes in FS-85

Holes ½ in. square were machined through 0.125-in.-thick FS-85 columbium alloy (nominal alloy content: 28% tantalum, 10% tungsten, 1% zirconium, remainder columbium), using a carbon electrode, in a dielectric of transformer oil at 10 psi. At 7 amp, 4 mfd and 16 kc, machining time per hole was 14.4 min, for a removal rate of 0.130 cu in. per hr. Wear ratio was 2.1 to 1; surface roughness, 225 micro-in.

Surface roughness was reduced to 150 micro-in. when the ½-in.-square holes were machined using a brass electrode. Here, a hole ⅜ in. in diameter was drilled through the 0.125-in.-thick FS-85 before production of the square hole that had the same axis. This operation was done at 3 amp, 0.9 mfd and 65 kc. Machining each hole took 58 min for a removal rate of 0.018 cu in. per hr. Wear ratio was 1.3 to 1.

Example 449 (h). Round Holes in Ti-6 Al-4 V

An electrode of brass, ½ in. in diameter, with a ⅛-in.-diam flushing hole at the center, was used to machine holes in Ti-6 Al-4 V (hardness, Rockwell B 71), with transformer oil as the dielectric, at 7 to 13 psi. With a current of 20 amp, capacitance of 14 mfd, and pulse frequency of 36 kc, a removal rate of 0.53 cu in. per hr was obtained, with surface roughness of 250 to 300 micro-in. Ratio of linear end wear was 3.9 to 1.

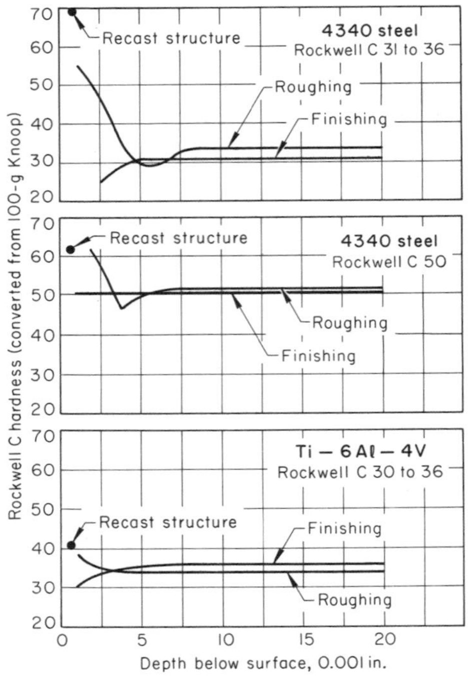

Fig. 5. Effect of electrical discharge machining on hardness of the machined surface, in roughing and finishing of 4340 steel at two hardness levels and Ti-6 Al-4 V at Rockwell C 30 to 36

A similar electrode of copper produced a surface roughness of 60 to 70 micro-in. at a slower removal rate (0.00736 cu in. per hr). The copper electrode was used at 1 amp, 1 mfd and 130 kc, for an end wear ratio of 4 to 1.

Example 449 (i). Square Holes in TD Nickel

Holes ½ in. square were machined through a thickness of 0.090 in. of thoria-dispersed nickel, using a carbon electrode, in a dielectric of transformer oil at 10 psi. At 7 amp, 4 mfd and 16 kc, machining time per hole was 4.6 min, for a removal rate of 0.03 cu in. per hr. Wear ratio was 1.2 to 1; surface roughness, 250 micro-in.

Surface roughness was reduced to 125 micro-in. when the ½-in.-square holes were machined using a brass electrode. A hole ⅜ in. in diameter had been drilled through the 0.090-in. material before making the square hole that had the same axis. At 3 amp, 0.9 mfd and 65 kc, each hole was machined in 29 min, for a removal rate of 0.026 cu in. per hr. Wear ratio was 2.0 to 1.

Example 449 (j). Round Holes in Tungsten Carbide at Rockwell C 78

Holes 1.125 in. in diameter were rough machined to a depth of 0.180 in. in tungsten carbide, on the same centers as previously made smaller holes. An electrode made of a silver-tungsten alloy was used, at 16 amp, 42 mfd and 4 kc. At a removal rate of 0.63 cu in. per hr, time per hole was 17 min. Overcut was 0.004 in. per side.

Holes 1.116 in. in diameter and 1.10 in. deep also were machined on the same centers as smaller holes. Silver-tungsten electrodes were used at 17 amp, 50 mfd and 4 kc. Machining time per hole was 105 min, at a removal rate of 0.61 cu in. per hr. Overcut was 0.0025 in. per side.

Process Characteristics

Accuracy of electrical discharge machining can readily meet tolerances of ±0.002 to ±0.005 in., and tolerances as small as ±0.0001 to ±0.0005 in. have been met with close control. Removal rates range from 0.01 to 30 cu in. of material per hour; a brass electrode removes about 0.00025 cu in. per amp per min, and a graphite electrode about two to three times as much.

Electrical discharge machining produces taper, overcut (half the difference between the hole size and the original size of the electrode), and corner radii. Typical taper is 0.0005 to 0.005 in. per in. per side, typical overcut is 0.0002 to 0.005 in. per side, and minimum corner radius is equal to overcut.

Surface Finish. Roughness of the machined surface is greater for higher metal removal rates, as illustrated in Table 2.

Effect on Work-Metal Hardness. The high temperatures attained in melting and vaporizing metal from the workpiece affect a shallow layer (0.0001 to 0.005 in.) of the surface machined.

The outermost layer after machining is metal that was rapidly chilled from a molten condition, and is therefore extremely hard. The layer directly below the hard surface is in a slightly tempered condition. In hardened steel, the outermost layer is about 0.0001 in. thick for finishing cuts and 0.0005 in. thick for roughing cuts, and has a final hardness greater than Rockwell C 60.

The tempered layer in hardened steel is about 0.002 in. thick for finishing cuts and 0.008 in. thick for roughing cuts, and is about 2 points (finishing) to 5 points (roughing) lower on the Rockwell C scale than the workpiece body.

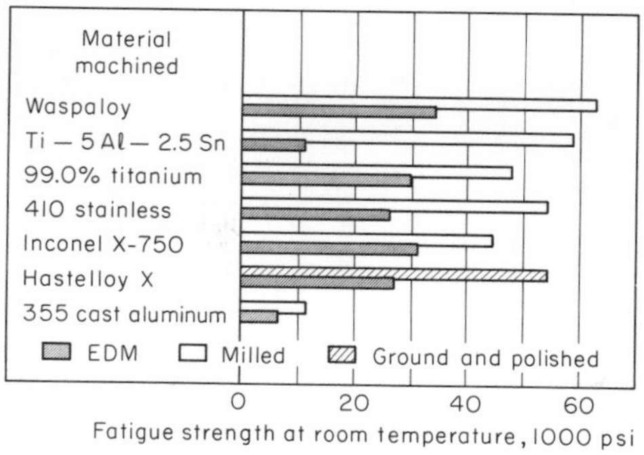

Fig. 6. Fatigue strength of seven workpiece materials after electrical discharge machining and two other processes

Figure 5 illustrates the effect of EDM on 4340 steel (two hardnesses) and on Ti – 6 Al – 4 V at Rockwell C 30 to 36.

Die surfaces are affected by EDM as shown in Fig. 5. Dies made by EDM are satisfactory for most applications, although premature cracking has been observed in some instances. Harmful surface effects can be minimized or avoided by careful die design and close control over EDM processing conditions. Improved die life sometimes results from EDM surface effects.

Effect on Fatigue Strength. Figure 6 compares the effect of EDM and two other processes on the room-temperature fatigue strength of seven metals. As shown, all seven metals had lower fatigue strength after EDM than after mechanical machining. For some high-stress applications, it may be necessary to restore fatigue life by removing the damaged surface layer or by peening or burnishing to produce a compressively stressed surface.

Other Examples

See list at bottom of column 3, page 230.

Electrochemical Machining (ECM)

By John F. Kahles*

ELECTROCHEMICAL MACHINING (ECM) is the controlled removal of metal by anodic dissolution in an electrolytic cell in which the workpiece is the anode and the tool the cathode. The electrolyte is pumped through the gap between the tool and the workpiece (the cutting gap), while direct current is passed through the cell at a low voltage, to dissolve metal from the workpiece at approximately 100% efficiency.

Electrochemical machining can be used to do work that would be difficult or impossible by mechanical machining. The work includes machining hard materials (such as hardened steel and heat-resisting alloys) and odd-shaped, small, deep holes. Electrochemical machining is used for operations as widely different as face milling, deburring, etching and marking.

Although electrochemical machining is sometimes applicable to small-lot production, the process is best suited to mass-production applications, because of high tooling and setup costs and high capital equipment costs. A 10,000-amp machine tool to remove metal at about 1 cu in. per min may cost $75,000 to $100,000 (not including the cost of accessory equipment and facilities). The most frequent application of ECM is in the production of jet engine parts and for other aerospace applications; it is also used in automotive and general manufacturing applications.

Figure 1 shows a typical setup for electrochemical machining. The electric current might be 50 to 20,000 amp at 4 to 30 volts dc, for a current density of 100 to 2000 amp per sq in. (asi) across a gap of 0.001 to 0.030 in. between the tool and the workpiece. The electrolyte flows through this cutting gap at a velocity of 20 to 200 ft per sec, forced by a pressure of 10 to 400 psi. Temperature of the electrolyte may be 75 to 150 F; suspended solids are removed by settling, centrifuging or filtering (or a combination of these) and circulated for re-use.

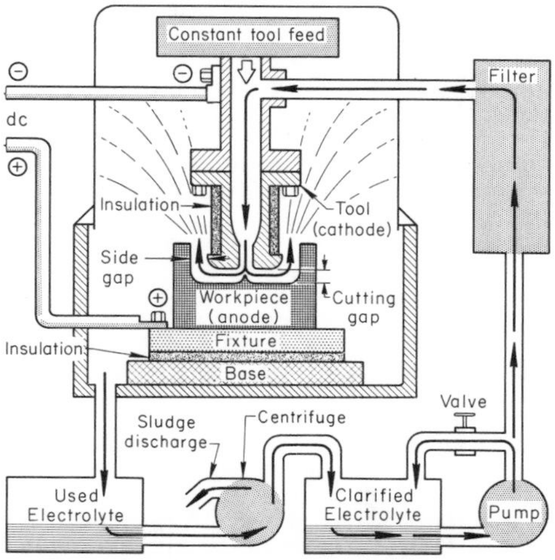

Fig. 1. Typical setup for electrochemical machining

Electrolytes are usually aqueous solutions of inorganic salts such as sodium chloride, potassium chloride, sodium nitrate or sodium chlorate; they may contain proprietary additives. Other electrolytes such as sulfuric acid or sodium hydroxide solutions may be used for machining certain metals.

The tool may be fed into the workpiece at the rate of 0.020 to 0.750 in. per min. In many applications, machining continues while the tool is held stationary for a specified "dwell" interval after completion of the feed travel. With electrolytes based on sodium chlorate, tool and workpiece can be held stationary for the entire machining period to do "embossing" or precision finishing. The tool may be made of brass, copper, stainless steel, titanium, platinum, a sintered copper-tungsten alloy, aluminum or graphite. The workpiece must be electrically conductive material.

Machine. The machine must be rigid enough to withstand the forces caused by the high pressure of the electrolyte, which tend to separate the tool from the workpiece. These forces are caused by the hydraulic pressure of the electrolyte as it flows through the gap between the tool and the workpiece. The electrolyte system includes pumps, filters, tanks and a heat exchanger. A servomechanism can be used to control the movement of the tool. Different types of automatic fast-acting cutoff devices are available to prevent catastrophic short circuits across the electrodes. One device monitors rate of

*Vice President, Metcut Research Associates Inc. The information in this article includes contributions from Guy Bellows, General Electric Co., and Edward Krabacher, Cincinnati Milling Machine Co. Data were also supplied by: J. R. Campbell, General Electric Co.; "Electrochemical Machining", Nimrod Press, 1966; F. M. Garlasco, Grumman Aircraft Engineering Corp.; H. Hudolin, Bendix Corp.; A. J. Mitchell, Oldsmobile Div., General Motors Corp.; J. H. Molinelli, Hanson – VanWinkle – Munning Div., M & T Chemicals, Inc.; B. H. Moschenross, McDonnell Douglas Corp.; R. L. Paden, Sundstrand Aviation Div., Sundstrand Corp.; R. A. Simpson, McDonnell Douglas Corp.

Table 1. Electrolytes for Electrochemical Machining of Various Metals

Work metal	Electrolyte: Major constituent	Electrolyte: Concentration (max), lb per gal H_2O	Removal rate, cu in. per min per 1000 amp
Steel; iron-base, Ni-base and Co-base alloys	NaCl or KCl	2½	0.13
	$NaNO_3$	5	0.13
Steel; hardened tool steel	$NaClO_3$	6½	0.12
Gray iron	NaCl	2½	0.12(a)(b)
	$NaNO_3$	5	0.12(a)(b)
White cast iron	$NaNO_3$	5	0.10(c)
Aluminum and aluminum alloys(d)	$NaNO_3$	5	0.13
	NaCl or KCl	2½	0.13
Titanium alloys	NaCl or KCl(e)	1	0.10
Tungsten	NaOH(f)	1½(g)	0.06
Molybdenum	NaOH(h)	1½	0.06
	NaCl or KCl	2½	0.06
Copper and copper alloys(d)	NaCl or KCl	2½	0.27
	$NaNO_3$	5	0.20
Zirconium	NaCl or KCl	2½	0.13

(a) Feed rates limited by graphite particle size. (b) Maximum; can vary widely. (c) Rough surface finish. (d) $NaNO_3$ electrolyte provides better surface finish. (e) Voltage must be greater than 11. (f) NaOH used up in process and must be replenished. (g) Minimum of ¾ lb per gal. (h) pH of electrolyte decreases with use; maintain pH by adding NaOH or KOH.

current change and backs off tool feed when an abnormal rise in current is detected.

Because corrosive spray or mist can easily be carried into the surrounding atmosphere, machines should be suitably isolated — preferably in a separate room away from other machine tools and work and tool-storage areas.

Control of many variables is needed for good results in ECM, the most important of these being: *(a)* tool feed rate; *(b)* current density; *(c)* electrolyte composition, suspended solids content, temperature, and flow rate; *(d)* tool and fixture material, construction and finish; *(e)* workpiece material and condition; and *(f)* cutting gap.

For accurate machining, a steady-state condition should be established, in which the dissolution of the workpiece material is balanced by the feed of the tool. This requires a uniform, controllable tool-feed rate. For a constant current, changes in feed cause changes in size of cut. Faster feeds cause the tool to cut a smaller hole.

As shown in Tables 7 and 8 and the examples in this article, most ECM is done at constant voltage with a fixed feed rate. At constant voltage, both cutting gap and side gap (see Fig. 1) are inversely proportional to the feed rate; the effect on the side gap is about 60% of that on the cutting gap. Feed and metal removal rates are limited by the permissible current density.

Typical penetration rates for different types of ECM operations on steel are:

Round through holes	0.5 ipm
Square through holes	0.4
Round or square blind holes	0.3
Simple cavities	0.25
Planing	6.0

Current density, in amperes per square inch of cutting area, is the chief factor in determining the permissible rate of tool feed, as the metal removal process is governed by Faraday's Law. Other factors remaining constant (such as electrolyte composition, flow and temperature), the rate of penetration varies directly with the current. For instance, a hole machined at 0.100 in. per min, at 10 volts and 1000 amp, would be made at 0.200 in. per min (twice the rate) if the current were raised to 2000 amp. This would require a potential of about 20 volts, and would increase power consumption to 40,000 from 10,000 watts. The power used is changed

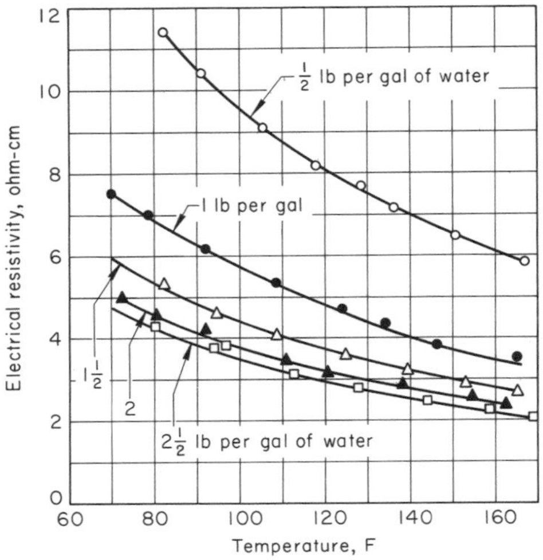

Fig. 2. Effect of temperature on resistivity of five sodium chloride solutions

into heat, and increased cooling capacity may be required at the higher current.

Current density also affects the surface finish of the work. Some metals can be polished in simple salt solutions, if the current density is great enough. Polishing action is more pronounced at higher current densities, and is influenced also by other factors, such as flow and temperature of electrolyte. Often the bottom of a hole made by ECM is polished whereas the sides have a dull finish. This is partly explained by local variations in current density. Most of the current flows through the cutting face of the tool. Some current leaks to the sides, behind the leading edge. The sides of the hole are machined somewhat by the leakage current at a lower current density, producing a dull finish. The greater current density at the cutting face yields a fine finish.

Electrolyte

The electrolyte has three main functions in ECM: It carries the current between the tool and the workpiece; it removes the products of the reaction from the cutting region; and it removes heat produced in the operation.

Electrolytes must have high electrical conductivity, low toxicity and corrosivity, chemical and electrochemical stability, and an absence of passivating effects. The work metal should dissolve at a single valence or, if there is a dual reaction, the ratio between the reactions should be constant; any secondary electrolytic oxidation must proceed at a constant rate.

General compositions of electrolytes for ECM processing of different types of metals are described in Table 1. Compositions that have been used in specific applications are listed in Tables 7 and 8, on pages 239 and 240.

Sludging Electrolytes. Solutions of sodium chloride and other salts are sludging electrolytes; they produce an insoluble reaction product, or sludge.

Sodium chloride solution is the most widely used electrolyte. It can be kept at constant strength by adding water to keep the volume constant. The electrical conductivity of sodium chloride varies little from pH 0 to 13. As an electrolyte, sodium chloride has some disadvantages. It is fairly corrosive, and produces large amounts of sludge. Some metals, such as tungsten carbide and pure titanium, cannot be machined in a sodium chloride electrolyte. Rough finishes are produced on silicon-containing alloys of aluminum in this solution.

Sodium nitrate is used in some applications, as shown in Tables 1, 7 and 8, either alone or in combination with sodium chloride. It gives smoother finishes on alloys of aluminum or copper, and is less corrosive than sodium chloride; however, it is more expensive and is more likely to cause passivity of the work surface.

Sodium chlorate solution has some unusual properties as an ECM electrolyte, and can be used in special applications, as described later in this article under "Embossing" by ECM.

Nonsludging Electrolytes. Solutions of strong acids or alkalis retain the anodically removed metal in solution and do not produce sludge under ECM conditions. An example is the use of sodium hydroxide as electrolyte for the machining of tungsten or molybdenum. Filtration of this kind of electrolyte is less of a problem; however, chemical control is more difficult, because the electrolyte changes more rapidly in composition. In addition, a large content of dissolved metal gives a greater tendency for metal to plate out of solution onto the tool. This cannot be permitted in accurate machining. The metal must be removed by some method, such as ion exchange or the periodic reversal of the current for short intervals. This latter method is more useful for work using a small current, because it is difficult to reverse large currents supplied from a rectifier.

Sludge, consisting of insoluble hydroxides or hydrated oxides of the work metal, is produced in salt electrolytes at the rate of about 100 to 150 cu in. of sludge per cubic inch of metal removed. A solution of 2 lb of sodium chloride per gallon becomes more viscous quickly after its sludge content exceeds 2.3% by weight. A thinner (less viscous) electrolyte is important for use with smaller cutting gaps and with higher electrolyte flow rates. The electrolyte usually should contain no more than 2% by weight of sludge.

A dirty electrolyte (with up to 2% by weight of sludge) machines as efficiently as a clean solution. There is little difference in the conductivity, rate of penetration, surface finish, or accuracy of machining. A dirty solution may deposit more precipitate on the sides of the workpiece, depending mainly on the rate of flow of the electrolyte. There is a danger that dried precipitate may stick in the cutting gap, causing a short circuit. For this reason in particular, a clean electrolyte is preferred.

Filtering, centrifuging and settling are generally used to remove sludge. It is usually more practical to purify even the cheapest electrolyte (sodium chloride) than to discard and replace it.

Strength of the electrolyte solution for ECM usually is a compromise. A concentrated solution has the advantages of better conductivity (lower voltage and power requirements), faster rate of penetration, and greater precision (because the conductivity of a concentrated solution varies less with changes in temperature and concentration). Dilute solutions have the advantages of costing less, dissolving more readily, being less likley to crystallize, and giving a smoother surface on some work.

Conductivity of the electrolyte, which depends primarily on its concentration and temperature, is important, because it affects power requirements and rate of penetration. For higher conductivity, the penetration rates are faster.

An over-concentrated solution may become saturated and allow the formation of crystals that can damage pumps, valves, instruments and pipes. A very weak solution causes local or intermittent passivity of the work, which makes machining difficult. A solution of 1 to 2.5 lb of sodium chloride per gallon of water works well as an electrolyte. A change in the pH of a salt electrolyte has little effect on its conductivity. The conductivity of sodium chloride solution increases less than 10% on lowering the pH to 1 or raising it to 13. In ECM operations, the chemical and electrochemical reactions and the presence of metallic hydroxides have a buffering effect, holding pH in the "neutral" range of 4 to 10 without the use of special control procedures.

The conductivity of an electrolyte changes greatly with temperature. Solutions of sodium chloride, for instance, are 100% more conductive at 160 F than at 75 F. Figure 2 shows the effect of temperature on resistivity of five solutions of sodium chloride. Any change in electrolyte conductivity will affect the accuracy of machining, because the dimensions of cutting gap and side gap depend on the conductivity. This is the reason for maintaining a constant electrolyte temperature. Selection of operating temperature usually requires a compromise. For higher temperatures less electricity is used, but additional capacity may be needed to heat the electrolyte. To some extent, conductivity of the electrolyte limits the current that can be used.

Rate of flow of the electrolyte is important, because the electrolyte must remove the heat and the products of the chemical reaction. Flow can be related to the amount of current used; the larger the ratio of flow to current, the better the removal of heat and reaction products. However, the cost of pumping increases as the flow increases, and excessive flow rates can cause cavitation effects and nonuniform metal removal. There is a minimum ratio of fluid flow to current that varies with the work metal and the cutting gap; 0.25 gal per min per 100 amp is a safe minimum flow rate for machining steel with an electrolyte of sodium chloride.

Rate of flow also has an effect on surface finish and on accuracy of machining. High electrolyte flow rate often improves the uniformity of metal removal with a given electrolyte without reducing the removal rate. Low rates of flow may cause precipitates to stick to the workpiece. This may cause changes in the pattern of flow that could affect the work. Local chemical attack may also be affected, causing

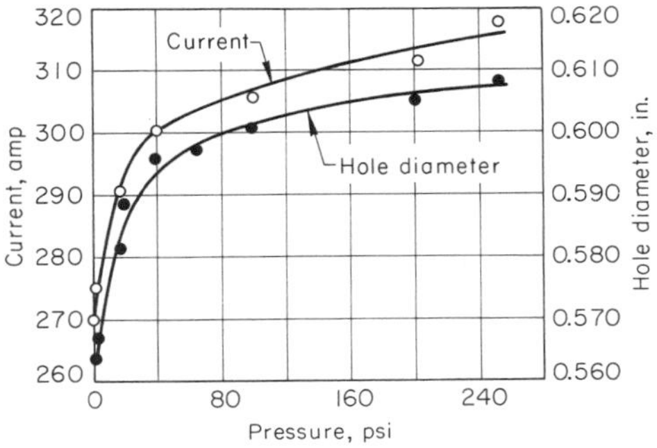

Fig. 3. Effect of electrolyte back pressure on hole size and current at constant voltage

changes in the surface finish. The flow rate sometimes affects the location and the thickness of deposits on the tool; high rates minimize the formation of deposits. The rate of flow also has a small effect on the voltage required.

Tool design limits the rate of electrolyte flow, and is the major factor governing pattern and uniformity of flow. (See "Tool Design", next column.)

Machining with back pressure is a useful form of ECM in some applications. The work is enclosed, restricting the outflow of the electrolyte, so that the pump raises the pressure. If the voltage is kept constant, the current increases, causing the tool to cut a proportionately larger hole. These changes are shown in Fig. 3. Even a small rise in pressure makes the tool cut a larger hole, but at pressures over 80 psi the changes become slight. Studies suggest that the current increases because the pressure makes the hydrogen bubbles smaller in the cutting gap, causing a greater effective conductivity of the electrolyte. Another effect of using back pressure in ECM is the reduction or the elimination of flow lines in the work.

Safety Precautions. Sodium chloride and potassium chloride, used as electrolytes, present no unusual hazards. Oxidants such as sodium nitrate and sodium chlorate must not be exposed to combustible materials, particularly in storage. The alkalis are dangerous to body tissue. Mists, vapors and dusts of alkalis must not be inhaled. Ventilation should be provided on equipment and for handling of chemicals. Protective gloves and face shields or masks may be required for handling certain chemicals. Hydrogen, freed at the ECM tool, must be vented from the high point of the work enclosure, to prevent hydrogen explosions.

Proper design of equipment and tools, together with sound operating procedures, minimizes the likelihood of short circuits, which can cause explosions or melting of tool or workpiece. Acids and chloride salts can be extremely corrosive; hence their use requires the selection of suitable construction materials, and safe operating practice.

Tools (Electrodes)

The design and construction of tools, although one of the most critical aspects of ECM, is largely empirical.

Tool Materials. The metal for an electrode or tool should have the needed stiffness and machinability, in addition to electrical and thermal conductivity and chemical resistance to the electrolyte. Copper, brass, stainless steel and titanium are the materials most used for ECM tools. Copper or brass usually is the best choice, except where greater stiffness is needed. Titanium is especially useful when machining with an electrolyte that anodizes it (sulfuric acid, for instance). Then the current can be reversed to remove plated deposits without harming the tool.

Protective devices on ECM equipment limit the amount of current passed by a short circuit. Copper and brass are less likely than other metals to be seriously damaged by such a minor short circuit, because these highly conductive metals conduct the heat away rapidly. The same kind of short circuit with a tool of stainless steel or titanium could concentrate much more heat at the affected point, because of low thermal conductivity, and severe damage could occur. The tool usually would have to be removed for repair or replacement. Table 2 compares properties of four metals used for ECM tools, and Table 3 has a more complete list of materials for ECM tools.

Tool Design. The tool or electrode usually is shaped approximately like a

Table 2. Relative Properties of Four Metals Used as Tools (Electrodes) in ECM

Properties	Tool (electrode) material: Copper	Brass	Stainless	Titanium
Electrical resistivity	1	4	53	48
Stiffness	1.1	1	1.9	1.1
Machinability	6.0	8.0	2.5	1.0
Thermal conductivity	25	7.5	1.0	2.6

Table 3. Materials for ECM Tools (Electrodes)

Aluminum
Carbon (graphite)
Copper alloys:
- 110, electrolytic tough pitch copper
- 145, free-cutting copper (½% Te)
- 187, free-cutting copper (1% Pb)
- 220, commercial bronze, 90%
- 260, cartridge brass
- 360, free-cutting brass
- 464, naval brass
- 639, aluminum-silicon bronze
- 706, copper nickel, 10%
- Copper-manganese alloy

Platinum
316 stainless steel
Titanium (99%)
Tungsten 80%, copper 20% (sintered)

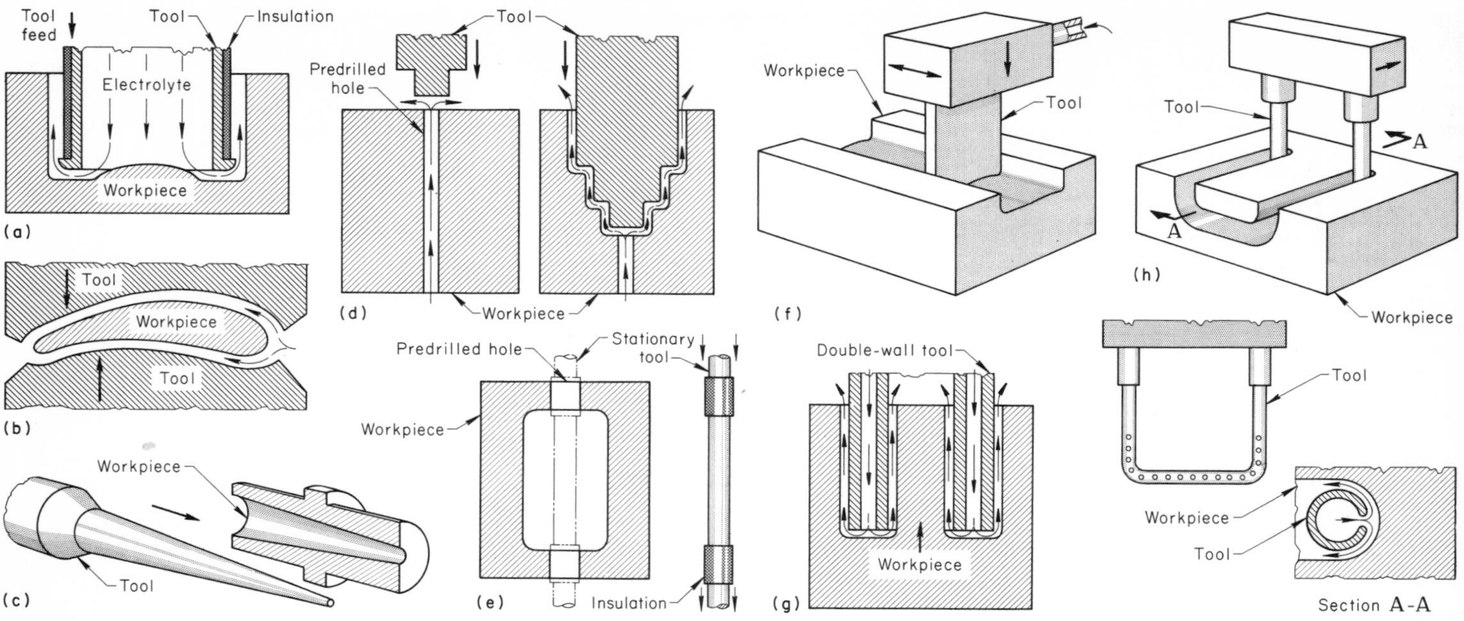

(a) Hole-sinking tool of the free-flow type, with insulated side wall. Holes of uniform curvature can be cut with curved tool. **(b)** Dual external-cutting tool, edge-flow type. Special fixtures are required to confine electrolyte. **(c)** Tool for tapering a predrilled hole; this type of tool was used on the interior of the nozzle shown in Fig. 5 (Example 452). **(d)** Tool for sinking a stepped through-hole. Electrolyte enters gap through predrilled hole. Electrolyte can be fed through tool to drill stepped blind holes. **(e)** Tool for enlarging interior section of a hole. A stub tool of similar design can be used to enlarge the interior of a blind hole. **(f)** "Surfacing" tool, through which electrolyte flows, can be used for planar or contoured cuts; or for turning, facing, grooving, trepanning and contouring in an ECM lathe. **(g)** Double-wall trepanning tool; entire wall is insulated. A single-wall tool can be used, with electrolyte entering on one side and leaving on the other side, but flow rates must be high and control is less precise. Special types are available for slug cutoff. Odd-shaped or tapered holes can be made. **(h)** "Wire" cutting or "hogging" tool. Electrolyte exits through row of holes in shaped tubing (tool), which is fed in direction of exit holes. Straight "wire" tools can be used for straight cuts or "sawing"; for heavy-duty work, tube is attached to a support and may be flattened.

Fig. 4. Tools for electrochemical machining

mirror image of the machined area of the completed part. Its function is to provide a defined path for the ECM current. The designer must determine the nature and extent of required deviation from the mirror-image configuration, while providing for a uniform and sufficiently high flow rate of electrolyte in the gap to allow a practical rate of metal removal.

Tool dimensions must be slightly different from the nominal dimensions of the completed part to allow for overcut, which can range between 0.001 and 0.030 in., depending on electrolyte flow and required dimensional accuracy. Cross section must be large enough to conduct the machining current and to provide strength and rigidity. To avoid arcing, the tool and workpiece surfaces should approximately conform at the start of cutting; stock is sometimes added to or removed from the workpiece if the tool is pointed.

Tool design must permit electrolyte flow in all machining areas at a rate sufficient to dissipate the heat generated and to keep the composition of the electrolyte near the work and the tool surfaces effectively the same as in the body of the liquid. (Excessively high flow rates, however, are expensive and may cause local erosion on workpiece or tool.) To produce a smooth and uniform surface on the workpiece, tool design must enable a uniform flow rate over the entire machining area. Ideally, flow should be laminar at all points and free from stray currents and eddies. In practice, the effects of changes in tool design on flow rates and patterns are difficult to predict — gap dimensions usually are less than 0.020 in., and electrolyte flow through the gap is often about 200 gpm.

General types of tool design for various ECM applications are illustrated in Fig. 4. The most common tool design is the "free-flow" type (Fig. 4a), in which electrolyte enters the gap through a channel in the center of the tool, and leaves around the outside of the tool; tools for hole-sinking usually are of this type. Holes free from taper can be drilled with the insulated construction shown. The dimensions of the lip on the leading edge of the tool and the location of the insulation govern the overcut and the extent of side cutting. For optimum surface finish, side cutting can be reduced by making the lip smaller (or by eliminating it and extending the insulation to the end of the tool).

Tools for external machining may be of the "edge-flow" type (Fig. 4b), in which electrolyte enters at one end of the workpiece and exits at the opposite end of the workpiece. This may require special fixtures to confine the electrolyte flow to the space between the workpiece and the tool. With "reverse-flow" tools, the electrolyte either is pulled through the gap and out through the tool by a downstream pump or is forced through the same path under pressure, using special fixtures to confine the liquid. This type of tool is sometimes needed to provide laminar flow for long or deep cuts, or to meet close tolerance or low-microinch finish requirements.

The illustrations of Fig. 4(c) to (h) show other tools for a variety of ECM applications. Because of the interaction of working-tip shape and dimensions, location of insulation, current density and feed rate, the design of tools to machine complex shapes requires at least an empirical understanding of electrical and electrochemical principles, plus experience and ingenuity. Although tool design may be difficult and time-consuming for complex shapes or close-tolerance applications, the cost of additional or replacement tooling usually is much less expensive than for conventional machining.

In critical work, the tendency for the current density to be high on tool edges and low at recesses can be counteracted by using "back-machining" to make the tool. To do this, a conventionally machined part is first used as a tool (cathode) in an electrochemical machining operation, and the part produced then serves as the tool for producing parts by ECM.

A peculiarity of ECM is the production of striations, ridges or protuberances on the workpiece, opposite or near the electrolyte flow channels in the tool, or at other points where sudden changes in flow direction cause a stagnant condition. The flow pattern can be improved and the surface irregularities reduced in number and in size by using a larger number of smaller holes or slots in the tool, but it is often still necessary to do an additional operation to remove these irregularities.

Standard tools for hole-sinking, sawing, cutting test coupons, and other simple operations are available from manufacturers of electrochemical machining equipment, who also design and produce nonstandard tools for specific applications.

Tool surfaces should be polished to a smooth finish. Any slight defect in the tool may affect the machining, leaving marks on the machined surface. Nicks, scratches, notches, burrs and lines can cause matching defects in the work. Any flaw in the tool that disturbs the flow of electrolyte can cause a flow line or flow pattern to be machined into the work. Mechanical polishing of tools is sometimes followed by chemical polishing, which can reach recessed or internal surfaces inaccessible to mechanical finishing.

Insulation is important in ECM, to control the path of the current. The tool can be insulated in a number of ways, depending on its shape, as discussed in the preceding section on Tool Design. Spraying or dipping may be the simplest applications of insulation, but a more durable insulation may be needed. The following qualities are essential:

1 Adhesion to the tool. Preformed insulation may be held to the tool by shrink fit, by adhesives, or by fasteners.
2 Sealing without pores or leaks that could cause stray machining by current leakage
3 Adequate thickness (0.002 in. is ample), for tools that must be insulated all the way to the cutting end
4 Smoothness, to avoid disturbing the flow of electrolyte
5 Resistance to heat, for continuous service at 400 F without breakdown
6 Curing temperature of 450 F or less, to prevent harm to the tool
7 Durability, to resist wear in guides and fixtures
8 Chemical resistance to the electrolyte
9 High electrical resistivity
10 Uniform application, for least disturbance of the flow of electrolyte, and to prevent interference.

For insulation, high-temperature varnish, vinyl, Teflon, polyester, urethane, phenolic, epoxy, tape, and other materials are commonly used. Most of these materials are satisfactory insulators and give adequate life where the tool has a lip to protect the edge of the insulation from the flow force of the electrolyte, when used with low fluid flow rates and low current density.

Few materials will last long enough to be fully satisfactory as insulation for ECM operations at high metal removal rates (high fluid flow rate and high current density). Sprayed or dipped coatings of enamels and epoxy electrical resins are among the most effective insulating materials for these applications; to take full advantage of these coatings, they should be used with a protective lip on the tool. Nylon, acetal and fiberglass-reinforced epoxy are among the best self-supporting preformed materials for insulation, but no insulation less than 0.002 in. thick gives long life in heavy-duty ECM service unless protected at the edge against the force of electrolyte flow.

Workpiece

Workpieces of almost any material that conducts electricity can be machined by ECM. Table 1 gives the selection of electrolytes and rates of machining for various materials.

Microstructure. There is little information on the effects that different work-metal microstructures would have on ECM. Experience in similar slower processes, electropickling and electropolishing, suggests that the following effects may occur:

1 Large grain size may cause a rougher finish than a fine grain.
2 Insoluble inclusions (graphite in cast iron, for instance) may cause roughness.
3 Variations in composition, as in case hardened steel, may cause differences in machining.
4 Precipitation of intermetallic compounds at the grain boundaries, as in heat sensitizing of some stainless steels, may cause serious intergranular attack.

Hardness. Electrochemical machining can be used to cut hardened metals. Although metal removal rate is not directly related to hardness of work metal, it may be affected by heat treatment and other operations that alter the microstructure of the material. Because of this dependence of machining rate on microstructure, constant current and feed cannot by themselves hold workpieces within close tolerances. Data on the rate of metal removal (cubic inches of metal removed per minute per 1000 amp) for 4340 steel after three different double tempering treatments are shown in Table 4. All machining was done with a sodium chloride solution testing 22° Bé at 80 F. The table shows that metal removal was faster at lower hardness; other metals and heat treatments might show the reverse relation or no change in removal rate with hardness.

Table 4. Effects of Double Tempering Treatments on Metal Removal Rates for 4340 Steel in ECM

Double tempering treatment (after quenching to 120 F)	Rockwell C hardness	Removal rate, cu in./min/1000 amp	Appearance of machined surface
425 F, 2 hr; 450 F, 2 hr	54	0.105	Dark, dull
800 F, 2 hr; 800 F, 2 hr	44	0.115	Dark, dull
1200 F, 2 hr; 1200 F, 2 hr	32	0.123	Bright

Removal Rate. As shown in Table 5, theoretical rates are 0.04 to 0.27 cu in. per min per 1000 amp. With suitable selection of electrolyte and operating conditions, work metals dissolve at close to the theoretical efficiency. If metal dissolution proceeds at substantially less than theoretical efficiency, the evolution of oxygen or chlorine or another undesirable product at the workpiece is indicated; such conditions should be avoided. As a first approximation, a value of 0.1 cu in. per min per 1000 amp (see columns 5 and 7 in Table 5) can be assumed for most metals in preliminary planning; this neglects effects of valence, work-metal density, and other factors.

Table 5. Theoretical Removal Rates in ECM

Metal	Valence	Density, lb/cu in.	Removal rate for current of 1000 amp(a): 100% efficiency, Lb/hr	100% efficiency, Cu in./min	90% efficiency, Lb/hr	90% efficiency, Cu in./min
Pure Metals						
Al	3	0.098	0.74	0.13	0.66	0.12
Be	2	0.067	0.37	0.09	0.33	0.08
Cb	3	0.310	2.55	0.14	2.29	0.13
	4	0.310	1.92	0.10	1.72	0.09
	5	0.310	1.53	0.08	1.37	0.07
Cu	1	0.324	5.22	0.27	4.70	0.24
	2	0.324	2.61	0.13	2.35	0.12
Fe	2	0.284	2.30	0.14	2.07	0.13
	3	0.284	1.53	0.09	1.38	0.08
Mg	2	0.063	1.00	0.27	0.90	0.24
Mo	3	0.369	2.63	0.12	2.36	0.11
	4	0.369	1.97	0.09	1.77	0.08
	6	0.369	1.32	0.06	1.18	0.05
Ni	2	0.322	2.41	0.13	2.16	0.12
	3	0.322	1.61	0.08	1.44	0.07
Ta	5	0.600	2.98	0.08	2.68	0.07
Ti	3	0.163	1.31	0.13	1.18	0.12
	4	0.163	0.99	0.10	0.89	0.09
W	6	0.697	2.52	0.06	2.26	0.05
	8	0.697	1.89	0.05	1.70	0.04
Commercial Alloys						
4340 ...	.	....	...	0.133	...	0.120
17-4 PH	.	....	...	0.123	...	0.111
A-286 ..	.	....	...	0.117	...	0.105
M-252 .	.	....	...	0.110	...	0.099
René 41	.	....	...	0.108	...	0.097
U-500 ..	.	....	...	0.110	...	0.099
U-700 ..	.	....	...	0.108	...	0.097
L-605 ..	.	....	...	0.107	...	0.096

(a) It is not always possible to predict the valence at which some metals will dissolve nor how much current will flow through the circuit of the workpiece, fluid, and electrode. Also, there may be other practical factors, such as the shape of the electrode, that limit the effective current flow. Pilot testing is required for accurate determination of penetration rates in specific applications.

Accuracy. The usual dimensional tolerance for ECM is ±0.005 in., but it is possible to control the process to ±0.0005 in. It is difficult to machine internal radii smaller than 0.007 in.; external radii can be of the order of 0.002 in. Overcut, taper and corner radii depend on the shape of the tool. Common values are 0.001-in. taper per inch of depth, 0.005-in. overcut, and 0.015-in. corner radius. The contour of internal radii can be approximated on the basis that overcut opposite an edge of the tool is about 60% of the overcut on adjacent areas of the workpiece.

Accurate predictions of metal removal, penetration rate, and cut configuration in specific applications require pilot testing.

Cleaning of the workpiece is nearly always necessary after ECM, to prevent corrosion. Cleaning should be done before any residue has hardened on the work. A rinse in water may be all that is needed for metals that resist corrosion. Steel and cast iron are usually treated in alkaline cleaning solutions, with or without a water rinse, or in a water-displacing compound that may leave a protective coating on the workpiece.

Surface finish of electrochemically machined parts is usually 4 to 30 micro-in. for the cutting-gap area (opposite the end of the tool), although it can be as rough as 200 micro-in. for the side-gap area. Important variables that affect surface finish are feed rate and gap dimensions, and the electrolyte composition, viscosity, temperature and flow. Electrolyte flow may depend on the work and the tooling. Very coarse surfaces, such as 1000 micro-in., may result from defective adjustment, setup or setting of the important variables, or from poor tooling.

Microscopic surface defects may be caused by selective attack on certain constituents in an alloy. They are usually associated with low current densities and with metallic precipitates at grain boundaries, as in age-hardened nickel alloys. One kind of surface defect is associated with intergranular attack, which can shorten the fatigue life of metal, and cannot be tolerated in parts subjected to high stress.

Surfaces that have been electrochemically machined have little or no residual stress. When ECM replaces mechanical machining, the effect on

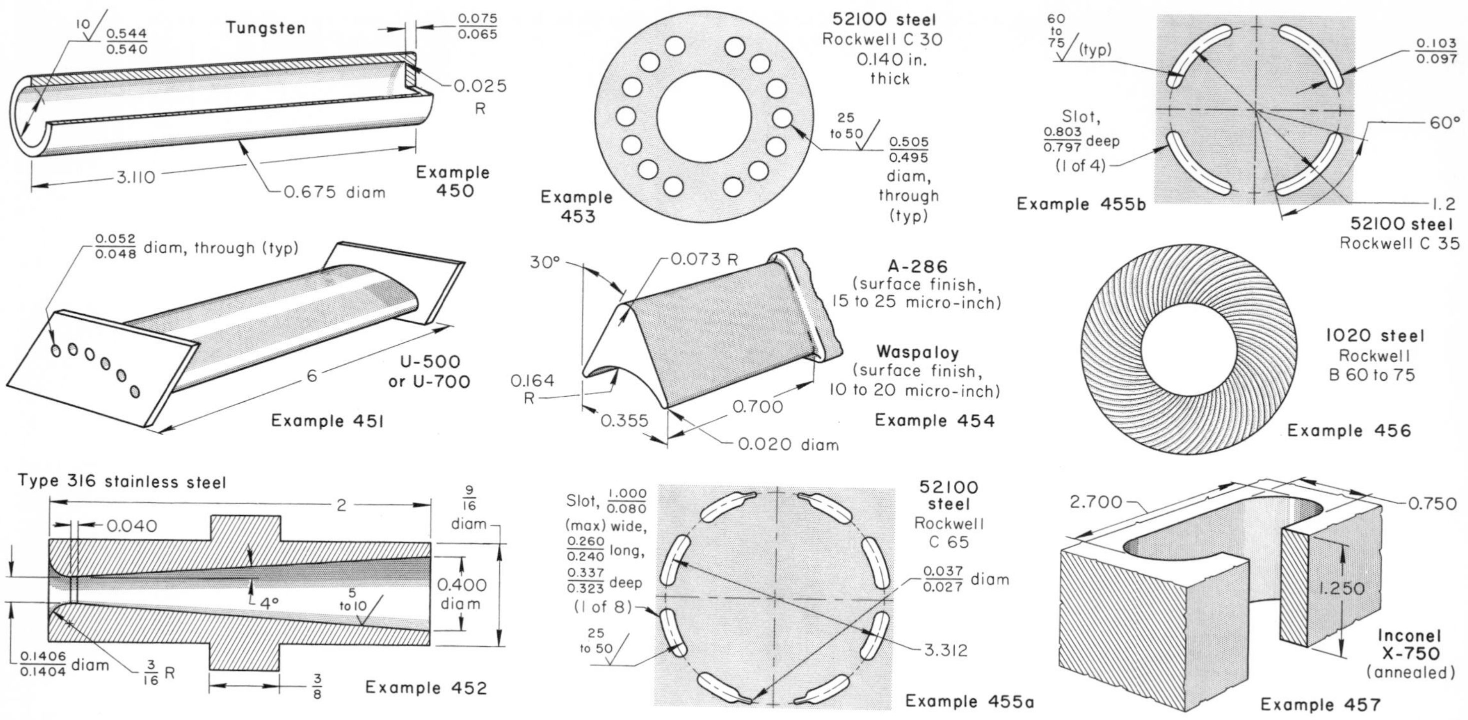

Ex. 450: Reaming a closed-end tungsten tube. Ex. 451: Drilling a jet-engine turbine blade. Ex. 452: Finishing a conical hole in a nozzle. Ex. 453: Drilling fourteen holes in a pilot plate. Ex. 454: Contouring a turbine-blade surface. Ex. 455(a): Cutting slots in a valve plate. Ex. 455(b): Cutting slots in a port plate. Ex. 456: Cutting spiral grooves in a friction disk. Ex. 457: Cutting a slot through Inconel X-750.

Fig. 5. Nine applications of electrochemical machining (Examples 450 to 457)

fatigue life should be considered, because a compressive stress may be required for adequate fatigue life.

Hydrogen embrittlement does not occur during ECM, because hydrogen is given off at the tool and not at the workpiece. However, the entry of hydrogen may be possible when a workpiece is in an acid solution with no electric current. A hydrogen-sensitive workpiece should not be immersed in an acidic electrolyte unless the current is flowing. Immediate, thorough rinsing should follow ECM. Neutral electrolytes, such as salt solutions, are unlikely to cause hydrogen embrittlement.

Reversing the current to clean the tool may subject the workpiece to hydrogen embrittlement and so should be avoided (or carefully controlled) when machining hydrogen-sensitive work.

"Embossing" by ECM

"Embossing" is done by holding the tool and the workpiece stationary during the entire machining period in an electrolyte containing sodium chlorate, for improved dimensional accuracy and surface finish.

This modified ECM process uses an electrolyte of a solution of 3.5 to 6.5 lb of sodium chlorate per gallon of water, that may also contain proprietary additives. Because of the unique low "throwing power" of this electrolyte, cutting action is completely absent at gap spacing greater than about 0.050 in., and there is no need for masking or sealing off the adjacent areas of the workpiece or the tool from the electrolyte. Chemical corrosion of adjacent work surfaces is also eliminated with the chlorate solution, which holds a pH of 7 to 9 in ECM operation. Sodium chlorate electrolyte can also be used for machining with controlled feed rates, as in conventional ECM.

The method is particularly well-suited for finish machining of hardened steel, for which conventional ECM yields only mediocre results. Data on four experimental and pilot-run applications are given in Table 8, on page 240; these parts (of 5160 steel or L6 tool steel, both at Rockwell C 60) could not be finished satisfactorily by conventional electrochemical machining.

Because sodium chlorate is a strong oxidant, precautions must be taken to prevent contact with combustible materials. Stainless steel, copper, methyl methacrylate, and polyvinyl chloride materials are suitable for long-term exposure to the electrolyte. Electrolyte cost is higher than for conventional electrochemical machining.

Examples of Application

Details of production applications of electrochemical machining are given in four examples in sections of this volume dealing with other processes:

Example	Application
373	Cost comparison of end milling, ECM and EDM for making complex slots in 4340 steel
786	Machining the airfoil and platform sections of type 403 stainless steel turbine blades by ECM
852	Machining the platform area of Inconel X-750 turbine blades by ECM
853	Comparison of mechanical milling and ECM for machining the root form of Inconel X-750 turbine blades.

Deburring in automated, high-production applications, particularly on points not practically accessible by conventional machining methods, is a major application of ECM. It is also used to rough machine massive forgings and other large, complex shapes.

The variety of work done by electrochemical machining is further illustrated by the examples that follow:

Example 450. Electrochemical Reaming of a Tungsten Tube (Fig. 5)

Figure 5 shows a cutaway view of a tungsten tube with a closed end. The hole in the tube was enlarged from 0.535 in. in diameter to 0.544/0.540 in. by ECM in a machine that could provide 1000 amp at 2 to 24 volts dc. A copper tool was used, with a machining current of 450 amp at 10 volts, in an electrolyte of 1.5 lb of sodium hydroxide per gallon of water, at a temperature of 80 F. A pressure of 50 psi caused electrolyte flow of 3 gal per min, with 50-micron filtration. The tool was stationary during machining, extending 3.04 in. into the tube. A cutting time of 1.25 min produced the part shown in Fig. 5, with internal smoothness of 10 micro-in.

Example 451. Electrochemical Drilling of a Heat-Resisting Alloy (Fig. 5)

Six through holes were drilled at the same time by ECM in the turbine blade shown in Fig. 5. The machine could provide 500 amp at 24 volts dc and less. Titanium tubes were used as the tool, with a current beginning at 3 amp and ending at 10 amp, at 9 volts. The polarity was reversed briefly at intervals, to clean the tool by deplating. The electrolyte, 10% H_2SO_4, was used at a temperature of 95 F. A pressure of 15 psi caused the electrolyte to flow at 0.6 gal per min, with 10-micron filtration. Tool penetration was 6 in., with a feed rate of 0.050 in. per min. Cutting time was 2 hr.

Example 452. Electrochemical Machining of a Stainless Steel Nozzle (Fig. 5)

Figure 5 shows the cross section of a nozzle of 316 stainless steel, made from a tube in a machine that could provide 500 amp at 24 volts dc or less. A copper tool was fed into one end of the tube to machine the hole to a conical shape, with a current beginning at 20 amp and ending at 310 amp, at 17 volts.

The electrolyte was 1 lb of sodium chloride per gallon of water, at a temperature of 80 F. A pressure of 80 psi caused the electrolyte to flow at 2 gal per min, with 50-micron filtration. Tool penetration was 1.74 in., with

Table 6. Comparison of Time and Cost for ECM vs Previous Machining Method in Five Production Applications (Examples 458 to 462)

Item	Example 458 Two slots in Waspaloy ECM	Example 458 End milling	Example 459 Pocket in A-286 ECM	Example 459 End milling	Example 460 Through hole in M-252 ECM	Example 460 End milling	Example 461 Square hole in tool steel (R_C 52) ECM(a)	Example 461 EDM	Example 462 Parallel holes in U-700 ECM	Example 462 EDM
Time per Piece, Minutes										
Machining	6	126	20	84	10	81	6	31	90	1800
Loading and unloading	4	3	10	5	5	2	2	2	15	5
Changing tools	..	6	..	12	..	12	..	..	..	...
Total	10	135	30	101	15	95	8	33	105	1805
Cost per Piece										
Labor and overhead	$2.50	$33.70	$6.00	$16.76	$3.00	$14.20	$1.60	$6.60	$14.00	$301.00
Tool use	...	...	...	14.00(b)	...	2.40(c)	...	2.00	...	8.00
Total	$2.50	$33.70	$6.00	$30.76	$3.00	$16.60	$1.60	$8.60	$14.00	$309.00

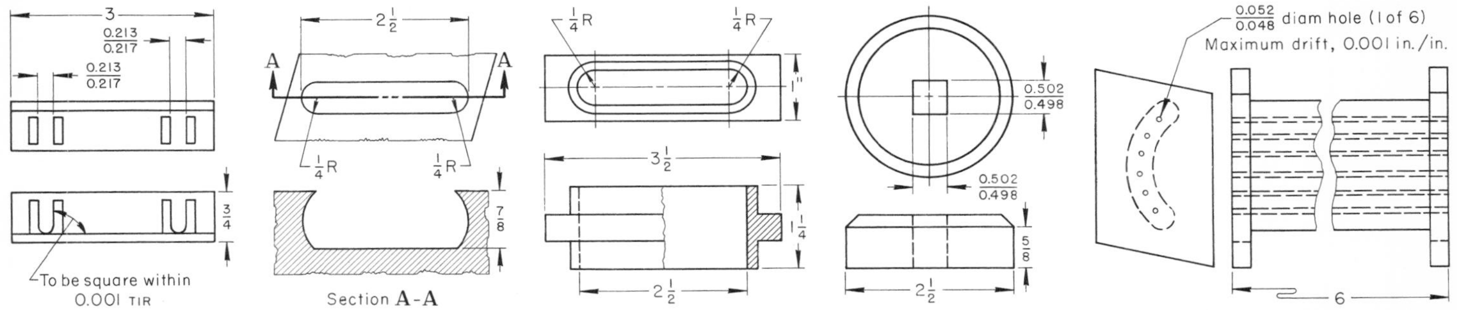

Example 458 Example 459 Example 460 Example 461 Example 462

(a) Final sizing (not shown) was done on electrochemically machined parts in one third the time required for electrical discharge machined parts. (b) Tool breakage averaged four cutters per pocket. (c) Cutter required three regrinds per hole. (SOURCE: F. A. Pitschke, "General Applications of Electrochemical Machining", SAE, Rockford-Beloit Section, Technical Paper No. S350, May 8, 1962)

a feed rate of 0.230 in. per min. A cutting time of 7.6 min produced internal smoothness of 5 to 10 micro-in.

After this first operation the part was inverted, and another copper tool was used to machine the radius at the other end of the hole. The current began at 20 amp and ended at 220 amp. The electrolyte was the same as before, with the same circulation. Tool penetration was 0.195 in., with a feed of 0.100 in. per min. Cutting time was 2 min, producing internal finish of 5 to 10 micro-in.

Example 453. Electrochemical Drilling of Alloy Steel (Fig. 5)

Electrochemical machining was used to drill fourteen ½-in.-diam holes at the same time through the 0.140-in.-thick pilot plate of 52100 steel (Rockwell C 30) shown in Fig. 5. The drilling was done in a machine that could provide 5000 amp at 2 to 20 volts dc. A brass tool was used, with a current beginning at 1200 amp and ending at 1700 amp, at 12 volts. The electrolyte was a solution of 1.7 lb of sodium chloride per gallon of water, at a temperature of 90 F. Pressure of 60 to 100 psi caused electrolyte flow of 17 gal per min, with 50-micron filtration. Drilling the 0.140-in. thickness at 0.130 in. per min took 1.1 min, with a final dwell of 3 sec, to make holes with roughness of 25 to 50 micro-in.

Example 454. Electrochemical Machining of a Turbine Blade (Fig. 5)

The constant-section portion of the turbine blade shown in Fig. 5 was electrochemically machined from either of two heat-resisting alloys (A-286 or Waspaloy) in a machine that could provide 5000 amp at 2 to 20 volts dc, using a tool made of a copper-tungsten alloy.

To make the blade of A-286, the current began at 100 amp, rose to 170, and ended at 150 amp, at 11 volts. The electrolyte was a solution of 2.2 lb of sodium nitrate per gallon of water, at a temperature of 110 F. Pressure of 130 to 200 psi caused electrolyte flow of 2 gal per min, with 50-micron filtration. Penetration of the 0.7-in. length at the rate of 0.300 in. per min took 2.33 min, machining the surface to a final roughness of 15 to 25 micro-in.

To make the blade of Waspaloy, the current began at 100 amp, rose to 160, and ended at 150 amp, at 12 volts. The electrolyte was a solution of 1.7 lb of sodium chloride per gallon of water, at a temperature of 90 F. A pressure of 130 to 200 psi caused electrolyte flow of 2.5 gal per min, with 50-micron filtration. Penetration of the 0.7-in. length at the rate of 0.325 in. per min took 2.15 min; surface finish was 10 to 20 micro-in.

Table 7. Conditions and Results in Five Applications of Electrochemical Machining

Condition or result	Work material: D-6ac steel, 240,000 psi	Nitrided steel, R_C 45	4340 steel, 140 Bhn	303 stainless steel	18% Ni maraging steel
Shape produced	Hole(a)	Holes(b)	...	Contour(c)	Contour
Equipment and Operating Conditions					
Electrode material	Stainless; brass face	Stainless; Cu-W tip	Cu-W alloy	Cu-W alloy	Copper
D-c power source	10,000 amp, 200 v	3000 amp, 2 to 20 v	3000 amp, 2 to 20 v	1500 amp, 25 v	5 to 20 v
Voltage	6	5	12.5	20	6.5
Current, amp:					
Start	4500	0	550	200	1000
Maximum	4900	50	2200	220	2600
End	4900	50	2200	180	2600
Electrolyte Conditions					
NaCl, lb per gal	1.5	1.0	1.0	1.0	1.25
$NaNO_3$, lb per gal	...	0.5	0.5	0.17	...
Pressure, psi	170	0	70	80	60 to 100
Flow rate, gal/min	...	17	...	...	17
Temperature, F	90	100	100	68 to 70	110
Filtration, microns	75	18	18	25	100
Penetration					
Total, in.	1.000	5.0	2.5	0.010(d)	0.090
Rate, in. per min	0.041	0.083	0.208	0.020(d)	0.076
Cutting time, minutes	24	60	12	0.5	1.2
Tolerance and Finish					
Tolerance, in.	±0.005(e)	±0.0005	±0.010	...	±0.0003
Finish, micro-in.	45 to 55	16	60 to 70	8	4 to 10

(a) 5-in. diam, 1 in. deep. (b) Three holes, ¼-in. diam by 5 in. deep. (c) On both ends of a bar, ½-in. square by 2¼ in. (d) On each end of bar. (e) On diameter. Tolerance on depth, ±0.002 in.

Example 455. Electrochemical Machining of Slots in 52100 Steel Plates

Example 455(a) — Valve Plate (Fig. 5). Eight slots 0.330 ± 0.007 in. deep, in a valve plate made of 52100 steel hardened to Rockwell C 65, were machined at the same time. The holes were made by ECM in a setup that could provide 5000 amp at 2 to 20 volts dc. A brass tool was used, with a current beginning at 1500 amp and ending at 2200 amp, at 13 volts. The electrolyte was a solution of 1.7 lb of sodium chloride per gallon of water, at a temperature of 90 F. A pressure of 100 to 150 psi caused the electrolyte to flow at 18 to 20 gal per min, with 50-micron filtration. Tool penetration was 0.330 in., with a feed rate of 0.150 in. per min. Cutting time was 2.2 min; finish was 25 to 50 micro-in.

Example 455(b) — Port Plate (Fig. 5). Four slots 0.800 ± 0.003 in. deep, in 52100 steel hardened to Rockwell C 35, were machined at the same time in the port plate shown in Fig. 5. The holes were made by electrochemical machining in a setup that could provide 5000 amp at 2 to 20 volts dc. A brass tool was used, with a current beginning at 300 amp and ending at 330 amp, at 12 to 13 volts. The electrolyte was a solution of 1.7 lb of sodium chloride per gallon of water, at a temperature of 90 F. A pressure of 140 to 160 psi made the electrolyte flow at 8 gal per min, with 50-micron filtration. Tool penetration was 0.800 in., with a feed

Table 8. Conditions and Results in Experimental and Pilot-Run Applications of Electrochemical Machining

Work material and hardness	Workpiece or shape machined (dimensions in footnotes)	Operating conditions: D-c source Volts	D-c source Amp	Voltage	Current, amp Start	Current, amp Max	Current, amp End	Electrolyte: NaCl, lb/gal	Pressure, psi	Flow, gpm	Temp, F	Penetration: Total, in.	Rate, ipm	Time, min	Tolerance, in.	Surface finish, micro-in.
5160 steel, Rc 60	Gear-tooth face	20	500	16	...	...	...	4.0(a)	140	....	86	0.0007	.....	...	.....	12-15
	Gear-hole wall	20	500	16	...	...	...	4.0(a)	140	....	86	0.0010	.....	...	±0.0001	2-4
	Needle-bearing race	20	500	16	...	...	...	4.0(a)	140	....	86	0.005	0.20	0.025	.....	2-5
L6 tool steel, Rc 60	Bushing(b)	20	500	16	250 amp/sq in.			3.75(a)	140	....	86	0.002	0.017	0.12	±0.0001	2-5
20-29 Cu-Mo stainless	Grooves(c)	18	5000	18(d)	81	...	123	0.67	155-130	1.4-1.5	84	0.076	0.0076	10	±0.002	2-6
A-286, Rc 25	Cylinder segment(e)	18	5000	12	....	...	735	5.0(f)	240	3.6	100	0.507	0.040	13	±0.005	10-36
M-252, Rc 35	Uniform airfoil(g)	25	3000	20	150	630	550	2.05	205-265	....	103	4.00	0.2	20	±0.001(h)	26-120
Hastelloy X, Rc 85-90	Slots(j)	18	5000	10	1040	...	65	2.05	260-200	3	75	.....	.....	1.5(k)	.....	......
	Slots(j)	18	5000	8	383	...	33	2.05	265-210	2.5-3	75	.....	.....	2.3(m)	±0.004	......
René 41, Rc 31	Grooves(c)	18	5000	10	280	...	93	2.1	250-195	1.5-1.6	73	0.069	0.0069	10	±0.006	12-20
René 41, Rc 35	Rectangular hole(n)	25	3000	28	250	650	580	2.1	320-355	....	103	4.525	0.203	22	±0.001	15-30
	Cylinder segment(p)	18	5000	11	....	...	663	2.1	240	3.9	94	0.190	0.040	4.8	±0.002	7-18
Ti – 8 Al – 1 Mo – 1 V	Uniform airfoil(g)	25	3000	20	100	500	460	0.8	205-265	....	103	4.00	0.2	20	±0.001(q)	220-280
	Tapered airfoil(r)	25	3000	20	100	550	500	0.8	205-265	....	103	3.50	0.2	17.5	.....	120-150
Tungsten (sintered), Rc 41	Slots in sheets(s)	18	5000	5	510	...	60	2.04(t)	170-145	1.8-2.0	...	.....	.....	22(u)	.....	......

(a) Modified method, using $NaClO_3$, instead of NaCl; tool and work stationary during processing. (b) 0.300-in. ID by 1.5 in. (c) ¼ by 2 in., 1/16 in. deep and ¼ in. apart. (d) 6 volts for first minute. (e) 1-in. radius, 1.509-in. chord, 0.920 in. wide; contoured in workpiece 1 by 1¾ in., to ½-in. maximum depth. (f) $NaNO_3$, instead of NaCl.
(g) 1.250 by 4 in., and 0.143 in. thick at center; trepanned from bar ¼ by 2½ in. (h) On 0.143-in. thickness; tolerance on 1.250-in. dimension was ±0.010 in. (j) ¼ by 2 in., ¼ in. apart, through 0.030-in. sheet. (k) Plus 1-min dwell. (m) Plus 2.7-min dwell. (n) 0.465 by 0.618 in., 4.5 in. deep. (p) Dimensions and operation same as in footnote e. Workpiece was premachined, except for 0.190-in. thickness of finish stock. (q) On 0.143-in. thickness; ±0.020 in. on 1.250-in. dimension.
(r) 1.257-in. width and 0.142-in. center thickness were tapered to 1.020 and 0.123 in., respectively. Airfoil was trepanned from bar ¼ by 2½ in. (s) ¼ by 2 in., ¼ in. apart, through 0.008-in. sheet. (t) NaOH, instead of NaCl. (u) Plus 38-min dwell.

rate of 0.180 in. per min. Cutting time was 4.45 min; finish was 60 to 75 micro-in.

Example 456. Electrochemical Machining of Spiral Grooves (Fig. 5)

Seventy-two equally spaced spiral grooves, 0.015 in. deep by 0.040 in. wide, were machined in a friction disk in an ECM machine that could provide 12,800 amp at 14 to 24 volts dc. A brass tool was used, with current beginning at 650 amp and ending at 600 amp, at 20 volts. The electrolyte was a solution of 1.25 lb of sodium chloride per gallon of water, at a temperature between 85 and 90 F. A pressure of 100 psi caused the electrolyte to flow at 10 gal per min, through a clarifier. Tool penetration, 0.015 ± 0.005 in., was at a feed rate of 0.050 in. per min, with 5 sec final dwell, in cutting time of 0.3 min. The 72 grooves were machined at one time, and the operation was repeated on the other side.

Example 457. Electrochemical Machining of Inconel X-750 (Fig. 5)

Figure 5 shows a slot machined through a 1.250-in. thickness of annealed Inconel X-750 in a machine that could provide 10,000 amp at low direct-current voltages. A tool made of a copper-tungsten alloy was used, with a current beginning at 400 amp and ending at 1400 amp, at 17 volts. The electrolyte was a solution of 1⅓ lb sodium chloride plus ⅔ lb sodium nitrate per gallon of water. The slot was machined at a feed rate of 0.080 in. per min, in 15.6 min cutting time. The machined surface had a finish of 35 to 50 micro-in.

Examples 458 to 462. ECM vs Alternative Methods of Machining (Table 6)

Data on time and cost for processing five different pieces by ECM compared with other processes are given in Table 6.

Table 7 presents results for five other applications of ECM. Table 8 presents data from experimental and pilot uses of ECM, which may suggest further production capabilities.

Other Examples

For other examples of ECM applications in this book, see list on page 238.

Chemical Machining (CHM)

By EDWARD A. DURAND*

CHEMICAL MACHINING (CHM) is the production of desired shapes and dimensions through selective or over-all removal of metal by controlled chemical attack or etching. Areas from which metal is not to be removed are protected from attack by masking. The process ordinarily is not electrically assisted.

Chemical machining is an extension of the metal finishing processes of etching, chemical brightening and chemical polishing, in which controlled chemical attack is used to alter the surface condition of metals. The same types of chemical solutions are used for chemical machining, with appropriate modification of concentration or composition, and of operating conditions, to increase the rate of metal removal. The process is also closely related to the etching of metal printing and engraving plates and of nameplates.

Nearly all metals can be chemically machined; Table 1 is a partial list of metals and alloys that have been chemically machined on a production basis.

There are two types of chemical machining: *chemical blanking*, for cutting or "stamping out" parts from thin sheet material; and *chemical contour machining*, or *chemical milling*, for the selective or over-all removal of metal from thicker material.

These processes are employed chiefly when the desired blanking or removal of metal by conventional methods is difficult or impractical because of hardness, toughness or brittleness of the work metal, or because of size of part, complexity of shape, or thinness of final section.

CHEMICAL BLANKING

Chemical blanking is used chiefly on thin sheet and foil for the kind of work normally produced in a blanking press. In most applications, photoresist (photosensitive masking) is used to define the locations on the workpiece at which the metal will be etched through and to protect areas not to be etched. A flow chart showing the principal process steps for chemical blanking by the photoresist method is given in Fig.

* Associate Editor, METALS HANDBOOK

1. [For more detailed information on photoresist techniques, see: T. R. Bates, *Plating*, July 1965, p 673-676; and T. D. Schlabach and D. K. Rider, "Printed and Integrated Circuitry: Materials and Processes" (McGraw-Hill, 1963).]

Preparation of Workpiece. From one to five steps may be required in preparing the workpiece, as indicated in Fig. 1, for the resist to remain impervious and adherent during the etching operation and to be readily removable from the blanked parts. (A rigorous pretreatment cycle used on nickel parts is described in Example 463b.) Selecting a pretreatment cycle involves the same principles as selecting a preparation cycle for painting (see Volume 2 of this Handbook, pages 550 and 551).

Preparation of Masters

Preparation of masters, which are the "tools" for chemical blanking by the photoresist method, begins with the generation of oversize artwork on paper, polyester drafting film, or polyester-base or glass-base scribing film (listed in order of increasing dimensional stability and permanence). The original artwork usually is made four times actual size, but it may range from two to 200 times actual size, depending on equipment, part size and accuracy required. Individual part size can vary from micro dimensions to a normal maximum of 18 by 22 in.

It is often economical and convenient to expose, develop and etch or blank a number of parts simultaneously from a single sheet of metal, and full-size multiple-image masters are required. Replication of images can be done in a step-and-repeat camera before, during or after reduction.

Provision is made in the preparation of masters for the reclaiming of the blanked-out parts after etching. In one method, called "tabbing", small lines are added to the artwork to produce connections (or "tabs") that hold the parts together after etching; these tabs must be removed from the work later. "Backcoating", by providing connecting lines on only one of a pair of mirror-image masters (to allow etching on only one side of the work at these locations), holds the completed parts together in a similar manner. In another technique, the part images are isolated, and the blanked parts drop out of the scrap skeleton into a collector basket when etching is complete.

Masking With Photoresists

In masking with photoresists (proprietary formulations), three operations are involved: application, exposure and development.

Application of photoresist to the workpiece is best done immediately after cleaning and pretreatment, although work can be covered and stored in a controlled environment for several hours to several days before applying the photoresist. The work must not be handled before the resist is applied.

Photoresists are applied by dipping, whirl-coating or spraying. Dipping is the simplest method, but whirl-coating gives the most uniform thickness, and spraying is the most versatile method.

Resists are dried at room temperature and then baked for about 15 min at a maximum of 250 F to remove residual solvent. Baking temperature is not critical, and longer baking times at lower temperatures can be used.

Exposure of conventional photoresists to ultraviolet light partly polymerizes the exposed areas of light-sensitive resin, increasing the resistance of these areas to the organic solvents used as developers. Each side of the workpiece panel can be exposed individually, or the two sides can be exposed at the same time between a pair of mirror-image masters in precise register. A vacuum "printing frame" is used, with the emulsion side of the master pattern toward the work panel. A vacuum of about 500 mm (20 in.) of mercury will insure good contact. Also, the printing frame must be padded appropriately or the glass masters will break in the evacuated frame.

Development is done by immersion with agitation in a suitable organic solvent or in a spray developer or degreaser. Conditions and time are determined by the nature and thickness of the resist. After the panel is removed from the developer, it should be rinsed in running water or spray rinsed, to remove the developer and dissolved polymer from the nonimage areas without leaving residual scum. If the nonimage areas are still not clean (not fully developed), development can be repeated without damaging the image.

After development, the resist is dried at room temperature. It is then baked again at 250 F for approximately 15 min to remove residual developer and to increase hardness and chemical resistance to the etchant.

Table 1. Partial List of Metals That Have Been Chemically Machined

Carbon and Low-Alloy Steels: 1010; 1020; 1095; 4130; 4140; 4340
Ultra-High-Strength Steels: D-6ac; H11; maraging steel, 18%
Tool Steels: H11; T5; 6H2
Stainless Steels: 301; 302; 304; 310; 316; 321; 347; 410; 430. Precipitation-hardening grades: 17-4 PH; 17-7 PH; PH 15-7 Mo; 350; 355
Heat-Resisting Alloys: A-286; Hastelloy X; Inconel 600; Inconel 718; Inconel 722; Inconel X-750; N-155; René 41; 19-9 DL
Columbium Alloys: C-103; C-129; Cb-752; D-14
Aluminum Alloys: 1100; 2014; Alclad 2014; 2020; 2024; Alclad 2024; 3003; 5052; 6061; 6063; 7072; 7075; Alclad 7075; 7079; 7178
Beryllium
Copper
Magnesium Alloys: AZ31; AZ63; AZ80; AZ81; AZ91; AZ92; EK30; EK41; EZ33; HK31; HM21; HM31; HZ32; QE22; ZK51; ZK60; ZK61
Molybdenum Alloys
Nickel (see also Heat-Resisting Alloys)
Titanium Alloys: Commercially pure titanium; Ti-2.5Al-16V; Ti-5Al-2.5Sn; Ti-8Al-1Mo; Ti-4Al-4Mn; Ti-4Al-3Mo-1V; Ti-6Al-4V; Ti-7Al-4Mo; Ti-8Al-1Mo-1V; Ti-8Mn
Zinc Alloys

Other Masking Techniques

Masking techniques other than photoresist are sometimes used for selective masking of individual workpieces or multiple-image panels for etching, particularly for high-volume production, for large parts, for parts that do not require the high dimensional accuracy of the photographic method, and for applications in which photoresists have inadequate chemical resistance to the etchant.

Maskant coatings can be applied directly to the work by screening or by offset printing, with a somewhat lower degree of dimensional accuracy and reproduction of detail. At a further sacrifice of accuracy and detail, the scribe-and-peel method may be used. In this method, parts are completely covered with maskant, the design to be etched is scribed through the maskant with the aid of a template, and the maskant is peeled off in the areas to be etched away.

The maskant pattern is duplicated in accurate register on the two sides of the work to allow etching to proceed from both sides at once (except for the etching of printed-circuit cards, which is discussed later in this article as a special case of chemical blanking).

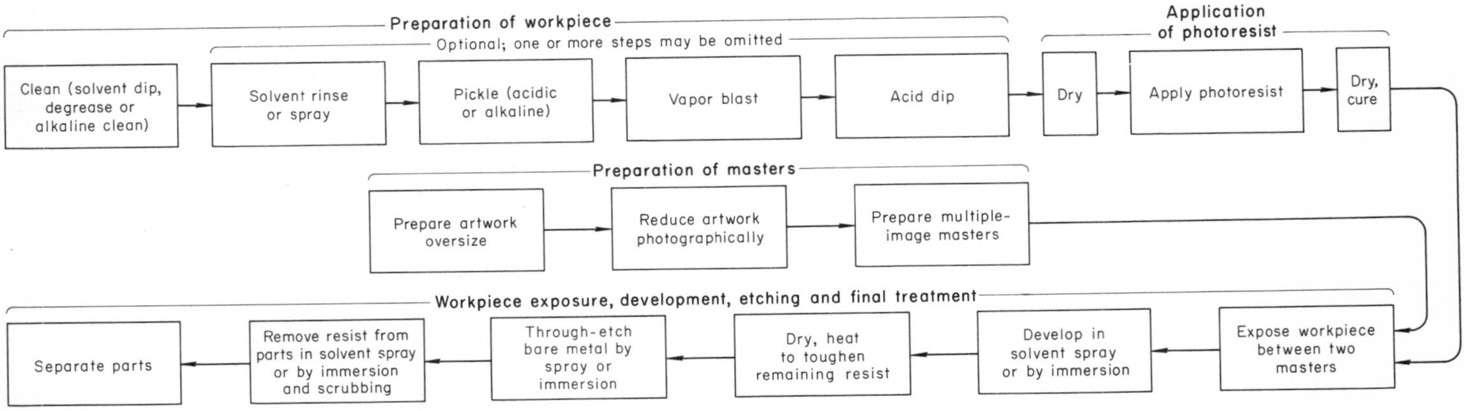

Fig. 1. Flow chart of principal process steps for chemical blanking

Table 2. Etchants for Chemical Blanking of Various Metals

Work metal	Etchant solution(a)	Temperature, F	Removal rate per side, ipm	Etch factor (b)	Source (see list below)
Alfenol (Fe, 16 Al)	$FeCl_3$, 4½-5 lb/gal(c)	120	......	....	1
Aluminum and aluminum alloys	NaOH, 21-24 oz/gal, + Al, 0.8-3 oz/gal(d)	165-180	0.0005-0.001	....	2
	NaOH, 10-16 oz/gal, + Al, 1-9 oz/gal(e)	180-200	0.0005-0.001	....	3
	$FeCl_3$, 16-24 oz/gal(f)	120	0.001	1.5-2.0	1
	HCl, 50% (vol), + HNO_3, 5% (vol)	120	0.001-0.002	2.0	1
Beryllium	NH_4HF_2, 12-24 oz/gal	80-90	0.0005-0.0006	....	4
Columbium	HNO_3 + HF	90-130	0.0005-0.001	....	5
Copper and copper alloys(g)	$FeCl_3$, 4½-5 lb/gal(c)	120	0.002	2.5-3.0	1
	$(NH_4)_2S_2O_8$, 1-2 lb/gal	90-120	0.0005-0.001	2.0-3.0	1
	CrO_3, 3-4 lb/gal	120	0.001-0.0015	2.0-3.0	1
	$CuCl_2$, 4-4½ lb/gal	130	0.0005-0.0006	2.5-3.0	1
Germanium	HF + HNO_3	....	......	....	1
Gold	HCl, 75% (vol), + HNO_3, 25% (vol)	90-100	0.001-0.002	....	1
Inconel and Inconel X-750	$FeCl_3$, 4½-5 lb/gal(c)	130	......	....	1
Kovar (Fe, 29 Ni, 17 Co)	CrO_3 3-4 lb/gal	120	0.001	2.0-2.5	1
	$FeCl_3$, 4½-5 lb/gal(c)	120	0.001	2.0	1
Lead	$FeCl_3$, 4½-5 lb/gal(c)	130	......	....	1
Magnesium	HNO_3, 12-15% (vol) (h)	90-120	0.001-0.002	....	1
Molybdenum	HNO_3 + HF	70-100	0.001	....	6
	H_2SO_4, 15-33% (vol), + HNO_3, 15-33% (vol)	130	0.001	....	1
	HNO_3, 25-33% (vol), + HCl, 25-33% (vol)	....	......	....	1
Moly Permalloy	$FeCl_3$, 4½-5 lb/gal(c)	130	......	....	1
Nickel, Monel, and Ni-Fe alloys	HNO_3, 48% (vol), + H_2SO_4, 5.5% (vol), + H_3PO_4, 11% (vol), + $HC_2H_3O_2$, 5.5% (vol) (j)	110-120	0.001	....	7
	$FeCl_3$, 4½-5 lb/gal(c)	120	0.0005-0.001	1.0-3.0	1
Silver	HNO_3, 50-90% (vol)	100-120	0.0005-0.001	....	1
	$Fe(NO_3)_3$, 4 lb/gal(k)	130	0.0008	....	1
Steels, carbon and alloy	HNO_3, 20% (vol), + H_2SO_4, 5% (vol), + H_3PO_4, 5% (vol) (m)	135-160	0.0007-0.001	....	8
	$H_2C_2O_4$, 3.3 oz/gal, + H_2O_2, 1.7 oz/gal, + H_2SO_4, 0.01 oz/gal	70-80	......	....	9
	$FeCl_3$, 4½-5 lb/gal(c)	120	0.001	2.0	1
	HNO_3, 10-15% (vol)	120	0.001	1.5-2.0	1
Steel, 1% Cr-Mo	H_2SO_4, 18% (vol), + HNO_3, 5% (vol) (n)	145-155	0.0005-0.001	....	8
Steel, 3% Cr-Mo	HNO_3, 20% (vol), + H_3PO_4, 5% (vol) (p)	140-160	0.0008-0.0012	....	8
Steel, 5% Cr-Mo-V	HNO_3, 20% (vol) (q)	145-155	0.0007-0.0017	....	8
Steel, silicon	$FeCl_3$, 4½-5 lb/gal(c)	130	0.001	1.5-2.0	1
Steel, stainless	HCl, 50% (vol), + HNO_3, 5% (vol), + H_3PO_4, 2.5% (vol) (r)	150	0.0003	....	10
	$FeCl_3$, 4.5-5 oz/gal(c)	130	0.0008	1.5-2.0	1
	HCl, 25% (vol) (s)	70-90	......	....	11
Tin	$FeCl_3$, 4.5-5 oz/gal(c)	130	......	....	1
Titanium	HF, 10-50% (vol)	85-120	0.0005-0.001	....	1
	HF + CrO_3	100-120	......	....	12
	HF + HNO_3	100-120	......	....	1
	NH_4HF_2 + HCl	100-120	......	....	1
Zinc alloys	HNO_3, 10-15% (vol)	100-120	0.001	....	1
Zirconium and Zircaloy	H_2SO_4 + HF(t)	100	0.0008	....	10
	HF + HNO_3(u)	100	0.0004	....	10

Footnotes

(a) Concentrations are expressed as ounces or pounds per gallon of solution, or as percentages (by volume) of concentrated commercial grades of liquid chemicals; remainder is water. (b) Etch factor in table for chemical blanking is depth of cut (from one side) divided by undercut. (Etch factor in chemical contour machining is undercut divided by depth of cut.) Results may vary with lot, temper, or etchant velocity.

(c) Control at 42° Bé. (d) For smooth finish. Can be regenerated by precipitating $Al(OH)_3$ at 70 to 90 F in seeded, air-agitated solution. (e) For etching to depth of ¼ in. or more. May contain 1 to 5% (depending on NaOH content) of a sequestrant such as gluconate, glucamine or sorbitol to retain Al in solution; addition of sulfides or electrically assisted action gives smoother surfaces. (f) Control at 12° to 18° Bé. (g) Adjust conditions as necessary for different copper alloys (etch phosphor bronze at 80 F for removal rate of 0.0003 to 0.0005 ipm and etch factor of 2.0); see Table 4 regarding copper.

(h) May contain proprietary organic additives. (j) Dilute with water for use on Monel. (k) Control at 36° Bé. (m) Maintain by 5% additions of HNO_3 until iron content reaches 6.7 oz per gal; adjust temperature according to alloy (1% Cr-Mo, 135 to 145 F; 3% Cr-Mo, 145 to 155 F; 5% Cr-Mo-V, 150 to 160 F). (n) Maintain by 5% additions of HNO_3 until iron content reaches 6.7 oz per gal. (p) Maintain as in footnote n; adjust temperature according to iron content of etchant (up to 1.6 oz per gal, 140 F; 1.6 to 2.7 oz per gal, 150 F; 2.7 to 6.7 oz per gal, 160 F). (q) Maintain by adding HNO_3 when removal rate falls to 0.0007 ipm; discard when iron content of etchant reaches 6.7 oz per gal. (r) For smoothest finish, dissolved metal content should be 8 to 16 oz per gal; adjust composition for optimum results on different alloys. (s) Electrically assisted (pass direct current at a low voltage with work anodic); avoid for high-stress applications. (t) For satin finish. (u) For bright finish.

Sources

1. R. K. Springborn (ed), "Non-Traditional Machining Processes" (ASTME, 1967), p 74-75. 2. *Aircraft Production* (England), Jan 1957, p 28-40. 3. J. E. Spessard, *Plating,* Nov 1961, p 1221-1222. 4. L. Missel and M. E. Shaheen, *Metal Finishing,* Nov 1965, p 69-71. 5. R. C. Movich, ASTME technical paper MR66-712, March 1966. 6. J. C. Roni, *Machinery,* Feb 1966, p 90-92. 7. L. Missel and G. W. Allen, *Plating,* Oct 1962, p 1076-1078. 8. P. F. Langstone, D. R. Connor and I. H. Gibson, *Machine Shop* (England), Sept 1964, p 418-426. 9. D. Fishlock and K. W. Hards, "New Ways of Working Metals" (Philosophical Library, 1965), p 47. 10. P. F. Langstone and J. C. Wright, *Production Technology* (England), April 1963. 11. Eastman Kodak Co., Technical Bulletin KMER, 1959. 12. W. C. Rockwell, technical paper, 8th Annual Corrosion Conference, NACE, Nov 1958.

Maskant materials are selected primarily for resistance of the cured maskant and the maskant-to-workpiece bond against the etchant. Properties of maskant materials other than photoresists are summarized in Tables 6 and 7, in the section on Chemical Contouring. (These materials are used more extensively in chemical contouring than in chemical blanking.) Maskant thickness is in the range of 3 to 15 mils; rubber-base materials are usually applied in somewhat greater thicknesses than resinous materials.

Etching for Blanking

Etching in chemical blanking is done either by immersion in mechanically agitated or air agitated chemical baths or in specially designed spray etching machines. In most production operations, composition and concentration of etchant, and other process conditions, are regulated for a removal rate of about 0.0005 to 0.002 ipm. Faster rates can be obtained, particularly in spray etching, but usually only at the cost of reduced accuracy, more frequent failure of the resist by penetration or by bond failure at pattern edges, and accelerated corrosion of equipment.

Etchants for chemical blanking of various metals are listed in Table 2, together with operating characteristics of each. Etch factor for chemical blanking equals depth of cut (from one side) divided by undercut. Important note: In chemical contour machining, the same term, "etch factor", means just the opposite (undercut divided by depth of cut).

Ferric chloride solutions can be used for the chemical blanking of a wide variety of metals, as indicated in Table 2. Strong mineral acids (including some oxidizing acids), other strong oxidants, and fluorides are the basis for most of the etchants; sodium hydroxide is used extensively on aluminum and aluminum alloys. Most acid etchants can be maintained by the addition of fresh acid until their chemical activity is altered excessively by the dissolved metal content — at which point they are discarded (see footnotes in Table 2). Sodium hydroxide etchants can be maintained by additions and regenerated when aluminum content becomes excessive. The effect of aging on etching rate and uniformity varies with the etchant and the work metal.

Etchant compositions can be adjusted to meet the requirements of specific applications, and proprietary additives can be included to control foaming or wetting characteristics, increase or decrease etching rate, or make etching more uniform. Many formulations resemble those used in bright dipping, chemical polishing, or electropolishing. A comparison of compositions of solutions used in the etching of printed-circuit cards is given in Table 4.

Applications of Chemical Blanking

One of the major applications of chemical blanking is the manufacture of burr-free, intricate, thin "stampings". For parts of this type, chemical blanking often is more economical than punch-press or press-brake blanking for quantities of up to 5000. For most jobs, a pair of masters for etching can be made for less than $200 — much less than the usual cost for design and manufacture of a set of dies for a complex part.

Typical chemically blanked parts include laminations for electric motors or magnetic recording heads, rotors, slotted spring disks and gaskets, meter parts, vanes for high-speed cameras, strain-gage loops or grids, electrical contacts and terminals, fine screens, helicopter vent screens, templates, electronic-conductor matrices, and printed-circuit cards. Shadow masks for color television also are made by chemical blanking; about 320,000 conical holes, each with a minimum diameter of 0.011 in., are blanked in 0.006-in.-thick, full-hard 1010 steel foil, for a 21-in. television picture tube. Corrosion-resistant filter screens for chemical applications have been made with 0.006-in.-diam holes on 0.011-in. centers in type 316 stainless steel foil 0.005 in. thick.

Chemical blanking is sometimes used to eliminate deburring or to reduce assembly time. Electronic chassis are made in small to medium quantities by using punch presses for routine holes and chemical blanking for odd-shaped holes and slots.

Thin intricate parts that are impractical to blank mechanically because of hardness or brittleness of the work material can often be made with ease by chemical blanking, as illustrated in Example 463, which follows.

Example 463(a) and (b). Chemical Blanking of Intricate Parts From Hard or Brittle Materials

Example 463(a) — Molybdenum Alloy Parts That Delaminated in Punch-Press Blanking. The conventional blanking of small, complex, close-tolerance aerospace parts from sheet molybdenum alloys was excessively slow, and rejection rates were high because of edge delamination. Production rate and yield were increased by the adoption of chemical blanking in nitric-hydrofluoric acid etchant, using photoresists.

Parts were spaced as close together as possible on a panel (minimum spacing, 0.100 in.), and the area to be etched away was kept as small as possible to conserve etchant and to simplify control of the etching process. The multiple-part panel was then etched through on the unmasked areas at a penetration rate of 0.001 ipm by immersion in the nitric-hydrofluoric acid bath. Maskant was removed from the completed parts by a combination of solvent spray and brushing. A dimensional accuracy of ±0.010 in. was maintained on material up to 0.060 in. thick. A controlled period of overetching was used on some parts for deburring and radiusing. [SOURCE: J. C. Roni, *Machinery*, Feb 1966, p 90-92]

Example 463(b) — Nickel Electronic Connector Network (Fig. 2). Chemical blanking was the only practical way to manufacture the connector network shown in Fig. 2 from predrilled 0.042-in.-thick nickel. This matrix, used in high-density packaging of electronic circuits, was made of nickel for strength, electrical conductivity, corrosion resistance, and suitability for spot welding. The processing sequence and the etchant composition were as follows:

1 Remove mill markings from precut sheet in organic solvent.
2 Immerse for 5 min in nonsilicated alkaline cleaner, 4 to 6 oz per gal, at 170 to 190 F.
3 Rinse thoroughly.
4 Treat anodically in hydrochloric acid (25% by volume) for 5 sec, at current density of 100 to 200 amp per sq ft.
5 Rinse thoroughly.
6 Oven dry at 200 to 250 F.
7 Coat with diluted photosensitive resist (proprietary material).
8 Bake at 250 F for 10 min (typical).
9 Mount artwork.
10 Expose to ultraviolet light.
11 Develop image for 2 to 3 min by immersion in resist developer (organic solvent).
12 Postbake 20 min at 250 F (typical).
13 Preactivate by anodic treatment as in step 4.
14 Rinse thoroughly without delay.
15 Without delay, etch by immersion for 20 to 30 min in the following solution at 110 to 120 F, using work agitation:

Nitric acid, 70%	48% (vol)
Sulfuric acid, 96%	5.5
Phosphoric acid, 85%	11
Acetic acid, 99%	5.5
Water	30

16 Remove from bath as soon as blanking is complete.
17 Rinse thoroughly.
18 Remove resist with organic solvent plus scrubbing.

The completed matrix was deburred and smoothed, when necessary, in a bright dip or chemical polishing bath. Large areas of bare nickel adjacent to the masked area were avoided to conserve etchant and to minimize gas evolution and local heating, which could affect adhesion of the resist or cause local variation in removal rate. A chemically resistant screen at the bottom of the tank was used to remove pieces of nickel that became detached from the work and would unnecessarily shorten bath life if left to dissolve.

Support legs around the periphery of the matrix were cut away after processing. Minimum line width was 0.021 in. Time required for complete blanking, 20 to 30 min, was reduced to about 4 min in test runs by spray etching preactivated surfaces. Monel matrices were produced experimentally by chemical blanking in a similar but more dilute etchant. [SOURCE: L. Missel and G. W. Allen, *Plating*, Oct 1962, p 1076-1078]

Cost Comparison With Mechanical Blanking. Equipment and operating costs for the manufacture of a volume-production part by chemical blanking and by mechanical blanking are compared in Table 3. The part, illustrated in Table 3, could be produced by either method from 0.008-in.-thick 1095 steel (Rockwell C 52 to 54) to tolerances of ±0.002 in.

Excluding the amortization of equipment and tooling, unit costs for chemical blanking were three to five times the unit cost for mechanical blanking (see totals in Table 3). Taking tooling and equipment costs into account, the low-production chemical method was cheaper than the mechanical method for quantities of less than about 600,000 ($0.038 each at the crossover point); the high-production chemical method was the most expensive method for all quantities.

If equipment were already available and only tooling costs were included, the low-production chemical method

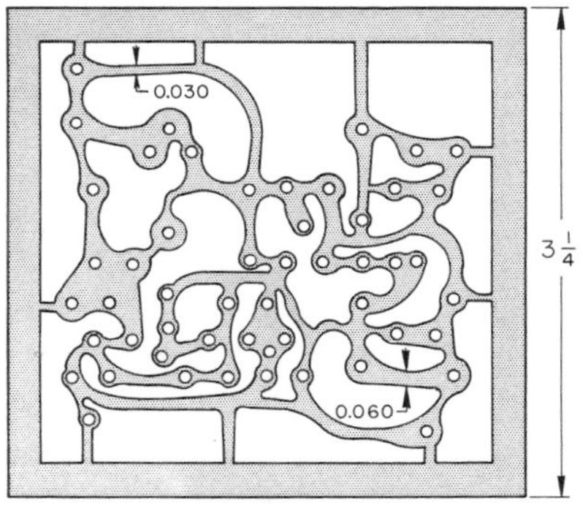

Fig. 2. Electronic connector network chemically blanked from predrilled 0.042-in.-thick nickel sheet (Example 463b)

Table 3. Costs for Making a Small Steel Part by Mechanical Blanking vs Chemical Blanking

Item	Mechanical blanking	Chemical blanking: Low-production equipment	Chemical blanking: High-production equipment
Operators	1	1	9
Production/hr	8000 pcs	300 pcs	5000 pcs
Cost:			
Equipment .	$13,500(a)	$6450(b)	$21,850(c)
Tooling ...	$ 6,950(d)	$ 300(e)	$ 300(e)
Costs per 1000 Pieces			
Steel	$2.30	$ 2.30	$ 2.30
Chemicals ...	....	4.20	4.20
Tool maint. ..	1.77	0.02	0.02
Labor+overhd	1.25(f)	21.17(g)	11.25(g)
Total	$5.32	$27.69	$17.77

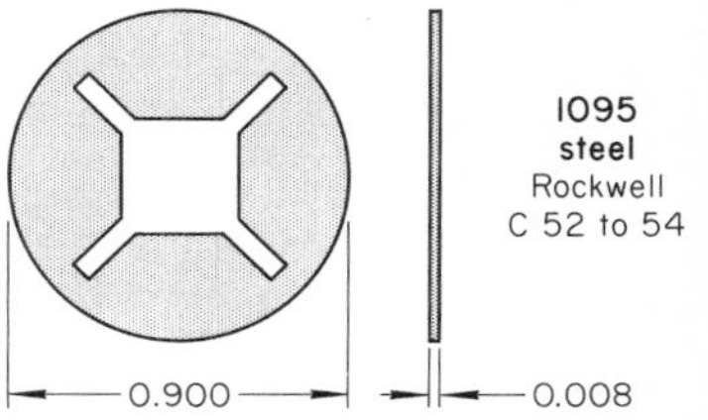

(a) Punch press and conveyor. (b) Stationary spray etcher, $2750; photoprinter, $1000; degreaser, tanks, oven, $1650; stereo microscope, $350; accessories, $700. (c) Conveyor spray etcher, $10,000; two photoprinters, $2000; spray developer, $2500; degreaser, tanks, ovens, $3550; optical comparator, $1800; stereo microscope, $350; accessories, $1645. (d) Carbide dies. (e) Artwork and masters. (f) At $10 per hour. (g) At an average of $6.25 per hour.

was less expensive for up to 300,000 parts ($0.029 each at the crossover point); the high-production chemical method was less expensive than the mechanical method for up to 500,000 parts ($0.019 each at the crossover point); and the high-production method was the less expensive of the chemical methods for all quantities (although the difference was small for quantities of a few thousand parts).

Printed-Circuit Etching. A special use of chemical blanking is in the manufacture of printed-circuit cards, to etch away the copper cladding from defined areas of plastic laminate, leaving a pattern of resist-protected conductor circuits on the plastic panel. The techniques are essentially those for other chemical blanking, but usually are applied to 1-oz or 2-oz copper foil (0.0014 or 0.0028 in. thick) bonded to plastic panels about 0.010 to 0.250 in. thick. In some applications, the maskant is used only as an intermediate coating to define the areas on which a metallic etch-resist (such as solder, nickel, tin-nickel alloy, palladium or gold) is then electroplated over the copper foil. Etching is done in specially designed spray etchers, using horizontal conveyor-type machines for volume production.

Etchants used on printed-circuit cards include solutions of: (*a*) chromic acid plus sulfuric acid or sodium sulfate, (*b*) ammonium persulfate, (*c*) ferric chloride, and (*d*) cupric chloride. Selection of an etchant depends on type of product, nature of resist or resists, subsequent soldering or welding requirements, removal rate, undercutting behavior, compatibility with plastic substrate (chemical attack, absorption, deposition of insoluble films), material cost, and ease and cost of control, regeneration and waste disposal. Table 4 compares the performance

Table 4. Effect of Etchant Composition on Production of 10-Mil Lines in 2-Oz Copper Foil Bonded to a Plastic Base (a)

Etchant composition — Constituent	Oz/gal	Etching time, sec(b)	Undercut, $R - T$, in.(b)	Etching taper, $B - T$, in.(c)
$(NH_4)_2S_2O_8$	29	88	0.0036	0.0026
$HgCl_2$	0.00086			
H_2SO_4	2.26(d)			
Copper	0.65-1.08			
$(NH_4)_2S_2O_8$	29	90	0.0035	0.0035
NH_4Cl	2.16			
$HgCl_2$	0.00086			
Copper	0.65-1.78			
$(NH_4)_2S_2O_8$	29	134	0.0029	0.0045
NH_4Cl	2.16			
Copper	0.65-1.78			
$(NH_4)_2S_2O_8$	29	182	0.0021	0.0040
NaCl	19			
Copper	0.87-1.32			
$CuCl_2$	36	143	0.0029	0.0018
NH_4Cl	8.64			
Copper	0.65-1.02			
$FeCl_3$	51	76	0.0026	0.0018

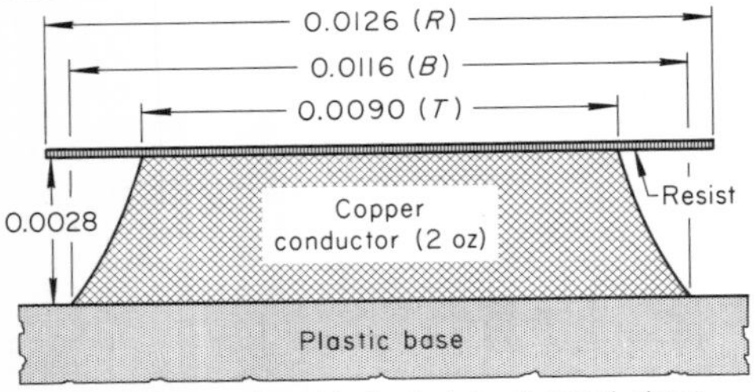

10-mil line produced in first etchant listed above

Undercut (both sides) $= R - T = 0.0036$ in.
Etching taper $= B - T = 0.0026$ in.

(a) Undercut and etching taper are influenced by etchant composition, operating conditions and foil thickness; undercut and taper would be substantially smaller for 1-oz (0.0014-in.-thick) copper foil; controlled overetching will reduce taper. (b) At 99 to 100 F. (c) See illustration; etch factor as calculated for other chemical blanking operations is not applicable to printed-circuit etching; etching taper $(B - T)$ is used instead. (d) Fluid ounces per gallon.

of six different etching solutions in producing 10-mil (0.010-in.) lines in 2-oz copper foil bonded to a plastic base. Space between lines was 5 to 30 mils (0.005 to 0.030 in.). The data in Table 4 show that etching rate, undercut and etching taper can be changed by altering the etchant composition; these variables can be changed also by adjusting the operating temperature or the spray velocity.

Under rigidly controlled conditions, patterns with line widths and spacings of 5 mils (0.005 in.) can be etched on 1-oz or 2-oz copper foil at constant etching time, with ammonium persulfate, chromic acid plus sulfuric acid, or ferric chloride etchants. Etching of patterns with lines and spacings narrower than 5 mils presents serious problems, chiefly because of variation in foil thickness. Patterns with line widths and spacings of 20 to 30 mils (0.020 to 0.030 in.) can be etched on a production basis without the critical control of etchant composition, temperature, uniformity of spray distribution, etching time, foil thickness and surface condition required for fine-line etching:

Example 464. Printed-Circuit Card Etched in Volume Production (Fig. 3)

The printed-circuit card in Fig. 3 illustrates a conductor pattern typical of cards produced in large quantities for wiring of electronic equipment. This card was produced by the photoresist method from 0.060-in.-thick epoxy-glass laminate clad on one side only with 1-oz copper foil, and predrilled as shown in Fig. 3. The dark-colored areas represent the copper conductor pattern remaining after etching. A 16-card composite master was used to expose the photoresist on a 10-by-13-in. panel, which was then developed, spray etched in ammonium persulfate, and cut into individual cards.

In use, component leads or wires were inserted through designated holes from the reverse side of the card, crimped against the "land" areas around the holes and soldered in place. The card was inserted into a connector-holder in which spring contact was made to each of the tabs. Dimensions are given in the table below Fig. 3.

Large quantities of cards, each with a different circuit pattern (if desired), can be made on a highly automated basis in a single production line, employing reusable exposure masters and drilling templates or tapes, with composite panels made to standard dimensions for efficient handling.

Panels are made with copper circuitry on both sides by starting with double-clad laminate stock. Panels with a number of layers of internal circuitry are made by etching a conductor pattern on each side of double-clad stock and then laminating additional layers of pre-etched single-clad stock in accurate register on each side of the core material. Each individual plane of circuitry may be different.

Holes are drilled in the final multiplane panel, and electrical connections are established between the several layers of etched copper circuitry by plating copper on the walls of the drilled holes. Etching of the outermost layers of copper may be delayed until a metallic etch-resist that is also suitable for soldering or welding (or one that will retain low electrical-contact resistance for long periods) has been applied by electroplating.

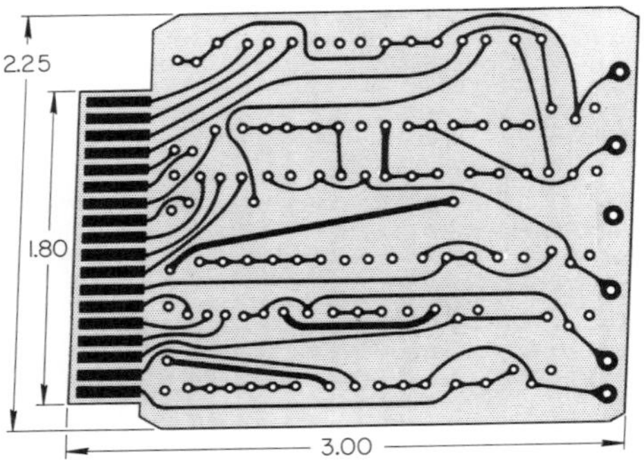

Composite panel size	10 by 13 in.
Number of cards per panel	16
Panel thickness	0.060 in.
Thickness of copper foil	0.0014 in.
Line width	0.010 and 0.030 in.
Minimum spacing between circuitry	0.010 in.
Tab dimensions	0.080 by 0.400 in.
Spacing between tabs	0.020 in.
Hole diameter	0.040 in.
Outside diameter of land	0.080 in.

Fig. 3. Etched printed-circuit card made from epoxy-glass laminate clad on one side only with 1-oz copper foil (Example 464)

Design Considerations for Chemical Blanking

The mechanical properties of the work metal have no effect on etching rate, nor does workpiece shape (unless it prevents uniform access of fresh etchant to the surface). Figure 4 illustrates progressive stages of metal removal in chemical blanking and the effect of undercut on design.

Because chemical blanking is concerned primarily with the etched surfaces that become the edges of the blanked-out part, undercut refers only to attack just below the resist edge on one side of the cut. Etch factor is defined as depth of cut divided by undercut; higher values are preferred to lower values. In Fig. 4(d), 6-mils-thick stock is shown blanked with an undercut of 1 mil and an etch factor of 3.0. Straightness of the side walls of the cut can be improved substantially by overetching, as shown in Fig. 4(f), for an undercut of 2 mils and an etch factor of 1.5. Allowance is made for undercut and etch factor in the layout of artwork, on the basis of trial processing or of experience.

The maximum thickness of sheet from which parts are chemically blanked on a production basis is 1/16 in. (However, cold rolled steel parts 1/8 in. thick have been blanked to a tolerance of ±0.015 in. under special conditions.) Parts can be blanked to an inside corner radius approximately equal to the stock thickness (T), and to an outside corner radius of about $\frac{1}{3}T$.

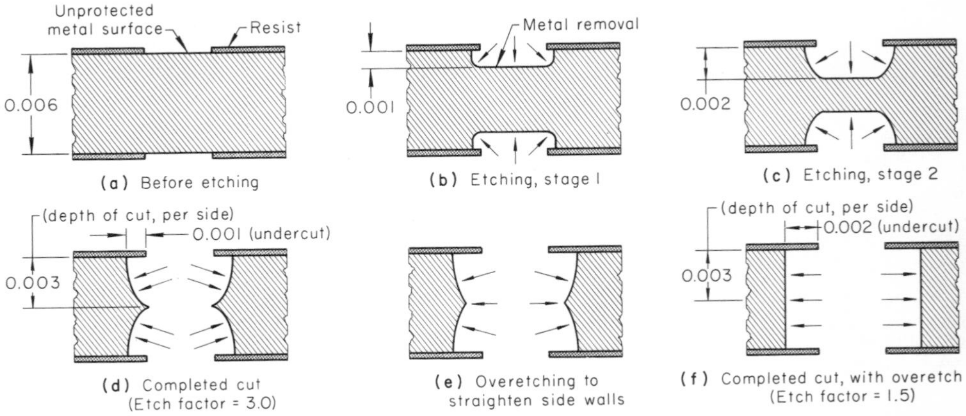

Metal is removed by etching on all work-metal surfaces not covered by resist. Workpieces can be taken from etchant as soon as blanking is completed (stage d), for an undercut of 0.001 in.; or etching can be continued to improve straightness of side walls, for an undercut of 0.002 in. (stage f). Workpiece dimensions depend on resist dimensions and control of undercut.

Fig. 4. Progressive stages of metal removal in chemical blanking

Minimum slot width or hole diameter for production chemical blanking of some commonly used metals is approximately as follows:

Steels, carbon and alloy	1.0*T*
Stainless steels	1.4*T*
Aluminum alloys	1.4*T*
Copper alloys	0.7*T*

Industry tolerances for dimensions of parts chemically blanked from various metals are listed in Table 5 for thicknesses of 0.002 to 0.060 in. The values shown range from ±10% of stock thickness for production blanking of steel, nickel, copper and copper alloys with rigid control to ±100% of stock thickness for routine production blanking of 0.002-in.-thick aluminum alloy foil. Under special conditions, accuracy of ±5% of thickness and part reproducibility of ±2% to ±3% of thickness can be maintained.

Although burrs are not produced in chemical blanking, the edges obtained at the instant of complete breakthrough may be irregular and rough to varying degrees. Edge uniformity depends on the uniformity and fineness of the grain structure of the workpiece, local stresses, edge orientation, uniformity of resist edge, and adherence of resist, as well as on local variation in etchant concentration, impingement velocity, and direction of flow against the surface being cut. Slower etching rates usually produce more uniform edges. Edge quality can be improved by controlled overetching (see Fig. 4), or by subsequent bright dipping or chemical or electrolytic polishing.

Advantages and Disadvantages of Chemical Blanking

The chief advantages of chemical blanking are:

1. Setup and "tooling" costs are extremely low (often less than $200).
2. Initial quantities of newly designed parts can be produced on short notice — sometimes within a few hours after the design has been conceived.
3. Design-change costs are low, since only artwork is altered.
4. The process does not produce burrs.
5. Extremely thin metal can easily be blanked without distortion. Accuracy actually increases as metal thickness decreases, because the extent of undercutting is decreased.
6. Metal hardness has no significant effect on ease of blanking.
7. The temper, stress and other physical properties of the metal are not changed.
8. Brittle metals (such as the silicon electrical steels, which often fracture during conventional blanking) are blanked without difficulty.
9. The process allows great design flexibility.

Table 5. Industry Tolerances for Chemical Blanking of Various Metals

Stock thickness, in.	Tolerance (±), in. — Aluminum alloys	Copper and alloys	Nickel	Stainless steel	Low-alloy steel
For Routine Production					
0.002	0.002	0.001	0.001	0.001	0.001
0.005	0.003	0.002	0.003	0.002	0.002
0.010	0.004	0.003	0.005	0.003	0.004
0.020	0.006	0.005	0.010	0.005	0.006
0.040	0.008	0.006	....	0.010	0.010
0.060	0.012	0.007	....	0.014	0.012
For Production With Rigid Control					
0.002	0.0003	0.0002	0.0002	0.0005	0.0002
0.005	0.0007	0.0005	0.0005	0.001	0.0005
0.010	0.0015	0.001	0.001	0.002	0.001
0.020	0.003	0.002	0.002	0.004	0.002
0.040	0.005	0.004	0.005	0.008	0.005
0.060	0.007	0.006	0.008	0.012	0.007

Tolerances are applicable to a dimension of 2 in. or less; proportionate value applies for a larger dimension. Closer tolerances are possible.

Disadvantages associated with chemical blanking are:

1. A relatively high level of operator skill is required.
2. Special safety precautions are needed in handling of chemicals; the etchant vapors also are very corrosive. Etching equipment must usually be isolated from other plant equipment.
3. Production yields are relatively low.
4. Suitable photographic facilities are not always available, and are costly.
5. Maximum metal thickness that can be blanked is about 1/16 in.
6. Sharp radii cannot be produced.

CHEMICAL CONTOUR MACHINING

Chemical contour machining, or chemical milling (also known as chemical contouring, dimensional etching, or chemical machining) is used chiefly to produce three-dimensional shapes by selective or over-all removal of metal from relatively large surfaces. The objective usually is the production of shallow pockets or odd-shaped cavities, reduction of weight, tapering of parts, over-all reduction in dimensions, or removal of an undesirable surface skin. The process is particularly useful in machining large, complex shapes or sections that are too thin to tolerate the stress of conventional machining, and in removing metal from exceptionally hard or brittle materials. Fragile parts can be machined after heat treatment, to avoid thermal distortion. Chemical contouring is not competitive in the manufacture of parts that can be produced readily with conventional metal-cutting tools; most applications are in the aerospace industries.

Procedure

The procedure for chemical contouring (chemical milling) resembles that for chemical blanking: *(a)* A metal workpiece is cleaned and coated with a liquid maskant, *(b)* the mask is dried and cured, *(c)* the pattern outline is scribed through the mask, *(d)* the mask is peeled away in the areas to be machined, *(e)* the desired thickness of metal is dissolved away by immersion in an etching solution for a controlled period, and *(f)* the remainder of the mask is removed. [The production of structural panels with a high strength-to-weight ratio by masking and chemical etching was patented by M. C. Sanz in 1956 (U. S. Patent 2,739,047); other patents cover various aspects of selective metal removal by masking and chemical etching.]

A flow chart showing the principal steps is given in Fig. 5. Rinsing and drying operations, not shown in the flow chart, are also required.

Preparation of workpieces is done in the same manner as for chemical blanking, except that preliminary operations such as vapor blasting are seldom used because they could cause difficulty in peeling the mask from the surfaces to be etched. Degreasing (or solvent cleaning) is sometimes the only pretreatment required; this is usually omitted when alkaline cleaning is used, unless grease or heavy soil is present on the work surface.

Masking and Scribing

Maskant is applied by dipping, spraying, flow coating, or brushing. Maskant materials must provide continuous, impermeable, chemically resistant coatings that adhere at cut edges during etching but can be readily peeled off before (and preferably also after) etching.

Resistance to acids, oxidizing acids, and alkalis and to heat is given in Table 6 for the elastomers and plastics used as maskants for chemical contouring. Table 7 gives additional information on five maskant materials that are used most widely in the chemical contouring of aluminum (exposure to alkalis or acids) and of steel (exposure to oxidizing acids).

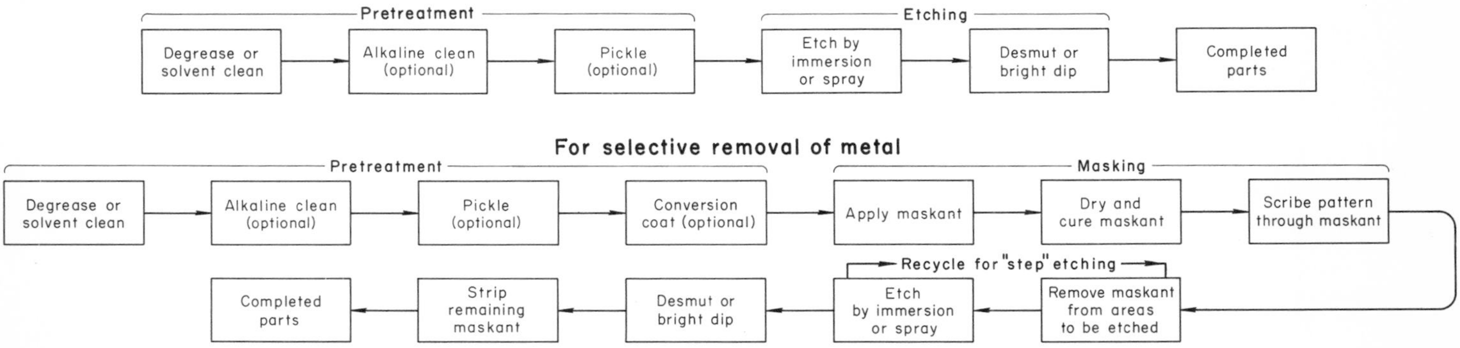

Fig. 5. Flow chart of principal process steps for chemical contour machining (chemical milling)

Table 6. Chemical and Thermal Resistance of Maskant Materials for Chemical Contouring

(E = Excellent, G = Good, F = Fair, P = Poor)

Maskant material	Resistance to: Acids	Oxidizing acids	Alkalis	Temperature, F(a)
Elastomers				
Acrylonitrile	G	F-P	E	250
Butyl rubber	E	G	E	300
Neoprene	G	F-P	E	200
Styrene-butadiene	E	F-P	E	200
Plastics				
Chlorinated rubber resins	E	G	E	150
Polyvinyl chloride	E	G-E	G-E	160
Polyvinylidene chloride	E	G-E	F	160
Polystyrene	E	G	E	150
Polyethylene	E	G	E	140

(a) Maximum for intermittent exposure; normally used also as curing temperature.

Thickness of maskant coatings can be 3 to 15 mils. Usually, the pretreatment of work metal, and the composition, cure and thickness of maskant coating, are regulated to give peel adhesion values of 1 to 3 lb per inch of width and a tensile strength of at least 800 psi. High maskant adhesion requires increased coating thickness and tensile strength and makes manual stripping more difficult; low adhesion increases the likelihood of pattern edge failure during handling or etching.

The pattern is scribed through the mask with a knife or heated scribing tool, using a template, and the mask is peeled off areas to be etched. Pinholes and other defects are then touched up with a patching material or tape.

Other Masking Methods. Screening or photoresist techniques, as described for chemical blanking, are used for the shallow chemical contouring of relatively small parts that require greater dimensional accuracy or finer detail. Applicability and tolerances for the three major masking methods are given in Table 8. These are based on "normal" production conditions; deeper cuts, narrower line widths or spacings, and greater dimensional accuracy can be obtained under special processing conditions. Because they are extremely thin, photoresist coatings can be used only for shallow cuts and are not suitable for use with hot, strongly alkaline etchants or with vigorously reacting oxidizing acids. Screened maskants are similarly limited by their resistance to etchants, but to a lesser degree.

Etching for Contouring

Etching for chemical contouring is ordinarily done by immersion, although spray etching is sometimes used, particularly on small workpieces. "Step etching" is done by repeated cycles of scribing and peeling off unwanted mask areas, then etching. "Taper etching" is done by immersing or withdrawing the workpiece from the etching bath at a controlled slow rate.

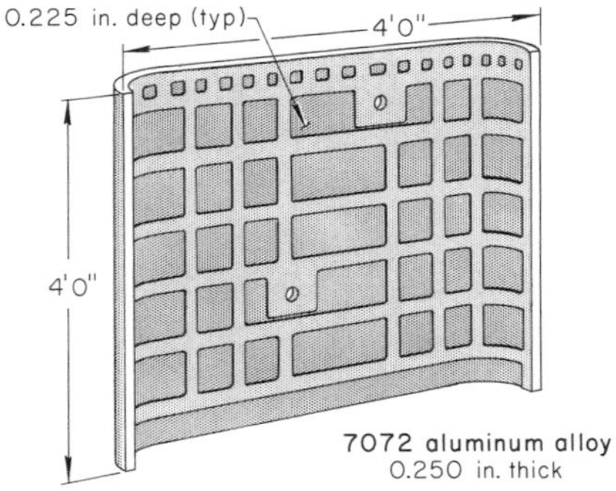

Fig. 6. Preformed aircraft skin section chemically contoured to reduce weight (Example 465a)

Workpieces should be positioned in such a way as to prevent entrapment of gases, which can prevent attack on areas to be etched, or which can interfere with dissipation of heat from masked areas. Sometimes it is necessary to change the position of workpieces after partial etching, to release entrapped gases. Test panels may be etched and checked with a micrometer to determine rate of attack and desired immersion time for each load of work to be etched.

When control of metal removal is critical, the work is exposed to the etchant for about 80% of the calculated time, remeasured, and then returned for a recalculated final period of etching. Some large workpieces that must be machined to close tolerances are removed after partial etching and returned in a reversed position to improve uniformity of metal removal. Particularly critical work may be stored in a rinse tank at the processing temperature to equalize temperature differences, before being returned to the etching tank.

After etching, the remaining maskant is peeled off (or stripped in a "paint remover" formulation, if necessary). Some coatings, such as neoprene, can be made to peel off readily by a vapor degreasing operation or a solvent treatment. Desmutting, bright dipping, or chemical polishing is sometimes necessary for removal of residual films from the completed work or for meeting surface finish requirements.

Etchants. The formulations used for chemical contouring are similar to those for chemical blanking described in Table 2, and the principles of selection and control are the same as for chemical blanking. Because of the generally much larger areas being etched and the larger volumes of potentially hazardous chemical solutions used in chemical contouring, several factors in etchant selection and use are more critical than for chemical blanking. These include: (*a*) cost of chemicals; (*b*) ease and cost of control, regeneration and waste disposal; (*c*) materials of construction; and (*d*) safety precautions and ventilation.

Materials of Construction. Mild steel is adequate for all equipment that is in

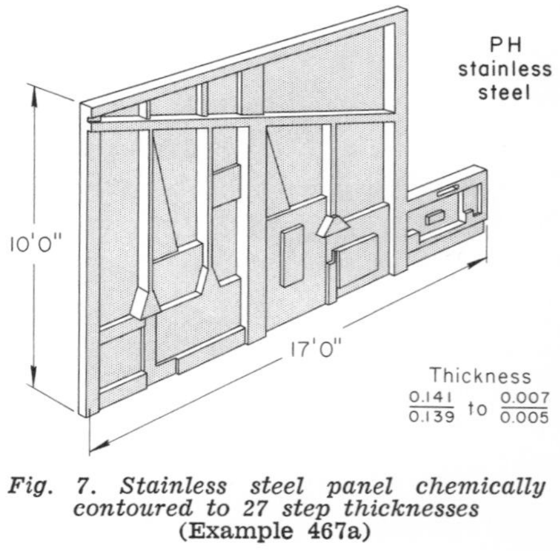

Fig. 7. Stainless steel panel chemically contoured to 27 step thicknesses (Example 467a)

Table 7. Properties of Maskant Materials Widely Used in Chemical Contouring

Property	Maskant material — Exposure to oxidizing acids(a): Polyvinyl chloride	Polyethylene	Exposure to acids or alkalis(b): Butyl rubber	Acrylonitrile rubber	Neoprene rubber
Ease of manufacture	Good(c)	Good(d)	Fair(e)	Fair(e)	Good(f)
Shelf life, months	6 to 12	6 to 12	4 to 6	3 to 6	6 to 8
Solids, %	25 to 55	60 to 100	20 to 25	15 to 25	25 to 35
Ease of application:					
Dipping	Good to fair	Poor to fair	Good	Good	Good
Flow coating	Good to fair	Poor to fair	Good	Good	Good
Air spraying	Good	Good	Poor	Poor	Fair
Type of cure	Air or heat	Heat(g)	Heat	Air or heat	Air or heat
Tensile strength, 1000 psi:					
Air dried (24 hr)	....	....	....	1.0 max	2.0 max
Heat cured(h)	1.0 to 2.5	0.8 to 1.5	0.8 to 1.5	1.5 to 2.5	1.5 to 3.0
Resistance to etchant:					
Deterioration	Good to excellent	Very good	Very good	Very good	Very good
Permeation	Fair to good	Very good	Excellent	Very good	Very good

(a) As in contouring of steel (see Table 2). (b) As in contouring of aluminum alloys (see Table 2). (c) Solution or dispersion. (d) Dispersion or hot melt. (e) Rubber mastication mandatory. (f) Rubber mastication preferable but not mandatory. (g) For dispersion coatings only. (h) Curing cycle is usually about 30 min at the temperatures listed in Table 6.

Table 8. Applicability and Tolerances for Major Masking Methods

Item	Method: Scribe-and-peel maskant	Screened maskant	Photoresist
Maximum workpiece size, in.	Limited only by tank size	48 by 48(a)	18 by 22(a)
Suitable workpiece shape	Flat to deeply contoured	Flat or simply curved to large radius	
Minimum width or spacing, in.	0.125(b)	0.010	0.0005
Maximum depth of cut, in.	0.500	0.060(c)	0.030(c)
Tolerance on lateral dimensions, in.:			
Maskant or resist image	±0.007	±0.003	±0.001 to 0.0002
Completed cut	±0.015(d)	±0.010	±0.002 to 0.005

(a) For ordinary production. (b) Must be twice the depth of cut for cuts deeper than 0.062 in., but need not be greater than 0.500 in. (c) Limited by chemical resistance and adherence of maskant or resist. (d) ±0.025 for cuts deeper than 0.050 in.

contact with alkaline etching solutions.

Nonoxidizing acids require tanks lined with vinyl plastisol coatings, and racks or baskets coated with this material. Pipes, pumps, filters and related equipment can be lined with vinyl plastisols or glass or made of solid PVC (polyvinyl chloride) for service at temperatures up to 140 F. For use at higher temperatures, this type of equipment can be made of glass or be lined with glass, PVDC (polyvinylidene chloride), ABS (acrylonitrile butadiene styrene), or chlorinated polyether plastics; or it can be made of corrosion-resistant metals such as Monel, Hastelloy C, titanium or tantalum.

Tank linings are often protected from physical damage by rigid sheets of plastic or plastic-coated steel. Steam coils can be made of the corrosion-resistant metals listed above, from special grades of graphite, or from glass or glass-coated steel.

The same materials used with nonoxidizing acids are also used with oxidizing acid solutions, except that 18–8 stainless steel is used instead of Monel.

Applications of Chemical Contouring

Chemical contouring (chemical milling) is used primarily to etch preformed aerospace parts to obtain maximum strength-to-weight ratio. Aircraft wing and fuselage sections are made with integral stiffeners of optimum cross section throughout their entire length and with minimum skin thickness. Spherical, conical or parabolic bulkheads for missiles are chemically contoured from spun blanks to almost any desired shape up to 13 ft in diameter. For least weight and most interior space, thicknesses are varied from 3⁄16 in. down to 0.020 in. or less by step or taper contouring to a final thickness tolerance of ±0.003 in. This technique also reduces the number of parts and assembly operations.

Example 931, in the article on Machining of Beryllium, describes how a beryllium missile component was reduced from 13 to 6 lb by CHM, in 15 to 20% sulfuric acid solution. The example that follows describes two other applications of CHM for weight reduction.

Example 465(a) and (b). Chemical Contouring of Integrally Stiffened Skin Sections

Example 465(a) — Fuselage Section Made From Preformed 7072 Aluminum Alloy Plate (Fig. 6). The fuselage skin section shown in Fig. 6 was chemically contour machined after stretch forming. The web areas comprising about 80% of the surface area (one side) of the originally ¼-in.-thick section were etched to a thickness of 0.025 in., reducing the weight of the part from 60 to 15 lb.

Before the development of chemical contour machining, parts of this type were made by welding or riveting reinforcing sheet sections to a formed 0.025-in.-thick skin, there being no practical method to form such a panel after machining or to machine such a panel after forming. Chemical contouring lowered manufacturing cost by greatly reducing the number of parts and eliminating assembly time. [SOURCE: L. P. Street, ASTME technical paper MR66-165 (1966)]

Example 465(b) — Leading Edge of Wing Made From Titanium Alloy. A 12-ft-long by 0.125-in.-thick flat panel of Ti – 5 Al – 2.5 Sn was chemically contour machined to reduce weight. The part tapered uniformly in width from 11 in. at one end to 6 in. at the other end. The weight of the part was reduced from 24 to 16 lb by etching rectangular 0.070-in.-deep pockets in a grid pattern that covered about 60% of the surface of one side of the panel. Typical roughness produced on parts of this type was 15 to 80 micro-in., depending on the alloy used. [SOURCE: L. P. Street, ASTME technical paper MR66-165 (1966)]

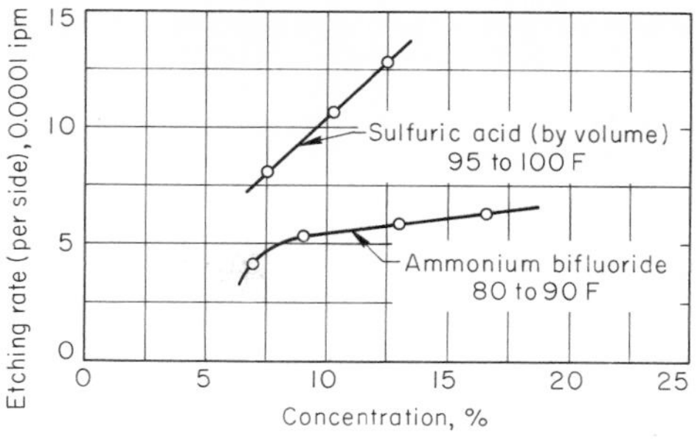

Fig. 8. Effect of etchant concentration on etching rate in chemical contouring of beryllium (Example 467b)

Electrically assisted chemical contouring, using low-amperage direct current at 4 to 6 volts during etching, speeds up metal removal on corrosion-resistant metals, and also is used in some applications on aluminum alloys to improve surface finish — as in the following example:

Example 466. Use of Auxiliary Anodic Current in Chemical Contouring Aluminum Alloy Parts

Poor yield was obtained in the production of aircraft landing-gear access doors from 2024 aluminum alloy by chemical machining in a sodium hydroxide bath. The part was contoured to six different levels by step etching. A total thickness of 0.308 in. was removed from the area of the sixth step. The final thickness at any point on this 11-sq-ft step was 0.014 in. The surface produced on many parts failed to meet dimensional tolerances and was too rough.

Making the work anodic during immersion and passing a current of 2 to 8 amp per sq ft greatly improved the yield of acceptable parts, as shown by inspection records for more than 7 months for each method:

Disposition of work	Standard method	Electrically assisted method
Immediately acceptable	4%	88%
Acceptable after repair	55%	12%
Total acceptable parts	59%	100%

The parts were wired, or several parts were clamped to a metal basket or frame, to provide electrical contact for processing; the tank walls served as the cathode. Rate of metal removal was uniform, and a smooth finish was obtained on all the parts in a load, with the basket spaced at about 10 to 12 in. from the tank wall. Etchant concentration was maintained at 10 to 12 oz NaOH per gal and 1 to 9 oz Al per gal. About 98% of the metal was removed chemically, and only 2% electrolytically. The improvement was attributed primarily to the presence of a positive potential on the work, which prevented local plating-out of copper and zinc on the aluminum.

The electrically assisted method was used satisfactorily on other production parts made of aluminum alloys 2024, 2219, 5052, 6061, 7075 and 7178. Acceptable results were also obtained by the addition of sulfide to the etchant to form insoluble compounds with the interfering metal ions. [SOURCE: J. E. Spessard, *Plating*, Nov 1961, p 1221-1222]

The three parts of the next example illustrate the application of chemical contouring to the manufacture of complex parts that were very large, or that were made of hard or brittle metal difficult to machine by ordinary means.

Example 467(a), (b) and (c). Chemical Contouring of Large Parts and Parts Made of Difficult-to-Machine Alloys

Example 467(a) — Large Stainless Steel Panel With 27 Different Thicknesses (Fig. 7). A 10-by-17-ft panel of a precipitation-hardening stainless steel was chemically machined to the complex configuration shown in Fig. 7. A total of 27 different step thicknesses that ranged from 0.140 to 0.006 in. were produced to a tolerance of ±0.001 in. [SOURCE: D. Fishlock and K. W. Hards, "New Ways of Working Metals" (Philosophical Library, 1965), p 51]

Example 467(b) — Etchant Developed for Machining Brittle Beryllium Alloy (Fig. 8). Conventional machining of space-vehicle parts from beryllium resulted in excessive rejection rates because of cracking. No acceptable method of repairing the defective parts could be found.

Accordingly, techniques were developed for making taper sections, integral stiffening ribs and other parts with a high strength-to-weight ratio by chemical contouring. A weight saving of 50% was obtained on guidance-package doors by this method of production.

The preferred etchant was a 9 to 17% solution of ammonium bifluoride, which had a metal-removal rate of 0.0005 to 0.0006 ipm per side at 80 to 90 F. Sulfuric acid etchant (8 to 13% by volume) removed metal more rapidly but was too sensitive to concentration changes for good control. The nearly constant etching rate of the ammonium bifluoride etchant is compared in Fig. 8 with the etching rate for sulfuric acid solutions. Temperature control was required, as etching rate in either solution was nearly doubled by a 15 F rise in bath temperature. A loose smut, which was readily removed by wiping, remained on the beryllium surface after etching. A neoprene-base maskant was used at a thickness of about 0.008 in. [SOURCE: L. Missel and M. E. Shaheen, *Metal Finishing*, Nov 1965, p 69-71]

Example 467(c) — Cb-752 Skin Panel for Re-entry Vehicle (Fig. 9). The stiffened skin panel illustrated in Fig. 9 was made of columbium alloy 752 (Cb, 10 W, 2.5 Zr) because of its combination of tensile properties at 2600 F with formability and weldability. The L-shaped stiffeners shown in the enlarged cross-sectional view were attached by electron beam welding before chemical machining of the 0.040-in.-deep pockets in the skin panel.

It was originally planned to form the pockets by conventional machining, but difficulties were encountered in meeting skin-thickness

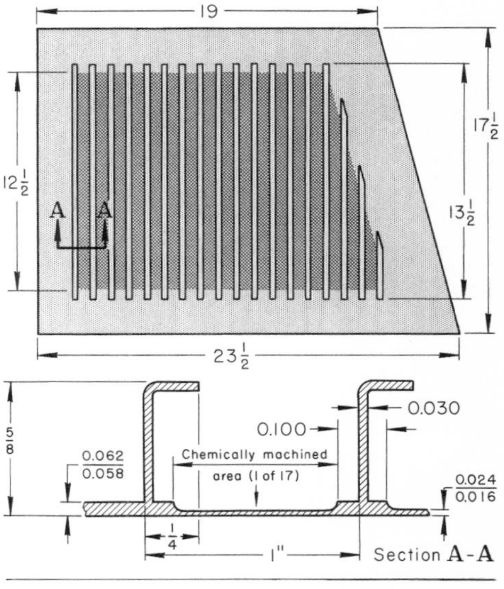

Etchant	HNO_3 plus HF
Temperature	90 to 130 F
Surface tension, maximum	30 dynes per cm
Etching rate	0.0005 to 0.001 ipm
Etching time	40 to 80 min
Surface finish, initial	20 micro-in.
Surface finish, final	40 micro-in.

Fig. 9. Stiffened skin panel of Cb-752 recessed by chemical contouring (Example 467c)

tolerances and in producing a smooth surface finish, and cutter life was very short. Therefore, it was decided to use chemical contour machining to form the parts instead.

The surface was pre-etched for 30 sec to provide adhesion for a translucent maskant 0.012 to 0.014 in. thick, which was applied in four dip coats and touched up by brushing. The pattern was scribed, using a knife and template, and the maskant was peeled from the machining area before etching.

Processing details are given with Fig. 9. Special precautions had to be taken to prevent local temperature differences on the work because of nonuniform dissipation of the heat generated by the chemical reaction. The bath was agitated, and the work was removed at intervals and allowed to equalize in temperature in a rinse tank held at etching temperature. The maximum variation in final thickness of the recessed area on a single panel was ±0.001 in. It was necessary to hold the surface tension of the bath at 30 dynes per cm or less to avoid channeling on the skin adjacent to the fillet and to keep undercut ratio at 1.0 for a true radius. [SOURCE: R. C. Movich, ASTME technical paper MR66-712, March 1966]

Other types of parts made by chemical contouring include: aircraft doors and access panels, integrally stiffened tubing, shells for missiles, helicopter blades, stator cases, spherical pressure vessels, and architectural trim panels.

Design Considerations for Chemical Contouring

Some important considerations in the design of parts to be processed by chemical contouring are illustrated in Fig. 10. Undercut behavior in simple contouring (Fig. 10a) is essentially the same as in chemical blanking or printed-circuit etching. Undercut *per edge* is approximately equal to the depth of cut. "Etch factor" is defined as the undercut divided by the depth of cut — the exact opposite of the definition used in connection with chemical blanking. In multistep contouring, fillet radii are approximately equal to the *total* depth of cut for each step (Fig. 10b). Allowance for undercut is made in layout. Tolerance on edge position of cut is illustrated in Fig. 10(c), and average tolerance values are given for shallow and deep cuts.

As indicated in Fig. 10(d), work should be laid out with the longest dimension of a pocket parallel to the grain, because etching is less uniform across the grain (particularly for cuts deeper than 0.100 in.).

Because chemical contouring does not usually remove deep dents or scratches, any necessary removal of such gross defects must be done before etching.

Depth of cut is limited by the uniformity of etching action obtainable on the work surface, and hence deep cuts require fine-grained, homogeneous metal, uniformly mechanically worked or heat treated, free from stress concentrations, inclusions and internal faults. The maximum depth of cut obtainable in ordinary production practice varies with the form of work material approximately as follows:

Sheet and plate	0.500 in.
Extrusions	0.150
Forgings	0.250

Results obtained on castings are highly variable, but depth of cut does not usually exceed 0.100 to 0.200 in.

Tolerances on depth of cut for aluminum alloys, copper alloys, magnesium alloys, steel, stainless steel and heat-resisting alloys are usually as follows:

Less than 0.020-in. depth	±0.001 in.
0.020 to 0.060	±0.002
More than 0.060	±0.003

Tolerances on depth of cut for titanium are about twice the above values. These tolerances include only the variation in the thickness of metal removed by etching; the original variation in stock thickness as purchased must be added to obtain over-all tolerances on final thickness of section. Final thickness tolerance can be improved by using narrower widths of standard flat stock (which are manufactured to closer thickness limits), by grouping incoming stock according to thickness, by grinding purchased stock to the desired thickness, or by timing parts individually according to thickness in etching. Table 9 illustrates the effect of material form and thickness on stock-thickness tolerances for aluminum alloys, as purchased. As the values in Table 9 indicate, individual control of etching time is necessary for close-tolerance work on thick material.

Table 9. Mill Tolerances on Thickness of Aluminum Alloy Flat Stock

Nominal thickness, in.	Tolerance (±), in.	Nominal thickness, in.	Tolerance (±), in.
Sheet and Plate		0.500	0.009
Up to 0.040	0.001	0.750	0.0125
0.050-0.071	0.0015	1.000	0.015
0.080-0.100	0.002	**Extrusions**	
0.125	0.0025		
0.160	0.003	Up to 0.124	0.003
0.190	0.0035	0.125-0.249	0.0035
0.250	0.005	0.250-0.499	0.004
0.313	0.006	0.500-0.749	0.0045
0.375	0.007	0.750-0.999	0.005

To estimate final thickness tolerances, the tolerances listed here must be combined with those on depth of cut given in the text.

Lateral dimensions of cuts are influenced by depth of cut. In ordinary practice, cuts deeper than 0.125 in. should have a width of at least 0.125 in. plus twice the depth of cut; shallower cuts should have a width of at least 0.060 in. plus twice the depth of cut. Minimum land width should be:

Depth of cut, in.	Land width, in.
Up to 0.062	0.125
0.063 to 0.250	2 times depth
Greater than 0.250	0.500

Maximum taper, when produced by controlled slow immersion or withdrawal rates, is usually 0.010 in. per foot for steel and 0.100 in. per foot for aluminum alloys. "Step tapering" eliminates less nonfunctional weight than continuous tapering, but may be cheaper and allows greater design flexibility.

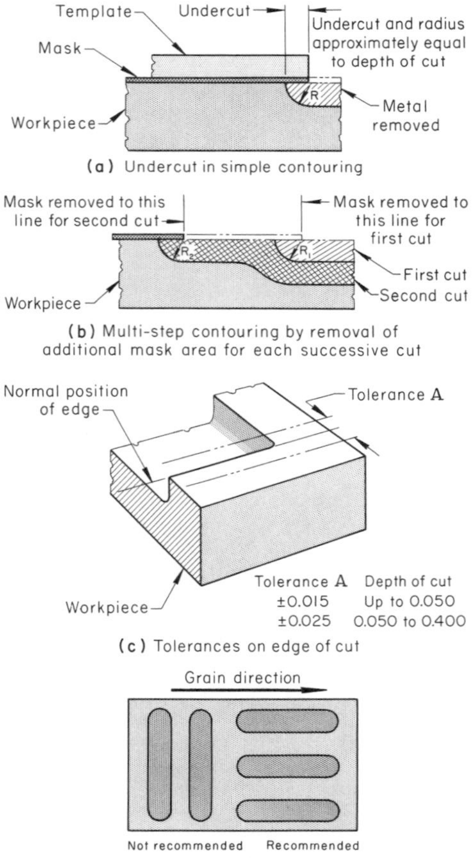

(a) Undercut in simple contouring

(b) Multi-step contouring by removal of additional mask area for each successive cut

(c) Tolerances on edge of cut

(d) Orientation for cuts deeper than 0.100 in.

Fig. 10. Design considerations for chemical contouring

Properties of Etched Surfaces

Initial surface waviness and defects are not altered greatly in contouring most metals, but may be smoothed out on magnesium alloys. Typical values for surface finish produced on sheet or plate for various work metals are given in Table 10. Quality of finish is lower for extrusions, forgings or castings (for example, 200 to 250 micro-in. for extruded 7075 aluminum alloy). Nonhomogeneous structures can produce gross deviations from flatness in chemical contouring (for example, nodules ⅜ in. high had to be removed after cutting ¾-in.-deep pockets in 2219-T39 aluminum alloy plates).

The mechanical properties of most metals are not affected by chemical contouring. Stresses are not induced by the process, as neither mechanical deformation nor exposure to high temperature is involved. In some instances, elimination of surface residual stress is beneficial; fatigue strength can be improved by imparting a uniform compressive stress to the chemically machined surface by peening, wet blasting, or other suitable techniques.

Embrittlement by hydrogen absorption may occur during the etching of some metals with nonoxidizing chemical solutions. Aluminum alloys are not subject to hydrogen embrittlement, and no effect is observed on steels, stainless steels, copper alloys, nickel alloys, titanium and other metals when strongly oxidizing etchants are used. Chemical machining of beryllium reduces the brittleness inherent in this material. If etching conditions permit embrittlement, the completed work can be heated to drive out absorbed hydrogen (1 to 4 hr at 250 to 400 F).

Intergranular attack can occur in etching certain metals, but it usually can be prevented by changing the composition or temperature of the etchant, or can be removed by a final mechanical polishing operation. The chemical contouring of workpieces made of René 41 and Hastelloy X to remove a thickness of 0.020 in. has been observed to reduce the fatigue limit of those alloys by about 15%, as a result of intergranular attack to a depth of 0.0004 to 0.0006 in.; no effect was observed on similarly treated A-286 alloy. Chemical contouring procedures for components subject to high service stress should be qualified by microscopic and mechanical examination of processed parts for intergranular attack and for embrittlement.

Advantages and Disadvantages of Chemical Contouring

Advantages of chemical contouring include the following:

1 Many pieces can be etched in a tank at one time, and metal can be removed from one or several sides simultaneously.
2 Workpiece size is limited only by size of etching tank; pieces 7 ft wide by 50 ft long have been processed commercially.
3 Intricate shapes and thin sections can be produced to close tolerances, even in metals that are extremely hard or brittle.
4 Design usually is not limited by tool size or travel, or by shape of the workpiece; preformed pieces can be machined readily.
5 Tool cost and tool maintenance cost are low, and tool life is long.
6 Lead time between design and production of first pieces is usually only a few hours or a few days. Design changes can be made quickly and inexpensively merely by preparing a new template.
7 Burrs are not produced.
8 Many shapes that cannot be extruded, cast or forged can be made by chemical contouring.
9 Distortion can be avoided by chemical contouring after hardening, when mechanical machining would not be satisfactory.

Table 10. Typical Surface Roughness Produced by Chemical Contour Machining of Sheet or Plate

Work metal	Roughness, micro-in. Range	Avg
Aluminum alloys (except clad material):		
Cuts up to 0.250 in. deep	70 to 125	90
Cuts deeper than 0.250 in.	40 to 165	115
Magnesium alloys(a)	30 to 70	50
Steel	30 to 250	100
Titanium	15 to 50	25

(a) Applies to most sheet and plate alloys; AZ31C averages about 120 micro-in.

Disadvantages of chemical contouring are:

1 The rate of metal removal is slow, 0.001 to 0.002 ipm.
2 The process usually is not competitive for machining operations that can be done readily by conventional methods, or for extremely long production runs.
3 Depth of cut is limited to ½ in. or less; sharp inside radii cannot be produced.
4 Interior surfaces of tubes or cylinders, or other shapes that limit circulation of etchant or that entrap gases, often cannot be etched in a simple manner.
5 Work materials of homogeneous composition and structure are required. Results are often unacceptable on welded or brazed parts and on porous or otherwise defective castings; clad surfaces present special problems.
6 Surface waviness, defects and thickness variation usually remain essentially unchanged. (Exception: surfaces of magnesium alloys may be improved by chemical contour machining.)
7 Special safety precautions are needed in handling of chemicals; also, etchant vapors are very corrosive. Etching equipment must usually be isolated from other plant equipment.

Ultrasonic Machining (USM)

ULTRASONIC MACHINING (USM) is the removal of material by particles of abrasive that vibrate in a water slurry circulating through a narrow gap between the workpiece and a tool that oscillates at about 20,000 cycles per second. The tool reproduces its shape in the workpiece, generally to an accuracy of ±0.001 in., and sometimes to a tolerance of 0.0005 in. or less, without burrs. Accuracy depends on the size of the tool, rigidity of the machine and the tool, temperature of the slurry, grit size, and the procedure for roughing and finishing.

Ultrasonic machining is used chiefly on hard, brittle materials that do not conduct electricity; however, it is used on both metals and nonmetals, and on ductile as well as brittle materials. It is particularly well suited to the production of relatively shallow, irregular cavities, and is one of the few processes suitable for machining extremely fragile material, such as honeycomb. The main disadvantages of the process are low metal removal rate and high cost.

Equipment and Procedure. Ultrasonic machining is done in a machine that can feed the tool down into the workpiece, and that has a worktable capable of moving in three directions. A typical setup is shown in Fig. 1. A magnetostrictive stack makes the tool vibrate up and down 0.0005 to 0.0025 in. at 19,000 to 25,000 cycles per second, driving the abrasive grains across a gap of about 0.001 to 0.004 in. against the workpiece. The stack produces the vibration by changing slightly in length with the rapidly alternating magnetic field. The magnetostrictive material is brazed to a connecting body of Monel that transmits and amplifies the changes in length. A removable tool holder, fastened to the connecting body, also amplifies the vibration. The tool holder is made of Monel or of stainless steel. The tool, usually made of low-carbon or stainless steel to the shape of the desired cavity and a few thousandths of an inch smaller, is brazed or soldered to the tool holder. All these parts, including the tool, act as one long elastic body, carrying and amplifying the vibration (by resonance) to the tip of the tool.

This article is based primarily on information in Chapter 2 of "Non-Traditional Machining Processes", R. K. Springborn, editor, ASTME, Dearborn, Mich., 1967.

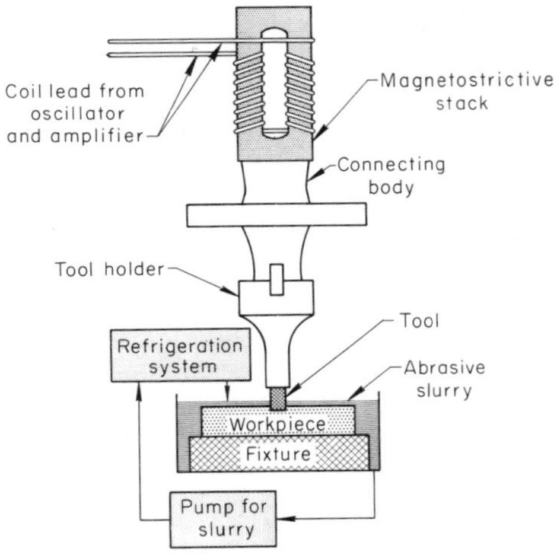

Fig. 1. Schematic of typical setup for ultrasonic machining

Table 1. Effect of Work Material on Performance in "Roughing" by USM

Work material	Removal rate: Cu in. per min	Removal rate: In. per min(a)	Max area, sq in. (b)	Wear ratio(c)
Glass	0.236	0.150	4.0	100
Ferrite	0.196	0.125	3.5	100
Mica(d)	0.196	0.125	3.5	100
Germanium	0.133	0.085	3.5	100
Graphite	0.125	0.080	3.0	100
Quartz	0.102	0.065	3.0	50
Ceramic(e)	0.094	0.060	3.0	75
Boron carbide	0.024	0.015	0.9	2.5
Tungsten carbide	0.022	0.014	1.2	1.5
Tool steel(f)	0.016	0.010	1.2	1

NOTE. Tool material was low-carbon steel; slurry was 30 to 40% of 180 to 240-grit boron carbide; amplitude of vibration was 0.001 to 0.0015 in. at a frequency of 25,000 cps.

(a) Linear penetration rate for a solid cylindrical tool ½ in. in diameter. (b) Maximum practical machining area. (c) Volume of work material removed divided by volume wear of tool. (d) Glass-bonded. (e) Average; results vary with hardness, brittleness and density. (f) Hardened. (SOURCE: M. C. Shaw, Ultrasonic Grinding, *Microtechnic*, June 1956, p 257-265)

The abrasive slurry is circulated by pumping and is cooled to 35 to 40 F to remove the heat that develops in USM. Much of the work is cemented onto glass plates, and cooling is required to keep the cement from softening. In addition, cooling is needed to prevent boiling in the cutting gap and to avoid undesirable temperature-dependent cavitation effects.

Workpieces. Nearly all materials can be cut effectively by USM, including (contrary to early reports) such ductile materials as soft brass. In general, however, workpiece material for USM is harder than Rockwell C 64, and it is not usually economical to use the process on steel that is softer than Rockwell C 45. In addition to hardened alloy steel, metals machined by USM include tool steel, stainless steel, nickel-base and cobalt-base heat-resisting alloys, and germanium. Other work materials include glass, ceramic, carbide and semiconductors. Table 1 lists average removal rate, maximum practical machining area, and average wear ratio for various work materials, based on the rough cutting of holes ½ in. in diameter and in depth. In this comparison, low-carbon steel tools were used with a 30 to 40% slurry of 180 to 240-grit boron carbide abrasive. Amplitude of vibration of tool tip was 0.001 to 0.0015 in. at a frequency of 25,000 cps. (Removal rates in cubic inches per minute would be proportionately lower for smaller cutting areas, but penetration rates in inches per minute would be of the same order of magnitude.)

Vibration of the workpiece must be prevented for the greatest efficiency in penetration. If the workpiece has little mass or rigidity, it should be held or clamped to a massive fixture to reduce or damp the vibration. Fixtures generally are made of stainless steel, brass or aluminum, with small areas that locate the work.

The workpiece may chip at the breakthrough of a hole unless the work material is cemented to a backing. Thin workpieces are almost always cemented to a backing.

Cored or predrilled holes in the workpiece help the flow of abrasive slurry to the cutting zone. A smaller through hole in the bottom of the workpiece allows the slurry to be pumped directly to the center of the cutting zone.

Workpieces are rotated during USM to increase the penetration rate and to improve uniformity in machining counterbores and other round holes and centered work. For certain operations, such as slicing, it is useful to move the work back and forth. Indexing devices and angle plates are used for some work, and lead screws are used for threading.

Tool holders for USM must transfer vibration, and must provide resonance without failure by fatigue. A tool holder must be fitted to the application; with proper design for resonance, a tool holder can give the tool edge an amplitude gain of six over the stack. Generally, the tool holder is in the shape of a cylinder, a cone, or a modified cone, with the center of mass of the tool on the centerline of the tool holder. The upper portion of the tool is identical to or slightly smaller than the adjacent portion of the tool holder, as illustrated in Fig. 1.

Standard tool holders are stocked, and the suppliers specify limits of tool area and length for each tool holder, so that it can resonate most usefully. The specified range of use avoids failure of the tool or of the brazed joint by overstress. The lowest resonant frequency is specified, permitting maximum reduction of tool length by wear before the tool must be replaced.

Fatigue is the primary cause of failure for tool holders, which are subjected to high-frequency reversals of stress between tension and compression. As in all highly stressed members, surface damage (such as nicks, scratches and tool marks) and excessive grain growth from repeated brazing can cause early failure. Tool holders should be polished, and handled with care. Surface damage such as nicks and scratches must be repaired to restore the polished surface. After 50 cycles of brazing, a tool holder should be heated to 1100 F for 2 hr, to reduce possible grain growth.

Tools for USM must be ductile and tough, rather than hard; but metals that are extremely ductile, such as copper, brass and aluminum, give a short tool life. Low-carbon steel is a good tool material; and 52100 steel, stainless steel, and molybdenum give superior performance. Many commercial forms of material can be used as tools without additional machining—for instance, music wire, gage wire, drill rod, stainless steel tubing, and hypodermic tubing.

The mass and the length of the tool are important. Too great a mass absorbs much of the ultrasonic energy, reducing the efficiency of machining. Too long a tool causes overstress of the tool and of the brazed joint, resulting in failure. Most tools for USM are less than 1 in. long, but some tools as long as 1½ in. are used; tools as long as 6 in. are rare.

Long, thin tools with too great a "slenderness ratio" will whip. (Slenderness ratio is the ratio of length of a

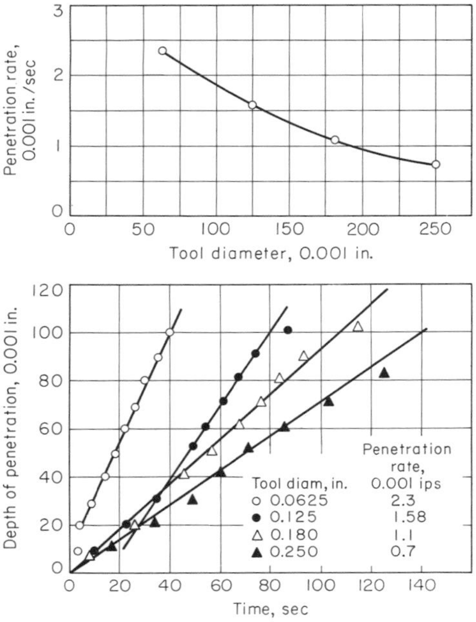

SOURCE: John Krawczyk, Ultrasonic Grinding Techniques in Microminiaturization, Diamond Ordnance Fuze Laboratories, TR-950, 1961.

Fig. 2. Effect of tool diameter on penetration rate in ultrasonic machining of ceramic with solid stainless steel tools

structural column to its least radius of gyration.) Slenderness ratio of a tool should not exceed 20. For instance, if the tool is a solid cylinder with a diameter of 0.060 in. (radius of gyration = 0.015 in.), its length should be no greater than 20 × 0.015 = 0.30 in. A hollow cylinder of 0.060-in. OD and 0.047-in. ID (radius of gyration = 0.019 in.) may have a length no greater than 20 × 0.019 = 0.38 in.

Cutting efficiency is at its best when the tool vibrates at a specified optimum amplitude or stroke for the machine tool and for the size of grit. Reasonable combinations are:

800-grit	Stroke, 0.0005 in.
400	0.0015
240	0.0025

For efficient operation, the assembly must be resonant at the designed frequency of the system, when vibrating at the optimum stroke. This condition of resonance will give these proofs:

1. Cavitation of water in the slurry will cause the loudest sound.
2. The feed indicator of the machine will show the greatest rate of feed.
3. The ends of the tool holder give the greatest sensation at a light touch.

The stroke of the tool can be observed in a microscope. Such viewing is important when experimenting with USM, because some tools and workpieces are too delicate or too brittle for a long stroke. It may be necessary to use a stroke as short as 0.0005 in. to prevent damage.

Rate of penetration in USM is limited chiefly by the degree to which the required circulation of slurry can be maintained on all parts of the area being machined. Thus, penetration is slower in machining large areas or cavities with a high ratio of depth to smallest lateral dimension. The normal maximum hole depth for USM is 1 to 2 in.; holes are sometimes made to a depth of 6 in., with special provision for circulation of the abrasive slurry.

A hollow "trepanning" tool has a faster rate of penetration than a solid tool of equal outer size, because of the smaller cutting area. A hollow tool of ½-in. OD by 7⁄16-in. ID can penetrate the work at more than four times the speed of a solid tool to make a hole of equal diameter, because the hollow tool has a cutting area that is only 23% as great as that of the solid tool.

Figure 2 shows penetration rates used by one manufacturer in ultrasonic machining of ceramic with solid stainless steel tools and a 33% slurry of 320-grit boron carbide abrasive. The penetration rate was slower for larger tools; for the 0.250-in.-diam tool, penetration rate was about a third of that for the 0.0625-in.-diam tool.

A volume removal rate 16 times as great would be required to maintain the same penetration rate as for the 0.0625-in. tool. But because slurry circulation could not be kept at the same level for the larger cutting area as for the smaller area, the volume removal rate for the larger tool had to be restricted to five times that for the smaller one.

Removal rate, or volume of work material removed per unit of time, is approximately proportional to the cutting area of the tool, provided slurry circulation and other operating conditions are held constant. However, in most production applications, conditions are not changed to correspond to the requirements of larger cutting areas, and therefore removal rate usually cannot be increased in proportion to the increase in cutting area (as shown above).

Tool vibration also affects removal rate. Although the relations are complex, removal rate is roughly proportional to the frequency and to the amplitude of tool oscillation.

The wide variation in removal rate for different types of work material is shown in Table 1. Early information on USM indicated that hard or brittle materials can be cut more readily than soft or ductile materials, but the contrary has sometimes been observed.

In one series of tests done under typical USM conditions, 4140 steel in the annealed condition (Rockwell B 95) machined 15 to 30% faster than after being oil quenched (Rockwell C 50), but normalized material (Rockwell C 34) machined almost as rapidly as annealed 4140. Copper alloy 260 (cartridge brass, 70%) machined twice as fast as annealed 4140 steel.

Nature of abrasive, particle size, and concentration of slurry also directly affect removal rate. Boron carbide is the hardest and fastest-cutting abrasive used in ultrasonic machining. Removal rate is roughly proportional to abrasive particle size up to a size approximately equal to the tool amplitude; for sizes substantially larger than tool amplitude, the relation is reversed. Removal rate increases with increasing slurry concentration up to about 30 to 40% (by volume) of abrasive; at very high concentrations, removal rate drops off rapidly.

Metal removal in USM appears to proceed by a complex mechanism involving both fracture and plastic deformation to varying degrees, depending in a given instance on work material and other process variables.

Wear Ratio. The effect of work material on wear ratio (volume of material removed from the workpiece divided by volume worn from the tool) is given in Table 1 for typical USM applications. Large differences in wear ratio for low-carbon steel tools are shown, depending on the hardness of the work material.

Table 2 illustrates the effect of tool material on wear ratio in the machining of glass and steatite, using stainless steel, carbon steel and brass tools.

All of the factors that affect removal rate (see preceding section) also influence wear ratio, except under conditions for which they affect tool and workpiece identically.

Size of hole that is produced by a given tool is affected by the size of the abrasive grit that is used with the tool. A circular hole produced by USM has a minimum diameter equal to the tool diameter plus an overcut of twice the size of the abrasive particles. (See table with Fig. 3 for relation between grit-size number and average particle size.) With size 180 grit, a ¼-in. tool makes a hole $0.250 + (2 \times 0.0034) = 0.257$ in. in diameter. Using No. 240 grit (0.0025 in.), a tool cuts a hole at least 0.005 in. larger than the tool.

Another consideration in hole size is taper — in some materials, taper may exceed 0.005 in. on the diameter per inch of depth. A finishing cut, to enlarge a roughed hole, should remove about 0.004 in. (on the diameter) from the largest portion of the roughed hole. If a through hole with a diameter of 0.502/0.500 in. must be drilled with minimum taper through a 1-in.-thick workpiece, using 240-grit abrasive, the hole should be roughed with a tool 0.487-in. in diameter, and finished with a tool 0.496 in. in diameter. If a finer abrasive were used in finishing, the diameter of the finishing tool would be correspondingly larger, and the roughing tool (still used with the coarser abrasive) also would be larger. These figures would be valid also for blind holes, but a greater number of tool passes would be needed to get a small radius at the bottom corner of the hole, because the tools become rounded as they wear.

Accurate detail at the bottom of a hole must be made by using a greater number of cutters, although they are duplicates except for wear (needing no increase in size). A large number of duplicate tools may be needed for some accurate work. Accuracy also may demand frequent changes of abrasive.

Surface roughness produced in USM depends on size of abrasive particles, work material, tool amplitude, and slurry circulation. Typical effect of grit size (a factor that can readily be adjusted to control roughness) is illustrated in Fig. 3.

Abrasives and Slurry. Silicon carbide, boron carbide and aluminum oxide are the abrasives most used for USM. Boron carbide is harder, faster-cutting and more durable than the other materials, and is the most widely used, although it costs 20 times as much.

The abrasive is carried in a slurry of water with 30 to 60% of abrasive by volume. When using larger tools, concentration of abrasive is usually held in the lower part of the range, to avoid difficulty in maintaining slurry circulation in the less accessible areas of the workpiece.

Just as in conventional grinding, the finer abrasives make the smoother finishes (as shown in Fig. 3), but the finer grit cuts at a slower speed. The finest grit does the most accurate work; 800 grit cuts within 0.00025 in.

Table 2. Wear Ratios of Three Tool Materials in Ultrasonic Machining Glass and Steatite

Tool material	Wear ratio for tools used on: Glass	Steatite
Stainless steel	100	40
Carbon steel, cold rolled	100	35
Brass	40	10

Wear ratio is depth of cut divided by linear wear on tool. Ratios are for tools ¼ in. in diameter on tapered tool holders, with 320-grit boron carbide abrasive supplied at a pressure of 1½ psi. (Source: John Krawczyk, Ultrasonic Grinding Techniques in Microminiaturization, Diamond Ordnance Fuze Laboratories, Report No. TR-950, July 28, 1961)

Grit sizes 200 to 400 are used for roughing, and 800 to 1000 for finishing. Fresh abrasive cuts better, so that grit must be added to the slurry from time to time. At intervals the slurry should be replaced completely. For a dependable, uniform finish, the grit must be uniform; therefore, abrasives should be segregated so that one grade does not contaminate or mix with another.

To use two grades of abrasive, one for roughing and one for finishing, it is necessary to use two separate fixtures to hold the work and two separate abrasive systems (pumps, tubes, and other components).

Efficient cutting demands an adequate supply of abrasive at the cutting face. When cutting deep holes or machining large surfaces, special techniques are needed to help supply the abrasive as needed. These include:

1. Feed of the slurry through the tool holder to supplement the external flow
2. Predrilled holes to permit the flow of abrasive up through the workpiece, exiting at the cutting face
3. Flutes on the tool (somewhat like the flutes of a twist drill)
4. Relief of the tool behind the cutting face, to provide clearance for abrasive flow
5. Automatic feeding that provides easier abrasive flow along the sides of the tool.

Flow of the abrasive slurry must also carry away the material that is removed from the workpiece. When rust inhibitors are used in the slurry, they should not cause foaming. Steel workpieces may have to be treated after USM to prevent rusting.

A predrilled through hole in the workpiece permits better circulation of the abrasive, and prevents any kind of compression that would retard the motion of the tool. Other work must be vented, as by holes in the tool. Cross holes (0.030-in.-diam or smaller) can be drilled in the hollow tool a third of the length back from the cutting face. New holes must be made after the tool wears to the old ones.

Typical Applications

Five typical applications of ultrasonic machining are summarized below:

Application 1. Four narrow rectangular holes were cut at the same time in the moving part of a hydraulic servo valve, of 52100 steel at Rockwell C 60 to 62, removing 0.005 to 0.010 in. of stock with a corner radius of 0.0015 in.

Application 2. A carbon flat, 3 by 4 by 0.040 in., was machined by USM, making 2176 holes through it, each 0.031 in. square, in less than 10 min.

Application 3. Dense ceramic, $\frac{1}{16}$ in. thick, was machined by USM, making 27 through holes in 3 rows of 9, the centers accurate to ±0.001 in. The holes, about $\frac{3}{16}$ in. in diameter, were made simultaneously by a tool that resembled 27 tubes. The tool made 150 parts before it needed sharpening.

Application 4. A bundle of 97 hypodermic needles served as the tool to cut wafers of silicon or germanium in the making of transistors. The wafers, 0.008 to 0.030 in. thick, were cemented to a glass plate before the blanks, 0.030 in. in diameter and larger, were cut and removed from the backing. Each of many such arrangements produced thousands of blanks daily. Each unit was rated at 1000 watts of electric power.

Application 5. A round through-hole having a final diameter of 0.5000 ± 0.0002 in. was trepanned in a 0.187-in.-thick carbide wire-drawing die, using a combination roughing and finishing tool. The abrasive for both cuts was boron carbide, 320-grit for roughing and 600-grit for finishing. Roughing (tool diameter, 0.490 in.) produced a tapered hole with a diameter of 0.493 in. at the top and 0.489 in. at the bottom in 15 min. A 10-min finishing operation (tool diameter, 0.4992 in.) eliminated the taper, for a final hole diameter of 0.5000 ± 0.0002 in. Surface roughness on completing the roughing cut was 22 micro-in.; this was improved to 15 micro-in. by the finishing cut.

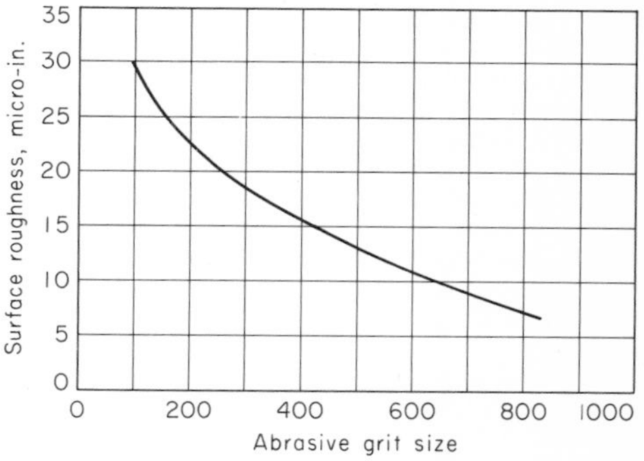

Grit size	Average particle size In.	Microns	Grit size	Average particle size In.	Microns
180 ...	0.0034	86	400 ...	0.00090	23
220 ...	0.0026	66	500 ...	0.00065	16
240 ...	0.00248	63	600 ...	0.00033	8
280 ...	0.00175	44	800 ...	0.00028	7
320 ...	0.00128	32	900 ...	0.00024	6

SOURCE: A. L. Roses, Techniques of Ultrasonic Machining, *Tool and Manufacturing Engineer*, Apr 1961, p 71-75.

Fig. 3. Effect of abrasive grit size on surface roughness produced in ultrasonic machining. The minimum overcut is calculated by doubling the average particle size.

Abrasive Jet Machining (AJM)

ABRASIVE JET MACHINING (AJM) is the removal of material from a workpiece by a high-speed stream of abrasive particles carried by gas from a nozzle. The process is used chiefly to cut materials that are sensitive to heat damage and thin sections of hard materials that chip easily, and to cut intricate holes that would be more difficult to produce by other methods.

Procedure and Equipment. The abrasive powder is fed from a mixing chamber that vibrates at 60 cycles per second into an orifice chamber, where it is entrained in the gas stream and then passed through a connecting hose, finally emerging from a small nozzle at high velocity. Powder feed rate is controlled by the amplitude of the mixing vibration, and a pressure regulator controls the gas flow. Duplex units allow uninterrupted production while reloading, or can perform independent operations with different abrasives. The pressure can be released through blow-off outlets; in some units, abrasive flow from the nozzle can be stopped in 10 to 15 milliseconds.

The nozzle is mounted in a fixture for automatic operation, either the workpiece or the nozzle being moved by cam drives, pantographs or other suitable mechanisms. Hand operation of the nozzle is satisfactory for removal of surface contamination or for noncritical cutting. A dust removal system is required, and suitable equipment is needed to insure a dry, clean, oil-free supply of propellant gas.

Nozzles must be highly resistant to abrasion, and are made of tungsten carbide or synthetic sapphire. Tungsten carbide is used for round nozzles 0.005 to 0.032 in. in diameter, and for rectangular nozzles 0.003 by 0.020 in. to 0.007 by 0.150 in., or 0.026 in. square. Sapphire nozzles are made only round, from 0.008 to 0.026 in. in diameter.

For average material removal, nozzles of tungsten carbide have a useful life of 12 to 30 hr, and nozzles of sapphire last 300 hr. For precision cutting, nozzles are made with an external taper on the tip to minimize secondary ricochet of abrasive particles that rebound from the workpiece.

Table 1. Effect of Distance of Nozzle From Work on Diameter of Cut and Rate of Material Removal in AJM (a)

Distance of nozzle tip from work, in.	Diameter of cut, in.	Distance of nozzle tip from work, in.	Rate of material removal, mg/min
0.031	0.018	1/8	26
0.197	0.025	3/16	52
0.394	0.059	9/32	60
0.590	0.079	13/32	60
		1/2	60
		19/32	54
		25/32	44

(a) Conditions: work material, plate glass at Knoop hardness of 450 to 510; nozzle-orifice diam, 0.018 in.; abrasive, 27-micron aluminum oxide; abrasive flow rate, 10 g per min; carrier gas, air (75 psi).

Distance of nozzle from workpiece affects the size of the machined area and the rate of material removal, as shown in Table 1 for the cutting of glass with aluminum oxide abrasive. The abrasive particles from any nozzle follow parallel paths for a short distance, and then the abrasive jet flares outward like a narrow cone.

Table 1 shows the diameter of the cut produced by the abrasive jet from a 0.018-in.-diam nozzle at various distances, together with the material removal rate for various nozzle distances. The jet from this nozzle is a cylinder for a distance of about 1/16 in. from the nozzle and then becomes a cone with 7° included angle, so that larger cuts are made with the nozzle farther from the work. Because of the acceleration

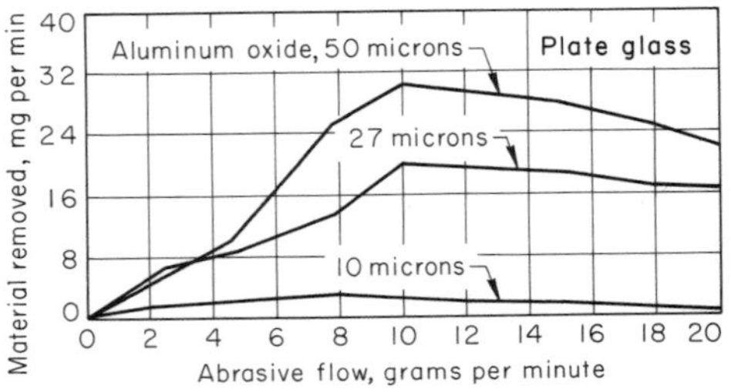

Conditions: work material, plate glass at Knoop hardness of 450 to 510; diameter of nozzle orifice, 0.018 in.; distance of nozzle tip from work, 1/32 in.; carrier gas, air at 75 psi.

Fig. 1. Effect of particle size of aluminum oxide on removal rate in AJM

of the particles after leaving the nozzle, the material removal rate for the conditions described in Table 1 increases as distance from the nozzle increases, up to about 9/32 in. At distances greater than about 1/2 in., the removal rate drops off, because of the increase in machining area for the same amount of abrasive, and because of a decrease in particle velocity.

Abrasive materials used in abrasive jet machining include aluminum oxide, silicon carbide, dolomite (calcium magnesium carbonate), sodium bicarbonate, and small glass beads. The hardness, strength, particle size and particle shape of the abrasive all affect its cutting performance and life. Aluminum oxide is a general-purpose abrasive, and is used in nominal diameters of 10, 27 and 50 microns. Silicon carbide is used in 25 and 50-micron sizes for faster cutting on extremely hard materials. Dolomite (about 200 mesh) is suitable for light cleaning and etching, and specially processed sodium bicarbonate is used for extra fine cleaning, as on critical potentiometer parts. Glass beads 0.025 to 0.050 in. in diameter are used for light polishing and fine deburring.

Abrasives are not ordinarily re-used, because of the reduced cutting action they give and because contamination with material abraded from the work can clog small orifices in the equipment and the nozzle. In cutting with sodium bicarbonate, special precautions must be taken to avoid exposure of the powder to moisture, including the use of special bottled or dried carrier gases, and temperatures above 120 F must be avoided to prevent moisture-producing decomposition of this material.

The effect of particle size on removal rate is illustrated in Fig. 1 for the cutting of plate glass at a Knoop hardness of 450 to 510 with aluminum oxide powder of three different particle sizes. Silicon carbide abrasive cuts plate glass at the same rate as aluminum oxide of the same particle size, but cuts ceramics (which are much harder) at a rate 50% faster than aluminum oxide.

Abrasive flow rate (mass flow rate) directly affects the rate at which material is removed from the workpiece. Figure 1 and Table 2 illustrate this relation for the cutting of plate glass at 1/32-in. nozzle distance. These data show that the fastest cutting is done with an abrasive flow of 8 to 18 grams per minute.

In operation, the voltage across the vibrator is adjusted to control abrasive flow rate, while holding gas pressure constant. Increasing abrasive flow rate above the normal range for the nozzle pressure results in a lower abrasive stream velocity and slower cutting, as shown in Fig. 1 and Table 2. Use of the lowest acceptable rate of flow conserves abrasive and increases nozzle life.

Carrier Gas. Air, nitrogen or carbon dioxide ordinarily is used as the carrier or propellant gas. (CAUTION: Do not use oxygen!) The air must be filtered to remove water, oil and other contaminants; commercial cylinder gases are usually of satisfactory purity.

Nozzle pressure can range between 30 and 120 psi, but ordinarily is about 75 psi. High pressure results in rapid nozzle wear; low pressure gives slow removal rates. The effect of carrier gas pressure on removal rate is illustrated in Table 2 for cutting plate glass with 27-micron aluminum oxide abrasive.

Table 2. Effects of Pressure of Carrier Gas and Abrasive Flow Rate on Rate of Material Removal in AJM (a)

Gas pressure, psi	Material removal, mg per min	Abrasive flow rate, g per min	Material removal, mg per min
75	18	2	8
90	21	5	13
100	23	10	20
125	26	15	19
		18	18
		21	14
		26	4

(a) Conditions: work material, plate glass at Knoop hardness of 450 to 510; nozzle-orifice diam, 0.018 in.; abrasive, 27-micron aluminum oxide; nozzle tip, 1/32 in. from work; carrier gas, air; gas pressure for abrasive-flow data, 75 psi; abrasive flow rate for gas-pressure data, 10 g per min.

Process Characteristics. The velocity of the abrasive stream as it emerges from the nozzle is about 1100 ft per sec. Propellant consumption in normal operation at a nozzle pressure of 75 psi is about ⅓ cu ft per min; consumption of abrasive at a flow of 5 grams per min is about 150 grams (⅔ lb) per hr.

A typical material removal rate for abrasive jet machining is 0.001 cu in. per min; this will cut a slot 0.020 in. wide by 0.010 in. deep by 5 in. long in one minute.

Minimum practical width of cut (about 0.005 in.) can be obtained by using a rectangular nozzle with an orifice 0.003 by 0.060 in. at a distance of 1/32 in. from the work. With close control, dimensions can be held within ±0.002 in.; an accuracy of ±0.005 in. is more nearly representative of normal production operations.

Masks defining the machining area are sometimes used to prevent stray cutting. Copper is a good all-purpose masking material; glass gives excellent definition but has short life; rubber has long life but gives poor definition.

Minimum corner radius is about 0.004 in.; taper is 0.005 in. per inch of penetration; surface finish ranges from 20 to 50 micro-in. in most applications.

Typical roughness values produced on glass with aluminum oxide or silicon carbide abrasive are:

Average particle size, microns	Roughness, micro-in.
10	6 to 8
25 or 27	14 to 20
50	38 to 55

There is no heat damage, as the work surface remains at room temperature; damage from impact or embedding of abrasive particles can extend only to a depth of about 0.0001 in. The nozzle tip and the rubber pinchcock in the shutoff valve are the parts most subject to wear. Nozzle life varies with operating conditions; an 0.018-in.-diam nozzle at 75 psi pressure will handle about 35 lb of 27-micron aluminum oxide abrasive before requiring replacement. The average life of the rubber pinchcock is about 50 hr (46,000 on-off cycles of 4-sec duration) for an abrasive flow rate of 10 grams per minute.

Advantages of AJM include:

1 Ability to cut intricate hole shapes in material of any hardness
2 Ability to cut fragile, brittle or heat-sensitive material without damage
3 Absence of mechanical contact between tool and work
4 Low capital cost.

Disadvantages of AJM include:

1 Limited applicability, because only small amounts of metal can be removed and because the nozzle must be close to the workpiece
2 Slow removal rate and inefficient use of power
3 Stray cutting
4 Embedding of abrasive in the workpiece.

Applications of AJM include: abrading and frosting glass; cleaning; cutting fine lines; exposing an area for electrical contact; machining semiconductors such as germanium, silicon and gallium; cutting and etching materials such as quartz, sapphire, mica and glass; deburring; marking.

In one application, AJM was used to cut 0.005-in.-thick tungsten sheet after all other methods that had been tried failed because of cracking or splitting of the workpiece. Shallow, inclined crevices 0.0002 to 0.0004 in. deep (previously hand lapped in 8 hr) were produced by AJM in 15 min to closer tolerances. Other applications to metals are: drilling and cutting thin sections of hardened metal; cutting or etching trade names or numbers on parts; removing plating, anodic or thermal oxide coatings, surface contamination, or corrosion products; and removing broken tools from holes.

Electron Beam Machining (EBM)

ELECTRON BEAM MACHINING (EBM) is a method of cutting material in a vacuum using a focused beam of high-velocity electrons. On impact of electrons with the workpiece, the kinetic energy of the electrons changes into heat, which vaporizes a small amount of the workpiece. The vacuum is necessary to prevent scattering of the electrons by collision with gas molecules. By controlling beam energy at a lower level, the process is used for welding instead of machining.

In machining, electrons are accelerated in an electrostatic field to velocities of more than half the speed of light. The electron beam, and the laser beam (p 255), exceed ordinary heat or light sources in energy density, precision and mobility. By focusing the beam with optical precision on a 0.0005 to 0.001-sq-in. area of the workpiece, energy is delivered at a power density of 10 billion watts per square inch and can vaporize any material instantly.

Electron beam machining is applicable to parts 0.010 to 0.250 in. thick, and can drill holes as small as 0.0005 in. in diameter in all materials, including ceramics, at a penetration rate of 0.010 in. per second or faster. It cuts slots as narrow as 0.001 in. at a spacing as close as 0.005 in. The process is used also to scribe thin films and to remove small, broken taps from holes.

Process Principles. A typical setup for electron beam machining is illustrated in the schematic diagram of Fig. 1. A stream of electrons is emitted from the tip of a hairpin tungsten filament 0.008 in. in diameter that is heated to 2500 C in a vacuum of about 10^{-5} mm of mercury. The cloud of electrons is shaped into a cylindrical stream by the magnetic field produced by the grid cup, and is directed through the hole in the anode without colliding with the anode itself. The stream is accelerated toward the anode by a potential difference of 50 to 150 kilovolts between the filament (cathode) and the anode.

The electrons reach maximum velocity as they leave the anode and (because of the vacuum) maintain this velocity until they strike the workpiece.

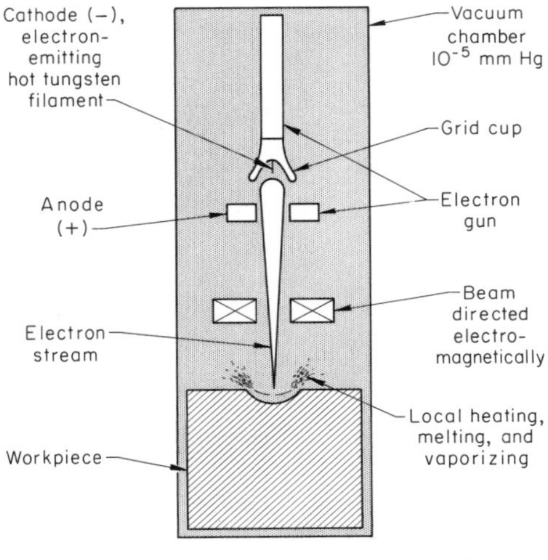

Fig. 1. Setup for electron beam machining

The beam may be redirected or focused by magnetic fields before reaching the workpiece. Beam current usually is 100 to 1000 micro amp, with continuous power of 100 to 1150 watts. Pulse duration is 4 to 64,000 microseconds at a frequency of 0.1 to 16,000 cps.

The distance from electron gun to workpiece usually is about 4 in. The chamber must be shielded to absorb the x-ray emission produced, as with commercial x-ray equipment.

Control of the accelerating potential, pulse duration, pulse frequency, and other factors involves different power settings for various cutting applications. Electromagnetic focusing makes beams of full power only 0.001 in. in diameter, and can make weaker beams as small as 0.0005 in. in diameter.

The electron beam is focused by a magnetic lens. Magnetic deflection coils beneath the focusing lens can deflect the beam anywhere in an area ¼ in. square on the workpiece. The beam can be programed in this area by saw-tooth-wave and sine-wave generators that drive the deflection coils. This system can cut in many different patterns, varying from a small round spot to a square or a rectangle.

Cutting conditions can be adjusted over a wide range. The electron beam is controlled to suit the work material, and the size and shape of the cut. High-melting alloys and thicker stock generally are machined by electron beams with greater beam current in longer pulses and at higher frequencies. Materials that have high melting and boiling temperatures, high specific heat, and high heats of fusion and va-

This article is based primarily on information on electron beam machining presented in Chapter 6 of "Non-Traditional Machining Processes", R. K. Springborn, editor, ASTME, Dearborn, Mich., 1967.

porization require more heat for cutting by EBM, which is essentially controlled vaporization of material. Relative power requirements to remove equal volumes of various metals in equal time, based on aluminum as 1.0, are:

Aluminum	1.0
Titanium	1.5
Iron	1.8
Molybdenum	2.2
Tungsten	2.9

The heat-affected zone may extend to a depth of 0.010 in. Although heat damage cannot be eliminated completely, heat flow into the workpiece can be minimized by using pulses of shorter duration. Shorter pulses can minimize surface effects such as local recasting, and an electron beam of lower amperage in short pulses is essential to prevent ceramic workpieces from cracking during machining.

Applications

Ten applications of EBM are summarized in Table 1. Holes and slots that are only a few thousandths of an inch wide are cut with a focused beam. Larger holes are made by trepanning, using magnetic deflection coils, with rotation of the workpiece.

An optical tracing device, a "flying spot scanner", can be used with EBM to copy patterns from negatives made by photographing the pattern. The magnetic deflection coils deflect the electron beam to the correct position on the workpiece to cut a pattern that reproduces the negative, with a linear reduction of 10 to 1. This method is used in drilling accurate grids, in etching copper gravure plates, and in making accurate film resistors.

Drilling Holes. In drilling holes, the beam usually focuses on one spot and evaporates material until it has completely penetrated the workpiece, or until it is switched off after a specified hole depth has been reached. Hole diameter depends on beam diameter and energy density, and can be changed by varying the amplitude of the voltage generator connected to the electromagnetic deflection system. If holes larger than the beam diameter are required, the beam is deflected electromagnetically in a circular path. For extremely large holes, the workpiece can be moved off-center and rotated.

Holes 10 to 20 diameters deep are produced readily by EBM (see examples in Table 1); maximum depth-to-diameter ratio is about 200 to 1. Figure 2 shows a portion of the length of 0.0008-in.-diam holes through an investment casting (Ni-15Co-10Cr-5.5Al-4.7Ti-3Mo-1V-0.06Zr-0.014B). These holes, 100 diameters in length, could not be produced practically in any other way.

The contour of the holes shown in Fig. 2 illustrates the effects of separate pulses of the electron beam. The hairline cracks visible did not constitute a problem in this application, but exposure to service stress sometimes requires the removal of a heat-damaged layer up to 0.010 in. thick in EBM products. Depth of heat damage is much less in welding with an electron beam.

Typical tolerances are ±0.001 in. on $\frac{1}{8}$-in.-diam holes, and ±0.00005 in. on 0.0005-in.-diam holes.

Cutting Slots. Cutting speed, in general, depends on the amount of material to be removed — that is, on the cross section of the slot to be cut.

All slots cut by EBM exhibit a small amount of material spatter on the side where the beam enters, which can usually be removed by light abrasive cleaning. Electron beam machined slots in material less than 0.005 in. thick have parallel sides with essentially no wall taper. In thicker material, slots show some taper because of beam divergence and nonuniformity of heat flow. The walls of electron beam machined slots in material 0.005 to 0.125 in. thick exhibit a taper of 1° to 2°. The edges of the walls can be maintained parallel to a tolerance of 0.002 in. The narrowest slots cut to date by EBM have been in material approximately 0.001 in. thick and have had a width slightly less than 0.001 in. When cutting slots of these dimensions, it is often necessary to make more than one pass in order to obtain a sharp, smooth edge.

Less than a third of the 100-diameters length of the holes is shown. Holes are bell-mouthed and irregular at entrance end (top of picture) and are irregular in cross section. (Compare with holes produced by laser beam machining, shown on page 256.) Cracks extend to a depth about equal to the hole diameter.

Fig. 2. Holes about 0.0008 in. in diameter made by electron beam machining a nickel-base alloy investment casting

Advantages of EBM include:

1 Capability of making very small holes and slots with high precision, in a short time, in any material (holes, slots and orifices not producible by any other method)
2 Absence of mechanical contact between workpiece and tool
3 Suitability for automatic machining.

Disadvantages of EBM include:

1 High cost of equipment
2 Limited applicability (Depth of cut is $\frac{1}{4}$ in.; vacuum chamber limits the size of workpiece; only small amounts of metal can be removed.)
3 Slow production rate, because of slow removal rate and time required to evacuate the chamber
4 Nonuniformity of holes and slots (Holes are tapered, and entrance to a hole usually is cratered.)
5 Need for skilled operators.

Table 1. Typical Applications of Electron Beam Machining

Work material and thickness (footnotes describe shapes machined)	Machining time or speed	Accelerating voltage, kv	Average beam current, microamp	Pulse duration, microsec	Pulse frequency, cps
Low-carbon steel, 0.040 in.(a)	30 in./min	150	9000	2100	300
Hardened steel, 0.125 in.(b)	10 min	140	150	80	50
304 stainless, 0.250 in.(c)	10-20 in./min	130	5000	5300	35
410 stainless, 0.250 in.(d)	......	150	7000	1000	3.3
Hastelloy, 0.450 in.(e)	1 min, 10 sec	130	5000	5300	100
Molybdenum, 0.010 in.(f)	Less than 1 sec	140	20	20	50
Tungsten, 0.010 in.(g)	Less than 1 sec	140	50	20	50
90 Ta – 10 W, 0.010 in.(h)	10 sec	140	100	80	50
Alumina, 0.030 in.(j)	30 sec	125	60	80	50
Quartz crystal, 0.125 in.(k)	Less than 1 sec	140	10	12	50

(a) Cut. (b) Rectangular hole, 0.018 by 0.072 in. (c) Cut to reopen welded container. (d) Slot, 0.030 in. wide at entrance, 0.010 in. wide at exit. (e) Hole, 0.100-in. diam. (f) Holes less than 0.002 in. in diameter, 0.003 in. between centers. (g) Hole, 0.001-in. diam. (h) Hole, 0.005-in. diam. (j) Hole, 0.012-in. diam. (k) Hole, 0.001-in. diam.

Commercial Equipment

One general-purpose commercial machine for EBM uses accelerating voltages as high as 150,000 v to produce a power output of 100 watts and a maximum power density of about six billion watts per square inch. The beam can be pulsed at frequencies as high as 10,000 cps. For continuous-beam operation, the maximum beam current is 800 microamp, but a much higher current can be used for pulsed-beam operation.

The machine is equipped with a beam-deflection system that allows beam movement of about 0.040 in. Mechanical worktable movement is used for machining larger areas. The workpiece is viewed from above through a microscope.

Accuracy of ±0.0002 in. can be obtained with this machine in cuts 0.020 to 0.040 in. deep, as follows:

Round holes: 0.002 to 0.008 in.
Slots: 0.002 to 0.004 by 0.040 to 0.080 in.

Manipulation is slower and more difficult for smaller shapes; larger ones can be made, but with less accuracy.

The high temperatures necessary for practical removal rates require the use of high beam currents. Beam current density at the cathode tip is limited to about 14 amp per sq in. at the operating temperature of 4580 F for the tungsten cathode. Cathode life drops off sharply at higher temperatures.

A major factor in the efficiency of the process, particularly in machining metals that have high thermal conductivity, is the conduction of heat away from the electron-impact zone. A pulsed electron beam is used to improve efficiency, because heating of the machining zone is much more rapid than heat loss by conduction.

Laser Beam Machining (LBM)

LASER BEAM MACHINING (LBM) is a method of cutting in which the work material is melted and vaporized by a narrow beam of intense monochromatic light (a laser beam). When the beam strikes the workpiece, the heat produced melts and vaporizes even the most refractory work materials.

Because of its high cost, laser beam machining is used only when no other method is satisfactory. It can make small holes in thin material and can produce small, precision cuts. By controlling the energy of the beam at lower levels, the laser method can also be used to weld fine wire.

Principle of the Laser. The word "laser" is an acronym for "light amplification by stimulated emission of radiation". This phenomenon can be explained in a simplified manner as follows: The absorption of a quantum of energy from a light source causes an orbital electron of an atom to jump to a higher energy level (an orbit farther from the nucleus of the atom). This electron in the "excited" atom may later drop back spontaneously to its original orbit, emitting the absorbed energy. The absorption of a second quantum of energy by an electron that is at the higher energy level results in the emission of two quanta of energy, and the electron returns to its ground state or original orbit.

The radiated energy has the same wave length as the stimulating energy and is in phase with it. By placing a laser rod in an optical cavity and using mirrors to focus the light on the laser rod, the energy is captured in the rod. The energy builds up in the rod while undergoing successive internal reflections, until a highly amplified light beam is emitted.

Machining

A typical setup for laser beam machining is shown schematically in Fig. 1. The stimulating light source usually is a linear arc-discharge lamp, such as a xenon flash lamp.

Laser Materials. Only the most powerful and reliable of the many different laser systems are suitable for use in machining operations. The most widely used laser materials are ruby and neodymium-in-glass.

The ruby laser material is crystalline aluminum oxide (corundum) that contains about 0.1% of chromic oxide. The laser rod can be a single crystal of synthetic ruby 1 cm in diameter by 10 cm long. The neodymium-in-glass material contains 2 to 6% neodymium and is fabricated into a rod similar to the ruby rod. The ends are finished as optical surfaces. Neodymium-in-glass is two to three times as efficient as ruby and is less sensitive to temperature changes. Both materials are nonconductors of electricity and hence are powered by a pulsed light flux, using a direct-current power supply and a bank of capacitors, instead of by direct electrical excitation.

This article is based primarily on information presented in Chapter 6 of "Non-Traditional Machining Processes", R. K. Springborn, editor, ASTME, Dearborn, Mich., 1967.

Equipment and Procedure. Laser beam machining systems are operated at room temperature. In a typical operation, the capacitors are charged to 4000 volts and a 3000-joule pulse is then discharged in one millisecond through the pre-ionized xenon gas in the flash lamp.

The laser rod and the flash lamp are located at the foci of an elliptical polished aluminum reflector, so that nearly all radiation from the flash lamp is focused on the laser rod. The ends of the rod have reflective coatings. The coating on the exit end is partially reflective, to permit escape of the laser beam at 6 to 120 pulses per minute when the light has been amplified to a suitable intensity. The light emitted is an almost completely parallel beam, having a typical divergence angle (θ) of 10^{-2} to 10^{-4} radian. Because of its low divergence and monochromatic nature, the beam can be focused with a simple lens to obtain high power densities in small areas 1 to 6 in. from the lens. The relation between focal length, divergence angle, and diameter of machining spot is given with Fig. 1.

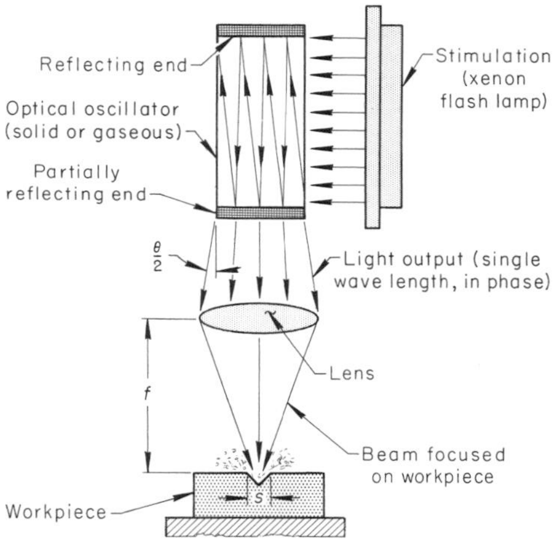

Machining spot diameter (s) = focal length of lens (f) times beam divergence (θ) in radians.

Fig. 1. Typical setup for laser beam machining

Additional equipment required for laser beam machining includes a triocular microscope for viewing the workpiece and for focusing the beam and a workholder to move the workpiece in three directions for accurate positioning at the focal point of the beam. The workpiece can be viewed from a distance by television. Water or air cooling is required, to dissipate the heat generated in the process.

Process Characteristics. A typical laser system can have an energy output of 20 joules with a pulse duration of one millisecond for a peak power of 20,000 watts. With a beam divergence of 0.002 radian, a power density of 7 × 10^9 watts per square inch is produced on a spot 0.002 in. in diameter at 1 in. from the lens. A power density of this magnitude can vaporize any known material.

Laser beam machining is very inefficient in energy consumption. The conversion of electrical energy to laser light energy for solid-state lenses has an efficiency in the range of 0.3 to 5%. There is a further loss of energy by partial reflection of the laser beam from the workpiece.

In machining, a short high-intensity pulse is desirable, to minimize the depth of the heat-damaged zone and to provide accurate dimensional control. The depth of heat damage is about 0.005 in.

Removal rate is only about 0.0004 cu in. per hour, the slowest of any machining process and less than 1/10 that of electron beam machining. The approximate amount of energy needed to remove a given amount of metal can be calculated from the specific heat and the heats of fusion and vaporization of the work material, and the estimated efficiency of energy conversion for the particular equipment. Relative power requirements for the removal of the same volume of various metals in a given time are:

Aluminum	1.0
Titanium	1.5
Iron	1.8
Molybdenum	2.2
Tungsten	2.9

Dimensional characteristics of holes produced by laser beam machining are:

Dimensional accuracy	±0.001 in.
Corner radii, minimum	0.010 in.
Taper per inch	0.050 in.

Taper is noticeable in holes deeper than 0.010 in.

Maintenance requirements are those for ordinary electronic and cooling equipment. Flash lamps require frequent replacement, their life being dependent primarily on the energy input and the current pulse shape. Commercial pulsed laser systems give a flash-lamp life of 10,000 to 100,000 pulses.

Cost. Both capital equipment cost and direct operating cost for laser beam machining are substantially higher than for conventional equipment and methods. Operating cost in cents per pulse is estimated as follows:

Flash lamp	2.0¢
Maintenance	0.2
Labor and overhead	0.5
Utilities	0.01
Depreciation	0.2 to 2.0
Total	2.9 to 4.7¢

Advantages of LBM include:

1. Applicability to any known material
2. Absence of direct contact and large forces between tool and workpiece
3. Ability to machine through air, inert gas, vacuum, or optically transparent liquids or solids
4. Accuracy and ability to make very small holes and cuts
5. Suitability for cutting ceramic and other materials that are readily damaged by heat shock.

Disadvantages of LBM include:

1. High capital and operating cost
2. Limited applicability (thin workpieces and removal of small amounts of material)
3. Slow production rate, because precise alignment is required
4. Nonuniformity of holes and cuts
5. Heat damage effects on workpieces
6. Need for skilled operators.

Applications. Laser beam machining is at present suitable only for exceptional applications that involve micro or high-precision operations difficult to perform by other methods. Although LBM can be applied to various metals, major use has been on ceramics. It is suitable for producing holes up to 1/8-in. diam in thicknesses up to 1/2 in.

Typical applications include drilling holes in tungsten, brass and ceramic, as described in the following tabulation. Less than one millisecond was required for drilling each of these holes.

Material	Thickness	Diameter
Tungsten	0.020 in.	0.020 in.
Brass	0.010	0.250
Ceramic	0.010	0.050

The characteristics of holes drilled in metals are illustrated in Fig. 2. The typical shape of a hole made in a single pulse is shown in Fig. 2(a); this air-flow hole did not require a uniform cross section but only a minimum diameter. A more uniform contour can be obtained with multiple pulses at lower energy level, as shown in Fig. 2(b). Figure 2(c) shows a 45° hole that takes advantage of the absence both of direct contact and of substantial forces between tool and work to avoid drift, curvature or mislocation.

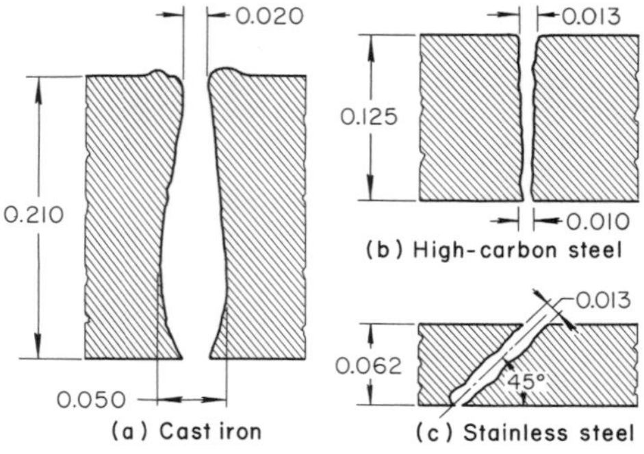

(a) Irregularly shaped hole produced with a single pulse of 146 joules in 5 milliseconds. (b) Hole with 12-to-1 depth-to-diameter ratio drilled with multiple pulses. (c) Hole drilled at 45° angle with four pulses of 2.2 joules each.

Fig. 2. Holes drilled by laser beams

Laser beam machining has been used to drill a matrix of 100 holes spaced on 0.080-in. centers in 0.078-in.-thick zirconia. These 0.005-in.-diam holes were drilled by this method only after ultrasonic, abrasive jet, and electron beam techniques had failed to hold tolerances or had caused cracking.

Gas Laser. The CO_2-N_2 laser provides a high, continuous power output and a conversion efficiency greater than 13% (potentially above 20%), and is the most promising gas laser. Low power density of gas units is compensated for by a continuous output, lower cost and greater convenience. The infrared gas laser beam (wave length, 10.6 microns) is focused by mirrors instead of lenses, because most lens materials absorb radiation of this wave length.

Plasma Arc Machining (PAM)

PLASMA ARC MACHINING (PAM) is done with a high-velocity jet of high-temperature ionized gas. The relatively narrow plasma jet melts and displaces the workpiece material in its path. Because plasma machining does not depend on a chemical reaction between the gas and the work material, and because plasma temperatures are extremely high, the process can be used on almost any metal, including those that are resistant to oxy-fuel gas cutting. The method is of commercial importance in the United States mainly for profile cutting of stainless steel and aluminum alloys.

Principles. At temperatures above about 10,000 F (as in a welding arc), gases are partially ionized and exist as a plasma (a mixture of free electrons, positively charged ions and neutral atoms). The plasma torch confines the plasma-forming gas in an arc chamber, and the arc supplies a large input of electrical energy. The central zone of the plasma reaches a temperature of 20,000 to 50,000 F, and is completely ionized.

Figure 1 shows the construction of a typical plasma arc cutting torch. It is like a tungsten-inert-gas welding torch with the electrode recessed into a nozzle with a small opening, but it is more rugged. A high-frequency spark is used to initiate a pilot arc between the tungsten electrode (cathode, −) and the copper nozzle (anode, +), both of which are water cooled. For cutting electrically conductive materials (the usual application), the pilot or internal arc initiates an external or "transferred" arc between the torch and the workpiece, which is connected as an anode (+). The pilot arc is then shut off, and the external arc does the cutting.

The plasma jet heats the workpiece by bombardment with electrons and by transfer of energy from the high-temperature, high-energy gas. In thick material, most of the heat input that is effective for cutting takes place in the top 1 to 2 in. of material, and cutting to greater depths depends largely on gravity or forced flow of superheated molten metal from this upper region (except for oxidation-assisted cutting).

Selection of Gas. Any gas or gas mixture that does not adversely affect the tungsten electrode or the workpiece can be used in the plasma torch. Carbon and alloy steels and cast irons are usually cut with a nitrogen-hydrogen mixture or with compressed air. Stainless steel, aluminum, and other nonferrous metals are cut with argon-hydrogen or nitrogen-hydrogen.

Flow Rates. Typical total gas flow rates are between 70 and 400 cu ft per hr. Arc current ranges between 150 and 1000 amp for typical cutting rates of 10 to 70 ipm. Size of orifice (usually 1/16 to 1/4 in. in diameter) depends on the arc current and gas flow required.

Power sources (direct current) rated at about 400 volts (open circuit), 200 volts (under load), 200 kw output, are required.

Torch standoff distance is usually 1/4 to 5/8 in. from the workpiece. For manual operation, the nozzle is insulated to prevent accidental shorting against the workpiece. Eye shielding and ear protection are normally required.

Process Characteristics. Surfaces of plasma cuts are usually smoother than gas cuts, but the edges are rounded. In addition, the walls of the cut often have a V-shaped included angle, which may be 5° to 10°; multiport nozzles under proper operating conditions reduce this bevel to 1° to 2°. Width of kerf is usually 3/16 to 3/8 in., but can exceed 1/2 in. for thick material; this also determines the minimum inside radius of the cut. Faster cutting speeds result in rougher cuts. Accuracy is ordinarily ±3/32 to 1/8 in., and with close control can be held to ±1/16 in. The depth of the heat-affected zone depends on the work metal, its thickness, and the cutting speed; maximum depth on stock up to 1 in. thick is about 3/16 in., and is much less at high speeds.

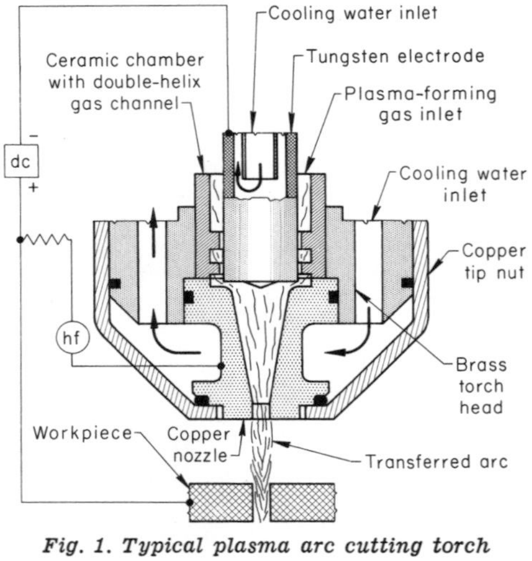

Fig. 1. Typical plasma arc cutting torch

Applications. Plasma arc cutting is used chiefly on stainless steel and on aluminum alloys. Oxy-fuel gas cutting of stainless steel requires the addition of iron powder or chemical flux; plasma cutting is preferred because it produces comparatively smooth cuts free from contaminants. Aluminum alloys cannot practically be cut by the oxy-fuel gas method. Heavy-duty plasma torches cut stainless steel up to 4 or 5 in. thick; aluminum alloys up to about 6 in. thick can be cut.

Other metals that are resistant to oxy-fuel gas cutting are sometimes cut by the plasma method. These include magnesium, titanium, copper, nickel, and alloys of copper and nickel.

In spite of high equipment and operating costs, a rapid cutting rate makes plasma cutting economical for straight cuts in mild steel in large quantities, in thicknesses up to 2 in. For efficient use of equipment, and because the comparative costs of plasma and oxy-fuel cutting vary widely for different applications, multitorch cutting machines equipped with both types of cutting torches are sometimes used in warehouse cutting and by plate fabricators. Cutting speeds of 2 to 240 ipm are available on one large machine with a cutting area of 44 by 82½ ft. A variety of automated guidance techniques are used for profile cutting, and 0.8-in. radii can be cut at the maximum speed of the machine.

Machining Development. The plasma arc method has been considered for lathe turning, milling and planing. It has been tried for the rough turning of bar stock in moderate sizes, and may be applicable to the turning of rolls for structural-shape rolling mills or of large hardened shafts, and to pulley grooving. Cost to remove metal at 7 cu in. per min has been calculated to be about $0.23 per cubic inch. The hardened and uneven surface produced may require the later removal of 0.030 to 0.050 in., depending on the application.

Abstract from "Electric Arc Cutting", which will appear in Volume 4 of this Handbook.

GRINDING, HONING AND LAPPING

CONTENTS

Grinding

*By the ASM Committee on Grinding**

IN ALL grinding, small chips of metal are removed from the workpiece by the mechanical action of irregularly shaped grains. This article discusses grinding with abrasive wheels; belt grinding is described in a separate article beginning on page 277.

Grinding ratio, defined as the volume of material removed from the work per unit volume of wheel wear, is a useful measure of ease of grinding — or grindability, a term analogous to machinability. The higher its grinding ratio, the easier a work material is to grind.

Any grinding ratio is found experimentally under a specific set of conditions and is the grindability index for those conditions *only*. The grinding ratio of a material may vary for different types of grinding operations, such as internal, cylindrical or surface grinding. However, the ranking of a group of materials with respect to grindability will generally remain about the same for all grinding operations.

The grinding ratio can be greatly affected by the grinding wheel, the grinding fluid, and the operating speeds and feeds.

Grinding Wheels

Every grinding wheel has two constituents, the abrasive that does the cutting and the bond that holds the abrasive grains. Variations of these constituents can be selected to give a large number of combinations.

Classification. Figure 1 shows the system of markings, adopted by the American Standards Association, that is widely used for identifying characteristics of grinding wheels as follows:

Abrasive Type. Aluminum oxide and silicon carbide are designated by the letters A and C, respectively. These letters are optionally prefixed by a proprietary symbol or number that denotes the manufacturer's subtype of abrasive. The subtype may be a single variety or a mixture of two varieties.

Grain Size. Abrasive grain size is designated by numbers that indicate the meshes per linear inch of screen through which grains will pass. (Sizes finer than 240 are obtained by sedimentation or other nonscreening methods, but are expressed in terms of hypothetical screen sizes.) Although the marking system shows a range of 10 (coarse) to 600 (very fine), sizes from 4 to 1000 are available.

Grade, the power of the bond to hold abrasive grains in place, is designated by letters ranging from A to Z in the order of increasing strength. Although it is sometimes called hardness, this designation does not refer to the penetration hardness of the abrasive or of the bond material. Grade letters are not equivalent in terms of bond strength for the different types of bonds.

Structure, the proportion of abrasive to bond, is designated by number. Dense wheels, in which the abrasive particles are close together in relation to their grain size, are designated by lower structure numbers. Open wheels, with wider spacing of abrasive particles in relation to grain size, are designated by higher structure numbers. Some wheels are made with a duplex structure, in which the grains are spaced in clusters that give a porous appearance to the wheel face. Structure designations are sometimes omitted from wheel classifications in this article.

Bond. A letter indicates the type of material used for holding the abrasive grains: vitrified, silicate, rubber, resinoid (with or without fiber reinforcement), shellac, or oxychloride.

Manufacturer's Record. Proprietary symbols indicate bond modification and other variations. Use of proprietary symbols is optional.

Wheels marked according to the first five parts of this system will not necessarily act the same way even when the nonproprietary symbols are identical. This is because: (*a*) the ingredients in the wheels may differ even though they are of the same general type; (*b*) the wheels may have been processed differently during their manufacture; and (*c*) the exact significance of the symbols for grain size, grade and structure varies among different wheel manufacturers.

This article will use a modified marking system that incorporates just the significant information necessary for general consideration. In this system, the numerous varieties of aluminum oxide abrasive are classified in terms of their relative toughness in grinding operations: extra tough, tough, semifriable and friable. These categories are respectively denoted by subscripts: A_e, A_t, A_s and A_f. The other elements that comprise this modified marking system are the grain-size number, grade letter, structure number and bond-type letter.

T. L. COUNIHAN, *Chairman,* Retired from Hyatt Bearings Div., General Motors Corp.; L. P. TARASOV, *Vice Chairman,* Research and Development Dept., Norton Co.; ROBERT W. CAMPBELL, Chief Manufacturing Research Engineer, SKF Industries, Inc.; GEORGE HAYS, Industrial Engineer, Transmission Div., Clark Equipment Co.

RALPH S. JONES, Work Standards Supervisor, Caterpillar Tractor Co.; FRANK H. LUKEN, Grinding Wheel and Diamond Engineer, Delco Products Div., General Motors Corp.; GEORGE B. MORSE, Industrial Engineer, Ex-Cell-O Corp.; JOHN A. MUELLER, Manager, Abrasive Systems Development, Bonded Abrasives Div., Carborundum Co.; L. K. PRUETT, Manufacturing Development Office, Ford Motor Co.; FRANK SETELE, Cleveland Pneumatic Tool Co. Div., Cleveland Pneumatic Industries, Inc.

THOMAS L. STILWELL, Works Manager, Warner & Swasey Co.; WALTER SZANCILO, Chief Tool and Manufacturing Engineer, Utica Div., Bendix Corp.; T. W. TOWNSEND, Manufacturing Engineering, Data Systems Div., International Business Machines Corp.; G. C. WALCOTT, Abrasive Engineer, Buick Motor Div., General Motors Corp.; HOWARD E. BOYER, *Secretary,* Managing Editor – Metals Handbook, ASM.

This modified system provides a convenient shorthand notation to describe wheels in terms that are meaningful to those with at least a little grinding experience. Discriminating selection of wheels must depend on experience with similar applications. Wheels for a wide variety of conditions are identified in the specific examples presented in this article.

Selection of a wheel for grinding carbon or low-alloy steel depends largely on whether the steel has been hardened. Table 1 lists wheels recommended for grinding unhardened steel, and general-purpose wheels for use when unhardened and hardened steels must be ground without changing wheels. Table 2 lists wheels recommended for grinding hardened steel.

In general practice, the harder the workpiece, the softer the wheel used to grind it, and vice versa. The reason for this is that hard steel is more easily damaged by grinding heat than soft steel. Therefore, a softer wheel, which generates less heat, should be selected for the harder steel.

Sharpness of abrasive grains affects heat generation. How sharp the grains remain depends on the inherent physical properties of the grains, such as toughness, on the way the wheel is dressed prior to grinding, and in general on the way the grains wear during the operation. There are three types of wear: attritious wear of the grain, grain fracture, and bond fracture. As it cuts, an initially sharp abrasive grain develops a small flat area. This area increases in size by attritious wear until friction causes the grain to fracture and create a new cutting edge. This cycle of attritious wear and grain fracture continues until the bond holding the remainder of the grain in place is sufficiently weakened to fracture and release the grain.

Attritious wear without fracture is undesirable because the resulting dull or glazed surface generates excessive heat. Some wheel wear by grain fracture is desirable, to maintain a sharp, cool-cutting wheel face.

Other factors besides the hardness of the steel should be considered in wheel selection. The type and severity of the grinding operation, the amount of metal to be removed, and the required surface finish all influence the choice of grit size and bond. A coarse grit can remove stock rapidly for rough grinding; a fine grit can produce a smooth surface finish. Most precision grinding is best performed with vitrified wheels, but there are some operations, like centerless and thread grinding, in which both vitrified and organic bonds are used, depending on the specific circumstances. For instance, extremely fine finishes on cylindrical surfaces call for organic bonds. So do cutoff wheels. Vitrified wheels should ordinarily be used at speeds of 6500 sfm or less; higher speeds are permissible on special machines if certain safety requirements are met. Organic wheels are generally used at considerably higher speeds than are vitrified wheels.

In grinding steel, wet grinding generally calls for a wheel one grade harder than for dry grinding. An even harder wheel can be used with a grinding oil. Grade selection should be based on minimum production cost (or sometimes maximum production rate) of parts passing inspection, rather than on minimum wheel cost alone.

Truing and dressing are terms for operations in the maintenance of a grinding wheel. *Truing* means the removal of material from the cutting face of a wheel so that the resultant surface runs true; also, restoring the cutting face to its original shape or contour. *Dressing* is the operation of cleaning or restoring the sharpness of a wheel face that has become dulled or loaded with the material being ground.

Safety. Grinding wheels can break in use. Therefore, the wheels must be mounted and used with adequate care and protection. Table 3 lists essential precautions to be observed. More complete regulations for mounting and use of grinding wheels are in the American Standard Safety Code, B7.1.

Grinding Fluids

The main functions of grinding fluids are cooling and the maintenance of wheel face. Grinding fluids can also carry chips away and may help to improve surface finish. Water-base fluids cool the workpiece. Grinding oils help preserve accurate wheel shape, as in form grinding.

It is important to distinguish between reduced generation of heat and removal of heat. Although less heat is generated with a grinding oil than with a water-base fluid, relatively little heat can be removed by the oil, because it is an inefficient coolant. Thus, although a change from water to oil may reduce the momentary surface temperature at grinding contact, the average temperature of the work will be higher with a grinding oil than with a water-base fluid.

Glazing, loading and gumming of the wheel face are causes of grinding heat. Glazing occurs when the cutting grains are dulled by attritious wear and there is insufficient grain fracture. Loading is welding of chips to the abrasive grains or mechanical trapping of chips in the pores of the wheel. Loading can be reduced by the use of a fluid that inhibits welding of the material being ground. Gumming occurs when the grinding fluid deteriorates and forms a sludge. The grinding fluid can have an important influence on these condi-

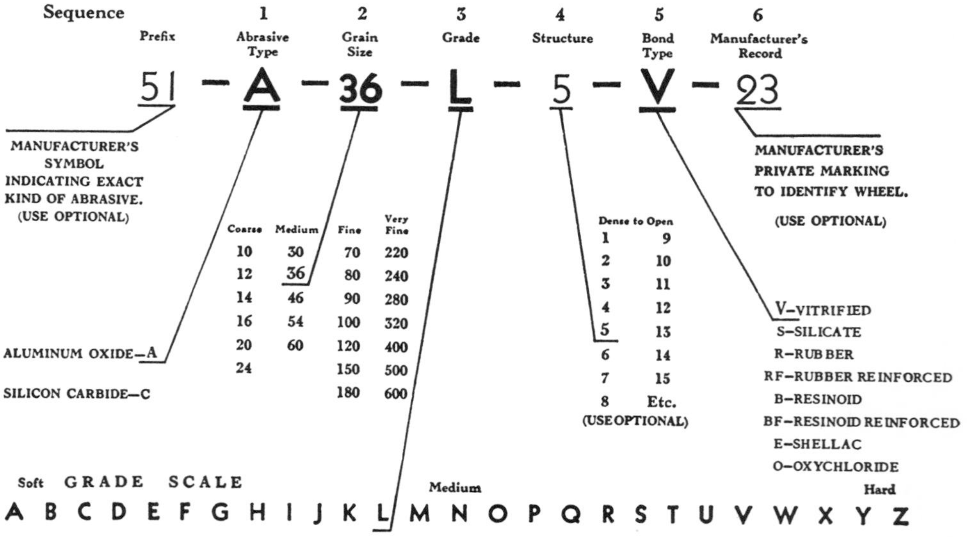

Fig. 1. Standard marking system for identifying grinding wheels (American Standard B5.17)

Table 1. Wheels for Grinding Unhardened Carbon or Low-Alloy Steel

Wheel type and/or size	Wet or dry	Wheel recommended: First choice	Wheel recommended: General-purpose(a)
Surface Grinding			
Straight, 14-in. diam or less	Wet	As-46-K8-V	As-46-J8-V
	Dry	As-46-J8-V(b)	As-46-J8-V
Straight, over 14-in. diam	Wet	As-36-K8-V	As-36-J8-V
Segment, rim 1½ in. or less(c)	Wet	As-24-H8-V(d)	As-24-H8-V
Cylinder, rim 1½ in. or less(c)	Wet	As-24-I8-V(e)	As-24-H8-V
Cup, rim ¾ in. or less(c)	Wet	As-24-H8-V(d)	As-30-H8-V
Cylindrical Grinding			
14-in. diam or less	Wet	As-60-M5-V	As-60-L5-V
16-in. diam or more	Wet	As-54-M5-V	As-54-L5-V
Centerless Grinding			
All sizes	Wet	As-54-N5-V	As-60-M5-V
Internal Grinding			
Less than ½-in. diam	Wet	As-60-M5-V	As-80-L6-V
½ to 1-in. diam	Wet	As-60-L5-V	As-60-K5-V
1 to 3-in. diam	Wet	As-54-K5-V	As-54-J5-V
Over 3-in. diam	Wet	As-46-K5-V	As-46-J5-V

(a) For use when hardened and unhardened steels must be ground without changing wheels. (b) Alternate: As-46-H12-V. (c) For wider rims, use next softer grade. (d) Alternate: As-30-F12-V. (e) Alternate: As-30-G12-V.

tions; therefore, it can influence the amount of grinding heat generated.

In conventional dry grinding, air serves effectively as a grinding fluid. Grinding forces would be many times greater in an oxygen-free inert-gas atmosphere, because the freshly formed surfaces of the chips and workpiece would be so clean that the chips would weld to the work surface immediately upon contact. Thus, the same chip would have to be ground many times before it permanently left the work surface. However, with even a slight amount of oxygen, the surfaces are oxidized sufficiently to prevent welding.

Water-base fluids can be divided into soluble-oil emulsions and synthetic compounds, also known as chemical fluids. In addition, there are mixtures of these two principal subdivisions, which are sometimes referred to as semisynthetics.

The soluble oils consist primarily of emulsified mineral oil; they may also contain soaps and fatty materials. Heavy-duty soluble oils are those to which sulfur and chlorine have been added to improve grinding action on materials like stainless steel by preventing wheel loading and reducing wheel wear.

Table 2. Wheels for Grinding Hardened or Carburized Carbon or Low-Alloy Steel(a)

Wheel type and/or size	Wet or dry	Wheel recommended
Surface Grinding		
Straight, 14-in. diam or less	Wet	As-46-I8-V
	Dry	As-46-H8-V(b)
Straight, over 14-in. diam	Wet	As-36-I8-V
Segment, rim 1½ in. or less(c)	Wet	As-30-H8-V(d)
Cylinder, rim 1½ in. or less(c)	Wet	As-30-H8-V(e)
Cup, rim ¾-in. or less(c)	Wet	As-36-H8-V(b)
Form and Radius Grinding		
8-in. diam or less	Wet	As-60-L7-V to As-100-M8-V
	Dry	As-60-K8-V to As-100-L8-V
10-in. diam or more	Wet	As-60-L7-V to As-80-M7-V
Cylindrical Grinding — Work Diameter 1 In. or Less		
14-in. diam or less	Wet	As-80-L6-V
16-in. diam or more	Wet	As-60-L5-V
Cylindrical Grinding — Work Diameter Over 1 In.		
14-in. diam or less	Wet	As-80-K5-V
16-in. diam or more	Wet	As-60-L5-V
Centerless Grinding		
All sizes	Wet	As-80-M6-V
Internal Grinding		
Less than ½-in. diam	Wet	As-80-N6-V
	Dry	As-80-L6-V
½ to 1-in. diam	Wet	As-60-M5-V
	Dry	As-70-K8-V
1 to 3-in. diam	Wet	As-54-L5-V
	Dry	As-60-J8-V(f)
Over 3-in. diam	Wet	As-46-K5-V
	Dry	As-46-J8-V(g)

(a) See last column of Table 1 for general-purpose wheels recommended when hardened and unhardened steels must be ground without changing wheels. (b) Alternate: As-46-F12-V (porous). (c) For wider rims, use next softer grade. (d) Alternate: As-36-F12-V (porous). (e) Alternate: As-36-E12-V (porous). (f) Alternate: As-60-H12-V (porous). (g) Alternate: As-54-H12-V (porous).

Table 3. Precautions in Mounting and Use of Grinding Wheels

Precautions in Mounting

1 When the correct wheel for the operation has been selected, "ring" the wheel to be sure it is not cracked. "Ringing" consists of gently tapping the suspended wheel with a light implement—a screwdriver handle for light wheels, or a wooden mallet for heavier wheels. Wheels that sound cracked should not be used.
2 Do not alter the hole in the wheel or attempt to force the wheel on the spindle.
3 Use clean, recessed matching flanges of a size equivalent to not less than one-third the wheel diameter.
4 Use a clean, smooth blotter on each side of the wheel under each flange.
5 Tighten the nut on the spindle only enough to hold the grinding wheel firmly in position.
6 Before starting the wheel, adjust the wheel guard and put on safety glasses.

Precautions in Use

1 When a dust hood and coolant nozzle are employed, they should be properly adjusted before grinding begins. On bench or floor-stand grinders, keep the work rest adjusted within ⅛ in. of wheel face (periphery).
2 Before starting to grind, stand aside and allow the wheel to run idle for a full minute.
3 Make certain that the machine speed is not excessive for the wheel to be used. Never exceed the maximum safe speed for the grinding wheel.
4 True the wheel if it is not running true.
5 Do not bump the wheel against the work when making grinding contact. Feeding should be smooth and gradual and without impact.
6 Grind only on the face of straight wheels. Use disk wheels for side grinding. Light side grinding is permitted on cup or dish wheels.
7 Never force grinding to the extent that the motor slows noticeably or the work gets hot.
8 Whenever a wheel breaks, carefully inspect the protective hood for possible damage and determine whether the flanges have been bent or sprung out of true. Spindle and nuts should also be inspected.
9 Wheels used in wet grinding should not be allowed to stand partly immersed in water or grinding fluid; the immersed portion may throw the wheel dangerously out of balance.
10 Protect grinding wheels from damage when they are not in use. Store wheels in storage rooms that are dry and are not subject to extremes in temperature.

The synthetic compounds contain a wide variety of organic and inorganic materials. They may be true solutions, like nitrite-amine rust-inhibitors, or they may be colloidal emulsions. The solutions have little or no lubricity, and are widely used in broad-contact grinding to inhibit foaming. Some colloidal emulsions have considerable lubricity and compete with soluble oils.

Grinding oils are mineral oils containing fatty materials to provide wetting and lubricating action. They may also contain sulfur or chlorine, or both. In comparison with water-base fluids, grinding oils limit wheel wear and heat generation very well, but they are poor coolants, messy to use, and a fire hazard. Consequently, they are used only when water-base fluids cannot do a satisfactory job.

Effect on Grinding Ratio. Generally, much higher grinding ratios are obtained with grinding oils than with water-base fluids. When vitrified-bond wheels are used, the grinding ratios of steels are somewhat higher in dry grinding than in grinding with water-base fluids.

Surface Finish and Quality

The following table relating grit size to surface finish can serve as a starting point for producing a specific finish:

54 grit	30 to 40 micro-in.
60 grit	20 to 30 micro-in.
80 grit	10 to 20 micro-in.

Surface roughness values given above refer to arithmetical average of the deviation from a mean centerline adopted by the American Standards Association (ASA B46.1). Numerically, arithmetical-average readings are approximately 10% less than root-mean-square readings — a difference that is rarely significant in practice. All references to micro-inches in this article are arithmetical-average values unless indicated otherwise.

The method of dressing the grinding wheel is important in controlling the surface finish obtained with a given grit size. A wheel dressed too rapidly produces a rough finish on the work; a wheel dressed too slowly is likely to burn the work.

Chatter marks are a common surface imperfection. They may be the result of any of the following:

1 **Wheel Out of Balance.** This condition can sometimes be corrected by rebalancing the wheel on its own mountings. Out-of-balance caused by allowing part of a wheel to stand in the grinding fluid can often be corrected by spinning off the excess fluid.
2 **Wheel Too Hard.** This condition can sometimes be corrected by an increase in work speed, traverse speed, and wheel pressure (infeed), or by sharper dressing of the wheel (which opens up the wheel face, reducing heat generation). However, it may be necessary to select a wheel of softer grade, of more open structure, or of coarser grit. The latter two changes may result in a harder wheel for the same letter marking.
3 **Work Centers Not True, or Improperly Lubricated.** Centers must be properly aligned, and corrective procedure may include the installation of centralized or automatic lubrication.
4 **Faulty Machine Conditions.** Chatter can be caused by loose bearings, uneven or improperly spliced belts, belt slippage, worn gear and ways, inadequate foundation, or general vibration.

Scratching is also undesirable. Its various forms and causes, and preventive measures, are listed below.

1 **Narrow and deep regular marks** are caused by too coarse a wheel. A wheel of finer grain size should be used.
2 **Wide, irregular marks of varying depth** are generally the result of too soft a wheel. There are two ways to make it perform like a harder wheel: (*a*) operate it at slower feeds and speeds, and reduce infeed pressure; or (*b*) dress it more slowly to give it a closed surface. If these procedures do not work, a harder wheel is needed.
3 **Fine spiral or thread on work surface** (often referred to as "diamond marks") may be prevented by reducing the traverse speed during wheel dressing; it may also be necessary to reduce the depth of dressing penetration. The dressing diamond should not be cracked or chipped. The diamond holder must be firmly clamped on the machine. It is advisable to rotate the diamond frequently. Dressing with a diamond nib or roll, containing numerous fine diamond particles, will also dress the wheel to prevent these marks.
4 **Wavy traverse lines** are usually caused by ragged wheel edges. Rounding of wheel edges corrects this condition.
5 **Irregular marks of various lengths and widths** often are caused by foreign material in the grinding fluid. A filtering system or frequent cleaning of the supply tank is required. It is good practice to flush clean the wheel guards when changing to a finer-grit wheel; this removes any coarse material that may be carried by the fluid into the grinding system.

Grinding burn may show as a surface discoloration (in various shades of straw, brown or blue) caused by the formation of a thin oxide film on the surface of the metal. However, absence of discoloration does not necessarily mean that the surface remained cool during grinding. Discoloration may have been removed immediately by the wheel in its travel across the surface, or it may have been removed in a subsequent light cut. (Dark stains that occur occasionally when grinding oil is used may be charred oil and should not be mistaken for grinding burn.)

If the microstructure of the work material is heat-sensitive, grinding may change both the microstructure and hardness of a shallow layer. This condition is sometimes called "metallurgical burn", to distinguish it from visible burn, or discoloration. In hardened and tempered steel, grinding heat may overtemper and soften the surface; or, if the transformation temperature is exceeded, austenite will form and will immediately be quenched by the cold metal beneath the surface, to form martensite. Such microstructural changes can be detected readily by nondestructive macro-etching or by metallographic examination. In most materials other than hardened steel, however, grinding heat has no direct effect on microstructure, and it is impossible to detect heat effects or surface damage by etching.

Residual stress can result from any operation in which heat or mechanical force causes inhomogeneous plastic deformation. Grinding stress may be entirely tensile, entirely compressive, or tensile in one layer and compressive in an adjoining layer. Tensile stress is believed to be caused primarily by grinding heat, and compressive stress by the plastic deformation of the surface that occurs when chips are formed. The magnitude of the stress below the ground surface decreases rapidly with depth, becoming negligible at a depth that varies with material and with grinding conditions (it may be 0.002 in. for hardened steel, or five to ten times as much for annealed steel or heat-resisting alloys). Residual stress that is fairly uniform over large areas can cause warping of thin or delicate parts.

Grinding Sensitivity and Cracking. Materials sensitive to grinding heat may develop shallow cracks during or after grinding. The greater the sensitivity, the less heat is required to cause cracking. If a material is insensitive to heat, excessive grinding heat will not, of itself, cause cracking. Soft metals, for example, cannot be cracked by abusive grinding, because of their considerable ductility.

In magnetic materials, grinding cracks invisible to the naked eye can be detected by magnetic-particle inspection. Fluorescent or dye penetrants can be used for the same purpose when the material is nonmagnetic; however, they are not successful when the grinding operation has smeared the surface and covered the cracks.

Suitable acid etchants will, of course, widen cracks in any material and make them readily visible. However, some acids can actually *produce* cracks in a crack-free surface containing high residual tensile stress. This happens when the metal becomes so embrittled by hydrogen absorbed from the acid that it cannot withstand the surface tensile stress. Hardened steels are embrittled in this manner by sulfuric and hydrochloric acids.

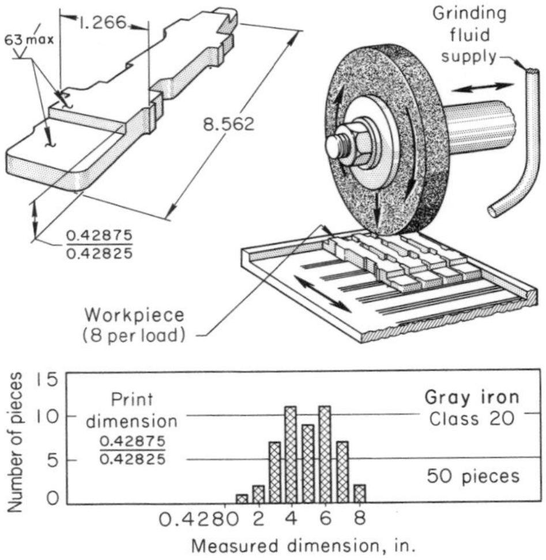

Wheel classification	Ar-46-I8-V
Wheel size	10 by 1½ by 3 in.

Operating Conditions

Speed	2000 rpm (5236 sfm)
Downfeed	0.0003 in.
Traverse speed	600 ipm
Crossfeed	0.125 in. per pass
Metal removed per side	0.0035 in.
Grinding fluid	Synthetic:water (1:40)
Setup time	0.3 hr
Production rate	20 pieces per hour
Wheel life per dressing	24 pieces
Method of dressing	Single-point diamond

Fig. 2. Close-tolerance surface grinding in a horizontal-spindle machine (Example 468)

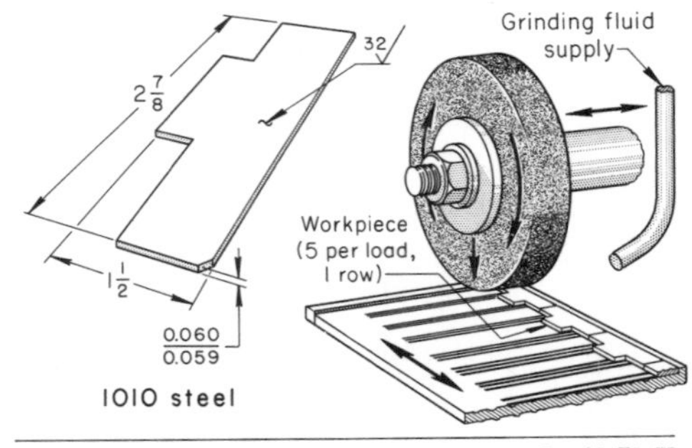

Wheel classification	Ar-46-I8-V
Wheel size	10 by 2 by 3 in.

Operating Conditions

Speed	2000 rpm (5236 sfm)
Downfeed	0.0002 in.(a)
Traverse speed	600 ipm
Crossfeed	0.125 in. per pass
Metal removed per side	0.002 in.
Grinding fluid	Synthetic:water (1:40)
Setup time	0.3 hr
Production rate	44 pieces per hour
Wheel life per dressing	10 pieces
Method of dressing	Single-point diamond

(a) A downfeed of 0.0001 in. was used for finish grinding.

Fig. 3. Surface grinding thin flat parts in a horizontal-spindle machine (Example 469)

Surface Grinding With Horizontal-Spindle Machines

Horizontal-spindle surface grinding machines, with either reciprocating or rotary tables, are used primarily for grinding flat surfaces on parts held directly on magnetic chucks. Metal is removed by the periphery of the grinding wheel. Standard horizontal-spindle surface grinders are available in several sizes, identified by the working area of the work table.

Of the three types of horizontal-spindle machines, those with reciprocating tables are the most common. Surfaces ground on these machines have a scratch pattern parallel to the traverse motion of the reciprocating table.

Rotary-table machines may be equipped with stationary or tilting tables. A scratch pattern of concentric circular marks is produced on the ground surface of a workpiece mounted on a stationary table. Tilting-table machines are generally used for grinding convex or concave surfaces, but flat surfaces also can be ground when necessary.

Face grinders are the third principal type of horizontal-spindle machine. These are large machines in which the workpiece is mounted on a vertical table and ground with either cylindrical or segmental wheels. Face grinders may have either traveling tables or traveling wheels.

The two examples that follow describe techniques and results in typical applications of surface grinding with horizontal-spindle machines.

Example 468. Close Tolerance (Fig. 2)

When both sides of gray iron castings like that shown in Fig. 2 were ground in a double-wheel grinder, it was difficult to meet the ±0.00025-in. tolerance on the 0.4285-in. dimension. By changing to a horizontal-spindle surface grinder, this difficulty was substantially eliminated, as the dimensions plotted in the graph in Fig. 2 indicate.

The horizontal-spindle machine had a work table 8 by 24 in. Eight pieces were ground at one time. They were placed against a guide rail in a good holding area of the magnetic chuck, and blocked in to prevent movement during grinding. Loading of the chuck with more than eight pieces induced excessive wear of the grinding wheel and caused difficulty in keeping within the dimensional tolerance. Processing details are given with Fig. 2.

Example 469. Thin Flat Part (Fig. 3)

A horizontal-spindle surface grinder with an 8-by-24-in. work table was used for grinding both surfaces of the 1010 steel card guide shown in Fig. 3. Five of these parts were ground in each load, placed in one row against a guide rail of the magnetic chuck. A load of more than five caused excessive wear of the grinding wheel and made it difficult to meet the 0.001-in. thickness tolerance. Because these parts were likely to warp and buckle when too much grinding pressure was applied, a 46-grit wheel was used to provide sharp grinding action. Other wheel details, and operating conditions, are given below Fig. 3.

Slots and Other Shapes. Horizontal-spindle surface grinders equipped with work-holding fixtures can be used for successful production grinding of flats, grooves, angles and forms in almost any workpiece configuration. Production operations involving the grinding of slots and step flats are described in the two examples that follow.

Example 470. Grinding vs Milling of Slots (Fig. 4)

An open-side 6-by-18-in. surface grinder, equipped with a pump and a filtering system for grinding fluid, was used to grind four slots in 8740 hardened steel parts (Rockwell C 34 to 38) of round cross section. Figure 4 shows the part and the setup used and gives processing details.

Formerly, the slots had been made by milling and finish grinding. This method was not satisfactory, because in finish grinding, metal removal from the sides of the milled slot was unequal, making it impossible to meet finish and tolerance requirements. Also, rough milling did not decrease grinding time; the downfeed per grinding pass could not be appreciably increased over that used when the slots were produced entirely by grinding, because slot width was controlled by the width of the wheel and because appreciably increased downfeeds caused breakdown of the sides of the wheel.

Example 471. Step Grinding (Fig. 5)

The shape of the part shown in Fig. 5 is typical of those that are step ground by a reciprocating surface grinder. This part was made of resulfurized low-carbon steel plate, using the following operations:

1 Rough grind both wide faces in a rotary grinder.
2 Straddle mill ends.
3 Straddle mill sides.
4 Vertical mill step cuts.
5 Finish mill ¾-in. key and necks in a horizontal milling machine.
6 Finish grind flat face in a reciprocating grinder.
7 Finish grind steps in a reciprocating grinder.

Processing details for step grinding (operation 7) are given below Fig. 5. Operation 6 was done in the same machine, using the same type and size of wheel, at the same speed and with the same type of grinding fluid, but with twice as many pieces per load (fourteen) as in step grinding (seven). [See also Example 521 and Fig. 44 for additional information on this same part.]

Surface Grinding With Vertical-Spindle Machines

Vertical-spindle surface grinders are available with either reciprocating or rotary tables. Reciprocating-table machines use cup, cylinder or segmental grinding wheels. The column supporting the wheel head may be fixed, or it may slide laterally on ways, for the grinding of workpieces that are wider than the grinding wheel.

Rotary-table machines use cylinder or segmental wheels, and some have as many as five wheel spindles mounted on a central column. On multiple-spindle machines, a ring-type rotating table carries the work under the wheels. Roughing, semifinishing and finishing

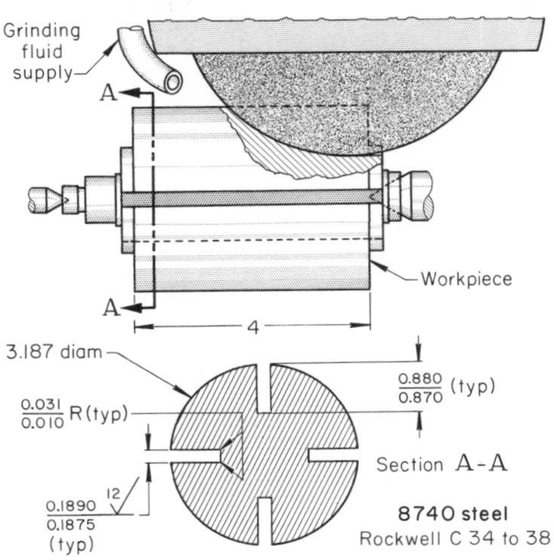

Wheel classification	A-80-L-V
Wheel size	8 by ¼(a) by 1¼ in.

Operating Conditions

Speed	2850 rpm (6000 sfm)
Downfeed	0.001 in.(b)
Traverse speed	225 ipm
Total metal removed	⅞ in.
Grinding fluid	(c)
Setup time	2⅓ hr
Grinding time per piece	1⅔ hr
Wheel life per dressing	1 slot
Method of dressing	Single-point diamond(d)
Total wheel life (average)	50 pieces (200 slots)
Wheel cost	$3 (6¢ per piece)

(a) Dressed to cut the slot width. (b) 50 strokes per min. (c) Grinding fluid was a mixture of 3 parts mineral oil (light viscosity) and 1 part high-sulfur concentrate. (d) Traversed across periphery of wheel. Wheel corners were dressed sharp; normal breakdown of corners during grinding of slot produced the 0.031/0.010-in. radii at bottom.

Fig. 4. Use of an open-side horizontal-spindle surface grinder for producing slots (Example 470)

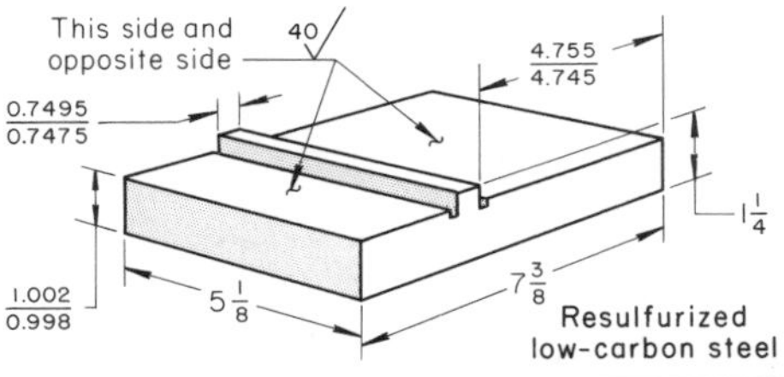

Wheel classification	A-46-J5-V
Wheel size	20 by 3 by 10 in.
Size of reciprocating table	20 by 72 in.

Conditions in Step Grinding

Speed	1100 rpm (5760 sfm)
Downfeed	0.0012 in. per pass
Amount of metal removed	0.016 in.
Grinding fluid	Soluble-oil:water (1:50)
Pieces per load	7
Setup time	0.4 hr
Time per piece	0.042 hr(a)
Production rate	24 pieces per hour(b)
Method of wheel dressing	Built-in diamond
Wheel life	140 hr of grinding
Wheel cost per piece	$0.011(c)
Total cost per piece	$0.195(d)

(a) Includes time for dressing. (b) Based on a 7-piece load. (c) Based on cost of $55 per wheel. (d) Based on wheel cost per piece plus amortization of setup time at $4 per standard hour over a 100-piece lot.

Fig. 5. Part finished by step grinding in a horizontal reciprocating surface grinder (Example 471)

cuts can be taken on parts as large as engine blocks with only one pass through machines like these rotary-table grinding machines.

Vertical-spindle surface grinders are especially efficient for grinding parts having two opposed flat surfaces. But the following types of parts must be blocked in position or the downfeed must be reduced, or both, for successful surface grinding:

1 Very small parts that make insufficient contact with the magnetic chuck to prevent sliding
2 Very large parts that have only a small proportion of their total area in contact with the magnetic chuck
3 Odd-shaped parts for which the locating surface overhangs chuck-contact area.

Because of its fast stock removal, large chuck capacity and ease of setup, the vertical-spindle rotary-table surface grinder can handle large or small production lots equally well. These machines are used primarily for work with dimensional tolerances no closer than 0.001 in. and required surface finish no smoother than 32 micro-in.

Some of these machines, however, can produce extreme accuracy of size, parallelism, and flatness, as well as excellent finish. Size can be held within limits of ±0.0002 in., and parallelism to better than 0.0001 in. per inch. Flatness can be produced that is measurable only with an optical flat. Surface finish of less than 10 micro-in. is possible. Results like these have been obtained under production conditions. For example, 7-in.-diam cast iron compressor heads have been ground to an over-all flatness variation of 7 millionths of an inch and a finish of 6 micro-in. at a rate of 40 per hour.

The example that follows is typical of many applications in which flat workpieces are ground instead of being machined by milling, planing, or shaping (even though the amount of metal to be removed indicates the use of a method other than grinding), because the large table loads that rotary surface grinders can accommodate often offset the faster removal rates in machining loads of one or two pieces:

Example 472. Cost Reduction Through Elimination of Milling (Fig. 6)

Originally, milling and grinding were used for removing a total of ⅛-in. from the two side faces of the 4615 steel chuck jaw shown in Fig. 6. In milling, one piece at a time was mounted in a rack vise, and one face was milled with a carbide cutter. Then 40 pieces were loaded into a rotary-table surface grinder, where the other face was ground to finish dimension.

Later, the milling operation was eliminated, and both faces were ground in the rotary-table vertical-spindle surface grinder (see processing details with Fig. 6). Mainly because large table loads could be accommodated, the change of method resulted in the following savings:

	Milling and grinding	Grinding only
Setup time, hr	1.10	0.50
Processing time per piece, hr	0.039	0.025
Production, pieces per hour	25	40
Cost per piece	$0.204	$0.125

The six examples that follow describe workpiece shapes and sizes, production quantities, tolerances, and surface finishes typical of vertical-spindle grinding operations. Five of these examples present data that show the superior performance of rotary-table vertical-spindle grinders over that of reciprocating-table or cylindrical horizontal-spindle grinders for the workpieces being processed.

Example 473. Efficiency and Dimensional Accuracy (Fig. 7)

The grooved face of the part shown in Fig. 7 reduced the grinding area and provided for efficient cooling during grinding in a vertical-spindle rotary surface grinder. These parts were made of 1018 steel and case hardened to the equivalent of Rockwell C 62 to 65 to a depth of 0.007 to 0.009 in. Grinding removed 0.002 in. of metal. The setup for grinding a full magnetic chuck load of 190 pieces is illustrated in Fig. 7. Grinding, under conditions listed with Fig. 7, consistently produced parts to specified surface finish (32 micro-in.) and dimensional tolerance (see graph in Fig. 7).

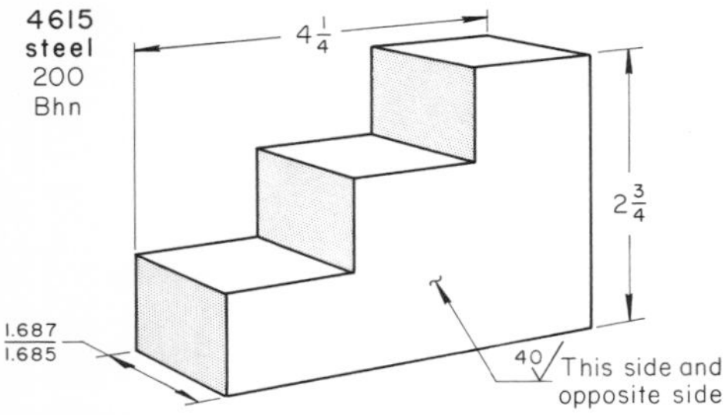

Wheel
 classification . . Segmental, A_s-30-G-V (porous)
Wheel size . . . . 18-in. diam, 5 in. wide
Diameter of rotary table . . . . 30 in.

Operating Conditions

Speed . . . . 720 rpm (3400 sfm)
Downfeed . . . . 0.012 ipm
Metal removed (total, both sides) . . . . 1/8 in.
Grinding fluid . . . . Soluble-oil:water (1:50)
Method of wheel dressing . . . . Star dresser(a)
Wheel life . . . . 7470 pieces(b)
Wheel cost per piece . . . . $0.005(c)
Total cost per piece . . . . $0.125(d)

(a) Wheel dressed during grinding; 20% of grinding time allowed for dressing. (b) Based on about 84 hr of grinding time; about 27 min of grinding time was required for each load of 40 pieces. (c) Based on cost of $40 per set of wheel segments. (d) Based on wheel cost plus labor cost.

Fig. 6. Drop forged chuck jaw that was surface ground on both side faces with a vertical-spindle rotary machine. For advantages over previous method (milling followed by grinding), see Example 472.

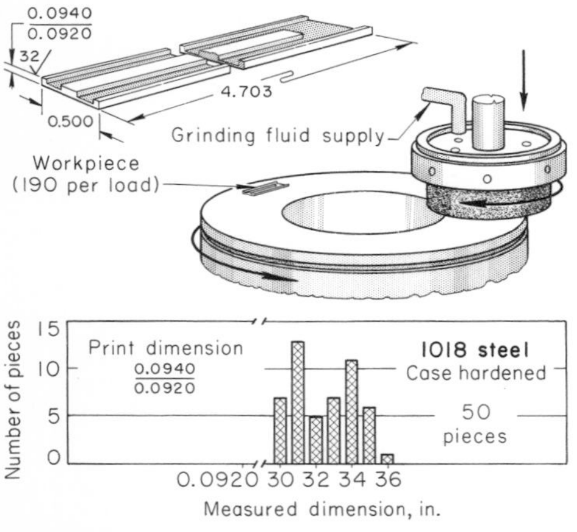

Wheel classification . . . . A_s-46-H-V
Wheel size . . . . 20 by 5 by 16½ in.
Diameter of rotary table . . . . 42 in.

Operating Conditions

Wheel speed . . . . 720 rpm (3750 sfm)
Table speed . . . . 6 rpm
Infeed . . . . 0.004 in. per min(a)
Amount of metal removed . . . . 0.002 in.
Grinding fluid . . . . Synthetic:water (1:40)
Setup time . . . . 0.3 hr
Production rate . . . . 400 pieces per hour
Method of wheel dressing . . . . Star dresser(b)

(a) Automatic cutoff control. (b) Wheel dressed when indicated by pressure indicator.

Fig. 7. Case hardened part consistently ground to specified tolerance and finish by a vertical-spindle rotary surface grinder (Example 473)

Examples 474 to 477. Rotary Vertical-Spindle vs Reciprocating Horizontal-Spindle Surface Grinders

Example 474 (Table 4). A vertical-spindle surface grinder with a rotary table was used to remove a total of ⅛ in. of metal from the top and bottom surfaces of shanks for cutters used in lathe turning. These shanks were made of class 30 gray iron and were about 1¼ in. wide, 1⅜ in. thick (after grinding), and 6 in. long. Because finish and tolerance for these parts were of minor importance, the rotary grinder, with its high rate of metal removal, was more efficient than a reciprocating-table (horizontal-spindle) machine — giving increased production rate and wheel life, and lower cost per piece (Table 4).

Example 475. Rectangular-section parts made of case hardened 1018 steel (hardness, Rockwell C 62 to 65), which were 7.928 in. long and 0.563 in. high, required the removal of 0.004 in. of metal to produce a thickness of 0.312 ± 0.002 in. Originally, these parts were ground in a horizontal-spindle surface grinder with a reciprocating table. The table size (8 by 24 in.) limited each grinding load to 25 pieces, and production rate was only 59 pieces per hour.

The tolerance was liberal enough for a change to a vertical-spindle machine with a 42-in.-diam rotary table, which could accommodate a load of 120 pieces. With this machine, output was increased to 190 pieces per hour — more than three times that of the horizontal machine. (The increase in production rate was not proportional to the increase in number of parts on the table because more time was consumed in loading and unloading the vertical machine.) The parts were ground with an A_s-36-F12-V (porous) wheel 20 in. in diameter and 5 in. thick. Wheel speed was 720 rpm (3770 sfm); a mixture of soluble synthetic and water (in a ratio of 1 to 40) was used as the grinding fluid.

Examples 476 and 477 (Table 5). The increased production rates and decreased costs obtained by grinding two different class 30 gray iron castings with a vertical-spindle rotary surface grinder instead of a horizontal-spindle reciprocating machine are shown by the comparison of data in Table 5.

Stock removal was 1/16 in. for the pushbutton plate (Example 476), which was ground on only one side, and ⅛ in. total for the clamp yoke (Example 477), which was ground on both sides (see sketches in Table 5).

Example 478. Vertical-Spindle Rotary vs Cylindrical Grinder (Fig. 8)

The composite hub (low-carbon steel ringed with molded rubber) shown at the left in Fig. 8 originally was ground in a cylindrical grinder, using the setup shown in the center sketch of Fig. 8. Setup time was 0.3 hr, and production rate was 196 pieces per hour.

By changing to an automatic vertical-spindle rotary grinder, setup time was reduced to 0.2 hr, and production rate was increased to 750 pieces per hour. The tolerance on the

Table 4. Vertical Rotary vs Horizontal Reciprocating Machines for Surface Grinding of Gray Iron Cutter Shanks (Example 474)

Item	Vertical-spindle rotary machine	Horizontal-spindle reciprocating machine
Dimensions of table, in.	30 diam	16 by 72
Number of pieces per load	65	99
Wheel classification	A_s-30-G15-V	A_s-46-J5-V
Wheel type	Segmental	Straight
Wheel size, in.	18 OD by 5 wide	20 by 3 by 10
Wheel cost, each	$40	$55
Setup time, hr	0.5	1.2
Grinding time per piece, min	0.41	1.08
Total time per piece, hr	0.018	0.027
Production rate, pieces per hour	55	37
Wheel life, pieces ground	12,290(a)	7780(b)
Wheel cost per piece	$0.003	$0.007
Total cost per piece(c)	$0.095	$0.163

(a) 84 hr of grinding. (b) 140 hr of grinding. (c) Setup and grinding costs, at $4 per standard hour, amortized over a 100-piece lot, plus wheel cost per piece.

Table 5. Vertical Rotary vs Horizontal Reciprocating Machines for Surface Grinding of Two Different Class 30 Gray Iron Castings (Examples 476 and 477)

Item	Example 476: Vertical rotary(a)	Example 476: Horizontal reciprocating(b)	Example 477: Vertical rotary(a)	Example 477: Horizontal reciprocating(b)
Number of pieces per load	20	44	40	72
Setup time, hr	0.30	0.80	0.40	1.40
Grinding time per piece, min	0.43	1.30	0.42	1.77
Total time per piece, hr	0.012	0.026	0.019	0.039
Production rate, pieces per hour	83	38	52	25
Wheel life, pieces ground	11,700(c)	6460(d)	12,000(c)	4750(d)
Wheel cost per piece	$0.0034(e)	$0.0085(f)	$0.0033(e)	$0.0116(f)
Total cost per piece(g)	$0.063	$0.145	$0.095	$0.224

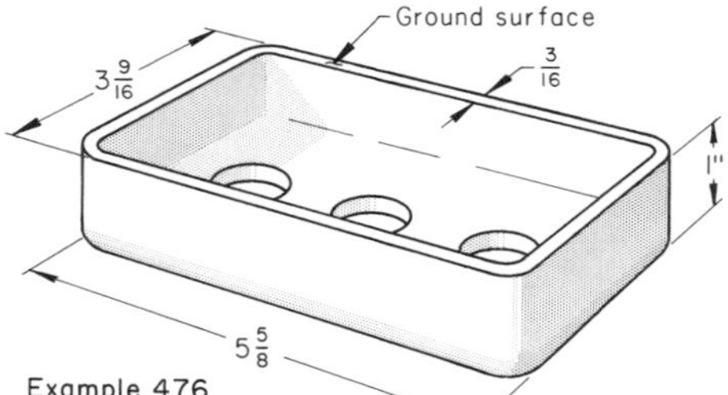

Example 476
Pushbutton plate

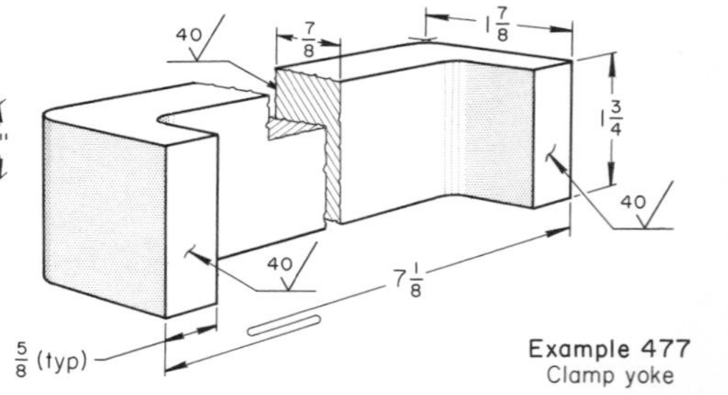

Example 477
Clamp yoke

(a) Diameter of rotary table, 30 in. Wheels, 30-grit aluminum oxide, segmental, 18 in. in diameter by 5 in wide. (b) Table, 16 by 72 in. Wheels, 46-grit aluminum oxide, straight, 20 in. in diameter by 3 in. wide. (c) 84 hr of grinding. (d) 140 hr of grinding. (e) Based on cost of $40 per wheel. (f) Based on cost of $55 per wheel. (g) Setup and grinding costs, at $4 per standard hour, amortized over a 100-piece lot, plus wheel cost per piece.

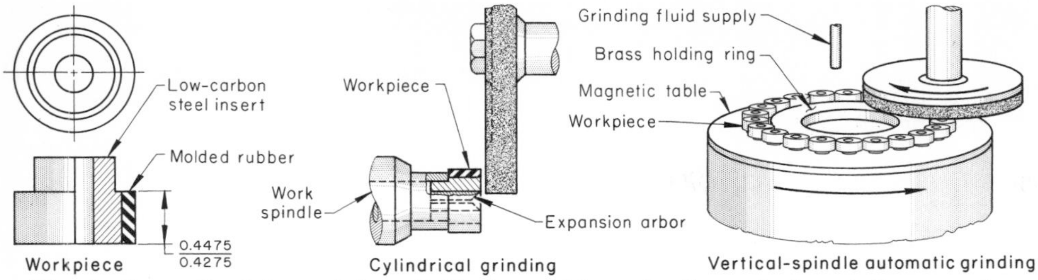

Fig. 8. Composite hub workpiece (left) *for which production rate in grinding was increased almost fourfold by changing from cylindrical to vertical-spindle automatic method* (Example 478)

0.4475/0.4275-in. dimension was large enough to permit loading of the pieces on the hub face (as indicated in the setup for the rotary machine shown at the right in Fig. 8), rather than on the shoulder from which the surface to be ground was dimensioned.

Each piece was loaded against a brass supporting ring on the continually turning 36-in.-diam rotary table. The table was magnetic only in the grinding area of the machine; with this arrangement, ground pieces could be removed without shutting down the operation, and the operator was free to load the chuck continuously. Grinding was done with an A_r-46-H-V wheel, 18 by 5 by 10 in., operated at 1175 rpm (5535 sfm); a synthetic solution was used as the grinding fluid.

Surface Grinding With Double-Wheel Machines

Parts with opposed flat surfaces can be ground in double-wheel grinders. The outer edges of the opposed faces, however, should be of the same contour, so that the two faces support each other and are ground evenly as the part enters and leaves the faces of the opposed grinding wheels.

Two types of work carrier, the rotary-disk type and the shuttle type, carry workpieces between the wheels. Rotary carriers are used for parts of small to medium size (from ¼ to 4 in. wide). Larger parts, with more than about 20 sq in. of area on each face, are transported by shuttle carriers. (Shuttle carriers can also transport small parts, but not as productively as rotary carriers.)

Although the grinding efficiency of double-wheel grinders is high, they require from ½ to 4 hr of setup time as well as special work carriers. Consequently, production should be sufficient to justify setting up the machine.

Close tolerances on thickness and flatness can be met with double-wheel grinders. These machines are particularly good at grinding parts to close flatness tolerance, because the parts are not subjected to the pull-down and release forces of a magnetic chuck (as are parts ground on vertical-spindle or horizontal-spindle surface grinders).

The six examples that follow describe the relation of various workpiece requirements to the operating characteristics of double-wheel grinders.

Example 479. Accurate Dimension on Springs (Fig. 9)

Music-wire springs 0.281 in. in diameter were ground to a height of 0.381/0.369 in. by a vertical-spindle double-wheel grinder. As shown in Fig. 9, the springs were fed into the wheels by means of a rotary carrier centered over a stationary steel plate. The springs were ejected through a trapdoor after being ground. The carrier rotated at the rate of one revolution every 6 min. Carrier speed was determined by the amount of time required for removing the necessary amount of metal (about 0.050 in. from each end of the springs) in one pass between the wheels. The bottom wheel was parallel with the carrier, whereas the top wheel was tilted so that the opening between the wheels where the springs entered was greater by an amount equal to the total stock removal (about 0.1 in.) than the opening where the springs exited. Operating conditions and cost data are given in the table below Fig. 9.

Specifications for these springs designated that the 0.375-in. height be deflected to 0.281 in. under a load of 25 lb ± 5%. In tests conducted on 50 springs selected from a 500-piece lot, the load required for obtaining the 0.281-in. deflected height varied from 24.6 to 25.2 lb — well within tolerance.

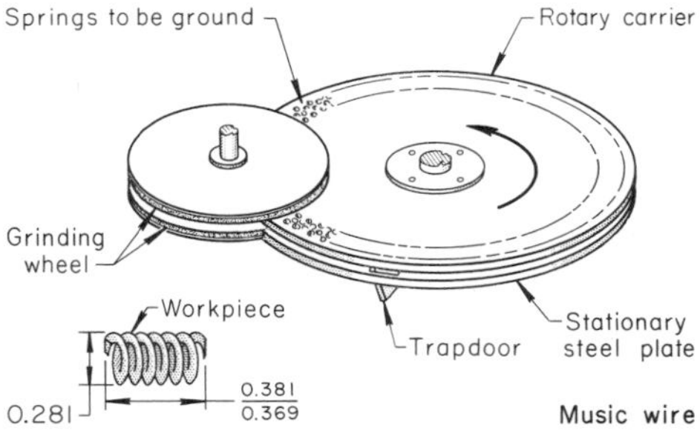

Wheel classification	A_s-46-N/M12-B(a)
Wheel size	18-in. diam, 1 in. wide(b)

Operating Conditions

Wheel speed	1270 rpm (5985 sfm)(c)
Rotary-carrier speed	⅙ rpm(d)
Grinding fluid	None
Metal removed, each end	0.050 in.
Setup time	30 min(e)
Production rate	3000 springs per hour
Wheel life per dressing	12,000 springs(f)
Total wheel life (approx)	250,000 springs

Cost per 1000 Springs

Wheels	$0.25
Labor	0.80
Amortization, other expenses	0.30
Total	$1.35

(a) Hardness grade N from periphery to 4 in. from center, grade M to center. (b) No arbor hole (secured by tapped nuts molded into the back). (c) Surface speed at periphery (direction of rotation reversed every 2 to 3 hr as an aid in maintaining flatness). (d) Diameter of rotary carrier, 32 in. (e) Time required for adjusting setup to accommodate springs of a different size. (f) 4 hr of grinding. Wheels were dressed with a diamond or mechanical dresser, on a swinging arm attached to the machine and moving in one plane.

Fig. 9. Grinding of music-wire springs in a vertical-spindle double-wheel machine (Example 479)

Example 480. Close Tolerance on Flatness of Sun Gears (Fig. 10)

Both faces of sun gears made of 1330 steel (187 to 217 Bhn) were rough ground in a 30-in. horizontal-spindle double-wheel grinder equipped with an automatic loading-and-unloading device. The setup is shown in Fig. 10. These gears were 2.360 in. in outside diameter and 0.960 in. thick. Grinding removed a total of 0.011 to 0.016 in. of metal from both faces. It was important that the machine be level, to prevent the removal of unequal amounts of metal from the two faces. Tolerances, operating conditions, and cost data are given in the tabulation accompanying Fig. 10.

Example 481. Flatness and Dimensional Accuracy (Fig. 11)

Silicon iron (1% Si) yokes were ground to within 0.001 in. of absolute flatness, and to within ±0.0005 in. of a basic thickness in a horizontal-spindle double-wheel grinder. Figure 11 shows the workpiece and setup, and plots variations in thickness and flatness on 50 pieces.

The yokes were fed automatically from a vibrating hopper into a 20-hole rotary carrier, which conveyed them to the wheels. After being ground, the yokes were automatically ejected. Thus relieved of loading and unloading, the operator was free to measure pieces and make machine adjustments to maintain dimensional accuracy. Processing details are given below Fig. 11.

Example 482. Flatness and Parallelism (Fig. 12)

A horizontal-spindle double-wheel grinder was used to remove 0.015 in. of metal per side from the magnetic yoke assembly shown in Fig. 12. The ground sides were required to be parallel within 0.005 in. and flat within 0.003 in. Formerly, a vertical-spindle rotary surface grinder had been used, but this machine could not produce parts to the required flatness because of the pulldown-and-release action of the magnetic chuck.

Before being ground, each part was straightened to within 0.005 in. Then the parts were fed into the wheels by a hydraulically actuated reciprocating slide carrier, as shown in Fig. 12. The yoke assembly was placed on the slide carrier at an angle of 45° so that it did not overhang the grinding wheels and thereby require a second grinding. One piece was ground at a time, and the wheels were fed automatically. Complete infeeding required 93 sec. This rather slow feed minimized the

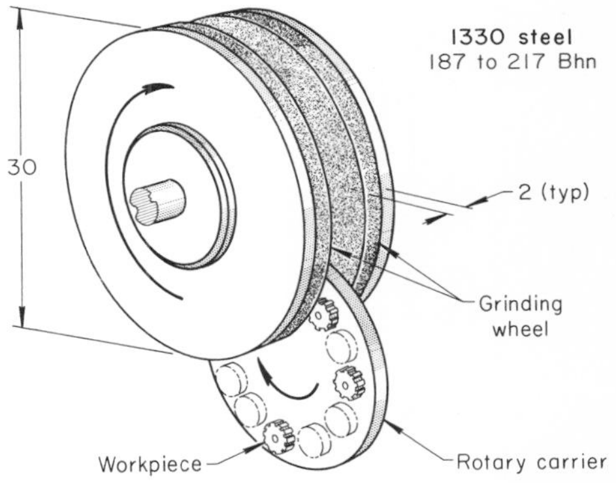

Tolerances

Flatness of faces	Within 0.0005 in. per in.
Squareness of faces with bore	Within 0.003 in.
Thickness	±0.002 in.

Operating Conditions

Wheel classification	A_s-60-O/L11-B(a)
Wheel size	30 by 2 by 16
Wheel speed	715 rpm (5615 sfm)(b)
Carrier speed	1 rpm
Total metal removed(c)	0.011 to 0.016 in.
Grinding fluid	Soluble-oil emulsion
Production rate	960 to 1320 pieces per hour
Setup time	4 hr
Wheel life per dressing(d)	950 to 1000 pieces
Total wheel life (average)	122,500 pieces

Costs per 1000 Pieces

Wheels	$1.76
Labor (at $3 per hr)	3.00
Grinding fluid	0.33

(a) Hardness grade O from 30 to 26 in. of wheel diameter, grade L from 26 to 16 in. (b) Surface speed at periphery. (c) Both sides. (d) Wheel dressed with diamond tools.

Fig. 10. Rough grinding of both faces of sun gears in a horizontal-spindle double-wheel machine (Example 480)

grinding pressure on the face of the magnetic cores and avoided bending from excessive side pressure. Because surface finish was not critical, free-cutting grinding wheels (see table below Fig. 12) were used to maintain the flatness tolerance of 0.003 in.

Example 483. Dimensional Accuracy of Narrow Part (Fig. 13)

The small carbon steel part shown in Fig. 13 was ground in a horizontal-spindle double-wheel grinder equipped with a 20-hole rotary carrier similar to the carrier shown in Fig. 11. Each part was positioned in the carrier so that it entered the grinding area lengthwise. This was necessary because the part was narrow (0.125 in.), and would roll slightly if fed sidewise into the grinding area.

The coarse-grained aluminum oxide wheels (see table of conditions below Fig. 13) provided good cutting efficiency and moderate wheel breakdown, because the ground area of the part was small in comparison with the grinding area of the wheel. The ability of the grinder to hold tolerance is indicated by the chart in Fig. 13.

Example 484. Special Carrier for Assuring Squareness (Fig. 14)

A horizontal-spindle double-wheel grinder removed 0.0042 in. of metal from each end of the 1144 steel bearing insert shown in Fig. 14 to make it 0.4991 ± 0.0003 in. long. Average hardness of the pieces was Rockwell C 30. The pieces were fed between the wheels by a 24-hole rotary carrier similar to the one shown in Fig. 11 except that each hole contained a precision-made carbide nest for a close fit on the cylindrical surface of the bearing insert.

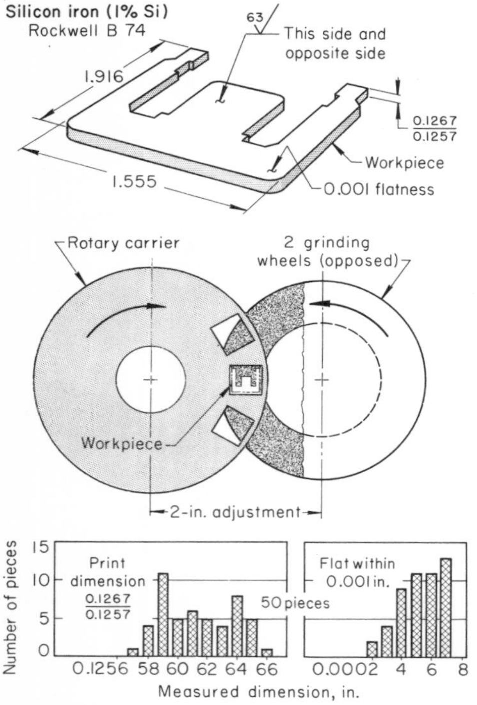

Wheel classification	At-80-J/G12-B(a)
Wheel size(b)	26-in. diam, 3 in. wide

Operating Conditions

Wheel speed	750 rpm (5100 sfm)(c)
Carrier speed	2 rpm
Metal removed per side	0.0015 in.
Grinding fluid	Synthetic:water (1:40)
Production rate	1200 pieces per hour
Setup time	0.6 hr
Wheel life per dressing(d)	4800 pieces

(a) Grade J to midway from periphery; grade G from there to inside diameter. (b) Wheel was metal-backed. (c) Surface speed at periphery. (d) Wheels dressed with diamond-cluster tool.

Fig. 11. Grinding of silicon iron yokes in a horizontal-spindle double-wheel machine (Example 481)

The grinding wheels were solid, having no relief holes through which the small inserts might fall during the grinding cycle.

The high degree of accuracy attained in this operation is shown by the dimensional variations in 50 pieces plotted in Fig. 14. Wheel details and operating conditions are given in the table below Fig. 14.

Cylindrical Grinding

Cylindrical grinding is a method of grinding outside surfaces of cylindrical parts. It entails four essential movements: *(a)* the workpiece rotates on centers or on a mandrel; *(b)* the grinding wheel rotates; *(c)* the wheel is moved toward and away from the workpiece; and *(d)* the wheel is traversed by the workpiece, or plunges into it. On very large machines the wheel may traverse the work.

Centers. In cylindrical grinding, accuracy depends greatly on the condition of centers and center holes. These should be accurate (exactly 60°), large enough to provide adequate bearing surface, clean, and properly lubricated. Centers are normally made of hardened steel or carbide.

Steady Rests. Workpieces that may spring or vibrate during cylindrical grinding — particularly, long slender pieces — should be adequately supported by steady rests. The number of steady rests used for a grinding operation is largely a matter of judgment and experience. In general, steady rests should be placed about one foot apart if the workpiece is 3 in. in diameter or less, and about two feet apart for workpieces of larger diameter. When more than one steady rest is required for a symmetrical workpiece, one is positioned under the middle of the workpiece, and an equal number are positioned on both sides of that one.

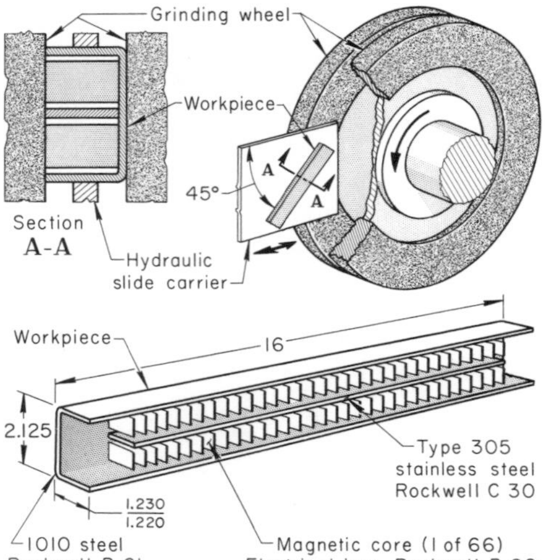

Wheel classification	As-46-G11-B
Wheel size	30-in. diam, 3 in. wide

Operating Conditions

Wheel speed	750 rpm (5890 sfm)(a)
Total infeed time	93 sec
Metal removed per side	0.015 in.
Grinding fluid	Synthetic:water (1:40)
Production rate	23 pieces per hour
Setup time	0.6 hr
Wheel life per dressing	10 pieces

(a) Surface speed at periphery

Fig. 12. Grinding of magnetic yoke assembly in a horizontal-spindle double-wheel machine (Example 482)

Speeds. Wheel speeds in cylindrical grinding are generally restricted to the range of 5500 to 6500 sfm. However, the work speed may be adjusted to provide an optimum relationship, depending to some degree on the hardness of the work. Speeds up to 8500 sfm are used when the machine and the wheel are designed for the higher speeds.

Shapes suitable for cylindrical grinding are the following:

1 Round stepped shafts (intermittent surfaces or multiple diameters)
2 Parts with eccentric cylindrical surfaces, like crankpins
3 Annular or cylindrical parts, such as rings and bushings, that require concentric inside and outside surfaces
4 Cylindrical parts that require grinding of radial grooves into the outer surface.

The equipment and procedures used in cylindrical grinding of these shapes

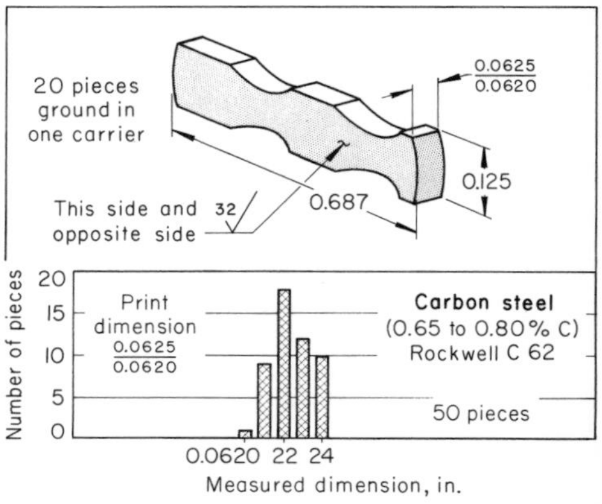

Wheel classification	As-46-N10-B
Wheel size	20-in. diam, 3 in. wide

Operating Conditions

Wheel speed	800 rpm (4190 sfm)(a)
Carrier speed	2 rpm
Metal removed per side	0.002 in.
Grinding fluid	Synthetic:water (1:40)
Production rate	1320 pieces per hour
Setup time	0.6 hr
Wheel life per dressing(b)	2500 pieces

(a) Surface speed at periphery. (b) Wheels dressed with diamond-cluster tool.

Fig. 13. Dimensional accuracy obtained in grinding with a horizontal-spindle double-wheel machine (Example 483)

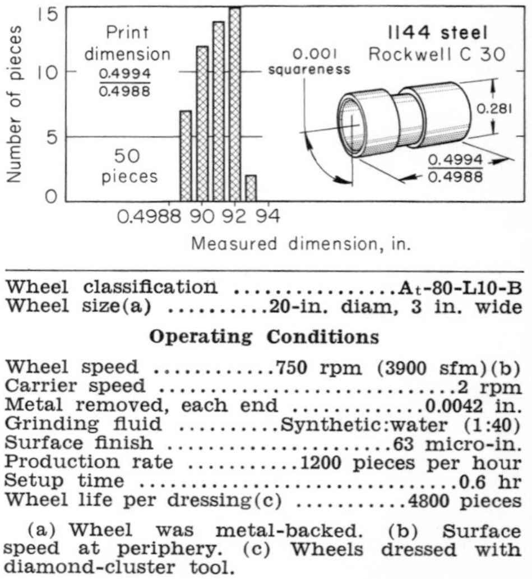

Wheel classification	At-80-L10-B
Wheel size(a)	20-in. diam, 3 in. wide

Operating Conditions

Wheel speed	750 rpm (3900 sfm)(b)
Carrier speed	2 rpm
Metal removed, each end	0.0042 in.
Grinding fluid	Synthetic:water (1:40)
Surface finish	63 micro-in.
Production rate	1200 pieces per hour
Setup time	0.6 hr
Wheel life per dressing(c)	4800 pieces

(a) Wheel was metal-backed. (b) Surface speed at periphery. (c) Wheels dressed with diamond-cluster tool.

Fig. 14. Dimensional accuracy obtained in grinding bearing inserts in a horizontal-spindle double-wheel machine (Example 484)

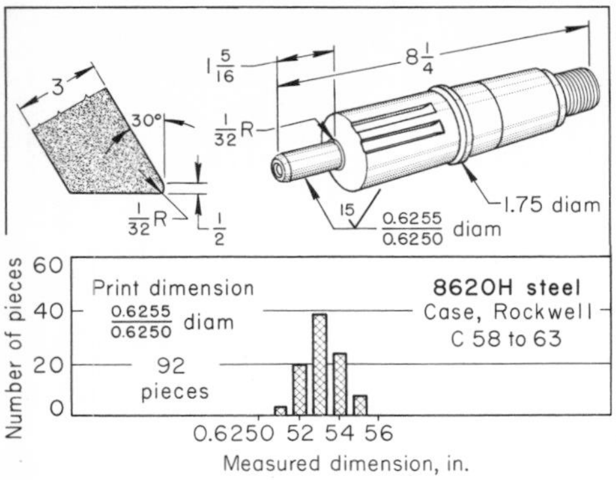

Wheel classification	A_s-80-L5-V
Wheel size	30 by 3 by 12 in.(a)

Operating Conditions

Wheel speed	700 rpm (5500 sfm)
Work-rotation speed	215 rpm (35 sfm)(b)
Metal removed from radius	0.0105 in.
Grinding fluid	Soluble-oil emulsion
Production rate	132 pieces per hour
Setup time	20 min
Wheel life per dressing(c)	43 pieces
Total wheel life (approx)	162,000 pieces(d)

Costs per 1000 Pieces

Grinding wheel(e)	$ 0.90
Labor (at $2.44 per hr)	17.60
Grinding fluid (estimated)	0.20
Amortization	1.60
Total	$20.30
Cost per piece	$0.0203

(a) Wheel face 30° from perpendicular (see above sketch). (b) Surface speed of pilot end being ground. (c) Wheel was dressed on both periphery and sides in single passes in each direction, using a diamond tool. (d) Based on wearing and dressing wheel to a minimum diameter of 20 in. (e) Initial cost, $150 each.

Fig. 15. Dimensional accuracy obtained in cylindrical plunge grinding the pilot-end diameter of a splined shaft. Angular wheel also produced fillet between pilot and splined section. (Example 485)

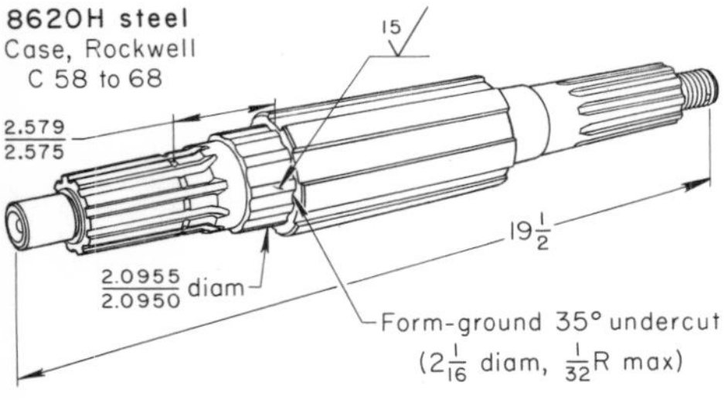

Wheel classification	A_s-80-L5-V
Wheel size	30 by 3 by 12 in.

Operating Conditions

Wheel speed	700 rpm (5500 sfm)
Work-rotation speed	125 rpm (68 sfm)(a)
Metal removed from diameter	0.017 in.
Metal removed from adjacent wall	0.009 in.
Grinding fluid	Soluble-oil emulsion
Production rate	53 pieces per hour
Setup time	26 min
Wheel life per dressing(b)	12 to 14 pieces
Total wheel life (approx)	33,000 pieces(c)

Costs per 1000 Pieces

Grinding wheel(d)	$ 4.50
Labor (at $2.44 per hr)	46.70
Grinding fluid	0.20
Amortization	10.40
Total	$61.80
Cost per piece	$0.0618

(a) Surface speed of fluted section being ground. (b) Wheel was dressed on both periphery and sides in single passes in each direction, using a diamond tool. (c) Based on wearing and dressing wheel to a minimum diameter of 20 in. (d) Initial cost, $150.

Fig. 16. Splined shaft on which fluted diameter, undercut, and adjacent wall were cylindrical plunge ground in an angular-wheel machine (Example 486)

are described in the four sections that follow. These sections also present ten production examples that give details of applications for specific pieces.

Cylindrical Grinding of Round Stepped Shafts

The five examples that follow represent typical practice in cylindrical plunge grinding of one or more outside diameters on shafts. Some of these examples involve profile grinding between centers. This type of operation is limited to workpieces that do not bend from the pressure applied by the grinding wheel, and is also contingent on the availability of wide wheels and of machines having adequate capacity.

Examples 485 and 486. Splined Shafts of 8620H Steel Case Hardened to Rockwell C 58 to 63

(Depth of case, 0.035 to 0.050 in.)

Example 485 (Fig. 15). Cylindrical plunge grinding with an angular wheel removed a total of 0.021 in. from the pilot-end diameter and formed a ¹⁄₃₂-in.-radius fillet on an 8620H steel splined shaft. Figure 15 shows the wheel and the shaft, and plots variations in dimensions of the ground pilot end as measured on

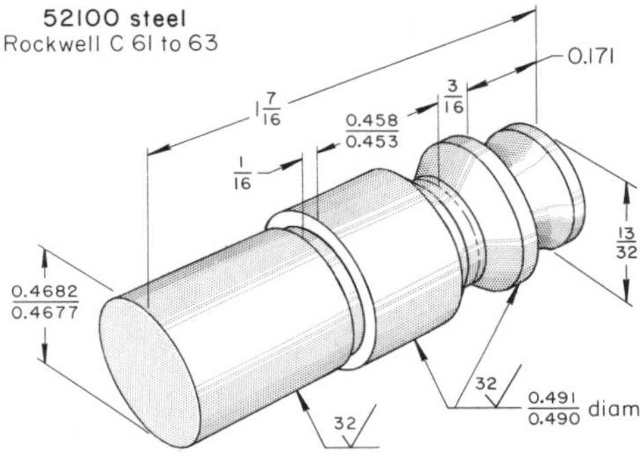

Wheel classification	A_t-80-N5-V
Wheel size	20 by 2 by 12 in.

Operating Conditions

Wheel speed	1240 rpm (6500 sfm)
Work-rotation speed	250 rpm (32 sfm)
Metal removed from diameter	0.010 to 0.012 in.
Grinding fluid	Soluble-oil emulsion
Production rate	125 pieces per hour(a)
Setup time	48 min
Wheel life per dressing(b)	125 pieces

(a) Labor cost per piece, at $3.50 per hr: $0.028. (b) Wheel dressed with a chisel-point diamond tool.

Fig. 17. Shaft on which profile plunge grinding was used for finishing the 0.491-in. and 0.4682-in. diameters simultaneously (Example 487)

92 pieces. Processing details and costs are given in the table below the illustration.

The grinding machine, classified as a semiautomatic angular-wheel slide grinder, was capable of accommodating parts up to 10 in. in diameter and 36 in. long. A hydraulically driven wheel-truing device, template or form-bar governed, was mounted on the wheelhead. This device permitted rapid setup and was designed for use in processing parts of various diameters; varying its speed controlled the finish of the ground surface. Speeds used varied from 1.5 ipm, for a finish of 15 micro-in., to 3.5 ipm, for 25 micro-in. Metal-removal rate, which was determined by tolerance and specified finish, varied up to 0.5 cu in. per min. Special material-handling or automatic gaging devices were not required in this operation, because production quantities were low, usually 75 to 300 pieces.

Example 486 (Fig. 16). The machine described in Example 485 was used also for plunge grinding the 2.095-in. fluted diameter on the 8620H steel splined shaft shown in Fig. 16. During the operation, the adjacent shoulder was ground perpendicular to the axis of the shaft to establish the 2.579/2.575-in. length. The 35° undercut at the base of the shoulder was also ground. Processing details and cost data for the grinding operation are given in the table accompanying Fig. 16.

Examples 487, 488 and 489. Profile Grinding, Undercutting and Radiusing

Example 487 (Fig. 17). The 0.491-in. and 0.4682-in. diameters on the 52100 steel shaft shown in Fig. 17 were finish ground simultaneously by profile plunge grinding. The 6-by-30-in. external grinding machine used was equipped with a mechanical-contact gage. Processing details are given in the table below Fig. 17.

This part was readily adaptable to profile grinding, because of the ¹⁄₁₆-in.-wide undercut between the larger and smaller diameters ground. For production quantities of 25 pieces or more, drive dogs were used on the ¹³⁄₃₂-in. diameter, and the wheel was profiled to grind the two diameters simultaneously. For fewer than 25 pieces it was more economical to grind the two diameters separately.

Example 488 (Fig. 18). The four diameters on the 4140 steel shaft shown in Fig. 18 were profile plunge ground to a final maximum surface roughness of 32 micro-in. in a sequence of four operations. Processing details are presented with Fig. 18. The 6-by-30-in. external grinder used was equipped with a mechanical-contact gage. The gage was used for all operations except the third.

After the shaft was ground, an oil groove was cut into diameter A in a thread mill, and a worm thread was ground in diameter B. The purpose of the finish grinding in operations 3 and 4 was to provide concentric locating diameters for grinding the worm.

Example 489 (Fig. 19). The hardened 52100 steel shaft shown in Fig. 19 was plunge ground to remove 0.012 in. from the 3-in. and the 2.75-in. diameters and to clean up and radius the shoulder. A 6-by-30-in. automatic external grinder equipped with a mechanical-contact gage was used for the operation. Processing details are given below Fig. 19.

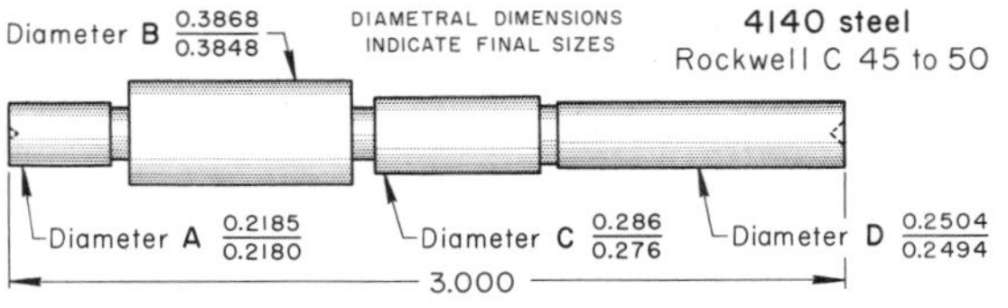

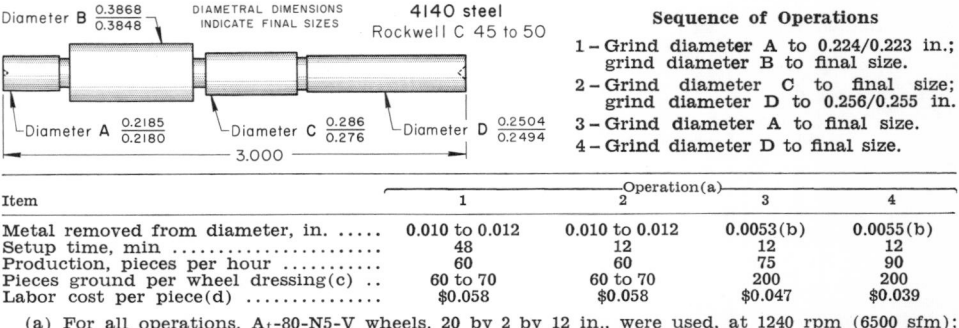

Sequence of Operations

1 – Grind diameter A to 0.224/0.223 in.; grind diameter B to final size.
2 – Grind diameter C to final size; grind diameter D to 0.256/0.255 in.
3 – Grind diameter A to final size.
4 – Grind diameter D to final size.

Item	Operation(a) 1	2	3	4
Metal removed from diameter, in.	0.010 to 0.012	0.010 to 0.012	0.0053(b)	0.0055(b)
Setup time, min	48	12	12	12
Production, pieces per hour	60	60	75	90
Pieces ground per wheel dressing(c)	60 to 70	60 to 70	200	200
Labor cost per piece(d)	$0.058	$0.058	$0.047	$0.039

(a) For all operations, A_t-80-N5-V wheels, 20 by 2 by 12 in., were used, at 1240 rpm (6500 sfm); work rotated at 250 rpm (25 sfm, max); and a soluble-oil emulsion was used as the grinding fluid. (b) To mean limit. (c) Wheels dressed with a chisel-point diamond tool. (d) At $3.50 per hr.

Fig. 18. Four-operation profile plunge grinding of multidiameter shaft, in a 6-by-30-in. external grinder (Example 488)

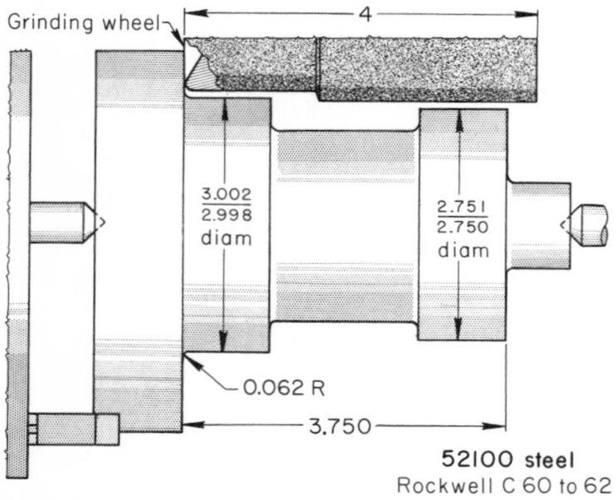

Wheel classification	A_t-60-K5-V
Wheel size	20 by 4 by 12 in.

Operating Conditions

Wheel speed	1240 rpm (6500 sfm)
Work-rotation speed	100 rpm (78 sfm)
Metal removed from diameter	0.012 in.
Grinding fluid	Soluble-oil emulsion
Production rate	33 pieces per hour
Setup time	30 min
Wheel life per dressing(a)	25 to 30 pieces

(a) Dressed with a single-point diamond tool

Fig. 19. Profile plunge grinding for finishing two diameters and radiusing a shoulder (Example 489)

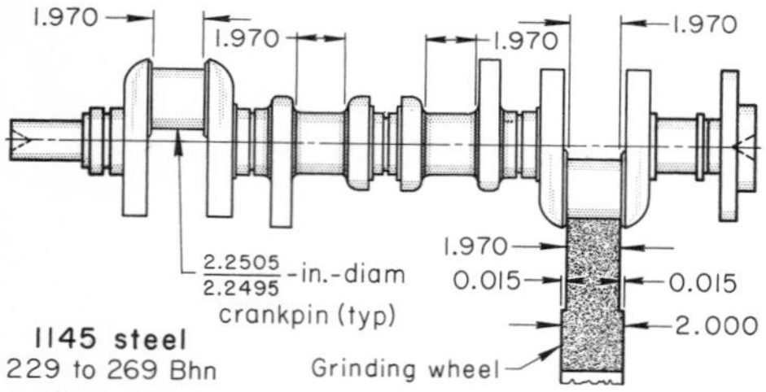

Wheel classification	A_s-54-P5-V
Wheel size	42 by 2 by 12 in.

Operating Conditions

Wheel speed	590 rpm (6500 sfm)
Work-rotation speed	95 rpm (56 sfm)
Metal removed from diameter	0.030 in.
Metal removed from adjacent wall	0.015 in.
Grinding fluid	Soluble-oil emulsion
Production rate	8 pieces per hour
Setup time	55 min
Wheel life per dressing	4 crankpins
Total wheel life	1800 to 3000 pieces

Finish and Tolerances

Surface finish	30 to 40 micro-in.
Tolerances on crankpin:	
Diameter	±0.0005 in.
Taper	0.0005 in. max
Out-of-roundness	0.0005 in. max

Costs per Crankshaft

Grinding wheel	$0.039
Labor	$0.250
Grinding fluid	$0.008

Fig. 20. Grinding crankpins and adjacent cheeks of a crankshaft in a crankpin grinder equipped with a formed wheel (Example 490)

Cylindrical Grinding of Crankpins

Machines for grinding crankpins of crankshafts are designed so as to hold the crankshafts in a special fixture and to permit cylindrical grinding of the crankpins on the individual cranks one at a time. Low production quantities can be processed satisfactorily with manually controlled and hand-loaded machines. Automatic grinders should be considered for intermediate quantities; transfer-pin grinders are used for maximum, high-quantity production.

Aluminum oxide wheels of 36-in. or 42-in. diameter are generally used for grinding crankpins. The larger wheel has greater productivity, because more pieces can be ground per wheel, thus reducing downtime for wheel changing. The width of the wheel is determined by the length of the crankpin.

In truing the wheel, it is important that equal amounts of material (generally, 0.015 in.) be removed from each side of the wheel. Otherwise, crankpin cheeks will not be ground equally, and it may be hard or impossible to keep linear dimensions within tolerance. The equipment and wheel used in one application of crankpin grinding are indicated in the example that follows:

Example 490. Crankpins and Cheeks (Fig. 20)

The crankpins and adjacent cheeks of an automotive crankshaft made of 1145 steel (229 to 269 Bhn) were ground in a 16-by-32-in. crankpin grinder. A special fixture was used to hold the crankshaft between centers of the grinder. Figure 20 shows the crankshaft; processing details and costs for grinding are given below the illustration.

Cylindrical Grinding of Rings

Rings, such as bearing rings, with outside diameters larger than 8 to 10 in. generally are ground on mandrels that are held between two dead centers. During grinding, the mandrels are rotated by a drive dog on the headstock end of the mandrel.

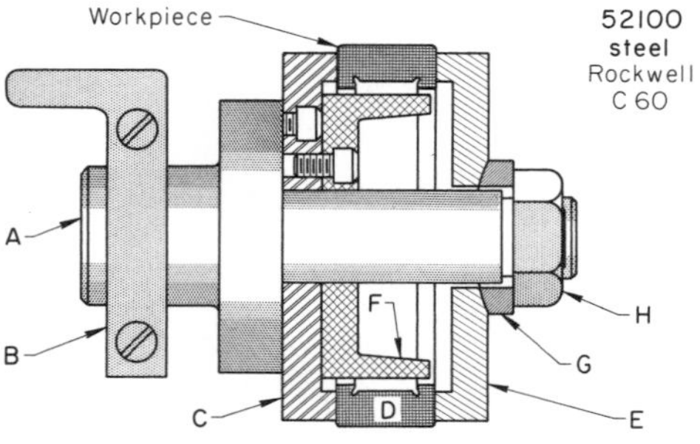

A – Mandrel shaft on body. B – Drive dog. C – Fixed clamp plate (usually relieved below face to facilitate grinding). D – Workpiece, rough outside diameter. E – Removable clamp plate (sliding fit on mandrel shaft). F – Centering pilot or spider (sometimes not used). Outside diameter of pilot must be smaller than bore of any ring to be ground. G – Self-aligning washer (sometimes not used). H – Clamp nut.

Wheel classification	A_s-54-J5-V
Wheel size	30 by 6 by 12 in.

Operating Conditions

Wheel speed	825 rpm (6500 sfm)
Work-rotation speed	46 rpm (152 sfm)
Table-reciprocation speed	80 in. per min
Table-reciprocation travel	10.3 in.
Feed rate on diameter	0.005 in. per min
Metal removed from diameter	0.040 in.
Grinding fluid	Soluble-oil:water (1:50)
Power consumed:	
Grinding	33 amp
Idling	22 amp
Production rate	19 pieces per hour
Setup time	1 hr
Wheel life per dressing(a)	1 race
Total wheel life(b)	13,000 races

Finish and Tolerance

Surface finish	35 micro-in.
Tolerance	0.002 in.

Costs per Piece

Grinding wheel	$0.0148
Labor, including setup	0.149

(a) Dressed with a single-point diamond tool. (b) Wheel replaced when worn to 20-in. diam.

Fig. 21. Tap-up mandrel setup for rough grinding outside diameter of roller bearing rings (Example 491)

There are two general types of mandrels: (*a*) tap-up mandrels, for rings whose inside diameters have not been previously ground or accurately finished and (*b*) pilot mandrels, for rings whose inside diameters have been accurately finished and which are located on these inside diameters for external grinding.

The following two examples describe production operations employing mandrels of each type for grinding roller bearing rings.

Example 491. Tap-Up Mandrel (Fig. 21)

The tap-up mandrel shown in Fig. 21 was used for rough grinding outer rings of cylindrical roller bearings. These rings were made of 52100 steel and hardened to Rockwell C 60. Size of each was 12.59-in. OD by 10.31-in. ID by 2.55 in. wide.

A ring was placed on the mandrel, and the mandrel nut was tightened moderately. Then, the loaded mandrel was placed in the grinding machine, the ring was centered to within about 0.005 in. of true position by tapping the ring with a brass hammer while reading runout on a dial indicator, and the mandrel nut was tightened securely. Finally, the grinding wheel was fed in manually to contact the ring, and the power feed was engaged.

The machine used was a reciprocating-table, plain outside-diameter grinder, 14-by-36-in., equipped with dead-center headstock and tailstock. Dimensional control was manual, either with a handwheel reading or a jump-on dial-indicator frame gage. Other processing details are given below Fig. 21.

Example 492. Pilot Mandrel (Fig. 22)

The pilot mandrel shown in Fig. 22 was used for finish grinding the races on cylindrical roller bearing inner rings made of 52100 steel hardened to Rockwell C 60. The size of each ring was 7.625-in. OD by 5.905-in. ID by 2.55 in. wide.

The races were ground on a reciprocating-table, plain outside-diameter grinder, 10-by-24-in., equipped with dead-center headstock and tailstock. Dimensional control was manual, either by use of a handwheel reading or a jump-on dial-indicator frame gage. To control eccentricity, the centers of the mandrel over which the race was placed had to be true with the bore of the race and the pilot diameter had to fit closely. Other processing details are given below Fig. 22.

An expanding or internal collet type of mandrel is used when concentricity (wall-thickness variation) must be held closer than is possible with a solid mandrel such as shown in Fig. 22.

Cylindrical Grinding of Grooves

Cylindrical grinding of grooves is advisable when tolerances are close and good surface finish is required, and when grooves are to be cut into interrupted surfaces, slots and drilled holes. Results obtained by plunge groove grinding are better than those obtained by machining plus grinding or by traverse grinding. More material can be removed at a pass, the wheel holds up better than with other methods, and consequently the workpiece finish is better.

Many groove-grinding machines use 14-in.-diam wheels, although larger wheels can be used. The smaller wheels have the advantage of reducing the cost of grooving, because dressing a wheel for groove grinding limits its use for other purposes. Figure 23 shows two shapes to which wheels are dressed for grinding grooves. The wheel with sides dressed perpendicular to the face (section A-A in Fig. 23) is preferred for plunge grinding from a solid surface with no starting groove. Groove width is constant, and the wheel has longer life. When small fillet radii are required, the wheel should be harder than would be necessary otherwise. The two examples that follow give details of production groove-grinding.

Example 493. Grooving a Shaft (Fig. 24)

The groove in the 4340 steel shaft shown in Fig. 24 was produced by plunge grinding in a universal grinding machine. The maximum size of workpiece that this machine could accommodate was 10-in. OD by 40 in. long. The grinder was equipped with a standard wheel-dresser (diamond-holder) faceplate fixture. Processing details are given in the table below Fig. 24.

Example 494. Plunge Grinder vs Traversing Grinder (Fig. 25)

Originally, a traversing cylindrical grinder was used to form the groove in the steel piston shown in Fig. 25. Excessive wheel dressing was required, because of breakdown of the radius on the edge of the wheel face. Also, there was danger of producing grinding cracks on the surface of the piston because of inability to supply enough grinding fluid to the grinding area. Production was only 10 pieces per hour.

A change was made to a plunge grinding machine with an automatic wheel dresser. This machine produced parts with improved quality, and production increased 330%. Also, elimination of the comparatively rapid tangential traversing motion made it easier to flood the wheel and the ground surface with grinding fluid. Processing details for plunge grinding are given with Fig. 25.

Applicability of Cylindrical Grinders

Conventional cylindrical grinders of various sizes are available, and the distance between centers is adjustable. These grinders can be adapted to manual control for efficient grinding of small production lots, or they can be automated for high production.

Cylindrical grinding may be more economical than a machining operation for the production of small parts:

Example 495. Grinding vs Lathe Turning (Fig. 26; Table 6)

Circular-section tensile specimens (Fig. 26) were machined from 1¼-in.-square bar stock by turning in an engine lathe and by grinding in a 10-by-18-in. cylindrical grinder. Table 6 compares processing and cost factors of these operations. A tungsten carbide tool was used for turning. Grinding was done with a vitrified aluminum oxide wheel. Specimens were processed individually in each method.

As shown in Table 6, the rate of metal removal in turning was considerably greater than in grinding, but the time saved in grinding, because of fewer processing operations, resulted in 35% greater productivity and 13% lower total cost. Note that the cost of polishing accounted for half the total cost of specimen machining by turning.

Production quantity influences the type and size of machine to be used. For instance, the semiautomatic grinder used to cylindrical plunge grind the outside diameters of the shafts discussed in Example 485 was satisfactory for handling production quantities of 75 to 300 pieces. These quantities did not justify the use of special material-handling or automatic gaging devices. For the shaft discussed in Example 487, a cylindrical plunge grinder that ground one outside diameter at a time was used for quantities up to 25 pieces, but for more than 25 pieces it was more economical to use a profile plunge grinder that could grind two or more outside diameters at the same time.

The two examples that follow show the influence of production quantity on the grinding method (and hence the type of machine) used.

Examples 496 and 497. Time vs Production Quantity in Centerless or Cylindrical Grinding of Bearing Rings

Example 496 — Roller Bearings (Fig. 27). Outer rings of larger roller bearings (8.85-in. OD and 2.28 in. wide) were rough ground to remove 0.022 in. of metal. Two methods were compared — grinding in through-feed centerless grinders, and grinding between centers in plain cylindrical grinders with the workpiece mounted in a tap-up mandrel. Figure 27 shows the effect of production quantity on the setup and machining times for the two methods. Processing details are compared in the table below the graph.

Example 497 — Ball Bearings (Fig. 28). Small ball bearing rings were ground by the same two methods as for the roller bearing rings in Example 496, above. The ball bearing rings were rough and finish ground in one operation to remove 0.015 in. of metal from the outside diameter. Nominal dimensions of these rings were 2.05-in. OD, 1.73-in. ID and 0.59 in. wide. Figure 28 compares time versus production quantity for the two methods. Processing details are compared below the graph.

The break-even points for the two methods compared in Examples 496 and 497 may be higher than shown in Fig. 27 and 28, because in centerless grinding there is often a greater chance of producing a few out-of-tolerance pieces at the start of the final

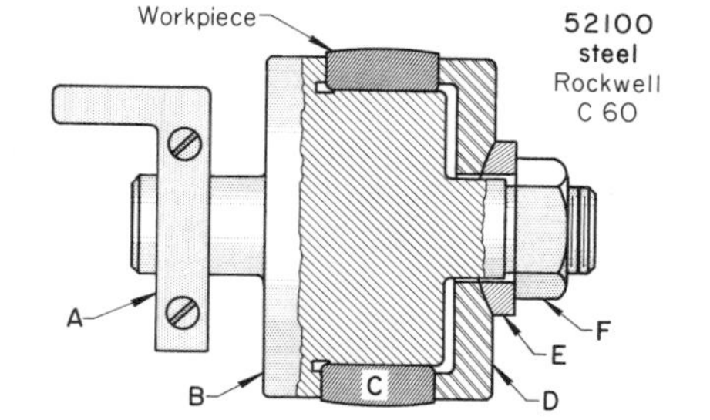

A – Drive dog. B – Mandrel body. C – Workpiece, finished inside diameter. D – Removable clamp plate (sliding fit on mandrel body). E – Self-aligning washer (sometimes not used). F – Clamp nut.

Wheel classification	A_t-80-K8-V
Wheel size	24 in. by 40 mm by 12 in.

Operating Conditions

Wheel speed	1040 rpm (6500 sfm)
Work-rotation speed	45 rpm (90 sfm)
Feed rate on diameter	0.005 in. per min
Metal removed from diameter	0.008 in.
Grinding fluid	Soluble-oil:water (1:50)
Power consumed:	
Grinding	18 amp
Idling	12 amp
Production rate	24 pieces per hour
Setup time	0.7 hr
Wheel life per dressing(a)	5
Total wheel life(b)	7000 rings

Finish and Tolerance

Surface finish	15 micro.-in. max
Tolerance	0.001 in.

Costs per Piece

Grinding wheel	$0.006
Labor, including setup	$0.1231

(a) Dressed with a single-point diamond tool. (b) Wheel replaced when worn to 17-in. diam.

Fig. 22. Pilot mandrel setup for finish grinding outer surface of roller bearing inner rings (Example 492)

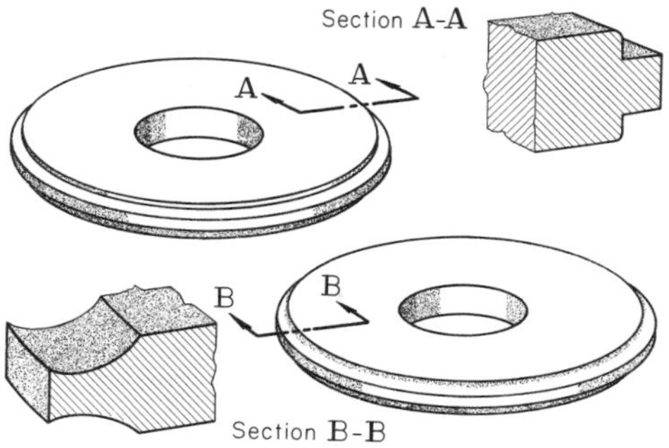

Wheel dressed to shape in section A-A is used to make the entire groove from solid stock, in one operation. Wheel dressed to shape in section B-B is used for finish grinding a groove previously rough cut.

Fig. 23. Wheels for plunge grinding of grooves

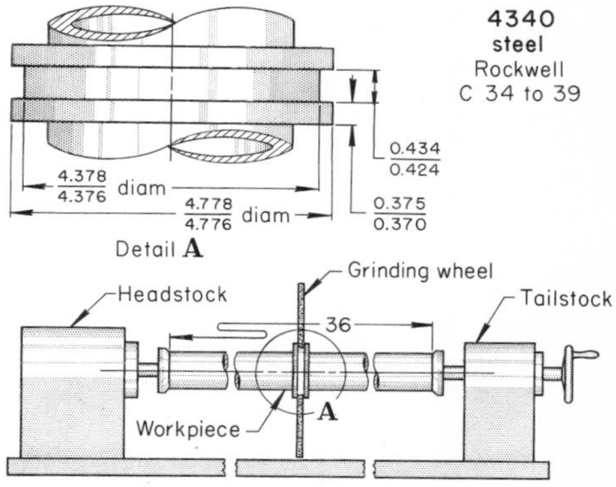

Wheel classification	A_s-80-M7-V
Wheel diameter	14 in.

Operating Conditions

Wheel speed	About 1800 rpm (6600 sfm)
Work-rotation speed	100 rpm (125 sfm)
Metal removed from diameter	0.400 in.
Grinding fluid	Grinding oil
Production rate	3 pieces per hour
Setup time, including wheel change	90 min
Wheel life per dressing(a)	1 piece
Total wheel life (approx)	200 pieces
Surface finish	63 micro-in.

(a) Dressed with a single-point diamond tool

Fig. 24. Grooving a shaft by plunge grinding (Example 493)

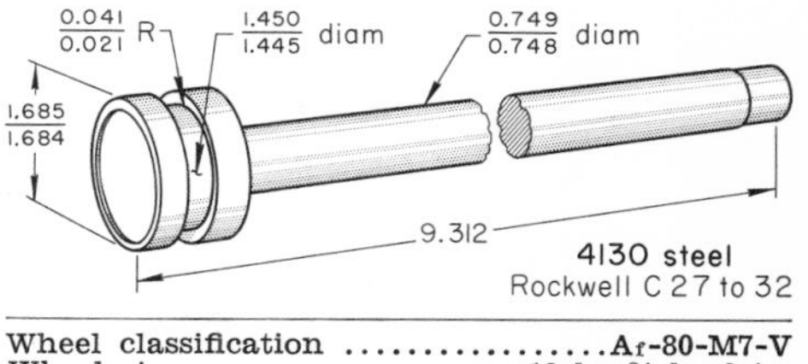

Wheel classification	A_f-80-M7-V
Wheel size	18 by ⅜ by 9 in.

Operating Conditions

Wheel speed	2100 rpm (9900 sfm)
Work-rotation speed	60 rpm (23 sfm)
Metal removed from diameter	0.237 in.
Grinding fluid	Grinding oil
Production rate(a)	43 pieces per hour
Setup time	1.5 hr
Wheel life per dressing(b)	1 piece
Total wheel life(c)	6000 pieces
Surface finish	32 micro-in. max
Cost of labor(d)	$0.08 per piece

(a) At 80% efficiency. (b) After each piece was ground, wheel was skin dressed (0.0005 in.) automatically with a single-point diamond tool. (c) Wheel replaced when worn to 14-in. diameter. (d) At rate of $3.50 per hour.

Fig. 25. Steel piston grooved in a plunge grinder (Example 494)

pass than in cylindrical grinding with mandrels. For both charts a break-even point of 100 pieces is probably more realistic.

The effect of production quantity on both time and cost is shown in the following example:

Example 498. Cylindrical vs Centerless Cylindrical Grinding (Fig. 29)

Production quantity determined which was the more economical of two methods for grinding the bearing surfaces and flange faces of a 1045 steel shaft. As Fig. 29 indicates, centerless grinding was more economical when more than 20 shafts were being finished.

The shaft was ground for removal of 0.021 in. of metal from the diameter of each bearing journal, and of 0.013 in. of metal from each flange face of the center section. A maximum surface roughness of 40 micro-in. was specified for all ground surfaces.

Cylindrical grinding on centers was done in a plain external grinder. First, one bearing end section and one flange face were ground; then the shaft was reversed manually for grinding the second bearing end and flange face. This procedure required one machine operator.

In the centerless method, both bearing journals were ground simultaneously in a double-wheel centerless grinder; then the shaft was transferred to a double-angle head grinder for simultaneous grinding of both flange faces. Each of these machines required one operator.

Centerless Grinding of Pins and Bars

Centerless grinding is a method of grinding unmounted cylindrical surfaces. Figure 30 shows the principal components of a centerless grinder.

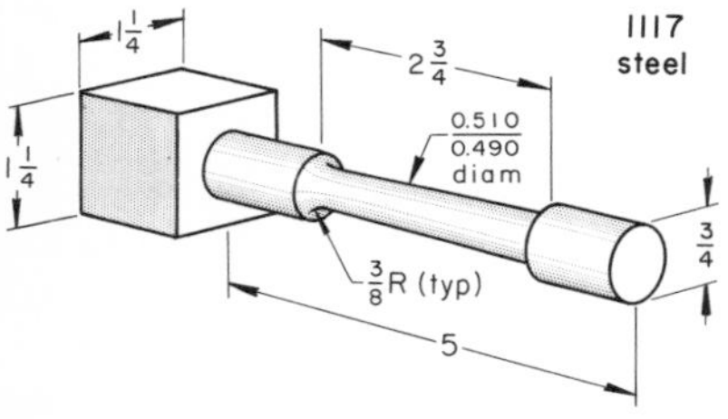

Fig. 26. Tensile specimen produced more economically by grinding than by lathe turning, as shown in Table 6 (Example 495)

There are two basic methods of centerless grinding — through-feed grinding and infeed grinding.

In through-feed grinding, the workpiece passes laterally, or axially, between the grinding wheel and the regulating wheel. Only straight cylindrical shapes without interfering shoulders can be ground by this method.

In infeed grinding, the workpiece has no relative axial movement. Infeed grinding is used when the workpiece has a shoulder, head, or other projection larger than the diameter being ground, or has a taper or any irregular profile. In general, this method corresponds to plunge grinding on a cylindrical grinding machine.

A variation of the infeed method, sometimes referred to as end-feed, is used for taper work that is fed into the machine from the front, manually or mechanically, to a fixed end-stop.

Centerless grinding machines are the most efficient for production grinding of outer surfaces of solid bars and pins, or rings and tubing. The maximum diameter of solid bars that commercially available centerless grinders can accommodate is about 7 in. For long bars of this diameter, auxiliary handling or rotating equipment is often necessary, because of the great weight of the workpiece and consequent high friction on the support blade. The maximum

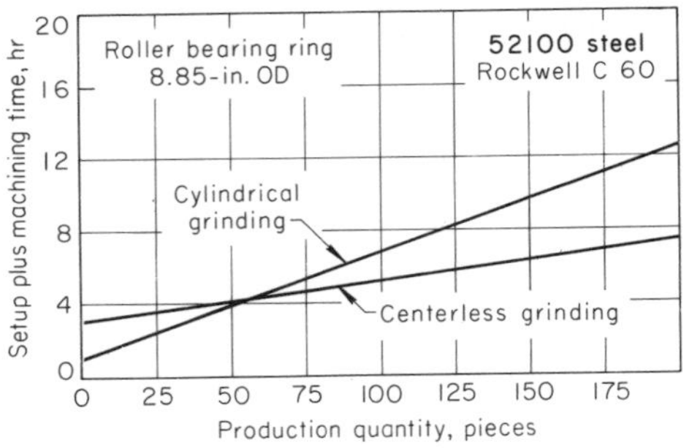

Item	Centerless (through feed) (a)	Cylindrical (tap-up mandrel) (b)
Grinder capacity, in. ..	10	16 x 36
Wheel classification ..	A_t-60-M15-V	A_s-54-J5-V
Wheel size, in.	24 x 10 x 14	30 x 6 x 12
Operating Conditions(c)		
Wheel speed, rpm	1040	825
Wheel speed, sfm	6500	6500
Work speed, rpm	33	65
Work speed, sfm	76	150
Through feed, ipm ...	20	...
Feed on diam, ipm ...	...	0.0065
Production, pcs/hr ...	87	17.2
Setup time, hr	0.5	1.0
Wheel dressing, hr ...	1(d)	...
Manpower required ...	2(e)	1(f)

(a) Ten passes required. (b) Machine was a plain center grinder; mandrel held three rings for grinding. (c) In both methods, 0.022 in. of metal was removed from the diameter, to a tolerance of 0.0015 in., and a 1-to-50 mixture of soluble oil and water was used as the grinding fluid. (d) Per job lot; includes resetting time. (e) Operator and helper. Helper assisted with setup, caught rings, and carried rings back to feed side for next pass. (f) Operator only.

Fig. 27. Centerless vs cylindrical method for rough grinding various quantities of roller bearing rings (Example 496)

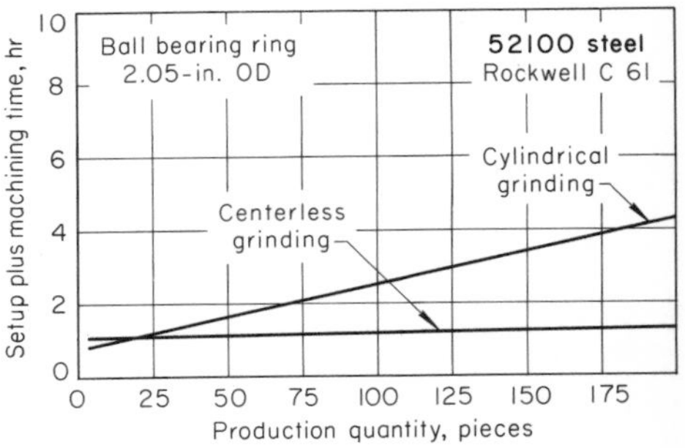

Item	Centerless (through feed) (a)	Cylindrical (tap-up mandrel) (b)
Grinder capacity, in. ...	4	6 x 18
Wheel classification	A_t-80-M6-V	A_s-60-L8-V
Wheel size, in.	24 x 8 x 12	20 x 4 x 12
Operating Conditions(c)		
Wheel speed, rpm	1040	1240
Wheel speed, sfm	6500	6500
Work speed, rpm	134(d)	280
Work speed, sfm	72(d)	150
Through feed, ipm	35 to 40	...
Feed on diam, ipm	...	0.006
Production, pcs/hr	756	54
Setup time, hr	0.5	0.7
Wheel dressing, hr	0.5(e)	...
Manpower required	1	1

(a) Three passes required. (b) Machine was a plain center grinder; mandrel held three rings for grinding. (c) In both methods, 0.015 in. of metal was removed from the diameter, to a tolerance of 0.0005 in., and a 1-to-50 mixture of soluble oil and water was used as the grinding fluid. (d) In first pass. Work speed in second pass was 170 rpm (91 sfm); in third pass, 200 rpm (105 sfm). (e) Per job lot; includes resetting time.

Fig. 28. Centerless vs cylindrical method for grinding various quantities of ball bearing rings (Example 497)

Table 6. Lathe Turning vs Grinding for Production of Tensile Specimen Shown in Fig. 26 (Example 495)

Item	Turning	Grinding
Machine	Engine lathe	Cylindrical grinder
Horsepower	15	25(a); 1(b)
Speed	400 sfm	8500 sfm(c); 240 rpm(d)
Feed	0.015 ipr	...
Metal removed per piece, cu in.	6.250	6.250
Metal removal rate, cu in. per min	3.70	1.14
Machining time per piece, min	1.69	5.50
Floor-to-floor time per piece, min	12	8.8

Cost Factors

Item	Turning: Time, min	Turning: Cost	Grinding: Time, min	Grinding: Cost
Setup(e)	15	$1.00	35	$2.33
Machining, per piece(e):				
Handling workpiece	0.85	$0.057	1.00	$0.067
Positioning tool	1.75	0.117	0.30	0.020
Machining	1.69	0.113	5.50	0.366
Tool changes and dressing	...	....	2.00	0.133
Measuring	0.95	0.063	...	....
Polishing	6.75	0.450	...	....
Machine operation, per piece:				
Power	...	0.005	...	0.027
Maintenance	...	0.050	...	0.022
Tool charges, per piece:				
Replacement	...	0.041	...	0.148
Sharpening	...	0.002	...	....
Total cost per piece, excluding setup		$0.898		$0.783

(a) Grinding-wheel motor. (b) Workpiece-rotation motor. (c) Grinding wheel. (d) Workpiece rotation. (e) Labor and fringe costs at $4 per hour.

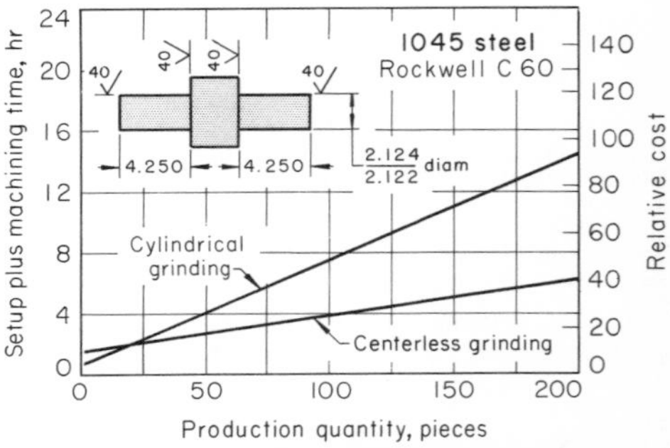

Fig. 29. Effect of production quantity on time and cost for two methods of grinding bearing surfaces and flange faces of a shaft (Example 498)

diameter for rings or tubing in centerless grinding machines is about 10 in.

Specially designed machines with a regulating wheel and work-rest blade have been built to accommodate workpieces up to 24 in. in diameter. Workpieces of even larger diameters have been ground on special machines that use a roller support arrangement instead of a regulating wheel and work-rest blade.

Grinding wheels for solid or tubular products range from 20 to 24 in. in diameter and 6 to 24 in. in width. Regulating wheels range from 10 to 15 in. in diameter and 6 to 24 in. in width. Motors of 25 to 75 hp are required for the grinding wheel.

The influence of workpiece size and shape on techniques used in centerless grinding is described in the two examples that follow.

Example 499. Grinding Small Pins (Table 7)

Small solid steel pins (sketch in Table 7) were ground in a centerless grinder to remove 0.003 in. of metal from the diameter in one pass. The work-rest blade (carbide-edged, 1/16 in. wide, and with a 20° top rake) was positioned so that the workpiece was 3/64 in. above the centerline of the grinding wheel. A vibratory feeder was used to feed each piece into the grinder. Because the feeder could orient and feed the pieces faster than required by the grinder, a short length of copper tubing (3/16-in. OD), which ended at the work-rest blade, was used to transfer the workpieces from the vibratory hopper to the grinding wheels. This prevented overfeeding and improper positioning of the workpieces, and kept them from falling from the work-rest blade. Each piece was deflected from the blade into a container after grinding. Other processing details are given in Table 7.

Example 500. Reduction in Number of Grinding Setups (Fig. 31)

When the oil-seal and trunnion diameters and the radii of a universal-joint spider were ground as shown in Fig. 31(a), it was difficult to produce the required radii. Four grinding operations (two setups) were necessary to meet the quality standards. One centerless grinder with two grinding wheels and a spacer was used to grind the oil-seal diameters and the radii on two opposite sides of the spider. A second centerless grinder was used to grind the trunnion bearing diameters. The wheels all had to be dressed after every 100 pieces. In the setup shown in Fig. 31(b), only two grinding operations were necessary, because of the development of an adjustable cam and a tungsten carbide cam follower and the use of a suitable diamond dressing tool. This equipment used two form-dressed grinding wheels. The wheel-dressing tool, a three-stone blade with elongated, extra-fine lapped diamonds

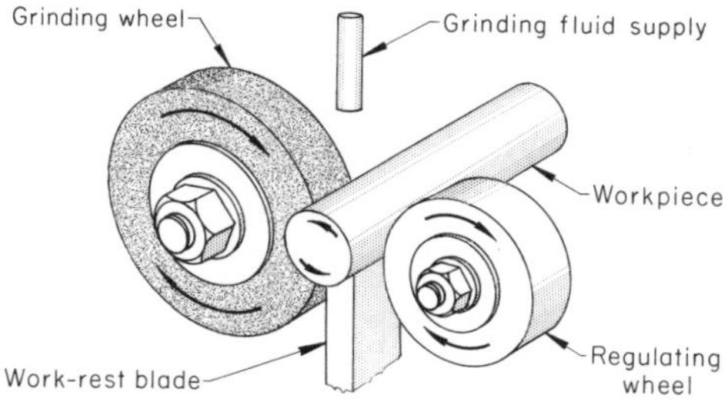

Fig. 30. Components of a centerless grinder

Table 7. Centerless Grinding of Small Pins (Example 499)

Wheel classification	A_s-80-M6-V
Wheel size	14 by 4 by 8 in.(a)
Operating Conditions	
Wheel speed	1750 rpm (6400 sfm)
Infeed rate	3 ft per min
Metal removed from diameter	0.003 in.
Grinding fluid	Soluble-oil:water (1:30)
Setup time	1½ hr
Production rate (net)	6000 pieces per hour
Wheel life per dressing(b)	6000 pieces
Total wheel life	1,000,000 pieces
Costs per 1000 Pieces	
Labor	$0.50
Grinding wheel	$0.67
Amortization and other expenses	$0.55

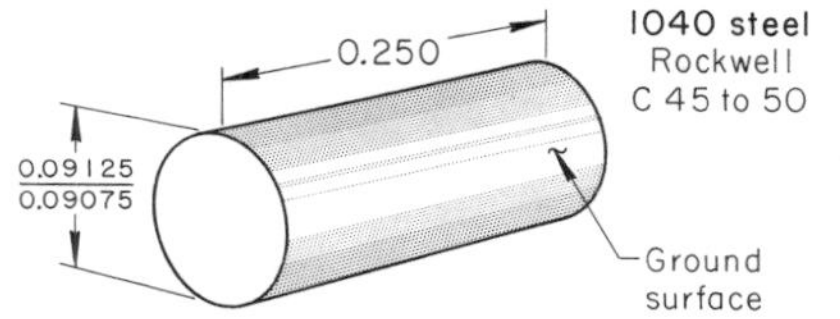

(a) Each side of wheel had a recess 10 in. in diameter by ½ in. wide. (b) Grinding wheel was dressed every hour with a single-point diamond weighing about 1 carat; regulating wheel was dressed once during each 8-hr shift.

(weight, 25 to 35 points), is shown in the upper right corner of Fig. 31(b). The cam follower and dresser cam are shown in the lower right corner of Fig. 31(b). Dimensional variation was 0.6569 to 0.6574 in. for the trunnion diameter, 0.743 to 0.748 in. for the oil-seal diameter, and 0.035 to 0.065 in. for the radii. Processing details of the improved method, together with a comparison of wheel costs and labor costs for the two methods, are given in the table accompanying Fig. 31.

Centerless Grinding of Rings and Tubing

Commercial centerless grinders can be used to grind rings and tubing up to about 10 in. in outside diameter. Larger workpieces require specially designed machines, as mentioned in the previous section on pins and bars.

The next example describes the grinding of rings of near-maximum diameter for commercial centerless grinding.

Example 501. Grinding of Bearing Rings (Table 8)

The 9.8-in.-OD surfaces of three 3310 steel bearing rings case hardened to Rockwell C 60 were rough ground in one cycle of an infeed grinding operation. Each ring had a 9.0-in. ID and a width of 7.3 in.

The rings were mounted on a loose mandrel that consisted of a tube and two end plates. The end plates clamped the rings together face to face. [Such a mandrel usually has a center tube to facilitate handling of the loaded mandrel. The tube must have a minimum radial clearance equal to or more than the grinding stock to permit radial shifting of the rings so they can round up individually.] Other processing details are given in Table 8.

Example 502. Centerless vs Cylindrical Grinding (Fig. 32)

Centerless grinding of the outside and the shoulder of the sleeve bushing shown in Fig. 32 was 11% more productive than cylindrical grinding on centers.

The infeed grinder used for centerless grinding took 0.94 min for rough grinding each bushing and 0.78 min for finish grinding, and produced 30 bushings per hour. Other processing details for the centerless method are given below Fig. 32.

For cylindrical grinding on centers, the bushing was placed on a standard arbor that was held between headstock and tailstock

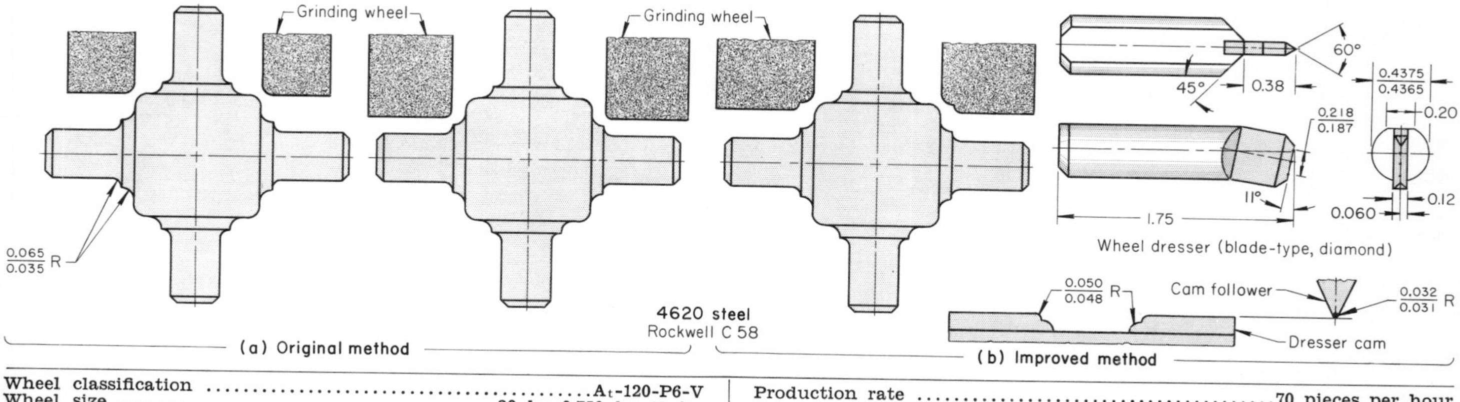

Wheel classification	A_t-120-P6-V
Wheel size	20 by 0.750 by 12 in.
Tolerance and Finish	
Dimensional tolerance	0.0005 in.
Maximum surface roughness	20 micro-in.
Operating Conditions for Improved Method of Centerless Grinding	
Wheel speed	1200 rpm (6300 sfm)
Work-rotation speed	38 rpm
Feed	0.0002 ipr
Metal removed from diameter	0.012 in.
Grinding fluid	Synthetic solution
Production rate	70 pieces per hour
Setup time	2 hr
Wheel life per dressing(a)	100 pieces
Total wheel life (per 2-wheel set)	41,040 pieces

Costs per Piece by the Two Methods

Grinding wheel:	
Original method	$0.00688
Improved method	$0.00172
Labor:	
Original method	$0.388
Improved method	$0.194

(a) Wheel was dressed with diamond tool shown above.

Fig. 31. Original and improved methods of centerless grinding diameters and radii of universal-joint spiders (Example 500)

Table 8. Centerless Grinding of 9.8-In.-OD Bearing Rings (Example 501)

Wheel classification	As-54-J5-V
Wheel size	20 by 24 by 12 in.
Operating Conditions	
Wheel speed(a)	1240 rpm (6500 sfm)
Infeed rate	0.070 ipm
Metal removed from diameter	0.020 in.
Grinding fluid	Soluble oil:water (1:50)
Setup time	1.5 hr
Production rate	42 pieces per hour
Wheel life per dressing	3 pcs (1 load)
Total wheel life	10,000 pieces
Tolerance	0.0015 in.

(a) Grinding wheel was driven by a 50-hp motor and feed-controlled by a cam. (b) Wheel was dressed with a single-point diamond tool.

centers. Total grinding time by this method was 1.934 min per piece, and production rate was 27 pieces per hour.

Tolerance and Finish Capabilities of Centerless Grinders

Close tolerances can be met by centerless grinding. Dimensions can be kept within tolerance ranges from 0.005 to 0.00004 in. Out-of-roundness can be held within 0.002 to 0.00001 in. The closer tolerances always increase the cost of grinding.

Greater dimensional accuracy and smoother finishes are produced when less metal is removed. In Example 501 (Table 8) a tolerance of 0.0015 in. was held when 0.020 in. of metal was removed by rough grinding, whereas in Example 500 (Fig. 31) a tolerance of 0.0005 in. was met and a surface roughness of 20 micro-in. was produced during the removal of 0.012 in. of metal. The example that follows describes a through-feed centerless grinding operation in which no difficulty was encountered in staying within a tolerance of 0.0003 in.

Example 503. Dimensional Accuracy

A pilot run of 250 steel rods was processed in a through-feed centerless grinder to determine the dimensional accuracy obtainable in removal of 0.0005 to 0.0007 in. from the diameter. These rods, 10 ft long and ½ in. in diameter, were made of 1040 steel and were not heat treated.

Measurements of every fifth rod (a total of 50) showed that dimensional variation for the outside diameter was 0.4993 to 0.4994 in. — well within the permissible range of 0.4992 to 0.4995 in.

The rods were ground with an A-100-L15-B wheel, 24 by 12 by 12 in., at a speed of 1000 rpm (6300 sfm) and an infeed rate of 10 ft per min. A water-soluble synthetic (2% concentration in water) was used as the grinding fluid. The grinding wheel was dressed, and the machine adjusted for size, before (but not during) the operation. A multipoint diamond tool was used for dressing. During the production grinding of similar rods, wheel life per dressing averaged 800 rods.

Internal Grinding

Internal surfaces are ground in chucking and centerless internal grinding machines.

A chuck is a satisfactory holding device when workpieces vary in size and shape and when small production quantities are involved. For grinding large quantities of identical parts, quick-acting collet chucks and special fixtures that operate mechanically, hydraulically, or by compressed air are more efficient. Although chucking machines can grind a wide range of inside diameters, the tendency of a long arbor to deflect limits the depth of hole that can be ground.

In a centerless grinding machine, the workpiece has no fixed center, but instead rolls on its outer surface in a centerless workhead. Consequently, the ground bore is generated from the outside diameter, so that nearly perfect concentricity is produced.

In centerless internal grinding, the workpiece is between and in direct contact with three rolls: a regulating roll, a support roll, and a pressure roll (Fig. 33). The regulating roll drives the work and regulates its speed. The support roll is fixed below the work. The pressure roll is mounted in a swinging bracket and holds the work in contact with the two other rolls. The regulating roll and support roll have fixed centers. Support shoes can be used instead of rolls (see Fig. 39).

The on-center type of centerless internal grinder has rolls positioned so that the axes of the work, grinding wheel, and regulating wheel are all in the same horizontal plane, as shown in Fig. 33(a). This provides maximum support to the work, and makes it possible to grind parts with thin walls accurately and without distortion.

In off-center machines, the rolls are positioned so that the centerlines of the work and of the grinding wheel are above that of the regulating roll, as shown in Fig. 33(b). The angular relation between the support roll and the regulating roll in an off-center machine is such that successive workpieces, even those with considerable variation in outside diameter, remain on the same vertical centerline. As a result, such workpieces can be ground to close dimensional tolerances. The off-center method also makes it possible to grind several parts simultaneously, all to the same dimension.

Centerless internal grinders are particularly efficient and economical to use on rings, sleeves, bearing rings (including cups and cones for tapered roller bearings), and cylinder liners. Tapered holes can be ground in some machines, and unsymmetrical parts can be handled by using auxiliary cylindrical holding devices.

The three examples that follow describe internal grinding for production workpieces varying from 0.046 in. to 1.1263 in. in diameter.

Example 504. Use of Special Grinder for Miniature Bearing Rings (Table 9)

A miniature machine equipped with a precision-mounted wheel was used to plunge grind the bores of miniature ball-bearing inner rings of 440C stainless steel hardened to Rockwell C 62 to 64. Grinding removed 0.004 to 0.005 in. of metal and produced a hole 0.046 in. in diameter by 0.062 in. long. A very hard (grade T) vitrified aluminum oxide wheel of fine grit size (320) was used. Other details of the operation are given in Table 9.

Example 505. Chucking Internal Grinder vs High-Speed Grinder (Table 10)

Hardened steel drill bushings (Rockwell C 62 to 65), 0.375 in. in diameter and 0.500 in. long, were ground to remove 0.004 to 0.008 in. of metal from the inside diameter. When chucking automatic grinders were used, production was only 55 to 58 pieces per hour per machine.

Changing to automatic high-speed internal centerless grinders increased the production rate to 90 pieces per hour per machine. A 45°-indexing head was used as auxiliary equipment for loading and unloading the bushings in these machines. Other processing details for the high-speed centerless method are given in Table 10.

Example 506. Effect of Machine Rigidity on Production Time

An internal grinder with a No. 3 head was used to remove an average of 0.008 in. of metal from an internal diameter of a stator shaft assembly. The finished hole was 1.1263 in. in diameter by 2.590 in. long. Production time for this operation was 1.53 min per piece, but manufacturing demands required reduction of the time to 1 min per piece.

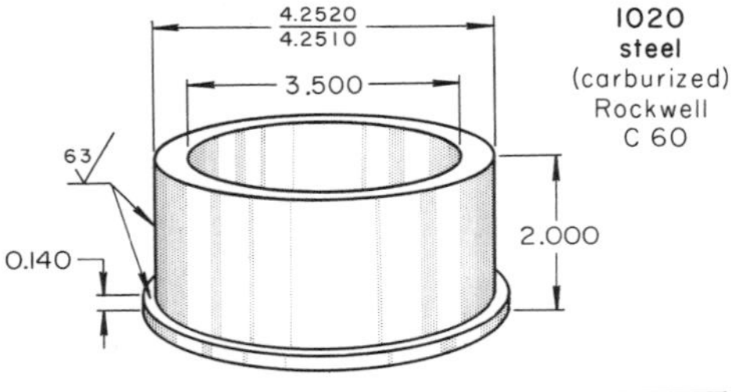

Wheel classification	As-60-L5-V
Wheel size	24 by 6 by 12 in.
Operating Conditions	
Wheel speed	1000 rpm (6250 sfm)
Infeed, per revolution of workpiece	0.0003 in.
Metal removed from diameter	0.0215 in.(a)
Grinding fluid	Soluble-oil emulsion
Setup time	0.5 hr
Production rate	30 pieces per hour
Wheel life per dressing(b)	9 pieces
Total wheel life	6000 pieces

(a) First grind removed 0.015 in.; second grind, 0.0065 in. (b) With single-point diamond tool.

Fig. 32. Sleeve bushing ground on outside and shoulder by centerless method (Example 502)

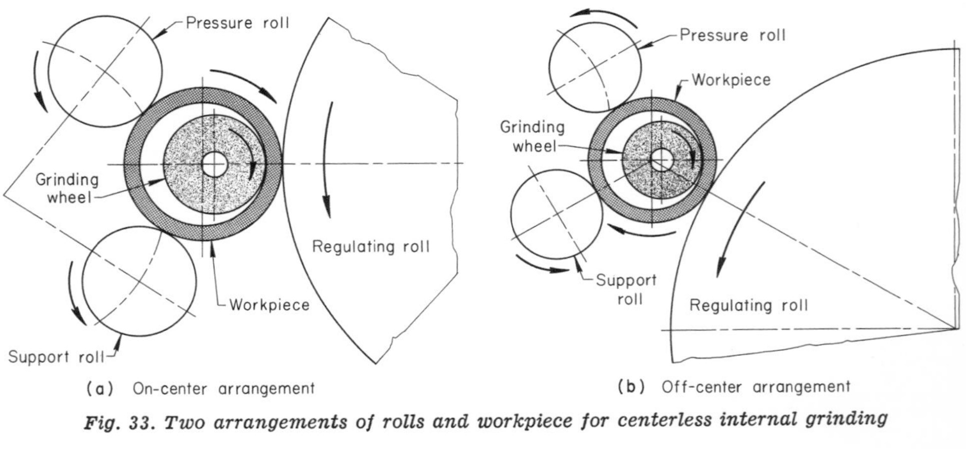

Fig. 33. Two arrangements of rolls and workpiece for centerless internal grinding

The No. 3 head was not rigid enough to prevent flexing or vibration of the grinding spindle when it was operated at the feed rate necessary to grind one piece per minute. A larger, No. 5 head provided the necessary rigidity, as shown by the following comparison:

Operation	No. 3 head	No. 5 head
Rough grinding	0.71 min	0.28 min
Sparkout	0.12	0.09
Wheel dressing	0.17	0.07
Finish grinding	0.53	0.46
Total time per cycle	1.53 min	0.90 min

With both heads, the grinding wheel (A-60-L6-V; 1 by 1 by ⅜ in.) was operated at 26,000 rpm (6750 sfm). With the No. 3 head, feed was 0.010 ipm for roughing and 0.0019 ipm for finishing; with the No. 5 head, roughing feed was increased to 0.025 ipm and finishing feed to 0.0021 ipm. The finished hole was within ±0.0005 in. of basic diameter, and a surface finish of 30 micro-in. or better was maintained. The wheel was dressed with a single-point diamond tool after grinding each piece. Total life of the wheel was 40 pieces.

Accuracy and Finish Capabilities of Internal Grinders

Single-spindle internal grinding machines can be set up efficiently for low or high production. In high production, an automatic gaging or sizing system is generally used to help maintain dimensional accuracy.

In some automatic gaging systems, the wheel is withdrawn from the inner surface on a signal from a size-sensing unit. Common sizing units are the reciprocating gage plug, reciprocating air plug, stationary crescent air fork, and various types of caliper fingers actuated by air or electronic mechanisms.

Another automatic sizing system uses a fixed amount of grinding infeed for each piece, either from the start of grinding or, more often, from the dress cycle at some intermediate point during grinding of each piece. This sizing system depends on accurate feed motion and uniform wheel action from piece to piece.

The two examples that follow demonstrate the high-production and close-tolerance capabilities of internal grinders operating with automatic gaging.

Examples 507 and 508. Automatic Gaging in Grinding of Bearing Inner Rings

Example 507 — Ball Bearings (Fig. 34). The 1.377-in.-diam bores of ball bearing inner rings (1.909-in. OD, and 0.810-in. bore width to corner radii) were ground in a 7½-hp automatic, reciprocating-wheel spindle machine. The machine had a maximum bore-size capacity of 2.5 in., and used shoe-type chucking. A reciprocating gage-plug sizing system was used during the fine-feed cycle, after the wheel-dressing cycle.

Grinding removed 0.020 in. of metal from the bore, which was held to a tolerance of 0.00043 in. Figure 34 shows deviations from the nominal bore diameter obtained during production grinding, using the operating conditions listed below the graph.

Example 508 — Roller Bearings (Fig. 35). The 5.905-in.-diam bores of roller bearing inner rings (8.188-in. OD, and 3.875-in. bore width to corner radii) were ground in a 15-hp chucking bore grinder. The reciprocating-wheel spindle of the grinder had a maximum bore-size capacity of 9 in., an automatic control for bore size, and automatic dressing cycles. The rings were located on their outside diameters and clamped to a face plate.

Grinding removed 0.050 in. of metal from the bore. Tolerances were 0.001 in. on bore diameter and 0.0007 in. for out-of-roundness. Variation from nominal bore size of 50 ground pieces is shown in Fig. 35; details of the operation are given in the accompanying table.

Table 9. Internal Grinding of Miniature Ball Bearing Inner Rings (Example 504)

Wheel classification	A_t-320-T-V
Wheel size	0.046 by 0.095 by 0.025 in.
Operating Conditions	
Wheel speed	150,000 rpm (1806 sfm)
Infeed rate	0.001 in. per sec
Metal removed from diam	0.004 to 0.005 in.
Grinding fluid	Activated grinding oil(a)
Production rate	300 pieces per hour
Setup time	About 30 min
Wheel life per dressing(b)	1 or 2 pieces
Total wheel life	80 to 100 pieces
Tolerances and Finish	
Tolerance on taper	0.000050 in.
Tolerance on roundness	0.000020 in.
Tolerance on diameter	0.0002 in.
Specified finish	8 micro-in. max

(a) Mixture of low-viscosity blending oil (100 SUS at 100 F) containing 4% sulfochlorinated additive. (b) Wheel initially trued to below hole size, then dressed with single-point diamond after each piece to remove 0.0001 in. on wheel diameter, or after every two pieces to remove 0.0002 in. from wheel diameter.

Table 10. Centerless Internal Grinding of Drill-Bushing Bores (Example 505)

Wheel classification	A-80-K5-V
Wheel size	⅜ by ½ in. (mounted in quill)
Operating Conditions	
Wheel speed	75,000 rpm (7400 sfm)
Work-rotation speed	1000 rpm (98 sfm max)
Infeed rate	0.001 in. per sec
Metal removed from diameter	0.005 in.
Grinding fluid	Soluble-oil emulsion
Production per machine(a)	90 pieces per hr
Setup time	2 hr
Wheel life per dressing(b)	1 piece
Total wheel life	100 pieces
Tolerance, Finish and Cost	
Tolerance	0.0003 to 0.0004 in.
Surface finish	8 to 12 micro-in.
Labor cost per piece(c)	$0.039

(a) Two grinding machines were used. (b) Wheel dressed automatically with single-point diamond tool. Dressing removed maximum of 0.05 in. of wheel material. (c) At $3.50 per hr.

The efficiency of internal grinding machines in grinding holes to close tolerances and fine finishes depends on the amount of stock to be removed. In one operation, accuracy within 0.0005 in. and a finish of 12 to 16 micro-in. were obtained in the removal of 0.009 to 0.011 in. from the inside diameter. In another operation, accuracy within 0.002 in. and a finish of 16 micro-in. were obtained in the removal of 0.030 to 0.035 in.

Wider tolerances and rougher finishes usually are specified when a greater amount of metal is removed in a given length of time. But specification of larger amounts of stock removal does not always mean that larger tolerances are required, provided an increase in time or cost can be accepted. Examples 509 and 510, which follow, present processing details for removing 0.016 and 0.036 in. of metal, respectively, from bearing inner rings and compare costs for holding two different tolerances. In these examples, grinding to closer tolerances resulted in a lower production rate and thus in a higher cost per piece.

Examples 509 and 510. Effect of Tolerances on Production Rate in Internal Grinding

Example 509. Bearing inner rings were ground in an internal grinding machine to remove 0.016 in. of metal from the diameter. The rings, made of 52100 steel and hardened to Rockwell C 61, measured 1.350-in. OD, 0.984-in. ID, and 0.590 in. wide. The grinding wheel (A_s-80-L6-V; 1 by ⅝ by ⅜ in.) was operated at 21,700 rpm (5700 sfm), and the workpiece revolved at 590 rpm (150 sfm).

Under the conditions listed below, a tolerance of 0.0004 in. could be met using a fully automatic machine; a tolerance of 0.0002 in. was held by a hand-operated machine, but at a 47% decrease in production rate. Grinding to the closer tolerance also resulted in an 89% increase in cost.

Item	Tolerance, in. 0.0004	0.0002
Coarse feed (diametral), ipm	0.200	0.125
Fine feed (diametral), ipm	0.078	0.050
Wheel dressings per cycle	1	2
Production, pieces per hour	170	90
Relative cost, arbitrary units	100	189

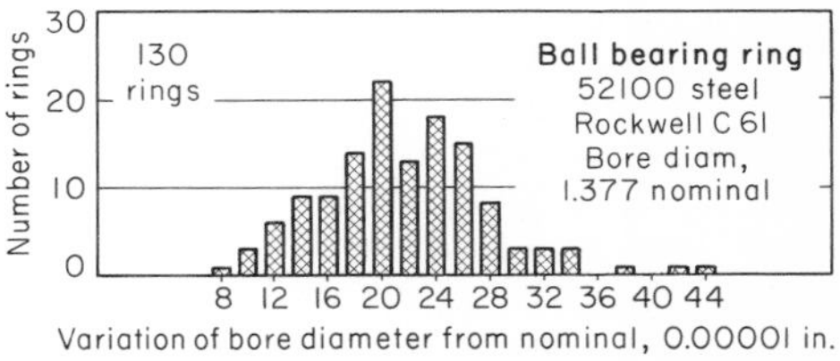

Wheel classification	A_s-80-L6-V(a)
Wheel size	1⁵⁄₁₆ by ¾ by ⅜ in.
Operating Conditions	
Wheel speed	16,500 rpm (5720 sfm)
Work-rotation speed	420 rpm (150 sfm)
Coarse feed, diametral	0.167 ipm
Fine feed, diametral	0.078 ipm
Stroke length, roughing	0.060 in.
Stroke length, finishing	0.250 in.
Stroke frequency, roughing	180 per minute
Stroke frequency, finishing	60 per minute
Metal removed from diameter	0.020 in.
Grinding fluid	Soluble-oil:water (1:50)
Production rate	145 pieces per hour
Setup time	2 hr
Wheel life per dressing	1 piece
Total wheel life (avg)	250 pieces
Dressing tool	Single-point diamond
Dress compensation(b)	0.0008 in.
Grinding wheel cost per piece	$0.11

(a) Sulfur treated. (b) Compensation is the diametral infeed of the wheel toward the diamond tool at each dressing cycle.

Fig. 34. Variation in diameter of bores of ball bearing inner rings ground in an automatic reciprocating-wheel grinder with automatic sizing system (Example 507)

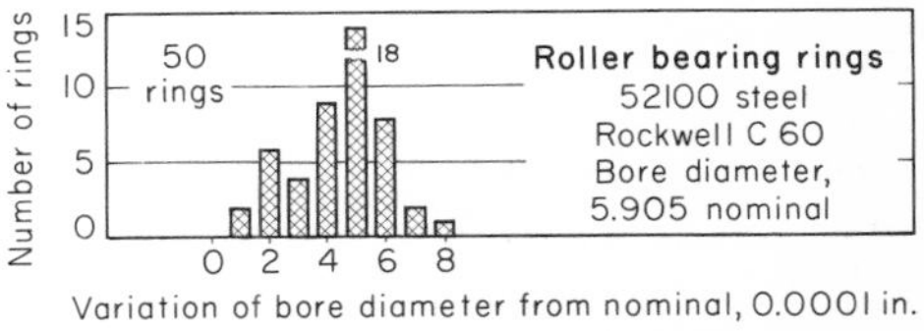

Wheel classification	A_r-60-L7-V
Wheel size	5 by 2½ by 2 in.
Operating Conditions	
Wheel speed	4550 rpm (6000 sfm)
Work-rotation speed	127 rpm (200 sfm)
Coarse feed, diametral	0.025 ipm
Fine feed, diametral	0.005 ipm
Stroke length	1⅞ in.
Stroke frequency	40 per minute
Metal removed from diameter	0.050 in.
Current drawn during grinding	35 amp
Grinding fluid	Soluble-oil:water (1:50)
Production rate	17 pieces per hour
Setup time	2.5 hr
Wheel dressing cycle	2 dressings per piece
Total wheel life	300 pieces
Dressing tool	Single-point diamond
Dress compensation(a)	0.005 in.
Grinding wheel cost per piece	$0.025

(a) Compensation is the diametral infeed of the wheel toward the diamond tool at each dressing cycle.

Fig. 35. Variation in diameter of bores of roller bearing inner rings ground in a chucking grinder with automatic internal sizing (Example 508)

Table 11. Internal Grinding of Bearing Inner Rings to Two Different Tolerances (Example 510)

Condition or result	Single grinding operation (tolerance, 0.0008 in.)	Double grinding operation (tolerance, 0.0003 in.) — Rough grinding	Double grinding operation (tolerance, 0.0003 in.) — Finish grinding
Grinding wheel:			
Classification	At-60-L5-V	At-60-L5-V	At-100-J6-V
Size, in.	4 by 2 by ⅞	4 by 2 by ⅞	3 by 2 by ⅞
Speed, rpm	5700 (6000 sfm)	5700 (6000 sfm)	7000 (5500 sfm)
Work speed, rpm	162 (200 sfm)	162 (200 sfm)	120 (150 sfm)
Feed (diametral), ipm:			
Coarse	0.036	0.056	0.016
Fine	0.018	0.028	0.008
Stock removed from diam, in.	0.036	0.030	0.006
Dimensional tolerance, in.	0.0008	0.002	0.0003
Wheel dressing per cycle	1	1	1
Production, pieces per hour	31	55	40

Example 510 (Table 11). Bearing inner rings made of 52100 steel, hardened to Rockwell C 61, and measuring 5.900-in. OD, 4.724-in. ID, and 1.574 in. wide, were ground in an internal grinding machine to remove 0.036 in. of metal from the diameter. Processing details for a single grinding operation that maintained a tolerance of 0.0008 in. and for a double operation that maintained a tolerance of 0.0003 in. are given in Table 11.

The production rate for the double operation (23 pieces per machine hour) was considerably less than that for the single operation (31 pieces per machine hour). This lower production rate and the need for two machine setups made the cost for producing the closer tolerance 48% higher than that for producing the wider tolerance.

The example that follows indicates the surface-finish capabilities of internal grinders and the importance of correct operation in controlling the quality of the finish produced.

Example 511. Internal Grinding to an 8-Micro-In. Finish (Fig. 36)

The inside of the carburized steel part shown in the setup in Fig. 36 was ground in a double-spindle (horizontal) internal grinder to produce a surface finish of 8 micro-in. or less. The internal grinder had a maximum swing of 14 in. over the ways, and was equipped with a central system that permitted continuous circulation of the grinding fluid. A roughing wheel and a finishing wheel removed 0.009 to 0.011 in. of metal from the 1¹⁄₁₆-in.-long internal surfaces.

Surfaces were rough ground within 0.0005 in. of finish size, after which they were finish ground. Processing details for the two grinding operations are given in Fig. 36.

The condition of the machine and the shape of the part were important factors in finish grinding to an 8-micro-in. finish. Minute vibrations in any part of the machine, especially in the workhead and grinding spindles, could have affected the quality of finish. Parts with thin walls were difficult to finish grind.

The finishing portion of the operation required extreme care. The sparkout period was longer than when grinding to rougher finishes. Wheel dressing required a sharp diamond and a steady dressing rate, which had to be determined empirically, as dressing too fast or too slow affected the finish adversely. The grinding fluid was passed through dual filters to remove all particles 10 microns or more in size. Under these conditions, a finish of 8 micro-in. or smoother could be produced; however, reproducibility depended on operator skill.

Form Grinding

Cylindrical grinders are used to grind complex cylindrical forms in rough workpieces, and horizontal-spindle surface grinders are used for producing complex forms of almost any shape. The suitability of form grinding for a given operation depends on the production quantity entailed. Quantities that warrant the cost of tooling and setup vary according to the complexity of the form and the cost of making the part by some other suitable method.

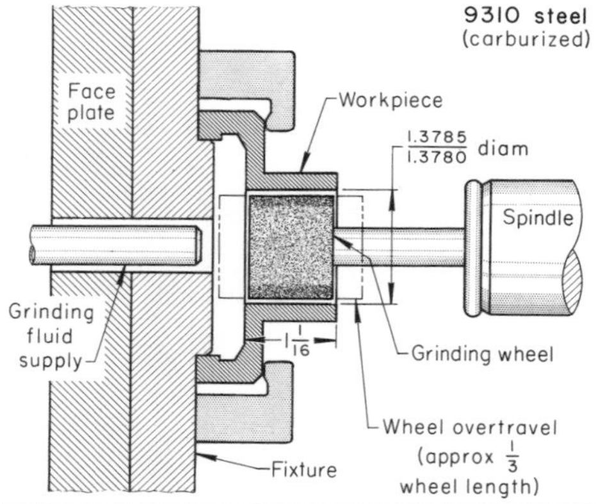

Wheel classification, roughing At-60-L5-V
Wheel classification, finishing At-60-K5-V
Wheel size,
roughing and finishing ...1¼ by 1 by ⅜ in.

Operating Conditions

Wheel speed, roughing ...12,000 rpm (3925 sfm)
Wheel speed, finishing ...14,000 rpm (4579 sfm)
Work-rotation speed ....150 rpm (54 sfm)
Metal removed, roughing ....0.0002 in./stroke(a)
Metal removed, finishing ..0.00005 in./stroke(a)
Total removed from diam ......0.009 to 0.011 in.
Stroke frequency ....40 per minute
Grinding fluid ....Soluble-oil emulsion(b)
Production rate, approx ......9 pieces per hour
Setup time, approx ....3½ hr(c)
Wheel life per dressing, roughing ......3 pieces
Wheel life per dressing, finishing ......1 piece
Wheel cost, both wheels ....$0.02 per piece

(a) Approximate amount of metal removed from diameter. (b) Heavy-duty soluble oil. (c) Includes grinding of first piece.

Fig. 36. Grinding a bore to an 8-micro-in. finish in a double-spindle internal grinder (Example 511)

The face of the grinding wheel can be formed by crush truing or by diamond truing. In crush truing, carbide, high speed steel, or cast iron rolls shaped to the profile desired in the workpiece are applied under pressure against the face of the grinding wheel to contour-form the wheel. High speed steel crush rolls are used for small production quantities and carbide rolls for larger quantities. If wheels are to be crush trued, the grinder spindle must be sturdy, to withstand the side loads.

Advantages of crush-trued wheels over diamond-trued wheels are:

1 Complex contours can be formed in the wheel in one fast operation.
2 More sharp cutting points are produced on the wheel, resulting in more stock removal per revolution.
3 Surface finish and accuracy of contour are uniform between workpieces.
4 More pieces are ground per dressing, because the wheel cuts more freely.
5 Wheels do not load up with metal, even when grinding soft materials such as aluminum and brass.
6 Truing is faster. It is done with wheel and roll operating at 200 to 300 sfm.

On the other hand, diamond-trued wheels have these advantages:

1 They produce better surface finishes.
2 They can be contoured to grind deeper grooves and grooves with shoulders having almost vertical sides.
3 They provide more accurate ground form.

When truing or grinding with crush-trued wheels, a grinding oil should be used. During truing, the oil should clean the wheel and reduce wear on the roll.

The two examples that follow describe form grinding two production parts.

Example 512. Grinding Small Laminations to Close Tolerance (Fig. 37)

Small laminations of the shape shown in Fig. 37 were form ground in a horizontal-spindle surface grinder that was equipped with a magnetic chuck and a form-truing attachment. A row of 50 pieces was placed against a guide rail in a good holding area of the magnetic chuck (Fig. 37). The pieces were blocked to prevent movement during grinding. About 0.007 in. of metal was removed per side from the laminations, which had been blanked on a press.

The wheel cut freely and maintained accuracy of form, because the form was fairly flat and had no weak, protruding areas. The wheel was trued to a template after each load, to maintain form and grinding action. Figure 37 also indicates process capability of holding the 0.030-in. dimension within the ±0.0002-in. tolerance.

Example 513. One Operation vs Two (Fig. 38)

Originally, the part shown in Fig. 38 was form ground from a rough-turned blank in two operations using two grinding wheels.

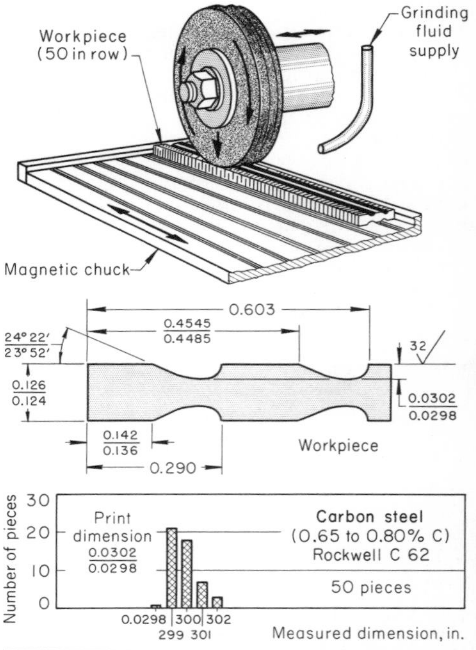

Wheel classification As-60-I8-V
Wheel size ....10 by ¾ by 5 in.

Operating Conditions

Wheel speed ....2000 rpm (5236 sfm)
Downfeed ....0.0003 in. per stroke
Traverse speed ....600 ipm
Metal removed per side ....0.007 in.
Grinding fluid ....Synthetic:water (1:40)
Setup time ....0.3 hr
Production rate ....286 pieces per hour
Wheel life per dressing(a) ....50 pieces

(a) Wheel was dressed with a V-shaped diamond in a form-truing attachment that used a template to guide the diamond.

Fig. 37. Accurate form grinding of steel laminations in a horizontal-spindle reciprocating surface grinder (Example 512)

First, the groove was form ground with one wheel, locating on the surface where the ball was to be ground. Next, the ball was contour ground with a different wheel, locating on the edge of the ground groove. This procedure removed 0.025 in. of metal during grinding of the ball. The 1.782/1.781-in. dimension could not be held within tolerance, and production was only 12 pieces per hour (of which 4% was scrap and 18% was reworked). Both wheels were trued by a diamond-truing attachment on the machine.

The two-operation method was replaced by one in which the ball and groove were ground simultaneously with one crush-trued grinding wheel. The part was held on centers. This procedure increased the production rate to 36 pieces per hour; the required tolerance was held, and scrap and rework were negligible.

Dimensional Accuracy

Dimensional accuracy obtained in grinding can vary widely, depending on the type of operation used. If wide tolerances are assigned, the choice of equipment and grinding procedure is not critical, except from the standpoint of cost.

When close tolerances are assigned, every condition of the grinding operation becomes critical. The machine must be of the proper type and size and in excellent working condition, with particular emphasis on the condition of the spindle bearings. Selection of a grinding wheel of the correct abrasive type, grain size and grade is important. Usually, close tolerances require a fine-grained wheel. The wheel should be hard enough to prevent excessive breakdown. Accurate wheel dressing with a good-quality diamond is important.

If a grinding fluid is used, a water-base type is preferred, except for grinding threads or other forms to close tolerances; for these a grinding oil is preferable. The grinding fluid should be filtered. For grinding to extremely close tolerances, refrigeration of the grinding fluid may be necessary, to keep the workpiece at room temperature during grinding.

When more accurate dimensions are necessary, less stock is removed in the final few passes. Particular emphasis is given to the sparkout or dwell time of the wheel. Thus, as dimensions become more critical, more time is required for grinding, and grinding costs rise.

The example that follows illustrates the effect of grinding method on dimensional accuracy.

Example 514. Process Change to Meet Concentricity Tolerance on Bearing Rings (Fig. 39)

Variation in the wall thickness of cylindrical bearing outer rings was beyond the specified tolerance, and a change in the process was required to reduce rejections and improve quality. The inside was to be ground, and eccentricity was not to exceed 0.0003 in. TIR.

Original Method. Originally, the ring was ground in a chucking internal grinder, using a contracting collet-type chuck mounted on a live-workhead spindle, as shown in Fig. 39(a). At each setup, the internal diameter of the chuck fingers was ground to eliminate repeating runout of the workhead spindle. Nevertheless, some nonrepeating runout was still present. The action of chuck fingers did not repeat perfectly at each chucking, and dirt was likely to accumulate between the outside diameter of the workpiece and the chuck fingers; both contributed to runout of the workpiece. It was possible to hold a maximum runout of 0.0003 in. only by accepting a high rejection rate and maintenance of the workhead spindle. In addition, the action of chuck fingers, even though they were clamped very lightly, created a lobe pattern on the internal surface of the thin ring.

Improved Method. An improved procedure consisted of rotating the workpiece by means of a drive plate affixed to the live-workhead spindle nose of a shoe-type internal grinder, as shown in Fig. 39(b). The center of the drive plate was offset in relation to the workpiece center. This setup imparted a force on the workpiece, causing it to ride firmly on the support shoes. The workpiece was held axially against the drive plate by two clamp rollers mounted on pressure-actuated arms. With this arrangement, the accuracy of the workhead spindle was less critical and chuck grinding was eliminated. Variation of wall section could be easily held to 0.0001 in. TIR, and rejects were eliminated. The lobes on the internal ground surface caused by the former chucking method were also eliminated. Other processing details for the shoe-type procedure are given below Fig. 39.

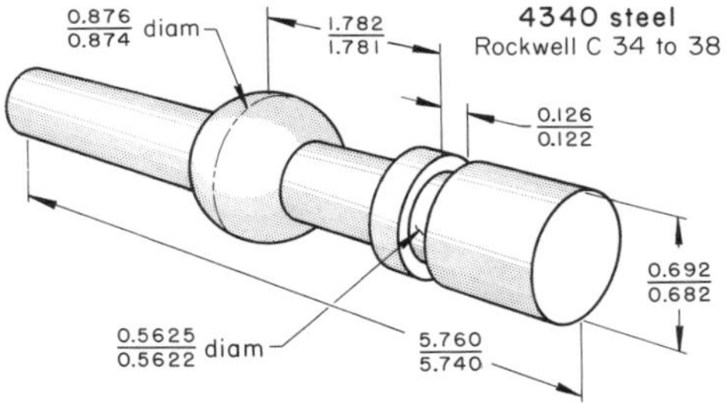

Fig. 38. Part in which ball and groove were contour ground simultaneously with one crush-trued grinding wheel (Example 513)

Cost

Dimensional tolerances and surface finish requirements greatly influence the cost of production grinding.

Effect of Tolerance. Close tolerances increase the cost of grinding because:

1. Different amounts of stock may have to be removed from different pieces of the same production part. This usually requires slower feed to size-out at a uniform grinding pressure.
2. Wheel sharpness varies between dressings. Thus, additional dressings are necessary when grinding to close tolerances.
3. Surface speed of the grinding wheel varies as it wears down, and speed adjustments must be made.
4. Variations in temperature of the workpiece often require slower feed rates or temperature control of the grinding fluid.
5. Deflections of the machine and tooling call for more rigid machines or slower feed rates.

Cost examples pertaining to cylindrical grinding on centers, centerless grinding, surface grinding (vertical rotary and reciprocating), internal grinding, and form grinding are presented below to emphasize the increase in grinding cost associated with close tolerances.

Example 515. Effect of Tolerance on Cost of Grinding Gear Blanks (Fig. 40)

Gear blanks were ground to produce a surface finish of 15 micro-in. and an outside diameter of 1.498 to 1.500 in. The blanks were used to make oil-pump gears, ⅞ in. wide with ten teeth of 8 pitch.

Originally, the outside diameter was specified as 1.4995 to 1.5000 in., then modified to 1.499 to 1.500 in., and finally to 1.498 to 1.500 in. These changes reduced the cost of grinding each blank, as indicated by Fig. 40. The blanks were ground with an A-80-L5-V wheel, 20 by 1½ by 12 in.

Example 516. Cost of Tolerance and Surface Finish in Plunge Grinding Pinions (Fig. 41)

An 8622 steel pinion was plunge ground on centers in a cylindrical grinder (Fig. 41) to remove 0.004 in. of metal from the face of the

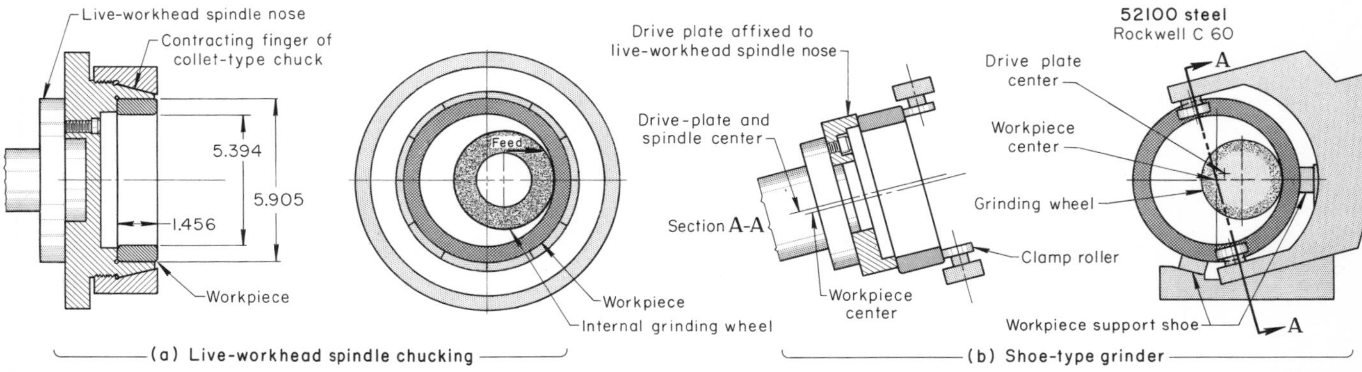

Wheel classification	A_t-100-J6-V
Wheel size	3¾ by 2½ by ⅞ in.
Operating Conditions, Shoe-Type Grinder	
Wheel speed	5600 rpm (5500 sfm)
Work-rotation speed	89 rpm (125 sfm)
Infeed on diameter	0.008 ipm
Metal removed from diameter	0.006 to 0.008 in.
Grinding fluid	Soluble-oil:water (1:50)
Setup time	2.5 hr
Production rate	32 pieces per hour
Wheel life per dressing	1 piece
Total wheel life	300 pieces
Tolerance on eccentricity	0.0003 in. TIR

Fig. 39. (a) *Live-workhead spindle chucking method of holding bearing outer rings, which caused excessive variation in wall thickness.* (b) *Shoe-type internal grinding arrangement that reduced rejection rate.* (Example 514)

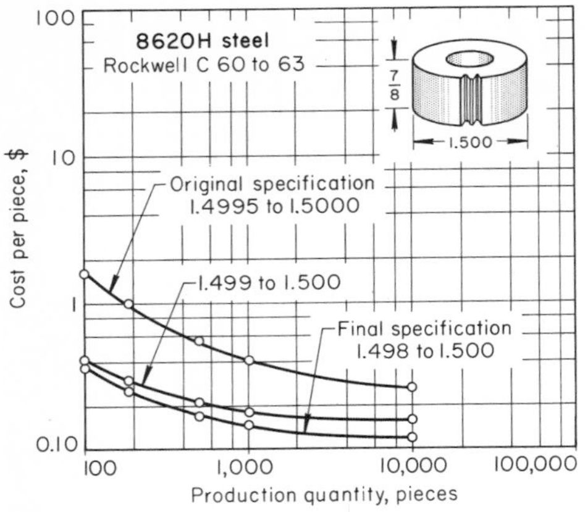

Reduction in grinding cost per gear blank as a result of changing from a tolerance of 0.0005 in. to one of 0.002 in. on the ground diameter. Setup and overhead charges are included.

Fig. 40. Effect of production quantity and tolerance on cost (Example 515)

shoulder to produce a finished width of 3.103/3.097 in., and to remove 0.020 in. of metal from the adjacent section to produce an outside diameter of 2.8150/2.8140 in. The specified maximum surface roughness of 63 micro-in. was maintained by a dished grinding wheel (A_s-60-L5-V) 30 by 6 by 12 in. The data that accompany Fig. 41 show the effect of closer tolerances and finer finishes on cycle time and cost of grinding.

Example 517. Effect of Tolerance on Production Rate (Table 12)

Closer tolerance reduced the production rate and resulted in a higher cost per piece for through-feed centerless grinding of rings. The workpiece was made of 52100 steel and hardened to Rockwell C 60, and was 2.83-in. OD by 2.35-in. ID by 0.66 in. long. Stock allowance on the outside diameter was 0.020 in. The grinding wheel (A_t-80-M6-V) was 20 by 8 by 12 in. Sufficient time was allowed between grinding passes to dress and reposition the grinding wheel, move the workpiece to the wheel, adjust angle, and change the regulating-roll speeds. The data in Table 12 show the effect of reducing tolerances on productivity.

Example 518. Cost of Grinding Shafts to Close Tolerance

Governor rack lever shafts made of 1045 steel and hardened to Rockwell C 60 were fed automatically from a hopper into a centerless grinder to remove a maximum of 0.0125 in. of metal from the outside diameter. The grinding wheel (A_s-46-M6-V; 20 by 6 by 12 in.) was operated at 1250 rpm (6500 sfm), and the regulating wheel at 29 rpm.

The outside diameter of these 7-in.-long shafts was ground to 0.5000/0.4995 in. The influence on time and cost for grinding to a closer tolerance is indicated in the following table (based on grinding 1600-piece lots):

Item, per piece	Tolerance, in. 0.0005	Less than 0.0005
Total time, min(a)	0.3359	0.4463
Increase in time	.....	32.9%
Grinding cost	$0.045	$0.059
Increase in cost	.....	28.3%

(a) Includes time for grinding and for dressing the wheel, but not setup time.

The increase in cost resulted mainly because an additional grinding pass was required for meeting the closer tolerance.

Example 519. Effect of Closer Tolerance on Cost of Surface Grinding Small Gears

Small gears (2.796-in. OD, 1.2508-in. ID) were ground on both sides to produce a finished width of 0.625 ± 0.0003 in. Each side was ground in a separate operation. Grinding the second side required the close tolerance; 0.011 in. was ground from that side. The gears were made of 8617H steel, carburized and hardened to Rockwell C 59 to 64.

The gears were ground in a vertical-spindle rotary surface grinder with a worktable 30 in. in diameter. Fifty-two gears were placed on the worktable and ground with a ring grinding wheel (A_f-60-H8-V) 18 by 5 by 15 in. The influence of tolerance on time and cost for grinding the second side of these gears in 250-piece lots is as follows:

Item, per piece	Tolerance, in. Over 0.001	0.001 or less
Cycle time, min(a)	9.078	11.466
Grinding cost	$0.021	$0.027
Increase in cost	....	29%

(a) Based on 52-piece load

The effects of dimensional tolerance and surface finish on cost of reciprocating surface grinding are shown in Fig. 42. The table below Fig. 42 shows the number of sparkout passes required to attain specific combinations of finish and tolerance. When a small amount of grinding stock is to be removed, an excessive number of sparkout passes can almost double the grinding time per load.

Cost data for two production parts ground on reciprocating surface grinders are presented in Examples 520 and 521 (Fig. 43 and 44), which follow. The grinding times to obtain the surface finishes and accuracy indicated by the tabular data below Fig. 43 and 44, are based on the number of sparkout passes indicated in the tabulation that accompanies Fig. 42.

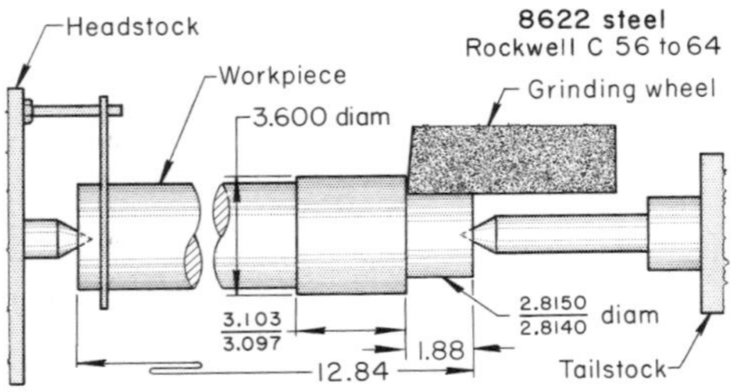

Item, per piece(a)	Tolerance, in. On 2.8145-in. dimension 0.0010	Under 0.0010	On 3.100-in. dimension Over 0.006	0.006 or less
Cycle time, min	2.418	2.488	2.258	2.418
Cycle cost	$0.302	$0.310	$0.283	$0.302
Increase in cost	...	2.6%	...	6.7%

Item, per piece(a)	Specified finish, micro-in. 63	32	16
Cycle time, min	2.418	2.681	2.874
Cycle cost	$0.302	$0.338	$0.361
Wheel cost	$0.018	$0.025	$0.025
Total cost	$0.320	$0.363	$0.386
Increase in cost	....	13.4%	20.6%

(a) Pinions were processed in 250-piece lots.

Fig. 41. Plunge grinding the bearing end of a pinion, and effect of tolerance and finish on time and cost for the operation (Example 516)

Table 12. Effect of Tolerance on Production Rate in Centerless Grinding (Example 517) (a)

Item	Dimensional tolerance, in. 0.0005	0.0004	0.0003
Number of passes	3	4	5
Regulating-roll speed, rpm:			
First pass	29	29	29
Second pass	34	34	34
Third pass	39	39	39
Fourth pass	(b)	39	39
Fifth pass	(b)	(b)	39
Production, pcs/hr	720	575	475
Increase in cost	...	24.4%	51.0%

(a) For production quantity of 3000 pieces (b) Pass not required.

Examples 520 and 521. Effects of Tolerance and Finish on Time and Cost of Grinding

Example 520 — Class 20 Gray Iron (Fig. 43). Both faces of a class 20 gray iron cover plate, shown in Fig. 43, were ground in a surface grinder to remove a total of ⅛ in. of metal. An A-46-J5-V wheel was used. The influence of tolerance and finish on time and cost for this operation is shown in Fig. 43 and the accompanying table. Note the sharp rise in cost as tolerance dropped below 0.001 in. at 40 and 25 micro-in.

Example 521 — Resulfurized Low-Carbon Steel (Fig. 44). A total of 0.008 in. of stock was removed by grinding two sides of the resulfurized (free-cutting) low-carbon steel plate shown in Fig. 44. An aluminum oxide wheel (20-in. diam, 6 in. wide) was used. The increase in time and cost resulting from increasing dimensional accuracy and smoother finishes is shown in Fig. 44 and the data in the table below it. As shown in the graph, cost rose sharply as tolerance went below 0.001 in. at 40 and 25 micro-in. [See also Example 471 and Fig. 5 for additional information on this same part.]

Example 522. Greater Productivity With Crush-Trued Wheel (Fig. 45)

The contoured shaft shown in Fig. 45 was form ground with a crush-trued grinding wheel. For the ball section, a maximum roughness of 8 micro-in. was specified; and tolerances were +0 and −0.001 in. on the diameter, and sphericity was required to be held within 0.0005 in. A check on these two dimensions was made to determine the amount of variation that resulted while grinding 85 pieces — the number of pieces ground per wheel dressing. Dimensional data are shown in Fig. 45.

This part was also ground by a diamond-trued wheel, to compare productivity and cost of the two forming procedures. Both wheels used the same method — grinding on centers. Comparative results are tabulated below Fig. 45.

Example 523. Effect of Tolerance on Tool and Grinding Costs (Fig. 46)

The effect of tolerances on cost of grinding the four dimensions indicated on the part in Fig. 46 is shown in the accompanying graph. Tolerances had a greater effect on cost of grinding than on tool cost. The part, of 8150 steel hardened to Rockwell C 58 to 60, was contour ground in one operation. A total of 0.020 in. was removed from the diameters and 0.010 in. from the face.

Effect of Surface Finish. The cost of producing surface finishes by grinding varies considerably with the type of equipment being used, the type and hardness of work material, the type of grinding wheel and the number of redressings required, and the roughness that is acceptable. Increases in grind-

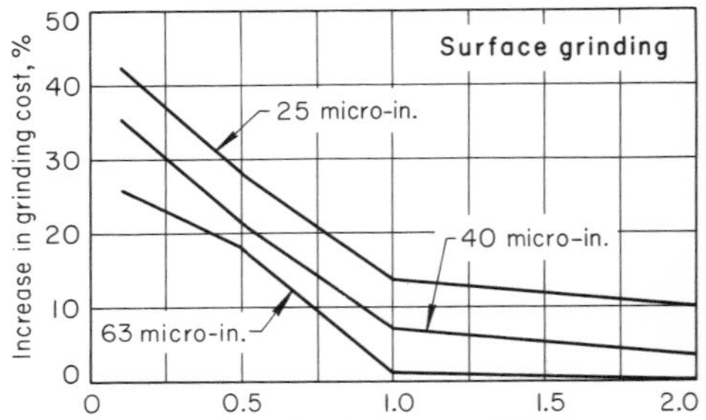

Surface roughness, micro-in.	Sparkout passes required for tolerance, in., of: 0.0005	0.001	0.003	0.005	>0.005
25	10	9	8	7	6
40	8	7	6	5	4
80	..	5	4	3	3
Over 80	..	..	2	1	1

Fig. 42. Effects of permissible surface roughness and dimensional tolerance on cost of reciprocating surface grinding, based on the sparkout passes required

ing time and sparkout time contribute a major part of the extra cost for smoother finish. Wheel costs per piece processed and wheel dressing costs are also important factors in the total cost of producing a smoother finish.

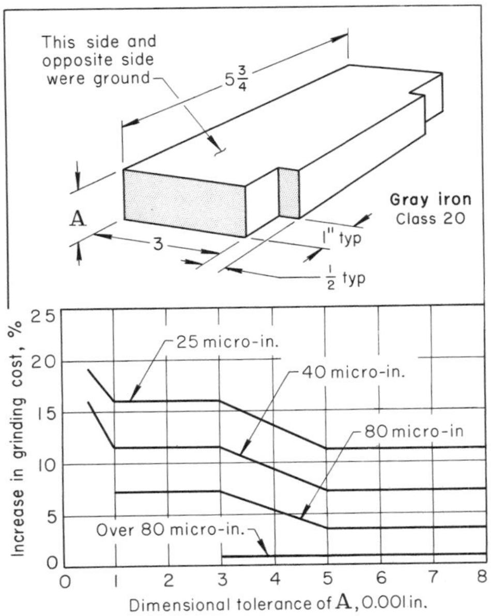

Surface roughness, micro-in.	Allowed standard hours per piece(a), for tolerance, in., of: 0.0005	0.001	0.003	0.005	>0.005
25	0.031	0.030	0.030	0.029	0.029
40	0.030	0.029	0.029	0.028	0.028
80	....	0.028	0.028	0.027	0.027
Over 80 ..	....	....	0.026	0.026	0.026

(a) Based on number of sparkout passes shown in table below Fig. 42.

Fig. 43. Increase in cost and time for grinding gray iron to finer finishes and closer tolerances (Example 520)

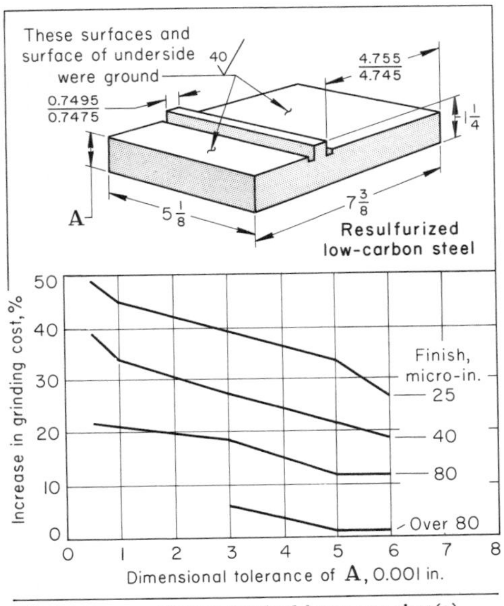

Surface roughness, micro-in.	Allowed standard hours per piece(a), for tolerance, in., of: 0.0005	0.001	0.003	0.005	>0.005
25	0.049	0.048	0.046	0.044	0.042
40	0.046	0.044	0.042	0.040	0.039
80	....	0.040	0.039	0.037	0.037
Over 80 ..	....	....	0.035	0.033	0.033

(a) Based on number of sparkout passes shown in the table below Fig. 42.

Fig. 44. Increase in cost and time for grinding free-cutting steel to finer finishes and closer tolerances (Example 521)

Table 13. Effect of Surface Finish on Time and Cost of Internal Grinding (Example 524)

Item, per piece	Surface finish, micro-in. 63	32	12
Wheel dressing time, min .	0.070	0.130	0.130
Grinding time, min	0.382	0.382	0.478
Sparkout time, min	None	0.200	1.150
Total, min	0.452	0.712	1.758
Added time for finish finer than 63 micro-in., min ..	...	0.260	1.306
Increase in cost of labor ..	...	26%	130%

Production quantity was 300 pieces.

To produce fine finishes, the dressing tool must travel across the wheel at speeds that are slow enough to produce the specified finish. Normally, the slower the rate of travel of the dressing tool, the better the finish, but this type of wheel dress will decrease the rate of stock removal. Damage caused by trying to remove stock too rapidly with a fine dress on the wheel includes grinding cracks in a hardened steel workpiece surface, out-of-roundness, or changes in size.

On a cylindrical grinder with workpiece centers, the finish can be controlled by (*a*) wheel dressing (traverse rate of dressing tool and frequency of dressing), (*b*) feed rate (plunge grinding), (*c*) traverse rate and infeed per pass (traverse grinding), (*d*) sparkout time, and (*e*) type of wheel employed. Example 516 (Fig. 41) shows the effect of surface finish on time and cost in a cylindrical plunge grinding operation.

The surface finish produced in centerless grinding depends mainly on the grit size of the wheel, the traverse rate, and the number of passes through the machine. The effect of traverse rate on surface finish and grinding cost in centerless grinding is shown in Fig. 47.

Surface finish can be controlled on an internal grinder by control of (*a*) grit size of the grinding wheel, (*b*) rates of traverse and infeed during finishing, (*c*) amount of stock remaining for finish grinding, and (*d*) amount of sparkout time. Generally, traverse rate is reduced after wheel dressing and throughout the sparkout time, depending on the finish required. The following example illustrates the increase in cost for various degrees of finish.

Example 524. Effect of Finish on Cost of Internal Grinding (Table 13)

The 1.375-in.-long bores of gears were ground in a semiautomatic internal grinder to remove 0.012 in. from the diameter. The gears were made of 1035 steel with a hardness of Rockwell C 23 to 30. Finish diameter of the bore was 1.3130/1.3125 in. An A_s-60-K5-V wheel, 1¼ by 1¼ by ⅜ in., was used to produce a maximum surface roughness of 63 micro-in. Finer finishes increased time and cost of grinding (see data in Table 13).

The surface finish obtained on surface grinders is controlled primarily by the amount of sparkout time. The degree to which finer finishes increase grinding costs of two production parts ground on reciprocating grinders has been illustrated in Examples 520 and 521. In both examples, for finishes coarser than 80 micro-in. the minimum tolerance was 0.003 in. Tolerances under 0.003 in. generally require a finish of 80 micro-in. or less.

The increase in cost of abrasive and cost of facility for producing six pro-

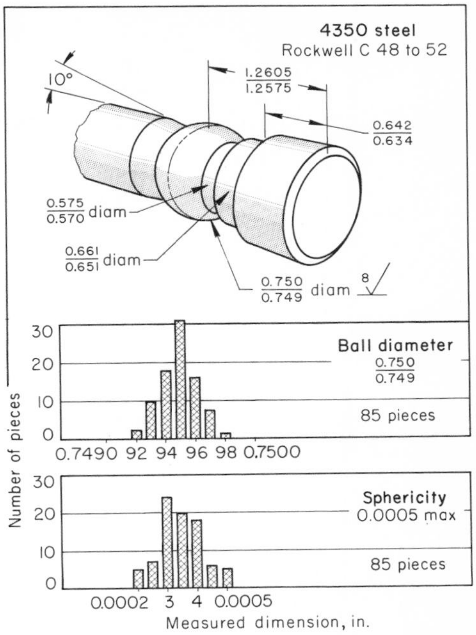

Item	Method of grinding: Diamond-trued wheel	Crush-trued wheel
Production, pcs/hr ...	7	24
Number of setups	3	1
Setup time, hr	18	4
Tool cost	$75	$400
Production efficiency	78%	90%
Rework and scrap	4%	½%
Wheel life per dressing, pieces	35	85

Fig. 45. Variation in dimensions of shafts ground during 85-piece life per crush truing of the grinding wheel, and results obtained with diamond-trued vs crush-trued wheels (Example 522)

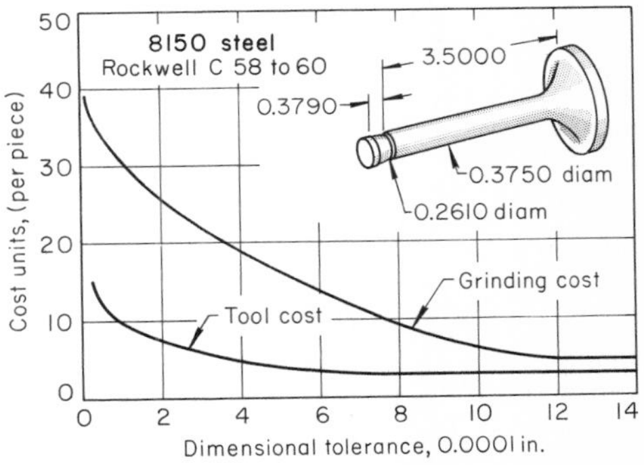

Tool cost includes wheels and crush rolls. Data are based on contour grinding of 500 parts.

Fig. 46. Effect of tolerance on tool cost and grinding cost (Example 523)

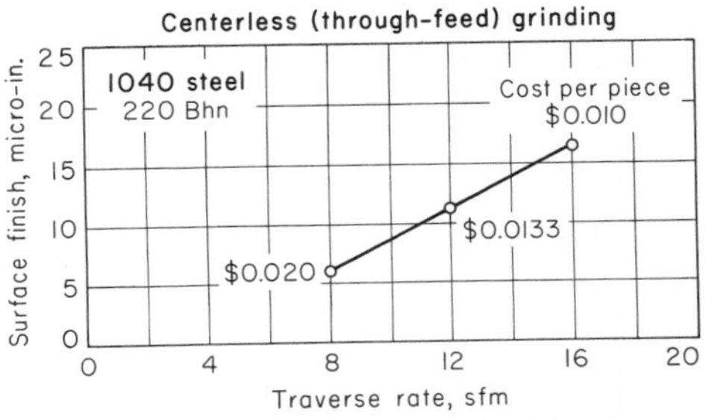

Workpiece, 12 in. long, was ground on the 0.500-in. outside diameter with a 100-grit, medium-grade, resinoid-bond wheel.

Fig. 47. Effect of traverse rate on surface finish and cost

Table 14. Effect of Surface Finish on Costs of Abrasive and Facility for Centerless Grinding Piston Pins

Surface finish, micro-in.	Stock removed, in.(a)	Grinding wheel classification	Cost of abrasive, per piece	Accumulated abrasive cost	Additional cost of abrasive, %(a)	Additional cost of facility, %(a)
Rough	0.004	A_t-60-K-V	$0.000131	$0.000131	...	...
80	0.004	A_t-60-K-V	0.000131	0.000262	100	100
30	0.002	A_t-80-L-V	0.000136	0.000398	50	50
15	0.0015	A_t-100-L-V	0.000109	0.000507	27	25
6	0.0010	A_t-120-L-B	0.000070	0.000577	14	20
4	0.0005	A_t-220-L-B	0.000060	0.000637	10	17

(a) In addition to next rougher finish. For instance, total stock removal for 4-micro-in. finish would be 0.0130 in., and total additional cost of abrasive would be about five times as much for a 4-micro-in. finish as for a rough finish.

Table 15. Efficiency and Costs for Milling vs Grinding of Gray Iron Motor Bases (Example 525)

Item	Milling	Grinding
Metal removed per piece, cu in.	35.5	35.5
Metal removal rate, cu in. per min	4.6	3.65
Machining time per piece, min	7.68	9.72
Floor-to-floor time per piece, min	26.18	20.72

Cost Factors

	Milling		Grinding	
	Time, min	Cost	Time, min	Cost
Setup (a)	34.00	$2.268	14.00	$0.933
Machining, per piece (a):				
Workpiece handling	12.50	0.835	7.00	0.467
Positioning tool	1.00	0.067	...	...
Machining	7.68	0.513	9.72	0.648
Measuring	5.00	0.334	4.00	0.267
Machine operation, per piece:				
Power	...	0.031	...	0.068
Maintenance	...	0.042	...	0.068
Tooling, per piece:				
Replacement	...	0.230	...	0.382
Sharpening (a)	...	0.276	...	...
Grinding wheel for sharpening tool	...	0.018	...	...
Tool cost per piece, excluding setup		$2.346		$1.900

(a) Labor and fringe costs at $4 per hour, including personal time allowance.

gressively smoother finishes during centerless grinding of piston pins is shown in Table 14.

Effect of Quantity. Grinding method used for producing 100 pieces per month normally is quite different from that for producing 10,000 pieces per month. Cost includes labor cost, fixed cost and machine and tool costs. The effect of quantity on time consumed, and hence on cost, is shown in Fig. 27, 28 and 29, each of which compares two different operations for grinding a specific part. Figure 40 also reflects the influence of quantity on cost.

Heavy Stock Removal

In some applications, grinding has supplanted planing, shaping, turning or milling for removing 0.10 to 0.25 in. of metal. Example 495 compares turning and cylindrical grinding. Example 530, in "Abrasive Belt Grinding", compares resurfacing in a planer with the same application using a wide abrasive belt. The following example compares milling and wheel grinding.

Example 525. Milling vs Grinding (Table 15)

The top and bottom surfaces of a gray iron motor base, 15 by 16 by 2⅜ in., were machined to make them flat and parallel and to produce a commercial finish. The top surface had an area of 240 sq in.; the four legs that comprised the bottom surface had an area of 43.6 sq in. Machining involved the removal of ⅛ in. of metal from the top and bottom surfaces, and was accomplished in two roughing cuts and two finishing cuts at normal speeds. A total of 35.5 cu in. of metal was removed from each piece. Only one piece at a time was processed.

Cost and efficiency of milling and grinding are compared in Table 15. Milling was done in a 20-hp bed-type vertical milling machine equipped with an 8-in. carbide face mill. Grinding was done in a 35-hp machine with an eight-segment wheel (A_s-24-H-V; porous). As shown in Table 15, milling required less machining time per piece and removed a greater volume of metal per unit of time, but grinding was less costly because of lower handling costs. [Less time is required to place the workpieces on the magnetic chuck of a grinder, blocking them if necessary, than to clamp workpieces to the table or fixture on a milling machine.]

Safety

The nature of the hazards in grinding (with grinding wheels) makes it necessary to follow rigid rules of safety that cover methods of grinding, machine conditions, safety guards, wheel mounting, grinding speeds, and everything else that may affect safety. These matters and others are covered fully in ASA B7.1-1964 (see the first reference below for exact title and availability of the standard safety code). Exceptions not covered are: wheels of natural stone, or of metal, wood, cloth, or paper, with abrasive surfaces.

Thread Grinding

Cylindrical and centerless grinding of threads in hardened steel and other workpieces are discussed in the article beginning on page 127. Six examples of production practice are included.

Gear Grinding

The two basic methods of grinding gears are form grinding and generating. These methods, as well as the "threading" of worms, are dealt with in the article "Grinding of Gears", which begins on page 213.

Selected References

"American Standard Safety Code for the Use, Care and Protection of Abrasive Wheels (B7.1)", American Standards Association, New York, 1964 (or later edition). This code is the authoritative statement on grinding safety, embodied in many state legal codes. It is also a useful source of terminology for grinding wheels and associated components. Copies are provided on request by wheel manufacturers.

K. B. Lewis, "The Grinding Wheel" (revised edition), Grinding Wheel Institute, Cleveland, 1959. Subtitled "A Textbook of Modern Grinding Practice", this is a good source of information on the subject. Highly readable and purposely avoids operational details. Also presents historical background of grinding.

L. P. Tarasov, Grinding Fluids, *The Tool and Manufacturing Engineer*, **46**, 67-73 (June 1961); **47**, 60-67 (July 1961); **47**, 57-63 (Aug 1961). A comprehensive review of the composition, behavior, selection and use of the various types of grinding fluids.

Other Examples of Grinding in This Volume

Work material	Example
Surface Grinding	
O1 tool steel	715
H11 tool steel	718
M1 tool steel	720, 721
420 stainless steel	787
303 stainless steel	788
U-500	854, 855
Ti – 6 Al – 4 V	1006
Cylindrical Grinding	
Gray iron, class 40	673
Malleable iron, pearlitic	675
Chilled cast iron	676
O2 tool steel	717
M10 tool steel	722, 723
M36 tool steel	724
440C stainless steel	789
303 stainless steel	790
Tungsten	866
Aluminum	924
Ti – 6 Al – 4 V	1007
Centerless Grinding	
Gray iron, class 40	674
W1 tool steel	714
M10 tool steel	725, 726, 727
302 stainless steel	791
416 stainless steel	792
Internal Grinding	
H11 tool steel	719
High speed steel	728, 729
440C stainless steel	793
Form Grinding	
17-4 PH stainless steel	794
AMS 5645 stainless steel	795
416 stainless steel	796
R-235	856
DCM	857
HS-31	858
Inconel	859
Thread Grinding	
Stainless steel	259, 262
Forged steel	260
4340	261
4330	263, 264
O1 tool steel	716
M2 tool steel	730
M7 tool steel	731
Gear Grinding	
9310	425, 426, 431
4140	427
7140	428
1118	429
4145	430
Alloy steel (carburized)	432

Abrasive Belt Grinding

ENDLESS BELTS precoated with abrasive are widely used for both grinding and polishing. This article deals with the use of these belts when stock removal and dimensional accuracy are the main objectives. Polishing is discussed in the article "Polishing and Buffing", which begins on page 371 of Volume 2 of this Handbook.

Contact Wheels. The contact wheel, over which the abrasive belt rides, provides an opposing pressure to the workpiece. Depending on its hardness, the contact wheel can provide either high unit pressure (hard wheel) or low unit pressure (soft wheel). Selection of contact wheel directly affects the rate of stock removal, the ability to blend, the surface finish obtained, and the cost of the grinding operation.

The manufacturer of contact wheels is responsible for speed-testing and balancing the wheels, as well as dressing the wheel faces for the operating speed at which they will be run. Although it is possible to operate a contact wheel satisfactorily at speeds from 2000 to 10,000 sfm, operating speeds usually range from 3500 to 7500 sfm.

Table 1 illustrates and describes the principal types of contact wheels and indicates their applicability to various grinding or polishing operations.

Applicability. Originally, the use of coated abrasive belts was limited to the grinding of flat surfaces, using straight-face contact wheels. However, after resin bonding of abrasives became practical, it was possible to produce belts with greater flexibility and improved joints, and to introduce improvements in machinery that permitted the use of coated belts in contour grinding.

Typical parts or operations that are or are not adaptable to belt grinding and polishing are listed below.

Adaptable

- Caps and barrels for fountain pens
- Golf-club heads and shafts
- Die-cast fry pans
- Automobile-bumper flat stock and bumpers
- Soleplates for electric irons
- Acorn faucets
- Bicycle cranks
- Percolator bodies
- Stainless steel and aluminum panels
- Screwdrivers and end wrenches
- Jet-engine turbine blades; nose cones
- Capacitor spacers for computers
- Hydraulic pistons
- Surface finishing of welded areas
- Centerless grinding of round shafting
- Beveling of glass products
- Flat-surfaced gears and other parts for watches and instruments
- Parts that are over ½ in. in diameter and over 0.025 in. thick, and that do not require less than 0.001-in. parallelism of top and bottom surfaces.

Not Readily Adaptable

- Very small parts and those with contoured surfaces, such as pivot ends, crowns, attachments, rounded or sculptured-form sections of cases
- Parts requiring a high degree of geometric accuracy for flatness and parallelism and for which dimensional tolerances of less than 0.001 in. are specified
- Contoured surfaces of gear teeth
- Cylindrical surfaces, such as those of pivots.

Limitations. Abrasive belts, disks and drums are seldom efficient or economical for removing thick stock or fins from sections adjacent to shoulders or projections, because the edges of the belt are fragile and break down rapidly. Also, coated abrasives cannot produce close accuracy during form grinding, although they are practical and economical for polishing forms on which close dimensional accuracy is not required. The strength of the backing usually limits the use of belts to applications in which the power requirement is less than 5 to 6 hp per inch of contact width.

Contour Grinding. There are three basic types of contour belt grinding:

1. Offhand — in which the work is handled entirely by a skilled operator
2. Semiautomatic — in which the operator feeds the work to the belt by means of mechanical tooling
3. Automatic — in which processing is entirely mechanical, except for loading and unloading.

In its simplest form, offhand belt grinding and polishing with contact wheels is performed on two-spindle polishing jacks, with backstand idlers mounted to the rear of each jack. The backstands provide tension on the belts

Table 1. Characteristics and Uses of Principal Types of Abrasive-Belt Contact Wheels

Wheel	Type	Material	Hardness	Purpose	Characteristics
1	Knurled or spiral grooved(a)	Steel	Rockwell C 52 to 55	Heavy grinding	Provides most aggressive action.
2	Cog tooth(b)	Rubber	70 to 90 durometer	Grinding(c)	Fast-cutting; allows long belt life.
3	Standard serrated(d)	Rubber	30 to 50 durometer(e)	Grinding(f)	Leaves rough-to-medium surface; excellent life.
4	X-shaped serrations(g)	Rubber	30 to 60 durometer	Grinding, polishing(h)	Flexibility allows entry to contours.
5	Plain face	Rubber	20 to 40 durometer(j)	Grinding, polishing(k)	Allows controlled penetration of abrasive grain.
6	Flexible	Compressed canvas	(m)	Grinding, polishing(n)	Tough and durable
7	Flexible	Rubber-coated canvas	Medium	Contour polishing	Contours well, yet gives substantial stock removal.
8	Flexible	Solid-section canvas	Soft, medium, hard	Polishing(p)	A low-cost wheel with uniform face density
9	Flexible	Buff-section canvas(q)	Soft	Contour polishing	For fine polishing and finishing; low-cost.
10	Pneumatic drum	Inflated rubber	(r)	Grinding, polishing	Gives uniform finishes; adjusts to contours.
11	Plastic foam	Polyurethane	Extremely soft	Fine polishing	Most flexible; for extreme contours.

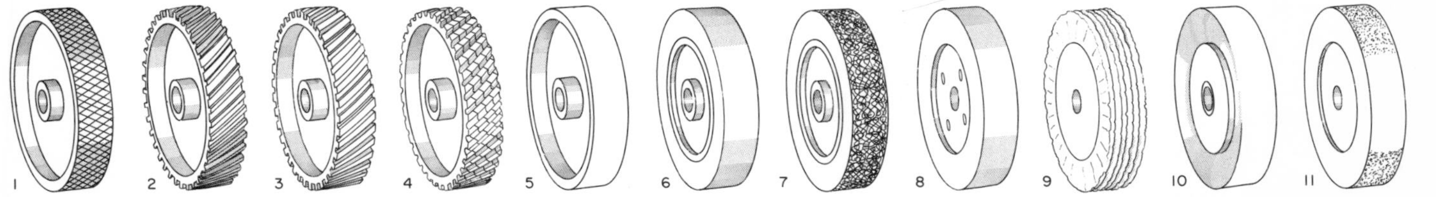

(a) No. 14 standard face; 4-pitch, 1/16 by 1/16 in. (b) Land, 3/16 in.; groove, 9/16 in.; depth, 5/16 in.; cushion, ¾ in. (c) For cutting down projections, such as weld beads, gates, risers and sprues. (d) Land, ⅜ in.; groove, ⅜ in.; depth, ⅜ in.; cushion, ⅞ in. (e) Wheel also may be of dual density, with harder rubber (60 durometer) at hub, softer rubber (20 to 40 durometer) at working surface. (f) For smoothing or blending cut-down projections or surface defects.

(g) Land, 3/16 in.; groove, 9/16 in.; depth, 5/16 in.; slit, ½-in. spaced; cushion, ⅞ in. (h) For light stock removal and medium polishing; preferred to standard serrated wheel for softer nonferrous materials. (j) Softer wheels give better finishes. (k) For flat surfaces. (m) Nine densities (very hard to very soft). Hard wheels can remove metal, but slower than wheel 2; softer wheels can polish the fine smoothness.

(n) Good for medium-range grinding and polishing; see footnote m. (p) Handles all types of polishing, giving uniform results without leaving abrasive pattern on work; adjusts to contours or can be pre-formed for contours. (q) Can be widened or narrowed by addition or removal of sections. (r) Hardness controlled by air pressure.

Table 2. Grit Sizes and Belt Speeds Recommended for Abrasive Belt Roughing and Polishing Applications(a)

Product	Roughing — Obstruction or roughness removed	Roughing — Grit size, mesh	Roughing — Belt speed, sfm	Rough polishing — Grit size, mesh	Rough polishing — Belt speed, sfm	Polishing — Grit size (mesh) for successive stages	Polishing — Belt speed, sfm	Polishing aid(b)
Aluminum:								
Die castings	Flash	220	5500	....	....	320	5500	G
Extrusions	Draw marks	180	5500	(c)	....	....	....	G
Pots and pans	....	....	....	80	5500	180, 240	5500	O
Sand castings	Gates	50	5500	80	5500	320	5500	G
Sheets	....	....	....	220	5200	(c)	....	G
Tubes	Die marks	....	....	....	....	220, 320	5000	G
Armatures (rotors), laminated	....	....	....	....	....	50	3600	WSO
Automobile bumpers (sheets)	Inclusions	100	3500	120	3500	150, 180(d)	3500	G
Axes — edging	Scale	36	5400	....	....	80	5500	G
Axes — sharpening	....	....	....	50	5500	....	....	G
Axles, cylindrical	....	....	....	50	5500	....	....	O
Band saws, steel	Pits	100	3500	....	....	150	3500	O
Bearings, inner or outer race	....	....	....	....	....	240	(e)	O
Beryllium, sheets	Pits	60(d)	2100	100(d)	2100	150(d)	2100	WSO
Billets, alloy or stainless steel	....	....	....	50	3500	....	....	G
Bits, steel — auger or flute	....	....	....	50	3500	150	5200	G
Brake lining(f)	....	....	....	36(d)	3500	....	....	....
Brass:								
Die castings	Flash	220	5500	....	....	320	5500	G
Sand castings	Gates	60	5500	....	....	180	5500	G
Sheet or strip	....	....	....	....	....	220, 320	4500	WSO
Bronze:								
Sand castings	Scale	60	3500	....	....	180	5500	G
Sheet or strip	....	....	....	....	....	220	4500	G
Tubes or bars	....	....	....	....	....	220, 320	5000	G
Cams, lobes(g)	....	....	....	80	5000	....	....	O
Cast iron (small castings)	Gates	50	3500	....	....	80	3500	....
Chilled iron rolls	....	....	....	50	3500	80, 120, 150, 220(d), 320(d)	3500	WSO
Chisels (woodworking), steel	....	....	....	80	5000	150	5000	G
Copper:								
Plumbing fixtures	Gates	60	5000	80	5200	220	5200	G
Rolls	....	....	....	....	....	320(d), 400(d)	5500	WSO
Sand castings	Scale	60	5500	80	5500	180	5500	G
Sheet or strip	....	....	....	....	....	320, 400	5000	O
Tubes or bars	....	....	....	50	3500	180	5000	WSO
Crankshaft pins and journals	....	....	....	....	....	320	(e)	O
Cutlery, stainless steel:								
Blades — tapering	....	50	5500	80	5500	180	5500	G
Forks or knives	....	....	....	80	5200	150	5200	G
Spoons	....	....	....	....	....	150, 220	5200	G
Dies, steel(h)	....	....	....	180	5000	320(d)	5000	WSO
Dies, tungsten carbide(h)	....	....	....	200(j)	5000	52 microns(j), 20 microns(j)	5000	WSO
Drive shafts, forged(k)	....	....	....	50	3500	150	3500	O
Electric irons, aluminum	....	....	....	150(d)	3500	220(d), 280(d), 320(d)	3500	O
Files (hand), hardened steel	....	....	....	....	....	50	5500	....
Gears, steel	Burrs	....	....	50	5000	....	....	....
Golf clubs, irons (forgings)	Scale	120	5800	....	....	150, 220	5800	G
Golf clubs, shafts	Weld excess	150	4500	....	....	220, 320	5500	WSO
Hammers, forged	....	....	....	50	5000	80	5200	G
Hypodermic needles, stainless	....	....	....	....	....	320(d), 400(d)	4600	WSO
Jet blades, Inconel	....	....	....	50	5500	120	5500	O
Jet blades, stainless steel:								
Airfoil	....	....	....	50	5500	120	5500	O
Longitudinal	....	....	....	....	....	80, 100, 120, 150, 180	(m)	O
Plow disks	Scale	50	3500	....	....	80	4200	G
Plowshares	Scale	50	3500	80	3500	....	....	G
Railroad track, butt welded	....	....	....	50	3500	....	....	....
Razor-blade strip(n)	Pits	100(d)	2100	120(d)	2100	....	....	O
Refrigerator doors, steel	Weld excess	80	5000	....	....	....	....	G
Relays, nickel	....	....	....	....	....	320	3500	....
Rifle barrels(k)	....	....	....	50	3500	80, 120, 180, 220, 320	4500	O
Rifle levers	....	....	....	80	5200	120	5200	G
Rifle receivers	....	....	....	50	4500	80, 120, 180, 240	4500	O
Saws, circular	Oxide	150	3500	....	....	....	....	WSO
Saws, strip	Scale	100	3500	....	....	....	....	O
Shears (bows, necks, sides)	....	....	....	80	5000	150, 240	5000	G
Shears (rings)	Flash	60	3000	....	....	150	4000	G
Shovel blades	....	....	....	50	3500	....	....	....
Silicon steel, rod or sheet	....	....	....	50(d)	3000	150(d)	3000	WSO
Skate blades, forged	Pits	80	3500	150	3500	240, 320	4000	G
Springs, coil(p)	....	....	....	....	....	120	3500	G
Springs, leaf	....	....	....	50	3500	....	....	O
Stainless steel:								
Coil (series 300)	Pits	60	3400	80	3400	120, 150	3400	O
Pots and pans	Wrinkles	80	5000	....	....	220, 320(d)	5000	G
Press plates	Scratches	80	4000	100	4000	120, 150, 180, 240, 320	4000	G
Sheets, No. 3 finish	....	....	....	80	4000	100	4000	G
Sheets, No. 4 finish	Inclusions	100	4000	120	4000	150(d)	4000	G
Sheets, No. 7 finish	Inclusions	100	4000	150	4000	180(d), 240(d), 280(d)	4000	G
Tubes	....	....	....	150	3500	220, 280, 320	4500	O
Turbine nozzles and buckets	....	....	....	80	5000	120	4500	G
Steel, mild:								
Centerless or cylindrical	....	....	....	50	3500	150, 220, 320	3500	O
Stampings	....	....	....	....	....	120	4500	G
Titanium, sheets	....	....	....	80(d)	2800	100(d), 120(d), 150(d)	2800	(q)
Tools (hand), forged	Flash	50	3500	80	4500	100, 150, 240, 320	4500	G
Wrought iron	Burrs(r)	....	....	50	3500	100	4000	....
Zinc-base die castings	Flash	80	5000	....	....	220	5000	G
Zinc sheets	Pits	100	5000	150(d)	5000	220(d), 240(d), 280(d), 400(d)	5000	O

(a) Abrasive belts coated with aluminum oxide, unless grit size is footnoted to indicate otherwise. (b) G, grease; O, oil; WSO, water-soluble oil. (c) Operation was completed with abrasive-impregnated nylon wheel. (d) Silicon carbide. (e) Fixtured abrasive. (f) Molded or metal mix. (g) Hardened steel cams for diesel engines. (h) Drawing and sinking dies. (j) Diamond abrasive. (k) Centerless. (m) Fixtured abrasive, reciprocating. (n) Grinding of crown. (p) Grind end. (q) Solution of K_3PO_4 or nitrate amine. (r) And excess weld metal.

by means of springs or air cylinders, and also track the belts accurately over the contact wheel. Most jacks have motors of 5 or 7½ hp, capable of giving belt speeds of 3500 to 7500 sfm.

A more complicated operation requires the use of a machine in which the contact wheel is an idler mounted on the yoke in front of the machine, and uniform belt tension is maintained by a screw-actuated or air-tensioned idler wheel mounted over the drive pulley. Because they employ lower belt speeds and have more uniform belt tension, these machines can handle a variety of deep contouring operations and can accommodate wheels of a more complex shape. Consequently, these machines are used to grind and polish workpieces with complicated shapes, such as surgical instruments, scissors, jet-engine blades, plumbing fixtures, cutlery and propellers. Even narrow belts, from ½ to 3 in. in width, can be readily used.

In offhand formed-contact-wheel abrasive belt grinding and polishing, bias buff wheels, compressed-canvas wheels, and muslin polishing wheels made from spiral-sewed buff sections are most widely used. Formed rubber and felt wheels are usually reserved for special jobs.

Belt Speed. Too slow a belt speed results in the rapid fracture of abrasive grains, thereby lowering cutting efficiency and causing the belt to shed abrasive. Too fast a belt speed results in glazing or dulling of the abrasive, and greatly shortens belt life.

For heavy stock removal, speeds of less than 3500 sfm are seldom used. Belt speeds in excess of 7500 sfm are not recommended, because they result in high frictional heat and rapid glazing of the abrasive. It is general practice to use belt speeds ranging from 3500 to 5500 sfm for heavy stock removal, and from 4500 to 7500 sfm for polishing.

Belt speeds and abrasive grit sizes used for a variety of applications are given in Table 2.

Lubricants are applied to belts to extend their life and to improve surface finish. Choice of lubricant is influenced largely by the type of metal being ground and the degree of metal cutting.

Belt lubricants are available in grease-stick tube form for offhand grinding and polishing operations. Their principal function is the elimination of excessive heat, which causes discoloration, distortion and warping. In polishing low-melting-point metals, selection of the proper lubricant prevents surface fusion and greatly simplifies any subsequent buffing.

Within limits, abrasive-belt lubricants help to control surface finish. For example, a heavy-bodied lubricant loads between the abrasive grains and serves as a cushion; consequently, only the top of the abrasive grit is permitted to penetrate the work surface, thus reducing the depth of cut and refining the surface finish. In contrast, a light-bodied lubricant serves to keep the belt "open", thus assisting in stock removal (in this case, the belt surface stays wet and oily, and grinding debris is prevented from redepositing and clogging the coated abrasive surface).

It is sometimes possible to reduce grinding and polishing time and improve surface finish by using a coarse-grit belt with a lubricant, rather than a fine-grit belt without a lubricant. By eliminating dry patches and providing a more uniform cutting action over the whole surface of the belt, the lubricant permits greater stock removal without burning.

Lubricants should be applied in small amounts and at frequent intervals as the grinding operation progresses. Great caution must be exercised in applying lubricants to belts that are operating on semiautomatic or automatic machines. Although kerosine and mixtures of kerosine and machine oil are frequently ideal in their lubricating properties, the low flash points of these liquids make them entirely unsuitable for semiautomatic and automatic applications; safe lubricants for use on grinding belts include mineral oil and emulsions of soluble oil and water.

Stock Removal, Finish, and Tolerance. Stock removal rates of ¼ to ⅜ in. per minute per inch of contact width have been achieved with coarse-grit belts and contact wheels on cast iron and soft steel parts on a through-feed basis while maintaining tolerances of ±0.002 in. on flatness and parallelism. In centerless grinding operations, stock removal rates of 40 to 100 lb of steel per hour are not uncommon. With finer grit sizes, tolerances of ±0.0005 in. are readily obtainable. In addition to the type and hardness of contact wheel used, finish is determined by the grit size. It is relatively easy to obtain finishes of 10 micro-in. with fine grit sizes, but stock removal rates and belt life will be decreased. Maximum economy is usually associated with the coarsest grit size that will produce an acceptable finish.

Examples of Practice

The four examples that follow deal with the use of coated abrasive belts for removing stock to close tolerances.

Example 526. Rough and Finish Grinding in One Pass

Hedge shear blades, made of carbon steel heat treated to Rockwell C 47 to 53, 0.209 in. thick by 1⅜ in. wide by 9½ in. long, were rough and finish ground in one pass in a two-head belt grinder with a reciprocating table. Aluminum oxide belts 10 in. wide operating at 3500 sfm removed up to 0.009 in. of stock per side from the blade. A 60-grit belt was used to rough 1000 blades and was then replaced with a new belt. The used belt was moved to the finishing head to finish grind 1000 pieces. Thus each belt rough and finish ground 1000 blades.

A magnetic chuck held 32 pieces per load. Table speed for the first side was 3.5 fpm and removed 0.004 to 0.005 in. per belt. The blade was then turned over and ground to a thickness of 0.195 in. at a table speed of 7 fpm.

Production rate was 300 finished pieces per hour (ground both sides). This machine replaced two single-disk grinders that produced 100 pieces per hour.

Example 527. Belt Grinding of Tool Steel

A four-head centerless belt grinder was used to remove stock from M1 and M2 tool steel bars ¼ in. in diameter by 12 ft long. The machine was equipped with four coated abrasive belts, 5 in. wide by 84 in. long, of 80, 180, 320 and 400 grit, respectively. The four belts removed 0.005 to 0.006 in. of stock per pass, and the production rate was 900 bars per shift (40 ft per min). The bars had a final surface finish of 15 micro-in. and a tolerance of 0.0003 in. TIR. A sulfurized grinding oil was used. Four or five belts were required during each shift (one belt per head per shift).

Example 528. Belt Grinding of Steel Tubing

Low-carbon seamless steel tubes, 2¾ to 8 in. in outside diameter, were ground on a single-head centerless belt grinder. Three belts of different grit sizes were used: 24 to 50 grit for roughing, 150 to 180 grit for intermediate finishing, and 220 to 400 grit for final polishing. Grinding of the 8-in.-diam tubing removed 0.005 to 0.006 in. of metal per pass at 60 in. per minute; 0.004 in. of metal per pass was removed at 130 in. per minute from tubing 3 in. in diameter. After rough grinding, tubes were round within 0.002 in. TIR and had a 120-micro-in. finish. After intermediate grinding, roundness improved to 0.001 in. TIR and surface finish to 30 to 40 micro-in. After final polishing, roundness remained at 0.001 in. TIR, but finish had further improved to 14 to 18 micro-in. A water-soluble grinding fluid was used. The service life of each belt was 60 to 80 lb of metal removed.

Example 529. Belt Grinding of Large Rolls

Paper mill rolls made from gray iron (25,000 to 40,000 psi), 10 to 15 ft in diameter and as long as 20 ft, were ground by a traveling belt grinder equipped with an abrasive belt 4 in. wide. Rough grinding was done dry, beginning with a 36-grit belt that removed 10 to 25 lb of metal per hour. For rough grinding of rolls less than 10 ft long, the 36 grit was followed by 80 and 180-grit sizes. For grinding of rolls longer than 10 ft, initial grinding with 36 grit was followed by 60, 120 and 180-grit sizes in succession, each finer grit removing less metal than the preceding grit. The finishing operation was the same for all rolls and was accomplished with a belt of 320 grit and a water-soluble grinding fluid. A total of 0.060 to 0.080 in. was removed from the diameter of each roll. Final surface finish and dimensional tolerance were 10 to 15 micro-in., and 0.0005 to 0.0015 in. TIR, respectively. Roughing belts were consumed at the rate of approximately one per roll, whereas the final finishing belts (320 grit) lasted for four to six rolls.

Example 530. Planing vs Grinding

Large 4140 steel foundry plates, 88 by 76 by 2 in., weighing 3000 lb, used for setting up sand molds in the pouring of zinc alloy dies, had to be flat and level. After years of service, these plates became warped and had to be machined to their original flatness. When done on a planer, resurfacing both sides of each plate required a total time of 8 hr.

Tests to determine if flat and parallel surfaces could be obtained on a large belt grinding machine yielded good results. Not only was the 60-micro-in. surface finish obtained an improvement over that produced previously, but total grinding time of about 4 hr was 50% less than the time required for planing.

The machine used an abrasive belt 86 in. wide and was powered by a 250-hp motor. Table speed was 6 sfm; belt speed, 5000 sfm. Waterproof cloth aluminum-oxide abrasive belts were used. Rough grinding, in which 36-grit abrasive was used, removed 0.500 in. of material from each side in approximately 1½ hr per side; finish grinding, using 60-grit abrasive, removed 0.010 in. in about 20 min. Water-soluble oil was the grinding fluid.

Wide-sheet grinding uses wide abrasive belts in machine-tool-type equipment in a smooth, continuous precision operation. Applications range from heavy stock removal to fine polishing, including: sizing of extrusions and of all kinds of sheet and coil stock, and applications of "special ground" or satin finishes to stainless steel.

Other Examples of Abrasive Belt Grinding in This Volume

Work material	Example number
403, 422 stainless steel	797
CF-20 (302) cast stainless steel	798
310 stainless steel	799
HS-31 heat-resisting alloy	860

Electrical Discharge Grinding (EDG)

By John F. Kahles*

ELECTRICAL DISCHARGE GRINDING (EDG) is much like electrical discharge machining (see article beginning on page 227), except that the electrode (tool) is a rotating graphite wheel. The work is fed to the wheel by a servo-controlled worktable. The workpiece is cut by the action of a stream of electric sparks between a negatively charged wheel and a positively charged workpiece immersed in a dielectric fluid. Each spark discharge melts or vaporizes a small amount of metal from the workpiece surface, producing a small crater at the discharge site, as in EDM.

The stream of sparks is produced by high-frequency pulses of direct current in an arrangement like the one shown in Fig. 1. The power supply and the dielectric fluid are similar to those used in EDM, but lower amperage is used in most EDG applications, because the cutting area is usually small and the method is used primarily to achieve accuracy and smooth finish.

Grinder. The graphite wheel is rotated at 100 to 600 sfm, the spindle being insulated from the wheel to isolate the electrical circuit. High wheel speed causes oil splash; excessively low speed may result in nonuniform wheel wear and in out-of-roundness. The spark gap is normally held at 0.0005 to 0.0030 in. by a servomechanism that controls the motion of the worktable. The machining gap is immersed in or flooded by a dielectric fluid like those used in EDM, usually a hydrocarbon oil having a viscosity of about 40 SUS at 100 F.

The power supply may be rated at 30 to 400 volts, 20 to 100 amp, up to 50 mfd capacitance, and pulse frequency of 2 to 260 kc. Machining current for most applications is 0.5 to 15 amp, at a potential of 40 to 80 volts.

When work loads in grinding do not justify an EDG machine, it is possible to use a conventional EDM machine in which the EDG wheel is mounted and rotated on the vertical spindle. The EDM machine is modified for servo feed of the worktable (instead of tool feed).

The grinding wheel, rotating at approximately 1500 sfm, is dressed by a tool arranged on the machine as shown in Fig. 2. The grinding wheel may be rough dressed at 0.050 in. per pass of the tool of hardened steel, followed by a finishing pass of 0.005 in.

For precision grinding, extreme rigidity is needed for minimum deflection during grinding and in-process wheel dressing. Spindle runout can be held to a maximum of 0.00004 in. TIR; deflection in wheel dressing can be held to 0.00015 in., for traversing 8 in. on hardened and ground V-ways.

Control. Higher voltage permits larger spark gaps; this is of value in plunge grinding, for ease of flushing with dielectric fluid. An average spark gap is about 0.001 in. Higher electric current cuts faster but leaves a rougher, more damaged surface — crater size is proportional to spark energy.

*Vice President, Metcut Research Associates, Inc.

Smaller current is used to produce smoother, less damaged surfaces, especially in the grinding of carbide. Higher pulse frequency makes a smoother surface. Greater capacitance generally is used for faster cutting.

In conventional EDM, it is not practical to plan on producing a surface finish finer than 20 to 40 micro-in. with graphite electrodes. In EDG, because of the "wiping" action of the wheel past the workpiece, surface finish of 10 micro-in. is practical.

Once the machining cycle has been started, operator attention is not required on automatic EDG machines. The servo drive for the worktable is controlled by the voltage between the grinding wheel and the workpiece. When the voltage is high (about 80 volts), the workpiece is rapidly traversed toward the grinding wheel until the first spark occurs. At this point, the voltage drops to the normal machining range (40 to 60 volts), and the servo device maintains a constant spacing between the grinding wheel and the workpiece (normally in the range of 0.0005 to 0.0030 in., depending on the power supply settings. The servo system automatically backs the work away from the grinding wheel if the voltage drops for any reason.

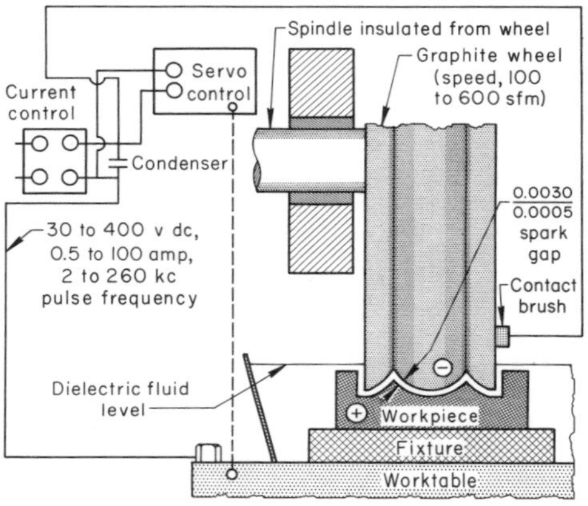

Fig. 1. Setup for electrical discharge grinding

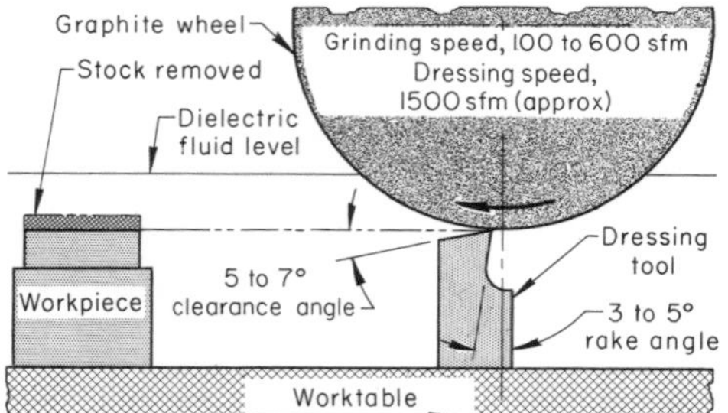

Fig. 2. Setup for in-process dressing of an electrical discharge grinding wheel

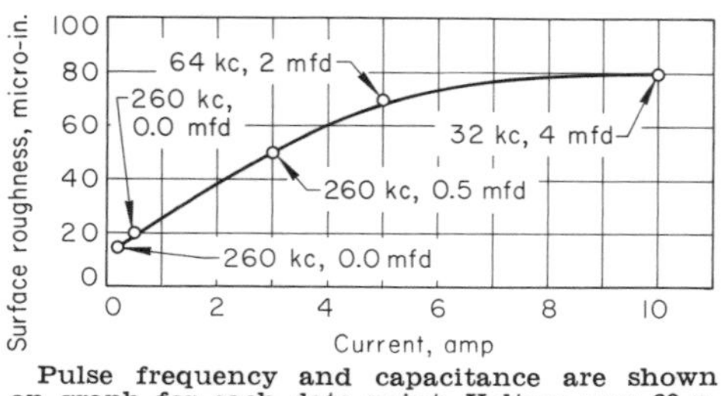

Pulse frequency and capacitance are shown on graph for each data point. Voltage was 60 v, except 50 v at 0.2 amp. Dielectric fluid was a hydrocarbon (petroleum) oil with viscosity of about 40 SUS at 100 F. Wheel was graphite.

Fig. 3. Effect of operating conditions on surface roughness in electrical discharge grinding of tungsten carbide

Applications. Electrical discharge grinding is used for work that demands great accuracy, such as the making of form tools. Tolerances of ±0.0002 in. are common; ±0.00005 in. can be obtained in some applications. It is a slow process, removing only 0.01 to 0.15 cu in. of stock per hour. Higher metal removal rates result in a quality of surface finish that is usually acceptable only for certain roughing applications. Besides making carbide form tools, EDG is used to grind carbide in shapes such as lamination dies, crushing rolls, and tools of other kinds. It is used also to grind other hard materials such as gear racks, for making closely spaced thin slots in hard materials, for grinding brittle or fragile parts, and for production grinding of complex shapes.

Cast iron is not ordinarily processed by EDG, because it is readily ground by conventional methods, and because nonconductive impurities (sand and slag) are not removed by the spark discharge and can damage the wheel.

Process Characteristics. Surface roughness depends primarily on the metal removal rate, as shown below for the grinding of carbide:

0.150 cu in. per hr	125 micro-in.
0.075	40
0.012	15

The effect of operating conditions on the grinding of tungsten carbide is illustrated in Fig. 3. Further decreases in frequency and increases in capacitance beyond the values shown in Fig. 3, while holding the current at 10 amp, will increase surface roughness substantially. For example, roughness was 110 micro-in. at 16 kc and 10 mfd, and 150 micro-in. at 8 kc and 14 mfd. Results vary for other metals and grinding conditions.

Corner radius depends on overcut; minimum corner radius in typical EDG applications is 0.0005 to 0.005 in.

The grinding of stainless steel is illustrated in Table 1, which shows workpiece and wheel configurations for four parts, and gives processing details. The wheel used in making Part 3 has a herringbone pattern cut in the working surface to improve the flushing action.

Wheel Wear. The wear ratio in EDG depends on current density, tool material, work material, and dielectric fluid. Volume-wear ratio (ratio of work volume removed to wheel volume removed) may range from 100:1 to 0.1:1; average volume-wear ratio is about 3:1.

Wheel wear, however, is spread over the entire periphery of the wheel; thus, assuming uniform distribution of wear, linear-wear ratio (ratio of depth of cut to depth of wheel wear) is much higher. For a 1-in. length of cut, average linear-wear ratio would be 75:1 for an 8-in. wheel or 110:1 for a 12-in. wheel. In grinding irregular contours, wheel wear is concentrated on the high points and sharp edges of the profile, and more frequent redressing is required than for uniform wear.

Dressing EDG graphite wheels is faster and cheaper than dressing diamond wheels for the grinding of carbides.

Brass wheels are sometimes used to cut sections thinner than 0.015 in., or when dielectric circulation is difficult.

Effect on the Workpiece. As in EDM the high temperatures attained in melting and vaporizing metal from the workpiece affect a thin layer (0.0001 to 0.0015 in.) of the surfaces ground by EDG. Figure 4 shows typical changes caused by EDG in the hardness of four materials in roughing and in finishing cuts. Carbide and other materials are also affected. For this reason, EDG is more widely used in forming carbide tools than in sharpening them. Although some carbides are damaged by EDG, and transverse strength may be reduced, form tools shaped by EDG are satisfactory. For high-stress applications, the surface layer affected by EDG may have to be removed.

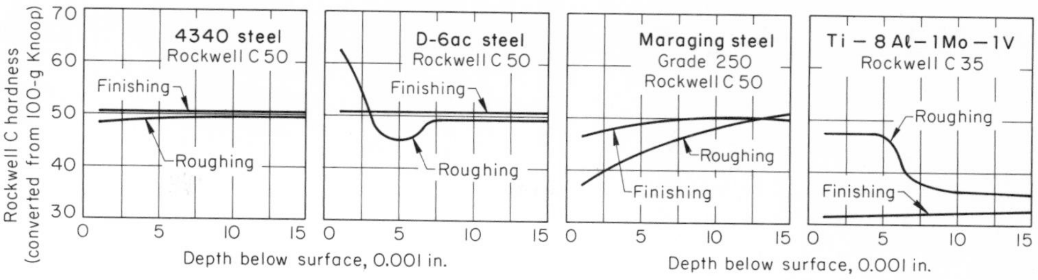

Fig. 4. Effect of heat in EDG on surface hardness of various work metals

Table 1. Typical Applications and Conditions for Electrical Discharge Grinding of Stainless Steels, Using 12-In.-Diameter Wheels

Work					Operating conditions					Results				
Part No.	Type of stainless steel	Description of workpiece	Shape produced	Dimensions of shape produced	Speed, rpm	Volts	Amp	Capacitance, mfd	Pulse frequency, kc/sec	Grinding rate, in.³/hr	Cutting time, min	Volume wear ratio	Overcut, in. per side	Finish, micro-in.
1	303	Rod, 0.531-in. diam by 1 7/32 in. long	3 grooves	3/16 in. wide, 0.218 in. deep; full-radius bottom	20	70	10	6	32	0.470	6	3:1	0.0017	200
2	304	Strip, 0.104 by 4.000 by 6.500 in.	Rib	0.600 in. wide, 0.010 in. deep; central web 0.010 in. wide	20	70	0.5	0.5	32	0.06	44	3:1	0.001	60
3	304	Strip, 1/8 by 3 by 20 in.	2 grooves	2.800 in. wide, 0.020 in. deep	20	70	2	2	130	0.156	400	6:1	0.001	60
4	304	Hexagonal tubing, 2 1/4 in. by 0.050-in. wall	Face, step-cut end	Step, 0.187 in. deep	34	80	8	2	32	....	30	...	0.001	125

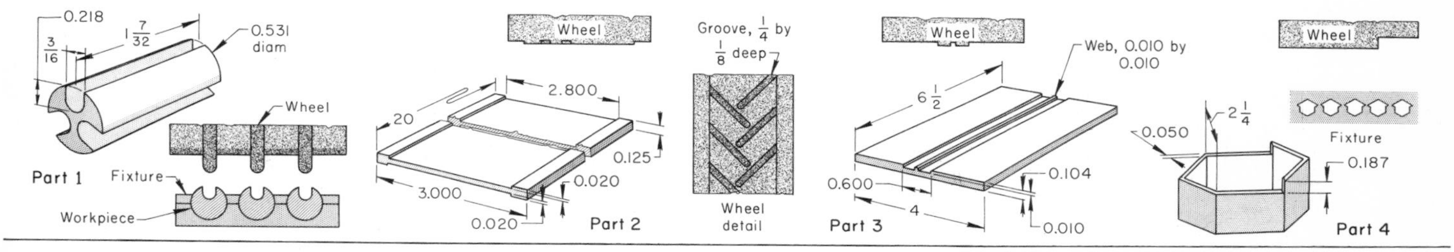

Electrochemical Grinding (ECG)

ELECTROCHEMICAL GRINDING (ECG), also called electrolytic grinding, is a combination of wheel grinding with electrochemical action. The abrasive action of the grinding wheel removes less than 10% of the stock, most of the material being removed by anodic dissolution, as in electrochemical machining (ECM). Electrochemical grinding is similar to ECM, except that the cathode is a specially constructed grinding wheel instead of a tool shaped like the contour to be machined. Both the workpiece and the grinding wheel must be electrically conductive.

Electrochemical grinding is used primarily to grind carbide tools, metals of extremely high hardness, and parts that are fragile or susceptible to heat damage.

Description of Process. Electrolyte is flooded onto the workpiece, instead of being forced through the cutting gap at high pressure as in ECM. The grinding wheel throws off a spray of electrolyte, the liquid collecting for return to the supply tank. Then the electrolyte is pumped through a filter before it flows again onto the wheel and the work. Figure 1 is a schematic diagram of an ECG setup for plunge grinding.

The current flows from the d-c source through the workpiece (anode, positive) and the electrolyte to the grinding wheel (cathode, negative) and back to the d-c source. The workpiece metal goes into solution as metal ions (anodic dissolution), and bubbles of hydrogen are generated at the wheel. Either the wheel and spindle or the workpiece must be insulated to isolate the electrical circuit from the surroundings. The protruding parts of the nonconductive grains of abrasive shown in Fig. 1 prevent the conductive body of the grinding wheel from shorting against the workpiece and define the electrolytic cutting gap.

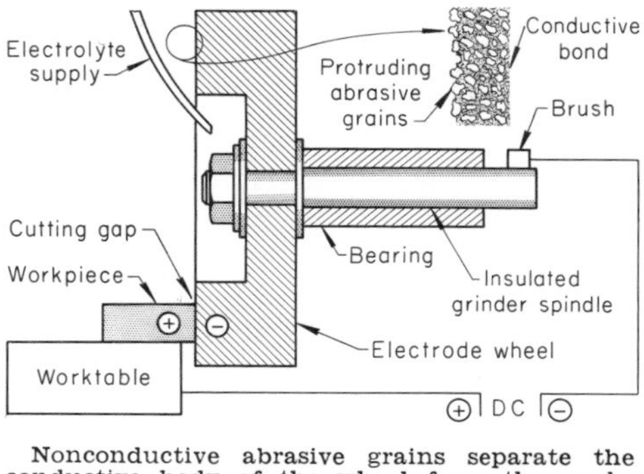

Nonconductive abrasive grains separate the conductive body of the wheel from the workpiece, and determine the thickness of the cutting gap, which is flooded with electrolyte during grinding.

Fig. 1. Schematic diagram of setup for electrochemical plunge grinding

Electrolyte. The space between the wheel and the work must be filled with electrolyte at all times during electrochemical grinding. Failure to do this, or to maintain flow rate or electrolyte strength, will reduce the rate of metal removal and cause needless wear of the wheel.

Electrolytes for ECG resemble those used for ECM in that they are electrically conductive aqueous solutions containing chiefly inorganic salts, and in that many of the same chemicals used in ECM are also present in ECG electrolytes. However, the formulations for ECG are distinctly different. They are designed to enable the electrochemical formation of oxide films on the positively charged work metal faster than the film dissolves in the electrolyte, whereas in ECM any oxides formed on the work must dissolve at once in the electrolyte. The abrading action of the

ECG wheel continuously exposes fresh metal for the electrochemical reaction.

Concentration of dissolved salts (usually sodium or potassium salts) is ordinarily in the range of 1 to 2 lb per gal, to provide an electrical conductance of about 0.05 to 0.15 mho per cm. Compositions that have been described in the literature for use on carbide are listed in Table 1. (See also Example 531 and Table 3.) The cobalt binder in sintered carbides dissolves anodically at 1.2 volts; tungsten carbide forms the oxide WO_3 at 1.7 volts; and titanium carbide forms the oxide TiO_2 at 3.0 volts. Electrolytes may contain chemicals selected to provide added solubility for the reaction products. Rochelle salts (sodium potassium tartrate) or phosphates aid in dissolving WO_3 by complex formation. Phosphates have the disadvantage of forming insoluble cobalt compounds. Dissolution of cobalt is aided by the formation of soluble complexes with ammonia, which is produced by reduction of nitrites or nitrates at the cathode.

Major components, such as nitrites or alkaline sodium or potassium compounds (borate, carbonate, phosphate or tartrate), reduce corrosive attack on the equipment, which is usually unalloyed steel. Tungstate salts produced during machining also help to reduce corrosion, and small amounts of inhibitors such as chromates, molybdates, benzoates, silicates, amines or certain soluble oils are sometimes included in the electrolyte. Chlorides increase corrosion of the equipment.

Potassium salts cost about two to five times as much as the corresponding sodium salts, but are much more soluble in water.

Encrustation of equipment with salts and grinding sludge is a major problem in equipment maintenance. The use of readily soluble salts and the presence in the electrolyte of chemicals that keep encrusted material from caking and drying to a hard, practically insoluble mass are of particular value in toolroom grinding installations.

The general composition of electrolytes used for several metals in addition to carbide is indicated in Table 3 and Example 531. Metals that are highly resistant to chemical attack may require the use of electrolytes containing chlorides. In spite of their corrosive action on equipment, compositions that are essentially sodium or potassium chloride are sometimes used for roughing applications where high removal rates are required.

The electrolytes generally used on carbide are sometimes used also on tool steel to avoid having to change solutions, although they give somewhat slower removal rates. When carbide and steel must be ground in a single cut, a mixture of the two types of electrolytes is sometimes used.

Electrical Variables. In general, less power is needed for ECG than for ECM, because the machining area is smaller. Total current ranges from 50 to 3000 amp, at 4 to 10 volts, through an electrolyte gap of about 0.001 in. The process is usually operated at room temperature, at a wheel speed of 4000 to 6000 sfm. Operating voltage is adjusted to give the maximum removal rate consistent with surface-finish requirements and acceptable tool wear. This adjustment is often made by increasing voltage setting until audible, blue sparking is observed and then reducing the voltage slightly.

Feed rate for plunge grinding at a current density of 500 amp per sq in. (asi) is 0.050 in. per min and at 2000 asi is 0.200 in. per min. Feed rate for surface grinding depends on depth of cut, current density, and wheel diameter. Depth of cut usually does not exceed 0.100 in. A typical current density, 1000 asi, will permit table feed of about 1 in. per min for a cut 0.100 in. deep in surface grinding.

Grinding wheels for ECG are made of abrasive material and a bonding agent. Electrochemical grinding wheels with aluminum oxide abrasive can be used for grinding steel. They have brass or other alloys as the bonding agent, or a copper-impregnated resin (especially for form grinding). The particle size of the aluminum oxide is 60 to 80 mesh for the metal-bond wheels; 100-mesh aluminum oxide is used for resin-bond wheels. Diamond is also used as abrasive in grinding wheels for carbide and for steel harder than Rockwell C 65; the bonding agent is a copper alloy or a copper-impregnated resin, and diamond particle size is 100 to 120 mesh.

Wheels for ECG are specially constructed for the desired combination of electrochemical and mechanical grinding action. The nonconducting abrasive grains protrude above the metal bond, defining the electrolytic gap between the wheel and the work and assisting in the machining operation by the mechanical removal of small amounts of metal from the work surface. This mechanical action removes nonreactive constituents, metal oxides or hydroxides, and other insoluble material from the surface, exposing fresh metal for further electrochemical attack.

Metal-bond wheels are prepared for ECG by removing a layer of metal to expose the grains of abrasive on the working surface of the wheel, as shown in Fig. 1. Metal is dissolved anodically ("deplated") from the wheel surface by passing the current in the reverse direction from that normally used in the process. Deplating must be repeated after each wheel-truing operation.

Copper-impregnated resin-bond wheels have adequate electrical conductivity for ECG, can be dressed easily, and do not need deplating; they are prepared by a prerun on a scrap piece. In normal operation, the surface layer of copper-impregnated resin gradually sloughs off, to expose an insulating layer of abrasive grains. If quality of finish is not critical, resin-bond wheels can be "worn in" on a production run.

It has been found by experiment that as much as 99% of the metal removal is by electrochemical action, and 1% by mechanical grinding; 90-to-10 is the accepted ratio for the usual conditions of production. Excessive wear of the grinding wheel, excessive marking, burning or burring of the work, and continuous rise of the load on the spindle indicate incorrect operating conditions or equipment malfunction.

Wheel-workpiece pressure usually is in the range of 50 to 200 psi. In one mode of operation, the pressure is controlled by regulating the feed rate, on the basis of calculations and experience. In a second mode of operation, a predetermined pressure is maintained by a hydraulic cylinder.

Table 1. Compositions of Five ECG Electrolytes for Use on Carbide (a)

Constituent	Electrolyte A	B	C(b)	D	E
$NaNO_2$	4.4	1.5	8.7	...	6.6
KNO_2	...	...	...	8.0	...
KNO_3	...	10.1	...	...	...
Na_2SO_4	7.1	...	...	...	...
Na_3PO_4 ...	...	...	3.7	...	...
$Na_2B_4O_7$ ...	...	...	1.7	...	0.6
Na_2CO_3 ...	...	...	...	...	1.8
Rochelle salt	...	7.6	...	5.3	...
Na_2WO_4 ...	...	...	...	...	4.0
Sulfonamide ..	2.8	...	...	...	...
Oleic acid .	3.7	...	...	...	...
Sodium soap	10.4	...	...	...	...
Oil(c)	2.0	...	...	...	...
Total ...	30.4	19.2	14.1	13.3	13.0

(a) Approximate compositions in ounces per gallon of solution, as described in: H. Reinhart and W. Grünwald, Electrolytic Stock Removal of Hard Metal and Carbide by Diamond Grinding Wheels, *Werkstatt und Bertrieb*, April 1962, p 212-218 (English translation by Diametal A G, Biel, Switzerland, and by *Machine Tool Engineering and Production News*).
(b) Also shown at half these concentrations.
(c) Unsaponifiable.

Contact Arc. The wheel should not touch the work along the cutting path in an arc longer than 0.75 in., because ordinarily this is the greatest contact length in which the electrolyte can be active. In a longer arc of contact, the electrolyte would build up excessive amounts of hydrogen, dissolved metal, and insoluble oxide or hydroxide. In order to grind by ECG along an arc longer than 0.75 in., either the feed rate must be reduced or special techniques must be used to supply fresh electrolyte to the grinding area at an increased rate.

Surface Finish. It is usual to obtain a surface finish of 5 to 10 micro-in. by electrochemical plunge grinding of carbide, and of 10 to 15 micro-in. by surface or traverse grinding. Surface finish of steel is ordinarily 15 to 30 micro-in. after ECG. A smoother finish is obtained at higher current density. Because of the mechanical abrading action, ECG finishes are less sensitive than ECM finishes to lack of homogeneity in the work metal. Finish passes are not needed to improve the surface, but sometimes a finish pass by mechanical grinding (without electric current) is useful when extreme dimensional accuracy is required.

Accuracy of ECG, depending on the processing conditions, can be as close as 0.0005 in., except for sharp corners. Dimensional accuracy can be improved still further by a final mechanical finishing pass without the use of electric current. For the greatest accuracy, most of the stock is removed by ECG, leaving 0.0005 to 0.0010 in. of finishing stock. After the ECG pass, the current is turned off to make a finishing pass by mechanical grinding without disturbing the setup further.

Because of grit size and electrolytic overcut, minimum corner radius for ECG is 0.010 to 0.015 in., depending some-

Table 2. Maximum Current Densities for Electrochemical Grinding
(Based on active cutting area)

Work material	Current density, amp per sq in.
Carbide, straight tungsten grades for machining cast iron	500 to 800
Carbide, grades containing added tantalum or titanium carbide for machining steel	800 to 1000
Steel, low-carbon	3000 to 4000
Steel, high-carbon	2000 to 3000
Stainless steel	3000 to 4000
Stellite	300 to 1000
U-500 heat-resisting alloy	3000 to 4000

what on the work material. The grinding wheel can be dressed to make any inside radius greater than the minimum. Outside corners can be ground sharp without any limiting minimum radius.

Cutting rate, or rate of metal removal, depends on current density. Table 2 shows the maximum allowable current densities for various metals. The amount of current used in a specific ECG operation is the product of the current density and the area of the cut. For purposes of preliminary planning, a metal removal rate of 0.1 cu in. per minute per 1000 amp can be assumed for most metals. The actual value for any given work metal depends on its density and on the valence at which it dissolves. Metal removal rates range between 0.04 and 0.3 cu in. per minute per 1000 amp. See Tables 1 and 5 (pages 234 and 237) in the article "Electrochemical Machining" for a list of removal rates for various metals.

To obtain maximum cutting rate, the cutting area should be as large as possible. However, because of equipment limitations, it is sometimes necessary to use a small cutting area and a low metal removal rate.

To estimate the time needed for electrochemical grinding, the following sequence of steps is necessary.

1 Selection of the best setup
2 Determination of the area of the cut
3 Selection of current density. This determines the number of amperes needed, and sets the rate of cutting (cubic inches removed per minute per 1000 amperes).
4 Calculation of cutting time per piece
5 Determination of work handling time (loading and unloading) per piece.

This procedure will give the total time and power needed. If there is insufficient power for the maximum cutting rate, the work can be done at a slower rate.

In sharpening cutters, the grinding of both carbide and tool steel in the same cut is sometimes required. An average current density can be calculated, based on the ratio of the areas of the two materials. In surface grinding of carbide-tipped tools, where the wheel would first grind carbide and then pass to steel, the power needed should be calculated for the current density for steel. The feed rate should be set on the basis of the current density for carbide.

Methods

The following is a brief discussion on five methods of electrochemical grinding and a listing of advantages and disadvantages. Typical applications are then indicated and are followed by three examples of production use.

Plunge grinding, with the area to be ground fed against the face of a wheel (as shown in Fig. 1), is the fastest method of ECG. The wheel should move back and forth in the grinding plane to make the wheel wear evenly, thus avoiding needless truing of the wheel, and producing a smoother finish. Hand feed with positive stops can produce good results in tool work and in production of small lots. For larger lots the feed should be automatic.

The procedure for estimating ECG power requirements, cutting time, and feed rate is illustrated below for the removal of 0.0625 in. from a flat 0.500 in. by 1.000 in. on a steel-cutting grade of carbide.

The average current density indicated for this material in Table 2 is 900 amp per sq in. To find the current needed, multiply the current density by the area to be ground:

$$900 \times (0.500 \times 1.000) = 450 \text{ amp}$$

This operation, then, must be done with a power supply that can deliver at least 450 amp.

A current of 450 amp removes 0.045 cu in. of metal per minute (at the previously assumed rate of 0.1 cu in. per min per 1000 amp). The volume of metal to be removed is $0.500 \times 1.000 \times 0.0625 = 0.03125$ cu in. The cutting time is 0.03125 cu in. divided by 0.045 cu in. per min = 0.69 min, or 41 sec.

Feed rate can be obtained by dividing penetration depth by cutting time.

$$\frac{0.0625 \text{ in.}}{0.69 \text{ min}} = 0.090 \text{ in. per min}$$

Feed rate can also be found by multiplying the current density by the assumed rate of metal removal:

$$\frac{900 \text{ amp}}{\text{sq in.}} \times \frac{0.1 \text{ cu in.}}{\text{min} \times 1000 \text{ amp}} = 0.090 \text{ in. per min}$$

If the power supply cannot deliver the needed 450 amp, the machining should be done more slowly, at a rate proportional to the available current. Using a d-c source capable of delivering 300 amp, cutting time would be:

$$\frac{450 \text{ amp}}{300 \text{ amp}} \times 41 \text{ sec} = 62 \text{ sec}$$

(as compared with 41 sec for a current of 450 amp), and the feed rate would be:

$$\frac{300 \text{ amp}}{450 \text{ amp}} \times 0.090 = 0.060 \text{ in. per min}$$

as compared with 0.090 in. per min for the 450-amp current.

Surface Grinding. The area of grinding contact varies logarithmically with the depth of cut, for a given diameter of wheel. The grinding pass should be full depth for best results, using the largest practical grinding wheel, preferably one wide enough to engage in one pass all the surface to be ground.

Figure 2 interrelates depth of cut, wheel diameter, length of wheel contact, and feed rate for ECG operations at a total current of 1000 amp. It can be used to estimate current requirements and feed rate for surface grinding. Figure 2(a) is used to determine the machining area, and current requirements are then found with the aid of Table 2. Figure 2(b) is then used to determine feed rate.

The procedure is illustrated below for grinding 0.042 in. from a flat surface on a steel-cutting grade of carbide with a wheel 6 in. in diameter by 2 in. wide. The full depth of cut is removed in a single pass.

On Fig. 2(a), the wheel contact length is found by following the vertical dotted line corresponding to a cut of 0.042 in. to its intersection with the slant line representing the specified wheel diameter of 6 in. Proceeding horizontally to the left scale gives a reading of 0.5 in. for the contact length. Multiplying this wheel contact length by the wheel width of 2 in. gives a machining area of 1 sq in. Table 2 gives an average current density of 900 amp per sq in. for this grade of carbide. Total current for the machining area of 1 sq in. is then 900 amp.

To determine feed rate from Fig. 2(b), the vertical dotted line corresponding to a cut of 0.042 in. is followed to its intersection with the slant line representing a 6-in. wheel diameter. A horizontal line drawn from this intersection gives a reading of 1.2 in. per min. Since the chart is based on the use of a current density of 1000 amp per sq in., the indicated feed rate must be multiplied by the ratio of current densities (900/1000) in order to arrive at the recommended feed rate of 1.1 in. per min for this example.

Although surface grinding can be done with hand feed, power feed is recommended. Too slow a feed causes excessive overcut, poor surface finish, and inaccuracy in grinding. Too fast a feed causes excessive wear of the grinding wheel.

Cylindrical grinding by ECG is slower than other methods, because the small

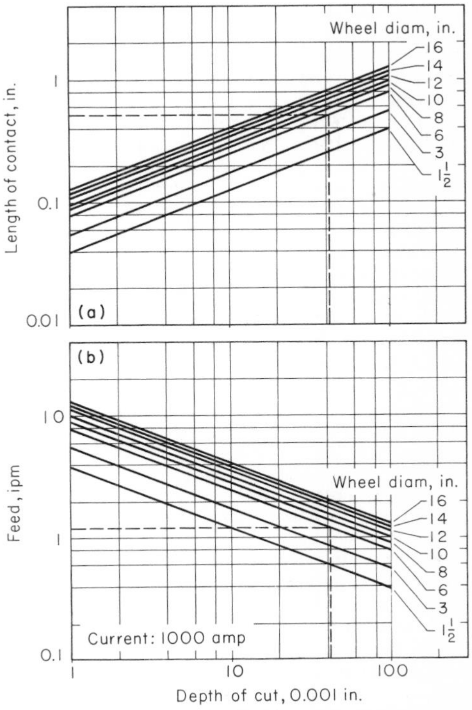

Fig. 2. Charts for determination of operating conditions for electrochemical surface grinding

Table 3. Operating Conditions and Results in Typical Applications of Electrochemical Grinding

Work material (see footnotes for details of operation)	Wheel diameter and width, in.	Volts	Current, amp	Electrolyte: Chemical (see note)	Electrolyte: Lb per gal	Wheel velocity: Sfm	Wheel velocity: Rpm	Spindle load(a), amp	Table feed, in./min	Depth of cut, in.	Results: Tolerance, in.	Results: Roughness, micro-in.
M2 tool steel(b)	8 by ½	10	225	(1)	1.7	7300	3500	..	0.67	0.100	......	..
Stainless steel(c)	10 by 1⁄16	8	25	(1)	1.7	5900	2250	..	3.00	....	0.001 runout	..
U-700(d)	18 by 3	6	2700	(2)	1.0	5100	1080	..	1.50	0.150	......	..
Waspaloy(e)	18 by ½(f)	6	450	...	...	6600	1400	..	2.50	0.030	......	..
Stellite weld(g)	6 by 1¼	7	30	(3)	2.0	6000	3800	..	4.00	0.030-0.050	±0.0005	..
Tungsten (99% density) (h)	12 by 0.080	8	150	(3)	1.5	6000	1900	..	0.75	0.040	......	..
Stellite weld(j)	5 by 0.485	7	60	(1)	1.7	6000	4600	..	1.25	0.250-0.500	±0.002 width	..
Carbide, 0.277 by 0.750 in.(k)	5 by ⅜(m)	5	80	(4)	1 to 2	....	....	2.5	0.032	....	±0.010 diam	20
	5 by ⅜(m)	7	160	(4)	1 to 2	....	....	2.5	0.043	....	±0.010 diam	20
Carbide, ⅜ by 0.135 in. thick(n)	6 by 0.063(p)	7	40	(4)	1 to 2	....	....	2	0.070	....	±0.010 diam	20
Carbide, ¼ by 7⁄16 in.(q)	6 by 1(m)	10	50	(4)	1 to 2	....	....	1.1	0.028	....	±0.010 diam	20
High speed steel, ⅜ by ⅜ in.(q)	6 by 1(m)	10	70	(4)	1 to 2	....	....	1.5	0.055	....	±0.010 diam	16
Carbide, 3 by 0.400 in. thick(n)	6 by 0.063(p)	6	....	(4)	1 to 2	....	....	..	0.067	....	±0.010 diam	20
René 41, 0.187 in., half round(r)	8 by ½(s)	9	150	(3)	...	....	....	2	0.155	....	......	..

NOTE. Numbers in parentheses refer to the following electrolyte compositions (constituents are listed in order of decreasing concentration): (1) $NaNO_2$, $NaNO_3$, amine salt; (2) $NaNO_3$; (3) KCl, KNO_3, Rochelle salt; (4) $NaNO_2$ or KNO_2 (or mixture of these) and organic corrosion inhibitor.

(a) Spindle load amperage is a measure of the power required to rotate the wheel during machining; a significant change indicates malfunction. (b) ½-in.-square face with two 0.125-in.-diam parallel half rounds on it. (c) Cutting off tubing ½-in. OD by 0.015-in. wall. (d) 3 by 2⅜ in. flat surface grinding. (e) 0.187-in.-radius bulb end on a flat, 10 in. wide. (f) Wide-shaped. (g) Curved surface. (h) Two parallel grooves 0.080 in. wide with semicircular bottom. (j) Internal spline slots in exhaust nozzle 4 ft in diameter. Slots ¼ to ½ in. deep by 0.500 in. wide. (k) Plunge grind. (m) Nonmetallic bond, diamond. (n) Cutting off. (p) Metallic bond, diamond. (q) Plunge grind. (r) Form 0.200 in. deep by 2 in. long. (s) Nonmetallic bond, aluminum oxide.

contact area restricts the amount of current that can be used. Cylindrical surfaces shorter than the width of the grinding wheel are ground by electrochemical plunge grinding to the full depth of cut and then by slowly rotating the work to complete the grinding. Generally, accuracy of about 0.001 in. on the diameter can be obtained. If closer tolerances are needed, 0.003 to 0.005 in. of stock can be removed in a second grind by cylindrical traverse grinding. Cylindrical traverse grinding is slower than the plunge-and-rotate method, but it produces better dimensional control.

Other circular work, such as cylindrical parts and milling cutters, can be ground with the edge of a cup grinding wheel. This is a poor method, because the small contact area limits productivity markedly. Sometimes the wheel can be dressed for a traverse cut or set at an angle to make a larger contact area and permit rapid metal removal. Various combinations of grinding cuts can be made, depending on shape of work, accuracy and surface-finish requirements, and the clearance for the grinding wheel. The plunge-and-rotate method can be combined with traverse or surface grinding for high dimensional accuracy or low-micro-inch finishes, or to remove large amounts of metal from cylindrical parts longer than the wheel width. Automatic feed is recommended for all cylindrical grinding.

Internal grinding by ECG should be done with the largest wheel possible, for maximum contact area. Best practice includes the use of a wheel that is wide enough for the work to be done in a plunge cut. If this cannot be arranged, the work should be done by traverse grinding.

Form grinding by ECG with aluminum oxide wheels (copper-impregnated resin bond) is used on all conductive work metals other than carbide. The wheels are trued with the ordinary diamond truing attachment. Carbide can be form ground by ECG with metal-bond diamond wheels, but this is not practical except for high production. As in other kinds of ECG, the inside corners cannot be made to a radius smaller than 0.010 to 0.015 in.

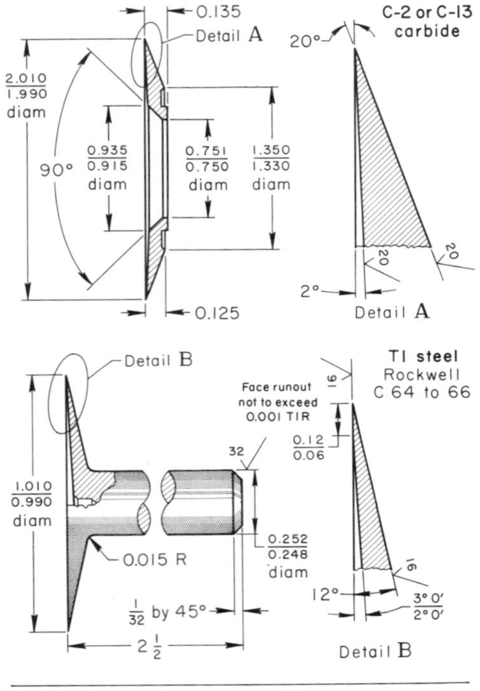

Carbide Cutter

Electrolyte ...... $NaNO_2$ or KNO_2 (or mixture of these), plus organic corrosion inhibitor; 0.8 to 2 lb per gal
Wheel abrasive(a) .... Diamond
Voltage, approx .... 9 volts

High Speed Steel Cutter

Electrolyte ...... KCl, KNO_3 and Rochelle salt; 2 lb per gal
Wheel abrasive(a) .... Aluminum oxide
Voltage, approx .... 8 volts

(a) 100-grit, resin bond; wheel diameter, 8 in.

Fig. 3. Carbide and high speed steel cutters for step-machining of aluminum alloy honeycomb, which were resharpened by ECG (Example 531a)

Advantages of ECG include:

1 Ability to grind any electrically conductive material, regardless of hardness
2 Removal rates 5 to 10 times those for milling, broaching or conventional grinding of metals harder than Rockwell C 60
3 Long wheel life and low wheel cost per cubic inch of metal removed
4 Low downtime because of low frequency of wheel-truing operations
5 Dimensional accuracy of ±0.0005 in.
6 Finish of 5 to 30 micro-in., depending on the work metal and type of cutting
7 Freedom from heat damage, residual stress, or burrs
8 No distortion of thin or fragile parts.

Disadvantages of ECG include:

1 High capital cost. Standard machines with 300 to 1500-amp power supplies cost $15,000 to $30,000; larger machines and those with special equipment may cost $50,000 or more.
2 Metal removal rates not competitive with those of conventional machining methods for readily machinable metals.
3 Inability to avoid some arcing damage, because of deviation from ideal maintenance of the insulating layer of abrasive grains on the working surface of the wheel. This defect prevents application of the method to highly stressed parts.
4 Chemical attack on work (particularly steel) and equipment by corrosive electrolytes; need for special rinsing of work.
5 Difficulty in providing required electric current in some applications.

Typical Applications. The largest single use of ECG is for grinding carbide cutting tools, because of the comparatively rapid removal rate on these hard, abrasive materials. Electrochemical grinding also has a special advantage that greatly reduces total sharpening time of milling cutters. During conventional sharpening, the cutter must be indexed a number of turns before all teeth are sharpened, as only 0.001 in. can be removed per pass. However, because the full depth of cut can be taken at one time with ECG, only one revolution of the cutter is needed to grind each clearance angle. Also, wheel wear with a diamond wheel is only about 15% of that for conventional grinding, and a complete cutter can be ground with a cutting-edge accuracy of ±0.0005 to ±0.0008 in. without compensation for wheel wear. In addition, tools ground by ECG usually have increased life because of the absence of the "saw-tooth" edges usually obtained with conventional grinding.

Because ECG work is not subject to overheating, the method is favored for grinding some metals that work harden rapidly when machined by conventional methods. Absence of burring, burning, smearing or "layover" permits its use on thin-wall tubing, hypodermic needles, honeycomb and laminated materials. Low rate of wheel wear allows long runs without interruption for wheel truing.

Some specific applications of ECG are described in the examples that follow and in Table 3.

Example 531. Grinding of Tools by ECG

The resharpening of carbide and high speed steel cutting tools, the commonest application of ECG, is illustrated in Example 531(a); the use of ECG in the manufacture of a reamer having cutters of the two materials is described in Example 531(b).

Example 531(a) — Resharpening of Honeycomb Cutters (Fig. 3). ECG was used in grinding carbide and high speed steel cutters (Fig. 3) for step-machining 2024-T81 aluminum alloy honeycomb structures for aircraft. In step machining, the cutting edge of the grinding tool sliced into the honeycomb structure, guided by a hand router. The back surface of the cutters was ground by ECG to produce a sharp knife edge free from burrs or nicks. On the steel cutters, a flat extending 1/16 to 1/8 in. inward from the cutting edge was also ground on the face.

Buildup of aluminum on the cutters was removed by chemical machining in sodium hydroxide solution, thus eliminating the need to grind the front surfaces. Cutter dimensions and tolerances are shown in Fig. 3, together with ECG operating conditions. Cutters were successively reground to reduce the OD in 1/16-in. increments (4 regrinds for the carbide cutters, 8 for the high speed steel).

The ECG wheels were required to run true within ±0.0005 in. The aluminum oxide wheels

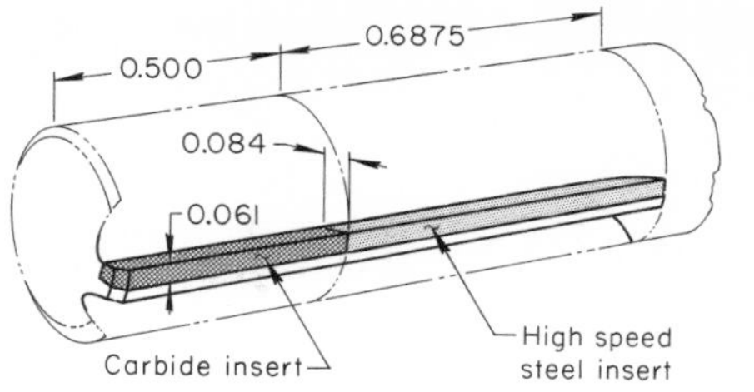

Work material	Metal removal rate, cu in. per min	Current density, amp per sq in.	Finish, micro-in.
Carbide, grade C-2	0.0007	91	8
	0.0030	510	9.5
M1 high speed steel ...	0.0005	91	12
	0.0014	560	16

Fig. 4. Reamer inserts electrochemically ground in regular production (Example 531b)

were dressed with a rigidly mounted single-point diamond, removing not more than 0.001 in. per pass. The diamond wheels were conditioned by a few passes with a dressing stick. The wheels were deplated after dressing or when excessive sparking was observed.

Example 531(b) — Grinding a Reamer (Fig. 4). Electrochemical grinding was used in the manufacture of a reamer with flutes 1.188 in. long, shown in Fig. 4. The reamer body was machined by conventional methods from a round bar of alloy steel. The cutting end of the reamer had carbide inserts 0.500 in. long, with inserts of high speed steel, 0.6875 in. long, facing the remainder of the length of each flute. Reamer diameter was 0.500 in., and the inserts were 0.061 in. thick by 0.084 in. wide. A diamond wheel, 60 to 80 grit, was used. The current densities, removal rates, and surface finish produced in a single pass (54 sec) across the combined insert length of 1.188 in. at two different operating voltages are listed in the table with Fig. 4. The ECG operation was essentially one of finish grinding. The electrolyte was a sodium nitrite formulation at 1 to 2 lb per gal.

Example 532. Slotting Inconel X-750 (Fig. 5)

Electrochemical grinding was used to form a slot in the end of an Inconel X-750 tube with 1/8-in. OD and 1/64-in. wall, shown in Fig. 5. The slot was 0.020 in. wide by 1/4 in. long, with 0.007-in. radius at the corners. The slotting was done with a wheel 5 in. in diameter and a power supply that could provide 50 amp. Actual current used was 3 amp at 3 volts. Wheel speed was 4600 rpm; table feed, 2 ipm. Grinding tolerance was ±0.001 in.

Another type of slotting application for which ECG was suitable is described in Example 800, in the article on Grinding of Stainless Steel.

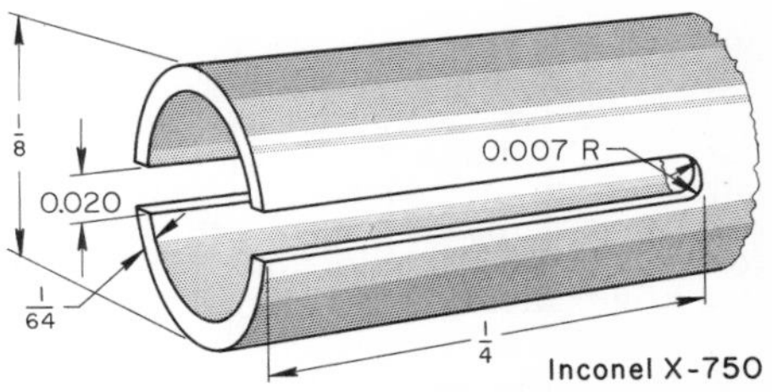

Fig. 5. Slots electrochemically ground in a tube of Inconel X-750 (Example 532)

Electrochemical Honing (ECH)

Electrochemical honing (ECH) is a modification of conventional honing, in which anodic dissolution of the work metal is combined with mechanical abrasion. It offers the same potential advantages over honing that electrochemical grinding (ECG) offers over grinding: faster metal removal, improved deburring action, and increased life of bonded abrasive. The finished surfaces are virtually free from stress or heat damage. The operations that can be done by ECH are the same as those done by conventional honing, and the mechanical aspects of the two processes are closely similar. (See the article "Honing", page 288.)

In its chemical and electrical aspects, the ECH process most closely resembles ECM. The workpiece is the anode, and the metal tool is the cathode. The gap between workpiece and tool is usually about 0.003 to 0.005 in. at the start of the cycle, and increases by the amount of stock removed per surface. The gap can increase to 0.020 in. or more.

ECM electrolytes (see page 233) can be used for ECH also. Composition of electrolyte is less critical than for ECM, because unreactive materials are removed continuously by the stones. A solution of sodium chloride is suitable for most work metals. Most of the metal removal is by electrochemical action.

Tool Design. The stainless steel tool (Fig. 1) is rotated and reciprocated on a rigid, precision spindle. The body of the tool, accurately dimensioned for the bore to be honed, covers the full length of the bore during the honing stroke. Electrolyte is fed in through the tool body, and exits through holes in the tool body into the tool-workpiece gap.

Bonded-abrasive honing stones are mounted on the tool, extending through slots in the tool body. The stones are forced outward by a cone in the tool, and exert pressure continuously against the work. Three or more stones, each about half the length of the bore, are mounted on the tool.

The stones preferentially remove metal at high spots, by mechanical abrasion and by exposing fresh metal to electrolytic attack — thus truing the bore with a minimum removal of stock. The bonding material for ECH stones must be chemically resistant to the aqueous electrolytes used.

Equipment. Commercial ECH equipment is available only for internal cylindrical honing. Shields confine the electrolyte to the working area. Machine components exposed to the electrolyte are made from stainless steel or other corrosion-resistant materials.

A 14-gpm pump circulates the electrolyte, which is filtered as in ECM and is stored in an 85-gal tank. Temperature of the electrolyte is controlled to enable accurate dimensioning. A mist collector removes spray from the honing station and returns it to the electrolyte tank; the compartment enclosing the spindle and guide bars is pressurized to prevent the entry of corrosive vapors. An air gage (see page 292) is used for automatic dimensional

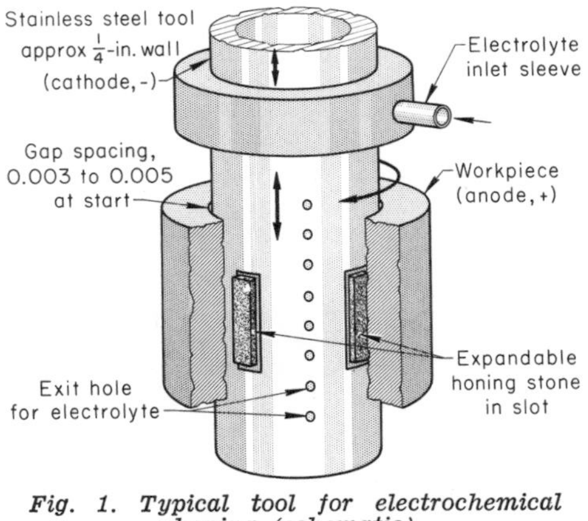

Fig. 1. Typical tool for electrochemical honing (schematic)

control. The direct-current power source for the machine described is a 3000-amp, 24-volt rectifier.

Operating Variables. Current density is usually about 120 to 130 asi (amp per sq in.), but may be as high as 300 asi, and electrolyte pressure is normally 150 psi. Other operating variables are as described for honing (page 288). For a controlled surface finish, the stones are allowed to cut for a few seconds after the current has been turned off. Bore diameters about 3/8 to 6 in. can be honed in lengths up to 12 in.

Applications. The advantages of the process are greatest in honing hard metals, as illustrated in the process trials described below. An electrolyte of 2 lb of sodium chloride per gallon of water was used throughout.

Application 1. The bore of a hardened pinion gear made of 8620 steel (Rockwell C 60 to 62) was honed by ECH. Approximately 0.002 in. was removed on the 1-in.-long by 3/4-in.-diam bore in 4 sec, to a tolerance of ±0.0001 in. The same operation required 18 sec by conventional honing, and consumed three times as much abrasive. The ECH cycle required a current density of 250 asi for 3 sec, followed by honing without current for 1 sec.

Application 2. The 2-in.-long by 1 5/8-in.-diam bore of a hardened transmission gear (8620 steel, Rockwell C 60) was honed by ECH to a tolerance of ±0.0002 in. and a surface finish of 10 to 12 micro-in. Total time to remove 0.008 in. of stock on the diameter was about 30 sec by ECH, as compared to an estimated 160 sec by conventional honing.

Application 3. Blind-end bores 9/16 in. in diameter and 1 5/16-in. deep were honed to a depth of 1 3/16 in. by ECH. A 3/16-in.-diam opening at the blind end of the hole facilitated circulation of electrolyte. The workpiece was a pump body made of M1 steel and hardened to Rockwell C 64. Ten seconds was required for increasing the bore diameter 0.003 in. by ECH, as compared to 30 sec for producing the same result by conventional honing.

Electrochemical Discharge Grinding (ECDG)

ELECTROCHEMICAL DISCHARGE GRINDING (ECDG), sometimes referred to as ECDM grinding, is a combination of the processes of electrochemical grinding (ECG) and electrical discharge grinding (EDG), with some modification of each.* The process resembles ECG in the electrochemical formation of oxides on a positively charged workpiece (anode); however, it employs alternating current or pulsing direct current, and does not use an abrasive-coated wheel. It resembles EDG in the use of a graphite wheel that does no mechanical grinding and in the use of intermittent spark discharges to remove material from the workpiece surface, but differs from EDG in using a highly conductive electrolyte instead of a dielectric fluid and in using low-voltage, high-frequency current.

Like ECG, the process is most useful for grinding carbide tools, hardened tool steel, nickel-base alloys, and parts that are fragile or sensitive to heat.

Equipment. Figure 1 shows a setup for ECDG using a solid bonded graphite wheel and an enlarged sectional view of the grinding interface. The wheel is made of graphite and a bonding agent; most commercial grades with particle size of 300 mesh or finer are satisfactory. Like an EDG wheel, it contains no abrasive; dressing gives it a finish of about 25 micro-in. or less, usually producing the final contour in a single pass.

The spindle is electrically insulated to isolate the electrical circuit. Versatile table positioning and feed mechanisms are provided. In sharpening single-point tools, the workpiece (such as a disposable carbide insert) is held against a flat surface of the graphite wheel. In profile grinding, the workpiece passes over the periphery of a preformed graphite wheel.

Single-point grinders for sharpening carbide tools have a self-contained 200-amp, 12-volt, 60-cps alternating-current power source. Commercial ECDG units for profile grinding and surface grinding are equipped with dual power sources, to provide either an a-c output like that of the single-point grinder, or a pulsing d-c output of 200 amp or more at 4 to 12 volts, 120 cps. At a given rate of power consumption, metal removal on steel and most other metals is greater for pulsing dc than for ac. However, ac must be used in grinding carbide.

The equipment includes an electrolyte mist collector, and a supply tank in which the electrolyte is stored and to which used electrolyte is returned. The electrolyte is pumped through a filter before flowing again onto the work and the wheel. Accessories may include equipment to form, true and dress the wheel without removing it from the machine. Formed plastic or graphite "scrapers" are used during profile grinding to provide uniform distribution of electrolyte.

Electrolytes. As with ECG, the electrolytes used for ECDG are conductive liquids (dilute aqueous solutions of inorganic salts). A solution containing 14 oz KNO_3 per gal plus 7 oz Na_2CO_3 (anhydrous) per gal is a general-purpose electrolyte suitable for the grinding of carbide and most metals; the Na_2CO_3 can be omitted except for carbide.

Concentration of the solution usually is maintained at about 1½ to 2 lb per gal (specific gravity of 1.11 to 1.15).

Mechanism of Process. The mechanism of ECDG can be understood in relation to the ECM, ECG and EDG processes. In the EDG process, metal removal takes place entirely by high-voltage spark discharges through a dielectric fluid, whereas anodic oxidation in a conductive electrolyte is the primary mechanism for metal removal in ECM, ECG and ECDG. In these three electrochemical processes, work metal can continue to dissolve anodically at a practical rate only if any continuous and adherent oxide films that are formed electrochemically on the surface of the work are continuously removed at a sufficiently rapid rate.

Both ECM and ECG make use of low-voltage, high-amperage direct current to dissolve metal from the workpiece. In ECM, electrolyte composition and current density are regulated so that no interfering adherent oxide films are produced; any oxide films that form dissolve chemically in the electrolyte as rapidly as they are formed. In ECG, the mechanical abrading action of the protruding surface grains of abrasive on the wheel removes interfering films and nonreacting particles, thus exposing fresh metal for the electrochemical reaction.

In ECDG, metal is removed by first transforming it into a continuous, adherent, poorly conductive oxide film about 10 to 50 micro-in. thick. When alternating current is used, the oxide film builds up during a positive current pulse (workpiece positively charged), and is removed at discharge sites when the breakdown voltage of the film is exceeded during the following negative pulse, and the cycle is repeated. When pulsing direct current is used, the oxide film builds up during the low-voltage portion of a pulse, and is removed at discharge sites when the breakdown voltage of the film is exceeded. Over a period of a few seconds, discharge sites are randomly distributed in the cutting area.

Depending on its energy level, an individual spark can remove a small amount of metal (as well as the oxide film) from the work, leaving a small crater in the surface. However, cratering is not observed on the workpiece under normal operating conditions. Cratering occurs at spark sites on the graphite wheel, and is a source of wheel wear.

Current density usually is controlled by a voltage adjustment on the current source. Current density can also be regulated by adjusting the gap distance. On a tool grinder this is done by changing the spring loading that holds the workpiece against the wheel; on a profile grinder the feed rate is changed. The relation between pressure and gap at two gap voltages is shown in Fig. 2. Because of increased gassing, a greater pressure is required at higher voltage to maintain the gap. Workpiece pressure is held between 5 and 20 psi to maintain gap distance between 0.0005 and 0.0012 in.

Total current in typical ECDG applications is 200 to 2000 amp at a potential of 4 to 12 volts.

Metal could be removed more rapidly by increasing the current, but current density when using alternating current is restricted to about 600 amp per sq in. for carbides, and to about 800 amp per sq in. for other metals. When a pulsing direct-current source is employed, a current density of about 1200 amp per sq in. can be used in grinding steel; intermediate current densities are used for other metals. Heat damage on the work and wheel wear are greater at high current density.

Wheel speed for most applications is between 4000 and 6000 sfm. Lower speed does not permit the flushing of fresh electrolyte through the grinding gap

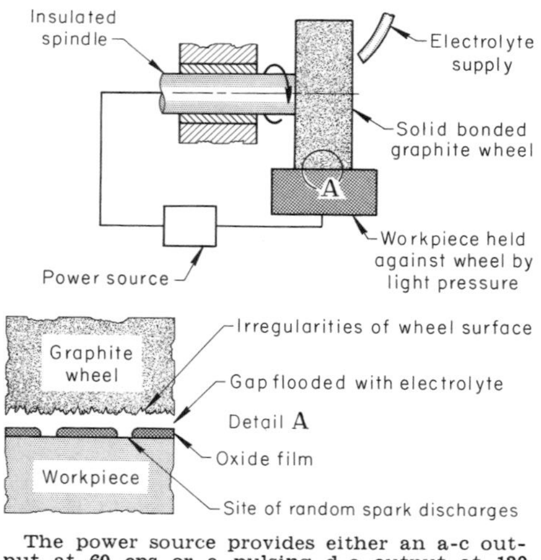

The power source provides either an a-c output at 60 cps or a pulsing d-c output at 120 cps (see text). The workpiece is positively charged (anodic) when direct current is used.

Fig. 1. Schematic of setup for electrochemical discharge grinding

*The terminology used in this article is consistent with that generally accepted for related processes (EDM and EDG for electrical discharge machining and grinding; ECM and ECG for electrochemical machining and grinding). Thus, ECDM would properly describe electrochemical discharge *machining,* done with a shaped tool (a process that is still undergoing development), and ECDG denotes electrochemical discharge *grinding,* a commercial process employing a graphite wheel.

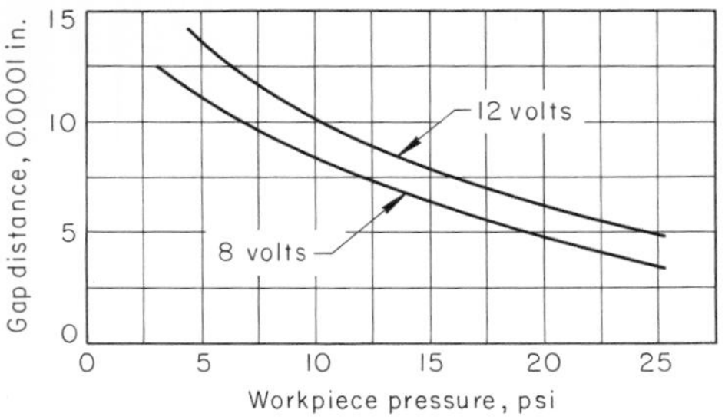

Fig. 2. Effect of workpiece pressure on gap distance in ECDG

at a rate sufficient to maintain the electrolyte composition in the gap. Lower speed also increases the electrical resistance across the gap by permitting the formation of larger gas bubbles in the gap. The maximum operational current density drops off steeply for wheel speeds below about 2000 sfm.

Wear ratio (the volume of metal removed from the workpiece divided by the volume of graphite worn from the wheel) is affected by gap voltage as shown in Fig. 3. Operation at a gap voltage of about 8 volts gives maximum wheel life or wear ratio. Below about 4 volts, wheel wear by mechanical abrasion increases; above about 12 volts, cratering of the wheel surface results from high-energy spark discharges; in either situation, wheel wear is excessive. When using alternating current on carbides or on tool steel, the wear ratio is about 7 to 1; when using direct current on other ferrous workpieces, the wear ratio is about 40 to 1.

Table feed rates in inches per minute are tabulated below for typical operations at a current density of 500 to 600 amp per sq in.

Work metal	Plunge grinding	Surface grinding(a)
Carbide	0.020	0.15
Steel	0.060	0.50

(a) For 0.10-in. depth of cut; 8-in.-diam wheel

Typical metal removal rates are 0.006 cu in. per min for carbide and 0.015 cu in. per min for steel, at a machining current of 200 amp. Typical depth of cut in a single pass is about ¼ in.

Accuracy and Finish. Dimensional accuracy of ±0.0005 in. can be obtained under carefully controlled conditions in plunge or surface grinding. Similar tolerances can be met in profile grinding, with the use of auxiliary plastic or graphite scrapers to control the distribution of the electrolyte on the wheel surface. The accuracy obtained in ordinary production operations is ±0.001 in. Typical surface roughness values are 5 to 15 micro-in. for carbide and 15 to 30 micro-in. for steel.

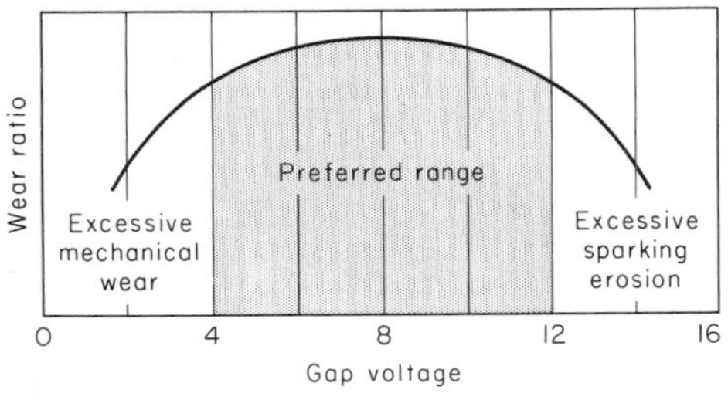

Fig. 3. Effect of gap voltage on wear ratio in ECDG

Wheel Maintenance. Flat surfaces of a graphite wheel can be dressed with a single-point carbide or high speed steel tool on the grinder. Frequent dressing of the wheel is unnecessary; good results can be obtained even with a wheel surface that shows scratches or gouges. Wheel life depends chiefly on the grade of graphite, operating voltage and type of power supply.

For profile or form grinding, the wheel can be formed in place on the grinder by plunge cutting with a high speed steel "master". While in use, the wheel can be dressed in the same manner when necessary.

Profile Grinding. The accuracy with which ECDG profile grinding reproduces the dimensions of the master is limited primarily by the uniformity of electrolyte film thickness on the formed wheel at the grinding interface. Figure 4 illustrates the nonuniform pattern of electrolyte distribution that is obtained at the grinding interface of a rotating

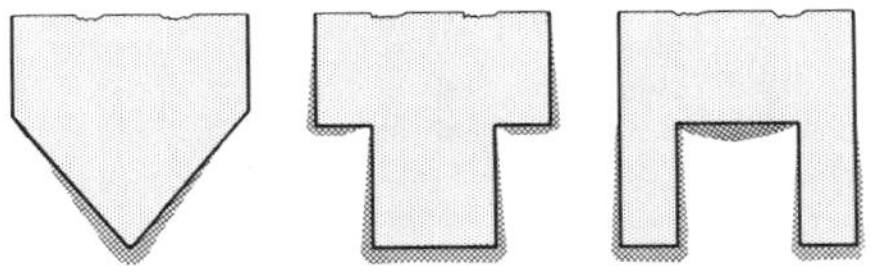

Fig. 4. Nonuniform electrolyte distribution on surface of rotating graphite ECDG wheel

formed wheel unless auxiliary devices such as scrapers are provided to distribute the liquid more uniformly over the contours of the wheel.

For profile grinding of single-point tools that do not have flat vertical or horizontal surfaces, a flat piece of 0.006-in.-thick fluorocarbon plastic sheet is held against the wheel peak as shown in Fig. 5, to scrape off excessive accumulation of electrolyte at the wheel peak.

For grinding multiple-contour profiles that do not have flat vertical or horizontal surfaces (such as chaser tools), conforming graphite scrapers about ⅜ in. thick are held against the wheel at a pressure of about 10 psi. The graphite scrapers are formed on the profile grinding machine in a normal ECDG operation, using pulsing direct current (200 to 450 amp per sq in.) and a workpiece pressure of 4 to 7 psi (gap spacing of 0.0005 to 0.0015 in.). At the pressures and current densities used, wear on the wheel is negligible, because the gassing and the electrolyte fluid pressure almost completely eliminate direct physical contact between workpiece and wheel.

For grinding complex profiles that have both curved contours and flat vertical or horizontal surfaces, compressed air is injected through a hollow conforming graphite scraper to control the electrolyte distribution, particularly on the flat vertical or horizontal surfaces. Best machining accuracy is obtained by using a scraper pressure of about 15 to 30 psi while feeding air at a pressure of about 40 to 60 psi through a 0.08-in.-wide slot extending across the scraper. Under these conditions, the distance between scraper and wheel is about 0.002 to 0.007 in.

In a well-controlled operation that makes use of scrapers, dimensional deviation from the wheel-forming master averages less than ±0.0005 in.

Comparison With EDG and ECG. The ECDG process has the same general range of applications as EDG and ECG, and shows the same advantages in grinding materials and shapes that present problems in conventional grinding with abrasive wheels.

ECDG requires 10 to 15 times as much current as EDG to remove metal at the same rate, but ECDG has much higher metal removal capability and produces smooth surfaces at much faster metal removal rates, as shown below:

Work metal	Finish, micro-in.	Removal, in.^{3}/hr EDG	Removal, in.^{3}/hr ECDG
Tool steel	30	0.02	1.0
Carbide	10	0.004	0.9

However, dimensional accuracy is lower for ECDG than for EDG:

	EDG	ECDG
Close control, in.	±0.0001	±0.0005
Routine production, in.	±0.0005	±0.0010

ECDG has the advantage over ECG of using much less expensive wheels than the specially manufactured abrasive-coated wheels required for ECG. Also, the ECDG graphite wheels are readily formed to intricate shapes and dressed while in place on the grinder. They have long life — a single cup-type ECDG wheel can be used to grind more than 35,000 disposable carbide inserts to a depth of 0.010 in. In addition, it is necessary to stock wheels of only one material, instead of the several different types needed for a range of applications in ECG.

Because ECDG uses a lower pressure of workpiece against wheel, it can do more delicate operations in grinding stress-free, burr-free surfaces on honeycomb and other fragile structures difficult to grind by other methods.

Applications. Single-point carbide disposable inserts have been ground to a depth of 0.010 in. with a surface finish of 15 to 25 micro-in. at a rate of one insert per minute. In a typical profile grinding operation, three C-5 carbide chaser tools were machined at the same time, removing 0.1 in. of metal in a single pass in 15 min (plus 8 min for forming a graphite scraper). Mean thread height deviation from master dimensions was ±0.0003 in., and pitch deviation was half this amount. Using air injection, brazed C-6 carbide dovetail form tools were ground to an average depth of 0.3 in. over a 0.8-in. length in 37 min per piece (plus 25 min for forming the scraper).

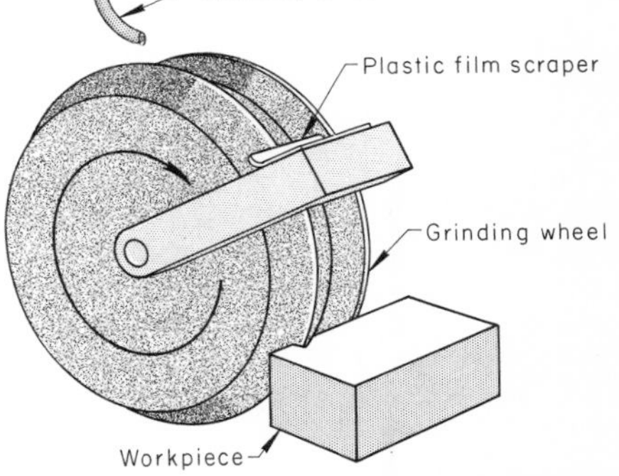

Fig. 5. Use of a plastic film scraper to equalize distribution of electrolyte on graphite wheel in profile grinding by ECDG

Honing

*By the ASM Committee on Honing**

HONING is a low-speed surface-finishing process in which stock is removed by the shearing action of the bonded abrasive grains of a honing stone or "stick". The usual purpose of honing is to produce uniform high accuracy and fine finish, most often on inside cylindrical surfaces, and in the most common applications only a few thousandths of an inch of stock is removed.

In honing, a simultaneous rotating and reciprocating action of the stone results in a characteristic crosshatch lay pattern (Fig. 1). For some applications, such as cylinder bores, angles between the crosshatched lines are important and may be specified within a few degrees. Because honing is a low-speed operation, metal is removed without the increase in workpiece temperature that accompanies grinding, and thus surface damage caused by heat is avoided.

The most frequent application of honing is for finishing inside cylindrical surfaces, but numerous outside surfaces also are honed. Gear teeth, valve components, and races for ball bearings and roller bearings are typical applications of external honing.

Process Capabilities

Although cast iron and steel are the materials most commonly honed, the process has been used for finishing materials ranging from the softer metals, like aluminum alloys, to extremely hard materials, like nitrided cases or tungsten carbide. Honing has also been used for finishing ceramics and plastics.

Bore Size. Bores as small as 1/16 in. in diameter can be honed. The maximum diameter of bore that can be honed is governed mainly by the ability of the machine to drive the honing tool and accommodate the workpiece. Machines powered by motors of up to 50 hp are available that can hone bores up to about 50 in. in diameter. Honing of bores up to 30 in. in diameter is common practice.

Bores of almost any length-to-diameter ratio can be honed. In oil-well applications, holes 1¼ in. in diameter and 32 ft long (a length-to-diameter ratio of 307 to 1) are honed. At the opposite extreme, the process has been used for 1½-in.-diam arbor holes as short as 1/64 in. (a length-to-diameter ratio of 1 to 96).

Bore Shape. Although most internal honing is done on simple, straight-through holes, blind holes and tapered holes also can be honed. It is not feasible to hone the sides of a blind hole flush with the bottom; because of the two-motion action that characterizes honing, some relief must be provided at the end of the hole. In holes like engine cylinder bores, a minimum relief of ⅛ in. is preferred, although in some operations it has been possible to hone within 0.015 in. of the blind end.

Bores having keyways can be honed, and so can male or female splines.

Stock Removal. In honing, a general rule is to remove twice as much stock as the existing error in the workpiece. For instance, if a cylinder is 0.002 in. out-of-round or tapered, the removal of about 0.004 in. will be required for complete cleanup.

Because honing is seldom economical for removing large amounts of stock, preceding operations in high-production work are usually planned so that the amount of stock removed in honing is minimized, as in the following example:

Example 533. Minimum Stock Allowance

In an automated engine plant, cylinder bores (slightly less than 4 in. in diameter) in as-cast gray iron engine blocks were rough and finish bored using modern, rigid boring equipment with sharp tools. The finish bored holes were held to a roughness range of 75 to 125 micro-in. — optimum for dressing the honing stones during the first few strokes. Removing 0.002 to 0.003 in. from the diameter by honing sized the bores to tolerance and produced a finish of 30 to 45 micro-in. This procedure resulted in optimum total machining time and in minimum stone wear.

In some applications, much more stock is honed than in the preceding example. For instance, as much as 0.100 in. is honed from the inside diameter of hydraulic cylinders, because stock removal by honing is more practical and economical than attaining close preliminary dimensions by grinding or boring. In finishing the bores of long tubes, even larger amounts (as much as 0.250 in.) may be removed by honing, because it is the only practical method. Such tubes are finished by honing immediately after drawing. In operations such as these, as much as 2 cu in. per minute can be removed from soft steel surfaces. For steel hardened to about Rockwell C 60, the rate of removal decreases to about 1 cu in. per minute.

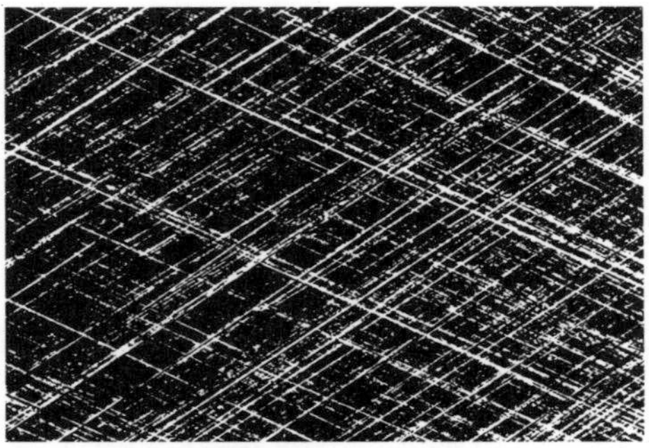

Fig. 1. Typical crosshatch lay pattern obtained in honing a cylinder bore. 5×.

Rough honing usually is employed before finish honing when large amounts of stock are to be removed and specific finishes are required. Stones containing abrasive as coarse as 80 grit, or even coarser, are used for rough honing, to obtain maximum rate of stock removal. Finish honing would use abrasives of 180 to 320 grit, or finer.

Honing vs Other Processes

For some shapes, honing is the only practical means of attaining the required accuracy. A typical example is holes whose length greatly exceeds the diameter. For finishing these holes, grinding is precluded because of the long spindle overhang, and lapping is excessively tedious and expensive.

When inside diameter approaches or exceeds bore length, acceptable results can often be produced by either grinding or honing. A choice between the two methods then depends on cost, on availability of equipment, and sometimes on established policies within a plant.

Example 534. Honing vs Finish Grinding and Lapping (Fig. 2)

Hydraulic valve lifters (tappets) made of hardened cast iron had to be finished on the inside to extremely close tolerances in order to attain the precise amount of "leakdown" of lubricant in engine operation. Originally, rough grinding, finish grinding, and lapping were used to attain required dimensions. Then finish grinding and lapping were replaced by honing for removing 0.004 to 0.005 in. of stock from the diameter. A complete lifter, and the surfaces that were honed, are illustrated in Fig. 2.

Honing provided straightness and roundness within 0.00003 in. and finish of 12 to 14 micro-in. The honing operation was performed in 18 sec. Honing not only was more economical, but also improved the quality of the finished parts. The typical lay pattern produced was a series of diamond-shaped plateaus that helped to carry the load of the sliding plunger. The corresponding valleys increased lubricant retention and thus enabled more consistent "leakdown".

Example 535. Honing vs Grinding of Crankpin Bores (Table 1)

Honing and grinding gave equally acceptable results in finishing the inside diameters of crankpin bores in automotive connecting rods. As shown by the comparative data in Table 1, honing enabled greater productivity

*D. A. PAULL, *Chairman*, Chief Metallurgist, Sealed Power Corp.; DEREK DAWSON, Chief Gear Engineer, Eaton Axle Div., Eaton Yale & Towne, Inc.; B. R. MCCONNELL, Senior Honing Engineer, Sunnen Products Co.; WALTER T. MICHAEL, Master Mechanic, Chrysler Tank Plant, Chrysler Corp.; ROBERT W. MILITZER, Director of Research and Engineering, Micromatic Hone Corp.; JULIUS PIERONEK, Divisional Master Mechanic, American Motors Corp.; HOWARD E. BOYER, *Secretary*, Managing Editor – Metals Handbook, American Society for Metals.

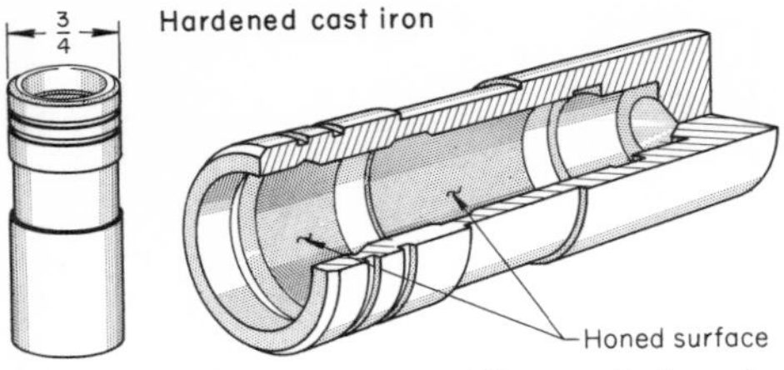

Fig. 2. Hydraulic valve lifter, and honed surfaces that formerly were produced by finish grinding and lapping (Example 534)

with a lower capital investment. The connecting rods were fixtured and honed on a "merry-go-round" type of machine.

Honing also was less costly, but not to the degree suggested by Table 1. Only 0.0025 in. was removed in honing, as compared with 0.0130 in. in grinding. Thus, prior boring was more critical for parts to be honed; two boring operations were required, whereas one sufficed for parts to be finished by grinding.

Machines

When only a few parts are to be finished and operators are skilled, parts can be honed successfully on a drill press or an engine lathe, on which arrangements can be made for simultaneous rotating and reciprocating motions. Vertical drill presses have often been used to drive honing tools. The tool is mounted in the chuck, and the workpiece is fixtured in such a way that it can float. The spindle provides rotary motion, and the reciprocating motion (stroking) can be done manually or by power, depending on the equipment. Feed-out of the honing stones is necessarily a manual operation. Various types of lathes and boring mills also have been tooled for honing. For some applications, portable machines like electric drills have been used to rotate the honing tools while stroking is done manually. Portable machines are used for honing bores in structures (such as mill or refinery equipment) that are too large to be transported to a stationary machine. The bores honed need not be large; holes ranging from 2½ to 20 in. in diameter have been honed using portable machines.

Most production honing, however, is done with machines built for the purpose. These machines are available in a wide range of sizes and designs, in both vertical and horizontal types. Special machines that drive the honing tools at an angle are frequently used for honing bores in V-engine blocks. For high-production honing of similar parts, installations may even include automatic gaging.

Some honing machines require manual stroking of the workpiece; others have power-stroking mechanisms.

In manual stroking, the machine rotates the tool at a pre-established speed while the operator holds the workpiece and strokes it back and forth over the tool. Because the axis of the honing tool is horizontal, stroking must also be horizontal. These machines may be equipped with devices for controlled feed-out of the honing stones.

Figure 3 illustrates and identifies important components of a typical manual-stroke honing machine. In this machine, feed-out and subsequent size control are accomplished by spring loading. Simpler machines of this general type are available that use manual feed-out. Components of the machine shown in Fig. 3 function as follows:

Table 1. Honing vs Grinding for Finishing Crankpin Bores (Example 535) (a)

(Honing was preceded by rough and finish boring; grinding, by rough boring only.)

Item	Honing	Grinding
Stock removed, in.	0.0025	0.0130
Abrasive used (b)	A-180-P-V	A-54-L-V
Life, pieces	385 (c)	250 (d)
Cost per piece	$0.00311	$0.00208
Honing fluid	Mineral seal oil	Soluble oil (e)
Production, pcs/hr	820	457
Number of operators	2	2
Number of machines	2	7
Cost per machine	$75,000	$35,000
Total cost, machines	$150,000	$245,000

(a) Operation consisted of finishing diameter to 2.5005/2.5000 in. (b) In honing, a set of five aluminum oxide stones was used, each 5/16 in. wide by 1¼ in. long by 45/64 in. high. Grinding wheel was 2¼ in. in diameter by ⅞ in. wide, with ⅝-in.-diam hole. (c) Per set. (d) Per wheel. (e) One part mixed with 50 parts of water.

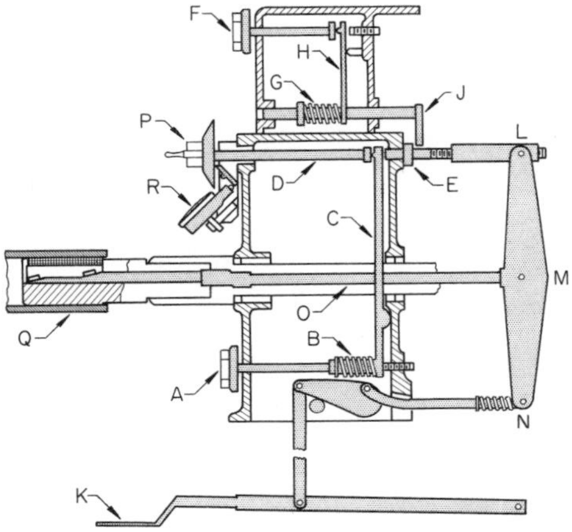

A – Heavy-cutting-pressure control. B – Spring. C – Lever. D – Feed screw. E – Collar. F – Light-cutting-pressure control. G – Spring. H – Lever. J – Rod and fork assembly. K – Foot pedal. L, M and N – Feed arm. O – Honing-stone-expansion link. P – Feed-out dial. Q – Workpiece. R – Honing dial.

Fig. 3. Typical manual-stroke honing machine employing automatic size control. Functions of components identified above are described in the text.

Setting heavy-cutting-pressure control A preloads spring B to the desired honing pressure in the heavy range (for roughing and stock-removal on larger bores). The spring force, through lever C, forces feed screw D to the left until stopped by collar E.

When relatively light cutting pressure is required (as in small-bore honing and finishing operations), heavy-cutting-pressure control A is turned all the way counterclockwise, thus entirely unloading spring B. Then, setting the light-cutting-pressure control F preloads spring G, through lever H, to the desired honing pressure in the light range. This spring pressure forces rod and fork assembly J to the left, which in turn forces feed screw D to the left by acting on collar E. The resultant action on feed screw D is the same as that produced by heavy-cutting-pressure control A, except that forces are much lighter.

Depressing foot pedal K causes feed arm L-M-N to pivot around point L and advance the honing-stone-expansion link O by a fixed amount. Clockwise rotation of feed-out dial P also advances the honing stone by moving point L to the left with N as a pivot, advancing link O until the honing stone contacts workpiece Q.

Additional clockwise rotation of feed-out dial P cannot expand the honing stone further, and points L, M and N remain fixed. However, this additional rotation moves feed screw D to the right and "compresses" either spring B through lever C, or spring G through rod and fork assembly J (depending on which cutting-pressure control is being used). This endwise movement of feed screw D to the right also actuates honing dial R. The reading on this dial now shows the amount of stock to be removed, which was preselected by advancing feed-out dial P.

During the honing operation, either spring B or spring G (depending on which cutting-pressure control is being used) acts on feed screw D through its respective linkage and causes points L and M, as well as link O, to move to the left, thus forcing the honing stone outward under the preset honing pressure. As the diameter of the honed hole gets larger, feed screw D moves to the left until honing dial R registers zero, at which time the honing is stopped by releasing foot pedal K. The work is now ready for gaging.

The operating cycle is repeated from part to part. The honing-tool-expanding mechanism is set for size on the first part and, except for a slight advance of the stone to compensate for wear, additional parts require no resetting of controls.

In power stroking, the workpiece usually is held stationary in a rigid fixture while the honing tool (which is generally powered hydraulically) is rotated and reciprocated.

Length of workpiece often dictates whether a vertical or a horizontal machine can be used. Vertical machines are often preferred because they permit easier fixturing of workpieces. Also, it is easier to obtain straight holes when vertical machines are used. Vertical machines have been built that can hone workpieces 6 ft long, but these machines are 23 ft high — a practical limit. Workpieces longer than 6 ft (even this length is unusual for vertical stroking) are stroked on a horizontal machine. As on vertical machines, the workpiece usually remains stationary while the tool rotates and reciprocates, although there are numerous instances in which it is advantageous to rotate the workpiece. For example, in honing bores in long tubes that are held stationary during the operation, occasionally the entire finished bore is slightly off-center. The error is caused by the weight of the honing head and driving shank; it is corrected by rotating the tube during honing.

Feed-out of the honing stones can be controlled manually, but automatic control is more common in production hon-

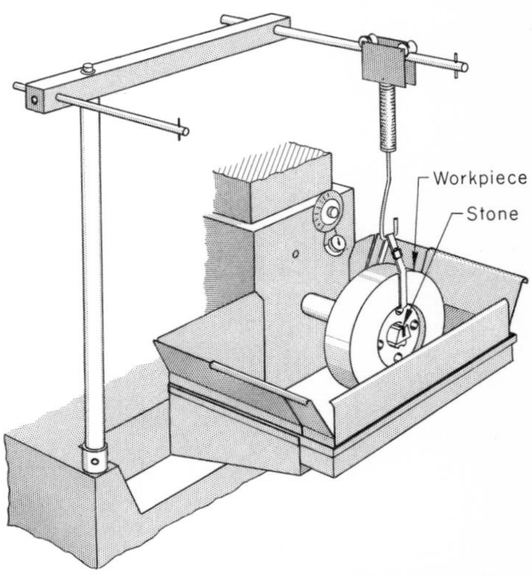

Fig. 4. Typical device used for supporting heavy or cumbersome workpieces during manual-stroke honing

Table 2. Typical Abrasives for Honing Various Metals

Metal honed	Brinell hardness	Abrasive(a)		Grit size for finish (micro-in.) of:						
		Type	Grade	3 to 5	6 to 9	10 to 14	15 to 20	21 to 26	27 to 30	>30
Steel	200 to 300	Al_2O_3	R	600	500	400	320	280	220	150
Steel	330 to 470	Al_2O_3	O	600	500	400	320	280	220	150
Steel	R_C 50 to 65	Al_2O_3	J	500	400	320	280	220	220	150
Cast iron	200 to 470	SiC	Q	500	400	280	280	220	150	150
Cast iron	R_C 50 to 65	SiC	J	400	280	220	150	...	...	...
Aluminum	All	SiC	R	600(b)	500(b)	400	320	280	220	180
Copper	120 to 140	SiC	R	600(b)	500(b)	400	320	280	220	180
Copper	180 to 200	SiC	R	600(b)	500(b)	400	320	280	220	180

(a) In vitrified bond, except where footnoted otherwise in grit-size columns. (b) In resinoid bond.

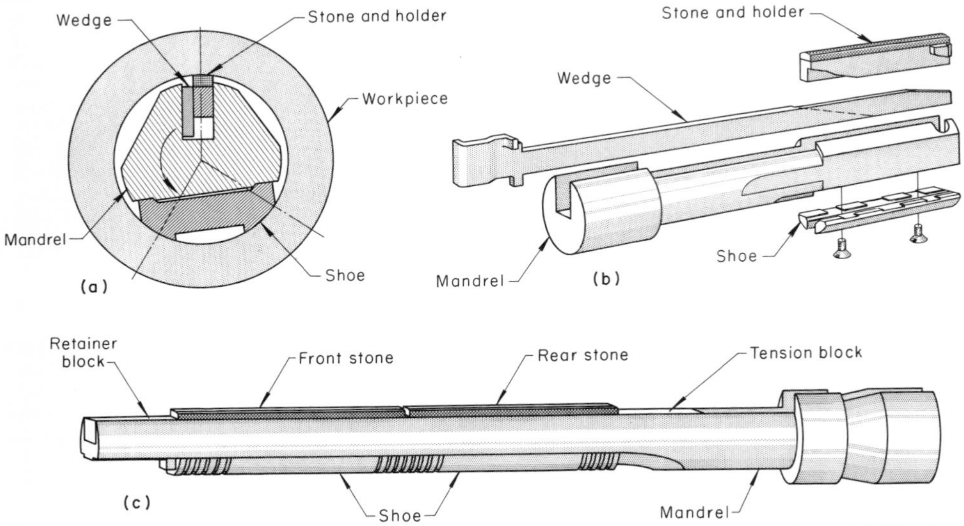

(a) End view showing how self-alignment is provided by three-point contact of shoes and single honing stone with bore. (b) Exploded view showing how axial displacement of wedge controls feed of the honing stone. (c) Manual-stroke honing tool with two stones; on tools for honing longer bores (up to 18 in.), as many as five stones can be mounted in line.

Fig. 5. Tools for manual-stroke honing

ing. Either hydraulic or pneumatic force can be used to keep a predetermined constant pressure on the honing stones. Some machines employ an electromechanical means, which feeds out the stones at a constant rate instead of under constant pressure.

Selection of Machine

Size and shape of the workpieces are usually the major factors that determine whether manual or power stroking is the more appropriate. However, the quantity of similar pieces to be honed, tolerance requirements, availability of equipment, availability of skilled operators, and specific plant policies also affect the choice of honing method and subsequently the choice of machine. Examples presented later illustrate manual and power stroking.

Manual stroking is widely used and often preferred for parts that an operator is able and permitted to hold. Most bores honed by manual stroking are 1 in. in diameter or less, although bores up to about 5 in. in diameter (and even much larger, in rare instances) have been successfully finished. Bores up to about 18 in. long have been satisfactorily honed by manual stroking.

Supports may be used for workpieces that are too heavy or cumbersome for an operator to hold (Fig. 4). However, supports are practical only for honing a few parts of a kind, as in reconditioning of tools by honing.

Manual stroking may be used in preference to power stroking for large quantities when tolerances are extremely close and size and shape of the workpiece permit. One advantage of manual stroking is that workpieces need not be fixtured, which reduces tooling investment and permits immediate changeover from one job to another.

Because manual honing is controlled largely by the operator, who can instantly gage the part he holds, closer tolerances often can be obtained. Techniques used to obtain the accuracy required include end-for-end reversal of the workpiece, change of stroke length, and quick "hone and try". Also, when various areas of a given part require differing degrees of correction (because of bellmouth, taper or other irregularities), the operator can favor those areas as stroking proceeds.

Manual honing is sometimes used as an adjunct to power honing in high production. Most of the honing is done by power, after which the "final touch" for tolerance of finish is achieved manually by skilled operators.

Power stroking can be used for honing virtually all types and sizes of workpieces. In high production of small parts, power stroking may prove more economical than manual stroking. The valve lifters discussed in Example 534 (Fig. 2) are typical of small parts that are power stroked when production quantities are high (in this application, 50,000 or more). Power stroking and fixtured honing are required for workpieces that exceed the size or weight that can be handled manually — for instance, the part shown in Fig. 17.

Honing Stones

Honing stones (known also as honing sticks) consist of particles of aluminum oxide, silicon carbide, or diamond bonded together with vitrified clay, resinoid, cork, carbon, or metal. The abrasive particles, or grits, which provide the cutting action, must be able to withstand the pressure required for removing metal. The bond must be strong enough to hold the grit, but it must not be hard enough to rub the bore and thus retard cutting. The hardness and type of bond are indicated by code letters in the identification of the stone. The porosity of the honing stone, which facilitates chip clearance and minimizes heat generation, is controlled during molding.

Grit size may range from 36 to 600, but 120 to 320 is the range most widely used. Suitable sizes are available for every type and size of bore honed.

Selection of grit size depends mainly on the desired rate of metal removal and the required finish. Coarse grit removes metal faster, but results in a rougher finish. For this reason, rough honing followed by finish honing is often economical. In some plants, stones of different grit sizes are alternated to obtain a compromise. The value of this practice is controversial, but it has been found that by alternating 150-grit and 180-grit stones on the same tool, cutting action approached that of 150 grit and surface finish approached that normally obtained with 180 grit (see Example 542).

Selection of abrasive depends mainly on the composition and hardness of the metal being honed, the finish required, and cost. Typical abrasives for honing various metals are listed in Table 2.

Aluminum oxide and silicon carbide stones are comparable in initial cost. However, one may be more economical than the other because of increased service life.

Diamond stones initially cost up to 20 times as much as aluminum oxide or silicon carbide stones, depending on diamond concentration and thickness of abrasive layer. Diamond stones are

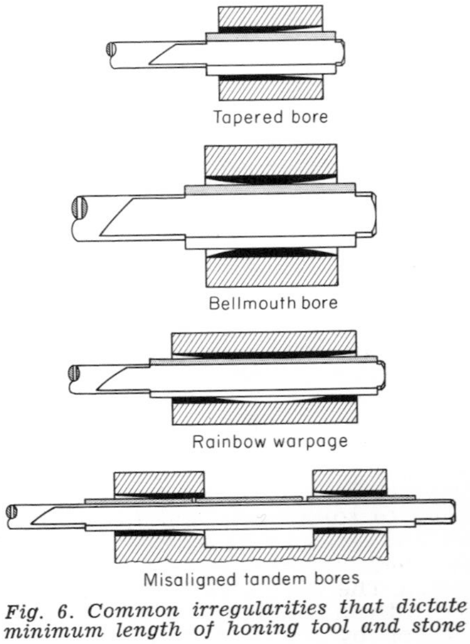

Fig. 6. Common irregularities that dictate minimum length of honing tool and stone

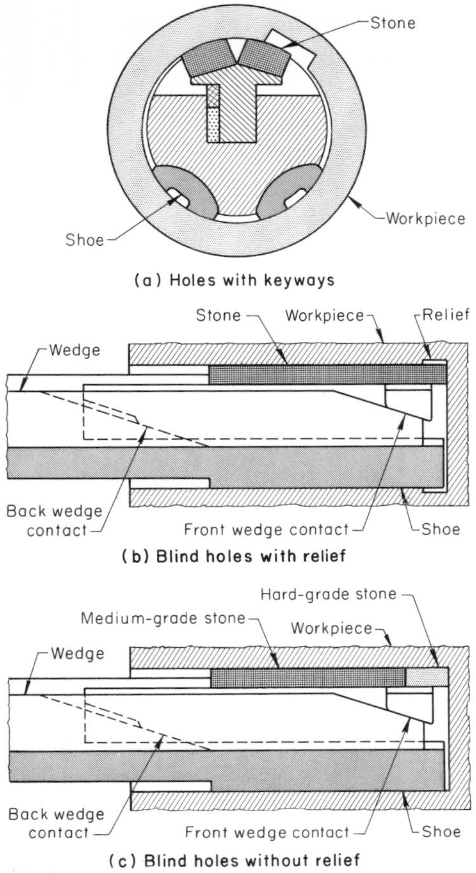

Fig. 7. Tools for manual-stroke honing of holes having keyways and blind holes with and without relief

almost mandatory, however, for honing extremely hard, wear-resistant materials such as tungsten carbide or ceramics. For honing nitrided cases or chromium plate, diamond stones have often been more economical on the basis of metal removed per unit of time.

Designations. An abrasive marking system that applies to both grinding wheels and honing stones has been established by the abrasive manufacturers. Details of this system are given in the article "Grinding". The four most significant characteristics are: type of grit, grit size, hardness grade, and type of bond. These characteristics are identified by letters and numbers in the above order. For example, an aluminum oxide stone having a grit size of 180, a grade of R and a vitrified bond is identified as A-180-R-V. This method of stone designation is used in this article.

Tools

Honing tools differ in design depending on whether they are to be used with manual or power stroking.

Manual Stroking. A tool for manual stroking consists of one or more abrasive stones, a mandrel and a wedge, and guide shoes. The simplest type is illustrated in Fig. 5(a) and (b). The purpose of the unequal angular spacing of the stones with respect to the shoes (Fig. 5a) is to facilitate removal of stock from the high spots until roundness is attained. The wedge, which controls feed-out of the stone, can be actuated manually or by an automatic mechanism such as that shown in Fig. 3. The two parallel shoes (Fig. 5b) stabilize and guide the workpiece. Because the shoes wear very slowly, alignment with the bore is maintained. Shoes are made of materials that are wear-resistant with respect to the workpiece material. Bronze, cast iron, steel or even plastics have been used. Sintered shoes made by powder metallurgy can retain oil.

Honing tools of the type illustrated in Fig. 5 are available for honing bores with diameters of from 1⁄16 to about 4 in.

Tools for manual-stroke honing of long bores (up to 18 in.) have two or more short stones mounted in line, as shown in Fig. 5(c). Tools and stones should be long enough to permit bridging of common irregularities (Fig. 6).

Tools incorporating modifications of the design shown in Fig. 5 are available for honing holes having surface irregularities such as keyways (Fig. 7a) and for honing blind holes with and without relief (Fig. 7b and c). When honing blind holes, stone and shoe should be of equal length and shorter than the depth of the hole. In Fig. 7(b) and (c), stone and shoes have been equally shortened, to assure uniform wear. Note the shoe clearance at the blind end.

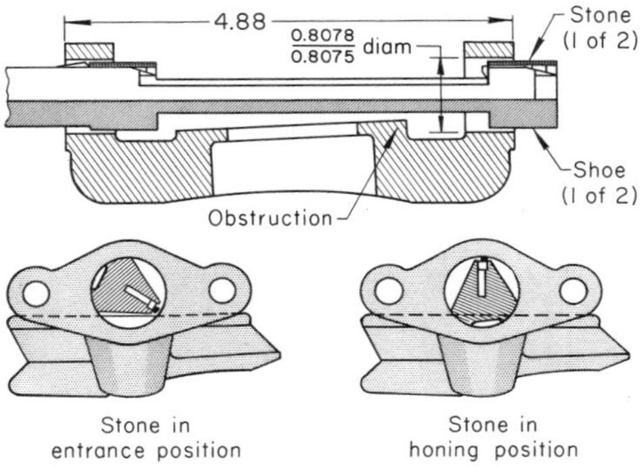

Fig. 8. Specially designed tool for manual honing of parts having an obstruction between bores (Example 536)

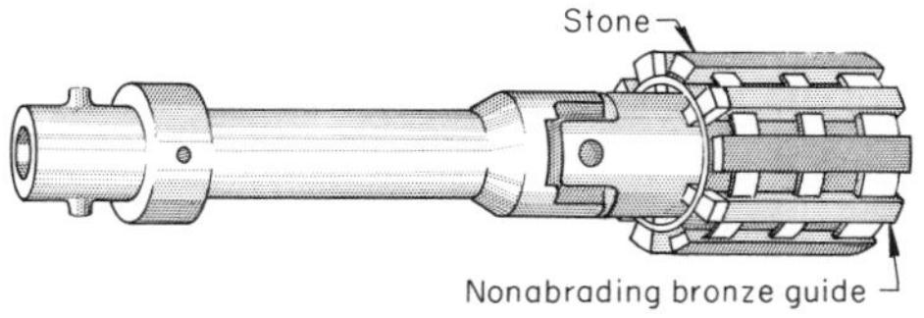

Fig. 9. Tool used for power-stroke (fixtured) honing of automotive cylinder bores. This type of tool was used in Example 542.

Special tools must sometimes be used, as in the following example:

Example 536. Tool for Honing Tandem Bores With an Obstruction Between Them (Fig. 8)

The obstruction between the tandem bores shown in Fig. 8 prevented the use of a long honing tool or any standard tandem alteration for manual honing. The honing tool had to be capable of entering both bores from either end, because frequent end-for-end reversal of the workpiece was necessary to keep the tooling straight. Figure 8 shows the tool designed for the operation. The stones and shoes had to be long enough to permit the overstroking at both ends that was required to equalize stone and shoe wear. The obstruction established the length of the stroke.

Power Stroking. Tools for power stroking (fixtured honing) usually have stones spaced at equal distances around the circumference and may or may not include guide elements (Fig. 9). Expanding cones (Fig. 10) control feed-out. Although the cones may be actuated manually, they are usually actuated automatically by constant-pressure or constant-feed methods. As in manual stroking, the tool may incorporate numerous modifications, depending on the application.

Figure 9 shows a typical tool used in fixtured honing. Tools of this type are used for multiple-spindle honing of parts such as motor blocks. For this application, tools must be self-aligning, because it is impossible to align each cylinder bore with each spindle centerline. Therefore, each tool incorporates a double universal joint. The nonabrading guides that are placed between the stones (Fig. 9) are kept within 0.020 to 0.030 in. of the cylinder wall, to prevent excessive eccentric wear of the stone, which will cause out-of-roundness or other deviations in bore shape.

Figure 10 shows a typical tool assembly for honing large-diameter bores. In this assembly, which was used for honing a bore 41 in. in diameter, the stones are mounted in a holder that will accept as many as four stones in line. Each stone is 8 in. long, making the total effective length 32 in. Depending on bore size, up to 24 stone holders can be spaced around a tool of this type (although 12 holders are indicated in Fig. 10). Because this tool is used on a single-spindle machine, no universal joints are needed. Guide elements are seldom used with this type of tool, but in horizontal honing of long bores, outside support of the spindle (driveshaft) may be required (see Example 545 and Fig. 17).

In power stroking, the honing stones must be encased, to prevent wear on the tool body and to permit quick changing of worn stones. The material used for

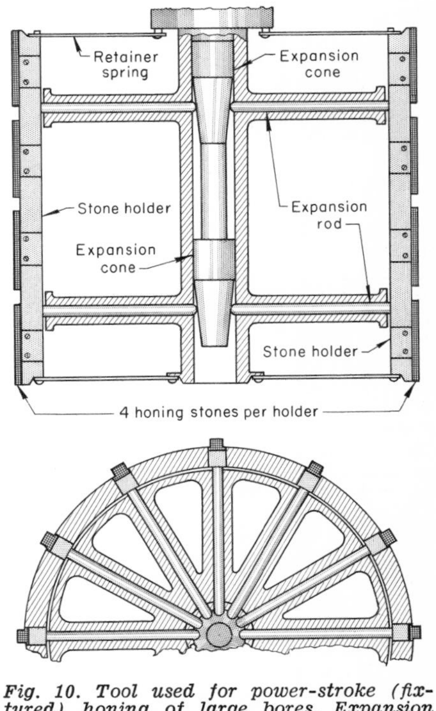

Fig. 10. Tool used for power-stroke (fixtured) honing of large bores. Expansion cones are used for feed-out of honing stones. See text for discussion.

mounting the stones must not damage the bore surface by scratching or spalling. Two widely used types of holders are shown in Fig. 11: a stone mounted in a plastic holder and a stone cemented to a metal die casting.

The body of the honing tool must have open areas that permit a copious flow of honing fluid around the abrasive stones during honing. Note the open spaces, both axial and radial, in the tool shown in Fig. 9.

The design of the honing tool can have an important effect on results, as in the example that follows.

Example 537. Guides for Close-Tolerance Honing (Fig. 12)

In simultaneous honing of five 2¾-in.-diam bearing bores in gray iron engine blocks (top portion of Fig. 12), tools having six banks of stones but no guides (Fig. 12a) could maintain accuracy of only 0.002 in. for straightness and bore-to-bore alignment. This was because the length-to-diameter ratio (26 to 2¾ in., or about 9½ to 1) made it impossible to provide a tool of this design with enough rigidity.

The tool was redesigned to incorporate a single, central bank of stones alternated with plastic guides, which was flanked by three equally spaced banks of plastic guides. The redesigned tool (Fig. 12b) could hone to straightness and alignment within 0.001 in. over the entire length of the five bores.

Gages

Automatic size control in power stroking may be accomplished by adaptations of at least five types of gages — air, ring, expanding, plug, and bar gages. Use of these gages is described below and, except for the air gage, methods are illustrated in Fig. 13.

An air gage is an integral part of the honing tool. With each stroke of the tool, the gage portion enters the bore with sufficient clearance to permit pressurized air emitted from gage orifices to escape to the atmosphere. As the bore size increases, back pressure in the air system decreases. When the bore is to size, a previously calibrated pressure switch cuts off the cycle. This type of gage is particularly well adapted to controlling multispindle machines in honing cylinder bores. By adjusting the calibrated control, various diameters can be honed without interrupting the cycle. Air gaging can hold diametral tolerances of 0.0003 in. and can be adjusted within a range of 0.004 in.

A ring gage is mounted just above the workpiece (Fig. 13a). The ring, whose inside diameter is equal to the specified bore diameter, is positioned so that only the plastic or metal tabs placed on the upper ends of the abrasive stones enter the ring at the top of each stroke. Because the abrasives and the tabs wear at the same rate, the diameter of the expanded tool is equal to the bore diameter. When the tool reaches gage-ring size, friction from the tabs causes the ring to swing through a small arc and initiates the end of the cycle. This method of control is best adapted to bore diameters of 0.120 to 4.0 in. It is capable of obtaining diametral accuracy of 0.0003 in. or better, and adjustments within 0.0005 in. can be made to allow for wear or to vary the desired size.

An expanding gage, which consists mainly of a split sleeve held together with a ring (Fig. 13b), reciprocates with the tool but is not attached to it. The gaging member, whose diameter is smaller than the bore diameter, enters the bore with each downstroke. At the bottom of the stroke, a lever on the side of the sleeve contacts a post, causing the split sleeve to expand until the gaging member touches the bore surface. Controls are preset so that two electrical contacts on the lever of the split sleeve meet and end the cycle when the diameter of the gaging member equals the desired bore diameter. This type of gage has been used successfully for size control of bores larger than 0.750 in. in diameter (there is no maximum size). A calibrated dial allows for fine adjustment of the size within 0.010 in. A tolerance of 0.0003 in. can be maintained at any dial setting.

A plug gage is independent of the tool and approaches the bore from the end opposite that at which the honing tool is introduced (Fig. 13c). The plug, whose diameter equals the desired bore size, attempts to enter the bore with each stroke. When entry is made, controls are activated and the cycle is terminated. This method can be used to control accuracy within 0.0002 in.

A bar gage consists of two bars that float in the body of the tool (Fig. 13d). The bars are fastened to a split ring and held against the bore surface by spring pressure. Bore diameter is measured by the distance between the contact faces of the bars. When the tool enters a bore, the bars are pressed inward and two low-potential electrical contacts on the split ring are held open. As the bore becomes larger, the contacts move closer together; when they meet (as preadjusted), the cycle is stopped. The use of this type of gage is usually restricted to size control of bores larger than 2 in. in diameter. However, this gage accepts adjustments within 0.040 in. Also, control of honed diameters within 0.0003 in. is feasible.

Rotation Speed

Spindle speed depends mainly on the diameter of the bore being honed, because surface speed is usually the basic consideration in honing. The choice of

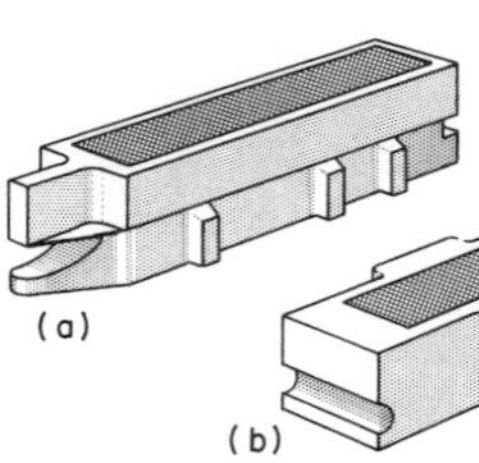

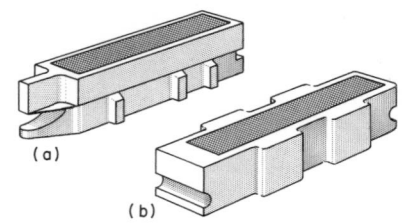

Fig 11. Mountings for abrasive stones used in fixtured honing: (a) *stone encased in a plastic holder;* (b) *stone cemented to a metal die casting*

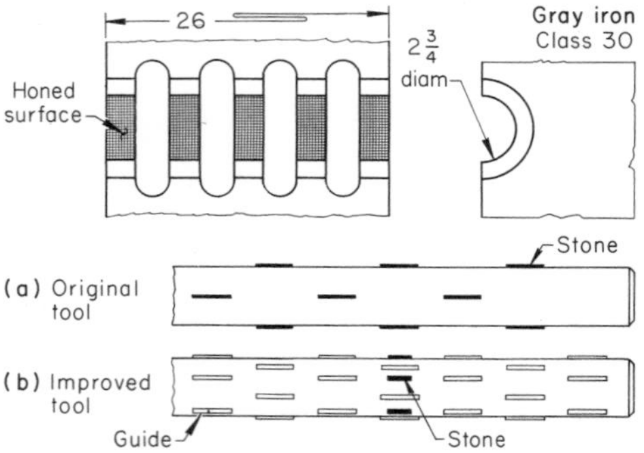

Fig. 12. Redesign of honing tool to permit attainment of greater accuracy in simultaneous honing of five bearing bores in gray iron engine blocks (Example 537)

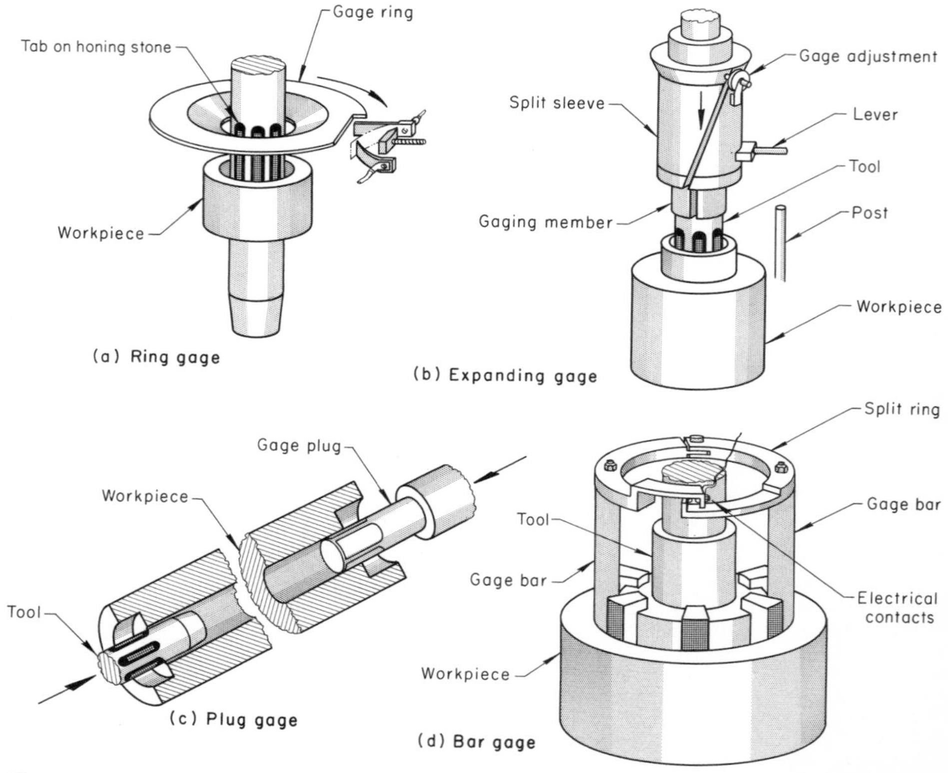

Fig. 13. Gages for automatic size control of fixtured workpieces honed in power-stroking machines. See text for discussion.

an optimum surface speed is influenced by the following five factors:

1. **Material Being Honed.** Higher speed can be used for metals that shear easily, such as cast iron and some of the softer nonferrous metals.
2. **Hardness.** Harder workpiece surfaces require lower speed.
3. **Surface Roughness.** Rougher surfaces that mechanically dress the abrasive stone permit higher speed.
4. **Number and Width of Stones in the Tool.** Speed should be decreased as the area of abrasive per unit area of bore increases.
5. **Finish Requirements.** Higher speed usually results in finer surface finish.

Because of the variables listed above, rotation speed cannot be standardized. However, the speeds given in Table 3 serve as a starting point, and, in general, are close to those given in the examples in this article.

Experience with a particular application may indicate advantages for higher or lower speed. Rotation speeds as high as 600 sfm have been used successfully (see Example 925, in the article on Machining of Aluminum). Conversely, in the following example, a reduction in spindle speed, and thus in surface speed, reduced the number of rejects:

Example 538. Decrease in Honing Speed for Reduced Rejection Rate

When cast iron cylinder liners (3.9-in. ID) in aluminum engine blocks were honed at a spindle speed of 231 rpm (about 235 sfm), the rejection rate for out-of-roundness and taper was 64.5%. A study based on 2000 workpieces showed that by reducing spindle speed to 154 rpm (about 157 sfm), the rejection rate could be reduced to 35.5%.

Excessive speeds contribute to decreased dimensional accuracy, overheating of the workpiece, and glazing (dulling) of the abrasive. Overheating causes breakdown of honing fluid and distortion of the workpiece; the latter frequently affects final dimensions.

Reciprocation Speed

Speed of reciprocation, which depends largely on the length of the honing tool and the depth of the bore, is most usefully expressed in surface feet per minute, the product of the number of stroke cycles per minute and twice the stroke length. Reciprocation speeds commonly used with four different work metals are listed in Table 3.

Because reciprocation speed, rotation speed, and crosshatch angle are related functions (see the next section), crosshatch angle can be controlled by varying the reciprocation speed when rotation is constant. Reciprocation speed also has some effect on the action of the abrasive; higher speed increases dressing action and thus usually produces a rougher finish.

Control of Crosshatch Angle

The crosshatch angle obtained on a honed surface depends on the ratio of surface speed of reciprocation (stroking) to surface speed of rotation. When the rotation and reciprocation speeds are equal, the crosshatch angle is 90° (Fig. 14a). When rotation speed exceeds reciprocation speed, the crosshatch angle is less than 90° (Fig. 14b).

The following formula can be used to determine the approximate angle that will result from given speeds (Fig. 14c):

$$\text{Tan}\ \alpha = \frac{\text{Reciprocation, sfm}}{\text{Rotation, sfm}}$$

$$\text{Crosshatch angle} = 2\alpha$$

Although the above formula may be useful as a guide when determining the speeds necessary for obtaining the desired angle for a new job, it is often more practical to resort to trial and error. In power stroking, a common practice is to establish rotation speed and then to vary reciprocation speed to get the desired crosshatch angle.

For some applications (engine cylinder bores are a notable example), crosshatch angle is important, and is noted in specifications. In the majority of applications, however, although an angle of 30° is commonly aimed at, any angle within the range of 20° to 45° usually is suitable. Angles within this range are practical with either manual or power stroking.

In manual honing, an experienced operator can instantly alter the practice to suit conditions. For instance, the workpiece can first be stroked at a rate that has proved most efficient for stock removal. The technique can then be changed so that the desired crosshatch pattern is produced in the few final strokes. Conditions that will produce a crosshatch angle of approximately 30° in manual-stroke honing are given in Table 4 for a range of workpiece diameters and lengths.

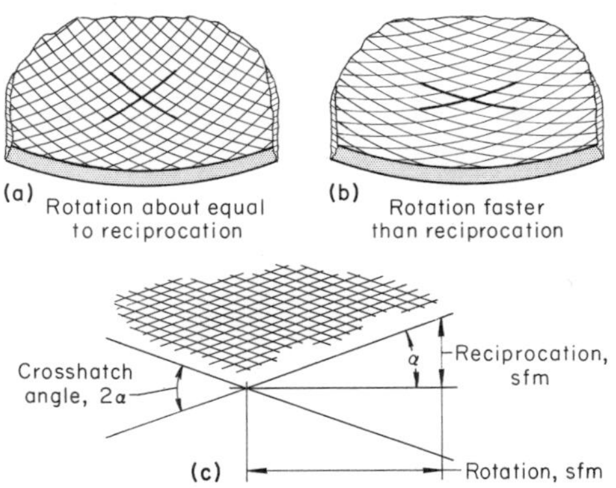

Fig. 14. Relation of crosshatch angle to rotation and reciprocation speeds. See text for formula.

Honing Pressure

A relatively wide range of pressures will yield acceptable efficiency and results. For example, in equipment using hydraulic force for feed-out, gage pressures have varied from 150 to 450 psi. However, honing is more often controlled by rate of feed-out than by gage pressure. For instance, in Example 543, feed-out rate was 0.009 in. per min for roughing and 0.007 in. per min for finishing 8½-in.-diam bores. These feed-out rates are larger than those used in honing smaller bores (as in Example 542, where 0.002 to 0.004 in. of stock was removed from 3.910-in.-diam bores).

Insufficient pressure will result in a subnormal rate of metal removal. When pressure is excessive, rougher finishes are obtained, because the abrasive is broken down too fast. This will result in increased stone cost, as well as decreased productivity caused by downtime required for replacing stones.

Trial and error is the usual method of determining optimum pressure for a new application in production honing. A common procedure is to start with low pressure and then gradually build up, using workpiece finish as an indicator, until best conditions are found. Pressure must be kept up by automatic feed-out to compensate for stone breakdown and hole growth.

The data in Table 5, based on manual honing with a single stone, show why machines for honing various bores must apply a wide range of force. If a force of 50 lb is applied to a stone with a contact area of 0.012 sq in., the pressure will be 4200 psi. Such a pressure would shatter the stone. But the same force applied to a stone with a contact area of 0.550 sq in. creates a pressure of only 91 psi — insufficient for cutting most materials.

Honing Fluids

Lubrication is more critical in honing than in most other metal-removing operations. No single honing fluid possesses a maximum of all properties

Table 3. Typical Speeds for Honing

Metal honed	Hardness	Speed, sfm: Rotation	Speed, sfm: Reciprocation
Steel	200 to 300 Bhn	80 to 180	70
	330 to 470 Bhn	60 to 150	60
	Rc 50 to 65	80 to 130	60
Cast iron	200 to 470 Bhn	160 to 210	80
	Rc 50 to 65	80 to 130	80
Aluminum	All	160 to 210	80
Copper alloys	120 to 140 Bhn	160 to 210	80
	180 to 200 Bhn	150 to 180	80

Table 4. Conditions for Producing 30° Crosshatch Angle in Manual-Stroke Honing

Bore diameter, in.	Rotation, rpm	Bore length, in.	Stone length, in.	Stroke length, in.(a)	Stroke cycles(a) per minute
¼	1600	1½	1¼	1.08	155
		3	1¼	2.58	65
		3	2¼	2.25	75
¾	640	3	2½	2.17	94
		6	2½	5.17	39
		6	4½	4.50	45
1½	320	4	3¼	2.92	70
		8	3¼	6.92	29
		8	6½	5.83	35
2½	200	4	3¼	2.92	72
		8	3¼	6.92	30
		8	6½	5.83	36

(a) In computing reciprocating surface speed, note that distance traveled during one stroke cycle comprises a forward and a return stroke.

Table 5. Relation of Stone Contact Area and Pressure With a 50-Lb Force(a)

Bore diameter, in.	Bore length, in.	Stone length, in.	Stone width, in.	Stone area, sq in.	Pressure, psi(b)
1/16	⅝	7/16	0.028	0.012	4166
⅛	¾	9/16	0.035	0.020	2500
3/16	1	¾	0.050	0.038	1316
¼	1½	1¼	0.070	0.088	568
½	3	2¼	0.145	0.326	154
⅝	3½	2½	0.220	0.550	91
⅝	9	7½	0.220	1.650	30
1½	4½	3¼	0.245	0.796	63
1½	20	16¼	0.245	3.981	13

(a) For manual honing with a single stone. (b) Pressure under a 50-lb force.

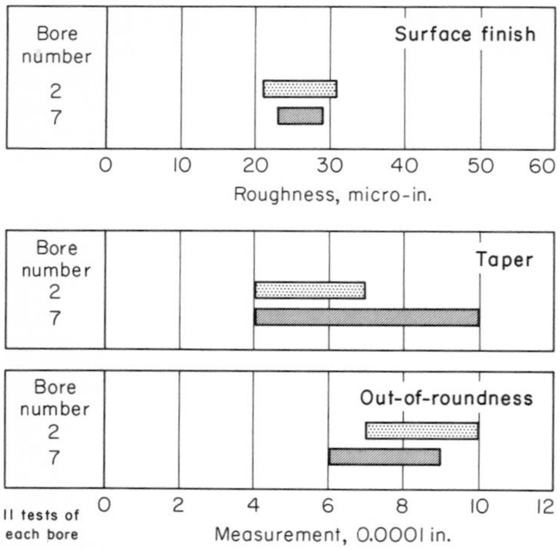

Data represent measurements on cylinder bores 2 and 7 in eleven gray iron blocks for V-8 engines, selected from a run of 900. Measurements were made on blocks 1, 50, 100, 200, 300, 400, 500, 600, 700, 800 and 900.

Fig. 15. Finish and dimensional variations obtained in honing (Example 540)

needed for honing. Therefore, some compromise must be made, and mixtures of two or more liquids are commonly used. The oils used in honing serve two main purposes:

1 They promote cutting action by flushing workpiece metal and particles of abrasive from the honing stones, thus preventing the stones from loading and glazing.
2 They maintain an almost constant workpiece temperature, and thus minimize dimensional variation due to expansion and contraction.

Honing fluid characteristics can directly influence quality or economy, or both. Viscous, gummy fluids, or fluids containing suspended solids, can cause a soft-bonded abrasive to lose efficiency and generate excessive heat from friction.

Water-base solutions are superior as coolants, but they are poor lubricants and have insufficient viscosity to prevent chatter. Water also causes rust. Because of these two characteristics, water-base solutions are seldom used for honing fluids.

Mineral seal oil is effective and is widely used for production honing (see Example 542). Mineral seal oil is a water-white product having a higher viscosity than kerosine (about 40 SUS, as against 31 SUS for kerosine). Its flash point also is higher than that of kerosine, and it is less likely to cause skin irritation. Mineral oils similar to those used for other machining operations have also proved satisfactory when one part of oil is diluted with four parts of kerosine (as in Example 543, involving cast iron cylinder liners).

Buffers are often added to honing fluids, to minimize or prevent chatter of the honing stones and thus prevent their premature disintegration. Buffer materials absorb shock and recoil from fluctuations in force. Animal oils, including tallow, lanolin and lard oils, are usually the most economical buffers, despite their relatively high cost, because of their long lasting qualities. These oils generally flow under pressure and cling to metal surfaces better than mineral oils. Prepared proprietary oils that contain buffers are widely used. Before use, these oils (which may also contain rust inhibitors and deodorants) are diluted up to 95% with kerosine.

Buffered honing fluids often are more economical than fluids without additives, as shown in the next example:

Example 539. Longer Stone Life With Buffered Honing Fluid

Crankpin bores in automobile connecting rods were honed with 150-grit stones that removed 0.0015 to 0.002 in. from the diameter. A change from straight mineral oil to an oil containing buffers lowered honing cost by 26% by increasing stone life and thereby decreasing downtime for changing stones.

The use of too much buffer may detract from its beneficial effects. An excessive amount (*a*) reduces the cutting action of the abrasive, (*b*) produces smoother finishes, (*c*) requires higher pressures or lower rotational speeds, (*d*) lowers the ability of the fluid to dissipate heat, (*e*) impairs fluid distribution, and (*f*) increases requirements for refrigeration and filtering.

Regardless of the type of fluid used, it should be delivered to the honing stones in a constant and generous supply. The fluid also should be filtered through a system that removes particles coarser than 15 microns. The system should be kept free of water and stray oil (such as from the hydraulic system), which adversely affect the properties of honing fluids.

Table 6. Processing Details for Honing Cylinder Bores in V-8 Engine Blocks (Example 542)

Processing Details(a)	
Machine production rate	70 blocks per hour
Spindle speed	204 rpm
Spindle reciprocation	78 strokes per minute
Stock removal:	
Amount	0.002 to 0.004 in.
Time	39 sec (approx)
Honing fluid	Mineral seal oil(b)
Stone life per set(c)	450 blocks
Size control	Spindle-mounted plug gage
Dimensional tolerance	Maximum out-of-roundness and taper, 0.001 in.
Finish	20 to 35 micro-in.
Crosshatch angle	22½°
Tool Cost per Block(d)	
Stones	$0.0474
Bronze guides	0.0173
Total	$0.0647

(a) Bores are classified in five sizes differing 0.0005 in. in diameter, for selective fitting of pistons. (b) At 68 F; heat exchanger is required for maintaining this temperature, and honing fluid must be free of water and tramp hydraulic oil. (c) Silicon carbide stones. (d) See Fig. 9 for honing tool used.

In many plants, 62 to 68 F is the preferred temperature range for honing fluids. Controlling the temperature becomes more important as tolerances become closer. If temperature is allowed to rise, dimensions may become inaccurate and the fluid may break down, causing excessive stone wear and changes in cutting characteristics. In production installations, heat exchangers are often used to maintain close control of honing-fluid temperature.

Dimensional Accuracy

Internal honing to tolerances of 0.001 to 0.0001 in. is common. For some high-precision parts, tolerances as close as a few millionths of an inch are specified and achieved.

In manual honing, the dimensional tolerances that can be achieved and reproduced depend to a great extent on the operator. Skilled operators develop a "feel", and can hone small parts to precision tolerances (sometimes to less than two millionths of an inch).

Close tolerances can be produced and repeated in fixtured honing (power stroking) if sources of variation, such as machine and honing fluid condition, are closely controlled, as described in the following example:

Example 540. Variations in Dimensions and Finish for 900 Cylinder Blocks (Fig. 15)

The data plotted in Fig. 15 represent results of a quality control check made on 3.910-in.-diam cylinder bores in gray iron blocks for V-8 engines. Bores 2 and 7 were measured in 11 blocks from a production run of 900. The techniques and conditions employed in honing these bores are presented in Example 542 and Table 6.

The honing fluid was maintained at 68 F by the use of a heat exchanger, and was constantly filtered. Less than 2% of the 7200 bores honed required a repair operation because either taper or out-of-roundness exceeded the specified 0.001 in.

Surface Finish

Surface finish of 10 to 15 micro-in. can be obtained easily in production honing, and finish of less than 2 micro-in. can be achieved and reproduced. A range of roughness is sometimes specified. For example, the cylinder liners discussed in Example 543 require a finish of 30 to 45 micro-in. In other applications, a maximum surface roughness is specified. Under carefully controlled conditions, surface roughness can be maintained within a close range, as indicated in Fig. 15 (Example 540).

Size of grit in the honing stones is the main factor controlling surface finish. When grit is fine, the finish will be fine (other factors being equal); but as grit size is decreased, rate of stock removal is also decreased, as described in the following example.

Example 541. Honing Gray Iron to a Finish of 10 to 15 Micro-In.

In honing gray iron (hardness, 170 to 195 Bhn), a finish of 10 to 15 micro-in. was desired. Silicon carbide stones with a grit size of 180 produced a roughness of 25 to 30 micro-in. The required finish could be obtained with 320-grit stones, but the time required for honing made the use of this grit size impractical. The problem was solved by first rough honing with 180-grit stones and then finish honing, in another setup, with 320-grit stones.

Rough finishes are sometimes improved by using a "dwell time" at the end of the honing cycle — that is, by

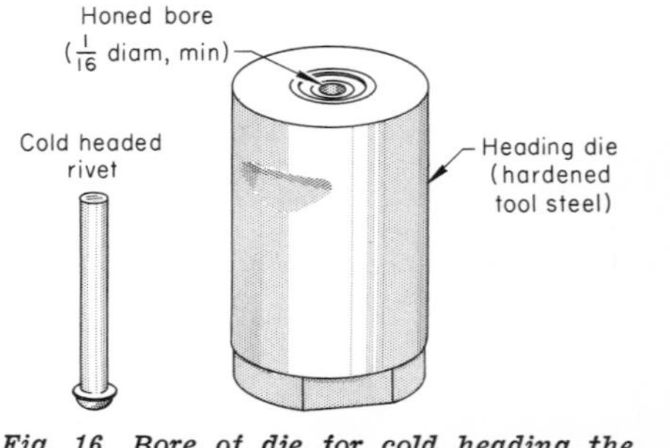

Fig. 16. Bore of die for cold heading the rivet shown at the left is typical of small bores finished by manual-stroke honing. (Example 544)

continuing the rotation and reciprocation action for a few strokes after feed-out ceases and pressure drops off. In manual honing of a particular bore, use of this technique reduced surface roughness from the normal 20 micro-in. to about 10 micro-in.

Honing Practice for Inside Diameters

Honing is widely used for finishing bores in engine cylinders, cylinder liners, and bearing bores. Procedures for honing similar parts may vary from one plant to another, depending on quantity, available equipment, and established plant practice. Procedures that represent experience from different plants in honing bores of various sizes and proportions are given in Examples 542 through 549, which follow.

Example 542. Eight Cylinder Bores Honed Simultaneously (Table 6)

Special eight-spindle V-type machines (with an included angle of 90° between each set of four spindles) were used for honing cylinder bores of 3.910-in. ID and 6-in. length in gray iron blocks for V-8 automobile engines. Each block was fixtured by being clamped lightly from the top to the pan on which it rested. Loading, unloading and size control were automatic, and all eight bores were honed simultaneously. Honing tools with universal drives (such as shown in Fig. 9) were used in a shell assembly. Each tool used six bronze guides and six abrasive stones. Stones of grade C-150-R-V abrasive (150 grit) were alternated with stones of grade C-180-R-V (180 grit) to obtain a compromise between metal-removal rate and finish. Processing details are given in Table 6. Workpieces of this type have also been honed by indexing in vertical machines.

Example 543. Honing Main and Relief Bores of a Cylinder Liner

Heavy-duty, single-spindle vertical machines with hydraulic power stroking were used for honing bores in alloy cast iron cylinder liners of 8½-in. ID and 22-in. length. The main bore, which ran the length of the liner, contained a relief bore (produced by contour boring) that was a concave band 4 in. wide and 0.007 in. deep at its lowest point.

The bores were honed in three passes because of the large amount of stock to be removed and because of the presence of the relief bore. In the first pass (roughing), 0.0025 in. was removed from the main bore, using a feed-out rate of 0.009 ipm, a spindle speed of 98 rpm and a reciprocating speed of 24 strokes per minute. The liners were then moved by roller conveyor to a second machine, and the relief bore was completely honed. For this pass, the holders for the 1½-in.-square honing stones were built with a high spot in the center that caused the stones to rock in their mounts for a distance of about 0.015 in. This rocking motion allowed the edges of the stones to follow the bore contour and produce the required finish. After time was allowed for the temperature of the liners to stabilize, the main bore was finish honed at a feed-out rate of 0.007 ipm, a spindle speed of 76 rpm, and a reciprocating speed of 24 strokes per minute.

The process was automatic except for loading and unloading. When the "start" button was pressed, a hydraulic platen lifted the cylinder into clamping position, the honing tool descended into the bore, and honing fluid started to flow. Eight holes in the upper clamp plates allowed a copious flow of honing fluid (one part mineral oil to four parts kerosine). The abrasive stones expanded and fed out rapidly until the bore wall was contacted. The feed rate then decreased to the preset rate. When the bore reached size, the cycle was terminated by an automatic sizing device.

Operating conditions (speed, feed and cycle stop points) were preset for the roughing and finishing passes. Resilient mounting of the fixture adapters prevented distortion of the liners during honing.

It was required that the main bore in the honed liners be less than 0.001 in. out-of-round, and straight within 0.0003 in. per inch of length. The relief bore must be less than 0.001 in. out-of-round, and its diameter must be kept within ±0.0015 in. Surface roughness was held to 30 to 45 micro-in.

As a rule, honing stones and techniques used for honing cast iron are different from those used for aluminum alloys. However, there are exceptions; for instance, in the section on honing in the article "Machining of Aluminum and Aluminum Alloys", Example 925 deals with an assembly of cast iron and aluminum where the two metals were honed simultaneously, with the same abrasive, in the simplest way to achieve a proper fit.

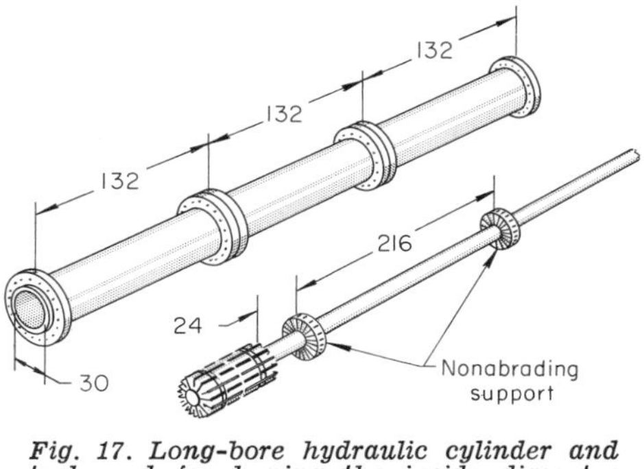

Fig. 17. Long-bore hydraulic cylinder and tool used for honing the inside diameter by "double ending" method (Example 545)

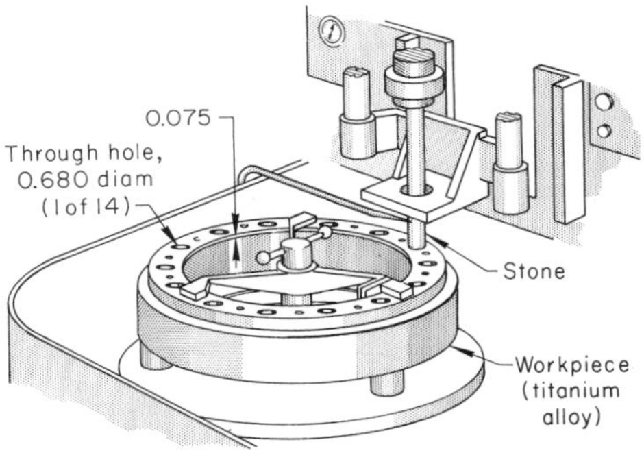

Fig. 18. Single-spindle rotary-indexing method of honing holes in compressor rotor-disk spacers (Example 546)

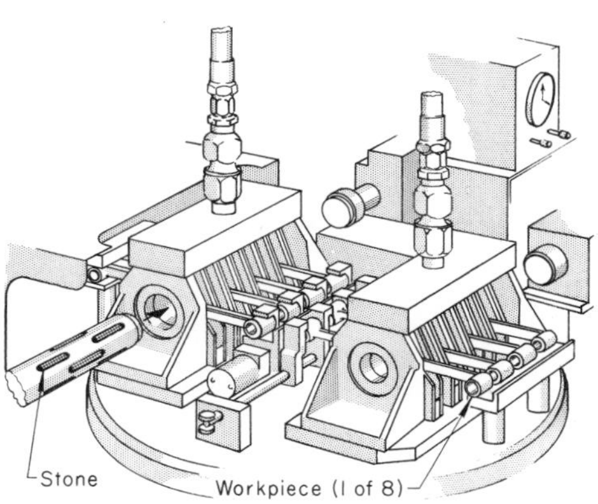

Fixture and honing tool for simultaneous honing of crankpin bores on eight automobile connecting rods. Rotating fixture permitted loading and unloading on one side while parts on the opposite side were being honed.

Fig. 19. High-production honing of automotive parts (Example 547)

Small Bores. Conventional manual-stroke honing tools (Fig. 5) are available for use in bores as small as ¹⁄₁₆ in. in diameter in parts such as fuel nozzles, miniature bearings, and heading dies, as in the following example.

Example 544. Honing Very Small Bores (Fig. 16)

Dies for cold heading tiny rivets and screw blanks had bores as small as ¹⁄₁₆ in. in diameter. Bore length varied, but was usually 1 to 2 in. Figure 16 shows one of the heading dies, which was made of tool steel, and a typical product of the die. Holes were drilled and reamed about 0.003 to 0.005 in. undersize before heat treatment. After hardening, they were honed, using manual stroking, to an accuracy of 0.0001 in. for both roundness and straightness.

Large Bores. The maximum diameter and length of bore that can be honed is limited mainly by the size of the equipment required for the workpiece and by the power required for the tools. Equipment with drive motors of up to 50 hp is available for honing steel shells of 41-in. ID and 63-ft length.

Cylinder shells for hydraulic hoists on regulating gates for dams are examples of large bores that are honed. In one honing operation, 0.030 in. of stock is removed from a 14,000-lb shell of 30-in. ID and 26-ft length to obtain a total envelope tolerance of 0.002 in. Before honing, the average out-of-roundness is 0.016 in.

Honing of a large hydraulic cylinder is described in the next example.

Example 545. "Double Ending" Technique for Large Bores (Fig. 17)

To prevent the drive shaft of the honing tool from sagging and marring the bore in honing the 30-in. ID of a 33-ft-long steel hydraulic cylinder (see upper sketch in Fig. 17), the tool used was provided with two supports of nonabrading material, as shown in the lower sketch. In honing, a technique called "double ending" was employed. This technique, which entails honing half the bore length and then reversing the workpiece and honing the other half, permitted the use of a machine with a stroke length shorter than the cylinder. Stock was removed at rates as high as 1.5 cu in. per min. Some cylinders required stock removal of up to 0.250 in. to obtain a tolerance of about 0.002 in. for roundness and straightness.

Short Bores. Several different techniques are used for honing short bores. These are particularly applicable when bore diameter exceeds length. In the simplest method, several pieces are stacked with bores aligned, clamped tightly by any suitable means, and honed as a unit. For example, ½-in.-long rings 1½ in. in inside diameter can be honed in stacks of eight. In effect, this would be the same as honing a single piece 4 in. long. Stacked parts may be either manually or power stroked. However, for successful results from this technique, the parts must have parallel sides, to permit building a straight stack that can be clamped tightly and provide a straight bore.

Other techniques that have proved successful for specific parts and requirements are described in the three examples that follow.

Examples 546, 547 and 548. Short-Bore Honing Techniques

Example 546 (Fig. 18). Fourteen holes of 0.680-in. diam and 0.075-in. length in compressor rotor-disk spacers made of a titanium alloy (Fig. 18) were honed on a single-spindle

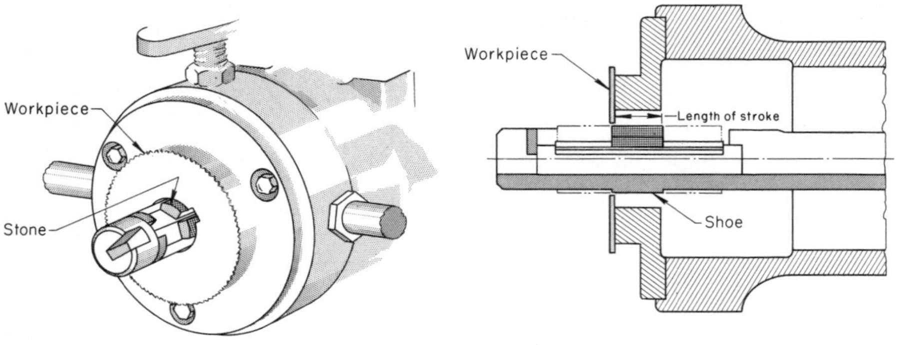

Fig. 20. Die honing guide used for manual honing of bores in circular slitting saws (Example 548)

machine equipped with hydraulic stroking. A rotary indexing table was used to position the parts. An average of 0.004 in. was removed from each hole, resulting in diametral accuracy within 0.0005 in. and a finish no rougher than 15 micro-in. Each part (14 holes) required 7 min, including loading and unloading.

Example 547 (Fig. 19). A power-stroking horizontal machine was used in high production for honing 2.423-in.-ID crankpin bores simultaneously in eight connecting rods. Figure 19 shows the fixture and the honing tool. Eight rods were stacked between 3/16-in.-wide parallel separator plates, resulting in an effective bore length of 10¼ in. The tool had three banks of four honing stones. Each stone was 3/8 in. square and 2¼ in. long. A two-station, rotary index table allowed the operator to unload eight completed rods and to load eight unfinished rods while eight other rods were being honed. A precheck plug probed the rods in the loading station to determine whether they had been bored to proper rough size. The operation completed one bank of rods in 45 sec, floor-to-floor time, and a production rate of about 600 rods per hour was obtained. In honing, 0.003 in. of stock was removed, a finish of 30 to 45 micro-in. was produced, and inside diameter was controlled within 0.0005 in.

Example 548 (Fig. 20). Keywayed bores in slitting saws made of hardened steel were honed after they had been ground in a stack to within a few thousandths of an inch of final size (1 to 1½ in. ID and 1/64 to 1/16 in. long). The bores were honed singly on a manual machine using a tool called a "die honing guide" (Fig. 20). Stack honing was not practicable, because the parts were thinner at the center and had teeth on the rims. With respect to the keyway, tool design was similar to that of Fig. 7(a).

The saw disk was pressed and held lightly by the operator against a flat circular boss on the face plate. The diameter of the boss was smaller than the outside diameter of the disk, as shown in Fig. 20. Both the saw disk and the face plate were stroked manually over the revolving tool, which protruded through the face plate.

Stops were used so that the operator did not overrun the tool. The work was centered by and on the expanding tool under a preset and automatically maintained pressure. Hole diameters were maintained within about 0.0002 in. Plug-gage and light-beam tests were used for inspection.

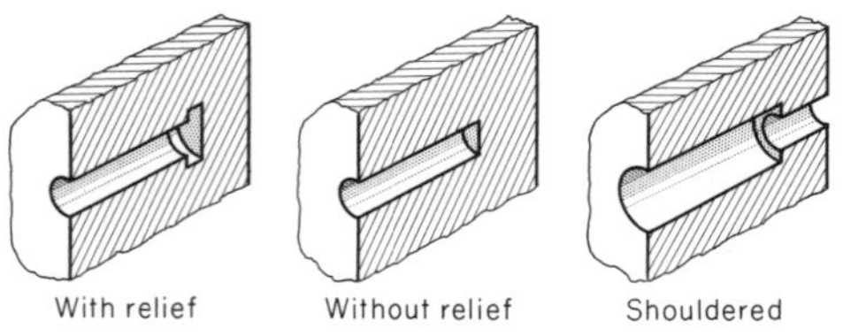

Fig. 21. Three types of blind holes

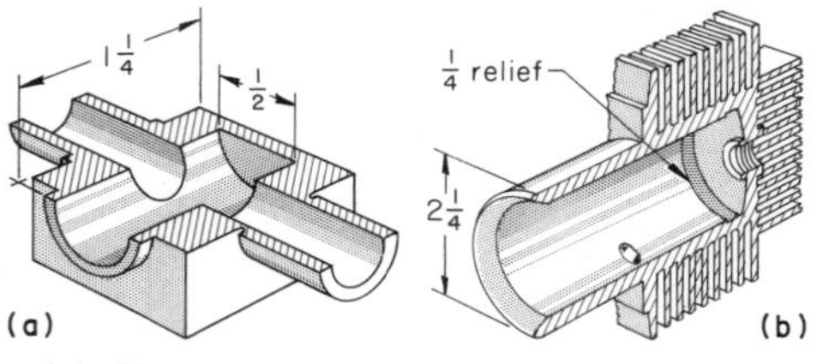

(a) Unrelieved blind hole that required a special tool (see Fig. 7c) for honing. (b) Relief in bore of a cylinder head for a lawn-mower engine. This relief permitted use of a conventional honing tool.

Fig. 22. Blind holes honed by different methods

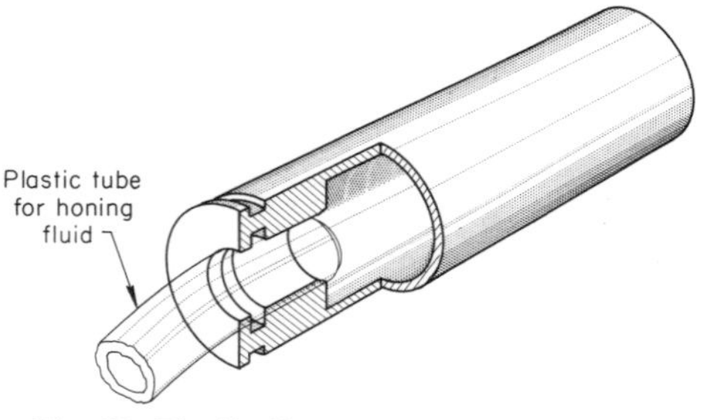

Fig. 23. Plastic line used to deliver honing fluid to the work area when blind holes are being honed

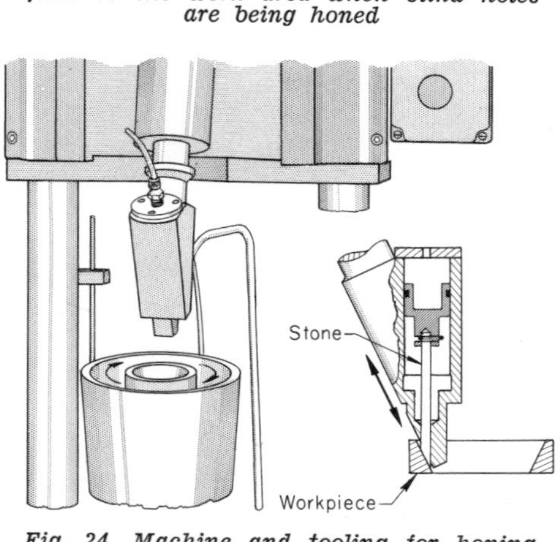

Fig. 24. Machine and tooling for honing short tapered bores

Blind holes are bores that have a bottom, shoulder or other obstruction that prevents a tool from passing completely through. The three most common types of blind holes are shown in Fig. 21. Most unrelieved blind holes can be honed satisfactorily, but there will always be some unfinished area at the bottom. The amount depends on length of bore, type of material, tolerance required, and amount of stock removed. Under best conditions, dead-blind holes can be honed to within about 0.015 in. of the end. Any relief will improve results; as much relief as possible is preferred. Sometimes an unrelieved blind hole is in effect provided with a relief because specified tolerance and finish need not be met at the bottom of the hole.

Special tools may be required, depending on whether or not relief (or on how much relief) is provided. For example, the unrelieved ½-in.-diam bore shown in Fig. 22(a) was manual-stroke honed to within about 0.015 in. of the end with a special tool having a hard-tipped honing stone (Fig. 7c). If adequate relief is provided, conventional tools are satisfactory. For example, cylinder heads in lawn-mower engines (Fig. 22b) can be manual-stroke honed in high production with conventional tools, because of the generous relief (about ¼ in. wide) at the blind end. Although both parts shown in Fig. 22 were manual-stroke honed, similar parts are frequently honed by power stroking.

Delivering enough honing fluid to the work area is often a problem in honing blind holes. When a hole has a bottom opening (Fig. 22b), fluid can be pumped through a plastic tube inserted in the opening, as illustrated in Fig. 23. When a hole has no bottom opening, the flow of fluid should be directed parallel to the mandrel, into the mouth of the bore.

In manual honing, blind holes are more difficult to keep straight than open holes. A truing sleeve (dummy workpiece) is frequently used to keep the shoes and stones straight and parallel; also, the stone and shoe are made shorter than the blind hole. Experienced operators have found that using a series of short strokes with an occasional stroke all the way out of the mouth is the best practice, until the hole is close to final diameter. This keeps the bottom slightly larger than the mouth. Straight strokes are then used for finish honing.

Tapered Bores. Part size, angle of taper, and length-to-diameter ratio determine the method used in taper honing. Short tapers are honed using a machine and tool such as that shown in Fig. 24. The machine has a head that can be positioned for any desired degree of taper, and the reciprocating tool holds a single stone. The workpiece is rigidly clamped in a fixture that rotates. This method is most commonly used for producing tapers on parts for which the length of honed area is less than the diameter. As the length of the taper increases in proportion to the diameter, however, the practicality of the method decreases, because the longer and more slender tools lack adequate rigidity.

Applications of this method of taper honing include special bearing rings and parts that use end tapers for sealing, and bores in gears that must fit tapered shafts. For example, drum-to-barrel seals in a 20-mm gun must have a taper of 0.050 in. per inch of length at each end and roughness less than 10 micro-in. To meet these requirements, 0.0005 to 0.002 in. of stock must be removed from the critical surfaces.

Taper honing long bores in large parts is far more complex than honing short tapers. Details of the procedure used in one application are given in the following example.

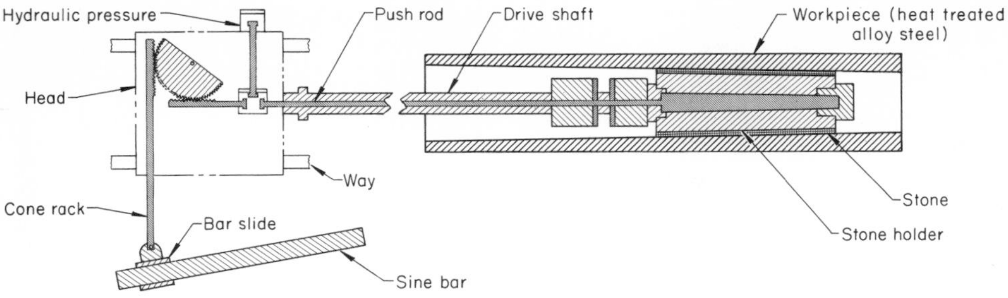

Fig. 25. Machine and tooling for taper honing of long bores (Example 549)

Example 549. Taper Honing by the Step Technique (Fig. 25)

To allow 177-mm gun jackets to separate from their mating tubes (they were shrunk together), both members required a taper of 0.0007 in. per inch over their entire length of 200 to 250 in. The tool used in honing the inside diameter of these parts contained ten sets of stones, 24 in. long, equally spaced around the periphery of the tool. Feed-out of these stones was controlled by hydraulically activated cones in the center of the tool. Because of the length of the parts, supports similar to those illustrated in Fig. 17 were needed on the drive shaft of the tool. A double universal joint between the support section and the honing section assured equal pressure in all directions.

The major portion of the stock was removed by "step honing". In this operation, a straight stroke was used, its length being progressively reduced to form a rough taper consisting of a series of small steps. The taper was finished in a second operation. The rod that moved the cone to expand the tool was linked to a sine bar on the side of the machine (see Fig. 25). As the tool was stroked forward through the bore, its diameter was decreased at a rate determined by the angle set on the sine bar. On the return stroke, tool diameter was gradually increased in the same manner. This phase of the operation produced a true taper for the full length of the bore.

A gaging device, which was mounted on the forward end of the tool, consisted of two selsyn motor and generator combinations. For one combination, the generator, which was operated by a small crank, was electrically connected to a motor in the gaging head on the tool. The motor controlled the feed-out of the gaging fingers. As the crank was turned, dials on the cabinet indicated how far the motor armature had turned. When the fingers were in contact with the bore, a light flashed on the cabinet. The bore diameter (at point of contact) could be read directly from the dials and plotted. In the other selsyn combination, the generator was geared to the stroking mechanism. The motor, wired to the generator, turned dials on the gaging cabinet that were calibrated to show the distance of the gaging fingers from the breech end of the jacket. This device permitted readings to be taken at any point in the bore.

Special Shapes. Machines and tools have been developed for honing various special shapes. For female splines, honing stones must be narrower than the spline width (preferably no wider than half the spline width), to allow for oscillation. Both machines and tools for honing splines are designed to produce simultaneous reciprocation and oscillation, rather than reciprocation and rotation. Relief bores are commonly honed by a procedure such as that described in Example 543.

Honing Practice for Outside Diameters

Honing has been used to only a limited extent for finishing outside diameters, largely because required dimensions and finish can be produced at less expense by other processes, such as centerless grinding. However, advances in metrology and improved honing techniques have resulted in an increase in the number and scope of applications of external honing.

Special machines and special adaptations of conventional machines (such as lathes) have been tooled to hone outside surfaces of metal parts. With these machines, either power or manual stroking may be employed.

Fixtured external honing (power stroking) is widely used for pieces that are not adaptable to competitive methods. A notable example is the finishing of grooves in bearing races. Special machines that simultaneously rotate the workpiece and oscillate the stones (Fig. 26) produce the crosshatch lay pattern characteristic of a honed surface. Such an operation is described in the following example.

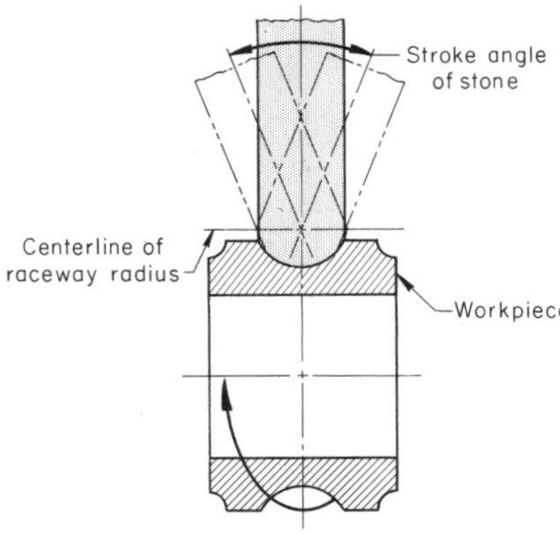

Fig. 26. Fixtured honing of grooves on external surface of bearing rings with simultaneous oscillation of honing stone and rotation of workpiece

Example 550. External Honing of an Internal Bearing Ring

An internal ring, 0.669-in. ID, 1.574-in. OD, and 0.472 in. wide, was rotated at 1560 rpm (650 sfm) during honing. Pressure rollers held the ring against a spindle drive adapter, which imparted the rotational force; a nonrotating bore-locating arbor was used for workpiece reference. A levigated alumina honing stone, ⅛ in. wide, ¼ in. thick and 6 in. long, was applied with an end pressure of 30 psi and was oscillated through an angle of 35° at 300 strokes per minute. This alloy steel ring (Rockwell C 60 to 63) was similar to that shown in Fig. 26.

In this operation, 0.0005 in. of stock was removed from the diameter in about 15 sec; finishes of less than 1 micro-in. parallel to the ball track, and of 2 to 4 micro-in. tangential to the track, were produced.

Manual external honing is applicable to the removal of small amounts of stock from external diameters of a wide variety of sizes and shapes. Honing of lengths up to 10 ft is common practice. Conventional honing machines are generally used for rotating workpieces up to 24 in. long. Lathes or drill presses are preferred for longer workpieces.

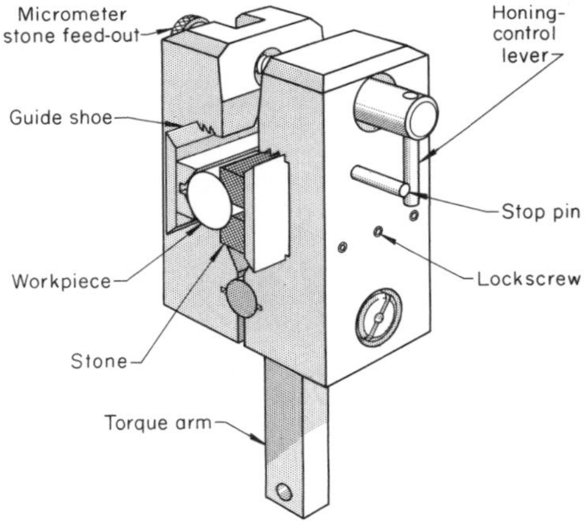

Fig. 27. Assembly used for manual-stroke honing of outside diameters. See text.

Tools such as that illustrated in Fig. 27 are available for honing parts ranging in outside diameter from about 0.120 to 2.750 in. With this setup, the operator grips the sides of the tool and strokes it over the rotating workpiece. Feed-out and cutting rate are controlled by applying pressure to the honing-control lever, which will move through a preset distance. Size is controlled automatically by setting the micrometer stone feed-out so that the honing-control lever will be against the stop pin when the correct size is attained. The only adjustment needed during the honing operation, even in production runs, is a slight additional stone feed-out to compensate for stone wear. A turn of the honing-control lever will instantly disengage the stone from the work for quick gaging or unloading, but will not change the setting on the micrometer stone feed-out.

With the setup shown in Fig. 27, a line of stones with opposing guide shoes, or opposing stones can be used. For honing long parts (up to 24 in.), multiple holders that contain as many as three stones or shoes in line may be used for correcting waviness. The torque arm can be used to offset the tendency for the tool to turn. A guide bar mounted on the machine acts as a stop for the torque arm. This type of

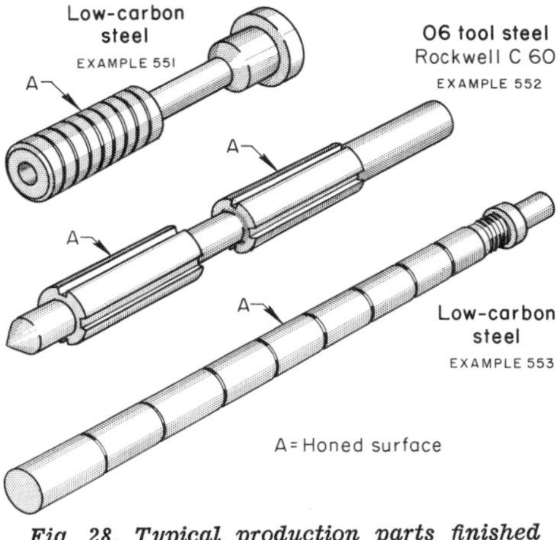

Fig. 28. Typical production parts finished on external surfaces by manual honing (Examples 551, 552 and 553)

tool can produce dimensional accuracy to 0.0001 in. or better and surface roughness as low as 2 micro-in.

Manual-stroke external honing has replaced lapping in some applications, because of the following advantages:

1 Honing is usually faster.
2 Soft metals can be honed without being impregnated with abrasive.
3 The use, in honing, of multiple-length stones and shoes allows better control of bow and waviness.

The following examples describe manual honing of external surfaces.

Examples 551, 552 and 553. Techniques for Manual External Honing

Example 551 (Fig. 28). A land 0.375 in. in diameter and 1.0 in. long on low-carbon steel metering rods was honed to a tolerance of ±0.0001 in. and a finish of 8 to 10 micro-in. Figure 28 shows a rod and the honed surfaces. A single stone and an opposing shoe were used in a tool like the one shown in Fig. 27, to remove 0.002 in. of stock.

Example 552 (Fig. 28). Two 1.0625-in.-long lands on valve needles made of O6 tool steel and hardened to Rockwell C 60 were honed to a diameter of 0.375 in., +0.0000, −0.0004 in. The resulting finish was 2 to 4 micro-in. Figure 28 shows a valve needle and indicates the honed surfaces. Two honing stones, with a combined length of 1.625 in., were used with opposing shoes for honing the lands.

Example 553 (Fig. 28). Low-carbon steel rams 18 in. long and 0.7450 in. in diameter were honed to diametral tolerance of +0.0000, −0.0001 in., straightness within 0.0002 in. in 6 in., and roughness of 8 to 10 micro-in. Total stock removed was 0.005 in. Figure 28 shows a ram and indicates the surface honed. Because of the length of these rams, multiple holders containing three 1.5-in.-long stones (total stone length, 4.5 in.) were used with three opposing shoes of the same length.

Long anodized aluminum tubes for in-flight refueling are honed externally in a lathe, the honing tool being moved by hand, and the nozzle for the honing fluid moving with the tool. Crankpins of some crankshafts are honed the same way at overhaul.

Honing Practice for Gear Teeth

The teeth of hardened gears are honed to remove nicks and burrs, to improve finish, and to make minor corrections in tooth shape. Gear teeth are honed on high-speed machines specially designed for the process (Fig. 29). The honing tool is like a gear driving the workpiece at high speed (up to 100 sfm) while oscillating so that the teeth slide axially against the workpiece.

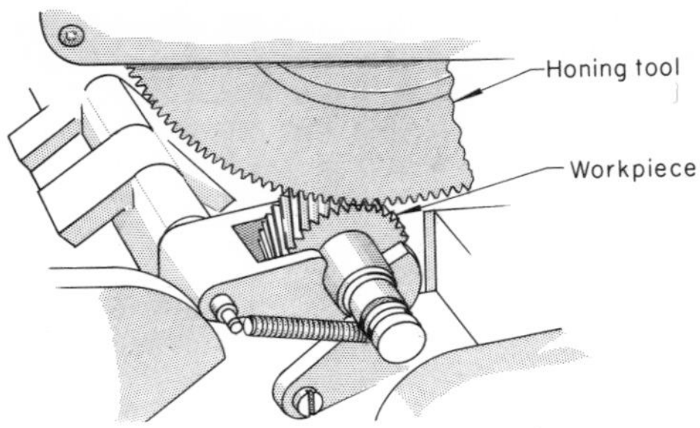

Fig. 29. Honing teeth of helical gears

Spur gears and internal or external helical gears ranging in diametral pitch from 24 to 2.5, in outside diameter from ¾ to 26½ in., and up to 3 in. in face width have been honed on these machines. Finishes of 30 micro-in. are easily achieved, and finishes of 3 to 4 micro-in. are possible. Both taper and crown honing can be done.

Tools used in honing gear teeth are of two types: (*a*) a helical-gear-shaped tool made of abrasive-impregnated plastic, and (*b*) a metal helical gear with a bonded abrasive coating that is renewable. The plastic tool, which is discarded at the end of its useful life, is widely used. The metal tool is used mainly for applications in which plastic tools would be likely to break.

Plastic tools are supplied with abrasives of 60 to 500 grit size. Size of abrasive, gear pitch and desired finish are usually related as follows:

Grit size	Gear pitch	Finish, micro-in.
60	Up to 16	30 to 35
100	16 to 20	25 to 30
180	Over 20	15 to 20
280	Over 20	10 to 12
500	Over 20	3 to 4

Honing tools do not load up, and a plastic honing tool can wear until its teeth break. Stock removal of 0.001 to 0.002 in., measured over pins, is recommended maximum.

Methods. The two methods used to hone gear teeth are (*a*) the zero-backlash method and (*b*) the constant-pressure method. In the zero-backlash method, which is used for gears made to commercial tolerances, the tool head is locked so that the distance between the center of the work gear and the center of the honing tool is fixed throughout the honing cycle. In the constant-pressure method, which is used for gears produced to dimensions outside commercial tolerance ranges, the tool and the work gear are kept in pressure-controlled tight mesh.

Applicability. The use of honing for removing nicks and burrs from hardened gears can result in a considerable cost saving in comparison to the usual method. In the usual method, the gears are tested against master specimens on sound-test machines. Nicks indicated are searched for and removed by a hand grinder. The gear is then retested to make certain the nick has been removed. When honing is used, all of these various tests and procedures can be eliminated.

Some shape correction can be achieved in the removal of 0.002 in. of stock by honing. A helical gear 5 in. in diameter may show lead correction of 0.0004 in., involute profile correction of 0.0003 in., and eccentricity correction of 0.0004 in.

The advisability of using honing for salvaging hardened gears hinges on cost considerations. As the error in tooth shape increases, honing time increases and tool life decreases. On the other hand, if the gears represent a large investment in production time and material, honing may be the most economical method.

Because honing is not designed for heavy stock removal or tooth correction, it cannot be substituted for grinding or shaving of gears. Rotary shaving usually leaves gear teeth smooth within 10 to 40 micro-in.

Lapping

*By the ASM Committee on Lapping**

LAPPING is a low-speed low-pressure abrading operation that accomplishes one or more of the following results: (*a*) extreme accuracy, (*b*) correction of minor imperfections in shape, (*c*) refinement of surface finish, and (*d*) extremely close fit between mating surfaces. In general, the quality that can be obtained by lapping is not easily or economically obtained by other processes.

Either loose or bonded abrasives may be used for lapping. When bonded abrasives are used, the lapping process resembles conventional grinding, except that lapping is done at low speeds and is nonsparking. Lapping with bonded abrasives differs from honing mainly in the type of tooling employed. Also, unlike honing, lapping is not necessarily a two-motion process.

Lapping operations usually fall into one of two categories: individual-piece lapping and matched-piece lapping.

In individual-piece lapping, abrasive is rubbed against the workpiece by means of a special tool called a lap

*T. W. MORRISON, *Chairman,* Vice President – Engineering and Research, SKF Industries, Inc.; ROGER D. COX, Project Engineer, Centralab Electronics Div., Globe-Union, Inc.; DEREK DAWSON, Chief Gear Engineer, Eaton Axle Div., Eaton Yale & Towne, Inc.

WILLIAM L. DENHART, Project Engineer, Perfect Circle Corp.; CONRAD P. FAHLMAN, Director of Quality Control, Industrial Products Div., Brown & Sharpe Manufacturing Co.; F. K. JONES, Chief Sales Engineer, Machine Tool Div., Norton Co.; DAVID W. PETHICK, Master Mechanic – Hart Plant, Bower Roller Bearing Div., Federal-Mogul-Bower Bearings, Inc.; J. GERALD REYNARD, Supervisor of Manufacturing, Scintilla Div., Bendix Corp.

PETER J. SOMMER, General Manager, Size Control Co.; B. H. STENBERG, Vice President of Manufacturing, Crane Packing Co.; JOSEPH B. WARGO, Assistant Manager of Manufacturing Engineering, Schick, Inc.

(usually of material softer than the workpiece), rather than by a mating workpiece surface. When loose abrasive is used, the lap usually is made of soft cast iron or a soft nonferrous metal. Laps made of bonded abrasive also can be used.

Individual-piece lapping is most effective on hard metals or other hard materials. It is used to produce optically flat surfaces, to produce accurate planes from which other planes can be located (as for gage blocks), and to finish parallel faces.

In matched-piece lapping, sometimes called "equalizing", two workpiece surfaces separated only by a layer of abrasive mixed with a vehicle are rubbed against each other. Each workpiece drives the abrasive so that the grit particles act on the opposing surfaces. Irregularities that prevent the surfaces from fitting together precisely are thus eliminated, and the surfaces are "mated". In many instances, a part is first lapped individually and is then mated with another part by this method, before the two are stocked as a pair of lapped-together parts.

Matched-piece lapping enables mating parts (such as the heads and blocks of internal-combustion engines) to form liquid-tight or gas-tight seals without the need for gaskets. It also eliminates the need for piston rings in fitting some plungers to cylinders. Other common uses of matched-piece lapping are for fitting tapered valve components (Fig. 1) and for mating two or more gears in a set.

Process Capabilities

Although most parts that are lapped are made of steel or cast iron, the process has also been used for finishing many other materials, from aluminum alloys to tungsten carbide and ceramics.

Size or weight of workpieces that can be lapped is limited only by the available equipment. Parts finished by lapping range in weight from a fraction of an ounce to hundreds of pounds.

Workpiece Shape. Tools and methods have been devised for lapping virtually every shape of workpiece on which a lapped surface is desired. Lapping is most widely used for finishing flat surfaces or outside and inside cylindrical surfaces. The process also can be applied, however, to balls, rollers, cones, double-curved surfaces, assembled bearings, and shapes such as gear teeth.

Metal Removal. Lapping is intended as a final finishing process that would be, in general, an impractical or uneconomical means of removing stock. In most applications, less than 0.0005 in. of metal is removed from a surface by lapping. However, on occasion (usually in flat lapping), 0.005 in. or even more may be removed. In a few instances it has proved more economical to remove stock by lapping than to add a preliminary grinding operation.

Selection of Abrasive

Silicon carbide and fused alumina are the abrasives most widely used for lapping. Silicon carbide is extremely hard, being rated at 9.5 on the Mohs scale or at about 2500 on the Knoop scale (100-g load). Its grit is sharp and brittle, making it nearly ideal as an abrasive for many lapping applications, because it continually breaks down to expose new cutting edges. Silicon carbide is used for lapping hardened steel or cast iron, particularly when an appreciable amount of stock is to be removed.

Fused alumina, rated at 9 on the Mohs scale (or about 2000 on the Knoop scale), also is sharp, but it is tougher than silicon carbide and breaks down less readily. Fused alumina is generally more suitable for lapping soft steels or nonferrous metals than is silicon carbide.

Boron carbide is next to diamond in hardness (9.75 Mohs; about 2800 Knoop) and is an excellent abrasive for lapping. However, because it costs 10 to 25 times as much as silicon carbide or fused alumina, boron carbide usually is used only for lapping dies and gages or for similar special applications. Relative costs for various quantities and grit sizes of silicon carbide, fused alumina, and boron carbide are compared in Table 1.

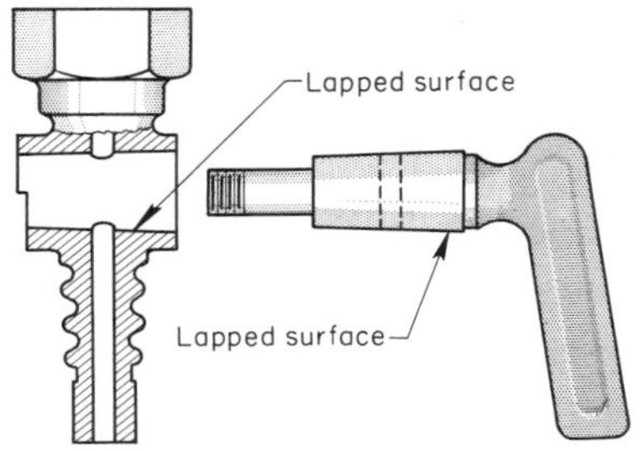

Fig. 1. Tapered valve components finished by matched-piece lapping for precise fit of mating surfaces

Table 1. Relative Costs of Abrasives

Quantity, lb	Size, mesh	Cost per pound: Fused alumina	Silicon carbide	Boron carbide
1	80	$1.20	$1.27	$12.50
	280	1.48	1.51	16.60
	800	1.88	2.10	23.55
5	80	0.70	0.77	9.70
	280	0.98	1.01	13.85
	800	1.38	1.60	20.80
10	80	0.50	0.57	9.35
	280	0.78	0.81	13.55
	800	1.18	1.40	20.45
25	80	0.38	0.45	9.00
	280	0.66	0.69	13.20
	800	1.06	1.28	20.10
50	80	0.33	0.40	8.70
	280	0.61	0.64	12.80
	800	1.01	1.23	19.75

Diamond is the hardest of all materials (10 Mohs; about 6500 Knoop), but because it costs about $3 or more per gram it is seldom used as an abrasive for lapping metals.

Softer abrasives, such as emery, garnet, unfused alumina, and chromium oxide, also are used for lapping, but to a far lesser extent. As indicated in Table 2, these softer abrasives are used for lapping soft metals or for final lapping of parts on which a highly reflective surface is required. In lapping to produce a reflective surface, no significant amount of stock is removed, and the finish is not necessarily finer than a matte finish.

Grit sizes most commonly employed in lapping range from 100 to 1000 (Table 2). However, abrasives usually are available in grit sizes from about 50 to 3800, and even finer.

For lapping hardened steel to remove about 0.0002 in. of stock and produce a finish of less than 2 micro-in., a grit size of 280 is appropriate. If finishing requirements are less stringent, 180-grit abrasive will be more economical, because it removes metal faster than finer grit does.

As the amount of stock to be removed increases, coarser grits are required; but for removing considerable amounts of stock, it is more economical to employ a roughing operation followed by a finishing operation.

When a substantial amount of stock is being removed, a fine finish can be produced without the use of a small grit size, because the originally coarse grit breaks down as lapping proceeds and progressively produces a finer finish. If this technique is used, there must be enough stock allowance for lapping so that the deeper scratches formed initially by the coarse grit will be removed by the time final dimensions are reached.

Grading. When an abrasive of a specified grit size is purchased, some of it will be finer and some coarser than the stated size. The degree of grading is an important consideration in the selection of any abrasive. Abrasives increase in cost as the grading becomes closer. However, the use of a low-cost,

Table 2. Types and Grit Sizes of Abrasives for Various Applications of Lapping

Abrasive	Relative hardness	Grit size	Typical applications
All-Purpose Compounds			
Silicon carbide	Hard and sharp	100,220,320,400	Tool-room lapping
Corundum	Medium soft	220,240,280	Tool-room lapping
Compounds for Roughing, Finishing or Polishing			
Corundum	Medium soft	400,500,600	Roughing softer steels
		700,800	Finishing softer steels
Alumina	Hard	500,600,900	Roughing harder steels, stainless, Cr plate
		2 to 10 microns	Finishing hard steels
Alumina	Medium hard	900	Polishing hard steels
		5,10,15 microns	Polishing hard steels
		1 to 3 microns	Polishing stainless, Cr plate
Alumina	Soft	1,2 microns	Polishing
Silicon carbide	Hard and sharp	600,800,1000	Roughing hardened steels; cast iron
Garnet	Medium soft	600,800	Finishing brass, bronze
		10 microns	Polishing brass, bronze
Emery	Medium soft	800	Polishing softer steels
Chromium oxide	Medium soft	1 micron	Polishing stainless
Ferric oxide	Soft	1 micron	Polishing soft metals
Cerium oxide	Medium hard	1,2 microns	Polishing

loosely graded abrasive is not always economical, as the experience described in the following example indicates.

Example 554. Closely Graded Abrasive for Greater Economy

A low-cost grade of silicon carbide that ranged in grit size from 100 to 800 was used for lapping piston rings. A change to an abrasive that was closely graded to a grit size of 600 reduced the over-all cost of abrasive 50%, even though the initial cost of the 600-grit abrasive was twice that of the low-cost grade. The saving was made possible because the 600-grit abrasive contained more of the grit size most efficient for lapping, and consequently only one fourth as much of it was required for removing the same amount of stock. The 600-grit abrasive also gave a smoother finish with less smudging.

Selection of Vehicle

Vehicles, or binders, for loose abrasives include a wide variety of compounds. Some shops prepare their own formulations or modify standard compositions. However, more consistent results can be obtained with standardized, commercial compounds.

Two major factors in the selection of a vehicle are the metal being lapped and the lapping method to be employed (inside or outside diameter, flat or spherical). Any vehicle should:

1. Retain abrasives in uniform suspension
2. Serve as a cushion between surfaces being lapped (to minimize metal-to-metal contact yet avoid rolling action on abrasive particles)
3. Adhere to laps, and thus minimize waste of compound
4. Be noncorrosive to the metal being lapped
5. Be nontoxic to operators
6. Be easily removable by cleaning
7. Respond to temperature variations with the viscosity characteristics (stability or flexibility) desired in a given application. (Although rapid changes of viscosity usually are undesirable, in some applications it is important that the vehicle be able to change quickly from a grease to an oil when under slight heat and pressure and then revert quickly to greaselike consistency when pressure is released.)

Most vehicles have an oil or grease base, although some are made of water-soluble compounds. The consistency of oil-base vehicles varies from that of mineral seal oil (a water-white product having a viscosity slightly higher than kerosine) to that of heavy grease. Common spindle oil is often used as a vehicle. Commercial compounds contain mixtures of animal fat, vegetable and mineral oils.

Vehicles with an oil or grease base are usually used for lapping ferrous metals. For specific applications where grease or oil would be objectionable (such as copper-base alloys and other nonferrous metals), water-soluble vehicles are available. These vehicles, which are readily removed with water, are low-viscosity compositions of starches, bentonite and soluble oils with rust inhibitors.

Lapping Outer Cylindrical Surfaces

Outer cylindrical surfaces usually are lapped by one of the following methods: (*a*) ring lapping (a manual operation), (*b*) machine lapping between plates, (*c*) centerless roll lapping with loose abrasive, and (*d*) centerless lapping with bonded abrasives. In addition to these, special methods are used for specific applications, such as the lapping of piston rings and crankshafts. Choice of method depends on part configuration, size of production lot to be lapped, and cost. Many outer cylindrical surfaces can be lapped with equal success by two or more methods.

Ring Lapping

Ring lapping is the simplest method of lapping outer surfaces. Designs of ring laps vary, but that illustrated in Fig. 2 is typical. The lapping ring (or ring lap), usually made of cast iron, is manually stroked back and forth over the workpiece, which is chucked in a lathe or polishing head and rotated. Lapping compound (usually of paste consistency) is applied frequently to

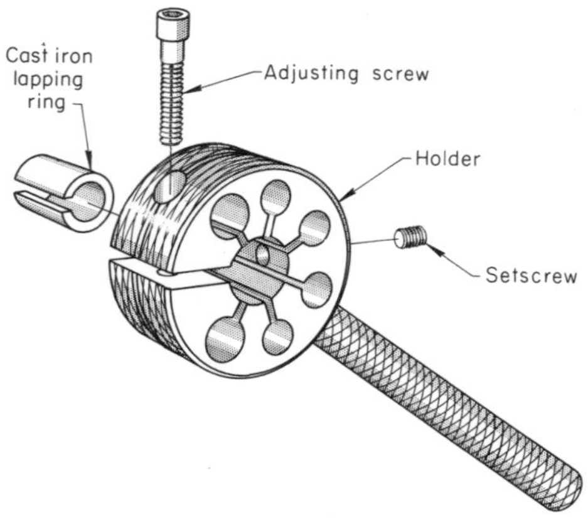

Fig. 2. Typical ring lapping assembly. Drilled holes and slots permit uniform adjustment.

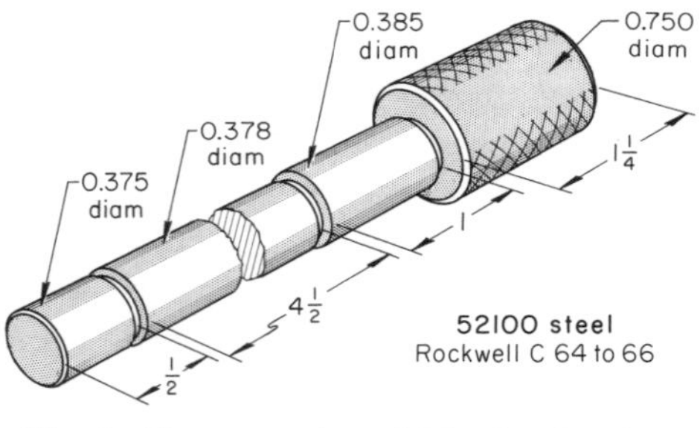

Fig. 3. Plug gage for which ring lapping was the best method of finishing, because three diameters required lapping and the handle unbalanced the part (Example 555)

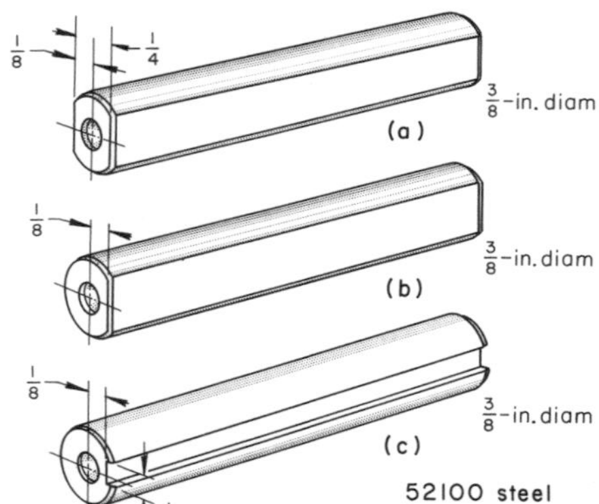

Fig. 4. Cylinders with flats or keyway, for which ring lapping was the most practical method (Example 556)

the surface of the workpiece. A manually adjusted screw is tightened, as required, to maintain a slight drag on the lap.

The ring lap should always be shorter than the workpiece, and if size permits, it should have adjustable slots. Finishing the bore of a ring lap is critical. It should be drilled, reamed and honed (or lapped) to a size very close to the starting diameter of the workpiece; the screw adjustment should be used only to compensate for the slight decrease in workpiece diameter as lapping proceeds.

Applicability. Ring lapping, when performed by a skilled operator, offers at least two advantages over machine methods: (*a*) parts can be produced to extremely close tolerances, and (*b*) out-of-roundness can be corrected to a degree not feasible by machine lapping. Aside from requiring operator skill, however, ring lapping is tedious and expensive, and it should be considered only when one or more of the following conditions prevail:

1. Equipment for any other method is not available.
2. Workpiece is out-of-round.
3. Weight of workpiece is unbalanced.
4. Workpiece has two or more different diameters that must be lapped.
5. Workpiece has flats, keyways or other interruptions on its cylindrical surface.
6. Only a few pieces are to be finished.

The four examples that follow describe specific applications in which some of the above conditions existed, and in which ring lapping therefore was the most suitable method.

Example 555. Three-Diameter Unbalanced Workpiece (Fig. 3)

The plug gage shown in Fig. 3 was ring lapped mainly because three diameters (0.375, 0.378 and 0.385 in.) had to be lapped and because the 0.750-in.-diam handle imposed a weight unbalance. This gage was lapped with cast iron ring laps of the type shown in Fig. 2. During lapping, the workpiece was rotated at 250 sfm in a 10-in. lathe and manually stroked at 30 to 40 strokes per minute. Each diameter was lapped straight within 35 millionths of an inch and concentric within 50 millionths. About 1 hr was required for a skilled operator to finish one piece (three diameters).

Example 556. Interrupted Cylindrical Surface (Fig. 4)

The parts shown in Fig. 4 are typical of workpieces for which ring lapping is the only practical method — even for large quantities — because of the flats or keyways that interrupt the cylindrical surface. These parts were chucked in the collet of a 10-in. lathe, rotated at 150 sfm, and stroked at 20 to 30 strokes per minute. To prevent dulling of the sharp corners of the flats and keyways, a fine (1000 to 1200-grit) aluminum oxide was used in a soluble-oil vehicle. About 0.0003 to 0.0004 in. of stock was removed to attain a finish of 3 micro-in. or better. One operator produced the parts shown in Fig. 4(a), (b) and (c) at a rate of 2, 3 and 4 pieces per hour, respectively.

Example 557. Small Quantities to Close Tolerances (Fig. 5)

Ring lapping was employed for finishing various sizes of plug gages (Fig. 5) when quantities were small and close tolerances had to be maintained. The gages were chucked by their tapered shanks in a polishing head or a lathe and were lapped with adjustable cast iron ring laps of the type shown at the left in Fig. 5. The lapping medium, which was applied manually, consisted of 900-grit aluminum oxide in a vegetable-compound vehicle of paste consistency. Rotation speeds were 150 to 600 rpm, depending on gage diameter. Lapping removed 0.0002 to 0.0003 in. of stock, achieved a finish of 1 to 2 micro-in. and met the dimensional tolerances given in the table with Fig. 5. Production was two to three gages per hour.

Maintaining close tolerances was made possible by strict adherence to the following operating procedure:

1 Measure to determine starting condition (amount of stock to be removed, taper and roundness).
2 Insert tapered shank of gage in chuck, and coat surface to be lapped with abrasive.
3 Loosen screw on lap and put lap on workpiece.
4 Tighten screw until lap turns with slight resistance.
5 Start machine and reciprocate lap evenly over the workpiece without overrunning ends; continue until lap runs smoothly from end to end.
6 Stop machine, remove lap and allow it to cool.
7 Measure workpiece and determine surface conditions.
8 Repeat process, except for reciprocation as in step 5, until desired results are obtained. Here, reciprocation depends on conditions found when the workpiece was measured in step 7. Oversize and out-of-roundness require slow, even reciprocation. Drop-off toward the ends requires reversal of reciprocation when the edge of the lap is within 1/16 in. of the end of the workpiece. Taper, or barrel or hourglass shape, requires that the reciprocation be localized at the high areas. Extremes of the above (in excess of 0.0002 in.) must be corrected by grinding.

Example 558. Preproduction vs Production Lapping (Fig. 6)

In many instances, ring lapping is used for parts being developed, and a more economical method is used when the parts are in production. This procedure was followed for the valve needle shown in Fig. 6, which was ring lapped in small quantities during development but was machine lapped between plates (see Example 561) in production lots. These needles, in diameters of 1/4 to 3/8 in., were made of alloy tool steel and hardened to Rockwell C 60 to 65.

For ring lapping, each needle was chucked by its stem and rotated in a lathe at 650 rpm. The lap (Fig. 6), which was made of cast iron, was stroked back and forth over the needle until grinding marks were eliminated. The lapping medium with which the needle was coated consisted of chromium oxide mixed with spindle oil. Lapping produced a finish of 2 micro-in., and maintained tolerances of 50 millionths of an inch for straightness and 25 millionths for roundness.

To insure straightness, the laps used had to be at least three fourths as long as the area to be lapped. The laps also had to be inspected frequently, and to be reconditioned by being lapped with internal laps of similar material.

Machine Lapping Between Plates

Machine lapping of outer cylindrical surfaces between plates employs as laps two opposed cast iron or bonded-abrasive circular plates that are held on vertical spindles of the machine (Fig. 7). The plates usually are 8 to 28 in. in diameter, although larger sizes are available. For the most part, plain-face laps are used, and for greatest accuracy, the width of the lap face should not exceed the length of the surface being lapped. The workpieces are retained between these laps in slotted plates and caused to rotate and slide. They are given an eccentric, or in-and-out, motion to break the pattern of motion and to insure that they move over the inside and outside edges of the lap. This prevents grooving the lap. For short runs, an eccentric motion is unnecessary if the laps are kept flat by reconditioning.

Cast Iron Laps. When cast iron laps are used, the lower lap is usually rotated and drives the workpieces. The upper lap is held stationary, but it is free-floating so that it can adjust to the variations in workpiece size. The lower lap regulates speed of rotation, because the workholder is not driven. As the diameter of the workpiece decreases, rotary speed is increased to maintain an almost constant surface speed.

The abrasive is used with a paste-type vehicle and is swabbed on the laps before the cycle is started. Oil or kerosine is then added during the cycle to prevent drying of the vehicle, which may result in scratching.

Because the upper lap floats, a quantity of parts must be lapped simultaneously. Although three parts will support the upper lap, when only three parts are lapped the machine will not produce straightness or a common size. Therefore, it is advisable to lap a minimum of five parts, and if they are not available, the machine should be loaded with dummy parts. The best practice is to put as many parts as possible in a load. This reduces the pressure on each part and slows the operation. Thus the operator has more control and can secure desired tolerances more easily.

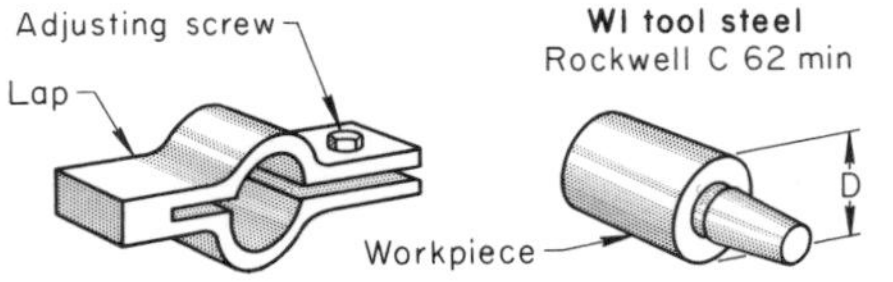

Workpiece diameter(D), in.	Tolerance, millionths of an inch, for gages of class: XX	X	Y
0.029 to 0.825	20	40	70
0.825 to 1.510	30	60	90
1.510 to 2.510	40	80	120
2.510 to 4.510	50	100	150
4.510 to 6.510	65	130	190
6.510 to 9.010	80	160	240
9.010 to 12.010	100	200	300

Fig. 5. Plug gage (workpiece) and cast iron ring lap for obtaining the dimensional tolerances tabulated (Example 557)

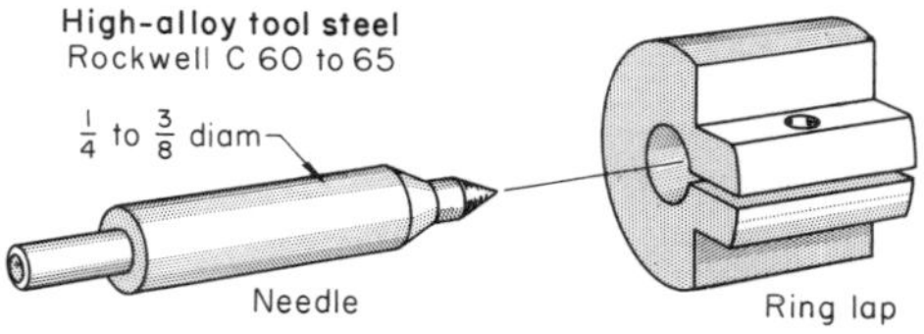

Fig. 6. Valve needle, and ring lap for finishing small, preproduction quantities (Example 558)

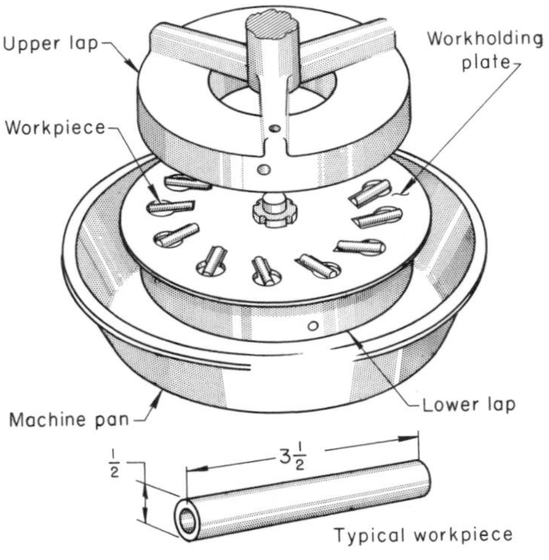

Fig. 7. Typical vertical lapping machine for finishing cylindrical surfaces in production quantities

Finishes as fine as 1 micro-in., with stock removal of 0.0001 to 0.0004 in., are feasible when cast iron laps are used. Diametral tolerances as low as 20 millionths of an inch, roundness within 5 millionths, and taper of less than 10 millionths have been achieved. However, such accuracy depends greatly on the accuracy achieved in prior machining operations.

Bonded-Abrasive Laps. When bonded-abrasive laps are used, both laps are rotated, with kerosine or a similar lubricant used as a coolant and to wash away chips or loose abrasive. Because both laps are driven at higher speeds than are used for cast iron laps, lapping action is more severe. Consequently, the machine will not produce the extreme accuracy possible with machines using cast iron laps. In addition, because bonded-abrasive laps must be dressed with diamond tools, it is not possible to make them as flat as cast iron laps, on which the machines regenerate flatness.

Quantity of parts being lapped is less critical for machines using bonded-abrasive laps than it is for machines using cast iron laps, because both bonded-abrasive laps are rigidly supported on spindles and separately driven. As few as three parts can be successfully processed in this type of machine.

Applicability. Machine lapping between plates is an economical method of finishing outside cylindrical surfaces, provided its use is warranted by production quantities and permitted by part configuration. The process can be used for lapping parts a few thousandths of an inch to 3 or 4 in. in diameter, and 1/4 to 9 in. long. Parts commonly lapped by this method include plug gages, piston pins, hypodermic plungers, ceramic pins, small valve pistons, cylindrical valves, small engine pistons, roller bearings, diesel injector valves, plungers, small rolls, and miscellaneous cylindrical pins.

Either hard or soft materials can be lapped, provided they are rigid enough to accept the pressure of the laps. Hard materials respond well to lapping, and achieve luster. Hard materials also are easier to control for tolerance, because the hardness slows the operation. Soft materials lap more rapidly and — especially when bonded-abrasive laps are used — often have a scratchy or dull appearance. This can be prevented by using a polishing abrasive, such as levigated alumina, which reduces the cutting ability of the bonded abrasive.

Limitations. A part with diameter greater than its length is difficult or impossible to machine lap between plates. For parts of this type, other methods of outer cylindrical-surface lapping are more practical.

Parts with shoulders require special workholders that permit the shoulder section to be placed on the inside or outside of the lap face. Parts with keyways, flats or interrupted surfaces are difficult to lap by machine, because the variations in pressure that occur are likely to cause out-of-roundness. If the relief extends over the entire length of the piece, this method of lapping cannot be used.

Parts with raised hubs in the middle require special laps that are cut in such a way that they clear the hub. Clearance is necessary between the hub and the work surface to allow for oscillation of the workpiece.

Thin-wall tubing can be lapped, but if the walls are so thin that deflection is significant, it will be difficult to maintain roundness. Parts that are hollow on one end but solid on the opposite end present problems in obtaining roundness and straightness, because the hollow end will deflect more under the weight of the upper lap. Sometimes, however, plugging the hollow end of the part will solve these problems.

Because it is impractical to keep more than one working surface on the face of cast iron laps flat, workpieces with work surfaces that have different diameters require a separate operation for each surface. It is usually impractical to machine lap workpieces with diameters that are greater than the diameter to be lapped.

Since the outside edges of the plates lap at a faster rate than the inside edges, care must be exerted to prevent workpieces from becoming tapered. One method of overcoming the problem consists of using short lapping cycles and, at the end of each cycle, turning the workpieces end for end in the slots in the workholder. Also, the workpieces should be removed from the slots after each short cycle, mixed, and then replaced at random in different slots. This prevents inadvertent placement of all larger pieces at one side of the workholder and smaller pieces at the opposite side — which, because the upper lap floats, would make it difficult to produce accurate parts. Taper may be minimized by positioning the workholder so that the parts in the slots are at a 15° angle to a radius, as illustrated in Fig. 8 and 10.

Because machine lapping between plates uses diametrically opposed laps, it cannot correct the out-of-roundness produced by centerless grinding. However, out-of-roundness of the type produced by grinding on centers can be corrected.

The following three examples describe procedures for machine lapping between plates. Two of the workpieces required special consideration because of their shapes.

Example 559. Clearing a Workpiece Projection (Fig. 8)

Fuel-injection plungers 3 to 30 mm in diameter and 3 to 7 in. long were lapped using the setup shown in Fig. 8. The plungers were ground to within 0.0002-in. variation, and 0.0008 in. of stock was left for removal in lapping. A rotary machine with upper and lower cast iron laps 24 to 30 in. in diameter was used. A workholder held each plunger tangent to a 2½-to-3-in.-diam circle in the center, as illustrated in Fig. 8, and positioned it so that a larger section cleared the lap. The bottom lap (which was grooved to prevent buildup of lapping compound) had a center driving pin set off-center ⅜ in. During lapping, the bottom lap rotated at 60 rpm; the top lap remained stationary. Lapping compound of soft, fine consistency was used. For each load, inspection and thorough cleaning were necessary after a 5-min run. Kerosine was then added with a finer compound, and the operation was continued for 2 min. The condition of the laps, which had to be kept flat, was checked with a straightedge.

Lapping caused roundness within 25 millionths of an inch, straightness within 50 millionths, and smoothness of less than 2 micro-in. An electrolimit gage with a setting plug was used to check the dimensions of one plunger in each load.

Example 560. Lapping a Plunger With a Recess (Fig. 9)

A special helix for fuel control was cut into some types of the plungers described in Example 559 and shown in Fig. 8. Figure 9 shows a typical helix, ⅛ in. deep. Originally, the plungers with helixes were ring lapped, because in conventional machine lapping, the compound built up excessively in the helix. It was found, however, that if both upper and lower laps were grooved, the buildup of compound would be minimized and machine lapping would be practicable. For machine lapping, essentially the same procedure as that described in Example 559 was used, and the parts were held in a workholder similar to that shown in Fig. 8.

Example 561. Lapping Valve Needles to Close Tolerance (Fig. 10)

The valve needles described in Example 558 and Fig. 6, although ring lapped in preproduction, were machine lapped between cast iron plates in production. Before being machine lapped, the parts were carefully ground for roundness and then (because the lap would ride on those parts that were largest in diameter) segregated into groups of 0.0001-to-0.0002-in. diametral variation. Both upper and lower laps were grooved to prevent breakdown of sharp edges during lapping. A laminated phenolic workholder designed to hold a maximum load of parts (Fig. 10) was eccentric to the laps, to provide an oscillating motion.

In this operation, the cycle was stopped so that the parts could be measured with an electrolimit gage, a visual shadow gage or an air gage. If the desired size had not been attained, more finish lapping compound was added and lapping was continued. Lapping produced a finish of 2 micro-in., roundness within 25 millionths of an inch and straightness of 50 millionths.

To recondition the laps, finish lapping compound was applied to the bottom lap. The laps were then brought together and rotated until the edges of the grooves were sharp. The laps required occasional regrinding to maintain a minimum groove depth of 1⁄16 in. and width of 0.030 in.

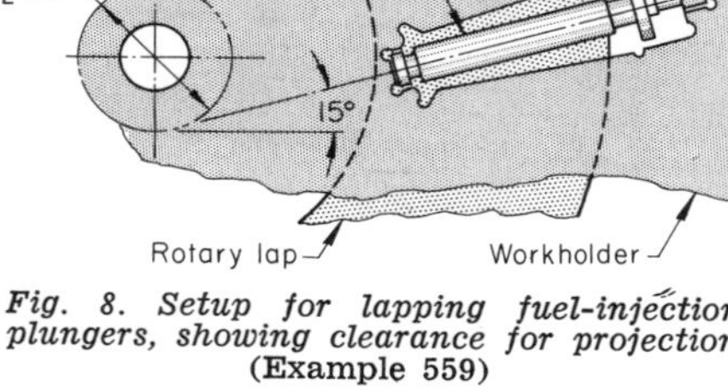

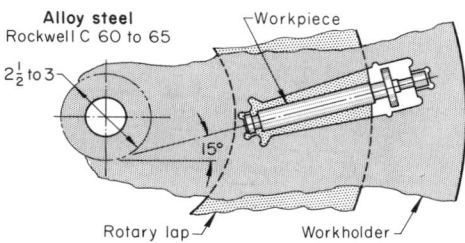

Fig. 8. Setup for lapping fuel-injection plungers, showing clearance for projection (Example 559)

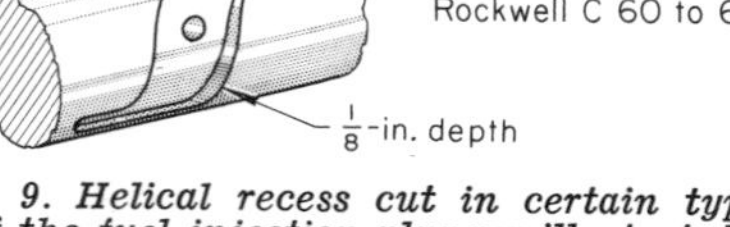

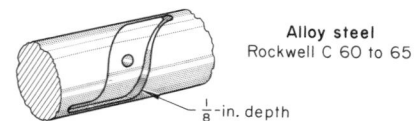

Fig. 9. Helical recess cut in certain types of the fuel-injection plunger illustrated in Fig. 8 (Example 560)

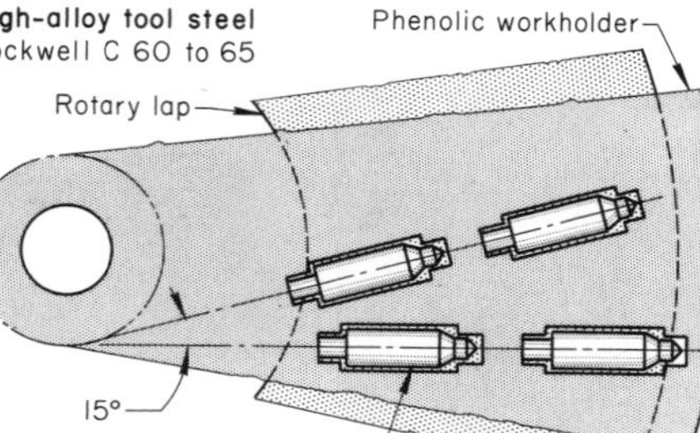

Fig. 10. Setup for lapping production quantities of the valve needle shown in Fig. 6 (Example 561)

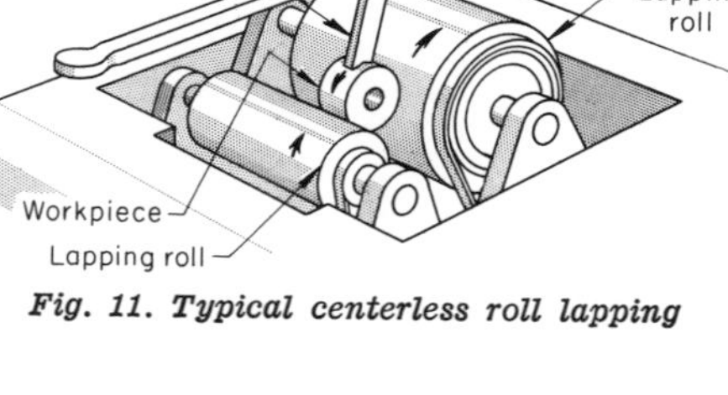

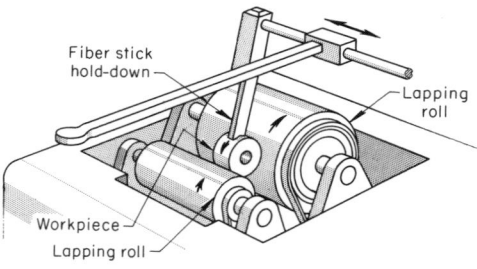

Fig. 11. Typical centerless roll lapping

Centerless Roll Lapping

In centerless roll lapping, only a single piece is processed at a time. Thus, this method is best suited to the lapping of small quantities of parts (usually, fewer than ten).

A typical machine (Fig. 11) consists essentially of two 6-in.-long cast iron rolls (one 6 in., and one 3 in., in diameter) and a reciprocating device for holding down the workpiece and controlling size. The end of the fiber stick that holds down the work is provided with a 120° V-groove. In operation, abrasive compound is applied to the rolls, and both rolls are rotated in the same direction — away from the operator and counter to the direction of workpiece rotation. The larger roll rotates at about 180 rpm, the smaller roll at about 90 rpm. The workpiece feeds across the rolls at about 2 ipm as the hold-down device is stroked back and forth to within ½ in. of each end of the workpiece.

The rate at which the workpiece feeds depends on the diameter of the piece. For instance, if a ½-in.-diam workpiece feeds at 2 ipm, a 1-in.-diam piece in the same setup will feed at approximately 1 ipm. Slow stroking is required, to obtain the best surface finish and control of size. Stock removal in centerless roll lapping is usually 0.0002 to 0.0003 in., depending on finish obtained in the previous operation.

The main advantage offered by centerless roll lapping is quick setup. The process is thus readily adaptable to frequent size changes in short production runs. Limitations on the shape of parts for centerless roll lapping are similar to, but more stringent than, those that apply to machine lapping between plates. When both processes are equally suitable for a given application, quantity of parts to be lapped determines which will be used, as indicated in the following example.

Example 562. Productivity — Centerless Roll vs Machine Lapping Between Plates

Hollow pins 1½ in. in diameter and 4 in. long, made of hardened steel, were lapped in a centerless roll lapper at a rate of only four per hour. When the same pins were lapped in a two-plate lapper, production rate was 30 parts per hour. However, in centerless roll lapping, there was no setup cost and the machine could have been immediately available for another job, whereas in two-plate lapping, setup cost was $100.

For a comparison between centerless roll lapping and two-plate machine lapping of hard anodized aluminum parts, see Example 926 in the article on Machining of Aluminum Alloys.

Centerless Lapping

Centerless lapping is a variation of centerless grinding (see the article "Grinding"). The machines for the two processes are generally similar in appearance, but the lapping machine is constructed to produce finishes of 2 micro-in. or better, diametral accuracy of 50 millionths of an inch, and roundness within 25 millionths. The lapping and regulating wheels are 22 in. wide, which is much wider than those ordinarily used for centerless grinding. Thus, the work remains in contact with the lapping wheel longer and receives a finer finish.

The regulating and the lapping wheels (both are bonded abrasive) can be angled so that their axes are not parallel. Ordinarily, the regulating wheel is adjusted to a positive angle of 1° to 3° (depending on the production and finish requirements), and the lapping wheel is adjusted to a negative angle, of about −4°. When trued, both wheels assume a slight hourglass shape, which then allows them to wrap around the workpiece as it passes between them. They also contact the workpiece at an angle to its axis, which is different from the axial-line contact of a grinding wheel. This eliminates lapping marks.

The finest finish obtainable in a centerless lapping machine requires at least three operations, each with a progressively finer lapping wheel, and a full flow of clean fluid (such as kerosine) as a coolant. During the first operation the workpiece is supported on a blade faced with hard steel or carbide. For correction of out-of-roundness, the center of the workpiece should be slightly above the center of the wheels. In the first operation, a maximum of 0.0005 in. of stock is removed, and a finish of 4 to 6 micro-in. is obtained. For the second and third operations, the workpiece is supported on a rubber blade and is centered on the wheels, so that scratches are minimized. During the second operation a maximum of 0.0001 in. of stock is removed, and a finish of 2 to 3 micro-in. is obtained; during the third operation, practically no stock is removed, and a finish of about 2 micro-in. is obtained.

Applicability. Centerless lapping is a high-production operation particularly suited to centerless ground parts that can be continuously fed, either manually or automatically. Parts ¼ to 6 in. in diameter by 15 in. long can be centerless lapped, and when a long bar feed is used, it is possible to lap parts ½ to 3 in. in diameter and 15 ft long. Typical parts finished by centerless lapping are pistons, piston pins, shafts, and bearing races.

Because little stock is removed in this process, only a small amount of correction can be made. Thus, parts must be previously ground to required straightness and roundness.

Parts with shapes that have no irregularities are ideally suited to centerless lapping, but irregularities such as those on the part shown in Fig. 12 can be tolerated. Such parts may, however, present problems in holding tolerances, because of the undercut and the keyway. Cross holes also add to the difficulty of holding extremely close dimensions in centerless lapping.

The production rates attained in centerless lapping and in two other processes for the part illustrated in Fig. 12 are compared in the example that follows:

Example 563. Production Rates — Centerless vs Centerless Roll vs Two-Plate Machine Lapping (Fig. 12)

The part shown in Fig. 12 (52100 steel hardened to Rockwell C 61 to 63) was lapped by three methods for removal of 0.0002 in. of stock to produce a finish of 1 micro-in. Productivity was as follows:

Method of lapping	Pieces per hour
Centerless	700
Centerless roll	10
Two-plate machine	100

Centerless lapping was done with bonded-abrasive wheels (14 in. in diameter and 22 in. long; grit size, 500) at a rotation speed of 52 rpm. A blade fixture (cost, $60) was used.

Centerless roll lapping was done in a machine with two 6-in.-long cast iron rolls, one 6 in. in diameter and one 3 in. The 1000-grit abrasive used was contained in a paste vehicle. Rotation of the smaller roll was at 100 rpm.

In machine lapping between plates, the two laps, which were of cast iron, were 16 in. in diameter and 3 in. thick. The "spider" fixture cost $60. Rotation speed was 100 rpm, and an 800-grit abrasive was used in a water vehicle.

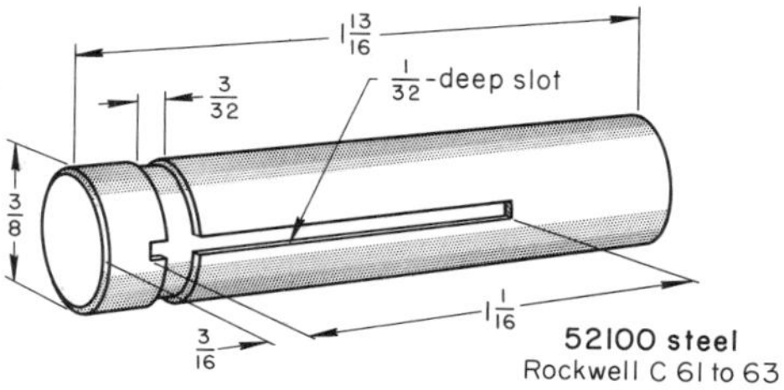

Fig. 12. Part lapped by three different methods (Example 563)

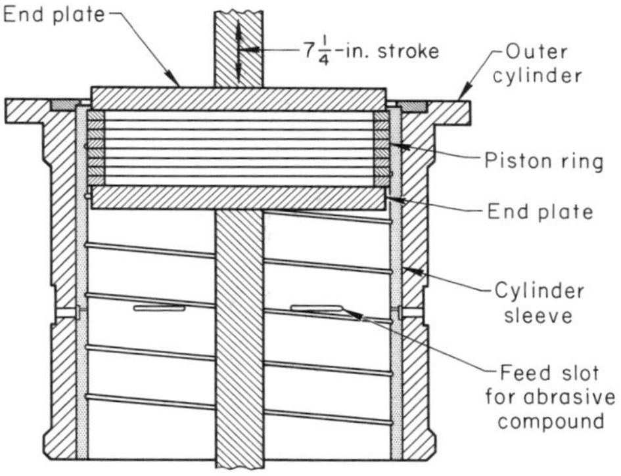

Fig. 13. Setup and fixture for lapping eight piston rings simultaneously (Example 564)

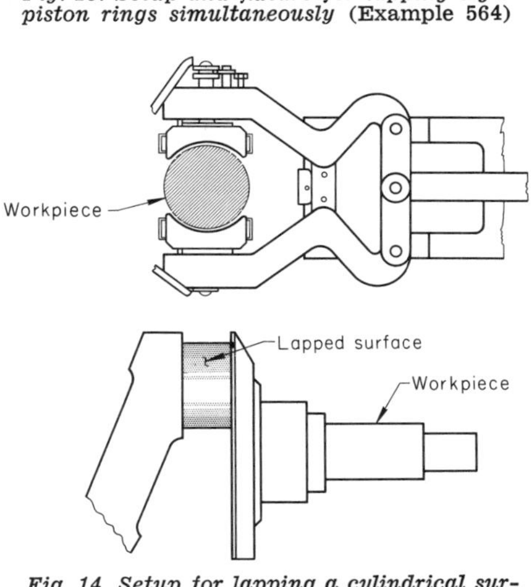

Fig. 14. Setup for lapping a cylindrical surface on a crankshaft (Example 565)

Lapping of Outer Surfaces of Piston Rings

Special procedures are required for lapping outer cylindrical surfaces of parts that are considerably greater in diameter than in axial length. Piston rings are typical of such parts. Lapping is especially necessary for a chromium-plated piston ring, because unless the minute chromium nodules are removed, the ring will quickly ruin a cylinder.

Because of slight variations in machining, rings may have areas that exert low pressure. During lapping, material will be removed faster from the high-pressure areas, thus causing a more even distribution of pressure around the ring, removal of chromium nodules, and smoothing of the surface.

A specific procedure employed in the lapping of piston rings is described in the example that follows.

Example 564. Lapping Eight Piston Rings Simultaneously (Fig. 13)

The stacking setup shown in Fig. 13 was used for simultaneously lapping eight chromium-plated steel piston rings (hardness, 775 Vickers). The lap consisted of an outer cylinder that was a solid casting and an inner sleeve that could be replaced when worn out. Replacing only the inner sleeve was more economical than replacing the entire cylinder. The piston rings were reciprocated in the sleeve at 150 cycles per minute by a special machine. During each reciprocation the stack of piston rings was rotated 45°. The abrasive, which was fed in through slots near the center of the sleeve, contained 10% of 600-grit aluminum oxide mixed with 90% (by weight) of a commercial lapping oil.

This practice was used for rings 2 to 8½ in. in diameter and 1/16 to ¼ in. thick. Productivity was 2 to 48 rings per minute, depending on ring size. Metal removal ranged from about 0.0010 to 0.0015 in. Size, which was controlled by the number of cycles, was checked by measuring the gap between the ends of the ring when installed in a gage.

Lapping of Crankshafts

Crankshaft journals and pins and a variety of similar cylindrical surfaces often are lapped when they require a finish better than that ordinarily produced by production grinding. The pin and journal surfaces on crankshafts, for example, are ground to finishes of 25 to 55 micro-in., but a finish of 4 to 8 micro-in. is required for some applications. This finer finish has been inexpensively achieved by the method described in the next example, in which all surfaces are lapped in one setup.

Example 565. Machine Lapping of Crankshafts (Fig. 14)

Crankshafts were lapped in a machine with a 14-in. swing and 32 in. between centers. Work shoes automatically clamped coated-abrasive paper or cloth (fused alumina, 240 to 320 grit) around the crankshaft surfaces to be lapped (Fig. 14). Mineral seal oil was constantly applied to cool the surface being lapped. At a rotation speed of 125 rpm and reciprocation of 80 cycles per minute, about 0.0002 in. of metal was removed, to produce a finish of less than 10 micro-in. Production rate was 70 crankshafts per hour.

Lapping of Inner Cylindrical Surfaces

Holes or bores are lapped by using either solid or adjustable laps, usually made of cast iron. The laps may be rotated by any one of a variety of machines, including honing machines, but lathes or polishing heads are most commonly used. The lap, which carries the abrasive, is rotated while the workpiece is manually stroked over it — a procedure similar to manual honing. Machines that reciprocate either the workpiece or the lap (usually the lap) in addition to rotating the lap also are used. These machines resemble those used for power stroking in honing (see the article "Honing").

In internal-surface lapping, virtually no stock is removed, because stock can be removed at lower cost by honing. When lapping follows honing, it is usually just a "touch-up" operation.

A variation of internal-surface lapping is employed for matching or mating male and female cylindrical components. (For instance, fuel-injection plungers like the one described in Example 559 are often lapped into cylinders to produce matched pairs.) In these applications, the male part, which rotates, becomes the lap. It is swabbed with abrasive, and the mating part is then manually stroked over it. Skilled operators are required for these operations.

Adjustable laps (see Fig. 15 for typical components) are available in almost any diameter larger than 1⁄16 in. These laps are expanded manually, as required, during operation. Although various means may be used for expanding the lap, adjusting screws (Fig. 15) are most often used.

Ring gages are examples of parts that are lapped to extremely accurate dimensions with adjustable laps. The following example describes a procedure used for lapping ring gages of various sizes.

Example 566. Adjustable Laps for Finishing Ring Gages (Table 3)

Screw-adjustable cast iron laps were used for finishing ring gages varying in diameter from 0.029 to 12.010 in. These gages were made of 8620 steel and were carburized and hardened to Rockwell C 62. Depending on gage diameter, polishing heads or lathes were used to rotate the laps at speeds ranging from 150 to 600 rpm, depending on gage diameter. The laps were swabbed with 900-grit abrasive in a vegetable oil vehicle of paste consistency. The gages were in a ground and stabilized condition, with 0.0003 to 0.0004 in. of stock for lapping, and round and straight within 0.0001 in. Tolerances specified for various diameters and classes of gages are shown in Table 3.

To obtain the accuracy required by the specifications in Table 3, it was necessary to adhere strictly to the following sequence of operations in lapping:

1 Determine initial condition of workpiece (amount of stock to be removed, and taper and roundness).
2 Insert shank of lap into polishing-head chuck.
3 Coat lap with abrasive compound.
4 Loosen screw in lap.
5 Place workpiece on lap.
6 Tighten screw in lap until workpiece turns with slight resistance.
7 Start the machine and reciprocate the workpiece evenly by hand over the length of the rotating lap, maintaining uniform resistance, until the piece runs smoothly from end to end.
8 Stop machine; remove the workpiece and allow it to cool.
9 Measure the workpiece to check for size, taper, barrel or hourglass shape, out-of-roundness and bellmouth.
10 Repeat the process, except for method of reciprocation as in step 7, until the desired results are obtained. At this point, method of reciprocation depends on conditions found in measuring the ring (step 9). Oversize and out-of-roundness require slow, even reciprocation. Bellmouth requires reversal before point of lowered resistance is reached. Barrel or hourglass shape and taper require faster reciprocation, localized at the high areas. Extremes of the above (more than 0.0002 in.) must be corrected by grinding.

Table 3. Lapping Tolerances for Various Sizes of Ring Gages (Example 566)

Diameter, in.	Tolerance, millionths of an inch, for gages of class: X	Y	Z
0.029 to 0.825	40	70	100
0.825 to 1.510	60	90	120
1.510 to 2.510	80	120	160
2.510 to 4.510	100	150	200
4.510 to 6.510	130	190	250
6.510 to 9.010	160	240	320
9.010 to 12.010	200	300	400

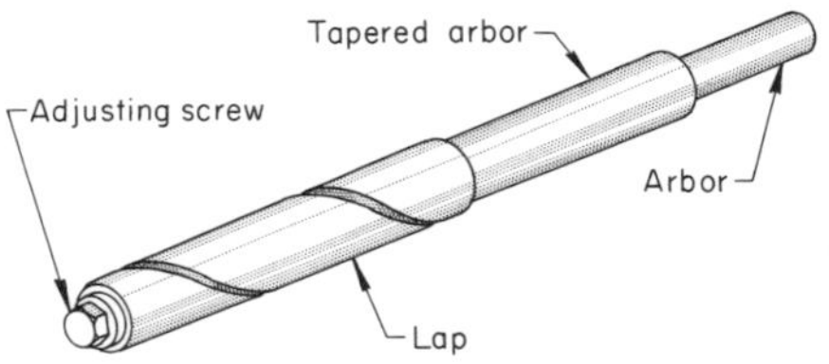

Fig. 15. Components of an adjustable lap

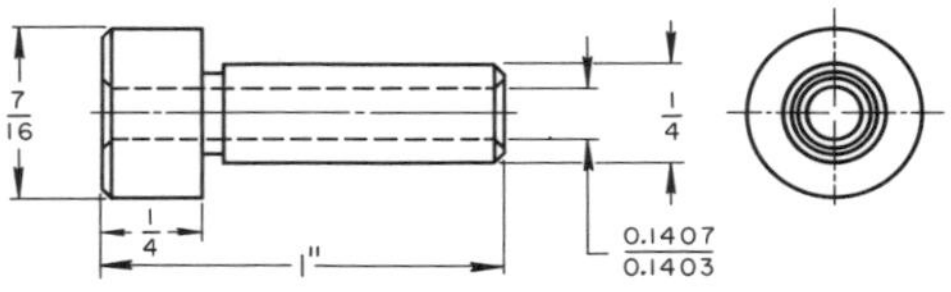

Fig. 16. Hardened steel part discussed in Example 567

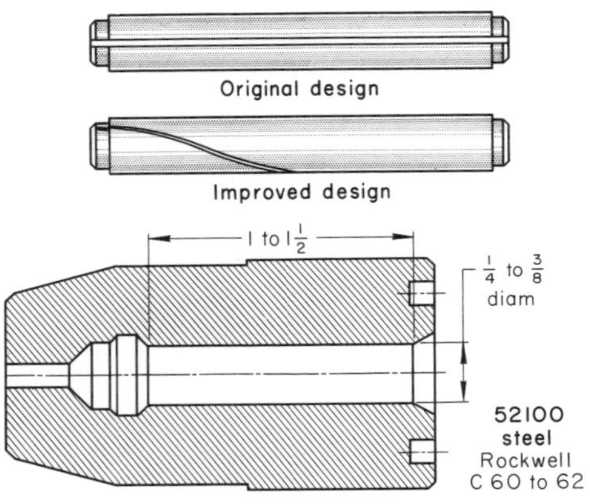

Fig. 17. Substitution of spiral for straight slot in lap for better distribution of abrasive in lapping a blind hole (Example 568)

Solid laps are low-cost round bars that are accurately finished to size. They usually are made of cast iron but, for extremely small workpieces, may be of copper or other nonferrous metal. Ordinarily, solid laps are used only when one or two odd-size pieces require finishing. However, solid laps *must* be used for finishing inside diameters of less than 1⁄16 in. (because this is the minimum diameter of adjustable laps), and they also can be used by skilled operators for correcting bow or "snake".

The chief disadvantage of solid laps is that they are useless once they become only slightly worn, unless they are refinished for lapping smaller bores.

The efficiency of solid laps is compared with that of adjustable laps in the following example.

Example 567. Solid vs Adjustable Laps (Fig. 16)

Hardened steel parts 1 in. long, like that shown in Fig. 16, were lapped internally with solid and adjustable cast iron laps, using the same grade of diamond abrasive in an olive oil vehicle. Solid laps processed 50% more parts per hour than adjustable laps (3 compared with 2), because the latter required time to adjust. Setup time for solid laps was two thirds that for adjustable laps (10 min, compared with 15 min). However, solid laps were too expensive, because they produced only four pieces per setup, whereas 20 pieces per setup were produced with adjustable laps.

Blind Holes. Lapping blind or partly blind holes presents problems because of uneven distribution of abrasive. The difficulty can sometimes be overcome by an improvement in lap design, as in the following example.

Example 568. Lapping Blind Holes (Fig. 17)

The part shown in section in the lower portion of Fig. 17 was made of 52100 steel and hardened to Rockwell C 60 to 62. Parts of this type had main bores 1⁄4 to 3⁄8 in. in diameter and 1 to 1½ in. in length. The bores originally were lapped with expansion laps made of cast iron and slotted in a straight line (Fig. 17). This type of lap did not allow enough lapping compound to reach the bottom of the bore; consequently, lapping action at the outer end of the hole was more rapid, and excessive taper was produced.

The problem was solved by redesigning the lap, providing it with a right-hand spiral that formed a carrier for the lapping compound (Fig. 17). The redesigned lap was held in a speed lathe (horizontal chucking head) and rotated clockwise at about 650 rpm; the part was rotated counterclockwise. A coarse abrasive (grit size, 600) was used. Lapping removed 0.0002 in. of stock, at a rate of 40 pieces per hour. The bores were held to a diametral tolerance of 50 millionths of an inch and to straightness within 25 millionths. Size and straightness were controlled by the use of an air gage and two master setting rings.

Lapping Flat Surfaces

Flat surfaces can be lapped by either manual or machine methods. In general, manual methods are used only when small quantities of parts are to be lapped or when special requirements must be met. Most flat lapping on a production basis is done with rotating two-plate machines similar to those used for lapping cylindrical surfaces.

Manual Methods. Hand rubbing of flat workpieces on a block or plate lap charged with loose abrasive is the simplest method of flat lapping. The lap, usually made of cast iron, has regularly spaced grooves about 1⁄16 in. deep to retain the lapping medium (usually an abrasive-containing paste). The flat workpiece is rubbed on the lap in a "figure eight" or similar motion that covers almost the entire lap surface, so that the lap will remain flat for a considerable amount of work. At best, this method of lapping is slow and tedious, and requires a high degree of skill for best results. It is used only when a few parts must be lapped or when more efficient equipment is not available.

Another and somewhat faster method of flat lapping single pieces makes use of a single-spindle vertical drill press. The lap, which is stationary, is mounted on the stand of the drill press. The workpiece is held by the spindle, which rotates it against the lap. Light pressures are applied by hand. This method is slow, and the lap is likely to wear unevenly. However, it may be preferable to other flat lapping methods for some applications. For example, certain round, flat sealing parts require a lapped surface with the concentric-line pattern produced by this method, because random scratch patterns are not leakproof. To achieve the concentric-line pattern, the rotating part is held against a rotating or nonrotating lap of the same size so that there is no motion except rotation between the workpiece and the lap.

When concentricity of scratch pattern is not important, the method described above is sometimes modified for faster lapping by oscillating the rotating workpiece back and forth over the lap. The workpiece should be mounted on the spindle of the drill press so that it is flexible and can float as it turns. A layer of rubber can be placed behind the workpiece to provide a suitably flexible mounting.

Machine Methods. The two general types of machines for flat lapping are: (*a*) those with two bonded-abrasive or cast iron laps (plates), one above and one below workpiece-carrier rings; and (*b*) those with a single rotating cast iron or bonded-abrasive lap (plate).

Machines with two bonded-abrasive laps are used for lapping both sides of the workpiece at the same time. The flatness of these laps is maintained by a diamond dressing attachment. The carrier rings rotate as the laps turn, imparting a cycloidal motion to the workpieces as they travel across the laps. These rings can be adjusted for eccentricity to provide even wear of the laps and to insure that the workpieces break the inside and the outside edges of the laps to prevent grooving.

Machines with two cast iron laps use loose abrasive and are useful for holding accuracy on gage blocks and similar parts that require critical control of parallelism, flatness and thickness.

Machines with a single rotating cast iron lap use loose abrasives and act much like a grinding wheel. When production quantities are low, the workpieces often are held and moved across the lap by hand. However, for larger quantities, workpieces are placed on carrier rings that hold them on the lap and rotate as the lap turns. These rings impart a cycloidal motion to the workpieces and must be positioned to distribute the wear evenly on the laps.

Lapping pressures used with the single-lap machines usually are 1 to 10 psi, although higher pressures are sometimes used. Added pressure may be applied to extremely light workpieces by means of a pressure plate with or without air cylinders. As pressure is increased, cycle time is decreased and the stock-removal rate is increased. During the operation, the

Table 4. Load Capacities of Planetary Flat-Lapping Machines

Workpiece diam, in.	Capacity, parts: Each ring	Capacity, parts: Full load
12-In.-Diam Laps; Three 4¼-In.-ID Conditioning Rings		
¼	235	705
½	55	165
¾	23	69
1	13	39
1¼	8	24
1½	5	15
2	2	6
3	1	3
4	1	3
24-In.-Diam Laps; Three 9¾-In.-ID Conditioning Rings		
¼	1300	3900
½	310	930
¾	130	390
1	70	210
1¼	45	135
1½	31	93
2	17	51
3	7	21
4	4	12
6	1	3
8	1	3
24-In.-Diam Laps; Four 8¼-In.-ID Conditioning Rings		
¼	920	3680
½	220	880
¾	90	360
1	55	220
1¼	32	128
1½	22	88
2	12	48
3	5	20
4	2	8
6	1	4
8	1	4
36-In.-Diam Laps; Three 14½-In.-ID Conditioning Rings		
½	700	2100
¾	300	900
1	165	495
1¼	105	315
1½	70	210
2	39	117
3	16	48
4	9	27
6	4	12
8	1	3
10	1	3
36-In.-Diam Laps; Four 12⅝-In.-ID Conditioning Rings		
½	560	2240
¾	245	980
1	130	520
1¼	80	320
1½	55	220
2	31	124
3	13	52
4	7	28
6	3	12
8	1	4
10	1	4
48-In.-Diam Laps; Four 17-In.-ID Conditioning Rings		
1	235	940
1¼	145	580
1½	100	400
2	55	220
3	23	92
4	13	52
6	5	20
8	2	8
10	1	4
72-In.-Diam Laps; Four 27¼-In.-ID Conditioning Rings		
1	620	2480
1¼	390	1560
1½	270	1080
2	145	580
3	60	240
4	34	136
6	14	56
8	8,	32
10	5	20
14-26	1	4
84-In.-Diam Laps; Four 32-In.-ID Conditioning Rings		
1½	375	1500
2	205	820
3	85	340
4	48	192
6	21	84
8	11	44
10	7	28
14	3	12
15	2	8
16	2	8
17-31	1	4

When using the table for determining capacity of machine with work separator, use the value for diameter next larger than that of the workpiece to be processed. Conditioning rings are carrier rings.

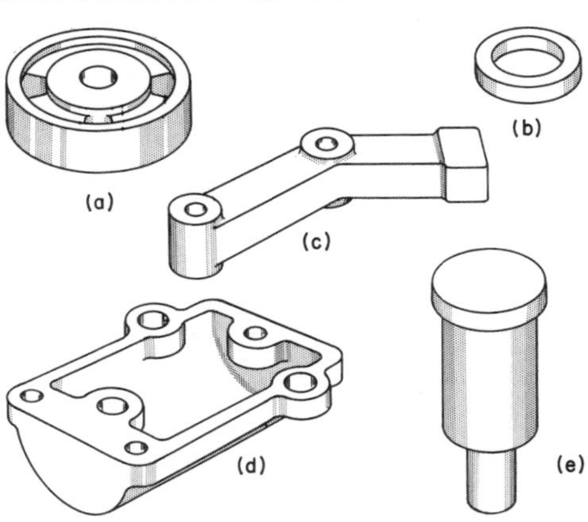

Parts like (a) and (b) do not require workholders for flat lapping. Parts like (c) and (d) require workholders to keep them separated from each other. Parts like (e) require workholders to keep them from tipping.

Fig. 18. Parts requiring different amounts of restraint or support in flat lapping

thick areas are lapped at a faster rate than the thin areas because of the pressure plate. Lapping is continued until all workpieces in the ring have the same thickness, each thus receiving the same pressure.

The laps for single-plate machines usually are made of cast iron, but for some purposes, laps made of copper or other materials may be used. Copper or other soft nonferrous metals often are preferred for lapping with diamond powders, because these metals readily become charged with the abrasive. On some single-plate machines, bonded-abrasive laps are used instead of metal laps.

Machines using a single metal lap and loose abrasive require more care to keep the lap flat than machines using two bonded-abrasive laps. The pressure plate and the lap must be lapped together if the workpieces are to be held to close tolerances for thickness, flatness or parallelism.

Some machines provide for changing abrasives for various jobs. Automatic machines are available that will feed, discharge and gage the workpieces, as well as compensate for abrasive wear.

Most planetary machines are provided with automatic timing devices for control of lapping cycles that have been established for production-quantity runs. These machines are provided also with a means for automatic control of the flow of lapping compound, which aids the operator in tending more than one machine or performing other duties during long lapping cycles. Some planetary machines are also equipped with pneumatic-cylinder lifts for raising and lowering the carrier rings and pressure plates, thus speeding loading and unloading. Pneumatic cylinders also can be used to exert additional downward force on the pressure plates for faster lapping.

Workholders are used in the carrier rings to hold parts of odd shape and to keep them from colliding or locking together as they turn during the operation. These workholders, which may be plastic, wood or sheet metal, have apertures to suit the workpieces.

Stock removal in flat lapping, when the process is used for improving flatness and finish of previously machined parts, usually is 0.0001 to 0.005 in. However, it may be economical to remove larger amounts if a machining operation can be eliminated. Tooling costs for flat lapping are often lower than for grinding or milling. Also, when parts require a long lapping time, one operator can tend two or more machines.

Lapping time can vary from a few seconds to an hour or more, depending on the stock to be removed, material being lapped, finish requirements, and other factors. Most parts, however, can be lapped in 10 min. or less. The rate of stock removal may vary from as high as 0.060 in. per hour, for brass, to as low as 0.003 in. per hour, for sintered carbide and hardened steel.

Workpiece Size and Shape. Parts ⅛ in. in diameter or smaller and as large as 32 in. in diameter can be flat lapped. Table 4 indicates the number of parts of given diameters that can be accommodated by planetary flat-lapping machines with laps 12 to 84 in. in diame-

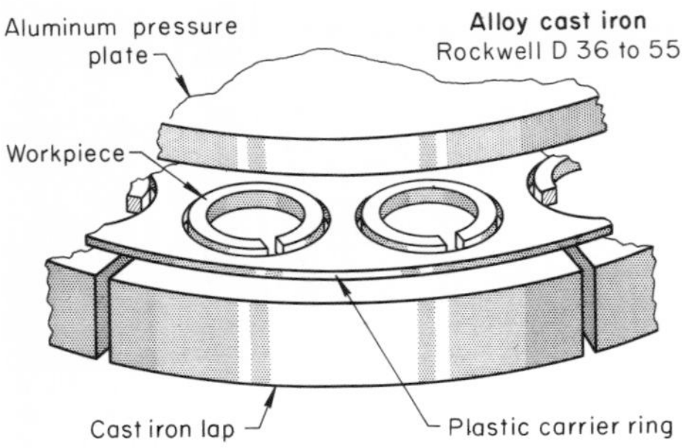

Fig. 19. Setup for lapping the sides of piston rings (Example 569)

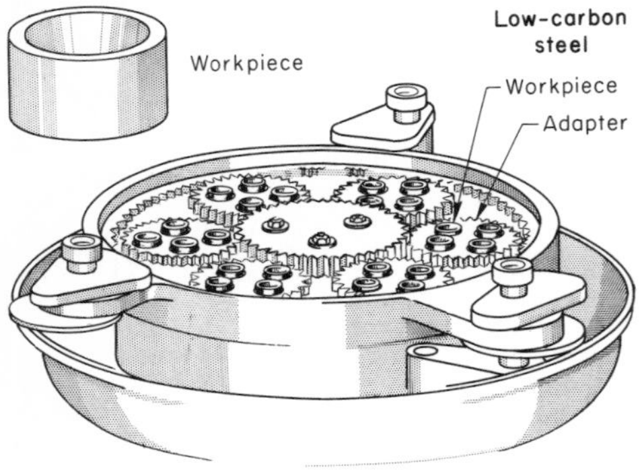

Fig. 20. Lapping setup for rings that had to be flat and parallel within 25 millionths of an inch (Example 570)

ter, in conjunction with various numbers and sizes of carrier rings. Note that large quantities of small parts can be lapped on large machines. Large parts can be lapped only on large machines.

With the correct workholders and operating conditions, parts as thin as 0.003 in. have been lapped. Workpiece height limitation is determined by machine clearances and by the ratio of height to lapped surface area. This ratio must be kept low enough to prevent tipping or rocking of the part during lapping, unless a workholder or fixture is provided. The restraint or support required for typical shapes that may be flat lapped is indicated in Fig. 18.

Flatness. Flat lapping can produce flatness within one light band (11.6 micro-in.) and smoothness better than 2 micro-in. To obtain these results, the workpieces must be stable during the operation, so that the possibility of stress relief that will result in distortion is eliminated. Also, flatness of the lap or laps must be kept within the flatness tolerance for the workpiece.

Size Tolerance and Parallelism. Parts having parallel faces, such as disks and seal rings, can be held to tolerances varying from ±0.0001 in., for small parts, to ±0.001 in., for large parts. Difficulty in maintaining accuracy increases for parts of uneven configuration; such parts may require fixtures, which then determine the accuracy attainable. The closer the tolerance requirements, the more difficult the operation is likely to be.

Surfaces of disks, seal rings and similar parts having parallel surfaces can be lapped on either the double-lap machines, which lap both sides in one operation, or the single-lap machines, which require two operations (one for each side). Surfaces can be held parallel within 0.0001 in., if the lap or laps and the pressure plate are kept flat. The operation becomes simpler as the number of parts to be lapped at one time increases and as the distribution of thick and thin parts improves. When only a few workpieces are lapped, or if the thickness of the part varies more than about 0.003 in., it may be necessary to distribute the thicker parts selectively or to remove and redistribute the parts before lapping the second side. Allowance for stock removal in this type of operation should be 1½ to 2 times the amount that the parts are out-of-parallel plus the amount of the variation in part sizes.

Examples of Procedure. Flat lapping is typically employed on piston rings, when side flatness is extremely critical, and on other ringlike parts. Although most ring-shaped parts can be lapped without elaborate procedures, special problems often arise.

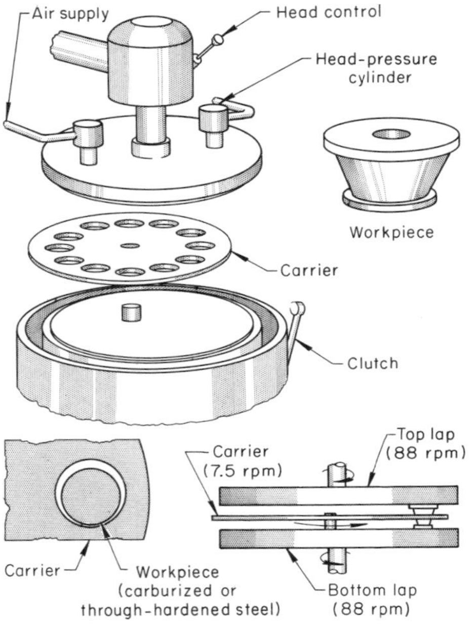

Fig. 21. Setup for lapping inner or outer bearing races (Example 571)

There are two main problems in lapping piston-ring sides: (*a*) the rings are flexible and can be easily distorted under load, and (*b*) some piston rings have a very smooth, polished finish on the circumference that must not be marred during lapping. Some load must be applied during lapping, because the rings are too light to lap without added load, but the applied load must not be great enough to distort the ring. An aluminum pressure plate is used, because it is light but also rigid enough to stay flat.

In the three examples that follow, procedures successfully employed for the flat lapping of ringlike parts are described in detail.

Examples 569, 570 and 571. Flat Lapping of Ringlike Parts

Example 569 (Fig. 19). The lapping setup shown in Fig. 19 was used for cast iron piston rings 2 to 8½ in. in outside diameter and 1/16 to 1/4 in. thick. The rings were lapped on a commercial, single 84-in.-diam cast iron lap revolving at 30 rpm. To prevent rubbing against each other during the lapping operation, the rings were placed in a carrier ring made of a sheet of plastic with a hole in it to accommodate each ring. (Urethane proved to be the best material for this purpose, because it is strong and wear-resistant and did not mar the workpiece; also, it was not appreciably affected by the lapping medium.) The medium used consisted of 10% aluminum oxide (average size, 14.5 microns) and 90% commercial lapping oil.

About 0.001 in. of stock (total from both sides) was removed in lapping, for thickness accuracy within ±0.0004 in. and finish of 10 micro-in. Final dimensions were controlled by shadow methods.

Example 570 (Fig. 20). The rings shown in Fig. 20 did not require close accuracy in width, but had to be flat and parallel within 25 millionths of an inch. These rings were made of soft steel, which made lapping still more difficult. Figure 20 shows the setup that enabled the stringent flatness and parallelism requirements to be met. The machine had two cast iron laps, the lower of which rotated at 40 rpm while the upper one did not rotate but floated. The workpieces were rotated at 20 rpm and oscillated at 40 strokes per minute by special adapters. Aluminum oxide (800-grit) in oil was used as the lapping medium. About 0.0005 in. of stock was removed from each part and 3 min was required for lapping one load (24 pieces).

Example 571 (Fig. 21). The setup shown in Fig. 21 was used for lapping the flat sides of inner and outer bearing races, made of carburized or through-hardened steel in diameters from 1 3/16 to 8½ in. The machine had two bonded-abrasive laps (400-grit silicon carbide) that rotated in opposite directions at 88 rpm. The head of the machine, which was like that of a vertical drill press, was air actuated. It raised and lowered the top lap, and could apply adjustable downward pressure (up to 60 psi) to the top lap. The bearing races were hand loaded in a horizontal circular fiber carrier that was eccentrically mounted over the bottom lap. The carrier rotated at 7½ rpm, and was adjusted so that eccentricity was up to 1 in. and part clearance was about 1/4 in. A viscous cutting oil was fed to the laps during the operation, and the laps were dressed two or three times during an 8-hr shift. A maxi-

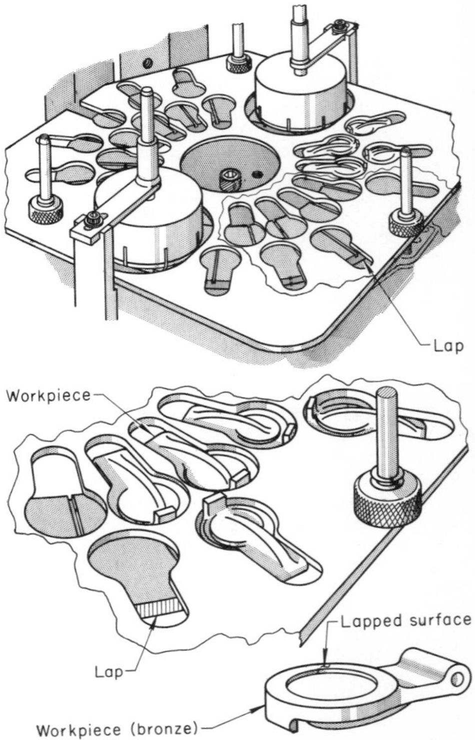

Fig. 22. Setup for lapping seats of swing check valves (Example 572)

mum of 0.0005 in. of stock was removed from the races, leaving a finish of 3 micro-in. When checked with an indicator (0.0001 in. per division), no deviation from parallelism was detected.

Parts of more complex shape can be flat lapped by using special laps and specially designed carriers or fixtures, as in the three examples that follow.

Examples 572, 573 and 574. Flat Lapping With Special Laps and Fixtures

Example 572 (Fig. 22). The seats of swing check valves were lapped to required flatness using the setup and relatively simple fixture shown in Fig. 22. This type of setup may be used for lapping similar offset flat surfaces. Cast iron laps were used, with loose abrasive. The portion of the workpiece that protruded beyond the lapped surface extended over the inside or outside diameter of the lap, and was loosely held in position by a cutout nesting fixture. To apply additional weight on the uneven back surfaces of the workpieces, rubber buttons on the underside of a pressure plate were placed so that they rested on the high points of the workpieces when lowered into lapping position. The pressure plate (not shown in Fig. 22) was indexed so that the buttons always rested in the correct position on the workpieces.

Example 573 (Fig. 23). Quartz crystal oscillators for the electronics applications required lapping to close tolerances. The crystals, which were less than 0.005 in. thick, were lapped using standard, commercially available diamond-footed coaster fixtures (Fig. 23). These fixtures were adjustable to permit the lapping of crystals as thin as 0.001 in. Parallelism within 50 millionths of an inch was obtained.

Example 574 (Fig. 24). Parts having a center flange 5½ in. in diameter and a hub on each side were lapped between two specially designed laps. Both sides of the flange were flat and parallel after lapping.

Conventional laps could not be used for these parts, because the hub extended on both sides of the flange. The problem was solved by providing each lap with a channel that divided its lapping surface into two parts and that was large enough to clear the hub on one side of the part.

Figure 24 shows the workpiece and the lapping setup. Both bonded-abrasive laps and laps requiring loose abrasive were used. The upper and lower laps, which were 26 in. in diameter, were driven by vertical spindles. A geared workholding adapter engaged the flange and rotated it.

Whether parts like those in Fig. 24 can be lapped satisfactorily with the type of setup shown depends on the dimensions of the workpiece. There should be enough flange surface resting on the laps to prevent the parts from tilting; and the flange face should have relieved areas so that the channel laps will cover the full surface to be lapped without marring the surface of the hub. Also, the hub extensions should be short enough to make the lap construction practical. For instance, if the flanges were 3 in. in diameter and the hub extensions were 7 or 8 in. long, construction of the laps would not be feasible.

Lapping End Surfaces

End lapping and conventional flat lapping are similar in principle, and the same machines are often used for both processes. As in flat lapping, fixtures are often necessary to prevent workpieces from tilting. In many instances, a workpiece whose height is several times the width of its lapped area is supported in a special fixture and processed in standard flat-lapping machines. Engine connecting rods are notable examples. Faces that hold the shims for the connecting-rod caps in assembly are supported by means of specially designed fixtures, and are forced, by weight or air pressure, against a rotating lap. Their mating caps are often lapped at the same time. For straight cylindrical parts (not tapered), fixtures for end lapping are simple, and various methods may be used, as in the two next examples.

Examples 575 and 576. End Lapping of Straight Cylindrical Parts

Example 575 (Fig. 25). The setup shown in Fig. 25 was used for lapping the ends of rollers when production quantities were small. The rollers were fixtured, as illustrated, and both ends were lapped at the same time with upper and lower laps that rotated at 125 rpm. Eccentric motion of the fixture was controlled by the operator. An air pressure system allowed adjustment of downward pressure on the upper lap. The lapping medium consisted of 800-grit unfused alumina in a water-soluble vehicle. Time cycles varied from 1 to 4 min, depending mainly on the depth of the grinding marks. Less than 0.0005 in. of stock was removed for end runout within 0.0001 in. and finish of 3 to 5 micro-in. One operator produced an average of 200 rollers per hour. Laps were reground after five shifts.

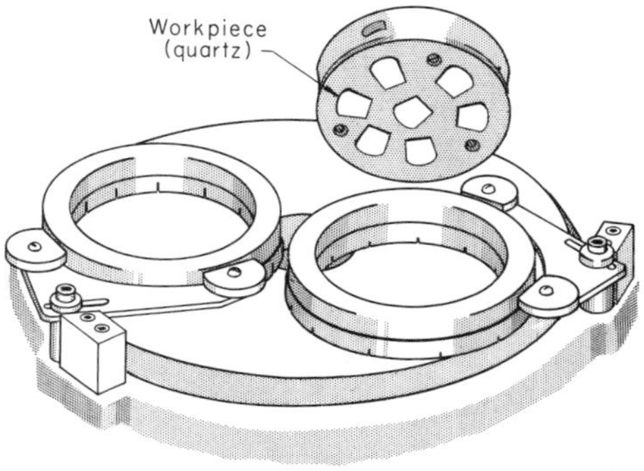

Fig. 23. Setup for lapping quartz crystal oscillators less than 0.005 in. thick (Example 573)

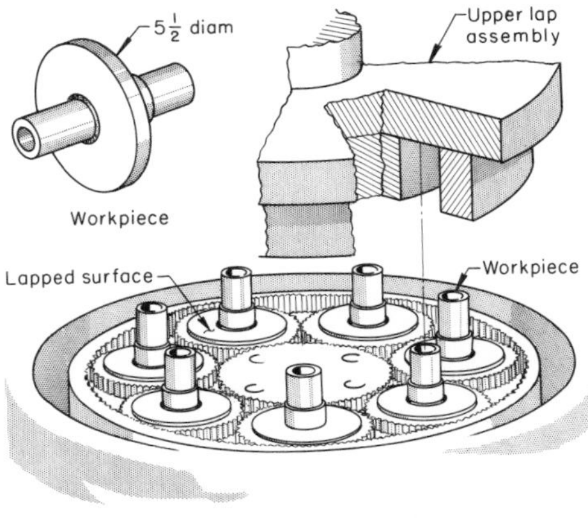

Fig. 24. Setup employed for lapping parts having a center flange and a hub on either side (Example 574)

Example 576 (Fig. 26). A special machine was used for high-production end lapping of rollers similar to those described in Example 575. Figure 26 shows the important components of this machine, which included an enclosed track that allowed the rollers to travel in a loop. The rollers were thus exposed to the bonded-abrasive wheels twice per trip around the track. The number of cycles required varied with the initial condition of the rollers. The laps, which were commercial vitrified wheels, rotated in the same direction at 1350 rpm and were cooled with a low-viscosity honing oil.

Problems in Flat and End Lapping

Problems encountered in flat and end lapping (and often in other methods of lapping, as well) usually are related to surface roughness or scratches, drop-off at edges, low rate of stock removal, improper size control, and failure to attain desired flatness and parallelism. Solution of these problems is obtained by proper control of the following conditions:

1 Preparation of workpiece
2 Selection and application of abrasive and vehicle
3 Sweep path of workpiece over the lap
4 Condition of lap surface
5 Interchange or transposition of workpieces during the lapping cycle
6 Duration of lapping cycle
7 Cleanness of environment.

Preparation of Workpiece. Parts to be lapped must have smooth, regular edges, because irregularities at the edge cause the abrasive grains in the lapping compound to burst free and form the "foxtail" pattern shown in Fig. 27(a). (This effect may result also from etching on the lapped surface.) To provide the smooth edges, it may be necessary to barrel finish workpieces in fine abrasive, or to buff them, prior to lapping.

Workpieces that have drop-off at edges, from previous operations, are subject to "hydraulic cut" in lapping. In hydraulic cut (Fig. 27b), the lapping abrasive builds up in the area of drop-off and perpetuates the condition. If drop-off cannot be eliminated, hydraulic cut can be minimized by the use of lesser amounts of abrasive in lapping. This remedy usually is uneconomical, however, because stock-removal rate is decreased when a lesser amount of abrasive is used, and the likelihood of glazing is increased. Glazing can be prevented by the use of a diamond-base abrasive that contains aluminum oxide as the main cutting agent. The diamond abrasive should be of smaller grit size than the aluminum oxide; ¼-

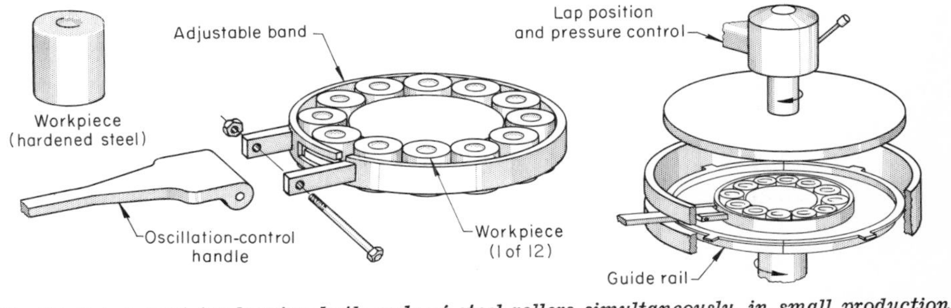

Fig. 25. Setup used for lapping both ends of steel rollers simultaneously, in small production lots (Example 575)

micron diamond has been successfully used with 1200-grit aluminum oxide.

Metal particles must be removed from the surfaces of workpieces to be lapped, so that the laps do not become charged with these particles and thus scratch the workpiece. Workpieces that have been ground should be freed of metal particles by being barrel finished in fine abrasive, before being lapped. Previously lapped workpieces also may have particles adhering to the surface. To remove these particles, the workpieces must be rubbed on a "dead" lapping block (a lightly charged, noncutting block).

Abrasives and Vehicles. Coarse finish, scratches, loss of flatness or parallelism, and inadequate or excess stock-removal rate often result from the use of improper abrasive or vehicle, or from improper method of application of the lapping medium.

In two earlier sections of this article, "Selection of Abrasive" and "Selection of Vehicle", the basic considerations in the choice of these mediums for a given application are discussed in detail. Excessive amounts of lapping abrasive cause dull finishes, loss of size control, edge drop-off, and low rates of stock removal. Abrasive films that are too thin react similarly, except that they produce bright finishes and may result in glazing.

Selection of Sweep Path. The sweep path illustrated in Fig. 28(a) is advantageous for rectangular pieces with height-to-area ratios greater than 2 to 1. One of the longer edges of the lapped area should be the leading edge. To keep the lap flat, the carrier must be positioned so that part of a workpiece sweeps over the outside and the inside of the lap face. The eccentric throw of the carrier must be reduced when the workpiece is large in relation to the width of the lap face, and thus practically straight-line lapping occurs. As a result, it is difficult to keep the lap flat, to control the size of the workpiece, and to obtain parallelism. The best lapping action is obtained when every new grain cut line crosses every previous grain cut line at an angle.

The path shown in Fig. 28(b) is advantageous for small rectangular pieces over 0.040 in. thick and with a height-to-area ratio less than 2 to 1. The amount of sweep is determined by the throw of the carrier. Excessive throw of workpieces of small area is detrimental because of the high rate of side motion at reversal points. Insufficient throw of workpieces of large area is detrimental because the lapping pattern approaches a straight line.

Sweep paths illustrated in Fig. 28(c) and (d) are derived from planetary action and are advantageous for cylindrical and square workpieces, and rectangular workpieces with height-to-area ratios of less than 2 to 1. These sweep paths help in reducing hydraulic cut, because the leading edge constantly changes — especially on shorter sweep paths. This provides a nondirectional pattern. As workpiece size is increased in relation to carrier size, the center of the workpiece tends to travel in a circular path and may increase the difficulty of maintaining flatness and parallelism.

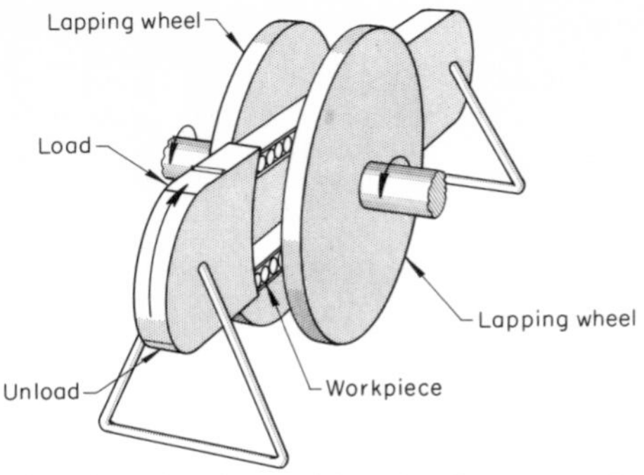

Fig. 26. Setup for end lapping large quantities of hardened steel rollers (Example 576)

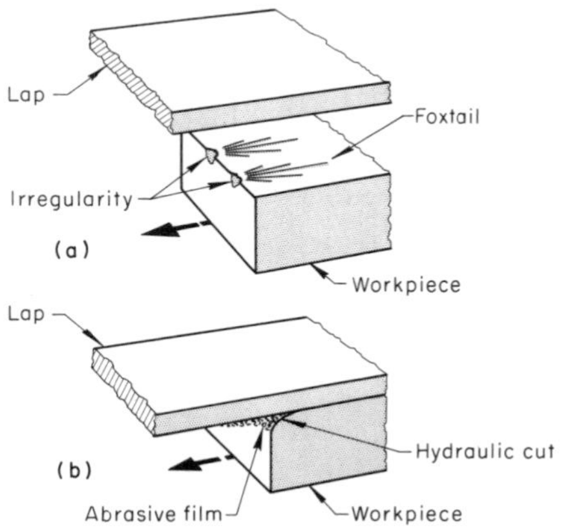

Fig. 27. Two undesirable consequences of improper preparation of workpieces for lapping. See text for discussion.

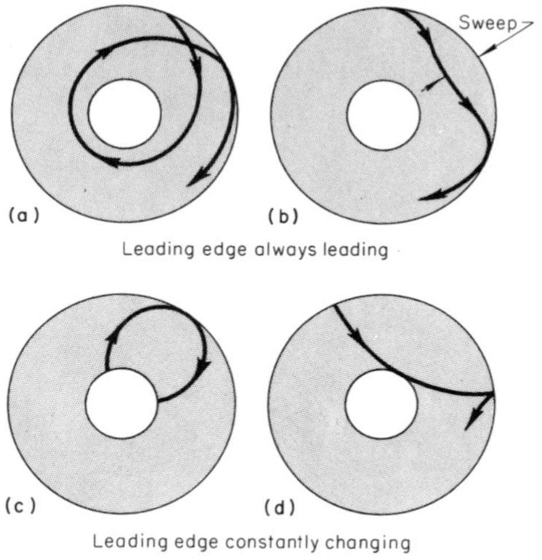

Fig. 28. Typical sweep paths of workpiece over lap face in flat lapping. See text for discussion.

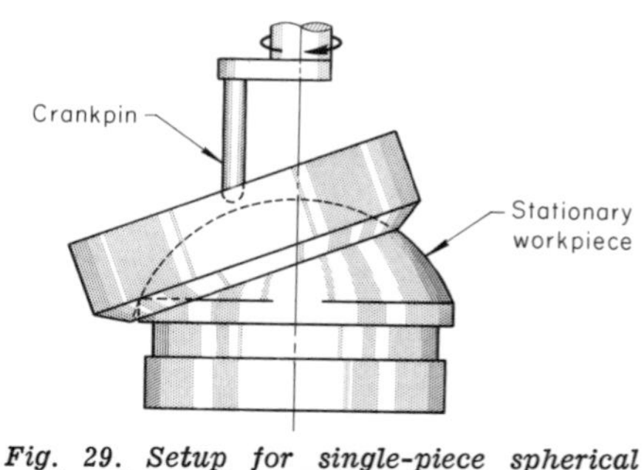

Fig. 29. Setup for single-piece spherical lapping with a one-spindle machine using a rotating lap. See text.

Condition of Lap Surface. A dull gray surface on the lap is best for stock removal but not for producing highly reflective finishes. Conversely, bright lap surfaces are excellent for producing highly reflective finishes, but poor for stock removal. When using laps having bright surfaces, the abrasive film must be thin. If not, scratching will result. However, a film that is too thin may cause glazing and loss of control of size and flatness.

Sand and other impurities in the lap surface sometimes break free and cause scratches, especially when heavy, viscous films of lapping compound are used.

A scleroscope hardness range of 27 to 32 (Rockwell B 89 to 99) has proved optimum for cast iron lap surfaces. Harder laps often cause glazing and scratching. Softer lap surfaces cause loss of flatness and parallelism and also produce grayer finishes.

Interchanging or transposing workpieces during the cycle is advantageous for producing consistent results. An increase in handling time and cost is the only disadvantage of this practice. Either of two methods may be used:

1 Workpieces in a load are interchanged between runs, and each load is processed independently until finished size is attained. Drop-off can be minimized by turning the workpieces end for end (reversing their leading edges) during the interchange.
2 Workpieces in a series of loads are intermixed at random outside the machine after each load is lapped for a given time. The process is repeated until size is reached. This method usually is the more economical.

Duration of Lapping Cycle. Required lapping time is usually determined experimentally for a new job. Extremely short cycles (in the range of 3 to 15 sec) are not economical, because too great a portion of the total time is used for loading and unloading. However, short cycles are preferred for size control. When abrasive is not continually fed to the laps, there is an optimum time for any job that must be determined by trial.

Cleanness of environment is important to the success of any lapping operation. Scratches, edge drop-off and related difficulties often can be attributed to the dropping of air-borne particles into open machines, the use of contaminated abrasives, or inadequate cleaning of workpieces.

Lapping Spherical Surfaces

Any of several methods may be used for lapping spherical surfaces. Size, quantity and required accuracy of the workpieces are the main factors that determine choice of method.

In single-piece lapping, concave or convex laps are individually contoured to the workpiece. The laps should be made of fine-grained cast iron, which is suitable for lapping virtually any metal if the process is continued for enough time. Any of several types of machines that have one or two rotating spindles, such as drill presses or milling machines, can be used.

When machines with one spindle are used, rotating the lap against the workpiece is preferred, because preparing a lap with either a straight or tapered shank to be held in a chuck is simpler than improvising a method of holding a workpiece for rotation. A magnetic chuck can hold workpieces made of ferrous metals. Clamping devices must be used for parts made of nonferrous materials. A crank, which is held by the chuck of the turning machine, is constructed with a ball-end crankpin that fits a drilled hole in the back of the lap (see Fig. 29) and causes the lap to rotate over the surface of the workpiece. The part is in line with the spindle of the turning machine; the crankpin is offset from center as required for the diameter of the workpiece. For best results, the lap should be heavy enough to provide the required lapping pressure (about 10 psi) on the workpiece. If necessary, added pressure can be applied to the lap by a hand feed lever, such as that on a drill press, but it should be applied carefully, because excessive pressure can throw the lap off the work.

When machines with two spindles are used, one spindle holds and rotates the workpiece while the other holds the lap in a floating position and oscillates it through an angle large enough to lap the required portion of the surface. A typical setup is illustrated in Fig. 30. One of the spindles must be designed so that it slides as the lap and the workpiece wear and thus keeps a constant pressure on the workpiece.

Multiple-Piece Lapping. Quantities of spherical parts are lapped on a concave or convex lap (Fig. 31). The lap may replace the lap on a conventional planetary lapping machine, or it may be fastened into the counterbore of the existing flat lap with holding brackets. Contoured laps should be made of fine-grained cast iron and should be machined to the required radii.

For continuous lapping operations, the conditioning (carrier) rings used should be made of the same material as the lap, so that the rings and the lap wear at the same rate. When more than one part is lapped within each conditioning ring, workholders made of fiber, wood, or similar materials are required. Workholders are machined to the same curvature as the lap plate and cut out so that the workpieces can fit into them.

Heavy workpieces may be lapped without additional weight applied, but pressure plates may be placed atop lighter pieces to provide sufficient weight for lapping. These plates can be of various weights, to suit requirements, but they must be shaped to conform to the final workpiece shape.

Planetary lapping machines converted to use for spherical workpieces are used to lap parts having radii of 60 to 120 in., the applications for a specific machine being limited by the dimension of its conditioning rings. The capacity of the machine will be the same as for flat lapping (see Table 4).

In plain planetary lapping machines that are prepared for contour lapping but not equipped with conditioning rings, workpieces are held by hand, or by improvised fixtures. In this instance, the workpieces should be moved over the entire area of the lap with reasonable constancy, so that the lap is worn evenly and its life is prolonged.

Lapping of Balls

Spherical parts such as balls for ball bearings can be economically lapped to close dimensional tolerances and smooth finishes. Two machines used in production are the multigroove lapper and the single-groove lapper.

A multigroove lapper is shown in Fig. 32. The machine consists of two cast iron laps (130 to 150 Bhn); one is stationary and one rotates. Each lap has a series of concentric grooves that correspond with the grooves in the other lap. The radii of the grooves are the same as the radii of the balls being lapped. The stationary lap is cut out for entrance and exit of the balls, which are fed in at spaced intervals.

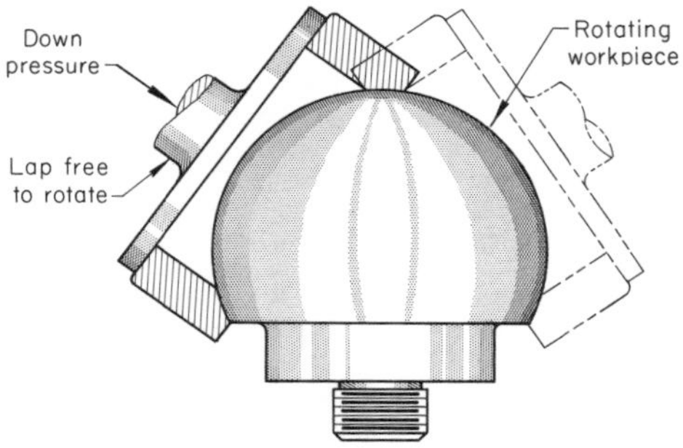

Fig. 30. Setup for single-piece spherical lapping with a two-spindle machine

Fig. 31. Setup for multiple-piece spherical lapping

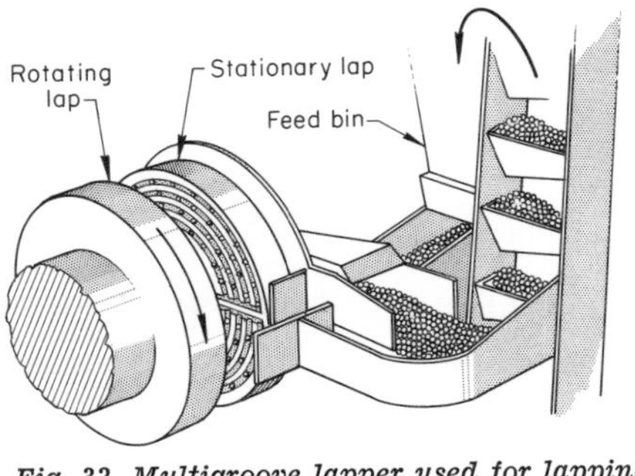

Fig. 32. Multigroove lapper used for lapping bearing balls

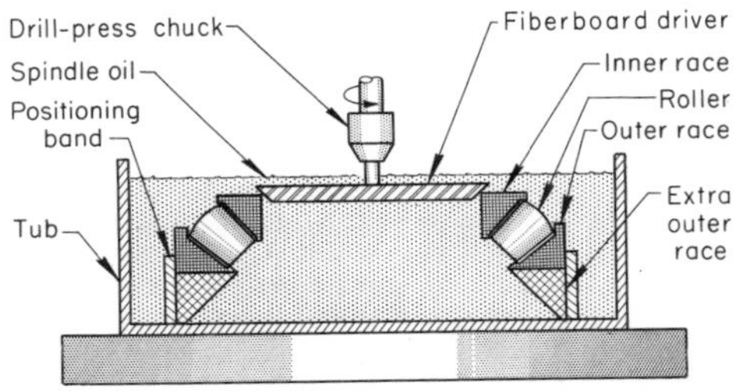

Fig. 33. Setup for lapping components of a large roller-bearing assembly, to accelerate wear-in (Example 577)

In the multigroove machine, the speed of the rotating lap is normally between 50 and 65 rpm and the load usually 7500 to 10,000 lb. Stock of 0.0004 to 0.0006 in. is removed from the diameters of the balls; the time required is 8 to 24 hr, depending on the dimensions and finish specified. Balls up to about 1¾ in. in diameter can be lapped in this type of machine to accuracy better than 25 millionths of an inch and a finish better than 2 micro-in.

The single-groove machine is used for balls larger than about 1¾ in. in diameter and for balls of any size that require greater accuracy and better surface finish than are obtainable in the multigroove machine. In the single-groove machine, which also employs two opposing cast iron laps, the shaft may be either horizontal or vertical. There is no cutout in either lap.

Balls to be lapped are alternated with spacer balls of slightly smaller diameter until the groove is filled. The speed of the rotating lap may vary from 30 to 150 rpm, depending on ball size and material and on the accuracy and surface finish desired. The load may be as low as 30 lb when extremes of accuracy and finish are sought, and the lapping time may extend to three days. Usually, 0.0002 to 0.0003 in. is removed from the ball diameters. Accuracy to less than 5 micro-in. and surface finish of 0.5 micro-in. are possible.

Assuming the pitch diameter of the groove is 15 in. and that spacer balls are used, 188 balls ⅛ in. in diameter or 9 balls 2⅝ in. in diameter could be finished in a single-groove machine in one run. However, less than the groove complement (even a single ball) can be lapped by using dummy balls of another material between the spacer balls to fill the groove. The material used to make the dummy balls must be different in some way (for example, color, density, magnetic properties, or reflectivity) from the material in the workpieces for easy identification.

In both types of machines, there is a constant flow of fluid lapping compound, which usually consists of fused alumina of grit size 5 to 10 microns suspended in 10% soluble oil and 90% water. Mineral oil may be used instead of soluble oil and water.

Although costs are greater for single-groove lapping than for multigroove lapping, in either process costs are proportional to the time required for obtaining desired accuracy and finish.

Most hard materials can be lapped to greater accuracy and better surface finish than soft materials. Rate of stock removal can be increased by using harder abrasives such as boron carbide or diamond. However, the use of harder or coarser abrasives results in some loss of surface smoothness.

Lapping to Accelerate Wear-In

Internal lapping is often employed as an accelerated wearing-in process for matching and aligning components of bearing assemblies. In most applications of this type, virtually no stock is removed, and sometimes the desired surface correction is so slight that no abrasive is needed. Typical tooling and techniques are described in the two examples that follow.

Examples 577 and 578. Lapping of Bearing Assemblies

Example 577 (Fig. 33). The lapping setup shown in Fig. 33 was used for removing rough surface crystals of zinc phosphate coating from critical areas of inner races of large bearings made of case hardened steel. The operation involved running the component under simulated load conditions. Because volume was low, a single-spindle drill press was used. The chuck pressed a fiberboard driver against the workpiece, using a pressure of 2.1 psi, while rotating at 450 rpm. The workpiece and the fiberboard driver were submerged in spindle oil during the operation; no abrasive was used. Lapping for 1 min removed the rough zinc phosphate crystals and produced the necessary amount of wear-in.

Example 578 (Fig. 34). The setup diagramed in Fig. 34 was used for simultaneous lapping of two roller-bearing cage assemblies into mating outer races. All components of these assemblies except cages were made of steel carburized and hardened to Rockwell C 60. As shown in Fig. 34, the cage assemblies were mounted at each end of a horizontal driving spindle. The outer races were positioned by horizontally actuated pressure heads through which the lapping compound was supplied.

Lapping was performed by rotating the cage assemblies against the races at 1063 rpm under pressure of 10 to 15 psi for 5 min. The lapping compound was prepared by mixing 24 oz of medium-hard, 800-grit silica with 10 gal of paraffin oil. The compound was recirculated, and was changed every ten shifts (80 hr). This machine could process cage assemblies of various outside diameters to a maximum of 7½ in.

Lapping of Springlike Parts

Special equipment and techniques are sometimes required for lapping unusual parts. Springlike parts such as those used in numerous precision mechanisms are examples of parts requiring specially designed equipment and techniques.

Example 579. Machine Lapping of a Springlike Part (Fig. 35)

Small, hardened springlike parts made of 440A stainless steel were lapped using the specially designed setup shown in Fig. 35. The machine, a horizontal reciprocating slide, oscillated the workpiece on a stationary, solid lap that was forced against the workpiece under a pressure of 3 psi. The laps were ⅛ to ½ in. wide, ¼ to ½ in. high, and up to 5 in. long. Because only one face of the lap was used, steel backing plates could be fastened to the unused side when the lap reached minimum height (see Fig. 35), thus prolonging the life of the lap.

The slide was rigidly held, to minimize swayback in the workpiece as the slide reversed direction when reciprocating. Oscillating motion was derived from a cam on a motor through a fork attached to the slide. Ball-and-socket jointed leaf springs attached to the machine provided pressure against a saddle that was, in turn, pressed against the workpiece. The saddle was made of steel, lined with rubber where it pressed on the workpiece. The rubber compressed to conform with the workpiece and thus prevent it from distorting during lapping.

The workpieces were reciprocated at 500 to 1000 strokes per minute; length of stroke was at least twice the length of the work surface. An average of 0.0025 in. of stock was removed from the surface in two operations: a roughing operation using 300-grit silicon carbide, followed by a finishing operation using 800-grit silicon carbide. Straightness within 0.0002 in. was required on the profile.

The number of parts that could be lapped on this machine varied from 1 to 30, depending on the size of the parts. Similar parts of various sizes were lapped by this method at a rate of about 30,000 parts per 8-hr shift.

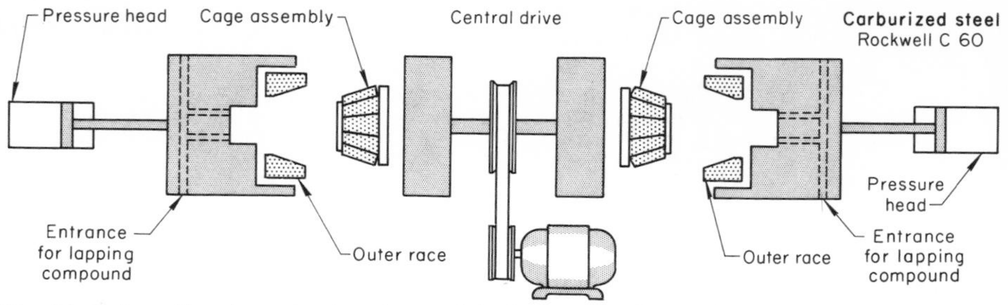

Fig. 34. Schematic view of setup for matched-piece lapping roller-bearing cage assemblies into mating outer races (Example 578)

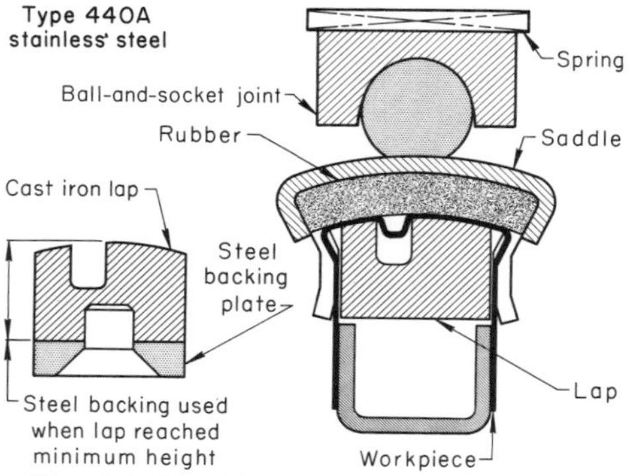

Fig. 35. Special setup for lapping small springlike parts (Example 579)

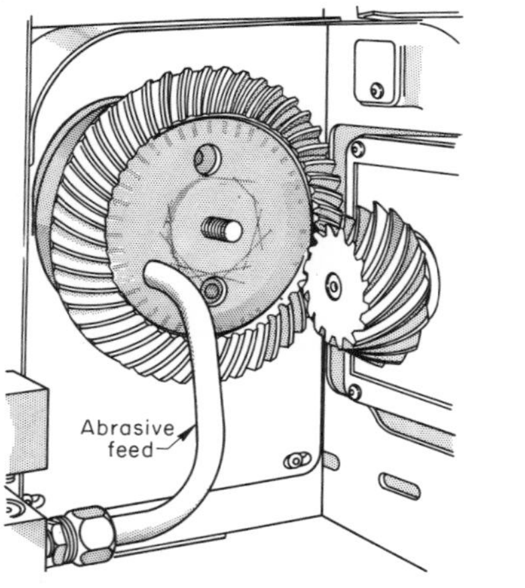

Fig. 36. Setup for lapping of hypoid gears

Lapping of Gears

Gear lapping corrects minute errors in involute profile, helix angle, tooth spacing, and concentricity, caused in forming or cutting, or in heat treatment of the gears. The lapping may be done by running a set of gears in mesh, or by running one gear with a gear-shaped master lapping tool.

Gear lapping is most often applied to sets of hardened gears that are required to run silently in service. Gear lapping is strictly a mating process, and is not intended for stock removal. Two gears that have been matched by lapping should be operated as a set — and they should be replaced as a set, rather than singly.

Gears are lapped in special machines, which can be arranged for manual, semiautomatic or automatic operation. In semiautomatic operation, loading and unloading are manual; in automatic operation, loading and unloading are done automatically, in accordance with a programed cycle.

Angular, spur and helical gears can be lapped, but the process is applied mainly to spiral bevel gears and hypoid gears. A typical setup used for lapping hypoid gears is shown in Fig. 36. Gears of up to 36-in. pitch diameter can be lapped in semiautomatic or automatic operation. Manual lapping, in special equipment, is employed for gears of approximately 100-in. pitch diameter down to the smallest gear that can be manufactured. Production lapping machines can be adjusted to lap gears with shaft angles of 0° to 180°.

Lapping Mediums. Optimum grit size varies with different types and sizes of gears. A 280-grit abrasive is used for spiral bevel gears; a finer abrasive (about 400-grit) is more suitable for hypoid gears, because the sliding action is greater. As a rule, coarser grit is used for gears having a coarse pitch, and finer grits are used for gears having a fine pitch. When compound is brushed on, as in manual operation, a paste-type vehicle is used. However, in semiautomatic or automatic lapping, the abrasive should be mixed with a thin oil (such as mineral seal oil), so that it can be pumped to the workpieces (Fig. 36).

Processing Techniques. It is important to roll all mating gears together before lapping, to detect nicks and burrs, which can be removed by a small portable hand grinder before the gears are lapped. This preliminary rolling also inspects tooth contact, which should be in the same location for each set of gears and is especially important in automatic lapping.

During the lapping operation, the pinion (smaller gear) is used as the driver, and the larger gear is the driven member. The driven spindle is also used for applying the necessary tooth-contact load by adjusting to a slight drag. Running cycles as short as 15 sec at about 250 sfm can frequently produce desired results. However, longer time cycles may be necessary, depending on initial gear-tooth finish and service requirements.

Low noise level is the criterion of successful gear-lapping. Because gear lapping is strictly a mating process and no stock removal is intended, measurements are not made as in most other lapping processes. Minor corrections in tooth bearing shape and position may be obtained, however. Lapping does improve the finish of gear teeth, but improved finish is seldom the purpose of gear lapping.

MATERIALS FOR CUTTING TOOLS

CONTENTS

High Speed Steel for Cutting Tools

*By the ASM Committee on Tool Steel**

HIGH SPEED STEEL is used for cutting tools because it retains enough hardness to cut metal at the rapid rates that generate high temperatures (1000 to 1100 F) at the cutting edge of the tool.

Because both high room-temperature hardness and high red hardness are necessary for good performance of cutting tools, high speed steels are highly alloyed with metallic elements and carbon. Hardness at elevated temperature depends on the specific steel, each having its own hot-hardness characteristics with some variation among grades. However, regardless of the grade, the original hardness of the high speed steel is completely regained upon cooling to room temperature, provided the original tempering temperature has not been exceeded. The many hard wear-resistant alloy carbides in these steels not only contribute to red hardness but also markedly increase wear resistance.

Availability. Table 1 lists nominal compositions and base prices for 33 high speed steels. These steels are available in various sizes in the annealed condition as round, hexagonal, square and flat bars, hot finished, cold finished and ground. For making milling cutters or special tools, some grades are produced as forged blanks in a series of standard sizes and by special order in almost any size or shape.

High speed steels are also available as annealed or heat treated drill rod for making small tools such as drills and reamers. All grades may be purchased as semifinished tools, heat treated and ready for finish grinding to the desired shape.

Tungsten High Speed Steel. Tungsten, chromium, vanadium, cobalt and carbon are the principal alloying elements in tungsten high speed steel. The high alloy and high carbon contents produce a large number of hard wear-resistant carbides in the microstructure, particularly in the grades containing more than 1.5% vanadium and 1.0% carbon. T15 is the most wear-resistant grade of tungsten steel, although it is somewhat lacking in toughness. Cobalt additions increase red hardness at a sacrifice in toughness. The presence of many wear-resistant carbides in a hard heat-resistant matrix makes these steels suitable for cutting tool applications; their toughness allows them to outperform sintered carbide in some delicate tools and in tools for interrupted cutting.

Molybdenum High Speed Steel. Molybdenum, tungsten, chromium, vanadium, cobalt and carbon are the principal alloying elements in molybdenum high speed steels. These steels are similar in properties to the tungsten high speed steels, but are generally considered to have slightly greater toughness at the same hardness. The main advantage of the molybdenum steels is their lower initial cost, almost 40% less than similar grades of tungsten steel. Higher carbon and vanadium contents increase wear resistance; an increase in cobalt content raises red hardness, as in the tungsten high speed steels. M15 is the most wear-resistant steel of the M group.

The M steels are somewhat more sensitive than the T steels to hardening conditions, particularly to temperature and atmosphere, because they decarburize easily under adverse treating conditions. This is especially true of the high-molybdenum grades. Approximately 90% of all the high speed steel produced in the United States is molybdenum steel.

Heat-Resisting Properties. The most important property of high speed steel is red hardness — that is, resistance to softening under the temperatures generated at the cutting edge of the tool. Even when cutting tools are flooded with oil or other coolant, wear and eventual failure depend largely on the red hardness of the steel.

Softening of hardened tool steel results from the precipitation and agglomeration of carbides from the hardened martensitic matrix. Steels high in alloying elements resist this precipitation effect. Resistance to the softening effect of heat also is improved by the presence in the steel of high-alloy carbides that retain their hardness at elevated temperature.

Hardenability. With the exception of M10, all of the high speed steels can be hardened to Rockwell C 64 to 66 throughout the entire cross section up to a diameter or thickness of about 1 in. by air cooling, and up to about 3 in. by quenching in oil or molten salt. However, except in unusual circumstances, they are seldom used in hardened sections thicker than 3 in. Even large cutting tools such as 4-in.-diam drills have a relatively small effective

*G. D. Dolch, *Chairman*, Materials Engineering Manager, Jet & Ordnance Div., TRW Inc.; Edward A. Dolega, Metallurgical Engineer, Bell Aerospace Corp.; Ural H. Gillett, Metallurgist, Cutting Tool Div., Barber-Colman Co.; C. W. Hangosky, Chief Metallurgist and Materials Engineer, Lansing Div., White Motor Co.

Elmer B. Hauser, Metallurgist, Weldon Tool Co.; John J. Hoffer, Manufacturing Technology, Apparatus and Optical Div., Eastman Kodak Co.; David P. Hughes, Manager of Metallurgy, Latrobe Steel Co.; Ralph G. Kennedy, Director of Laboratories, Cleveland Twist Drill Co.; Peter Leckie-Ewing, Chief Metallurgist, UTD Corp.; J. P. Long, Jr., Metallurgical Engineering Supervisor, Materials Engineering Dept., TRW Inc.; S. R. Prance, Chief Metallurgist, Inland Manufacturing Div., General Motors Corp.

D. A. Stewart, Senior Engineer, Thomson Engineering Laboratories, Small Aircraft Engine Dept., General Electric Co.; Rex F. Supernaw, Chief Metallurgist, National Twist Drill & Tool Co.; A. L. Trueax, Jr., Project Engineer, Ternstedt Div., General Motors Corp.; E. D. Wilson, Tool and Die Materials Div., Allegheny Ludlum Steel Corp.

[This article is a condensed and updated presentation of information on pages 637 to 654 of Volume 1 of this Handbook.]

Table 1. Nominal Compositions and Costs of High Speed Steels

Steel	C	Cr	V	W	Mo	Co	Cost(a)
Molybdenum High Speed Steels							
M1	0.80	3.75	1.15	1.75	8.75	...	$1.32
M2, class 1	0.85	4.00	2.00	6.25	5.00	...	1.36
M2, class 2	1.00	4.00	2.00	6.25	5.00	...	1.36
M3, class 1	1.05	4.00	2.50	6.25	5.75	...	1.72
M3, class 2	1.20	4.00	3.00	6.25	5.75	...	1.72
M4	1.30	4.00	4.00	5.50	4.75	...	1.72
M6	0.80	4.00	1.50	4.25	5.00	12.00	2.74
M7	1.02	3.75	2.00	1.75	8.75	...	1.32
M8	0.80	4.00	1.50	5.00	5.00	1.25 Cb	...
M10, class 1	0.89	4.00	2.00	0.70	8.00	...	1.32
M10, class 2	1.00	4.00	2.00	0.70	8.00	...	1.32
M15	1.50	4.00	5.00	6.50	8.50	5.00	2.805
M30	0.80	4.00	1.20	1.80	8.25	5.00	1.675
M33	0.88	3.75	1.15	1.75	9.50	8.25	1.96
M34	0.90	3.75	2.10	1.75	8.75	8.25	1.97
M35	0.85	4.00	2.00	6.00	5.00	5.00	2.25
M36	0.85	4.00	2.00	6.00	5.00	8.25	2.47
M41	1.10	4.25	2.00	6.75	3.75	5.25	2.07
M42	1.08	3.75	1.15	1.60	9.60	8.25	1.98
M43	1.20	3.75	1.60	2.70	8.00	8.20	1.98
M44	1.15	4.25	2.00	5.25	6.50	11.75	2.96
M45	1.27	4.20	1.60	8.25	5.20	5.50	2.21
M46	1.24	4.00	3.20	2.10	8.25	8.25	...
Tungsten High Speed Steels							
T1	0.73	4.00	1.00	18.00	...	...	$2.10
T2	0.85	4.00	2.00	18.00	...	...	2.30
T3	1.05	4.00	3.00	18.00	0.60	...	2.40
T4	0.75	4.00	1.00	18.00	0.60	5.00	2.87
T5	0.80	4.25	2.00	18.00	0.90	8.00	3.085
T6	0.80	4.25	1.60	20.50	0.90	12.25	4.655
T7	0.75	4.00	2.00	14.00	...	...	...
T8	0.80	4.00	2.00	14.00	0.90	5.00	2.72
T9	1.20	4.00	4.00	18.00	...	...	3.16
T15	1.55	4.50	5.00	12.50	0.60	5.00	2.915

(a) Typical base price per pound, August 1, 1967

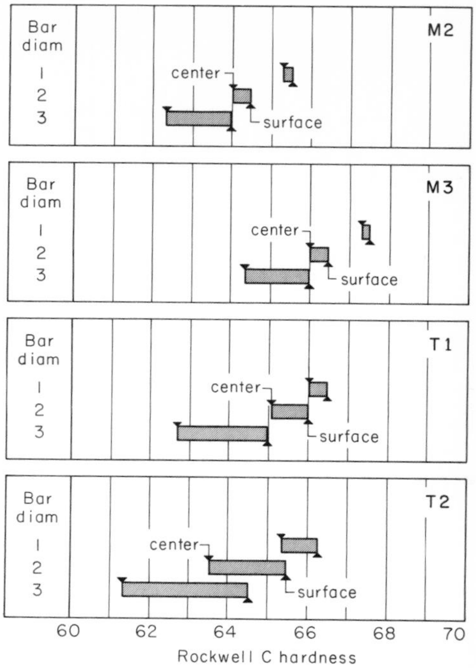

Fig. 1. Effect of bar diameter on range of surface-to-center hardness. (Steels were oil quenched: M2, from 2200 F; M3, from 2250 F; T1 and T2, from 2350 F.)

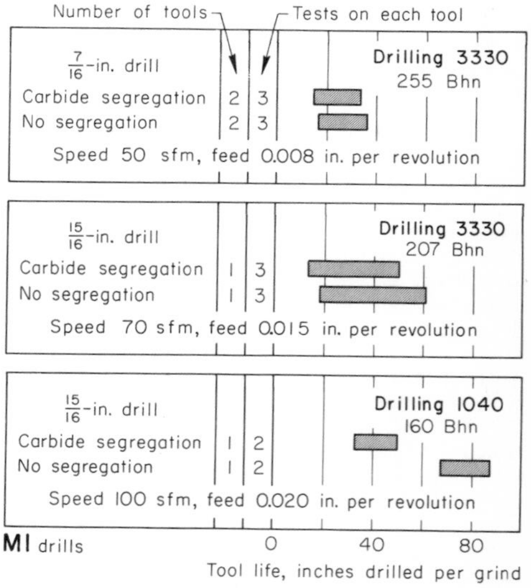

Fig. 2. Effect of carbide segregation on the life of M1 high speed steel drills

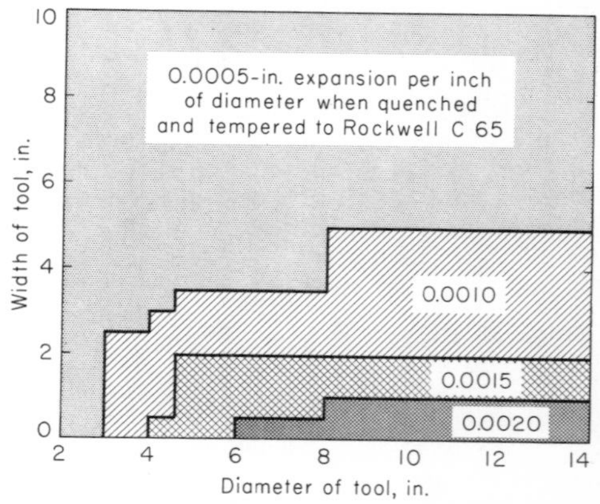

Fig. 3. Typical allowances for expansion in heat treating M2 high speed steel tools of various sizes

section for hardening, because of the removal of metal for flutes. Some solid tools of large diameter are made from high speed steel — for example, broaches up to 4 or 5 in. in diameter. However, with such tools, only the surface hardness is important. Figure 1 indicates a drop in center and surface hardness with increase in diameter of oil-quenched bars. For tools of large diameter and heavy section, it is common to use an accelerated oil quench that is effective in gaining one or two Rockwell C points over the more common hot-salt-quenching and air-cooling procedures. Direct oil quenching is preferred for full hardness in tools over 3 in. in diameter or thickness.

Frequently the word "hardenability", when used in connection with high speed steel, refers not so much to the depth of hardening as to the specific hardness that can be obtained under standard procedures of quenching and tempering. The maximum hardness of high speed steel varies somewhat with alloy content, and especially with carbon content. A hardness of Rockwell C 64.5 can be obtained on all high speed steels. Some grades, such as T15 and the 1.0% carbon grades of M2, M7, M41, M42, M43 and M44, because of their high carbon content and hard carbides, will harden to Rockwell C 67 to 68.

The M3, M4, M7 and M15 grades will harden to at least one point higher (usually to Rockwell C 66 or slightly higher) than the lower-carbon molybdenum high speed steels. When properly austenitized and quenched, most molybdenum steels will test one-half to one point Rockwell C harder than comparable tungsten high speed steels.

Effect of Composition on Tool Performance. Carbon in high speed steel is commonly held to ±0.02%, because of its pronounced effect on hardness and other properties. On the other hand, tungsten need be held to only ±0.75 or ±1.00%, because lesser variations do not affect eventual tool performance.

In recent years, with more advanced processing techniques in the steel mill, the effect of carbide segregation on high speed steel has become less severe. The results of cutting tests (Fig. 2) with high speed steel drills made from segregated and nonsegregated bars indicate segregation generally reduces drill life. This effect is especially significant in drills, because the greatest segregation is in the web — the most highly stressed section of the tool.

Some high speed steels are available with additions of sulfur to improve machinability. Sulfur additions must be carefully controlled to prevent large inclusions that would adversely affect tool performance. As presently added, sulfur for machinability is visible in the microstructure only under high magnification, and the thin elongated stringers of sulfide are dispersed so that the mechanical properties of the steel are not affected to any significant extent. In general, tool performance is not improved by the use of sulfurized high speed steel; the only advantage is improved machinability, resulting in a smoother surface finish on some tools.

Comparisons of different grades of high speed steel for the same application are given in numerous examples in this volume (see entries under *Tool Material Comparisons* in the index).

Dimensional changes resulting from heat treatment must be estimated and compensated for in machining allowances. Figure 3 shows that different sections of M2 increase in size by different amounts. This is an example of the effect of tool shape on growth.

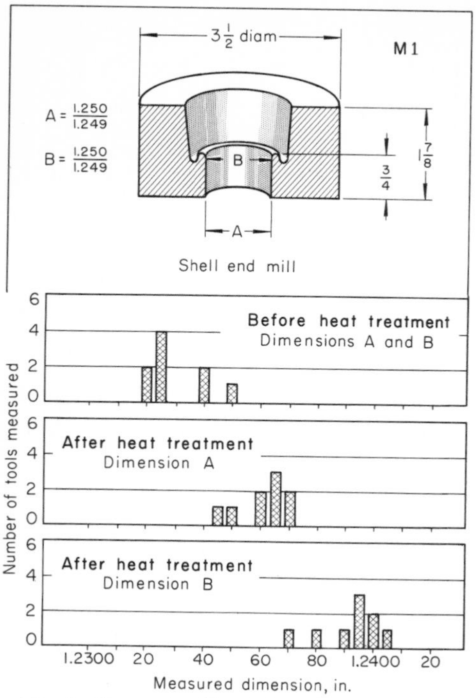

Fig. 4. Change in dimensions in heat treating tools made from M1 high speed steel. Tools were oil quenched from 2200 F and tempered at 1050 F.

The effect of section size and method of quenching is important. In Fig. 4, pronounced barreling of an oil-quenched end-mill section is apparent from the measurements given. Salt quenching would have substantially eliminated this effect, because lower thermal shock and more uniform cooling would have allowed the cross section to shrink more uniformly, regardless of section size.

Defects. The addition of alloying elements to tool steel during the melting operation increases the complexities of subsequent hot working of the steel. High speed steel and other high-alloy tool steels are likely to develop carbide segregation at the center of the ingot during normal solidification. This condition makes high speed steel difficult to fabricate by hot pressing, forging or rolling, because each of these operations can create internal fissures or bursts, despite good hot working practices. All of these grades must be heated and worked under exacting control; even with care, scrap losses are relatively high. Increasing the carbon range of M2, M7 and M10 also has emphasized the difficulties of hot working. The rigid control of mill procedures required to process these grades is partly reflected in the cost of the steels; the higher-priced steels are among the most difficult to forge and hot roll.

Decarburization. Tool steels decarburize in oxidizing atmospheres above 1400 F; those with significant molybdenum, silicon and cobalt contents are considered more susceptible. The effect of silicon (and probably cobalt), however, may be confused with effects of these elements in lowering the hardenability of low-carbon areas, as discussed by P. Payson in *Metal Progress* for December 1960.

Steel manufacturers work to decarburization allowances common to all of the grades of tool steel (see Table 2 for decarburization limits for various shapes and sizes). Individual suppliers of specific products, however, often are held to more restrictive limits for high speed steel. For example, high speed steel rounds more than ⅝ in. in diameter are usually supplied free from decarburization, even though the steel is ordered as hot rolled.

If mill bark, or scale, is not entirely removed, the performance of most tools will be adversely affected. A notable example is the surface of a drill. Mill bark is often more harmful than loss of a few points of carbon from the surface layers during heat treatment.

In addition to the elements mentioned above that promote decarburization, high speed steels requiring long soaking at the austenitizing temperature, because of the sluggish absorption of carbon in the austenite, usually are more likely to decarburize under adverse heat treating conditions. The molybdenum high speed steels and the cobalt-bearing tungsten steels are rated as generally poor in resisting decarburization and must be protected during heat treatment.

Grade Popularity. Molybdenum high speed steels received great impetus during the tungsten shortage of the second World War and the Korean

Table 2. Decarburization Allowances for Tool Steel Bars (AISI)

Ordered size, in.(a)	Hot rolled	Hammered	Rough turned	Cold drawn	Rough ground
Allowance per Side From Ordered Size for Rounds, Hexagons and Octagons, In.					
0 to ½	0.016	....	....	0.016	0.004
½ to 1	0.031	....	....	0.031	0.008
1 to 2	0.048	0.072	....	0.046	0.012
2 to 3	0.063	0.094	0.020	0.063	0.016
3 to 4	0.088	0.120	0.024	0.088	0.020
4 to 5	0.112	0.145	0.032	....	....
5 to 6	0.150	0.170	0.040	....	....
6 to 8	0.200	0.200	0.048	....	....
8	....	0.200	0.072	....	....

Ordered thickness, in.(a)	Side (see cut)	Ordered width, in. 0 to ½, incl	Over ½ to 1, incl	Over 1 to 2, incl	Over 2 to 3, incl	Over 3 to 4, incl	Over 4 to 5, incl	Over 5 to 6, incl	Over 6 to 7, incl	Over 7 to 8, incl	Over 8 to 9, incl	Over 9 to 10, incl
Hot Rolled Square and Flat Bars												
0 to ½	A	0.020	0.020	0.024	0.028	0.032	0.036	0.040	0.044	0.048	0.048	0.048
	B	0.020	0.036	0.044	0.056	0.068	0.092	0.104	0.120	0.136	0.144	0.152
½ to 1	A	....	0.036	0.036	0.040	0.044	0.048	0.056	0.056	0.060	0.060	0.060
	B	....	0.036	0.052	0.064	0.080	0.104	0.120	0.136	0.160	0.160	0.160
1 to 2	A	....	....	0.052	0.052	0.056	0.056	0.060	0.060	0.072	0.076	0.080
	B	....	....	0.052	0.068	0.084	0.112	0.124	0.144	0.168	0.180	0.180
2 to 3	A	....	....	....	0.068	0.068	0.068	0.068	0.072	0.080	0.080	0.080
	B	....	....	....	0.068	0.092	0.120	0.136	0.160	0.180	0.200	0.200
3 to 4	A	....	....	....	....	0.092	0.092	0.092	0.092	0.100	0.100	0.100
	B	....	....	....	....	0.092	0.120	0.140	0.180	0.200	0.200	0.200
4 to 5	A						0.120	0.120	0.120	0.120	0.120	0.120
	B						0.120	0.152	0.180	0.200	0.200	0.200
5 to 6	A							0.152	0.152	0.152	0.152	0.152
	B							0.152	0.200	0.200	0.200	0.200
6	A							....	0.200	0.200	0.200	0.200
	B							....	0.200	0.200	0.200	0.200
Hammered Square and Flat Bars												
0 to ½	A	0.024	0.024	0.028	0.032	0.036	0.044	0.052	0.056	0.060	....	....
	B	0.024	0.048	0.064	0.080	0.100	0.120	0.144	0.168	0.200	....	....
½ to 1	A	....	0.048	0.048	0.052	0.052	0.060	0.064	0.068	0.072	0.080	0.088
	B	....	0.048	0.072	0.084	0.100	0.120	0.144	0.168	0.200	0.200	0.200
1 to 2	A	....	....	0.072	0.072	0.072	0.080	0.088	0.092	0.100	0.112	0.120
	B	....	....	0.072	0.096	0.108	0.124	0.148	0.172	0.200	0.200	0.200
2 to 3	A	....	....	....	0.096	0.096	0.100	0.104	0.108	0.120	0.128	0.140
	B	....	....	....	0.096	0.120	0.128	0.148	0.172	0.200	0.200	0.200
3 to 4	A	....	....	....	....	0.120	0.120	0.128	0.144	0.152	0.168	0.180
	B	....	....	....	....	0.120	0.144	0.152	0.180	0.200	0.200	0.200
4 to 5	A						0.144	0.144	0.152	0.168	0.180	0.200
	B						0.144	0.168	0.200	0.200	0.200	0.200
5 to 6	A							0.168	0.180	0.180	0.200	0.200
	B							0.168	0.200	0.200	0.200	0.200
6	A							....	0.200	0.200	0.200	0.200
	B							....	0.200	0.200	0.200	0.200

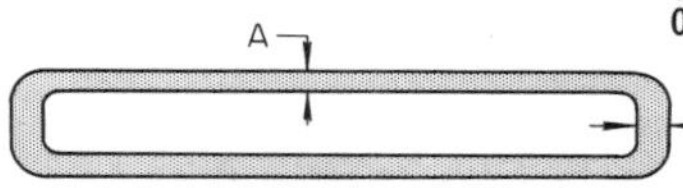

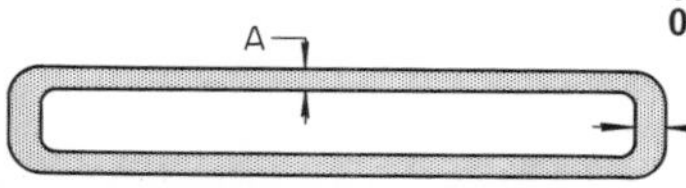

(a) Upper limit of range is inclusive; for example, "½ to 1" means "over ½ in. to and including 1 in."

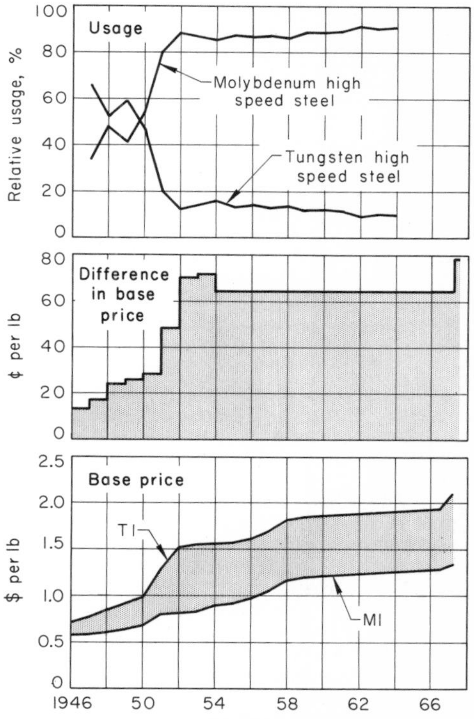

Fig. 5. Relative usage and difference in base price of molybdenum and tungsten high speed steels

Table 3. U. S. Production of High Speed Steels in 1964 (AISI)

Steel	Tons	
Molydenum High Speed Steels		
M2 and M8	8,755	
M3 and M4	1,357	
M1 and M7	6,297	
M10	2,267	
M6, M15, M30, M34, M35, M36 and other grades	1,743	
Total		20,419
Tungsten High Speed Steels		
T1, T2, T3, T7 and T9	1,400	
T4, T5, T6, T8 and T15	852	
Total		2,252
Total all high speed steels		22,671

War. In the period from 1950 to 1952, major increases in the price of tungsten brought about changes in the pricing of high speed steel (particularly for the grades containing a high percentage of tungsten), which are reflected in the relative usage of tungsten to molybdenum high speed steels shown in Fig. 5. The difference in price of 78¢ a pound, applied to 20,000 tons of high speed steel per year, amounts to a difference of more than $30 million per year in total cost — a large economic factor in the selection of steel.

The recent trend has been toward greater use of vanadium and carbon in high speed steels, because of better wear resistance and longer tool life imparted by the hard vanadium carbides. Use of these types (such as the 1.0% carbon grades of M2 and M10; M7; M3, class 1; M3, class 2; M4 and T15) has increased in recent years at about three times the rate of all other high speed steels.

Relative tonnages produced in the United States are shown in Table 3.

Cost. Previous discussion has indicated the effect of higher alloy content on the cost of high speed steel and its relation to manufacturing losses and fabrication problems. In addition, there is the cost involved in the actual price per pound of the various alloying elements used. This is particularly important in tool steels containing tungsten and cobalt.

To the base price of high speed steel are added fabricating costs, commonly known as extras, in arriving at a total price for any specific size, shape, condition or quantity. Typical magnitudes of price extras for M1 and T1 steels, expressed as a percentage of the base price for a group of blanks in various diameters, are given in Table 4, assuming that ten pieces of tool steel, each 12 in. long, are purchased from a warehouse, and that the order includes extras for annealing, hot rolled size, warehouse quantity, and cutting to length.

Table 4. Typical Tool Steel Extras Expressed as Percentage of Base Price (a)

Grade	Bar diameter, in. ½	1	2	4	8
M1	46	35	23	17	31
T1	31	24	15	12	14

(a) From a survey of eight tool steel suppliers, August 1965. (See text for explanation.)

Possibly the most important extra is that pertaining to quantity. Base prices usually apply to a quantity of 1000 lb or more, and therefore it is most economical to buy tool steel in lots of this amount. When production involves more than one size in small quantities, it may be practical to buy base quantities of large-size bars for producing a variety of smaller-size parts. However, the cost of machining large sizes to smaller sizes must be considered — it may be more economical to purchase smaller quantities of the correct size even though a small-order penalty must be paid. (See Table 3 on page 355 in the article "Machining of Tool Steel" in this volume.)

Grade standardization provides direct benefits and cost savings by reducing unit purchasing charges and materials handling, and by simplifying inventory records, steel identification, and storage. A typical decrease in cost per pound as the quantity of individual orders is increased is shown in Fig. 6.

Consumer Processing Costs. The ability to machine or otherwise fabricate tool steel in the annealed or soft condition usually is a relatively minor consideration in selection of grade; perfection of the finished product is of greater importance than the ease or low cost of machining. When several available grades have equivalent properties in the finished tools, it is, of course, more economical to select the grade having the best machinability and general workability.

For information on the machining and grinding of tool steel, see pages 353 to 374 in this volume.

Heat treating of high speed steel is discussed on pages 235 to 240 in Volume 2 of this Handbook.

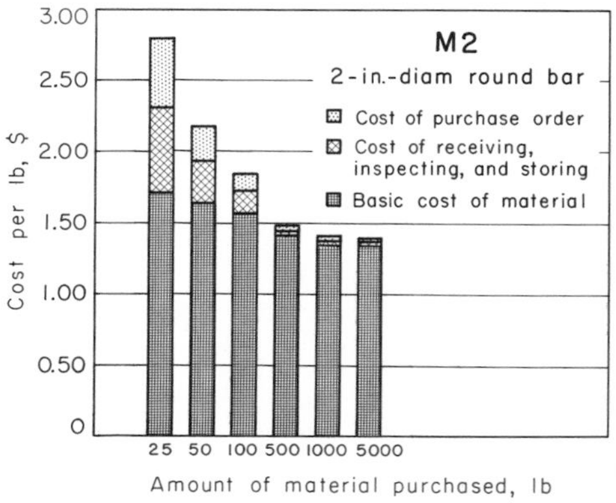

Fig. 6. Effect of quantity purchased on basic material cost and total cost of M2 high speed steel bars. Inspection costs are based on statistical quality control methods.

Cast Cobalt-Chromium-Tungsten-Molybdenum Alloys for Cutting Tools

ALLOYS of cobalt and chromium containing tungsten or molybdenum, or both, are made by a number of manufacturers in a variety of grades covering a wide range of hardness and other properties. The softer and tougher compositions are used for high-temperature applications such as gas-turbine vanes and buckets. The harder grades discussed here are used for cutting tools and wear-resistant parts.

For tool applications, these alloys usually contain from 25 to 32% chromium. The tungsten and molybdenum contents vary from 4 to 25%, or preferably from 6 to 20%, depending on the hardness desired. Carbon, present in amounts from 1 to 3%, exerts a marked hardening effect. The carbon content generally increases as the tungsten content increases. Manganese and silicon are present as deoxidizers, and other elements, such as vanadium, boron, tantalum, columbium and nickel, may be added to impart other special properties. Small amounts of iron or nickel are always present, usually as impurities; however, the nickel may be added intentionally to soften and toughen the alloys.

Table 1 indicates the property trends of these materials. Unlike steels, the harder grades are generally weaker than the softer grades. This is reflected in both tensile and impact strengths. Typical compositions and properties for several of the wear-resistant alloys are given in Table 2.

Structure. The metallographic structure of the medium and hard cast alloys is complicated. The most notable constituent is a large hexagonal carbide

Condensed from the article by G. A. Fritzlen and J. K. Elbaum on pages 669 to 671 in Volume 1 of this Handbook.

Table 1. Properties of Hard, Medium and Soft Cobalt-Base Alloys as Influenced by Tungsten and Carbon Contents

Tungsten and carbon contents	Hardness, R_C	Tensile strength, psi	Impact resistance, ft-lb	Castability	Machinability
18% W, 2.5% C	62	50,000	2 to 3	Poor	Finished by grinding only
11% W, 2% C	53	78,000	3 to 4	Fair to good	Simple machining with carbide tools
4% W, 1% C	41	133,000	8 to 10	Good	Relatively easy to machine and grind

crystal that usually appears in an elongated or acicular (needle-like) form and can be identified as the chromium carbide Cr_7C_3 in which some of the chromium may be replaced by cobalt or tungsten or both. The matrix consists of various binary and ternary eutectics containing all the constituents of the alloy. This structure is generally stable at temperatures as high as 1800 to 1900 F.

Outstanding resistance to wear makes these alloys suitable for metal-cutting tools. The success of their applications results from their "red hardness" — that is, their ability to retain hardness and strength at high temperature. High speed steel makes better cutting tools than carbon tool steel because high speed steel has a higher hardness at elevated temperature. Similarly, the cast cobalt-base alloys are generally superior to high speed steel in performance and tool life because of their greater retention of hardness at elevated temperature.

Red hardness also makes these alloys more capable of resisting wear under almost all conditions where high local surface temperatures are developed. Resistance to tempering effects is great, because the alloys do not undergo phase changes or transformations. In addition, these alloys have comparatively low coefficients of friction, which means that they develop lower temperatures in sliding contact.

Because the cobalt-chromium-tungsten alloys are generally weaker and less ductile than high speed steels, in tool form, they should not be subjected to extreme conditions of stress that might cause breakage. However, under some conditions, these tool alloys can be used for intermittent cutting better and more economically than either tungsten carbide or steel. Figure 1 (left) shows the variation of Brinell hardness with temperature for typical hard, medium and soft alloys, as compared with the variation for 18-4-1 high speed steel.

In Fig. 1 (right) is shown the variation in tensile strength with temperature for three classes of alloys. The correlation between hardness and strength that normally obtains for steels is not applicable to these materials. However, the retention of strength with increasing temperature is closely associated with the retention of hardness indicated in Fig. 1.

Ductility also remains fairly low with increasing temperature. In fact, for the medium and hard grades, it may be generally assumed that the yield strength and tensile strength are essentially the same. The alloys show almost no plastic deformation in tension tests at temperatures as high as 1500 F.

Metal-cutting tools are made from alloys of the hard type. Medium grades are used for parts subjected to wear and requiring greater impact resistance. Soft grades are used for valves, hot trimming dies, and the like.

The harder grades are resistant to heat treatment and are supplied as stress-relieved castings. Although the medium and soft grades may be finished by grinding or machining with carbide tools, the hard grades can usually be finished by grinding only. The latter are therefore cast close to size, whether intended for cutting tools or for other service. Grinding conditions must be controlled to avoid surface cracking or heat checks. Slow grinding speeds are desirable (2800 to 6000 sfm).

Cutting Applications. The cobalt-chromium-tungsten metal-cutting tools have been widely used for machining steel, gray iron, malleable iron, cast steel, stainless steel, brass, bronze, aluminum and most other machinable materials. They are selected for operations requiring speeds faster than high speed steel tools can withstand but slower than those at which tungsten carbide tools are generally used. The cast alloy tools are less tough than high speed steel, but they will withstand more impact, pressure and vibration than carbide tools.

Lathe Tools. In cutting-tool applications, these alloys are used as single-point blades, bits or tools. One manufacturer recommends cast cobalt-base tools for use at surface speeds up to twice those employed with high speed steel tools, using the same or heavier feed and depth of cut. Typical data are shown in Table 3.

Milling Cutters. Another application of these alloys is in milling cutter blades for large inserted-tooth cutters and in solid cast cutters of smaller sizes. Table 4 gives normal operating conditions for these cutters.

Wear Strips. Pilot bars for boring tools and the like must resist wear for accuracy of the part. A common procedure is to insert five or six alloy wear strips (cast, wrought or hard faced) around the bar.

Table 2. Nominal Compositions and Properties of Cast Cobalt-Chromium-Tungsten Alloys

Item		Medium grades			Hard grades	
Chromium		30.50	30.50	31.00	32.00	30.00
Tungsten		12.50	8.50	10.50	17.00	18.50
Molybdenum, max		....	....	....	....	0.80
Carbon		2.45	1.35	1.70	2.50	2.00
Manganese, max		1.00	1.00	1.00	1.00	1.00
Silicon, max		1.00	1.00	1.00	1.00	1.00
Nickel, max		3.00	3.00	3.00	2.50	3.50
Cobalt		Rem	Rem	Rem	Rem	Rem
Rockwell C hardness	Chill cast	60	51	55	62	63
	Sand cast	55	48	52	58	60
Tensile strength, psi	Chill cast	85,000	....	110,000	75,000	95,000
	Sand cast	55,000	76,000	105,000	62,000	75,000
Compressive strength, psi	Chill cast	310,000	193,000	310,000	335,000	370,000
Izod impact strength, ft-lb, unnotched	Chill cast	6	....	11.5	3.5	3
	Sand cast	2.5	7	3.5	2.5	3
Density, lb per cu in.		0.312	0.308	0.302	0.316	0.312
Electrical resistivity, microhm-in.		40.9	38.7	38.4	41.7	44.7

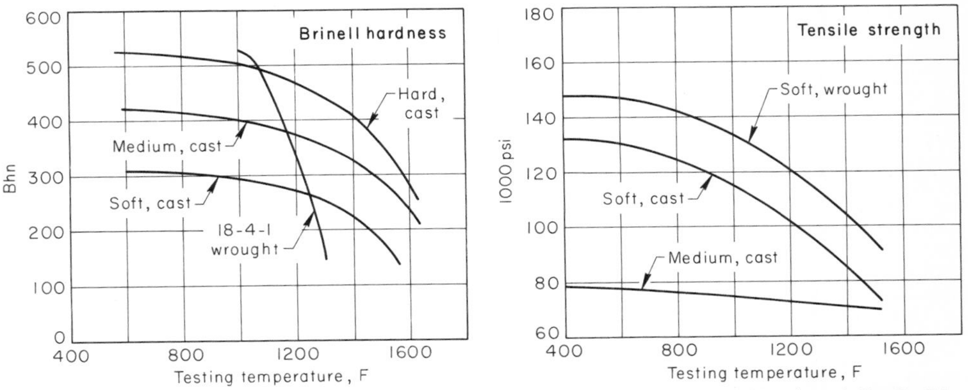

Fig. 1. Effect of testing temperature on the hardness and tensile strength of cast Co-Cr-W alloys. For purposes of comparison, hardness data on wrought 18-4-1 high speed steel are included in the chart at the left.

Table 3. Recommended Speeds and Depths of Cut at 1/32-In. Feed per Revolution

Metal being machined	Surface speed (sfm) for depth of cut (in.) of: 1/32	1/4	5/8
Wrought Steel			
Plain carbon:			
1010 to 1040	250	160	105
1080 to 1095	150	100	65
Free-cutting,			
11xx to 13xx	300	200	130
Low alloy, 4130 to 4820	150	100	65
High-chromium (52xxx)	125	85	70
18-8 stainless steel	225	170	120
Cast Steel			
115 to 140 Brinell	160	125	80
140 to 160 Brinell	150	110	65
Cast Iron			
160 to 180 Brinell	190	155	95
225 to 250 Brinell	150	115	70
Copper Alloys and Aluminum			
Brass	500	333	200
Bronze, soft	190	126	75
Bronze, hard	150	100	60
Aluminum	1200	870	520

Table 4. Recommended Speeds and Feeds for Milling Cutters

Material	Roughing: Speed, sfm	Roughing: Feed, ipt	Finishing: Speed, sfm	Finishing: Feed, ipt
Gray and malleable iron	80 to 140	0.010 to 0.015	150 to 300	0.005 to 0.010
Cast steel	60 to 80	0.010 to 0.015	80 to 100	0.005 to 0.010
Bronze	175	Up to 0.030	250	Up to 0.030
Aluminum	800	Up to 0.030	1200	Up to 0.030
Copper and brass	400	Up to 0.030	600	Up to 0.030

Sintered Carbide for Cutting Tools

*By the ASM Committee on Sintered Carbide**

SINTERED CARBIDE is a product of powder metallurgy, made of finely divided, hard particles of carbide of refractory metal, sintered with one or more metals of the iron group (iron, nickel or cobalt), forming a body of high hardness and compressive strength. The hard particles are tungsten carbide, usually in combination with lesser amounts of other carbides. The additional carbides are those of titanium and tantalum, with some occasional specialized use being made of the carbides of columbium, molybdenum, vanadium, chromium, zirconium and hafnium. The auxiliary, or binder, metal is usually cobalt; nickel or iron is used infrequently.

The carbides are present as individual grains, and also as a finely dispersed network resulting from the precipitation, during cooling, of carbide dissolved in the cobalt during sintering.

After solidification, the cobalt is present in the interstices as almost pure metal with its original ductility. Solid cobalt dissolves only about 1% of tungsten carbide at low temperature. The limit of solid solubility of tungsten carbide in nickel is 25% and in iron, 5%. It is this low solubility of tungsten carbide in cobalt, compared with the solubility in nickel or iron, which accounts for the use of cobalt as the binder metal. The higher solid solubility of carbide in iron or nickel would result in a more brittle auxiliary, or binder, phase. The cobalt also has superior ability to wet the carbide at elevated temperatures, which is important during sintering.

Classifications

The simplest classification of carbides recognizes two broad categories: (*a*) the "straight tungsten carbide" grades, used primarily for machining cast iron, austenitic steel, and nonferrous and nonmetallic materials, and (*b*) the grades containing major amounts of titanium and tantalum carbides, used primarily for machining ferritic steel.

The so-called straight tungsten carbides usually contain tungsten carbide and cobalt with no more than 2 to 5% of titanium and tantalum carbides. These straight tungsten grades are generally recommended for machining of cast iron and nonferrous metals. Cast irons such as pearlitic and martensitic malleable, however, are more often machined advantageously using the so-called steel-cutting grades, which usually contain from 10 to 40% titanium and tantalum carbides in addition to tungsten carbide.

A more detailed classification based on composition is shown in Table 1, which also lists typical uses. Groups 1 to 3 are the straight tungsten carbide grades; groups 4 to 9 contain more than 8% TiC plus TaC. Groups 4 to 8 encompass all the steel-cutting grades. Group 9, containing tantalum additions only, is used to a lesser extent for cutting tools and to a greater extent for heat-resisting and shock-resisting applications other than cutting tools.

An approximate correlation of the compositions of the common "C" grades with hardness, density and transverse rupture strength is given in Table 2. Composition, grain size and properties such as hardness and rupture strength vary considerably among products having the same "C" designation but made by different producers.

Table 1. Classification of Sintered Carbides

Carbide group	Composition, % (remainder WC) Co	TaC+TiC	Hardness, R_A	Density, g/cu cm
Straight Tungsten Carbide				
1	2.5-6.5	0-3	93-91	15.2-14.7
2	6.5-15	0-2	92-85	14.8-13.9
3	15-30	0-5	88-85	13.9-12.5
Added Carbide Predominantly TiC				
4	3-7	20-42	93.5-92.0	11.9-9.0
5	7-10	10-22	92.5-90.0	12.0-11.0
6	10-12	8-15	92.0-89.0	13.0-12.0
Added Carbide Predominantly TaC				
7	4.5-8	16-25	93.0-91.0	12.5-12.0
8	8-10	12-20	92.0-90.0	13.0-11.5
Added Carbide Exclusively TaC				
9	5.5-16	18-30	91.5-84.0	14.8-13.5

Typical Uses

Group 1. Finishing to medium roughing cuts on cast iron, nonferrous metals, superalloys and austenitic alloys; low-impact dies. **Group 2.** Rough cuts on cast iron, especially on planers; moderate-impact dies. **Group 3.** High-impact die applications.

Group 4. Light high-speed finishing cuts on steel. High crater resistance. Low shock resistance. **Group 5.** Medium cuts and speeds on steel. Good crater resistance and moderate shock resistance. Dies with moderate impact involving pickup. **Group 6.** Roughing cuts on steel. Good shock resistance together with wear and crater resistance. Moderate-impact die applications involving pickup.

Group 7. Light cuts on steel where a combination of edge wear and crater resistance is required. **Group 8.** General-purpose and heavy cutting of steel requiring resistance to wear and cratering. Also resists abrasive wear caused by scale.

Group 9. Wear-resistant applications particularly involving heat; gage elements, special machining applications. Special applications involving mechanical shock and heat such as hot trimming of flash.

Table 2. Approximate Identification of Commercial Metal-Cutting Grades of Sintered Carbide

Carbide grade	Composition, % WC	TiC	Co	Hardness, R_A	Density, g per cu cm	Transverse rupture strength, psi
C-1	94	..	6	91.2	14.95	317,000
C-2	91	..	9	90.3	14.60	275,000
C-3	95.5	..	4.5	92.2	15.05	200,000
C-4	97	..	3	92.8	15.15	175,000
C-6	82	8	10	90.5	12.55	215,000
C-7	80	12	8	91.5	11.15	175,000
C-8	84	10	6	92.0	12.85	207,000
C-50(a)	72	8	8.5	81.2	12.60	......

(a) Contains 11.5% TaC

Hardness

The exceptional tool performance of sintered carbide results from high hardness and compressive strength. The lowest hardness of sintered carbide is approximately the same as the highest hardness available in tool steel, Rockwell A 85 (Rockwell C 67), and ranges to Rockwell A 93, depending on grade.

Hardness is easily measured and offers some clue to the suitability of a carbide grade for a given application. For instance, groups 1, 2 and 3, having nominal Rockwell A hardness of 92, 89 and 86, respectively, are recommended for applications in the following order: (*a*) finishing and light to medium cutting of cast iron, (*b*) roughing cuts on cast iron, and (*c*) rugged cutting of cast iron, as in interrupted cuts. Each successive application requires higher impact properties, necessitating higher cobalt content, which results in lower hardness. Table 1 shows the magnitude of decrease in hardness with increasing cobalt content. The same need for

*ALFRED BORNEMANN, *Chairman,* Professor of Metallurgy, Stevens Institute of Technology; A. B. ALBRECHT, Technical Consultant, Monarch Machine Tool Co.; BENNETT BOVARNICK, Chief, Sintered Metals and Ceramics Branch, Rodman Laboratory, Watertown Arsenal; ERNEST CARLSON, Manufacturing Research Office, Ford Motor Co.; D. F. DICKEY, Director, Research and Development, Firth Sterling, Inc.; R. J. DORR, Manager, Advance Product Engineering, Metallurgical Products Dept., General Electric Co.

EDGAR W. ENGLE, Development Engineer, Kennametal, Inc.; J. W. FOUTCH, Project Engineer, Timken Roller Bearing Co.; W. D. GILDER, Chief Metallurgist, Reed Roller Bit Co; ROBERT T. HOOK, Chief Metallurgist, Warner & Swasey Co.; L. J. HULL, Chief Metallurgist, Ryan Aeronautical Co.; GEORGE G. LEITCH, Chief Metallurgist, Fellows Gear Shaper Co.; C. P. LITTLE, Metallurgist, Joy Manufacturing Co.; H. M. LUEHMANN, Chrysler Corp.

CARL LUGAR, Ladish Co.; WILLIAM PENTLAND, Research Supervisor, Cincinnati Milling Machine Co.; P. V. SCHNEIDER, Metallurgist, International Business Machines Corp.; K. J. TRIGGER, Professor of Mechanical Engineering, University of Illinois; W. B. WEBER, Heat Treat Engineer, Caterpillar Tractor Co.

[This article is a condensation, with modifications, of the article beginning on page 659 in Volume 1 of this Handbook.]

lower hardness with increased severity of cut exists for the steel-cutting grades of groups 4 to 8.

Hardness measurements alone will not discriminate between the straight WC grades and the TiC or TaC grades. Density, in conjunction with hardness testing, can be used for separating grades, as discussed in the following section. Figure 1 illustrates the range in hardness for individual grades and groups and the effect of increasing cobalt content from 3 to 13% in straight WC grades. Figure 2 illustrates the range of hardness found in a large number of shipments of several commercial grades of one nominal composition (94% WC, 6% Co).

Hardness readings should not be taken near cutting edges, because the indentation will act as a notch, nor in a straight line, for the same reason. In some plants a tool is reground if a large number of hardness readings have been taken in a critical area. Very fine microcracking occurs when carbides harder than Rockwell A 91 are being tested, but this does not appreciably affect the hardness values.

The Rockwell A scale (60-kg load) is used because the 150-kg load of the C-scale would create proportionately deeper indentations and might crack the carbide. No extensive calibration of the A-scale is needed; the only requirement is that the average of five readings on a test block should check within ±0.2 of a hardness number. A detailed statement of recommended practice is available in ASTM B294.

The hardness of sintered carbide is 9 on the Mohs' scale (talc is 1, diamond is 10). Specific hardness comparisons (Knoop indentations) with nonmetallic abrasive materials are shown below:

Material	Knoop hardness number
Tungsten carbide sintered with cobalt binder	1050 to 1500
Topaz	1250
Aluminum oxide	1625 to 1680
Silicon carbide	2130 to 2140
Boron carbide	2250 to 2260
Sapphire	1600 to 2200
Diamond	6000 to 6500

Hardness at elevated temperature is only slightly decreased up to the temperature where rapid oxidation begins (Fig. 3). The difference in hardness among grades at a given temperature is largely dependent on the amount of binder, and to a lesser extent on the grain size, porosity and impurities. At 1400 F the highest hardness in Fig. 3 is shown by a 6% Co grade of group 1, Rockwell A 85 (Rockwell C 67). Lowest is 13% Co, group 2, Rockwell A 72 (Rockwell C 43).

High-temperature hardness is useful in determining the relative resistance to plastic flow of a carbide at a given temperature, and is important where tool failure is the result of stress combined with temperature, as in hot impact extrusion. When carbide is exposed to extremely high temperatures for prolonged periods, a grade high in titanium carbide (such as group 4) is recommended because it oxidizes at a slower rate than tungsten carbide.

A specific advantage of using sintered carbide within its temperature range is that repeated cycling between high and low temperature or sustained holding at high temperature has no tempering effect that decreases the hardness. When the sintered carbide returns to room temperature, it has its original hardness.

Density

Density is readily determined by weighing the blank in air and then in water, as described in ASTM B311. Nominal density values of the groups are listed in Table 1. Density measurements on 1129 specimens of 65 grades in all nine groups are shown in Fig. 4.

The straight WC grades of groups 1 to 3 have high density, the TiC additions of groups 4 to 6 make these grades lighter, and the TaC additions of groups 7 to 9 result in densities almost equal to the straight WC grades. This is to be expected since the densities of the three pure carbides are as follows: WC 15.6, TiC 4.7, and TaC 14.0 g per cu cm. Cobalt has a density of 8.9 g per cu cm. The effect of TiC is illustrated in Fig. 4, where the lowest density readings were obtained with a grade having 32% TiC, 10% TaC, 7% Co.

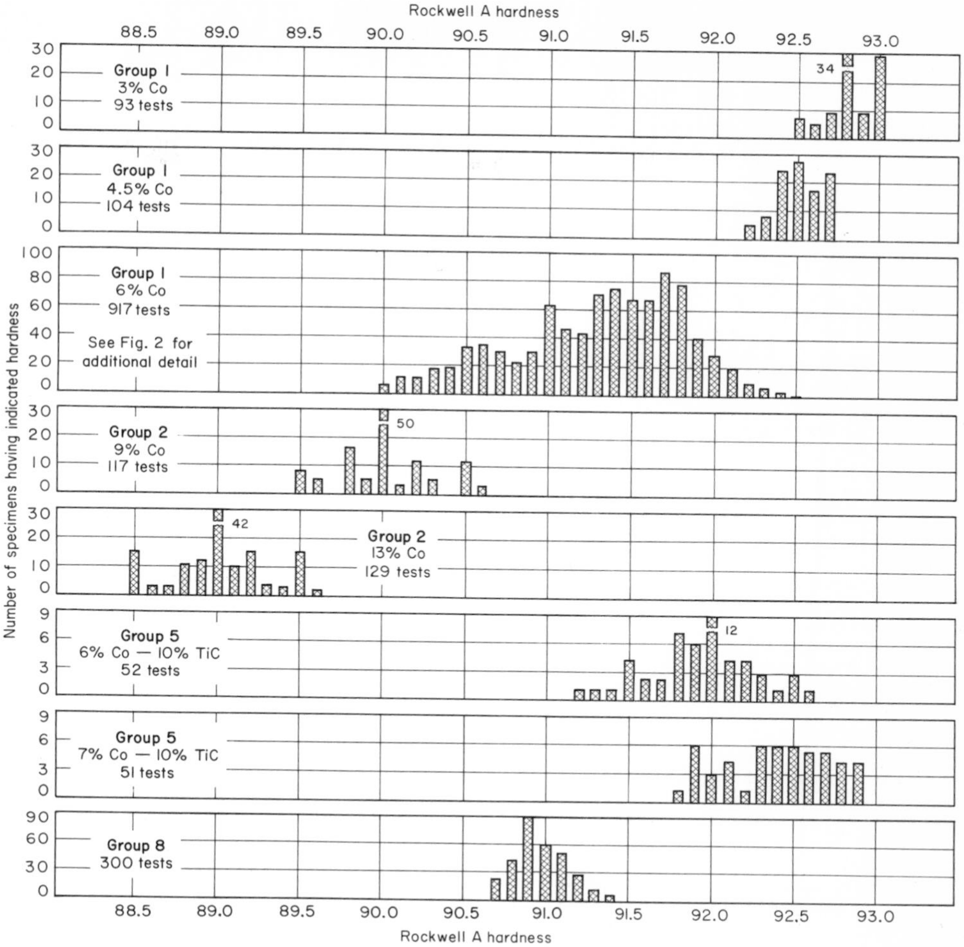

Fig. 1. Hardness of sintered carbides tested in accordance with ASTM B294

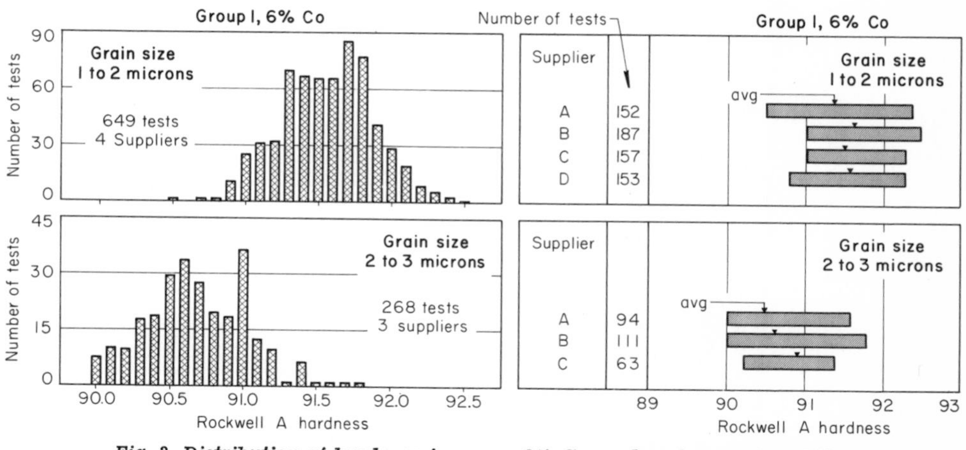

Fig. 2. Distribution of hardness for seven 6% Co grades of group 1 carbide

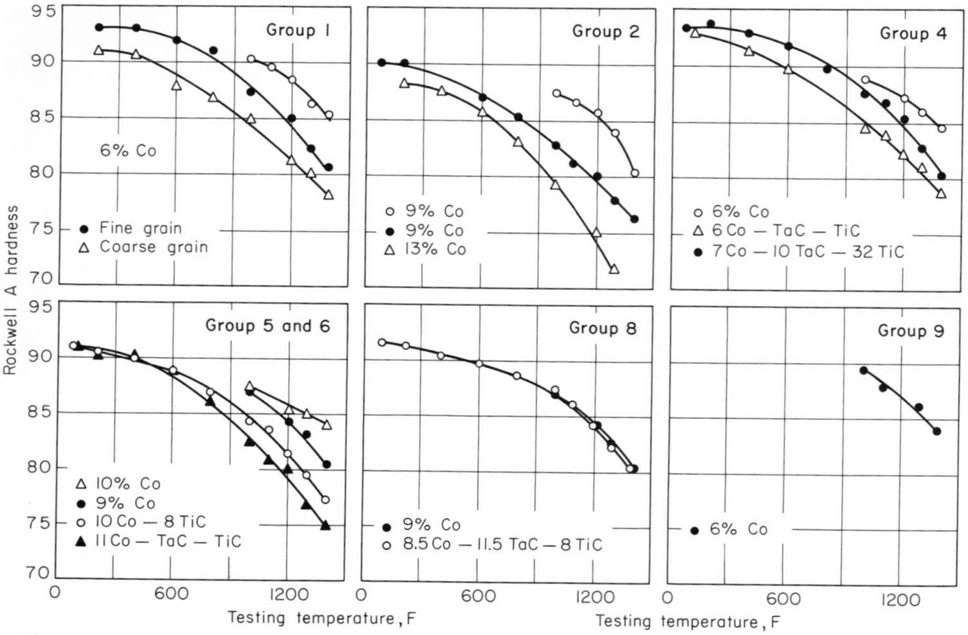

Fig. 3. Effect of testing temperature on the hardness of sintered carbides. Samples were protected by a hydrogen atmosphere during heating, and the hardness readings were taken at the elevated temperatures with an extension penetrator.

A more detailed analysis of seven WC grades is shown in Fig. 5.

Figure 6 shows the range of density values for five steel-cutting grades. Note the increase in density with decreasing TiC and increasing TaC. Based on nominal composition, the 7 Co – 10 TiC grade should be lighter than the 6 Co – 10 TiC grade, because more cobalt, with a density of 8.9, has replaced the heavier WC, which has a density of 15.6 g per cu cm. The fact that the 7 Co – 10 TiC grade measured heavier probably results from the presence of small amounts of TaC not shown in the nominal composition.

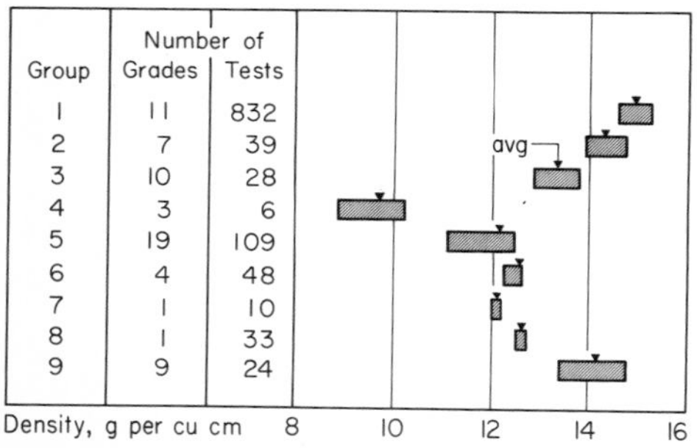

Fig. 4. Density as determined from incoming inspection measurements by four users of carbide for cutting tools

Density determination, along with hardness measurement, is a practical method for identifying tool inserts if the identity of a grade is lost or if grades are inadvertently mixed.

Mercury, with a density of 13.55 g per cu cm, offers an expedient method of identification or separation of the straight tungsten carbide grades from grades having appreciable TiC plus TaC. When placed in mercury, the straight tungsten grades will sink and the TiC-TaC grades will float. Some of the group 3 grades will float, but such grades are easily separated by hardness. Group 9 grades are also an exception. They will sink in mercury because the additional carbide is TaC, which is about equivalent to WC in density. However, users would be aware of the presence of these specialty grades in their plants. Final identification can usually be verified by hardness.

The most difficult to separate are groups 5 and 8. Both are steel-cutting grades containing TiC with TaC; hardness, density and tool applications of the two groups are similar.

Transverse Rupture Strength

Transverse rupture strength of commercial carbides varies from about 115,000 to 485,000 psi, and is useful in determining allowable angles for cutting edges and the amount of support required for tools. Figure 7 gives data on transverse strength by groups.

With increasing cobalt content, strength increases to a maximum at 10 to 15% Co. In greater amounts, cobalt acts to separate the carbide grains; the strengthening effect offered by mechanical interlocking of the grains is lessened; more soft cobalt increases the slip paths available for yielding.

Shock resistance also increases when the amount of cobalt in an impact tool is larger. The point of diminished return is at about 30% Co, where hardness and wear resistance become too low for any tool.

Transverse rupture, rather than simple tension, is used to determine the strength of carbides because (*a*) a small sample is less costly, (*b*) the alignment problem is increased with a small tension sample, and (*c*) straight tension testing is less suited for materials of low ductility. In transverse testing, the load is applied to a beam specimen, of either rectangular or round section. Although rupture strength is determined as pounds per square inch by the simple beam formula, the results are not true stress values because of the high magnitude of shear stresses involved. Also, at large deflections the bending causes deviation from true stress values that is not accounted for by the simple beam formula. This test method provides a useful, reproducible method of comparing strength among grades.

Various cross sections and center distances are in use. One practice recommended by a large portion of the industry specifies specimen dimensions of 0.200 by 0.250 in. and a distance between centers of 9/16 in. (ASTM B406).

Compressive Strength

Compressive strength may be determined according to the practice recommended to ASTM by the Cemented Carbide Producers Assoc., Specification CCPA P-104. The effect of cobalt content on compressive strength for the

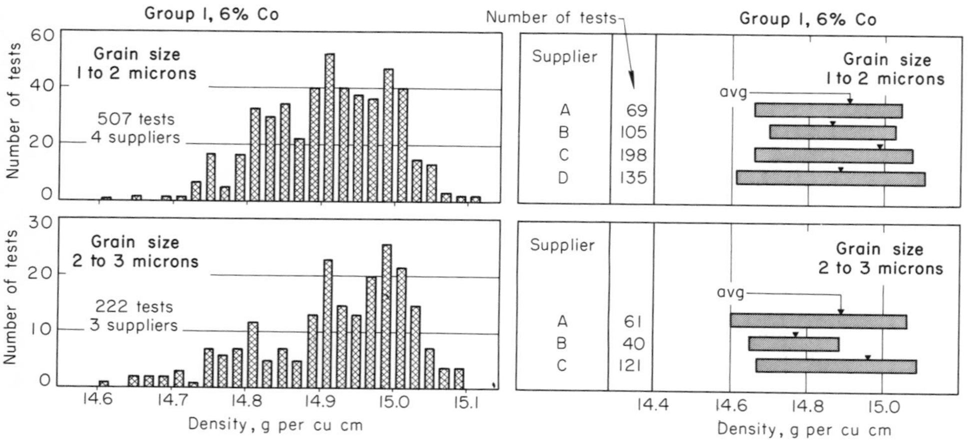

Fig. 5. Distribution of density in seven commercial grades of group 1 carbide. Measurements are the inspection results of one user. Density was measured in accordance with ASTM B311.

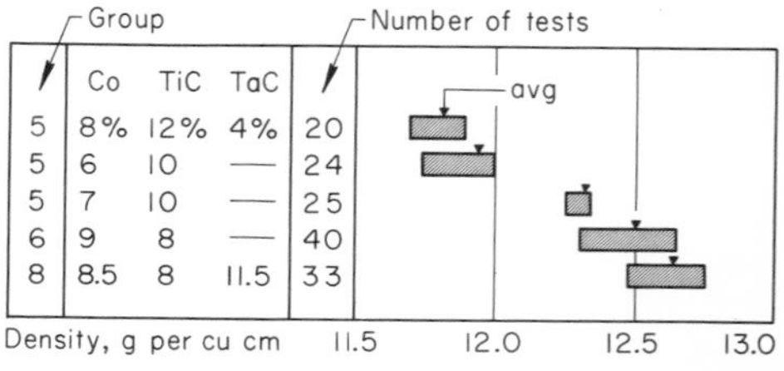

Fig. 6. Ranges of density for five carbide grades used for cutting steel. Incoming inspection measurements by two users.

straight tungsten carbide grades is illustrated in Fig. 8. The compressive strength and elastic limit in compression for most of the carbide groups are listed in Table 3. The decrease in modulus with increasing cobalt content is illustrated in Fig. 8.

Compressive strength values reported in Fig. 8 and Table 3 are, in most instances, the average of three readings taken at one time on three samples ⅜ in. in diameter and 1 in. long. There is obviously some disagreement relative to the effect of cobalt between Fig. 8 and Table 3. Several variables, including the exact composition of the carbide, may contribute to this discrepancy, but the difference is attributed mainly to an insufficient number of tests.

Data from one laboratory show the following cobalt – compressive strength relationship (average of three tests):

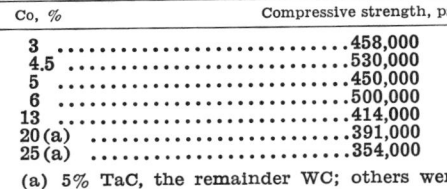

Co, %	Compressive strength, psi
3	458,000
4.5	530,000
5	450,000
6	500,000
13	414,000
20 (a)	391,000
25 (a)	354,000

(a) 5% TaC, the remainder WC; others were WC only with Co.

These data are in approximate agreement with those given in Fig. 8, although more tests would undoubtedly show a considerable spread in values.

Microstructure

Microstructure affects hardness and strength. The size of the carbide particles (grains), their distribution and porosity, and the quality of bond between cobalt and carbide crystals are influential factors. The effect of grain size on hardness was shown in Fig. 2.

Increasing tungsten carbide grain size lowers the hardness because the cobalt "lakes", which are interspersed between grains, are also larger. The ideal structure for high-strength carbides is one of small carbide grains separated by the thinnest possible layer of auxiliary binder. One experimental study has shown the transverse rupture strength to be a maximum when the average distance between carbide particles is in the range of 0.3 to 0.6 microns (12 to 24 micro-in.).

Titanium and tungsten form a double carbide, and about 35 to 50% of the double carbide is desirable for tools made from grades having a minimum of 10 to 15% TiC. The amount of double carbide is proportional to sintering time and temperature. Hardness and density increase, and porosity decreases with prolonged sintering.

A magnification of 1500× is used for microscopic examination and identification of carbide particles. At this magnification WC and TaC crystals are easily identified. The double carbide of TiC with WC is more difficult to distinguish. Polished carbide surfaces are etched in a one-to-one solution of 10% potassium ferrocyanide and 10% potassium hydroxide in water at room temperature.

Heat tinting is another method used to identify the types of carbides. The polished surface is etched with a Na_2CO_3 solution and then heated to 900 F, to give the individual carbides a

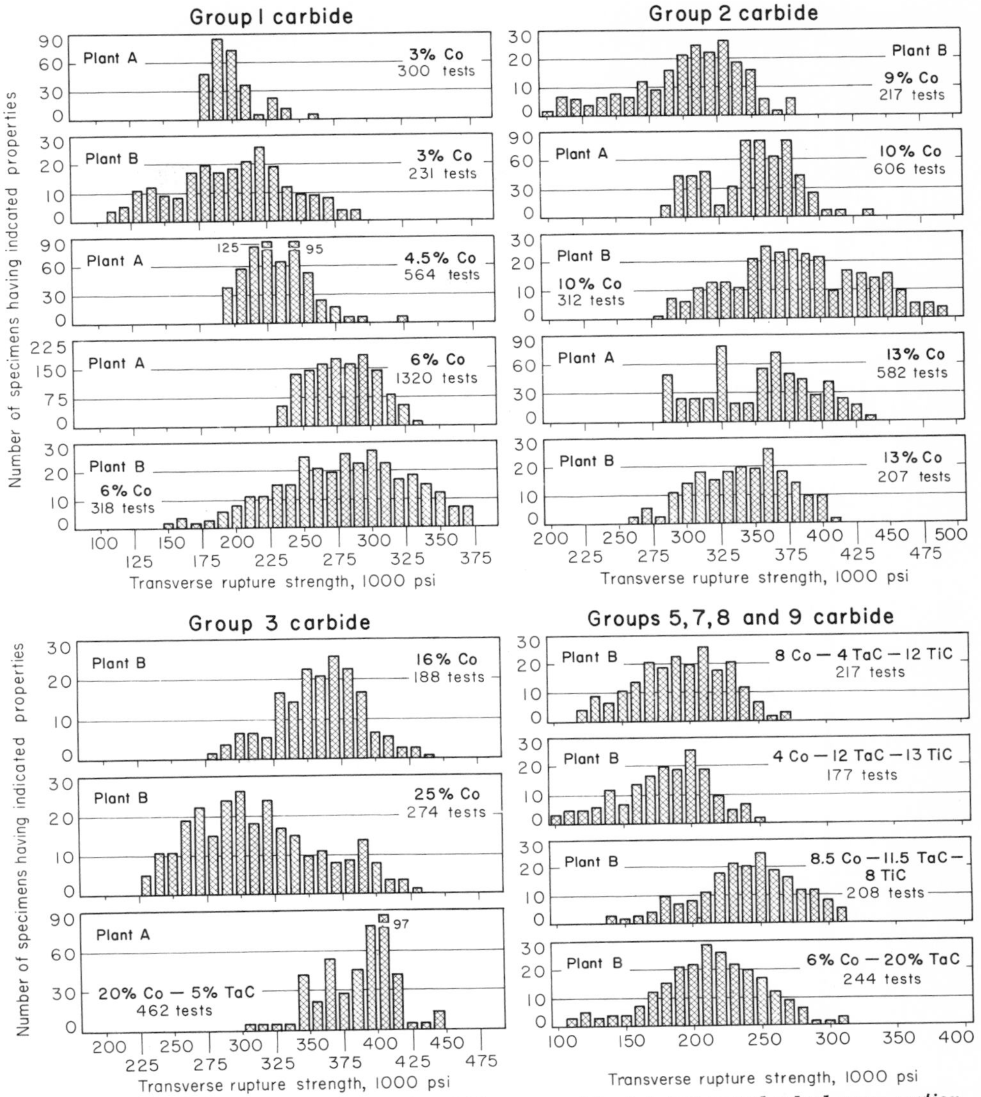

Fig. 7. Transverse rupture strength of carbide groups. Plant A test samples had cross section of 0.2 by 0.4 in. and support distance between centers of 9⁄16 in. Plant B test samples, ¾ in. long, had a cross section of 0.2 by 0.375 in. and support distance between centers of 9⁄16 in.

Table 3. Typical Physical and Compressive Mechanical Properties of Sintered Carbides

	Measured in compression								
Carbide group	Compressive strength, psi	Elastic limit, psi	Modulus of elasticity, million psi	Poisson's ratio	Ductility, %	Impact strength, ft-lb (a)	Fatigue limit, 1000 psi (b)	Coefficient of thermal expansion (c)	Electrical resistivity at 20 C, microhm-cm
1 (3% Co)	615,000	500,000	105	0.24	0.60	...	...	...	21.3
1 (6% Co)	614,000	286,000	105	0.28	0.85	0.73	95	5.0	...
2 (10% Co) ...	600,000	125,000	87	0.20	1.90	1.10 (d)	105 (d)	5.9 (d)	19.6 (d)
3 (16% Co) ...	545,000	95,000	76	0.22	2.70	1.75 (e)	...	...	29.2 (e)
5	625,000	230,000	78	0.22	1.00	0.60	90	...	...
6	533,000	97,000	80	0.22	2.00	0.40	90	6.8	...
7	635,000	173,000	82	0.21	0.90	...	...	...	...
8	631,000	250,000	81	0.22	1.00	0.60	85	6.00	...
9	705,000	240,000	86	0.22	1.70	0.60	85	6.00	...

(a) Values for impact strength are from unnotched specimens in sections approximately ¼ in. square. (b) Values for fatigue limit are based on 20,000,000 cycles of stress, for specimens of the R. R. Moore rotating-beam type. (c) Average coefficient of thermal expansion for the range 20 to 700 C (68 to 1290 F), in microinches per inch per °C. (d) 13% Co. (e) 20% Co.

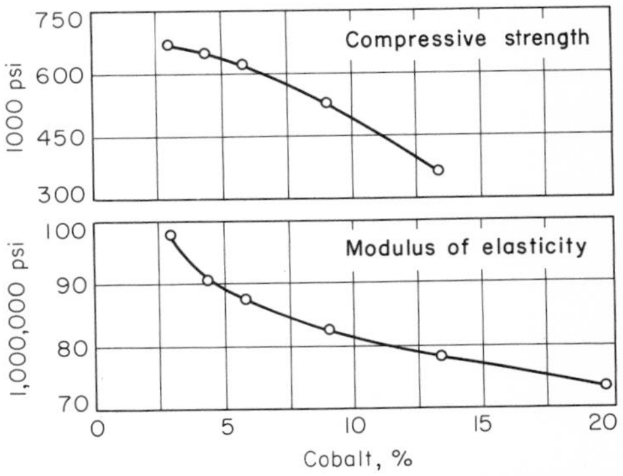

Fig. 8. Effect of cobalt on strength and modulus of sintered tungsten carbide

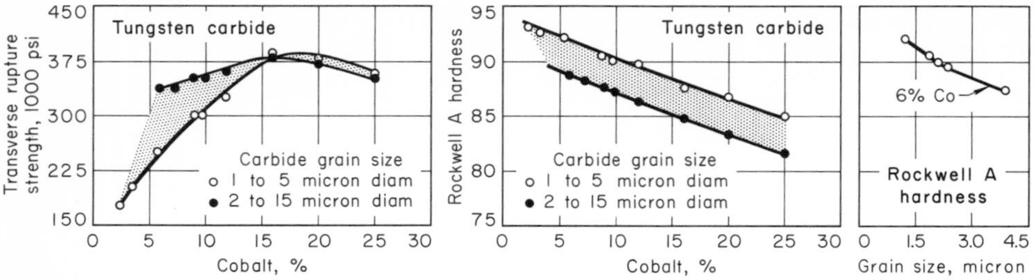

Fig. 9. Effect of cobalt content and carbide grain size on transverse rupture strength and hardness of straight tungsten carbide materials

characteristic yellow or orange color. Columbium carbide is most often used with tantalum carbide, and the two are difficult to separate by analytical or microscopic means.

The effect of grain size on properties is more pronounced in straight WC grades than in the other grades, which normally have coarser grain structures.

Figure 9 shows the effects of cobalt content and carbide grain size on transverse rupture strength and hardness of straight tungsten carbide grades.

Porosity is examined and rated at a magnification of 200×. The method of evaluating and classifying porosity is shown in ASTM B276. The *type* of porosity is classified as A, B or C. Type A designates porosity up to 10 microns diameter; type B from 10 to 40 microns; and type C includes porosity resulting from uncombined or excess carbon. Increasing *amounts* of porosity of each type are designated by numbers from 1 to 6. The results of 912 examinations on seven different grades of group 1 carbide are shown in Fig. 10.

Properties Shown in Table 3

Modulus of elasticity and Poisson's ratio are shown in Table 3, as well as some impact, fatigue, thermal expansion, and electrical resistivity values.

A carbide structural element will deflect only 33 to 40% as much as a similar steel one under the same loading conditions, because of the high modulus of elasticity of carbide. Thus carbides are valuable materials when stiffness is required, as in boring bars for use when hole dimensions impose rigid space limitations. The fact that a carbide section will not deflect as much as a steel one, under the same load, should be considered when composite carbide and steel assemblies are being designed. If this difference is not taken into account, the carbide insert may crack because of lack of stiffness in the steel support. The carbide section should be able to sustain the load placed upon it without exceeding its elastic limit. Under a heavy localized load, the steel support in the composite member must be designed for enough stiffness to carry about three times the load it is actually called upon to support, to make sure its deflection will match that of the sintered carbide.

The thermal expansion of carbide is about one third to one half that of steel, an important factor when carbide parts are attached to steel either mechanically or by brazing. If compressive loads are not excessive, shims of copper are inserted between the carbide and steel to supply a low-strength cushion that will yield and distribute stresses.

Tungsten carbide and the addition carbides exhibit properties that are largely metallic. The melting point ranges from 5000 to 7000 F. Electrical and heat conductivity and optical reflectivity are in the same range as for metals.

Standardization of Test Methods. Testing methods for hardness, density, transverse rupture, and porosity have been referred to in the earlier sections on these subjects. Other properties for which recommended procedures have been tentatively agreed upon by a majority of the industry, include compressive strength, modulus of elasticity, Poisson's ratio, thermal expansion, electrical resistivity, and metallographic methods.

Methods recommended by the Cemented Carbide Producers Assoc. for determining properties of carbides are covered by the following designations:

Density P-101
Poisson's ratio P-105
Compressive strength P-104
Transverse rupture strength P-102
Microstructure M-202
Apparent porosity M-201
Modulus of elasticity P-106

Carbides Other Than Tungsten Base

Recent developments include the use of metal carbides other than tungsten, of which the most prevalent are the carbides of titanium and chromium, with nickel or a nickel-base alloy as the binder metal. These materials are sometimes referred to as "cermets". (The term cermet would be as appropriate for the conventional WC-Co system as for TiC-Ni; both are produced by sintering a carbide with a metal.)

The TiC-Ni materials fall into several categories of end products, some of which overlap the common uses of WC-Co grades. In the most common type, the hard phase is predominantly titanium carbide with chromium carbide additions and 30 to 70% of nickel or nickel alloy binder. These grades combine high resistance to oxidation, high hardness, resistance to thermal shock, relatively low density, and good creep rupture properties for the temperatures involved (1800 to 2200 F). The greater solid solubility of the carbide in the nickel alloy results in a binder phase of low ductility having markedly lower impact values than WC-Co material. These range from 1 to 12 ft-lb when tested with a 0.394 by 0.394 by 2.165-in. unnotched impact specimen.

These materials, having a binder content of 30 to 70%, are generally used for tools or components other than cutting tools where high-temperature abrasion resistance is the primary objective.

Hardness and transverse rupture strength of these grades are given in Fig. 11, which shows that decreasing amounts of the nickel binder increase the rupture strength.

However, a second category of the so-called cermets contains the same basic ingredients as the above, but the binder content is generally less than 20%. These materials have been applied to cutting both steel and cast iron, particularly in finishing operations at high speed with medium to light chip loads. They are usually produced for mechanical attachment to the shank, but may be brazed to it.

Cutting Tools

More carbides are consumed for metal cutting than for any other type of application. Because of their ability to retain a sharp cutting edge, the straight tungsten carbide grades of group 1 are virtually the only tool material used to cut abrasive materials such as fiber glass and phenolic resins. Carbides of group 1, which have the highest hardness, are also being used for production cutting of white cast iron at Rockwell C 60. Thus, the straight WC grades serve for both extremes of the metal-cutting range, as defined by the type of chip produced in the machining operation. The steel-cutting grades containing TiC and TaC occupy an intermediate position; the steel chips have ductility and abrasive properties between the extremes encountered in machining practice.

The straight tungsten carbides are less suitable for machining steel, or grades of cast iron (chiefly pearlitic and martensitic malleable and nodular irons) that give a brittle chip, because the ductility and strength of these chips cause a severe wiping action along the top surface of the tool. Rapid cratering results in a sharper-angled cutting edge, and the extremely wear-resistant but relatively brittle thin edge fails by minute chipping. Grades of groups 4 to 8 are applied on the ba-

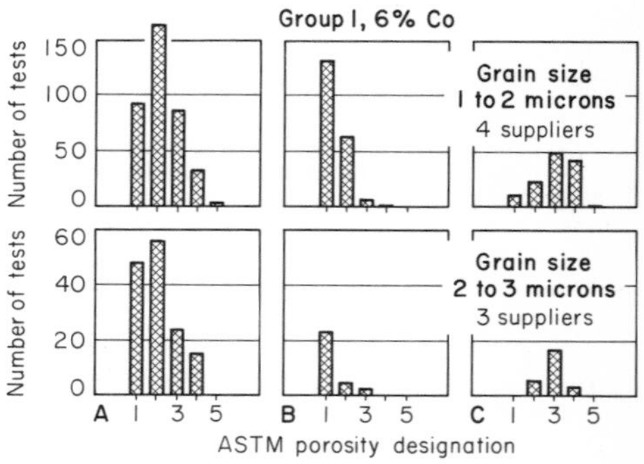

Data are summarized from the inspection records of one user. For the specific applications involved, the carbides were subject to rejection as follows: C-type porosity of C-3 or greater, B-type porosity of B-3 or greater, and A-type porosity of A-5.

Fig. 10. Porosity ratings for 912 samples of seven carbide grades from group 1

sis of their resistance to cratering; grades of group 5 are the most widely used.

The application of carbides in groups 4 to 8 differs in different plants. One specific plant prefers grades of group 4 for high-speed light finishing cuts on steel, group 5 for medium-speed medium-cutting of steel, and group 6 for slow to medium roughing cuts on steel. Grades of group 7 are used for special turning operations such as machining uranium, and group 8 is used more for applications other than cutting tools where a minimum of porosity is required, as for precision gage blocks.

There is also a divergence of opinion on the use of TiC and TaC grades, especially for high-temperature requirements. A choice between the two is frequently resolved on the basis of cost; the TiC grades are cheaper.

Recognition of the opposing nature of cutting tool properties (resistance to edge wear versus resistance to cratering) is the basis for selection of carbide tools; resistance to cratering is gained at the expense of edge wear. Most metal-cutting applications involve a compromise between these two factors, with the hardest grade that will not chip or break being selected.

The reasons for the improved resistance to cratering of TiC and TaC carbides are not well defined. Below a critical temperature range, temperature has only a minor effect on wear. Within the sensitive range, temperature is important because it affects the rates of adhesion and diffusion. The critical temperature for a particular grade depends on both the composition of the work material and the composition of the carbide tool, because both contribute material to the diffusion interface.

The hot abrasion resistance of this interface is the determining factor in wear life, rather than the hot hardness of the carbide in the as-received condition. For instance, group 1 carbide at 1400 F has a hardness of Rockwell A 85, while group 5 at the same temperature has Rockwell A 81.5. Yet the harder group 1 carbide will fail by cratering at speeds where the softer group 5 carbide will perform satisfactorily.

Columbium carbide is utilized in about one fifth of the steel-cutting grades. It is present in group 9 grades in amounts of 0.75 to 2%. In groups 5 and 8, 1.75 to 2.50% CbC is present. Columbium carbide appears to impart essentially the same properties as TaC.

Figure 12 illustrates cutting temperatures in machining 52100 steel with a group 5 carbide.

Full advantage of carbide tooling for metal-cutting operations can be gained only by selecting the grade that has the best combination of properties for the specific conditions. For example, carbide may have a high modulus of elasticity but exhibit little ability to undergo plastic deformation. The material supporting them must have adequate section to provide the assembly with enough stiffness to withstand high localized stresses occurring when heavy cuts are taken. Carbide grades having a hardness of Rockwell A 90 to 91.5 and a transverse rupture strength above 275,000 psi are usually recommended for heavy-duty cutting. Tool failure by thermal cracking is prevalent in rough cutting with carbide. If cracking prevails it is advisable to use a grade having a lower titanium and tantalum content. Higher cutting speeds require harder and more crater-resistant grades. These grades can be effectively used for rough machining if mechanically held inserts and lighter chip loads are employed. Table 4 lists carbide grades that have been found the most satisfactory in one plant for single-point turning under the conditions stated.

For specific examples and comparisons of the performance of sintered carbide tools with high speed steel and cast cobalt-base alloy tools, see the article "Selection of Material for Cutting Tools", beginning on page 325.

Brazed vs Disposable Tips. As a rule only extremely small cutting tools are made from solid carbide. Most tools are made by attaching carbide tips to alloy steel bodies either by brazing or by mechanical means. Where space permits, the latter method is usually preferred and is becoming more widely used.

When a tip is brazed to the body or holder, the tool must be removed from the machine for sharpening. After the tool has been resharpened to the extent that it can no longer be used, it must be removed and replaced. As a rule, under these conditions only one or two edges of the tip can be used.

In contrast, when the tip is mechanically secured in the holder, it can be loosened and turned or indexed to the next cutting edge without removing the tool from the machine. With this procedure, the six or eight cutting edges (depending on whether the carbide tip is triangular or square) can be used before the carbide insert is reground or discarded. After all edges have been used, common practice is to discard the carbide tip because it is less expensive to replace than to recondition it by grinding. Therefore, the

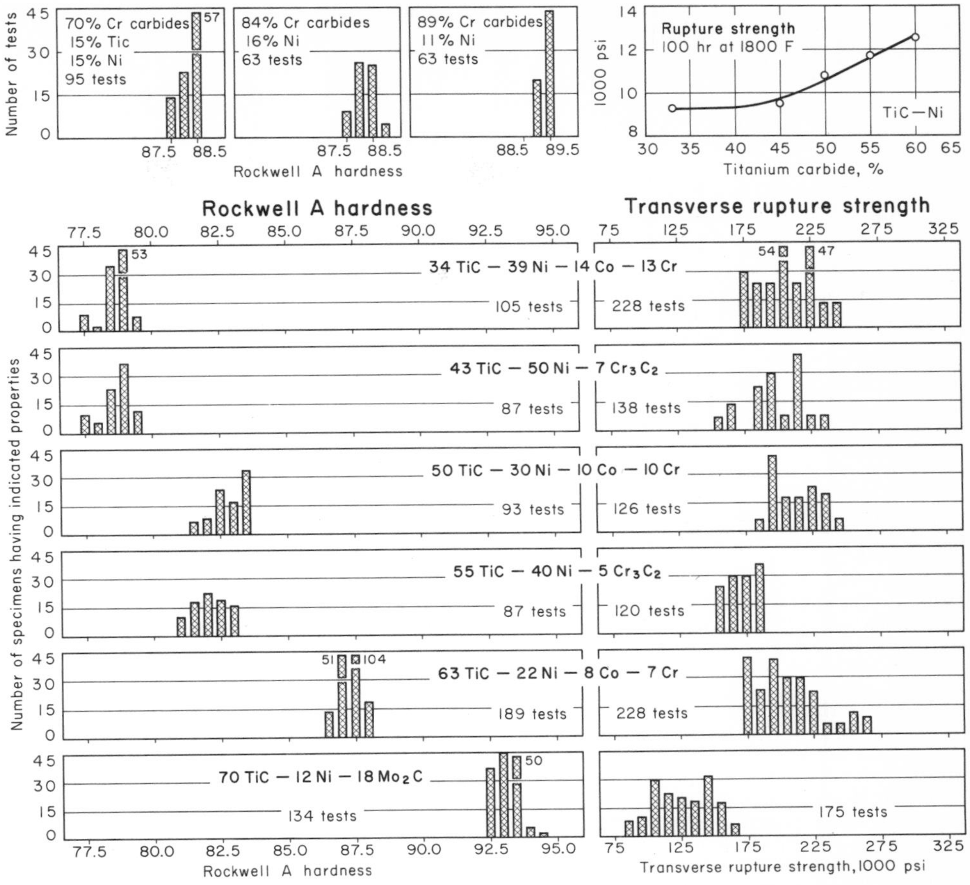

Fig. 11. Properties of commercial sintered materials composed of carbides other than tungsten and a binder phase other than cobalt

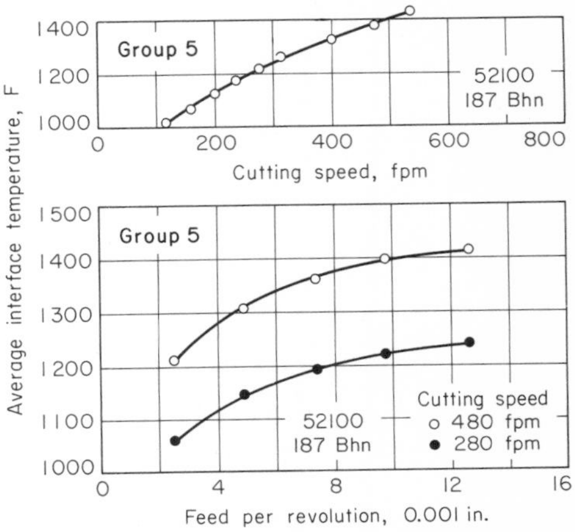

Tool shape: 0°, −2°, 7°, 7°, 8°, 0°, 3/64 in. (See Fig. 2, page 3 and Table 1, page 4 for explanation.) Effect of speed is for depth of cut of 0.102 in. at a feed rate of 0.0098 in. per revolution.

Fig. 12. Effect of speed and feed on tool interface temperature in single-point turning operations

Table 4. Typical Use of Carbides for Turning

Carbide group	Cutting conditions: Speed, sfm	Cutting conditions: Feed, ipr	Cutting conditions: Depth, in. (max)	Application
6	125 to 300(a)	0.030 to 0.072	1.125	Heavy turning of steel forgings and bar stock
5(b)	250 to 400	0.018 to 0.033	0.750	General turning of steel forgings and bar stock
1(c)	40 to 80	0.012 to 0.027	0.750	Turning cast steel and chilled rolls
1	150 to 300	0.018 to 0.040	1.000	Rough turning of cast iron

(a) Cast cobalt-chromium-tungsten alloy tools are recommended for cutting speeds below 100 sfm on heavy steel forgings or bar stock. (b) A harder grade of carbide should be used if excessive cratering occurs. (c) Bordering on carbide group 2.

term *disposable* carbide tip or insert has come into common usage.

In addition to the economic advantage of the mechanically secured carbide tip, the hazard of damage to the insert by brazing is eliminated.

Sharpening of Carbide Tools

The high hardness of carbide limits the number of materials that can effectively grind the surface; thus the shaping and reconditioning of carbide tools is an expensive procedure. In one test of grinding wheels, using 1.0 as the grinding rate of aluminum oxide, silicon carbide ground the sintered carbide at 5.5 times that rate, boron 12 times, boron carbide 15 times, and diamond dust 25 times the rate of aluminum oxide.

Silicon carbide abrasives are used for roughing and semifinishing, and resinoid-bond diamond wheels for finishing. Grinding of the steel shanks to which the carbide is attached is best done with an aluminum oxide wheel.

Electrochemical grinding is a process that combines electrochemical and abrasive action. It is sometimes used where conventional grinding of carbide is costly or impractical. For more details of ECG, see page 281.

Ultrasonic machining does not directly use electric current for stock removal. Cutting is accomplished by abrasive action at high frequency and low amplitude and, unlike electrolytic processes, the ultrasonic technique cuts nonconducting as well as conducting materials. The cutting or grinding tool is vibrated in the frequency range of 19,000 to 25,000 cycles per second through an amplitude of not more than a few thousandths of an inch. The abrasive (usually boron carbide) is carried in water to the tool and workpiece. Aluminum oxide and silicon carbide have been used but do not last as long as boron carbide. Removal rates of 0.0035 cu in. per min have been achieved when machining tungsten carbide with 240-grit abrasive. An accuracy of ±0.001 with a surface finish of 30 micro-in. can be obtained. Surface finish can be improved to about 8 micro-in. with 800-grit abrasive, but metal removal is much slower. (For more details, see the article on page 249.)

Electrical discharge machining can be used for contour shaping of carbide blanks. For a description of this process, see the article on page 227.

Cost

The cost of sintered tungsten carbide is approximately $0.06 per gram, or $27.00 per pound (April 1967). Grades containing other carbides such as titanium and tantalum cost about 10% more than the straight tungsten grades. In April 1967, about 475 grades of carbide are commercially available.

To the user, the cost per unit of weight is of little interest because carbide for cutting tools is usually sold as specific shapes. In addition, the condition of finish in which they are supplied has a marked effect on cost. For example, disposable tips of C-2 carbide ground for use as cutting tools cost about $0.70 each for a 3/8 in. square 1/8 in. thick; $1.07 each for a 1/2 in. square 3/16 in. thick; and $1.75 each for a 3/4 in. square 3/16 in. thick. Grinding to precise shape often accounts for a major portion of the cost. For instance, utility ground or as-molded carbide tips, 3/8 in. square by 1/8 in. thick, cost only about $0.35 each. (For comparative costs of carbide and other tool materials, see the article that begins on page 325.)

Ceramic Materials for Single-Point Turning Tools

By ALAN G. KING AND W. M. WHEILDON*

CERAMIC tool materials are dense polycrystalline aggregates averaging two to five microns in grain size. They are based on alumina with the corundum crystal structure. Small amounts of other ceramic materials have been added, either to refine the grain structure or to promote sintering. Tool inserts or tips of ceramic materials are manufactured by either sintering or hot pressing. Their strength depends on alumina-alumina grain-boundary adhesion rather than on an alumina-cement-alumina bond.

The principal elevated-temperature properties of alumina are high hardness, chemical inertness, and resistance to wear. The high hardness and wear resistance of alumina are the main reasons for its use in machining cast iron and hardened steel at high cutting speeds. The high wear resistance also permits machining of long cylindrical surfaces without taper. The inertness of alumina to iron at high temperature prevents welding of the tool to steel or cast iron workpieces and contributes to the production of good surface finish. Ceramic tools are satisfactory for general machining of steel where there are no heavy interrupted cuts and where negative rakes can be used.

Table 1 lists some mechanical properties of ceramic and other cutting-tool materials. Figure 1 compares the relations of tool life to cutting speed for a ceramic, a grade C-8 carbide, and a TiC-Ni cermet in machining 81B45 steel and gray iron. The ceramic tool was much more wear-resistant than the carbide tool, but the tests did not consider fracture, which often occurs before development of a 0.020-in. wear land (the end point in the tests).

Some failures of ceramic tools are caused by fatigue. This has been substantiated by the performance of reground ceramic tools in cutting brake drums, where the tool life of refinished tool tips was substantially lower than that of the original tools.

Photomicrographs of polished sections of tools showed that the original land (0.006 in. by 60°) had worn to a rounded configuration on the flank. A number of cracks were seen in the wear land and in the crater area at the top. Similar sections were photographed with polarized light so that structural damage in these areas could be studied. Fatigue cracks showed in approximately the same positions as before. The greatest fatigue damage was in the crater area, with less damage just below the chamfer, where wear was maximum.

The relation of hardness to temperature of several cutting-tool materials is shown in Fig. 2. Because the temperature at the tool edge increases with cutting speed, ceramic can function at higher speeds than other materials.

Chemical reactions between the tool and the workpiece cause shorter tool life by accelerated wear. Such reactions depend on chemical affinity and temperature. Aluminum oxide is inert to iron, manganese, cobalt, carbon and nickel. Magnesium reduces alumina at about 1650 F, and tool wear can be rapid if temperatures in this range are reached. Beryllium and aluminum oxide form chrysoberyl ($BeO \cdot Al_2O_3$) at 3300 F. In machining, this mixed-oxide film would be continuously removed by abrasion, permitting further chemical reaction between clean work metal and the tool, thus accelerating tool wear.

Because of reaction and bonding between aluminum metal and aluminum oxide, and a slight reaction between titanium or zirconium and alumina at 2550 F, with corrosion developing at 2900 F, ceramics are not recommended for machining aluminum alloys, titanium, and zirconium.

*Mr. King is with Zirconium Corp. of America. Mr. Wheildon is with Refractories Div., Norton Co.

Vanadium, columbium, tantalum, chromium, molybdenum and tungsten do not react with alumina at temperatures up to 3300 F.

Speed and Feed

At slower cutting speeds, tool loads are markedly higher and ceramic tools are likely to chip or fracture because of their lower tensile strength. Hence ceramic tools should run at high speeds and use the strongest tool shapes.

The curves in Fig. 3 show that ceramics are much less affected by speed than are carbides. Data for these curves were obtained in machining soft steel with C-8 carbide and ceramic tools. At cutting speeds to the left of the intersection of the curves, carbides last longer; to the right of this point, ceramics show longer life.

As the cutting speed or the hardness of the work material increases, the feed and the ratio of feed to depth of cut become more important. Deeper cuts at lighter feed are better than lighter cuts at heavier feed. The feed rate for each job must be established by trial. Typical rates are 0.020 ipr for cast iron, 0.017 ipr for heat treated steel, and 0.021 ipr for soft steel.

Depth of cut usually depends on the amount of stock to be removed; cuts up to half the width of the insert should not shorten the life of a ceramic tool.

[Nominal speeds and feeds for rough and finish turning of carbon and low-alloy steels of various hardnesses with ceramic tools are given in Table 4, page 7 in this volume. Similar data for machining ferritic and martensitic stainless steels with ceramic tools are given in Table 5, page 378.]

Tool Design

Tool holders should be designed for greatest rigidity with least overhang. The tool holder should not extend beyond its support more than 1½ times the shank thickness, except for light cuts. Overhang of 50 to 100% of the toolholder thickness is recommended.

Mechanically clamped holders are best, because the tool can be set easily at a negative rake and the mechanical chip breaker can distribute the clamping forces equally. The chip breaker must be adjusted to prevent loosely curled chips from rubbing on the edge of the tool, causing premature failure.

Precision-ground carbide seats are necessary for proper support of ceramic tools. Some users lap the ceramic tip to the carbide seat for full contact.

An aluminum or other soft metal shim 0.001 to 0.004 in. thick between the tip and anvil can help extend tool life.

Cementing the ceramic tip to the steel shank with epoxy will do for certain light machining operations.

The usual brazing and soldering techniques are not satisfactory for ceramic tools, because of poor wettability between metal and ceramic under ordinary conditions. Because of thermal stress during brazing and use, a brazing or soldering medium must be soft enough to accommodate the different thermal expansion of the ceramic tip and steel shank and still be strong enough to resist machining force.

Table 1. Mechanical Properties of Tool Materials

Property	Ceramic	High speed steel	C-2 carbide
Transverse rupture strength, psi	90,000	500,000	230,000
Compressive strength, psi	500,000	600,000	650,000
Modulus of elasticity, psi	60×10^6	32×10^6	100×10^6
Microhardness, Rockwell A	93	85	92
Microhardness, Knoop 100	1780	740	1800

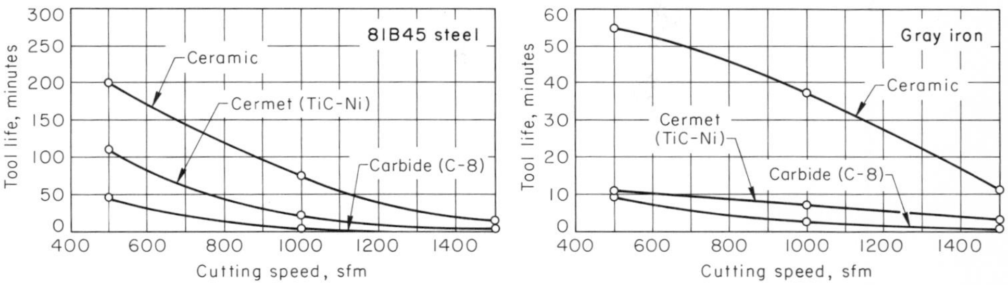

Depth of cut, 0.010 in.; feed, 0.005 ipr; side and back rakes, —5°; side and end cutting-edge angles, 15°. Tool-life criterion, 0.020-in. wear land. (Source: E. Krabacher and W. Haggerty, Performance Characteristics of Ceramic Tools in Turning and Milling, *ASTE Technical Paper* 145, 1958)

Fig. 1. Relation of tool life to cutting speed for ceramic, cermet and carbide tools

Table 2. General Range of Tool Angles and Nose Radii for Ceramic Tools

Work material	Side and back rake	End and side relief	Side cutting edge	End cutting edge	Nose radius, in.
Steel, to 200 Bhn	0 to —15°	2 to 10°	0 to 60°	5 to 20°	1/32 to 1/8
200 to 275 Bhn	0 to —15°	2 to 10°	0 to 60°	5 to 20°	1/32 to 1/8
275 to 350 Bhn	0 to —15°	2 to 10°	0 to 60°	5 to 20°	1/32 to 1/8
350 to 450 Bhn	5 to —10°	2 to 5°	0 to 60°	5 to 15°	1/32 to 1/16
450 to 600 Bhn	0 to —7°	2 to 5°	0 to 60°	5 to 15°	1/32 to 1/16
Cast iron	0 to —7°	2 to 10°	0 to 60°	5 to 20°	1/32 to 1/16
Nonmetallic	0 to 10°	6 to 18°	0 to 60°	5 to 20°	1/32 to 1/8

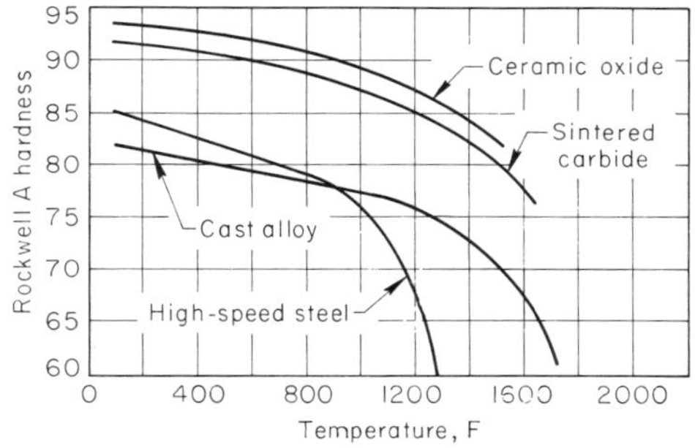

Fig. 2. Hardness as a function of temperature for various cutting-tool materials (Source of data: A. G. Metcalfe, Why Oxide Tools Can Cut Faster, American Machinist, *Dec 3, 1956)*

Tool Angles. A negative rake at the cutting edge for a distance at least equal to the feed per revolution is best for long tool life. From there on, the top of the tool may have positive or negative rake, depending on the chip control desired. The rake angle is usually built into the tool holder so that all cutting edges of a disposable insert may be used. Rake is usually a compromise between maximum edge strength and desired surface finish. With a decrease in the negative angle, strength decreases and finish improves. Ranges of tool angles are given in Table 2.

Side cutting-edge (lead) angles greater than 0° are desirable when the nature of the cut permits their use. Because edge pressure on ceramic tools is more critical than on carbides, a thin chip, which greatly extends the length of edge carrying the load, is an advantage. As much lead angle as the rigidity of the machine and workpiece will allow is usual. However, a large lead angle may push the work away from the tool, and for this reason large lead angles are not generally used on long slender workpieces.

Small (less than 10°) relief or clearance angles are desirable for maximum strength of the cutting edge.

The nose radius should be as large as possible without causing chatter. A sharp nose causes less vibration, but too small a nose radius can cause chipping of the tool.

A large nose radius is good because it acts like an increased lead angle for more gradual cutting but larger nose radii require more power and may cause chatter.

Tests in turning steel have indicated that a nose radius of 0.040 to 0.060 in. produces the least radial tool wear, with smooth finish. Further increase in nose radius increased radial tool wear. At increased surface speed, the smaller radii were vulnerable to cracking.

A narrow negative land honed onto the cutting edge of a tool substantially decreases the probability of fracture

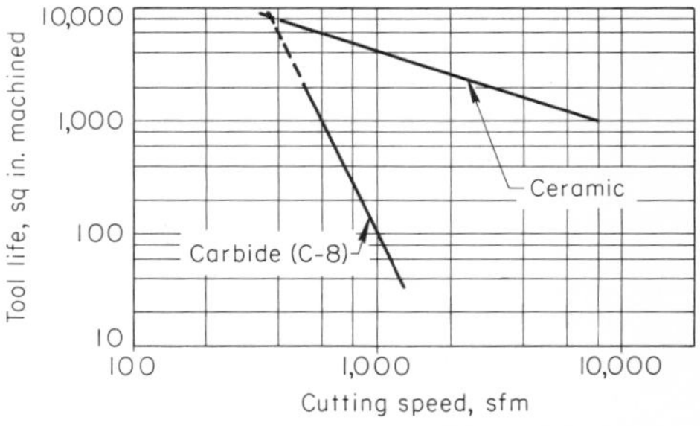

Fig. 3. Effect of cutting speed on tool life of ceramic and carbide tools in machining soft steel (Source: L. Fersing, Ceramic Tool Research, Production, *Sept 1958)*

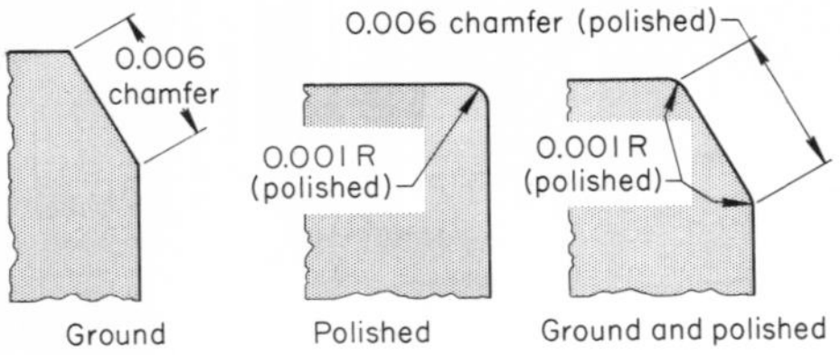

Fig. 4. Cutting-edge profiles of ceramic tools. See text for discussion.

of the tool tip. Edge lands generally are used for machining cast iron and for machining steel harder than Rockwell C 40, when feed is above 0.010 in. and depth of cut is more than 1/16 in.

A prehoned flat land width of 50 to 80% of the feed at an angle of 45° to 60° to the top tool surface, or a 0.005-in. radius made by tumbling, is generally satisfactory. Hand honing of the cutting edge improves tool life.

Tests have been made of the edge profiles shown in Fig. 4. Tools with ground and chemically polished chamfer showed a threefold increase in tool life over those with the ground chamfer, whereas the 0.001-in.-radius polished land had a tool life 30% less than that of the ground chamfer. The increase in tool life could not be attributed to either the edge profile or the chemical polish alone, but was a result of the combination of increased strength caused by polishing and the more satisfactory distribution of stress because of edge contour. The chamfer edge duplicated edge wear on a number of tools after short use and did not increase appreciably during the life of the tool.

Applications of Ceramic Tools

Ceramic tools are used successfully in a variety of turning operations. Significant expansion in the use of ceramics will require more machines that can operate routinely at the higher range of speeds where ceramic tools are most efficient. It will also be necessary to reconsider tool engineering on each job, or each type of job, where ceramic replaces another tool material.

Performance data of a ceramic tool machining transmission gears of 5135 steel at 170 to 207 Bhn are given in Table 3. As shown, cutting speed for the ceramic was twice that of carbide for the same feed and depth of cut, and production was increased 50% with four times the tool life.

In another application, a high-speed lathe designed for operation with ceramic tools was used to machine an artillery part 3.5 in. in diameter of 5135 steel at a hardness of 320 Bhn. Comparing previous production performance using carbide tools in a good but less complicated machine tool, the ceramic tools showed an increase in tool life from 80 to 270 pieces per insert and a decrease in cycle time from 0.48 to 0.10 min for the rough turning and facing operations. Speed and feed for the carbide and ceramic tools were 375 and 1100 rpm, and 0.008 and 0.013 ipr, respectively. Depth of cut for both tools was 0.020 to 0.048 in.

The same machine tools were used to finish turn and face, and to bore and chamfer the part in a second setup. Cycle time for machining with ceramic tools was 0.17 min, which was one third that required for carbide cutters. Ceramic tool life for turning and facing was 133 pieces per insert, and 532 pieces per insert for boring. The high-speed lathe had precision spindle bearings and a 60-hp motor capable of the rapid accelerations necessary for high-speed production work.

Table 3. Turning 5135 Steel at 170 to 207 Bhn With Ceramic Tools

Speed	970 sfm
Feed	0.013 ipr
Depth of cut	0.025 in.
Tool life per grind	1200 pieces
Tool life	4 × carbide
Cutting speed	2 × carbide
Production rate	1½ × carbide

The negligible effect of cutting speed on ceramic tool life or cost is most evident in facing cuts, with high speeds on the outside and low speeds near the center. When facing with carbide (Fig. 5a) the instantaneous total cost varies as the tool cuts on a decreasing diameter and at decreasing surface speed; cost goes through the minimum and up the other side of the curve. When using ceramic, cost is almost independent of cutting speed above a certain point, as illustrated in Fig. 5(b).

The cost of ceramic inserts is about twice that of precision-ground carbide inserts of the same size, as indicated in Table 7 on page 336.

An example of cost relations is the finish facing of a cylinder head of class 35 gray iron, 18.187-in. OD by 2.687-in. ID, with oval cutouts near the outside diameter. Facing caused a marked change in surface speed, depending on the diameter. Interrupted cuts occurred at the holes. Data for machining this part with carbide and ceramic tools are given in Table 4.

High stock removal from low-alloy gray iron (285 Bhn) is shown in the right-hand columns of Table 4. Ceramic tools were used for both the rough and finish cuts in a 50-hp turret lathe. The same feed and depth of cut were used for both carbide and ceramic tools, but the cutting speed and metal-removal rate for the ceramic tools were six times those of carbide.

Many nonferrous metals and nonmetallics can be machined with ceramic tools, success depending on the affinity of the work material for aluminum oxide. Table 5 summarizes general applicability for eleven nonferrous and nonmetallic materials.

Heat-resisting alloys may be grouped into two categories on the basis of their machinability:

1 Hard cobalt-base alloys and all series 400 stainless steels
2 Softer, work-hardening stainless steels and nickel-base alloys.

Alloys in the first group machine well with ceramic tools. Negative rake angles, large lead angles and large nose radii are recommended. Most carbides chip or wear excessively with this group of metals. Alloys in the second group are gummy and have high shear strength that requires positive tool angles in a strong tool material. Ceramic tools are not suited for these alloys.

Table 5. Machining Nonferrous and Nonmetallic Materials With Ceramic Tools

Material	Usual speed, sfm	Tool life
Carbon (graphite)	200 to 1000	Excellent
Tungsten	150 to 800	Excellent
Copper	600 to 2000	Excellent
Co-Cr-W alloy	60 to 140	Excellent
Brass	To 3000	Good
Bronze	To 3000	Good
Molybdenum	500 to 800	Fair
Titanium	Not recommended	Poor
Aluminum bronze	Not recommended	Poor
Plastics	300 to 3000	Good
Hard rubber	To 1000	Excellent

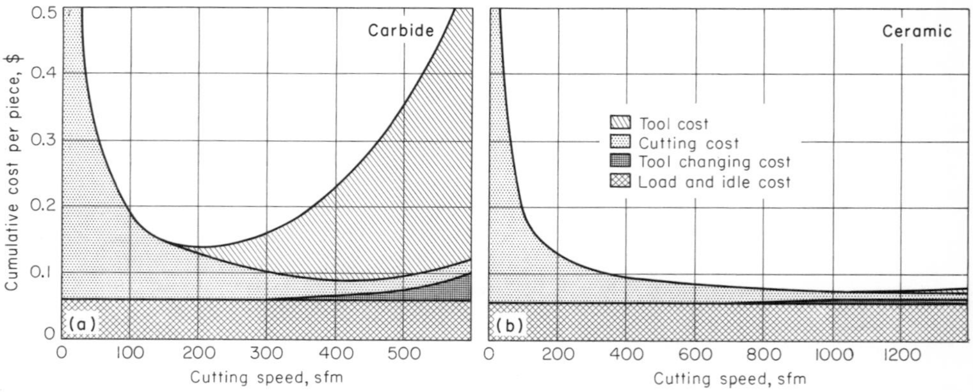

Fig. 5. Cost allocation versus cutting speed for carbide and ceramic tools (Source: A. O. Schmidt, J. R. Roubik, J. J. Lonergan and G. Hug, Comparative Carbide and Ceramic Milling Tests, ASME Paper *62-PROD-8; 1962)*

Table 4. Turning and Facing Gray Iron Parts With Carbide vs Ceramic Tools

	Part A		Part B	
	Carbide	Ceramic	Carbide	Ceramic
Speed, rpm	67	300	256	1547
Speed, sfm	46; 316(a)	210; 1418(a)	70	422
Feed, ipr	0.015	0.010	0.023; 0.006(b)	0.023; 0.006(b)
Depth of cut, in.	0.010	0.010	⅜ max	⅜ max
Time per piece, minutes	7.71	2.4	11.2	1.86
Tool life per edge, pieces	12	100	3 to 4	3 to 4
Stock removal, in.^{3}/min	....	....	22	133

(a) Minimum and maximum surface speeds. (b) Roughing and finishing cuts, respectively.

Selection of Material for Cutting Tools

*By the ASM Committee on Cutting Tools**

CUTTING TOOL MATERIALS most widely used for production machining are: high speed steel, cast cobalt-chromium-tungsten alloy, and sintered carbide. Tool steels of lower alloy content than high speed steel are seldom used in sustained production. Because of high initial cost, diamond tools are restricted to highly specialized work. "Ceramic" (aluminum oxide) tools and "cermets" are also in limited use.

High Speed Steel

Compared with carbide or cast cobalt-chromium-base alloy, high speed steel has greater resistance to shock, even when fully hardened, is readily shaped by forging and machining, and is available in a greater number of forms. For these reasons high speed steel is the preferred cutting tool material for a variety of metal-cutting operations and is applicable to every metal-cutting operation. However, except for short runs, carbide or cast alloy tools cost less per piece machined in most metal-cutting operations. Exceptions are drills, taps and large broaches.

Nominal composition and base price for 33 high speed steels are listed in Table 1 in the article "High Speed Steel for Cutting Tools", page 312. Table 3 in that article indicates relative quantities produced.

Choice of Grade. High hardness (above Rockwell C 50) at a temperature of 1000 F is a property common to all grades of high speed steel, although there is some variation depending on composition. Hardness of T1, M2 and M4 high speed steels at elevated temperatures is shown in Fig. 1. The three steels have nearly the same hardness up to about 1050 F, beyond which T1 steel is harder than the others.

Four grades, T1, M1, M2 and M10, closely similar in performance, make up a high percentage of the general-purpose high speed steel used for tools. The latter three grades have the lowest base price. T1 costs about 50% more than the average of the other three, although less than the higher-alloy M types. These four grades are the most readily available from warehouse stock and after recommended heat treatments are the toughest of the high speed steels. In the absence of experience with a specific application, it is advisable to select one of these grades and then to determine by tool performance whether the higher hot hardness or greater wear resistance of a more costly grade is required.

From 5 to 12% cobalt is present in certain high speed steels, for increased red hardness. The cobalt-containing steels cost more than the four high-volume grades, and are more difficult to machine, heat treat, and grind. For example, M2 can be hardened to Rockwell C 65 by heating to 2250 F, air cooling and tempering twice for 2 hr at 1050 F, with no special precautions during the tempering cycles. However, M6, which contains 12% cobalt, is more susceptible to surface decarburization, and a carefully controlled furnace atmosphere is required. Tempering also is critical. To prevent cracking, tools made of M6 must be heated slowly to 1050 F and cooled in the furnace no faster than 50 F per hr for the first tempering operation. This will increase heat treating costs measurably and must be considered when the use of such steel is contemplated. No special precautions are necessary in the second tempering cycle.

All high speed steels contain between 1 and 5% vanadium. As vanadium is increased, carbon is usually increased by at least 0.10% carbon for each 1.00% vanadium except when other alloy adjustments have been made. This results in free particles of vanadium carbide, the hardest carbide found in high speed steel (2400 Knoop). Vanadium carbide increases the resistance of the high speed steel to abrasion and may significantly increase tool life in some operations. However, vanadium carbide causes difficulty in tool grinding, and the cost of grinding equipment and labor often offsets the advantage of increased tool life.

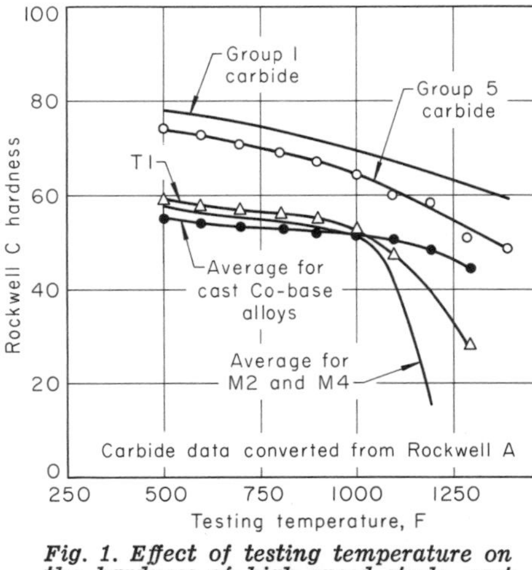

Fig. 1. Effect of testing temperature on the hardness of high speed steels, cast cobalt-base alloys and sintered carbides

For example, fine-pitch taps made from T1 steel and used for machine tapping 4140 failed in a short time. A change to taps made from T3 and hardened to the same Rockwell C 64 resulted in variable performance; life of the T3 taps varied from one half to double that of the taps made from T1 steel. Crests of certain teeth on the T3 taps were found to be tempered in grinding so that the true hardness on the crests was as low as Rockwell C 35 (converted from Knoop). The difficulty and cost of manufacturing reliable taps from T3 made it impractical for this application.

For roll-turning or parting tools for cutting aluminum bronze or heat treated alloy steel at hardnesses above Rockwell C 40, maximum hot hardness and abrasion resistance of the tool is required; for such applications one of the more highly alloyed grades such as T15 might be suitable. However, high initial cost and the increased cost of fabrication may make the use of these grades impractical. The cobalt-containing steels are also more brittle than the general-purpose types and require better support in the tool holder.

Molybdenum vs Tungsten Grades. Molybdenum grades of high speed steel are generally preferred because their initial cost is at least 30% less than that of their tungsten counterparts. Cost of fabricating and heat treating is about the same.

There is no technical reason for recommending a comparable grade of a tungsten high speed steel over a molybdenum grade, or vice versa. The important properties of hot hardness, abrasion resistance and toughness are the same. Extensive laboratory studies and production comparisons do not establish any consistent superiority for comparable grades of the same group (for example, T1 as compared with M2). Response to heat treatment, machining and grinding are about the

*Paul C. Farren, *Chairman,* Metallurgist, Hartford Machine Screw Co.; C. W. Andrews, Metallurgist, Jones & Lamson Machine Co.; R. M. Cage, Resident Metallurgist, Chrysler Corp.; J. E. Epprecht, Chief Production Engineer, Propeller Div., Curtiss-Wright Corp.; J. G. Gantner, Head, Metallurgical Research, National Cash Register Co.

D. C. Goldberg, Westinghouse Electric Corp.; Larry Higgins, Ladish Co.; C. C. Hoffman, Chief Metallurgist, Columbus Plant, Timken Roller Bearing Co.; J. R. Kunkel, Underwood Corp.; W. E. Matthews, Superintendent, Mechanical Dept., Bethlehem Steel Co.; William McLaury, General Superintendent, Transmission Div., Clark Equipment Co.; Joseph F. Mikulski, Waterbury Plant, Vickers, Inc.

Robert M. Prouty, Metallurgical Engineer, New Departure Div., General Motors Corp.; R. F. Schaffer, Chief Metallurgist, Gardner-Denver Co.; Burton C. Schwertfager, Assistant Superintendent, Machine Shop, Ohio Steel Foundry Co.; George J. Shubat, Chief Metallurgist, Diamond Chain Co., Inc.

[This article is a condensation, with modifications, of the article beginning on page 671 in Volume 1 of this Handbook.]

same with nearly equal vanadium and cobalt contents. Molybdenum grades are more susceptible to decarburization during heat treatment than comparable tungsten grades, but with proper atmosphere control or salt baths this is seldom a decisive factor in selection.

Certain special-purpose steels in each group, namely T6, T7, T8, T15, and M6, M8, M35 and M36, have no close counterparts. The unique compositions, properties or prices of these steels make their selection logical for specific applications without competition from any grade in the opposite group. For example, T15 inserts in milling cutters are used to machine series 300 stainless steels when the speed and horsepower required for carbide tools are not available. In another instance T15 proved advantageous for the heavy, rough and intermittent cuts encountered in resinking impressions in prehardened forging die blocks. Both T1 and M2 were tried for these tools, but were unsuitable because they required frequent resharpening.

Data on comparative wear and service life of two molybdenum high speed steels and three tungsten high speed steels are given in the five examples that follow.

Examples 580 and 581. Wear of Molybdenum and Tungsten High Speed Steel Tools

Example 580 — Hobbing (Fig. 2). Comparative performance of M2 and M36 molybdenum high speed steel tools in hobbing hot rolled 1022 steel (137 to 159 Bhn) is shown in Fig. 2. The hobbing was done at a speed of 245 sfm and feed of 0.075 ipr. The cutting fluid used was a mineral-base oil.

The M36 tools gave greater hob life because of the increased hot hardness and wear resistance imparted by the 8% cobalt content. However, the M2 tools were more economical in cost per inch of cut (Fig. 2).

Example 581 — Shaving (Fig. 2). T1 and T2 high speed steel tools were used for shaving 0.125-in.-thick patented 1050 steel having a hardness of Rockwell C 30 to 32. Cutter life was compared on the basis of wear per 10,000 pieces, as shown in Fig. 2. Both tool steels were liquid nitrided for 4 hr at 1050 F to a surface hardness of Rockwell C 64 to 65. Cutting speed was 16.56 sfm at contact, 7.51 sfm at through point, and depth of cut was 0.020 in. A 1-to-3 mixture of base and quenching oil was used as the cutting fluid. The slight increase in the wear resistance of T2 did not justify its higher cost for this application.

Examples 582, 583 and 584. Comparative Tool Life of Molybdenum and Tungsten High Speed Steels

Example 582 — Drilling (Fig. 2). A general-purpose high speed steel, M2, and a super high speed steel, T4 with 5% cobalt, were used in drilling 1045 steel. Performance was based on the number of pieces per grind. The 100% increase in drill life per grind for the cobalt-containing steel paralleled the tool life results in the hobbing application described in Example 580 (Fig. 2).

Example 583 — Drilling (Fig. 2). Tool life and tool cost for drilling sintered 0.7% carbon steel parts with M2, T4 and T1 high speed steel drills are plotted in Fig. 2. The work metal had a density of 6.50 g per cu cm (83% theoretical density) and a hardness of Rockwell B 80 to 85. Drills were coated with black oxide and operated at a speed of 50 sfm and feed of 0.001 ipr. A water-soluble oil was used as the cutting fluid.

Differences among the three steels, based only on pieces per grind, were not significant. However, T4 was the most expensive on the basis of tool cost per 1000 holes. The lower cost of M2 drills compared with T1 was just enough to offset their slightly inferior performance so that cost per 1000 holes was the same for M2 and T1.

Example 584 — Slotting (Fig. 2). M2, T4 and T1 cutters were used in milling slots 0.060 in. wide and 0.375 in. deep in the same work metal discussed in Example 583. Black-oxide-coated cutters, 4 in. in diameter with 32 teeth, were operated at speeds of 190 to 240 rpm (200 to 250 sfm), and a feed of 0.001 ipt. Water-soluble oil was the cutting fluid.

T1 performed better than either M2 or the more highly alloyed T4. Although the difference in number of pieces per grind was not great, it resulted in a significant advantage in tool cost per piece. More than 50 tools of each of the three high speed steels were used in making this evaluation.

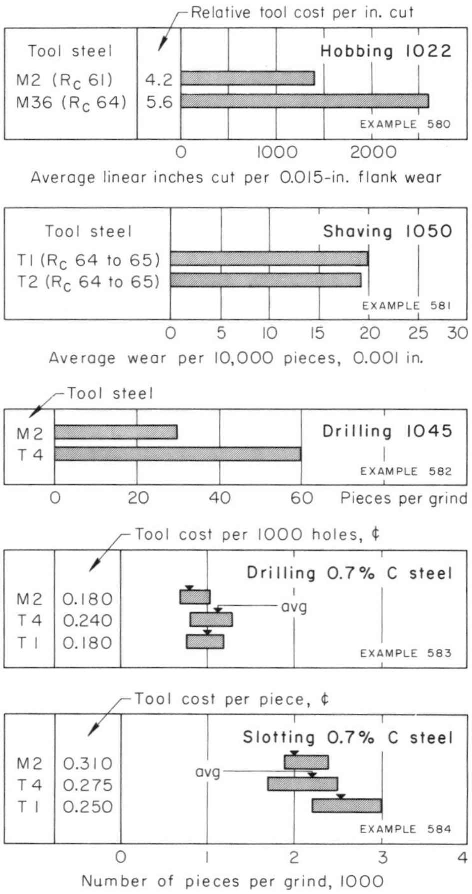

Fig. 2. Wear and life of high speed steel tools (Examples 580 to 584)

Surface treatments can increase the life of high speed steel tools. Any high speed steel tool may be coated with oxide either in an alkali-nitrate bath or by steam oxidizing. Both treatments are usually applied to finish-ground tools. Although these treatments do not increase hardness, they provide a film that prevents or minimizes adhesion of the tool to the workpiece, particularly in machining sticky materials such as non-free-cutting low-carbon steel or soft copper. Up to 100% increase in tool life has been achieved by using such coatings.

Plating high speed steel tools with 0.0001 to 0.0005 in. of hard chromium also prolongs their life by preventing adhesion of the tool to the workpiece. However, this treatment is not widely used, because of the cost and difficulty of plating and the danger of hydrogen embrittlement and subsequent cracking of the tools.

Nitriding increases life of a variety of shapes and compositions of high speed steel cutting tools. All types respond to nitriding. However, the ammonia-gas method has been successful only for specialized applications because it produces a case that is too brittle and may chip. Salt bath nitriding is cheaper and easier to control for the required light cases. This treatment increases both superficial hardness and resistance to adhesion.

In an evaluation of liquid nitrided tools and their unnitrided counterparts in one plant, nitriding was never detrimental. For single-point and form turning tools the difference in tool life varied from zero to 100% in machining annealed steels. A greater advantage of nitriding was reported for taps, drills and reamers used on similar steels. In a few instances nitrided taps excelled unnitrided taps by 700%, although the average increase in tool life was between 100 and 200%.

The moderate cost of nitriding can usually be justified on the basis of increased tool life but because the tools may require renitriding each time they are ground, the cost of handling and control is sometimes excessive. Some tools such as certain types of form tools need sharpening only on the cutting face and thus do not require nitriding after each grind.

Time in the liquid nitriding bath affects tool life. Data in Fig. 3 were obtained by nitriding shaving tools made of T1 at 1050 F for ½ to 4 hr. Machining details are given in Example 581.

Cast Alloy Tools

Cast cobalt-chromium-tungsten alloys for cutting tools are marketed as proprietary materials. The alloys usually contain 38 to 46% Co, 25 to 32% Cr, 10 to 20% W, and 1.50 to 2.50% C, depending on the properties desired. Molybdenum and boron are also present. Manganese and silicon are used in small amounts as deoxidizers. Some grades also contain small percentages of vanadium, tantalum and columbium. Iron and nickel are always present as impurities, and nickel is sometimes added intentionally as a toughening agent. Nominal compositions of three cast alloys are given in Table 1. See also the article on pages 314 and 315.

These cast alloys are available in a variety of sizes and shapes ready for finish grinding to final dimensions with wheels recommended by the manufacturer of the specific alloy. Hardness in the as-cast condition is Rockwell C 60 to 64; heat treatment by the user is not required. Cast alloys can withstand higher cutting temperatures than high speed steel without failure of the cutting edge (Fig. 1).

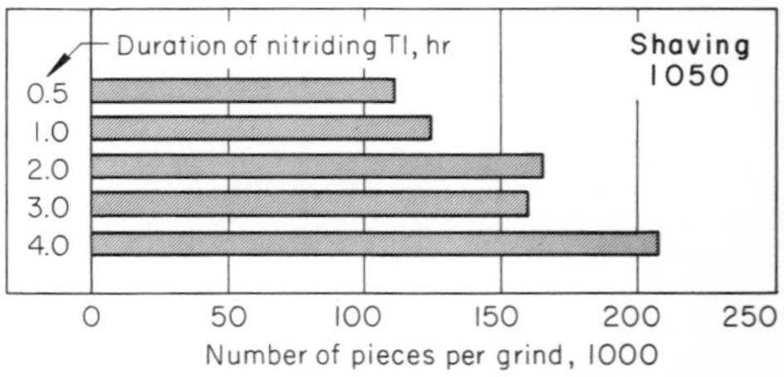

Fig. 3. Effect of duration of liquid nitriding at 1050 F on life of T1 high speed steel. Operation was the same as in Example 581.

The most noticeable constituent in cast alloys is chromium carbide, in which cobalt and tungsten replace some of the chromium.

Applications of cast alloy cutting tools are more limited than are those of high speed steel, because the cast alloys are weaker and more brittle; hence, they are unsuitable for most operations involving impact, such as interrupted cutting. In addition, cast alloys are more costly than high speed steels; consequently, tools are seldom made entirely of the cast alloy. This imposes some limitations on tool design because cast alloy inserts must be brazed, welded or mechanically secured to carbon or low-alloy steel shanks or bodies in constructing tools. For this reason cast alloys are not practical for most drills, reamers, taps and broaches.

Cast alloys are most useful as single-point turning and form tools, milling cutters, and a few special applications such as spotfacers and cutoff tools.

The most important application of cast alloy is for lathe tools. One manufacturer recommends surface speeds twice as high as for high speed steel tools in the same operation. Cast alloys are especially suitable for turning large forgings or castings, where tool temperature becomes quite high and cooling is impractical.

Milling cutters also are made from cast alloy. Inserts are used on large cutters; small cutters can be cast to shape. In milling, as well as in turning, cast alloy is especially useful where no cutting fluid is used.

Choice of grade depends on the type of operation and tool cost. The lower-carbon grades are recommended for tools subject to impact or vibration from lack of rigidity. The higher-carbon types give longer life where only abrasion and heat are involved.

Table 1. Nominal Compositions of Three Cast Alloys Used for Cutting Tools

Alloy	C	Co	Cr	W	Mo	V	B	Other
1	2.5	41	32	17	0.7	3	0.8	1 Ni
2	2.0	45	32	18	..	..	0.2	...
3	2.0	46	28	16	..	..	0.2	5 Ta

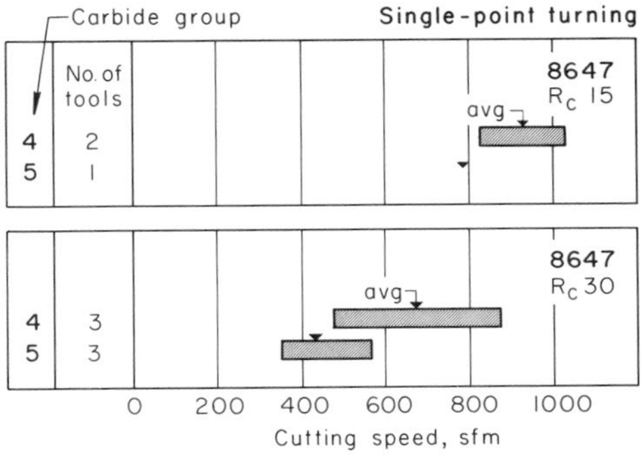

Fig. 4. Simulated production data comparing carbide groups 4 and 5 for allowable cutting speed (Example 585)

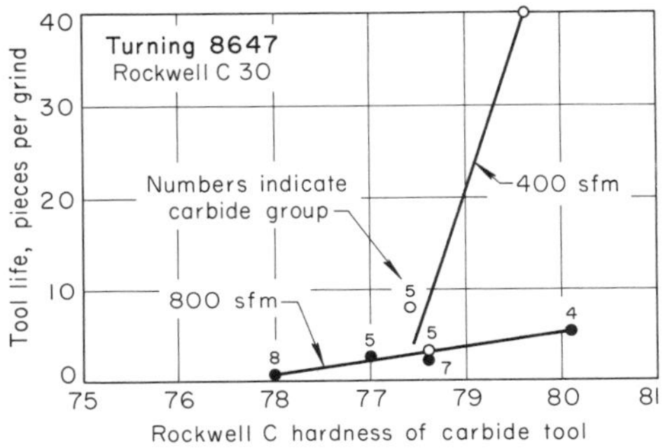

Fig. 5. Simulated production data showing effect of hardness of carbide tool on tool life (Example 586)

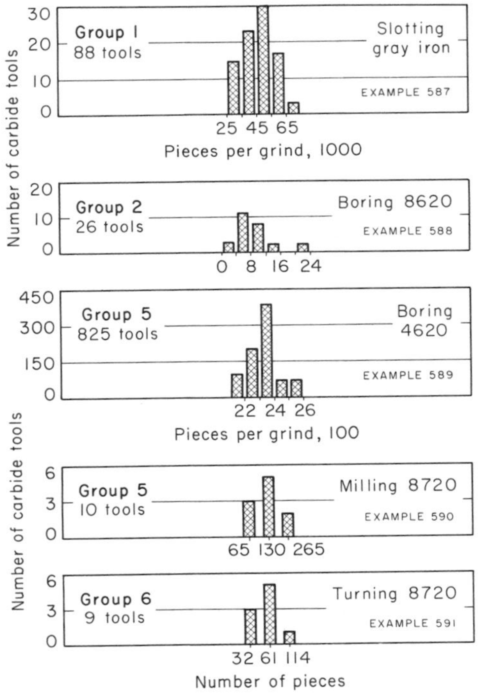

Fig. 6. Distribution of tool life for identical carbide tools. In each group, the tools were used under the same machining conditions. (Examples 587 to 591)

Sintered Carbide

Sintered carbides are usually marketed as proprietary materials rather than to specified ranges of composition or properties. Most of the 475 commercially available grades fall within the nine groups listed in Table 1, page 316.

Carbide tools are successfully used for most metal-cutting operations and are best suited for single-point cutting tools, form tools, milling cutters, shaving tools, boring tools and, in some instances, tools for planing and shaping. High speed steel is usually more practical for drills, taps and broaches; for these tools carbide is limited to special applications.

The metal being machined does not limit the use of carbide tools; they can cut every metal from soft brass or aluminum to white cast iron at Rockwell C 60 or heat-resisting alloys at hardnesses higher than can be machined by high speed steel or cast alloy.

Machine tool condition, age and type must be considered before a decision is made to use carbide. Carbide tools function more efficiently at high speeds than at low speeds and can withstand higher cutting speeds and temperatures than either high speed steels or cast alloys. However, they will withstand these high speeds only when the machine tool is rigid. For nonrigid machine tools, high speed steel or cast alloy tools are recommended (see Example 607).

Selection of carbide group depends mainly on the composition and hardness of the metal being machined and the amount of impact anticipated. The nine groups in Table 1, page 316, in the article "Sintered Carbide for Cutting Tools", are classified according to the predominant carbide added.

All sintered carbides have high hot hardness. Values for grades in groups 1 and 5 are shown in Fig. 1. Hot hardness of a sintered carbide is a rough qualitative measure of the ability of the tool material to resist deformation at elevated temperature, but small differences in hot hardness do not indicate differences in tool performance.

If failure of a tool is caused by local flow, the hot hardness can be correlated with tool performance. However, adhesion of the tool and work is more important than the hot hardness alone. Because of adhesion to the work metal, the tool material may wear away rapidly. Such wear results more from the specific tool and work pair than from any deficiency in hot hardness. For example, group 1 carbide at 1400 F has a hardness of Rockwell A 85; group 5 carbide at the same temperature, Rockwell A 81.5. Nevertheless, when group 1 tools are used for cutting steel at the same high speeds that are permissible for group 5, the group 1 tool craters and fails rapidly.

Simulated Production Data for Carbide Tools

Machining tests under controlled conditions have been made by machine tool manufacturers and others to evaluate the performance of carbide tools under various conditions. The variables investigated include differences in carbide tools, composition and hardness of the work metal, and cutting speed.

Simulated production tests comparing different carbide groups for allowable cutting speed and for the effect of carbide hardness on tool life are described in the following two examples.

Example 585. Effect of Tool Material Composition on Turning Speed (Fig. 4)

A comparison of cutting speed for single-point turning of 8647 steel at two hardnesses, using groups 4 and 5 carbide tools, is shown in Fig. 4. Data are based on the removal of 600 sq in. of metal and on tools reground at 0.020-in. wear. Feed was 0.015 ipr and depth of cut was 0.100-in.

Example 586. Effect of Carbide Hardness on Tool Life in Turning (Fig. 5)

The effect of the hardness of carbide tools on tool life in single-point turning 8647 steel at Rockwell C 30 is plotted in Fig. 5. Workpieces 2 in. in diameter by 6 in. long were turned at speeds of 400 and 800 sfm, using a feed of 0.015 ipr and 0.10-in. depth of cut. No cutting fluid was used. Tools were reground at 0.020 in. of wear. Each hardness value shown in Fig. 5 represents an average of several readings taken on the Rockwell C scale.

Performance of Carbide Tools

Table 1 in the article "Sintered Carbide for Cutting Tools" shows considerable variation in composition within each carbide group. Significant differ-

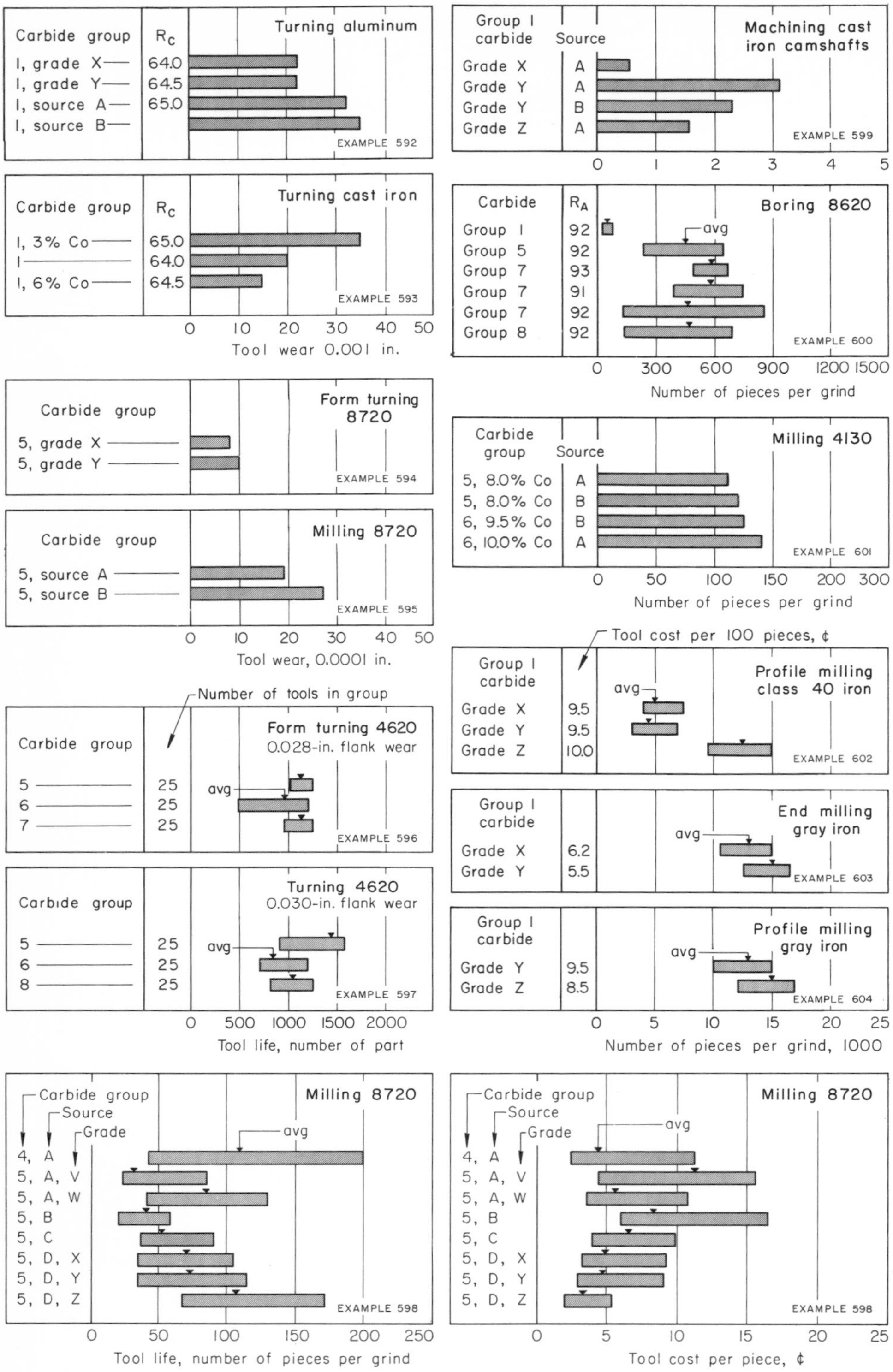

Fig. 7. Comparison of wear, life and cost of carbide tools of different groups, grades and sources **(Examples 592 to 604)**

ences in performance also are observed among the grades within each group. The wide range in performance of identical tools used in the same operation is shown in Fig. 6. Machining conditions are described in the next five examples.

Examples 587 to 591. Variations in Tool Life of Identical Carbide Tools

Example 587 — Slotting (Fig. 6). In the slotting operation of Fig. 6, group 1 carbide cutters were used for milling slots 0.038 in. wide by 0.75 in. deep in gray cast iron (180 Bhn) at a feed of 0.012 ipt and speed of 8 to 9 sfm (2500 rpm). No cutting fluid was required.

Example 588 — Boring (Fig. 6). A wide range in the tool life of 26 group 2 carbide tools boring 8620 steel tubing is shown in Fig. 6. The tubing, 1 in. long with an outside diameter of ⅞ in. and inside diameter of 9⁄16 in., was bored at a speed of 294 sfm and feed of 0.007 ipr. No cutting fluid was used.

Example 589 — Boring (Fig. 6). The number of pieces per grind for boring 4620 (180 Bhn) steel parts with group 5 carbide tools is plotted in Fig. 6. Parts were bored at a speed of 475 sfm and feed of 0.010 ipr. No cutting fluid was used.

Example 590 — Milling (Fig. 6). The tool life of group 5 carbide tools when milling 8720 (Rockwell C 22 to 23) steel forgings is shown in Fig. 6. The operation consisted of cutting V-notches in Y-bit lugs with no cutting fluid.

Example 591 — Turning (Fig. 6). Tool life on the basis of number of pieces turned is shown in Fig. 6. Group 6 carbide tools were used for turning 8720 steel (200 to 225 Bhn) head pin connections without a cutting fluid.

In addition to the effect of composition on tool life, carbide grades within each group and the source of the sintered carbide also influence tool life and cost. These variations are presented in Fig. 7 and are described in the 13 production examples that follow.

Examples 592 to 604. Effect of Group, Grade and Source of Sintered Carbides on Tool Life and Tool Cost

Example 592 — Turning (Fig. 7). Different grades and sources of group 1 carbides were compared for turning aluminum at speeds of 400 to 600 sfm. When machining soft metals such as aluminum, less variation in tool wear is likely to occur among carbide grades within one group than when cutting steel, because of the larger difference in hardness between the tool and the work metal. In this example, however, a difference of more than 50% was recorded (Fig. 7).

Example 593 — Turning (Fig. 7). Three grades of group 1 carbide were compared for turning cast iron at 180 to 220 Bhn. A speed of 250 to 300 sfm was used. In apparent contradiction to the general rule that wear resistance increases when cobalt content decreases, in this example, tools made from the 6% cobalt grade showed less than half the wear of those made from the 3% grade.

Example 594 — Form Turning (Fig. 7). Two grades of group 5 carbide were compared on the basis of tool wear for form turning of roller-bearing races from 8720 steel forgings. A difference of 25% in tool wear was reported between the two grades, as shown in Fig. 7.

Example 595 — Milling (Fig. 7). A difference of more than 25% in tool wear was recorded in a comparison of two group 5 carbides obtained from two sources (Fig. 7). In this operation a "V" was milled on Y-bit lugs in 8720 steel forgings.

Example 596 — Form Turning (Fig. 7). In the form-turning operation of Fig. 7, tools from three carbide groups were compared on the basis of number of parts machined when the tools reached 0.028-in. flank wear. The 4620 alloy steel (149 to 187 Bhn) was turned using a speed of 475 sfm, feed of 0.005 ipr, and 0.062-in. depth of cut. In making this evaluation, 25 tools from each carbide group were used.

Example 597 — Turning (Fig. 7). The tool life of 25 tools from each of three carbide groups was compared on the basis of number of parts machined until tools showed 0.030-in. flank wear. In single-point turning of 4620 steel (149 to 187 Bhn), a speed of 475 sfm and feed of 0.010 ipr were used. Depth of cut was 0.25 in. A comparison of these data with form turning of the same work metal (Example 596, Fig. 7) shows a significant difference in tool life among the group 5 carbides.

Example 598 — Milling (Fig. 7). Tool life and cost of cutters from two carbide groups, of several grades and sources, are compared in Fig. 7 on the basis of number of pieces per grind and tool cost per piece. Milling consisted of cutting a 120° "V" on Y-bit lugs in 8720 steel at Rockwell C 22 to 33.

Example 599 — Machining Camshafts (Fig. 7). The differences in tool life plotted in Fig. 7 were recorded in machining cast iron camshafts with tools of various grades and sources of group 1 carbide. The cast iron, with chilled surfaces, was machined at a speed of 220 sfm, 0.009-in. feed, and depth of cut was 0.060 in.

Example 600 — Boring (Fig. 7). Boring tools of several carbide groups, all of approximately the same hardness, were compared for tool life

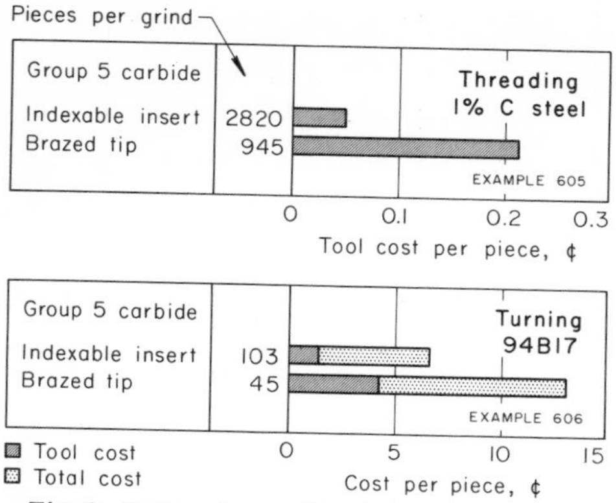

Fig. 8. Comparisons of tool life and cost for brazed and indexable-insert carbide tips (Examples 605 and 606)

on the basis of number of pieces per grind. In boring 8620 steel at a speed of 294 sfm and feed of 0.008 ipr, data reported on three tools from each group show a marked difference in performance of group 1 tools compared with tools from groups 5, 7 and 8.

Example 601 — Milling (Fig. 7). The effect of cobalt content and source of carbide on tool life for carbide groups 5 and 6 is shown in Fig. 7. Data are for milling 4130 steel (160 to 170 Bhn) at a speed of 600 sfm, feed of 0.003 ipt and 0.015-in. depth of cut.

Example 602 — Profile Milling (Fig. 7). Tool life in profile milling class 40 gray iron (Rockwell C 25 to 30) was measured for three grades of group 1 carbide. Workpieces 18 in. long were milled with 5-in.-diam cutters using a feed of 0.004 ipt at 2300 rpm, surface feed of 8 to 10 in. per minute, and 1/64-in. depth of cut. No cutting fluid was used.

Example 603 — End Milling (Fig. 7). Two grades of group 1 carbide, used for end-milling cutters 1 in. in diameter, were compared for tool life. The gray iron (180 Bhn) parts in 12-in. lengths were milled using a feed of 0.010 ipt at 3000 rpm, surface feed of 12 to 16 in. per minute, and 1/16-in. depth of cut. No cutting fluid was used.

Example 604 — Profile Milling (Fig. 7). Differences in tool life in profile milling 12-in. lengths of gray iron at 180 Bhn are shown in Fig. 7. Two grades of group 1 carbide were used for the 5-in.-diam cutters. Milling was done at a feed of 0.006 ipt at 3500 rpm, surface feed of 10 to 12 in. per minute, and 1/32-in. depth of cut. No cutting fluid was used.

Method of attaching carbide tips may have a marked effect on tool life. The carbide is commonly brazed to a body or shank of carbon or low-alloy steel. This method has two possible disadvantages: first, because of the different rates of expansion of the carbide, the body, and the bonding metal, there is danger of cracking; and, more important, the entire tool must be removed from the machine to be reground when the tip is worn.

Mechanically secured tips are used for several types of tools, such as form turning and single-point cutting tools and some milling cutters. Indexable tips are available for milling cutters and for single-point cutting, designed so that all corners may be used to the limit of permissible wear before the tool is discarded or reground. Triangular tips with negative rake angles can provide six cutting edges; three edges are the maximum that can be utilized for tools with positive rake angles. Similarly, with square tips, those with negative rake angles have eight available cutting edges, while those with positive rake angles have only four. Indexable carbide tips are discussed in greater detail later in this article.

The two examples that follow compare indexable inserts with brazed tips on the basis of number of pieces per grind and tool cost per piece.

Examples 605 and 606. Comparative Tool Life and Cost of Brazed vs Indexable-Insert Tips

Example 605 — Threading (Fig. 8). Brazed and indexable tips of group 5 carbide, used in threading 1% carbon steel (200 Bhn), were compared for tool life and tool cost. Results of the comparison are given in Fig. 8.

Example 606 — Turning (Fig. 8). A comparison identical to that discussed in Example 605 was made for rough turning 94B17 steel (230 Bhn), using a feed of 0.015 ipr and 1/4-in. depth of cut. Results are shown in Fig. 8.

Machine tool condition markedly affects the life of carbide tools, as illustrated in the next example. (See also Examples 319, 321 and 322, involving machine rigidity and carbide tools.)

Example 607. Effect of Machine Tool Condition on Performance of Carbide Tools (Fig. 9)

Counterweights were turned on automotive crankshafts of 1046 steel in two different plants of the same company. Square insert-type carbide tips permitted the use of eight corners before regrinding. In plant A, where cutting tools were used on new machine tools

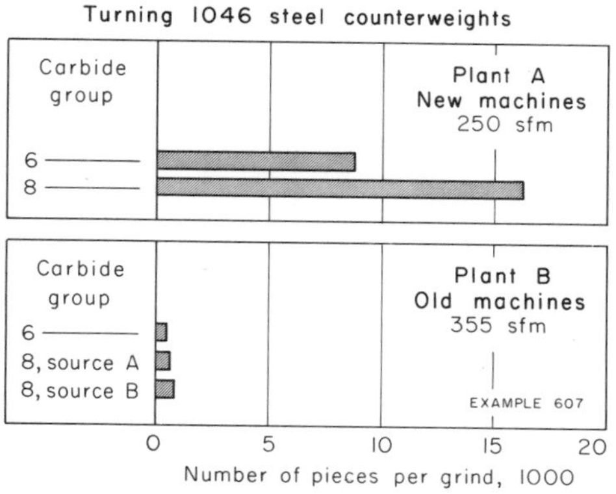

Fig. 9. Effect of machine tool condition on performance of sintered carbides in two plants turning counterweights on the same crankshafts (Example 607)

in first-class condition, group 6 carbide produced 8800 pieces per grind, compared with 16,300 for group 8. In plant B, making the same part, the machine tools were old, lacked rigidity and were unsuitable for carbide tooling. Here group 6 carbide gave only 480 pieces per grind (5.4% of the production in plant A), while group 8 carbide obtained from two different sources gave 600 and 696 pieces. In plant A, using new machines, feed was 0.020 in. and depth of cut 0.125 in. Plant B (old machines) used higher speed with lower feed (0.015 in.) and 0.125 to 0.187-in. depth of cut.

Performance details are illustrated by the graphs of Fig. 9.

Work-metal composition also has a major effect on life of carbide tools, as shown in the next three examples:

Example 608. Tool Life in Rough Turning Alloy Steels of Different Carbon Content (Fig. 10)

Group 3 carbide tools with high cobalt content were selected for machining large steel castings of different carbon content, annealed to a hardness of scleroscope C 35 to 40 (equivalent to Rockwell C 22 to 27). The castings were rough turned at a speed of 90 sfm and feed of 0.080 ipr. Depth of cut was 2.5 in. and no cutting fluid was used.

Tool life, based on the reported time between grinds, showed a decrease as carbon content of the steels increased. The composition of each alloy steel is tabulated with Fig. 10.

Examples 609 and 610. Tool Life of Group 8 Carbide Tools

Example 609 — Turning Steels of Similar Carbon Content (Fig. 11). In turning three steels having similar carbon content, the tool life of group 8 carbide tools, plotted in Fig. 11, showed no significant differences. In rough turning differential side gears of carbon steel and 0.25% Mo steels, a speed of 386 sfm and feed of 0.0169 ipr were used. Depth of cut was 0.25 in. (max).

Example 610 — Milling Five Different Metals (Fig. 11). The wide range in life of group 8 carbide cutters used in face milling five different metals is shown in Fig. 11. A 6-in.-diam cutter with −5° axial and radial rake angles was used at a speed of 638 sfm and feed of 0.0057 ipt. Depth of cut was 0.060 in.

Other Cutting Tool Materials

Cermets. Performance data for these materials are limited to the type composed mainly of 70 to 80% TiC with additions of molybdenum carbide and with nickel as the binder. The structure of cermets is different from conventional sintered carbides because the carbide solubility at sintering temperature is greater in the nickel than in the cobalt binder. For this reason cermets are more brittle than sintered carbides, which usually limits their use to light finishing cuts.

One field report showed that a steel-cutting grade of tungsten carbide used to finish machine gear blanks of 8620 alloy steel at 170 to 207 Bhn produced 1100 pieces per corner. A titanium carbide cermet machined 6300 pieces under like conditions.

Diamond tools are used for special-purpose cutting and usually give longer tool life than carbide. In the single-point turning operation of the next example, diamond tools outperformed carbide tools by a wide margin.

Example 611. Diamond vs Carbide (Fig. 12)

In single-point turning of aluminum die castings (85 to 100 Bhn), the tool life of group 1 carbide tools and industrial diamond tools was compared on the basis of 90 tools of each material. Results are shown in Fig. 12. Diamond tools gave average life of 14,500 pieces, compared with 500 for group 1 carbide tools. Turning was done at speeds of 722 to 1620 sfm and feed of 0.004 ipr. Depth of cut was 0.015 in.

Aluminum oxide ceramics are also used in production machining. They are extremely hard (Al_2O_3 is about 2400

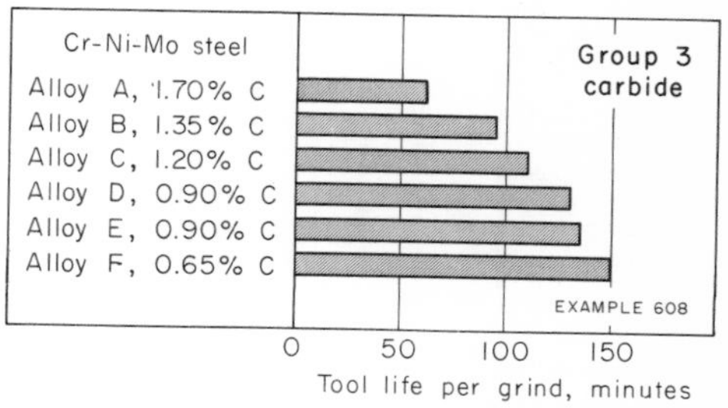

Alloy	C	Mn	Cr	Ni	Mo
A	1.70	1.45	1.05	0.20	0.30
B	1.35	0.90	0.95	0.20	0.50
C	1.20	0.90	0.95	0.20	0.50
D	0.90	0.90	0.95	0.20	0.50
E	0.90	0.65	1.05	0.25	0.40
F	0.65	0.70	0.40	1.30	0.25

Fig. 10. Effect of carbon content of annealed steel castings on life of carbide tools (Example 608)

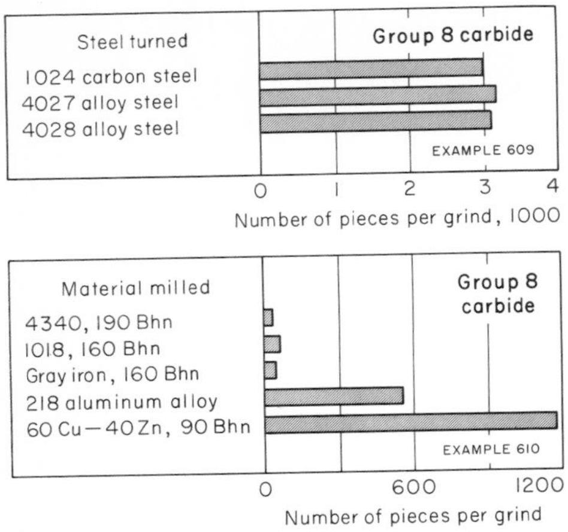

Fig. 11. Comparison of life of carbide tools cutting eight different work metals (Examples 609 and 610)

Knoop) but also very brittle. Thus, their use is limited. Additional information on the properties and applications of ceramic tools is given in the article that begins on page 322. Speeds and feeds for turning steel of various hardnesses with ceramic tools are given in Table 5 on page 8. Tool life of ceramic tools compared with carbide tools is illustrated in the example that follows.

Example 612. Ceramic vs Carbide (Fig. 12)

Aluminum oxide ceramic and group 1 carbide, used for single-point turning tools, were compared for tool life, with results as shown in Fig. 12. In turning pearlitic malleable iron (200 Bhn) at a speed of 650 sfm, feed of 0.006 ipr, and 0.015-in. depth of cut, ceramic tools averaged 570 pieces, compared with an average of 75 pieces for carbide tools. This evaluation was based on the use of 30 tools of each material.

Comparisons of Carbides, Cast Alloys and High Speed Steels

Performance data for the three most widely used types of cutting tool materials have so far been limited mainly to comparisons of grades within each of the three types. Data in Fig. 13 (Examples 613 to 631) and Fig. 14 (Examples 632 to 640) compare high speed steels, cast alloys and carbides for the same operations.

Allowable cutting speeds are compared in Examples 613 to 617 in Fig. 13. Consistently higher speeds are permissible with carbide regardless of the metal being machined. Speeds for cast alloy, shown in Examples 616 and 617 in Fig. 13, are intermediate between steel and carbide in machining both cast iron and aluminum. Cast alloys are also intermediate between T6 high speed steel and group 5 carbide for rate of wear in machining stainless steel and aluminum, Examples 618 and 619 in Fig. 13. Carbide is the economical choice for these operations because of the low initial cost (see caption) and the lowest rate of wear.

Example 620 in Fig. 13 compares M2 with M3 high speed steels for broaching splines in 5160H steel tubing. The M2 broach lasted 8 hr and cost $165.00, or $20.62 per service-hour; the M3 broach lasted 32 hr and cost $220.00, or $6.87 per service-hour.

Another comparison involving M3 high speed steel is given in Example 621 in Fig. 13. The average life of five carbide tools was about 47 times greater than that of the same number of M3 tools used for cutting off small-diameter modified 51100 steel (0.90 to 1.00% instead of 0.95 to 1.10% C).

High speed steel T1 is compared with two grades of group 1 carbide for facing turbine disks made of a heat-resisting alloy in Example 622, Fig. 13. T1 is not recommended for this application because one tool will not complete the facing operation on one disk at economical speeds and feeds, and changing tools in the middle of the operation is costly. Example 623 in Fig. 13 charts similar results in facing type 414 stainless (AMS 5615). The range for 16 tools of T1 steel is 0.3 to 1.5 pieces per grind, compared with 0.6 to 3 pieces per grind for M2, and 4 to 10 pieces for carbide.

Data in Example 624, Fig. 13, compare T1 with two cast alloys for cutting off low-alloy steel. T1 tools machined 6 to 10 pieces; one cast alloy, 48 to 70 pieces; and a competitive cast alloy, 75 to 100 pieces.

In machining aluminum alloy compressor spindles, Example 625 (Fig. 13), T1 lasted for 3 to 4 pieces per grind, compared with 4 to 5 for M2, 6 to 7 for cast alloy A, and 9 to 10 for cast alloy B. Cast alloys A and B are competitive proprietary alloys.

Six tool material comparisons based on both tool life and tool cost are given in Examples 626 to 631 in Fig. 13. In all six examples, except for drilling 1113, carbide tools gave better performance at a lower initial cost. For example, in turning aluminum, T8 tools cost $6.42 each, cast alloy $7.13 and the carbide tools only $3.40.

Cost per piece machined is the most realistic criterion for evaluation of cutting tools. Differences in tool design can affect cost, as shown in Fig. 14 (Examples 632 to 635) in which the use of end-milling cutters with right-hand spiral and left-hand spiral resulted in different costs for the same operation. The left-hand spiral has more shearing action at the teeth and does not exert forces that tend to lift the workpiece from the table.

The data in Fig. 14 compare the costs of tools made of high speed steels, cast alloys and sintered carbides for the operations described in the following eight examples.

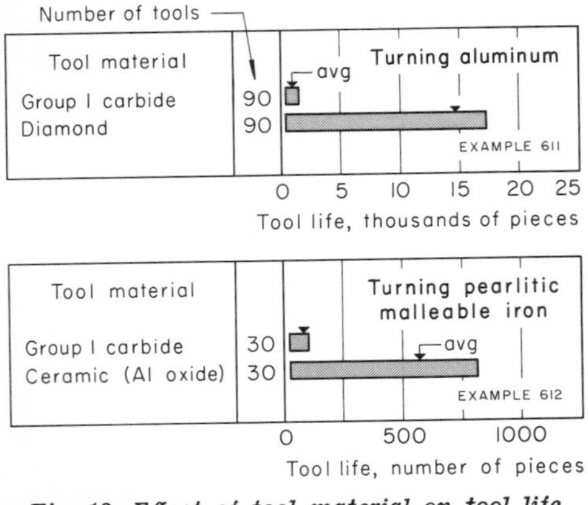

Fig. 12. Effect of tool material on tool life (Examples 611 and 612)

Examples 632 to 639. Comparative Tool Costs of High Speed Steels, Cast Alloys and Sintered Carbides

Example 632 — End Milling (Fig. 14). Two high speed steels and a group 1 carbide used for milling cutters were compared for tool cost per piece machined, with results as shown in Fig. 14. A profile milling machine incorporating a ¾-in.-diam cutter was used to end mill cast aluminum (70 to 80 Bhn), cutting ¼ in. on the side and end of the cutter. An oil made by addition of 5% fatty oil to mineral oil was used as the cutting fluid.

Example 633 — End Milling (Fig. 14). Comparative costs per piece machined of three high speed steels and a group 1 carbide used in milling vacuum-melted 52100 annealed steel forgings (200 to 207 Bhn) are shown in Fig. 14. Cuts from ⅛ to 3⁄16 in. deep were made using 1-in.-diam end mills on a profile milling machine. Mineral oil was the cutting fluid.

Example 634 — End Milling (Fig. 14). A comparison of tool cost per piece between two high speed steels and a group 1 carbide in milling grade 60-45-10, nodular cast iron (165 to 190 Bhn) is shown in Fig. 14. Side cutting was done on a profile milling machine using 1-in.-diam end mills at a speed of 1100 rpm without a cutting fluid.

Example 635 — End Milling (Fig. 14). Comparative tool costs for end cutting, under conditions identical to those described for side cutting in Example 634, are shown in Fig. 14.

Example 636 — Straddle Milling (Fig. 14). Group 6 carbide and T15 high speed steel tools were compared on the basis of the total cost per piece machined, as shown in Fig. 14. Straddle milling 4340 steel having a hardness of Rockwell C 42 was done on a horizontal milling machine at a speed of 320 sfm and feed of 6⅛ ipm for the carbide tools; 57 sfm and 1½ ipm for the high speed steel tools.

Example 637 — Turning (Fig. 14). The relative cost per piece machined is compared in Fig. 14 for tools from two high speed steels and two cast alloys. The tools were used for turning 8620 steel parts (143 to 163 Bhn) at a speed of 90 sfm and feed of 0.014 ipr. Depth of cut was 3⁄16 in. The cast alloy tools (Rockwell C 62 to 62.5) were significantly lower in cost than the steel tools.

Example 638 — Milling Slots (Fig. 14). Tool costs per piece are compared in Fig. 14 for high speed steel and group 1 carbide. In this operation 24 slots 1⁄32 in. wide by 1 in. deep were milled in manganese bronze (alloy 8A) castings (Rockwell B 75), using a 3-in.-diam saw. A 1-to-15 mixture of sulfurized oil and water was the cutting fluid. Cost of the high speed steel tools was nearly nine times that of the carbide tools; tool life differed by a factor of 35 (4 vs 140 pieces per grind).

Example 639 — Milling Slots (Fig. 14). The cost of high speed steel and group 1 carbide tools was compared on a per-piece basis, with results similar to those shown in Example 638. In milling ¼ to ⅜-in. by 3-in. slots in class 20 gray iron (Rockwell B 85 to 95), 3-in.-diam cutters were used at a speed of 145 rpm and feed of 8 ipm, without cutting fluid.

Disposable Carbide Inserts

Data comparing tool cost per piece machined using tools of solid high speed steel and indexable carbide inserts (often called "disposable" or "throwaway" inserts) are given in the following example.

Example 640. Cost of Solid High Speed Steel Tools vs Carbide Inserts (Fig. 14)

Group 5 carbide disposable inserts proved more economical than solid M2 high speed steel tools in the machining of 1% carbon steel at 200 Bhn, as shown in Fig. 14. Three different outside diameters were turned at a feed of 0.015 ipr and 1⁄16 to ¼-in. depth of cut without cutting fluid. At 0.015-in. flank wear, the solid steel tools were resharpened and the triangular inserts were indexed to a new cutting edge. Because the initial cost of the inserts was less than the cost of resharpening either type of tool, the inserts were discarded and new inserts installed after the six cutting edges on each insert were worn.

Caption Detail for Fig. 13

Example 613 — Form Turning. High speed steel compared with carbide on a basis of allowable cutting speed in form turning 4620 at 190 Bhn, using feeds of 0.010 ipr for carbide and 0.0025 ipr for M2. A 5% soluble-oil cutting fluid was employed.

Example 614 — Rough turning 94B17 hot rolled bars at 195 to 225 Bhn with straight form tool, using 1/32-in. nose radius, feed of 0.015 ipr, and 1/4-in. depth of cut. Carbide tip was brazed to holder. Carbide insert was triangular indexable with six cutting edges.

Example 615 — Rough Turning. Similar to Example 614 but work metal was leaded 8620 steel.

Example 616 — Turning. Allowable cutting speed for two high speed steels, a cast alloy and a group 1 carbide for turning gray iron at 180 to 220 Bhn, using a feed of 0.030 ipr, and 0.10-in. depth of cut.

Example 617 — Turning. Allowable cutting speed for three high speed steels, a cast alloy and a group 5 carbide for turning aluminum alloy using a feed of 0.010 ipr, and 1/4-in. depth of cut without cutting fluid. Cost of T1 tool was $5.00, T4 $5.40, T6 $7.00, cast alloy $11.02 and carbide $3.40.

Example 618 — Turning. Wear of tool material in turning type 304 stainless (150 Bhn) at 53 sfm, using a feed of 0.010 ipr and 1/4-in. depth of cut without cutting fluid. Cost of T6 tool was $7.00, cast alloy $11.02 and carbide $3.40.

Example 619 — Turning. Wear of tool material in turning aluminum alloy (139 Bhn) at 800 sfm, using a feed of 0.010 ipr and 1/4-in. depth of cut. Cost of T6 tool was $7.00, cast alloy $11.02, carbide $2.51.

Example 620 — Broaching. Tool life in broaching splines in 5160H steel tubing with a hardness of Rockwell B 85 to 95. A 0.002-in. depth of cut per tooth (0.040-in. total depth) at broach speed of 32 sfm and an oil cutting fluid were used. M2 broach lasted 8 hr and cost $165.00, or $20.62 per service-hour; M3 broach lasted 32 hr and cost $220.00, or $6.87 per service-hour.

Example 621 — Cutting Off. Life of blades for cutting off 1-mm-diam modified 51100 with a hardness of Rockwell B 85 to 90. M3 tools averaged 3.8 hr, compared with 178.6 hr for carbide.

Example 622 — Facing. High speed steel compared with two grades of group 1 carbide for tool life in facing heat-resisting alloy AMS 5733 (13.5 Cr, 26.0 Ni, 3.0 Mo, 1.80 Ti) at 248 to 302 Bhn, using a speed of 80 sfm, feed of 0.018 ipr, and a water-soluble cutting fluid.

Example 623 — Facing. Tool life in facing AMS 5615 (type 414 stainless) at 207 to 269 Bhn, a speed of 160 sfm, feed of 0.019 ipr, with water-soluble cutting fluid.

Example 624 — Cutting Off. High speed steel compared with cast alloys for cutoff tools for a variety of screw-machine parts. Chlorinated-oil cutting fluid was used.

Example 625 — Form Turning. High speed steels and cast alloys used for rough form turning aluminum alloy compressor spindles. Tool life for removing 30 cu in. of metal per piece; water-soluble cutting fluid was used.

Example 626 — Turning. Tool life and tool cost per piece for turning 2-in.-diam 2014-T6 aluminum alloy, using 1/4-in. depth by 30-in. length of cut at 800 sfm, feed of 0.010 ipr, and no cutting fluid.

Example 627 — Rough Milling. High speed steel compared with carbide. Tool life and tool cost per piece for rough milling 1113 steel, using 1/16-in. depth of cut, feed of 0.005 ipt at 6 to 8 sfm (200 rpm) for T1; and 1/16-in. depth of cut, feed of 0.006 ipt at 15 to 18 sfm (3500 rpm) for carbide. Mineral-base cutting oil was used with T1, no cutting fluid with carbide. Data are based on a minimum of 50 tool grinds.

Example 628 — Finish Milling. Tool life and tool cost per piece for finish milling 1113, using 1/64-in. depth of cut, feed of 0.005 ipt at 5 to 6 sfm (250 rpm) for M2 and T1; and 1/32-in. depth of cut, feed of 0.008 ipt at 5 to 6 sfm (3500 rpm) for carbide. Mineral-base cutting fluid was used with both tool materials. Data are based on a minimum of 50 tool grinds.

Example 629 — Drilling. High speed steel compared with carbide for drilling 0.509-in. holes at 1500 rpm (100 sfm), using a feed of 0.005 ipr, and no cutting fluid. Data are based on a minimum of 50 tool grinds.

Example 630 — Profile Milling. High speed steel compared with carbide for profile milling gray iron (180 Bhn) in 12-in. lengths, using 1/32-in. depth of cut, feed of 0.005 ipt at 6 to 8 sfm (150 to 200 rpm) for T1; and 1/32-in. depth of cut, feed of 0.006 ipt at 10 to 12 sfm (3500 rpm) for carbide. No cutting fluid was used for either tool material. Data are based on a minimum of 50 tool grinds.

Example 631 — Slotting. Cutting slots 0.038 in. wide by 0.75 in. deep with the same tool materials and work material as Example 630. Feed was 0.009 ipt at 6 to 8 sfm (200 rpm) for T1; and 0.012 ipt at 8 to 9 sfm (2500 rpm) for carbide. Cutters were 6 in. in diameter and ran without cutting fluid. Data are based on a minimum of 100 tool grinds.

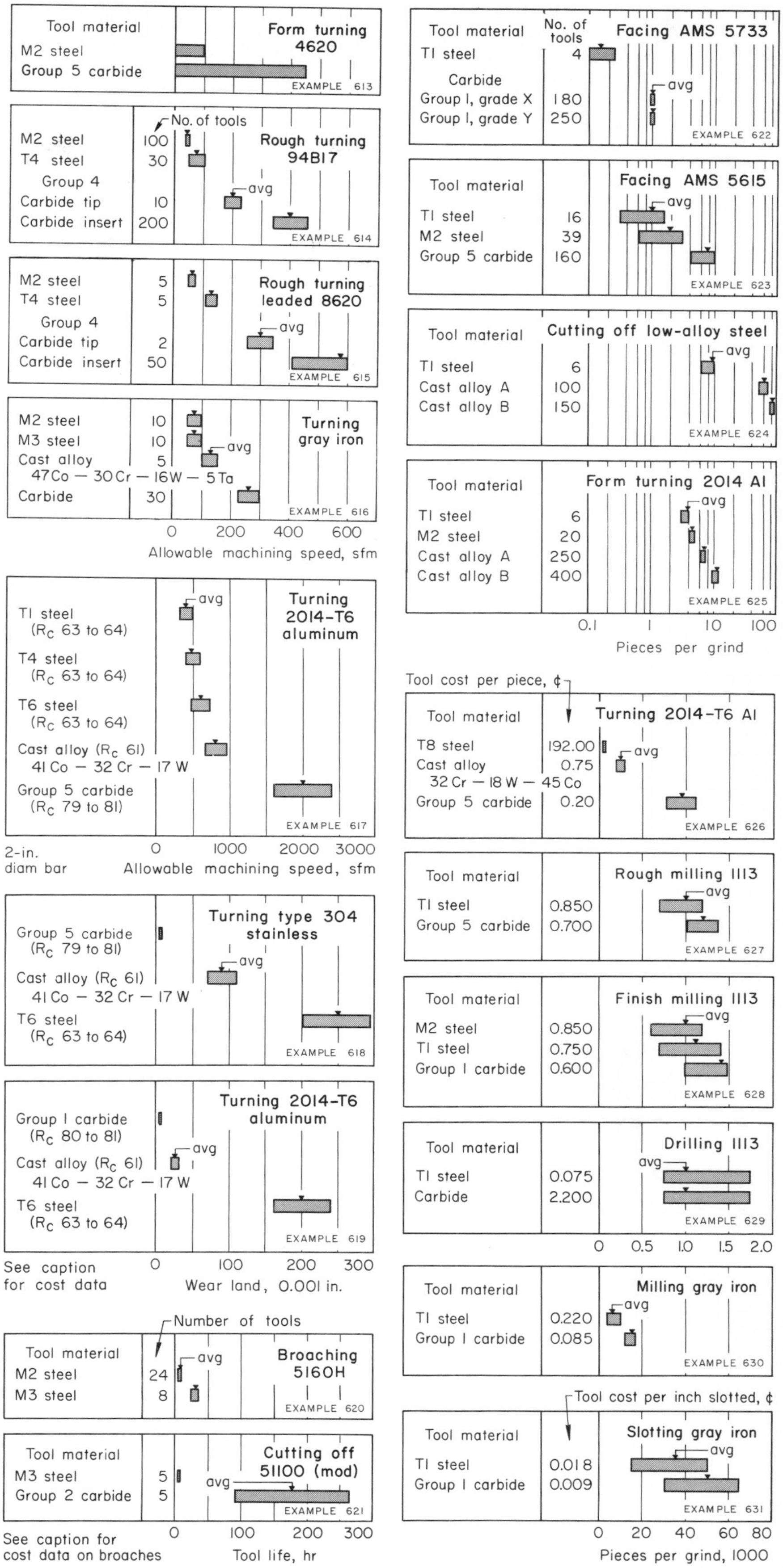

Fig. 13. Comparisons of allowable machining speed, tool life, wear and cost involving tools made of carbide, high speed steel, and cast cobalt-chromium-base alloy for use with seven different machining operations and 12 different work metals. A description of each chart is given in the column at the left. (Examples 613 to 631)

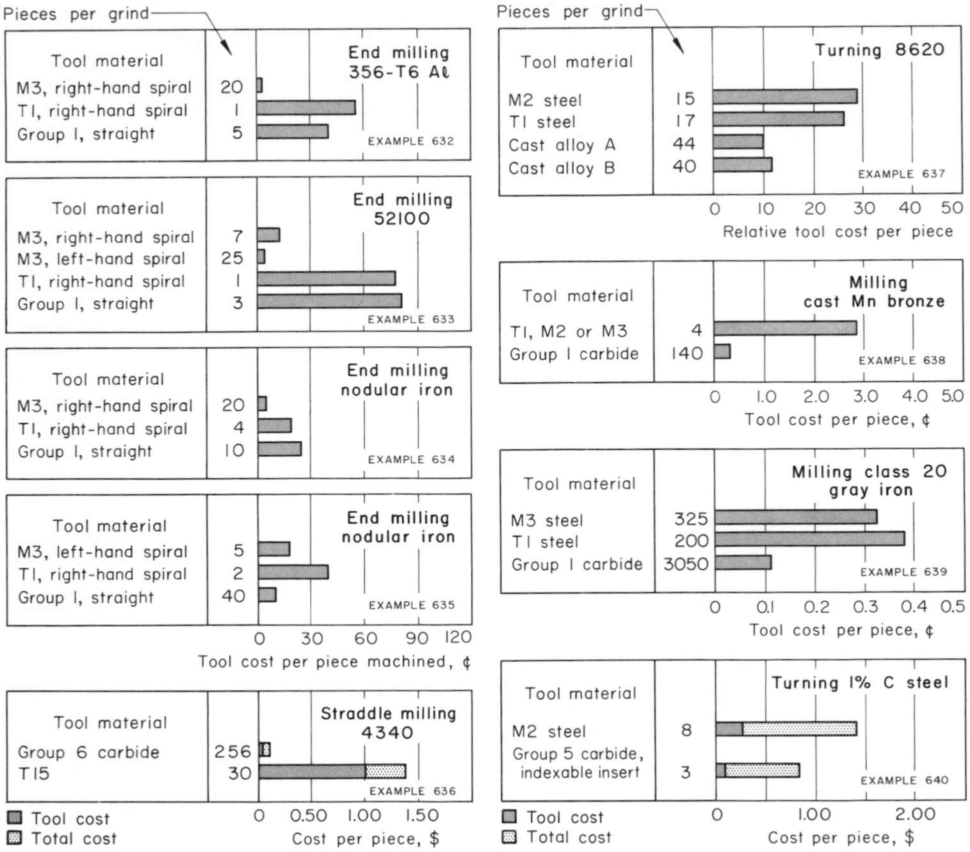

Fig. 14. Comparisons of tool cost (Examples 632 to 640)

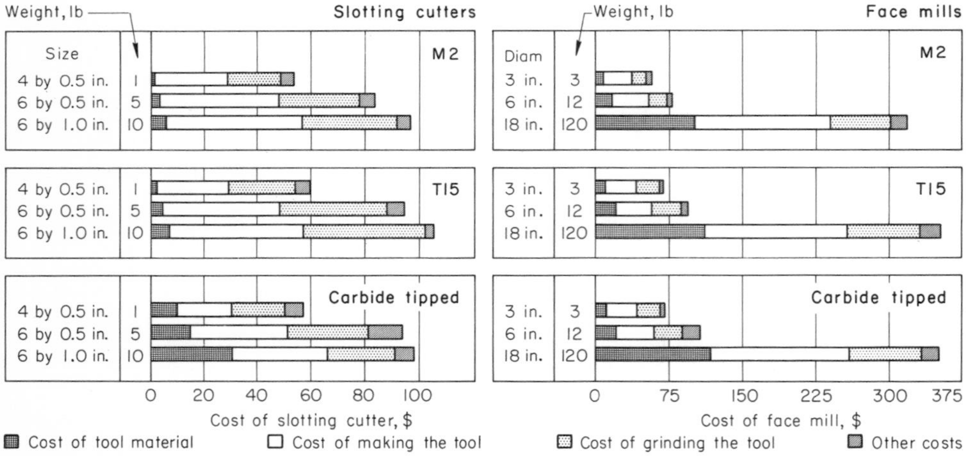

Fig. 15. Effect of tool size and weight on material cost, processing cost and total cost of slotting cutters and face mills

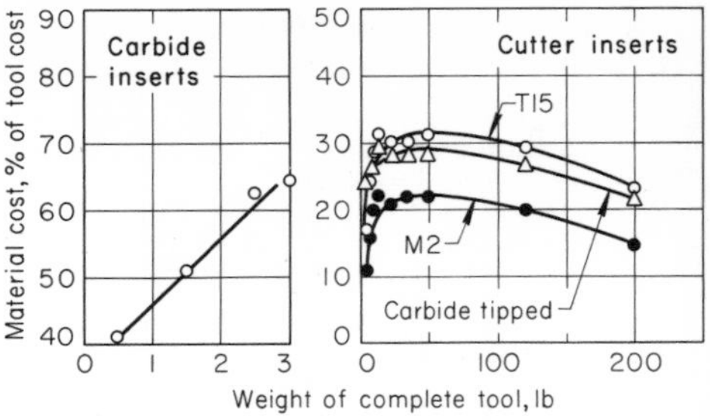

Fig. 16. Effect of tool size on cost. (Left) *Cost of carbide inserts related to weight of single-point cutting tools.* (Right) *Cost of carbide and high speed tool steel inserts in relation to the weight of milling cutters.*

The initial cost of the high speed steel tools was $0.262 per piece machined; the carbide inserts cost $0.079 per piece, as shown in Fig. 14. Machining costs other than tool costs also were significantly reduced by the use of disposable inserts. The following tabulation compares both tools on the basis of total cost per piece.

M2 High Speed Steel		
Machining and handling	13.85	min
Piecework labor	$0.613	
Machine burden (including tool cost)	0.8085	
Total cost per piece	$1.4215	
Group 5 Carbide Disposable Insert		
Machining and handling	8.02	min
Piecework labor	$0.386	
Machine burden (including tool cost)	0.469	
Total cost per piece	$0.855	

Disposable carbide inserts are widely used, because they are more economical for many applications, as indicated by Examples 605 and 607 in this article and Examples 647 and 648 in the article "Machining of Cast Iron".

Cost of Cutting Tools

The cost of the tool material is usually a small fraction of the total cost of small tools. The ratio changes as the tools increase in size. Elements that make up total tool cost for nine different slotting cutters are given in the three graphs on the left in Fig. 15. Similar comparisons are shown for face mills on the right of this figure.

For single-point cutting tools the ratio of cost of carbide insert to total cost is almost directly proportional to the weight of the tool (Fig. 16, left). The graph at the right in Fig. 16 shows the portion of total cost represented by the cost of inserts for milling cutters of several weights up to 200 lb. Small milling cutters are made from solid high speed steel, but slotting cutters wider than 0.5 in. and any face-milling cutters larger than 4 in. in diameter can usually be constructed at lower cost by using inserts. Narrow slotting cutters may require solid high speed steel construction because of limitations in space or rigidity, or both. Helical plain milling cutters are seldom made with inserts.

The T15 cutter inserts (Fig. 16) are more costly than carbide because they are solid pieces of high speed steel (as are the M2 inserts), whereas the carbide inserts are made by brazing carbide tips to carbon steel shanks. However, because of this fundamental difference in construction the thicker high speed steel inserts will permit a greater number of grinds before they must be replaced. All inserts in Fig. 16 are secured by serrated locking devices.

Other Examples of Selection of Material for Cutting Tools in This Volume

Type of tool	Example number
Carbide vs Carbide	
Single-point tools	305, 774
Milling cutters	358
Boring tools	745
Drills	832
Carbide vs High Speed Steel	
Planing tools	91, 92
Broaches	123
Drills	184, 190, 195, 832, 833
Reamers	206
Form tools	308
Milling cutters	341, 360, 370-372, 672, 697, 699
Boring tools	810
Circular saws	920
Carbide vs Cast Alloy	
Single-point tools	692
Carbide vs Ceramic	
Milling cutters	357
High Speed Steel vs High Speed Steel	
Broaches	123, 749, 750, 811, 818, 822, 823
Drills	183, 828-831
Form tools	303
Milling cutters	360, 782, 846-848
High Speed Steel vs Carbon Steel	
Band saws	447
High Speed Steel vs Cast Alloy	
Form tools	304

MACHINING OF CAST IRON

CONTENTS

Machining of Gray, Nodular and Malleable Irons

*By the ASM Committee on Machining of Cast Iron**

CAST IRONS vary greatly in machinability. For example, white irons, which are harder than glass, are extremely difficult to machine, whereas ferritic cast irons are among the easiest to machine of all metals. Between these two extremes lie the various commercial grades of gray, nodular and malleable cast irons.

Factors that influence machining, and four comparisons of the machinability of different types of cast iron, are included in the sections that immediately follow. Additional comparisons of machinability are presented in six examples of production practice that deal with specific machining operations later in this article (Examples 655, 656, 661, 662, 663 and 671).

Machining Characteristics of Gray Iron

Microstructure is a more fundamental indicator of the machining characteristics of gray iron than hardness and other mechanical properties. Table 1 shows the effect of matrix microstructure on tool life. As microconstituents in gray iron increase in hardness (Table 2), abrasive wear of the tool increases and tool life decreases. Because of its lower hardness, a structure containing coarse pearlite is easier to machine than one containing fine pearlite, and causes less tool wear.

Table 1. Effect of Microstructure on Tool Life in Machining Gray Iron (a)

Matrix microstructure(b) (in order of decreasing machinability)	Brinell hardness number	Tool-life index
Ferrite	120	20
50% ferrite, 50% pearlite	150	10
Coarse pearlite	195	2
Medium pearlite	215	1.5
Fine pearlite	218	1
Fine pearlite with 5% free carbide	240	0.3

(a) Data are based on USAF Machinability Reports. (b) Graphite content, 2.5%, approx.

Table 2. Hardness of Microconstituents of Gray Iron

Microconstituent	Knoop microhardness (100-gram load) Range	Average
Free graphite	15 to 40	20
Free ferrite	215 to 270	240
Pearlite	300 to 390	350
Steadite	600 to 1200	950
Free carbide	1000 to 2300	1500
Tool Materials (for Comparison)		
Hardened tool steel	730 to 760	740
Tungsten carbide	1700 to 1940	1800

Free graphite and ferrite — the softest microconstituents — are products of graphitization. They are formed by the decomposition of iron carbide (Fe_3C). Conditions that promote graphitization soften the structure of gray iron and improve its machinability. Conditions that prevent or inhibit graphitization (stabilize carbide) have the opposite effect. Graphite produces discontinuities in gray iron that break the chips, and provides lubrication during machining. It renders gray iron more machinable than most steels. The beneficial effects of graphite, however, can be diminished or canceled by:

1. The presence of chill at corners and in light sections
2. The presence of adhering sand on the surface of the casting
3. Swells (usually the result of soft molds)
4. Shifted castings (mismatch)
5. Shrinks.

Chill at corners and in light sections is mostly encountered with small castings, with higher-strength irons, and with designs that have light sections in the cope, or top section, of the mold. Chill can be effectively decreased by treating the molten iron with a small amount (1 to 5 lb per ton) of graphitizing alloy, such as ferrosilicon. It is better to avert chill by this method in the foundry than to correct it later by heat treatment of the solidified casting. Heat treating to remove chill is a large additional expense and often results in distortion beyond tolerance and a sacrifice in hardness and strength. Chill, and the marked increase in hardness associated with it, can shorten tool life markedly. This is illustrated by the following example.

Example 641. Effect of Chill on Tool Life in Facing Class 25 to 30 Gray Iron Castings

When gray iron castings in the normal hardness range (156 to 217 Bhn), and essentially free of chill, were faced with carbide inserts (½-in. diam by ⅛ in. thick), tool life was 175 pieces per tool. However, the occurrence of chill in sections of some

*WM. W. AUSTIN, *Chairman,* Head, Department of Mineral Industries, North Carolina State University; R. D. BENNETT, Chief Metallurgist, Oliver Corp.; INYONG HAM, Associate Professor, Department of Industrial Engineering, Pennsylvania State University; HANS J. HEINE, Technical Director, Malleable Founders Society; JULIAN W. HOEN, Superintendent, Plant 5, Rex Chainbelt Inc.; LOUIS IANNETTONI, Material and Process and Insulation Section, Buffalo Motor and Gearing Div., Westinghouse Electric Corp.; GERHARD J. MUELLER, formerly with Detroit Diesel Engine Div., General Motors Corp.; BEN E. STORRS, Service Engineer, Metallurgical Products Dept., General Electric Co.; R. C. TITTEL, Manager, Materials Laboratory, Cummins Engine Co., Inc.; C. F. WALTON, Technical Director, Gray and Ductile Iron Founders' Society, Inc.

castings produced localized hardness as high as 405 Bhn and lowered tool life to 13 to 25 pieces per tool. By instituting proper foundry controls, chills were eliminated and normal tool life was restored.

The machining operation from which these data were obtained was done on a double-index chucking machine and consisted of rough facing several surfaces on the castings, ranging from 1¾ to 5 in. in diameter, at a feed of 0.0165 ipr and speeds from 138 to 390 sfm (at 300 rpm).

Adhering sand can usually be removed by effective cleaning, but sand present as a result of penetration of the iron into the mold wall is extremely difficult to remove, and if allowed to remain may have a very deleterious effect on machinability and especially on tool wear. Carbide tools are better than high speed steel tools for resisting the extreme abrasiveness of embedded sand.

Swells are most troublesome in the more difficult machining operations, such as broaching, even when low cutting speeds are used, and in other machining operations associated with high production in which high cutting speeds are mandatory. The additional metal encountered in the area of the swell often places an excessive load on the tool, which may chip or dull but not fail until some time after the parts have been machined.

Shifted castings are similar to swells in their action on cutting tools. Both shifts and swells may cause excessive tool loads if these defects affect locating points. Thus, it is important to consider the position of locating points in design and to avoid indiscriminate grinding of these points in the foundry cleaning room.

Shrinks are a less common defect, but they can be troublesome in operations such as drilling. Often an increase in hardness is associated with an area of shrink, and this may cause the drill to break or to drift.

Shakeout practice may influence the microstructure and hardness of gray iron castings. If the iron is austenitic at the time the casting is "shaken out", higher hardness may result. Many types of microstructure may be obtained in a given casting, because the austenite in thin sections may transform in the mold whereas in heavier sections that cool more slowly the transformation may be delayed until the air cooling after shakeout. The effect of shakeout practice on hardness is negligible in unalloyed irons. Irons containing a total of 1 to 2% of carbide-forming elements (chromium, molybdenum and vanadium) are the most sensitive to shakeout practice. The effect of shakeout on a class 40 alloy gray iron is shown in Table 3. Highly alloyed martensitic or white irons show little, if any, difference after shakeout.

The effect of foundry variables on the machinability of gray iron is demonstrated in the next example:

Example 642. Machinability of Class 40 Gray Irons From Nine Different Foundries (Table 4)

Gray iron bars produced by nine different foundries to the same specification (ASTM A48, class 40) were machined in laboratory tests. Table 4 gives the composition, tensile strength, hardness and microstructure of the bars and compares their machinability on the basis of cutting speeds for attaining 60-min, 30-min and 15-min tool life in turning cylinders from the bars. As the comparison of results indicates, the nine irons showed a considerable difference in turning characteristics — the speeds for 60-min tool life, for example, ranged from 143 to 194 sfm. Tool details and machining conditions are given in footnote (a) in Table 4.

Table 3. Effect of Shakeout Practice on the Hardness of a Class 40 Alloy Gray Iron (a)

Time(b), min	Bhn
3	302
6	302
10	293
12	269
20	248

(a) Composition: 3.40 C, 2.10 Si, 0.60 Mn, 0.40 Cr, 0.93 Mo. Casting weighing 2.3 lb, with average section of 7/16 in., poured at about 2600 F. (b) Interval between pouring and shakeout.

Table 4. Machinability of Class 40 Gray Irons From Nine Foundries (Example 642) (a)

Foundry	Characteristics of iron: Tensile strength, psi	Bhn	Composition, %(b): Carbon, Total	Carbon, Graphitic	Carbon, Combined	Si	P	Pearlite and graphite: Size(c)	ASTM type	Speed, sfm(d), for tool life (to 0.010-in. flank wear) of: 60 min	30 min	15 min
A	42,390	210	3.25	2.49	0.76	2.13	0.21	M	B-3	194	221	253
B	42,230	207	3.07	2.39	0.68	2.10	0.11	M	A-3	190	221	258
C	41,110	217	3.22	2.45	0.77	1.88	0.19	M	A-3	186	219	256
D	51,360	190	3.27	2.53	0.74	1.90	0.07	M	A-3	177	212	255
E	36,260	207	3.08	2.28	0.80	1.79	0.12	F	A-3	176	205	235
F	48,870	212	3.00	2.29	0.71	1.96	0.10	F, M	A-4	170	195	225
G	38,780	197	3.04	2.21	0.83	1.26	0.15	M, F	C-3	162	197	242
H	46,720	217	3.27	2.60	0.67	1.46	0.15	M, F	A-3	155	189	230
I	48,800	217	2.82	2.07	0.75	1.46	0.05	M	A, C-4	143	172	204
Average	44,060	208	3.11	2.37	0.75	1.77	0.13	M	...	173	203	240

(a) Data were obtained on cylinders (6¾-in. OD, 4¼-in. ID, 24 in. long) turned in a laboratory lathe, using brazed cutting-tool tips made of C-2 carbide (94% WC, 6% Co; Rockwell A 92). Tool details: 0°, 7°, 7°, 7°, 8°, 0°, 1/32 in. (see Table 1 in the article "Turning" for conventional order of listing tool angles). Depth of cut was 0.160 in.; feed, 0.016 ipr. (b) Molybdenum varied from 0.08 to 0.54%, chromium from 0.03 to 0.15%, nickel from 0.09 to 1.15%, and copper from 0.06 to 0.64%. Tool life did not correlate with the contents of these elements. (c) M = medium; F = fine. (d) Speeds for each iron represent averages of five tests.

Machining Characteristics of Nodular Iron

In nodular iron, the graphite is present as tiny balls or spherulites (not as flakes, as in gray iron), which serve the same useful purposes of chip breaking and lubrication in machining as for gray iron. Although nodular iron has considerably higher tensile strength than gray iron at the same hardness, the machinability of nodular iron is superior in some applications. The data in Fig. 1, obtained in turning tests using carbide tools, show the differences in machinability at two different hardness levels. In the same series of turning tests, gray iron annealed to a fully ferritic condition (100 Bhn; 15,700 psi tensile strength) had the same cutting speed for 200-cu-in. tool life (960 sfm) as fully annealed (ferritized) nodular iron (170 Bhn). This comparison is not necessarily valid for machining operations in general, as contrary results have been observed in drilling gray iron and pearlitic nodular iron at the same hardness.

Machinability data comparing cutting speed and tool life for a ferritic nodular iron (grade 60) with two pearlitic nodular irons (grades 80 and 100), and also showing the effect of a spray cutting fluid on the machining characteristics of the ferritic iron, are given in the following example.

Example 643. Cutting Speed and Tool Life for Ferritic vs Pearlitic Nodular Irons (Fig. 2)

The relation between cutting speed and life of carbide tools (86.4 W, 5.8 C, 2 Ta, 5.75 Co; grade C-2) in turning one ferritic and two pearlitic nodular irons is shown in Fig. 2. Figure 2(a) shows the relation between cutting speed and tool life for ferritic iron (grade 60-45-10), affected by the use and nonuse of a cutting fluid (a 2% mixture of soluble oil in water applied as a spray mist). Improved tool life was obtained with the use of cutting fluid at speeds above about 700 sfm because of the ability of the fluid to reduce tool-flank buildup. Figure 2(b) and (c) show this relation for pearlitic irons (grades 80-60-03 and 100-70-03), as a function of feed rate. An increase in feed caused a decrease in tool life. These two pearlitic irons were machined dry.

In another investigation, a comparison was made between nodular iron and malleable iron castings. The machining operations included facing, boring, threading and drilling. There was no significant difference in machining costs between these two materials when the work was done on a production basis.

In a production test run, costs of machining nodular iron castings at 163 Bhn and steel castings at 149 Bhn were compared. The results, shown in Fig. 3, indicate superior machining qualities for nodular iron. The amount of stock removal was about the same, but the nodular iron castings were closer to pattern and were easier to chuck. It was estimated that about half the saving was a result of better machinability with the remainder caused by mechanical and production factors.

Machining Characteristics of Malleable Iron

A rule of thumb frequently quoted is that the machinability of malleable iron is 25% better than that of free-cutting steel. Although this rule applies to most applications of turning (the usual basis for machinability ratings),

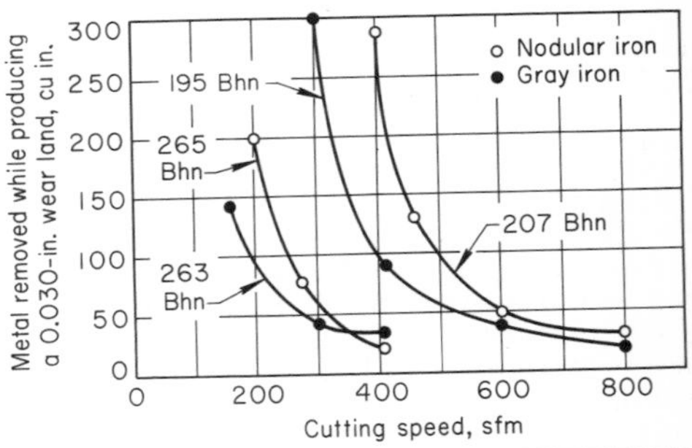

Hardness and type of iron	Tensile strength, psi	Relative speed, sfm(a)
263 Bhn, gray	59,000	150
265 Bhn, nodular	97,000	200
195 Bhn, gray	35,000	325
207 Bhn, nodular	85,000	420

(a) Cutting speed for removing 200 cu in. of metal while producing a wear land of 0.030 in.

Fig. 1. Machinability of gray and nodular irons

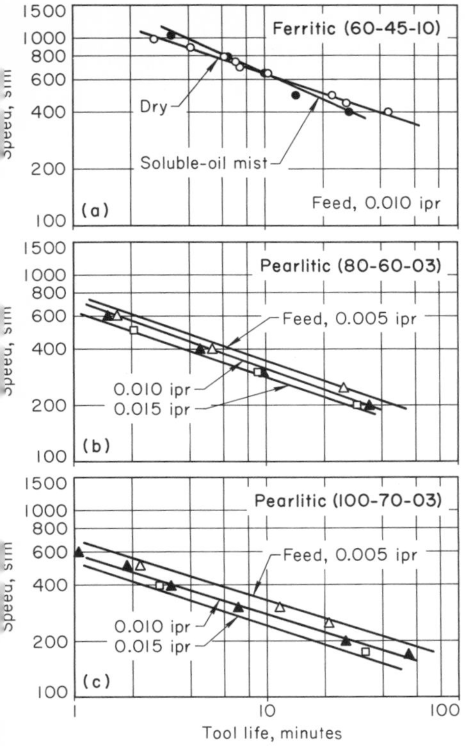

Item	Ferritic 60-45-10(a)	Pearlitic 80-60-03(b)	Pearlitic 100-70-03(c)
Brinell Hardness Number			
Range	159 to 170	204 to 232	229 to 248
Mean	165	214	237
Composition, %			
Carbon:			
Graphitic(d)	3.61	3.06	2.66
Combined(d)	0.18	0.46	0.70
Total	3.79	3.52	3.36
Silicon	2.22	2.23	2.35
Manganese	0.35	0.40	0.84
Phosphorus	0.024	0.059	0.058
Sulfur	0.010	0.022	0.018
Copper	0.061	0.08	0.44
Nickel	0.62	0.42	0.05

(a) Heat treatment: held at 1625 F for 8 hr; cooled to 1275 F, held for 5 hr; cooled to 800 F at 100° F per hour; doors opened. (b) Heat treatment: held at 1625 F for 2 hr; air cooled to 1000 F and held 4 hr; furnace cooled. (c) Heat treatment: held at 1000 F for 2 hr; furnace cooled. (d) Based on analysis of material as received.

For all three irons, the results plotted were obtained in turning test specimens (6½-in. OD, 19 in. long) in a 10-hp engine lathe equipped with a variable-speed drive motor, using C-2 carbide tools. Tool details: —5°, —5°, 5°, 5°, 15°, 15°, 1/16 in. (for explanation of conventional order of listing tool angles, see Table 1, on page 4, in the article "Turning"). Depth of cut was 0.100 in.; tool-life limit, 0.015-in. flank wear.

Fig. 2. Effect of variables on relation between cutting speed and tool life, for three nodular irons (Example 643)

it does not necessarily apply to broaching or some other machining operation. Data on machining of malleable iron are few, probably because machining is seldom a problem, except when some difficulty arises because of surface variations. Pearlitic or decarburized structures at or just below the surface of ferritic malleable castings reduce machinability. (Four surface and subsurface microstructures that represent decreasing suitability for machining are shown in Fig. 16 on page 371 of Volume 1 of this Handbook.)

In Example 644, which follows, a grade 32510 ferritic malleable iron casting was less costly to machine than the class 25 gray iron for which it was substituted. In Example 661, a slightly stronger grade of ferritic malleable iron (grade 35018) was more costly to machine than class 25 gray iron.

Example 644. Malleable vs Gray Iron

Malleable iron (grade 32510) was substituted for gray iron (class 25) as the material for castings on which a spherical boring operation was performed. These castings had a rough weight of 2.3 lb, and a finished weight of 1.87 lb. As indicated in the following comparison, the change reduced boring time by about 30% and boring cost by more than 50%, per piece machined:

	Gray iron	Malleable iron
Boring time, min	1.17	0.81
Boring cost	$0.113	$0.053

The machinability of pearlitic malleable iron is often significantly better than for steel of the same hardness, as illustrated in the following example:

Example 645. Pearlitic Malleable Iron vs 1145 Steel

To reduce machining costs, automotive universal-joint yokes that had formerly been produced as forgings from 1145 steel were cast from pearlitic malleable iron. Comparative data obtained in machining both materials at the same hardness showed that:

1 In broaching splines, steel gave 1800 pieces per grind; pearlitic malleable iron, 15,000 to 20,000 per grind.
2 Drilling production was increased from 600 to 900 pieces per sharpening.
3 Reaming output was increased from 800 to 2400 pieces per sharpening.
4 In grinding, wheels were dressed after every three trays of steel and after every five trays of pearlitic malleable.

Effects of Alloying Elements on Machining Characteristics

With two principal exceptions, alloying elements affect the machining characteristics of cast iron largely through their effects on the relative stability of iron carbide and graphite in the microstructure. The exceptions are phosphorus and tin, both of which affect the matrix.

Phosphorus can have an adverse effect on the machinability of cast iron. When present in quantities above about 0.15%, it occurs as the iron – iron phosphide eutectic, steadite. Steadite may occur in the microstructure independently in gray or nodular cast iron, or in association with the carbide in white or mottled cast irons. The extreme hardness of steadite (as shown in Table 2) and its abrasion resistance markedly reduce tool life in machining pearlitic iron.

Although the presence of more than about 0.2% P causes a significant decrease in machinability, the decrease is structure-sensitive and can be largely offset by converting the matrix in which steadite particles are embedded from its normal (pearlitic) condition to a relatively soft (ferritic) structure. In the latter, which can be produced by using inoculants or by annealing, the soft matrix lacks the rigidity to force steadite particles into abrasive contact with the cutting tools, and the adverse effect on machinability is minimized.

Tin. In contrast to the effect of phosphorus, the addition of tin in small amounts (0.05 to 0.15%) to otherwise unalloyed gray iron increases machinability and tool life, by reducing the range of hardness values throughout the castings and by eliminating hard spots and chilling at corners. Results obtained in machining tin-free and tin-alloyed gray iron castings are compared in the following example.

Example 646. Effect of Tin in Gray Iron on Machinability and Machining Cost (Table 5)

A comparison was made of machining conditions, production rate, tool life, and costs per piece for turning, facing, boring, chamfering and grooving, in a 2A turret lathe, flanged traveler wheels cast from an unalloyed class 25 gray iron and from gray iron of the same composition to which 0.1% tin (as grade A tin) had been added, as shown in Table 5. An illustration of the casting showing the areas machined is also included in Table 5. As these data indicate, the addition of tin, although increasing average hardness, enabled an increase in speed or feed, or both (depending on the surfaces being cut); and although increasing the initial cost per casting, resulted in savings in labor and tooling costs that reduced total cost per piece machined by $0.203.

Because of the increased speeds and feeds possible with the tin-alloyed castings, machining was transferred to an automatic lathe (see machining sequence and operating conditions in Table 5). This effected still further savings in production time and cost per piece, as noted in Table 5.

Effects of Annealing on Machining Characteristics

Castings that require extensive machining may be given suitable annealing treatments prior to machining to decompose any massive carbides present in the as-cast matrix. (For details of heat treating, see the article "Heat Treating of Cast Irons", which begins on page 203 of Volume 2 of this Handbook.)

Annealing for improved machinability is most economical when the casting is small and the amount of machining large; a typical example is a carburetor-flange sub-body. In general, however, gray iron is seldom annealed, because of cost, thermal distortion, and sacrifice of hardness and strength. For example, a typical class 35 gray iron will be downgraded to about class 20 in strength as a result of annealing (Table 6). Gray iron castings for which wear resistance is important, such as cylinder blocks, are not annealed, because of the unsatisfactory service performance of a ferritic matrix.

Cutting Fluid

Cast iron is frequently machined without a cutting fluid, except for certain operations, such as threading, where a lubricant is essential. Conventional cutting fluids are unsatisfactory in machining cast iron, as they form a

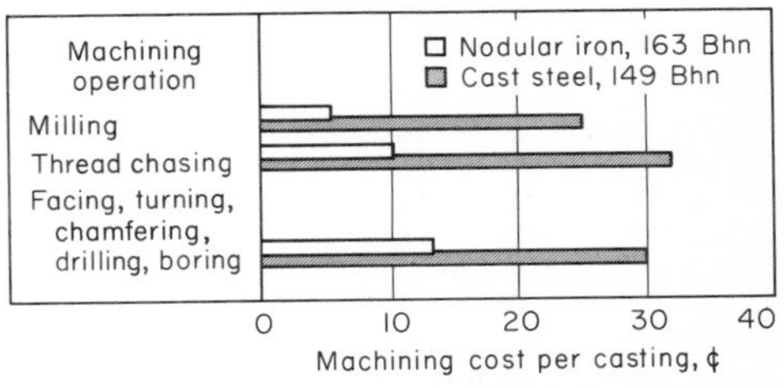

Fig. 3. Machining costs for nodular iron vs cast steel

Table 5. Effect of Addition of Tin to Class 25 Gray Iron on Machinability and Cost (Example 646) (a)

Item	Unalloyed iron	0.1% Sn iron	Item	Unalloyed iron	0.1% Sn iron
Machining in a Turret Lathe(b)					
Machining Conditions			Machining time/pc, min	18	12
Surfaces A to F; M and N:			Tool life, pieces	20	100
Speed, rpm	101	134	**Costs per Piece**		
Speed, sfm(c)	294	390	Material	$3.50	$4.00
Feed, ipr	0.011	0.015	Labor	0.829	0.496
Surfaces G to L:			Tooling	0.72	0.35
Speed, rpm	249	249	Total	$5.049	$4.846
Speed, sfm(c)	228	228	Saving		$0.203
Feed, ipr	0.011	0.015			

Station(d)	Operations	Surfaces machined	Speed, Rpm	Speed, Sfm	Feed, ipr(e)
Machining of 0.1% Sn Iron Castings in an Automatic Lathe(f)					
1	Turning, facing, chamfering, rough boring	A to H; M and N	158	460(c)	0.012
2	Grooving, chamfering	I, J, K and L	260	196	0.003
3	Finish boring	H	428	304	0.012

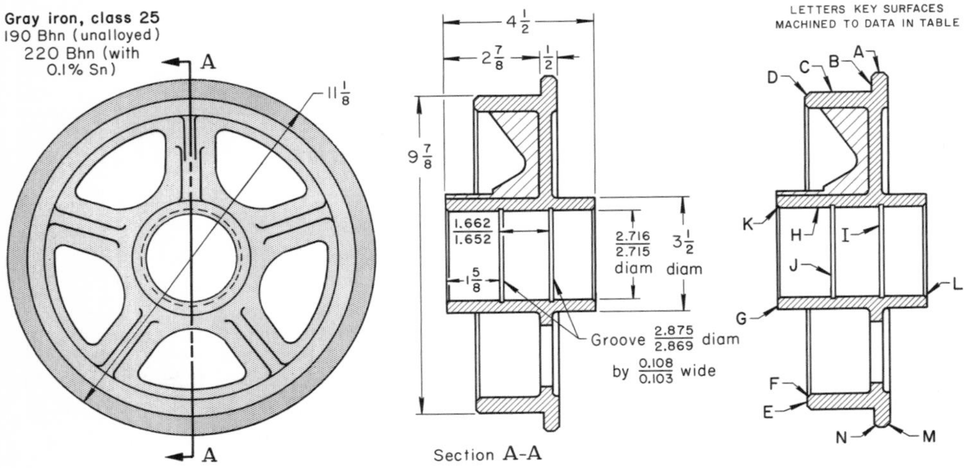

(a) Data are based on machining the letter-identified surfaces of the 27-lb flanged traveler wheel in the sketch above, cast either from an unalloyed class 25 gray iron (3.2 C, 2.22 Si, 0.102 P, 0.021 S, 0.98 Mn, 0.01 Ni, 0.02 Cr, 0.01 Mo) or from gray iron of the same composition to which 0.1% Sn (as Grade A tin) had been added. (b) Castings of both irons were machined with carbide tools, and without cutting fluid. (c) Maximum. (d) Single-spindle automatic lathe used had five stations, of which two were idle. (e) Feeds were lower than those used for the alloyed-iron castings on the turret lathe because several operations were done simultaneously at each station on the automatic lathe. (f) With carbide tools (average life, 150 pieces), and with a proprietary water-base chemical cutting fluid free of chlorine, sulfur and phosphorus. Total machining time per piece was 6 min; total cost per piece machined, $4.63.

slurry with the powdery portion of the iron chips generated in machining, and this may cake in the grooves and crevices of the machine tool. Detergent water-soluble emulsions have been developed specifically for machining iron castings. These fluids do not cause rusting or clogging and are beneficial to tool life.

Because of the excellent cooling properties of water-soluble fluids, rapid generation of thermal cracks may occur in carbide tools under roughing-cut conditions. The portion of the cutting edge that is "buried" in the cut becomes extremely hot, and after leaving the cut is immediately subjected to quenching. This rapid succession of heating and cooling in interrupted cutting causes small thermal cracks, which grow rapidly from the cutting edge and ultimately result in tool breakage. Tool breakage is even more likely to occur when the more crater-resistant grades of carbide are used.

When this type of thermal failure occurs, it is best to eliminate the water or coolant. When cooling of the workpiece is essential, the coolant flow is directed so that it does not strike the tool, but cools only the workpiece.

Dust Control. The machining of cast iron generally produces a quantity of "cast iron dust", which must be prevented from dispersing into the surrounding area. There are two methods for dust control, namely, the use of an acceptable coolant (water-soluble fluids containing a rust inhibitor are most commonly used), or the use of a vacuum or suction system, which has gained wide acceptance. The vacuum system keeps work areas clean and eliminates thermal checks and rusting of machined parts, and is often used to remove the chips themselves.

Turning

All of the common types of tool material (high speed steel, carbide, ceramic oxide, and cast Co-Cr-W alloy) are used in turning operations on cast irons. A comparison of tool material costs for tools of typical sizes is given in Table 7.

High speed steel and cast alloy tools are generally purchased as solid bits; carbide and ceramic oxide tools, as inserts. Steel and cast alloy bits are ground all over; carbide inserts may be purchased as-molded (completely unground), utility-ground (ground on top and bottom), or precision-ground (completely ground on all surfaces). As-molded and utility-ground inserts cost about the same, and are becoming more widely used than precision-ground inserts.

Carbide tools, in a wide range of shapes and rakes, are available as solid tools or as brazed or disposable inserts. Carbide grades C-1, C-2 and C-4 are best suited for roughing and finishing operations where resistance to wear is the sole requirement. A carbide of grade C-3 is preferred where some resistance to cratering is required. The more abrasive irons approximate the machining characteristics of steel and cause tool failure by cratering, especially as cutting speeds are increased. These irons, which contain graphite in nodular form or are rich in carbides, frequently require the use of C-7 or C-8 carbide tooling to resist cratering.

When using a carbide tool, it is often more economical to use a disposable insert in place of a brazed tool of similar composition. An indication of the savings that can be realized by the use of disposable inserts is given in the example that follows:

Example 647. Brazed vs Disposable Carbide Inserts in Turning Class 30 Gray Iron (Table 8)

In turning class 30 gray iron castings (10 in. in diameter by 12 in. long) at a hardness of 195 Bhn, the substitution of carbide inserts for brazed carbide tools of the same composition resulted in an appreciable reduction in machining costs. The initial cost of each disposable insert tool, including depreciation of the $12.15 insert holder, was only $1.53, whereas the initial cost of the brazed tool was $5.07, and cost per cutting edge was $1.10 less for the disposable inserts. When other cost factors, such as overhead, labor and tool-changing time, were included in the calculations, the use of disposable inserts resulted in a saving of 21¢ per casting machined, when both tools were operated at identical speed (230 sfm) and

Table 6. Effect of Annealing on Strength and Hardness of Class 35 Gray Iron(a)

Condition	Tensile strength, psi	Hardness, Bhn
As cast	38,900	217
Annealed	23,900	131

(a) Composition of iron: 3.30 total C, 2.22 Si, 0.027 P, 0.18 S, 0.61 Mn, 0.03 Cr, 0.03 Ni, 0.14 Cu, Mo nil. Annealing treatment consisted of 1 hr at 1425 F, followed by furnace cooling to 1000 F.

Table 7. Comparative Costs of Precision-Ground Tools and Inserts in Several Sizes and Four Materials

Material	Size, in.	Cost, each
Solid Tools		
High speed steel	½ sq, 4 long	$1.80
	1 sq, 7 long	9.80
Cast alloy	½ sq, 4 long	3.31
(Co-Cr-W)	1 sq, 6 long	16.21
Inserts		
C-2 carbide(a)	⅜ sq, ⅛ thick	0.70
	½ sq, 3/16 thick	1.07
	¾ sq, 3/16 thick	1.75
Ceramic oxide	⅜ sq, ⅛ thick	1.47
	½ sq, 3/16 thick	2.40
	¾ sq, 3/16 thick	3.71

(a) Utility-ground or as-molded carbide inserts cost $0.35, $0.70 and $1.38, respectively, for the three sizes listed.

feed (0.020 ipr). These savings were increased to 36¢ per part when the cutting speed for disposable inserts was increased to 310 sfm, despite the fact that tool life per disposable insert decreased. Thus, when disposable inserts were used, it was more efficient to operate at the higher cutting speed, because the benefits of increased production rate outweighed the sacrifice in tool life required to achieve it.

Details of the cost comparison are given in Table 8.

The following example confirms the superiority of disposable inserts over brazed carbide tools for a turning operation over a wide range of speeds.

Example 648. Brazed vs Disposable Inserts in Turning Class 40 Gray Iron (Fig. 4)

Elevator-drive-sleeve support brackets cast from class 40 gray iron were turned in a No. 3 ram-type turret lathe using brazed and disposable-insert tools. The brackets were 5½ in. in outside diameter and 8 in. long, and had an average hardness of 208 Bhn. Under identical conditions, the brazed and disposable inserts were operated at nine speeds, ranging from 100 to 600 sfm, to obtain a comparison of cost per piece and of tool life.

The resulting cost data are plotted in Fig. 4, and the tool-life comparison is tabulated below Fig. 4. As these data indicate, for a straight turning operation at any speed, a disposable-insert tool is preferable to a brazed tool. However, the better speed-cost ratio of the disposable tool was due entirely to reduced tool-replacement costs, and not to superior cutting performance.

Ceramic oxide tools have the highest red hardness of tool materials, but their lack of toughness renders them highly susceptible to chipping and

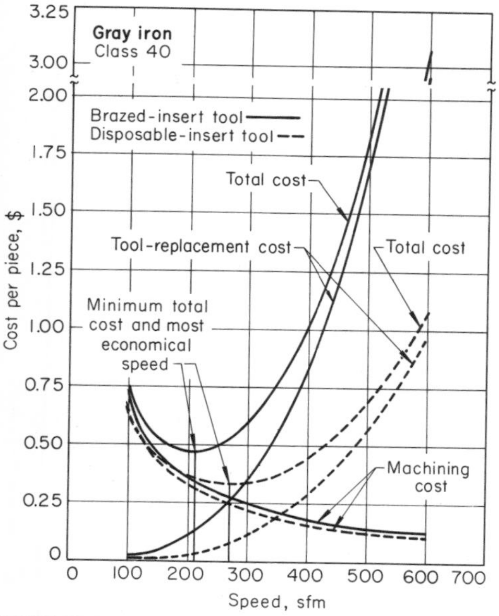

Speed, sfm	Tool life, min	Tool life, pieces machined: Brazed tool	Tool life, pieces machined: Disposable tool
100	700	87.1	97.0
150	140	26.2	34.3
210	35	9.17	10.2
270	12.5	4.31	4.67
300	8.15	3.05	3.40
350	4.40	1.92	2.14
400	2.60	1.29	1.44
500	1.05	0.65	0.73
600	0.50	0.37	0.42

Both tools were of C-2 carbide and of equivalent shape. Also, for both tools, feed was 0.0124 ipr and depth of cut was 0.200 in. No cutting fluid used. Tool-life limit: 0.010-in. flank wear.

Fig. 4. Comparison of costs and tool life for brazed and disposable-insert tools used in turning class 40 gray iron (Example 648)

Table 8. Brazed vs Disposable Carbide Inserts in Turning Class 30 Gray Iron (Example 647) (a)

Item	Brazed insert	Disposable insert
Initial cost of tool	$5.07	$1.53 (b)
Total cutting edges in life of tool	15	8
Grinding time per edge, min	6	None
Tool-changing time, min	5	2
Machine overhead per min (at $6/hr)	$0.10	$0.10
Machine operation per min (at $3/hr)	0.05	0.05
Total machining cost per min	$0.15	$0.15
Toolroom overhead per min (at $2.50/hr)	$0.0416	None
Tool grinding per min (at $2.50/hr)	0.0416	None
Total grinding cost per min	$0.083	None
Tool cost per cutting edge:		
Initial cost	$5.07/15 = $0.338	$1.53/8 = $0.19
Grinding	$0.083 × 6 = 0.50	...
Tool-change	$0.15 × 5 = 0.75	$0.15 × 2 = 0.30
Total	$1.59	$0.49
Saving per cutting edge		$1.10
Turning at 88 Rpm (230 Sfm)(c)		
Tool life per edge, pieces	5.4	5.4
Tool cost per piece	$1.59/5.4 = $0.30	$0.49/5.4 = $0.09
Turning cost per piece (6.8 min × $0.15)	1.02	1.02
	$1.32	$1.11
Saving per piece		$0.21
Turning at 119 Rpm (310 Sfm)(d)		
Tool life per edge, pieces	...	2.3
Tool cost per piece	...	$0.49/2.3 = $0.21
Turning cost per piece (5 min × $0.15)	...	0.75
Total cost per piece	...	$0.96
Saving per piece, over use of brazed tool at 230 sfm		$0.36

(a) For turning 10-in.-OD, 12-in.-long castings at 195 Bhn. Both types of tools were of the same grade of carbide. (b) Based on $1.47 per insert plus $0.06 for depreciation of $12.15 holder over use with 200 inserts. (c) Data are based on turning time per piece (at 0.020-ipr feed) of 6.8 min, and tool life of 37 min per edge, at this speed. (d) Data are based on turning time per piece (at 0.020-ipr feed) of 5 min, and tool life of 11.5 min per edge, at this speed. Calculations were not made for brazed tools, as use of this speed obviously would be uneconomical because of the high cost involved in frequent tool changing necessitated by shorter tool life.

breakage. They cannot be brazed to tool shanks, but can be attached with an adhesive. Thus, they must be ground with extreme care if damage to the adhesive bond is to be avoided. Because of this limitation, ceramic tools are generally used as disposable inserts. Also, because the tools are relatively weak, negative rakes are always used (in some applications as high as 25°), and the edges are honed to minimize failure by chipping. Ceramic inserts are limited to triangular, square or round shapes; all shapes are precision ground. Additional information on ceramic tools is given in the article "Ceramic Materials for Single-Point Turning Tools", which begins on page 322 of this volume.

Cast Co-Cr-W alloy tools can be used at about twice the surface cutting speed of high speed steel tools. In machining cast irons, they are used primarily in form turning, but are used also for interrupted cuts that might cause carbide tools to chip or break, or where the hardness of the work material prevents the satisfactory use of high speed steel tools.

Side cutting-edge angles (or lead angles) are recommended wherever the part design or machining operation does not require a square shoulder. With a lead angle, the tool can make a more gradual entrance to, and exit from, the cut. Whenever the tool is required to make a total exit, as in facing to a bore or hole, or in facing from the inside diameter to the outside diameter, cast iron is likely to break out at the exit edge unless a lead angle is used. The higher the feed rate and the duller the tool, the more accented is the breakout. Lead angles of 15° to 45° are used for turning cast irons. Although the 45° lead gives the least breakout and best tool life, it also increases the radial pressure on the workpiece, and in some applications may cause too much deflection.

An effective lead angle is also obtained through the use of round inserts; these are excellent for cutting workpieces that require interrupted

Table 9. Rake Angles of Brazed Carbide Tools for Turning Castings of Various Hardnesses and Surface Conditions

Hardness of casting, Bhn	Rake angle: Side-cutting tools (side rake)	Rake angle: End-cutting tools (end rake)
For Turning Clean Surfaces		
100 to 200	15°	10°
200 to 325	8°	8°
325 to 425	3° to 5°	5°
425 to 500	0°	0°
For Interrupted Cuts or Scaly Surfaces		
100 to 200	0°	0°
200 to 325	−3°	−5°
325 to 425	−5°	−8°
425 to 500	−8° to −10°	−10°

Table 10. Effect of Rake Angle on Cost of ½-In.-IC Triangular C-2 Carbide Inserts

Rake angle	Cost per insert	Number of edges	Cost per edge
Positive (a)	$1.62	3	$0.54
Negative (a)	1.18	6	0.20
Negative, with positive-rake groove (b)	0.87	6	0.15

(a) Precision-ground insert. (b) Precision-pressed insert with integral chip breaker.

Table 11. Nominal Speeds and Feeds for Turning of Cast Iron With Single-Point and Box Tools

ASTM grade	Brinell hardness	Rough turning (depth of cut, 0.150 in.) Speed, sfm(a) HSS tools(b)	Carbide tools(c) Brazed	Carbide tools(c) Disposable	Finish turning (depth of cut, 0.025 in.) Speed, sfm(d) HSS tools(b)	Carbide tools(e) Brazed	Carbide tools(e) Disposable
Gray Irons							
Classes 20 and 25	110 to 140	140	460	530	180	575	660
Class 30	150 to 190	85	350	400	135	460	530
Classes 35 and 40	190 to 220	70	280	325	110	350	400
Classes 45 and 50	220 to 260	50	225	265	80	275	325
Classes 55 and 60	250 to 320	30 (f)	115 (f)	130 (f)	45 (h)	160 (h)	180 (h)
Nodular Irons							
60-48-18; 65-45-12	140 to 190	140	460	530	180	575	660
80-55-06	190 to 225	100	325	375	130	400	460
	225 to 260	75	250	290	90	300	350
100-70-03	240 to 300	60 (f)	200 (f)	230 (f)	75 (h)	250 (h)	290 (h)
120-90-02	270 to 330	30 (g)	120 (g)	140 (g)	45 (h)	160 (h)	185 (h)
	330 to 400	...	50 (h)	65 (h)	...	65 (h)	80 (h)
Malleable Irons							
32510 and 35018	110 to 160	200	700	850	275	900	1100
45007, 45010, 48004, 50007	160 to 200	90	300	375	120	400	475
	200 to 240	70	225	300	95	325	400
53004 and 60003	200 to 255	60 (j)	200	260	85 (j)	300	375
80002	240 to 280	45 (g)	150 (g)	200 (g)	70 (h)	250 (h)	325 (h)

(a) Feed, 0.015 ipr. (b) High speed steels M2 and T5, except T15, M41, M42, M43 and M44 for hardness above about 220 to 240 Bhn. (c) Grade C-2 carbide. (d) Feed, 0.007 ipr. (e) Grade C-3 carbide. (f) Feed, 0.012 ipr. (g) Feed, 0.010 ipr. (h) Feed, 0.005 ipr. (j) High speed steels M2, T5 and T15. (Data are adapted from tables compiled by Metcut Research Associates, Inc.)

Table 12. Nominal Speeds and Feeds for Turning of Cast Iron With Form Tools

ASTM Grade	Brinell hardness	High speed steel tools(a) Speed, sfm	Feed, ipr, for tool width of: ½ in.	1 in.	2 in.	Carbide tools(b) Speed, sfm	Feed, ipr, for tool width of: ½ in.	1 in.	2 in.
Gray Irons									
Classes 20 and 25	110 to 140	105	0.008	0.006	0.004	345	0.016	0.012	0.008
Class 30	150 to 190	65	0.006	0.004	0.004	260	0.012	0.010	0.007
Classes 35 and 40	190 to 220	50	0.004	0.004	0.002	210	0.007	0.007	0.005
Classes 45 and 50	220 to 260	40	0.003	0.002	0.0015	165	0.005	0.004	0.003
Classes 55 and 60	250 to 320	20	0.0025	0.0015	0.0015	85	0.0045	0.0035	0.0025
Nodular Irons									
60-48-18; 65-45-12	140 to 190	105	0.006	0.004	0.004	345	0.012	0.010	0.007
80-55-06	190 to 225	75	0.0045	0.003	0.003	245	0.009	0.006	0.005
	225 to 260	55	0.003	0.002	0.0015	190	0.005	0.004	0.003
100-70-03	240 to 300	45	0.0025	0.0015	0.0015	150	0.0045	0.0035	0.003
120-90-02	270 to 330	20	0.0025	0.0015	0.0015	85	0.0045	0.0035	0.0025
	330 to 400	..	.....	.....	.....	35	0.004	0.003	0.002
Malleable Irons									
32510 and 35018	110 to 160	150	0.004	0.003	0.0025	525	0.0075	0.006	0.0045
45007, 45010, 48004, 50007	160 to 200	65	0.0035	0.0035	0.0025	225	0.007	0.0065	0.005
	200 to 240	50	0.0025	0.002	0.0015	170	0.0055	0.004	0.003
53004 and 60003	200 to 255	45	0.0025	0.002	0.0015	150	0.0055	0.004	0.003
80002	240 to 280	35	0.0025	0.002	0.0015	110	0.0045	0.003	0.002

(a) High speed steels M2 and T5, except T15, M41, M42, M43 and M44 for hardness above about 220 to 240 Bhn. (b) Grade C-2 carbide. (SOURCE: same as for Table 11)

Table 13. Nominal Speeds and Feeds for Turning of Cast Iron With Cutoff Tools

ASTM grade	Brinell hardness	High speed steel tools(a) Speed, sfm	Feed, ipr, for tool width of: 1/16 in.	⅛ in.	¼ in.	Carbide tools(b) Speed, sfm	Feed, ipr, for tool width of: 1/16 in.	⅛ in.	¼ in.
Gray Irons									
Classes 20 and 25	110 to 140	105	0.005	0.008	0.010	345	0.010	0.016	0.020
Class 30	150 to 190	65	0.004	0.006	0.008	260	0.008	0.012	0.015
Classes 35 and 40	190 to 220	50	0.003	0.004	0.005	210	0.007	0.008	0.010
Classes 45 and 50	220 to 260	40	0.002	0.003	0.003	165	0.004	0.006	0.007
Classes 50 and 60	250 to 320	20	0.0015	0.0025	0.0025	85	0.0035	0.0045	0.005
Nodular Irons									
60-48-18; 65-45-12	140 to 190	105	0.004	0.006	0.008	345	0.008	0.012	0.015
80-55-06	190 to 225	75	0.003	0.0045	0.0055	245	0.006	0.009	0.011
	225 to 260	55	0.002	0.003	0.003	190	0.004	0.006	0.007
100-70-03	240 to 300	45	0.0015	0.0025	0.0025	150	0.0035	0.0045	0.005
120-90-02	270 to 330	20	0.0015	0.0025	0.0025	85	0.0035	0.0045	0.005
	330 to 400	..	.....	.....	.....	35	0.003	0.004	0.0045
Malleable Irons									
32510 and 35018	110 to 160	150	0.003	0.004	0.005	525	0.0055	0.0075	0.009
45007, 45010, 48004, 50007	160 to 200	65	0.0035	0.004	0.005	225	0.0065	0.008	0.010
	200 to 240	50	0.002	0.003	0.003	170	0.004	0.005	0.006
53004 and 60003	200 to 255	45	0.002	0.003	0.003	150	0.004	0.005	0.006
80002	240 to 280	35	0.002	0.003	0.003	110	0.0035	0.004	0.005

(a) High speed steels M2 and T5, except T15, M41, M42, M43 and M44 for hardness above about 220 to 240 Bhn. (b) Grade C-2 carbide. (SOURCE: same as for Table 11)

cuts. Round inserts allow higher feed rates, while maintaining a good surface finish.

In the machining of chilled cast iron rolls, a lead angle of 75° is generally used, together with a small nose radius blending the side cutting edge and a 0° end cutting-edge angle. A negative-back-rake land of 5° to 10° strengthens the edge. The higher the hardness of the roll material, the higher the negative rake. In these applications, C-1 carbide is often used for roughing, and C-2 for finishing.

End Cutting-Edge Angle. When using inserts, the size of the end cutting-edge angle depends on the shape of the insert as well as on the size of the lead angle. A square insert is generally stronger because it has a 90°-included-angle nose, as compared with a 60° nose for a triangular insert. A square insert with a 15° lead angle also has a 15° end cutting-edge angle. In triangular inserts a 15° lead angle has a 45° end cutting-edge angle, whereas a 0° lead angle has an end cutting-edge angle of 30°.

For the best surface finishes, the use of a 1° end cutting-edge angle combined with 1/16-in. nose radius is recommended. This combination is intended for shallow finishing cuts (0.015 to 0.020 in. deep).

With high speed steel or brazed carbide tools, a broad-nosed tool with 0° end cutting-edge angle and positive back rake permits the use of heavy feed rates while yielding good surface finish.

Nose radius should be as large as possible, to obtain optimum surface finish, but not so large as to cause work deflection or chatter. Normal insert radii range from 1/64 to ⅛ in.; the finished part configuration often dictates the required shoulder radius, and consequently the nose radius to be used. When round inserts are used, the radius can vary from 3/16 to ⅝ in.

Rake Angles. High speed steel and cast Co-Cr-W alloy tools are provided with positive rake angles to obtain better cutting action at normal cutting speeds. Because these tool materials are much stronger than many of the carbides, they accommodate positive rake angles more easily. Most standard brazed carbide tools are ground with 4° to 10° side or back rake, depending on the direction of cutting and the style of tool used. But as the hardness of the iron or the degree of surface roughness increases, rake angle is decreased, as shown in Table 9.

With disposable carbide inserts, it is possible to select a positive rake, a negative rake, or a combination negative rake with a positive-rake groove. Tool costs vary, depending on which of these designs is selected, as shown by the data on C-2 carbide inserts presented in Table 10.

In addition to their cost advantage over positive-rake inserts, negative-rake inserts are much stronger and yield better results on workpieces that are of higher hardness or exhibit a scaly or uneven surface. Negative rakes are particularly effective in cutting the segmental, discontinuous type of chip that is characteristic of cast irons. In general, turning operations should be-

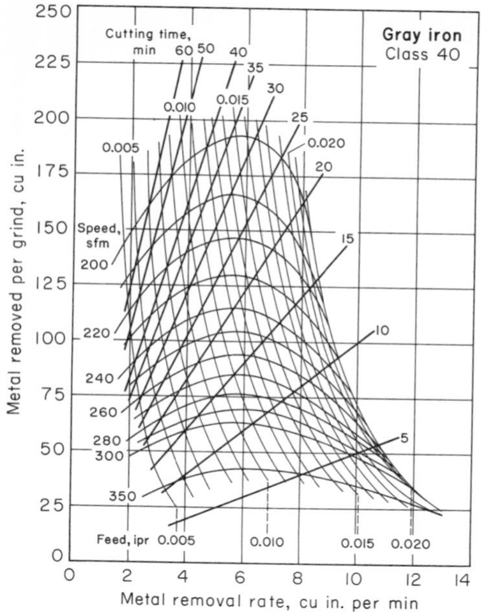

Data were obtained in turning with C-2 carbide tools, taking a 0.160-in.-deep cut, to a tool-life limit of 0.010-in. flank wear.

Fig. 5. Interrelation of machining variables in turning class 40 gray irons

gin with negative-rake tooling, except for workpieces of certain shapes, such as those with thin walls, that require the use of positive rakes.

Relief (Clearance) Angles. Relief angles for normal turning and facing tools of the 5°-negative-rake type are 5°; the normal side clearance on 6° positive-rake insert tooling is 5°, with 11° end clearance, and on brazed tools it is 5° to 7°. If a positive-rake insert is placed in a neutral-rake holder (0° back and side rake) an 11° clearance angle is obtained. This is because the insert has an 11° angle. This combination is sometimes used in finishing operations. Under these conditions, the wear land does not develop as rapidly as on a 5°-clearance insert, because the wear is spread over a larger area, and therefore cutting or feeding pressure remains lower. For example, when a tool with a clearance angle of 5° wears 0.0055 in. (radial wear from the cutting edge), the width of flank wear is 1/16 in. In contrast, when the clearance angle is 11°, the width of flank wear is only 1/32 in. for the same amount of radial wear. In boring, the end clearance angle must be increased as the bore size decreases, and boring tools often will have to be of the brazed or solid carbide type because there is not enough room for a properly designed holder and its parts.

Honing of Cutting Edges. In order to strengthen the cutting edges of carbide and ceramic tools, the entire cutting edge is sometimes lightly honed or rounded. This minimizes chipping or breaking of the tool edge, especially with ceramic tools.

The harder the workpiece, the less extensive the honing should be. Excessive honing usually makes cutting more difficult and results in increased breakage of the workpiece at exit edges. On ceramic tools, a 20°-negative-rake land, 0.010 in. wide, is sometimes substituted for honing, because it provides a sharper edge with adequate strength.

Speed and Feed. Among the major variables that affect the selection of turning speeds and feeds are the microstructure and hardness of the casting and the type of tool material used.

Nominal speeds and feeds for turning the frequently used grades of gray iron, nodular iron and malleable iron with several types of high speed steel and carbide tools, are listed in Tables 11, 12 and 13.

In production turning, it is often desirable — or even necessary — to select cutting speed and feed on the basis of a desired metal removal rate and tool life (in volume of metal removed per grind). The chart in Fig. 5, constructed from data obtained in turning the class 40 gray irons described in Example 642, represents a considerable range of chemical compositions, microstructures and hardnesses. From this chart, several machining variables can be readily estimated. For example, it is possible to estimate the speed to be used at a given feed, or the feed at a given speed, for attaining tool life of any specified time; or, inversely, to estimate the tool-life time that will result from various combinations of speed and feed. Maximum production rates can often be obtained by using the highest possible feed, reducing speed if necessary. Rigid setups are needed to make best use of this procedure.

Effects of feed, depth of cut, nose radius and side cutting-edge angle on speed in turning class 30 gray iron are indicated in Table 14 for high speed steel tools and Table 15 for carbide tools. The effects of the changes in nose radius and side cutting-edge angle of high speed steel tools on speed for turning gray iron are much smaller than for turning carbon and low-alloy steels. (Compare Tables 14, 15 and 16 here with Tables 7, 8 and 9, page 10 in the article "Turning" in this volume.)

Production examples describing conditions used in the turning of cast iron are given in the section on Multiple-Operation Machining in this article. In these examples, turning was one of several operations performed in a turret lathe or automatic machine. Five additional examples in which turning was done in conjunction with other operations are given in the article on Multiple-Operation Machining, which begins on page 147 in this volume, and three examples that describe the turning of gray iron appear in the article "Turning", which begins on page 1.

The following example indicates the superiority of turning over grinding in processing a cylindrical surface deformed by mold mismatch. Mismatch is not an uncommon problem in the production of castings, and this example describes a method for salvaging mismatched castings that might otherwise have had to be scrapped.

Example 649. Turning vs Grinding for Cleaning Up Mismatch (Fig. 6)

Mold mismatch in the white iron casting shown in Fig. 6 necessitated cleanup machining of 50% of the castings. Originally, center-

Table 14. Effect of Variables on Cutting Speed for 60-Min Tool Life in Turning Class 30 Gray Iron With T1 High Speed Steel Tools(a)

Depth of cut, in.	Speed, sfm, for feed, ipr, of: 0.002	0.004	0.008	1/64	1/32	1/16	1/8
Tool No. 1 (SCEA, 0°; NR, none)(b)							
1/32	169	127	97	77	63	62	62
1/16	168	126	96	76	61	52	49
1/8	168	126	96	74	58	48	41
1/4	166	126	94	73	56	45	37
1/2	165	124	93	71	53	41	32
1	165	123	92	68	51	37	28
Tool No. 2 (SCEA, 0°; NR, 1/16 in.)(b)							
1/32	227	174	131	103	84	73	66
1/16	203	153	116	91	73	58	54
1/8	186	140	107	82	66	54	47
1/4	178	132	100	77	60	48	41
1/2	171	128	96	73	56	43	35
1	168	125	93	70	52	39	28
Tool No. 3 (SCEA, 30°; NR, 1/8 in.)(b)							
1/32	282	212	159	122	96	77	69
1/16	230	172	130	100	78	63	56
1/8	206	154	122	89	69	56	47
1/4	192	143	107	82	63	50	41
1/2	185	137	102	77	58	45	35
1	180	134	99	74	55	41	30
Tool No. 4 (SCEA, 30°; NR, 1/4 in.)(b)							
1/32	302	226	171	131	101	80	69
1/16	281	210	157	120	92	71	60
1/8	225	171	128	97	75	59	48
1/4	205	153	114	88	67	52	41
1/2	191	143	105	80	60	46	36
1	183	136	101	76	56	41	28
Finishing Tool(c)							
0.005 ..	309	219	187	154	133	117	111
0.010 ..	263	202	156	127	106	93	87
0.015 ..	242	181	142	114	95	82	75

(a) Metal cut: Carbon, 2.88 total, 0.32 combined; silicon, 1.47; tensile strength, 30,000 psi; 177 Bhn. No cutting fluid used. (b) BR, 8°; SR, 14°; ER, 6°; SRF, 6°; ECEA, 6°. (c) BR, 20°; SR, 0°; ER, 6°; SRF, 6°; ECEA, 6°; SCEA, 0°; NR, 1/8 in.; flat, 1/8 in. (Source of table: ASME Manual on Cutting of Metals, 2nd ed, 1952)

Table 15. Effect of Variables on Cutting Speed for 60-Min Tool Life in Turning Class 30 Gray Iron With Carbide Tools(a)

Depth of cut, in.	Speed, sfm, for feed, ipr, of: 0.002	0.004	0.008	1/64	1/32	1/16	1/8
Tool No. 1 (SCEA, 0°; NR, none)(b)							
1/32 ...	592	444	334	255	201	201	201
1/16 ...	591	443	334	253	195	156	155
1/8	590	442	331	251	191	149	120
1/4	589	441	330	249	188	144	112
1/2	588	439	327	246	184	139	105
1	587	438	325	244	180	134	98
Tool No. 2 (SCEA, 0°; NR, 1/16 in.)(b)							
1/32 ...	814	611	461	382	289	243	222
1/16 ...	715	536	405	311	247	202	176
1/8	658	494	371	282	221	177	148
1/4	629	467	350	265	204	159	129
1/2	608	456	337	255	193	147	115
1	598	444	330	248	185	138	104
Tool No. 3 (SCEA, 30°; NR, 1/8 in.)(b)							
1/32 ...	1003	752	561	427	330	263	236
1/16 ...	812	608	456	348	267	213	186
1/8	730	544	431	309	236	185	154
1/4	681	506	379	287	217	167	135
1/2	654	486	360	273	205	155	120
1	630	475	353	264	197	146	109
Tool No. 4 (SCEA, 30°; NR, 1/4 in.)(b)							
1/32 ...	1076	805	606	460	353	276	237
1/16 ...	995	743	556	421	319	246	202
1/8	799	605	451	342	260	200	162
1/4	726	540	403	305	230	175	139
1/2	675	505	375	283	212	160	121
1	649	485	360	270	200	149	111
Finishing Tool(c)							
0.005 .	1100	779	660	543	469	414	392
0.010 .	938	717	548	445	371	326	302
0.015 .	859	654	502	398	329	285	261

(a) Metal cut: Carbon, 2.88 total, 0.32 combined; silicon, 1.41; tensile strength, 30,000 psi; 177 Bhn. No cutting fluid used. (b) BR, 8°; SR, 14°; ER, 6°; SRF, 6°; ECEA, 6°. (c) BR, 20°; SR, 0°; ER, 6°; SRF, 6°; ECEA, 6°; SCEA, 0°; NR, 1/8 in.; flat, 1/8 in. (Source of table: ASME Manual on Cutting of Metals, 2nd ed, 1952)

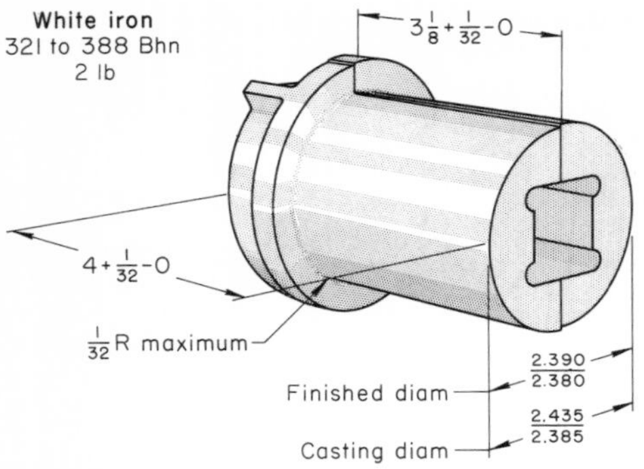

Operating Conditions for Turning

Machine	No. 5 ram-type turret lathe
Speed	274 rpm (172 sfm)
Feed	0.019 ipr
Depth of cut	0 to 0.030 in.
Cutting fluid	None
Tool	Disposable carbide insert (six edges)
Setup time	½ hr
Downtime for tool change	0.15 min
Tool life, pieces	17 per edge (102 per insert)
Production rate	33 pieces per hour

Turning vs Cylindrical Grinding

(Time and cost per piece)

	Grinding	Turning
Machine time, min	3.13	0.84
Handling time, min	1.00	0.97
Total time, min	4.13	1.81
Cost per piece	\$0.5213	\$0.1971
Saving		\$0.3242

Fig. 6. Casting for which lathe turning was more economical than cylindrical grinding for cleaning up mismatch (Example 649)

less grinding was tried, but could not be used because the mismatch caused wheel breakage — a safety hazard.

Cylindrical grinding was successful, but, despite the use of two mandrels to enable the operator to load and unload during the grinding cycle, total time per piece was too high. Moreover, wheels of all grades tried wore excessively.

Finally the casting was turned on a No. 5 ram-type turret lathe, under the conditions tabulated with Fig. 6. As the time and cost data show, turning reduced total time per piece by 56%, and cost per piece by 62%, in comparison with cylindrical grinding.

The following example describes an application in which it was necessary to perform secondary lathe-turning operations on gray iron castings after hardening.

Example 650. Eight Machining Operations on a Thin-Wall Cylinder Liner at Rockwell C 45 to 55 (Fig. 7)

Figure 7 shows a thin-wall (0.34 to 0.125 in.) cylinder liner, cast from class 30B gray iron and quenched and tempered to Rockwell C 45 to 55, on which eight machining operations were required prior to grinding and honing. Five of these operations (turning the outside diameter, boring, turning the recessed porthole band, drilling the portholes, and turning the flange) were performed on liners in the as-cast annealed condition. However, the three other operations — facing the inside of the flange, turning the 0.12-in.-wide undercut, and cutting a spiral scroll (like phonograph-record grooves) on the end — had to be done after the iron was hardened. Otherwise, warpage during heat treatment would have caused the machined castings to be outside dimensional tolerances.

The three secondary machining operations were done on an automatic lathe, using two carbide-insert tools (brazed, for facing and undercutting; disposable, for scrolling) on the rear carriage, as illustrated in Fig. 7. The use of the expanding mandrel, attached to the spindle face, provided the rigidity required for keeping the inherently fragile thin-wall casting on center. Tool life (see operating conditions with Fig. 7) was short because of the high hardness of the castings.

Boring

General aspects of the machining methods of boring and discussions on the equipment, tools and procedures used, together with 25 examples of boring cast iron parts, are given in the article "Boring", which begins on page 20.

Nominal speeds and feeds for boring the frequently used grades of gray iron, nodular iron and malleable iron with high speed steel and carbide tools are listed in Table 17.

Broaching

When high speed steel broaches are used, cutting speeds up to 30 sfm are feasible for certain grades of cast iron; cutting speeds do not exceed 20 sfm for most grades. With carbide broaches, much higher speeds (up to about 150 sfm) are attainable, if the power is available and the setup is rigid.

Table 18 lists nominal speeds and feeds for broaching cast iron with high speed steel tools.

Face angles of about 8° to 12° are recommended for the cutting teeth of broaches used on cast irons. Roughing teeth are usually given clearance of 2° to 3°, semifinishing teeth about 1°, and finishing teeth about ½°.

Fixtures are used to position the part accurately in relation to the broach and to avoid distortion of the parts during broaching. It is always preferable to have the fixture clamp over the heavier sections of the workpiece. Support at the surface being broached is essential to prevent chatter, hold tolerance, and attain acceptable tool life. A cutting fluid is sometimes used to cool the workpiece and reduce the possibility that it might suffer heat distortion.

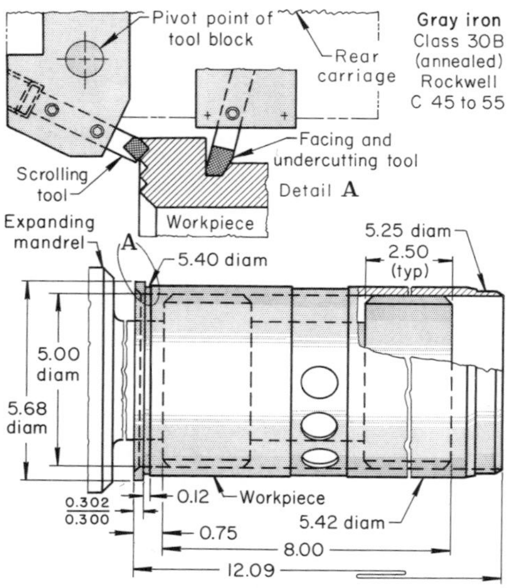

Speed	144 rpm (214 sfm max)
Feed	0.020 ipr
Depth of cut	0.025 in.
Cutting fluid	Soluble-oil:water (1:20)
Production rate	54.4 pieces per hour
Tool material	Carbide(a)
Tool life per grind or corner	24 pieces
Downtime for tool change	10 min

(a) Brazed insert for facing and undercutting, disposable insert for scrolling

Fig. 7. Tooling and workholding arrangement for facing, undercutting and scrolling a thin-wall cylinder liner after hardening (Example 650)

Table 16. Comparison of Cutting Speeds for 60-Min Tool Life in Turning Three Different Grades of Gray Iron With T1 High Speed Steel Tools(a)

Depth of cut, in.	Speed, sfm, for feed, ipr, of: 0.002	0.004	0.008	1/64	1/32	1/16	1/8
Soft Iron (127 Bhn)(b)							
1/32	473	354	266	204	160	129	115
1/16	383	287	217	167	130	105	93
1/8	344	257	204	149	115	93	79
1/4	320	239	179	137	105	83	68
1/2	308	229	171	129	97	75	58
1	301	223	165	124	92	68	50
Class 30 Iron (177 Bhn)(c)							
1/32	282	212	159	122	96	77	69
1/16	230	172	130	100	78	63	56
1/8	206	154	122	89	69	56	47
1/4	192	143	107	82	63	50	41
1/2	185	137	102	77	58	45	35
1	180	134	99	74	55	41	30
Class 50 Iron (224 Bhn)(d)							
1/32	169	126	95	73	57	46	41
1/16	137	102	77	60	46	37	33
1/8	123	92	73	53	41	33	28
1/4	114	85	64	49	37	30	24
1/2	110	82	61	46	35	27	21
1	107	80	59	44	33	24	18

(a) Tool angles: BR, 8°; SR, 14°; ER, 6°; SRF, 6°; ECEA, 6°; SCEA, 30°; NR, 1/8 in. (b) Carbon, 3.71 total; silicon, 1.80; tensile strength, 17,000 psi. No cutting fluid used. (c) Carbon, 2.88 total, 0.32 combined; silicon, 1.47; tensile strength, 30,000 psi. No cutting fluid used. (d) Carbon, 3.80 total, 0.90 combined; silicon, 2.85; tensile strength, 50,000 psi. No cutting fluid used. (Source of table: ASME Manual on Cutting of Metals, 2nd ed, 1952)

The three examples that follow describe broaching of gray and ferritic malleable iron castings. See also Examples 105, 115, 116, 130 and 131 on cast iron in the article "Broaching".

Example 651. Simultaneous Broaching of Four Class 30 Gray Iron Bearing Caps in Line (Fig. 8)

Because of high production output (206,000 pieces per year), broaching was used in preference to milling or boring for machining 3.760/3.740-in.-diam half-round openings in 1.38-in.-wide bearing caps cast from class 30 gray iron (Fig. 8). Milling or boring would have been used had the annual production been 6000 pieces or less. Four castings were clamped in a special fixture and were broached simultaneously (four halves in a line). Broaching was done in single-ram, 25-ton vertical machines with 66-in. maximum stroke; one man operated three machines.

Full-round broaches made of high speed steel were used, each consisting of four segments as detailed in Fig. 8. When regrinding was required, larger segments were ground to the dimensions of the next smaller one; thus only segment 4 had to be supplied.

Operating conditions, results and cost data are tabulated below Fig. 8. No surface finish was specified, because caps were finish bored in final assembly.

Example 652. Multiple-Operation Broaching of Ferritic Malleable Iron Bearing Caps (Fig. 9)

Seven separate areas of main-bearing caps cast from ferritic malleable iron were machined in one return pass of a multiple-cutter broach. The two side surfaces, the two parting-line faces, and the half-round surface were roughed by six successive broach segments like the one shown at the top center of Fig. 9. The side faces, the parting-line faces, and the chamfers were finished in the same return stroke by the six broach segments (top left in Fig. 9) on the same tool fixture. (The half-round surface was finished in a subsequent boring operation.)

Broaching was done in a two-way, 25-hp horizontal machine with hydraulic drive and a 125-in. maximum stroke. Three other operations (not detailed here) were performed on the forward stroke. Operating conditions and cost data for the return-stroke broaching are listed below Fig. 9.

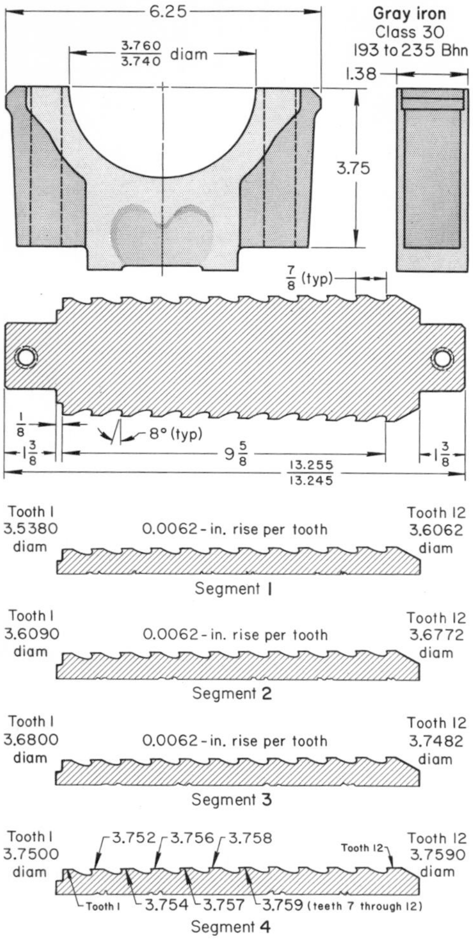

Operating Conditions

Broach speed, sfm	20 (cutting), 40 (return)
Metal removed per piece	0.3 lb
Length of cut	5.52 in.(a)
Depth of cut	0.087 in.
Cutting fluid	None
Broach material	High speed steel
Production rate	93.9 pieces per hour
Tool life per grind	50,000 pieces (25,000 pairs)
Downtime for tool change	½ hr

Cost Data

Initial cost of broaching machine	$35,000
Initial cost of broaches:	
Details 1, 2 and 3 (at $180 each)	$540
Detail 4	200
Total	$740
Regrinding time, each broach detail	18.15 hr

(a) Four castings, stacked, were broached simultaneously.

Fig. 8. Bearing cap (top), and details of the four-segment round broach used for sizing the half-round section in four castings simultaneously under conditions tabulated above (Example 651)

Example 653. Broaching to Align Seating Surfaces on Small Ferritic Malleable Iron Castings (Fig. 10)

Broaching was selected as the most economical method of correcting slight dimensional irregularities in the 90° seating surfaces of the ferritic malleable iron idler shaft bracket shown in Fig. 10. These irregularities had resulted in misalignment of the parts (originally intended for use as-cast) in final assembly.

Castings to be broached were supplied annealed, but no change in design was made. Consequently, broaching had to be done with a minimum of stock removal, and the broach cut (up to 0.025 in. deep) was mainly confined to the decarburized zone.

Broaching was done in a 24-ton-capacity horizontal hydraulic machine. Two castings, held opposite each other as shown at the left in Fig. 10, were broached in one pass of the square-section broach used. Additional processing details are tabulated below Fig. 10.

Planing and Shaping

Planing and shaping are used principally for the production of flat and angular surfaces. The machines employed in these operations are designed to make straight-line cuts, and the cutting tools used in both operations are identical except for size.

Tool Design. The principles that govern the shape of turning tools (see discussion in the section on Turning in this article) also apply to tools for planing. The amount of back rake and side rake provided depends on the hardness of the material, and the resultant rake and inclination should be negative. The end relief should be about 4° to 8° for planer tools, because a planer tool is held about square with the platen, whereas a lathe tool, the height and inclination of which can be varied, may not always be clamped in the same position.

(For illustrations showing details of planing and shaping tools suitable for use on cast iron, see the articles "Planing" and "Shaping", on pages 45 to 57 in this volume.)

Speeds and feeds for planing vary widely, depending on the composition and hardness of the work metal, and on the tool material used. Feed is also governed by the depth of cut, the nature of cut (whether roughing or finishing), and the rigidity of the workpiece when clamped in position for machining.

Table 19 gives nominal speeds and feeds for planing the frequently used grades of gray iron, nodular iron, and malleable iron with high speed steel and carbide tools. Speeds for carbide tools are about four to ten times those for comparable operations using high speed steel tools; recommended feeds are the same in most instances.

In shaping, rapid metal removal is of less importance than in planing. Speeds and feeds are often restricted to values substantially below those used for planing, because of limitations on power and rigidity, the generally smaller size of tools, and the higher frequency of interruptions in cutting. To avoid chatter, however, feed is almost invariably maintained above 0.010 in. per stroke. Data for some applications of shaping gray iron are given in Table 3, on page 55, in "Shaping".

Drilling

High speed steel drills are widely used for drilling cast irons; the cobalt-containing grades are preferred for drilling castings harder than about 220 Bhn. Except for drilling out cored holes and gun drilling, carbide drills are seldom used, because they cost much more than high speed steel drills and require more attention in handling and sharpening. Standard drills have a point angle of 118° and a helix angle of 32°.

Table 17. Nominal Speeds and Feeds for Boring of Cast Iron With High Speed Steel and Carbide Tools

ASTM grade	Brinell hardness	Rough boring, 0.100-in. depth: Speed, sfm, HSS (a)	Speed, sfm, Carbide (b)	Feed, ipr, HSS (a)	Feed, ipr, Carbide (b)	Finish boring, 0.010-in. depth: Speed, sfm, HSS (a)	Speed, sfm, Carbide (b)	Feed, ipr, HSS (a)	Feed, ipr, Carbide (b)
Gray Irons									
Classes 20 and 25	110 to 140	125	415	0.010	0.015	140	460	0.006	0.008
Class 30	150 to 190	75	315	0.010	0.015	85	350	0.006	0.008
Classes 35 and 40	190 to 220	65	250	0.008	0.010	70	280	0.005	0.007
Classes 45 and 50	220 to 260	45	200	0.008	0.010	50	225	0.005	0.007
Classes 55 and 60	250 to 320	25	105	0.005	0.008	30	115	0.003	0.004
Nodular Irons									
60-48-18 and 65-45-12	140 to 190	125	415	0.010	0.015	140	460	0.003	0.008
80-55-06	190 to 225	90	295	0.010	0.015	100	325	0.006	0.008
	225 to 260	65	230	0.010	0.015	75	250	0.006	0.008
100-70-03	240 to 300	55	180	0.008	0.010	60	200	0.005	0.007
120-90-02	270 to 330	25	110	0.005	0.008	30	120	0.003	0.004
	330 to 400	...	45	...	0.008	...	50	...	0.004
Malleable Irons									
32510 and 35018	110 to 160	180	630	0.010	0.015	200	700	0.006	0.008
45007, 45010, 48004, 50007	160 to 200	80	270	0.010	0.015	90	300	0.006	0.008
	200 to 240	65	205	0.008	0.010	70	225	0.005	0.007
53004 and 60003	200 to 255	55	180	0.008	0.010	60	200	0.005	0.007
80002	240 to 280	40	135	0.008	0.010	45	150	0.005	0.007

(a) High speed steels M2 and T5, except T15, M41, M42, M43 and M44 high speed steels for boring cast iron at hardness above about 220 to 240 Bhn. (b) Grade C-3 carbide. (Data are adapted from tables compiled by Metcut Research Associates, Inc.)

Table 18. Nominal Speeds and Feeds for Broaching of Cast Iron With High Speed Steel Tools(a)

ASTM grade	Brinell hardness	Speed, sfm	Feed (chip load), ipt
Gray Irons			
Classes 20 and 25	110 to 140	30	0.005
Class 30	150 to 190	30	0.004
Classes 35 and 40	190 to 220	25	0.003
Classes 45 and 50	220 to 260	20	0.003
Classes 55 and 60	250 to 320	15	0.002
Nodular Irons			
60-48-18 and 65-45-12	140 to 190	25	0.005
80-55-06	190 to 225	25	0.004
	225 to 260	20	0.004
100-70-03	240 to 300	10	0.002
120-90-02	270 to 330	10	0.002
	330 to 400	5	0.002
Malleable Irons			
32510 and 35018	110 to 160	30	0.004
45007, 45010, 48004 and 50007	160 to 200	20	0.003
	200 to 240	15	0.003
53004 and 60003	200 to 255	15	0.003
80002	240 to 280	10	0.002

(a) M2 high speed steel, except T5 and T15 for hardness above 240 Bhn. Grade C-2 carbide can be used for broaching gray iron classes 20 to 40, with speed of 150 sfm and feed of 0.003 to 0.005 ipt. (SOURCE: same as for Table 17)

Table 19. Nominal Speeds and Feeds for Planing of Cast Iron With High Speed Steel and Carbide Tools

ASTM grade	Brinell hardness	0.500-in. depth of cut: Speed, sfm, HSS (a)	0.500-in. depth of cut: Speed, sfm, Carbide (b)	0.500-in. depth of cut: Feed, in. per stroke, HSS (a)	0.500-in. depth of cut: Feed, in. per stroke, Carbide (b)	0.100-in. depth of cut: Speed, sfm, HSS (a)	0.100-in. depth of cut: Speed, sfm, Carbide (c)	0.100-in. depth of cut: Feed, in. per stroke, HSS (a)	0.100-in. depth of cut: Feed, in. per stroke, Carbide (c)	0.005-in. cut: Speed, sfm(d), HSS (a)	0.005-in. cut: Speed, sfm(d), Carbide (e)
Gray Irons											
Classes 20 and 25	110 to 140 ..	50	300	0.090	0.090	75	300	0.125	0.125	60	235
Class 30	150 to 190 ..	35	275	0.090	0.090	55	300	0.125	0.125	40	195
Classes 35 and 40	190 to 220 ..	20	225	0.090	0.090	30	300	0.100	0.125	35	125
Classes 45 and 50	220 to 260 ..	10	125	0.090	0.090	15	150	0.050	0.050	12	90
Nodular Irons											
60-48-18 and 65-45-12	140 to 190 ..	45	200	0.060	0.060	60	250	0.050	0.093	50	210
80-55-06	190 to 225 ..	35	180	0.060	0.060	55	240	0.050	0.093	40	190
	225 to 260 ..	20	125	0.060	0.060	35	100	0.050	0.093	25	90
100-70-03	240 to 300 ..	10	100	0.045	0.060	15	125	0.050	0.040	12	70
Malleable Irons											
32510 and 35018	110 to 160 ..	50	300	0.060	0.060	75	300	0.050	0.050	60	235
45007, 45010, 48004, 50007	160 to 200 ..	40	190	0.060	0.060	65	240	0.050	0.050	45	200
	200 to 240 ..	25	125	0.060	0.060	35	100	0.050	0.050	40	90
53004 and 60003	200 to 255 ..	20	115	0.060	0.060	35	90	0.050	0.050	25	80
80002	240 to 280 ..	10	100	0.045	0.045	15	125	0.050	0.050	12	70

(a) High speed steels M2 and T5, except M3 and T5 for planing cast iron at hardness above about 220 to 240 Bhn. (b) Grade C-1 carbide, except C-6 for gray irons at hardness above 190 Bhn. (c) Grade C-2 carbide, except C-7 for gray irons at hardness above 190 Bhn. (d) Feed, ¾ of width of square-nose finishing tool. (e) Grade C-2 carbide. (Data are adapted from tables compiled by Metcut Research Associates, Inc.)

Table 20. Nominal Speeds and Feeds for Drilling of Cast Iron With High Speed Steel Drills (a)

ASTM grade	Brinell hardness	Speed, sfm	Feed, ipr, for hole diameter of: ⅛ in.	¼ in.	½ in.	1 in.	1½ in.	2 in.
Gray Irons								
Classes 20 and 25	110 to 140	140	0.003	0.006	0.010	0.014	0.018	0.022
Class 30	150 to 190	95	0.003	0.005	0.008	0.012	0.014	0.015
Classes 35 and 40	190 to 220	85	0.003	0.005	0.008	0.012	0.014	0.015
Classes 45 and 50	220 to 290	70	0.002	0.004	0.006	0.010	0.012	0.014
Nodular Irons								
60-48-18 and 65-45-12	140 to 190	100	0.003	0.005	0.008	0.012	0.014	0.015
80-55-06	190 to 225	60	0.002	0.004	0.006	0.010	0.012	0.015
	225 to 260	45	0.002	0.003	0.006	0.010	0.012	0.012
100-70-03	240 to 300	40	0.002	0.003	0.006	0.010	0.012	0.012
Malleable Irons								
32510 and 35018	110 to 160	120	0.002	0.004	0.007	0.012	0.015	0.018
45007, 45010, 48004, 50007	160 to 200	90	0.002	0.004	0.006	0.010	0.015	0.015
	200 to 240	75	0.002	0.004	0.006	0.010	0.015	0.015
53004 and 60003	200 to 255	80	0.002	0.004	0.006	0.010	0.015	0.015
80002	240 to 280	70	0.002	0.004	0.006	0.010	0.015	0.015

(a) High speed steels M1, M7 and M10. (SOURCE: same as for Table 19)

Table 21. Nominal Speeds and Feeds for Drilling of Gray Iron With Carbide Drills (a)

ASTM class gray iron	Brinell hardness	Speed, sfm	Feed, ipr, for hole diameter of: ⅛ in.	¼ in.	½ in.	1 in.	1½ in.	2 in.
20 and 25	110 to 140	230	0.003	0.006	0.010	0.014	0.018	0.022
30	150 to 190	195	0.003	0.005	0.008	0.012	0.014	0.015
35 and 40	190 to 220	180	0.003	0.005	0.008	0.012	0.014	0.015
45 and 50	220 to 260	160	0.002	0.004	0.006	0.010	0.012	0.014
55 and 60	250 to 320	95	0.001	0.003	0.005	0.009	0.012	0.012

(a) Grade C-2 carbide (SOURCE: same as for Table 19)

Table 22. Nominal Speeds and Feeds for Gun Drilling of Cast Iron With Carbide Drills (a)

ASTM grade	Brinell hardness	Speed, sfm	Feed, ipr, for hole diameter, in., of: < ¼	¼ to ½	½ to ¾	1 to 2
Gray Irons						
Classes 20,25, 30, 35,	100 to 140	350	0.0008	0.0015	0.003	0.007
40, 45, 50, 55 and	150 to 190	300	0.0008	0.0015	0.003	0.007
60, at hardnesses	190 to 220	250	0.0008	0.0015	0.003	0.007
listed at right	220 to 260	200	0.0005	0.001	0.002	0.003
Nodular Irons						
60-48-18, 65-45-12,	140 to 190	300	0.0004	0.0006	0.0008	0.002
80-55-06, 100-70-03	190 to 225	250	0.0004	0.0006	0.0008	0.002
and 120-90-02, at	225 to 260	200	0.0004	0.0006	0.0008	0.002
hardnesses	240 to 300	150	0.0004	0.0006	0.0008	0.0015
listed at right	270 to 330	150	0.0004	0.0006	0.0008	0.0015
Malleable Irons						
32510, 35018, 45007,	110 to 160	350	0.0004	0.0006	0.0008	0.002
45010, 48004, 50007,	160 to 200	300	0.0004	0.0006	0.0008	0.002
53004, 60003 and	200 to 240	250	0.0004	0.0006	0.0008	0.002
80003, at hardnesses	200 to 255	225	0.0004	0.0006	0.0008	0.002
listed at right	240 to 280	200	0.0004	0.0006	0.0008	0.002

(a) Grade C-2 carbide. (SOURCE: same as for Table 19)

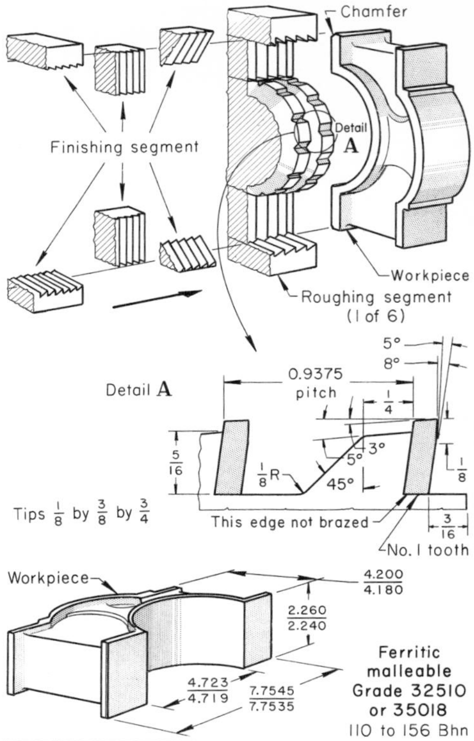

Operating Conditions

Broach speed ....7.5 sfm
Depth of cut ....0.003 to 0.005 ipt
Length of cut ....2¼ in.
Cutting fluid ....None
Setup time ....24 to 32 hr
Production rate ....62.1 pieces per hour
Tool material ....Carbide
Tool life per grind ....20,000 to 36,000 pieces
Downtime for tool change ....17 hr

Costs per Piece (a)

Labor (0.0161 hr at $3 per hour) $0.0483
Tool maintenance and replacement $0.0400
Power $0.0210
Supplies $0.0080

(a) Exclusive of costs of tools and machine ($118,000), which were amortized at 8.3% per yr.

Fig. 9. Broaching seven surfaces of bearing caps in one pass of a multiple-cutter broach (Example 652)

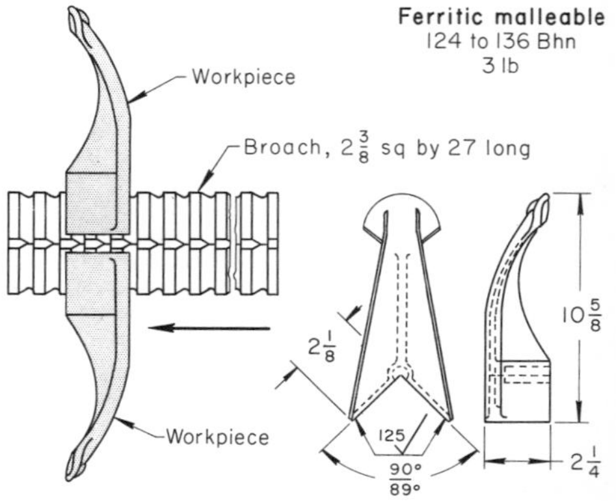

Broach speed ....22 sfm
Depth of cut ....0 to 0.025 in.
Cutting fluid ....Sulfurized mineral oil
Setup time ....1½ hr
Machining time ....0.96 min for two pieces
Production rate ....125 pieces per hour
Broach material ....M3 high speed steel
Face angle ....15°
Rise per tooth ....0.0015 in.
Tool life per grind ....36,000 pieces
Downtime for changing tools ....¼ hr

Fig. 10. Broaching 90° seating surfaces on two castings simultaneously, to improve alignment in assembly (Example 653)

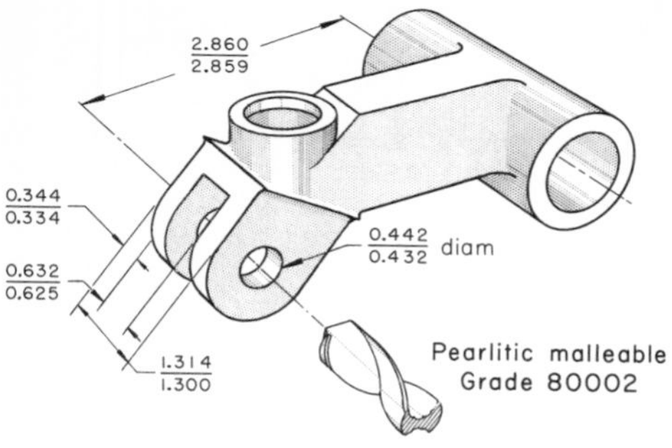

Item	1040 steel forging	Malleable iron casting
Tool Details		
Material	High speed steel	
Point angle	140°	118°
Helix angle	30°	30°
Machining Conditions		
Speed, rpm	890	890
Speed, sfm	100	100
Feed, ipr	0.006	0.006
Cutting fluid	Soluble oil:water(1:20)	
Production, pcs/hr	150	178.6
Labor time/pc, hr	0.0067	0.0056
Tool-change time/pc, hr	0.0094	0.0067
Tool cost/pc	$0.007	$0.003
Tool life per grind, pcs.	225	550

(a) Maintenance and replacement

Fig. 11. Cast lever of grade 80002 pearlitic malleable iron, formerly produced as a 1040 steel forging. Comparison of conditions and results for drilling two in-line holes shows benefits that resulted from the change of material (Example 656)

Table 23. Drilling Class 35 Gray Iron vs Grade 32510 Ferritic Malleable Iron (Example 655) (a)

Item	Gray iron (217 to 235 Bhn)	Ferritic malleable (134 Bhn)
Speed, rpm	336	480
Speed, sfm	37	53
Feed, ipr	0.011	0.015
Time per piece, min(b)	1.38	1.14
Production, pieces per hr	43	52
Drilling cost per piece	$0.076	$0.064
Drill life per grind, pieces	175	225

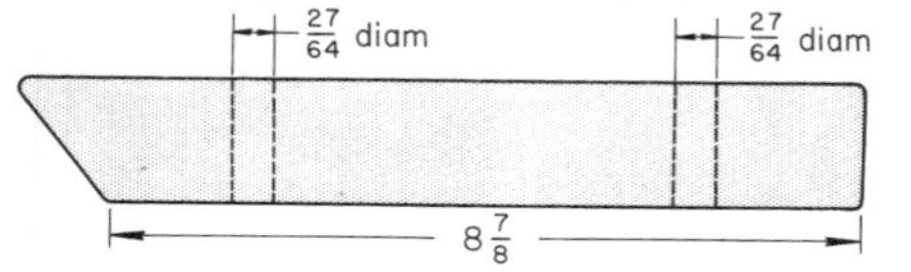

(a) Data are for drilling the 8.5-lb casting shown above. Castings of both materials were drilled in a multiple-spindle drill press with high speed steel twist drills of standard design (118° point angle), and were fixtured for simultaneous drilling of both holes; a 40-to-1 mixture of water and soluble oil was used as the cutting fluid. (b) Includes time for loading and unloading, which is the same for both work metals.

Speed and Feed. Tables 20, 21 and 22 list nominal speeds and feeds for drilling of cast irons — Table 20 for drilling gray, nodular and malleable cast irons with high speed steel tools; Table 21 for drilling only gray iron with carbide drills; and Table 22 for gun drilling gray, nodular and malleable cast irons with carbide drills.

At low feeds, power requirements per cubic inch of metal removed per minute are greater than at heavier feeds. For example, at feeds over 0.010 ipr, the power requirement is only 0.60 hp per cubic inch of metal removed per minute, as compared with 0.75 hp for feeds of less than 0.010 ipr.

Table 24. Drilling, Reaming and Tapping Gray Iron Cylinder Heads (Examples 657 and 658)

Item	Example 657 Drilling and reaming(a)	Example 658 Tapping four holes(b)
Operating Conditions		
Speed, rpm	290 to 1150(c)	534
Speed, sfm	40 to 80(c)	70
Feed, ipr	0.011	0.050(d)
Hole diam, in.	5⁄32 to 3⁄4	1⁄2
Hole depth, in.	7⁄16 to 2½	0.530 to 0.560
Cutting fluid	None	Sulfurized oil
Tool material	HSS(e)	HSS(f)
Results		
Time per piece	2.71 min	0.9 min
Production per hr	22.1 pcs	66.5 pcs
Tool life/grind	1500 pcs	204 pcs(g)
Tool-change time	10 min	10 min

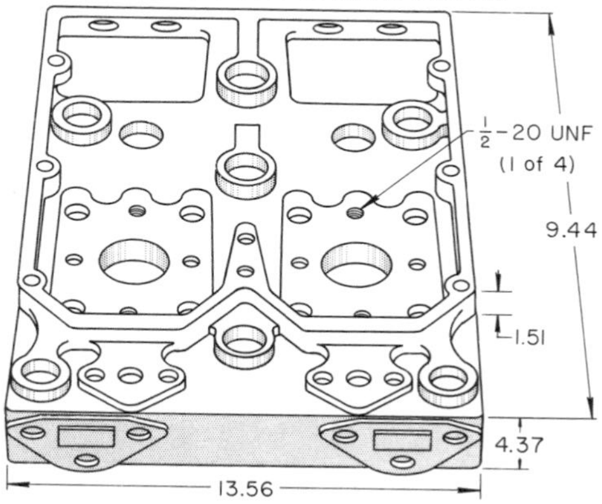

(a) A total of 97 drilling and reaming operations were performed progressively on the casting illustrated above, in five of the six stations on the rotary table of a multispindle vertical and horizontal drill press; one station was used for loading and unloading. Jobber's drills were used, with a point angle of 118° and helix angle of 32°; reamers were straight fluted (8 flutes) with 45° chamfer angle. (b) After being drilled and reamed, the cylinder head was moved to a two-spindle drill press equipped with a special tapping head, for tapping four holes (see sketch above) with ½-20 UNF threads. (c) Minimum speed, for reamer; maximum, for drill. All tools were gear driven; speed of all drills and reamers was controlled by maintaining the speed of the ¾-in drill (the tool with the shortest life) at 325 rpm (64 sfm). (d) Spindle advance was controlled by lead screw, to relieve axial pressure. (e) General-purpose high speed steel, steam oxide treated, for all tools except controlling tool (see footnote c), which was made of cobalt-containing high speed steel. (f) Treated with molybdenum disulfide; taps were of standard design, ½-20 UNF. (g) Tool maintenance and replacement cost per piece was $0.025.

Table 25. Standard Reamers for Cast Iron

Reamer detail	Reamer material: High speed steel	Reamer material: Carbide tipped
Chamfer angle	45°	30° to 45°
Clearance angle	3° to 7°	6° to 8°
Rake angle	0° to 5°	4° to 7°
Land, in.	0.008 to 0.015	0.007 to 0.020

Cutting fluid is less essential in drilling cast iron than for many other metals, because the graphite in cast iron provides lubrication and because chip removal is easier than with stringy-chip metals. Although a water-soluble fluid is often used in production drilling, much drilling is done dry; an air jet directed at the area of drilling will cool the work and remove chips.

Examples. The four examples that follow deal with drilling of various types of cast iron on a production basis. Two of these examples describe the benefits obtained by a change of work material — in one, from gray to ferritic nodular iron; in the other, from a steel forging to a pearlitic malleable iron casting. See also Examples 150, 164, 173 and 177 in "Drilling".

Example 654. Drilling ¾-In.-Diam Holes in Pearlitic Nodular Iron

A ¾-in.-diam through hole ⅞ in. deep was drilled in a pearlitic nodular iron casting. The drilling was done at a speed of 67 sfm (340 rpm) and a feed of 0.0068 ipr with high speed steel drills. Drill life averaged 300 pieces per grind.

Example 655. Gray Iron vs Malleable Iron (Table 23)

Table 23 shows a stabilizer-bar casting, and compares operating conditions and results for drilling two holes in castings originally made from class 35 gray iron (217 to 235 Bhn) and later from grade 32510 ferritic malleable iron (134 Bhn). As the comparison shows, changing to ferritic malleable iron permitted an increase in speed and feed, which resulted in a 20% increase in production rate and a 16% decrease in cost per piece. In addition, the ferritic malleable iron castings had greater strength and ductility than those made from gray iron.

Example 656. Steel Forging vs Malleable Iron Casting (Fig. 11)

The cam-follower lever shown in Fig. 11, cast from grade 80002 pearlitic malleable iron (241 to 269 Bhn), originally was produced (with a minor difference in design) as a 1040 steel forging heat treated to Rockwell C 28 to 35 before machining. A comparison of conditions and results for drilling the two in-line holes in the forging and the casting is tabulated below Fig. 11. As these data show, the change from 1040 steel to the pearlitic malleable iron enabled a 19% increase in production rate, decreased downtime for tool change by nearly 30% and labor time per piece by 16%, and reduced tool costs by 57%.

The change from forging to casting also resulted in a 20% decrease in weight; after machining, the casting weighed only 1.49 lb, as against 1.87 lb for the forging.

Example 657. High-Production Drilling and Reaming of Class 45 Gray Iron Cylinder Heads (Table 24)

As detailed in Table 24, a six-station multispindle vertical and horizontal drill press was used for 97 drilling and reaming operations on 71 holes, 5⁄32 to ¾ in. in diameter, in engine cylinder heads cast from class 45 gray iron (201 to 235 Bhn). By performing these operations progressively as each casting was indexed from station to station on the rotary table of the machine, total machining time per piece was only 2.71 min — which met production requirements of 450 pieces per day.

Reaming

Both high speed steel and carbide-tipped reamers are used for reaming cast irons; the latter are most often used in high production or for reaming the more-difficult-to-machine alloys. When carbide-tipped reamers are used, chatter must be eliminated completely, to avoid tool breakage. Tool angles for high speed steel and carbide-tipped reamers are given in Table 25.

Speed and Feed. Tables 26 and 27 list nominal speeds and feeds for reaming the cast irons — Table 26 for reaming with high speed steel reamers, and Table 27, with carbide reamers.

As shown in Tables 26 and 27, speed decreases as hardness of the cast iron increases. Also, speeds for nodular iron are substantially lower than those for gray and malleable irons at about 250

Table 26. Nominal Speeds and Feeds for Reaming of Cast Iron With High Speed Steel Reamers(a)

ASTM grade	Brinell hardness	Speed, sfm	Feed, ipr, for hole diameter of: ⅛ in.	¼ in.	½ in.	1 in.	1½ in.	2 in.
Gray Irons								
Classes 20 and 25	110 to 140	100	0.004	0.006	0.010	0.015	0.020	0.025
Classes 35 and 40	190 to 220	60	0.004	0.006	0.010	0.015	0.020	0.025
Classes 45 and 50	220 to 260	50	0.003	0.005	0.007	0.010	0.015	0.020
Nodular Irons								
60-48-18 and 65-45-12	140 to 190	70	0.003	0.004	0.006	0.010	0.015	0.020
80-55-06	190 to 225	60	0.003	0.004	0.006	0.010	0.015	0.020
	225 to 260	35	0.003	0.004	0.006	0.010	0.015	0.020
100-70-03	240 to 300	25	0.002	0.003	0.004	0.007	0.012	0.015
Malleable Irons								
32510 and 35018	110 to 160	90	0.004	0.008	0.012	0.018	0.020	0.025
45007, 45010, 48004, 50007	160 to 200	60	0.004	0.008	0.012	0.016	0.020	0.025
	200 to 240	50	0.004	0.008	0.012	0.016	0.020	0.025
53004 and 60003	200 to 255	45	0.004	0.008	0.012	0.016	0.020	0.025
80002	240 to 280	40	0.003	0.007	0.010	0.015	0.018	0.020

(a) Data are based on the use of six-flute reamers of high speed steels M1, M2 or M7, except T15 for reaming of cast iron at hardness above about 240 to 260 Bhn. (SOURCE: same as for Table 30)

Table 27. Nominal Speeds and Feeds for Reaming of Cast Iron With Carbide Reamers(a)

ASTM grade	Brinell hardness	Speed, sfm	Feed, ipr, for hole diameter of: ⅛ in.	¼ in.	½ in.	1 in.	1½ in.	2 in.
Gray Irons								
Classes 20 and 25	110 to 140	300	0.004	0.006	0.010	0.015	0.020	0.025
Classes 35 and 40	190 to 220	150	0.004	0.006	0.010	0.015	0.020	0.025
Classes 45 and 50	220 to 260	120	0.003	0.005	0.007	0.010	0.015	0.020
Nodular Irons								
60-48-18 and 65-45-12	140 to 190	225	0.003	0.004	0.006	0.010	0.015	0.020
80-55-06	190 to 225	190	0.003	0.004	0.006	0.010	0.015	0.020
	225 to 260	110	0.003	0.004	0.006	0.010	0.015	0.020
100-70-03	240 to 300	85	0.002	0.003	0.004	0.007	0.012	0.015
Malleable Irons								
32510 and 35018	110 to 160	230	0.004	0.008	0.012	0.018	0.020	0.025
45007, 45010, 48004, 50007	160 to 200	170	0.004	0.008	0.012	0.016	0.020	0.025
	200 to 240	140	0.004	0.008	0.012	0.016	0.020	0.025
53004 and 60003	200 to 255	170	0.004	0.008	0.012	0.016	0.020	0.025
80002	240 to 280	140	0.004	0.007	0.010	0.015	0.018	0.020

(a) Data are based on use of 6-flute reamers of C-2 carbide. (SOURCE: same as for Table 30)

Table 28. Nominal Speeds and Feeds for Counterboring and Spotfacing of Cast Iron With High Speed Steel Tools

ASTM grade	Brinell hardness	Speed, sfm	Feed, ipr, for hole diameter of: ¼ in.	½ in.	1 in.	2 in.	3 in.
Gray Irons							
Classes 20 and 25	110 to 140	110	0.0035	0.004	0.005	0.0065	0.0075
Classes 35 and 40	190 to 220	55	0.0025	0.003	0.004	0.005	0.006
Classes 45 and 50	220 to 260	40	0.002	0.0025	0.0035	0.0045	0.0055
Nodular Irons							
60-48-18 and 65-45-12	140 to 190	110	0.0035	0.004	0.005	0.0065	0.0075
80-55-06	190 to 225	80	0.002	0.003	0.004	0.005	0.006
	225 to 260	60	0.002	0.0025	0.0035	0.0045	0.0055
100-70-03	240 to 300	50	0.0015	0.002	0.003	0.004	0.005
Malleable Irons							
32510 and 35018	110 to 160	160	0.0035	0.004	0.005	0.006	0.007
45007, 45010, 48004, 50007	160 to 200	70	0.003	0.0035	0.0045	0.0055	0.0065
	200 to 240	55	0.002	0.0025	0.0035	0.0045	0.0055
80002	240 to 280	35	0.002	0.0025	0.003	0.004	0.005

Table 29. Nominal Speeds and Feeds for Counterboring and Spotfacing of Cast Iron With Carbide Tools

ASTM grade	Brinell hardness	Speed, sfm	Feed, ipr, for hole diameter of: ¼ in.	½ in.	1 in.	2 in.	3 in.
Gray Irons							
Classes 20 and 25	110 to 140	370	0.005	0.006	0.008	0.010	0.012
Classes 35 and 40	190 to 220	225	0.004	0.0045	0.0055	0.007	0.009
Classes 45 and 50	220 to 260	180	0.0035	0.004	0.005	0.006	0.007
Nodular Irons							
60-48-18 and 65-45-12	140 to 190	370	0.005	0.006	0.008	0.010	0.012
80-55-06	190 to 225	260	0.003	0.0035	0.0045	0.0055	0.0065
	225 to 260	200	0.003	0.004	0.005	0.006	0.0065
100-70-03	240 to 300	160	0.003	0.0035	0.0045	0.005	0.006
Malleable Irons							
32510 and 35018	110 to 160	560	0.005	0.006	0.008	0.010	0.012
45007, 45010, 48004, 50007	160 to 200	240	0.0045	0.0055	0.0075	0.0095	0.012
	200 to 240	180	0.004	0.005	0.007	0.009	0.011
80002	240 to 280	120	0.0035	0.004	0.006	0.0075	0.009

Bhn; differences in speed, however, are not significant at lower hardnesses. Nominal feeds for the three groups of cast irons are slightly lower at higher hardnesses, with the feed for nodular iron slightly lower than for gray and malleable irons, at equal hardness.

For reaming holes up to 1 in. in diameter, stock allowance should be from 0.005 to 0.008 in.; for larger holes, from 0.008 to 0.015 in.

Production Examples. Details of high-production reaming of holes ranging from ⁵⁄₃₂ to ¾ in. in diameter in class 45 gray iron are given in Example 657. See also Examples 205 and 207 in "Reaming".

Counterboring and Spotfacing

Procedures and equipment for these two closely related machining methods are described in the articles "Counterboring" and "Spotfacing", pages 103 and 104 in this volume.

Tables 28 and 29 list nominal speeds and feeds for counterboring and spotfacing the cast irons with high speed steel and carbide tools. Speeds and feeds are generally lower for the harder materials, and are higher for carbide tools than for high speed steel tools. Some differences also exist among the individual grades, because of differences in abrasiveness and other properties of the material.

Tapping

High speed steel taps are recommended for tapping cast irons. These tools usually employ a rake angle of 0°, although a rake angle of 3° to 5° is often preferred for tapping annealed material. To provide adequate lubrication, a sulfurized oil is recommended. As shown in Example 659, taps treated with molybdenum disulfide are capable of cutting more efficiently and of yielding a higher production rate than untreated taps.

Speed. Taps should be operated at the highest speed permitted by equipment, lubrication and type of work material. High speed not only increases production and thread accuracy, but also results in longer tap life. Most tap breakage occurs because of insufficient speed.

It is common practice to operate the tap at the same speed used for the tap drill. In some applications, an even higher speed will give excellent results. Table 30 gives nominal speeds for tapping cast irons with high speed steel taps. Lower speeds are employed at higher hardnesses; differences among individual grades are relatively small, comparing at equal hardness.

Examples. The first of the two examples that follow presents details of the conditions and results in high-production tapping; the second example illustrates the improved results obtained when taps treated with molybdenum disulfide were substituted for unlubricated taps.

Example 658. Tapping Four Holes in Class 45 Gray Iron Cylinder Heads (Table 24)

After it had been drilled and reamed (see Example 657), the class 45 gray iron cylinder head shown in Table 24 was moved to a two-spindle drill press for tapping four holes

Table 30. Nominal Speeds for Tapping of Cast Iron With High Speed Steel Taps(a)

ASTM grade	Brinell hardness	Speed, sfm
Gray Irons		
Classes 20 and 25	110 to 140	45
Class 30	150 to 190	40
Classes 35 and 40	190 to 220	35
Classes 45 and 50	220 to 260	30
Classes 55 and 60	250 to 320	10
Nodular Irons		
60-48-18 and 65-45-12	140 to 190	40
80-55-06	190 to 225	25
	225 to 260	20
100-70-03	240 to 300	15
120-90-02	270 to 330	10
Malleable Irons		
32510 and 35018	110 to 160	50
45007, 45010, 48004 and 50007	160 to 200	40
	200 to 240	30
53004 and 60003	200 to 255	30
80002	240 to 280	25

(a) High speed steels M1, M7 and M10. (Data are adapted from tables compiled by Metcut Research Associates, Inc.)

with ½-20 UNF threads. The machine was equipped with a special tapping head that had a screw behind each tap to feed the spindle down and relieve axial pressure. Production rate for tapping the four holes was 66.5 pieces per hour. Details of the tapping operation are given in Table 24.

Example 659. Effect of Molybdenum Disulfide Coating on Tap Performance

The taps used for the operation described in Example 658 (tapping four holes in a class 45 gray iron cylinder head) were treated with molybdenum disulfide. Originally, untreated taps had been used. Although the molybdenum disulfide coating increased the cost of each tap by 3¢, the use of the treated taps resulted in an over-all saving of $6652.80 per year, by improving productivity and tool life, as shown in the following comparison:

	Untreated taps	MoS_2-treated taps
Labor time per piece, hr ..	0.0172	0.0150
Production, pieces per hr .	58.2	66.5
Tap life per grind, pieces .	68	204
Tap cost per piece	$0.076	$0.025

Multiple-Operation Machining

Hand turret lathes, either horizontal or vertical, are widely used to produce parts in quantities of a few hundred or less. Whether a horizontal or vertical machine is selected depends primarily on the shape, size, and weight of the casting to be machined. The horizontal machine is easier to set up and operates at higher speeds, but is best suited to handling small parts. Castings weighing more than about 50 lb are more readily chucked and fixtured on a vertical machine, because the vertically positioned chuck facilitates entry of the workpiece, holding (by gravity) and positioning, and tightening. As production quantities increase, automatic turret lathes are more appropriate (see Table 1 on page 155, in the article on Multiple-Operation Machining).

Multiple-spindle machines and automatic machines of special design are preferred for mass production. In common with turret lathes, the multiple-spindle machines are available in both horizontal and vertical models. However, the multiple-spindle machine is equipped with several spindles that operate simultaneously, thus increasing production rate and reducing the machining cycle time per unit. A completed part is obtained with each index of the spindles. Automotive oil-pump bodies, clutch drums, and governor hubs are typical parts produced in horizontal multiple-spindle machines.

Table 31 shows the machines selected for multiple operations on 23 parts of different size, weight and shape.

Several types of machines are used in the production examples on multiple-operation machining (Examples 660 to 666). In some examples, a change from one type of machine to another resulted in a higher production rate and lower machining costs. In others, similar results were obtained by changing the material to be machined or by a change in tooling. Example 660, which follows, typifies the multiplicity of turning, boring, facing and chamfering operations that can be performed in a single-spindle machine.

Example 660. Eight Operations on Pearlitic Nodular Iron in a Single-Spindle Chucking Machine (Fig. 12)

A single-spindle semiautomatic chucking machine was used to perform eight machining operations (facing, turning, boring and chamfering) on the pearlitic nodular iron brake drum shown in Fig. 12. By using tools on front and rear cross slides and in a five-station turret, machining time per piece was 4.49 min. All tools were of group 1 carbide (2.5 to 6.5 Co, 0 to 3 TaC+TiC, rem WC) and, except for the chamfering tool, were of the disposable-insert type. Tool details and machining conditions for the eight operations are tabulated below Fig. 12.

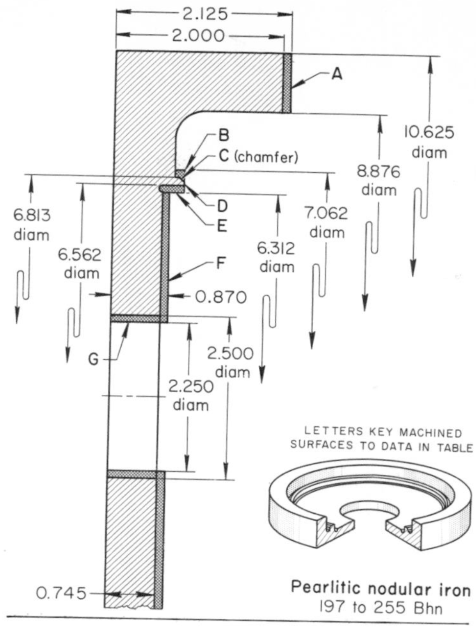

Surface cut(a)	Speed: Rpm	Speed: Sfm, max	Feed, ipr	Depth of cut, in.	Length of cut, in.	Tool life per edge, pcs(b)
A(c) ..	146	406	0.009	0.110	0.875	8
	292	814	0.007	0.015	0.875	23
B	178	329	0.007	0.125	0.156	40
C	292	520	0.007	0.031	0.031	133
D	146	260	0.009	0.125	0.375	35
E	248	427	0.009	0.125	0.375	12
F	178	295	0.009	0.125	2.031	17
G	292	191	0.007	0.125	0.745	58

(a) Sequence of operations: 1 — Rough face A (rear-slide tool), face D and F (tools on turret faces 1 and 2); 2 — turn B (tool on turret face 3); 3 — bore E (tool on turret face 4); 4 — bore G, chamfer C (two tools on turret face 5), and finish face A (front-slide tool). (b) All tools were of carbide, and of disposable-insert type except for chamfering. Insert for facing A was ½-in. round, with negative rake; all other inserts were ⅜-in.-IC triangles with 1/32-in. nose radius, with positive rake for B and G, negative rake for D, E and F. (c) Data are for rough and finish facing, respectively.

Fig. 12. Details of brake drum machined in eight operations in a semiautomatic chucking machine with a five-station turret (Example 660)

Effects of Changes in Work Material. Examples 661, 662 and 663, which follow, illustrate the influence of a change in work material on machining conditions and costs.

Example 661. Gray Iron vs Ferritic Malleable Iron (Table 32)

To increase the strength and ductility of a 3-lb input-shaft coupling (inset view in Table 32) without altering its design, the material used was changed from class 25 gray iron to grade 35018 ferritic malleable iron. Machining for this casting comprised core drilling, boring, reaming, turning, chamfering and facing, in a turret lathe. The change in material did not necessitate a revi-

Table 31. Machines Used for Multiple-Operation Machining of Castings of Various Sizes, in Low, Medium and High Production Quantities

No.	Part	Max diam, in.	Weight, lb	Machining operations	Machine used
				Low Production (Fewer Than 50 Pieces)	
1	Pulley	9.6	20	Turn, groove, bore, face	3-A turret lathe
2	Retaining ring ..	52	300	Turn, face, bore	6-ft vertical boring mill
3	Flywheel	84	...	Turn, face, bore	12-ft vertical boring mill
4	Roll	30	60,000	Turn, face	60-in. lathe
				Medium Production (50 to 500 Pieces)	
5	Cylinder	7¾	20	Face, bore	Automatic turret lathe
6	Cylinder	6	15	Face, bore, turn	Automatic turret lathe
7	End plate	2 3/16	1	Face, bore	Single-spindle automatic chucker
8	Pipe flange	13	80	Face, bore, thread	Semiautomatic lathe
				Continuous High Production	
9	Servo cover	...	1.1	Face, drill, groove, turn	8-spindle double-indexing chucker
10	Brake cylinder ..	1¼	1	Rough, finish ⅞-in. bore	4-spindle horiz. boring machine
11	Oil-pump body ..	5	2.5	Face, bore	6-spindle double-indexing chucker
12	Oil-pump body ..	9	8	Turn, groove, face, bore	6-spindle vertical chucking lathe
13	Oil-pump body ..	9	8	Turn, bore, face, groove	2-spindle horiz. boring machine
14	Crankshaft	5	5	Turn, face	Automatic-cycle lathe
15	Pump body	8 1/16	30	Face, chamfer bore	Semiautomatic lathe
16	Cylinder barrel ..	3¾	1	Face, turn	4-spindle vertical turner
17	Flange	5	3	Face, turn, bore	2-spindle vertical chucking lathe
18	Clutch drum	5.2	9	Face, bore, groove	6-spindle vertical chucking lathe
19	Clutch drum	6	10	Face, bore	2-spindle vertical chucking lathe
20	Governor hub ...	4	1.7	Face, turn, bore	6-spindle chucker
21	Brake drum	16½	40	Rough, finish bore; face	Automatic vertical turret lathe
22	Brake drum	11	50	Finish bore	Vertical boring machine
23	Piston	15	...	Turn, face	4-A turret lathe

Table 32. Multiple-Operation Machining of Class 25 Gray Iron vs Grade 35018 Ferritic Malleable Iron (Example 661) (a)

Operation or result	Gray iron Speed Rpm	Gray iron Speed Sfm	Gray iron Feed, ipr	Malleable iron Speed Rpm	Malleable iron Speed Sfm	Malleable iron Feed, ipr
Turret Tools(b)						
Core drilling (station 1)	480	126	0.020	264	69	0.016
Rough boring (station 2)	264	83	0.020	264	83	0.016
Semifinish boring (station 3)	360	116	0.020	264	85	0.016
Reaming (station 4)	62	20	Hand	48	16	Hand
Cross-Slide Tools(c)						
Semifinish turning outside diameter	264	170	0.020	264	170	0.016
Chamfering	264	86	0.020	264	86	0.016
Finish turning outside diameter	360	231	0.020	264	170	0.016
Rough facing flange	264	170	0.010	264	170	0.008
Finish facing flange	360	231	0.010	264	170	0.008
Results						
Machining time per piece, minutes		2.88			3.54	
Production rate, pieces per hour		21			17	
Cost per piece		$0.165			$0.203	

(a) Data are for machining the 3-lb input-shaft coupling shown at right, cast from either class 25 gray iron (170 to 211 Bhn) or grade 35018 ferritic malleable iron (tensile strength, 53,000 psi), in a manual four-station turret lathe. Castings of both materials were machined with tools of the same design, without cutting fluid. (b) Drill and reamer were of high speed steel; boring tools were brazed carbide. (c) All cross-slide tools were brazed carbide. Rough turning and chamfering were done with two tools on the same rear slide; finish turning was done with a tool on a second rear slide. Rough and finish facing were done in two successive passes with the same tool on a front slide.

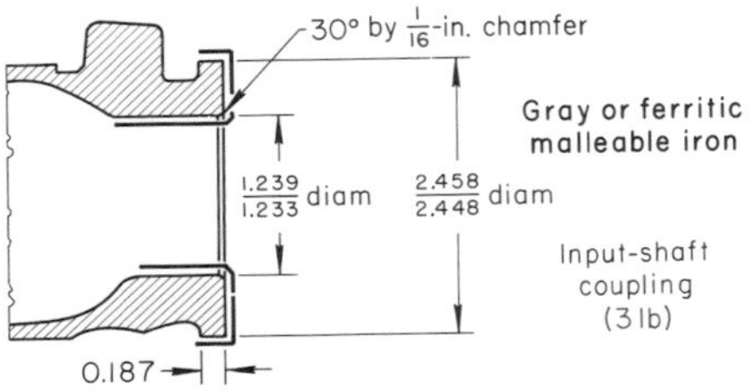

sion of tooling, but, as shown by the comparison in Table 32, did call for a reduction in speed and feed. Consequently, production rate was lowered by about 20%, and cost per piece was increased by 4¢.

Example 662. Steel Forging vs Malleable Iron Casting

When an idler gear, originally produced as a heat treated 1141 steel forging (Rockwell C 26 to 33), was made as a pearlitic malleable iron casting quenched and tempered to 269 to 302 Bhn before machining, a decrease in material cost of 25¢ per part and a 10% reduction in machining cost were realized. The design of the part remained essentially unchanged; in both forms, the part weighed 8.5 lb rough and 6.5 lb after machining.

Both materials were machined on a 12-in., eight-spindle chucking machine provided with double indexing, which permitted it to index and to operate two tooling stations simultaneously. Machining consisted of turning, facing and boring. Carbide tools were used in all operations, and although the grade was changed for the castings, tool costs were virtually unaffected.

Savings realized in machining the castings resulted primarily from an increase in production rate (from 32.4 to 35.9 pieces per hour) and a reduction of machining cost per piece (from $0.154 to $0.139).

Example 663. Class 35 Gray Iron Substituted for Class 25 After Tool Redesign (Fig. 13)

In the manufacture of the 2-lb hydraulic piston shown in Fig. 13, it was necessary to replace class 25 gray iron (170 to 211 Bhn) with class 35 (217 to 235 Bhn), to provide the casting with enough strength to meet an increase in pressure-resistance requirements. A total of 11 machining operations were required for these castings, as shown in Fig. 13. Normally, substitution of class 35 for class 25 gray iron results in an increase in machining costs, because of the higher hardness and strength and consequent lower machinability of class 35 gray iron. In this application, however, by revising the rake and side clearance of only the turning tools, it was possible to use the same speeds and feeds used for machining class 25 gray iron. Rake angles were changed from 6° to 0°, and side clearance angles from 5° to 7° on tools E and F (Fig. 13). This enabled the same machining time (8.9 min per piece) and production rate (7 pieces per hour) to be maintained, and machining cost per piece ($0.501) was unchanged.

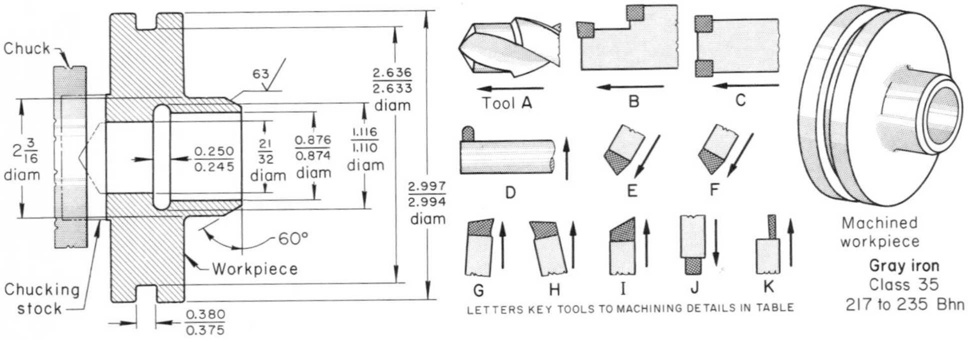

Tool(a)	Operation	Speed Rpm	Speed Sfm, max	Feed, ipr	Depth of cut, in.
A	Step drill (2 diam)	163	37	0.015	2.147
B	Bore c'bore; face hub	163	53	0.015	1.00
C	Ream c'bore	163	37	Hand	1.00
D	Form recess	163	48	Hand	0.117
E, F(b)	Turn OD, hub diam	163	128	0.015	0.844
G, H(b)	Face flange (2 sides)	226	177	0.009	1.187
I	Form 60° chamfer(c)	163	53	Hand	0.352
J	Rough form groove	102	80	0.003	0.180
	Turn groove bottom	53	36	Hand	0.015
K	Cut off	163	53	0.009	0.813

(a) All tools were of carbide, except for high speed steel step drill. Tools A, B, C and D were on individual turret stations; tools E, F and J were on rear slides; and tools G, H, I and K were on front slides. (b) Two tools, on one slide, cutting simultaneously. (c) Speeds shown are for cutting; tool dwelled at 53 rpm (17 sfm).

Fig. 13. Hydraulic piston that was machined from class 25 and class 35 gray irons with eleven tools on a turret lathe (Example 663)

Effect of Changes in Type of Machine. Demands for higher production and lower cost often justify a change to more complex machines. Two of the three examples that follow describe the benefits obtained when manual turret lathes were replaced by semiautomatics. The third describes a special indexing machine that was designed to take the place of several machines.

Examples 664 and 665. Manual vs Semiautomatic Machines

Example 664 — Nine-Tool Machining of Class 20 Gray Iron (Fig. 14). In machining a series of sizes of class 20 gray iron pillow blocks, one size of which is shown in Fig. 14, it was desired to maintain a high rate of production for the entire series with a minimum of changeover time from one size to another. Production quantities of 800 to 1000 pieces were machined every two months; there were eight different sizes of castings, weighing between 4.7 and 18 lb each. A cost study indicated that this range of sizes was great enough to warrant the use of semiautomatic turret lathes (machining sequence in Fig. 14) in place of manual turret lathes, which up to then had been used.

The semiautomatic machines had greater weight and rigidity, which in turn permitted the use of higher speeds and feeds. But their major advantage was in the reduction of labor costs; each manual turret lathe demanded the full time of one operator, whereas one operator could operate two semiautomatic machines simultaneously. The disadvantage of a slower indexing time, characteristic of semiautomatic machines, was more than offset by these advantages, and production rate per man-hour increased from 27 to 66 pieces.

Operating conditions on the semiautomatic lathes, and a comparison of results obtained on the semiautomatic and the manual turret lathes, are tabulated below Fig. 14.

Example 665 — Seven-Tool Machining of Ferritic Malleable Iron (Fig. 15). Originally, a 15½-lb ferritic malleable iron taper cap (Fig. 15) was machined in a manual ram-type turret lathe, in a sequence of operations that included facing, radiusing, turning, chamfering and taper boring. The lathe required the full time of one operator. A 63% reduction in machining costs, and tripled production per man-hour, were realized when machining was transferred to semiautomatic single-spindle chucking machines. Two men — an operator and his helper — could tend four of these semiautomatic machines.

Table 33. Cutter Angles for Face Mills Used on Cast Iron(a)

Angle	Cutter material HSS	Cutter material Carbide
Axial, radial rakes(b)	10° to 15°	4° to 6°
Corner(b)	0°(c)	0°(c)
Primary clearance	4° to 6°	3° to 6°
Secondary clearance	8° to 10°	8° to 10°

(a) All angles are positive, except as noted otherwise. (b) When heavy feeds are used, cutters are often provided with 45° or 60° corner angles, to prevent excessive breakout at the edges. When this is done, high speed steel cutters are given a 20° axial rake and −5° radial rake; carbide cutters, −5° axial and radial rakes. (c) 1/16-in. chamfer.

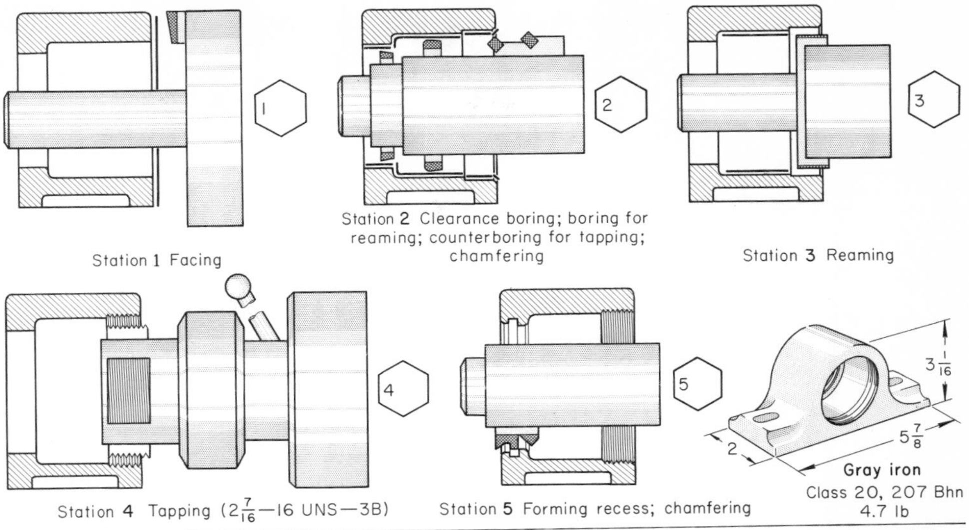

Station	Operation	Speed Rpm	Speed Sfm, max	Feed, ipr	Cycle time, min(a)
Operating Conditions, Semiautomatic Lathe(b)					
1	Face(c)	530	424	0.005	0.080
2	Finish bore; rough bore; c'bore & chamfer(d)..	530	330	0.021	0.150
3	Ream(e)	530	330	0.021	0.110
4	Tap(f)	68	44	Lead	0.120
5	Form recess; chamfer(g)..	530	288	0.0104	0.040

Item	Type of turret lathe: Manual (7½ hp)	Type of turret lathe: Semi-automatic (20 hp)
Time/Production Comparison, Semiautomatic vs Formerly Used Manual Turret Lathe		
Time per piece, min:		
Loading and unloading	0.95	0.26
Indexing	0.47	0.94
Cutting	0.80	0.50
Total (floor-to-floor)	2.22	1.70
Pieces per machine-hour	27	35
Pieces per man-hour	27	70(h)

(a) Total setup time for all operations was 2½ hr. (b) For all operations, a 1-to-30 mixture of soluble oil and water was used as the cutting fluid. (c) With brazed carbide tool, ⅝ in. square. (d) Boring tool was of the inserted-blade type with brazed carbide cutters (two edges for each diameter); cutters for counterboring and chamfering were ⅜-in.-square disposable carbide inserts. (e) With double-edge reaming bar with brazed carbide tips. (f) With high speed steel chasers in die head. (g) With sliding block containing two brazed form-ground carbide inserts. (h) One man operated two semiautomatic machines, merely loading (placing part on angle plate chuck, applying air clamps, and starting machine) and unloading (pressing clamp-release button and removing machined part).

Fig. 14. Machining of a pillow block in a semiautomatic turret lathe (Example 664)

Figure 15 shows the surfaces machined and the tools used in the semiautomatic machine; details of operations, and comparison of results with those obtained when the manual lathe was used, are tabulated below Fig. 15.

Example 666. Multistation Machine vs Four Different Machines (Fig. 16)

In machining class 30B gray iron rocker-shaft brackets (Fig. 16), production rate was increased from 46.1 to 91.7 pieces per hour by replacing two drill presses and two horizontal mills (used for progressive machining of each casting) with one multiple-station indexing machine. The cost of the new machine ($57,000) was approximately equal to the cost of the machines it replaced; tooling costs ($29,000), including the cost of fixtures, drill heads, and bushing plates, remained unchanged.

When four machines were used, the sequence of operations was: (*a*) drill, countersink, spotface and ream large hole in first drill press; (*b*) straddle mill ends on first horizontal mill; (*c*) finish mill large end on second horizontal mill; and (*d*) drill small hole on second drill press. Completing these operations required 0.0217 man-hr per part, as compared to 0.0109 man-hr per part in the indexing machine.

The sequence of operations employed for machining the bracket in the indexing machine is shown in Fig. 16. The machine consisted of a horizontal index table supporting nine identical work-holding fixtures. Each fixture contained, in addition to basic supports, three rest buttons, tungsten carbide-tipped cam clamps, and adjustable stops for use in the horizontal plane. Four vertical columns were located as follows: one for stations 2, 3 and 4 and one each at stations 5, 8 and 9. A three-spindle drill head comprised stations 2, 3 and 4, and received its power from a common source; all other stations were individually powered.

Details of machining and tool-life data are tabulated below Fig. 16. The maximum cycle of 23 sec afforded the operator ample time in which to unload a finished part, check it with gages, and load an unmachined casting at the first station. The 23-sec cycle, together with tool-change loading, unloading and gaging time, resulted in the total time of 0.0109 hr per part, thus accounting for the production rate of 91.7 pieces per hour.

Milling

The basic principles of the three general types of milling — face, peripheral (slab) and end — are discussed in the article "Milling", in this volume. Equipment, tool materials, tool design, and operating conditions are also considered there in relation to composition and hardness of work metal. Figure 10 in the article "Milling" relates rake angle to tool material and work metal. Recommended cutter angles for face mills used on cast iron are given in the present article in Table 33.

In face and end milling of cast iron, either high speed steel or carbide cutters are used, depending primarily on the nature and hardness of the work metal. Nearly all peripheral milling of cast iron is done with high speed steel cutters.

Speed and Feed. Tables 34 to 38 list nominal speeds and feeds for milling cast iron. Optimum milling conditions vary widely, as shown by these tables. With high speed steel cutters, peripheral milling speeds are somewhat higher than those for end or face milling; feeds are slightly lower than those for face milling, and are about two to ten times those used for end milling. Nominal conditions for the use of carbide tools show a different relation: Except for finishing at hardnesses above about 300 Bhn, speeds for face milling are greater than for end milling, the difference being greatest for roughing at low hardness; feeds for face milling with either high speed steel or carbide cutters are two to ten times, or more, those for end milling; carbide tools are not ordinarily used for peripheral milling because of the danger of their chipping.

Milling speeds and feeds are selected on the basis of the work done by a single cutting edge, and have a significant effect on cutter life and regrinding costs. Although an increase in cutter feed will generally reduce labor costs, it is seldom economical to employ maximum feeds and speeds, because of their adverse effect on tool life.

Examples. The six examples that follow describe techniques and conditions used in milling gray irons, and ferritic and pearlitic malleable irons. Four of these examples compare the results obtained under alternative conditions —

Table 34. Nominal Speeds and Feeds for Face Milling of Cast Iron With High Speed Steel Cutters(a)

ASTM grade	Brinell hardness	Roughing (0.150-in. cut)(b) Speed, sfm	Roughing (0.150-in. cut)(b) Feed, ipt	Finishing (0.025-in. cut)(b) Speed, sfm	Finishing (0.025-in. cut)(b) Feed, ipt
Gray Irons					
Classes 20 and 25	110 to 140	 175	0.016	225	0.014
Class 30	150 to 190	 100	0.016	135	0.014
Classes 35 and 40	190 to 220	 85	0.013	115	0.011
Classes 45 and 50	220 to 260	 60	0.010	80	0.008
Classes 55 and 60	250 to 320	 35	0.008	45	0.005
Nodular Irons					
60-48-18 and 65-45-12	140 to 190	 140	0.016	185	0.014
80-55-06	190 to 225	 100	0.012	135	0.010
	225 to 260	 85	0.012	110	0.010
100-70-03	240 to 300	 60	0.012	80	0.010
120-90-02	270 to 330	 30	0.011	40	0.009
Malleable Irons					
32510 and 35018	110 to 160	 240	0.016	320	0.014
45007, 45010, 48004, 50007	160 to 200	 125	0.012	165	0.010
	200 to 240	 85	0.012	115	0.010
53004 and 60003	200 to 255	 70	0.012	95	0.010
80002	240 to 280	 50	0.012	65	0.010

(a) High speed steels M2 and M7. (b) Depth of cut measured parallel to axis of cutter. (Data are adapted from tables compiled by Metcut Research Associates, Inc.)

two different types of machines, methods, work materials, or cutter materials. See also Examples 340 and 349 in the article "Milling".

Example 667. Knee-Type vs Duplex Machines for Straddle Milling Class 40 Gray Iron (Table 39)

When a knee-type machine was used for straddle milling the ends of the 142-lb power-takeoff-drive housing (cast from class 40 gray iron containing 0.80 to 1.00 Ni, 0.30 to 0.40 Cr, and 0.18 to 0.25 Mo) illustrated in Table 39, difficulty was encountered in machining and in holding the 4.500-in. dimension within the specified tolerance of ±0.001 in. Although several changes of tooling were tried, none reduced the machining cost per piece to an acceptable level.

The operation was transferred to a duplex mill. Because this machine was much more rigid than the knee-type mill, dimensional accuracy was improved, and speed and feed could be nearly tripled. Although the initial cost of the insert-type tooling for the duplex mill was higher than that of the standard tooling for the knee-type mill, tool maintenance cost was considerably lower. All of these improvements resulted in a two-thirds reduction in machining cost per piece. Comparative data for the two types of machines are presented in Table 39.

Example 668. Straddle Milling vs Face Milling of Pearlitic Malleable Iron (Fig. 17)

The 66-lb two-piece ball bearing housing shown in Fig. 17 was one unit of a self-aligning bearing subject to extremely high stress in service. The base and cap comprising this housing were cast in grade 45007 pearlitic malleable iron, because of its high strength and self-lubrication under load. Parallelism of the assembled two parts had to be closely controlled in milling two opposing sides to a 125-micro-in. finish.

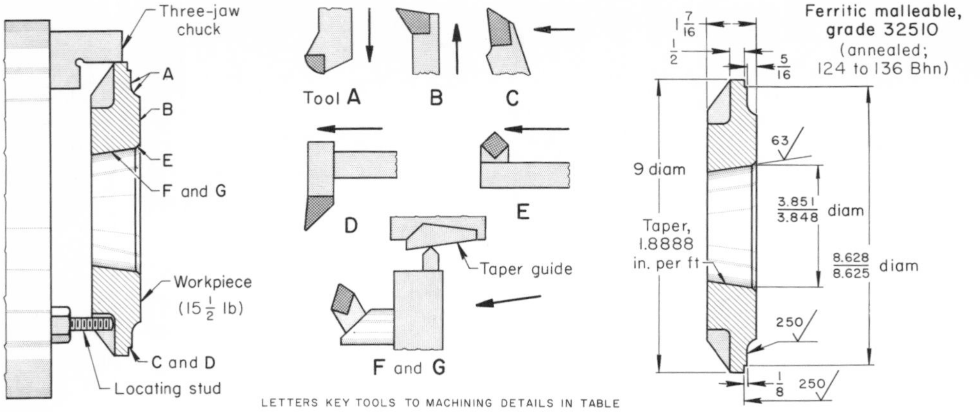

Tool(a)	Operation	Speed Rpm	Speed Sfm, max	Feed, ipr
Operating Conditions for Semiautomatic(b)				
A	Face flange; form radius	107	252	0.016
B	Face hub	107	196	0.016
C	Rough turn 8.625-in. OD	107	241	0.016
D	Finish turn 8.625-in. OD	107	241	0.016
E	Chamfer ID	107	109	0.016
F	Rough bore taper	248	246	0.016
G	Finish bore taper	298	300	0.006

Item	Manual turret lathe	Semi-automatic chucker
Time/Production Comparison, Semiautomatic vs Formerly Used Manual Turret Lathe		
Time per piece, min:		
Machining	4.41	3.78
Handling	4.46	1.70
Total (floor-to-floor)	8.87	5.48
Production per hour, pieces:		
Per machine	6.8	11
Per man	6.8	22(c)
Cost per piece	$1.00	$0.37

(a) Tools A and B were on rear and front slides, respectively; tool C was on turret station 1, tools D and E on station 2, tool F on station 3, and tool G on station 4 (station 5 idle). All tools were carbide, of the indexable, disposable-insert type; average life per edge, 125 pieces; insert-change time, 0.18 min. (b) Single-spindle semiautomatic chucker (three-jaw chuck) with 15½-in. swing over cross slides, 40/20-hp 2-speed motor, 5-station turret. Depths of cut, ⅛ to 3/16 in. Setup time, 3 hr. No cutting fluid used. (c) Two men operated four machines.

Fig. 15. Seven-tool machining of a malleable iron taper cap in a semiautomatic chucking machine that replaced a manually operated turret lathe. Data show time saving and cost reduction that resulted. (Example 665)

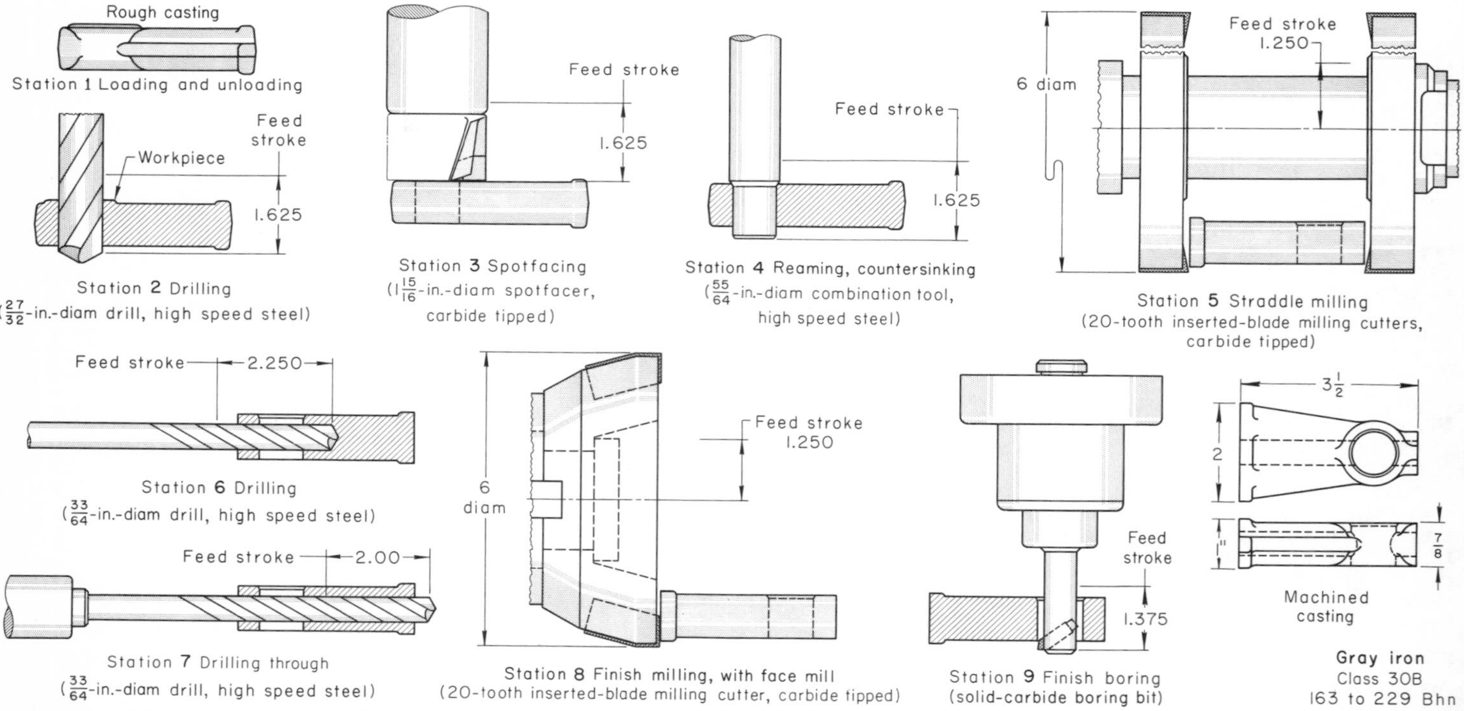

Station	Speed Rpm	Speed Sfm	Feed Ipr	Feed Ipm	Cycle time, sec Feed	Dwell	Advance	Return	Index	Total	Tool data Life, pieces (approx)	Tool data Changing time, min
2 ...	364	80	0.017	6.22	16	1	1	2	3	23	400	5
3 ...	355	180	0.017	6.22	16	1	1	2	3	23	800	5
4 ...	366	83	0.017	6.22	16	1	1	2	3	23	800	5
5 ...	160	251	0.040	6.40	12	1	1	2	3	19	6000	20
6 ...	623	84	0.016	9.97	14	1	2	3	3	23	400	5
7 ...	623	84	0.016	9.97	12	1	2	3	3	21	400	5
8 ...	180	282	0.040	7.20	10	1	1	2	3	17	800	20
9 ...	981	225	0.005	5.30	16	1	1	2	3	23	400	5

Fig. 16. Complete machining of a rocker-shaft bracket in nine stations of an automatic indexing machine. Production rate was double that obtained when machining was done progressively in two drill presses and two horizontal milling machines. (Example 666)

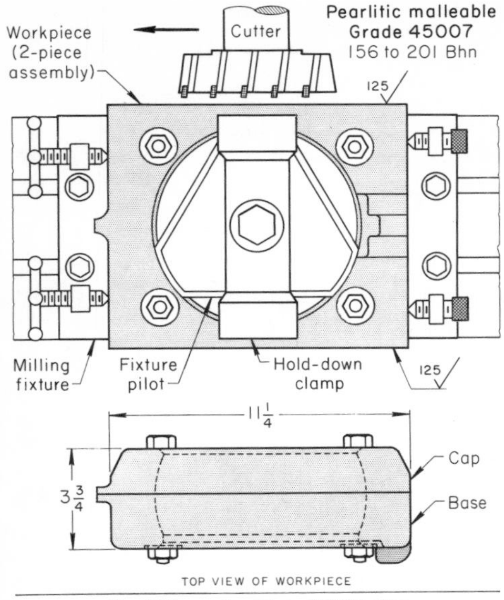

Conditions for Face Milling(a)

Speed	265 rpm (416 sfm)
Feed	0.007 ipt (18.5 ipm)
Depth of cut	⅛ in.
Cutting fluid	None
Setup time	45 min
Tool life per insert edge(b)	50 pieces
Downtime for changing inserts	10.2 min

Face vs Straddle Milling(c)

Time per piece, min:		
Machining	1.76	6.88
Handling	5.93	3.44
Total	7.69	10.32
Tool cost, per piece	0.24	0.44
Production, pieces per hour	7.8	5.8
Cost per piece	$0.86	$1.16

(a) Castings were milled on a 25-hp horizontal milling machine with a 6-in.-diam, 10-tooth cutter containing indexable, disposable carbide inserts having 1/16-in. negative land. (b) All ten inserts were changed after 50 pieces had been milled. (c) Straddle milling (second column) was done in one operation, using two 14-in.-diam high speed steel cutters.

Fig. 17. Face milling opposing sides of a two-piece ball bearing housing of pearlitic malleable iron. Data show both time saving and cost reduction obtained over straddle milling, the method formerly used. (Example 668)

Table 35. Nominal Speeds and Feeds for Face Milling of Cast Iron With Carbide Cutters

ASTM grade	Brinell hardness	Roughing (0.150-in. cut)(a): Speed, sfm, Brazed(b)	Roughing: Speed, sfm, Disposable(b)	Roughing: Feed, ipt	Finishing (0.025-in. cut)(a): Speed, sfm, Brazed(c)	Finishing: Speed, sfm, Disposable(c)	Finishing: Feed, ipt
Gray Irons							
Classes 20 & 25	110 to 140	475	525	0.020	630	695	0.018
Class 30	150 to 190	400	440	0.020	530	585	0.018
Classes 35 & 40	190 to 220	350	385	0.016	465	510	0.014
Classes 45 & 50	220 to 260	300	330	0.010	400	440	0.008
Classes 55 & 60	250 to 320	135	150	0.008	180	200	0.005
Nodular Irons							
60-48-18 and 65-45-12	140 to 190	500	550	0.020	665	730	0.018
80-55-06	190 to 225	350	385	0.014	465	510	0.012
	225 to 260	300	330	0.014	400	440	0.012
100-70-03	240 to 300	240	265	0.014	320	350	0.012
120-90-02	270 to 330	140	155	0.012	190	210	0.010
	330 to 400	70	80	0.008	90	100	0.006
Malleable Irons							
32510 and 35018	110 to 160	600	660	0.020	800	880	0.018
45007, 45010, 48004, 50007	160 to 200	375	415	0.016	500	550	0.014
	200 to 240	325	360	0.014	430	475	0.012
53004 and 60003	200 to 255	300	330	0.014	400	440	0.012
80002	240 to 280	200	220	0.014	265	290	0.012

(a) Depth of cut measured parallel to axis of cutter. (b) Grade C-2 carbide, except grade C-1 for hardness above about 240 to 260 Bhn, and grade C-6 for malleable irons. (c) Grade C-3 carbide, except grade C-2 for hardness above about 240 to 260 Bhn, and grade C-6 for malleable irons. (Data are adapted from tables compiled by Metcut Research Associates, Inc.)

Table 36. Nominal Speeds and Feeds for Peripheral (Slab) Milling of Cast Iron With High Speed Steel Cutters(a)

ASTM grade	Brinell hardness	Roughing (0.150-in. cut)(b): Speed, sfm	Roughing: Feed, ipt	Finishing (0.025-in. cut)(b): Speed, sfm	Finishing: Feed, ipt
Gray Irons					
Classes 20 and 25	110 to 140	175	0.014	225	0.012
Class 30	150 to 190	105	0.013	165	0.011
Classes 35 and 40	190 to 220	85	0.012	135	0.010
Classes 45 and 50	220 to 260	60	0.010	100	0.008
Classes 55 and 60	250 to 320	40	0.007	55	0.005
Nodular Irons					
60-48-18 and 65-45-12	140 to 190	175	0.014	225	0.012
80-55-06	190 to 225	125	0.012	160	0.010
	225 to 260	90	0.010	110	0.008
100-70-03	240 to 300	75	0.010	95	0.008
120-90-02	270 to 330	40	0.007	55	0.005
Malleable Irons					
32510 and 35018	110 to 160	250	0.014	340	0.012
45007, 45010, 48004, 50007	160 to 200	115	0.013	155	0.011
	200 to 240	85	0.010	120	0.008
53004 and 60003	200 to 255	75	0.010	105	0.008
80002	240 to 280	55	0.008	90	0.006

(a) High speed steels M2 and M7. (b) Depth of cut measured parallel to axis of cutter. (Data are adapted from tables compiled by Metcut Research Associates, Inc.)

Originally, the two sides of the assembly were milled simultaneously, by straddle milling with two 14-in.-diam cutters made of high speed steel. Although parallelism and finish were acceptable, production rate was unsatisfactory and the initial cost of the cutters and the cost of maintenance were both considered excessive.

Face milling the assembly, with a cutter containing indexable, disposable carbide inserts, was adopted as the alternative method. This operation consisted of milling one side of the assembly, then indexing it 180° and milling the opposite side, using the setup illustrated in Fig. 17. Details of the face milling operation, together with a comparison showing the increased production and lower tool and per-piece costs obtained, are tabulated below Fig. 17.

Example 669. Face Milling Grade 32510 Ferritic Malleable Iron (Fig. 18)

The 8½-lb idler shaft bracket shown in Fig. 18 was face milled in the annealed condition in a 25-hp horizontal milling machine, to provide a flat base for mounting on a structural channel. Although finish of the milled surface was not a significant factor, flatness and angular relationship to other functional machined surfaces of the part were of utmost importance.

High speed steel, rather than carbide, was selected for the milling cutter because its ability to withstand high chip loads without damage rendered its use more economical. The face milling setup and details of the machining operation are given with Fig. 18.

Example 670. High-Production Face Milling of Class 45 Gray Iron in a Two-Spindle Rotary Mill (Fig. 19)

Figure 19 shows the setup (and details of the carbide cutter inserts) used on a 40-hp two-spindle rotary mill with a 48-in.-diam table, to obtain high production in rough and finish face milling of cylinder heads cast from class 45 gray iron. The surface produced had a finish of 250 micro-in. and was flat within ±0.005 in. Operating conditions are tabulated below Fig. 19.

The worktable revolved continuously at 0.2 rpm, which was slow enough to permit the operator to unload and reload a jig as it passed his work station.

Example 671. Straddle Milling Gray Iron vs Pearlitic Malleable Iron

In straddle milling the thrust faces of crankshaft-bearing caps cast from class 30 gray iron at a feed of 25 ipm (0.00625 ipt), cutter life was more than double that obtained in milling identical castings of grade 60003 pearlitic malleable iron at a feed of only 10 ipm (0.0025 ipt). Castings of both materials weighed 5.6 lb rough and 5.4 lb finished, and were of comparable hardness (197 to 241 Bhn for the pearlitic malleable, and 183 to 235 Bhn for the gray iron). Both types were milled on identical equipment with two 9-in.-diam side milling cutters containing 32 inserted carbide blades, at a speed of 125 rpm (295 sfm). The increased feed and tool life for the gray iron increased production and lowered cost, as shown below:

	Malleable	Gray
Insert life, pieces	500	1200
Production per hour, pieces	58.4	114.7
Machining cost per piece	$0.086	$0.044

The straddle mill had dual 15-hp heads. Cut width was 3.75 in.; depth, 0.12 in.; section thickness, 1.380 ± 0.005 in. Cutting fluid was soluble oil (1 to 20).

When the milling machine and holding fixtures are rigid enough to withstand the additional forces imposed, the substitution of carbide for high speed steel milling cutters permits much higher speed and feed, thus increasing production rate — as shown in the following example:

Example 672. High Speed Steel vs Carbide Cutters for Face Milling Gray Iron (Fig. 20)

In face milling the bases of class 20 gray iron pillow blocks in the setup shown in Fig. 20, production rate was doubled by changing from high speed steel cutters to cutters containing indexable, disposable car-

Table 37. Nominal Speeds and Feeds for End Milling of Cast Iron With High Speed Steel Cutters (a)

ASTM grade	Brinell hardness	Roughing (0.050 in. cut)(b): Speed, sfm	Roughing: Feed, ipt, for cutter diam of: ¼ in.	½ in.	¾ in.	1 to 2 in.	Finishing (0.015-in. cut)(b): Speed, sfm	Finishing: Feed, ipt, for cutter diam of: ¼ in.	½ in.	¾ in.	1 to 2 in.
Gray Irons											
Classes 20 & 25	110 to 140 ...	135	0.002	0.004	0.006	0.008	175	0.001	0.002	0.005	0.007
Class 30	150 to 190 ...	100	0.002	0.003	0.005	0.007	130	0.001	0.002	0.004	0.006
Classes 35 & 40	190 to 220 ...	75	0.002	0.003	0.004	0.005	100	0.001	0.002	0.003	0.004
Classes 45 & 50	220 to 260 ...	65	0.002	0.0025	0.003	0.004	85	0.001	0.0015	0.002	0.003
Classes 55 & 60	250 to 320 ...	30	0.001	0.002	0.003	0.004	40	0.0005	0.001	0.002	0.003
Nodular Irons											
60-48-18 & 65-45-12	140 to 190 ...	120	0.002	0.004	0.006	0.008	155	0.001	0.002	0.005	0.007
80-55-06	190 to 225 ...	85	0.002	0.003	0.005	0.007	110	0.001	0.002	0.004	0.006
	225 to 260 ...	75	0.001	0.002	0.003	0.005	95	0.0005	0.001	0.002	0.004
100-70-03	240 to 300 ...	55	0.001	0.002	0.004	0.005	70	0.0005	0.001	0.003	0.004
120-90-02	270 to 330 ...	35	0.001	0.002	0.003	0.004	45	0.0005	0.001	0.002	0.003
Malleable Irons											
32510, 35018	110 to 160 ...	150	0.002	0.004	0.006	0.008	195	0.001	0.002	0.005	0.007
45007, 45010, 48004, 50007	160 to 200 ...	130	0.002	0.003	0.005	0.007	170	0.001	0.002	0.004	0.006
	200 to 240 ...	85	0.002	0.003	0.004	0.005	110	0.001	0.002	0.003	0.004
53004, 60003	200 to 255 ...	75	0.002	0.003	0.004	0.005	95	0.001	0.002	0.003	0.004
80002	240 to 280 ...	60	0.001	0.002	0.003	0.004	80	0.001	0.0015	0.002	0.003

(a) High speed steels M2 and M7 except T15, M33, M41, M42, M43 and M44 for hardness above about 240 to 260 Bhn. (b) Depth of cut measured parallel to cutter axis. (SOURCE: see Table 36.)

Table 38. Nominal Speeds and Feeds for End Milling of Cast Iron With Carbide Cutters (a)

ASTM grade	Brinell hardness	Roughing (0.050-in. cut)(b): Speed, sfm	Roughing: Feed, ipt, for cutter diam of: ¼ in.	½ in.	¾ in.	1 to 2 in.	Finishing (0.015-in. cut)(b): Speed, sfm	Finishing: Feed, ipt, for cutter diam of: ¼ in.	½ in.	¾ in.	1 to 2 in.
Gray Irons											
Classes 20 & 25	110 to 140 ...	450	0.002	0.005	0.009	0.010	585	0.001	0.003	0.007	0.009
Class 30	150 to 190 ...	350	0.002	0.004	0.007	0.008	455	0.001	0.003	0.005	0.007
Classes 35 & 40	190 to 220 ...	275	0.002	0.004	0.006	0.008	360	0.001	0.003	0.005	0.007
Classes 45 & 50	220 to 260 ...	225	0.002	0.003	0.004	0.006	290	0.001	0.002	0.003	0.005
Classes 55 & 60	250 to 320 ...	125	0.001	0.0025	0.004	0.005	160	0.0005	0.0015	0.003	0.004
Nodular Irons											
60-48-18 & 65-45-12	140 to 190 ...	400	0.002	0.005	0.009	0.010	520	0.001	0.003	0.007	0.009
80-55-06	190 to 225 ...	275	0.002	0.004	0.007	0.008	360	0.001	0.002	0.006	0.007
	225 to 260 ...	225	0.0015	0.004	0.006	0.007	290	0.001	0.002	0.005	0.006
100-70-03	240 to 300 ...	200	0.001	0.0025	0.005	0.006	260	0.0005	0.0015	0.004	0.005
120-90-02	270 to 330 ...	100	0.001	0.0025	0.004	0.005	130	0.0005	0.0015	0.003	0.004
Malleable Irons											
32510, 35018	110 to 160 ...	475	0.002	0.005	0.009	0.010	620	0.001	0.003	0.007	0.009
45007, 45010, 48004, 50007	160 to 200 ...	350	0.002	0.004	0.007	0.008	455	0.001	0.003	0.005	0.007
	200 to 240 ...	275	0.002	0.003	0.004	0.006	360	0.001	0.002	0.003	0.005
53004, 60003	200 to 255 ...	250	0.002	0.003	0.004	0.006	325	0.001	0.002	0.003	0.005
80002	240 to 280 ...	175	0.0015	0.003	0.004	0.005	230	0.001	0.002	0.0025	0.0035

(a) Grade C-2 carbide. (b) Depth of cut measured parallel to cutter axis. (SOURCE: see Table 36.)

bide inserts. A comparison of operating conditions and results for the two cutter materials is tabulated below Fig. 20.

Milling the bases of these pillow blocks was the first machining operation performed, because it provided a locating plane for all subsequent machining. Fixtures were designed so that several sizes of blocks could be milled with a minimum of setup time. The two-fixture setup permitted milling to be done simultaneously with unloading and loading.

Grinding

General principles, equipment, grinding wheels, and procedures of grinding are discussed in the article "Grinding", in this volume. Wheel designations and nominal speeds and feeds for surface, cylindrical, centerless and internal grinding of the cast irons are given in Table 40.

Grinding Fluid. Although cast iron is sometimes ground dry (without any cooling medium), for most applications the use of some type of grinding fluid is necessary. Selection of grinding fluid for cast iron is more critical than for steel under similar grinding conditions, mainly because of the graphite and other fines generated in grinding cast iron. Soluble-oil emulsions are commonly used, but because the graphite and fine metallic particles of the grinding residue mix readily with the oil and are difficult to separate, they are constantly recirculated over the areas being ground, causing excessive loading of the wheels. When synthetic chemical solutions containing sodium nitrite or potassium nitrite are used, the graphite and other fines float on the grinding fluid and can be skimmed off, thus preventing their being recirculated. Minimizing contamination of the grinding fluid improves the finish on the work and increases wheel life.

Examples. The four examples that follow present conditions and results in production grinding of gray, malleable and chilled iron castings. The first two examples discuss the basis for wheel selection for grinding gray iron at two widely different hardness levels.

Example 673. Cylindrical Grinding of Class 40 Gray Iron at 228 to 241 Bhn (Fig. 21)

For cylindrical grinding the gray iron clutch spider illustrated in Fig. 21, considerable experimentation was required in selecting the wheel and operating conditions (see tabulated details below Fig. 21) that provided specified

Table 39. Knee-Type vs Duplex Machines for Straddle Milling Class 40 Gray Iron (Example 667) (a)

Item	Knee-type machine	Duplex machine
Cutter Details(b)		
Number of cutters	2	2
Cutter diameter, in.	14	8
Number of teeth per cutter ..	26	15
Operating Conditions		
Speed, rpm	58	170
Speed, sfm	213	356
Feed, ipm	5⅛	15
Feed, ipt	0.0034	0.0058
Machining time per piece, min	2.94	1.62
Production, pieces per hour .	20.4	37
Cutter life per change, pieces	70	300
Costs		
Cutters, per set	$525	$840
Grinding, per set of cutters ..	$13	None
Labor per cutter change(c) .	$3	$1
Machining cost per piece ..	$0.162	$0.055

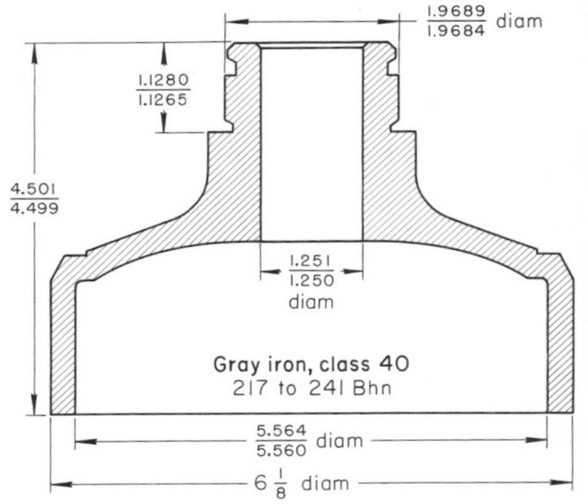

(a) Data compare the use of a high-speed knee-type milling machine and a duplex bed-type machine for straddle milling the ends of the drive housing illustrated above, to produce the 4.501/4.499-in. dimension. Depth of cut per side was 3⁄16 in.; no cutting fluid was used. (b) Carbide cutters of the same grade were used on both machines. Brazed, resharpenable inserts were used on the knee-type machine. Disposable inserts were used on the duplex machine. (c) Direct labor plus fringe allowance.

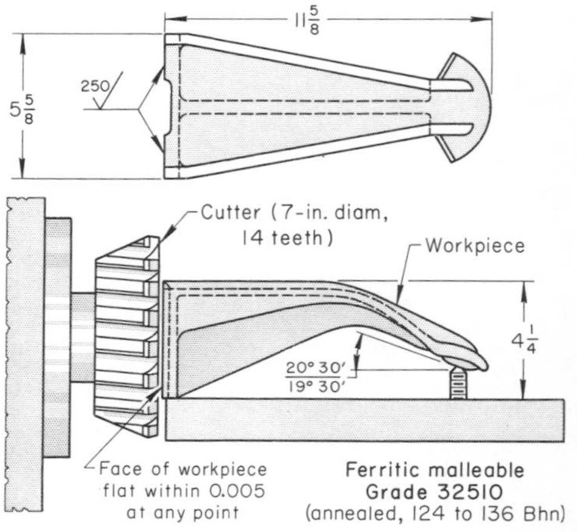

Speed	44 rpm (81 sfm)
Feed	0.025 ipt (15.4 ipm)
Depth of cut	1⁄16 to 3⁄16 in. (⅛ in. avg)
Cutting fluid	None
Setup time	45 min
Machining time per piece	1.31 min
Production rate per hour	45.8 pieces
Tool life per grind	250 pieces
Downtime for tool change	15 min

Fig. 18. Face milling a cast idler shaft bracket in a 25-hp horizontal machine (Example 669)

Table 40. Conditions for Grinding Cast Iron(a)

Surface Grinding	
Wheel classification	A-46-I-V
Wheel speed	5500 to 6500 sfm
Table speed	50 to 100 sfm
Downfeed per pass, roughing	0.003 in.
Downfeed per pass, finishing	0.001 in. max
Crossfeed per pass	⅓ wheel width
Cylindrical Grinding	
Wheel classification	A-60-L-V
Wheel speed	5500 to 6500 sfm
Work speed	100 sfm
Infeed per pass, roughing	0.002 in.
Infeed per pass, finishing	0.0005 in. max
Traverse per work revolution:	
Gray or malleable iron:	
Roughing	⅓ wheel width
Finishing	⅙ wheel width
Nodular iron:	
Roughing	¼ wheel width
Finishing	⅛ wheel width
Centerless Grinding	
Wheel classification	C-60-J-V or A-60-J-V
Wheel speed	5500 to 6500 sfm
Work feed	50 ipm
Infeed per pass, roughing	0.005 in.
Infeed per pass, finishing	0.0015 in. max
Regulating-wheel angle	3°
Regulating-wheel speed	30 rpm
Internal Grinding(b)	
Wheel classification	A-46-J-V(c)
Wheel speed	5000 to 6500 sfm
Work speed	80 to 160 sfm
Infeed per pass, roughing	0.002 in.
Infeed per pass, finishing	0.0002 in. max
Traverse per work revolution:	
Roughing	⅓ wheel width
Finishing	⅙ wheel width

(a) Conditions apply to cast irons with a maximum hardness of Rockwell C 52. (b) Based on grinding maximum hole length of 2½ times hole diameter. (c) Maximum wheel width is 1½ wheel diameters. (Data are adapted from tables compiled by Metcut Research Associates, Inc.)

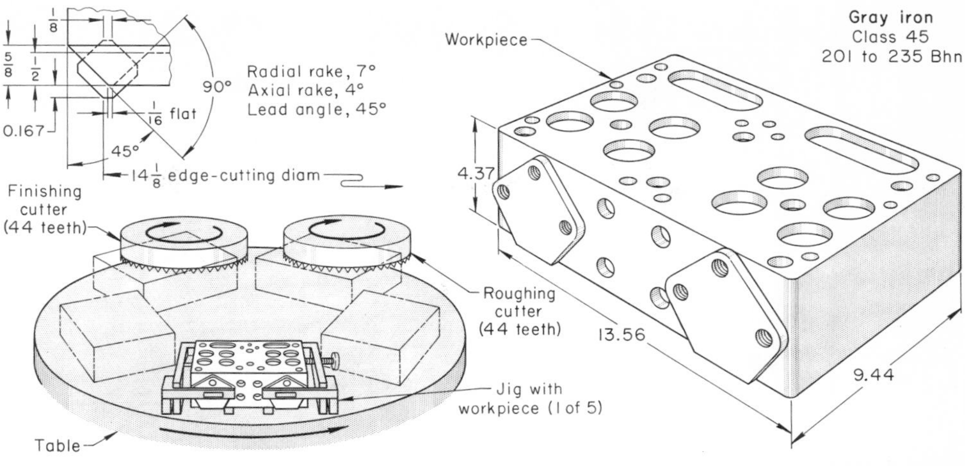

Roughing:	
Speed	75 rpm (275 sfm)
Feed	0.010 ipt (33 ipm)
Depth of cut	0.250 in
Finishing:	
Speed	90 rpm (330 sfm)
Feed	0.008 ipt (31.7 ipm)
Depth of cut	0.030 in.

Cutting fluid	None
Setup time	30 min
Time per piece	1.32 min
Production per hour	45.4 pieces
Insert material	Carbide
Tool life per grind	300 pieces
Downtime for changing tools	1 hr
Tool cost per piece	$0.017

Fig. 19. Rough and finish face milling of gray iron cylinder heads in a two-spindle rotary-table mill (Example 670)

finish and dimensional accuracy. The matrix structure of the iron (fine pearlite with randomly distributed type A graphite), grain size (5 to 6), and the strength of the matrix (150,000 psi) were among the factors considered in selecting the most suitable grinding wheel. (Alloy content of the iron was 0.80 to 1.00 Ni, 0.30 to 0.40 Cr, and 0.18 to 0.25 Mo.)

An A-54-M-V wheel was selected for the following reasons:

1 Aluminum oxide abrasive, because of the high-strength matrix and the relatively light cuts required
2 Medium grit size, because the material was relatively soft but brittle
3 Medium hardness, because the ground area was comparatively large and the wheel speed was relatively high
4 Medium-dense structure, because of the close tolerances and smooth finish specified for the brittle material.

To obtain the 25-micro-in. finish, it was also important to limit the amount of stock removed per pass and to control the frequency of wheel dressing.

Example 674. Centerless Grinding of Class 40 Gray Iron at 500 to 550 Bhn (Table 41)

Table 41 lists the conditions used for centerless grinding a hydraulic piston cast from alloy gray iron (0.20 to 0.30 Cr, 0.45 to 0.75 Mo) quenched and tempered to 500 to 550 Bhn. Except for the centerless ground 4.0020/4.0005-in. diameter, all surfaces on this casting had been finish machined before being heat treated. (Heat treatment consisted of holding at 1600 F for 1 hr, quenching in paraffin-base oil at 130 F, and tempering for 1 hr at 300 F. The casting was then blasted with No. 40 grit before being ground.)

The normal microstructure of the quenched and tempered iron was martensite with type A graphite randomly distributed and a grain size of 6 to 8. The A-80-J-V wheel (see Table 41 for wheel size and operating conditions) was selected for the following reasons:

1 Aluminum oxide abrasive, because of the high hardness of the heat treated iron, and the light cuts required

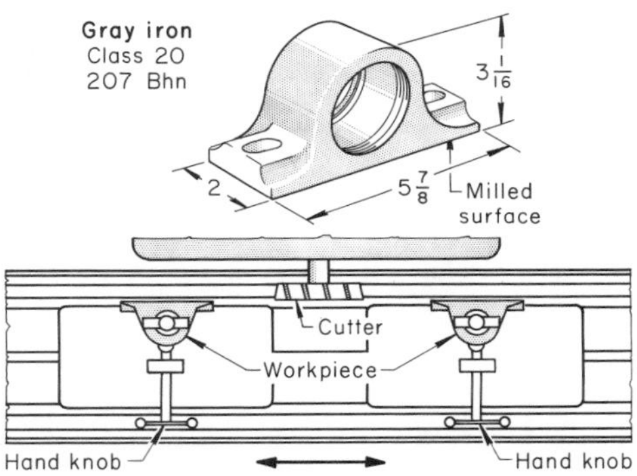

Condition or result(a)	Cutter(b): High speed steel (12-tooth)	Cutter(b): Carbide(c) (10-tooth)
Speed, rpm	131	173
Speed, sfm	206	272
Feed, ipm	6.0	15.6
Feed, ipt	0.0038	0.009
Tool life per grind or edge, pieces	200	800
Downtime for indexing or changing tools, min	10	10 to 15
Time per piece (floor-to-floor), min	1.10	0.54
Production per hour, pieces	50	100

(a) Both types of cutters were used on a horizontal machine with a 12-by-54-in. table. Depth of cut was ⅛ in.; no cutting fluid was used. Each fixture consisted of an air-actuated hydraulic pull-down clamp with a hand-knob locator. (b) Cutters of both materials were 6 in. in diameter. (c) Indexable, disposable inserts.

Fig. 20. Face milling bases of pillow blocks in a two-fixture setup, with high speed steel vs carbide cutters (Example 672)

2 Medium-fine grain, because it afforded fast stock removal but relatively light depth of grain penetration
3 Medium-soft wheel, because of high hardness of the iron
4 Medium-dense structure, because the iron was hard and brittle, and centerless grinding was to be used.

To obtain the 10 to 15-micro-in. finish, it was also important to limit the amount of stock removal per pass. A low grinding-wheel speed was used because of the condition of the equipment; the machine was 18 years old and in only fair condition.

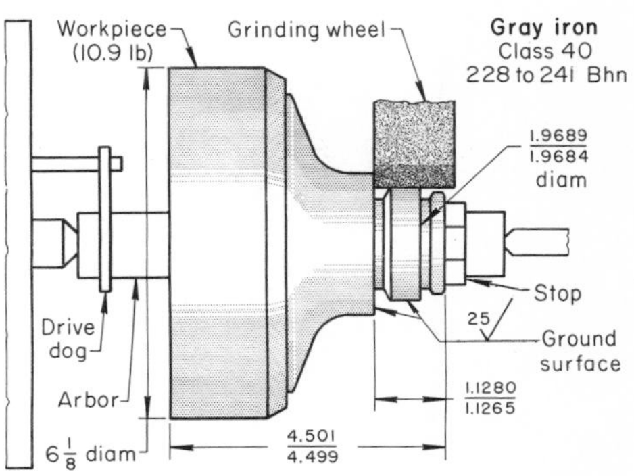

Machine size(a)	10 by 36 in.
Wheel classification	A-54-M-V
Wheel size	30 by 12 by 2½ in.
Operating Conditions	
Machine(a)	Semiautomatic, 10 by 18 in.
Wheel classification(b)	A-46-K6-V
Feed per revolution	0.0003 in.
Depth of cut per side	0.012 in.
Grinding fluid	Soluble oil:water (1:80)
Setup time	36 min
Production rate	38 pieces per hour
Wheel life per dressing	30 pieces

(a) Self-feed cylindrical grinder. (b) Surface speed of ground diameter.

Fig. 21. Cylindrical grinding of two surfaces of a clutch spider to close dimensional and finish specifications (Example 673)

Example 675. Cylindrical Finish Grinding of Pearlitic Malleable Iron (Fig. 22)

Figure 22 shows the setup used in three semiautomatic cylindrical grinders for finish grinding the contoured outside diameter of pistons cast from grade 60003 pearlitic malleable iron. As noted in the table of processing details that accompanies Fig. 22, one man operated all three machines. Castings were transported to and from the machines by conveyor.

After two turning operations, the castings had been rough ground in centerless grinders. Each casting was then placed in a cradle located between and below the two grinding centers of the cylindrical machine. Two pushbuttons actuated the hydraulic tailstock, lifting the casting from the cradle and securing it between centers (Fig. 22), and also started the grinding cycle. A straight plunge feed with a timed dwell for sparkout was em-

Table 41. Centerless Grinding of Class 40 Gray Iron at 500 to 550 Bhn (Example 674) (a)

Wheel classification	A-80-J-V
Wheel size	20 by 6 by 12 in.
Operating Conditions	
Grinding-wheel speed	500 rpm (2618 sfm)
Feed-wheel speed	18 rpm
Feed-wheel setting	3°
Depth of cut	0.015 in.(b)
Grinding fluid	Soluble-oil:water (1:45)
Production rate	67 pieces per hour
Wheel life per dressing	25 pieces

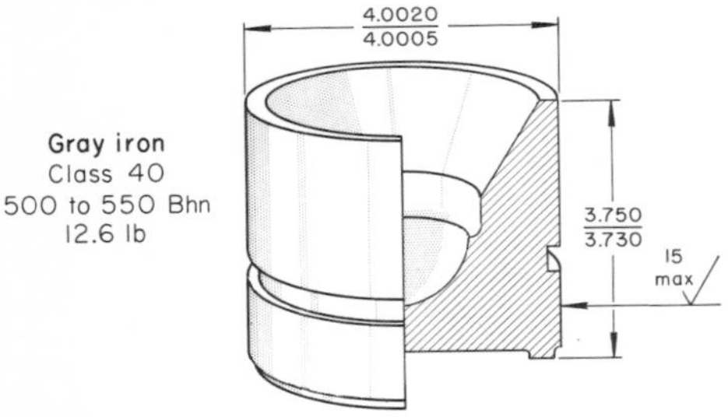

(a) Data are for finish grinding the 4-in. diameter on the hydraulic piston shown above, in a No. 12 centerless grinding machine. (b) Total in five passes. Each of the first three passes removed 0.004 in.; the remainder (0.002 to 0.003 in.) was removed in the two final passes to produce a finish of 10 to 15 micro-in.

ployed. The tailstock center automatically retracted at the end of the cycle.

Selection of wheel-hardness grade was critical, because of the interrupted cut at the piston-pin holes and because the trailing edges of these holes exerted a dressing action on the wheel. Also, pressure on the tailstock had to be kept to a minimum, to avoid distortion of the workpiece.

Example 676. Grinding vs Turning for Rough Sizing of Chilled Iron Rolls

Time per piece was reduced from 28 hr to 3½ hr when rough grinding was used instead of turning, for removing ¾ to 1 in. of stock from the body diameter of steel-mill work rolls cast from chilled iron, prior to finish grinding to size. These rolls had a body length of 98 in. and diameter (finished) of 27 in.; hardness was 75 to 80 scleroscope (Rockwell C 56 to 59). The change in roughing method also provided a saving in finish grinding, because turning left 0.125 in. of stock for removal, as against only 0.040 in. by rough grinding.

Turning was done in three passes with brazed-carbide tools. Tips were ½ in. thick, 1¼ in. long, and ¾ in. wide, and had 0° side rake, 5° primary and 10° secondary clearance angles, and ⅛-in.-wide by 10° negative back-rake land. Speed was 18 sfm for rolls at 75 scleroscope, and 10 to 12 sfm for those at 80; feed was from 0.040 to 0.060 ipr; no cutting fluid was used.

Grinding was done in a 125-hp roll grinder, using three A-54-M-V wheels, 36 in. in diameter by 3 in. wide, spaced 1 in. apart. Wheel speed started at 690 rpm and increased to 1125 rpm as the wheel wore, to maintain a surface speed of about 6500 sfm. Work rotation was 14 rpm (100 sfm), and traverse rate was 60 fpm. Sal soda and water was the grinding fluid.

Six additional production examples describing conditions used in the grinding of cast iron are given in the article "Grinding" (see table at right).

Honing and Lapping

Honing is the usual way to finish cylinder bores of automotive engines. The process can be applied to finishing of parts made from gray, nodular or malleable iron in any hardness range, although it is most widely used for the various grades of gray iron.

Outside diameters of cast iron parts can also be finished by honing, although grinding is usually satisfactory and is cheaper than honing.

Machines, tools and techniques that are applicable to honing of cast iron are described in the article "Honing", beginning on page 288 of this volume. Eight processing examples (533, 534, 537, 538, and 540 to 543) in that article deal with honing of cast iron.

Although there are exceptions, silicon carbide is almost always used as the abrasive in honing stones, and vitrified bond is the most common. The abrasive in stones for honing of cast iron may vary from 150 to 500 grit size, depending on finish requirements. A finish of 3 to 5 micro-in. can be produced on as-cast and hardened cast irons by stones having grit size of 400 to 500. For a finish of 6 to 9 micro-in., stones having grit size of 280 to 400 are used. Grit size of 280 will usually produce a surface finish of 15 to 25 micro-in.

In a majority of applications involving honing of cast iron, a range of surface finish is specified (as is usually true for automobile engine bores) rather than a maximum micro-inch value. The most common ranges of specified finish can usually be accommodated by abrasive grit sizes of 150 to 300. As is noted in Example 541 in the article on Honing, a change in abrasive grit size may result in an improvement in surface finish. Sometimes, to meet specific requirements, stones having different grit sizes are intermixed as described in Example 542 in the article on Honing. In this instance, C-150-R-V (150 grit) stones were intermixed with C-180-R-V (180 grit) stones to achieve a compromise between desired stock removal and surface finish in the honing of cylinder bores.

Because most applications for honing cast iron require a specific lay pattern, honing speed is critical. The speed of rotation for honing of cast irons having hardness in the range of 160 to 210 Bhn usually is from 160 to 210 sfm, which is decreased to a range of 80 to 130 sfm for work-metal hardness of Rockwell C 50 to 65. A speed of reciprocation of 80 sfm is common, although this may vary considerably, depending on the specified angle of crosshatch. The article on Honing gives a formula for determining the crosshatch angle that will result from different combinations of reciprocation and rotation speeds. However, in practice the desired angle is more often obtained by trial. The most common procedure is to establish a rotation speed and then to vary the speed of reciprocation until the desired angle of crosshatch is attained. Sometimes adjustments must be made in

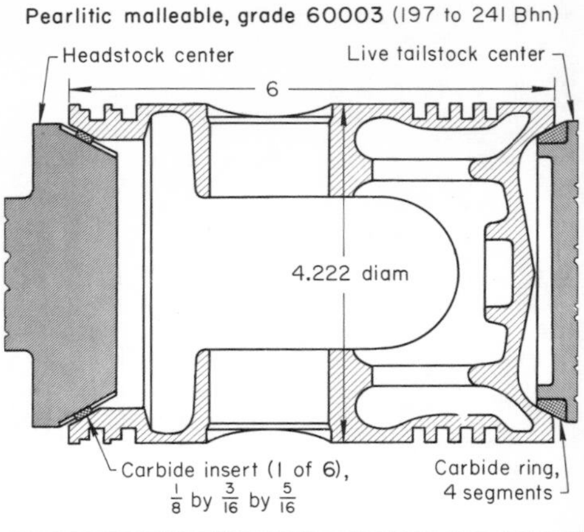

Machine(a)	Semiautomatic, 10 by 18 in.
Wheel classification(b)	A-46-K6-V
Wheel size	24 by 7 by 12 in.
Operating Conditions	
Wheel speed	1035 rpm (6500 sfm max)
Work speed	125 rpm (138 sfm)
Infeed	0.007 in. per min
Depth of cut per side	0.005 in.
Grinding fluid	Soluble-oil:water (1:100)
Machine-cycle time per piece	58 sec
Production per hour:	
Per machine	33 pieces
Per man	100 pieces(c)
Wheel life per dressing	40 to 50 pieces
Total wheel life, approx	25,000 pieces
Downtime for changing wheel	1 hr

(a) Grinding machine cost $40,000; tailstock center, $200; headstock center, $350. (b) Wheels cost $139.20 each in lots of 12. (c) One man operated three machines.

Fig. 22. Cylindrical finish grinding of pearlitic malleable iron pistons
(Example 675)

rotation speed for other reasons. For instance, in Example 538 in the article on Honing, it was necessary to reduce rotation speed from 235 to 157 sfm to reduce out-of-roundness and taper.

Dimensional accuracy within 0.001 to 0.0001 in. in diameter of cast iron bores is regularly attained by honing (note Example 540 in the article on Honing).

Acceptable results in honing cast iron depend greatly on a copious supply of lubricant at the areas being honed. Mineral seal oil is widely used, although higher-viscosity mineral oils diluted with kerosine and other lubricants are also used (see the section on Honing Fluids in the article "Honing").

Lapping with loose abrasive is not used extensively for finishing cast iron parts, mainly because the workpieces become charged with abrasive, which is difficult to remove. Matched-piece lapping is sometimes used for mating of cast iron parts such as valve components. Another application is lapping the sides of piston rings, as described in Example 569, on page 306.

Other Examples of Machining Cast Iron in This Volume

Gray Iron

Turning	Ex. 8, 10, 22
Boring	Ex. 40, 46, 47, 48, 51, 52, 54, 55, 61, 63, 66, 69, 70, 71, 73, 75, 77-80
Planing	Ex. 91
Broaching	Ex. 105, 112, 115, 116
Drilling	Ex. 150, 164, 173, 177
Reaming	Ex. 205, 207
Die threading	Ex. 251
Multiple-operation machining	Ex. 289, 295
Milling	Ex. 340, 349
Honing	Ex. 533, 534, 537, 538, 540-543
Lapping	Ex. 569
Grinding	Ex. 468, 474, 476, 477, 520, 525
Contour band sawing	Ex. 444

Nodular Iron

Boring	Ex. 36, 39, 56
Broaching	Ex. 105
Multiple-operation machining	Ex. 287

Malleable Iron

Boring	Ex. 42, 50
Broaching	Ex. 130
Die threading	Ex. 258
Multiple-operation machining	Ex. 278, 279

MACHINING AND GRINDING OF TOOL STEEL

CONTENTS

Machining of Tool Steel

*By the ASM Committee on Machining of Tool Steel**

THE HIGH CARBON and alloy contents that make tool steels serviceable as tools also make them more difficult to machine than the lower-carbon and the lower-alloy constructional steels. Table 1 gives nominal compositions of alloy tool steels except high speed steels, which are covered in Table 1 on page 312, in the article "High Speed Steel for Cutting Tools". Several of the alloying elements used in tool steel, especially chromium, tungsten, molybdenum and vanadium, readily form carbides that have adverse effects in machining. These effects are markedly influenced by the size, shape and distribution of the carbide particles in the matrix of the steel.

Most tool steels (notably the higher-carbon tool steels) are easiest to machine when they have been annealed to a microstructure that consists of small spheroidal carbides uniformly distributed in a matrix of ferrite.

In tool steels containing less than about 0.75% carbon, the spheroids are more likely to become large and widely dispersed in relatively large areas of ferrite. Carbides dispersed in this manner cause poor finish and low tool life. If the alloy content of the steel is low, the ferrite is characteristically gummy; if the alloy content is high, the ferrite is tough. Thus, the properties of the ferrite matrix, as well as the size and distribution of carbides, can be a major factor in the machinability of tool steel. The preferred structure usually is a mixture of spheroidite and lamellar pearlite obtained by controlled annealing. As the carbon content is increased to approximately 1% in unalloyed tool steel, the spheroids become finer, more numerous and more closely spaced.

To provide a basis for comparing the relative machinability of different types of tool steel, carbon tool steel containing 1% carbon is rated at 100; other tool steels are rated as a percentage of 100, as shown in Table 2.

The micrographs in Fig. 1 indicate the differences in microstructure characteristic of three different tool steels (W1 containing 1% C, A2 and M2) in the annealed condition. As shown, the microstructure of the W1 steel is a uniform distribution of small spheroids. In the A2 steel, massive alloy carbides appear, and in the M2 steel the carbides are larger and more numerous than in A2. As annealed, the hardness ranges are 156 to 196 Bhn for W1, 202 to 217 Bhn for A2, and 217 to 235 Bhn for M2. However, the increase in hardness is only partly indicative of the relative decrease in machinability encountered in a comparison of these steels. Compared to the iron carbide in the unalloyed steel, the more abrasive alloy carbides have a greater adverse effect on machining characteristics than the slightly higher hardness of the annealed steels containing them would indicate.

Hardness. Low-carbon tool steels are relatively soft in the annealed condition and have machining characteristics similar to those of their counterparts in tonnage carbon and alloy steels. For instance, P1 mold steel has machining characteristics similar to 1010, and P20 closely resembles 4130 in machinability, under conditions of similar annealing practice.

W1 steel can be annealed to a hardness of less than 200 Bhn, whereas the typical hardness of annealed T15 and M15 high speed steels is about 255 to 275 Bhn. Tool steels containing high percentages of cobalt, which strengthens the ferrite, also have lower machinability because of generally higher hardness, as annealed. T5 and T6 cobalt-containing high speed steels can be annealed no softer than about 250 to 275 Bhn.

*RICHARD C. STROKER, *Chairman,* Metallurgist, Barber-Colman Co.; HENRY BRANDOLF, Staff Metallurgist, United Greenfield Corp.; CHARLES A. DIVINE, JR., Metallurgical Department, Carpenter Steel Co.; DONALD F. GRIFFIN, Chief Metallurgist, Landis Machine Co.

R. G. KENNEDY, Director of Laboratories, Cleveland Twist Drill Co.; P. LECKIE-EWING, Manager of Research, Latrobe Steel Co. (now Chief Metallurgist, Union Twist Drill Co.); DAVID L. LEWIS, Production Engineer, Die & Machine Plant, Fisher Body Div., General Motors Corp.

H. E. MOHLER, Production Engineer, New Castle Forge Plant, Chrysler Corp.; REX SUPERNAW, Chief Metallurgist, National Twist Drill & Tool Co.; BRUCE E. WRIGHT, Research Engineer, Buick Motor Div., General Motors Corp.

As machinability decreases because of hardness or composition, or both, greater power and rigidity are required in the machine tool to perform a given machining operation.

Cost

In any machining operation in which a large quantity of chips is produced (as in turning or milling), the metal cost of the discarded chips is the major cost in machining tool steels. As shown in Table 3 and Fig. 2, the turning costs for a wide variety of tool steels are insignificant in relation to the cost of the lost material — even for the relatively low-cost W and O tool steels.

Table 1. Classification and Nominal Composition of Tool Steels Mentioned in This Article
(AISI except for last group of steels)

Steel	C	W	Mo	Cr	V	Other
Water-Hardening Tool Steels						
W1 ..	(a)	...	...	...	...	...
W2 ..	(a)	...	...	...	0.25	...
W3 ..	1.00	...	...	...	0.50	...
W5 ..	1.10	...	...	0.50	...	...
Shock-Resisting Tool Steel						
S1 ...	0.50	2.50	...	1.50	...	...
Oil-Hardening Cold Work Tool Steels						
O1 ...	0.90	0.50	...	0.50	...	1.00 Mn
O2 ...	0.90	...	...	...	...	1.60 Mn
O6 ...	1.45	...	0.25	...	...	1.00 Si
O7 ...	1.20	1.75	...	0.75	...	...
Medium-Alloy Air-Hardening Cold Work Tool Steels						
A2 ...	1.00	...	1.00	5.00	...	...
A4 ...	1.00	...	1.00	1.00	...	2.00 Mn
A5 ...	1.00	...	1.00	1.00	...	3.00 Mn
A6 ...	0.70	...	1.00	1.00	...	2.00 Mn
A7 ...	2.25	(b)	1.00	5.25	4.75	...
High-Carbon High-Chromium Cold Work Tool Steels						
D1 ...	1.00	...	1.00	12.00	...	...
D2 ...	1.50	...	1.00	12.00	...	...
D3 ...	2.25	...	...	12.00	...	...
D4 ...	2.25	...	1.00	12.00	...	...
D5 ...	1.50	...	1.00	12.00	...	3.00 Co
D6 ...	Now included with D3 by AISI					
D7 ...	2.35	...	1.00	12.00	4.00	...
Chromium Hot Work Tool Steels						
H11 ..	0.35	...	1.50	5.00	0.40	...
H12 ..	0.35	1.50	1.50	5.00	0.40	...
H13 ..	0.35	...	1.50	5.00	1.00	...
Tungsten Hot Work Tool Steels						
H21 ..	0.35	9.00	...	3.50	...	...
H26 ..	0.50	18.00	...	4.00	1.00	...
High Speed Steels						
(See Table 1 on page 312, in the article "High Speed Steel for Cutting Tools".)						
Low-Alloy Special-Purpose Tool Steels						
L1 ...	1.00	...	...	1.25	...	...
L2 ...	(c)	...	...	1.00	0.20	...
L3 ...	1.00	...	...	1.50	0.20	...
L6 ...	0.70	...	(d)	0.75	...	1.50 Ni
L7 ...	1.00	...	0.40	1.40	...	0.35 Mn
Carbon-Tungsten Special-Purpose Tool Steels						
F1 ...	1.00	1.25	...	...	...	...
F2 ...	1.25	3.50	...	...	...	...
F3 ...	1.25	3.50	...	0.75	...	...
Low-Carbon Mold Steels						
P1 ...	0.10	...	...	...	...	...
P4 ...	0.07	...	0.75	5.00	...	...
P6 ...	0.10	...	...	1.50	...	3.50 Ni
P20 ..	0.35	...	0.40	1.25	...	...
P21 ..	0.20	...	...	...	...	4.00 Ni, 1.20 Al
Other Alloy Tool Steels						
6F7 ..	0.40	...	0.75	1.50	...	4.25 Ni
6G ..	0.55	...	0.45	1.00	0.10	0.80 Mn

(a) Range 0.60 to 1.40. Available with various carbon contents, in increments of 0.10% carbon, within this range. (b) 1.00% tungsten optional. (c) Range 0.50 to 1.10. Available with various carbon contents, in increments of 0.10% carbon, within this range. (d) 0.25% Mo optional.

Table 2. Approximate Machinability Ratings for Annealed Tool Steels(a)

Steel or group(b)	Machinability rating(c)
W	100
S	60 to 70
O	45 to 60
A (except A7)	45 to 60
D and A7	30 to 40
H10 to H19(d)	60 to 70
H20 to H43(d)	45 to 55
M2 and T1	40 to 50
M3 (class 1) and T4	35 to 40
M15 and T15	25 to 30
L	65 to 75
F	55 to 60
P1 to P6	75 to 90
P20 and P21	65 to 80

(a) Based on the average cutting speeds for turning, boring, drilling, slab milling and end milling given in Tables 5, 6, 7, 9, 12 and 13. (b) For specific steels included in the H, M and T groups, see the tables mentioned in the first footnote. (c) As a percentage of the rating of 100 for W steels. (d) Applies only to hardness range of 150 to 200 Bhn.

The data in Fig. 2 and Table 3 take no account of the scrap value of the chips generated in machining. Careful identification, segregation and classification of tool steel scrap make it possible to recover as much as 10% of the original cost of the material through the sale of such scrap. This recovery can result in a significant dollar saving with the more expensive, higher-alloy steels (such as some of the cobalt-containing types, which have a base price of $3 to $4 per pound).

In addition to the cost of the steel, the cost of removal by cutting tools is also a significant factor and often influences choice of tool steel for a given application. For instance, in Example 698 the cost of milling the flutes in M1 reamer blanks was about one third the cost of milling similar blanks made from the more highly alloyed T15. And in Example 704, similar results were obtained in drilling M1 and T15. However, in removing metal by electrical discharge methods, although the alloy content still affects the cost of metal removal, it is a less important factor than in conventional cutting (see Example 706).

Turning

Tools made from high speed steel, carbide and cast Co-Cr-W alloy are all used for turning of tool steels. For continuous cutting where rigidity is sufficient that chatter will not develop, carbide tools usually provide greatest productivity at lowest tool cost per piece. However, for shock loads, as in interrupted cutting, in the turning of forged drill blanks, or where the setup lacks rigidity, high speed steel tools are more suitable than carbide. Cast alloy tools are especially suited for turning applications in which rugged cutting is necessary, or in which the use of cutting fluids is impractical.

Tool angles typically ground on carbide and high speed steel turning tools are listed in Table 4. As indicated, carbide turning tools are often ground with less back and side rake than similar tools made of high speed steel.

Many form tools are difficult to grind because of their shape or because they must maintain high accuracy. It is economical to use slower speeds and lighter feeds to prolong the life of such tools between grinds. Conversely, when maximum rate of metal removal is the primary objective, as in rough turning, tool grinding is usually simpler. For these conditions it is more economical to remove metal at the maximum rate and grind tools more frequently.

Drilling

Most tool steels, particularly those with carbon content of 1% or greater, respond best to drilling when the microstructure consists of ferrite and small spheroidized carbides. However, the smallest carbides should be large enough to be resolved clearly at a magnification of 1000×.

Carbon and lower-alloy tool steels, such as those in the W, O and L groups, are drilled with standard drills of high speed steel, at speeds of 40 to 80 sfm.

For drilling more highly alloyed tool steels, such as high speed steels (and particularly the high-carbon, high-vanadium types), special drills are used. These highly alloyed tool steels are not only harder (often up to 280 Bhn), but also more abrasive. Heavy-duty drills made of cobalt-bearing high speed steel (such as T5, T15, M6 or M36) are preferred. Nitriding the drills will prolong drill life. Lower speeds (often as low as 20 sfm) are usually best for drilling the more highly alloyed tool steels.

Drill points with the conventional included angle of 118° and normal lip relief angle (about 12° for a ½-in.-diam drill) are suitable for drilling tool steels of the W, O and L groups. However, drill points with a 130° included angle and lip relief about two-thirds normal are more suitable for drilling steels of the D and A groups and the high speed steels — particularly when hardness of the work material is 260 Bhn or higher.

Cutting Fluid. Water-soluble or sulfurized oil should be used as a cutting fluid when drilling tool steels. The cutting fluid should be directed onto the cut, and the rate of flow must be sufficient to cool the drill point. In vertical drilling of deep holes, an intermittent feed is best; that is, the drill should be withdrawn at regular intervals to remove chips, cool the point, and allow more cutting fluid to reach the cut. In horizontal drilling, the cutting fluid is directed along flutes of the drill to the point. Intermittent withdrawal of the drill flushes away chips and allows the drill to cool. For deep-hole drilling, regardless of workpiece composition, oil-hole drills should be used, to permit a continuous supply of cutting fluid at the critical area.

Speed and Feed

Nominal speeds and feeds for machining the various tool steels are given in Tables 5 to 15. These tables include turning, boring, broaching,

W1 (1.00% C) | A2 | M2

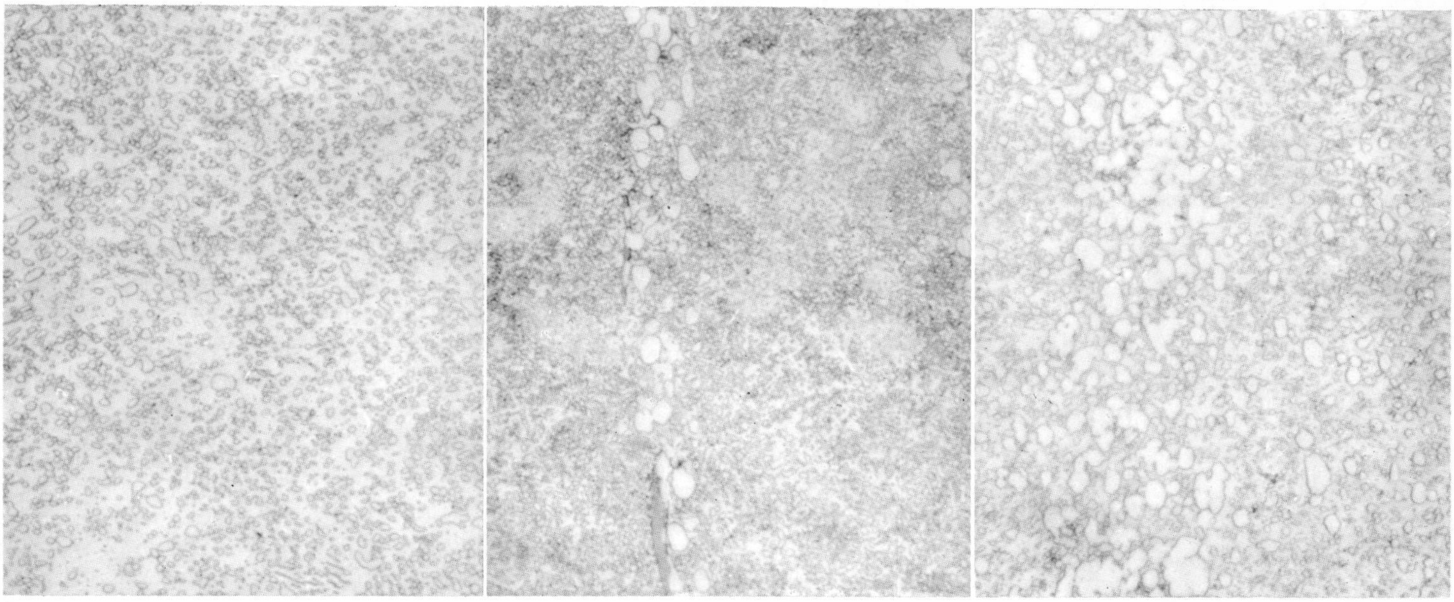

156 to 196 Bhn | 202 to 217 Bhn | 217 to 235 Bhn

Fig. 1. Annealed microstructure of three tool steels, indicating differences resulting from chemical composition that affect machining characteristics. (W1 and A2 etched in 2% nital, M2 in 5% nital; all micrographs at 750×)

Table 3. Cost of Machining Tool Steels (a)

Bar diam, in.	Cost: Machining (b)	Cost: Material removed	Cost: Total	Cost differential
2⅛	$0.23	$1.41	$1.64	(c)
2¼	0.25	2.89	3.14	$1.50
2½	0.52	6.25	6.77	5.13
2⅝	0.80	8.05	8.85	7.21

(a) Machining and material cost involved in turning 6-in.-long bars of various diameters to 2-in. diam. Material cost is figured at $1.155 per pound.
(b) One turning cut is required for reducing 2⅛ and 2¼-in. sizes to 2 in. Two turning cuts are required for reducing 2½-in. sizes to 2 in. Three turning cuts are required for reducing 2⅝-in. sizes to 2 in. Cutting speed, 80 sfm; feed, 0.015 ipr; depth of cut, variable, ⅛ in. max; labor rate, $3 per hr, including setup.
(c) It is assumed that 2⅛-in. stock is ordinarily used to produce a 2-in.-diam part, to insure the removal of any undesirable surface conditions.

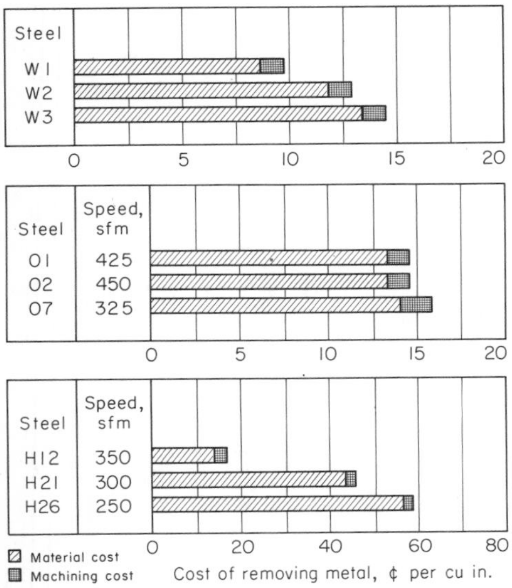

Fig. 2. Effect of composition of tool steel on cost per cubic inch removed by turning with carbide inserts. All steels were machined in the annealed condition. No credit included for scrap value of chips.

drilling, reaming, tapping, milling and sawing. Some of the tables also consider variables such as depth of cut, width of tool (in form turning) and diameter of hole to be drilled or reamed.

Speed. In Tables 5 to 15 the cutting speed is based on the use of rigid setups and effective cutting fluids. Speed depends largely on the composition and hardness of the steel being machined, and on the tool material. Speeds given in some of the processing examples in this article do not agree with those given in Tables 5 to 15. These variations are generally caused by specific conditions such as lack of rigidity, workpiece configuration, machine capacity, or other factors that are not considered in the tabulated nominal speeds.

Feed. Nominal feeds for the operations given in Tables 5 to 15 are also affected by work metal composition and hardness, although generally to a lesser degree than are speeds. Depth of cut has a marked influence on optimum feed in operations such as turning, boring and milling.

Water-Hardening Tool Steels

The machining characteristics of water-hardening tool steels are dealt with here in seven examples that describe the milling, drilling, sawing and electrical discharge machining (EDM) of these steels in production applications. Information on machining W2 tool steel in a shaper will be found in Example 98, in the article "Shaping".

Example 677. Face Milling W2 (Fig. 3)

After being cold sawed to desired lengths, various sizes of hot rolled sections of W2 tool steel (202 Bhn max) were face milled on a semiproduction basis using the setup shown in Fig. 3. To eliminate the clamping problem normally encountered in milling a mixture of steel sizes, the machine table was equipped with a 12-by-36-in. magnetic chuck. However, because the rough surface of the hot rolled sections did not always make full contact with the ground surface of the magnetic chuck, the feed rate had to be varied, according to the operator's judgment, and backup blocks sometimes had to be placed around the workpieces to prevent movement during milling (Fig. 3).

The sections were milled in a 30-hp vertical knee-type machine with a 9-in.-diam cutter that had 14 blades tipped with C-6 carbide. Axial rake of the blades was 7°; radial rake was 3°. The cutter was mounted on the face of the spindle. Additional processing conditions are listed in the table accompanying Fig. 3.

Table 4. Typical Design Details of Tools for Turning Tool Steels

Tool angle	Carbide tools	HSS tools: Continuous cutting	HSS tools: Interrupted cutting
Back rake	0°	0°-8°	—12°
Side rake	0°-8°	15°	14°
Front relief	7°	6°	6°
Side relief	7°	6°	6°
Side cutting edge	0°-15°	0°-15°	15°
Front cutting edge ...	8°-15°	5°-20°	17°
Nose radius, in.	1/32	1/32-1/8	3/32

All angles positive, except back rake for high speed steel tools used for interrupted cutting.

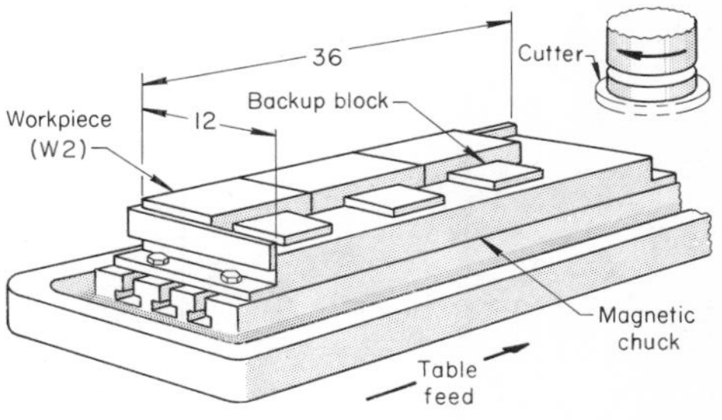

Speed	350 sfm
Feed	13 to 27 ipm (0.006 to 0.013 ipt)
Depth of cut	0.030 to 0.180 in.
Width of cut	2 to 6 in.
Length of cut	6 to 30 in.
Cutting rate	0.8 to 29.2 cu in. per minute
Cutting fluid	None
Tool life per grind	4 to 8 hr

Fig. 3. Face milling sections of W2 tool steel, using a magnetic chuck and backup blocks (Example 677)

Example 678. Straddle Milling W2 (Fig. 4)

Bars of W2 tool steel hot rolled to the T-section shown in Fig. 4 were machined simultaneously on four faces by straddle milling, using the setup shown in Fig. 4. Bars of four different lengths (25⅜, 26¾, 30¾ and 37⅜ in.) were milled in batches of 50. After milling, each length was sawed in half, and the halves were drilled; ultimately, these parts served as die guides.

Straddle milling was done in a 30-hp horizontal knee-type machine using two 7-in.-diam staggered-tooth cutters, each with 14 insert-type high speed steel blades. The blades had 15° axial rake and 11° radial rake. The cutters were mounted on an arbor to permit simultaneous milling of the width of the "T" and both adjacent flanges. Other processing conditions are tabulated with Fig. 4.

Example 679. Contour Milling W2 (Fig. 5)

A die section used in forming an automobile-body pillar was rough and finish contour milled in a 7½-hp spindle-drive horizontal tracer-controlled machine with work capacity of 5 by 10 ft. The die section (workpiece), machine setup, and direction of milling cuts are illustrated in Fig. 5.

The workpiece consisted of a large alloy iron casting to which two sections of 1% carbon W2 tool steel (hardness, 202 Bhn max) were fastened (Fig. 5). The two sections of tool steel weighed 150 lb before machining and 118 lb after.

An explanation of the procedure, and a table of processing details for rough and finish milling, are presented with Fig. 5.

In the production milling of flutes in carbon tool steel drills, accuracy is of the utmost importance. Rigidity of the milling machine and setup is essential. However, even with required rigidity, excessive variations in drill web and land dimensions may be experienced if the steel is not properly annealed. Specifically, the presence of lamellar pearlite in the annealed microstructure is objectionable because it may contribute to large variations in web and land dimensions and tearing of the surface metal. Also, despite the higher hardness of the pearlitic material, it has a lower resistance to machining as a result of the lower shear strength caused by the lamellae. Web and land dimensions, in addition to varying widely, are often undersize. Because it is extremely difficult to produce lamellar pearlite in suitably small and controlled amounts during annealing, it is necessary that the annealed structure be completely spheroidized. This is demonstrated by the application described in the following example:

Example 680. Milling of Flutes in W5 Drills

A cam-fed automatic milling machine and a 2½-in.-diam, 22-tooth cutter made of M10 high speed steel were used for milling flutes (climb rotation) in 5⁄16-in.-diam drill blanks of W5 tool steel containing 1.25% C. In the milling operation the cam rotated the spindle as the spindle fed the drill blank into the cutter, the helix being formed by this screw action.

In milling blanks that were annealed to a lamellar pearlite structure (hardness, 192 Bhn), flaky chips and torn surfaces were produced. Web thickness in these blanks was 0.070 to 0.078 in. (variation, 0.008 in.); land, 0.180 to 0.190 in. (variation, 0.010 in.). Under the same operating conditions blanks annealed to a 100% spheroidal structure (170 Bhn) yielded shiny surfaces without tearing; in these blanks, web thickness was 0.079 to 0.081 in., and land 0.197 to 0.200 in.

Milling speed was 250 rpm (163 sfm); feed was 6 ipm. (0.0011 ipt). Length of the cut was 4¾ in.; width and depth of cut were determined by the parabolic shape of the cutter tooth profile, which was 0.290 to 0.297 in. wide at the major axis. The cutter was angled to the longitudinal axis of the drill blank at 30°. A low-viscosity spindle oil was used as cutting fluid. Metal removal rate was 1.57 lb per hour; production rate, 42 drills per hour; cutters were reground after each 8-hr shift.

Example 681. Drilling W2 (Fig. 6)

Eight 21⁄32-in.-diam by 1.5-in. through holes were drilled in W2 die guide plates using the two-operation setup shown in Fig. 6. These plates ranged from 12½ to 18½ in. in length

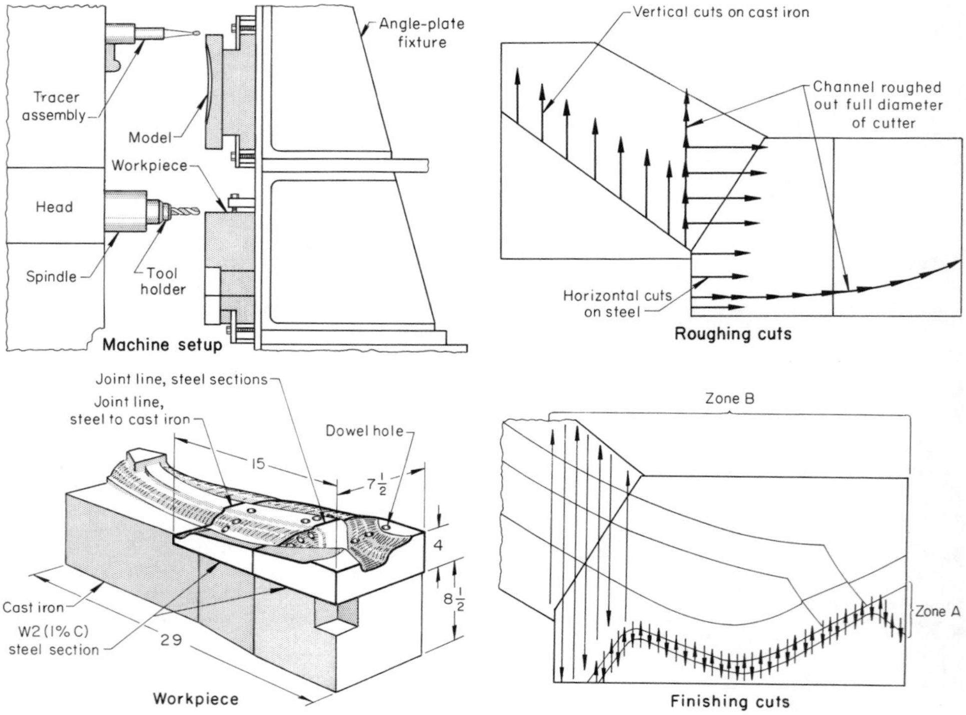

The layout operation consisted of establishing horizontal and vertical lines on both the workpiece and a model of the finished shape, to balance the machining stock approximately. A reference point was then located on the model and dimensioned so that the surface contour shape was located at the proper height from the base of the workpiece. After this layout had been established, the model and workpiece were mounted on a setup plate as shown above. The setup lines were used to establish the proper relative position of the workpiece and the model on the setup plate.

After preliminary layout and setup had been completed, the setup plate containing the rigidly mounted workpiece and plastic-coated, plaster-cast model was bolted to the vertical angle-plate fixture on the machine, as shown in the upper left-hand drawing above.

Diagrams of the cuts made in roughing and in finishing are presented in the plan views at the right, above. The two channels were first roughed by manual control to the full diameter of the cutter. As indicated in the diagram at the upper right, all roughing cuts on the cast iron portion were made vertically, and the steel portion was milled horizontally. Because of the type of cutter used, rough milling was done in one direction only. A rapid-return cycle (RRC) was used for all roughing. In finishing, all cuts were made vertically, each successive cut being in an alternate direction (lower right). A ball-type end mill was used for finish milling, which permitted the use of a continuous-cut cycle (CCC). Zone A was finish milled separately, as shown. Zone B was milled entirely by means of continuous cuts, as indicated by the arrows at the left of Zone B.

Roughing Cuts	
Tool	Four-flute M2 end mill(a)
Diameter of tracer buttons	2.700 in.
Speed	33 sfm
Feed, channel rough-out	1.5 ipm (0.007 ipt)
Feed, horiz cuts on steel	2 ipm (0.0093 ipt)
Depth of cut	1 in.
Width of cut (index distance)	1.2 in.
Cutting fluid	Water-soluble synthetic, in 1-to-20 mixture with water
Cutting rate	1.8-2.4 cu in./min

Finishing Cuts(b)	
Tool	Two-flute M10 end mill(c)
Diameter of tracer buttons	1.070 in.
Speed, zones A and B	67 sfm
Feed, zone A	4 ipm (0.008 ipt)
Feed, zone B	9 ipm (0.0175 ipt)
Depth of cut, zones A and B	0.090 in.
Width of cut, zone A (index dist)	0.300 in.
Width of cut, zone B (index dist)	0.200 in.
Cutting fluid	Same as for roughing
Cutting rate	0.108-0.164 cu in./min

(a) Mill was 2½ in. in diameter, had a 4-in. length of cut, 2-in. straight shank, and 30° right-hand spiral; hook angle was 15°, corner radius 1⁄16 in. (b) Vertical face cuts. In zone A, one horizontal cut was made at base of groove for relief, prior to face cutting. (c) Mill, of ball-end type, 1-in. diam, had 2-in. length of cut, 1-in. straight shank, and 30° helix with 15° hook angle.

Fig. 5. Contour milling of a die used for forming an automobile-body pillar (Example 679)

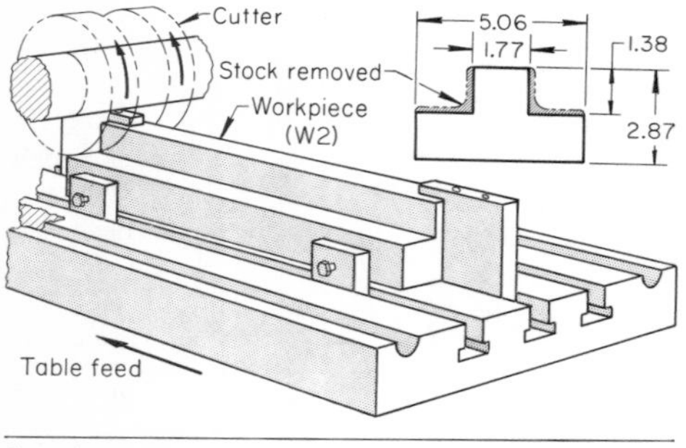

Speed	54 sfm
Feed	1.5 ipm (0.0073 ipt)
Cross-sectional area of cut	0.806 sq in.
Length of cut	25⅜, 26¾, 30¾, 37⅜ in.
Cutting rate	1.21 cu in. per minute
Cutting fluid	40-to-1 mixture of water and low-sulfur, water-soluble synthetic
Tool life per grind:	
Stock removed	1100 cu in.
Length cut	1350 in.

Length of blank, in.	Original weight, lb	Weight after milling, lb
25⅜	77½	71¾
26¾	81¾	75¾
30¾	94	87
37⅜	114	105½

Fig. 4. Straddle milling of four different lengths of T-section W2 tool steel, using two staggered-tooth cutters (Example 678)

Table 5. Nominal Speeds and Feeds for Turning of Tool Steels With High Speed Steel Tools (a)

Steel	Brinell hardness	Single-point and box tools — Speed, sfm		Form tools				Cutoff tools			
		Roughing (0.150-in. cut; feed, 0.015 ipr)	Finishing (0.025-in. cut; feed, 0.007 ipr)	Speed, sfm	Feed, ipr, for tool width of: ½ in.	1 in.	2 in.	Speed, sfm	Feed, ipr, for tool width of: 1/16 in.	⅛ in.	¼ in.
W group	150 to 200	130	175	95	0.0025	0.0015	0.001	95	0.0015	0.002	0.0025
S group	175 to 225	85	110	65	0.0025	0.0015	0.001	65	0.0015	0.002	0.0025
O group	200 to 250	70	90	50	0.0015	0.001	0.0007	50	0.001	0.0015	0.002
A group(b)	200 to 250	70	90	50	0.0015	0.001	0.0007	50	0.001	0.0015	0.002
D group and A7	200 to 250	40(h)	50(j)	30	0.0015	0.001	0.0007	30	0.001	0.001	0.0015
H11(c)	150 to 200	90	105	65	0.0025	0.0015	0.001	65	0.0015	0.002	0.0025
	200 to 250	75	90	55	0.0015	0.001	0.0007	55	0.001	0.0015	0.002
	325 to 375	50	65	35	0.0015	0.001	0.0007	35	0.001	0.001	0.0015
	Rc 48 to 50	20(h)	25(j)	..	...	...	...	..	...	...	...
	Rc 50 to 52	15(h)	20(j)	..	...	...	...	..	...	...	...
H20(d)	150 to 200	65	80	50	0.0025	0.0015	0.001	50	0.0015	0.002	0.0025
	200 to 250	60	80	45	0.0015	0.001	0.0007	45	0.001	0.0015	0.002
M2 and T1(e)	200 to 250	60	75	45	0.0015	0.001	0.0007	45	0.001	0.001	0.0015
M3 (cl 1) and T4(f)	225 to 275	50	60	35	0.0015	0.001	0.0007	35	0.001	0.001	0.0015
M15 and T15(g)	225 to 275	35(h)	45(j)	25	0.0015	0.001	0.0007	25	0.001	0.001	0.0015
L group	150 to 200	90	105	65	0.0025	0.0015	0.001	65	0.0015	0.002	0.0025
F group	200 to 250	75	90	55	0.0015	0.001	0.0007	55	0.001	0.0015	0.002
P1 to P6	100 to 150	110	140	80	0.0025	0.0015	0.001	80	0.0015	0.002	0.0025
P20 to P21	150 to 200	95	125	70	0.0025	0.0015	0.001	70	0.0015	0.002	0.0025

(a) High speed steels M2 and T5 for groups W, S, O, A, D, H20, L, F and P, and for group H11 to 200 Bhn; M2, T5 and T15 for groups T1 and T4, and for group H11 at 200 to 375 Bhn; T15, M41, M42, M43 and M44 for group T15 and for group H11 at hardness above 375 Bhn. (b) Except A7. (c) Includes also H10, H12, H13, H14, H16 and H19. (d) Includes also H21, H22, H23, H24, H25, H41, H42, and H43. (e) Includes also M1, M6, M10, T2, T6 and T7. (f) Includes also M4, M7, M30, M33, M34, M35, M36, M41, M42, M43, M44, T5 and T8. (g) Includes also M3 (class 2) and T9. (h) Feed, 0.010 ipr. (j) Feed, 0.005 ipr. (Data are adapted from tables compiled by Metcut Research Associates, Inc.)

Table 6. Nominal Speeds and Feeds for Turning of Tool Steels With Carbide Tools (a)

Steel	Brinell hardness	Speed, sfm: Single-point and box tools — Brazed		Disposable		Form tools				Cutoff tools			
		Roughing (0.150-in. cut; feed, 0.015 ipr)	Finishing (0.025-in. cut; feed, 0.007 ipr)	Roughing (0.150-in. cut; feed, 0.015 ipr)	Finishing (0.025-in. cut; feed, 0.007 ipr)	Speed, sfm	Feed, ipr, for tool width of: ½ in.	1 in.	2 in.	Speed, sfm	Feed, ipr, for tool width of: 1/16 in.	⅛ in.	¼ in.
W group	150 to 200	500	700	625	875	375	0.005	0.0035	0.0025	375	0.0045	0.006	0.0075
S group	175 to 225	340	400	425	500	255	0.005	0.0035	0.0025	255	0.0045	0.006	0.0075
O group	200 to 250	275	335	335	420	205	0.003	0.0025	0.0015	205	0.003	0.0045	0.006
A group(b)	200 to 250	275	335	335	420	205	0.003	0.0025	0.0015	205	0.003	0.0045	0.006
D group and A7	200 to 250	160(h)	200(j)	200(h)	250(j)	120	0.0025	0.0015	0.0015	120	0.002	0.002	0.003
H11(c)	150 to 200	325	400	415	500	245	0.005	0.0035	0.0025	245	0.0045	0.006	0.0075
	200 to 250	290	360	360	440	220	0.003	0.0025	0.0015	220	0.003	0.0045	0.006
	325 to 375	200	250	250	310	150	0.003	0.002	0.0015	150	0.003	0.003	0.0045
	Rc 48 to 50	95(h)	110(j)	120(h)	140(j)	...	...	...	...	...	...	...	...
	Rc 50 to 52	80(h)	100(j)	100(h)	120(j)	...	...	...	...	...	...	...	...
	Rc 52 to 54	65(k)	75(j)	80(k)	90(j)	...	...	...	...	...	...	...	...
	Rc 54 to 56	55(j)	65(j)	65(j)	80(j)	...	...	...	...	...	...	...	...
H20(d)	150 to 200	250	310	310	375	185	0.004	0.0025	0.002	185	0.004	0.005	0.0065
	200 to 250	235	300	300	365	175	0.003	0.0025	0.0015	175	0.003	0.0045	0.006
M2 and T1(e)	200 to 250	235	300	300	365	175	0.003	0.002	0.0015	175	0.002	0.003	0.0045
M3 (cl 1) and T4(f)	225 to 275	200	250	250	310	150	0.003	0.002	0.0015	150	0.002	0.003	0.0045
M15 and T15(g)	225 to 275	140(h)	180(j)	175(h)	225(j)	105	0.0025	0.0015	0.0015	105	0.002	0.002	0.003
L group	150 to 200	350	425	425	500	260	0.005	0.0035	0.0025	260	0.0045	0.006	0.0075
F group	200 to 250	300	350	375	425	225	0.003	0.0025	0.0015	225	0.003	0.0045	0.006
P1 to P6	100 to 150	450	500	560	625	340	0.005	0.0035	0.0025	340	0.0045	0.006	0.0075
P20 and P21	150 to 200	375	450	450	560	280	0.005	0.0035	0.0025	280	0.0045	0.006	0.0075

(a) For carbide grades C-6 for roughing and C-7 for finishing, except that grade C-8 is more suitable for turning steels at hardness above about Rc 48. (b) Except A7. (c) Includes also H10, H12, H13, H14, H16 and H19. (d) Includes also H21, H22, H23, H24, H25, H41, H42 and H43. (e) Includes also M1, M6, M10, T2, T6 and T7. (f) Includes also M4, M7, M30, M33, M34, M35, M36, M41, M42, M43, M44, T5 and T8. (g) Includes also M3 (class 2) and T9. (h) Feed, 0.010 ipr. (j) Feed, 0.005 ipr. (k) Feed, 0.007 ipr. (SOURCE: same as for Table 5)

and from 35.3 to 52.4 lb in weight. They were drilled in the annealed condition at 202 Bhn max. The 5-hp, box-column, vertical drill press had a geared drill head with four adjustable spindles and a guide-rod fixture base to accommodate two guide plates.

In the first operation (top view in Fig. 6), parts were placed in the fixture with one end located firmly against a removable gage block, and were clamped in this position. The drill press was cycled, and two holes were drilled in each workpiece.

For the second operation (middle view in Fig. 6), the removable gage block was withdrawn, and the parts were moved 1.25 in. to locate against a stationary gage block. Then the drill press was cycled, and two more holes were drilled in each workpiece. Additional processing details are given in the table that accompanies Fig. 6.

For removing stock from flat surfaces, sawing is often more economical than shaping, provided surface finish is not of primary importance and when only straight cuts, or simple or compound angles, are involved. Hydraulically fed band saws can perform such operations with a minimum of setup time. See speed and feed data on band sawing of tool steel in Table 2, page 225, in the article "Cutoff Band Sawing." For similar data on contour band sawing of tool steel, see Table 4 on page 221.

The next example describes production hydraulic band sawing.

Example 682. Sawing W2 Tool Steel

Die sections of W2 hot rolled bar (hardness, 202 Bhn max) measuring 2½ by 8 by 6 in. required removal of 9/16 in. of stock on the 2½ by 8-in. surface, reducing the 6-in. dimension to 5 7/16 in. The slabs (11¼ cu in., 3.3 lb) were removed by band sawing at a rate of 4 sq in. per min, total time per slab being 5 min. The same operation performed on a shaper required two roughing cuts and a finish cut, for a total time of 9 min (for details, see Example 98, in "Shaping").

A hydraulic-feed band saw with 18-in. stroke and 22-in. height capacity was used. Blades (high speed steel edges, carbon steel back) had raker-set hook teeth, four per inch. Blade speed was 180 sfm; hydraulic-feed pressure, 100 psi. Height of cut was 2½ in.; length, 8 in.; area, 20 sq in. A 7-to-1 mixture of water and a sulfurized water-soluble coolant containing extreme-pressure and antiseptic additives was used as the cutting fluid.

Example 683. Electrical Discharge Machining (EDM) of W2, A2 and S1 (Fig. 7)

A four-post, platen-type electrical discharge machine with 50-amp power supply and a 40-by-42-in. table was used in machining a set of dies for stamping automotive air-outlet grills. Three different tool steels were used for this die setup: W2, A2 and S1 — all of which were machined at a hardness of Rockwell C 60 to 62.

The die sections, shown schematically in Fig. 7(a) and (b), comprised: (1) the lower steel, having the male forming surface, male trimming edge and the punch die holes; (2) the stripper (S1) which served as the female forming surface, the clamp for trimming and as the punch stripper; (3) the upper steel (W2) which provided the female trimming edge; and (4) the piercing punches. The finished stamping is shown in Fig. 7(c).

The EDM operation was divided into two principal sequences. First the trimming edges of the die sections were eroded (Fig. 7a); then the punch die holes were eroded in the stripper and the lower steel section (Fig. 7b). The actual sequence of operations was:

1 Rough out upper and lower steels, leaving 1/16 in. of stock on cutting edges, and make undercuts.
2 Harden upper and lower steels, grind joints,

Table 7. Nominal Speeds and Feeds for Boring of Tool Steels With High Speed Steel and Carbide Tools

Steel	Brinell hardness	Rough boring (depth of cut, 0.100 in.) Speed, sfm HSS(a)	Carbide(b)	Feed, ipr HSS(a)	Carbide(b)	Finish boring (depth of cut, 0.010 in.) Speed, sfm HSS(a)	Carbide(b)	Feed, ipr HSS(a)	Carbide(b)
W group	150 to 200	115	450	0.010	0.015	130	500	0.005	0.006
S group	175 to 225	75	305	0.007	0.009	85	340	0.004	0.005
O group	200 to 250	65	245	0.006	0.008	70	275	0.003	0.004
A group(c)	200 to 250	65	245	0.006	0.008	70	275	0.003	0.004
D group and A7	200 to 250	35	145	0.006	0.008	40	160	0.003	0.004
H11(d)	150 to 200	80	295	0.008	0.010	90	325	0.005	0.006
	200 to 250	65	260	0.006	0.008	75	290	0.004	0.005
	325 to 375	45	180	0.006	0.008	50	200	0.004	0.005
	Rc 48 to 50	20	85	0.006	0.008	20	95	0.003	0.004
	Rc 50 to 52	15	70	0.006	0.008	15	80	0.003	0.004
	Rc 52 to 54	..	60	....	0.006	...	65	....	0.004
	Rc 54 to 56	..	50	....	0.006	...	55	....	0.003
H20(e)	150 to 200	60	225	0.006	0.008	65	250	0.004	0.005
	200 to 250	55	210	0.006	0.008	60	235	0.004	0.005
M2 and T1(f)	200 to 250	55	210	0.007	0.009	60	235	0.004	0.005
M3 (cl 1) and T4(g)	225 to 275	45	180	0.007	0.009	50	200	0.004	0.005
M15 and T15(h)	225 to 275	30	125	0.006	0.008	35	140	0.003	0.004
L group	150 to 200	80	315	0.010	0.015	90	350	0.005	0.006
F group	200 to 250	65	270	0.006	0.008	75	300	0.003	0.004
P1 to P6	100 to 150	100	405	0.010	0.015	110	450	0.005	0.006
P20 and P21	150 to 200	85	340	0.010	0.015	95	375	0.005	0.006

(a) High speed steels M2 and T5 for groups W, S, O, A, D, H20, L, F and P, and for group H11 to 200 Bhn; M2, T5 and T15 for groups T1 and T4, and for group H11 at 200 to 375 Bhn; T15, M41, M42, M43 and M44 for group T15, and for group H11 at hardness above 375 Bhn. (b) Carbide grade C-7, except that grade C-8 is more suitable for boring steels at hardness above about Rc 48. (c) Includes all of group A except A7. (d) Includes also H10, H12, H13, H14, H16 and H19. (e) Includes also H21, H22, H23, H24, H25, H41, H42 and H43. (f) Includes also M1, M6, M10, T2, T6 and T7. (g) Includes also M4, M7, M30, M33, M34, M35, M36, M41, M42, M43, M44, T5 and T8. (h) Includes also M3 (class 2) and T9. (SOURCE: same as for Table 5)

and assemble the two steels in shoes.

3 Rough out stripper to outside trim line, leaving about 1/32 in. of stock, and drill holes at punch-piercing locations.
4 Make up flat copper (half-hard) or graphite male electrode (3/4 in. thick), finished to developed outside trim line.
5 Rough saw flat copper (half-hard) female electrode (3/4 in. thick) with 1/16 in. of stock inside cutting line.
6 Set up male electrode, and erode female electrode and cutting edges of upper steel.
7 Erode outside edges of lower steel and stripper with female electrode.
8 Make up piercing punches with 1/2-in.-thick copper-tungsten tips, or add graphite tips to finished punches.
9 Set up piercing punches with tips; erode openings in lower steel and in stripper.
10 Remove electrode tips and assemble.

Volumes and rates of metal removal for the electrical discharge machining operations are given in the table that accompanies Fig. 7.

Shock-Resisting Tool Steels (S Steels)

The hardness of annealed S steels is usually between those of the W and O steels (Tables 5 to 15). Most machining of the S steels is done at speeds and feeds nearer those used for the O group than the W group. Accordingly, the data in Examples 677 to 683 of the previous section can be used as a starting point in the machining of S steels with a moderate downward adjustment of speed and feed. Likewise, the data in Examples 684, 685 and 686 in the section that follows can be used in the same way with a slight upward adjustment of speed and feed.

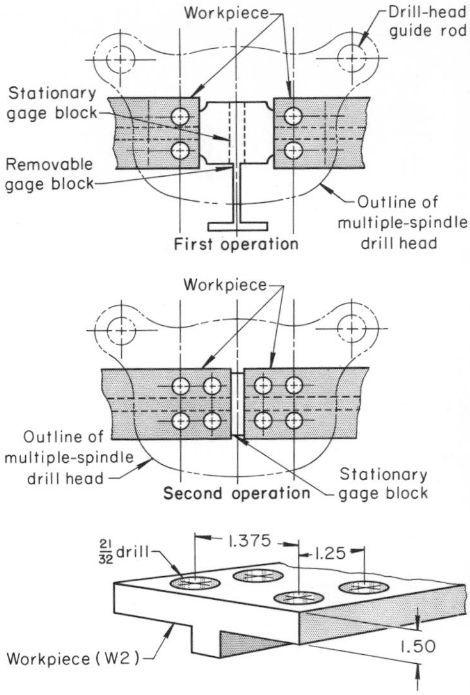

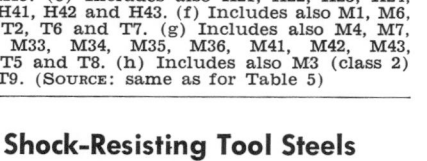

Drill Details

Material M7
Diameter ....21/32 in.
Length ....5 1/8 in.
Helix angle ....30°
Point angle (included) ....118°
Lip relief angle ....8° to 10°

Machining Conditions

Speed(a) ....220 rpm (38 sfm)
Feed(a) ....0.005 ipr (1.15 in. per min)
Depth of hole ....1.50 in.
Cutting fluid ....40-to-1 mixture of water and nonsulfurized water-soluble synthetic
Drilling time per cycle (4 holes) ....1.5 min
Tool life per drill ....300 to 500 holes

(a) Speed and feed were slightly lower than normal for drilling W2, to conform with the horsepower (5 hp) and rigidity of the machine and drill head used.

Fig. 6. Setup and conditions for multiple-spindle drilling of holes in W2 die guide plates (Example 681)

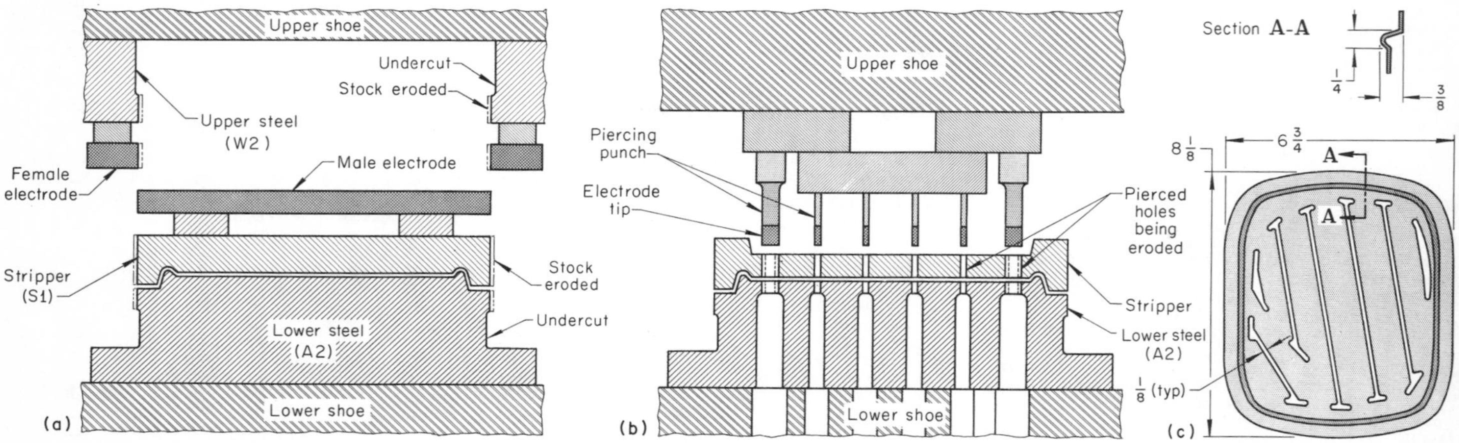

Upper Steel (W2), for Outside Trimming

Volume of metal removed (cutting edges) ....1.18 cu in.
Metal-removal rate ....0.35 cu in. per hour
Surface finish ....150 micro-in.
Overcut(a) ....0.0018 in.

Stripper (S1)

Volume of metal removed:
Piercing-punch holes ....1.72 cu in.
Outside edges ....0.10 cu in.
Metal-removal rate ....0.20 cu in. per hour
Surface finish ....130 micro-in.
Overcut(b) ....0.0012 in.

Lower Steel (A2), for Piercing

Volume of metal removed:
Pierced holes ....1.02 cu in.
Outside cutting edges ....0.59 cu in.
Metal-removal rate ....0.30 cu in. per hour
Surface finish ....150 micro-in.
Overcut(a) ....0.0018 in.

(a) Die clearance required, 0.0015 to 0.002 in. (b) Die clearance required, 0.0010 to 0.0015 in.

Fig. 7. (a) and (b) Setups used for electrical discharge machining of a stamping die made of W2, A2 and S1 tool steels. (c) Automotive air-outlet grill produced in die. (Example 683)

Type O Cold Work Tool Steels

The machinability of tool steels in group O is lower than that of the water-hardening tool steels discussed earlier (45 to 60, compared with 100). Hence, the data in Examples 677 to 683 can be applied to the O steels, provided speeds and feeds are reduced accordingly. Similarly, the three examples that follow, for O steels, are applicable to similar operations and setups for W (as well as S) steels with proportionately increased speeds and feeds.

Example 684. Turning O1 Tap Blanks

Before being heat treated and ground, tap blanks 1⁷⁄₁₆ in. in diameter by 3¾ in. long, made from O1 bar stock (hardness, 196 Bhn), were turned on a 20-hp tracer lathe. These blanks weighed 1.7 lb each before turning, and 1.5 lb after. The turning tool (indexable carbide tips) had 0° to 5° back rake, 6° side rake, and ¹⁄₁₆-in. nose radius.

Turning speed was 1225 rpm (460 sfm); feed, 0.016 in. per min; depth of cut, 0.323 in.; length of cut, 2 in. Time per cut was 6 sec. A 200-to-1 mixture of water and chemical solution was the cutting fluid. Tool life for the indexable tips was 45 pieces per corner.

Example 685. Milling Flutes in O1 Taps

A No. 2 plain mill was used for cutting the flutes in ¾-in.-diam four-flute hand taps made of O1 tool steel. Blanks for these taps were milled at a hardness of 196 Bhn; each blank weighed 0.25 lb before machining, and 0.17 lb after.

The milling cutter, of M10 high speed steel, was 4 in. in diameter by 0.260 in. wide, and had 32 teeth (10° clearance angle, 0° to 2° positive radial rake, 0.190-in. tooth radius). An average of 600 flutes could be cut between grinds.

Speed was 95 rpm (100 sfm), at a feed of 3.5 in. per min; a sulfur-base oil was used as the cutting fluid. Length of cut was 2⅜ in., depth 0.195 in. Time for milling each flute was 0.67 min.

As is evident from a comparison of Example 682, above, and Example 686, which follows, the sawing characteristics of W2 and O6 steels are similar; cutting rates for both steels are almost identical in these two examples.

Example 686. Sawing O6

The hydraulic band saw described in Example 682, above, and the same type of blades and cutting fluid, were used also for making four cuts in blocks of O6 oil-hardening tool steel, to produce T-sections. Before sawing, these blocks were 9 in. long, 4½ in. wide, and 8.62 in. high.

For all cuts, blade speed was 200 sfm, hydraulic-feed pressure was 100 psi, and height of cut was 8.62 in. For cuts 1 and 2 (which made the "leg" of the T), length of cut was 3.25 in., area cut was 28 sq in., cutting time was 6.75 min, and cutting rate was 4.15 sq in. per min. For cuts 3 and 4 (at right angles to cuts 1 and 2), length of cut was 1.5 in., area 13 sq in., cutting time 3.25 min, and cutting rate 4 sq in. per min.

Types A and D Cold Work Tool Steels

The high carbon and alloy content of tool steels in groups A and D promotes the formation of large alloy carbides and makes it difficult to obtain a low hardness in the annealed steels; both conditions affect machining characteristics adversely. Listed in order of decreasing machinability, the steels in the A and D groups may be rated as follows: A2, A6, A4, A5, D1, D2, D5, D6, D3, D4, A7, D7.

Because of their high content of carbon, chromium and vanadium, A7 and D7 have extremely poor machinability and are highly susceptible to grinding damage in the hardened condition. In general, the D steels are more susceptible to grinding damage than the A steels, because they have more massive carbides, but this susceptibility can be reduced somewhat by tempering at higher temperatures.

Table 8. Nominal Speeds and Feeds for Broaching of Tool Steels With High Speed Steel Broaches

Steel	Brinell hardness	Speed, sfm	Feed, ipt	Broach material
W group	150-200	20	0.003	M2
S group	175-225	15	0.003	T5, T15
O and A	200-250	15	0.003	T5, T15
D group & A7	200-250	10	0.002	T5, T15
H11(b)	150-200	20	0.003	M2
	200-250	15	0.002	M2
	325-375	10	0.002	T5, T15
H20(c)	150-200	15	0.002	M2
	200-250	10	0.002	T5, T15
M2 & T1(d)	200-250	10	0.002	T5, T15
M3 & T4(e)	225-275	5	0.002	T5, T15
L group	150-200	20	0.003	M2
F group	200-250	15	0.003	T5, T15
P1 to P6	100-150	20	0.003	M2
P20 & P21	150-200	20	0.003	M2

(a) Includes all of group A except A7. (b) Includes also H10, H12, H13, H14, H16 and H19. (c) Includes also H21, H22, H23, H24, H25, H41, H42 and H43. (d) Includes also M1, M6, M10, T2, T6 and T7. (e) M3 classes 1 and 2; also M4, M7, M30, M33 through M36, M41 through M44, T5, T8 and T15. (SOURCE: same as for Table 5)

Table 9. Nominal Speeds and Feeds for Drilling of Tool Steels With High Speed Steel Drills (a)

Steel	Brinell hardness	Speed, sfm	Feed, ipr, for hole diameter of: ⅛ in.	¼ in.	½ in.	¾ in.	1 in.	1½ in.	2 in.
W group	150 to 250	85	0.002	0.004	0.007	0.010	0.012	0.015	0.018
S group	175 to 225	50	0.002	0.003	0.005	0.009	0.011	0.014	0.016
O group	200 to 250	40	0.002	0.003	0.005	0.008	0.010	0.011	0.013
A group(b)	200 to 250	40	0.002	0.003	0.005	0.008	0.010	0.011	0.013
D group and A7	200 to 250	25	0.001	0.002	0.004	0.005	0.006	0.007	0.008
H11(c)	150 to 200	55	0.002	0.003	0.006	0.009	0.011	0.014	0.016
	200 to 250	45	0.002	0.003	0.005	0.008	0.010	0.011	0.013
	325 to 375	35	0.002	0.003	0.005	0.007	0.008	0.009	0.010
	Rc 48 to 50	15	0.0005	0.001	0.002	0.002	0.003	0.003	0.004
	Rc 50 to 52	10	0.0005	0.001	0.002	0.002	0.003	0.003	0.004
H20(d)	150 to 200	40	0.002	0.003	0.005	0.008	0.009	0.011	0.013
	200 to 250	30	0.002	0.003	0.005	0.008	0.010	0.011	0.013
M2 and T1(e)	200 to 250	40	0.002	0.003	0.005	0.008	0.009	0.011	0.013
M3 (cl 1) and T4(f)	225 to 275	30	0.002	0.003	0.005	0.008	0.010	0.011	0.013
M15 and T15(g)	225 to 275	20	0.001	0.002	0.004	0.005	0.006	0.007	0.008
L group	150 to 200	55	0.002	0.003	0.006	0.009	0.011	0.014	0.016
F group	200 to 250	45	0.002	0.003	0.005	0.008	0.010	0.011	0.013
P1 to P6	100 to 150	65	0.002	0.004	0.007	0.010	0.012	0.015	0.018
P20 and P21	150 to 200	55	0.002	0.003	0.006	0.009	0.011	0.014	0.016

(a) High speed steels M1, M7 and M10 for drilling all steels listed except T15 and M33 used for drilling D group and A7, and for H11 group at hardness above 325 Bhn. (b) Includes all of group A except A7. (c) Includes also H10, H12, H13, H14, H16 and H19. (d) Includes also H21, H22, H23, H24, H25, H41, H42 and H43. (e) Includes also M1, M6, M10, T2, T6 and T7. (f) Includes also M4, M7, M30, M33, M34, M35, M36, M41, M42, M43, M44, T5 and T8. (g) Includes also M3 (class 2) and T9. (SOURCE: same as for Table 5)

Table 10. Nominal Speeds and Feeds for Reaming of Tool Steels With High Speed Steel and Carbide Reamers

Steel	Brinell hardness	High speed steel reamers(a): Speed, sfm	Feed, ipr, for hole diameter of: ⅛ in.	¼ in.	½ in.	1 in.	1½ in.	2 in.	Carbide reamers(b): Speed, sfm	Feed, ipr, for hole diameter of: ⅛ in.	¼ in.	½ in.	1 in.	1½ in.	2 in.
W group	150 to 250	60	0.003	0.005	0.008	0.012	0.015	0.020	250	0.003	0.005	0.008	0.012	0.015	0.020
S group	175 to 225	50	0.003	0.005	0.008	0.012	0.015	0.020	200	0.003	0.005	0.008	0.012	0.015	0.020
O group	200 to 250	30	0.003	0.005	0.008	0.012	0.015	0.020	100	0.003	0.005	0.008	0.012	0.015	0.020
A group(c)	200 to 250	30	0.003	0.005	0.008	0.012	0.015	0.020	100	0.003	0.005	0.008	0.012	0.015	0.020
D group & A7	200 to 250	15	0.002	0.003	0.004	0.007	0.010	0.012	45	0.002	0.003	0.004	0.007	0.010	0.012
H11(d)	150 to 200	40	0.003	0.005	0.008	0.012	0.015	0.020	160	0.003	0.005	0.008	0.012	0.015	0.020
	200 to 250	35	0.003	0.005	0.008	0.012	0.015	0.020	140	0.003	0.005	0.008	0.012	0.015	0.020
	325 to 375	25	0.002	0.003	0.004	0.007	0.010	0.012	75	0.002	0.003	0.004	0.007	0.010	0.012
	Rc 48 to 50	..	....	....	....	....	....	....	30	0.002	0.003	0.004	0.006	0.008	0.010
	Rc 50 to 52	..	....	....	....	....	....	....	20	0.002	0.003	0.004	0.006	0.008	0.010
H20(e)	150 to 200	30	0.003	0.005	0.008	0.012	0.015	0.020	100	0.003	0.005	0.008	0.012	0.015	0.020
	200 to 250	25	0.002	0.005	0.008	0.012	0.015	0.020	75	0.003	0.005	0.008	0.012	0.015	0.020
M2 & T1(f)	200 to 250	30	0.002	0.005	0.010	0.016	0.020	0.025	100	0.002	0.005	0.010	0.016	0.020	0.025
M3 (cl 1) & T4(g)	225 to 275	20	0.002	0.005	0.010	0.016	0.020	0.025	60	0.002	0.005	0.010	0.020	0.020	0.025
M15 & T15(h)	225 to 275	15	0.002	0.005	0.008	0.012	0.015	0.020	50	0.002	0.005	0.008	0.012	0.015	0.020
L group	150 to 200	40	0.003	0.005	0.008	0.012	0.015	0.020	160	0.003	0.005	0.008	0.012	0.015	0.020
F group	200 to 250	30	0.003	0.005	0.008	0.012	0.015	0.020	100	0.003	0.005	0.008	0.012	0.015	0.020
P1 to P6	100 to 150	45	0.003	0.005	0.008	0.012	0.015	0.020	180	0.003	0.005	0.008	0.012	0.015	0.020
P20 and P21	150 to 200	40	0.003	0.005	0.008	0.012	0.015	0.020	160	0.003	0.005	0.008	0.012	0.015	0.020

(a) High speed steels M1, M2 and M7, except T15 for H11 group above 325 Bhn. (b) Grade C-2. (c) Except A7. (d) Also H10, H12, H13, H14, H16 and H19. (e) Also H21, H22, H23, H24, H25, H41, H42 and H43. (f) Also M1, M6, M10, T2, T6 and T7. (g) Also M4, M7, M30, M33, M34, M35, M36, M41, M42, M43, M44, T5 and T8. (h) Also M3 (class 2) and T9. (SOURCE: same as for Table 5)

Table 11. Nominal Speeds for Tapping of Tool Steels With High Speed Steel Taps(a)

Steel	Brinell hardness	Speed, sfm
W group	150 to 250	45
S group	175 to 225	25
O group	200 to 250	20
A group(b)	200 to 250	20
D group and A7	200 to 250	10
H11(c)	150 to 200	25
	200 to 250	20
	325 to 375	15
	Rc 48 to 50	5
	Rc 50 to 52	3
H20(d)	150 to 200	20
	200 to 250	20
M2 and T1(e)	200 to 250	20
M3 (cl 1) and T4(f)	225 to 275	15
M15 and T15(g)	225 to 275	10
L group	150 to 200	30
F group	200 to 250	20
P1 to P6	100 to 150	40
P20 and P21	150 to 200	30

(a) High speed steels M1, M7 and M10, except M3 and M40 for tapping group H11 steels at hardness above Rc 48. (b) Includes all of group A except A7. (c) Includes also H11, H12, H13, H14, H16 and H19. (d) Includes also H21, H22, H23, H24, H25, H41, H42 and H43. (e) Includes also M1, M6, M10, T2, T6 and T7. (f) Includes also M4, M7, M30, M33, M34, M35, M36, M41, M42, M43, M44, T5 and T8. (g) Includes also M3 (cl 2) and T9. (SOURCE: same as for Table 5)

The two following examples indicate the relative machinability of some of these tool steels. In addition, data comparing the shaping characteristics of D2 with W2 tool steel are given in Example 98, in the article "Shaping".

Example 687. Drilling, Facing, Turning, Boring and Broaching A2, A7, D2 and M1 (Table 16)

Identical thread rolling dies were produced from disk-shaped blanks forged from four different tool steels: A2 (hardness, 210 Bhn), A7 (250 to 265 Bhn), D2 (210 to 240 Bhn), and M1 (217 to 255 Bhn). As illustrated in Table 16, the forged blanks were 7½-in. OD, 1¼-in. thick and weighed 15 lb each; the finished dies were 7¼-in. OD, 3-in. ID, 1-in. thick and weighed 9 lb.

Production of these dies entailed the following sequence of operations:

1 Drill 2¾-in.-diam hole in blank
2 Face, to reduce thickness of blank to 1 in.
3 Turn, to reduce outside diameter of blank to 7¼ in.
4 Bore, to enlarge diameter of drilled hole to 3 in.
5 Broach keyway
6 Stamp identification data on face
7 Heat treat (M1 only)
8 Face grind
9 Internal grind

Table 12. Nominal Speeds and Feeds for Peripheral (Slab) Milling of Tool Steels With High Speed Steel Cutters(a)

Steel	Brinell hardness	Rough milling (depth of cut, 0.150 in.) Speed, sfm	Rough milling Feed, ipt	Finish milling (depth of cut, 0.025 in.) Speed, sfm	Finish milling Feed, ipt
W group	150 to 200	160	0.010	215	0.008
S group	175 to 225	105	0.010	125	0.008
O and A groups(b)	200 to 250	85	0.008	105	0.006
D group and A7	200 to 250	50	0.008	60	0.006
H11(c)	150 to 200	110	0.010	130	0.008
	200 to 250	90	0.008	110	0.006
	325 to 375	60	0.006	80	0.004
	Rc 48 to 50	25	0.003	35	0.002
H20(d)	150 to 200	80	0.010	100	0.008
	200 to 250	75	0.008	90	0.006
M2 and T1(e)	200 to 250(h)	75	0.008	90	0.006
M3 (cl 1) and T4(f)	225 to 275(h)	60	0.007	75	0.005
M15 and T15(g)	225 to 275(h)	40	0.006	55	0.004
L group	150 to 200	115	0.010	130	0.008
F group	200 to 250	95	0.008	115	0.006
P1 to P6	100 to 150	135	0.010	150	0.008
P20 and P21	150 to 200	115	0.010	135	0.008

(a) High speed steels M2 and M7, except M33 and T15 for milling of the H11 group at hardness above Rc 48. (b) Includes all of group A except A7. (c) Includes also H10, H12, H13, H14, H16 and H19. (d) Includes also H21, H22, H23, H24, H25, H41, H42 and H43. (e) Includes also M1, M6, M10, T2, T6 and T7. (f) Includes also M4, M7, M30, M33, M34, M35, M36, M41, M42, M43, M44, T5 and T8. (g) Includes also M3 (class 2) and T9. (h) Depth of cut in rough milling, 0.125 in. (Data are adapted from tables compiled by Metcut Research Associates, Inc.)

Table 13. Nominal Speeds and Feeds for End Milling of Tool Steels With High Speed Steel and Carbide Cutters

Steel	Brinell hardness	Rough milling (depth of cut, 0.050 in.) Speed, sfm	Rough feed, ipt, for cutter diameter of: ¼ in.	½ in.	¾ in.	1 to 2 in.	Finish milling (depth of cut, 0.015 in.) Speed, sfm	Finish feed, ipt, for cutter diameter of: ¼ in.	½ in.	¾ in.	1 to 2 in.
High Speed Steel Cutters(a)											
W group	150 to 200	120	0.002	0.003	0.005	0.006	155	0.001	0.002	0.004	0.005
S group	175 to 225	85	0.002	0.003	0.004	0.005	110	0.001	0.002	0.003	0.004
O group	200 to 250	70	0.001	0.002	0.003	0.004	90	0.0007	0.001	0.002	0.003
A group(b)	200 to 250	70	0.001	0.002	0.003	0.004	90	0.0007	0.001	0.002	0.003
D group and A7	200 to 250	40	0.001	0.002	0.003	0.004	50	0.0007	0.001	0.002	0.003
H11(c)	150 to 200	85	0.001	0.001	0.002	0.004	110	0.0005	0.001	0.001	0.002
	200 to 250	75	0.001	0.002	0.003	0.004	95	0.0007	0.001	0.002	0.003
	325 to 375	50	0.001	0.001	0.002	0.003	65	0.0005	0.001	0.001	0.002
	Rc 48 to 50	25	....	0.0005	0.0005	0.001	30	0.0005	0.0005	0.0005	0.001
H20(d)	150 to 200	70	0.001	0.001	0.0015	0.003	90	0.0005	0.001	0.001	0.002
	200 to 250	60	0.001	0.0015	0.002	0.003	80	0.0005	0.001	0.0015	0.002
M2 and T1(e)	200 to 250	60	0.001	0.002	0.003	0.004	80	0.0007	0.001	0.002	0.003
M3 (cl 1) and T4(f)	225 to 275	50	0.001	0.002	0.003	0.004	65	0.0007	0.001	0.002	0.003
M15 and T15(g)	225 to 275	35	0.0007	0.001	0.0015	0.0025	45	0.0005	0.001	0.0015	0.002
L group	150 to 200	85	0.002	0.003	0.004	0.005	110	0.001	0.002	0.003	0.004
F group	200 to 250	70	0.001	0.002	0.003	0.004	90	0.0007	0.001	0.002	0.003
P1 to P6	100 to 150	105	0.002	0.003	0.005	0.006	135	0.001	0.002	0.004	0.005
P20 and P21	150 to 200	90	0.002	0.003	0.004	0.005	120	0.001	0.002	0.003	0.004
Carbide Cutters(b)											
W group	150 to 200	500	0.0025	0.004	0.006	0.008	650	0.0015	0.0035	0.006	0.007
S group	175 to 225	365	0.002	0.003	0.005	0.007	475	0.001	0.002	0.004	0.005
O group	200 to 250	300	0.0015	0.0025	0.004	0.005	390	0.001	0.0015	0.0025	0.005
A group(b)	200 to 250	300	0.0015	0.0025	0.004	0.005	390	0.001	0.0015	0.0025	0.004
D group and A7	200 to 250	200	0.0015	0.0025	0.004	0.005	260	0.001	0.0015	0.0025	0.004
H11(c)	150 to 200	300	0.001	0.002	0.003	0.004	390	0.001	0.001	0.002	0.002
	200 to 250	275	0.0015	0.0025	0.004	0.005	360	0.001	0.0015	0.0025	0.004
	325 to 375	175	0.001	0.001	0.002	0.003	230	0.001	0.001	0.001	0.001
	Rc 48 to 50	70	....	0.0005	0.002	0.002	90	0.0005	0.0005	0.001	0.001
	Rc 50 to 52	50	....	0.0005	0.002	0.002	65	0.0005	0.0005	0.001	0.001
	Rc 52 to 54	40	....	0.0005	0.001	0.0015	50	0.0005	0.0005	0.001	0.001
	Rc 54 to 56	30	....	0.0005	0.001	0.001	40	0.0005	0.0005	0.001	0.001
H20(d)	150 to 200	230	0.001	0.002	0.003	0.004	300	0.001	0.001	0.002	0.002
	200 to 250	225	0.001	0.0015	0.0025	0.0035	290	0.001	0.0015	0.0015	0.0025
M2 and T1(e)	200 to 250	225	0.0015	0.0025	0.004	0.005	290	0.001	0.0015	0.0025	0.004
M3 (cl 1) and T4(f)	225 to 275	200	0.0015	0.0025	0.004	0.005	260	0.001	0.0015	0.0025	0.004
M15 and T15(g)	225 to 275	165	0.001	0.002	0.003	0.004	215	0.001	0.0015	0.002	0.003
L group	150 to 200	375	0.002	0.003	0.005	0.007	485	0.001	0.002	0.004	0.005
F group	200 to 250	325	0.0015	0.0025	0.004	0.005	420	0.001	0.0015	0.0025	0.004
P1 to P6	100 to 150	465	0.0025	0.004	0.006	0.008	605	0.0015	0.0035	0.006	0.007
P20 and P21	150 to 200	400	0.002	0.003	0.005	0.007	520	0.001	0.002	0.004	0.005

(a) High speed steels M2 and M7 except T15, M33, M41, M42, M43 and M44 for milling of M3 (class 1) and T4 groups, M15 and T15 groups and group H11 at hardness of Rc 48 to 50. (b) Includes all of group A except A7. (c) Includes also H10, H12, H13, H14, H16 and H19. (d) Includes also H21, H22, H23, H24, H25, H41, H42 and H43. (e) Includes also M1, M6, M10, T2, T6 and T7. (f) Includes also M4, M7, M30, M33, M34, M35, M36, M41, M42, M43, M44, T5 and T8. (g) Also M3 (cl 2) (h) Carbide grade C-2. (SOURCE: same as for Table 12)

10 Stress relieve (A2, D2 and A7 only)
11 Thread grind
12 Heat treat (A2, D2 and A7 only).

Details of equipment, tooling, processing conditions, and tool life for the drilling, facing, turning, boring and broaching operations are presented in Table 16.

Although machinability (as gaged by speeds, machining times, tool material and tool life) of the four steels is shown in Table 16 to have been equal or closely similar in drilling and broaching, a marked difference is apparent in their performance in facing, turning and boring. In these three operations, M1 consistently produced appreciably greater tool wear than A2 and D2, but less than A7— which, despite the use of slower speeds and tools of a different composition of carbide, yielded the lowest tool life of all. The cost of machining A7 greatly exceeded that of the three other steels, and the over-all cost of a finished A7 die was about 40% higher than that of one made of A2 or D2.

Example 688. Face Milling D2

A 30-hp vertical-spindle knee-type milling machine was used for face milling flat die sections of various lengths cut from hot rolled D2 bar stock at 255 Bhn. Several of these sections were machined simultaneously. The 8-in.-diam, 16-tooth milling cutter was mounted on the face of the spindle, and contained carbide-tip inserted blades with 7° axial rake and 3° radial rake.

Depth of cut was 0.030 to 0.180 in., width 2 to 6 in., and length 6 to 30 in. Milling speed was 200 sfm; feed, 9 ipm (0.006 ipt). No cutting fluid was used. Metal-removal rate was 0.54 to 9.7 cu in. per min.

Electrical Discharge Machining of A2. For a description of the techniques and conditions used in two applications involving electrical discharge machining of A2 tool steel, see Examples 683 and 706 in this article. See also the article on page 227.

Hot Work Tool Steels (H Steels)

When used for tools, the H steels are machined in the annealed condition, with machinability somewhat less than the A steels and better than the D steels. Type H11, usually containing 0.40% C instead of 0.35% C, is used also for structural parts in aerospace applications. Such parts generally are machined in the quenched and tempered condition at higher hardness, and information on such machining is included elsewhere in this volume (see *H11 steel* in the index).

Some hot work steels containing sulfur or lead additions have been used in special applications involving low amounts of shock. The two examples that follow describe applications in which sulfurized H13 permitted a reduction in machining time from that required for the regular nonsulfurized grade of H13 tool steel.

Example 689. Facing and Turning H13 vs Sulfurized H13

Blanks of H13 and sulfurized H13 tool steels were faced and turned in a 16-in. engine lathe, using carbide tools. Before machining, these blanks weighed 21¾ lb apiece; after machining, each blank weighed 17½ lb and was 8-in. OD by 1¼-in. thick. Depth of cut in rough turning and facing was 1⁄16 in.; in finishing, 0.005 to 0.010 in.

For the H13 blanks, speed in roughing and finishing was 180 rpm; feed was 0.012 ipr in roughing and 0.006 ipr in finishing. Total machining time, for roughing and finishing, was 50 min per piece.

The improved machinability of the sulfurized H13 blanks permitted roughing and finishing speed to be increased nearly 40% (to 250 rpm) and roughing feed to be doubled (to 0.024 ipr); feed in finishing remained the same (0.006 ipr). The increases in speed and feed resulted in a 20% decrease in machining time, which was 40 min per piece for the sulfurized H13.

Table 14. Nominal Speeds for Power Band Sawing of Tool Steels With High Speed Steel Blades (a)

Steel	Brinell hardness	Speed, sfm
W group	150 to 200	265
S group	175 to 225	185
O, A and D groups	200 to 250	100
H11(b)	150 to 200	180
	200 to 250	135
	325 to 375	110
H20(c)	150 to 200	150
	200 to 250	115
M2 and T1(d)	200 to 250	115
M3 (cl 1) and T4(e)	225 to 275	105
L and F groups	150 to 250	190
P group	100 to 200	225

(a) Pitch for sawing material less than ¼ in. thick, 8 to 10 teeth per in.; ¼ to 1½ in. thick, 6 to 8 teeth per in.; more than 1½ in. thick, 3 to 6 teeth per in. (b) Includes also H10, H12, H13, H14, H16 and H19. (c) Includes also H21, H22, H23, H24, H25, H41, H42 and H43. (d) Includes also M1, M6, M10, T2, T6 and T7. (e) Includes also M3 (class 2) M4, M7, M15, M30, M33, M34, M35, M36, M41, M42, M43, M44, T5, T8, T9 and T15. (SOURCE: same as for Table 12)

Table 15. Nominal Pitches, Speeds and Feeds for Power Hacksawing of Tool Steels With High Speed Steel Blades

Steel	Brinell hardness	Pitch, teeth per in. (a)	Speed, strokes per min	Feed, in. per stroke
W group	150 to 200	6	140	0.006
S group	175 to 225	6	90	0.003
O, A and D groups	200 to 250	10	55	0.005
H11(b)	150 to 200	6	100	0.003
	200 to 250	10	75	0.003
	325 to 375	10	45	0.003
H20(c)	150 to 200	6	80	0.003
	200 to 250	10	60	0.003
M2 and T1(d)	200 to 250	10	70	0.006
M3(cl 1) and T4(e)	225 to 275	10	60	0.006
L and F groups	150 to 250	6	105	0.006
P group	100 to 200	6	115	0.006

(a) Pitches listed are for sawing material ¼ to ¾ in. thick. Pitch for material less than ¼ in. thick, 10 teeth per in.; ¾ to 2 in. thick, 6 teeth per in.; more than 2 in. thick, 4 teeth per in. (b) Includes also H10, H12, H13, H14, H16 and H19. (c) Includes also H21, H22, H23, H24, H25, H41, H42 and H43. (d) Includes also M1, M6, M10, T2, T6 and T7. (e) Includes also M3 (class 2) M4, M7, M15, M30, M33, M34, M35, M36, M41, M42, M43, M44, T5, T8, T9 and T15. (SOURCE: same as for Table 12)

Example 690. Facing, Turning and Milling H13 vs Sulfurized H13 (Fig. 8)

Porthole extrusion dies (Fig. 8) were machined from H13 and sulfurized H13 forgings 12 in. in diameter and 5⅛ in. thick, weighing 186 lb. Machining consisted of facing and turning, and of milling the four ports.

Facing and turning, in which 86 lb of metal was removed, required 9 hr for the H13, as against 6⅔ hr for the sulfurized H13. Milling the H13 required 10 hr; sulfurized H13, 7 hr.

High Speed Steels

General-purpose types of high speed steel, such as T1, ordinarily machine at 50% of the rate for the W group (most easily machined). Annealed T1 steel, however, has been machined still faster, at 40% of the rate for 1112 steel. For instance, with a 0.060-in. depth of cut and at a feed of 0.010 ipr, annealed T1 has been turned with a high speed

Table 16. Machining A2, A7, D2 and M1 Thread Rolling Dies (Example 687)

Drilling(a)

Speed .... 60 rpm
Feed .... 0.004 ipr
Cutting fluid .... Soluble-oil:water (1:20)

Facing(b)

Speed, roughing:
A2, D2 and M1 .... 110 rpm
A7 .... 62 rpm
Speed, finishing:
A2, D2 and M1 .... 110 rpm
A7 .... 84 rpm
Feed, roughing and finishing (all) .... 0.013 ipr
Depth of cut, roughing .... 0.125 in.
Depth of cut, finishing .... 0.015 in.
Cutting fluid .... Soluble-oil:water (1:20)

Turning and Boring(b)

Speed, roughing:
A2, D2 and M1 .... 84 rpm
A7 .... 62 rpm
Speed, finishing:
A2, D2 and M1 .... 110 rpm
A7 .... 84 rpm
Feed, roughing and finishing (all) .... 0.011 ipr
Depth of cut, roughing .... 0.125 in.
Depth of cut, finishing .... 0.015 in.
Cutting fluid .... Soluble-oil:water (1:20)

Broaching(c)

Speed .... 15 ft per min
Feed .... 0.0047 ipt
Depth of cut .... 0.130 to 0.140 in.
Width of cut .... 0.505 in.
Cutting fluid .... Sulfurized thread-cutting oil

Tool Life

(Pieces per grind or per cutting edge)

Drilling, all steels(a) .... 150 to 200
Rough turning and facing(b):
A2 and D2 15
M1 10
A7 3
Finish turning and facing(b):
A2 and D2 25
M1 20
A7 6
Rough boring(b):
A2 and D2 30
M1 20
A7 5
Finish boring(b):
A2 and D2 45
M1 30
A7 10
Broaching, all steels(c) 200

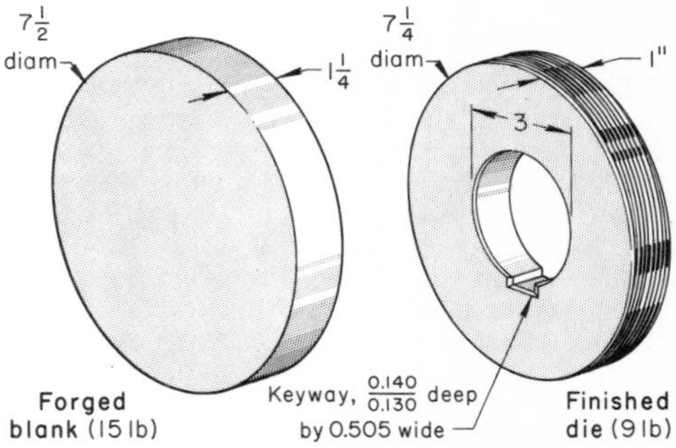

(a) Drill press was a vertical-spindle machine with 28-in. stroke and 3-in. drill capacity. Drills were of M1 high speed steel, had two flutes, 130° point angle and 8° lip relief angle. Three 1¼-in.-thick blanks, stacked and clamped, were drilled simultaneously; drilling time, 25 min (8⅓ min per piece). (b) Facing was a separate operation; turning and boring were done simultaneously. Total machining time for facing, turning and boring A2, D2 and M1 was 18 min; for A7, 22 to 23 min. For all three operations, a 40-hp horizontal turret lathe with a 16-in. chuck, and carbide tools (C-50 for A2, D2 and M1; C-2 for A7), were used. Tools for facing and turning (both roughing and finishing) were triangular disposable carbide, 3⁄16 in. thick and with ½-in. inscribed circle. Tools for rough boring had 20° rake, 7° clearance and 45° backoff; tools for finish boring had 15° rake, 7° clearance and 15° backoff. (c) Broaching was done in a 10-ton hydraulic machine. Broaches, of M1 high speed steel, were 53½ in. long and 0.505 in. wide, and had 41 teeth; rake angle was 15°, clearance angle 1° 30′, and side clearance angle 2°. Broaching time per piece was 20 to 30 sec.

Table 17. Cast Co-Cr-W Alloy Tool Bits vs Disposable Carbide Tips for Turning M10 Tap Blanks (Example 692) (a)

Item	Co-Cr-W	Carbide
Tool Details		
Side rake	10°	5°
Back rake	15°	5°
Lead rake	15°	15°
Nose radius, in.	1/32	1/32
Machining Conditions(b)		
Speed, rpm	550	2300
Speed, sfm	100	415
Feed, ipr	0.015	0.010
Machg. time per cut, sec	20	8
Cycle time per cut, sec	24	12
Tool life, pieces(c)	150	165

(a) Tap blanks, 1 1/16 in. in diameter and 9 in. long, were turned at a hardness of 228 Bhn in a 12-in. engine lathe. (b) For tools of both materials, depth of cut was 0.047 in., length of cut was 2¾ in. (c) Per grind (Co-Cr-W bits) or per tip (disposable carbide).

Table 18. Turning M10 vs Sulfurized M10 Reamer Blanks (Example 693) (a)

Item	M10	Sulfurized M10
Speed, rpm	230	325
Speed, sfm	120	170
Feed, ipr	0.025	0.025
Depth of cut, in.	0.125	0.125
Length of cut, in.	3¾	3¾
Power input, hp	4.5	5
Force on tool bit, lb	1050	900
Cutting rate, cu in./min	4.25	6
Cutting rate, lb per min	1.25	1.8
Tool life per grind, pieces	18	25

(a) Reamer blanks, 2 in. in diameter, were turned for removal of 0.250 in. of stock on the diameter. A 54-in. lathe with 5-hp capacity, and 0.75-in.-square tools of M2 high speed steel, were used for turning. Cutting fluid was a 1-to-25 mixture of soluble oil and water.

steel tool at 120 sfm, whereas for similar conditions 1112 steel is turned at 300 sfm.

Machinability of the more highly alloyed high speed steels decreases as hardness and abrasiveness increase. This is especially true of the high-carbon, high-vanadium types, such as M4, M15, T9 and T15. These steels are considerably more difficult to machine than T1, requiring lower cutting speeds or causing increased tool wear, or both. These more highly alloyed grades of high speed steel are comparable to the A7 and D7 cold work die steels with respect to machinability.

The machining characteristics of M1 high speed tool steel are compared with those of A2, A7 and D2 in Example 687, an application involving drilling, facing, turning, boring and broaching. The sixteen examples that follow provide details for a variety of machining operations on several types of tungsten or molybdenum high speed steel workpieces.

Example 691. Turning M10 Tap Blanks

Tap blanks 1⅛-in. in diameter and 5⅛-in. long (weight, 1.6 lb), of M10 bar stock with a hardness of 234 Bhn, were turned in a 10-hp 14-in. engine lathe. The tool holder and setup were rigid, the turning tool was well supported to prevent vibration, and the lathe motor provided ample reserve power — all necessary conditions when turning high speed steels.

Speed was 418 rpm (125 sfm), feed 0.008 ipr, depth of cut 0.220 in. and length of cut 2½ in. A 200-to-1 mixture of water and chemical synthetic was used as the cutting fluid. Metal removed per piece was 0.3 lb; machining time per piece was 45 sec. The turning tool had indexable carbide tips, with 6° side rake, 0° to 5° back rake, and 1/16-in. nose radius. Tool life was 30 to 35 pieces per corner.

Example 692. Turning M10 Tap Blanks (Table 17)

(Comparison of Turning-Tool Materials)

The performance of cast Co-Cr-W alloy tool bits was compared with disposable carbide tips for turning M10 tap blanks. These blanks, 1 1/16 in. in diameter and 9 in. long, were turned in the annealed condition (228 Bhn) on a 12-in. engine lathe.

As shown in Table 17, the carbide tips permitted the use of much higher speed, had slightly longer cutting life, and considerably reduced machining time and cycle time per cut. In this application, the use of carbide doubled production rate while only slightly increasing tooling cost.

Example 693. Turning M10 vs Sulfurized M10 Reamer Blanks (Table 18)

In turning 2-in.-diam reamer blanks to remove 0.250 in. of stock from the diameter, cutting speed was increased from 120 to 170 sfm when a sulfurized M10 steel was substituted for the regular grade. Both steels were machined in the annealed condition (228 Bhn). Processing conditions are given in Table 18.

Example 694. Milling Flutes in M10 Drills

A 2-hp automatic flute-milling machine was used for milling flutes in 5/16-in.-diam drill blanks of M10 high speed steel. These blanks weighed 0.105 lb before machining and 0.065 lb after, and were machined in the annealed condition (228 Bhn). Tool details, operating conditions, and results were the same as in Example 680.

Example 695. Milling Flutes in M10 vs T15 Drills

(Tool Life/Material Comparison)

A 1½-hp automatic flute-milling machine (cam-fed helix) was used for milling flutes in 17/64-in.-diam drill blanks of M10 high speed steel (Rockwell B 96 to 98). The milling cutter, 2½ in. in diameter, with 22 teeth, was M10. Speed was 250 rpm (163 sfm), and feed was 6 ipm (linear, not helical), or 0.0011 ipt. Cutting fluid was a low-viscosity spindle oil. Tool life per grind was 8 hr (336 drills).

When the M10 cutters were used under the same conditions for milling T15 drill blanks (Rockwell B 103 to 105), tool life was only ¼ hr (about 11 drills). However, when brazed carbide tips were substituted as the tool material (with other conditions unchanged), tool life in milling the T15 blanks increased to 28 hr (or about 1200 drills).

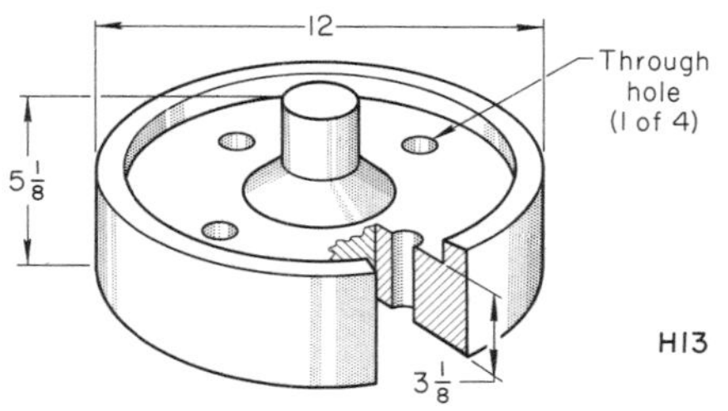

Fig. 8. Porthole extrusion die that was faced, turned and milled in 28% less time when made of sulfurized H13 than when made of H13 (Example 690)

Table 19. M10 vs Carbide Cutters for Milling Flutes in M10 Reamer Blanks (Example 697) (a)

Item	Cutter material: M10	Cutter material: Carbide
Tool Details		
Diameter, in.	2¼	3¼
Width, in.	⅜	⅜
Number of teeth	16	20
Rake angle	5°	5°
Clearance angle	10°	8°
Machining Conditions(b)		
Speed, rpm	210	224
Speed, sfm	125	190
Feed, in. per min	3⅛	9 7/16
Cutting time per piece, min	1.7	0.57
Tool life per grind, flutes	600	1200

(a) A 3-hp milling machine was used for cutting six flutes in each blank. Blanks, 1 1/16 in. in diameter and 10⅞ in. long, were machined in the annealed condition (hardness, 228 Bhn). Cutting fluid was a sulfur-base oil. (b) For tools of both materials, depth of cut was ⅛ in., width 5/16 in., and length 5 7/16 in.

Example 696. Milling Flutes in M10 vs Sulfurized M10 Reamers

A 15-hp gang mill was used for cutting flutes in ¾-in.-diam six-flute hand reamers made of M10 or sulfurized M10 high speed steel. The mill was set up to machine six blanks at a time, cutting one flute each per pass. The milling cutters, also of M10, were 3 in. in diameter, with 22 teeth. Chip load was 0.0008 ipt. A medium-viscosity sulfurized oil was used as the cutting fluid.

The lower resistance to machining of the sulfurized M10 reamers permitted an increase in speed and feed, as follows:

	M10	M10+S
Speed, rpm	116	145
Speed, sfm	90	115
Feed (climb), ipm	2	2.5

These increases resulted in a 20% increase in production rate over that for the regular M10 reamers.

Example 697. Milling Flutes in M10 Reamer Blanks (Table 19)

(Comparison of Cutter Materials)

In milling flutes in annealed (228 Bhn) M10 reamer blanks 1 1/16 in. in diameter by 10⅞ in. long, the performance of an M10 milling cutter was compared to that of a cutter with carbide teeth. As indicated by the data in Table 19, the use of carbide tooling doubled tool life and reduced cutting time 66%.

Example 698. Milling Flutes in M1 vs T15 Reamers

In milling six straight flutes in straight-shank chucking reamers made of M1 or T15 high speed steels, the following comparison of the machinability of the two steels, and of machining costs, was obtained:

	M1	T15
Cuts required per flute	1	2
Milling time per tool, min	13	81
Tool life per grind, pieces	150	24
Milling cost per reamer	$0.088	$0.223

The M1 blanks were easily milled with one heavy cut per flute, but two light cuts per flute were necessary for the T15 blanks in order to obtain an acceptable surface finish. The flute area milled was 0.395 in. in diameter and 3 in. long; each blank weighed 0.2543 lb before machining and 0.1560 lb after. The reamer blanks, chucked on shank ends and steadied on front ends by means of centers, were gang milled, six at a time, in automatic milling machines.

Example 699. Milling Flutes in T15 End Mills (Table 20)

(Comparison of Cutter Materials)

In milling helical flutes in ¾-in.-diam four-flute end mills made of T15 high speed steel, the machining characteristics of cutters made of M2 high speed steel were compared with those of carbide-tip cutters. Because T15 steel is much more difficult to machine than M1, M2 or M10, surface speed and feed were reduced to about 50% of the rates ordinarily used for these M steels, in the interest of tool life. Nevertheless, as shown in Table 20, which presents the results of the comparison, carbide tooling doubled the machining rate and nearly tripled the tool life provided by M2 tooling.

On the basis of these data, the use of carbide tooling for machining difficult high speed steels such as T15, M15 and M4 was recommended — provided machine tools are in good repair and the setup is rigid.

Example 700. Milling Flutes in M10 Taps (Table 21)

The data in Table 21 compare the tooling and conditions that were used for milling flutes in two sizes of four-flute hand taps made of M10 high speed steel. Blanks for

Table 20. M2 vs Carbide-Tip Cutters for Milling Flutes in T15 End Mills (Example 699) (a)

Item	Cutter(b) M2	Carbide
Speed, rpm	125	322
Speed, sfm	57	146
Feed, in. per min	1¾	3½
Machining time per cut, min	1.43	0.71
Tool life, number of cuts	70	200

(a) Milling four helical flutes in ¾-in.-diam end mills in a 3-hp "universal" mill. Depth of cut was ⅛ to $\frac{1}{16}$ in., width ⅜ in., and length 2¼ in. A sulfur-base oil was used as the cutting fluid. (b) Both M2 and carbide-tip cutters were 1¾ in. in diameter and ⅜ in. wide.

taps of both sizes (½ and 1½ in. in diameter) were machined in the annealed condition (228 Bhn).

Example 701. Milling M1 vs Sulfurized M1 Thread Chasers

In milling threads in tangential thread chasers made of sulfurized M1 high speed steel, machining time was 20% less than that for thread chasers made of regular M1, and surface finish was improved.

Before machining, the chaser blanks weighed 11.75 oz each; the finished tools (1¼-by-4-in., 11-pitch, Whitworth-taper pipe-thread chasers) weighed 8 oz each. Teeth were milled in a roughing pass, which removed about 0.060 in. of stock, and a finishing pass, which removed 0.005 in. Speed for the M1 was 120 rpm, in both roughing and finishing; this was increased to 145 rpm for the sulfurized M1. Feed for the M1 was 1⅝ ipm in roughing but was reduced to 1 ipm in finishing; for the sulfurized M1, 1⅝ ipm was used in finishing as well as roughing.

Tangential thread chasers ordinarily are made of M1 high speed steel, but M3 may be substituted when longer tool life is desired or a more difficult material is to be threaded. The following example compares the tool life obtained in milling "step and angle" dovetails in thread chasers made of these two steels.

Example 702. Milling M1 vs M3 Thread Chasers (Fig. 9)

The dovetail shown in Fig. 9 was produced in tangential thread chasers made of M1 or M3 high speed steel in one pass by a single milling cutter. (In service, this dovetail locks the chaser into the holder.) Blanks for these chasers weighed 3½ oz before machining, and 2½ oz after. At a speed of 95 rpm and table feed of 3⅛ ipm, tool life in milling the M1 chasers was 2400 pieces per grind, as against 1200 to 1440 for M3.

Example 703. Milling M2 Tap Chasers (Fig. 10)

A 10-hp milling machine with 18-in. table was used for cutting a 0.50-in. step in overhanging tap chasers made of M2 high speed steel. The workpiece and the machining setup are shown in Fig. 10; tool details and machining conditions are tabulated below the illustration. These chasers were milled in the annealed condition (217 to 255 Bhn). Blanks weighed 1.07 lb each; weight of the finished tap chaser was 0.8 lb.

Example 704. Drilling Oil Holes in M1 vs T15 Drill Blanks (Fig. 11)

In a production operation that involved drilling two 0.080-in.-diam oil holes in straight-shank drill blanks made of M1 or T15 high speed steel, time and cost for drilling the two holes in the T15 blanks were about triple those for the M1:

	M1	T15
Time per piece, min	21.05	63.10
Cost per piece	$1.247	$3.820

As shown in Fig. 11, the two holes were not drilled parallel to the axis of the drill blank. In order to obtain straight, accurately spaced holes, two shallow center holes were drilled at each end. The blank was then placed in a vertical position in a ½-hp drill press, with a center hole in the shank end pressed firmly onto a male center in the center of the work table. Blanks were held by hand on the male center, and drilling was started by hand-feeding an 0.080-in.-diam drill (M1 high speed steel) into the corresponding center hole at the point end of the blank. Holes were drilled in steps of ½ in., using longer drills as drilling progressed through the 7⅝-in. length of the blank. To keep each hole straight, the operator rotated the blank about one third of a turn, several times a minute, during drilling.

The blanks, which were machined at hardnesses of 255 Bhn (M1) and 290 Bhn (T15), weighed 0.2880 lb before drilling and 0.2659 lb after drilling.

Example 705. Shell vs Solid Reamers for M2 Hob Blanks

Through holes 3 in. deep, drilled to 1.203 in. in diameter in hob blanks of M2 high speed steel at 240 Bhn, required reaming to 1.241/1.240-in. finished diameter.

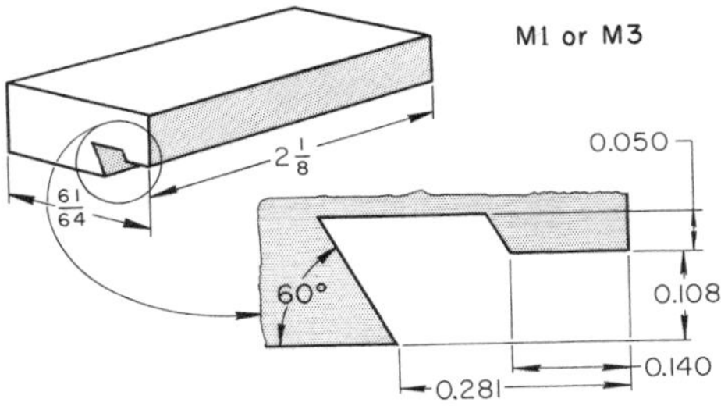

Fig. 9. Tangential thread chaser in which dovetail was milled (Example 702)

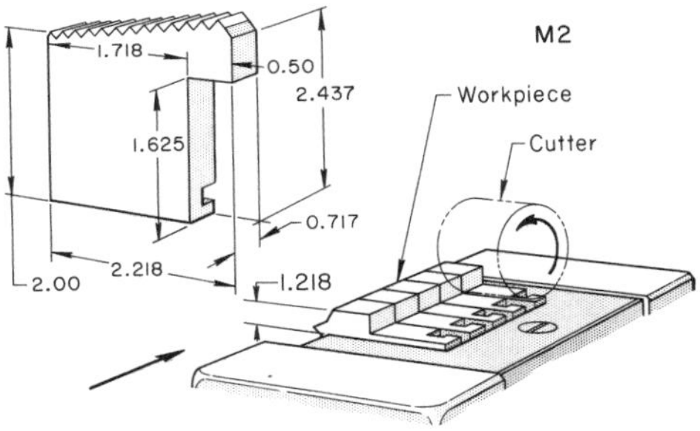

Details of Milling Cutter(a)

Material	M2 high speed steel
Diameter	3½ in.
Width(b)	1 in.
Number of teeth	20
Axial and radial rake angles	10°
Tooth angle	60°
Primary clearance angle	6°
Secondary clearance angle	30°

Machining Conditions

Speed	36 rpm (33 sfm)
Feed	0.010 ipr
Depth of cut	0.50 in.
Width of cut	$1\frac{3}{16}$ in.
Cutting fluid	Water-soluble oil
Cutting time per piece	4 min
Tool life per grind	175 to 200 pieces

(a) Cutter was mounted on 1-in.-diam arbor of a 10-hp milling machine with an 18-in. table; as shown in illustration, chasers were milled in groups of five. (b) Because of width of cutter, two passes were required.

Fig. 10. Milling recess in M2 overhanging tap chaser (Example 703)

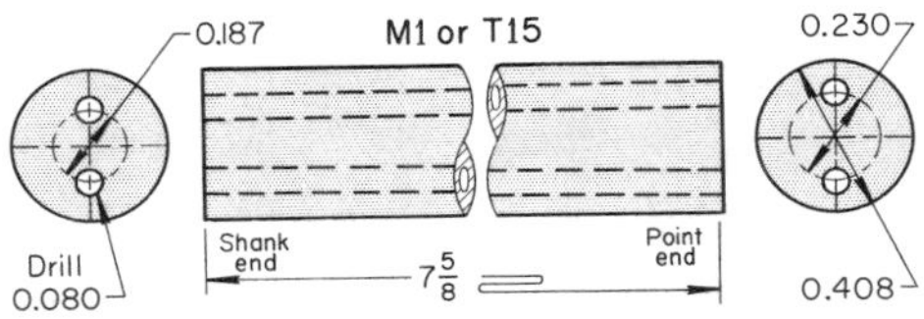

Fig. 11. Straight-shank drill blanks in which 0.080-in.-diam oil holes were drilled (Example 704)

When reaming was done in a single operation with a high speed steel solid reamer, the cutting edges loaded and galled, causing loss of accuracy. Also, reamer life was short; often only three holes could be reamed before regrinding was required.

The process was revised to consist of rough reaming with a solid reamer to a diameter of 1.232 in., and finish reaming with a carbide-tip expandable shell reamer for removal of the final 0.008 in. of metal. This method resulted in good finish (100 to 125 micro-in.), and the 0.001-in. tolerance was met. Reamer life increased to 50 holes per grind, with a total life of 500 holes.

All reaming was done in a turret lathe at a speed of 35 sfm and a feed of 0.011 ipr. Cutting fluid was soluble oil mixed 1-to-25 with water. Production rate, including rough and finish reaming, was 8 pieces per hour.

Example 706. Electrical Discharge Machining (EDM) of T15 or A2 Punching Dies (Fig. 12)

When electrical discharge machining was substituted for conventional machining in the production of the stator "slot" punching die shown in Fig. 12, machining time and cost were reduced, and the service life of the punch-and-die set was significantly increased. These tools were made of either T15 or A2 steel, depending on quantity of stator slots to be produced. (With a burr limit of 0.007 in., T15 tools produced 175,000 slots per grind, A2 tools about 50,000. On the basis of cost of producing the tool, number of regrinds, and setup costs, it had been found more economical to use T15 steel for production runs of more than one million slots.)

The punch was produced entirely by conventional machining methods and was used as the EDM electrode. The electrode material was attached to the punch before grinding, so that both components could be ground to size at the same time. The sequence of operations entailed in producing the punch was as follows: shape, square up, lay out, reshape, drill and tap, heat treat, grind to final size, lap dowel holes, and assemble to punch head.

The die section was roughed out in the annealed condition and then was hardened to Rockwell C 60 to 62 (A2) or Rockwell C 63 to 64 (T15). The die was set up on the electrical discharge unit with the top of the die on the face of the machine, so that the electrode worked in from the bottom face of the die. This arrangement resulted in increased machining speed, faster metal removal at the bottom of the die, and formation of a relief taper. The EDM machine was equipped with a rotary quill in the ram head, a servo feed, and a jig-borer table with a servo feed. Production of the die entailed the following sequence of operations: shape, lay out, drill and tap, saw, heat treat, grind top and bottom, lap dowel holes, assemble to die shoe, and complete the die by electrical discharge machining to final size.

Table 21. Milling Flutes in Two Sizes of M10 Hand Taps (Example 700) (a)

Item	Tap diameter ½ in.(b)	1½ in.(c)
Tool Details(d)		
Cutter width, in.	0.260	0.816
Number of teeth	30	20
Radial rake angle	5°	5°
Clearance angle	10°	10°
Tooth radius, in.	0.130	0.405
Machining Conditions		
Speed, rpm	125	105
Speed, sfm	130	110
Feed, in. per min	2½	1
Depth of cut, in.	0.139	0.405
Width of cut, in.	0.260	0.816
Length of cut, in.	$2\frac{1}{16}$	3½
Milling time per flute, min	0.82	3½
Tool life, number of flutes	650	600

(a) Taps (four-flute) of both diameters were milled in the annealed condition (228 Bhn) in a 5-hp machine, using a sulfur-base oil as the cutting fluid. (b) Over-all length, 3⅜ in.; thread length, $1\frac{21}{32}$ in.; weight, 0.15 lb before machining, 0.10 lb after. (c) Over-all length, 6⅜ in.; thread length, 3 in.; weight, 2.80 lb before machining, 1.85 lb after. (d) Cutters for both sizes of taps were 4 in. in diameter and made of M10 high speed steel.

Dies made by the electrical discharge machining process not only were less costly and time-consuming to produce than those made by conventional machining (see table below Fig. 12), but also produced 30% more blanks per grind — because of the harder cutting face and because the punch and die were so accurately fitted. The producer of these tools also reported that multiple-blank-and-slot dies of more intricate design required as much as 1000 hr of labor to manufacture by conventional methods, whereas the same dies could be completed in only 575 hr by electrical discharge machining.

Low-Alloy Special-Purpose Tool Steels

In the spheroidize-annealed condition (179 to 207 Bhn), steels L1, L2, L3 and L7 are 65% to 75% as machinable as a W1 steel containing 1% C. Steel L6, which contains 1.50% Ni, is slightly more difficult to machine.

Completely or nearly completely spheroidized stock is preferred for most machining operations. Occasionally, however, microstructures that contain some lamellar pearlite are preferred. Such applications usually involve those steels of lower carbon content, which can be specified for L2.

For the L steels with 1% carbon, microstructures of ferrite and spheroidized carbides are almost invariably preferred (and specified) for all machining operations. For these steels, microstructures containing lamellar pearlite usually result in rough surface finish and shorter tool life. The following example describes an application in which the sequence of operations was changed to avoid machining a microstructure that contained pearlite.

Example 707. Deferred Forging for Improved Machinability (Fig. 13)

The original and improved methods used for producing wood-drill shanks from L1 tool steel are shown in Fig. 13. In the original method, the blank was first forged to obtain the square tapered end, after which the recess was form turned in a 5-hp lathe. Even though the blanks were spheroidized, at least half of the recessed area had been heated to the forging temperature, and this resulted in the mixed microstructure denoted as "Poor machinability" in Fig. 13. Severe wear of the M34 form tools, especially at the corner nearest the forged end, occurred in form turning of workpieces made by the original method. Form tools required grinding after 5 to 20 pieces.

In the improved method, steps 1 and 2 were reversed, so that the blanks were formed before the microstructure (denoted in Fig. 13 as "Good machinability") was altered by heating for forging. Form tool life was increased to 150 pieces per grind. Machining conditions for the forming operation are given in the table below Fig. 13.

Turning. For turning operations on low-alloy special-purpose tool steels, single-point tools should have the relief, rake and cutting-edge angles and nose radii listed in Table 22, which gives recommended angles for both high speed steel and carbide tools.

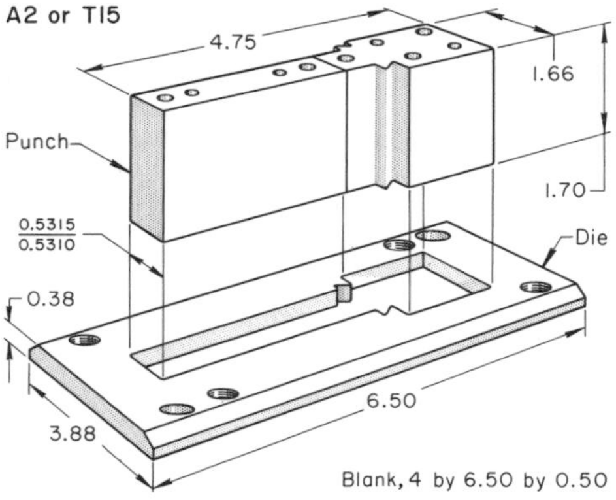

Item	Punch and die material(a) A2	T15
Punch(b)		
Weight of blank, lb	3.71	4.07
Finished weight, lb	2.04	2.24
Machining time, hr	14.56	18.50
Machining cost	$64.63	$78.29
Die		
Weight of blank, lb	3.64	4.00
Finished weight, lb	2.10	2.31
Machining time, hr:		
Conventional method	21.40	28.25
EDM method	13.86	18.39
Machining cost:		
Conventional method	$72.65	$94.20
EDM method	$47.36	$61.28

(a) Choice of A2 or T15 was determined by quantity of stators to be produced. (b) Punch, machined by conventional methods, was used as the electrode for electrical discharge machining of die.

Fig. 12. Electrical discharge machining vs conventional machining for production of die for punch-and-die set used for punching stators (Example 706)

Carbon-Tungsten Special-Purpose Tool Steels

As annealed (183 to 207 Bhn), F1 carbon-tungsten steel is approximately 75% as machinable as 1% carbon W1 steel of comparable structure. Steels F2 and F3, with normally higher hardness of 207 to 235 Bhn in the annealed condition, will machine approximately 60% as well as the annealed 1% carbon W1.

Turning. Recommended design for high speed steel or carbide single-point tools for turning the F steels is given in Table 23.

Milling. Recommended tool design for milling the F steels with high speed steel cutters is given in Table 24.

Low-Carbon Mold Steels

Many dies made from low-carbon mold steel are formed by a hubbing operation, in which a hard master form is pressed into the die to produce the die impression. Many of these steels have very low hardness in the annealed condition. This is especially true for P1, which is frequently supplied at 80 to 100 Bhn. As the alloy content increases, hardness of the annealed steel also increases and suitability for hubbing decreases. Thus, P4, P6, P20 and P21 are generally considered unsuitable for hubbing, so that molds of these steels must be produced by machining instead.

The low-carbon steels of the P group (P1 to P6) have poor machinability because of their softness; chips are gummy and readily build up on cutting edges and drill margins. Because of the low hardness of types P1 to P6, the surface of the mold impression must be carburized and hardened to resist wear, and the entire die must be heat treated to resist deformation of the impression. Considerable distortion occurs in quenching, particularly the water quenching of a relatively small die. Thus, size control is difficult and dies must be finished by grinding after hardening. When dies are ground, care must be taken not to penetrate the carburized case, because core hardness is insufficient for adequate resistance to abrasion or deformation.

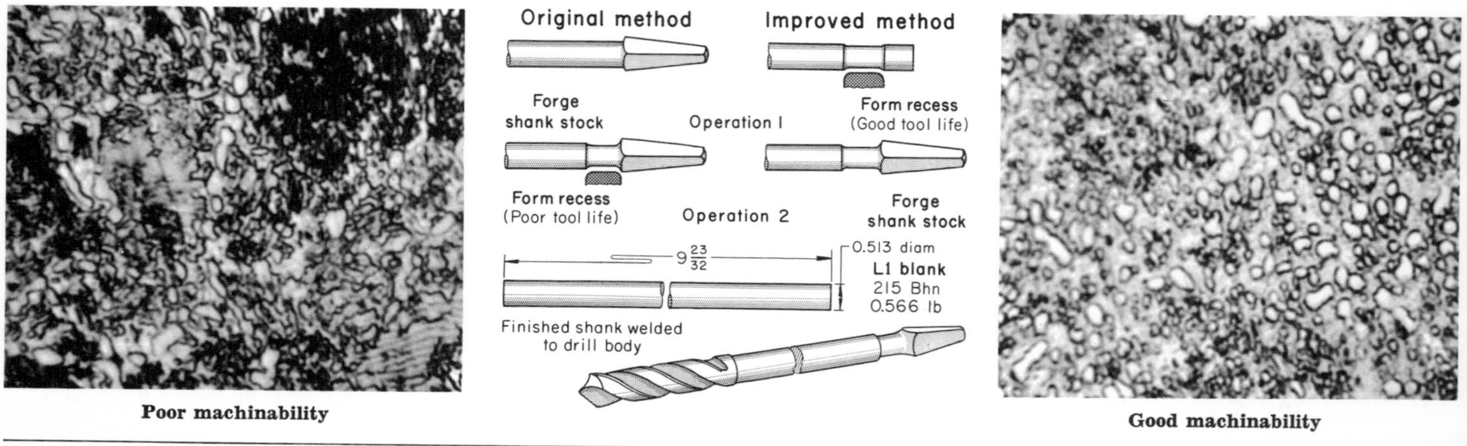

Speed .... 830 rpm (110 sfm)	Depth of cut .... 0.087 in.
Feed .... 0.00063 ipr	Cutting fluid .... Soluble oil:water (1:70)
Metal removed from each blank .... 0.016 lb	Rate of metal removal ...... 0.096 lb per minute

Fig. 13. Change of method that improved machinability and tool life in forming recess in wood-drill shanks made of hot rolled and annealed L1 tool steel. Specimens for micrographs were etched in 2% nital; magnification, 2000×. (Example 707)

Because the group P steels are used almost exclusively in the manufacture of molds, few, if any, turning operations are encountered. However, steels P1 through P6, depending on their composition, have machining characteristics like those of production carburizing steels of similar composition. The P20 steel resembles 4140.

Example 708. Drilling, Fly Cutting and Milling P20 (Fig. 14)

In the production of a P20 steel mold for forming plastic housings for television cabinets, the prehardened block (285 Bhn) was first ground square in a surface grinder, to facilitate layout and provide reference planes. Then the block (30 by 32 by 10 in.) was machined in the following sequence of operations (see Fig. 14):

1 After the block had been clamped into a large boring mill, a 3½-in.-diam hole was drilled in the center of one of the 30-by-32-in. faces, to a depth of 6 in.
2 With the block still in position in the boring mill, the drilled hole was enlarged to 26-in. diameter by a series of fly cutters.
3 The block was then placed in a tracer-controlled milling machine, which squared the corners of the impression and produced the final symmetrical contour.
4 The block was returned to the boring mill, and four 11⁄16-in.-diam through holes (later plugged at one end), for circulation of cooling water, were drilled through under the impression and along the sides.

Variation in Practice for P20. Practice described in the above example is typical for making plastics molds. Because P20 steel can be processed in several ways, it is used for many different mold types and sizes. The molds are machined at three or more different hardnesses.

The most economical way to make a plastic mold is to machine prehardened steel (usually 275 to 325 Bhn) for service without further heat treatment. Machinability for most operations is reasonably good at this hardness, and the cost of further heat treatment is eliminated.

At a hardness of 275 to 325 Bhn a high speed steel cutter can be operated at about 60 sfm and at a feed rate up to 0.005 ipt (somewhat less if the cutter shank lacks rigidity). When carbide cutters are used, the feed will be about the same, but the speed can be increased to about 240 sfm. Cooling ducts can be drilled with carbide-tipped gun drills at 250 sfm using a feed of 0.0004 to 0.0006 ipr for holes no larger than ½ in. in diameter.

For molds used in molding plastics that contain abrasive fillers, mold hardness must be higher to attain acceptable mold life. Under these conditions one of three procedures is followed:

The simplest procedure is to machine the steel in the fully annealed condition (175 to 225 Bhn) to finished or nearly finished size. At this hardness metal can be removed with high speed steel cutters at 90 sfm, or at 350 sfm with carbide cutters. Feed is commonly 0.005 to 0.007 ipt, although lesser feeds are necessary if the cutter lacks rigidity. Cooling ducts can be drilled with carbide-tipped gun drills at 300 sfm and feeds of 0.0004 to 0.0006 ipr for holes up to ½ in. in diameter. After machining, the mold is carburized and hardened so that the surface is near Rockwell C 60 and the core is approximately Rockwell C 50. Some grinding or polishing, or both, will be needed to finish the mold.

When molds are too intricate to withstand the carburizing treatment without excessive distortion, a second procedure is sometimes used. The prehardened steel is machined completely and gas nitrided for 30 hr.

The third machining procedure is also used for plastic molds that are too intricate to carburize in the finish machined condition. The fully annealed stock is rough machined to within about 1⁄16 in. of finish surface, then hardened to Rockwell C 45 to 50. After heat treatment the mold is finish machined. Carbide cutters are usually used. A speed of 85 sfm with a feed of about 0.002 ipt with grade C-2 carbide is common practice.

Table 22. Design of Single-Point Tools for Turning Low-Alloy Special-Purpose Tool Steels

Tool angle	Steel turned: L1, L2	L3, L7	L6
High Speed Steel Tools			
Side rake	7°	15°	8°
Back rake	7°	5°	7°
Side relief	9°	6°	8°
End relief	7°	3°	8°
End cutting edge	10°	10°	9°
Side cutting edge	12°	10°	16°
Nose radius	10% of depth of cut		
Carbide Tools			
Side rake	10°	6°	6°
Back rake	5°	2°	4°
Side relief	7°	6°	6°
End relief	7°	6°	7°
End cutting edge	10°	10°	10°
Side cutting edge	12°	10°	12°

Table 23. Design of Single-Point Tools for Turning Carbon-Tungsten Special-Purpose Tool Steels

Tool angle	Tool material: High speed steel	Carbide
Side rake	20°	5°
Back rake	5°	10°
Side relief	6°	4°
End relief	3°	4°
End cutting edge	10°	6°
Side cutting edge	10°	8°
Nose radius	...	1⁄32 to 1⁄16 in.

Table 24. Tool Design for Milling Carbon-Tungsten Special-Purpose Tool Steels With High Speed Steel Cutters

Rake angle	10° to 15°
Clearance angle	10° to 15°
End relief angle	3° to 5°
Tooth land radius	1⁄32 in.

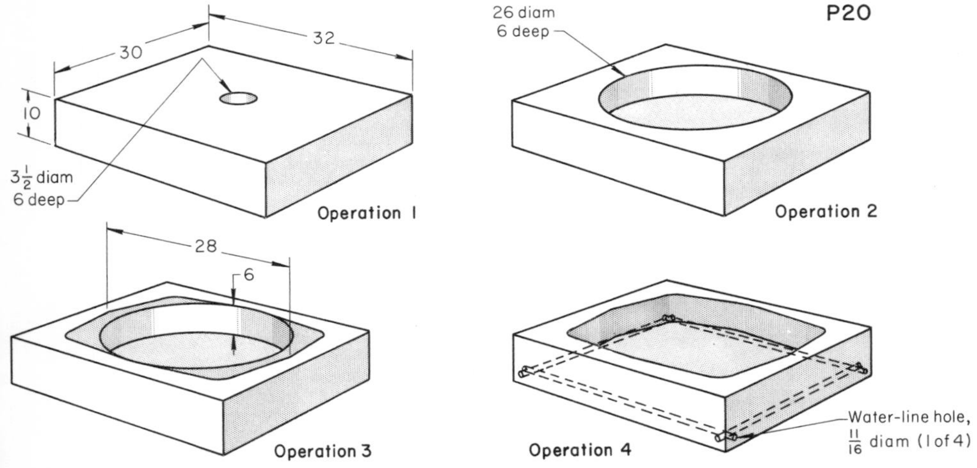

Operation 1 — Drilling

Tool material(a)	M2 high speed steel
Hole diameter	3½ in.
Hole depth	6 in.

Operation 2 — Boring

Tool material(b)	T5 or M34 high speed steel
Speed	32 to 16 rpm(c)
Feed	0.002 to 0.005 ipr
Final diameter	26 in.

Operation 3 — Die-Sink Milling

Tool material(d)	M2 high speed steel
Speed	80 rpm
Feed	0.8 to 1.4 ipm
Depth of cut	2 in.

Operation 4 — Drilling Water-Line Holes

Tool material(e)	M10 high speed steel
Speed	80 rpm
Feed	0.002 ipr

(a) A 3½-in.-diam twist drill of standard design was used; speed and feed not reported. (b) Fly-cutting tool bits used had 15° top rake angle, 10° end rake angle, 5° end cutting-edge angle, and 0° side cutting-edge angle. (c) Speed was decreased as diameter of hole was progressively increased by use of larger-diameter fly cutters. (d) Taper die-sinking cutter was 2 in. in diameter by 6 in. long. (e) An 11⁄16-in.-diam crankshaft drill was used.

Fig. 14. Four-operation machining of prehardened P20 steel mold for forming plastic television-cabinet housings. Blank weighed 2720 lb; finished mold, 1430 lb. (Example 708)

Machining of Tool Steel Gears

Gears that function in a hot or abrasive environment are sometimes made of a hot work tool steel such as H11, H12 or H13. Milling is the gear-production process most often used, because it is practical for the small quantities that are usually needed.

One of three procedures is usually followed, the choice of procedure depending largely on whether the primary requirement is abrasion resistance or heat resistance in service.

One procedure is to mill the gear teeth in the fully annealed condition (200 to 250 Bhn) followed by quenching and tempering to approximately Rockwell C 50. If this procedure causes too much distortion, a final grinding operation can be included (see "Grinding of Gears", page 213). When this procedure is used, a speed of about 100 sfm may be used for rough milling and 130 sfm for finishing with high speed steel cutters. For gears having diametral pitch of 1 to 3, a feed of 0.006 ipt is usually optimum. As pitch becomes finer the feed should be decreased gradually to 0.003 ipt for gears having diametral pitch of 25 to 32.

When the gears must resist abrasion, common practice is to quench and temper the blanks to 325 to 375 Bhn, mill the teeth, and then nitride the machined gear. At this higher hardness, speed must be reduced to about 65 sfm for rough cuts and 100 sfm for finishing with high speed steel cutters. Feed is also reduced to about 0.004 ipt, for gears having diametral pitch of 1 to 3, or about 0.003 ipt for gears having diametral pitch of 25 to 32.

In some instances it is desirable to mill the teeth at higher hardness and employ no further finishing operations. Milling of H11 at up to Rockwell C 55 is common practice (see Examples 329, 347, and 362 to 369 in the article "Milling", beginning on page 169).

Steels for Die Blocks

Steels 6G and 6F7 (Table 1) are typical members of a large group of proprietary compositions not identified by AISI numbers. The largest use of these steels is for die blocks or die inserts for closed-die or hot upset forging. Because of the application of these steels, carbon content, with a few exceptions, is in the range of 0.40 to 0.55%. Alloy content varies considerably within the group; for example, 6G is only slightly higher in alloy content than production steel 4140, whereas 6F7 has a total alloy content of more than 6%. Thus, the machinability of these steels also varies considerably. Steel 6G (annealed) is usually rated about 85% as machinable as the W steels, whereas the more highly alloyed types such as 6F7 (annealed) are rated at 50 to 75% of the machinability of W steels.

From the standpoint of machinability alone, these steels are most economically machined in the annealed condition; an annealed structure containing about 60% spheroidite and 40% lamellar pearlite is preferred. However, because of the applications served by these steels, they are ordinarily machined in the quenched and tempered condition in spite of the resulting loss in time and tool life.

When these steels are used for die blocks, the most common practice is to purchase the blocks as hardened and tempered forgings. Such forgings are available in several hardness ranges starting as low as 269 Bhn and as high as 477 Bhn. The most common range is 341 to 375 Bhn. Regardless of hardness, all machining is done on the hardened and tempered blocks. Machining operations for resinking used dies are also performed without annealing the hardened and tempered dies.

Machining these steels at hardnesses higher than 302 Bhn is difficult and is done only at a sacrifice in cutting speed and tool life.

The four examples that follow describe the conditions and tooling for machining die blocks of 6F7 and 6G tool steels. All these die blocks were machined without a cutting fluid. Contrary to customary practice, the dies discussed in Example 709 were hardened after being machined.

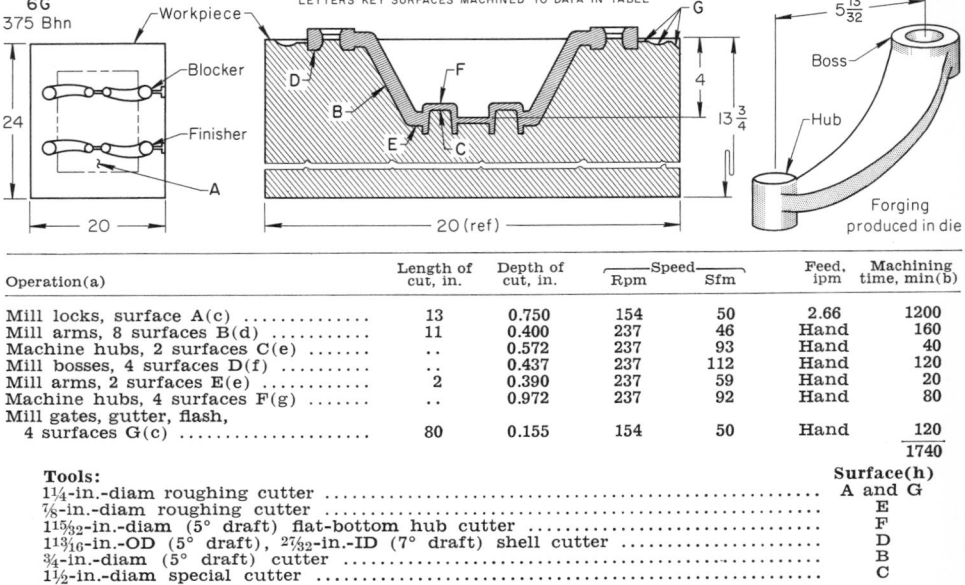

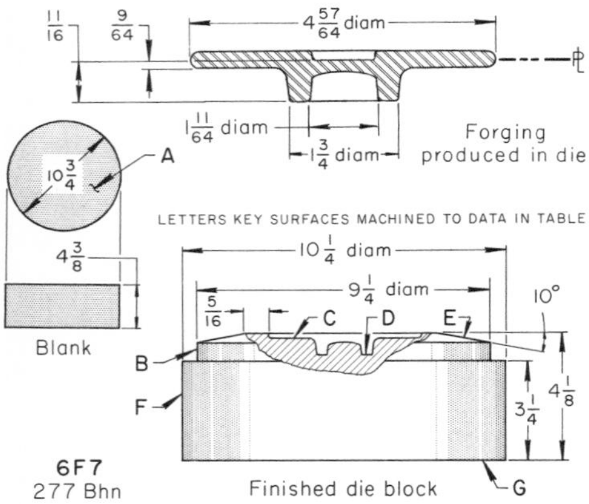

Operation(a)	Surface	Speed, rpm	Machining time, min
Semifinish facing	A	75	20
Rough turning	B	37	65
Finish turning	B	50	35
Turning flange section	C	100	30
Turning hub section(b)	D	100	60
Turning 10° face	E	75	30
Turning OD	F	21	40
Facing to length	G	50	30
Total			310

(a) A 36-in. vertical turret lathe was used for all operations; no cutting fluid was used. Feed for all operations was 0.0085 ipr. Carbide cutting tools (1¼ by ⅝ in.) were used for all operations except turning the hub. (b) Cutting tool, ¾-in. square, was of T15 high speed steel.

Fig. 15. Production of dies for forging transmission gears (Example 709)

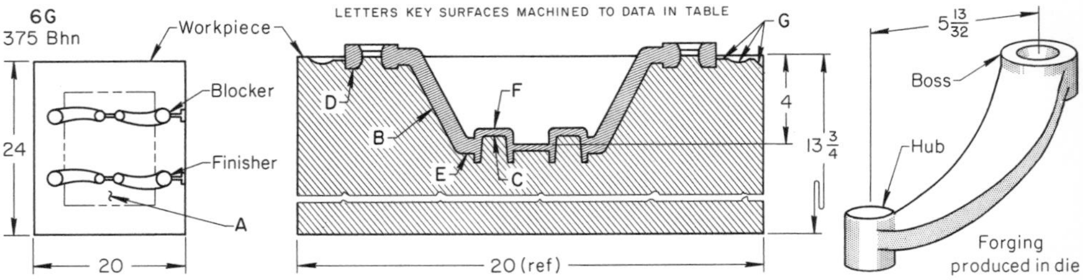

Operation(a)	Length of cut, in.	Depth of cut, in.	Speed Rpm	Speed Sfm	Feed, ipm	Machining time, min(b)
Mill locks, surface A(c)	13	0.750	154	50	2.66	1200
Mill arms, 8 surfaces B(d)	11	0.400	237	46	Hand	160
Machine hubs, 2 surfaces C(e)	..	0.572	237	93	Hand	40
Mill bosses, 4 surfaces D(f)	..	0.437	237	112	Hand	120
Mill arms, 2 surfaces E(e)	2	0.390	237	59	Hand	20
Machine hubs, 4 surfaces F(g)	..	0.972	237	92	Hand	80
Mill gates, gutter, flash, 4 surfaces G(c)	80	0.155	154	50	Hand	120
						1740

Tools:	Surface(h)
1¼-in.-diam roughing cutter	A and G
⅞-in.-diam roughing cutter	E
1 15/32-in.-diam (5° draft) flat-bottom hub cutter	F
1 13/16-in.-OD (5° draft), 27/32-in.-ID (7° draft) shell cutter	D
¾-in.-diam (5° draft) cutter	B
1½-in.-diam special cutter	C

(a) All operations were performed in a 28-by-96-in. vertical milling machine, without cutting fluid. All tools were made of M2 high speed steel. (b) Total for both top and bottom dies where the operations applied to both. (c) Applies to both top and bottom dies. (d) Finishing and blocking impressions in both dies. (e) Finishing impression in bottom die only. (f) Finishing impressions in top and bottom dies. (g) Blocking and finishing impressions in top die only. (h) Identified in illustration.

Fig. 16. Production of dies for forging the workpiece shown (Example 710)

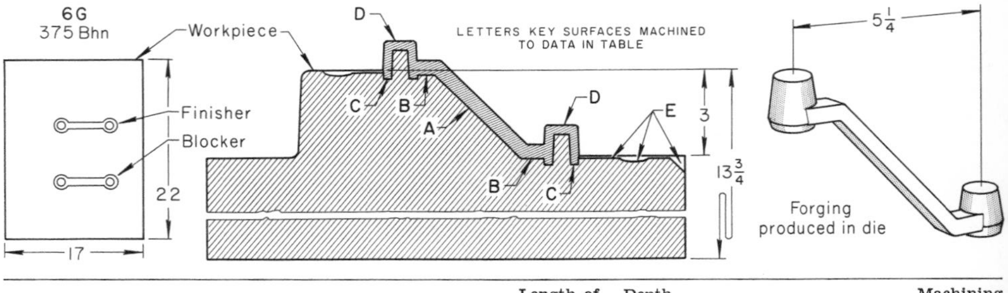

Operation(a)	Length of cut, in.	Depth of cut, in.	Speed Rpm	Speed Sfm	Machining time, min(b)
Mill arm (four), surface A(c)	9	0.375	237	54 max	120
Mill arm (four), surface B(c)	4	0.250	237	54 max	80
Sink socket (two), surface C(d)	..	0.320	122	55	40
Sink socket (four), surface D(e)	..	0.972	122	46	160
Mill gates, gutter, flash, surface E(f)	24	0.155	154	50	90
					490

Tools:	Surface(g)
⅞-in.-diam roughing cutter	A and B
⅝-in.-diam (5° draft) spiral cutter	A and B
1.710-in.-diam (5° draft) flat-bottom hub cutter	C
1.430-in.-diam (5° draft) flat-bottom hub cutter	D
1¼-in.-diam roughing cutter	E

(a) All operations were performed in a 28-by-96-in. vertical milling machine, using hand feed and no cutting fluid. All tools were of M2 high speed steel. (b) Total for both top and bottom dies where the operation applies to both. (c) Blocking and finishing impressions in both top and bottom dies. (d) Finishing impression, bottom die. (e) Blocking and finishing impressions, bottom die. (f) Applies to both top and bottom dies. (g) Identified in illustration.

Fig. 17. Production of dies for forging the workpiece shown (Example 711)

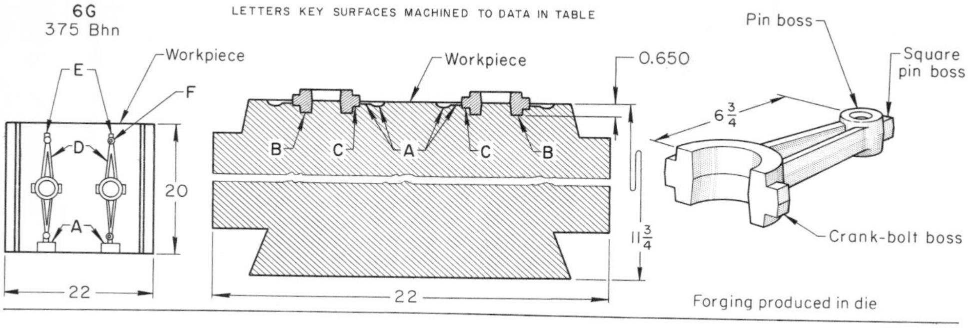

Area milled(a)	Length of cut, in.	Depth of cut, in.	Speed Rpm	Speed Sfm	Machining time, min(b)
Gates, gutter, flash, surface A(c)	24	0.375	190	62	45
Crank boss (four), surface B(d)	4	0.500	237	39	80
Crank-bolt boss, surface C(d)	1	0.300	237	39	240
Rib section, first cut, surface D(d)	10	0.250	237	31	320
Rib section, second cut, surface D(d)	10	0.060	237	39	160
Square pin boss, surface E(d)	$\frac{5}{8}$	0.543	237	39	80
Pin boss, surface F(e)	..	0.543	237	..	160
					1085

Tools:	Surface(f)
$1\frac{1}{4}$-in.-diam roughing cutter	A
$\frac{5}{8}$-in.-diam cutters (5° and 7° draft)	B, C, D (second cut), E
$\frac{1}{2}$-in.-diam cutters (5°, 7° and 10° draft)	D (first cut)
Two special preformed shell cutters	F

(a) All operations were performed in a universal die sinking machine, using hand feed and no cutting fluid. All tools were made of M2 high speed steel. (b) Total for both top and bottom dies where operations applied to both. (c) Applies to both top and bottom dies. (d) Applies to blocking and finishing impressions in both top and bottom dies. (e) Finishing impressions only in both top and bottom dies. (f) Identified in illustration.

Fig. 18. Production of dies for forging connecting rods (Example 712)

Example 709. Production of Dies From 6F7 (Fig. 15)

A 36-in. vertical turret lathe was used for turning and facing die blocks made of 6F7 tool steel (Fig. 15). The rough blocks, which weighed 118 lb, were machined at a hardness of 277 Bhn, and weighed 88.85 lb finished. After machining, the dies were heat treated to 388 to 401 Bhn. Tool details and machining conditions are tabulated below Fig. 15.

Examples 710, 711 and 712. Production of Dies from 6G

Example 710 (Fig. 16). A 28-by-96-in. vertical milling machine was used in the production of die blocks made of 6G tool steel. The lower die and the forging to be produced are illustrated in Fig. 16; machining conditions are tabulated below the illustrations. Blanks for these die blocks were 14 by 20 by 24 in., weighed 1900 lb each, and were machined at a hardness of 375 Bhn. The two finished blocks weighed 2776 lb, total.

Example 711 (Fig. 17). Die blocks for forging the part shown in Fig. 17 were machined from blanks of 6G tool steel at a hardness of 375 Bhn, using the same vertical milling machine (28 by 96 in.) employed in Example 710. The blanks, 14 by 17 by 22 in., weighed 1518 lb each. The finished die blocks weighed 2312 lb, total. Details are given in the table below Fig. 17.

Example 712 (Fig. 18). The die block shown in Fig. 18 was machined from 6G tool steel (375 Bhn) in a universal diesinking machine. Blanks were 12 by 20 by 22 in. and weighed 1530 lb each; finished die blocks weighed a total of 2356 lb. Details of machining operations and tools are given with Fig. 18.

Grinding of Tool Steel

*By the ASM Committee on Grinding and the ASM Committee on Machining of Tool Steel**

THE WIDE differences in composition among tool steels give rise to wide variations in grinding characteristics. The grindability index† is about 100 times as great for the easiest tool steel to grind as for the most difficult. This relation is evident in Fig. 1.

In general, the grindability index has direct significance only below some limiting value that decreases as the proportion of wheel wear ascribable to dressing increases. Indirectly, however, the grindability index can be helpful in rating a group of work materials, even when most of the wheel wear is through dressing. Thus, the indexes for a number of similar materials can sometimes be related to the number of pieces per dressing for a particular operation. Likewise, as size of wheel is increased relative to the area of the ground surface, the highest value of the grindability index that is directly significant becomes less, but the index may have indirect significance even though it exceeds the limiting value.

The grindability index is unimportant with easy-to-grind materials. It is much more important when difficult-to-grind tool steels are considered.

Because the grindability index is an inverse measure of wheel wear, its ranking of work materials can be used to predict the relative ease of maintaining dimensional accuracy and also the relative production rate, provided surface roughness or grinding damage are not controlling factors. These may be affected by entirely different properties of the work material than those that affect wheel performance. For example, the susceptibility of hardened steel to the formation of grinding cracks, known as grinding sensitivity, can be markedly affected by changes in the processing (especially heat treating) to which the steel is subjected before grinding. At the same time, these processing changes may have no effect on the grindability index. The relative ease of producing acceptable parts from different steels may depend on either the grindability index or the grinding sensitivity. A similar situation may arise with respect to the ease of producing a desired finish.

In operations such as cylindrical or thread grinding, in which the wheel normally wears only to a negligible extent before it has to be dressed, the grindability index has little or no significance.

Steel Classification for Grindability

Classification of steels as low, medium or high in grindability is usually precise enough for practical purposes. The classification of that kind shown in Table 1 correlates satisfactorily with the grindability index relationships of Fig. 1. All the steels shown in Table 1 as having low grindability are generally comparable with T15 (Fig. 1) in terms of grindability index. Similarly, the grades listed as "medium" are similar to D3, and those indicated as having high grindability usually show an index equal to, or slightly higher than, that of O2 (Fig. 1). Note that all the steels classified as having low grindability contain 3% or more vanadium; see also Fig. 2. Some tool steels that contain about 2% V plus cobalt additions, such as M43 and M44, are also difficult to grind and are placed in the "low" classification. See "Vanadium" in the following section "Effect of Steel Composition on Grindability".

In general, as the wear resistance of steel is increased, grindability is sacrificed. The abrasion-resistant high-vanadium high speed and die steels, when properly applied, offer considerably longer tool life than the lower-alloy easier-to-grind materials, and this helps to compensate for the extra cost in fabricating them into tools. But the use of a difficult-to-grind steel for an

* For committee lists, see pages 257 and 353.

† The grindability index of a material is a measure of the ease of removing stock by grinding, expressed in terms of wheel wear. Numerically it is equal to the grinding ratio obtained under a specified set of grinding conditions, the grinding ratio being the volume of work material removed per volume of wheel wear. The higher this index, the easier the material is to grind. This concept of grindability does not include grinding sensitivity, which is the susceptibility of the work material to cracking during or after grinding. Nor does this concept involve the ease of obtaining a good surface finish. (L. P. Tarasov, *Trans ASM,* 43, 1144, 1951).

Table 1. Relative Grindability of Tool Steels

Grindability	Steels
Low(a)	A7, D7, M3 (class 2), M4, M15, M43, M44, T3, T9, T15
Medium(b)	A2 to A6, A8 to A10, D1 to D5, H steels (and other hot work steels, such as 6G), M1, M2, M7, M10, T1, T4, F steels, P4
High(c)	O steels, W steels, S steels, L steels, P steels except P4

(a) Grindability index generally comparable with that for T15 in Fig. 1. (b) Grindability index generally comparable with that for D3 in Fig. 1. (c) Grindability index equivalent to, or greater than, that for O2 in Fig. 1. See also discussion of grindability index in first four paragraphs.

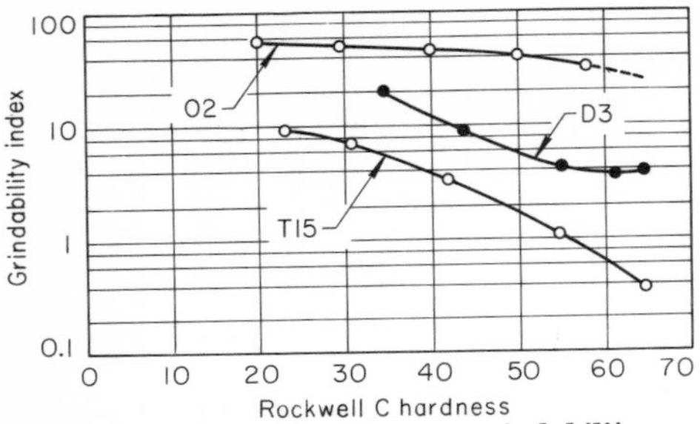

Fig. 1. Effect of hardness on grindability

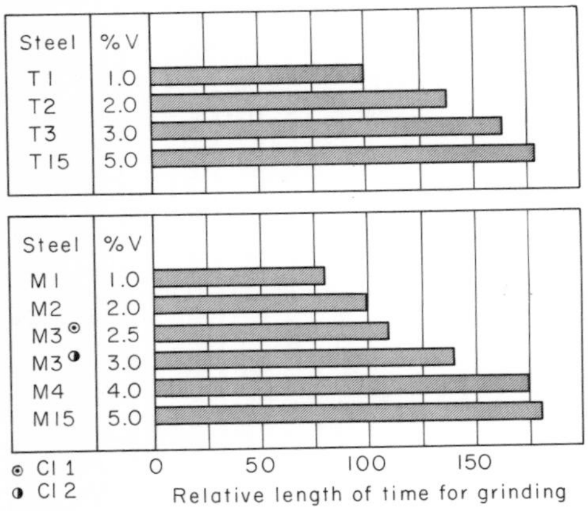

Fig. 2. Effect of vanadium content of high speed steel on grinding time required for removal of equal volumes of metal with the same type of wheel

intricate tool such as a tap, small twist drill, compacting die, or spline broach, may increase the cost of fabrication enough to defeat the application.

Effect of Steel Composition on Grindability

Ease of grinding after heat treatment is usually inversely proportional to the base hardness, the volume of carbide phase present, and the hardness of individual carbide particles. Steels containing high percentages of carbon and carbide-forming alloying elements are all difficult to grind. Tool steels relatively high in carbide-forming elements are more difficult to grind than the carbon or low-alloy types, even though hardness and carbon content may be higher for the low-alloy steels.

Vanadium has the greatest effect of all alloying elements on grindability, and all steels containing more than about 1% V are difficult to grind. Vanadium up to about 1% is soluble in austenite in most tool steel compositions, and little if any undissolved vanadium carbide remains in the normal heat treated structure. Beyond 1% V, however, excess undissolved vanadium carbide begins to appear in the microstructure, and the carbide particles increase rapidly in size and number at higher vanadium concentrations. T1 high speed steel contains only about 0.5% undissolved vanadium-rich carbide after conventional heat treatment, whereas T15 contains approximately 8% (F. Kayser and M. Cohen, Carbides in High Speed Steel—Their Nature and Quantity, *Metal Progress,* June 1952, p 79). Because of this relationship, increasing the vanadium content of a high speed steel from 1 to 4% by weight reduces the grindability index by a factor of close to 30, if there is enough carbon in the steel to convert the vanadium into vanadium carbide.

Vanadium carbides are relatively pure carbides formed during solidification of the steel; they contain very little iron or other metallic elements. These carbides have a hardness of 2300 to 2700 Knoop, averaging about 2500. Aluminum oxide grinding-wheel abrasive has a hardness of 1900 to 2900 Knoop, averaging 2440. The near equality in hardness of these two substances partly explains the difficulty in grinding high-vanadium steels.

Figure 2 shows the relative length of time for grinding high speed steels of different vanadium contents. The same relative time to grind T1 and M2 steels is indicated, even though M2 has a higher vanadium content. However, wheel wear is greater when grinding M2 than when grinding T1, and this factor has not been taken into consideration in the presentation of data on grinding time. The adverse effect of vanadium on grindability is reflected also in the grindability-index comparison plotted in Fig. 3.

Chromium. Although less potent than vanadium, chromium also has a marked effect on grindability index. In the A and D series of cold work die steels, the same effects of vanadium on grindability have been observed as in high speed steel. A7 and D7, however, are difficult to grind not only because of the high volume of vanadium carbide present but also because of the presence of a large number of complex iron-chromium carbides. The effect of chromium on grindability index is indicated in Fig. 4.

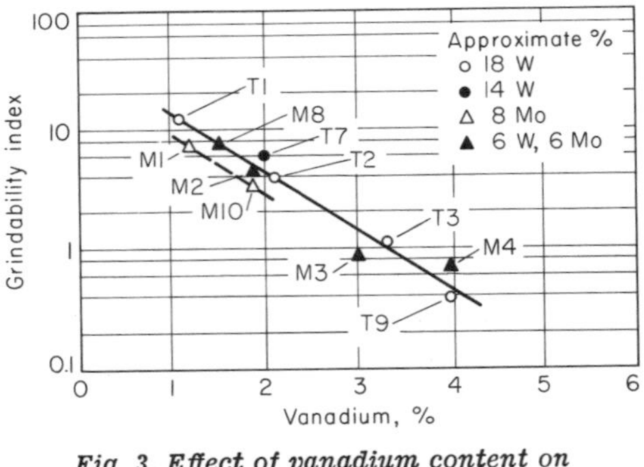

Fig. 3. Effect of vanadium content on grindability

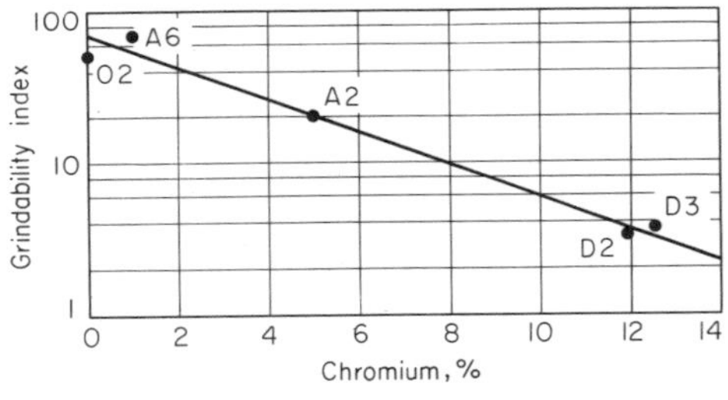

Fig. 4. Effect of chromium content on grindability

Sulfur. The effect of sulfide inclusions in tool steel appears to be predominantly chemical in nature; sulfide inclusions greatly reduce wheel wear without marked degradation of the mechanical properties of the steel. In the hardened condition, sulfurized tool steels have better grindability than the same grades without sulfur. Data are summarized in Tables 2 and 3.

Effect of Hardness of Steel on Grindability

Grindability of tool steel decreases as hardness increases. However, the magnitude of the difference contributed by hardness varies considerably with different compositions.

For tool steels that contain few if any particles of alloy carbide, such as the W and O types, hardness has a relatively small effect on grindability index, as indicated in Fig. 1. For instance, O2 steel has a grindability of 60 at a hardness of Rockwell C 20 (annealed), but as hardness is increased to Rockwell C 60 the grindability decreases to about 30.

The decrease in grindability index with increasing hardness is more pronounced (on a logarithmic scale) for the more highly alloyed tool steels such as D3 and T15 (Fig. 1). For instance, the grindability index for T15 is only about 10 in the annealed condition (Rockwell C 23), and decreases rapidly to about 0.6 at Rockwell C 60. Thus, it is always more economical to do as much of the grinding as possible prior to heat treatment. However, from the relations of grindability index and hardness shown in Fig. 1, it is evident that whether stock is removed in the soft or the hard condition is more critical for highly alloyed steels like T15.

Effect of Hardness on Finishability

Hardness influences the surface finish that results from grinding of tool steel when other factors remain the same. Factors that increase grindability generally cause a rougher finish. Figure 5 shows relations of hardness and surface roughness for one of the easier-to-grind steels (O2) and one of the more highly alloyed and more difficult-to-grind steels (D3). For both steels, surface roughness increases as hardness decreases. However, this increase is more pronounced for O2 than for D3. To maintain a constant surface

Table 2. Effect of Sulfurization of Tool Steel on Grindability (a)

Steel	Grindability index: Regular grade	Sulfurized (b)	Increase, %
Dry Grinding			
M2	17	34	100
M3 (class 1)	5.5	15.4	180
M4	2.8	9.5	240
Wet Grinding			
M2	6.4	9.6	50
M3 (class 1)	2.7	4.2	60
M4	0.9	2.1	130
D7	0.9	3.1	240

(a) Data are for surface grinding; source: L. P. Tarasov, Grinding Sulfurized Tool Steels, *Tool Engineer,* Feb 1959. (b) Free-machining.

Table 3. Effect of Sulfurization and Hardening Temperature of M3 High Speed Steel on Grindability (a)

Temp, F	Dry grinding: Regular grade	Sulfurized (b)	Wet grinding: Regular grade	Sulfurized (b)
Grindability Index				
2210	5.7	18.7	2.9	4.4
2240	5.5	15.4	2.7	4.2
2270	5.5	14.6	2.5	3.2
Net Power Input (c)				
2210	8.7	8.3	10.8	10.3
2240	9.2	8.9	10.6	10.2
2270	10.2	9.2	10.7	9.4

(a) L. P. Tarasov, Grinding Sulfurized Tool Steels, *Tool Engineer,* Feb 1959. (b) Free-machining. (c) Expressed in arbitrary units.

roughness, it is necessary to change to a harder wheel for the softer steels, which is in keeping with general grinding practice.

Effect of Steel Composition on Grinding Cost

In the production of intricate tools and dies where considerable finish grinding after heat treatment is involved, the cost of finish grinding can be an important consideration. Usually this is of greater significance than is the comparative machinability or workability of the steel in the annealed state. Finishing operations that involve form grinding, thread grinding or the internal grinding of small holes separate the difficult-to-grind tool steels from the easy-to-grind grades more than does surface grinding of flats. However, in surface grinding of the more abrasion-resistant and longer-wearing grades of high speed steel and die steel, the rate of wheel wear often equals or exceeds the rate of metal removal. The consequent wheel dressing in part accounts for the higher costs.

An example of relative cost is indicated by the data in Fig. 6. The higher cost of grinding H12 compared with O2 is attributable to the more rapid loading of the grinding wheel in grinding H12 at Rockwell C 48 than with O2 at Rockwell C 60. T4, because of its higher tungsten, vanadium and cobalt contents, is not only more costly to grind but the metal removed costs more.

General Practice

Equipment for grinding tool steel is seldom different from that used for similar operations on other metals. Equipment is discussed in detail in the article "Grinding", which begins on page 257 in this volume.

Selection of Wheel. Composition and hardness of the tool steel being ground, workpiece shape, and tolerance and finish requirements are significant factors in selecting a grinding wheel for a given application. The type of grinding operation may also influence the characteristics of the wheel used (Table 4). Details of the ASA system of grinding wheel identification, as well as of a modified system used in these articles, and a more complete discussion of grinding wheels, are given in the article "Grinding". (Structure number has been omitted from some wheel designations in this article.)

In most grinding applications on tool steel, aluminum oxide wheels are used. Silicon carbide wheels are sometimes used for grinding tool steels that have an extremely low grindability index.

Selection of abrasive grain size depends mainly on the surface finish required. As grain size decreases, finish improves, but the rate of metal removal usually decreases. Wheels having grain size as coarse as 36 are used for rough grinding. Grain sizes of 60 to 80 are most common for finish grinding. Much finer grain sizes are available for special applications such as roll and thread grinding.

As in the grinding of production steels, softer wheels are normally used for the harder materials, and vice versa. Most tool steels are ground in the hardened condition, for which soft to medium-grade wheels are selected because wheel breakdown should be rapid, to expose new cutting edges of the abrasive. Hard wheels are likely to glaze and burn the surface of hardened steel. Wheels softer than E in a porous structure or H in a normal structure are seldom used on tool steel.

Selection of wheels for thread grinding does not necessarily follow the pattern for other types of tool steel grinding, because it is important to minimize the rate of wheel breakdown to keep the wheel accurate in thread form. Therefore, wheels of R to Z hardness are commonly used for thread grinding.

Structure (density) numbers from 5 to 9 are common, and a majority of wheels fall within this range. Structure numbers, specified by each manufacturer, are related to other wheel characteristics and to the specific operation. Structure numbers are not necessarily related to the hardness of the steel being ground.

Vitrified bond is the most widely used for grinding tool steel. Such a bond is strong, has a high yield in terms of metal removal rate, is not affected by any grinding fluid and resists all temperature changes normally involved in grinding operations. With some exceptions, a vitrified-bond wheel should be operated at speeds not exceeding 6500 sfm.

Wheels bonded with resinoid are generally less efficient for grinding tool steel than those having a vitrified bond. However, the resinoid bond is

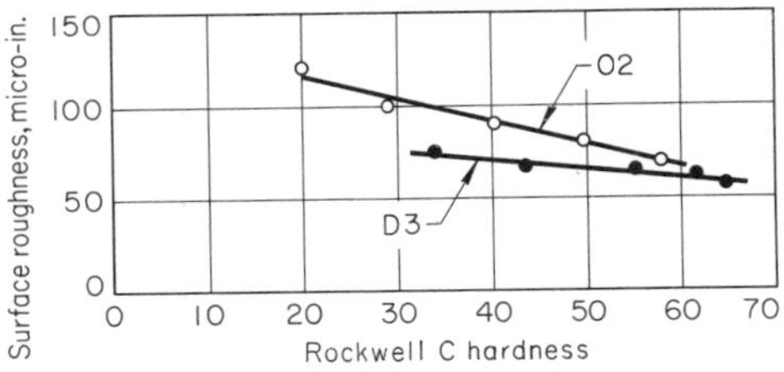

Fig. 5. Effect of hardness on ground finish

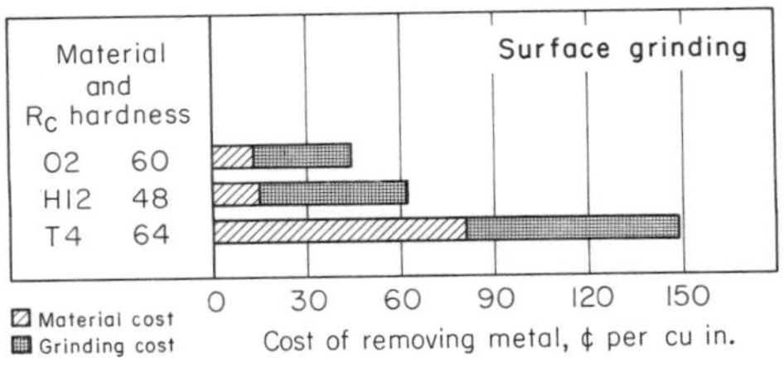

Fig. 6. Effect of composition of tool steel on grinding cost

Table 4. Typical Conditions for Grinding of Tool Steel

Operating condition	Work material condition and hardness: Annealed (150-275 Bhn)	Quenched & tempered (R_c 56-65)
Surface Grinding (a)		
Wheel classification	A_s-46-I-V	A_s-46-I-V
Wheel speed, sfm	5500-6500	5500-6500
Table speed, sfm	50-100	50-100
Downfeed, in. per pass:		
Roughing	0.002	0.002
Finishing	0.0005 max	0.0005 max
Crossfeed, fraction of wheel width per pass	1/5	1/10
Cylindrical Grinding (b)		
Wheel classification	A_s-46-K-V	A_s-46-L-V
Wheel speed, sfm	5500-6500	5500-6500
Work speed, sfm	60	50
Infeed, in. per pass:		
Roughing	0.002	0.002
Finishing	0.0005 max	0.0005 max
Traverse per work rotation, fraction of wheel width:		
Roughing	1/2	1/4
Finishing	1/6	1/8
Centerless Grinding (c)		
Wheel classification	A_s-60-M-V	A_s-80-L-V
Wheel speed, sfm	5500-6500	5500-6500
Work feed, in./min	50	50
Infeed, in. per pass:		
Roughing	0.005	0.005
Finishing	0.0015 max	0.0015 max
Regulating wheel:		
Angle	3°	3°
Speed, rpm	30	30
Internal Grinding (d)		
Wheel classification	A_s-80-L-V	A_s-80-L-V
Wheel speed, sfm	5000-6500	5000-6500
Work speed, sfm	75-150	75-150
Infeed, in. per pass:		
Roughing	0.0005	0.0005
Finishing	0.0002 max	0.0002 max
Traverse per work rotation, fraction of wheel width:		
Roughing	1/3	1/3
Finishing	1/6	1/6

(a) Applicable to all tool steels except A7 and the D, T, M and F groups when they are quenched and tempered. For these groups an A_s-60-I-V wheel is recommended. (b) Applicable to all tool steels except A7, D7, T9, T15, M3, M4, M15 and the F group when they are quenched and tempered. For these steels either an A_s-46-J-V, or a C-46-J-V should be used, and traverse for rough grinding should be no more than 1/8 wheel width per work rotation.

(c) Applicable to all tool steels except A7 and the D, T, M and F groups when they are quenched and tempered. For these steels, infeed per pass should be no more than 0.003 in. per pass for roughing and 0.001 in. per pass for finishing. For grinding A7, D7, T9, T15, M3, M4, M15 and the F group in the quenched and tempered condition, an A_s-80-K-V wheel should be used. (d) Applicable to all tool steels in all conditions. (Data are adapted from tables compiled by Metcut Research Associates, Inc.)

stronger than the vitrified and thus can be safely operated at higher speeds. Wheels with resinoid bond are often used for centerless and thread grinding of hardened tool steel and also for cutting off, slotting, and flute grinding.

Rubber-bond wheels are often used in specialized applications such as flute grinding. Rubber bonds have the disadvantage of being affected by oil.

Shellac-bond wheels are useful for roll grinding and for producing burr-free edges on cutting tools. Shellac is adversely affected by alkaline fluids.

Speed. Most tools and other workpieces made of tool steel are ground at speeds of 4000 to 6500 sfm. However, the specific grinding operation, as indicated in the section "Types of Grinding", is a major factor in selection of wheel speed (see Table 4).

Grinding Fluid. Most tool and cutter grinding (sharpening) is done dry and some internal, external and surface grinding is done dry. In most other grinding of tool steel, however, one of the following fluids is used: (*a*) soluble-oil emulsion, (*b*) synthetic solution, or (*c*) grinding oil.

Emulsions of about one part soluble oil to 25 to 40 parts water are the fluids most widely used for grinding tool steel. For grinding threads, or for operations involving heavy cuts and hard wheels, specially compounded oils give greater accuracy and smoother finish.

In some applications in which the conventional use of a flow of grinding fluid is not practical, oil or a water-base fluid sprayed into a mist and directed over the work has proved effective. Compressed air has also proved effective for applications where liquids are impractical.

In some applications, careful selection among grinding fluids is necessary to obtain desired results. The following example describes one such instance.

Example 713. Soluble-oil Emulsion vs Straight Oil for Centerless Grinding

Bars of annealed tool steel (¼-in. diam by 12 ft long) were ground in a centerless grinder using soluble oil mixed 1-to-60 with water as grinding fluid. The grinding wheel was A_s-80-N5-V and operated at 1200 rpm. The regulating wheel (A_s-80-R2-R), 12 in. in diameter by 6 in. wide with a 5-in.-diam arbor hole, was angled 7° and operated at 130 rpm. A tungsten carbide work-rest blade having a top angle of 30° was placed 3/32 in. above the centerline of the grinding wheel, to support the workpiece.

Use of the soluble-oil mixture with stock removal of 0.001 in. per pass produced a poor surface pattern containing deep spiral marks. Because of this poor finish, the ground bars were rejected. When straight oil was used, bar finish was acceptable; the bars had a uniform finish without spiral marks, even when stock removal was increased to 0.006 in. per pass. With the straight oil, the grinding ratio was 96; there was no measurable taper; maximum workpiece runout was 0.0002 in. TIR; and abrasive cost $0.03 per 12 ft of bar.

Types of Grinding

Grinding of tool steel includes surface, cylindrical, centerless, internal, thread and flute grinding, and sharpening or clearing of tools. Flute grinding is used mainly in the manufacture of taps, drills and reamers. Sharpening or clearing is used for finishing or reconditioning various tools, and seldom involves removal of much stock.

Surface grinding of tool steel is commonly done in both of the principal types of surface grinders: horizontal spindle and vertical spindle. (For a description of the two types, see the article "Grinding", in this volume.) The first method is more flexible in accommodating various workpiece shapes and sizes, and the second is especially well adapted to the grinding of many identical pieces in one load, as in grinding the sides of milling cutter blanks. Lower speeds (often as low as 4000 sfm) are used in reciprocating-table operations, where it is difficult to keep grinding fluid trained on the working surfaces or where workpiece sections are thin, or both. The surface grinding of knives made of carbon tool steel is an application in which extreme care (including low speed) is necessary. One advantage of rotary-table grinding is the ease of supplying a flood of grinding fluid to the critical areas.

Cylindrical grinding of workpieces between centers is extensively used for tool steel, because of the large number of round tools that require grinding of two or more diameters. This type of grinding is least likely to damage workpieces, because of the small area of contact between wheel and workpiece. Minimum contact makes possible most efficient use of the grinding fluid and, therefore, the use of speeds as high as allowable for the particular wheel. Speed of workpiece rotation in grinding tool steel is essentially the same as in cylindrical grinding of any other metal (75 to 150 sfm is a common range). Stock removal per pass may be as high as 0.005 in. on the diameter in the rough grinding of hardened tool steel, and from 0.0005 to 0.001 in. in finishing.

Table 5. Centerless Grinding of W1 Drill Rod (Example 714) (a)

Wheel classification	A_s-70-P7-B
Wheel size	20 by 6 by 12 in.
Operating Conditions	
Wheel speed	1220 rpm (6375 sfm) (b)
Feed (lineal), roughing	12 fpm
Feed (lineal), finishing	8 fpm
Stock removal, roughing	0.006 in. (c)
Stock removal, finishing	0.004 in. (c)
Grinding fluid	Soluble oil:water (1:40)
Roughing time per piece	1 min
Finishing time per piece	1½ min

(a) Twelve-foot lengths of cold drawn rod, annealed (Rockwell B 95 to 100), were ground in a No. 2 centerless grinder, to reduce diameter from 0.291 in. to 0.281 in. (b) Speed of regulating wheel, 29 rpm. (c) From diameter.

Centerless grinding is used in preference to cylindrical grinding on centers when the workpiece shape permits. It is not applicable if more than one diameter is to be ground, or if a shoulder or protuberance interferes.

Internal grinding involves greater contact of wheel and workpiece than external grinding. Thus, there is more possibility of surface damage. Although this danger exists for internal grinding of all metals, it is more critical for highly hardened tool steel. Common practice is to use a wheel diameter no more than 90% of the diameter of the bore to be ground when the bore diameter is smaller than 1 in. For grinding of bores larger than 1 in., the wheel diameter should be no more than 70% of the bore diameter.

Stock removal per pass must be light (seldom more than 0.0005 in. on the diameter) or burning may result. When it is impractical to use grinding fluid, as when fluid would impair the operator's vision into small holes, prevention of damage from excessive heat may be difficult. Under these conditions, air-blast cooling is sometimes used.

Thread Grinding. Practice for thread grinding of tool steel is not necessarily different from that for grinding of threads in production steels of similar hardness; see the article "Thread Grinding", page 127 in this volume. Thread grinding of tool steel is often critical, because of the end use. For instance, in grinding the cutting teeth in taps from the hardened solid, extreme care must be used to avoid burning the crests of the teeth.

A relatively fine grit is ordinarily used for grinding threads in hardened tool steel (note Examples 730 and 731 in Table 8). The type of bond depends largely on the accuracy required. Vitrified wheels give greater accuracy because they deflect less than resinoid-bond wheels. The latter are used where high production rate is more important than accuracy.

A constant flood of grinding oil over the area being ground is mandatory for successful thread grinding. Water-base cutting fluids are unsuitable for thread grinding.

Flute Grinding. Spiral or straight flutes are often ground in tool blanks after heat treatment, rather than being cut in a prior milling operation. Grinding is preferred for producing accurate flutes. However, because of the relatively long contact between the wheel and the work and because the wheel is buried in the work, this method calls for extreme caution.

In most applications, relatively hard aluminum oxide resinoid-bond wheels are used. Larded grinding oil (or some type specially compounded for the purpose) is recommended over water-oil emulsions, which are used for most other grinding operations. Details of typical flute grinding practice are given in Table 8, in the section on High Speed Steels.

Sharpening or clearing is needed in final finishing of new tools, as well as in reconditioning almost all types of cutting tools and many types of dies.

Machines for this use are special in most instances; tools like end mills and cutters need one type, whereas drills need a different type of machine.

Hand grinding of tools is not recommended, because it is impossible to obtain accuracy as high as in machine grinding, and damage to cutting edges is more likely in hand grinding.

Examples of wheel selection and other processing details for sharpening drills and cutters are given in Table 8, page 374. See also text on page 373.

W, O, S and L Steels

Although there is considerable variation in grindability among steels in the W, O, S and L groups, they are all within the general classification of high-grindability steels (Table 1). Depending on hardness, a grindability index approximating that shown for O2 in Fig. 1 can be expected.

All tool steels are to some degree susceptible to tempering from overheating during grinding. However, the W, O, S and L steels are more susceptible than the more highly alloyed steels. Surface hardness begins to decrease from the maximum value when these steels are heated higher than 250 or 300 F.

Specific practices are indicated in the following four examples:

Example 714. Centerless Grinding of W1 Drill Rod (Table 5)

In two passes in a No. 2 centerless grinder, 12-ft lengths of cold drawn W1 rod (annealed; Rockwell B 95 to 100) were ground from a diameter of 0.293/0.289 in. to 0.2815/0.2805 in., before being cut into shorter lengths for tool blanks. (This is common practice for producing lengths of tool steel that are free of decarburization, straight, and within desired diametral tolerance. This method often is more economical than cutting the long lengths into pieces and then grinding the pieces individually in a later stage of manufacturing small tools.) Before being ground, these rods weighed 2 lb, 11 oz each.

The 12-ft lengths of rod were laid flat on a table and were automatically discharged, one at a time, into a power-roll feed trough. In grinding, each rod was driven by the regulating wheel, set at a 5° inclined angle, which provided the feed motion and held the rod rigidly against the grinding wheel and guide throughout the operation. Additional details of this operation are given in Table 5.

Example 715. Surface Grinding of O1 (Fig. 7)

A horizontal-spindle surface grinder with a reciprocating magnetic worktable was used for removing 0.003 in. from each of two sides of interposer stops made of O1 tool steel and hardened to Rockwell C 62. The workpiece and setup are shown in Fig. 7. Because of the relatively small area of each workpiece, 180 of these parts could be loaded on the magnetic table; the shape of the parts made supporting blocks unnecessary when the workpieces were stacked as shown in Fig. 7 (alternating open and closed ends). A slow downfeed (0.0002 in. per pass) was necessary for parallelism of the two ground sides. Wheel details and operating conditions are tabulated with Fig. 7.

Example 716. Grinding Threads in O1 Lead Screws

A standard thread grinder was used to grind 1–8 threads a distance of 7¼ in. in lead screws made of O1 tool steel and hardened to Rockwell C 58. Wheels 17 by ⅜ by 10 in., A_s-120-L3-V, were used in this operation. Wheel speed was 6200 sfm; workpieces were rotated at 15 rpm. Seven passes, using 0.010 in. infeed per pass, were required to grind threads in these lead screws at a rate of one screw per hour. Grinding fluid was thread-grinding oil.

Example 717. Dimensional Variation in Cylindrical Form Grinding of O2 (Fig. 8)

Workpieces illustrated in Fig. 8 were ground from the solid in one cylindrical grinding operation with a wheel dressed by a crush roll. As also shown in Fig. 8, the two grooves were required to be within +0.0005, −0.0000 in. and the ground diameter was allowed a variation of +0.001, −0.000 in.

The graph in Fig. 8 shows how the two dimensions varied within one wheel dressing; after grinding of 60 to 65 parts, redressing was required, to prevent the grooves from going out of tolerance, even though the 1.114-in. diameter had increased only a minute amount.

Grinding time was 65 sec per piece or 41 pieces per hour at 85% efficiency. Eighteen to 22 crushings were obtained per roll regrind.

A and D Steels

With the exception of A7 and D7, the cold work tool steels of the A and D groups are classified as "medium" in grindability (Table 1). Although there

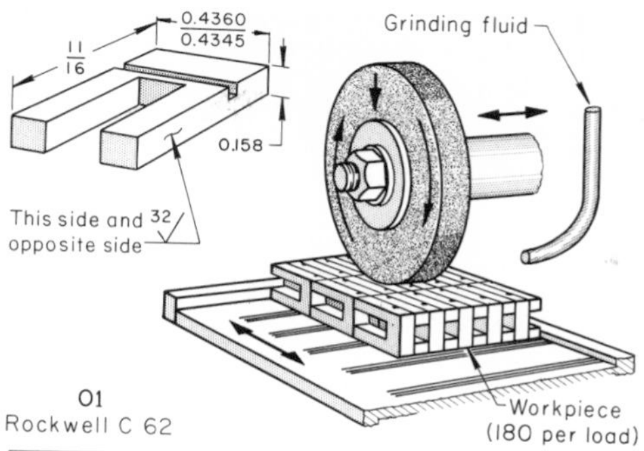

Wheel classification	A_s-46-I8-V
Wheel size	10 by 1½ by 3 in.

Operating Conditions

Wheel speed	1800 rpm (4700 sfm)
Downfeed	0.0002 in. per pass
Traverse speed	100 fpm
Depth of cut	0.003 in. per side
Grinding fluid	Soluble oil:water (1:40)
Production rate	360 pieces per hour
Wheel life per dressing(a)	180 pieces, one side

(a) Wheels were dressed with a single-point diamond tool before each final pass.

Fig. 7. Surface grinding of interposer stops made of an O1 tool steel (Example 715)

is considerable variation within the group, a grindability index approximating that for D3 (Fig. 1) can be expected. The variation in chromium content among the different types will have some effect on grindability, as indicated in Fig. 4. The amount of vanadium in the A and D steels (other than A7 and D7) is not sufficient to affect grindability significantly.

Because they contain 4% or more vanadium, A7 and D7 are classified as "low" in grindability (Table 1), and a grindability index approximating that shown for T15 in Fig. 1 can be expected. Steels such as A7 and D7 are used where resistance to abrasion is necessary, and thus are expected to be extremely low in grindability.

Hot Work Steels (H Types)

The chromium, tungsten and molybdenum hot work steels are generally classified as "medium" in grindability (Table 1). Steels 6G, 6F2 and others in the group denoted as "Other Alloy Tool Steels" (see composition table on page 354) also are classified with the H steels in grindability. A grindability index approximating that of D3 shown in Fig. 1 would be expected for the higher-alloy steels in the H group, and a somewhat higher index for the lower-alloy steels such as 6G or H10.

There are some differences in grinding a low-alloy steel like 6G (total alloy content, about 2.50%) and in grinding the highest-alloy steel of the group (H26, with an alloy content of 23%). However, none of these steels contains more than about 2% V, which is a major factor affecting grindability. In addition, all hot work steels are relatively low in carbon content (0.65% is the highest, and most of them have less than 0.55%). Therefore, massive carbides are not likely to occur. These steels are seldom harder than Rockwell C 55 when they are ground. Thus their grindability is generally better than that of tool steel hardened to Rockwell C 60 or higher.

Loading of the grinding wheel is a greater problem in grinding the hot work steels than in grinding high-carbon tool steels, and more frequent dressing of wheels is usually required. Selection of soft (K or softer) aluminum oxide wheels that have a structure of 5 or lower in density is usually helpful in minimizing wheel loading.

Typical practice employed in the surface grinding and internal grinding of hot work tool steels is demonstrated in the following two examples.

Example 718. Surface Grinding H11 (Fig. 9)

An H11 steel key (Rockwell C 50 to 53) originally was ground to produce 0.020/0.010-in. radii at the bottom corners of the slot, as shown at the left in Fig. 9. This required rough and finish grinding of the sides and bottom of the slot, and caused excessive scrap because of surface damage by the hard (grade L) grinding wheel that had to be used to hold tolerance on the radii.

Changing the design to incorporate ⅛-in. undercuts in the slot, as shown at the right in Fig. 9, made possible the use of a softer grinding wheel, eliminated rejections, and increased the production rate from 1½ to 3 pieces per hour. In this method, first the sides of the part were ground with the ⅛-in. radii, then the bottom of the slot was ground with another wheel. Processing details for the improved method are given with Fig. 9.

Example 719. Internal Grinding of H11 (Table 6)

Details of operation for internal grinding of H11 pistons at Rockwell C 53 to 55 are given in Table 6. These pistons were 21.560 in. long and, before grinding, 11.280 in. in inside diameter. Grinding increased the inside diameter to 11.310 in.

High Speed Steels

The T and M types of high speed steel comprise a group of about 30 members. The lower-alloy, general-purpose types are generally classified "medium" in grindability (Table 1). However, this depends to some extent on their carbon content. The 1.0% carbon grades of M2, M7 and M10 are very close to M3 (class 2) in grindability (Table 1). The more highly alloyed types, particularly those containing 3% or more vanadium, are "low" in grindability and will have a grindability index near that shown for T15 in Fig. 1.

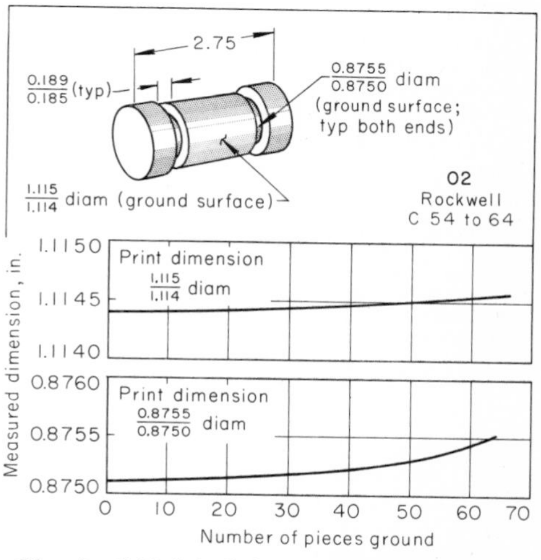

Fig. 8. Cylindrical form grinding of two diameters. Graph shows dimensional change in the 0.875 and 1.114-in. diameters during grinding of 60 to 65 pieces without wheel dressing. (Example 717)

The low grindability and consequent high grinding cost of the highly alloyed steels are major factors in deterring their more widespread use.

A more recent development in high speed steels is the M40 group. These grades can be heat treated as high as Rockwell C 70 in small sections, but are less difficult to grind than the high-vanadium types like T15, which are two or three points lower in hardness. The reason for the appreciably better grindability of the M40 steels is that they do not contain the large amounts of the extremely hard and abrasion-resistant particles of vanadium carbide that are present in T15.

The M40 steels, all heat treated to approximately the same hardness, differ considerably among themselves in grindability, presumably because of differences in the amount and hardness of the carbide particles present.

As shown in Table 7, the grindability of the M40 steels is distributed over most of the range between that of T15 on the low side and M2 on the high side. Measurements of grinding power showed the 46-grit wheel to be somewhat harder than the 60-grit wheel, although both wheels were well within the normal hardness range for H-grade wheels. The consistently lower grinding ratios obtained with the coarser grit size indicate that 60 grit was superior to 46 grit from the standpoint of stock removal for all these steels. That is, more material was removed at the same power consumption.

This is equivalent to removing the same amount of material at a lower power level, which is the same as saying that the 60-grit abrasive is cooler cutting than 46 under these grinding conditions. A cooler-cutting wheel is less likely to damage the work surface, and since a finer grit size normally results in a better finish, 60 grit is superior to 46 with respect to both grinding damage and surface finish. In many applications, however, a cooler-cutting wheel will produce a poorer finish and the relative quality of two wheels will then depend on whether it is more important to minimize grinding heat at the same production rate or to obtain a better finish.

Similar power comparisons have shown that the 80-grit wheel was a little softer than the 60-grit wheel, which accounts for the somewhat lower grinding ratios obtained with the finer wheel for all the steels except M1. When the slight grade difference between the two wheels was taken into account, the 60-grit abrasive was found to be slightly cooler cutting than the 80-grit material for the T15, M44 and M42 steels, while the reverse was true for M2, M41 and M43 steels. The finer grit was markedly superior for the M1 steel, as shown in Table 7.

These results illustrate two conditions. First, in grinding two high speed steels of the same type having essentially the same grindability rating under a specified set of grinding conditions, one wheel may perform better on one steel and another one on the other steel. Second, the grindability ratings of two similar steels may differ by a small amount for one wheel and considerably for another, as can be seen by comparing the grinding ratios for the M1 and M2 steels and the three grit sizes.

Present knowledge on the effects of alloying elements on the grindability of high speed steel can be summarized as follows:

1 Vanadium carbide has a pronounced effect in reducing grindability.
2 Iron-tungsten carbide, in which molybdenum may substitute for part or all of the tungsten, has very little effect in comparison with vanadium carbide.
3 Reducing the hardness of the steel by tempering increases the grindability. The effect is small for a change of a few points on the Rockwell C scale but can be quite large if the hardness is reduced considerably below the range in which these steels are used in practice.
4 Sulfurizing the steel to make it free-machining can increase the grindability appreciably. The degree of improvement appears to be affected by the grindability of the steel in the unsulfurized condition, but the results are contradictory as to whether high speed steels of low or high grindability benefit more from sulfur.
5 Cobalt moderately reduces the grindability of high speed steel.
6 In molybdenum high speed steel, raising the tungsten content and reducing the molybdenum appears to decrease the grindability.
7 The mechanisms by which vanadium and sulfur affect grindability are understood but this is not yet true of tungsten, molybdenum or cobalt.

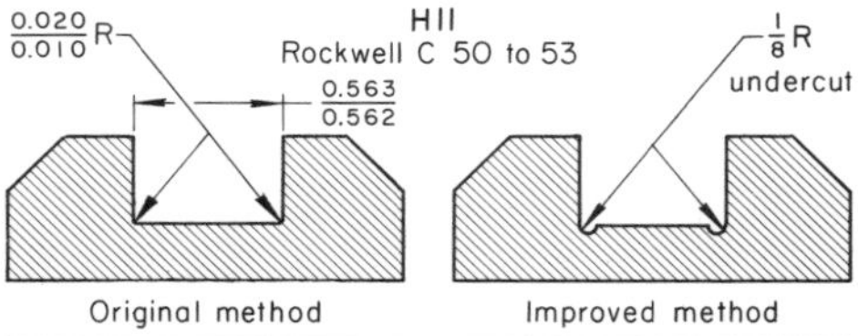

Machine	Surface grinder(a)
Wheel classification	A_s-60-K5-V
Wheel size	12 by ½ by 3 in.

Operating Conditions

Wheel speed	1700 rpm (5300 sfm)
Traverse speed	56 passes per minute
Stock removed per pass	0.001 in.
Total depth of cut	0.020 in.
Grinding fluid	Soluble oil:water (1:3)
Tolerance	+0.001, −0.000 in.
Finish specified	32 micro-in. max roughness
Production rate	3 pieces per hour
Wheel life per dressing	10 pieces

(a) 1½-hp, horizontal spindle; 10-by-36-in. table

Fig. 9. Change in surface grinding method, substituting undercuts for radii in the slot, for elimination of rejects. Processing conditions tabulated are for the improved method. (Example 718)

Table 6. Internal Grinding of H11 Pistons (Example 719)

Machine	Extended-bridge internal grinder, 42-in. swing
Wheel classification	A_s-46-I8-V
Wheel size	8-in. diam, 2-in. thickness

Operating Conditions

Wheel speed:	
Roughing	2850 rpm (5950 sfm)
Finishing	2100 rpm (4400 sfm)
Work speed:	
Roughing	24 rpm (70 sfm)
Finishing	17 rpm (50 sfm)
Infeed:	
Roughing	0.001 in. per pass
Finishing	0.0005 in. per pass
Traverse rate:	
Roughing	50 sfm
Finishing	40 sfm
Depth	0.015 in. per side (21.56-in. length)
Stock removed	11.474 cu in.
Grinding fluid	Soluble-oil emulsion
Grinding time per piston	40 min

Table 7. Grinding Ratios for High Speed Steels

Steel	Hardness, R_C	Ratio for wheel type: A_s-46-H8-V	A_s-60-H8-V	A_s-80-H8-V
T15	65.7	0.49	0.62	0.51
M44	67.7	0.97	0.99	0.88
M41	68.7	1.2	1.6	1.4
M43	67.5	1.4	2.2	1.7
M42	68.8	4.8	6.5	3.8
M2	64.9	6.1	7.2	6.7
M1	64.9	7.8	8.0	11.9

For grinding hardened high speed steel in a horizontal-spindle, reciprocating surface grinder.

Typical practices followed in grinding high speed steel are described in the examples that follow.

Examples 720 to 737. Summary of Practice in 18 Applications and 7 Methods (Table 8)

Eighteen applications that typify grinding practice used for four general-purpose high speed steels and one higher-alloy type (M36) are presented in summarized form in Table 8 (page 374). These examples include all seven of the general methods of grinding.

Aluminum oxide wheels were used without exception. Other wheel characteristics varied to some extent, depending on conditions. Abrasive grain sizes of 60 to 80 were used for grinding hardened tools, except for form grinding (thread and flute) for which a finer grain was selected. A coarser grain was used for grinding the soft cutter blanks (Example 721), and for resharpening twist drills (Example 736). Exclusive of thread and flute grinding, for which hard wheels were used, a wheel hardness of H to N was chosen, except for Example 722 where a D hardness was used for cylindrical grinding.

In all instances of grinding hardened steel except Example 735 wheels having a density of 4 to 10 were used. For grinding the soft cutter blanks in Example 721, density was much lower (16). Vitrified-bond wheels were chosen in all of the examples except thread or flute grinding, where resinoid or rubber bond was used.

The example that follows describes internal grinding of one of the more highly alloyed high speed steels:

Example 738. Internal Grinding of M4

Heading-die inserts made of M4 high speed steel at Rockwell C 62 to 63 were ground to a finished inside diameter of 1.1255/1.1250 in. Length of the insert bore was approximately 2 in. overall.

A silicon carbide wheel (C-60-I7-V), ¾ by ⅝ by ¼ in., was used for roughing, during which a total of 0.006 in. was removed from the diameter at 0.0002 in. per pass. Rough grinding resulted in a surface finish of 25 to 30 micro-in. Finish grinding was done with a similar wheel except the grit size was 120 and removed a total of 0.002 in. from the diameter at 0.0002 in. per pass, after which the surface finish was 8 to 10 micro-in. For both roughing and finishing, wheel speed was 4300 sfm and the workpiece was rotated at 100 sfm.

Tool steel parts are sometimes made by form grinding with wheels shaped by a crush roll on an arbor. A typical procedure is described in the following example:

Example 739. Form Grinding of M2 (Fig. 10)

The spherical end of the workpiece shown in Fig. 10 was produced by a form grinder equipped with a collet containing a stop and adapter for holding the workpiece and with a crush roll on an arbor. The workpiece was made of sulfurized M2 high speed steel hardened to Rockwell C 63 to 66. Grinding formed the 21° 30′ angle, the 0.050/0.040-in. radius, and the 0.3750/0.3745-in.-diam spherical surface (which had to be spherical within 0.0004 in.). The ground shape had to be concentric with the locating diameter within 0.002 in. TIR. The amount of stock removed varied from 0.023 to 0.015 in. Other processing details are given with Fig. 10.

F Steels

The carbon-tungsten special-purpose tool steels (F types) are classified as "medium" in grindability, despite their relatively low alloy content. They are all high in carbon content and are nearly always used in the fully hardened condition (Rockwell C 65 to 67), thus placing them lower in grindability than the W or L types.

Grinding practice for the general-purpose types of high speed steel (see Table 8) is satisfactory also for grinding the F types.

P Steels

The low-carbon mold steels are seldom ground in the soft condition. Steels P1 through P6 commonly are carburized, hardened and tempered, after which a grinding operation is required for correcting dimensions. Steels P20 and P21 also are hardened before being ground. Provided reasonable care is exercised to avoid grinding burn, overheating, and heavy grinding of sharp internal angles, these steels, with the exception of P4, are rated "high" in grindability (Table 1). In general, the grinding characteristics of the carburized surfaces are comparable to those of 1% C water-hardening tool steel or to low-alloy tool steel. Because of its higher chromium content, however, carburized P4 is more susceptible to grinding burn and cracking, and hence is usually classified as "medium" in grindability (Table 1).

APPENDIX

Sharpening High Speed Steel Tools

High speed steel tools are most commonly sharpened by grinding with semifriable wheels of aluminum oxide abrasive. The grade of wheel used for sharpening usually is the same as for general grinding of the same steel. Straight, cup, or dish wheels are used. Typical wheel selections are given in Table 8 (Examples 734 to 737). Diamond wheels may be used to sharpen tools of high speed steel that contains more than 4% vanadium (such as T15).

Speed and Feed. Speeds for sharpening are usually 4000 to 6500 sfm, depending on the tool and the amount of stock to be ground off. The slower speeds reduce the danger of burning the tool. Feed per sharpening pass is like that for a finish pass in production grinding (0.0005 in.), although it may be as much as 0.003 in. (Table 8).

Grinding fluid is seldom needed in sharpening because so little metal is removed. Dry grinding permits better visibility of the work, for better control. Grinding fluid may be a help when appreciable stock is to be ground from a tool. Soluble oil with water (1 part oil to 15 of water) or a spray mist may be used.

Stoning the edges that have been sharpened extends tool life while causing the tool to make smoother cuts with less friction. Stones come in grit grades to suit the grit grade of the grinding wheel. Stoning is done by stroking the stone toward the cutting edge.

Single-point tools usually are easier to sharpen than rotary tools. Surfaces that rub the workpiece need the most grinding. Except for severe cratering, back rake and side rake need no regrinding until the tool has been made enough shorter so that rake is affected. Round-nose tools are sharpened in a swivel fixture.

Drills wear by rounding of corners, followed by wear of the lips and the chisel edge to a cone. Because wear accelerates with continued use of a dull drill, sharpening should not be postponed. For instance, a 1-in. drill cut 100 holes before becoming so dull that it refused to cut. The margins had worn undersize a distance of one inch back from the point, so that the drill had to be shortened an inch in sharpening. If it had been sharpened after 75 holes, the margin wear would have affected only one third of an inch, permitting two more sharpenings, or 225 holes instead of 100, for equal tool use.

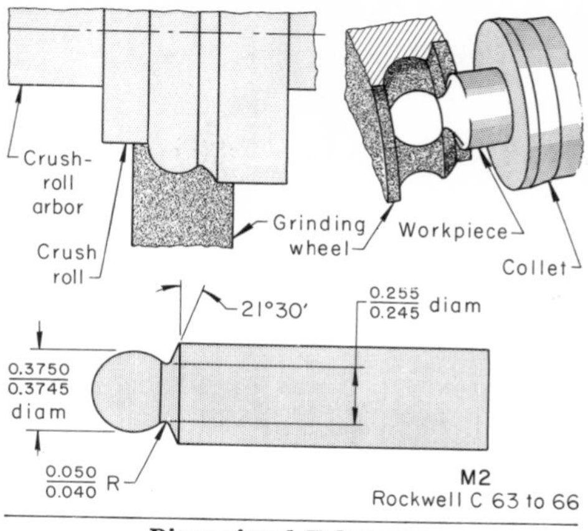

Dimensional Tolerances

Diameter of sphere	+0.0000, −0.0005 in.
Roundness of sphere	Within 0.0004 in.
Angles	±1°
Radius	±0.005 in.
Concentricity	0.002 in. TIR (a)
Finish	8 micro-in. max roughness

Wheel Details

Wheel classification	A_s-220-M9-V
Wheel size	24 by 1 by 12 in.

Processing Conditions

Wheel speed	1115 rpm (7000 sfm)
Feed rate	0.015 in. per min
Grinding fluid	Grinding oil
Production rate	42 pieces per hour
Wheel life per dressing	100 pieces
Total wheel life	80,000 pieces

Costs per Piece

Grinding wheel	$0.003
Labor	0.250
Grinding fluid, other supplies	0.008

(a) Ground shape had to be concentric with locating diameter within 0.002 in. TIR.

Fig. 10. Cylindrical form grinding of M2 high speed steel using a crush-trued wheel (Example 739)

The chisel edge is restored when the drill is sharpened. The point and lip relief are reground in a drill grinder that has a cam for straight or cone relief. Straight relief gives a straight chisel edge and cone relief a slightly S-shaped chisel edge. Cone relief is better for self-centering than is straight relief.

Webs of twist drills usually become thicker from point to shank, so that the web near the point is thicker after the drill has been shortened. The web should be thinned, especially at the point, preferably in a web-thinning grinder.

Reamers usually need sharpening only on the starting chamfer. This can be done by any of three methods: (*a*) holding the reamer by the shank and grinding with a cup wheel while rotating the reamer to grind the chamfer, (*b*) rotating the chamfer against a straight wheel, and (*c*) holding the reamer between centers and rotating it while the chamfer is ground. Taper in a taper reamer must be ground first, and then the chamfer.

Taps usually need sharpening only at the tip, but sometimes the flutes must be ground. The tap is held between centers in a universal grinder, and the back of the land is held against a tooth rest.

Milling cutters must be sharpened on arbors or on centers and held by the shank. Plain cutters are sharpened by grinding a narrow land behind the cutting edge on the periphery. The land is at an angle to the tangent at the cutting edge. This is done either with a straight grinding wheel or with a cup wheel. Either way, the clearance is ground by offsetting the axis of the wheel to suit while the cutting edge is held fixed.

The narrow land is ground to the clearance angle. The amount of offset for a given diameter of cutter and a given clearance angle can be found in charts supplied by makers of cutter grinders. It may be simpler to set the clearance angle by use of a clearance-setting dial on the grinder.

Profile cutters that are not form relieved are sharpened by grinding radial relief, side relief, chamfer and radius. The three kinds of radial relief are: flat, concave and eccentric.

Flat relief is produced by the face of a cup wheel. The degree of relief is controlled by rocking the cutter. Concave relief is produced by the periphery of a straight wheel. The amount of concavity is a function of wheel diameter. Degree of relief may be varied by adjusting offset or changing wheel diameter. Eccentric relief, applicable only to helical cutters, differs from concave relief in production only in that the wheel periphery is dressed at an angle, or the wheel is tipped at an angle to the cutter axis. The degree of relief is varied by changing the angle of wheel inclination or the angle dressed on the wheel. Staggered-tooth cutters also may be ground in a similar manner, except that a double-beveled tooth rest is usually used.

Side relief may be ground on profile cutters, either to a sharp edge or to a narrow margin.

Chamfers on corners usually are sharpened with the cutter fixed in position. Radii (concave, convex, or at a corner) can be sharpened with the cutter held as for sharpening chamfers, but so that the cutter swings to generate the radius against the grinding wheel.

Form-relieved cutters are sharpened by grinding only on the face of the teeth; thus a tooth rest cannot be used against the face of a tooth for positioning the cutter in sharpening. The cutter is positioned and indexed in one of three ways:

1. By an index head connected to the cutter by arbor or by the shank. This method gives accurate spacing of cutter teeth.
2. By a fixed stop or indicator for each tooth in succession. This method may give less accurate spacing of cutter teeth than the index-head method.
3. By a stop that is positioned against the back of each tooth. A ground spot may be provided on the back of each tooth for this purpose, by the cutter maker.

Face-milling cutters are sharpened like peripheral cutters. Face mills up to 8 in. in diameter may be mounted on the work head of a grinder. Larger face mills are ground in an indexing fixture.

End mills usually are reconditioned by sharpening the relief and the clearance surfaces of the peripheral teeth, causing a reduction in the diameter of the cutter. To avoid this decrease in size, end mills may be sharpened by grinding the flute face and fillet to remove the wear land and restore the shape of the flute. A disadvantage of this method of sharpening is the possible generation of excessive heat, so that extra care is needed to prevent harm to the cutter. If the end mill has centers it can be held between them; otherwise the cutter must be held by the shank.

End teeth of end mills are sharpened by first grinding the intersection of the peripheral and the end teeth. The end mill can be held in a chuck and rotated against a flat or a cup wheel (for a square end) or against a concave radius-dressed wheel (for a ball end). The primary relief and secondary relief are then sharpened on the end teeth.

Counterbores and spotfacers are sharpened by grinding the end cutting edges only. As these edges are repeatedly sharpened, the chip spaces become smaller. It is therefore necessary periodically to grind additional chip spaces in front of the cutting edges.

In common practice, the first step is to grind the large relief (usually 30° to 40°), leaving the desired width of land (normally 1/16 in.) and reestablishing the original chip space. The machine is then reset for grinding the desired primary relief angle, which is ordinarily 6° to 8°. All cutting edges must be equally sharp and evenly located, because any projecting teeth will be overloaded, probably resulting in tool breakage.

Table 8. Typical Grinding Practice for High Speed Steels (Examples 720 to 737)

Example number	Workpiece: Steel	Workpiece: Hardness, Rc	Workpiece: Name; and dimensions, in. (D = diam; L = long)	Stock removed, in.	Wheel classification (and size, in.)	Wheel speed: Rpm	Wheel speed: Sfm (approx)	Feed, in.	Grinding fluid	Time per piece	Other processing data
Surface Grinding											
720	M1	65	Cutoff blades; 8 by 1 by ⅛	0.005 per side	A_s-60-I10-V (10 by ¾ by 1¼)	2500	6600	0.001/pass	Soluble-oil: water (1:40)	6 min	2 blades were ground at one time
721	M1	240 Bhn	Cutter blanks; 8¼ D by ¼ L	0.025 per side	A_s-30-H16-V (18 diam) (a)	720	3400	0.016/min	Synthetic: water (1:50)	3¾ min(b)	Table rotation 18 rpm
Cylindrical Grinding											
722	M10	65	Reamer blanks; 0.316 D, 6 L	0.008, for 4½-in. length	A_s-60-D8-V (20 by 1½ by 8)	1200	6300	0.001/pass	Soluble-oil: water (1:40)	40 sec	8 passes; work was rotated at 154 rpm
723	M10	45	4-flute end mill; 1D	0.018, for 2-in. length	A_s-80-L9-V (24 by 2 by 12)	1100	6800	0.0018/pass	Soluble-oil: water (1:40)	18 sec	10 passes; work was rotated at 75 rpm
724	M36	65	Twist drills; 0.875 D, 17 L	0.018	A_s-80-L9-V (24 by 2 by 12)	1100	6800	0.0015/pass	Soluble-oil: water (1:40)	35 sec	6 passes; work was rotated at 120 rpm
Centerless Grinding											
725	M10	65	Reamer blanks; 0.258 D, 6 L	0.007, rough; 0.001, finish	A_s-80-N6-V (20 by 8 by 12)	1140	5900	0.0004/sec	Soluble-oil: water (1:25)	18 sec(c)	Feed wheel rotated at 15 rpm
726	M10	65	Twist drills; 15/32 D, 7½ L	0.013, rough; 0.002, finish	A_s-80-N6-V (20 by 8 by 12)	1140	5900	0.001/sec	Soluble-oil: water (1:25)	20 sec	Feed wheel rotated at 12 rpm
727	M10	20	Solid blank; 1 D, 9 L	0.015, one operation	A_s-80-N6-V (20 by 10 by 12)	1140	5900	0.0015/sec	Soluble-oil: water (1:25)	15 sec	Feed wheel rotated at 12 rpm
Internal Grinding											
728	M2	65	Spiral mill(d); 4½ OD, 2 ID, 6 L	0.008 per side	A_s-60-K6-V (2 by ½ by ⅜)	11000	5700	0.0002/pass	None	30 min(e)	Work was rotated at 70 rpm
729	M10	65	Sleeve; 2⅛ OD, 1.5 ID, 3 L	0.010 on ID	A_s-80-N6-V (1⅜ by ½ by ⅜)	14000	5100	0.0002/pass	None	20 min	Work was rotated at 125 rpm
Thread Grinding											
730	M2	45	Tap; ⅞–14	(f)	A_s-150-R9-B (17 by ⅜ by 10)	1750	7800	0.015/pass(g)	Thread-grinding oil	4 min	(h)
731	M7	65	Tap; ⅝–18	(j)	A_s-150-Z4-B (17 by ⅜ by 9)	2000	8900	0.012/pass(g)	Thread-grinding oil	2 min	(h)
Flute Grinding											
732	M1	65	4-flute end mill; ⅜ D	Flutes formed	A_s-100-O8-B (18 by ⅜ by 8)	2500	12000	4/min	Grinding oil	1 min	One pass per flute
733	M10	65	Jobber's drill; ⅛ D	Flutes formed	A_s-80-O-R (18 by 0.2 by 8)	2500	12000	15/min	Larded grinding oil	12 sec	One pass per flute
Sharpening or Clearing											
734	M2	65	6-flute end mill; 2 D	(k)	A_s-60-I8-V (3¼ by 2¾ by 1½) (m)	5000	4250	0.001/pass	None	2¾ min	(k)
735	M2	65	Side mill(n); 6 D, ½ wide	0.007 by 1-in., each tooth(n)	A_s-60-J0-V (3¼ by 2¾ by 1½) (m)	5000	4250	0.002/pass	None	9 min(p)	2 passes (1 roughing, 1 cleanup)
736	M10	65	Twist drill; ¾ D	0.010(q)	A_s-46-L5-V (8 by 5½ by 2) (r)	2300	4800	0.002/pass	Soluble-oil: water (1:15)	4 min	....
737	M10	65	Jobber's drill; ¼ D	0.005 to 0.007(q)	A_s-60-I8-V (5 by 3½ by 1) (r)	3600	4700	0.003/pass	Soluble-oil: water (1:15)	30 sec	....

(a) Eight-segment wheel. (b) Eight pieces (16 sides) were ground in 30 min. (c) 12 sec for roughing, 6 sec for finishing. (d) 2-in.-long bearing was ground in each end. (e) 15 min per bearing. (f) ⅞–14 thread was ground for 37/64-in. length on shank. (g) For three roughing passes; one final 0.001-in. pass was made for finishing. (h) Grinding was done in three roughing passes (with work rotated at 30 rpm) and one finishing pass (with work rotated at 50 rpm). (j) ⅝–18 thread was ground for 1⅞-in. length on shank. (k) Six edges were ground on both sides; stock removal, each edge: 0.007 to 0.008 in., one side, 0.0005 to 0.001 in., other side. (m) With ½-in. cup. (n) 28 teeth. (p) For both sides. (q) Resharpening. (r) Plate mounted.

MACHINING OF STAINLESS STEEL AND HEAT-RESISTING ALLOYS

CONTENTS

Machining of Stainless Steel

*By the ASM Committee on Machining of Stainless Steel**

PROPERTIES of stainless steels that make them more difficult to machine than carbon steels are:

1 The tensile strength of annealed stainless steel is generally higher than that of annealed carbon steel.
2 Compared to hot rolled or annealed carbon steel, the spread between yield strength and tensile strength is usually greater for annealed stainless steel.
3 Most grades of stainless steel have a higher rate of work hardening than carbon steel.
4 The higher-carbon grades of stainless steel (notably types 440A, B and C) contain substantial amounts of free particles of alloy carbide, which increase machining difficulty by hardening the matrix and cause greater tool wear because of the abrasiveness of the particles.

Austenitic steels such as 302, 303, 304 and 316 have tensile strengths of 85,000 to 90,000 psi in the annealed condition. This range is about the same as that of 1045, 1050 and 1055 carbon steels. Of greater importance, however, is the spread between tensile and yield strengths, which is much greater for austenitic stainless steels than for low-carbon or medium-carbon ferritic steels. Tensile and yield strength ranges for two grades of stainless, one carbon steel, and a brass are compared in Fig. 1. The marked spread between tensile and yield strengths indicated for annealed type 303 in Fig. 1 causes "gumminess" in machining, which results in buildup on tool edges, poor finish, excessive heat and short tool life.

Heavier feeds and slower speeds are used for machining austenitic stainless steels than are used for carbon steels, in order to avoid work hardening and reduce tool buildup. A tripod punch is preferred to a conventional center punch for locating holes to be drilled, to prevent work hardening of the spot first touched by the drill. Chip-curler tools also are recommended for machining all austenitic grades (particularly the high-alloy grades, such as type 309), which produce exceptionally tough and stringy chips.

Martensitic Grades. Annealed low-carbon grades of martensitic stainless, such as type 410, have machining characteristics generally similar to those of annealed low-carbon alloy steels such as 8620. The hardness range, however, is usually higher for annealed low-carbon martensitic stainless steels, and therefore more power is needed for machining these stainless steels.

For many applications, type 410 or similar grades of martensitic stainless steel must be machined in the quenched and tempered condition (usually in the hardness range of Rockwell C 26 to 32). Machining at this hardness requires a proportionate increase in power and decreased speed and feed. Although tool life decreases with increasing hardness, excellent surface finish and accuracy can be obtained when machining the lower-carbon martensitic grades in the above hardness range.

Higher-carbon martensitic grades, such as types 420 and 440 (particularly type 440C), are increasingly difficult to machine for two reasons: (*a*) hardness of the annealed steels is relatively high (195 to 230 Bhn), and (*b*) particles of hard chromium carbide are present. The high hardness of annealed types 414 and 431 (235 and 260 Bhn, respectively) also makes these steels difficult to machine. Consequently, the higher-carbon grades as well as types 414 and 431 require more power for machining than the lower-carbon martensitic grades. Tool life is shortened because of the presence of abrasive carbide particles in the work metal, or high hardness, or both. Machining practices for these more difficult-to-machine grades are generally similar to those used for the higher-carbon alloy tool steels (see the article "Machining of Tool Steel", which begins on page 353).

Ferritic grades that contain less than 18% chromium, such as types 405 and 430, have good machining characteristics because the structure is somewhat brittle, causing good chip breakage.

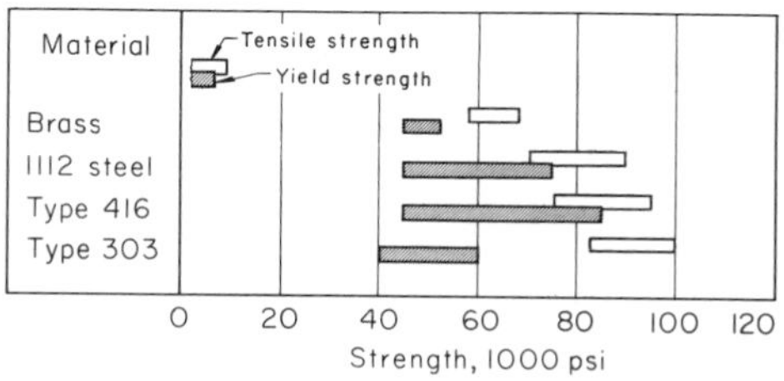

Fig. 1. Ranges of tensile and yield strengths for two grades of stainless steel, compared with the same for carbon steel and brass

*WALTER O. DOW, JR., *Chairman,* Plant Manager, Manning Products Co., Sunbeam Corp.; S. P. COOK, Chief Industrial Engineer, DeLaval Separator Co.; CHARLES A. DIVINE, JR., Metallurgist, Stainless Steels, Carpenter Steel Co.; R. DOUGHTON, JR., Supervisor of Product Development, Stainless and Strip Div., Jones and Laughlin Steel Corp.

EDWARD T. GALE, Laboratory Supervisor, Sunbeam Corp.; JOHN V. GOULD, Manufacturing Engineering, Research and Development Section, Hamilton Standard Div., United Aircraft Corp.; L. EDWARD JORGENSEN, General Superintendent, Equipment Div., Pennsalt Chemicals Corp.; H. K. KEEVER, Management Consultant, Case and Co., Inc.

JAMES F. MAHONEY, Manufacturing Engineer, Small Steam and Gas Turbine Div., Westinghouse Electric Corp.; GEORGE J. STEVENS, Machining Engineer, Metallurgical Dept., Baltimore Works, Armco Steel Corp.; JENS L. WENNBERG, Manager of Machinability Services, Therm Electric, Inc.; I. H. WHEELER, JR., Methods Engineer, Machining, Chattanooga Div., Combustion Engineering, Inc.

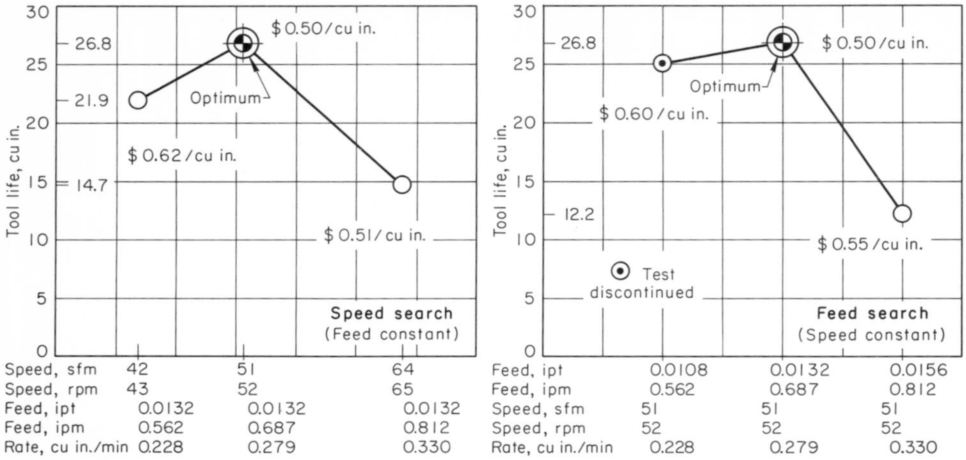

Fig. 2. Influence of speed and feed on tool life and cost of face milling PH 15-7 Mo age hardened to 200,000-psi tensile strength (Rockwell C 43). Cutters were T15 high speed steel.

Table 1. Comparisons of Tool Life, Metal Removal Rate, and Cost of Machining PH 15-7 Mo (200,000 Psi) and 4130 (100,000 Psi) in Twelve Machining Operations

Machining operation	Tool life, cu in. of metal removed		Rate of metal removal, cu in. per min		Rate of PH 15-7 Mo removal relative to 4130, %	Cost per cubic inch	
	4130	PH 15-7 Mo	4130	PH 15-7 Mo		4130	PH 15-7 Mo
Face milling	63.0	26.8	2.67	0.279	10.5	$0.06	$ 0.50
End milling	207.0	73.0	4.4	0.42	9.5	0.04	0.32
Straddle milling	270.0	25.5	4.87	0.675	13.9	0.15	1.37
Turning	576.0	60.4	11.5	1.32	11.5	0.01	0.10
Threading 1¼–12	4.8	0.3	0.297	0.112	37.7	0.88	2.34
Band sawing(a)	1220.0	156.0	5.25	1.4	26.7	0.06	0.23
Drilling, ¼-in. diam(b)	3.37	0.113	0.59	0.084	14.2	0.22	6.67
Drilling, ½-in. diam	10.3	1.53	1.44	0.101	7.0	0.09	1.64
Reaming, ¼-in. diam	1.179	0.063	0.021	0.008	38.1	6.16	25.55
Reaming, ½-in. diam	1.937	0.0785	0.0402	0.007	17.4	3.26	20.25
Tapping, ¼–28, through	0.46	0.0595	0.092	0.009	9.8	6.59	29.37
Tapping, ½–20, through	0.782	0.1640	0.1764	0.040	22.7	1.99	10.15
Average for all operations					18.2%	$1.63	$ 8.21

(a) Metal removal is in square inches. (b) Drill for PH 15-7 Mo was 0.199 in. in diameter and had a point angle of 118°; drill for 4130 was 0.250 in. in diameter and had a point angle of 135°.

These grades are classified with the lower-carbon types of martensitic stainless for machinability.

The high-chromium ferritic grades, like 446, are difficult to machine because they are "gummy" and chips are stringy. Machining these grades is similar to machining austenitic grades.

Precipitation-hardening grades vary considerably in machining characteristics because of differences in structure. They may be ferritic, austenitic or two-phase (semi-austenitic). The grades having ferritic structures are preferred for machining because the rate of work hardening is low and they are relatively brittle, resulting in good chip breakage. Because of the various heat treatments that are applied to precipitation-hardening grades, machining characteristics vary from being similar to the lower-chromium ferritic steels mentioned above, to being more nearly like the austenitic grades.

PH 15-7 Mo, one of the precipitation-hardening stainless steels having a semi-austenitic structure, has machining characteristics in the unhardened condition similar to those of an austenitic grade at the same strength level. Often, however, PH 15-7 Mo is machined at a tensile strength of 200,000 psi in order to produce parts within closer tolerances than could be obtained by machining before quenching and tempering. At this high strength, the rate of metal removal is low and tool life is short.

Relation of Machinability to Machining Cost

In machining precipitation-hardening grades, as well as other grades of stainless steel, machining costs increase as hardness increases. In an investigation to determine the difficulty and cost of machining, age-hardened PH 15-7 Mo at 200,000 psi tensile strength (Rockwell C 43) was compared with 4130 steel at 100,000 psi tensile strength (Rockwell C 15). Optimum speeds and feeds were first determined for machining PH 15-7 Mo, on the basis of cost per cubic inch of metal removed, by varying speed at constant feed and feed at constant speed. Results of one of these speed and feed searches are shown in Fig. 2.

Using the optimum feeds and speeds determined for PH 15-7 Mo in various machining operations, the investigation was continued to obtain comparisons of tool life, rate of metal removal, and cost per cubic inch of metal removed, as shown in Table 1. As expected, because of the great difference in strength, 4130 can be machined far more efficiently and at lower cost than PH 15-7 Mo. However, of equal significance is the variation in machinability among the different operations. For instance, Table 1 indicates that the cost of metal removal for PH 15-7 Mo was about 30 times that for 4130 when drilling a ¼-in. hole, but only about four times greater for reaming a ¼-in. hole.

Table 2. Steel Designations Used in Speed and Feed Tables in This Article

Designation(a)	Steels covered by designation
FM Fer	430F, 430F(Se)
FM Mar	416, 416F
FM Aus	303, 303Se, 303FF, 347F(Se)
Ferritic	405, 430, 434, 436, 442, 443, 446, 449, 502
Mar(410)	403, 410, 420, 501
Mar(431)	414, 422, 431
Mar(440)	418, 440A, 440B, 440C
Aus(304)	201, 202, 301, 302, 304, 304L, 305, 321, 347, 348
Aus(316)	302B, 309, 309S, 310, 310S, 314, 316, 316L, 317, 318, 329, 330
PH	17-4 Ph, 17-7 Ph, PH 15-7 Mo, AM-350, AM-355, AM-359
Cast FM	CF-16F (303), CN-7M
Cast Fer	CA-15 (410), CA-40 (420), CB-30 (431), CC-50 (446)
Cast Aus	CF-3 (304L), CF-3M (316L), CF-8 (304), CF-8C (347), CF8M (316), CF-12M (316), CF-20 (302), CG-8M (317), CH-20 (309), CK-20 (310)

(a) FM Fer = Free-machining ferritic; FM Mar = Free-machining martensitic; FM Aus = Free-machining austenitic; Mar(410), (431), (440) = Martensitic; Aus(304), (316) = Austenitic; PH = Precipitation hardening; Cast FM = Cast free-machining; Cast Fer = Cast ferritic (including martensitic); Cast Aus = Cast austenitic.

Additives for Free Machining

Sulfur, selenium, and lead (singly, or in combination) are added to some grades of stainless steel to increase machinability. Types 303, 416 and 430F are examples of free-machining grades.

Sulfur functions mainly to minimize tool-edge buildup, thus allowing greater speeds, reducing power requirements, and prolonging tool life. To some extent, selenium has the same effect as sulfur, although the main function of selenium is to improve surface finish. Lead is used to a limited extent as an additive to improve machinability of stainless steels.

Free-machining austenitic grades show about 15% improvement in machinability over other austenitic grades. For instance, types 301, 302 and 304 are commonly machined in turret lathes at speeds in the range of 75 to 100 sfm, using high speed steel tools. Type 303 (free-machining) can be machined at 90 to 115 sfm under the same conditions.

Additions of sulfur or selenium, or both, also improve machinability of the 400 series. For instance, types 416 and 430F have machinability ratings of about 85 compared with screw stock (1112) rated at 100. This machinability rating of 85 is substantially better than the ratings for the non-free-machining counterparts of types 416 and 430F (types 410 and 430, respectively). Tool life is also considerably better when machining types 416 or 430F than when machining types 410 and 430 under the same conditions.

The higher-carbon grades of the 400 series (types 420 and 440) are also available with free-machining additives. However, the influence of sulfur or selenium on the machinability of high-carbon grades is not so great as in low-carbon grades, because the abrasive carbide particles in the high-carbon grades cause rapid tool wear, regardless of free-machining additives.

Selection of a free-machining over a non-free-machining grade depends mostly on material versus machining costs. Other fabricating operations, as well as end use, must also be considered. These latter considerations are often minor. However, there have been applications in which free-machining additives impaired operations such as cold heading; under some service conditions, these additives have reduced corrosion resistance and strength.

Better surface finish is another economic consideration in the use of free-machining grades. In one example, small shafts made from type 410 required a second turning operation to attain the required finish. Changing to type 416 provided a suitable finish in the first turning. Savings in cost resulted from both increased machining speed and elimination of one operation.

The free-machining grades cost more. The difference for types 416 and 430F amounts to about $0.50 minimum per 100 lb (1 to 1.5% above base price). The cost increase for 303 may be 6% more above base price than for 302. Nevertheless, the extra cost for the free-machining stainless is readily justified if the parts are to be machined extensively, and particularly if the properties of the steel still fulfill the requirements of the service. Each application has to be considered separately, but when the generated scrap for a specific part exceeds about 10%, the free-machining grade should be considered.

Classification for Speed and Feed

Subsequent sections of this article present 18 tables dealing with nominal speeds and feeds for various machining operations on stainless steels. The wrought and cast stainless steels are classified into several groups bearing abbreviated designations. Table 2 lists the stainless grades that are classified under the various designations used in the speed and feed tables beginning with Table 4 in the section on Turning.

Table 3. Design of Single-Point Turning Tools for Stainless Steels Compared With Carbon and Alloy Steels (a)

Material	Brinell hardness	High speed steel and cast alloy tools: BR	SR	ER	SRF	ECEA	Carbide tools: Brazed BR	Brazed SR	Disposable BR	Disposable SR	ER	SRF	ECEA
Stainless Steels													
Free-machining	135 to 425 ..	5°	8°	6°	6°	5°	0°	6°	—5°	—5°	5°	5°	5°
Ferritic	135 to 185 ..	5°	8°	6°	6°	5°	0°	6°	0°	5°	5°	5°	5°
Austenitic	135 to 275 ..	0°	15°	6°	6°	5°	0°	6°	0°	5°	5°	5°	5°
Martensitic	135 to 200 ..	0°	15°	6°	6°	5°	0°	6°	—5°	—5°	5°	5°	5°
Martensitic	200 to 425 ..	0°	15°	5°	5°	5°	0°	6°	—5°	—5°	5°	5°	5°
Precipitation-hardening	150 to 440 ..	0°	15°	5°	5°	5°	0°	6°	—5°	—5°	5°	5°	5°
Carbon and Alloy Steels													
Plain carbon	100 to 225 ..	10°	12°	6°	6°	5°	0°	6°	—5°	—5°	5°	5°	5°
Alloy (b)	225 to 325 ..	8°	10°	6°	6°	5°	0°	6°	—5°	—5°	5°	5°	5°
Ultrahigh-strength	325 to 425 ..	0°	8°	6°	6°	5°	0°	6°	—5°	—5°	5°	5°	5°

(a) For an explanation of the abbreviations used for tool angles, see Table 1 in "Turning", page 4 in this volume. Nose radius and side cutting-edge angle will generally be dictated by type of operation being performed. When not specified, use 3/64-in. nose radius and 15° side cutting-edge angle. On insert-type tools with 15° side cutting-edge angle, the end cutting-edge angle will be 15°. High speed steel disposable inserts may be used with positive rake. Carbide holders have 0° back rake and 5° side rake. (b) Includes free-machining types.

Table 4. Nominal Speeds and Feeds for Turning Stainless Steels With Single-Point and Box Tools

Type of steel (a)	Condition (b)	Brinell hardness	Rough turning (c) (0.150-in. depth) Speed (sfm) of: HSS tools	Carbide tools: Brazed	Carbide tools: Disposable	Finish turning (d) (0.025-in. depth) Speed (sfm) of: HSS tools	Carbide tools: Brazed	Carbide tools: Disposable
FM Fer	Ann	135 to 185	150	500	575	170	560	640
FM Mar	Ann	135 to 185	150	500	575	170	560	640
	Ann or CD	185 to 240	140	450	515	160	500	575
	Q and T	275 to 325	70	325	375	80	375	425
	Q and T (e)	375 to 425	40	150	170	50	200	225
FM Aus	Ann	135 to 185	95	400	460	115	450	515
	CD	225 to 275	90	350	400	110	400	460
Ferritic	Ann	135 to 185	110	450	515	130	500	575
Mar (410)	Ann	135 to 185	110	450	515	130	500	575
	Ann	175 to 225	100	400	460	120	450	520
	Q and T	275 to 325	60	250	285	75	300	345
	Q and T	375 to 425	40	150	175	50	175	200
Mar (431)	Ann	225 to 275	70	300	350	85	350	400
	Q and T	275 to 325	55	225	260	80	275	315
	Q and T (f)	375 to 425	40	150	175	50	175	200
Mar (440)	Ann	225 to 275	60	275	315	75	335	385
	Q and T	275 to 325	50	200	230	60	240	275
	Q and T (f)	375 to 425	40	150	175	50	175	200
	Q and T (e)	R_C 48 to 52	20	100	115	30	125	140
	Q and T (g)	R_C 54 to 56	..	55	65	..	70	80
Aus (304)	Ann	135 to 185	80	275	315	100	335	385
	CD	225 to 275	75	250	285	95	300	345
Aus (316)	Ann	135 to 185	70	250	285	90	300	345
PH	Ann	150 to 200	65	275	315	85	335	385
	Hard	275 to 325	60	250	280	80	300	350
	Hard	325 to 375	55	225	250	75	275	310
	Hard (e)	375 to 440	35	150	175	40	175	200
Cast FM	Ann	140 to 170	80	325	400	110	400	500
Cast Fer	N and T	175 to 225	70	275	325	90	350	425
Cast Aus	Ann	140 to 190	50	225	275	65	275	325

(a) See Table 2 for types of steel in each group. (b) Ann = Annealed; CD = Cold drawn; Q and T = Quenched and tempered; Hard = Hardened; N and T = Normalized and tempered. (c) Feed, 0.015 ipr. (d) Feed, 0.007 ipr. (e) Feed, high speed steel and carbide, 0.010 ipr for roughing, 0.005 ipr for finishing. (f) Feed, high speed steel only, 0.010 ipr for roughing, 0.005 ipr for finishing. (g) Feed, carbide only, 0.005 ipr for roughing and finishing. (Data are adapted from tables compiled by Metcut Research Associates, Inc.)

Cutting Fluid

Machining stainless steel without a cutting fluid is usually restricted to low production quantities or to specific operating conditions in which use of cutting fluid is impractical, such as machining of large workpieces or complex shapes. Sometimes complex shapes are machined dry to avoid entrapment of fluid that would impair subsequent processing or service.

The use of a cutting fluid is more desirable for machining stainless steels than for machining carbon or alloy steels for two reasons: (*a*) stainless steels are generally less machinable than carbon or alloy steels, and (*b*) the lower heat conductivity of stainless steels increases the need for cooling.

Water-soluble oils (usually in proportions of 1 part oil to 12 to 20 parts water) and sulfochlorinated cutting oils (having a viscosity of 300 SUS maximum at 100 F) are the cutting fluids most widely used in machining stainless steels.

Soluble oils are used for most single-point tool operations such as turning and boring. Soluble oils cost less than sulfochlorinated oils, are easy to supply to the cutting area in copious amounts, and function as an acceptable means of cooling and flushing away chips. Soluble oils are also used successfully for milling, and for machining in turret lathes and bar and chucking machines when several operations take place consecutively or simultaneously (note Examples 776, 777 and 778).

Sulfochlorinated or other additive-type cutting oils are infrequently used for turning, boring or milling of stainless steels, although there are operating conditions for which sulfochlorinated oils have proved to be the best choice. Examples of such conditions are: excessively hard work metal, the use of high speed steel tools (because of interrupted cutting), and critical surface finish requirements.

Stainless steels are drilled with twist drills using soluble oil, although as the depth of hole increases the frequency of using sulfochlorinated or other additive oils increases. Soluble oil is usually used for reaming of stainless steels. Gun drilling or other deep-hole drilling of stainless steels is generally done with sulfochlorinated or other additive-type oils (see Example 760). When additive oils are used, viscosity should be no higher than 300 SUS at 100 F, in order to permit the necessary flow.

For broaching of stainless steels, best results are obtained with additive-type cutting oils. The same applies to tapping and to die threading. Soluble oil is used for sawing stainless steels.

Table 5. Nominal Speeds and Feeds for Turning Stainless Steels With Ceramic Tools

Type of steel(a)	Condition(b)	Brinell hardness	Rough turning (over 0.062-in. depth) Speed, sfm	Rough turning Feed, ipr	Finish turning (under 0.062-in. depth) Speed, sfm	Finish turning Feed, ipr
FM Fer	Ann	135 to 185	500 to 1000	0.005 to 0.012	650 to 1100	0.005 to 0.010
FM Mar	Ann	135 to 185	500 to 1000	0.005 to 0.012	650 to 1100	0.005 to 0.010
	Ann or CD	185 to 240	450 to 900	0.005 to 0.012	550 to 1000	0.005 to 0.010
	Q and T	275 to 325	350 to 700	0.005 to 0.015	400 to 800	0.004 to 0.010
	Q and T	375 to 425	150 to 500	0.005 to 0.015	200 to 600	0.004 to 0.010
Ferritic	Ann	135 to 185	300 to 700	0.005 to 0.020	400 to 900	0.005 to 0.010
Mar (all)	Ann	135 to 275	300 to 700	0.005 to 0.012	350 to 750	0.005 to 0.010
	Q and T	275 to 325	200 to 550	0.005 to 0.015	250 to 650	0.004 to 0.008
	Q and T	375 to 425	175 to 450	0.005 to 0.012	200 to 550	0.004 to 0.008
	Q and T	Rc 48 to 52	....	....	150 to 300	0.003 to 0.006
	Q and T	Rc 54 to 56	....	....	100 to 200	0.002 to 0.005

(a) See Table 2 for types of steel in each group. (b) Ann = Annealed; CD = Cold drawn; Q and T = Quenched and tempered. (SOURCE: same as for Table 4)

Turning

Single-point tools for turning the austenitic chromium-nickel grades must have adequate clearance to avoid work hardening of freshly cut surfaces. The back rake angle should be as large as permissible, to aid in breaking of chips. Chip breakers are helpful, but their design must be such that the cutting edges will not be weakened. Improperly designed chip curlers can cause chip crowding and tool damage (Example 6, in the article "Turning", shows the design of a chip-curler groove in a box tool used for turning type 304 stainless).

In Table 3, the design of single-point tools (made of high speed steel, cast alloy, and carbide) for turning stainless steels is compared with designs for turning plain carbon, alloy, and ultra-high-strength steels.

Speed and Feed for Single-Point Tools. The free-machining stainless steels (types 303, 416 and 430F) can be turned at speeds about 85% as high as those used for turning carbon steel screw stock (1113). Table 4 gives nominal speeds for rough and finish turning of stainless steels with single-point high speed steel and carbide tools, based on the specific feeds and depths of cut shown. Carbide tools permit faster speeds than high speed steel tools by a factor of three or more, but maximum rigidity in the machine and setup is mandatory. Interrupted cutting may damage carbide tools (see Example 5, involving type 410 stainless, in the article "Turning"). Speeds for cutting with cast alloy tools are between those for high speed steel and carbide tools.

Table 5 shows nominal speeds and feeds for use with ceramic tools in rough and finish turning of ferritic and martensitic grades of stainless steel. Ceramic tools permit higher speeds at similar feeds than carbide tools. However, rigidity of machine and setup is even more critical for ceramic than for carbide tools.

Rigidity is a major factor influencing speed, feed and depth of cut. To avoid unwanted vibration, surface conditions such as heavy scale may require changes in speed or feed from those given in Tables 4 and 5. In turning workpieces that are several times longer than their diameter, marked deviations from normal procedure or special techniques are also often required, to avoid vibration. Example 29, in "Turning", describes the machining of a type 416 stainless steel shaft with a spindle arrangement that provided necessary rigidity. The two examples that follow deal with conditions in which lack of rigidity was a problem with two other types of stainless steel.

Example 740. Turning a Forged 17-4 PH Shaft (Fig. 3)

Heavily scaled hammer-forged shafts 10 ft long and 8 in. in diameter made of 17-4 PH were turned at a hardness of 340 to 360 Bhn. A cast-iron-cutting grade of disposable carbide insert was used for roughing (depth of cut, 0.350 to 0.500 in.) and a steel-cutting grade (also disposable) for finishing. Inserts were mounted in a 2-in.-square tool holder. Operating details and tool angles are given in the tabulation accompanying Fig. 3.

Because of the especially heavy depth of cut used in roughing, speed was necessarily reduced to a fraction of that ordinarily used for turning 17-4 PH at the above hardness with carbide tools (Table 4). Excessive vibration was avoided by using heavy-duty equipment — a 25-in. engine lathe with a 26-ft bed and a 60-hp motor. The shaft was held by a four-jaw chuck and was supported by a live center and a follower rest.

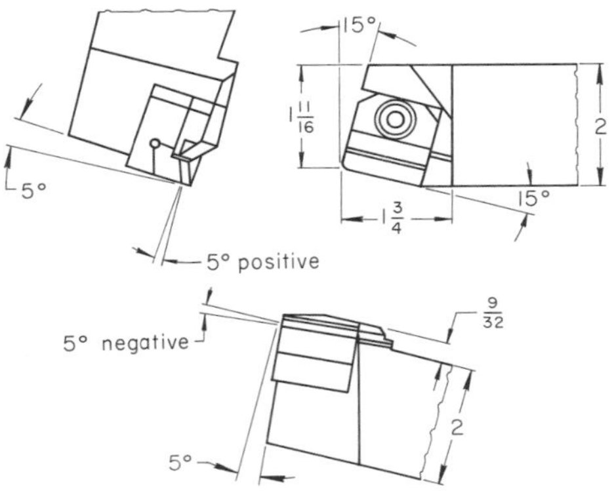

Roughing(a)

Speed .... 73 sfm (35 rpm)
Feed .... 0.035 ipr
Depth of cut .... 0.350 to 0.500 in.
Tool material .... Carbide(b)
Tool life .... 6 to 10 ft of bar

Finishing(a)

Speed .... 147 sfm (70 rpm)
Feed .... 0.032 ipr
Depth of cut .... 0.075 in.
Tool material .... Carbide(c)
Tool life .... 10 ft of bar

(a) Soluble oil was used as the cutting fluid. (b) Disposable carbide insert of cast-iron-cutting grade. (c) Disposable carbide insert of steel-cutting grade.

Fig. 3. Design of single-point tool for turning 17-4 PH shaft (8-in. diam by 10-ft length) with disposable carbide inserts (Example 740)

Example 741. Rubber Insert for Reduced Chatter During Turning of Tubing

Chatter was a problem in turning the outside diameter of guide pipes made of 304 stainless steel tubing having a hardness of 180 Bhn. The tubes were 3-in. OD and 44 in. long with 0.250-in.-thick walls. Chatter was largely eliminated by inserting 2½-in.-diam split rubber tubing in the workpiece before turning. Turning was done in an engine lathe equipped with a three-jaw chuck and a steady rest. A mist-type cutting fluid was used. Rough and finish turning to a final outside diameter of 2.887/2.882 in. was done in three cuts at a speed of 175 sfm (233 rpm) with a carbide tool. Feed during turning was 0.010 ipr, and depth of cut was 0.025 in. per cut for roughing and 0.010 in. for finishing. Finish machining produced a surface roughness of 63 to 125 micro-in. The required final finish of 16 micro-in. was obtained by grinding.

Cutoff tools for stainless steel are larger and stronger than those used for carbon steel, because of the need for greater strength and increased capacity to absorb and transfer heat. Carbide-tipped tools, unless of a shock-resistant carbide (Example 774), are not satisfactory for interrupted cutting because of the severe shock encountered, which cracks and breaks the carbide.

Blade-type tools should have end clearance of 7° to 9° and side clearance of 2° to 3° on each side of the tool. For relatively small diameter work, the end cutting-edge angle should be 10° to 15°, decreased to 5° or less as the diameter of the work increases. Frequently a shallow concavity is ground into the top of the tool immediately behind the cutting lip to facilitate cutting action and chip disposal.

Tool design for one cutoff application is described in Example 742, which follows. In the article "Turning" in this book, Example 3 describes a carbide tool used for various cutoff applications, and Example 4 describes a tool for cutoff on thin-wall stainless steel tubing.

Example 742. Cutoff-and-Trim Tool for Sheet Metal Cylinders and Tubing (Fig. 4)

The specially designed tool shown in Fig. 4 was used to cut off stainless steel tubing and trim excess stock from deep drawn cups made of type 317 stainless steel having a wall thickness of 0.007 in. This tool removed the burrs from the outside and inside diameters as it passed through the workpiece. Several grades of carbide were tested but a grade containing 8.5% Co, 72% WC and 8% TiC, having a hardness of Rockwell A 91.2 and a density of 12.60 g per cu cm was the most satisfactory in this application.

The life of the tool made of this carbide was 2000 pieces per grind. Life of tools made of all other carbides tested was low because the points did not withstand the impact when contacting the workpiece. To protect the tool point, a hydraulic control was installed on the cross slide of the lathe, thus minimizing crash impact of the tool with the workpiece. These changes increased production from 500 to 1000 pieces per hour.

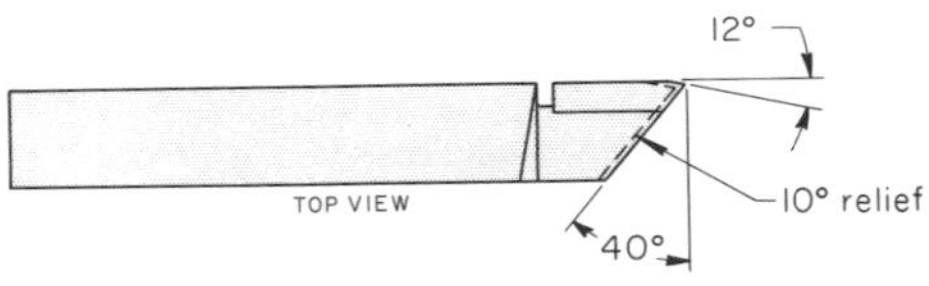

Fig. 4. Tool for parting and trimming deep drawn cups of type 317 stainless steel (Example 742)

The design of circular cutoff tools follows that of the blade type. Circular tools usually have a back rake of 7° to 10°. The end relief angle on circular tools causes the tool to deflect under pressure, which, in turn, causes rapid wear on the tool point. To overcome this condition, a small flat portion is ground on the cutoff side of the tool at 90° to the workpiece.

Circular tools are limited in the distance they can travel into a cut. However, they are more rigid than the blade type, have greater resistance to shock and greater capacity for dissipating heat, and hence they are often preferred for stainless steel.

Table 6 shows nominal speeds and feeds for turning stainless steels with high speed steel and carbide cutoff tools. Feeds for blade and circular-type tools made of high speed steel usually range from 0.001 to 0.003 ipr for tools 0.062 to 0.250 in. wide. As indicated in Table 6, similar cutoff tools made of carbide are operated with heavier feeds (0.003 to 0.0075 ipr). Example 769, in a subsequent section of this article, shows typical speeds and feeds for a carbide-tipped cutoff tool.

Form Tools. Standard circular and dovetail tools are used for form turning of stainless steel. Form tools commonly are made of high speed steel, although cast alloy and carbide-tipped tools can be used when sufficient power is available to take advantage of higher cutting speeds. Carbide-tipped tools are not well suited for shock-load conditions encountered when forming noncircular stock such as square and hexagon shapes.

In some production operations, the life of high speed steel form tools may be so short that it is more economical to use carbide-tipped tools. The following example compares the life of both types of tools for a specific application.

Example 743. Carbide vs High Speed Steel for Form Turning 420F (Fig. 5)

The cutter wheel illustrated in Fig. 5 was form turned from 1³⁄₁₆-in.-diam unground stock. Form tools were originally high speed steel but tool life was less than one hour, which was unacceptable. A change to carbide tools increased tool life to seven hours. The carbide tools were rigidly mounted on the cross slide of the machine to retain sharpness of tool edges and required workpiece finish. Operating details are tabulated below Fig. 5.

Form tools must have side clearance to prevent rubbing and galling of freshly cut surfaces. As depth of cut increases or as finish contours become more intricate, clearance requirements necessitate the use of form cutters for roughing to size, followed by finish-form or shaving tools for obtaining the final form. For close tolerances, the recommended practice is to leave 0.004 to 0.005 in. of stock for finishing with a finish-form or shaving tool. For roughing cuts, tools should have rounded corners when possible.

Side relief angles for form tools range from 3° to 5°, or slightly higher for deep cuts. End clearance angles range from 7° to 10° but should not be so large that support of the cutting edge is weakened. Back rake angles usually range from 4° to 8°; rough cuts are made with an angle of 8° and fine cuts with an angle of about 4°. In the application described in the example that follows, the back rake angle greatly affected tool life.

Example 744. Effect of Back Rake Angle on Tool Life in Form Turning Type 303 (Fig. 6)

When the type 303 forging shown in Fig. 6 was form turned with brazed carbide tools having zero back rake, tool life per grind was only 10 pieces. Providing the tools with an 8° back rake (improved design in Fig. 6) resulted in an increase in tool life to 100 pieces per grind. The redesigned tools also improved surface finish, from about 90 to 63 micro-in.

Table 6. Nominal Speeds and Feeds for Turning Stainless Steels With Cutoff Tools

Type of steel(a)	Condition(b)	Brinell hardness	High speed steel tools: Speed, sfm	HSS Feed (ipr) for tool width (in.) of: 0.062	0.125	0.250	Carbide tools: Speed, sfm	Carbide Feed (ipr) for tool width (in.) of: 0.062	0.125	0.250
FM Fer	Ann	135 to 185	110	0.002	0.0025	0.003	375	0.004	0.0055	0.007
FM Mar	Ann	135 to 185	110	0.002	0.0025	0.003	375	0.004	0.0055	0.007
	Ann or CD	185 to 240	105	0.002	0.0025	0.003	340	0.004	0.0055	0.007
	Q and T	275 to 325	50	0.001	0.001	0.0015	255	0.003	0.003	0.0045
	Q and T	375 to 425	30	0.001	0.001	0.0015	110	0.003	0.003	0.0045
FM Aus	Ann	135 to 185	70	0.0015	0.002	0.003	300	0.0045	0.006	0.009
	CD	225 to 275	65	0.002	0.0025	0.003	260	0.0045	0.006	0.009
Ferritic	Ann	135 to 185	85	0.002	0.0025	0.003	330	0.004	0.0055	0.007
Mar(410)	Ann	135 to 185	85	0.002	0.0025	0.003	340	0.004	0.0055	0.007
	Ann	175 to 225	75	0.002	0.0025	0.003	300	0.004	0.0055	0.007
	Ann	275 to 325	45	0.001	0.001	0.0015	190	0.003	0.003	0.0045
	Q and T	375 to 425	30	0.001	0.001	0.0015	110	0.003	0.003	0.0045
Mar(431)	Ann	225 to 275	50	0.0015	0.002	0.003	225	0.004	0.0055	0.007
	Q and T	275 to 325	40	0.001	0.001	0.0015	150	0.003	0.003	0.0045
	Q and T	375 to 425	30	0.001	0.001	0.0015	110	0.003	0.003	0.0045
Mar(440)	Ann	225 to 275	45	0.0015	0.002	0.003	205	0.004	0.0055	0.007
	Q and T	275 to 325	40	0.001	0.001	0.0015	150	0.003	0.003	0.0045
	Q and T	375 to 425	30	0.001	0.001	0.0015	110	0.003	0.003	0.0045
Aus(304)	Ann	135 to 185	60	0.002	0.0025	0.003	205	0.004	0.0055	0.007
	CD	225 to 275	55	0.0015	0.002	0.003	190	0.004	0.0055	0.007
Aus(316)	Ann	135 to 185	55	0.002	0.0025	0.003	190	0.004	0.0055	0.007
PH	Ann	150 to 200	50	0.002	0.0025	0.003	205	0.004	0.0055	0.007
	Hard	275 to 325	45	0.001	0.001	0.0015	190	0.003	0.003	0.0045
	Hard	325 to 375	40	0.001	0.001	0.0015	170	0.003	0.003	0.0045
	Hard	375 to 440	25	0.001	0.001	0.0015	110	0.003	0.003	0.0045
Cast FM	Ann	140 to 170	60	0.0015	0.002	0.0025	245	0.0045	0.006	0.0075
Cast Fer	N and T	175 to 225	50	0.001	0.0015	0.002	205	0.003	0.0045	0.006
Cast Aus	Ann	140 to 190	35	0.001	0.0015	0.002	170	0.003	0.0045	0.006

(a) See Table 2 for types of steel in each group. (b) Ann = Annealed; CD = Cold drawn; Q and T = Quenched and tempered; Hard = Hardened; N and T = Normalized and tempered. (SOURCE: same as for Table 4)

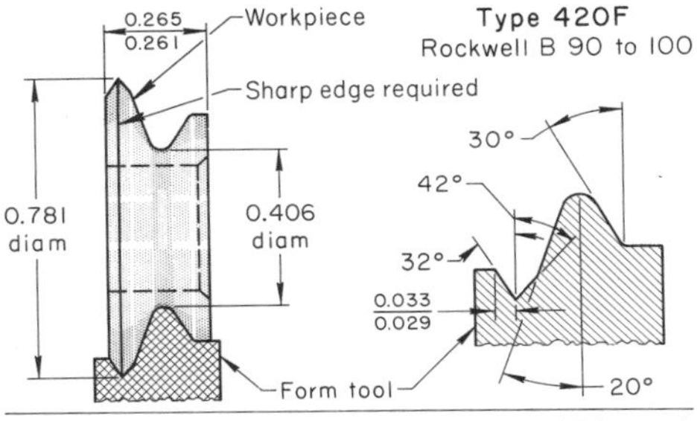

Speed	98 sfm (480 rpm)
Feed	0.0012 ipr
Tool material	Carbide
Cutting fluid	Sulfurized oil
Surface finish	32 micro-in.
Tool life per grind	2000 pieces
Machining time per piece	34 sec

Fig. 5. Cutter wheel that was form turned, and the tool used (Example 743)

Tools for form turning stainless steel should be no wider than 1½ times the diameter of the stock being turned. Form tools exceeding this width-to-diameter ratio require more rigid support to prevent chatter and must be operated with a light feed. However, when light feeds are used, the work metal is more susceptible to work hardening.

Speeds for form turning do not differ greatly from those used for single-point turning. As the width of the form tools varies and as the contour of the workpiece becomes more intricate, some adjustment in speed will be required, depending largely on the machinability of the steel being turned. Nominal speeds used for form turning with high speed steel and carbide tools are given in Table 7.

Optimum feed depends mainly on the width of form tool and the composition and hardness of the work metal. Nominal feeds for form turning various grades of stainless steel with high speed steel and carbide tools of three different widths are given in Table 7.

Boring

Rigidity problems are accentuated in boring stainless steel. The provision of an adequate supply of cutting fluid is more important in boring stainless steel than in boring carbon steel or cast iron, because of the lower heat conductivity of stainless steel.

Since the above factors are critical when boring stainless steel, speed, feed and depth of cut are generally less than those used for turning outside diameters. Nominal speeds and feeds for boring various stainless steels with high speed steel and carbide tools are given in Table 8.

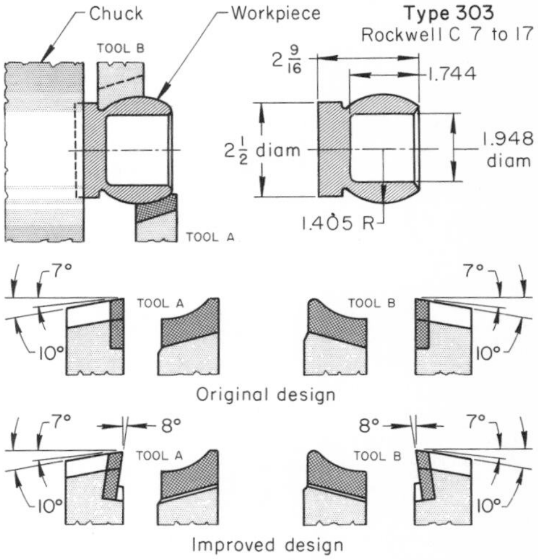

Fig. 6. Setup for form turning a type 303 forging, and original and improved brazed carbide tools used. Note increase in back rake from 0° to 8°. (Example 744)

Table 7. Nominal Speeds and Feeds for Turning Stainless Steels With Form Tools

Type of steel(a)	Condition(b)	Brinell hardness	High speed steel tools: Speed, sfm	Feed (ipr) for tool width (in.) of: 0.500	1.000	2.000	Carbide tools: Speed, sfm	Feed (ipr) for tool width (in.) of: 0.500	1.000	2.000
FM Fer	Ann	135 to 185	110	0.003	0.0025	0.002	375	0.005	0.004	0.0035
FM Mar	Ann	135 to 185	110	0.003	0.0025	0.002	375	0.005	0.004	0.0035
	Ann or CD	185 to 240	105	0.003	0.0025	0.002	340	0.005	0.004	0.0035
	Q and T	275 to 325	50	0.0015	0.001	0.0007	255	0.003	0.002	0.002
	Q and T	375 to 425	30	0.0015	0.001	0.0007	110	0.003	0.002	0.002
FM Aus	Ann	135 to 185	70	0.003	0.0025	0.0015	300	0.006	0.004	0.003
	CD	225 to 275	65	0.003	0.0025	0.002	260	0.006	0.004	0.004
Ferritic	Ann	135 to 185	85	0.003	0.0025	0.002	330	0.005	0.004	0.0035
Mar(410)	Ann	135 to 185	85	0.003	0.0025	0.002	340	0.005	0.004	0.0035
	Ann	175 to 225	75	0.003	0.0025	0.002	300	0.005	0.004	0.0035
	Ann	275 to 325	45	0.0015	0.001	0.0007	190	0.003	0.002	0.002
	Q and T	375 to 425	30	0.0015	0.001	0.0007	110	0.003	0.002	0.002
Mar(431)	Ann	225 to 275	50	0.003	0.0025	0.0015	225	0.005	0.004	0.0035
	Q and T	275 to 325	40	0.0015	0.001	0.0007	170	0.003	0.002	0.002
	Q and T	375 to 425	30	0.0015	0.001	0.0007	110	0.003	0.002	0.002
Mar(440)	Ann	225 to 275	45	0.003	0.0025	0.0015	205	0.005	0.004	0.0035
	Q and T	275 to 325	40	0.0015	0.001	0.0007	150	0.003	0.002	0.002
	Q and T	375 to 425	30	0.0015	0.001	0.0007	110	0.003	0.002	0.002
Aus(304)	Ann	135 to 185	60	0.003	0.0025	0.002	205	0.005	0.004	0.0035
	CD	225 to 275	55	0.003	0.0025	0.0015	190	0.005	0.004	0.0035
Aus(316)	Ann	135 to 185	55	0.003	0.0025	0.002	190	0.005	0.004	0.0035
PH	Ann	150 to 200	50	0.003	0.0025	0.002	205	0.005	0.004	0.0035
	Hard	275 to 325	45	0.0015	0.001	0.0007	190	0.003	0.002	0.002
	Hard	325 to 375	40	0.0015	0.001	0.0007	170	0.003	0.002	0.002
	Hard	375 to 440	25	0.0015	0.001	0.0007	110	0.003	0.002	0.002
Cast FM	Ann	140 to 170	60	0.0025	0.0015	0.001	245	0.005	0.0035	0.0025
Cast Fer	N and T	175 to 225	50	0.0015	0.001	0.0007	205	0.003	0.0025	0.0015
Cast Aus	Ann	140 to 190	35	0.0015	0.001	0.0007	170	0.003	0.0025	0.0015

(a) See Table 2 for types of steel in each group. (b) Ann = Annealed; CD = Cold drawn; Q and T = Quenched and tempered; Hard = Hardened; N and T = Normalized and tempered. (SOURCE: same as for Table 4)

Table 8. Nominal Speeds and Feeds for Boring Stainless Steels

Type of steel(a)	Condition(b)	Brinell hardness	Rough boring (0.100-in. depth): Speed, sfm: HSS	Carbide	Feed, ipr: HSS	Carbide	Finish boring (0.010-in. depth): Speed, sfm: HSS	Carbide	Feed, ipr: HSS	Carbide
FM Fer	Ann	135 to 185	135	450	0.008	0.010	150	500	0.005	0.006
FM Mar	Ann	135 to 185	135	450	0.008	0.010	150	500	0.005	0.006
	Q and T	275 to 325	65	295	0.007	0.009	70	325	0.004	0.005
	Q and T	375 to 425	35	135	0.006	0.008	40	150	0.003	0.004
FM Aus	Ann	135 to 185	85	360	0.008	0.010	95	400	0.005	0.006
Ferritic	Ann	135 to 185	100	405	0.008	0.010	110	450	0.005	0.006
Mar(410)	Ann	135 to 185	100	405	0.008	0.010	110	450	0.005	0.006
	Ann	175 to 225	90	360	0.008	0.010	100	400	0.005	0.006
	Q and T	275 to 325	55	225	0.006	0.008	60	250	0.003	0.004
	Q and T	375 to 425	35	135	0.006	0.008	40	150	0.003	0.004
Mar(431)	Ann	225 to 275	65	270	0.007	0.009	70	300	0.004	0.005
	Q and T	275 to 325	50	205	0.006	0.008	55	225	0.003	0.004
	Q and T	375 to 425	35	135	0.006	0.008	40	150	0.003	0.004
Mar(440)	Ann	225 to 275	55	245	0.007	0.009	60	275	0.004	0.005
	Q and T	275 to 325	45	180	0.006	0.008	50	200	0.003	0.004
	Q and T	375 to 425	35	135	0.006	0.008	40	150	0.003	0.004
	Q and T	Rc 48 to 52	..	50	....	0.005	...	55	....	0.003
	Q and T	Rc 54 to 56	20	90	0.006	0.008	20	100	0.003	0.004
Aus(304)	Ann	135 to 185	70	250	0.008	0.010	80	275	0.005	0.006
Aus(316)	Ann	135 to 185	65	225	0.007	0.009	75	250	0.004	0.005
PH	Ann	150 to 200	60	245	0.008	0.010	65	275	0.005	0.006
	Hard	275 to 325	55	225	0.006	0.008	60	250	0.003	0.004
	Hard	325 to 375	50	205	0.006	0.008	55	225	0.003	0.004
	Hard	375 to 440	30	130	0.006	0.008	35	150	0.003	0.004
Cast FM	Ann	140 to 170	70	295	0.008	0.012	80	325	0.005	0.006
Cast Fer	N and T	175 to 225	65	245	0.008	0.012	70	275	0.005	0.006
Cast Aus	Ann	140 to 190	45	205	0.008	0.012	50	225	0.005	0.006

(a) See Table 2 for types of steel in each group. (b) Ann = Annealed; Q and T = Quenched and tempered; Hard = Hardened; N and T = Normalized and tempered. (Data are adapted from tables compiled by Metcut Research Associates, Inc.)

Tool Material. Both high speed steel and carbide tools are used for boring stainless steels. Tools of grade C-3, C-7 or C-8 carbide will be more economical than high speed steel tools under favorable boring conditions: adequate power for the recommended speeds (Table 8), minimum shock loading, and use of the optimum grade of carbide. Importance of carbide selection is exemplified in the following application.

Example 745. Effect of Carbide Grade on Tool Life (Fig. 7)

When boring tools for machining type 302 stainless steel were tipped with grade C-5 carbide (WC with TaC+TiC), tool life was 10 to 15 pieces per grind. Changing to a C-3 grade increased tool life to 100 to 110 pieces per grind. Both tools had the same design, which is shown in Fig. 7. The C-5 carbide is the general-purpose type, whereas C-3 is generally recommended for light finishing cuts in which no shock is encountered. Operating conditions for boring the stainless steel part are shown in the tabulation accompanying Fig. 7.

Precision boring is used to produce holes to closer tolerances and finer finishes than can be obtained by drilling and, under certain conditions, by reaming. Precision boring is done at higher speeds and shallower cuts than conventional boring. Carbide tools are used almost exclusively for precision boring. Tool angles recommended for precision boring of stainless steels are compared with those for precision boring of alloy steels in Table 9.

Example 759, in the section on Drilling in this article, discusses boring after rough drilling of type 304 stainless steel. Other applications of boring of stainless steel are discussed in Examples 41, 67, 72, 81 and 83 in the article on Boring in this volume.

Broaching

Broaches for cutting stainless steel should be designed with a land behind each cutting edge to serve as a guide for the following cutting edge. The width of the land should be held to a minimum to reduce rubbing and galling. The remainder of the land is relieved by grinding an angular clearance of up to 3°, as indicated in Table 10. Greater clearance may be required for certain applications, such as the 5° clearance used in Example 746.

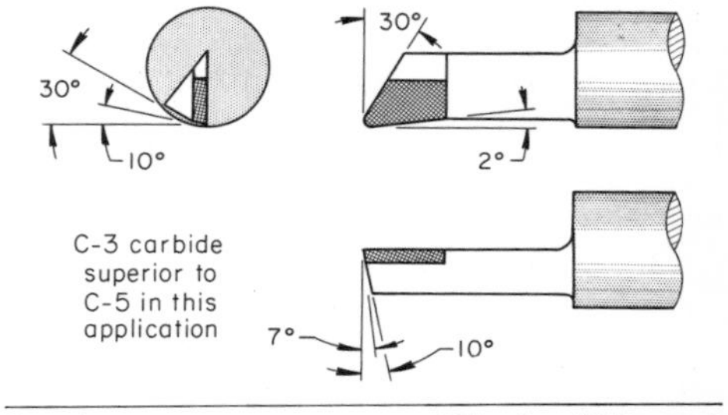

Speed	325 sfm (622 rpm)
Feed	0.005 ipr
Depth of cut:	
Roughing	3/32 in.
Finishing	0.040 in.
Depth of bored hole	1.405 in.
Tool material	C-3 carbide
Cutting fluid	Soluble-oil emulsion
Surface finish	125 micro-in.
Tool life per grind	100 to 110 pieces

Fig. 7. Tool for boring type 302 stainless steel (Example 745)

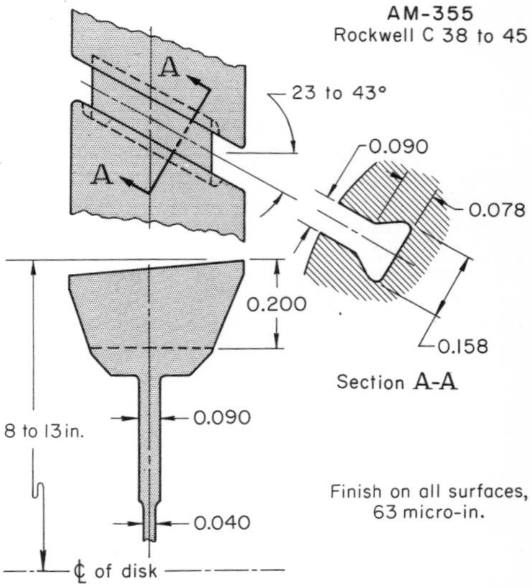

Tool detail	Roughing	Semi-finishing	Finishing
Length, each insert, in.	16	20	16
Pitch, in.	1/4	5/16	3/8
Face angle	15°	15°	0°
Backoff clearance	1° 30′	1° 30′	5°
Land width, in.	5/64	3/32	3/16
Rise per tooth, in.	0.0015	0.0014	0.0002

Fig. 8. Compressor disk and small dovetail slot broached in the periphery (Example 746)

Tools can be designed for roughing only, for combined roughing and finishing, or for finishing only, depending on the application. Sometimes a semifinishing broach is necessary, as for the application described in Example 746. Two types of tool design problems in broaching of stainless steel are discussed in Examples 110 and 122 in the article on Broaching.

Face angle varies with the grade and hardness of stainless steel being broached. The usual range is 8° to 15°, as indicated in Table 10. However, tools with face angles outside the ranges shown in Table 10 may be necessary in some applications. This feature of broach design is illustrated in the three examples that follow. The tool for finish broaching the part in Example 746 had a face angle of 0°, whereas tools with face angles up to 20° were used to produce a fine surface finish on the parts in Examples 747 and 748.

Example 746. Angle Broaching of Dovetail Slots in AM-355 Compressor Disks (Fig. 8)

The following design and operating details relate to the broaching of dovetail slots in AM-355 compressor disks at Rockwell C 38 to 45. Details of the disk and slot are shown in Fig. 8; the accompanying table lists details of the two-insert broaching tools used for roughing, semifinishing and finishing.

The slots were broached at angles of 23° to 43° from the axial centerline of the disk. The tool material, M3 high speed steel, was nitrided and steam treated; cutting was done at 15 sfm. A medium-active sulfochlorinated mineral oil of about 300 SUS viscosity was used as cutting fluid.

With the above operating conditions, approximately 700 slots were broached before a tool regrind was required. Tools could be reground six to eight times before they were scrapped.

Special attention was given to the rigidity of work-holding fixtures, to meet tolerances and minimize distortion.

Example 747. Redesigned Insert for Finish Broaching of Type 410 Rotor Disks (Table 11)

In broaching the ninth rotor disks of a turbine assembly, short tool life and poor surface finish became apparent. To maintain specified finishes of 32 micro-in. (dovetail) and 45 micro-in. (radii), a new finishing insert was designed. Instead of having all teeth cutting the full slot envelope, the new finisher had one set of teeth cutting the dovetail and the remainder cutting the radii. Table 11 lists details for the original and revised designs of the finishing insert.

The original finisher had 21 teeth, which, after roughing, were required to remove about 0.008 in. of metal all around the form. In the redesigned finisher, which also had 21 teeth, the first ten teeth generated the dovetail form, and the eleventh tooth did the sizing. The following nine teeth were used for cutting the radii, and the last tooth was used to size the 0.040-in. radius. Top-flow cutting fluid was replaced by forced-flow cutting fluid fed through the fixture.

Full tool life of the original broach was 15,000 to 18,000 slots. Full tool life of the redesigned broach was 40,000 to 45,000 slots, during all of which the required finishes (32 and 45 micro-in.) were maintained.

Example 748. Added Insert for Finish Broaching of Type 410 Compressor Wheels (Fig. 9)

On the dovetail form broached in compressor wheels made of type 410 stainless steel at 241 to 311 Bhn, it was necessary to eliminate tears in radii and to provide a better finish than was being obtained (63 micro-in.). This was accomplished by adding a three-stage, 13-tooth shave detail to the nine-piece insert set that generated the form. The shave insert cleaned up the torn surfaces; it also provided required control of dimensions and confined most problems of tool maintenance to one insert set.

Table 9. Typical Angles Used on Carbide Tools for Precision Boring

Angle	Tool angle: Stainless steel (all types)	Tool angle: Typical alloy steels
Back rake	3° to 10°	0° to −6°
Side rake	0° to 15°	−3° to −8°
End relief	5° to 10°	5° to 10°
Side relief	2° to 3°	2° to 3°
End cutting edge	5°	5°
Side cutting edge	15°	15°

Table 10. Face and Clearance Angles for Tools for Broaching Stainless Steels

Type of steel	Brinell hardness	Face angle	Clearance angle
Free-machining	135 to 425	8°-12°	1°-2°
Ferritic	135 to 185	12°-15°	2°-3°
Austenitic	135 to 185	12°-15°	1°-2°
Martensitic	140 to 425	8°-12°	1°-2°
Precipitation-hardening	150 to 440	10°-15°	2°

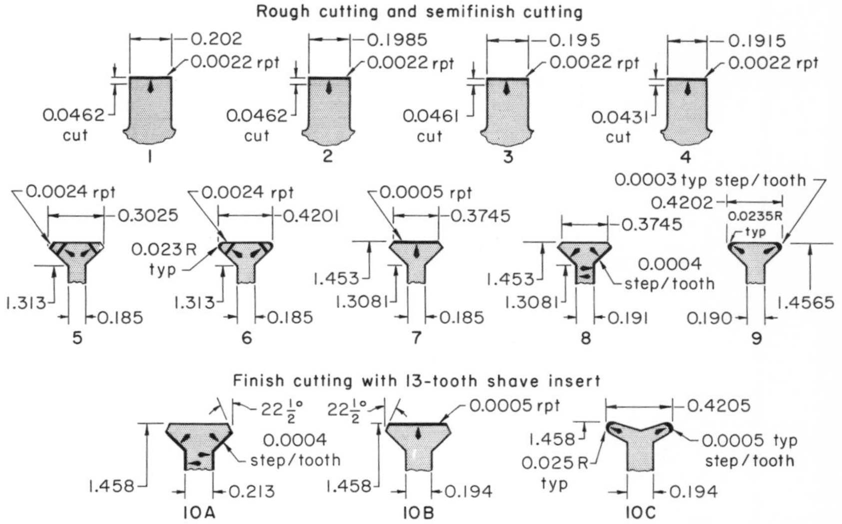

Tool detail	Detail No. 1	Detail No. 10	Tool detail	Detail No. 1	Detail No. 10
Length, in.	8.000	5.000	Backoff relief	2°	2°
Pitch, in.	0.375	0.375	Face (rake) angle	18°	20°
Depth of flute, in.	0.140	0.140	Tooth land, in.	0.125	0.125
Flute radius, in.	0.078	0.047	Form relief	....	2°

Details 1 through 9 show typical tooth forms of nine generating inserts. The finishing detail (10A, B and C) utilized only 5 in. of length, but duplicated cutting of entire contour. Problems of tool maintenance and surface finish were largely confined to the short insert, which provided a 32-micro-in. finish. Broach was T15 steel at Rockwell C 66 to 68.

Fig. 9. Progression of inserts of broach for dovetail slotting type 410 stainless steel (AMS 5613) compressor wheels (Example 748)

Table 11. Details of Original and Improved Designs of Finishing Inserts Used in Broaching Type 410 Stainless Steel Rotor Disks (Example 747) (a)

Item	Dovetail form(b): Original	Dovetail form(b): Improved	0.040-in.-radius corners(c): Original	0.040-in.-radius corners(c): Improved
Face angle	15°	20°	20°	10°
Shear angle	0°	20°	5°	10°
Backoff clearance	1°5′	2°	1°5′	2°
Tooth pitch, in.	0.5	0.5	0.5	0.5
Tooth thickness, in.	0.15	0.15	0.15	0.15
Tooth depth, in.	0.22	0.22	0.22	0.22
Removed per tooth, in.	0.0007(d)	0.0011(e)	0.0007(d)	0.0011(e)
Broaching speed, sfm	15	22	15	22
Cutting fluid flow	Top flow	(f)	Top flow	(f)

(a) Both original and improved broaches were T5 steel at Rockwell C 64 to 66. Both broaches had 21 teeth removing approximately 0.008 in. left by roughing operation. (b) 32-micro-in. finish. (c) 45-micro-in. finish. (d) Two finishing teeth. (e) One finishing tooth. (f) Forced through fixture.

Details 1 through 9 in Fig. 9 show typical tooth forms of the nine-piece inserts that generated the form; details 10A, B and C show typical tooth forms of the three stages of the 13-tooth shaver. The first four of the thirteen teeth were stepped 0.0004 in. on the angle of the dovetail. The next four teeth (5 through 8), which cut the base of the slot, were stepped at 0.0005 in., as were the last five teeth (9 through 13), used to cut the radii. All backoff angles were 2° up sharp, with no wear land.

The shave detail, with an insert length of only 5 in., thus duplicated the passes of the roughing and semifinishing sets. Capable of being easily replaced when worn, the shave insert added more life to the broach. Also, because it was able to satisfy all finish dimensional tolerances, it made possible variations in rough and semifinish dimensions of the bar. Finally, it greatly improved the condition of radii and slots, reducing surface roughness significantly, from 63 to 32 micro-in.

This operation was performed on a 15-ton surface broaching machine that had a 72-in. stroke; cutting fluid for the operation consisted of mineral oil with 1% active sulfur, chlorine and synthetic additions.

Broach Material. Broaches are usually made from high speed steel; M2, M3, T5 and T15 are the grades most commonly used. Grade M3 is widely used as a broach material for stainless steel. In some plants an established practice is to use M3 as standard and to change to one of the more highly alloyed (and more expensive) grades only in specific applications when the need has been

Table 12. Nominal Speeds and Chip Loads for Broaching Stainless Steels With High Speed Steel Tools

Type of steel(a)	Condition(b)	Brinell hardness	Speed, sfm	Chip load, ipt
FM Fer	Ann	135 to 185	30	0.004
FM Mar	Ann	135 to 185	25	0.004
	Ann or CD	185 to 240	20	0.002
	Q and T	275 to 325	10	0.002
	Q and T	375 to 425	8	0.002
FM Aus	Ann	135 to 185	25	0.004
	CD	225 to 275	20	0.003
Ferritic	Ann	135 to 185	20	0.003
Mar(all)	Ann	140 to 225	25	0.004
	Ann	225 to 275	20	0.003
	Q and T	275 to 325	15	0.002
	Q and T	375 to 425	5	0.001
Aus(all)	Ann	135 to 185	20	0.003
	CD	225 to 275	15	0.003
PH	Ann	150 to 200	15	0.002
	Hard	275 to 325	15	0.002
	Hard	325 to 375	8	0.002
	Hard	375 to 440	5	0.001
Cast FM	Ann	140 to 170	20	0.003
Cast Fer	N and T	175 to 225	20	0.003
Cast Aus	Ann	140 to 190	20	0.003

(a) See Table 1 for types of steel in each group. (b) Ann = Annealed; CD = Cold drawn; Q and T = Quenched and tempered; Hard = Hardened; N and T = Normalized and tempered. (Data are adapted from tables compiled by Metcut Research Associates, Inc.)

Table 13. Tool Angles of High Speed Steel Twist Drills for Drilling All Grades of Stainless Steel

Tool angle	Hardness of stainless steel, Bhn 135-200	200-325	200-325
Point angle	118°	118°	118-135°
Lip relief	10-12°	7-10°	7-10°
Chisel edge	125-135°	125-135°	120-130°
Helix angle	24-32°	24-32°	24-32°
Point grind	Standard	Crankshaft (both)	

proved. In the production application described in the example that follows, broaches made of M3 equalled those made of T15 in tool life, and cost substantially less than T15.

Example 749. M3 vs T15 for Broaching Type 410 Stator Blades

Broaches made from M3 (class 2) and T15 tool steels were used for broaching the saddle and ends of roots of stator blades made of type 410 at high hardness (Rockwell C 40 to 45) on a 180-in. horizontal broaching machine. Although it was assumed that T15 cutters would be more effective at this hardness, it was demonstrated that the M3 cutters were just as effective, and, in terms of both initial cost and maintenance, much less expensive.

A gear-tooth design, with a 45° corner chamfer to generate the cut, was used for both the M3 and T15 inserts. Other tool details were as follows: face angle, 20°; backoff, 2°; pitch, 0.411 in.; tooth depth, 11/32 in.; shear angle, 12°. Machine speed was held constant at 10 sfm; mineral oil with 1% active sulfur and chlorine and synthetic additions was used as cutting fluid in all tests.

Tool life was found to be the same for both steels (6000 pieces per grind). However, the average cost per insert with the M3 steel was only $84, compared with $169 for T15. Also, the time required for grinding M3 (3 hr) was 25% less than that required for grinding T15 (4 hr).

Speed. Table 12 shows nominal speeds ranging from 5 to 30 sfm for broaching various stainless steels with tools made of high speed steel. Specific conditions may alter the optimum speed by a factor of three or more from the nominal speed shown in Table 12. For instance, a speed of 25 sfm is shown in Table 12 for broaching types 410 and 422. However, in the following example an increase in speed to 90 sfm improved surface finish and tool life when broaching these grades of stainless steel.

Example 750. Speed Increase That Improved Finish and Tool Life in Broaching Types 410 and 422

In broaching the dovetail slots in annealed type 422 compressor wheels, an appreciable increase in ram speed (from 28 to 90 sfm) resulted in an improvement in surface finish (from 100 to 120 micro-in., to 40 to 45 micro-in.) and a 500% increase in tool life.

At the increased ram speed, an M3 (class 2) steel was used for roughing and a T5 steel for finishing, and flow of the cutting fluid (a medium-active sulfochlorinated mineral oil of about 50 SUS viscosity) was increased. The broach had a land 5/32 in. wide; pitch was 15/32 in., depth of gullet 5/32 in., face angle 22°. The broach was inserted in a standard holder, and cutting was done in a 90-in. vertical machine that had been converted to high-speed operation. Aluminum or brass plates were used for backup, and the slots were wire brushed on the return stroke. Tool finish was 8 to 12 micro-in.

On annealed type 410 stainless, comparable results were obtained, and the increase in cutting speed resulted in lowering cost per groove from $0.0263 to $0.0185. Surface finish was improved and tool life was doubled.

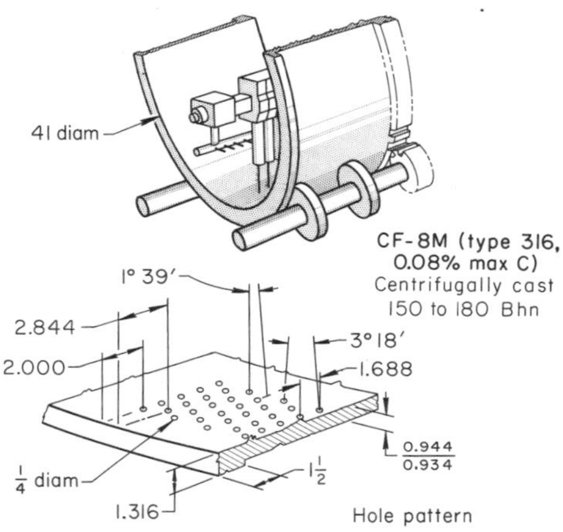

Speed .... 36 sfm (550 rpm)
Feed .... 0.002 ipr
Length of cut .... 0.939 in.
Cutting fluid .... Soluble-oil emulsion
Tolerance, hole location .... ±0.005 in.
Surface finish .... 125 micro-in.
Drill life(a) .... 200 holes per drill
Total time per piece .... 6 hr(b)

(a) Standard 1/4-in. high speed steel twist drills with 118° point angle and thinned web. (b) One cycle, consisting of indexing and drilling one row, required 1.1 min. Remainder of time was used for setting up and tool changing.

Fig. 10. Stainless steel casting in which 2725 holes were drilled, and hole pattern (Example 751)

Feed per tooth varies from light shaving cuts of 0.001 in. to cuts of 0.004 in., as shown in Table 12. When broaching steels susceptible to work hardening, each cutting edge of the broach must cut under the work-hardened layer left by the preceding tooth.

Rigidity of Setup. Broaching, like other machining operations for stainless steel, requires a rigid setup. In Example 136 in the article on Broaching in this volume, broaching was better than milling for producing flats on a type 416 stainless steel crankpin because rigidity of the milling setup was inadequate to meet close tolerance and production-rate requirements.

Drilling

In drilling stainless steel, more power is required for the same amount of metal removed per unit of time than in drilling carbon or alloy steel, and rigidity in the machine and tooling setup is more critical. Features of equipment that are especially desirable for drilling stainless steel are as follows:

1. Spindle bearings must be kept in condition to permit the drills to run true.
2. Drilling machines with controlled feed and with steplessly variable speed are preferred.
3. Drill chucks should permit adjustment of the drill for minimum overhang, to prevent whip and oversize holes.
4. Use of drill jigs is especially desirable and should always be considered when tolerances are critical.
5. Drill condition is also critical; sharp, machine-ground drills are recommended.

Drill design recommended for drilling all grades of stainless steel is given in Table 13. The included angle of the drill point for twist drills is usually 118°. However, when work metal hardness is in the range of 325 to 425 Bhn, better results can be obtained by increasing the point angle to 135°.

Web thickness at the point should be reduced to about 1/6 to 1/8 of the hole diameter, to minimize rubbing at the bottom of the hole. Thus, work hardening is reduced and excessive heating is avoided, resulting in longer tool life and closer dimensional control. Web thinning also reduces cutting pressure and makes starting easier.

Chip curling grooves usually are ground into drills, to avoid chip

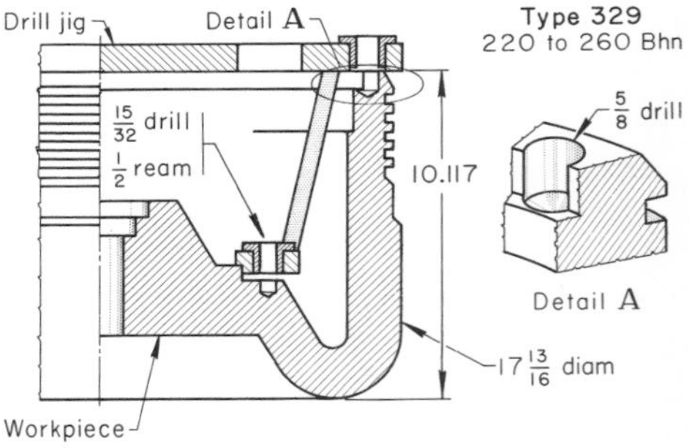

Speed(a):
Core drill .... 43 sfm
Twist drill .... 32 sfm
Reamer .... 34 sfm
Feed:
Core drill .... 0.004 ipr
Twist drill .... 0.003 ipr
Reamer .... 0.012 ipr
Length of cut:
Core drill .... 3/4 in.
Twist drill and reamer .... 1/2 in.
Cutting fluid .... Soluble oil
Tolerance:
On location of slot and hole .... 0.008 in.
On diameter of reamed hole .... 0.0008 in.
Surface finish, slot and hole ... 63 micro-in. max
Tool life(b):
Core drill .... 20 pieces per grind
Twist drill .... 10 pieces per grind
Reamer .... 25 pieces per grind
Total machining time .... 1.88 minutes(c)

(a) Spindle speed of the machine was 260 rpm. (b) Tools consisted of a 5/8-in. core drill with 1/16-in. radius on the corner of each flute, a 15/32-in. standard twist drill and a 0.500-in. reamer. Each tool was made of high speed steel and had a taper shank. (c) Machining time consisted of 0.89 min for the core drill, 0.82 min for the twist drill, and 0.17 min for reaming.

Fig. 11. Forged part in which slot and hole were drilled with core and twist drills in a four-spindle drill press with power feed (Example 752)

congestion when drilling the tougher grades of stainless steel. A high helix angle also assists chip removal.

Step drills are sometimes used to combine drilling and counterboring or countersinking in one operation. An application of the latter in type 302 stainless is given in Example 161 in the article "Drilling". Another combination tool, in type 410, is dealt with in Example 171 in the same article.

Frequently, short drills are used to start the drilling of deep holes (for example, when depth exceeds 8 times the diameter of the hole). Drills with heavier web and relatively short flutes provide increased torsional strength and less whipping action.

Standard twist drills are used for most applications in drilling stainless steel. Several types of special drills and the applications in stainless steel for which they proved successful are described in Examples 153, 154 and 159 in "Drilling". The five examples that follow describe results obtained with different types of drills.

Example 751. Multiple Drilling of CF-8M Centrifugal Castings (Fig. 10)

The 2725 holes in the centrifugally cast CF-8M (316) stainless steel shell, a section of which is shown in Fig. 10, were drilled in a special machine capable of drilling 13 holes simultaneously. There were 218 rows of holes around the circumference. Each odd-numbered row contained 13 holes; each even-numbered row contained 12 holes. The odd-numbered rows were 3° 18′ apart; the even-numbered rows were in between at 1° 39′. All holes in each row were evenly spaced (1.688 in. apart) from front to back.

Drilling was done with standard twist drills that had point angles of 118° and thinned webs. A small flat surface was straddle milled on each drill shank for added grip. Drill bushings were not used.

The drilling machine was completely automatic and had four speeds. The workpiece rested on two gear-operated rollers that indexed the workpiece after each row of holes had been drilled. Drill spindles were adjustable lengthwise and removable. The position of the spindles in relation to each other was fixed for each part. All spindles and drills were raised and lowered together by a cam.

After setting up for a row of 13 holes, all 13-hole rows were drilled and indexed in sequence. The machine was then positioned for the 12-hole rows, one drill removed, and each of these rows was drilled and indexed in sequence to completion. Cutting fluid was supplied directly to the drill point through a petcock that controlled the flow. Other processing details are listed below Fig. 10.

Example 752. Drilling a Slot in Type 329 Using Core Drill and Jig (Fig. 11)

A ⅝-in.-diam core drill was used to make the slot (detail A) in the type 329 forging shown in Fig. 11. The core drill was centered close to the inside surface of the part so that the drill broke through the wall, forming the slot. This operation was followed by drilling and reaming with a 15⁄32-in.-diam standard twist drill and a reamer to produce the 0.500-in. hole in the base section. A jig, consisting of a flat plate and an offset arm, was clamped across the top of the part, as shown in Fig. 11. The jig was equipped with drill bushings to control location and straightness of the slot and the hole. The workpiece was heavy enough (180 lb) so that clamping it to the drill press table was not required. Processing details are tabulated below Fig. 11.

Example 753. Use of a Subland Drill to Replace Two Twist Drills (Fig. 12)

The 1-in.-diam holes shown in Fig. 12 were originally drilled through the 1⅟16-in. section of the bowl shell by two twist drills — first a ¾-in.-diam pilot drill and then a second drill to produce the required size. Tool life was 20 to 25 pieces for each drill.

Because of an increase in production requirements, the drilling operation was transferred to a radial drill press with an indexing fixture to locate the hole. A subland drill was used to drill each hole to size in one operation. Twelve holes in each piece were drilled in this manner. The subland drill increased the production rate, and surface finish of the holes was superior to that obtained with the original procedure.

Six 5⁄16-in.-diam holes also were drilled in the same 1⅟16-in. section (Fig. 12) with standard twist drills. Subsequently they were tapped for ⅜–16 threads. Additional processing details are given in the tabulation with Fig. 12.

Example 754. Double-Margin Drills for Hardened 17-7 PH Stainless Steel (Table 14)

Standard twist drills were used originally to drill 5⁄16-in.-diam blind holes in 17-7 PH stainless steel at Rockwell C 41 to 42. Holes were drilled to a depth of 0.600 in. in sections 0.850 in. thick. With this technique, holes were consistently 0.003 to 0.005 in. oversize. Various attempts with different drills and different grinds failed to solve the problem of oversize holes.

The holes were produced within the required tolerance by using double-margin, short-flute drills. The greater rigidity of these drills provided the required cutting stability, and this was further improved by grinding a 5° to 7° primary relief flat, about 0.032 in. wide, on the drill lip.

Drilling was done with a jig having a ¾-in.-long slip bushing. Other drill details and processing data are given in Table 14.

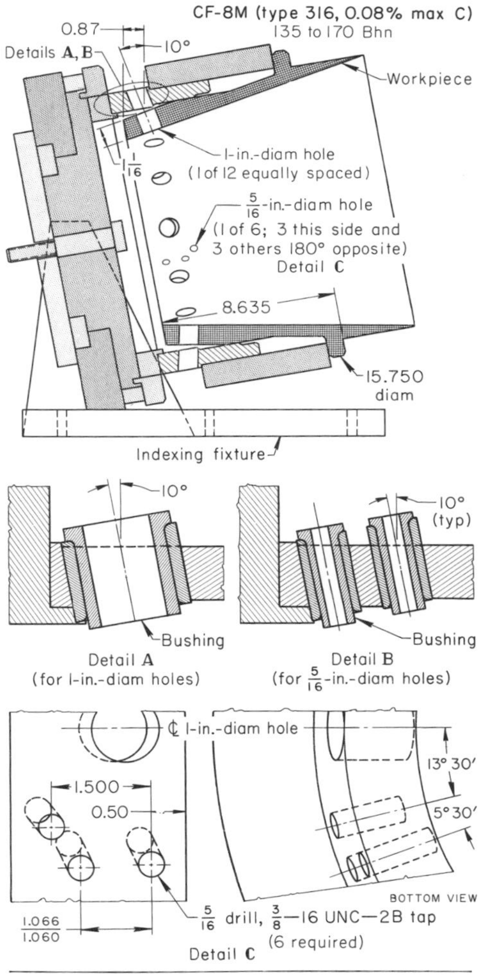

Speed:	
Subland drill	38 sfm (147 rpm)
Twist drill	38 sfm (460 rpm)
Tap	9 sfm (88 rpm)
Feed:	
Subland drill	0.008 ipr(a)
Twist drill	0.006 ipr(a)
Tap	Hand feed
Cutting fluid	Sulfurized oil
Surface finish	125 micro-in.
Tool life(b)	12 to 18 pieces per grind
Total time	76 min per piece(c)

(a) Drill was power fed. (b) Subland drill had ¾-in. minor diameter and 1-in. major diameter. Twist drill was 5⁄16 in. in diameter. Tap size was ⅜–16. (c) Time per hole was as follows: 1-in. holes, 2.20 min; 5⁄16 holes, 0.65 min; tapping, 0.91 min. Remaining time was used for setting up, indexing and handling.

Fig. 12. Bowl shell in which 1-in. and 5⁄16-in. holes were drilled in a 5-ft radial drill press (Example 753)

Table 14. Drilling of 17-7 PH Stainless Steel at Rockwell C 41 to 42 (Example 754)

Tool Design	
Type of drill	Double margin
Point angle	130° (point split to zero)
Flute length	1½ to 2 in.
Web thickness at point	0.080 to 0.090 in.
Positive axial rake	3° to 4° (on split edge)
Web taper	0.016 in. per in.
Drill material	High speed steel
Operating Conditions	
Diameter of hole	5⁄16 in.
Depth of hole	0.600 in.
Speed	20 sfm (250 rpm)
Feed	0.003 to 0.005 ipr
Drill life	18 holes per grind

Example 755. Short-Flute Stub Drills for Drilling Four Holes in True Position (Fig. 13)

To drill four holes within 0.003 in. of true position, in a part made of cold drawn and centerless ground type 430 stainless (Fig. 13), a high degree of rigidity was required. As shown in Fig. 13, the diameter of these holes was 0.159/0.153 in., and they were drilled on a bolt circle measuring 0.265 in. in diameter. High accuracy was essential because a subsequent operation involved turning a 0.4385/0.4375-in.-diam step (see Fig. 13) on the outside diameter surrounding the four smaller holes and reducing the resulting wall thickness to a minimum of 0.0035 in.

The holes were drilled successfully with stub screw-machine drills 5⁄32 in. in diameter and made of high speed steel. These drills had a flute length of only ⅜ in. and an included point angle of 135°.

Drill Material. Virtually all twist drills used for drilling stainless steel are made of high speed steel. Twist drills made of solid carbide or having carbide tips are used in highly specialized applications only, although gun drills usually have carbide tips (see subsequent text on Gun Drilling, page 385 in this article).

M1, M7 and M10 are the high speed steels most used for making twist drills and are recommended for drilling all stainless steels at hardnesses no higher

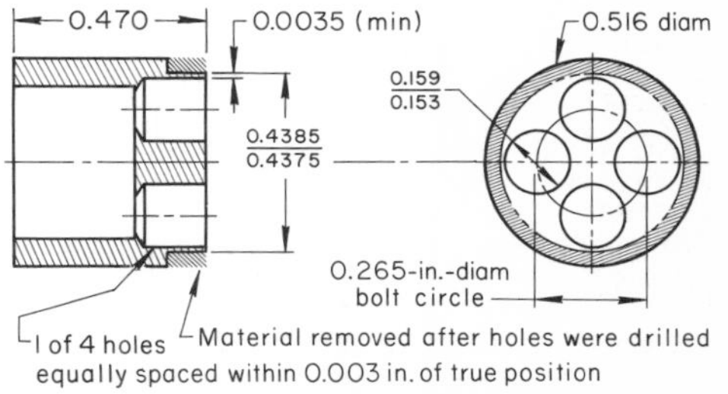

Part made of type 430 stainless steel, cold drawn and centerless ground, for which high speed steel drills having a flute length of ⅜ in. were used successfully to drill the four 0.159/0.153-in.-diam holes shown. Short drills gave increased rigidity for true positioning of holes.

Fig. 13. Part in which four holes having close location tolerances were drilled (Example 755)

Table 15. Nominal Speeds and Feeds for Drilling Stainless Steels With High Speed Steel Drills

Type of steel(a)	Condition(b)	Brinell hardness	Speed, sfm	Feed (ipr) for nominal diam (in.) of: 0.125	0.250	0.500	0.750	1.000	1.500	2.000
FM Fer	Ann	135 to 185	140	0.003	0.005	0.010	0.014	0.018	0.020	0.025
FM Mar	Ann	135 to 185	140	0.003	0.005	0.010	0.014	0.018	0.020	0.025
	Ann or CD	185 to 240	130	0.003	0.005	0.010	0.014	0.018	0.020	0.025
	Q and T	275 to 325	65	0.002	0.004	0.006	0.008	0.010	0.014	0.018
	Q and T	375 to 425	40	0.001	0.002	0.004	0.006	0.008	0.009	0.010
FM Aus	Ann	135 to 185	100	0.003	0.005	0.010	0.014	0.018	0.020	0.025
	CD	225 to 275	90	0.003	0.005	0.010	0.014	0.018	0.020	0.025
Ferritic	Ann	135 to 185	60	0.002	0.003	0.006	0.008	0.010	0.014	0.018
Mar(410)	Ann	135 to 185	70	0.003	0.004	0.006	0.008	0.010	0.014	0.018
	Ann	175 to 225	60	0.002	0.003	0.006	0.008	0.011	0.014	0.018
	Q and T	275 to 325	50	0.002	0.003	0.005	0.008	0.011	0.013	0.016
	Q and T	375 to 425	40	0.001	0.002	0.004	0.006	0.008	0.009	0.010
Mar(431)	Ann	225 to 275	50	0.002	0.003	0.005	0.008	0.011	0.013	0.016
	Q and T	275 to 325	45	0.002	0.003	0.005	0.008	0.011	0.013	0.016
	Q and T	375 to 425	40	0.001	0.002	0.004	0.006	0.008	0.009	0.010
Mar(440)	Ann	225 to 275	40	0.002	0.003	0.005	0.009	0.010	0.012	0.013
	Q and T	275 to 325	35	0.001	0.002	0.003	0.005	0.006	0.008	0.009
	Q and T	375 to 425	25	0.001	0.002	0.003	0.004	0.005	0.006	0.007
	Q and T	Rc 48 to 52	20	0.0005	0.001	0.002	0.002	0.003	0.003	0.004
Aus(304)	Ann	135 to 185	50	0.002	0.003	0.005	0.009	0.010	0.013	0.016
	CD	225 to 275	45	0.002	0.003	0.005	0.008	0.011	0.013	0.016
Aus(316)	Ann	135 to 185	45	0.002	0.003	0.005	0.008	0.011	0.013	0.016
PH	Ann	150 to 200	45	0.002	0.003	0.005	0.008	0.010	0.012	0.015
	Hard	275 to 325	40	0.001	0.003	0.005	0.005	0.008	0.010	0.012
	Hard	325 to 375	30	0.001	0.003	0.004	0.005	0.007	0.010	0.012
	Hard	375 to 440	20	0.001	0.002	0.003	0.004	0.005	0.006	0.007
Cast FM	Ann	140 to 170	55	0.003	0.004	0.007	0.010	0.012	0.015	0.018
Cast Fer	N and T	175 to 225	45	0.002	0.003	0.005	0.008	0.009	0.011	0.013
Cast Aus	Ann	140 to 190	35	0.002	0.003	0.006	0.008	0.009	0.010	0.011

(a) See Table 2 for types of steel in each group. (b) Ann = Annealed; CD = Cold drawn; Q and T = Quenched and tempered; Hard = Hardened; N and T = Normalized and tempered. (Data are adapted from tables compiled by Metcut Research Associates, Inc.)

than 325 Bhn. For drilling stainless steel harder than 325 Bhn, drills made of the more highly alloyed grades such as T15 or M33 are recommended. Drills made of the latter grades frequently cost more than twice as much as the lower-alloy grades of high speed steel; however, for drilling hard steel, the cost is justified.

Speed and Feed. Nominal speeds for drilling various grades of stainless steel at different hardnesses with twist drills are given in Table 15. Recommended speeds range from 20 sfm for the precipitation-hardening grades to 140 sfm for free-machining ferritic grades in the annealed condition.

Feed for drilling stainless steel is influenced to some extent by the composition and hardness of the work metal, although diameter of drill has a greater influence on optimum feed, as shown in Table 15. When drilling steels that are strongly susceptible to work hardening, it is especially important to keep the rate of feed high enough to cut below the work-hardened surface produced by the preceding cut. Heavy feed may require slower speed because of the generation of excessive heat, or from lack of power.

Drilling Deep Holes. Deep holes are usually drilled by special machines (see article on Drilling in this volume). In most deep hole drilling, the workpiece is rotated while the drill remains stationary. Gun drills are usually employed when the depth of the hole is greater than about six times the diameter. However, special equipment is not always available, and other techniques are often used to achieve the desired results. One such technique is described in the example that follows:

Example 756. Technique for Drilling Deep Holes With Twist Drills (Fig. 14)

Because quantities were small and designs varied, deep hole drilling equipment was not considered practical for drilling the deep holes in the forged 304 stainless steel bowl top, shown in Fig. 14. Both the 5/16 and 3/8-in.-diam holes shown had depths over seven times the diameter. The nine holes were drilled separately by placing the workpiece in a jig and spot drilling each hole to a depth of 1/4 in. The workpiece was then removed from the drill jig, placed in an indexing fixture, and the six 3/8-in. holes were drilled by power feed. While the 3/8-in.-diam holes were being drilled, the operator was spotting holes in another workpiece and drilling the 5/16-in.-diam holes using hand feed.

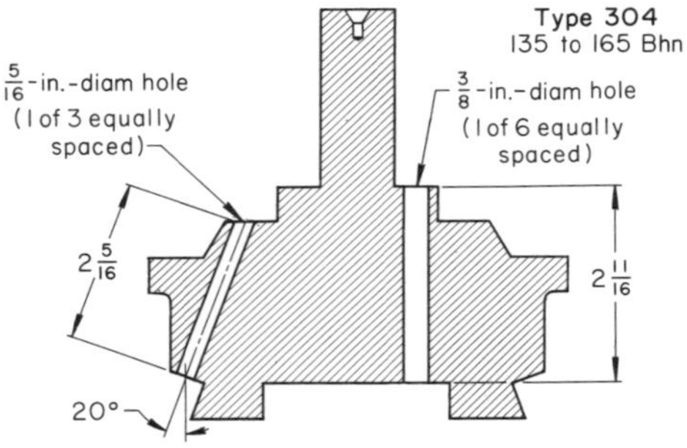

Speed:
- Spot drilling:
  - 5/16-in. holes .... 36 sfm (445 rpm)
  - 3/8-in. holes .... 44 sfm (445 rpm)
- Through drilling:
  - 5/16-in. holes .... 33 sfm (400 rpm)
  - 3/8-in. holes .... 39 sfm (400 rpm)

Feed:
- Spot drilling 5/16-in. holes .... 0.003 ipr
- Spot and through drilling 3/8-in. holes .... 0.006 ipr
- Through drilling 5/16-in. holes .... Hand feed

Length of cut (spot drilling) .... 1/4 in.
Cutting fluid .... Soluble oil
Tolerances:
- Location .... ±0.005 in.
- Diameter .... +0.010, −0.000 in.
- Straightness .... 0.010 in. in 6 in.

Surface finish .... 125 micro-in.
Tool life(a) .... 10 to 15 pieces per grind
Total machining time .... 30 min per piece(b)

(a) Tools were 118°-point, high speed steel twist drills with webs thinned to 0.062 in. (b) Machining time for each operation was as follows: Spot and through drilling of 5/16-in. holes, 0.82 and 5.50 min, respectively; spot and through drilling of 3/8-in. holes, 1.33 and 1.54 min, respectively. Remainder of the 30 min was used for setup in fixture, indexing and handling.

Fig. 14. Bowl top in which deep holes were spot and through drilled (Example 756)

Drilling was done on a four-spindle drill press with steplessly variable speed. A tachometer, accurate within 5%, was used to indicate spindle speed. The operator began drilling at the speed recommended on the work order for the part, after which he increased or decreased the speed according to the cutting action of the drill. Operating details are tabulated below Fig. 14.

Starting the drill is often a greater problem in drilling stainless steel than in carbon or alloy steel, mainly because stainless steel is more easily work hardened. When a spot is severely work hardened, it will cause the drill to wander or may overheat and dull the drill in a few revolutions.

When conventional center punches are used, they must be tapped lightly (especially when the higher-nickel grades of stainless are being drilled) to avoid creating hard spots. Tripod punches are preferred because they are less likely to cause work hardening at the center. The use of drill templates is another means of avoiding work hardening. When starting or re-entering a hole, the drill should be at full speed with positive feed. Dwell periods should not be permitted.

When numerically controlled equipment is available, center drilling is often used for locating and starting holes. The two examples that follow describe operations in which center drilling and the use of numerically controlled machines eliminated the need for drill jigs. In some applications, the use of spiral point drills has eliminated the need for jigs or center drilling when numerical control is used on the machine.

Examples 757 and 758. Use of Center Drills on Types 303 and 304 Stainless Steels

Example 757 (Table 16). The four 17/64-in.-diam holes in the 303 stainless steel (200 Bhn) clamping ring shown in Table 16 were drilled with center and taper shank twist drills in two operations on a single-spindle numerically controlled drill press equipped with a three-jaw chuck. First, each hole was started with a 3/16-in-diam center drill; then the holes were drilled to size by a taper shank drill. Center drilling prevented the taper shank drill from moving off center. Because the hole locations were programmed from tape, a drill jig was not required. Operating conditions for drilling are given in Table 16.

The 2-lb blank for the clamping ring was cut from bar stock and machined all over in two operations on a conventional turret lathe to a surface finish of 63 micro-in. After drilling, both sides of the holes were deburred on an adjacent single-spindle machine.

Example 758 (Table 17). Drilling the eight holes in the 304 stainless steel bracket shown in Table 17 was done on the numerically controlled drill press and in the manner described in Example 757. Conditions for drilling the bracket are given in Table 17. The bracket was held for drilling by nesting and clamping in standard step blocks.

The blank for the bracket was sheared to shape from plate stock having a hardness of 135 to 150 Bhn. The sheared blank weighed 8 1/2 lb. After shearing, the corner radii were hand ground with a 12-in.-diam grinding wheel that was mounted on a standard polishing machine.

Tolerance and Finish. When close-tolerance holes with a surface finish smoother than 125 micro-in. are specified, recommended practices are as follows:

1 Rough drill with a drill 1/32-in. under finish size, followed by a second drill about 0.010 in. undersize. Feed rate should be

Table 16. Conditions for Drilling Type 303 Stainless Steel Clamping Ring on Numerically Controlled Drill Press Using Center Drill and Taper Shank Twist Drill (Example 757)

Speed (each drill)	764 rpm(a)
Feed (each drill)	0.004 ipr
Cutting fluid	Soluble oil
Tool material	High speed steel
Tool life:	
Center drill	30 pieces per grind
Taper shank drill	10 pieces per grind
Total drilling time	0.488 min(b)
Tolerance:	
Hole diameter	±0.004 in.
Hole location	±0.010 in.
Surface finish (max roughness):	
Holes	63 micro-in.
Other surfaces	90 micro-in.

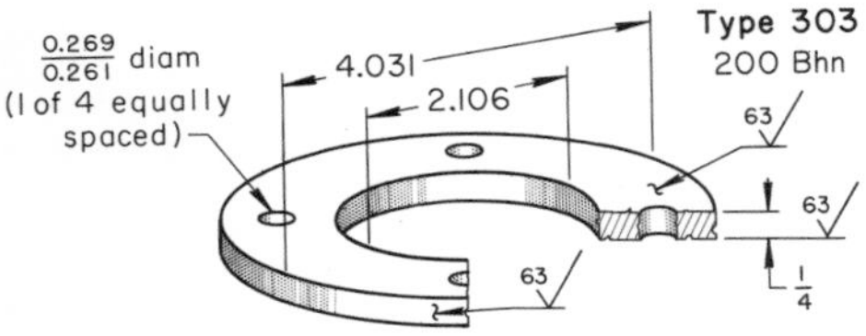

(a) Speed of center and taper shank drills was approximately 53 sfm. (b) Drilling time for four holes for center drill and taper shank drill was 0.16 and 0.328 min, respectively.

reduced during the second drilling for improved surface finish.

2 Ream with a high speed steel tool operating at 15 to 40 sfm and a feed of 0.003 to 0.0075 ipr. Finer finishes and closer tolerances can be produced by increasing the speed (between 40 and 100 sfm) but using the same feed. The best surface finish usually is produced by a carbide-tipped reamer with narrowed lands and a secondary lead angle, and operating at 100 to 300 sfm.
3 Hone, when necessary, for surface finishes that are difficult to obtain by other methods.

Other means of finishing a hole may be necessary if the required accuracy is beyond the capability of the drilling operation. The following example describes the use of rough drilling and boring to produce large holes with a close diametral tolerance.

Example 759. Drilling and Boring of Welded Assembly to Close Diametral Tolerances (Fig. 15)

Rough drilling and boring of 169 holes on each side (total of 338 holes) of a reactor core support assembly (Fig. 15) was necessary to obtain the required diametral tolerances (2.313 +0.002 and −0.000 in.). After welding, the assembly was rough machined all over and one side was drilled in quadrants, using a drilling template equipped with alignment pins. The holes were drilled singly in four settings as follows: First setting, seven rows of seven; second setting, six rows of seven; third setting, seven rows of six; fourth setting, six rows of six. The template was aligned for each next setting by extending alignment pins through two idle holes of the template into two holes previously drilled. It cost less to make the template for drilling in four settings than for drilling all the holes in one setting. The same drilling procedure was used for the opposite side. All drilling was done on a radial drill press.

After drilling with a 2⅛-in. drill, the core support plate was stress relieved, finish machined all over, and the holes were finish bored to size. Boring was done on a 5-in. table-type horizontal boring mill. A special tool was attached to a boring bar to machine the four slots in the ten holes shown in the center portion of one side. Each of these holes needed more machining as shown in Fig. 15.

A surface finish of 32 micro-in. was required for each bored hole. A few of the holes that did not meet this requirement were honed using a portable machine. Additional processing details are given with Fig. 15.

Gun Drilling. Stainless steels can be gun drilled with carbide-tipped tools having a bevel point, an outer point angle of 30° and an inner point angle of 20°. The tools should be provided with a relief angle of 6° to 15° on the outer point and 10° to 15° on the inner point. The outer relief angle should have a secondary clearance of 15° to 25°. The apex distance of the point for drills of this type is ¼ of the diameter. Back taper should be 0.0006 in. per linear inch.

Gun drills having step points are also used for drilling some grades of stainless steel — mainly the 300 series and 17-4 PH. The step points provide better chip breakage than those having bevel points, thus facilitating ejection of chips.

Table 17. Conditions for Drilling Type 304 Stainless Steel Bracket on Numerically Controlled Drill Press Using Center Drill and Taper Shank Twist Drills (Example 758)

Speed:	
5⁄16-in. center drill	65 sfm (800 rpm)
21⁄32-in. taper shank drill	33 sfm (190 rpm)
17⁄32-in. taper shank drill	26 sfm (190 rpm)
Feed:	
Center drill	0.003 ipr
Taper shank drills	0.005 ipr
Cutting fluid	Soluble oil
Tool material	High speed steel
Tool life:	
Center drill	30 pieces per grind
Each taper shank drill	4 pieces per grind
Total drilling time	6.192 min(a)
Tolerance, hole diameter	±0.010 in.
Surface finish	125 micro-in.

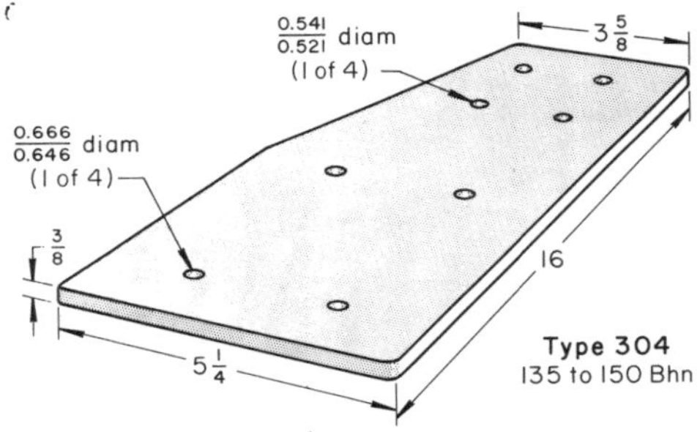

(a) Breakdown of time: center drilling, 0.512 min; drilling 21⁄32-in.-diam holes, 2.92 min; drilling 17⁄32-in.-diam holes, 2.76 min.

Nominal speeds and feeds for gun drilling with carbide tools are given in Table 18, which shows that speeds vary by as much as a factor of four, depending on composition and hardness of the work metal.

Hole straightness, out-of-roundness, and size can be held within closer limits with a gun drill than with a twist drill. Example 760 below and Examples 163 (for 17-7 PH) and 164 (for type 304) in the article on Drilling in this volume discuss applications of gun drilling. The latter two exemplify the advantages of gun drills over twist drills.

Example 760. Gun Drilling CA-15 Stainless Steel Castings (Fig. 16)

The eight cooling holes in the CA-15 stainless steel cast base shown in Fig. 16 were produced with a carbide-tipped gun drill. All holes were 0.1875 in. in diameter; however, the depth-to-diameter ratios varied from about 4-to-1 to 15-to-1. Operating conditions for gun drilling the cooling holes are given in the table that accompanies Fig. 16.

Reaming

Difficulties in reaming stainless steel are most often caused by previous operations. For example, if the feed in drilling is too light the hole wall can be severely work hardened and can resist cutting by the reamer. Drilling practice (particularly when the high-nickel grades of stainless are being drilled) is more critical when the holes are to be subsequently reamed. Also, because stainless steels are strongly susceptible to work hardening, it is important that sufficient stock remain on the workpiece to insure positive cutting by the reamer.

Reamer Design. Reamers of straight or spiral-flute design are used for both straight and tapered holes. Usually spiral-flute reamers are preferred because they are less susceptible to chatter, can better dispose of chips from deep holes, and are capable of producing a better finish.

Recommended design for high speed steel reamers for all grades of stainless steel at 135 to 425 Bhn is as follows: margin width, 0.005 in. to 0.015 in.; chamfer angle, 30° to 40°; chamfer length, 1⁄16 in., chamfer relief angle, 4° to 5°; radial rake angle, 5° to 8°; helix angle, 0° to 10°; and primary relief angle, 4° to 5°.

For carbide-tipped reamers, margin width should be 0.002 to 0.005 in. for reaming all free-machining stainless steels (135 to 425 Bhn) and martensitic grades up to Rockwell C 52. For reaming non-free-machining ferritic and

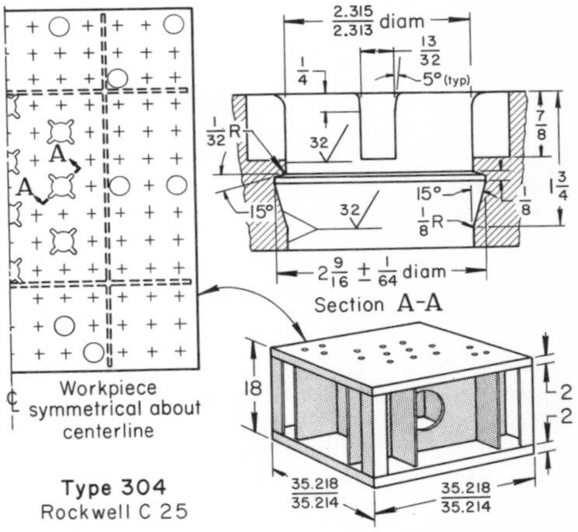

Speed:	
Rough drilling	30 sfm (54 rpm)
Boring	44 sfm (72 rpm)
Feed:	
Rough drilling	0.020 ipr
Boring	0.008 ipr
Cutting fluid	Soluble oil
Surface finish:	
After rough drilling	250 micro-in.
After boring or honing	32 micro-in.
Tool life, both tools(a)	1 hr per grind
Rough drilling time	6 min per hole(b)
Boring time	3 min per hole(c)

(a) Cutting tools were made of high speed steel. Drill was 2⅛ in. in diameter, with 135° point angle. (b) Average time per hole, including setting up and positioning. Actual drilling time was 3.5 min per hole. Floor-to-floor time for each side was 16.9 man-hr. (c) Three minutes required for boring the 2.313-in.-diam hole, not including tapered detail. Thirty additional minutes per hole was required for machining the tapered detail and the slots.

Fig. 15. Nuclear reactor core support assembly in which 338 holes were drilled and bored (Example 759)

Table 18. Nominal Speeds and Feeds for Gun Drilling Stainless Steels With Carbide Drills

Type of steel(a)	Condition(b)	Brinell hardness	Speed, sfm	Feed (ipr) for nominal diam (in.) of: Under 0.250	0.250 to 0.500	0.500 to 0.750	0.750 to 1.000	1.000 to 2.000
FM Fer	Ann	135 to 185	300	0.0004	0.0006	0.0008	0.001	0.0015
FM Mar	Ann	135 to 185	300	0.0004	0.0006	0.0008	0.001	0.0015
	Ann or CD	185 to 240	275	0.0004	0.0006	0.0008	0.001	0.0015
	Q and T	275 to 325	225	0.0004	0.0006	0.0008	0.001	0.0015
	Q and T	375 to 425	150	0.0003	0.0005	0.0007	0.0008	0.001
FM Aus	Ann	135 to 185	275	0.0004	0.0006	0.0008	0.001	0.0015
	CD	225 to 275	250	0.0004	0.0006	0.0008	0.001	0.0015
Ferritic	Ann	135 to 185	275	0.0004	0.0006	0.0008	0.001	0.0015
Mar(410)	Ann	135 to 185	275	0.0004	0.0006	0.0008	0.001	0.0015
	Ann	175 to 225	250	0.0004	0.0006	0.0008	0.001	0.0015
	Q and T	275 to 325	175	0.0003	0.0005	0.0006	0.0008	0.001
	Q and T	375 to 425	125	0.0002	0.0003	0.0004	0.0005	0.0007
Mar(431)	Ann	225 to 275	200	0.0003	0.0005	0.0006	0.0008	0.001
	Q and T	275 to 325	175	0.0003	0.0005	0.0006	0.0008	0.001
	Q and T	375 to 425	125	0.0002	0.0003	0.0004	0.0005	0.0007
Mar(440)	Ann	225 to 275	200	0.0003	0.0005	0.0006	0.0008	0.001
	Q and T	275 to 325	150	0.0003	0.0005	0.0006	0.0008	0.001
	Q and T	375 to 425	100	0.0002	0.0003	0.0004	0.0005	0.0007
	Q and T	Rc 48 to 52	75	0.0002	0.0003	0.0004	0.0005	0.0006
Aus(304)	Ann	135 to 185	250	0.0004	0.0006	0.0008	0.001	0.0015
	CD	225 to 275	200	0.0003	0.0005	0.0006	0.0008	0.001
Aus(316)	Ann	135 to 185	275	0.0004	0.0006	0.0008	0.001	0.0015
PH	Ann	150 to 200	250	0.0004	0.0006	0.0008	0.001	0.0015
	Hard	275 to 325	150	0.0003	0.0005	0.0006	0.0008	0.001
	Hard	325 to 375	100	0.0003	0.0005	0.0006	0.0008	0.001
	Hard	375 to 440	100	0.0002	0.0003	0.0004	0.0005	0.0006
Cast FM	Ann	140 to 170	300	0.0004	0.0006	0.0008	0.001	0.0015
Cast Fer	N and T	175 to 225	250	0.0003	0.0005	0.0006	0.0008	0.001
Cast Aus	Ann	140 to 190	200	0.0003	0.0005	0.0006	0.0008	0.001

(a) See Table 2 for types of steel in each group. (b) Ann = Annealed; CD = Cold drawn; Q and T = Quenched and tempered; Hard = Hardened; N and T = Normalized and tempered. (SOURCE: same as for Table 15)

austenitic grades, and precipitation-hardening grades, the margin should be increased to 0.005 to 0.010 in. For reaming all grades, carbide-tipped reamers should have a chamfer (lead) angle of 2° and chamfer length of 3/16 in., radial rake angle of 7° to 10°, helix angle of 5° to 8°, and primary relief angle of 7° to 15°.

For accuracy, reamers should be held in fixtures when being sharpened. Reamer edges should be stoned after grinding to remove grinding marks.

Speed and Feed. Table 19 shows nominal speeds and feeds for reaming stainless steels with six-flute reamers made of high speed steel and carbide. These operating conditions will produce accurate reamed holes. If surface finish is a primary requirement, it may be necssary to decrease speeds from the values shown in Table 19; for example, a decrease of as much as 50% may be necessary for the free-machining grades. For applications requiring both accuracy and fine finish, reaming in two stages, roughing and finishing, is recommended practice — it is often essential for tool life, as well.

Speeds for reaming vary widely, depending on work metal composition and hardness, and tool material, as indicated in Table 19. Work metal composition and hardness also influence selection of optimum feed, although the size of hole being reamed is a more important factor, as shown in Table 19. Specific conditions often permit or require some deviation in feed from those shown in Table 19. For instance, in Example 752 (Fig. 11) a feed of 0.012 ipr was used to ream type 329 stainless steel (precipitation hardening).

Tapping

More power is required to tap a hole in stainless steel than in carbon or alloy steel; tool life and production rates are lower, as indicated in Examples 228 to 231 in the article on Tapping in this volume. Whenever possible, it is desirable to use free-machining grades for tapping, especially when blind holes are specified, in order to minimize the difficulty of removing and disposing of chips. The gummy, stringy chips resulting from the non-free-machining grades of stainless steel are a source of difficulty in tapping.

In tapping all grades of stainless steel, and especially the non-free-machining grades, the following recommendations are made: (*a*) use taps that are as large as permissible in diameter (high side of the tolerance); (*b*) keep thread pitch as fine as possible, because the finer the pitch the less metal removed per tooth; (*c*) keep the percentage of full thread as low as permissible (60 to 75% is a preferred

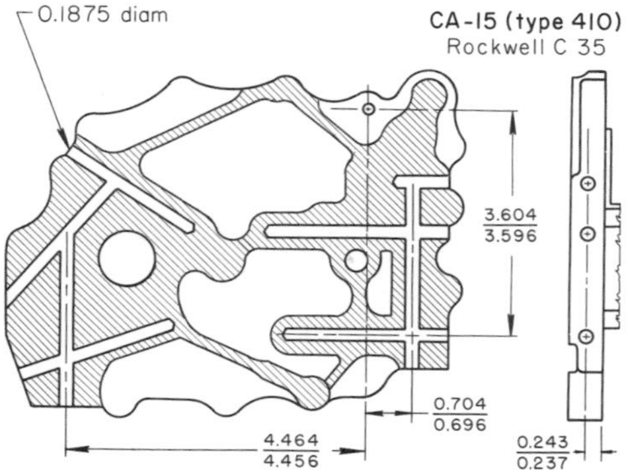

Speed .... 150 sfm (3000 rpm)
Feed .... ½ in. per min
Cutting fluid .... Sulfochlorinated oil(a)
Tool material .... Carbide tip
Tool life(b) .... 30 to 35 holes
Drilling time/in. of depth .... 2.14 min, avg

(a) Oil flow was 2 gpm at a pressure of 500 psi. (b) A 0.1875-in.-diam gun drill was used.

Fig. 16. Stainless steel base in which eight cooling holes were gun drilled (Example 760)

range); and (*d*) use a flood of cutting oil (under pressure of at least 5 psi when tapping blind holes).

Difficulties encountered in tapping stainless steel are often a result of work-hardened surfaces caused by previous drilling or reaming operations. Thus, when tapping problems arise, an investigation of the drilling and reaming conditions is recommended. Chips must be cut in either drilling or reaming; consequently when drills or reamers are permitted to burnish rather than cut, surfaces become work hardened. The degree of work hardening varies among the different grades of stainless steel; the higher-nickel austenitic grades are the most susceptible.

Tap Material and Design. High speed steel taps are nearly always used for tapping stainless steel. The general-purpose types of high speed steel, such as M1, M2, M7 and M10, are usually used for tapping free-machining ferritic, austenitic and martensitic grades with hardness up to 325 Bhn and for the precipitation-hardening steels with hardness up to 375 Bhn. The more highly alloyed high speed steels, such as M3, M44 and T15, are usually used for tapping the martensitic and precipitation-hardening grades at hardnesses of 375 Bhn and higher. Standard taps made of the general-purpose types of high speed steel are commercially available for tapping classes 1, 2 and 3 threads. Taps made of the more highly alloyed grades are available by special order.

Spiral-point (gun) taps with two or three flutes are used for the straight ferritic and austenitic grades. These taps are provided with a hook or rake angle of 15° to 20°, and a chamfer relief angle of 10°. Plug taps are provided with a chamfer angle of 10°.

Spiral-point taps produce good results in through holes ½ in. in diameter and smaller. They can be used also for blind holes, provided the depth of the hole is sufficiently greater than the length of thread to accommodate the chips at the bottom of the hole. When tapping to the bottom of the hole with a spiral-point tap, chip congestion will cause problems, as in the application described in the following example.

Example 761. Modified Tap for Small Blind Hole

A conventional two-flute high speed steel gun tap produced unsatisfactory results when tapping an 8–32 thread in a blind hole in small studs made of annealed 303 stainless steel (180 to 200 Bhn). It was required that the tap penetrate to a depth of 9/16 in. Chips packed at the bottom of the hole necessitated a secondary cleaning operation. This condition also resulted in poor tap life and frequent tap breakage.

These problems were eliminated by removing the points of the first three threads on the tap by grinding a flat at the end of each flute. This type of grind, which is used in tapping brass, provided more space for the chips and increased tap life.

Tapping was done on a standard drill press equipped with a tapping head and a rapid-acting fixture that held the workpiece.

Straight-flute taps with four flutes are recommended for free-machining, martensitic and precipitation-hardening grades. For tapping free-machining and martensitic grades, taps having a hook angle of 8° to 12° and chamfer relief of 10° are used, whereas a hook angle of 15° to 20° and chamfer relief of 8° are used on precipitation-hardening grades. A chamfer relief of 5° is provided on taper taps and of 10° on plug taps for tapping free-machining, martensitic and precipitation-hardening grades of stainless steel.

Straight-flute taps are used for holes larger than ½ in. in diameter. Collapsible taps are available for holes larger than 1 in. in diameter. Their use avoids the difficulties that occur in backing out solid taps.

For cutting class 3 threads, taps should have two flutes for holes up to size No. 6. Three-flute taps are satisfactory for hole sizes No. 6 to ½ in. in diameter. Three-flute taps reduce the possibility of cutting oversize but provide less chip clearance than two-flute taps. Holes larger than ½ in. in diameter are tapped with four-flute taps.

For tapping all classes of threads in deep holes, the lands of the tap should be thinned by grinding the heels to reduce the bearing areas. A tap with interrupted threads also is satisfactory.

Chamfer is provided on the tap to facilitate entry into the hole. This chamfer must be ground accurately. The chamfer must be short for blind holes that require threading close to the bottom, whereas the chamfer may extend over three to five threads for through holes. The chamfer angle with the axis of the tap should be 10° or more.

Tap design often is modified to improve performance. Modifications may be made by grinding longitudinal grooves along the lands, narrowing the land width, omitting the cutting edges on alternate threads, and providing relief behind the cutting edges. Figure 17 shows several modifications of tap design for tapping stainless steel.

For a given set of operating conditions, the style or design of the tap can greatly influence the quality of threads produced and the life of the tap. Example 224, in the article "Tapping", compares a shell tap and a collapsible tap in type 347 stainless steel. In the following example, tap design was progressively modified until high-quality threads and satisfactory tool life were obtained.

Table 19. Nominal Speeds and Feeds for Reaming Stainless Steels With Six-Flute Reamers

Type of steel(a)	Condition(b)	Brinell hardness	Speed (sfm) for tools of: HSS	Carbide	Feed (ipr) for nominal diam (in.) of: 0.125	0.250	0.500	1.000	1.500	2.000
FM Fer	Ann	135 to 185	75	300	0.002	0.005	0.010	0.016	0.020	0.025
FM Mar	Ann	135 to 185	75	300	0.002	0.005	0.010	0.016	0.020	0.025
	Ann or CD	185 to 240	65	250	0.002	0.005	0.010	0.016	0.020	0.025
	Q and T	275 to 325	35	140	0.002	0.005	0.010	0.016	0.020	0.025
	Q and T	375 to 425	25	75	0.001	0.003	0.007	0.010	0.012	0.015
FM Aus	Ann	135 to 185	50	200	0.003	0.005	0.010	0.016	0.020	0.025
	CD	225 to 275	45	180	0.003	0.005	0.010	0.016	0.020	0.025
Ferritic	Ann	135 to 185	45	180	0.004	0.007	0.010	0.016	0.020	0.025
Mar(410)	Ann	135 to 185	50	200	0.003	0.005	0.010	0.016	0.020	0.025
	Ann	175 to 225	45	180	0.002	0.005	0.010	0.016	0.020	0.025
	Q and T	275 to 325	30	100	0.002	0.005	0.010	0.016	0.020	0.025
	Q and T	375 to 425	20	60	0.001	0.003	0.007	0.010	0.012	0.015
Mar(431)	Ann	225 to 275	35	140	0.002	0.005	0.010	0.016	0.020	0.025
	Q and T	275 to 325	25	75	0.001	0.003	0.007	0.010	0.012	0.015
	Q and T	375 to 425	20	60	0.001	0.003	0.005	0.008	0.010	0.012
Mar(440)	Ann	225 to 275	30	100	0.002	0.005	0.010	0.016	0.020	0.020
	Q and T	275 to 325	20	60	0.001	0.003	0.007	0.010	0.012	0.015
	Q and T	375 to 425	15	50	0.001	0.002	0.005	0.008	0.010	0.012
	Q and T	R_C 48 to 52	10	25	0.001	0.002	0.003	0.005	0.008	0.010
Aus(304)	Ann	135 to 185	35	140	0.002	0.005	0.010	0.016	0.020	0.025
	CD	225 to 275	30	100	0.002	0.005	0.010	0.016	0.020	0.025
Aus(316)	Ann	135 to 185	35	140	0.002	0.005	0.010	0.016	0.020	0.025
PH	Ann	150 to 200	35	140	0.003	0.005	0.010	0.016	0.020	0.025
	Hard	275 to 325	25	75	0.003	0.005	0.008	0.010	0.012	0.015
	Hard	325 to 375	20	60	0.002	0.003	0.004	0.007	0.010	0.012
	Hard	375 to 440	15	50	0.002	0.003	0.004	0.007	0.010	0.012
Cast FM	Ann	140 to 170	40	160	0.003	0.004	0.008	0.012	0.015	0.020
Cast Fer	N and T	175 to 225	30	100	0.002	0.004	0.008	0.012	0.015	0.018
Cast Aus	Ann	140 to 190	25	75	0.003	0.004	0.007	0.010	0.012	0.015

(a) See Table 2 for types of steel in each group. (b) Ann = Annealed; CD = Cold drawn; Q and T = Quenched and tempered; Hard = Hardened; N and T = Normalized and tempered. (Data are adapted from tables compiled by Metcut Research Associates, Inc.)

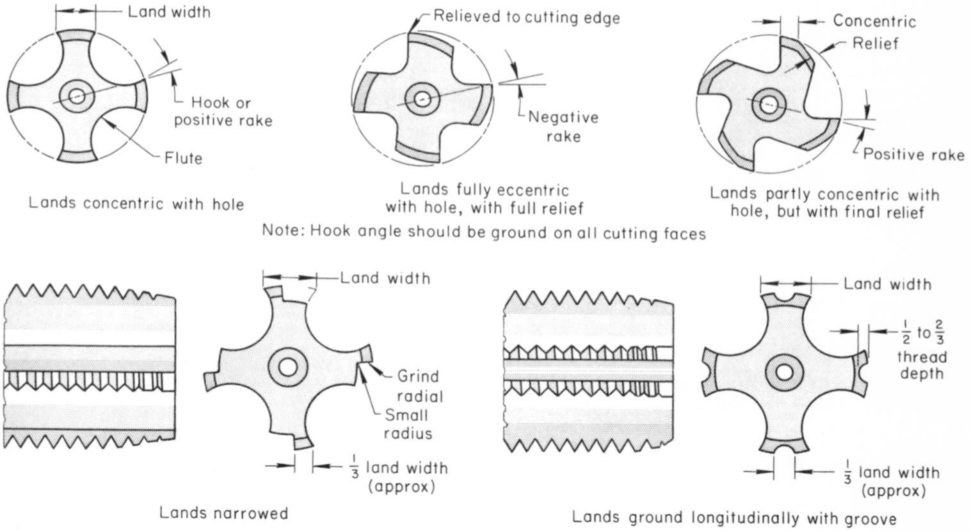

Fig. 17. Modification of tap design for tapping stainless steels

Example 762. Progressive Modification of Tap Design for Soft Austenitic Stainless (Fig. 18 and Table 20)

As the result of a series of modifications in tap design, the tool life of taps used to thread 304, 316 and 330 stainless steels on a single-spindle automatic machine was extended from 2 to 3000 holes per tap. Before the final (and most satisfactory) tap design was developed, tap breakage had been caused by the jamming of chips in the lands of the tap and by the tapping of holes previously work hardened in a drilling operation. In addition, the generation of excessive heat during tapping had caused breakdown of the tap teeth at the cutting tips.

The three austenitic stainless grades tapped were all in the annealed condition, with a hardness of Rockwell B 95 (208 Bhn) or less. The application consisted of drilling and tapping ¼-in.-diam holes in the valve bonnet shown in Table 20. Tap size was ¼-32. All parts were required to have a class 3 fit on 80% of the threads, and threads had to be smooth and free of tear marks.

The final tap design was achieved in six steps, the details of which are summarized in Table 20. Taps of all six designs were made of grade M2 high speed steel, and received no special surface treatment. The original tap and three of the redesigns — including the final one — are illustrated in Fig. 18.

In the initial setup, a standard four-flute, conventionally relieved, ground plug tap (Fig. 18a) was used. With two machine speeds available, tapping was performed at 275 rpm (approximately 18 sfm), and the tap was withdrawn at a speed of 610 rpm (approximately 40 sfm). Thus, the ratio of withdrawal speed to threading speed was 2.2 to 1. For lubrication, a mineral-base, extreme-pressure oil containing fatty oils and active sulfur was used; its viscosity was similar to that of SAE 20 oil. Under these conditions, not more than two holes could be tapped before heavy chips became packed in the flutes of the tap, which resulted in tap breakage.

Because greater chip relief was obviously required, a two-flute tap (Fig. 18b) was tried. This tap, which provided a land larger and stronger in cross section, was ground to a spiral point that afforded a path for chip disposal. Tapping was performed with this two-flute tap at the same speeds and feeds and with the same cutting oil that had been used with the original, four-flute taps. This tap resulted in more rubbing; galling occurred during withdrawal of the tap at high speed; and chips jammed the flutes, restricting flow of the cutting fluid.

The two-flute tap was modified to full relief, which allowed a greater flow of cutting oil around the cutting tips. This modification helped preserve cutting edges, reduced galling, and increased tap life to 22 holes.

Next, to increase the flow of cutting fluid to the tips, all threads to the rear of the seventeenth tooth (seventeen being the minimum number of teeth required for threading the part) were removed. Under these conditions, thread quality was improved and tool life was extended to 85 holes per tap.

The two-flute tap was modified again by removing approximately 75% of the land behind the cutting edge to the depth of the root diameter at the trailing edge of the land (Fig. 18c). This decrease in cutting-tool area permitted an increase in the flow of cutting fluid to the cutting edges and also reduced the area of the thread drag that occurred when the tap was withdrawn from the hole at high speeds.

With this tap, speeds and feeds were not altered, but the cutting fluid was changed to a highly chlorinated mineral-base oil to which fatty compounds were added. This oil contained a high percentage of sulfur, and its viscosity was similar to, or less than, that of SAE 10.

The three-flute tap, representing the ultimate improvement in design, incorporated an increase in the number of cutting edges (from two to three), thus providing increased distribution of cutting fluid around each row of cutting edges. Except for its having three flutes (Fig. 18d), it retained the same design as that shown for the two-flute tap.

To reduce the amount of work-hardened metal developed as a result of drilling, drill size was changed from a No. 5 (0.2055-in. diam) to a No. 6 (0.2040-in. diam), and a 5.3-mm (0.2087-in.) drill was used to finish the hole before tapping. (Finishing feed was 0.006 ipr, with a spindle speed of 610 rpm.) The cutting fluid was changed to include a 10% addition containing 45% sulfur compounded with mineral oil; this was a heavy mineral oil that had a viscosity closely similar to that of SAE 40 or 50.

After producing 3000 holes, the new tap showed little sign of wear. Galling and metal flow at the tips of the stainless steel threads were virtually eliminated. The threads were smooth, and gaged satisfactorily with a class 3 thread gage.

Speed for tapping may range from 5 to 50 sfm, depending on composition and hardness of the work metal, as shown in Table 21. Other factors also influence tapping speed. Depth of hole is one of these factors. It is recommended that speed be reduced 5% every time the depth of the tapped hole is doubled. Thread pitch also influences speed; slower speeds are required for tapping coarser threads.

Withdrawal speed can be the same as that used for cutting the threads, but is often increased in order to reduce total machining time per hole. In Example 762, for instance, withdrawal speed was more than twice the cutting speed.

Equipment and Operation. Tapping can be accomplished in different types of machines, including drill presses, lathes, automatics, and boring mills. A comparison between a drill press and a boring mill for one operation is described in the following example.

Example 763. Change From Drill Press to Boring Mill to Reduce Tap Cost (Fig. 19)

Tool cost for tapping 1–8 UNC–2B threads ¾ in. deep in 24 holes in the 304 stainless steel support plate shown in Fig. 19 was less when done in a horizontal boring mill than when a radial drill press was used. The drill press had a 9-ft arm. The horizontal mill was equipped with a 7-in. bar. The workpiece was set up in a nonindexing fixture attached to an angle plate. Tapping was done with a straight-flute high speed steel tap that had been treated by wet blasting. Taps were also wet blasted after each sharpening.

In addition to the lower tool cost per hole, tapping in the horizontal boring mill resulted in a better finish, less time for tool changes, lower tool-sharpening cost, and a smaller tool inventory. Processing details and comparisons are shown in Fig. 19.

Tapping is often done on a manually operated tapping machine when the application involves small lots of workpieces for which the cost of a more productive machine is not warranted. Accurate and high-quality threads can be produced by such hand tapping, as in the low-volume operation described in the following example.

Example 764. Hand Tapping Small Lots of Type 304 Stainless Steel Disks

Because of the small quantity (40 pieces), tapping ½–20 UNF–3B threads in four through holes was done in a hand tapping machine. The workpiece was a 6-in.-diam disk ½ in. thick, made of 304 stainless steel (200 Bhn). Each hole was drilled and reamed to 29/64-in. diam prior to tapping.

A four-flute high speed steel precision-ground (GH3) tap with a 15° hook angle was used. The hook grind included the first full tooth. It was required that the tap, whether new or resharpened, be checked before being used to insure concentricity of 0.002-in. max TIR at the last tooth on the chamfer adjacent to the first full tooth.

The workpiece was clamped to the platen of the machine. The tap was aligned with the hole and hand-fed through. Pitch-diameter tolerance, as measured by gage, was GO 0.4675 in., NOT GO 0.4701 in. The tap was reground every 28 holes to insure accurate thread. Sulfurized oil was used as the cutting fluid.

Blind holes pose more problems in tapping than through holes, especially when minimum space is provided at the bottom of the hole for chips. When tapping close to the bottom is required, final hand tapping is generally necessary, as in the following example.

Example 765. Tapping to the Bottom of Blind Holes (Table 22)

The following procedure was used for tapping 10–24 UNC–3B threads within 0.010 in. of the bottom of four ½-in.-deep blind holes in a 410 stainless steel aircraft casting (see inset section in Table 22):

1 A four-spindle drill press was used for drilling the holes and tapping them to a depth of 7/16 in. with a bottoming tap. (Countersinking the holes made it possible to begin tapping with a bottoming tap rather than the more usual plug tap.)
2 The casting was removed from the machine and the holes were hand tapped to within 0.010 in. of full depth with a special tap.

Table 22 gives details of both taps (identified there as taps 1 and 2, respectively), and lists operating conditions and cost data for this application.

Table 20. Details and Results of Progressive Redesigns of M2 High Speed Steel Taps for High-Speed Tapping of Stainless Steels (Example 762) (a)

Tap design changes	Number of flutes	Condition of threads	Holes per tap, max
Original tap (Fig. 18a)	4	Ragged and torn	2
Relief of 70% of land length; change to spiral point (Fig. 18b)	2	Slight improvement	8
Full relief of land length	2	About 40% of thread area galled	22
Removal of excess threads, to allow cutting fluid to reach cutting edges	2	Very slight galling	85
Removal of 75% of land behind cutting edge (Fig. 18c)	2	Good	264
Three flutes instead of two (Fig. 18d)	3	Excellent	3000(b)

NOTE. The only operational changes were: (1) change from a mineral-base, extreme-pressure oil to a mineral-base highly chlorinated oil at tool life of 85 holes per tap; and (2) change of drill size from No. 5 (0.2055-in. diam) to No. 6 (0.2040-in. diam), followed by a reaming operation with a 5.3-mm (0.2087-in.) drill, at tool life of 3000 holes per tap; a 10% sulfurized compound was added to the cutting fluid at this point.

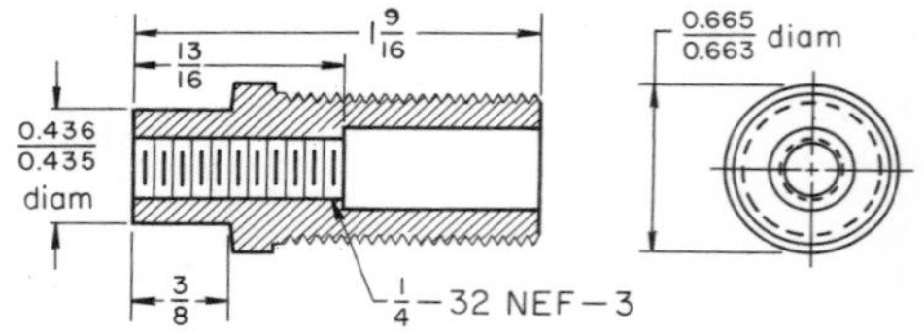

(a) Operation consisted of drilling and tapping ¼-in.-diam holes in the stainless steel valve bonnet shown above. (b) Tap showed little wear after 3000 holes.

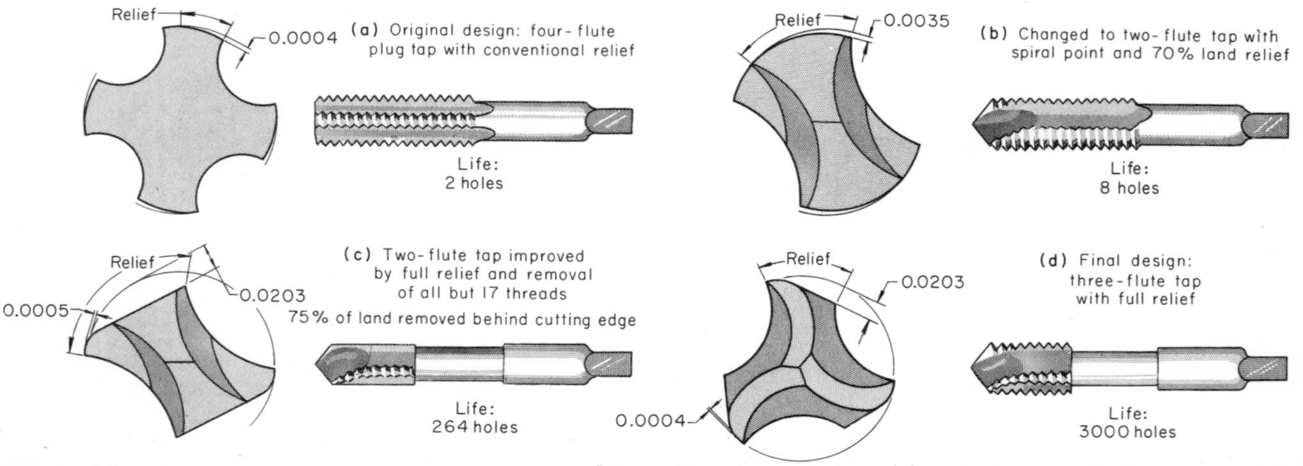

Tap shown in (*a*) underwent five revisions before final design (*d*), which produced a 1500-fold increase in tool life in tapping ¼-in.-diam holes in valve bonnets (see sketch in Table 20, above) of soft austenitic stainless steels (types 304, 316 and 330). Two intermediate redesigns are shown in (*b*) and (*c*). Taps of all designs were of M2 high speed steel and had standard lead and hook angles.

Fig. 18. Progressive modification of tap design for tapping ¼–32 threads in stainless steel valve bonnets (Example 762)

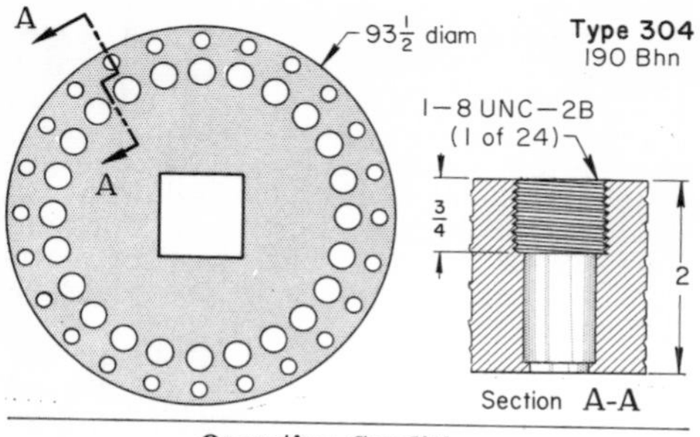

Operating Conditions

Speed .... 15 sfm
Cutting fluid .... Soluble-oil emulsion
Production rate .... 1 min per hole

Cost of Tools

Item	Drill press	Boring mill
Cost per tap (approx)	$8.00	$8.00
Number of holes tapped before sharpening	12	24
Tool cost per hole	$0.666	$0.333

Fig. 19. Support plate in which 24 holes were tapped in a radial drill press vs a horizontal boring mill (Example 763)

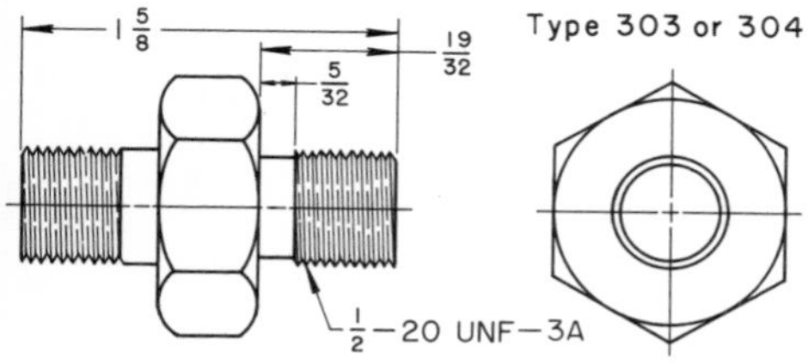

Item	Stainless steel(a) 303	Stainless steel(a) 304
Speed, sfm	20	12
Production, pcs/hr..	110	95
Chaser life, pcs(b) ..	300	225
Chaser cost	$17.15(c)	$22.75(d)

(a) Fittings of both steels were threaded in a turret lathe, using soluble oil as cutting fluid. (b) Pieces threaded per set of chasers. (c) Includes three sets of chasers at $4.90 per set and seven grinds at $0.35 per grind. (d) Includes four sets of chasers at $4.90 per set and nine grinds at $0.35 per grind.

Fig. 20. Threaded fitting produced from two different grades of stainless steel (Example 766)

Die Threading

Cutting edges of threading dies (chasers) are made of high speed steel, regardless of whether the die is self-opening or solid. General-purpose high speed steels such as M1, M2, M7 and M10 are satisfactory for most threading applications. Dies made of the more highly alloyed grades such as M3, M44 or T15 are preferred for threading martensitic or precipitation-hardening stainless at a hardness of 375 Bhn or higher.

Tool Design. Standard chasers for threads of 32 to 13 pitch have a chamfer angle of 25°. Chasers should have a lead of 1½ to 3 threads for economical and satisfactory operation.

Rake angles for the cutting teeth of a chaser vary with the grade of stainless steel being threaded and with the type of chaser. Tangent and circular chasers are provided with a rake of 20° to 28° for threading non-free-machining straight-chromium grades with normal carbon content, such as types 403, 410, 430, 431, 442 and 446, and for chromium-nickel grades such as types 302, 304, 309, 310, 316, 321 and 347. A rake angle of 15° to 20° is used for threading types 420 and 440A, B, and C. Tangential chasers for threading the free-machining grades are provided with rake angles of 10° to 20°; larger angles are used on circular chasers.

The first few cutting edges of the chasers are provided with clearance to reduce rubbing and generation of frictional heat. Clearance is helpful especially when threads expand as cutting proceeds — for example, fine threads cut to close tolerances. For tangential chasers, a clearance angle of 22° to 25° is usual; for circular chasers, a clearance angle of 7° to 10° is preferred.

Table 21. Nominal Speeds for Tapping Stainless Steels(a)

Type of steel(b)	Condition(c)	Brinell hardness	Speed, sfm
FM Fer	Ann	135 to 185	50
FM Mar	Ann	135 to 185	50
	Ann or CD	185 to 240	40
	Q and T	275 to 325	30
	Q and T	375 to 425	10
FM Aus	Ann	135 to 185	40
	CD	225 to 275	35
Ferritic	Ann	135 to 185	30
Mar(410)	Ann	135 to 185	35
	Ann	175 to 225	30
	Q and T	275 to 325	20
	Q and T	375 to 425	10
Mar(431)	Ann	225 to 275	25
	Q and T	275 to 325	20
	Q and T	375 to 425	10
Mar(440)	Ann	225 to 275	20
	Q and T	275 to 325	15
	Q and T	375 to 425	10
	Q and T	Rc 48 to 52	5
Aus(304)	Ann	135 to 185	25
	CD	225 to 275	20
Aus(316)	Ann	135 to 185	20
PH	Ann	150 to 200	25
	Hard	275 to 325	20
	Hard	325 to 375	15
	Hard	375 to 440	10
Cast FM	Ann	140 to 170	25
Cast Fer	N and T	175 to 225	20
Cast Aus	Ann	140 to 190	15

(a) For tapping steels under 375 Bhn, M10, M7 and M1 high speed steel taps. For steels over 375 Bhn, M3 and M40 taps. (b) See Table 2 for types of steel in each group. (c) Ann = Annealed; CD = Cold drawn; Q and T = Quenched and tempered; Hard = Hardened; N and T = Normalized and tempered. (Data are adapted from tables compiled by Metcut Research Associates, Inc.)

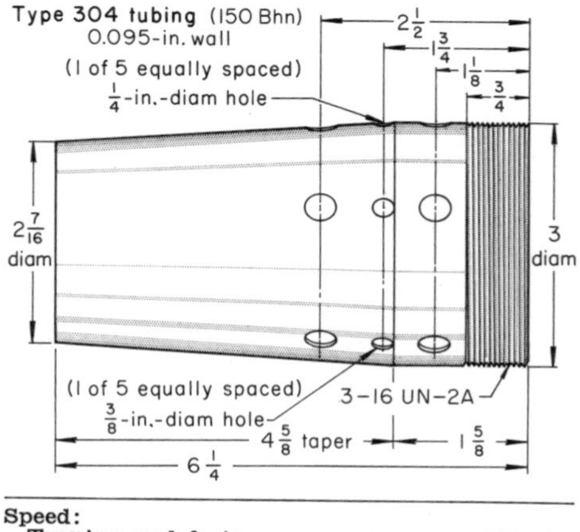

Speed:
Turning and facing .... 250 sfm
Threading .... 25 sfm
Feed: turning and facing .... 0.006 in.
Cutting fluid .... Sulfurized oil
Surface finish .... 125 micro-in.
Machining time (total) .... 15 min per piece

Fig. 21. Fire tube trued and threaded in an engine lathe (Example 767)

Speed for threading the free-machining grades of stainless steel is about 25 sfm; when all conditions are most favorable, a speed of 30 to 35 sfm is used for types 430F and 416. The other grades are threaded at speeds of 10 to 20 sfm. The production of threads of extreme accuracy and high surface finish may require the use of speeds of less than 10 sfm.

Threading speed depends on the machinability of the stainless steel. The following example is a typical comparison of speed, production rate and tool cost for tapping two austenitic stainless steels, one of which is free-machining.

Example 766. Productivity and Tool Costs for Threading Type 303 vs Type 304 (Fig. 20)

A self-opening die was used in a turret lathe to cut threads on one end of the stainless steel fitting illustrated in Fig. 20. Tool costs and production rates in threading types 303 and 304 stainless steel are compared in the table below the illustration. As these data show, productivity was about 15% higher for the free-machining type 303 than for type 304.

Production Practice. In practice, specific conditions often require special techniques or changes in tooling or procedure to obtain satisfactory results. A change in procedure that eliminated chaser damage in stainless steel is described in Example 256 in the article on Die Threading in this volume. The three examples that follow describe techniques used to meet specific requirements in the threading of stainless steel.

Example 767. Single-Point Chaser for Threading 0.095-In.-Wall Tubing (Fig. 21)

A single-point high speed steel chaser was required for threading the 0.095-in.-wall fire tube shown in Fig. 21. Threading with a die

Table 22. Tap and Processing Details for Example 765

(Tapping to the bottom of a blind hole)

Tap Details

	Tap 1(a)	Tap 2(b)
Type of chamfer ...	Bottoming	No-lead(c)
Number of flutes ...	3	3
Pitch diameter limit.	GH2	GH1
Cost, each	$2.86	$3.23

Operating Conditions

Speed, tap 1 .... 90 rpm (4.5 sfm)
Speed, tap 2 .... Hand tapped
Cutting fluid .... High-viscosity sulfurized oil
Setup time .... 30 minutes
Production rate .. 32 holes (8 pieces) per hour
Tap life per grind:
Tap 1 .... 40 holes
Tap 2 .... 60 holes
Downtime for tool change .... 20 minutes
Labor cost .... $2.75 per hour
Tool maintenance cost .... $3.75 per hour

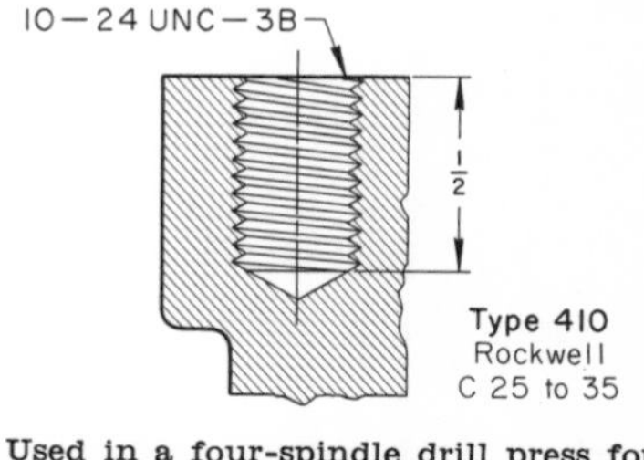

(a) Used in a four-spindle drill press for tapping the drilled and countersunk hole to 7/16-in. depth. (b) Used for hand tapping hole to full depth. (c) Chamfer, 0.010 in. by 45°.

had been attempted but this tool caused out-of-roundness in the thread area. The fire tube was made of type 304 stainless steel tubing (150 Bhn).

Before the thread was cut, it was necessary to true the part, because the preceding forming operation had caused a slight out-of-roundness. A tapered 3-in. plug was inserted into the tapered section. The part was placed in the four-jaw chuck of an engine lathe for truing the straight section, facing the end and machining a small chamfer in the inside diameter. This was followed by positioning a bell center firmly in the end to be threaded, after which 3–16 UN–2A threads were cut. To prevent distortion, a 0.010 to 0.015-in. depth of cut was used in all machining operations. Other processing details are given with Fig. 21.

Example 768. Four-Chaser vs Five-Chaser Die for Cutting Class 3 Threads

Workpieces made of type 303 stainless steel (180 Bhn) required 1–8 class 3 threads. Because the chips were tough and stringy, tolerances could not be maintained when a four-chaser die was used. A five-chaser die was tried, and the improvement was sufficient to meet class 3 requirements consistently.

Example 769. Die Threading Type 304 Torque Rods (Fig. 22)

Two self-opening dies with high speed steel chasers were used to thread tapered ⅜–18 NPT and straight ⅝–11 UNC–2A threads on the 304 stainless steel cabinet torque rod shown in Fig. 22. The part was made from ⅝-in.-diam rod. Machining involved facing one end, threading the ⅝-in. length, cutting off, rechucking, facing the opposite end, beveling the end for turning with a roller turning tool, turning the 0.500-in. diameter, and threading over a length of 3 in. The workpiece was held in a ⅝-in. collet of a turret lathe for all machining operations. Other processing details are given with Fig. 22.

Thread Milling

Thread milling is recommended for cutting internal or external threads on stainless steel workpieces when one or more of the following conditions exist: (*a*) when the pitch of the thread is too coarse for cutting with a tap or die; (*b*) when the size of the hole requiring an internal thread is too large to be practical for tapping; (*c*) when surface finish or dimensional accuracy is critical; (*d*) when thread milling is the only applicable method because of proximity to adjacent surfaces; (*e*) when the workpiece is too large for a drilling or tapping machine or a lathe.

Dimensional accuracy and surface finish often are the reasons for using the process. It is possible to mill threads with a finish of 55 micro-in. Lead error can be held to 0.001 in. per ft, and spacing errors on multiple-start threads can be held within 0.0003 to 0.0004 in. To prevent distortion on long or multiple-start screws, two or three passes of the cutter may be required.

Tooling and Equipment. Both single-thread and multiple-thread cutters are employed. Multiple cutters are of either the topping or the nontopping type. Topping cutters mill the flanks, root and outside diameter, and produce threads with concentric major, minor, and pitch diameters. Approximately 0.010 in. of stock must be allowed for finishing by topping cutters. A nontopping cutter is used when the crest of a thread is of the required size prior to thread milling.

In conventional thread milling the work is held in a chuck and rotated about a fixed axis. The cutter rotates on an axis parallel to the axis of the work. Universal thread millers can produce any type of thread, and can use either single or multiple cutters.

In planetary milling the workpiece does not revolve, but is held in a fixture, and the cutter revolves around the workpiece. Feed is accomplished by means of two eccentric quills. The planetary machine can thread mill odd-shaped workpieces. A typical planetary machine is electronically controlled for both feed-in and feed-around. A planetary machine was used in the application described in Example 770.

Speed and feed for thread milling stainless steels are given in Table 23, which shows nominal speeds varying from 45 to 150 sfm for wrought stainless steel, and from 55 to 85 sfm for three different groups of cast stainless steel. Nominal feed for stainless steel is 0.001 to 0.002 ipr, as indicated in Table 23. Values in Table 23 are for initial guidance only.

Production Example. In the following example, thread milling was selected for more than one of the reasons outlined at the beginning of this section. Size of the internal thread (8-in. diameter) and quality requirements were the principal reasons.

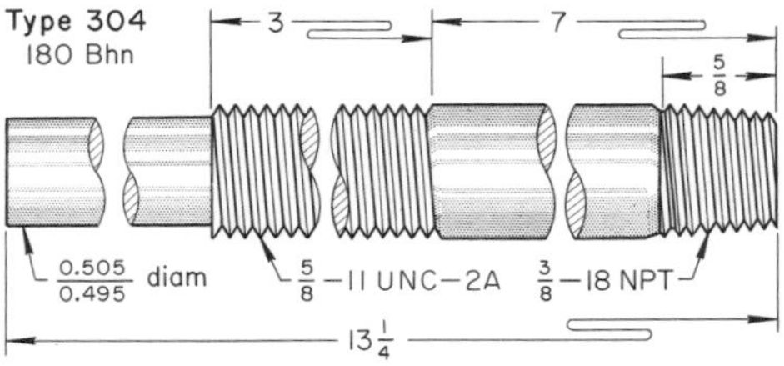

Speed:
Facing and turning ....200 sfm (1222 rpm)
Cutting off ....150 sfm (917 rpm)
Threading ....10 sfm (62 rpm)
Feed:
Facing and turning ....0.010 ipr
Cutting off ....0.003 ipr
Cutting fluid ....Soluble oil
Surface finish ....63 micro-in.
Tool life(a) ....100 pieces per grind(b)
Machining time ....0.16 hr per piece

(a) Carbide-tipped tools were used for facing, turning and cutting off, and two self-opening dies with high speed steel chasers were used for threading. Carbide had medium shock resistance and medium wear resistance, and contained tungsten carbide and cobalt. (b) Tool life of carbide-tipped facing, turning and cut-off tools; life of threading tools was 30 pieces.

Fig. 22. Torque rod machined by facing, turning, threading and cutting off in a turret lathe (Example 769)

Example 770. Milling an 8-In.-Diam Thread in a Tubular Housing (Table 24)

The inside diameter of a type 304 (200 Bhn) stainless steel tubular housing was threaded with a 5½ pitch modified Acme 14½°–5° thread by milling with a planetary mill that was mounted in a horizontal milling machine. Prior to threading, the housing was bored and honed to an inside diameter of 8.000 in.

Because the cost of these workpieces was high at the stages of processing immediately preceding thread milling, subsequent operations had to be completed under conditions that would insure an acceptable product. Therefore, threading was done in three cuts: roughing, semifinishing, and finishing. The cutter was ground after every third thread was completed. A chlorinated oil was used for cutting fluid; specifications did not permit the use of a sulfurized oil. Other processing details are given in Table 24.

Multiple-Operation Machining in Automatic Bar and Chucking Machines

Turret lathes, hand-operated and automatic, single-spindle and multiple-spindle automatic bar machines and chucking machines are used for multiple-operation machining of stainless steel when production quantities are high enough to warrant the use of such mass-production equipment. (Typical comparisons with operation of engine lathes are given in Examples 12 and 14 in the article on Turning.)

Many kinds of attachments and accessories can be added to the machines,

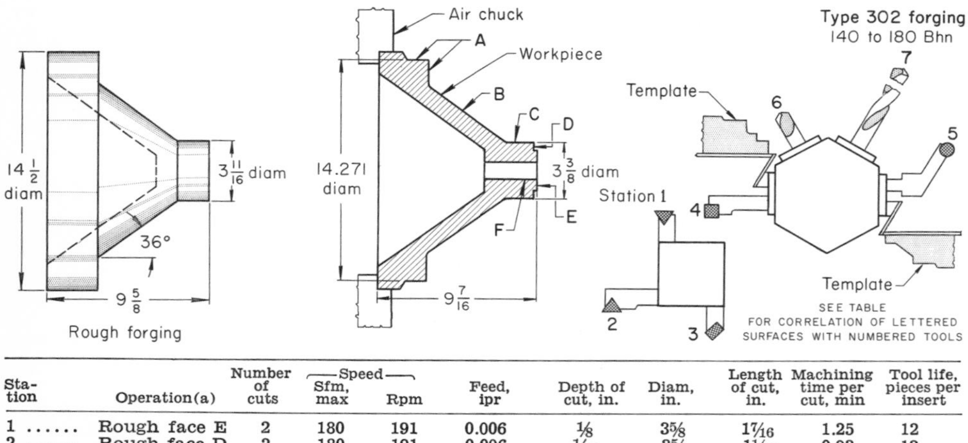

Station	Operation(a)	Number of cuts	Speed: Sfm, max	Speed: Rpm	Feed, ipr	Depth of cut, in.	Diam, in.	Length of cut, in.	Machining time per cut, min	Tool life, pieces per insert
1	Rough face E	2	180	191	0.006	⅛	3⅝	1 7/16	1.25	12
2	Rough face D	2	180	191	0.006	1/16	3⅝	1 1/16	0.93	12
3	Rough turn C	1	170	191	0.012	⅛	3⅜	1 7/16	0.61	12
	Rough face A		305	83	0.0095	⅛	14¼	1⅝	2.04	12
4	Finish turn C, finish face D and E	1	250	284	0.012	0.020	3⅜	2 7/16	0.71	30
5	Finish turn B	2	790	284	0.012	0.020	10⅝	12¼	3.58	30
	Finish face A		1050	284	0.012	0.020	14¼			
6	Spot drill F	1	28	108	0.007	....	1	0.280	0.37	12(b)
7	Drill F	1	25	108	0.007	....	⅞	2.000	2.64	10(b)

(a) Carbide insert tools were used for all turning and facing operations. Drills were made of high speed steel. (b) Number of pieces per grind.

Fig. 23. Bowl top that was machined on its external surfaces, and the tools used (Example 771)

Table 23. Nominal Speeds and Feeds for Thread Milling Stainless Steels

Type of steel(a)	Condition(b)	Brinell hardness	Speed, sfm	Feed, ipt/rev
FM Fer	Ann	135 to 185	150	0.002
FM Mar	Ann	135 to 185	150	0.002
	Ann or CD	185 to 240	135	0.002
	Q and T	275 to 325	75	0.001
FM Aus	Ann	135 to 185	100	0.002
	CD	225 to 275	90	0.0015
Ferritic	Ann	135 to 185	110	0.002
Mar(410)	Ann	135 to 185	110	0.002
	Ann	175 to 225	110	0.002
	Q and T	275 to 325	65	0.001
Mar(431)	Ann	225 to 275	70	0.0015
	Q and T	275 to 325	55	0.001
Mar(440)	Ann	225 to 275	65	0.0015
	Q and T	275 to 325	50	0.001
Aus(304)	Ann	135 to 185	90	0.002
	CD	225 to 275	80	0.0015
Aus(316)	Ann	135 to 275	80	0.002
PH	Ann	150 to 200	70	0.002
	Hard	275 to 325	60	0.001
	Hard	325 to 375	45	0.002
Cast FM	Ann	140 to 170	85	0.002
Cast Fer	N and T	175 to 225	75	0.002
Cast Aus	Ann	140 to 190	55	0.002

(a) See Table 2 for types of steel in each group. (b) Ann = Annealed; CD = Cold drawn; Q and T = Quenched and tempered; Hard = Hardened; N and T = Normalized and tempered. (Data are adapted from tables compiled by Metcut Research Associates, Inc.)

as, for instance, tracer units for control. A tracer-controlled automatic machine usually can increase the rate of production over other multiple-operation machines, as illustrated in the two examples that follow.

Example 771. Sequence of Machining Operations to Maintain Tolerances and Finish (Fig. 23)

Facing and turning operations were required to produce the part shown in Fig. 23 with a surface finish of 125 micro-in. and a tolerance of ±0.020 in., from a 302 stainless steel forging. The forged blank weighed 110 lb and had a hardness of 140 to 180 Bhn. After rough machining the exterior surfaces of the forging, internal surfaces were rough and finish machined. These operations were followed by finish machining the external surfaces in a fixed sequence. Deviations from this sequence resulted in out-of-tolerance parts. The ⅞-in. hole was drilled after finish machining of the exterior. The sequence of operations and other details for machining the exterior surfaces are shown in Fig. 23. Machining removed 50 lb of metal.

The forging was machined in a turret lathe equipped with tracer slides mounted on the face of the turret. A speed cam working in relation to the forward motion of the turret provided constant surface speed through a variable-speed drive. This arrangement enabled the cutting tool to produce a satisfactory surface finish as it progressed down the cone from the small to the large diameter. Production was at the rate of two pieces per hour.

Previously, a vertical turret lathe had been used to machine the part. However, this machine required about twice as much time as the tracer-equipped turret lathe. Also, polishing was necessary for the desired finish.

Example 772. Tracer-Controlled Turret Lathe for Machining a Forged Bowl Top (Fig. 24)

Figure 24 shows the setup and tools and gives processing data for rough and partial finish machining a 304 stainless steel bowl top from a forging in two chuckings in a tracer-controlled turret lathe. Production quantities of this part averaged 10 pieces per lot; seldom were more than 25 pieces per lot required. The use of a forging for the bowl top resulted in removal of about 11 lb of metal; weights of the forging and the finished part were 19 and 8⅝ lb, respectively.

Formerly, a standard turret lathe with a hand-operated chuck had been used to rough machine the part. It had been necessary to machine the large end to provide it with a suitable chucking surface, after which the part had been chucked for rough machining of the shank end and adjacent surfaces.

To improve the production rate, subsequent production lots were machined on a tracer-controlled turret lathe. This equipment reduced setup time and machine handling, permitted greater stock removal because of power chucking of the part, eliminated the need for turning the large end to provide a chucking surface, and accomplished most of the finishing operations. Tool overhang was kept at a minimum for greater rigidity. Longer tool life was achieved by removing the rough, uneven forged surface prior to tracing.

Total time for the first chucking (using a three-jaw, hard-jawed chuck) was 2.74 hr per 10 pieces (16.44 min per piece). Processing details for the first chucking are given below Fig. 24.

A three-jaw power chuck with soft jaws was used for the second chucking. Approximately ¼ lb of metal was removed during the second chucking operations and it was important that the machined surfaces be dimensionally accurate, square, and concentric. A thread was milled on diameter G (see Fig. 24) after finish machining. It was required that the thread be concentric within 0.005 in. with the chucking diameter and square within 0.005 in. per foot with the centerline of the part. For this reason the part was chucked (see second chucking in Fig. 24) to permit a back facing operation on surface P just before removal of the part from the machine. Total time for the second chucking operations averaged 15 min per piece. Processing details for these operations are given with Fig. 24.

Even though production rates often can be improved by the use of an automatic machine, other factors may preclude the use of such equipment, as shown by the example on the next page.

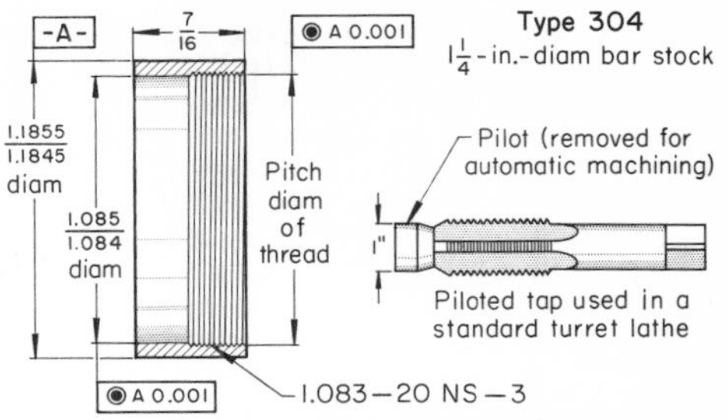

Fig. 25. Type 304 sleeve and the piloted tap used in threading operation (Example 773)

Table 24. Milling Internal Threads in Type 304 Tubing (Example 770)

Machine	Planetary thread mill(a)
Threading tool	Milling cutter(b)
Cutter material	T15 high speed steel
Operating Conditions	
Speed	35 sfm (28 rpm)
Feed	0.33 in. per cutter revolution
Length of threaded section	3½ in.
Depth of cut:	
Roughing	0.060 in.
Semifinishing	0.039 in.
Finishing	0.007 in.
Machining time	28 minutes(c)
Cutting fluid	Chlorinated oil(d)
Tool life	3 threads per grind
Surface finish	63 micro-in.

(a) Planetary mill was mounted on a 7-in. horizontal milling machine. (b) Cutter (4.785-in. diam) was form ground to produce a 5½-pitch modified Acme thread (standard 14½° on one side and modified to 5° on the opposite side). (c) For each planetary cycle; total threading time, including measurements and tool inspection after each pass, was 3 hr. (d) Cutting fluid had high chlorine and high fat content.

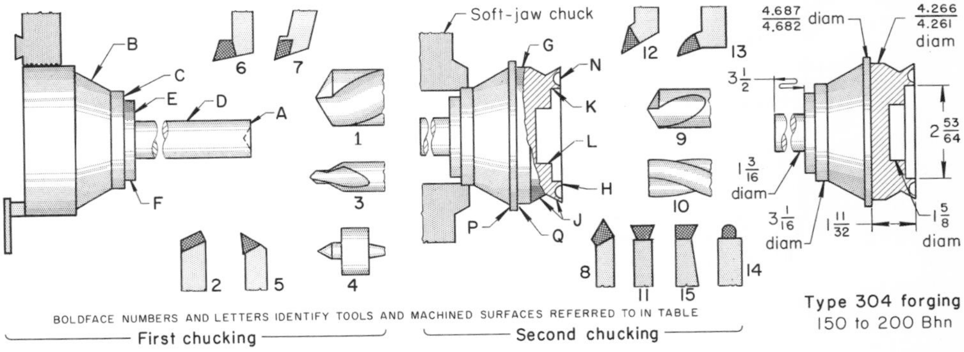

Tool No.	Operation and surface	Speed, rpm(a)	Feed, ipr	Machining time, min
	Sequence of Operations, First Chucking(b)			
1	Spot drill A(c)	220	0.008	0.52
2	Finish face A(d)	439	0.005	0.57
3	Center A	439	0.002	0.55
4	Position live center	...	....	0.25
2	Rough form B	220	0.005	1.14
2	Rough face C	220	0.005	1.14
5	Rough turn D	220	0.011	1.07
6	Rough trace, full length	220	0.011	3.24
7	Finish trace(e)	439	0.011	3.20
7	Finish trace(e)	220	0.011	3.20

Tool No.	Operation and surface	Speed, rpm(a)	Feed, ipr	Machining time, min
	Sequence of Operations, Second Chucking(f)			
8	Rough turn G	86	0.011	1.52
8	Rough face H	161	0.011	0.59
8	Rough form J	161	0.004	0.87
9	Drill K	126	0.004	0.65
10	Flat bottom drill	126	0.004	0.65
11	Rough slab face L	161	0.011	0.42
11	Rough bore K	161	0.011	0.42
12	Finish G	321	0.011	1.82
13	Finish K	321	0.011	1.82
14	Groove N	161	0.002	0.56
15	Back face P	161	0.002	0.55
15	Rough radius Q	321	0.005	0.59

(a) Speed for all turning and facing operations was about 250 sfm; speed for a final tracing cut was 300 sfm.
(b) Total stock removal was 3/16 in. on the radius. Cutting fluid was water-base chemical emulsion. Facing and turning tools were cemented or indexable carbide with a hardness of Rockwell A 92 and a density of 14.90 g per cu cm. Drills were made of high speed steel. Tolerance was ±1/64 in. Finish was 125 micro-in. Total machine time was 16.44 min per piece.
(c) A 1¾-in.-diam short drill was used for spot drilling. (d) Surface was finish machined. (e) Finish trace to surface C (right to left) at high rpm, then at reduced speed for the remainder of the cut. Surface F is the diameter, and surface C was generated as the facing tool withdrew.
(f) Cutting fluid was water-base chemical emulsion with EP additive. Facing and turning tools were cemented or indexable carbide of the type used in the first chucking. Drills were made of high speed steel. Tolerance ranged from −0.005 to ±0.016 in. Surface finish was 125 micro-in. Total machine time was 15 min per piece.

Fig. 24. Bowl top that was rough and partially finish machined in a tracer-controlled turret lathe, and the tools used (Example 772)

Example 773. Single-Spindle Automatic vs Turret Lathe (Fig. 25)

In an effort to reduce costs, a single-spindle bar machine was substituted for a manual turret lathe for drilling, boring and tapping 1¼-in.-diam type 304 stainless steel cold rolled bar stock to form the sleeves shown in Fig. 25.

Although acceptable sleeves were produced by the turret lathe, this method necessitated drilling and boring of a pilot hole 1¼ in. deep into the bar stock to guide the 1-in.-diam pilot on the end of the tap. After finish machining and cutting off the sleeve, the hole remaining in the bar stock was rebored to the size required for tapping the thread on the next piece.

When using the automatic bar machine, the bar stock was held in the collet of the machine and a standard holder was used for the tap. Tapping of the sleeve in the automatic bar machine, however, was not satisfactory. In order to produce acceptable threads, it was necessary to apply a special cutting oil by hand. This procedure was not practical for automatic bar machine operation and it was necessary, therefore, to return to the manual turret lathe operation.

Carbide tools are used in many applications because they result in higher production rates and improved tool life. Sometimes the life of a carbide tool can be improved by changing to a grade of carbide that is better suited to the particular machining operation. For example, in the following production application, a change in the grade of carbide increased tool life about seven times.

Example 774. Shock-Resistant Carbide for Machining Interrupted Cuts (Fig. 26)

A change from a general-purpose grade of carbide to a shock-resistant grade (both grades disposable inserts) increased tool life considerably when machining the wings of the CF-20 (type 302) stainless steel precision-cast part shown in Fig. 26. Because of interrupted cuts, the general-purpose carbide chipped readily and had a life of only two to four pieces per tool, whereas the shock-resistant grade, which was in the form of a triangular disposable tip, had a life of 20 pieces per tip.

Turning of the wings was the third operation in the machining sequence. Approximately 0.025 in. of metal was removed from the wings to produce the 1.078 and 2.909-in. diameters.

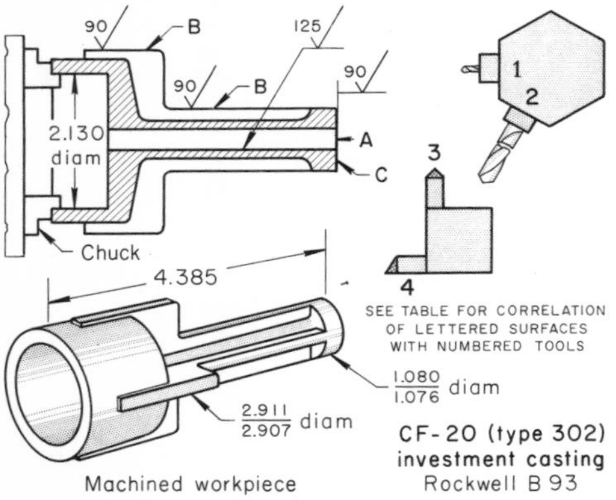

Tool No.	Operation	Speed Sfm	Speed Rpm	Feed, ipr	Machining time, min
	Processing Details(a)				
1	Spot drill A ...	15	464	0.003	0.17
2	Drill A	18	188	0.002	9.30
3	Turn outside diameters B	482 and 185	640	0.004	1.10
4	Face C	185	640	0.004	0.17

(a) Cutting fluid was water-soluble oil for all operations. Each operation was accomplished in one cut. Total machining time was 11 min per piece. Tool life of the ⅛-in.-diam spot drill and the ⅜-in.-diam drill was 4 pieces per grind. Both drills were made of high speed steel. The turning tool had a disposable triangular carbide insert with a hardness of Rockwell A 92 and a density of 14.90 g per cu cm. Production rate was slightly more than five pieces per hour.

***Fig. 26.** Casting that was machined in a turret lathe, and the tools used* (Example 774)

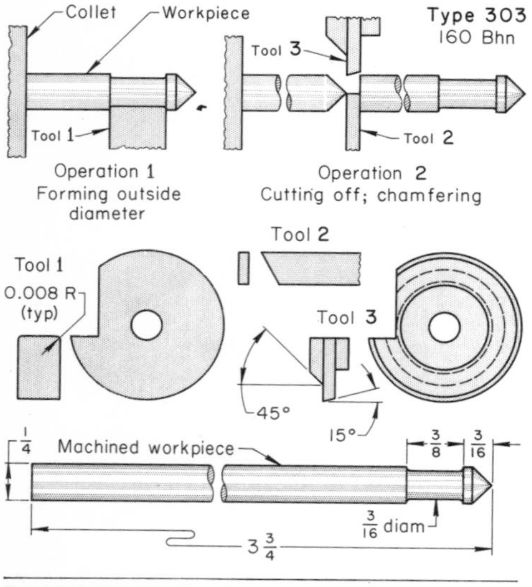

Speed (all operations) ....92 sfm (1400 rpm)
Feed:
Form turning groove ....0.0006 ipr
Cutting off ....0.0008 ipr
Chamfering ....0.0008 ipr
Cutting fluid ....Sulfurized oil
Tolerance ....±0.004 in.
Surface finish of recess ....63 micro-in.
Tool life(a) ....500 pieces per grind
Machining time per piece ....15 sec
Production rate per hour ....240 pieces

(a) All tools were high speed steel.

***Fig. 27.** Valve rod that was form turned, cut off, and chamfered in an automatic bar machine, and the tools used* (Example 775)

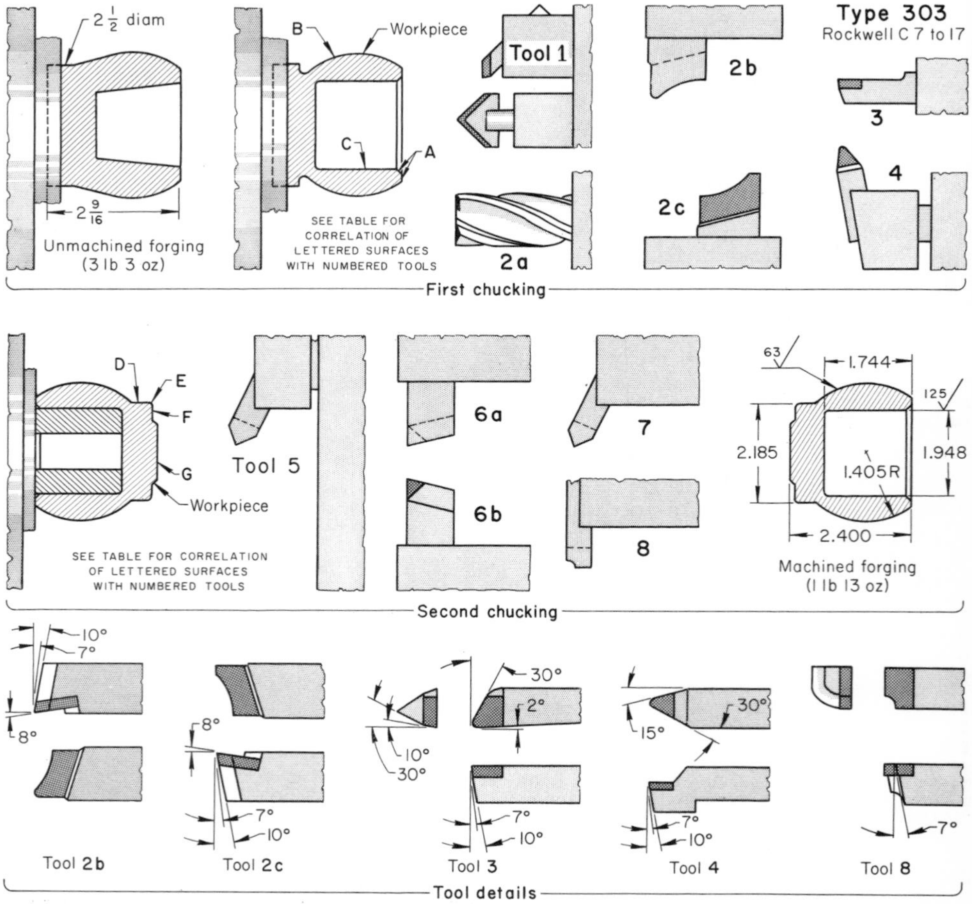

Tool No.	Operation	Speed Sfm	Speed Rpm	Feed, ipr	Tool material	Tool life, pcs per grind
	First Chucking(a)					
1	Face and chamfer A(b)	75	134	0.0077	Disposable carbide insert	100
2a	Drill C	66	134	0.007	High speed steel(c)	100
2b, c	Rough form B	95	134	0.007	Brazed carbide tip	150
3	Bore C	325	622	0.005	Brazed carbide tip	100
4	Finish form B	830	1058	0.005	Brazed carbide tip	50
	Second Chucking(a)					
5	Rough turn D	247	378	0.011	Disposable carbide insert	50(d)
6a, b	Face F and G	224	622	0.007	Disposable carbide insert	50(d)
7	Finish turn D	610	1058	0.007	Disposable carbide insert	100(d)
8	Form radius E	356	622	0.007	Brazed carbide tip	100

(a) A cutting fluid of soluble oil mixed with water was used for all operations. Production rates of the first and second chucking operations were 15 and 24 pieces per hour, respectively. (b) Chamfer made by a carbide-tipped spade drill. (c) Twist drill was 1⅞ in. in diameter and had a flat bottom. (d) Life expressed as pieces per cutting edge.

***Fig. 28.** Forging and part machined from it, and the tools used. Less time was required for machining the part from a forging than from bar stock.* (Example 776)

It was required that these diameters be concentric with each other within 0.004 in. TIR.

Machining was done in a horizontal ram-type turret lathe equipped with a three-jaw chuck. The inside jaws of the chuck gripped the part on the 2.130-in.-diam cast bore. The part weighed 1 lb, 6 oz before machining and 1 lb after. Total machining time was 11 min per piece, resulting in a production rate of slightly more than five pieces per hour. Processing details for all machining operations are tabulated below Fig. 26.

By modifying variables such as cutting fluid, form of stock, method of machining, or operating techniques, a marked improvement in results can often be obtained. The following four examples discuss operations in which a processing change was necessary in order to produce parts more efficiently. Example 775 involves a change from water-soluble-oil to sulfurized-oil cutting fluid to eliminate chatter marks produced by a form-turning tool. Example 776 discusses the machining of a stainless steel part in less time when machined from a forging than when machined from bar stock. Example 777 concerns the method of machining used to prevent out-of-roundness of rings. Example 778 refers to the use of a machine with a special dwell feature to prevent chatter.

Example 775. Change in Cutting Fluid to Eliminate Polishing Operation (Fig. 27)

The use of a heavy grade of sulfurized cutting fluid produced the required surface finish of 63 micro-in. or better during form turning the 3⁄16-in.-diam by 3⁄8-in. recess in the type 303 stainless steel valve rod shown in Fig. 27. Originally soluble cutting oil was used; however, the rod developed sufficient chatter to cause a rough finish. This condition necessitated a subsequent polishing operation to produce the 63 micro-in. finish. Polishing was unnecessary when the sulfurized cutting fluid was employed.

The valve rod was machined from 1⁄4-in.-diam bar stock in an automatic bar machine. Processing consisted of turning a recess with a circular form tool mounted on the front slide, feeding the bar stock to a stop, cutting off, and chamfering the end of the bar for the next piece by a second circular form tool mounted on the rear slide. The blank stock weighed 0.053 lb and the finished piece weighed 0.045 lb. Other processing details are given with Fig. 27.

Example 776. Change in Material Form to Reduce Machining Time (Fig. 28)

Total machining time was 6.17 min when the type 303 stainless steel part shown in Fig. 28 was machined from a forging in two chucking operations, compared to total time of 9.10 min when machined from bar stock. The first and second chucking operations required 4 min and 2.17 min, respectively. The change from bar stock to a forging also resulted in improved surface finish on the bore and exterior surfaces, respectively.

Machining of the forging was done in a single-spindle automatic chucking machine. Two carbide form tools rough machined the exterior form, removing most of the material. The finish form was generated by a carbide-tipped single-point tool whose path of travel was controlled by a cam mounted on the rear slide. Weight of the forging blank was 3 lb, 3 oz. After the first and second chucking operations, the workpiece weighed 2 lb, 6 oz and 1 lb, 3 oz, respectively. Processing details for the forging are given with Fig. 28.

Previously, the part was machined from bar stock on a 4¾-in. single-spindle automatic for the first chucking and on a turret lathe for the second chucking operations.

Example 777. Method of Machining Rings to Prevent Out-of-Roundness (Fig. 29)

In the original method of making the shell rings as shown in Fig. 29 the part distorted on removal from the machine after the second chucking. It was essential to maintain exact roundness after machining, and large and small inside diameters had to be concentric within 0.005 in.

The machining procedure that eliminated out-of-roundness was rough and finish turning the outside in one operation on a 30-in. vertical turret lathe, then reversing the part in the chuck and rough boring all inside diameters. About 0.020 in. of stock was left on each inside diameter for removal during finish turning. Prior to final machining, the chuck jaws were loosened to relieve stresses within the part, then retightened just enough to hold the part for finish turning. The forging blank weighed 20 lb, and the finish-machined ring weighed 13 lb. Total machining time was 13.59 min per piece. Tool shapes and processing details for the second chucking operations are shown with Fig. 29.

Example 778. Special Dwell Feature That Prevented Chatter (Fig. 30)

A horizontal automatic bar machine with a special dwell feature was used to machine oil-gun caps from 2⅛-in.-diam cold finished hexagonal bar stock of type 416 stainless steel. A cross-sectional view of the cap and schematic view of the tooling are shown in Fig. 30. The special dwell feature of the machine was used at station 3 to facilitate machining of the 3⁄8-in. radius (surface K in Fig. 30) and the thread-relief groove with the 45° chamfer (surface D) without chatter. Pressure from the tool at station 3 steadied the tool for cutting the chamfer at station 3A.

The use of a solid tap for the threading operation resulted in some damage to the threads when the machine was reversed for tap withdrawal.

When a collapsible tap was used, satisfactory threads were obtained only after the tap threads were nitrided.

To produce the finish, it was necessary to hone the tools periodically. Tests with other grades of carbide and with variations of speed and feed did not improve economy or accuracy. Sequence of operations and processing details are given with Fig. 30.

Milling

Milling of stainless steel requires more power, more rigid setups and lower speeds and feeds than does ordinary carbon steel. For example, when milling carbon steels and nonferrous metals, power is usually available for using large-diameter cutters to obtain high rates of metal removal. However, when these tools are applied to stainless steel, depth of cut and feed must be reduced to prevent overloading.

Cutter Design. Standard milling cutters employed for carbon steel are adaptable for stainless steel. Cutters having helical teeth are especially desirable for milling stainless steel when width of cut is over ¾ in. For these widths the helical teeth cut continuously and provide smoother action than straight teeth. When slots are being milled, similar advantages are gained with cutters having staggered teeth so that they cut successively on alternate sides of the slot. This practice reduces the cutting load per tooth and generates smaller chips, which are more readily removed. A different method for distributing cutting load, when ganged cutters are used, is illustrated in Example 320, for type 410 stainless, in the article "Milling".

Table 25 shows the design of high speed steel and carbide face mills for milling stainless steels within the hardness range of 135 to 440 Bhn. Sometimes tool angles different from those shown in Table 25 are necessary for a particular application. In the first example that follows, axial rake angles

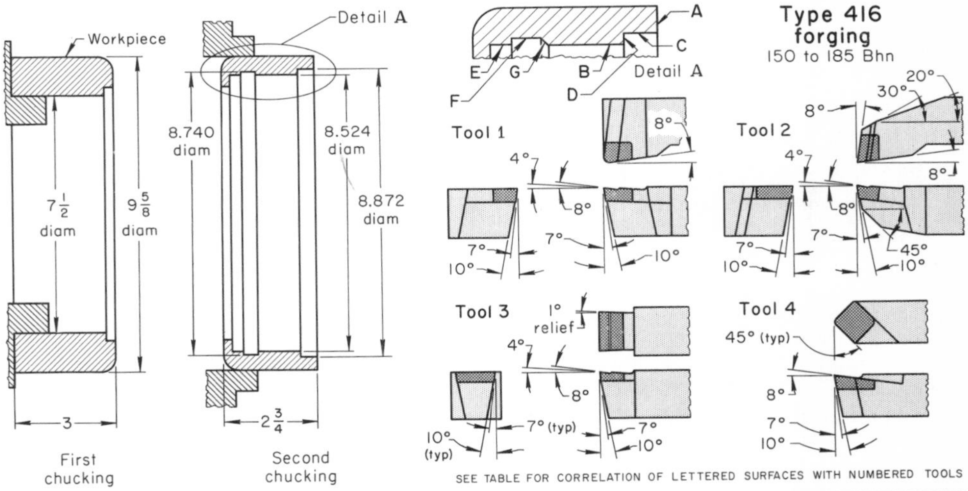

Operation	Tool No.	Description	Diameter machined, approx, in.	Speed Sfm	Speed Rpm	Feed, ipr	Length of cut, in.	Machining time, min per cut(b)
		Processing Details for Second Chucking(c)						
1	1	Rough face surface A	9⅝	216	86	0.014	¾	0.71
2(a)	2	Rough bore B and E	8½	191	86	0.014	2¾	4.48
3(a)	2	Rough bore C	8⅞	200	86	0.014	1⅛	2.00
4	1	Finish face surface A	9⅝	303	120	0.007	½	0.71
5	2	Rough face D	8⅞	279	120	0.007	3⁄16	0.36
6	2	Finish bore C	8⅞	279	120	0.007	1⅛	1.38
7	2	Finish face D	8⅞	279	120	0.007	3⁄16	0.31
8	2	Finish bore B and E	8½	266	120	0.007	1¼	1.46
9	3	Form recess F	8¾	130	57	0.003(d)	3⁄32	0.65
10	4	Form chamfer G	9⅝	143	57	0.003(d)	3⁄32	0.65

(a) Each operation required one cut, except the second and third operations, each of which required two cuts. (b) Total machining time was 13.59 min per piece. Production rate was 4 pieces per hour. (c) Carbide-tipped tools were used. Tool life was 4 pieces per grind for the facing and boring tools, and 15 pieces per grind for the recessing and chamfering tools. A cutting fluid of soluble oil mixed with water was used for all operations. Tolerances were +0.002, −0.000 in. Finish was 90 micro-in. (d) Tool was fed by hand.

Fig. 29. Rings machined to accurate roundness requirements, and the tools used (Example 777)

Table 25. Cutter Angles for High Speed Steel and Carbide Face Mills for Milling Stainless Steels

Material	Brinell hardness	High speed steel: Axial rake	High speed steel: Radial rake	Carbide, Disposable: Axial rake	Carbide, Disposable: Radial rake	Carbide, Brazed: Axial rake	Carbide, Brazed: Radial rake	High speed steel and carbide: Corner angle	End cutting edge	End relief	Peripheral relief
Free-machining	135 to 425	0°	0°	5° to 11°	−5° to −11°	0°	0°	45°	5°	8° to 10°	8° to 10°
Austenitic	135 to 275	0° to 5°	0° to 5°	5° to 11°	−5° to −11°	0° to 5°	0° to −5°	45°	5°	8° to 10°	8° to 10°
Martensitic	135 to 425	0°	0°	5° to 11°	−5° to −11°	0°	0°	45°	5°	8° to 10°	8° to 10°
Precipitation-hardening	150 to 440	0°	0°	5° to 7°	0° to 5°	0°	0°	45°	5°	8° to 10°	8° to 10°

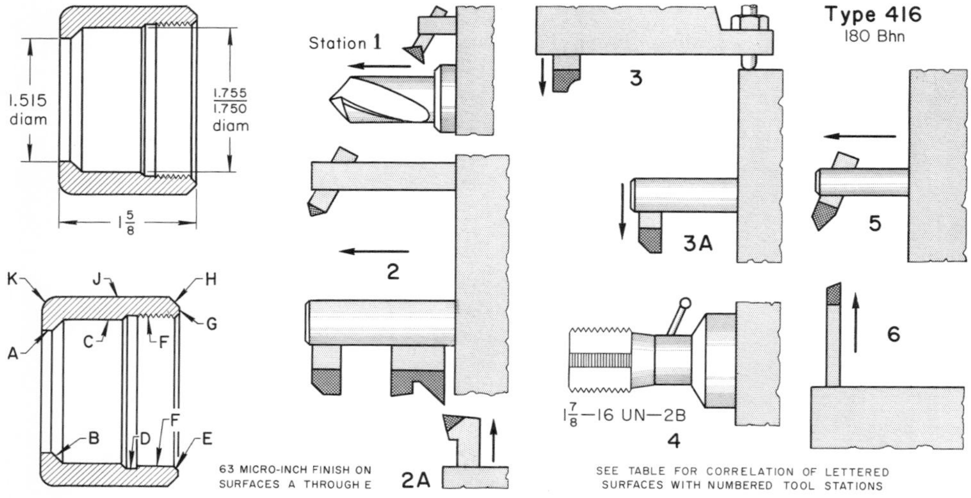

Station	Surface	Tool
		Sequence of Operations
1	A	High speed steel drill(a)
1	H	Chamfer cutter(b)(c)
2	J	Turning cutter(d)
2	C,F,B,E	Boring and forming cutters(e)
2A	G	Facing cutter(f)
3	K	Forming cutter(g)(c)
3A	D	Forming cutter(g)
4	F	Collapsible tap(h)
5	A	Boring cutter(j)(c)
6		Cutoff tool

Operating Conditions(k)

Speed:	
Drilling	60 sfm
Tapping	30 sfm
Carbide tools	275 sfm
Feed:	
Drilling	0.020 ipr
Carbide tools	0.015 ipr
Cutting fluid	Water-soluble oil
Surface finish	63 micro-in.(m)
Tool life:	
Drills and taps	100 pieces per grind
Carbide-tipped tools	300 pieces per grind
Total machining time	4.7 min per piece

(a) 1 7/16-in.-diam drill with 140° point. (b) ¾-in. triangular carbide tip insert with a negative rake. (c) Steel-cutting grade of carbide had a hardness of Rockwell A 91.3. (d) ¾-in. triangular tip insert of steel-cutting grade of carbide for heavy-duty interrupted cuts. Cutting edge had a negative rake.

(e) Special brazed carbide-tipped boring and forming tool. (f) ¾-in. triangular carbide-tip insert with positive rake. Carbide had a hardness of Rockwell A 92 and a density of 12.50 g per cu cm. (g) Special form tool with brazed carbide tip. (h) Nitrided high speed steel tap of 1⅞-in. diameter. (j) Brazed carbide-tipped boring tool.

(k) Method of holding and feeding workpiece consisted of a hydraulically operated collet chuck and bar feed with 2⅛-in.-diam hexagon collet bushings and feed finger pads. (m) Finish for specific surfaces, as indicated in illustration.

Fig. 30. Oil-gun cap machined from hexagonal bar stock, and the tools used (Example 778)

were essentially as recommended in Table 25, whereas in the second example (Example 780) results were improved by increasing rake angles.

Example 779. Face Milling Type 420 Stainless at Rockwell C 50 to 52

On the basis of power consumption and metal removal rate, the most efficient tool for face milling 420 stainless steel at Rockwell C 50 to 52 was a 6-in.-diam cutter (disposable carbide blades) having axial and radial rakes of 5° and a corner angle of 0.120 in. by 45°. The most efficient processing conditions comprised a speed of 122 sfm, feed of 0.0057 ipt, and depth of cut of 0.125 in. Under these conditions, this cutter yielded a metal-removal rate of 1.36 cu in. per min and a power consumption rating of 0.86 cu in. per hp per min. Width of cut was 3 in. Milling was done on a No. 5 vertical machine. Tools were permitted to wear to a land width of 1/32 in.

For maximum production rate, regardless of efficiency rating, the same cutter was capable of a 0.250-in. depth of cut and a feed of 0.0042 ipt. The metal removal rate under these conditions was 1.59 cu in. per min. Power consumption rating, however, dropped to 0.55 cu in. per hp per min.

In general, efficiency was affected adversely when feed was decreased or when a corner radius was substituted for the chamfer. Combinations of 0° radial rake with axial rakes of −10°, −7°, or −5° also produced unsatisfactory results.

Example 780. Change in Axial and Radial Rake for Greater Cutter Life (Table 26)

A major change in the axial and radial rake angles of a face mill resulted in a 20% increase in tool life while maintaining 125-micro-in. surface finish when milling 17-4 PH stainless steel in the solution-treated condition (150,000 psi tensile strength). Cutter design (disposable carbide blades were used) and processing details for the original and improved cutters are given in Table 26.

The larger axial and radial rake proved successful despite the high hardness of the work material. The improved cutter had previously been used successfully in machining 17-4 PH parts prior to heat treatment, provided that tolerances were no closer than ±0.0005 in. and that proper allowance had been made for shrinkage of the parts during heat treatment.

When cuts are continuous, face milling is most often done with the largest cutters that can be driven with the available power. For interrupted cuts, however, the rapid metal removal rate obtainable with a large face mill must often be sacrificed, because interrupted cutting causes excessive vibration, resulting in premature failure of cutter blades. Sometimes it is necessary to change the type of cutter or the setup, or both, for interrupted cutting, as in the following example.

Example 781. Change in Cutter Size and Workpiece Setup to Improve Cutter Life (Fig. 31)

An 8-in.-diam face mill having eight carbide blades was originally used to face mill cast stainless steel travel rails (Fig. 31). The procedure was to place the rail on its side and mill one side of one rail (two separate surfaces) simultaneously. Speeds of 150 to 600 sfm were tried with feeds from 0.005 to 0.015 ipt. This procedure was unsatisfactory because intermittent cutting and vibration resulted in rapid tool failure.

The problem was solved by placing two castings side by side, which permitted the use of a smaller-diameter tool. An improvised 4-in.-diam face-type milling cutter having only two blades was used. The excess stock was milled in a single pass from surfaces B and C shown in Fig. 31, then from surface A, and finally

Table 26. Effect of Cutter Design on Cutter Life in Face Milling 17-4 PH Stainless Steel (Example 780) (a)

Item	Original cutter	Improved cutter
Cutter Design		
Diameter of cutter	8 in.	8 in.
Number of teeth	10	8
Axial rake	12°	35°
Radial rake	10°	25°
Processing Details(b)		
Speed	40 sfm (19 rpm)	60 sfm (29 rpm)
Feed	0.005 ipt	0.008 ipt
Depth of cut	0.125 in.	0.125 in.
Width of cut	6 in.	6 in.

(a) Stainless steel was solution treated to a tensile strength of 150,000 psi. (b) Cutting fluid was a sulfurized paraffin-base oil.

Table 27. Evaluation of Cutter Material for End Milling PH 15-7 Mo at Rockwell C 45 to 50 (Example 782) (a)

Cutter Design

Number of teeth	8
Diameter of cutter	2 in.
Radial rake	15°
Axial rake	15°
Radius of corner	0.12 in.
Outside-diameter relief	5°

Operating Conditions

Speed	28 sfm
Feed	0.0046 ipt
Depth of cut	0.06 in.
Width of cut	1 in.
Length of cut	1 in.
Cutting fluid	Water-soluble oil

Performance Results

Item	Climb milling M30	Climb milling T15	M2	Conventional milling M30	Conventional milling T15
Number of cuts	1	38	2	1	4
Area cut, sq in.	1	38	2	1	4
Wear on OD	..	..	..	(b)	(c)
Wear on corner	(d)	(d)	(d)	..	..

(a) Cutter design and processing details were identical for all end mills. (b) Excessive. (c) Slight. (d) Cutters broke down.

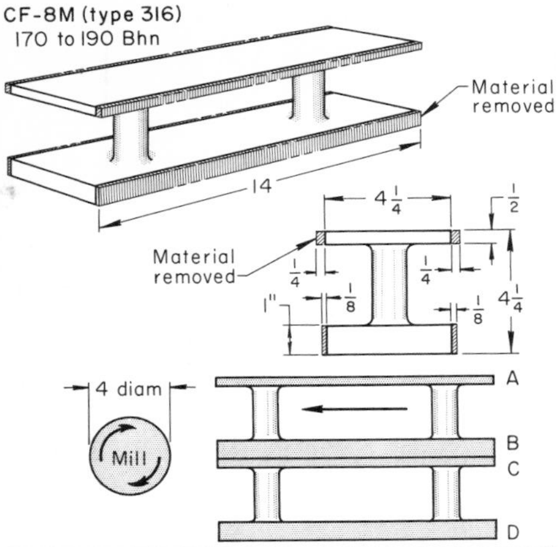

Speed ....463 rpm (485 sfm)
Feed ....0.008 ipt
Cutting fluid ....None
Tool life ....10 pieces per grind
Machining time ....1.9 min per pass

Fig. 31. Cast travel rail that was face milled, and revised procedure (Example 781)

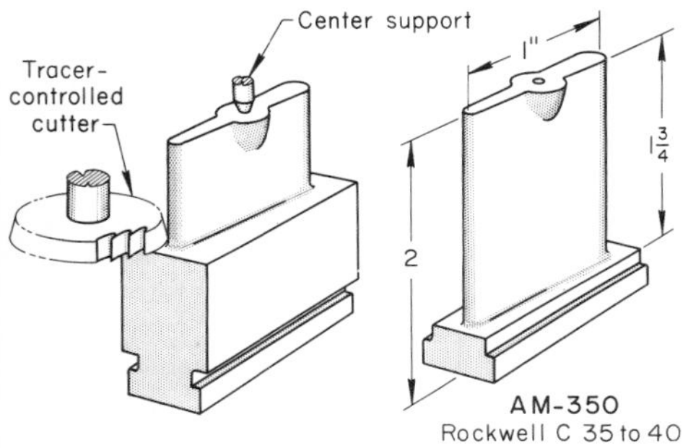

Cutter speed ....60 sfm
Workpiece rotation ....2 rpm
Downfeed of workpiece ....0.030 ipr
Depth of cut ....Varied
Length of cut ....1¾ in.
Cutter life ....9 pieces per grind
Production rate ....2 hr per blade

Fig. 32. Airfoil section of a turbine blade that was milled from bar stock with a carbide cutter (Example 783)

from surface D. Had there been a larger production run, it might have been better to use a 4-in.-diam face mill with four to eight teeth. Processing details are tabulated below the illustration in Fig. 31.

Recommended design of end mills is the same for all grades of stainless steel, including the martensitic stainless steels that have been heat treated to a hardness as high as Rockwell C 52. End mills should be provided with helix angle of 35°, radial rake angle of 15°, end cutting-edge angle of 3°, end relief of 3° to 7°, and peripheral relief of 10°.

Cutter Material. Milling cutters made of high speed steel are used in most applications on stainless steel. Carbide inserts are used most frequently when milling the more difficult-to-machine grades, such as the precipitation-hardened grades. Small end mills made of solid carbide have been used successfully in a few applications. Because of the higher modulus of elasticity, carbide end mills deflect less under a given force than steel end mills.

The more highly alloyed grades of high speed steel usually outperform the general-purpose grades used for cutters or cutter blades, as shown in the following example, in which T15 proved greatly superior to M2 and M30. These results indicate that the high vanadium content of T15, rather than cobalt, was the important factor, as M30 contains cobalt but M2 does not.

Table 28. Nominal Speeds and Feeds for Face Milling Stainless Steels With High Speed Steel Cutters

Type of steel(a)	Condition(b)	Brinell hardness	For 0.150-in. depth: Speed, sfm	For 0.150-in. depth: Feed, ipt	For 0.025-in. depth: Speed, sfm	For 0.025-in. depth: Feed, ipt
FM Fer	Ann	135 to 185	175	0.010	235	0.008
FM Mar	Ann	135 to 185	175	0.010	230	0.008
	Ann or CD	185 to 240	125	0.008	165	0.006
	Q and T	275 to 325	85	0.006	110	0.005
	Q and T	375 to 425	40	0.005	55	0.004
FM Aus	Ann	135 to 185	120	0.010	150	0.008
	CD	225 to 275	110	0.010	140	0.008
Ferritic	Ann	135 to 185	135	0.006	180	0.005
Mar(410)	Ann	135 to 185	125	0.006	165	0.005
	Ann	175 to 225	110	0.006	145	0.005
	Q and T	275 to 325	70	0.005	95	0.004
	Q and T	375 to 425	40	0.004	55	0.003
Mar(431)	Ann	225 to 275	85	0.006	115	0.005
	Q and T	275 to 325	65	0.005	90	0.004
	Q and T	375 to 425	40	0.004	55	0.003
Mar(440)	Ann	225 to 275	75	0.006	100	0.005
	Q and T	275 to 325	55	0.005	75	0.004
	Q and T	375 to 425	40	0.004	55	0.003
Aus(304)	Ann	135 to 185	95	0.006	125	0.005
	CD	225 to 275	85	0.006	110	0.005
Aus(316)	Ann	135 to 185	85	0.006	110	0.005
PH	Ann	150 to 200	80	0.006	105	0.005
	Hard	275 to 325	75	0.005	100	0.004
	Hard	325 to 375	50	0.005	65	0.004
	Hard	375 to 440	40	0.004	55	0.003
Cast FM	Ann	140 to 170	95	0.012	125	0.010
Cast Fer	N and T	175 to 225	85	0.012	115	0.010
Cast Aus	Ann	140 to 190	60	0.010	80	0.008

(a) See Table 2 for types of steel in each group. (b) Ann = Annealed; CD = Cold drawn; Q and T = Quenched and tempered; Hard = Hardened; N and T = Normalized and tempered. (Data are adapted from tables compiled by Metcut Research Associates, Inc.)

Table 29. Nominal Speeds and Feeds for Face Milling Stainless Steels With Carbide Cutters

Type of steel(a)	Condition(b)	Brinell hardness	For 0.150-in. depth: Speed (sfm) for: Brazed	For 0.150-in. depth: Speed (sfm) for: Disposable	For 0.150-in. depth: Feed, ipt	For 0.025-in. depth: Speed (sfm) for: Brazed	For 0.025-in. depth: Speed (sfm) for: Disposable	For 0.025-in. depth: Feed, ipt
FM Fer	Ann	135 to 185	470	520	0.014	625	690	0.012
FM Mar	Ann	135 to 185	470	520	0.014	625	690	0.012
	Ann or CD	185 to 240	430	475	0.010	570	630	0.008
	Q and T	275 to 325	300	330	0.008	400	440	0.006
	Q and T	375 to 425	150	165	0.005	200	220	0.004
FM Aus	Ann	135 to 185	375	415	0.014	500	550	0.012
	CD	225 to 275	325	360	0.014	430	475	0.012
Ferritic	Ann	135 to 185	425	470	0.010	565	620	0.008
Mar(410)	Ann	135 to 185	475	525	0.010	630	685	0.008
	Ann	175 to 225	425	470	0.010	565	620	0.008
	Q and T	275 to 325	300	330	0.008	400	440	0.006
	Q and T	375 to 425	135	150	0.005	180	200	0.004
Mar(431)	Ann	225 to 275	350	385	0.010	465	510	0.008
	Q and T	275 to 325	300	330	0.006	400	440	0.005
	Q and T	375 to 425	135	150	0.005	180	200	0.004
Mar(440)	Ann	225 to 275	325	360	0.010	430	475	0.008
	Q and T	275 to 325	275	305	0.006	370	410	0.005
	Q and T	375 to 425	135	150	0.005	180	200	0.004
Aus(304)	Ann	135 to 185	325	360	0.010	430	475	0.008
	CD	225 to 275	300	330	0.010	400	440	0.008
Aus(316)	Ann	135 to 185	300	330	0.010	400	440	0.008
PH	Ann	150 to 200	175	195	0.010	230	255	0.008
	Hard	275 to 325	130	145	0.008	170	190	0.006
	Hard	325 to 375	120	130	0.007	160	175	0.005
	Hard	375 to 440	120	130	0.005	150	165	0.004
Cast FM	Ann	140 to 170	400	440	0.014	530	585	0.012
Cast Fer	N and T	175 to 225	350	385	0.014	465	510	0.012
Cast Aus	Ann	140 to 190	300	330	0.012	400	440	0.010

(a) See Table 2 for types of steel in each group. (b) Ann = Annealed; CD = Cold drawn; Q and T = Quenched and tempered; Hard = Hardened; N and T = Normalized and tempered. (Data are adapted from tables compiled by Metcut Research Associates, Inc.)

Example 782. M2 vs M30 vs T15 for End Milling PH 15-7 Mo (Table 27)

End mills made of M2, M30 and T15 high speed steels were evaluated for performance in climb-cut end milling of PH 15-7 Mo stainless steel at Rockwell C 45 to 50. Grades M30 and T15 were also evaluated in conventional end milling of the same steel. Cutter design and processing details were identical for all tools, as shown in Table 27.

Only the T15 cutters could end mill the hard stainless steel successfully. As shown in Table 27, the T15 cutters made more cuts in climb milling, but corner breakdown was more severe than in conventional cutting.

The use of carbide cutters is governed partly by over-all economy and by their ability to hold a sharp cutting edge. Selection of carbide cutters is influenced also by the ability of the machine to perform at the higher speeds at which these tools are most efficient, as in the following example.

Example 783. Carbide Cutters for Milling Turbine Blades from AM-350 (Fig. 32)

Turbine blades were milled from bar stock of AM-350 alloy heat treated to Rockwell C 35 to 40. A vertical tracer-controlled milling machine with carbide cutters was used to gen-

Table 30. Nominal Speeds and Feeds for End Milling Stainless Steels With High Speed Steel Cutters

Type of steel(a)	Condition(b)	Brinell hardness	For 0.050-in. depth: Speed, sfm	Feed (ipt) for diam (in.) of: 0.250	0.500	0.750	1.0 to 2.000	For 0.015-in. depth: Speed, sfm	Feed (ipt) for diam (in.) of: 0.250	0.500	0.750	1.0 to 2.000	Tool material
FM Fer	Ann	135 to 185	140	0.001	0.002	0.004	0.005	180	0.0005	0.001	0.003	0.004	M2, M7
FM Mar	Ann	135 to 185	140	0.001	0.002	0.004	0.005	180	0.0005	0.001	0.003	0.004	M2, M7
	Ann or CD	185 to 240	125	0.001	0.002	0.004	0.005	160	0.0005	0.001	0.003	0.004	M2, M7
	Q and T	275 to 325	65	0.001	0.002	0.003	0.004	85	0.0005	0.001	0.002	0.003	M2, M7
	Q and T	375 to 425	40	0.0005	0.001	0.002	0.003	50	0.0005	0.0007	0.001	0.002	T15, M33
FM Aus	Ann	135 to 185	135	0.001	0.002	0.004	0.005	175	0.0005	0.001	0.003	0.004	M2, M7
	CD	225 to 275	110	0.001	0.002	0.004	0.005	145	0.0005	0.001	0.003	0.004	M2, M7
Ferritic	Ann	135 to 185	110	0.001	0.002	0.003	0.004	145	0.0005	0.001	0.002	0.003	M2, M7
Mar(410)	Ann	135 to 185	110	0.001	0.002	0.003	0.004	145	0.0005	0.001	0.002	0.003	M2, M7
	Ann	175 to 225	100	0.001	0.002	0.003	0.004	130	0.0005	0.001	0.002	0.003	M2, M7
	Q and T	275 to 325	60	0.001	0.002	0.003	0.004	80	0.0005	0.001	0.002	0.003	M2, M7
	Q and T	375 to 425	40	0.0005	0.001	0.002	0.003	50	0.0005	0.0007	0.001	0.002	T15, M33
Mar(431)	Ann	225 to 275	70	0.001	0.002	0.003	0.004	90	0.0005	0.001	0.002	0.003	M2, M7
	Q and T	275 to 325	55	0.001	0.002	0.003	0.004	70	0.0005	0.001	0.002	0.003	M2, M7
	Q and T	375 to 425	40	0.0005	0.001	0.002	0.003	50	0.0005	0.0007	0.001	0.002	T15, M33
Mar(440)	Ann	225 to 275	65	0.001	0.002	0.003	0.004	85	0.0005	0.001	0.002	0.003	M2, M7
	Q and T	275 to 325	50	0.001	0.002	0.003	0.004	65	0.0005	0.001	0.002	0.003	M2, M7
	Q and T	375 to 425	35	0.0005	0.001	0.002	0.003	45	0.0005	0.0007	0.001	0.002	T15, M33
	Q and T	Rc 48 to 52	20	.....	0.0005	0.0005	0.0015	25	0.0005	0.0005	0.0005	0.001	T15, M33
Aus(304)	Ann	135 to 185	85	0.001	0.002	0.003	0.004	110	0.0005	0.001	0.002	0.003	M2, M7
	CD	225 to 275	75	0.001	0.002	0.002	0.003	95	0.001	0.001	0.0015	0.002	M2, M7
Aus(316)	Ann	135 to 185	75	0.001	0.002	0.003	0.004	95	0.0005	0.001	0.002	0.003	M2, M7
PH	Ann	150 to 200	70	0.001	0.002	0.003	0.004	90	0.0005	0.001	0.002	0.003	M2, M7
	Hard	275 to 325	55	0.001	0.002	0.003	0.004	70	0.0005	0.001	0.002	0.003	M2, M7
	Hard	325 to 375	50	0.0005	0.001	0.002	0.003	65	0.0005	0.0007	0.001	0.002	M2, M7
	Hard	375 to 440	40	0.0005	0.001	0.002	0.003	50	0.0005	0.0007	0.001	0.002	M2, M7
Cast FM	Ann	140 to 170	80	0.001	0.003	0.004	0.005	105	0.001	0.002	0.003	0.004	M2, M7
Cast Fer	N and T	175 to 225	70	0.001	0.002	0.004	0.005	90	0.0007	0.0015	0.003	0.004	M2, M7
Cast Aus	Ann	140 to 190	50	0.001	0.002	0.004	0.005	65	0.0007	0.0015	0.003	0.004	M2, M7

(a) See Table 2 for types of steel in each group. (b) Ann = Annealed; CD = Cold drawn; Q and T = Quenched and tempered; Hard = Hardened; N and T = Normalized and tempered. (SOURCE: same as for Table 29)

erate the airfoil contour. For this operation the part was held upright in a fixture designed to accommodate the previously machined root section; a dead center supported the other end of the part. Milling of the airfoil section began at the end opposite the root, as illustrated in Fig. 32. Processing data are listed under the illustration.

Speed and feed for face milling and end milling with high speed steel and carbide tools are shown in Tables 28, 29, 30 and 31. Table 32 shows nominal speeds and feeds for slab milling with high speed steel cutters.

Heavy feed and slow speed are often preferred to the opposite combination. For example, when milling any grade of stainless that is strongly susceptible to work hardening, feed must be great enough to insure that each tooth of the cutter will cut under the work-hardened zone left by the preceding tooth. Under these conditions a reduction in speed may be required because of inadequate power. Hand feed, although not often employed in milling operations, is sometimes necessary, as indicated in the following example.

Example 784. Use of Light Feed for Longer Tool Life (Fig. 33)

Service requirements of the cast CF-8M (type 316) stainless steel part shown in Fig. 33 permitted only a 1⅛-in. radius for runout of the cutter at the bottom of the slot for each wing. This necessitated the use of 2¼-in.-diam side milling cutters for producing the wings by straddle milling. Because of the small cutter diameter, it was necessary to operate the cutters at low feed to obtain acceptable tool life.

Hand feed was used at the start and finish of each cut. Power feed of ⅝ in. per min was used in between; even at this low feed rate, tool life was only four pieces per grind.

The two side milling cutters were ground as a pair in order to prevent mismatch in the bottom of each slot where the cuts overlapped. Each of the 12 equally spaced wings was machined in two passes of the cutters. Total depth of cut for the two passes was about 7/16 in.

A dividing head with a three-jaw chuck was used to hold and index the part during milling of the wings. The small end of the part was supported by a revolving center mounted in a tail stock on the machine table. The weight of the casting before and after milling was 20 lb and 16 lb. Other processing details are given in Fig. 33.

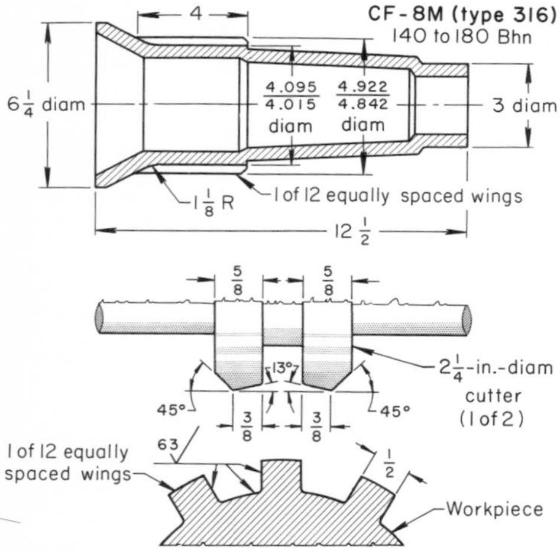

Speed	37 sfm (63 rpm)
Feed	⅝ in. per min(a)
Number of passes	2
Length of cut	6½ in.
Total depth of cut	7/16 in.(b)
Cutting fluid	Soluble oil
Tool life	4 pieces per grind
Total machining time	267.36 min(c)

(a) Hand feed was used to start the cut and to mill the 1⅛-in. radius. Power feed was used between these two operations. (b) Approximate depth of cut for two passes for each wing. (c) Time required to make 24 cuts for forming the 12 wings. Machining time per cut was: 0.58 min for starting cut, 9.7 min for cutting slot, and 0.86 min for milling radius.

Fig. 33. Cast tubular shaft on which wings were straddle milled with high speed steel cutter shown (Example 784)

Rigidity is especially important when milling stainless steel. Tool and workpiece setups that are satisfactory for milling of the easier-to-machine metals often prove unacceptable for milling stainless, and special procedures are required. The following example demonstrates an effective means of obtaining acceptable rigidity for simultaneous milling of two surfaces.

Example 785. Use of Special Vise Jaws for Rigidity (Fig. 34)

Rigidity of setup to prevent chatter was essential for producing a 63-micro-in. finish when milling, in one pass, one end and a slot on the ¼-in.-diam part shown in Fig. 34. Rigidity was provided by a standard milling-machine vise with jaws that were machined to hold each piece in the same location in relation to the two milling cutters. A 6-in.-diam standard side milling cutter ground 0.014 in. undersize on the diameter was used for milling the ⅞-in.-wide slot. A 3-in.-diam

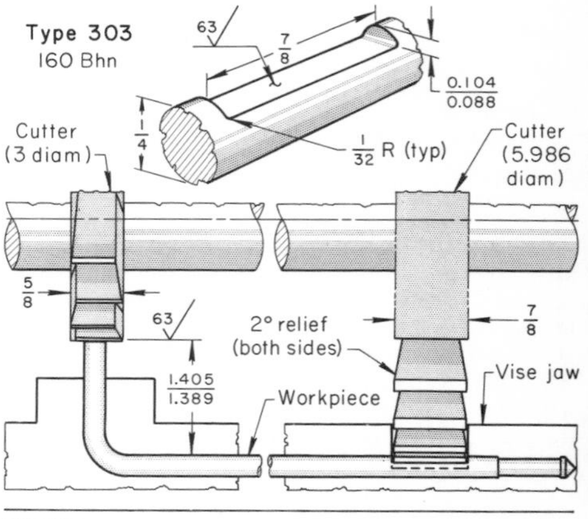

Speed:	
3-in.-diam cutter	102 sfm (130 rpm)
5.984-in.-diam cutter	204 sfm (130 rpm)
Feed	2⅜ in. per min
Length of cut	1.057 in.(a)
Number of passes	1
Cutting fluid	Soluble oil
Tolerance	±0.008 in.
Tool life(b)	4000 pieces per grind
Machining time	0.45 min per piece
Production rate	130 pieces per hour

(a) Includes tool approach. (b) Standard staggered-tooth and side milling cutters made of high speed steel were used.

Fig. 34. Valve part on which two surfaces were milled simultaneously in a horizontal milling machine (Example 785)

Table 31. Nominal Speeds and Feeds for End Milling Stainless Steels With Carbide Cutters

Type of steel(a)	Condition(b)	Brinell hardness	For 0.050-in. depth: Speed, sfm	Feed (ipt) for diam (in.) of: 0.250	0.500	0.750	1.0 to 2.000	For 0.015-in. depth: Speed, sfm	Feed (ipt) for diam (in.) of: 0.250	0.500	0.750	1.0 to 2.000
FM Fer	Ann	135 to 185	400	0.001	0.002	0.005	0.007	520	0.0005	0.001	0.004	0.006
FM Mar	Ann	135 to 185	400	0.001	0.003	0.005	0.007	520	0.0005	0.002	0.004	0.007
	Ann or CD	185 to 240	350	0.001	0.002	0.005	0.007	455	0.0005	0.001	0.004	0.006
	Q and T	275 to 325	250	0.001	0.002	0.003	0.005	325	0.0005	0.001	0.002	0.004
	Q and T	375 to 425	100	0.001	0.002	0.003	0.004	130	0.001	0.001	0.002	0.003
FM Aus	Ann	135 to 185	350	0.001	0.002	0.005	0.007	455	0.0005	0.001	0.004	0.006
	CD	225 to 275	325	0.001	0.002	0.005	0.007	420	0.0005	0.001	0.004	0.006
Ferritic	Ann	135 to 185	350	0.001	0.002	0.004	0.006	455	0.0005	0.001	0.003	0.005
Mar(410)	Ann	135 to 185	350	0.001	0.002	0.004	0.006	455	0.0005	0.001	0.003	0.005
	Ann	175 to 225	300	0.001	0.002	0.004	0.006	390	0.0005	0.001	0.003	0.005
	Q and T	275 to 325	225	0.001	0.002	0.004	0.006	290	0.0005	0.001	0.003	0.005
	Q and T	375 to 425	100	0.001	0.002	0.003	0.004	130	0.001	0.001	0.002	0.003
Mar(431)	Ann	225 to 275	250	0.001	0.002	0.004	0.006	325	0.0005	0.001	0.003	0.005
	Q and T	275 to 325	200	0.001	0.002	0.004	0.006	260	0.0005	0.001	0.003	0.005
	Q and T	375 to 425	100	0.001	0.002	0.003	0.004	130	0.001	0.001	0.002	0.003
Mar(440)	Ann	225 to 275	225	0.001	0.002	0.004	0.006	290	0.0005	0.001	0.003	0.005
	Q and T	275 to 325	175	0.001	0.002	0.004	0.006	230	0.0005	0.001	0.003	0.005
	Q and T	375 to 425	90	0.001	0.002	0.003	0.004	120	0.001	0.001	0.002	0.003
	Q and T	Rc 48 to 52	60	....	0.0005	0.002	0.002	80	0.0005	0.0005	0.001	0.001
	Q and T	Rc 54 to 56	35	....	0.0005	0.001	0.0015	45	0.0005	0.0005	0.0005	0.001
Aus(304)	Ann	135 to 185	275	0.001	0.002	0.003	0.005	360	0.0005	0.001	0.002	0.004
	CD	225 to 275	250	0.001	0.002	0.003	0.004	325	0.0005	0.001	0.002	0.003
Aus(316)	Ann	135 to 185	250	0.001	0.002	0.003	0.004	325	0.0005	0.001	0.002	0.004
PH	Ann	150 to 200	275	0.001	0.002	0.004	0.006	360	0.0005	0.001	0.003	0.005
	Hard	275 to 325	225	0.001	0.002	0.004	0.006	290	0.0005	0.001	0.003	0.005
	Hard	325 to 375	200	0.001	0.002	0.003	0.004	260	0.001	0.001	0.002	0.003
	Hard	375 to 440	75	0.001	0.002	0.003	0.004	100	0.001	0.001	0.002	0.003
Cast FM	Ann	140 to 170	350	0.0025	0.004	0.006	0.007	455	0.0015	0.003	0.005	0.006
Cast Fer	N and T	175 to 225	300	0.002	0.0025	0.005	0.006	390	0.001	0.002	0.004	0.005
Cast Aus	Ann	140 to 190	250	0.002	0.0025	0.005	0.006	325	0.001	0.002	0.004	0.005

(a) See Table 2 for types of steel included in each group. (b) Ann = Annealed; CD = Cold drawn; Q and T = Quenched and tempered; Hard = Hardened; N and T = Normalized and tempered. (Data are adapted from tables compiled by Metcut Research Associates, Inc.)

standard stagger-tooth cutter, mounted on the same arbor, was used to mill the upright end of the workpiece.

Originally two separate operations were required to produce the two cuts within the ±0.008-in. tolerance required. Total machining time for these two operations was 0.75 min. Simultaneous milling saved 0.30 min per piece in addition to savings in setup and handling time. Processing details are listed below the illustration for Fig. 34.

Sawing

High speed steel blades are used for cutting wrought and cast stainless steel by band sawing and by power hacksawing. Pitches for band saw blades vary from 8 to 10 teeth per inch for cutting material up to ¼ in. thick, to a range of 3 to 6 teeth per inch for material 1½ in. or more in thickness (Table 33).

Nominal speeds for band sawing stainless steel depend on the hardness of the material to be cut, and range from 55 sfm for the precipitation-hardening grades hardened to 325 to 375 Bhn, to 100 sfm for the annealed ferritic and martensitic grades within a hardness range of 135 to 185 Bhn. Table 33 shows the nominal speeds for band sawing all grades of stainless. For additional data on band sawing of stainless steel, see Table 6 on page 221 and Table 2, page 225.

The effect of band speed on tool life and over-all cost is illustrated by the following comparison for cutoff band sawing of PH 15-7 Mo stainless steel bars 1.4 in. thick (Rockwell C 43) with a high speed steel band:

Band speed, sfm	Band life, sq in. cut	Cost per sq in.
75	156	$0.23
102	104	0.30

The sawing comparison was made at a hydraulically controlled feed rate of 1.0 ipm for a cutting rate of 1.4 sq in. per min, with flow application of a 1-to-1 mixture of sulfurized oil and mineral oil. A 15½-ft-long saw band 1 in. wide, 0.035 in. thick, regular tooth, raker set, 4-pitch, with 0.060-in. set dimension, was used. The over-all machining cost in the tabulation above was based on a tool cost of $22.10 per band, tool-change cost of $0.58, and operating cost of $0.116 per minute.

Although increasing band speed from 75 to 102 sfm resulted in higher over-all sawing cost, as shown in the foregoing comparison, decreasing band speed substantially below 75 sfm could also give higher over-all cost; feed rate, too, can influence comparisons of sawing cost.

Power hacksaw blades of 10 teeth per inch are recommended for material up to ¾ in. thick. Coarser blades of 6 or 4 teeth per inch are used for material from ¾ to 2 in. and for 2 in. and over, respectively.

Nominal speeds and feeds for power hacksawing are influenced primarily by the hardness of the material to be cut, as indicated in Table 34. Speeds vary from 45 strokes per minute for precipitation-hardening grades hardened within a range of 325 to 375 Bhn to 110

Table 32. Nominal Speeds and Feeds for Slab Milling Stainless Steels With High Speed Steel Cutters

Type of steel(a)	Condition(b)	Brinell hardness	For 0.150-in. depth: Speed, sfm	Feed, ipt	For 0.025-in. depth: Speed, sfm	Feed, ipt	Tool material
FM Fer	Ann	135 to 185	185	0.008	210	0.006	M2, M7
FM Mar	Ann	135 to 185	185	0.008	210	0.006	M2, M7
	Ann or CD	185 to 240	175	0.008	200	0.006	M2, M7
	Q and T	275 to 325	85	0.006	100	0.004	M2, M7
	Q and T	375 to 425	50	0.004	60	0.002	T15, M33
FM Aus	Ann	135 to 185	115	0.009	145	0.007	M2, M7
	CD	225 to 275	115	0.007	135	0.005	M2, M7
Ferritic	Ann	135 to 185	135	0.007	170	0.005	M2, M7
Mar(410)	Ann	135 to 185	135	0.007	160	0.005	M2, M7
	Ann	175 to 225	125	0.007	150	0.005	M2, M7
	Q and T	275 to 325	75	0.006	90	0.004	M2, M7
	Q and T	375 to 425	50	0.004	65	0.002	T15, M33
Mar(431)	Ann	225 to 275	85	0.006	105	0.004	M2, M7
	Q and T	275 to 325	65	0.006	100	0.004	M2, M7
	Q and T	375 to 425	50	0.003	65	0.002	T15, M33
Mar(440)	Ann	225 to 275	75	0.006	90	0.004	M2, M7
	Q and T	275 to 325	60	0.006	75	0.004	M2, M7
	Q and T	375 to 425	50	0.003	65	0.002	T15, M33
Aus(304)	Ann	135 to 185	100	0.007	125	0.005	M2, M7
	CD	225 to 275	95	0.006	115	0.004	M2, M7
Aus(316)	Ann	135 to 185	90	0.007	110	0.005	M2, M7
PH	Ann	150 to 200	80	0.007	105	0.005	M2, M7
	Hard	275 to 325	75	0.006	100	0.004	M2, M7
	Hard	325 to 375	65	0.005	90	0.003	M2, M7
	Hard	375 to 440	45	0.003	50	0.002	T15, M33
Cast FM	Ann	140 to 170	100	0.010	135	0.008	M2, M7
Cast Fer	N and T	175 to 225	90	0.010	110	0.008	M2, M7
Cast Aus	Ann	140 to 190	60	0.010	80	0.008	M2, M7

(a) See Table 2 for types of steel included in each group. (b) Ann = Annealed; CD = Cold drawn; Q and T = Quenched and tempered; Hard = Hardened; N and T = Normalized and tempered. (SOURCE: same as for Table 31)

Table 33. Nominal Pitches, Speeds and Feeds for Power Band Sawing Stainless Steels With High Speed Steel Blades (a)

Type of steel (b)	Condition (c)	Brinell hardness	Speed, sfm	Feed, in. per stroke
Ferritic	Ann	135 to 185 ...	100	0.006
Mar (all)	Ann	135 to 185 ...	100	0.006
	Ann	175 to 225 ...	90	0.006
	Ann	225 to 275 ...	75	0.005
	Q and T	275 to 325 ...	60	0.004
Aus (all)	Ann	135 to 185 ...	90	0.006
	CD	225 to 275 ...	70	0.005
PH	Ann	150 to 200 ...	90	0.006
	Hard	275 to 325 ...	70	0.005
	Hard	325 to 375 ...	55	0.004
Cast FM	Ann	150 to 225 ...	80	0.006
Cast Fer	N and T	150 to 225 ...	80	0.006
Cast Aus	Ann	140 to 190 ...	75	0.004

(a) Speeds and feeds for all steels in all conditions are for saws with pitches as follows: 8 to 10 tpi (teeth per inch) for material up to ¼ in. thick, 6 to 8 tpi for thickness of ¼ to 1¼ in., and 3 to 6 tpi for 1½ in. and over. (b) See Table 2 for types of steel in each group. (c) Ann = Annealed; Q and T = Quenched and tempered; CD = Cold drawn; Hard = Hardened; N and T = Normalized and tempered. (Data are adapted from tables compiled by Metcut Research Associates, Inc.)

Table 34. Nominal Pitches, Speeds and Feeds for Power Hacksawing Stainless Steels With High Speed Steel Blades (a)

Type of steel (b)	Condition (c)	Brinell hardness	Speed, strokes per min	Feed, in. per stroke
Ferritic	Ann	135 to 185 ...	110	0.006
Mar (all)	Ann	135 to 185 ...	100	0.006
	Ann	175 to 225 ...	90	0.006
	Ann	225 to 275 ...	75	0.005
	Q and T	275 to 325 ...	60	0.004
Aus (all)	Ann	135 to 185 ...	100	0.006
	CD	225 to 275 ...	80	0.005
PH	Ann	150 to 200 ...	80	0.006
	Hard	275 to 325 ...	55	0.005
	Hard	325 to 375 ...	45	0.004
Cast FM	Ann	150 to 225 ...	75	0.006
Cast Fer	N and T	150 to 225 ...	75	0.006
Cast Aus	Ann	140 to 190 ...	65	0.004

(a) Speeds and feeds for all steels in all conditions are for saws with pitches as follows: 10 tpi (teeth per inch) for material up to ¾ in. thick, 6 tpi for thickness of ¾ to 2 in., and 4 tpi for 2 in. and over. (b) See Table 2 for types of steel in each group. (c) Ann = Annealed; Q and T = Quenched and tempered; CD = Cold drawn; Hard = Hardened; N and T = Normalized and tempered. (SOURCE: same as for Table 33)

strokes per minute for annealed ferritic grades at 135 to 185 Bhn. Cast stainless steels are usually cut at speeds of 65 to 75 strokes per minute.

Feeds for both wrought and cast stainless steels range from 0.004 to 0.006 in. per stroke, as shown in Table 34.

Electrical Machining

The methods most used for machining stainless steel with the aid of electric current are: (*a*) electrical discharge machining, (*b*) electrochemical machining, (*c*) electrochemical grinding, and (*d*) arc cutting. Power requirements and the machining capabilities of each of these electrical machining processes are summarized in Table 35.

Electrical discharge machining uses a pulsed current to form sparks in a dielectric fluid between the preshaped tool (electrode) and the workpiece. The spark (arc) causes a minute portion of the workpiece and electrode to melt and vaporize at the surface, causing a crater. Rapid repetition of the tiny arc at 5000 to 40,000 cycles per second erodes the part to the configuration of the electrode. Because the electrode also is eroded during machining, used electrodes are employed for roughing and unused electrodes for finishing. As shown in Table 35, dimensional accuracy as close as ±0.0002 in. can be obtained with this process.

In general, electrodes for machining stainless steel are made of brass, graphite or one of the copper-tungsten alloys. Selection of electrode material is based on economy of operation for producing the desired shape of the part. Brass is cheaper to purchase and prepare, but electrodes of graphite or copper-tungsten alloys have longer life.

The selection of dielectric fluid for the spark gap also is based on economy of operation. Transformer oil and kerosine are commonly used; however, the more expensive proprietary blends and silicone oils have better electrical characteristics that result in faster metal removal and finer surface finish.

Electrochemical machining is a reverse plating process. In contrast to plating, in which ionized metal atoms are removed from solution and deposited on the workpiece, electrochemical machining reverses the direction of the current to ionize the surface atoms of the workpiece and put them into solution. By placing the tool (electrode) close to the workpiece, the electrolytic action is confined and the workpiece conforms to the shape of the electrode. There is no tool wear.

Electrolytes employed are either acid, mainly dilute sulfuric (H_2SO_4), or high concentrations of sodium chloride ($NaCl$), sodium nitrate ($NaNO_3$), or sodium nitrite ($NaNO_2$) in water. Because of their lower resistivity and higher ion concentration, salt solutions result in faster metal removal. Salt solutions, however, cause the metal removed to form a precipitate that must be filtered out prior to re-use of the electrolyte. Acid electrolytes do not form this precipitate; therefore, they are preferred for drilling small holes and for other operations in which a particle of precipitate could cause blocking of the electrolyte and short circuits.

Electrodes are made of titanium for use in acid electrolytes, to prevent etching of the tool. Usually brass electrodes are used for salt solutions. A copper electrode was used in the following example.

Example 786. Electrochemical Machining of a Turbine Blade (Fig. 35)

Trepanning the airfoil and the platform section of the type 403 stainless steel turbine blade shown in Fig. 35 was done by placing 1-in. square bar stock in a fixture and electrochemical machining in a salt solution (25% NaCl) with a preshaped copper electrode. The slots in the base section were milled prior to machining of the foil and platform. Operating details are given with Fig. 35.

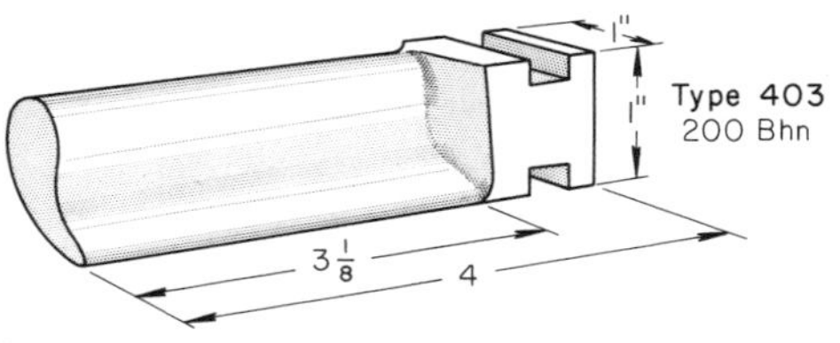

Machine rating	3000 amp
Electrode	Preshaped copper
Electrolyte	25% NaCl solution
Number of cuts	1
Metal removal rate	0.125 ipm
Current strength	850 amp
Length of cut	3⅛ in.
Machining time	30 min

Fig. 35. Airfoil and platform sections of turbine blades that were electrochemically machined (Example 786)

Electrochemical grinding combines the electrochemical machining process with grinding. An abrasive wheel with an electrically conductive bonding agent is used as an electrode and as a grinding wheel.

When machining stainless steel, the action can be changed from grinding only (no current flow) to electrochemical machining only (no grinding when a high current is applied). This extreme of electrochemical machining without grinding cannot be achieved with some materials, such as tungsten carbide.

Usually, a machining condition consisting of 90% electrolytic action and 10% grinding produces the highest metal removal rate coupled with low wheel wear and an accurate surface. Most operations on stainless steel use proprietary electrolytes; however, sodium nitrate ($NaNO_3$) can be used.

Table 35. Comparison of Methods for Electrical Machining of Stainless Steel

Item	Electrical discharge machining	Electrochemical machining	Electrochemical grinding	Arc cutting
Potential, volts	2 to 300	2 to 30	5 to 30	60 to 300
Current, amp	15 to 200	50 to 20,000	15 to 3000	30 to 10,000
Removal rate, cu in. per min	0.004 to 0.025	0.03 to 2.0	0.01 to 0.35	10 to 200 (a)
Finish, micro-in.	3 to 400	2 to 60	2 to 60	250 to 400
Tolerance, in.	±0.0002 to 0.0003	±0.001 to 0.005	±0.0002	±0.010 to 0.050
Repeatability, in.	±0.0001	±0.0005	±0.0002	...

(a) Linear rate of machining per minute

Other Examples of Machining of Stainless Steel Elsewhere in This Volume

Article	Example number
Austenitic Steels	
Turning	3, 4, 6
Boring	41
Drilling	154, 159, 161, 164
Tapping	224, 228, 230, 231, 237
Die threading	256
Multiple-operation machining	298, 303
Grinding	788, 790, 791, 795, 798-800
Martensitic Steels	
Turning	5, 11, 12, 14, 19, 23, 29
Broaching	122, 136
Drilling	171
Tapping	229
Thread grinding	262
Multiple-operation machining	277, 297
Milling	320
Lapping	579
Grinding	504, 787, 789, 792, 793, 796, 797
Precipitation-Hardening Steels	
Drilling	153, 163
Grinding	794

Grinding of Stainless Steel

*By the ASM Committee on Machining of Stainless Steel**

STAINLESS STEEL can be ground with the same general procedures and wheel speeds that are used for grinding carbon and low-alloy steels (see the article "Grinding", page 257). However, the avoidance of uneven or localized heating is of major importance in grinding stainless steel. The low thermal conductivity of stainless contributes to increased thermal distortion, particularly in the austenitic grades, whose coefficients of thermal expansion are about 60% higher than those of ordinary steel and cast iron.

Grinding Wheels

The ASA system of marking for identifying grinding wheels is described on pages 257 and 258, in the article "Grinding". In the tables and examples in the present article, most designations of aluminum oxide wheels also include a small subscript letter f, s or t, which denotes friable, semifriable or tough abrasive, respectively.

Table 1 shows the range of aluminum oxide wheels ordinarily used for surface, cylindrical, centerless and internal grinding of stainless steel. For any of these operations, the same wheel can be used for rough grinding and finish grinding; often, however, a finer grain size than indicated in Table 1 would be used for finish grinding. As is true also for carbon and low-alloy steels, wheels for thread grinding of stainless steel are of finer grain and harder than those used for other grinding operations, because of the importance of retaining wheel contour. The finer the thread pitch, the finer the grain and the harder the wheel (see wheel classifications in Table 2).

*For committee list, see page 375.

Type of Abrasive. Aluminum oxide wheels are used almost exclusively in grinding stainless steel. Silicon carbide wheels are generally used only for specialized applications such as roll grinding, where silicon carbide of extremely fine grit sizes provides fine surface finishes on stainless steel rolls used for cold rolling.

The superiority of aluminum oxide over silicon carbide for surface grinding is demonstrated by Table 3; grinding ratio is greater by as much as a factor of seven for the aluminum oxide wheel.

Grain size of readily available wheels ranges from less than 10 to over 600. Selection of the most suitable grain size depends primarily on the surface finish required. For any given abrasive, a finer grain size produces a finer finish; however, metal removal rate decreases as grain size decreases. Although only two grain sizes (46 and 60) are listed in Table 1, wheels with grain size as fine as 220 have been used in production grinding of stainless steel, and are cited in examples here.

Grade (hardness) of the wheel is designated by letter, and ranges from A (very soft) to Z (very hard). Most stainless steels are ground with medium-hard wheels (grades H to L) except for thread grinding, in which harder wheels are used. (See, for instance, Example 262, involving 410 stainless.)

Structure. Wheels having structure numbers from 5 to 13 are commonly used for grinding stainless steel, the same as for carbon steel. The definition of structure number varies among different wheel manufacturers; however, they all agree that as the structure number increases, the distance between grains is greater. Structure numbers do not appear in some wheel designations in this article.

Type of Bond. Vitrified bond (designated by the letter V) is the type most commonly used for grinding stainless steel. Other types are used in some applications; note, for example, the references to resinoid-bond wheels (letter B) in Table 2, for thread grinding. Resinoid bond is stronger than vitrified, and thus can be operated safely at higher speeds.

Grinding Fluids

A grinding fluid, used to cool and lubricate the wheel and the workpiece, minimizes wheel loading and glazing of the abrasive grains, both of which cause poor cutting action, excessive heat buildup, heat checking, and poor finish.

Selection of fluid for grinding stainless steel is more important than for grinding carbon or low-alloy steel. In some applications (see subsequent section on Factors Affecting Grinding Ratio), the grinding fluid has proved to be, by far, the most significant variable in grinding of stainless steel. In grinding stainless steel, either water-base fluids (soluble-oil emulsion or synthetic solutions) or grinding oils can be used.

Soluble oils are based on emulsified mineral oil or its constituents. The synthetic solutions contain organic compounds, but no petroleum compounds. Synthetic solutions of high nitrite concentration generally perform poorly in grinding of austenitic stainless steel. Heavy-duty soluble oils containing chlorine and sulfur are by far the best water-base compounds for grinding all grades of stainless. Grinding oils are recommended for use only in thread grinding and in other specialized applications.

Table 1. Wheels for Grinding of Stainless Steel

Method of grinding	Wheel classification: Ferritic steels(a)	Austenitic steels(a)	Martensitic steels(b)	PH steels(c)
Surface	A_s-46-I-V	A_s-46-J-V	A_s-46-J-V(d)	A_s-46-H-V
Cylindrical	A_s-60-J-V	A_s-60-I-V	A_s-60-I-V	A_s-60-I-V
Centerless	A_s-60-K-V	A_s-60-K-V	A_s-60-L-V	A_s-60-L-V
Internal	A_s-46-J-V	A_s-46-J-V	A_s-46-J-V	A_s-46-J-V
Thread	See Table 2			

(a) Annealed (150 to 220 Bhn). (b) Annealed (150 to 220 Bhn) or, except for surface grinding, quenched and tempered (Rockwell C 45). (c) Annealed (160 to 180 Bhn) or solution treated and aged (380 to 440 Bhn). (d) A_s-46-H-V wheel for quenched and tempered steel (Rockwell C 45).

Table 2. Wheels and Speeds for Thread Grinding of Stainless Steel(a)
(F = Ferritic, A = Austenitic, M = Martensitic, PH = Precipitation hardening)

Threads per inch	Annealed F, A, M & PH steels(b): Wheel classification	Wheel speed, sfm(c)	Hardened M & PH steels(d): Wheel classification	Wheel speed, sfm(e)
4 to 13	A_s- 90-R-B	8500	A_f- 80-I-V	7000
14 to 28	A_s-120-S-B	9000	A_f-120-J-V	7500
29 to 64	A_s-180-T-B	9500	A_f-180-M-V	8500
65 to 80	A_s-220-U-B	10000	A_f-220-P-V	9000

(a) Grinding fluid for all materials may be sulfurized oil, chlorinated oil, sulfochlorinated oil, or grinding oil. (b) 150 to 220 Bhn for ferritic, austenitic and martensitic steels, 160 to 180 Bhn for PH steels. (c) Work speed, 4 sfm. (d) Martensitic steels quenched and tempered (Rockwell C 45); PH steels solution treated and aged (380 to 440 Bhn). (e) Work speed, 6 sfm.

Table 3. Effect of Wheel and Fluid on Grinding Ratio of Type 302(a)

Grinding fluid, and concentration in water	Grinding ratio(b): With A_s-60-H8-V wheel	With C-60-I8-V wheel
Soluble oil, 10% (c)	20	2.8
Soluble oil, 10% (d)	9	3.5
Soluble oil, 10% (e)	8	2.4
Synthetic solution, 10% (f)	5	1.7
Soluble oil, 1¼% (g)	1.5	1.1

(a) Data were obtained in surface grinding, at a downfeed of 0.001 in. (b) Ratio of the volume of metal removed in grinding to the volume of wheel wear. (c) Heavy-duty oil emulsion containing sulfurized fats; designed for stainless steels. (d) Heavy-duty oil emulsion containing sulfur, extreme-pressure additives, and a high percentage of fats. (e) Heavy-duty oil emulsion containing fatty materials and synthetic soaps; designed for stainless steels. (f) Based on synthetic wax. (g) Emulsion containing soap.

Table 4. Grinding Ratios for Stainless Steels
(One tool steel and two plain carbon steels are listed for comparison.)

Steel	Condition	Rockwell hardness	Grinding ratio
Group 1			
AM-355	Solution annealed	B 95	7
310	Hot rolled	B 92	8
AM-355	Precipitation hardened	C 42	9
304	Hot rolled	B 77	9
17-4 PH	Precipitation hardened	C 45	9
D3	*Hardened tool steel*	*C 60*	*9*
Group 2			
302	Hot rolled	B 81	15
316	Hot rolled	B 76	17
440C	Hardened	C 55	19
430	Hot rolled	B 91	21
440A	Hardened	C 53	23
Group 3			
440A	Annealed	B 91	40
440C	Annealed	C 22	40
202	Hot rolled	B 83	50
410	Annealed	B 98	55
314	Hot rolled	B 81	65
1020	*Hot rolled carbon steel*	*B 67*	*65*
1019	*Cold drawn carbon steel*	*B 85*	*85*
410	Hardened	C 41	85
Group 4			
303(a)	Annealed	B 85	110
303(a)	Cold drawn	B 98	110
303	Hot rolled	B 78	220
430F	Hot rolled	B 81	240
416	Hardened	C 42	550
416	Hot rolled	B 89	600

(a) Low sulfur content; see entries for 303 in Table 5.

Table 5. Effects of Heat Treatment and Composition on Grinding Ratio

Steel	Condition or constituent	Rockwell hardness	Grinding ratio
Effect of Heat Treatment			
AM-355	Soln. annealed	B 95	7
	Precip. hardened	C 42	9
440A	Annealed	B 91	40
	Hardened	C 53	23
440C	Annealed	C 22	40
	Hardened	C 55	19
410	Annealed	B 98	55
	Hardened	C 41	85
416	Hot rolled	B 89	600
	Hardened	C 42	550
Effect of Carbon Content			
430	0.06 C	B 91	21
440A	0.60 C	B 91	40
440C	1.00 C	C 22	40
440A	0.60 C	C 53	23
440C	1.00 C	C 55	19
Effect of Sulfur Content			
304	0.03 S	B 77	9
302	0.02 S	B 81	15
303	0.16 S	B 85	110
303	0.35 S	B 78	220
430	0.02 S	B 91	21
430F	0.34 S	B 81	330
410	0.02 S	B 98	55
416	0.28 S	B 89	600
410	0.02 S	C 41	85
416	0.28 S	C 42	550
Effect of Silicon Content			
310	0.4 Si	B 92	8
314	2.0 Si	B 81	65
Effect of Nickel Content			
430	0.4 Ni	B 91	21
302	8.2 Ni	B 81	15
304	9.0 Ni	B 77	9
Effect of Molybdenum Content			
304	0.2 Mo	B 77	9
302	0.3 Mo	B 81	15
316	2.7 Mo	B 76	17
Effect of Manganese Content			
304	1.3 Mn, 9.0 Ni	B 77	9
302	0.9 Mn, 8.2 Ni	B 81	15
202	8.7 Mn, 5.0 Ni	B 83	50

Table 6. Nominal Processing Conditions for Surface Grinding of Stainless Steel With Straight Wheels

Steel classification and hardness	Wheel: Classification	Wheel: Speed, sfm	Crossfeed per pass, fraction of wheel width
Ferritic, 135 to 185 Bhn	A_s-46-I-V	5500 to 6500	1/4
Austenitic, 135 to 275 Bhn	A_s-46-J-V	5500 to 6500	1/4
Martensitic, 135 to 275 Bhn	A_s-46-J-V	5500 to 6500	1/4
Martensitic, over 275 Bhn	A_s-46-H-V	5500 to 6500	1/8
Precipitation hardening, 150 to 200 Bhn	A_s-46-H-V	5500 to 6500	1/4
Precipitation hardening, 275 to 440 Bhn	A_s-46-H-V	5500 to 6500	1/8

Conditions given are for table speed of 50 or 100 fpm, downfeed of 0.002 in. per pass for roughing, and 0.0005 in. max for finishing, of annealed steels and precipitation-hardened grades; 0.001 in. per pass for roughing, and 0.0005 in. max for finishing, of quenched and tempered martensitic grades. Grinding fluid may be water-base soluble-oil emulsion or synthetic solution, or sulfurized oil.

Factors Affecting Grinding Ratio

Table 3 shows the large effect of grinding fluid on grinding ratio for 302 stainless; the ratio is about 13 times as high with a high-concentration emulsion of heavy-duty soluble oil as with one of regular soluble oil at low concentration.

Although composition and condition of work metal also affect the grinding ratio, grinding fluid is the largest single factor, as Table 3 suggests.

Table 4 shows the results of an extensive series of tests to determine the effects of several variables on grinding ratio for 14 different grades of stainless steel. All test pieces were 6 in. long by 1½ in. wide and were ground on a surface grinder using A_s-60-I-V wheels. The wheels were operated at 6000 sfm (idling), and table speed was 60 fpm. Unit of lateral index (crossfeed) was 0.050 in. after each table traverse. Unit of downfeed was 0.002 in. after each complete series of passes.

Unit downfeed of 0.002 in., instead of 0.001 in., was selected because all the stainless steels could be ground satisfactorily this way and the time required for measurable wheel wear was reduced for the high-grindability steels. (Increasing unit downfeed from 0.001 to 0.002 in. reduces the grinding ratio for 304 stainless steel by a factor of 4 or 5.) Grinding was continued as long as necessary to get far enough beyond the initial nonlinear portion of the curve of wheel wear against downfeed to obtain reliable grinding ratios. For the steel with the highest grinding ratio, this amounted to a total downfeed of more than 0.7 in., but usually it was possible to keep this below 0.2 in. Extended runs, to remove this much stock at 0.002 in. per pass, were necessary because any change in the rate of stock removal to speed up the rate of wheel wear for these high-ratio steels would have caused unsatisfactory grinding of the steels at the other end of the grindability spectrum.

Three nonstainless steels were included in the tests, to serve as "bench marks": plain carbon steels 1019 and 1020, which would normally be expected to have a relatively high grinding ratio, and D3 tool steel, for which a low ratio would normally be expected.

The grinding ratios determined for all these steels are summarized in Table 4, in the order of increasing grindability. The grades tested fall into four groups, as indicated in the table.

Grinding fluid was discovered to be by far the most important factor in grinding the stainless steels successfully. The most satisfactory fluid, a 10% emulsion of a heavy-duty soluble oil containing active sulfur and designed for use with stainless steel, raised the grinding ratio by a factor of 10 for 304 stainless steel over the value obtained with a general-purpose soluble oil.

The steels of lowest grindability (group 1 in Table 4) all have about the same grindability ratio as D3 tool steel, which is generally considered to be a difficult steel to grind. This group includes the two precipitation-hardening steels and austenitic steels 304 and 310. However, changing from the special heavy-duty soluble oil used in this study to a general-purpose soluble oil greatly reduced the grindability of the stainless steels. The effect of this change in grinding fluid was much smaller for the tool steel. Unless a heavy-duty soluble oil was used for grinding these stainless steels, they were considerably more difficult to grind than D3 and were more nearly in the grindability category of the high-vanadium high-speed steels (for grindability data, see the article "Grinding of Tool Steel", pages 367 to 374).

Group 2 in Table 4 includes austenitic, martensitic and ferritic grades. It is not clear why the grinding ratio for 302 is so much higher than for 304, as these steels are similar in composition. The principal difference is the lower carbon content of 304, but this is the same as that of 316, which matches 302 in grindability, as Table 4 indicates.

Table 7. Processing Data for Surface Grinding of Type 420 (Example 787)

Wheel classification	A_s-80-I8-V
Wheel size	14 by 1 by 5 in.
Operating Conditions	
Wheel speed	5500 sfm
Rotary-table speed	100 rpm
Downfeed	0.001 in. per pass
Metal removal (total)	0.006 in. per side
Grinding fluid	Synthetic (a)
Setup time	25 min
Production rate	288 pieces per hour
Wheel life per dressing (b)	600 pieces

(a) Contained rust inhibitor, in 1% concentration of KNO_2. (b) Wheel was dressed with a single-point diamond tool.

Table 8. Rotary Surface Grinding of Type 303 Brackets (Example 788) (a)

Grinder	Vertical-spindle, 36-in.-diam rotary table
Wheel classification	A_s-30-G15-V (porous)
Wheel size:	8 segmts 18-in. diam, 1½ in. wide
Operating Conditions	
Wheel speed	705 rpm (3300 sfm)
Table speed	18 rpm
Downfeed	0.024 in. per min
Metal removed from each side	0.062 in.
Metal removed from each end	0.076 in.
Grinding fluid	Rust-inhibitor solution
Setup time	0.3 hr (b)
Production rate:	
Grinding both ends	55 pcs/hr
Grinding two opposing sides	41 pcs/hr
Labor cost per piece (c)	
Grinding both ends	$0.064
Grinding two opposing sides	$0.085
Wheel life per dressing (d)	36 pieces

(a) Brackets, of 303 stainless steel, were 2 in. square and 3¼ in. long. (b) 0.05 hr for each side and each end. (c) At $3.50 per hr. (d) Wheel was dressed with star wheel, at sparkout after grinding of each 36-piece load.

Group 3 includes austenitic and martensitic stainless steels and the two plain carbon steels. Group 4 includes the free-machining versions of the austenitic, martensitic and ferritic types. When a general-purpose soluble oil was used for grinding the stainless steels in groups 3 and 4, the grinding ratios for those in group 3 became similar to the ratio for the D3 tool steel, and those in group 4 showed a grindability ratio more nearly like those in group 3.

Composition and Condition. To indicate the effects of composition and condition, the data from Table 4 are rearranged as shown in Table 5.

Surface Grinding

Table 6 shows nominal processing conditions for surface grinding all grades of stainless steel, using straight wheels. When cup or segmented wheels are called for, the following wheels give satisfactory results:

Type of stainless steel	Wheel: Cup	Wheel: Segmented
Ferritic; austenitic	A_s-36-G12-V	A_s-60-E8-V
Martensitic; PH	A_s-24-G8-V	A_s-30-E12-V (porous)

Specific methods used in production surface grinding of a martensitic and an austenitic stainless steel are described in the following two examples.

Example 787. Type 420 Washers (Table 7)

To obtain a 10-micro-in. finish and hold thickness to ±0.0005 in., washers made of 420 stainless steel were ground on both sides with a horizontal-spindle rotary-table surface grinder, by the procedure detailed in Table 7. These washers, which had been quenched and tempered to Rockwell C 45, were 1.750 in. in diameter and 0.032 in. thick, and had an 0.875-in.-diam hole. The washers were held, 48 at a time, by means of a magnetic chuck.

Example 788. Six Surfaces on Type 303 Bracket (Table 8)

Type 303 stainless steel brackets, 2 in. square by 3¼ in. long, were sawed from bar stock, after which all surfaces were ground on a vertical-spindle rotary surface grinder. Grinding removed 0.062 in. of metal from each side face, and a total of 0.152 in. from the two ends; tolerance was 0.005 in. A segmented vitrified wheel of aluminum oxide was used to grind 36-piece loads, which were placed in a work-holding device on the chuck because the stainless steel was nonmagnetic. Each piece was polished to a maximum roughness of 32 micro-in. after being ground. Processing details for grinding are shown in Table 8.

Cylindrical Grinding

Table 9 shows nominal processing conditions for cylindrical grinding of stainless steel. Two production applications are illustrated by the two examples that follow.

Example 789. Type 440C Bushings (Table 10)

Bushings (1.750-in. OD, 1.500-in. ID, 3.5 in. long) made of 440C stainless steel and hardened to Rockwell C 60 were cylindrically ground to remove 0.015 in. from the outside diameter and to achieve a maximum surface roughness of 16 micro-in. In this application, the workpieces were traversed, rather than the grinding wheel. Wheel details and processing data are listed in Table 10.

Example 790. Plunge Grinding Type 303 Shafts (Table 11)

Table 11 gives processing data for cylindrical plunge grinding 2½-in.-long, 0.498 to 0.500-in.-OD shafts of 303 stainless steel at Rockwell B 71, for producing final outside diameter of 0.475 in. and maximum surface roughness of 15 micro-in.

Centerless Grinding

Centerless grinding can be done at slightly higher wheel speeds, and with considerably greater rates of infeed, than are used for cylindrical grinding between centers. Nominal processing conditions for through-feed centerless grinding of stainless steel are given in Table 12.

The two examples that follow describe centerless grinding of thin-wall tubing (in which distortion is a danger) and of short lengths of rod that required a 7-micro-in. finish.

Example 791. Thin-Wall Type 302 Tubing (Table 13)

Six-and-a-half-inch lengths of 3-in.-OD, ⅛-in.-wall, 302 stainless steel tubing (hardness, 180 Bhn) were centerless ground for removal of approximately 0.021 in. from the outside diameter. The ground tubing had to be straight and round within 0.001 in., with a tolerance of 0.001 in. on wall thickness.

Table 9. Nominal Processing Conditions for Cylindrical Grinding of Stainless Steel

Steel classification and hardness	Wheel: Classification	Wheel: Speed, sfm	Work speed, sfm	Traverse per work revolution, fraction of wheel width: Roughing	Finishing
Ferritic, 135 to 185 Bhn	A_s-60-J-V	5500 to 6500	50	½	⅙
Austenitic, 135 to 275 Bhn	A_s-60-I-V	5500 to 6500	50	½	⅙
Martensitic, 135 to 275 Bhn	A_s-60-I-V	5500 to 6500	50	½	⅙
Martensitic, over 275 Bhn	A_s-60-I-V	5500 to 6500	50	¼	⅛
Precipitation hardening, 150 to 200 Bhn	A_s-60-I-V	5500 to 6500	80	¼	⅛
Precipitation hardening, 275 to 440 Bhn	A_s-60-I-V	5500 to 6500	70	¼	⅛

Conditions given are for infeed of 0.002 in. per pass in roughing, and 0.0005 in. max in finishing. Grinding fluid may be water-base soluble-oil emulsion or synthetic solution, or sulfurized oil.

Table 10. Processing Data for Cylindrical Grinding of Type 440C (Example 789)

Wheel classification	A_s-80-K5-V
Wheel size	20 by 2 by 12 in.
Operating Conditions	
Wheel speed	6000 sfm
Work-rotation speed	150 rpm
Infeed on diameter, per traverse	0.001 in.
Traverse rate (a)	50 in. per min
Metal removed from diameter	0.015 in.
Grinding fluid	Synthetic solution (b)
Setup time	45 min
Production rate	60 pieces per hour
Wheel life per dressing (c)	120 pieces

(a) Workpiece was traversed. (b) Synthetic compound; 2% in water. (c) Wheel was dressed with a single-point diamond tool.

Table 11. Processing Data for Cylindrical Plunge Grinding of Type 303 (Example 790)

Wheel classification	A_s-80-K5-V
Wheel size	16 by 3 by 8 in.
Operating Conditions	
Wheel speed	6500 sfm
Work-rotation speed	20 rpm
Metal removed from diameter	0.024 in.
Grinding fluid	Soluble oil:water (1:20) (a)
Setup time	40 min
Production rate	85 to 90 pieces per hour
Wheel life per dressing (b)	120 pieces

(a) Heavy-duty soluble oil. (b) Wheel was dressed with a single-point diamond tool.

Table 12. Nominal Conditions for Through-Feed Centerless Grinding of Stainless Steel

Wheel classification	A_s-60-K-V
Wheel speed	5500 to 6500 sfm
Infeed, roughing	0.005 in. per pass
Infeed, finishing	0.0015 in. per pass
Work feed, approx	50 in. per min
Regulating-wheel angle	3°
Regulating-wheel speed	30 rpm
Grinding fluid	Water-base, or sulfurized oil

All conditions are applicable to grinding of: annealed (135 to 275 Bhn) ferritic, austenitic or martensitic steels; hardened (over 275 Bhn) martensitic steels; and annealed (150 to 200 Bhn) or hardened (to 440 Bhn) precipitation-hardening steels.

Table 13. Processing Data for Centerless Grinding of Type 302 (Example 791)

Grinding wheel classification	A_s-80-K5-V
Grinding wheel size	20 by 6 by 12 in.
Regulating wheel size	12 by 6 by 5 in.
Operating Conditions	
Grinding wheel speed	6500 sfm
Regulating wheel speed	32 rpm
Feed	20 in. per min
Metal removed	0.021 in. (a)
Grinding fluid	Activated grinding oil
Setup time	60 min
Production rate	15 pieces per hour
Wheel life per dressing (b)	60 pieces

(a) Total (from diameter), in four roughing and three finishing passes. (b) Wheel was dressed with a single-point diamond tool.

Table 14. Processing Data for Centerless Grinding of Type 416 (Example 792)

Grinding wheel classification	As-150-K8-V
Grinding wheel size	20 by 6 by 12 in.
Regulating wheel size	12 by 6 by 5 in.
Operating Conditions	
Grinding wheel speed	6500 sfm
Traverse speed	25 in. per min
Infeed on diameter	0.005 in. per pass
Metal removed from diameter	0.026 in.
Grinding fluid	General-purpose soluble-oil emulsion
Setup time	60 min
Production rate	50 pieces per hour
Wheel life per dressing(a)	200 pieces

(a) With a single-point diamond tool

Table 15. Nominal Processing Conditions for Internal Grinding of Stainless Steel(a)

Steel type and hardness, Bhn	Wheel classification	Speed, sfm	Work speed, sfm	Traverse per work revolution, fraction of wheel width: Roughing	Finishing
Ferritic, 135 to 185	As-46-J-V	5000 to 6500	75 to 150	1/3	1/6
Austenitic, 135 to 275	As-46-J-V	5000 to 6500	75 to 150	1/3	1/6
Martensitic, 135 to 275	As-46-J-V	5000 to 6500	50 to 100	1/3	1/6
PH, 150 to 200	As-46-J-V	5000 to 6500	75 to 150	1/3	1/6
PH, 275 to 440	As-46-I-V	5000 to 6500	50 to 100	1/3	1/6

Data are for infeed of 0.0005 in. per pass in roughing and 0.0002 in. max in finishing; grinding fluid may be soluble-oil emulsion, synthetic solution or sulfurized oil; all data are applicable to holes with a maximum length-to-diameter ratio of 2.5 to 1, and for grinding wheels with a width-to-diameter ratio of 1.5 to 1.

The removal of 0.021 in. of metal necessitated a rough grinding operation. This operation could not be severe; otherwise, distortion would result. Furthermore, too much down pressure on the work caused small particles of stainless steel to weld onto the carbide-tipped work-rest blade, causing scratches and rings on the work. Elevating the work-rest blade to about ¾ in. above the centerline of the wheels minimized the welding of particles and improved the surface condition, but produced objectionable chatter.

Many adjustments were made in height of work-rest blade, angle of regulating wheel, feed, speed, and type of grinding wheel. Best results were obtained with the regulating wheel set at an angle of 3° to 4° and operating at a speed of about 32 rpm. Four passes were needed for rough grinding: In each of the first two, 0.006 in. of metal was removed; in each of the last two, 0.003 in. There was no measurable distortion.

Finish grinding consisted of three passes; 0.0015 in. of metal was removed in the first pass, and 0.001 in. in each of the text two passes. During finish grinding, a work-rest blade tipped with aluminum bronze was used, to make possible a scratch-free finish with a maximum roughness of 25 micro-in. Additional processing data are given in Table 13.

Example 792. Fine Finish on Type 416 Rod (Table 14)

One-inch lengths of 0.150 to 0.155-in.-OD 416 stainless steel rod, at 180 Bhn, were centerless ground to reduce the outside diameter to 0.130/0.128 in. and obtain a maximum surface roughness of 7 micro-in. Wheel details and processing data are given in Table 14.

Internal Grinding

Nominal processing conditions for internal grinding of stainless steel are presented in Table 15. Finer-grit wheels, higher work-rotation speeds, and other variations from these nominal conditions are sometimes used with satisfactory results, as indicated in the example that follows.

Example 793. Type 440C Bushings (Table 16)

Type 440C bushings 2 in. in outside diameter, 3½ in. long, and hardened to Rockwell C 60 were internally ground for removal of 0.006 in. of metal from the bore, to produce a final bore diameter of 1.625 in. and a maximum surface roughness of 5 micro-in. Wheel details and processing data for this internal grinding application are listed in Table 16.

For finishing similar type 440C bushings of smaller bore diameters, finer-grit aluminum oxide (vitrified bond) wheels were used as bore diameter decreased:

Bore diameter, in.	Grit size
1 to 2	80 or 90
0.250 to 1	100 to 150
0.038 to 0.250	150 to 320

Form Grinding

Three production applications of form grinding, in which a crush-true grinder (equipped with a crusher roll to form the grinding wheel to the required contour) was used, are described in the three examples that follow.

Table 16. Processing Data for Internal Grinding of Type 440C (Example 793)

Wheel classification(a)	As-80-J5-V
Wheel size	1½ by ¾ by ⅜ in.
Operating Conditions	
Wheel speed	5000 sfm
Work-rotation speed	225 rpm (118 sfm)
Infeed on diameter	0.0002 in. per pass
Traverse rate	40 in. per min
Metal removed from diameter	0.012 in.
Grinding fluid	Synthetic:water (1:50)
Setup time	45 min
Production rate	10 pieces per hour
Wheel wear (diametral)	0.004 in. per piece
Wheel life per dressing(b)	25 pieces

(a) For finer grit sizes used in grinding smaller-diameter bores, see text of Example 793. (b) With a single-point diamond tool.

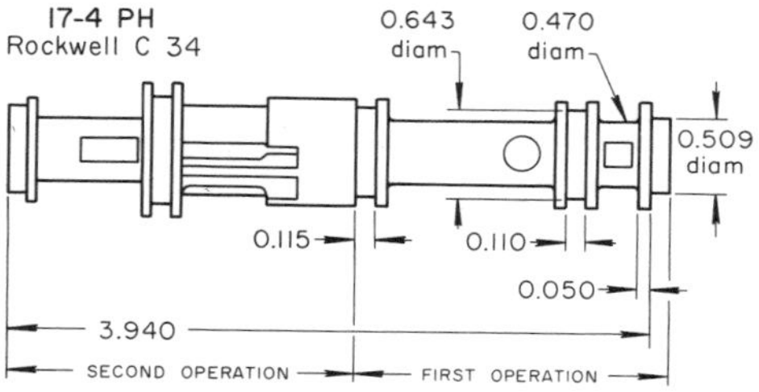

Wheel classification	Ar-220-K13-V
Wheel size	14 by 2 by 5 in.
Operating Conditions	
Wheel speed	6000 sfm
Work-rotation speed	25 sfm
Fluid	Heavy thread-grinding sulfurized oil
Setup time	65 min
Production rate	12 to 18 pieces per hour
Wheel life per dressing	145 to 150 pieces

Fig. 1. Two-operation form grinding, with crush-trued wheels, for producing grooves in a valve sleeve (Example 794)

Example 794. Grooves in 17-4 PH (Fig. 1)

Grooves in throttle-valve sleeves made of 17-4 PH stainless steel were formed by crush-trued grinding wheels. As shown in Fig. 1, these sleeves were ground in two operations, each involving about half the length of the workpiece.

Grinding produced a maximum roughness of 10 micro-in.; it was important that the grinding fluid be introduced at the point of contact between the wheel and the work, because of the large amount of heat generated in form grinding. Wheel details and operating conditions are tabulated with Fig. 1.

Example 795. Forged AMS 5645 Blanks (Fig. 2)

Blanks forged from AMS 5645 stainless steel (18 Cr – 10 Ni – Ti), with a hardness of 185 Bhn, were ground with a crush-trued wheel to form the shape shown in Fig. 2. Loading of the grinding wheel, which readily occurs with this material, was prevented by the use of a 46-grit wheel and a supply of grinding fluid sufficiently large to eliminate sparking. (Wheels containing 80-grit and 100-grit abrasive proved unsatisfactory.)

The fluid, which was stored in a 450-gal tank equipped with a leaf-type filter, and with refrigeration for maintaining the fluid below 100 F, was supplied to the grinding area through a nozzle. A 25-hp motor drove the grinding wheel, which was adjusted to a fast infeed until the motor ammeter registered 70% of rated load and then automatically readjusted to an infeed of 0.010 in. per min for the remainder of the grinding cycle. Other processing data are tabulated with Fig. 2.

Example 796. Effect of Infeed Rate on Cost, Grinding Time, and Wheel Life (Fig. 3)

Tests were made to determine the infeed rate that would result in lowest total cost per piece in form grinding the part shown in Fig. 3. The workpiece material was 416 stainless steel bar stock, cold finished and heat treated to Rockwell C 38 to 40. Form grinding each bar to the contour shown required the removal of 3.27 cu in. of stock; specified finish was 40 micro-in. maximum surface roughness.

Each part was positioned on a solid steel arbor (details of the inside of the hollow part are omitted in Fig. 3) and ground with an As-220-P10-V wheel. Wheel speed was 1340 rpm (5500 to 6750 sfm); work speed was 350 rpm (52 to 92 sfm); infeed total travel was 0.260 in. The grinding fluid consisted of 70% paraffin oil, 2½% sperm oil, 1½% sulfur, and 26% chlorinated paraffin.

Lowest total cost per piece, 42.5¢, resulted from the use of infeeds of 0.140, 0.150 and 0.160 in. per min. The grinding time required and the number of pieces ground per crush truing for the different infeed rates are given in the table accompanying Fig. 3; the effect of infeed rate on cost per piece is shown in the graph (note the rise in crush-roll cost with increasing feed rate).

The crush-roll costs were established at $210 basic cost plus one regrind at $40, giving a total of $250. Ten wheel truings were obtained per crush roll, five from a new roll and five after regrind. The total crush-roll cost ($250) divided by the number of wheel truings (10) yields a cost of $25 per truing. The crush-roll cost of each workpiece was obtained by dividing crush-truing cost ($25) by the number of pieces produced at a given rate of feed. For example, at an infeed rate of 0.130 in. per min, 250 pieces were finished before it became necessary to true the wheel. Crush-truing cost ($25) divided by number of pieces (250) yields a crush-roll cost of 10¢ per piece. Operating costs were taken as $10 per hour (16⅔¢ per min) of grinding time. Total grinding cost per piece equals crush-roll cost plus operating cost.

Belt Grinding

Belt grinding may be used on stainless steel. An application involving three different stainless steels is described in the following example.

Example 797. Turbine Buckets and Blades (Table 17)

Forged turbine buckets and turbine blades were ground with resin-bond abrasive belts in a belt-type polishing machine to the specified size and maximum surface roughness of 40 to 50 micro-in. The buckets were forged from either 403 or 422 stainless steel and hardened to 200 Bhn. The blades were forged from AM-350 stainless steel and hardened to 420 Bhn. Both parts were rough ground with a dry belt, then finish ground using oil as a grinding fluid. Other processing details are given in Table 17.

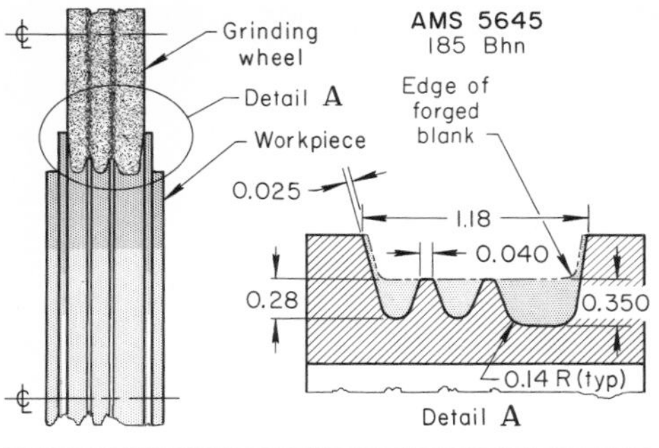

Wheel classification ....A_s-46-M-V
Wheel size ....24 by 1¼ by 12 in.

Operating Conditions

Wheel speed ....1050 rpm (6600 sfm)
Work-rotation speed ....200 sfm
Infeed on diameter ....(a)
Metal removed ....3.93 lb
Grinding fluid ....Grinding oil
Grinding time per piece ....25 min
Wheel life per dressing(b) ....8 pieces

(a) Fast infeed until 70% rated motor load, then 0.010 in. per min for remaining portion of cycle. (b) Wheel, trued with crush roll, lost 0.040 in. on diameter during each truing.

Fig. 2. Use of crush-trued wheel for form grinding of forgings (Example 795)

The two examples that follow illustrate application of a grinding machine with an 86-in.-wide abrasive belt, powered by a 250-hp motor. Belt speed was fixed at 5000 sfm. The 86-in. belt traveled over a conventional vertical-head assembly consisting of a dynamically balanced upper idler roll, of steel, and a rubber-covered serrated lower contact roll. A pneumatic belt-centering device was used to assure positive tracking of the abrasive belt and was adjustable to accommodate belts of different widths.

Example 798. Large Sand Castings

Type CF-20 stainless steel (similar to wrought type 302) sand cast heat treating fixtures, each 60 in. long, 32 in. wide and 8 in. thick, and weighing 600 lb, were refinished to 100 micro-in. maximum roughness on the working surfaces. With belt speed at 5000 sfm and table speed at 6 to 8 sfm, the fixtures were rough ground and finish ground, using waterproof-cloth belts coated with aluminum oxide abrasive. Abrasive was 36-grit for rough grinding, 60-grit for finish grinding. Soluble oil was used as grinding fluid.

To attain the required dimension and specified 100-micro-in. maximum roughness, approximately 0.050 in. of material was removed from each side of each fixture during rough grinding, and 0.010 in. in finish grinding. The rough grinding cycle required about 2½ hr for each side, and finish grinding about ½ hr. Planing, previously used for refinishing these fixtures, had required 4 hr for each side.

Example 799. Type 310 Plates

Surface plates of 310 stainless steel were finished to a maximum surface roughness of 20 micro-in., and the time taken for belt grinding was compared with that for wheel grinding the same kind of plate. Approximately 25 plates, most ranging in size from 30 by 6 by 1¼ in. to 18 by 30 by 1 in., were ground; the largest plate processed was 10 ft long and 18 in. wide.

The plates were ground with waterproof-cloth aluminum oxide abrasive belts of 36-grit for roughing, 60-grit for finishing. Soluble-oil emulsion was used as grinding fluid. Belt speed was 5000 sfm; table speed was 5 to 6 sfm. In rough grinding, 0.012 to 0.016 in. of material was removed (this included removal of hard scale on the top surface of each plate); in finish grinding, 0.006 to 0.008 in. was removed.

The required maximum roughness limit was held. Total grinding time for the largest plate was 2½ hr; this compared with 6 hr needed for resurfacing these plates with a wheel in a large surface grinder.

With the exception of the precipitation-hardening stainless steels, the hardness of the steel has a greater effect than its composition on the life of a grinding belt. Hardness also affects finish, and it is easier to obtain a high-quality finish on a harder stainless than on one that is softer. With the precipitation-hardening alloys, best grinding results are obtained with a waterproof-cloth belt and soluble-oil emulsion as a grinding fluid.

When grinding fluids are used, they should be of a type that will maintain free-cutting (nonloading) edges and a cool cutting surface, and be easy to apply. Grease sticks or waxes are sometimes used instead of grinding fluids.

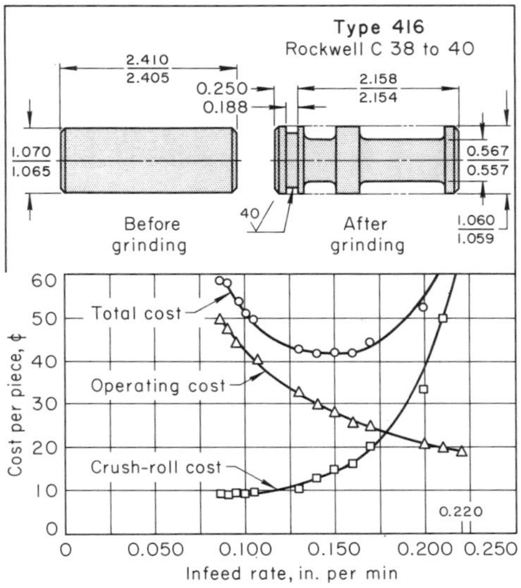

Infeed rate, ipm	Grinding time, min/pc	Pieces per crush truing	Infeed rate, ipm	Grinding time, min/pc	Pieces per crush truing
0.087	3.0	270	0.150	1.7	175
0.095	2.7	270	0.160	1.6	150
0.100	2.6	265	0.170	1.5	125
0.104	2.5	260	0.200	1.3	75
0.130	2.0	250	0.210	1.2	50
0.140	1.8	200	0.220	1.18	25

Fig. 3. Effect of infeed rate on cost, grinding time, and wheel life in form grinding, under the other operating conditions described in Example 796

Cutting oils diluted with kerosine (1 part oil to 4 parts kerosine) have often been used as fluids for belt grinding.

Safety. Metal fines collected in a container near the machine during the belt grinding of stainless steel should be removed regularly, because the fines, together with polishing compounds or oils that are collected with them, constitute a potential fire hazard. A fire in the duct system can be extremely dangerous, because of the high air flow in the ducts. Fire-extinguishing equipment should be close to the machines.

Electrochemical Grinding

Electrochemical grinding (ECG) can be applied to stainless steel workpieces (see process description in the article beginning on page 281; Table 3 in that article includes operating conditions for an application to stainless steel. Benefits of this electrochemical process are most likely to be realized with workpieces that are especially intricate or fragile, or both. The slot grinding application described in the following example was favorable for ECG.

Example 800. Burr-Free Slots in Type 316 Tubing (Fig. 4)

Electrochemical grinding, with metal-bond aluminum oxide wheels and with sodium chloride (4½ lb) and buffers mixed with 5 gal of water as the electrolyte, produced the three 0.050-in.-deep slots in the thin-wall sleeve shown in Fig. 4. These sleeves, made of 316 stainless steel tubing, were ground at a hardness of 285 Bhn. The 0.375-in.-wide slot was ground to the full depth in one pass, after which the two narrower slots were ground simultaneously in a second pass by two wheels of appropriate width mounted ⅛ in. apart on one spindle.

Not only were the ground sleeves free from distortion, but the edges of the slots were free of the burrs that ordinarily are produced in conventional wheel grinding of a tubular part like this one.

Electrical Discharge Grinding

Electrical discharge grinding (EDG) can be applied to stainless steel workpieces. Table 1 on page 281 gives typical conditions for electrical discharge grinding of type 303 and 304 stainless.

Table 17. Processing Data for Belt Grinding of Turbine Parts (Example 797)

Item	Buckets (type 403 or 422)(a)	Blades (alloy AM-350)(a)
Roughing		
Grit size, Al_2O_3 ...	80	80
Size of belt, in. ...	2½ by 60(b)	2½ by 60 (c)
Belt speed, sfm ...	2000 to 4000	2000 to 3000
Grinding fluid ...	None	None
Finishing		
Grit size, Al_2O_3 ...	120	180
Size of belt, in. ...	2½ by 60(b)	2½ by 60(b)
Belt speed, sfm ...	6000	4000
Grinding fluid	Oil	Oil

(a) Approximately 0.005 in. of stock was removed from the surface. (b) Highly flexible and light weight. (c) Heavy-duty, low flexibility.

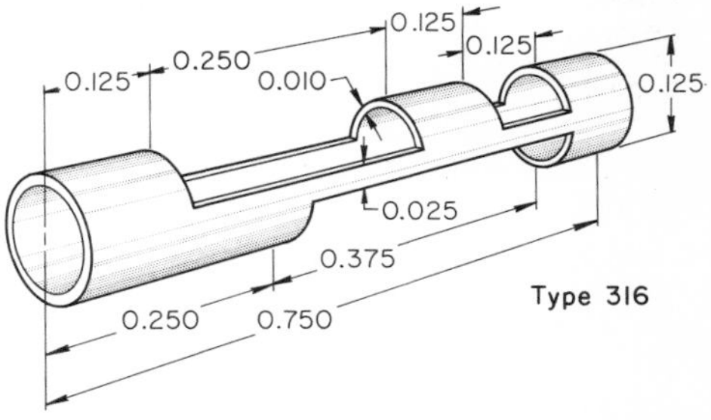

Type of wheel ..Metal-bond aluminum oxide(a)
Wheel diameter(b) ....6 in.

Operating Conditions

Wheel speed ....3800 rpm (6000 sfm)
Electrolyte ....Sodium chloride(c)
Grinding fluid ....None
Setup time ....40 min
Production rate ....12 pieces per hour
Method of wheel dressing ....Deplating(d)

(a) Grit size, 80. (b) With 1-in.-diam arbor hole; wheel widths were the same as slot widths. (c) Commercial sodium chloride (4½ lb) plus buffers mixed with 5 gal of water. (d) Deplating removed metal and exposed abrasive particles.

Fig. 4. Thin-wall sleeve in which burr-free slots were produced without distortion by electrochemical grinding (Example 800)

Machining of Maraging Steels

MARAGING STEELS in the annealed condition can be machined successfully by practice that is generally similar to that used for cold drawn austenitic stainless steels such as 304 (see "Machining of Stainless Steel", page 375). For maraging steel in the hardened condition (Rockwell C 50 to 52), practice is similar to that used for alloy steels such as 4340 at the same hardness. Tool design is essentially the same as that used for stainless or alloy steel at the same hardness.

Speed and Feed. Nominal speeds and feeds for machining the 18% and 25% nickel grades of maraging steel at varior hardness levels are presented in the eight tables below.

Tool Life. In tests to evaluate the effect of speed on life of high speed steel turning tools, a 0.062-in. depth of cut was used and tool life end point was established at 0.060-in. wear land. Tool design was the same for all tools.

In turning the 18% nickel grade of maraging steel at 302 Bhn with M2 high speed steel tools and a feed of 0.009 ipr, tool life was 45 min at a cutting speed of 80 sfm. However, at 70 sfm, a wear land of only 0.020 in. was obtained in 80 min, when the test was stopped. In turning the same steel at Rockwell C 52, small changes in cutting speed had much larger effects. In one test using M2 high speed steel tools and a feed of 0.005 ipr, tool life was only 10 min for a speed of 60 sfm. When speed was decreased to 50 sfm the tool life end point increased to 47 min, and when speed was further decreased to 45 sfm the tool had worn only 0.020 in. in 80 min.

Cutting Fluid. Soluble oil mixed 1-to-20 with water is an effective cutting fluid, as are chlorinated oils.

Nominal Speeds and Feeds for Machining of Maraging Steels

Turning With High Speed Steel and Carbide Single-Point and Box Tools

Steel	Brinell hardness	Roughing (0.150-in. cut) Speed, sfm	Roughing Feed, ipr	Finishing (0.025-in. cut) Speed, sfm	Finishing Feed, ipr
High Speed Steel Tools(a)					
18% Ni(b)	275-325(c)	60	0.015	80	0.007
	Rc 50-52(d)	40	0.010	55	0.005
25% Ni	175-225(c)	70	0.015	100	0.007
	Rc 50-52(d)	35	0.010	45	0.005

Steel	Brinell hardness	Roughing Speed, sfm Brazed	Roughing Speed, sfm Dispos	Roughing Feed, ipr	Finishing Speed, sfm Brazed	Finishing Speed, sfm Dispos	Finishing Feed, ipr
Carbide Tools(e)							
18% Ni(b)	275-325(c)	325	400	0.015	375	460	0.007
	Rc 50-52(d)	150	190	0.010	200	250	0.005
25% Ni	175-225(c)	275	335	0.015	335	420	0.007
	Rc 50-52(d)	125	160	0.010	160	200	0.005

Broaching With High Speed Steel Tools(f)

Steel	Brinell hardness	Speed, sfm	Feed (chip load), ipt
18% Ni(b)	275 to 325(c)	10	0.002
25% Ni	175 to 225(c)	15	0.003

Drilling With High Speed Steel Tools(g)

Steel	Brinell hardness	Speed, sfm	Feed, ipr, for hole diam of: ⅛ in.	½ in.	1½ in.
18% Ni(b)	275 to 325(c)	45	0.002	0.005	0.011
	Rc 50 to 52(d)	30	0.001	0.003	0.005
25% Ni	175 to 225(c)	50	0.002	0.006	0.014
	Rc 50 to 52(d)	20	0.001	0.003	0.005

Reaming With High Speed Steel and Carbide Tools

Steel	Brinell hardness	Speed, sfm	Feed, ipr, for tool diam of: ⅛ in.	½ in.	1½ in.
High Speed Steel Tools(h)					
18% Ni(b)	275 to 325(c)	30	0.002	0.008	0.015
	Rc 50 to 52(d)	..	....	....	....
25% Ni	175 to 225(c)	35	0.0025	0.008	0.015
	Rc 50 to 52(d)	..	....	....	....
Carbide Tools(j)					
18% Ni(b)	275 to 325(c)	100	0.003	0.008	0.015
	Rc 50 to 52(d)	40	0.002	0.004	0.008
25% Ni	175 to 225(c)	140	0.003	0.008	0.015
	Rc 50 to 52(d)	25	0.002	0.004	0.008

Tapping With High Speed Steel Tools

Steel	Brinell hardness	Speed, sfm	Tool material
18% Ni(b)	275 to 325(c)	20	M10, M7, M1
	Rc 50 to 52(d)	5	M3, M40
25% Ni	175 to 225(c)	25	M10, M7, M1
	Rc 50 to 52(d)	5	M3, M40

Peripheral (Slab) Milling With High Speed Steel Tools(k)

Steel	Brinell hardness	Roughing (0.150-in. cut) Speed, sfm	Roughing Feed, ipr	Finishing (0.025-in. cut) Speed, sfm	Finishing Feed, ipr
18% Ni(b)	275 to 325(c)	75	0.006	95	0.004
25% Ni	325 to 375(c)	80	0.006	105	0.004

Face Milling With High Speed Steel and Carbide Tools

Steel	Brinell hardness	Roughing (0.150-in. cut) Speed, sfm	Roughing Feed, ipr	Finishing (0.025-in. cut) Speed, sfm	Finishing Feed, ipr
High Speed Steel Tools(m)					
18% Ni(b)	275-325(c)	75	0.007	100	0.005
	Rc 50-52(d)	35	0.005	45	0.003
25% Ni	325-375(c)	80	0.007	105	0.005
	Rc 50-52(d)	25	0.005	35	0.003

Steel	Brinell hardness	Roughing Speed, sfm Brazed	Roughing Speed, sfm Dispos	Roughing Feed, ipr	Finishing Speed, sfm Brazed	Finishing Speed, sfm Dispos	Finishing Feed, ipr
Carbide Tools(j)							
18% Ni(b)	275-325(c)	250	275	0.006	330	360	0.005
	Rc 50-52(d)	100	110	0.005	130	145	0.004
25% Ni	325-375(c)	200	220	0.006	265	290	0.005
	Rc 50-52(d)	75	85	0.005	100	110	0.004

End Milling With High Speed Steel and Carbide Tools

Steel	Brinell hardness	Roughing (0.050-in. cut) Speed, sfm	Roughing Feed, ipr, for tool diam of: ½ in.	Roughing 1 to 2 in.	Finishing (0.015-in. cut) Speed, sfm	Finishing Feed, ipr, for tool diam of: ½ in.	Finishing 1 to 2 in.
High Speed Steel Tools(n)							
18% Ni(b)	275-325(c)	65	0.002	0.005	85	0.0015	0.004
	Rc 50-52(d)	30	0.001	0.003	40	0.001	0.002
25% Ni	175-225(c)	75	0.002	0.005	95	0.0015	0.004
	Rc 50-52(d)	25	0.001	0.002	30	0.001	0.001
Carbide Tools(j)							
18% Ni(b)	275-325(c)	300	0.002	0.005	390	0.0015	0.004
	Rc 50-52(d)	75	0.002	0.004	100	0.001	0.003
25% Ni	175-225(c)	275	0.002	0.005	360	0.0015	0.004
	Rc 50-52(d)	70	0.001	0.002	90	0.001	0.001

Footnotes for Tables. (a) High speed steel M2, T5 or T15 for 18% Ni at 275 to 325 Bhn; M2 or T5 for 25% Ni at 175 to 225 Bhn; T15, M41, M42, M43 or M44 for all steels at Rc 50 to 52. (b) Grades 200, 250 and 300. (c) Annealed. (d) Quenched and tempered. (e) Carbide grade C-2 for roughing 18% Ni at 275 to 325 Bhn, and for 25% Ni at 175 to 225 Bhn and Rc 50 to 52; grade C-3 for roughing 18% Ni at Rc 50 to 52, and for all finishing. (f) High speed steel T5 or T15 for 18% Ni; M2 for 25% Ni. (g) High speed steel T15 or M33. (h) High speed steel M2, M7 or M1. (j) Carbide grade C-2. (k) High speed steel M2 or M7. (m) High speed steel M2 or M7 for 18% Ni at 275 to 325 Bhn, and 25% Ni at 325 to 327 Bhn; T15 or M33 for all steels at Rc 50 to 52. (n) High speed steel M2 or M7 for 18% Ni at 275 to 325 Bhn, and 25% Ni at 175 to 225 Bhn; T15 for all steels at Rc 50 to 52. M33, M41, M42, M43 or M44 may be used as alternate to T15.

All tables and other data on this page have been adapted from data compiled by Metcut Research Associates, Inc.

Machining of Heat-Resisting Alloys

*By the ASM Committee on Machining of Heat-Resisting Alloys**

HEAT-RESISTING ALLOYS usually are classified as iron-base, nickel-base and cobalt-base. Most of the cobalt-base alloys are more accurately referred to as cobalt-chromium-nickel-base alloys, and one of the "iron-base" alloys (N-155) contains 60% Co + Cr + Ni. The three basic categories of alloys include a wide range of compositions, of which 37 are listed in Table 1. In presenting nominal speeds and feeds for machining operations in this article, heat-resisting alloys (wrought and cast) are classified into the eight groups defined by Table 2.

Heat-resisting alloys are difficult to machine. The iron-base alloys, some of which can be properly designated as stainless steels, usually machine more easily than the nickel-base and cobalt-base alloys, in similar conditions of heat treatment.

The nickel-base and cobalt-base alloys have several characteristics in common that contribute to difficulty in machining and cause rapid tool wear and high machining cost. These characteristics are:

1 High shear strength, which causes high forces at the cutting edges of tools
2 High capacity for work hardening
3 Presence of hard, abrasive intermetallic compounds in the microstructure
4 Low thermal conductivity, resulting in heat concentration in the cutting area.

Machining Comparisons

Figure 1 shows relative machinability of several heat-resisting alloys, stainless steels, refractory metals and alloy steels, using cutting speed in face milling as a basis for comparison. For the alloy steels and most of the other metals, cutters with carbide inserts were employed. For the nickel alloys, the speeds shown are based on cutters with high speed steel inserts. The slowest speeds (about 20 sfm) were required for the three nickel-base alloys, even though the hardness of two of these was only slightly higher (and of one alloy, lower) than that of the 4340 steel (340 Bhn, in this comparison), which was milled at the highest speed shown, 525 sfm.

In addition to the large variations in machinability among different alloys, the same alloy will differ in its response to different machining operations. This is illustrated by Tables 3 and 4.

In Table 3, the machinability of PH 15-7 Mo and A-286, both precipitation-hardening iron-base alloys, is compared with that of 4130 steel, arbitrarily rated at 100% for each of the operations considered. The 4130 steel was heat treated to a tensile strength of 100,000 psi (Rockwell C 15). The iron-base heat-resisting alloys were in the solution-treated-and-aged condition at a tensile strength of 200,000 psi (Rockwell C 43) for PH 15-7 Mo and 163,000 psi (Rockwell C 35) for A-286.

As shown in Table 3, average rates of metal removal for the two heat-resisting alloys for the twelve machining operations are almost identical — 18.25% for PH 15-7 Mo and 18.30% for A-286. Nevertheless, in comparing the ratings for specific machining operations, several marked differences appear. For example, although the machinability ratings for both alloys are similar in face milling and straddle milling, PH 15-7 Mo is approximately three times as difficult to machine as A-286 in end milling. Other marked differences are recorded for turning, for drilling and reaming the smaller-diameter holes, and for tapping.

Table 4 compares machining characteristics of three widely used heat-resisting alloys representing the three alloy classes — iron-base (A-286), nickel-base (Inconel X-750), and cobalt-base (HS-25). Despite the fact that the average machinability ratings of the three alloys are closely similar, marked differences occur for several processes — for example, threading, reaming, end milling, and drilling of ¼-in.-diam holes.

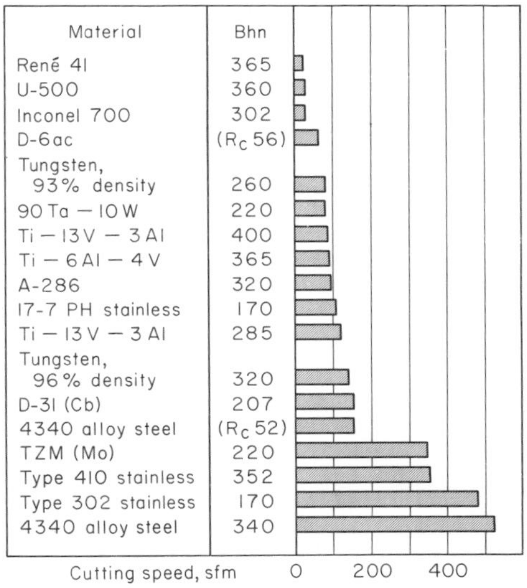

Fig. 1. Typical speeds in face milling twelve heat-resisting alloys and six steels

Manufacturing Comparisons. Machinability ratings based on cutting speed or metal-removal rate have limited utility. Ratings that permit estimating machining costs and shop load for production scheduling are more useful. Such manufacturing ratings reflect the consideration of noncutting time, as well as of cutting time. Thus, allowance is made for such time-consuming factors as tool changes and setup adjustments (to obtain the greater rigidity needed in machining a more difficult material).

In a development program for an aerospace vehicle, simulated service tests were conducted on identical structural parts made from two nickel-base alloys (Hastelloy X and René 41) and a cobalt-base alloy (HS-25). Although production of acceptable parts was the primary concern, the machining program afforded an opportunity to compile comparative information on the three alloys. Milling predominated in the machining schedule, but enough drilling, single-point cutting, shaping and abrasive sawing were involved to provide a fair knowledge of the production capabilities of the three alloys in these operations also.

Fittings for assembling one body joint, one wing joint, and four wing-to-body joints were produced in 14 different shapes of various degrees of complexity (see illustrations in Table 5). In all, 102 pieces were machined, 34 of each of the three alloys, in approximately one man-year (2119 hr) of manufacturing time. Table 5 analyzes production time per alloy for each of the 14 parts. Table 6 rates the three alloys on the basis of the development program and again on the basis of subsequent manufacturing experience with the same alloys.

Cost Comparisons. The ultimate comparison of machinability is the relative cost of producing a given machined part from various alloys. Because such information is seldom available until machining production is well under

*W. R. Freeman, Jr., *Chairman,* Manager, Materials Laboratory Section, Engineering and Development Operations, Lycoming Div., Avco Corp.; Peter R. Arzt, Senior Engineer, Pressure Vessel Components, Materials Advanced Technology, Aerojet-General Corp.; Clarence W. Forsyth, Manufacturing Process and Tool Planning Engineer, Cleveland Pneumatic Tool Co.; Arnold L. Havens, Manager, Producibility Dept., Sundstrand Aviation Div., Sundstrand Corp.

E. R. Hinman, Chief Process Engineer, Lycoming Div., Avco Corp.; Waldon F. Huston, Process Engineering Manager, Fafnir Bearing Co.; John Maranchik, Jr., Vice President, Metcut Research Associates, Inc.; John F. McAuliffe, Geometric Tool Div., United Greenfield Corp.; L. W. McBride, Assistant Plant Metallurgist, Aerodynamic Products, Allison Div., General Motors Corp.

John W. Mezas, Cleveland Pneumatic Tool Co. (formerly with Brush Beryllium Co.); J. M. Schaefer, Supervisor, Machining Engineering, Taylor Forge & Pipe Works, Inc.; E. Peter Schellens, President, Schellens True Corp.; D. A. Stewart, Senior Engineer, Thomson Engineering Laboratories, General Electric Co.

Table 1. Nominal Compositions of Heat-Resisting Alloys Dealt With in This Article

Alloy	Alloy group(a)	AISI No.	C	Mn	Si	Cr	Ni	Co	Mo	W	Cb	Ti	Al	Fe	Other
Iron-Base Alloys															
16-25-6(b)	Fe Wrt	650	0.05	1.75	...	16.00	25.00	...	6.00	...	...	...	...	Rem	0.15 N
19-9 DL(b)	Fe Wrt	651	0.32	0.15	0.55	18.50	9.00	...	1.40	1.35	0.40	0.25	...	Rem	...
17-14 Cu, Mo(b)	...	653	0.12	0.75	0.50	15.90	14.10	...	2.50	...	0.45	0.25	...	Rem	3.00 Cu
A-286(c)	Fe Wrt	660	0.05	1.45	0.60	14.75	25.20	...	1.30	...	...	2.15	0.22	Rem	0.28 V, 0.004 B
N-155(c)	Fe Wrt	661	0.12	1.50	0.70	20.75	19.85	19.50	2.95	2.35	1.15	...	...	Rem	0.13 N
Discaloy(c)	Fe Wrt	662	0.04	0.90	0.80	13.50	26.00	...	2.75	...	...	1.75	0.07	Rem	0.005 B
D-979(c)	...	664	0.06	0.25	0.20	14.90	44.30	...	4.05	3.65	...	3.00	1.05	Rem	0.01 B
Nickel-Base Alloys															
Hastelloy X	Ni Wrt 2	680	0.10	0.65	0.60	21.50	Rem	1.50	9.00	0.60	...	...	...	18.50	...
Incoloy 901	Ni Wrt 1	681	0.05	0.24	0.12	12.50	42.50	...	6.00	...	...	2.50	0.20	Rem	0.015 B
René 41	Ni Wrt 1	683	0.09	...	...	19.00	Rem	11.00	10.00	...	...	3.10	1.50	1.80	0.005 B
U-500	Ni Wrt 1(d)	684	0.10	0.10	0.10	17.50	Rem	18.45	4.25	...	...	3.00	3.00	0.50	0.005 B
Waspaloy	Ni Wrt 1	685	0.07	0.10	0.10	19.75	Rem	13.50	4.45	...	...	3.00	1.40	0.75	0.005 B, 0.04 Zr
Alloy R-235	...	686	0.12	...	...	15.00	Rem	...	5.00	...	...	2.50	2.00	10.00	...
U-700	Ni Wrt 1(d)	687	0.07	...	...	15.00	Rem	18.50	5.25	...	...	3.50	4.25	0.50	0.03 B
Inconel X-750	Ni Wrt 1	688	...	...	...	15.00	73.00	...	...	...	0.85	2.50	0.80	6.75	...
M-252	Ni Wrt 1(d)	689	0.15	...	...	20.00	Rem	10.00	10.00	...	...	2.60	1.00	...	0.005 B
Refractaloy 26	Ni Wrt 2	690	0.03	0.80	1.00	18.00	38.00	20.00	3.20	...	...	2.75	0.20	Rem	...
Astroloy	...	...	0.06	...	...	15.00	Rem	15.00	5.00	...	...	3.50	4.40	...	0.03 B
DCM	...	...	0.05	...	...	14.30	61.00	...	5.30	...	...	3.40	4.30	Rem	0.08 B
Hastelloy B	Ni Wrt 2(d)	...	0.10	...	...	...	Rem	...	28.00	...	...	...	...	5.00	...
Hastelloy C	Ni Cast	...	0.15	...	...	16.50	Rem	...	17.00	4.50	...	...	...	6.00	...
Hastelloy W	...	...	0.12	...	...	5.00	Rem	...	25.00	...	...	...	...	5.50	0.6 V max
Inconel 600	...	...	0.04	...	...	15.00	Rem	...	...	...	...	...	...	7.00	...
Inconel 700	Ni Wrt 1	...	0.13	0.08	0.25	15.00	45.00	30.00	3.00	...	...	2.20	3.20	1.00	...
Alloy 713C	Ni Cast	...	0.12	...	...	12.50	Rem	...	4.00	...	2.00	0.80	6.10	...	0.10 Zr
Inconel 718	Ni Wrt 1	...	0.04	...	...	19.00	Rem	...	3.00	...	5.20	0.80	0.60	18.00	...
K-42-B	...	...	0.05	0.70	0.70	18.00	43.00	22.00	...	...	...	2.50	0.20	...	...
M-308	...	...	0.08	...	...	14.00	33.00	...	4.00	6.50	...	2.00	0.25	Rem	0.25 Zr, tr B
Nimonic 75	Ni Wrt 1(d)	...	0.12	1.00	1.00	20.00	Rem	...	...	...	...	0.40	...	5.00	...
Nimonic 80	Ni Wrt 1(d)	...	0.10	1.00	1.00	20.00	Rem	2.00	...	...	...	2.25	1.25	5.00	...
Nimonic 90	Ni Wrt 1(d)	...	0.10	1.00	1.00	20.00	Rem	18.00	...	...	...	2.50	1.50	5.00	...
Cobalt-Chromium-Nickel-Base Alloys															
HS-25 (L-605)	Co Wrt	670	0.12	1.65	0.60	19.85	9.90	Rem	...	15.25	...	...	...	1.60	...
S-816	Co Wrt	671	0.42	1.05	0.45	19.65	20.35	43.60	4.15	3.95	4.10	...	...	Rem	...
HS-21	Co Cast	...	0.25	...	...	27.00	3.00	Rem	5.50	...	...	...	...	1.00	...
HS-31 (X-40)	Co Cast	...	0.50	...	...	25.50	10.50	Rem	...	7.50	...	...	...	1.00	...
J-1570	Co Wrt	...	0.20	...	...	20.00	28.00	Rem	...	7.00	...	4.00	...	2.00	...
Stellite J	...	...	2.20	1.00	1.00	31.00	2.50	Rem	...	16.00	...	...	...	3.00	...

(a) See Table 2 for group designations of alloys on which speed and feed data are included in this article. (b) Austenitic alloys, strengthened by "hot-cold" work. (c) Austenitic alloys, iron base. (d) Also Ni Cast.

Table 2. Group Designations Used in Tables of Nominal Speed and Feed in This Article

Group(a)	Alloys
Fe Wrt	16-25-6, 19-9 DL, A-286, Discaloy, Incoloy 800, Incoloy 801, Incoloy 805, N-155, V-57, W-545
Ni Wrt 1	Incoloy 901, Inconel 700, Inconel 702, Inconel 718, Inconel 721, Inconel 722, Inconel 751, Inconel X-750, M-252, Nimonic 75, Nimonic 80, Nimonic 90, Nimonic 95, René 41, René 62, U-500, U-700, Waspaloy
Ni Wrt 2	Hastelloy B, Hastelloy X, Incoloy 804, Refractaloy 26
Ni Cast	GMR-235, Hastelloy B, Hastelloy C, Alloy 713C, IN-100, MAR-M200, M-252, Nimonic 75, Nimonic 80, Nimonic 90, Nimonic 95, Nimonic 100, U-500, U-700
Co Wrt	HS-25, J-1570, J-1650, S-816, V-36
Co Cast	HS-6, HS-21, HS-31, HS-36, MAR-M302, MAR-M322, WI-52
HR Cst 1	HA, HC, HD, HT, HU, HW, HX
HR Cst 2	HE, HF, HH, HI, HK, HL, HM

(a) Fe Wrt = Iron-base wrought alloys; Ni Wrt 1 and 2 = Nickel-base wrought alloys; Ni Cast = Nickel-base casting alloys; Co Wrt = Cobalt-chromium-nickel-base wrought alloys; Co Cast = Cobalt-chromium-nickel-base casting alloys; HR Cst 1 and 2 = Heat-resistant casting alloys (ACI).

Table 3. Comparison of Machining Characteristics of PH 15-7 Mo (Rockwell C 43) and A-286 (Rockwell C 35)

(Relative to 4130 steel at Rockwell C 15 as 100%)

Operation	Rate of metal removal relative to 4130, %: PH 15-7 Mo	A-286
Face milling	10.5	8.5
End milling	9.5	25.0
Straddle milling	13.9	11.5
Turning	11.5	15.6
Threading, 1¼–12	37.7	47.0
Band sawing	26.7	28.6
Drilling, ¼-in. diam	14.2	3.6
Drilling, ½-in. diam	7.0	7.1
Reaming, ¼-in. diam	38.1	20.9
Reaming, ½-in. diam	17.4	22.4
Tapping, ¼–28	9.8	15.2
Tapping, ½–20	22.7	14.2
Average, all operations	*18.25*	*18.30*

Table 4. Comparison of Machining Characteristics of Inconel X-750 (Rockwell C 35), HS-25 (Rockwell C 24), and A-286 (Rockwell C 35)

(Relative to 4130 steel at Rc 15 as 100%)

Operation	Rate of metal removal relative to 4130, %: Inconel X-750	HS-25	A-286
Face milling	4.5	2.6	8.5
End milling	11.4	10.2	25.0
Straddle milling	11.6	9.6	11.5
Turning	15.2	23.2	15.6
Threading, 1¼–12	83.0	96.0	47.0
Band sawing	22.8	19.0	28.6
Drilling, ¼-in. diam	10.6	12.0	3.6
Drilling, ½-in. diam	9.3	9.4	7.1
Reaming, ¼-in. diam	7.2	15.7	20.9
Reaming, ½-in. diam	10.0	16.7	22.4
Tapping, ¼–28	18.9	7.4	15.2
Tapping, ½–20	13.9	14.1	14.2
Average, all operations	*18.2*	*19.7*	*18.3*

way, test data on the cost per cubic inch for metal removal are sometimes developed ahead of production. Figure 2 summarizes this type of information for A-286 machined by several different processes. For further information on the method used for arriving at optimum feed and speed in these tests, see the discussion on page 185.

Manufacturing of sample parts is a more meaningful method of evaluating cost relations in advance of production. Figure 3 shows a 6-lb part for which machining would cost $10 if the part were made from a 10-lb piece of 1112 steel bar stock. (This particular steel is frequently used as the reference material in comparing machinability of steels.) If the same part is made from bar stock of various heat-resisting alloys, machining costs increase as shown in Fig. 3. If a forging or casting is substituted for bar stock, considerably less machining is required, which is reflected in the lower cost of machining the workpiece. Tooling costs are not included in the data in Fig. 3, but any preconditioning costs (for example, for heat treating) are included.

Turning

In turning, the force for cutting heat-resisting alloys is about double that for annealed medium-carbon alloy steel, and great rigidity in the machine, tooling, and workpiece setup is mandatory, because of the power required per unit of metal removed (Table 7).

Tool design is of particular importance in single-point turning of heat-resisting alloys. Recommended angles and tool materials are presented in Table 8. Although the data in Table 8 are applicable to most turning operations on heat-resisting alloys, experience often indicates the need for changes in tool angles for a specific contour. Tools that proved successful for single-point turning are described in the four examples that follow:

Example 801. Tool for Turning the Inside of an A-286 Turbine Casing (Fig. 4)

A carbide insert and a holder were designed for turning the inside contour of a turbine casing made of A-286 (Rockwell C 24 to 36), and removing approximately 0.010 in. of material. The insert (Fig. 4) was of grade C-2 carbide, and had 6° end and side relief, and 0.250-in. nose radius. Holder size was 1¼ by 1½ in. The cutter produced a surface finish of 80 to 100 micro-in., and a soluble-oil cutting fluid was used. Turning speed was 140 to 170 sfm; feed was 0.015 ipr; tool life (volume of metal removed per cutting edge) was 91 cu in.

Example 802. Tool for Rough Turning Compressor-Rotor Hub (Fig. 5)

The carbide insert and the tool holder designed for rough turning the cone of a compressor-rotor hub made of Incoloy 901 (Rockwell C 28 to 38) are shown in Fig. 5. The insert was 0.500 in. square, 0.125 in. thick, and had a maximum radius of 0.047 in. and 0° back and side rakes. The hub was turned in a vertical turret lathe, and the surface finish obtained was 80 to 100 micro-in. Cutting speed was 170 sfm, and feed, 0.010 ipr. A soluble-oil cutting fluid was used. Tool life was 21.3 cu in. of metal removed per edge.

Example 803. Tool for Turning Cone on Compressor-Rotor Hub (Fig. 6)

To turn the cone and blend the radius on the hub of a compressor rotor made of Incoloy 901 (Rockwell C 28 to 38), the turning-tool assembly shown in Fig. 6 was used. The grade C-2 carbide insert had 0° back and side rakes. Surface finish on the parts was 80 to 100 micro-in. Cutting speed for turning was 57 to 170 sfm (40 rpm), at a feed of 0.010 ipr. A soluble-oil cutting fluid was used, and tool life was 21.3 cu in. of metal removed per edge.

Example 804. Tool for Tracing and Turning Compressor Hub (Fig. 7)

A carbide tool of the disposable-insert type, with a suitable holder, was used for machining the cone and hub section of a compressor rotor made of Incoloy 901 (Rockwell C 28 to 38). The cutter (Fig. 7), which incorporated a chip breaker, had 5° back rake, 5° end relief, 3° end cutting-edge angle, and a nose radius of 0.062 in. This tool provided a surface finish of 80 to 100 micro-in. Operating conditions for cutting the hub sections were as follows: speed, 100 to 275 sfm; feed, 0.010 ipr; depth of cut, 0.093 to 0.3125 in. Tool life was 15 to 18 cu in. of metal removed per cutting edge. A soluble-oil cutting fluid was used.

Tool-holding devices must be given consideration equal to that of tool design when heat-resisting alloys are being turned. A fivefold difference in tool life often results because of variations in tool positioning. Holders designed for specific operations are described in the two following examples:

Example 805. Mechanical Tool Holder and Tool-Setting Gage for Plunge-Cutting Tool (Fig. 8)

To reduce the time for accurately positioning a brazed carbide tool used for close-tolerance (0.010-in. total) plunge grooving of a 0.250-in.-wide A-286 weldment flange, the mechanical holder and tool illustrated in Fig. 8 (ordinarily used for cutting off) were employed. A tool-setting gage of the flush-pin type helped position the tool accurately. The ease of inserting tools, together with the positive positioning afforded by the gage, resulted in a decrease of tool-setting time from 30 min per tool to less than 5 min per tool. A 20% increase in tool life also resulted, because of the mechanical tool holder.

Example 806. Tool for Turning a Radius on Waspaloy Turbine Blades (Fig. 9a)

A special tool and holder (Fig. 9a) were designed for turning a radius on turbine blades made of Waspaloy (Rockwell C 32 to 38). The tool, which had a nose radius of 0.160 in. (other dimensions are given in Fig. 9a), was made of either M3 or T15 high speed steel. A special tool post operated with a cam-actuated tool slide. To turn the radius, the blade was clamped at the serrated butt with a conforming-serration holder. After turning, surface finish was 80 to 100 micro-in.

Turning was done at a cutting speed of 25 sfm, a feed of 0.004 ipr, and a depth of cut of 0.100 in., and a sulfochlorinated cutting oil was used. In terms of volume of metal removed, tool life was 1.6 cu in. per grind (equivalent to four loads, two blades per load).

Cutoff Tool. In cutting off Inconel 600 tubing (3-in. diam, ⅜-in. wall), the cast cobalt-base alloy tool shown in Fig. 9(b) provided excellent surface finish and had a minimum life of 40 pieces per grind. The principal features of this tool are the 4° side relief on each side, and the curved nose. The tool was used at a speed of 30 sfm and 0.004-ipr feed, with a 1-to-20 mixture of soluble oil and water as the cutting fluid.

Table 5. Manufacturing Time Required to Produce the Same Part From Hastelloy X, René 41 and HS-25, and for Total Production of Each Part (See Table 6 for Manufacturing Ratings)

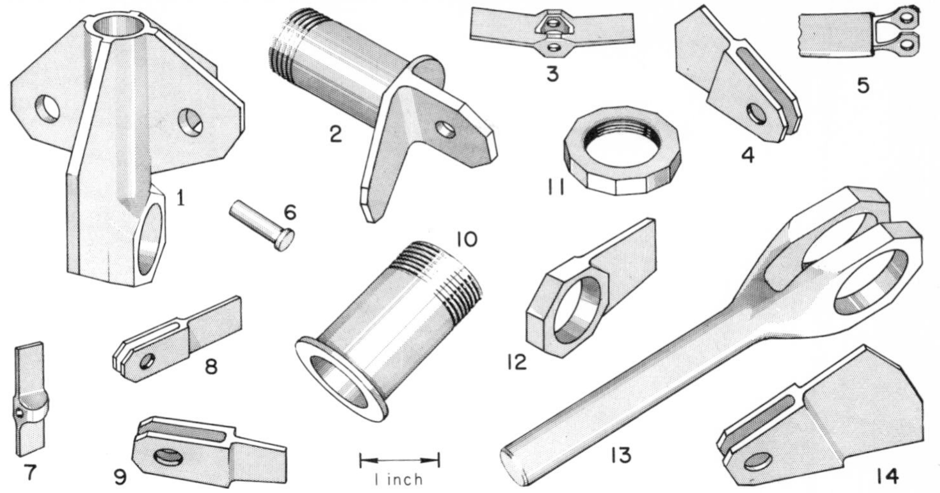

Part No.	Production time per piece, hr: Hastelloy X	René 41	HS-25	Quantity machined of each alloy	Total production time, hr
1	71.8	116.5	126.0	4	1257.2
2	27.0	39.3	25.0	1	91.3
3	15.8	9.5	6.0	1	31.3
4	11.2	10.0	15.8	4	148.0
5	13.0	10.5	13.5	1	37.0
6	7.0	13.0	11.5	1	31.5
7	10.5	14.0	21.3	1	45.8
8	4.6	7.3	5.3	5	86.0
9	5.4	6.3	4.6	4	65.2
10	4.1	7.3	6.1	4	70.0
11	1.6	1.8	2.0	5	27.0
12	20.5	20.0	51.0	1	91.5
13	18.0	25.0	19.5	1	62.5
14	18.5	36.0	20.5	1	75.0
Total	229.0	316.5	328.1	34	2119.3

Table 6. Manufacturing Ratings for the Alloys for Which Production Time Is Given in Table 5

Alloy	Development program: Hours	Rating, %	Subsequent manufacturing rating, %
Hastelloy X	531.3	100	100
René 41	773.2	69	72
HS-25	814.8	65	61

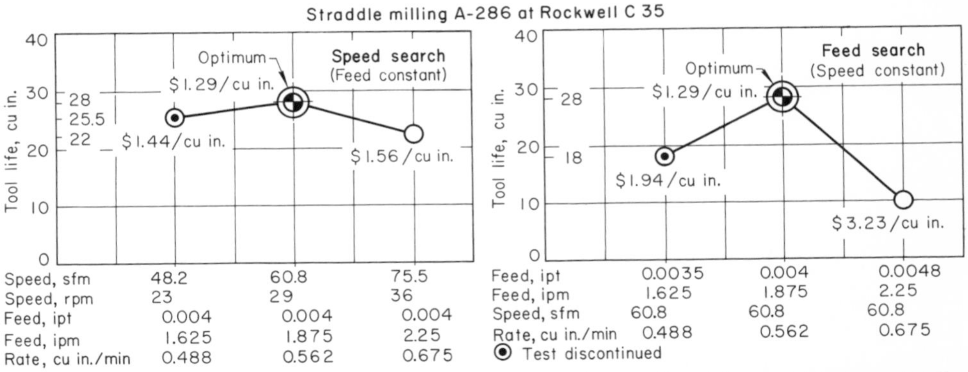

Fig. 2. Effect of speed and feed on tool life and cost of straddle milling A-286 at Rockwell C 35. For similar data on turning, drilling and reaming this alloy, see pages 11, 87 and 100.

Table 7. Power Requirements in Turning Heat-Resisting Alloys With Carbide Tools

Alloy	Hp/cu in./min	Alloy	Hp/cu in./min
16-25-6	1.10	Inconel X-750	0.90
A-286	1.20	Nimonic 80 ...	1.10
S-816	1.25	Nimonic 90 ...	1.30
J-1570	1.30	Inconel 713C .	1.06
Refractaloy 26	1.30	Inconel 700 ..	1.40

Table 8. Tool Material and Design for Turning Heat-Resisting Alloys

Alloy type and type of cut	Tool material	Side rake angle	Back rake angle	End and side relief	Side cutting-edge angle	Remarks
Age-hardenable and austenitic:						Hone cutting edge to
Roughing	Carbide	6°	0° to 3°	6°	15° to 30°	minimize cratering
Finishing	Carbide	6°	0°	6°	0°	and abrasion
Cobalt-base	Carbide	0°	0°	3° to 5°	15° to 30°	Abrasive wear
Intermittent cuts (all alloys)	HSS	6°	0°	5°	30°	3/64-in. nose radius

Tool Material. Carbide tools are usually used in turning heat-resisting alloys. Although the most efficient carbide grade for one application may not be best for another, a C-2 grade containing about 88.25% W, 5.75% C and 6.0% Co is frequently selected.

High speed steel tools are seldom used in turning heat-resisting alloys, except for interrupted cuts. In such applications, high speed steel tools are more practical than carbide tools because of their greater shock resistance. The general-purpose, highly alloyed grades such as T15, M36 or M44 are usually selected despite higher cost. Tools of these grades have longer life than general-purpose grades such as M2 or T1. However, cutting speed must be much slower for high speed steel tools than for carbide tools.

Speeds for turning heat-resisting alloys with single-point and box tools are given in Table 9, and speeds for form turning and cutoff turning are listed in Tables 10 and 11, respectively. In all three tables, speeds are given for both high speed steel tools and carbide tools.

The effects of speed on tool life in turning three different iron-base heat-resisting alloys are shown in Fig. 10(a). The workpieces used in collecting these data were bars 3 to 4 in. in diameter by 18 in. long. Alloy N-155 was turned in the solution-treated condition; 19-9 DL, in the stress-relieved condition. Thus, their hardnesses were lower than that of A-286, which was turned in the solution-treated-and-aged condition. All three curves are steep, indicating a rapid decrease in tool life as speed is increased. Tool details and operating conditions are given in the table that accompanies Fig. 10.

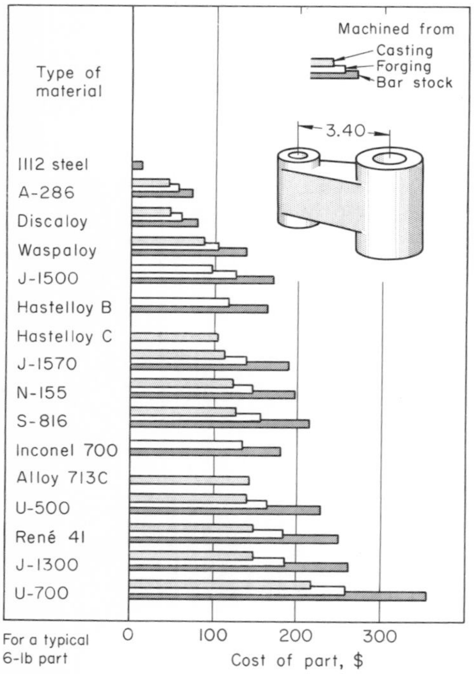

Comparison is based on a 6-lb part for which machining would cost $10 if the part were made from a 10-lb piece of 1112 steel bar stock.

Fig. 3. Comparison of machinability in terms of approximate cost to produce a machined part from various alloys

The relation of speed to tool life in turning four nickel-base heat-resisting alloys is plotted in Fig. 10(b). All four alloys were turned in the solution-treated condition. For 20-min tool life, cutting speed cannot exceed 90 sfm for Incoloy 901 (262 Bhn) and Inconel 700 (302 Bhn). For equivalent tool life in turning U-500 (340 Bhn), cutting speed must be no more than about 65 sfm, and for Hastelloy R-235 (285 Bhn), speed must not exceed 35 sfm. The curves in Fig. 10(b) show that speed and tool life relations do not correlate closely with hardness; Hastelloy R-235 has the lowest hardness of the four alloys, but requires the slowest speed for machining operations like turning.

Figure 11 shows the effect of speed, work-metal condition, and tool material on tool life in turning René 41. Other machining conditions, such as tool angles and cutting fluid, were optimum for this alloy (see table accompanying Fig. 11). Better tool life was obtained with both T15 high speed steel and C-2 carbide tools when René 41 was turned in the solution-treated condition (321 Bhn), rather than in the solution-treated-and-aged condition (365 Bhn). However, in either condition, relatively low cutting speed was mandatory, with the high speed steel tools showing greater sensitivity to an increase in cutting speed.

Feeds typically used in turning heat-resisting alloys are listed in Tables 9, 10 and 11. Tool life usually increases as feed decreases. Both feed and depth of cut must be great enough to avoid glazing. Depths of cut for rough and finish turning with single-point and box tools are given in footnotes (d) and (e) of Table 9.

Cutting Fluid. Water-soluble oils in mixtures of one part oil with 20 to 40 parts water are most frequently used in turning heat-resisting alloys (see specific examples). Water-base chemical emulsions (usually proprietary) also have proved acceptable. Supplying a constant flood of cutting fluid to the cutting area is frequently more important than the composition of the fluid.

Sulfurized or chlorinated cutting oils, applied straight or diluted 1 to 1 with low-viscosity mineral oil, are used in some applications. Diluting the cutting oil with mineral oil permits better mobility (and cooling) without seriously impairing the properties of these chemically active oils. Two conditions in which active cutting oils are preferred to soluble oils are: (*a*) when surface finishes are critical, and (*b*) when high speed steel cutting tools are being used.

If sulfurized or chlorinated oil is used as a cutting fluid, the workpieces must be thoroughly cleaned before heat treatment or high-temperature service. Serious damage to workpieces during heating cycles may result if any residue remains.

Effect of Alloy Composition on Conditions for Turning. Results of a study of tool life expectancy in rough and finish turning of Inconel 718 (two hardnesses) and in rough turning of Waspaloy (two hardnesses) and A-286 are summarized in Table 12. For the

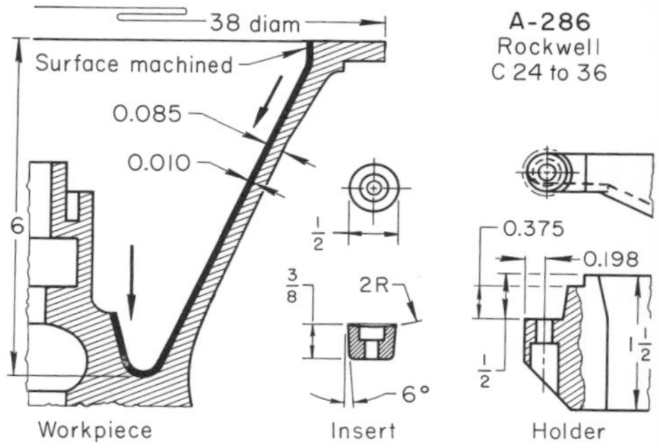

Fig. 4. Special tool designed for turning inside surface of the A-286 workpiece shown (Example 801)

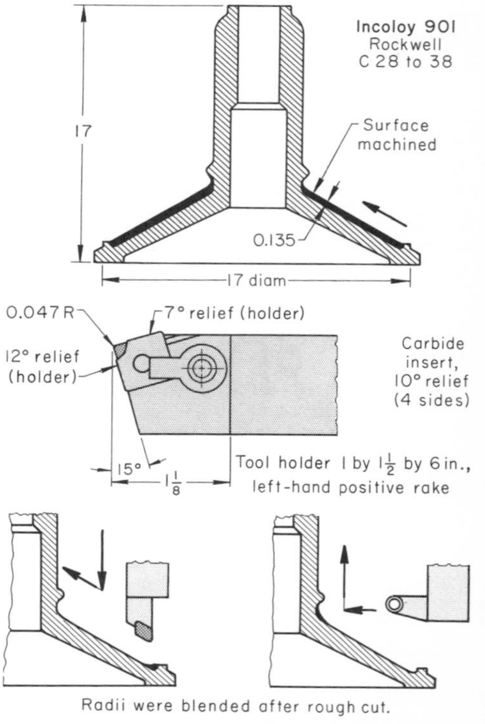

Fig. 5. Carbide insert and tool holder for rough turning the Incoloy 901 compressor-rotor hub cone shown in the top sketch (Example 802)

conditions of the test, tool life is quite short for all three alloys. Carbide (C-2) insert-type cutters were used exclusively. A lead angle of 45° was found to provide a longer tool life than a 0° lead angle. Stock-removal rate and tool life were the principal considerations; surface finish was of no concern.

As was discussed in relation to Table 5, identically shaped aerospace parts are sometimes made from two or more different alloys. This practice has permitted machining comparisons among different alloys, as in the three examples that follow.

Example 807. Turning Forged Rings: Hastelloy X vs René 41 (Table 13)

Processing details and results (in terms of metal-removal rate) for turning forged rings of identical shape from Hastelloy X and René 41 are compared in Table 13. The ring cross section with turning tools in position is shown in the figure in Table 13. Rings of both materials were machined with the same equipment, using the same tooling; thus, variations in metal-removal rate are a result of differences in the machining characteristics of the materials. The rings were held in the lathe chuck by clamping the rim so that half of both the inside and outside diameters could be turned during each setup. Because the chips generated were not troublesome, chip breakers were not used.

In preliminary tests, square carbide inserts were found to give better tool life than triangular inserts in turning outside diameters, and square inserts with negative-rake insert holders doubled tool life, because each insert was used twice on each corner.

All cuts were continuous roughing cuts and were produced with the aid of automatic feed control. In terms of metal-removal rate, René 41 in the age-hardened condition was more than twice as difficult to turn as Hastelloy X in the solution-treated condition. Furthermore, productivity in ID turning was considerably less than in OD turning, for both alloys.

Example 808. Turning Turbine Parts: Incoloy 901 vs Waspaloy vs Astroloy (Table 14)

Identical turbine parts of Incoloy 901, Waspaloy and Astroloy, all in the age-hardened condition, were turned under the conditions given in Table 14. Workpieces were held in a 30-in. horizontal lathe by a three-jaw chuck,

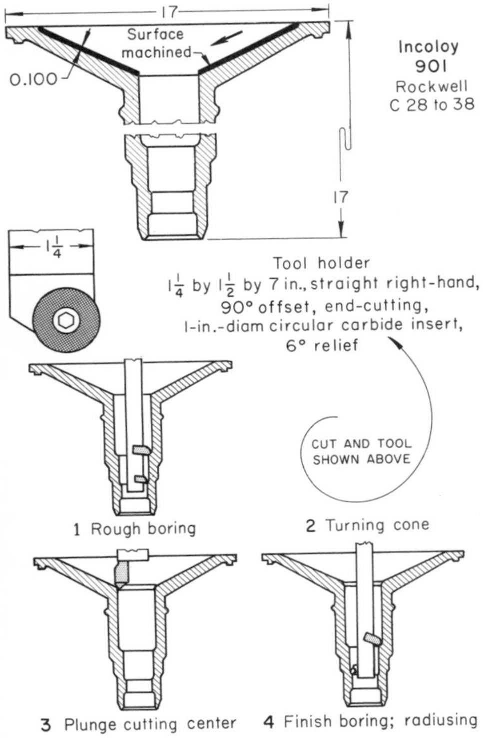

Fig. 6. Operations and tooling for machining the compressor-rotor hub shown (Example 803)

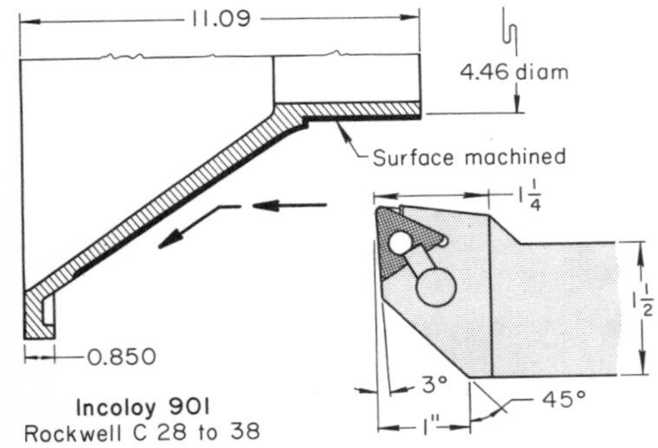

Fig. 7. Carbide insert and tool holder for tracer turning and facing the compressor hub shown (Example 804)

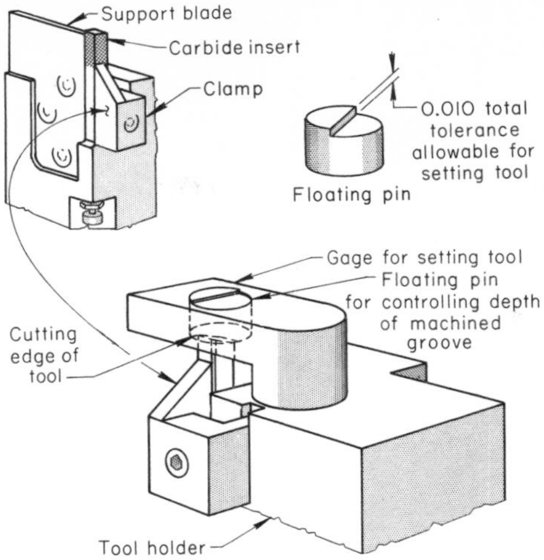

Fig. 8. Cutoff tool, holder and tool-setting gage used in plunge grooving (Example 805)

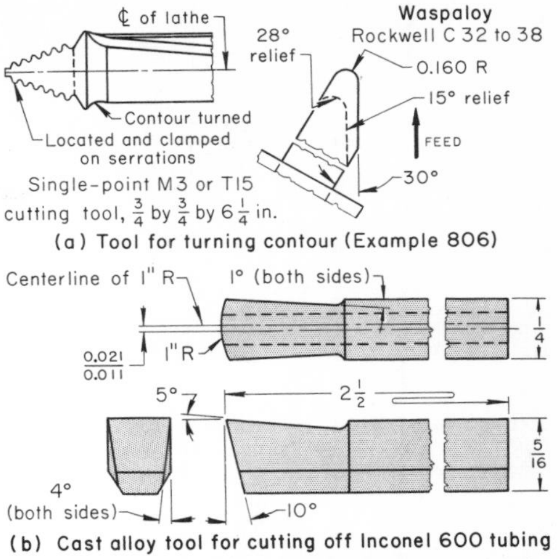

Fig. 9. (a) *Tool and holder to turn radius on blade* (Example 806). (b) *Cutoff tool.*

Table 9. Nominal Speeds for Turning Heat-Resisting Alloys With Single-Point and Box Tools (a)

			Rough turning(d) — Speed, sfm			Finish turning(e) — Speed, sfm		
				Carbide tools(g)			Carbide tools(h)	
Alloy group(b)	Condition(c)	Brinell hardness	HSS tools(f)	Brazed	Disposable	HSS tools(f)	Brazed	Disposable
Fe Wrt	ST(j)	180 to 230 ..	30	125	150	35	150	180
	ST, A	250 to 320 ..	25	110	135	30	135	160
Ni Wrt 1	Ann or ST	200 to 300 ..	15	60	70	20	70	80
	ST, A	300 to 400 ..	15	60	70	20	70	80
Ni Wrt 2	Ann(j)	140 to 220 ..	45	125	160	60	175	215
	CD(j)	240 to 310 ..	35	100	125	45	125	150
Ni Cast	AC(k)	250 to 350 ..	10	30	35	15	40	50
Co Wrt	ST	180 to 230 ..	20	80	90	25	90	100
	ST, A	270 to 320 ..	15	60	70	20	70	80
Co Cast	AC(k)	220 to 290 ..	10	30	35	15	40	50
HR Cst 1	AC(j)	160 to 210 ..	65(m)	275	325	80(m)	325	400
HR Cst 2	AC(j)	160 to 210 ..	50(m)	225	275	65(m)	275	325

(a) High speed steel tool design: 0° back rake, 15° side rake, 5° end relief, 5° side relief, 15° end cutting-edge angle. Carbide tool design: (brazed) 0° back rake, 6° side rake, 5° end relief, 5° side relief, 5° end cutting-edge angle; (disposable) —5° back rake, —5° side rake, 5° end relief, 5° side relief, 5° end cutting-edge angle. Nose radius and side cutting-edge angle are usually dictated by type of operation being performed. A chemical emulsion is recommended as the cutting fluid. (b) See Table 2 for alloys in each group. (c) ST = Solution treated; A = Aged; Ann = Annealed; CD = Cold drawn; AC = As cast. (d) Depth of cut, 0.150 in.; feed, 0.010 ipr, except for conditions footnoted (j).
(e) Depth of cut, 0.025 in.; feed, 0.007 ipr, except for conditions footnoted (k). (f) T15, M41, M42, M43 and M44. (g) Grade C-2. (h) Grade C-3. (j) Roughing feed, 0.015 ipr. (k) Finishing feed, 0.005 ipr. (m) M2 and T5.

Table 10. Nominal Speeds and Feeds for Turning Heat-Resisting Alloys With Form Tools (a)

			High speed steel tools(d)				Carbide tools(e)			
				Feed (ipr) for tool width (in.) of:				Feed (ipr) for tool width (in.) of:		
Alloy group(b)	Condition(c)	Brinell hardness	Speed, sfm	0.500	1.000	2.000	Speed, sfm	0.500	1.000	2.000
Fe Wrt	ST	180 to 230	20	0.002	0.002	0.001	95	0.004	0.003	0.002
	ST, A	250 to 320	20	0.002	0.002	0.001	80	0.004	0.003	0.0015
Ni Wrt 1	Ann or ST	200 to 300	10	0.002	0.0015	0.0007	45	0.004	0.003	0.0015
	ST, A	300 to 400	10	0.0015	0.001	0.0007	45	0.003	0.0025	0.001
Ni Wrt 2	Ann	140 to 220	35	0.002	0.002	0.001	95	0.004	0.003	0.002
	CD	240 to 310	25	0.002	0.002	0.001	75	0.004	0.003	0.0015
Ni Cast	AC	250 to 350	7	0.0015	0.001	0.0007	20	0.003	0.0025	0.0015
Co Wrt	ST	180 to 230	15	0.002	0.0015	0.0007	60	0.004	0.003	0.0015
	ST, A	270 to 320	10	0.0015	0.001	0.0007	45	0.003	0.0025	0.0015
Co Cast	AC	220 to 290	7	0.0015	0.001	0.0007	20	0.003	0.0025	0.0015
HR Cst 1	AC	160 to 210	50	0.0015	0.001	0.0007	205	0.003	0.0025	0.0015
HR Cst 2	AC	160 to 210	35	0.0015	0.001	0.0007	170	0.003	0.0025	0.0015

(a) A chemical emulsion is recommended as the cutting fluid. (b) See Table 2 for alloys in each group. (c) ST = Solution treated; A = Aged; Ann = Annealed; CD = Cold drawn; AC = As cast. (d) T15, M41, M42, M43 and M44, except M2 and T5 for alloy groups HR Cst 1 and 2. (e) Grade C-2, except grade C-6 for alloy groups HR Cst 1 and 2.

Table 11. Nominal Speeds and Feeds for Turning Heat-Resisting Alloys With Cutoff Tools(a)

Alloy group(b)	Condition(c)	Brinell hardness	High speed steel tools(d): Speed, sfm	Feed (ipr) for tool width (in.) of: 0.062	0.125	0.250	Carbide tools(e): Speed, sfm	Feed (ipr) for tool width (in.) of: 0.062	0.125	0.250
Fe Wrt	ST	180 to 230 ..	20	0.001	0.002	0.0025	95	0.003	0.005	0.007
	ST, A	250 to 320 ..	20	0.001	0.002	0.0025	80	0.003	0.005	0.007
Ni Wrt 1	Ann or ST	200 to 300 ..	10	0.001	0.0015	0.002	45	0.003	0.0045	0.006
	ST, A	300 to 400 ..	10	0.001	0.001	0.0015	45	0.003	0.003	0.0045
Ni Wrt 2	Ann	140 to 220 ..	35	0.001	0.002	0.0025	95	0.003	0.005	0.007
	CD	240 to 310 ..	25	0.001	0.002	0.0025	75	0.003	0.005	0.007
Ni Cast	AC	250 to 350 ..	7	0.001	0.001	0.0015	20	0.003	0.003	0.0045
Co Wrt	ST	180 to 230 ..	15	0.001	0.0015	0.002	60	0.003	0.0045	0.006
	ST, A	270 to 320 ..	10	0.001	0.001	0.0015	45	0.003	0.003	0.0045
Co Cast	AC	220 to 290 ..	7	0.001	0.001	0.0015	20	0.003	0.003	0.0045
HR Cst 1	AC	160 to 210 ..	50	0.001	0.0015	0.002	205	0.003	0.0045	0.006
HR Cst 2	AC	160 to 210 ..	35	0.001	0.0015	0.002	170	0.003	0.0045	0.006

(a) A chemical emulsion is recommended as the cutting fluid. (b) See Table 2 for alloys in each group. (c) ST = Solution treated; A = Aged; Ann = Annealed; CD = Cold drawn; AC = As cast. (d) T15, M41, M42, M43 and M44, except M2 and T5 for alloy groups HR Cst 1 and 2. (e) Grade C-2, except grade C-6 for alloy groups HR Cst 1 and 2.

without the use of special fixtures. Identical carbide tools were used for turning all three metals; chip breakers were not required. Speeds and feeds were selected to yield an average tool life of 30 min per cutting edge. All cuts were continuous roughing cuts, produced with automatic feed control. The figure in Table 14 shows a section of the turbine part and the tools used for turning the shaft, web-contour, and rim-face areas.

Example 809. Turning Inlet Nozzles: HS-25 vs HS-31 (Table 15)

Processing details for turning identical inlet nozzles made from HS-25 weldments and HS-31 investment castings are compared in Table 15. The workpiece cross section with tools in position is shown in the inset figure.

Five interrupted cuts per revolution for both the weldments and castings presented a major problem. Although interrupted cutting usually requires high speed steel tools, carbide tools were used for this application, but their cutting edges were mounted 0.020 in. above the centerline, which minimized shock caused by the interruptions. For the castings, filling the spaces between the vanes with a low-melting alloy increased rigidity; this practice was not required for the weldments.

At different times, both vertical and horizontal lathes were used for turning the weldments; operating details for both are compared in Table 15. A vertical lathe was used exclusively for turning the castings. All turning was done with automatic feed control.

Boring and Trepanning

Heat-resisting alloys are bored by methods similar to those used for turning. Back and side rake angles should be 0° to +5°; clearance angles, 3° to 5°. End relief angle of boring tools must be varied inversely with the diameter being bored.

Tool Materials. The choice between carbide and high speed steel for tool material depends largely on the setup. If maximum rigidity can be obtained and cuts are not interrupted, carbide is usually selected; otherwise, one of the more highly alloyed grades of high speed steel is a better choice (Tables 16 and 17).

Speed, Feed and Depth of Cut. Nominal speeds and feeds for boring heat-resisting alloys are given in Table 16; the values assume rigid setups and a chemical emulsion cutting fluid. Speed is up to five times greater for carbide tools than for high speed steel tools. In practice, variables other than those considered in Table 16 often influence optimum speed or feed. The following example of boring three nickel-base alloys involves speeds substantially less than those shown in Table 16.

Example 810. Speeds for Boring Hastelloy X, René 41 and HS-25 (Table 17)

Speeds used for rough and finish boring of 1 and 1¼-in.-diam holes in Hastelloy X, René 41 and HS-25 are given in Table 17. In this operation, both M30 high speed steel and carbide were satisfactory tool materials. Feeds near the high side of the recommended range (0.006 ipr) were used for roughing. Feed rate was about 0.002 ipr for finishing.

Trepanning has not been used extensively as a method for machining heat-resisting alloys, although in some applications, iron-base casting alloys (groups HR Cst 1 and HR Cst 2 in Table 2) have been trepanned. Limited experience indicates that speeds, feeds and tool materials suitable for boring are satisfactory for trepanning under similar conditions. Several cast alloys of the above groups have been successfully trepanned in the as-cast condition (160 to 210 Bhn) with cutting tools made of M2 and T5 high speed steels; speeds of 40 to 50 sfm and feeds of 0.005 ipr were used.

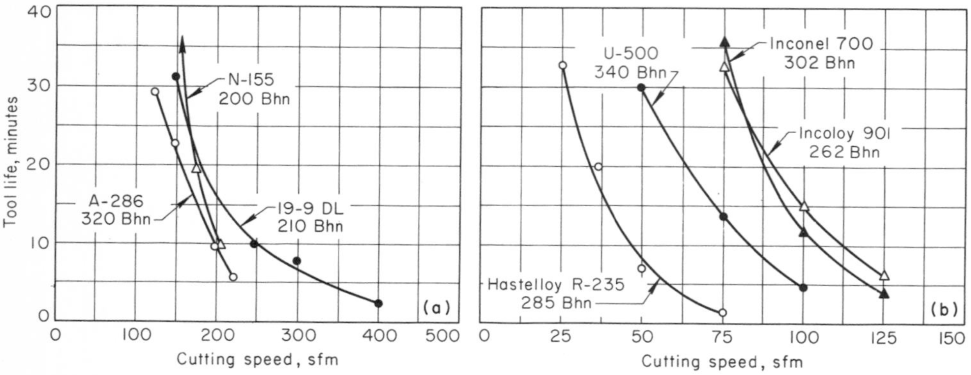

Turning Conditions

Feed ....0.009 ipr
Depth of cut ....0.100 in.
Cutting fluid ....None
Criterion of wear ....0.015-in. wear land

Tool Details

Back rake: −5° (chart a), 0° (chart b). Side rake: −5°. Relief: 5°. End cutting-edge angle: 15°. Side cutting-edge angle: 15°. Nose radius: 0.032 in. Mechanical chip breaker.

Fig. 10. Effect of speed on tool life in turning heat-resisting alloys with C-2 carbide tools. Note difference in horizontal scale of the two graphs.

Planing and Shaping

Planing has been done on some large heat-resisting alloy castings, but is seldom done on wrought heat-resisting products. Nominal speeds for rough and finish planing of the casting alloys

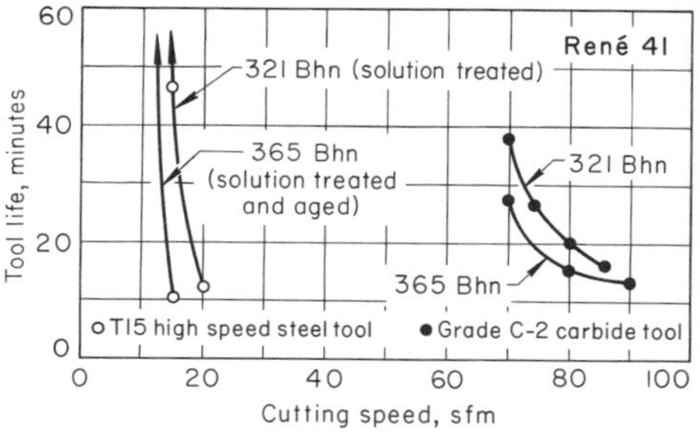

Machining Conditions(a)

Feed ....0.009 ipr
Depth of cut ....0.062 in.
Cutting fluid ....Oil(b)

Tool Details

	T15 HSS	C-2 carbide
Back rake angle	0°	0°
Side rake angle	15°	5°
Relief angle	5°	5°
End cutting-edge angle	5°	15°
Side cutting-edge angle	0°	15°
Nose radius, in.	1/32	1/32

(a) A wear land of 0.060 in. was used as tool life end point for turning with T15 tools; arrow on the curve for the solution-treated-and-aged material turned with T15 indicates test was stopped after 81 min and 0.030-in. wear land; likewise, test on solution treated material was stopped after 75 min and 0.010-in. wear land. (b) Chlorinated oil was used for turning the solution-treated-and-aged material with T15; soluble oil (1 part oil to 20 parts water) was used for all other turning.

Fig. 11. Effect of cutting speed, work-metal condition, and tool material on tool life in turning René 41

Table 12. Comparison of Conditions for Turning of Inconel 718, Waspaloy and A-286 With Carbide Tools

Brinell hardness	Type of cut	Depth of cut, in.	Feed, ipr	Speed, sfm	Expected tool life, min
Inconel 718					
250 to 275 ..	Rough	¼	0.031	90	15
	Rough	¼	0.015	125	20
	Finish	1/32	0.010	135	30
400 to 415 ..	Rough	3/16	0.015	70	13
	Rough	3/16	0.020	56	12
	Finish	1/32	0.010	70	18
Waspaloy					
245 to 285 ..	Rough	¼	0.015	85	10
	Rough	¼	0.021	115	6
	Rough	½	0.005	115	10
355 to 375 ..	Rough	3/16	0.010	70	20
A-286					
315 to 350 ..	Rough	¼	0.020	200	10

identified as HR Cst 1 and 2 in Table 2 are given in Table 18. Workpieces are usually planed without a cutting fluid, but synthetic emulsions are sometimes used.

Shaping tools with +8° side rake, 0° to 3° back rake, 4° to 6° relief angle, and 0.045 to 0.060-in. nose radius are suitable for heat-resisting alloys. Ram speeds must be slow; 7 to 13 sfm is optimum, using a feed per stroke of 0.020 to 0.030 in. for roughing and 0.010 to 0.015 in. for finishing. Depths of cut range from 0.050 to 0.100 in. for roughing and 0.015 to 0.030 in. for finishing. Sulfur-free chlorinated oil applied with a brush is recommended for use as a cutting fluid in shaping.

Example 99, in the article "Shaping", presents details of operating conditions for three heat-resisting alloys.

Broaching

Although broaching is one of the more difficult machining operations, it is used extensively on heat-resisting alloys because it is often the only practical method for machining the complex contours of blades, wheels and related components of gas turbines. Successful broaching of heat-resisting alloys requires careful consideration of broach design, broach material, and technique.

Broach Design. Face (hook) angle, back angle, and gullet shape are important, because of the behavior of heat-resisting alloys in shearing and chip formation. The use of short, replaceable broach inserts can provide cost savings as well as better control of surface finish and accuracy. Tool design changes that improved results in broaching specific alloys and contours are illustrated by the seven examples that follow. The first five examples describe applications for internal broaching; the last two deal with external broaching.

Table 13. Comparison of Single-Point Turning Identical Forged Rings Made of Hastelloy X or René 41 (Example 807)

Operating condition(a)	Hastelloy X (230 Bhn)	René 41 (330 Bhn)
Turning Inside Diameter(b)		
Speed, sfm	165	115
Feed, ipr	0.005	0.005
Depth of cut, in.	0.100	0.072
Removal, cu in./min	2.90	0.79
Turning Outside Diameter(c)		
Speed, sfm	202	132
Feed, ipr	0.008	0.005
Depth of cut, in.	0.150	0.100
Removal, cu in./min	2.90	0.79

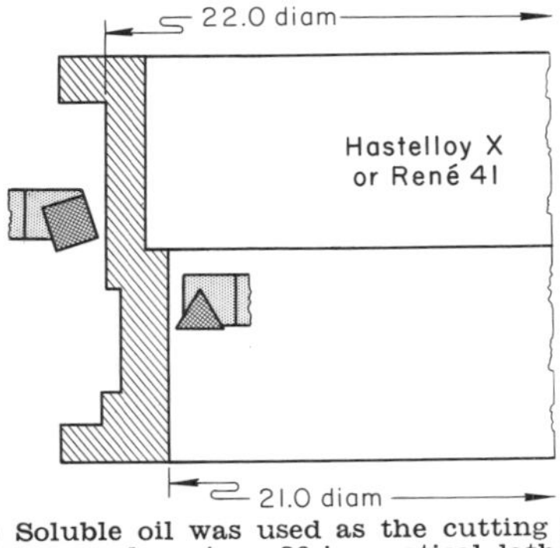

(a) Soluble oil was used as the cutting fluid; turning was done in a 36-in. vertical lathe. (b) Tool details: indexable, triangular, C-2 carbide insert, −5° rake angle, 3° side relief and end relief angles, and 0.060-in. nose radius. (c) Tool details: indexable, square, C-2 carbide insert, −5° rake angle, 3° side relief angle, 15° end relief angle, and 0.060-in. nose radius.

Example 811. Original and Improved Tools for Broaching Slots in Discaloy Turbine Wheels (Table 19)

In slotting a fir-tree shape in turbine wheels of Discaloy (228 to 269 Bhn), poor tool life was obtained with broaches made of T2 tool steel. Broach material was changed to T5, and broach design was revised in the manner indicated by the details given in Table 19. These modifications improved tool life 125% per setup and total broach life tenfold, and decreased the cost of each broach by $7. Aluminum backup disks were used; a wire brush removed chips on the return stroke.

Table 14. Comparison of Turning Identical Turbine Parts Made of Incoloy 901, Waspaloy or Astroloy (Example 808)

Operating condition(a)	Incoloy 901 (290 Bhn)	Waspaloy (325 Bhn)	Astroloy (300 Bhn)
Turning Shaft(b)			
Speed (avg), sfm	101.5	87.3	50.7
Feed, ipr	0.0067	0.0167	0.0083
Depth of cut, in.	0.050	0.050	0.100
Removal, in.³/min	0.40	0.875	0.505
Turning Web Contour(b)			
Speed (avg), sfm	63.8	46.1	46.1
Feed, ipr	0.0067	0.0083	0.0050
Depth of cut, in.	0.187	0.187	0.283
Removal, in.³/min	0.96	0.858	0.780
Turning Rim Face(b)			
Speed (avg), sfm	178.0	83.6	88.0
Feed, ipr	0.0067	0.0050	0.0083
Depth of cut, in.	0.187	0.046	0.044
Removal, in.³/min	2.68	0.230	0.39

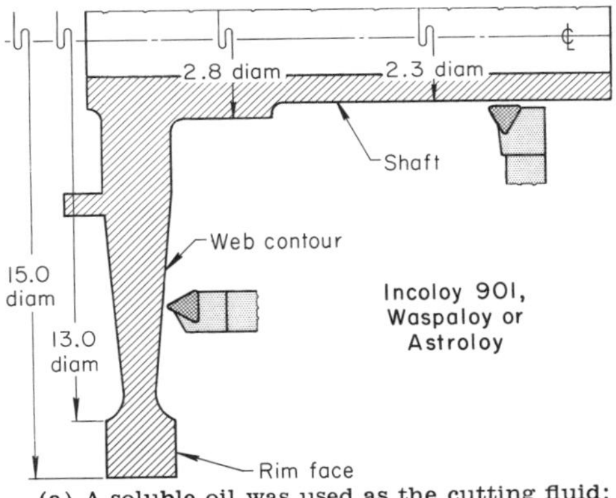

(a) A soluble oil was used as the cutting fluid; turning was done on a 30-in. horizontal lathe. (b) Tool details: indexable, triangular, C-2 carbide inserts, 5° rake angle, 3° side relief and end relief angles, and 0.030-in. nose radius.

Table 15. Comparison of Turning Welded HS-25 and Investment Cast HS-31 Turbine Inlet Nozzles (Example 809)

Operating condition(a)	HS-25 weldment (age-hardened) (b)	HS-25 weldment (age-hardened) (c)	HS-31 casting (solution-treated) (b)
Rough Turning(d)			
Speed, sfm	21.4	33.4	28.2
Feed, ipr	0.0052	0.004	0.006
Depth of cut, in.	0.009	0.008	0.006
Removal, in.³/min	0.012	0.012	0.012
Finish Turning(e)			
Speed, sfm	21.4	20.6	18.3
Feed, ipr	0.0052	0.004	0.001
Depth of cut, in.	0.009	0.008	0.006
Removal, in.³/min	0.012	0.008	0.0013

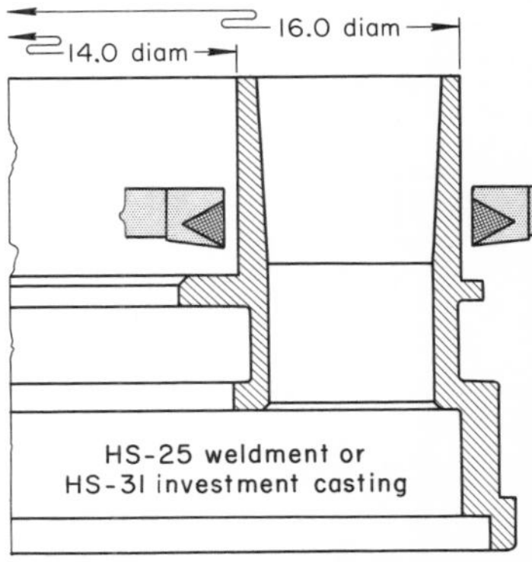

(a) A soluble oil was used as the cutting fluid; turning involved interrupted cuts. (b) A 36-in. vertical lathe was used. (c) A 36-in. horizontal lathe was used. (d) Tool details: indexable, triangular, C-2 carbide inserts, +5° rake angle, 3° side relief and end relief angles, and 0.30-in. nose radius. (e) Tool details for all finish turning were the same as for rough turning, except that a tool with a nose radius of 0.015 in. was used in finish turning the HS-25 weldment in the vertical lathe.

Example 812. Original and Improved Tool Designs for Broaching Splines in 16-25-6 Turbine Wheels (Table 20)

In broaching splines in turbine wheels of 16-25-6 alloy (Rockwell C 32 to 36), a change of broach design, broach material, and type of cutting fluid resulted in savings of 67% in broach costs and 576 man-hours per year. In addition, galling, tearing and undesirable tapering of splines were completely eliminated. Table 20 lists the changes made in broach design, and the footnotes indicate the improvement achieved by each change.

As broach material, T15 (Rockwell C 66 to 68) was substituted for M3, because T15 performed more satisfactorily over a wider range of tool hardness. Because the heavy-duty, high-sulfur-content thread-cutting oil that had been used originally resulted in excessive burning, galling, and buildup and welding of

Table 16. Nominal Speeds and Feeds for Boring Heat-Resisting Alloys(a)

Alloy group(b)	Condition(c)	Brinell hardness	Rough boring (0.100-in. depth): Speed, sfm, HSS	Rough: Speed, sfm, Carbide	Rough: Feed, ipr, HSS	Rough: Feed, ipr, Carbide	Finish boring (0.010-in. depth): Speed, sfm, HSS	Finish: Speed, sfm, Carbide	Finish: Feed, ipr, HSS	Finish: Feed, ipr, Carbide
Fe Wrt	ST	180 to 230	25	115	0.007	0.009	30	125	0.004	0.005
	ST, A	250 to 320	20	100	0.006	0.009	25	110	0.003	0.005
Ni Wrt 1	Ann or ST	200 to 300	15	55	0.006	0.008	15	60	0.003	0.004
	ST, A	300 to 400	15	55	0.006	0.008	15	60	0.003	0.004
Ni Wrt 2	Ann	140 to 220	40	115	0.007	0.009	45	125	0.004	0.005
	CD	240 to 310	30	90	0.007	0.009	35	100	0.004	0.005
Ni Cast	AC	250 to 350	10	25	0.005	0.006	10	30	0.002	0.003
Co Wrt	ST	180 to 230	20	70	0.006	0.008	20	80	0.003	0.004
	ST, A	270 to 320	15	55	0.006	0.008	15	60	0.003	0.004
Co Cast	AC	220 to 290	10	25	0.005	0.006	10	30	0.002	0.003
HR Cst 1(d)	AC	160 to 210	60	250	0.008	0.012	65	275	0.005	0.006
HR Cst 2(d)	AC	160 to 210	45	205	0.008	0.012	50	225	0.005	0.006

(a) High speed steel tools, T15, M41, M42, M43 and M44; carbide tools, grade C-3. A chemical emulsion is recommended as the cutting fluid. Tool design: 3° to 10° back rake, 0° to 15° side rake, 5° to 10° end relief, 2° to 3° side relief, 5° end cutting-edge angle, 15° side cutting-edge angle. (b) See Table 2 for alloys in each group. (c) ST = Solution treated; A = Aged; Ann = Annealed; CD = Cold drawn; AC = As cast. (d) M2 and T5 high speed steel tools.

Table 17. Speeds (Sfm) Used for Rough and Finish Boring With High Speed Steel and Carbide Tools (Example 810)

Operation	Hastelloy X	René 41	HS-25
M30 High Speed Steel Tools			
Roughing	30 to 40	20 to 30	15 to 20
Finishing	35 to 45	25 to 35	20 to 25
C-2 or C-5 Carbide Tools			
Roughing	60 to 70	35 to 40	30 to 35
Finishing	70 to 80	50 to 60	40 to 45

Table 18. Nominal Speeds for Planing Heat-Resisting Alloys(a)

Alloy group(b)	Condition	Brinell hardness	Speed, sfm: HSS tools(c)	Speed, sfm: Carbide tools(d)
Rough Planing(e)				
HR Cst 1	As cast	160 to 210 ..	30	190
HR Cst 2	As cast	160 to 210 ..	20	140
Finish Planing(f)				
HR Cst 1	As cast	160 to 210 ..	45	195
HR Cst 2	As cast	160 to 210 ..	25	150

(a) A chemical emulsion is recommended as cutting fluid. (b) See Table 2 for alloys in each group. (c) M2 or T5. (d) Grade C-6. (e) Depth of cut, 0.500 in.; feed, 0.060 in. per stroke. (f) Depth of cut, 0.005 in.; feed, ¾ the width of square-nose tool.

Table 19. Details of Original and Improved Designs of Broaches Used for Slotting Turbine Wheels of Discaloy (Example 811)

Broach detail	Original design	Improved design: Rougher	Improved design: Finisher
Tool steel	T2	T5	T5
Face angle	15°	18°	22°
Backoff clearance	2°; 1°	2°; 0°	2½°
Tooth pitch, in. .	9/16	½	½
Tooth thickness, in.	3/16	¼	5/32
Tooth depth, in. .	5/64	5/64	7/64
Radius, in.	3/64	1/16	1/32
Taper per tooth, in.	....	....	0.002
Broach life, slots	1794	18,000	18,000

chips, a cutting fluid composed of mineral oil with 1% active sulfur, chlorine and synthetic additions was substituted, and with this cutting fluid, the defects were eliminated.

With these changes, and the changes in broach design listed in Table 20, a greater number of pieces could be broached per tool sharpening. Thus, the number of setups, and setup certifications, was reduced, saving a total of 576 man-hours per year.

Examples 813 and 814. Redesign of Tools for Broaching Incoloy 901 Turbine Wheels

Example 813 (Table 21). By redesigning broach details, tool breakage was eliminated and misalignment corrected in cutting fir-tree slots in turbine wheels of Incoloy 901 (255 to 352 Bhn), on a 25-hp, 100-in. vertical broaching machine. The fir-tree slot, which had a prominent lobe at the root, is shown in Table 21. The numbered sections refer to individual broach inserts (details) used to rough-cut the slots.

As originally designed, broach details 1 to 7 roughed V-forms in the wheel. Detail 8 took a semifinishing cut and formed the width of the top lobe. Detail 9, a short section on the broach, finish-formed all of the slot contours except the top lobe radius, which was cut by detail 10, another short section. The total length of assembled broach inserts was 95 in.

Tool breakage occurred in detail 8, which cut only the width of the top lobe; this was caused by jamming of chips at the narrow serration immediately below this lobe.

Details of the redesigned broach (which solved the problem) are shown in Table 21. Tooth length and pitch of roughing details 1 to 7 were increased to provide a greater chip pocket and smoother cutting action. A new finishing detail (24½ in. long and containing 54 teeth) replaced former details 8, 9 and 10. The first 45 teeth of this detail (backed off 2° up sharp) cut the side angle contour of the lower lobes (see cross-section view in Table 21). The remaining teeth (46 to 54) were also backed off 2° up sharp and cut the top lobe radii. The lower portion of teeth 46 to 54 (which contacted side angles of lower lobes) were backed off 2° sharp and were straight (not stepped) and without face angle. These tooth areas were used as a pilot to keep the remainder of the contour in line with the top lobe.

Accuracy of detail alignment was accomplished by grinding the insert slot recess on the initial setup. The grinding wheel was mounted on compound fixtures, and the ram (minus details) passed over the wheel. The ground slot was true within 0.0005 in. TIR for the entire length of broach.

Roughers had the same angle on corners as the angle of the fir-tree slot, leaving only about 0.006 in. of metal around the radii for the finisher to remove. With this design, cutting edges seldom broke down.

Both the original and redesigned tool sections were made of T15 (Rockwell C 65 to 67). The cutting fluid was a mineral oil with 1% active sulfur, chlorine and synthetic additions. The redesigned broach was able to cut two turbine wheels (204 slots) per regrind. Total tool life was 16 wheels per broach.

Example 814. Poor surface finish, severe galling in critical areas, and excessive tool wear were encountered in broaching Incoloy 901 turbine wheels (255 Bhn min) with a conventional broach made of T5 (Rockwell C 64 to 66). Broaching was required to form 52 two-branch fir-tree contours in a wheel 22.750 in. in outside diameter by 1.600 in. thick. The angle of broaching was 19° 30′.

On the original broach, teeth had a 0.500-in. pitch, a 15° face angle, and a 2° backoff clearance angle. Finishing teeth were full-form and truncated.

An improved broach tooth more compatible with the cutting characteristics of the alloy solved the problem. In the new design, the face angle was increased to 18° and the backoff angle to 4°. Improved chip control enabled the full-form cutting to be postponed to the semifinishing stage, and final sizing could be done by inserted finishing teeth. The finishing teeth had a rise per tooth of 0.0007

Table 20. Details and Results of Changes in Design of Broach for Spline Broaching Turbine Wheels Made of 16-25-6 Alloy (Example 812)
(Length of cut was 1.189 to 1.846 in.)

Broach change No.	Item	Original design	Improved design
1(a)	Face angle	15°	18°
2(b)	Tooth pitch, in.	½ to ⅝	9/16; 19/32; 31/64(c)
3(d)	Length of teeth, in.	0.125	0.156
4(e)	Gullet radius, in.	5/32	5/32
5(e)	Tooth depth, in.	0.250	0.250
6(f)	Backoff clearance, outside diameter .	2° to ½°	2°; 2°; 1°(c)
7(g)	Number of roughing teeth	33	43 (2° backoff)
8(g)	Number of semifinishing teeth	32	42 (2° backoff)
9(e)	Number of finishing teeth	6	6 (1° backoff)
10(h)	Length of broach, in.	59.0	65.0
11(j)	Sides of teeth relieved up to 1/32 in. of top of teeth	...	1° ± ¼° backoff(k)

(a) Enabled bar to cut freely and provided efficient chip curl. (b) Eliminated harmonic rings. (c) Roughing, semifinishing and finishing, respectively. (d) Increased life of teeth. (e) No change. (f) Reduced drag and gall on broach. (g) Increased number of teeth; reduced rise per tooth. (h) Used full stroke of machine and improved broach design. (j) Eliminated all galling and tears. (k) Full form on sides of all spline teeth up sharp (no land).

Table 21. Details of Redesigned Broach for Slotting Turbine Wheels of Incoloy 901, and Stock Removed by Each Broach Detail (Example 813)

Broach design(a)	Roughing detail 1	Finishing detail 10
Length, in.	8.969	24.500
Tooth pitch, in.	0.344	0.437
Depth of flute, in.	0.125	0.065
Flute radius, in.	0.078	0.037
Face angle	15°	18°
Tooth land, in.	0.156	0.218
Form relief	....	2°
Broach detail No.	**Stock removed, in.**	**Rise per tooth, in.**
Details 1 through 7 — Stair-Step Roughers		
1	0.069	0.0027
2	0.069	0.0027
3	0.069	0.0027
4	0.068	0.0026
5	0.068	0.0026
6	0.0515	0.0022
7	0.041	0.0019
(Details 8 and 9 were eliminated)		
Detail 10 — 54-Tooth, 24½-In. Finisher		
Cutting Side Angle of Lower Lobes		
Tooth 1 to 39	0.0718	0.00189
Tooth 40 to 45	0.0130	0.00217
Cutting Bottom and Radii of Top Lobe		
Tooth 46 to 50	0.0035	0.0007
Tooth 51 to 54	0.0020	0.0005

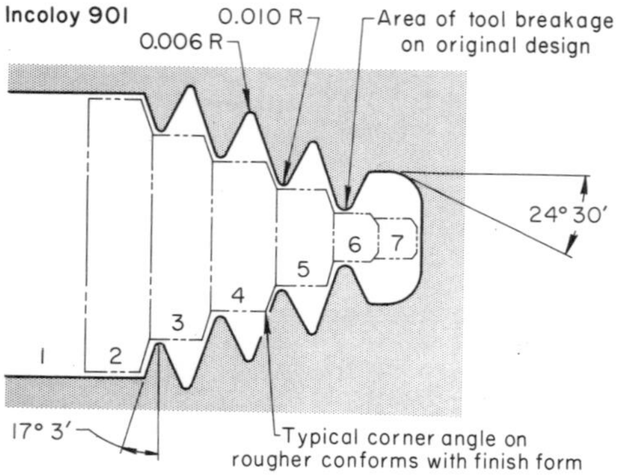

Details 8 and 9 of original broach were eliminated; detail 10 was replaced by 54-tooth finisher, which broached profile roughed by teeth 1 through 7.

(a) Back taper was 0.0040 in. per detail for roughing details 1 through 7. Backoff was 1° per tooth on each side for roughing details 1 through 7, 3° per tooth on top for details 1 through 6, 2° for details 7 and 10.

Table 22. Design of Broach for Production Broaching of Fir-Tree Slots in René 41 at Rockwell C 41 (Example 815)

Broach detail	Roughing	Semi-finishing	Finishing
Face angle	15°	15°	15°
Backoff clearance ..	3°	3°	3°
Pitch, in.	0.500	0.437	0.562
Land width, in.	0.165	0.150	0.175
Rise per tooth, in. ..	0.003	0.003	0.003
Length of insert, in..	345.0	44.0	79.0

Table 23. Improved Tool Design for Broaching a Root Form in Turbine Vanes Made of HS-31 (AMS 5382) (Example 816)

Broach detail	Original	Improved
Face angle	18°	12°
Backoff clearance	2°	4°
Pitch, in.	9/32	11/32
Tooth depth, in.	¼	3/16
Shear angle	5°	45°
Tool life per setup	300	13,000

to 0.0003 in. and removed the final 0.005 in. of metal. T5 high speed steel was used, and cutting speed was 11 sfm.

Example 815. Tooling for Broaching Unusual Slot Design in René 41 Turbine Wheels (Table 22)

A test program was conducted to develop tooling for broaching an unusual slot design in René 41 turbine wheels. The slot was a multibranched fir-tree form that was particularly difficult to broach because of an extended, thin heart-shaped lobe at the root. The length of the lobe was equal to the length of the fir tree.

As a result of the test program, new broaches were made from T5 steel, and wheels were broached in a 20-ton, 240-in. horizontal broaching machine, using two passes. Later a 15-ton, 180-in. horizontal machine was used to broach the wheels in three passes. In both machines, producing a few wheels on a development basis, five wheels (270 slots) were the average number produced per tool grind. Finish requirements were 63 micro-in. max, and slot tolerances, ±0.0005 in. max, using conventional checking methods.

The test program indicated that a 12° face angle and 2° clearance were maximum for finish-cutting teeth and that the largest positive rake possible was desired (just short of tool-edge chipping). In a production setup, the same combination of face angle and clearance angle used for roughing (15° and 3°, respectively) proved successful. Increased rigidity of setup, not present in the test program, made this possible; very heavy fixtures reinforced with "outboard" clamps were used.

Broaching the slots required a machine of 15 tons minimum capacity and maximum stroke length. Three passes were needed to complete the slot, and 468 in. of insert length was used for a machine stroke of 480 in. Tool details are shown in Table 22. Ram speed was 9 sfm. The cutting fluid, a sulfochlorinated-concentrate oil composed of mineral and fatty oils, was applied by flooding the tools.

Example 816. Redesign of Tool for Broaching HS-31 (AMS 5382) Turbine Vanes (Table 23)

Improvement in both tool life and surface finish was obtained in broaching the root form in HS-31 turbine vanes at low hardness (Rockwell C 10 to 15) when tools were altered to a large (45°) shear angle and a sharper positive face angle. For this soft cast alloy, chip formation was a problem when a small (5°) shear angle was tried, because of the probability of chipping the work at the exit of the cut. Details of the original and improved tools are given in Table 23. The changes in face angle and backoff clearance, and especially the increase in shear angle, almost completely eliminated chipping. Productive life of the high speed steel broach of the original design averaged 300 pieces per setup. However, after the tooth profile was redesigned, the broach averaged 13,000 pieces per setup. The operation utilized rigid fixturing, pressurized cutting fluid, and a horizontal broaching machine.

Example 817. Redesigned Broach for N-155 Nozzle-Diaphragm Blades (Fig. 12)

Nozzle-diaphragm blades were fabricated from flat-rolled N-155 at Rockwell C 30 to 40. A form die was used for folding over the sheet to form a hollow blade. Following this operation, the open ends were welded, using AMS 5732 (A-286) welding rod. The blade face and weld area were broached to a smooth contour. The blade is illustrated in Fig. 12.

Both the convex and concave sides of the blade were broached. Because the problems encountered with both sides were similar, only the broach used to cut the concave side will be considered.

The broach originally used consisted of two sections, each 13 in. long and containing 48 teeth. All teeth were made with full-form radii and 2° backoff angles. This broach was unsuccessful because the full-form radii did not permit the chips to curl, a condition that resulted in excessive weld buildup on the teeth, tooth breakage, and damaged work. Resharpening was required after each 100 to 125 pieces, and the broach was scrapped after broaching only 1800 pieces.

In a redesigned broach, the roughing teeth were changed from full-form radii to straight

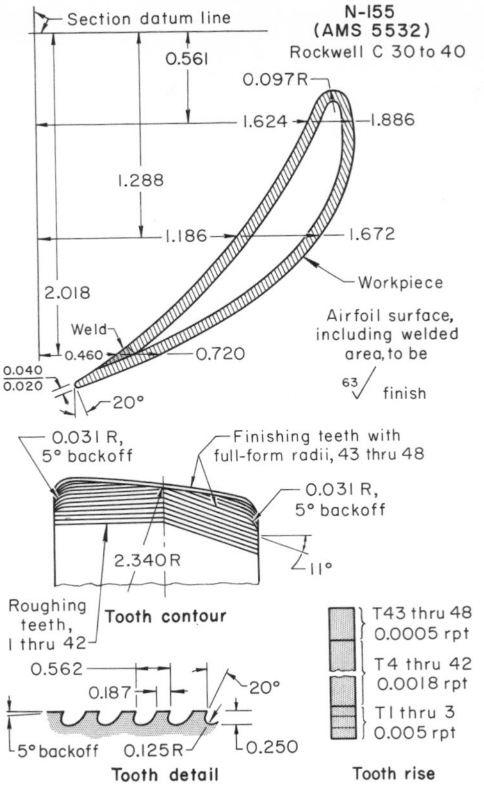

Fig. 12. Tooth details for redesigned broach used to finish both sides of the hollow blade shown (Example 817)

teeth cutting on both sides of center on all but the last five teeth. Thus, all but the last five teeth were used primarily for stock removal; the split-angle arrangement provided excellent chip control. The backoff clearance on all teeth was changed to 5°. Tooth details and tooth rise for the redesigned broach are shown in Fig. 12.

The new design provided free cutting action, with a minimum of weld buildup and tooth damage. From 350 to 600 blades could be broached before resharpening was required. Total life of the broach was extended to between 6000 and 9000 pieces.

The broach material was T15 steel (Rockwell C 66 to 68). The machine was a 36-in. vertical broaching machine (15-hp hydraulic ram), and speed was 12 sfm for a cutting length of 4 in. A cutting fluid consisting of mineral oil with 1% active sulfur and chlorine and synthetic additions was used.

Effect of Work Metal on Broach Design.

In producing gas-turbine components, a change in the work metal is sometimes necessary. Such a change may require revisions in broach design. The four examples that follow describe operations in which broach design was altered because work metal was changed.

Example 818. Redesign of Broach Because of Change in Work Metal From 16-25-6 to A-286 (Fig. 13)

In finish broaching fir-tree slots (internal broaching) in 2-in.-thick, 17.856-in.-diam turbine wheels made of 16-25-6 (235 to 293 Bhn), tool life was 4050 slots per regrind. However, tool life was reduced to only 38 slots when A-286 alloy (143 to 202 Bhn) was substituted as the turbine-wheel material, even though the same tooling setup was used as for broaching the 16-25-6 wheels.

The short tool life was caused by the greater tendency of the chips of A-286 to weld and abrade the tooth face and cutting edge. This welding prevented succeeding chips from sliding along the full face of the tooth and thus increased friction and heat. Teeth broke down at 0.035 to 0.050 in. from the cutting edges.

To extend tool life, the broach material was changed from M3 to T15. Only one wheel (54 slots) was broached with T15 inserts, and finish was poor, because chips welded to the cutting edges, again causing greater friction and heat — which, in turn, increased welding.

By changing from a full-radius gullet to a two-angle gullet (Fig. 13), while retaining T15 as the tool material, parts could be finish broached satisfactorily. The 18° face angle that had blended to a radius at the root of the gullet was changed to a combination of two angles, one of 18° and one of 20°. Redesigning the angles and radii of the T15 broach inserts permitted chips to flow into the gullet with minimum welding on the tooth face and edges, and broach life was extended to 378 slots before resharpening was required. Also, the surface finish of the turbine wheels was greatly improved because chips no longer interfered with the cutting edges but flowed away, curling neatly to clear the workpiece. Broach breakdown was appreciably reduced.

The two-angle-gullet design was used to advantage also in roughing where a 10°/20° combination was used for all but the last roughing detail and the semifinish detail, which did not present a chip problem. Broach details are listed in the table accompanying Fig. 13.

Speed was 18 sfm for roughing and semifinishing, and for finishing detail 1; for finishing details 2, 3 and 4, speed was 12 sfm. Cutting fluid was mineral oil with 1% active sulfur, chlorine and synthetic additions.

Example 819. Redesign of Broach Because of Change in Work Metal From 403 Stainless to A-286

When rotor blade material was changed from 403 stainless steel (Rockwell C 26 to 32) to A-286 alloy (Rockwell C 29 min), excessive tool wear and dimensional variation were encountered in broaching the root form (ex-

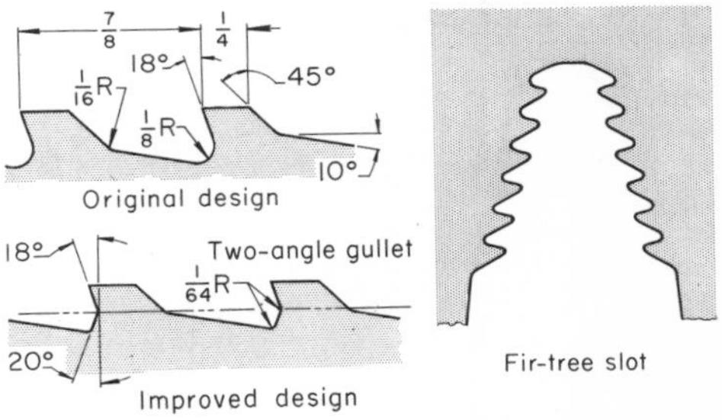

Detail No.	Length of insert, in.	Pitch, in.	Land width, in.	Rise per tooth, in.
Roughing(a)				
1 ...	16.625	0.500	0.156	0.004
2 ...	18.750	0.490	0.156	0.004
3 ...	18.750	0.490	0.156	0.004
4 ...	16.875	0.490	0.156	0.004
5 ...	16.625	0.500	0.156	0.004
6 ...	18.750	0.490	0.156	0.004
7 ...	18.750	0.490	0.156	0.004
8 ...	16.875	0.767(b)	0.250(b)	0.0067
Semifinishing				
Side cutting only, using detail No. 8				
Finishing(c)				
1 ...	15.750	0.500(d) 0.710(e)	0.1875(d) 0.500(e)	0.0018(d) 0.0006(e)
2 ...	15.750	0.875(e)	0.250(e)	0.0016
3 ...	15.750	0.875(e)	0.250(e)	0.0018
4 ...	15.750	0.875(e)	0.250	0.0005, 0.002(f)

(a) Rough-cutting with eight two-pass broach details; face angle was 10° plus 20°, except for detail 8 (side cutting only), where it was 15°; backoff clearance was 2°. (b) Alternate. (c) Detail 1: top cut, 13 teeth; side cut, 12 teeth. Details 2 and 3: side cut only. Detail 4: side cut, 13 teeth; straight cut, 6 teeth; top cut, 6 teeth; 0.005-in. step on top radius. Face angle was 18° plus 20°, and backoff clearance, 2°. (d) Top cut. (e) Side cut. (f) Top and side cuts.

Fig. 13. Original broach design for broaching a fir-tree slot in 16-25-6 and redesign for broaching the same slot in A-286. Fir-tree slot is shown at the right. Table shows broach details for the improved design. (Example 818)

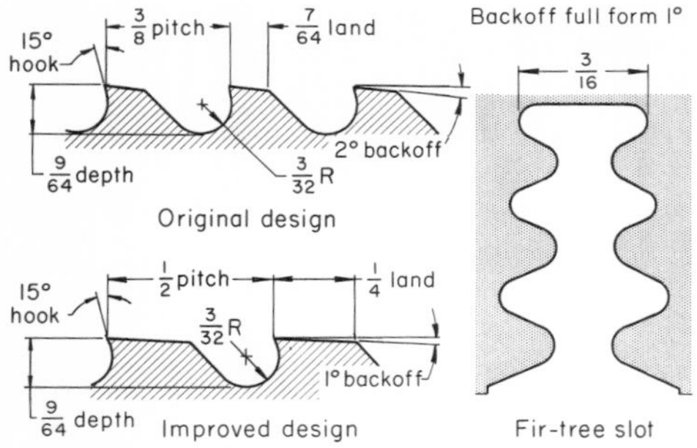

Fig. 14. Original broach design for broaching fir-tree slot in turbine wheel made from A-286 and redesign for broaching the same slot in René 41 (Example 820)

ternal broaching) in a chain-type broaching machine. The cutter material was M3 (class 2) high speed steel, and an ample supply of cutting fluid was used.

To achieve satisfactory results with the A-286 alloy, it was necessary to reduce the broach speed from 22 to 16 sfm, add three 11-in. cutters to the setup, and modify broach design as follows:

Broach detail	403	A-286
Face angle	18°	15°
Backoff clearance	3°	5°
Rise per tooth, in.	0.004	0.003

Example 820. Redesign of Broach Because of Change in Work Metal From A-286 to René 41 (Fig. 14)

Redesigning a broach by increasing pitch length and land width enabled the broaching of 7½ times as many fir-tree slots (internal broaching) in René 41 turbine wheels as with the conventional design. The wheels were first-stage and second-stage, requiring 119 and 109 slots, respectively, at an angle of 10° 52′, and were 30.250 in. in diameter and 1 in. thick.

The broach of the original conventional design had been used with fair success on similar parts made of A-286. However, when it was tried on the René 41 wheels using the same operating conditions as for A-286, only eight slots could be obtained per broach resharpening. Not only were tools being expended by wear and excessive grinding, but tooth breakout occurred after several grinds.

The revised design, with stronger teeth, enabled broaching of 60 or more slots per broach sharpening. Use of a backoff angle of only 1° for the full-form slot shown in Fig. 14 extended the life of a broach to 12 or more sharpenings. Broaches were sharpened as soon as chips fused to the cutting edge and could not be brushed off freely. Broaches had smooth surfaces (10 micro-in.), and teeth were ground to a sharp edge (no flat land).

A broaching speed of 6 sfm gave best results, and the machine used had sufficient capacity to provide smooth cutting at this low speed. M2 high speed steel was an acceptable tool material if nitrided and oxide coated by steam, but best results were obtained using T15 (Rockwell C 65 to 67). All tools made from T15 were tempered three times, and oxide coated after grinding.

Example 821. Tool Modifications Because of Change in Work Metal From Greek Ascoloy to S-816

To obtain satisfactory results in broaching a dovetail form, angle end, and slot in forged S-816 rotor blades (Rockwell C 32 to 40), using essentially the same tooling formerly used to broach Greek Ascoloy (AMS 5616), some tool modifications were required. The blades were mounted in a mechanical holding box for better rigidity before they were inserted in a heavier-than-normal broaching fixture. A 3° backoff clearance was specified for the cutting surfaces of side cutting teeth, to prevent galling of other tooth portions not cutting at the same time. Speed of the 66-in. dual-ram machine was reduced from 22 sfm to 12 sfm.

It was not necessary to change either the tool material (M3, class 2) or the cutting fluid (mineral oil with 1% sulfur, chlorine, and synthetic additions). The improved rigidity and the changes in tool design and cutting speed sufficed to provide a free-cutting action and to satisfy dimensional and surface-finish requirements.

Broach Material. High speed steel is used for broaches in most applications for broaching heat-resisting alloys. The selection of solid broaches versus those with inserted cutting edges depends on the size and design of the broach and on cost. Cost is usually the deciding factor. In many applications (particularly when large broaches are being used), cost can be decreased by using high speed steel inserts in an alloy steel body. Assuming other factors are constant, whether broaches are solid or have inserts will not influence broach performance.

The more highly alloyed grades of high speed steel, such as T2, T5 and T6, generally are superior in broach wear or life, or both, to the general-purpose grades, but they are harder to grind.

The following example describes an application where a change from M3 to T5 allowed a large increase in the number of parts per grind.

Example 822. M3 vs T5 for Broaching M-252

In broaching fir-tree slots in M-252 turbine buckets, a change in tool material resulted in a large increase in production rate and tool life. When T5 was the broach material, production of turbine buckets was 1400 to 1600 pieces per regrind, whereas when M3 had been used, yield was only 200 to 300 pieces per regrind.

Broach teeth had a rake of 15° to 18°, backoff clearance of 3°, and a shear angle of 15° to 20°. Broaching speed was 22 sfm; minimum rise was 0.0025 ipt.

In six of the 13 examples of broaching heat-resisting alloys, T15 high speed steel was used initially or a change was made to this grade. T5 was used in three examples. Although acceptable results were obtained with an M2 broach for the application described in Example 820, T15 performed better. M3 (class 2) has been satisfactory for numerous broaching applications as shown in Examples 819 and 821, but this grade is near the minimum in alloy content (only slightly higher than general-purpose grades) that is usually considered suitable for broaching heat-resisting alloys. In some plants, the highly alloyed grades such as T15 are not used because of difficulty in grinding them.

In broaching, the composition and condition of the work metal strongly influence selection of tool material. This is evidenced in Example 822, as well as in the example that follows:

Example 823. Tool Materials and Technique for Broaching A-286 and D-979 Turbine Wheels (Fig. 15)

For broaching of root forms (Fig. 15) in turbine wheels of A-286 (Rockwell C 30 to 36), M3 high speed steel broaches were used for roughing and T15 for finishing. When the work metal was changed to D-979 (Rockwell C 40 to 43), broaches made of T15 were used for both roughing and finishing. Details of cutter design and tooling setup are shown in Fig. 15.

The operation was performed in a vertical, 90-in., 15-ton hydraulic broaching machine. The work metal was solution treated and partially aged.

The broach consisted of eight sections, and was almost 90 in. long. The first three sections rough cut the blade root slot within 0.005 in. of finish depth. The fourth section semifinished the form within 0.005 in. of finished size. The fifth and sixth sections finished the shelf and form. The seventh section blended the cuts of the third and sixth sections to finish the bottom of the slot. The eighth section consisted of six qualifying teeth that held the size of the form when the sixth insert had been resharpened undersize. Thus, the eighth section was used only after resharpening of the sixth insert.

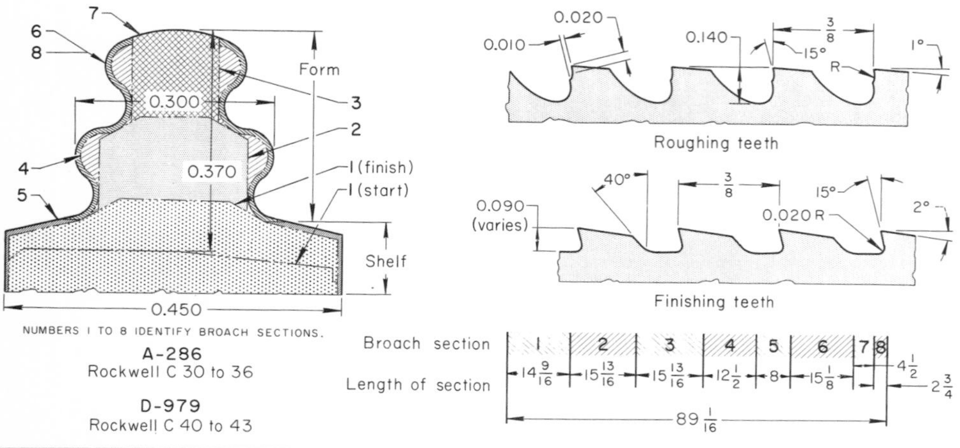

Item	A-286	D-979
Speed, sfm	10	6
Feed, ipt:		
Roughing	0.002	0.0015
Finishing	0.0006	0.0004

Item	A-286 and D-979
Cutting fluid	Viscous oil containing sulfur, chlorine and fat
Broach life, roughing	300 to 400 slots
Broach life, finishing	500 to 600 slots

Fig. 15. Broach design, and metal removed from turbine wheel by different broach sections (Example 823)

Speed and Rise per Tooth. Optimum speed for broaching heat-resisting alloys varies considerably, depending on the composition and hardness of the work metal. Nominal speeds for broaching five different groups of heat-resisting alloys are given in Table 24. These values are based on the use of T15 broaches (with the one exception noted in the table), and sulfurized or sulfochlorinated oil as cutting fluid. Speeds shown in Table 24 are conservative, particularly for the iron-base alloys. In many applications, speeds of 10 to 18 sfm will provide acceptable results when broaching the iron-base alloys (Examples 818 and 819). Common practice is to use a speed near the high side of the range for roughing, and then to finish at a lower speed, as in Example 818.

To obtain acceptable tool life when broaching the nickel-base and cobalt-base alloys, lower speeds are necessary; 5 to 10 sfm has proved satisfactory for broaching most of these alloys. For example, René 41 (one of the most difficult-to-broach alloys) is successfully broached at 6 to 9 sfm (see Examples 815 and 820); common practice is to rough and finish broach at the same low speed.

Nominal rise per tooth (chip load) for broaching heat-resisting alloys, expressed in inch per tooth (ipt), is included in Table 24; the values tabulated are conservative. For rough broaching, values of chip load up to 0.005 ipt are often used. For the finishing operation, 0.0005 to 0.001 ipt is not uncommon. A rise of less than 0.0005 ipt is not recommended, because the broach is likely to burnish rather than cut. Burnishing causes variations in work-metal finish and excessive broach wear.

Cutting Fluid. A flood of sulfochlorinated oil over the area being broached is preferred, and in most applications is mandatory for acceptable results. In some applications, cutting fluids similar to thread cutting oil have been used successfully, but the use of such fluids is usually a compromise, especially when broaching nickel-base or cobalt-base alloys. In the application described in Example 812, a change to sulfochlorinated oil improved results in broaching alloy 16-25-6 (ordinarily one of the easier-to-broach heat-resisting alloys).

Oils containing about 1% active sulfur, with chlorine and synthetic additions, are often used. A plentiful supply of cutting fluid in the area being broached is of equal, if not greater, importance than fluid composition. Preferably, cutting fluid is supplied under pressure up to about 5 psi. To obtain the viscosity required for use in pressure systems, the cutting oil can be diluted with plain mineral oil. A mixture of one part concentrated cutting oil and one part mineral oil has lower viscosity than concentrated cutting oil and is adequate for most applications. Cutting fluids with viscosity higher than 300 SUS are not recommended for broaching.

Thorough cleaning of workpieces broached with chemically active oils (sulfurized or chlorinated) is extremely important before heat treating or high-temperature service, to prevent damage to the workpiece.

Drilling

Selection and control of drills, machines and machining conditions are more important in drilling heat-resisting alloys than in drilling carbon or low-alloy steel. The high forces produced necessitate maximum rigidity of the machine, tools, and setup. Drill material and design, and speed and feed are also more critical than in drilling steel or cast iron.

Table 24. Nominal Speeds and Rise per Tooth for Broaching Heat-Resisting Alloys With High Speed Steel Tools(a)

Alloy group(b)	Brinell hardness	Speed, sfm	Rise per tooth, in.
Fe Wrt	180 to 230	10	0.002
	250 to 320	8	0.002
Ni Wrt 1	200 to 300	6	0.002
	300 to 400	8	0.002
Ni Wrt 2	140 to 220	10	0.001
	280 to 310	8	0.002
Co Wrt	180 to 230	6	0.002
	270 to 320	8	0.002
HR Cst 1	160 to 210	20	0.003

(a) T15 high speed steel tools are recommended for all alloy groups except HR Cst 1, for which M2 tools are recommended. Tool design: 15° to 20° face angle, 2° to 3° clearance angle. A sulfochlorinated fat-containing mineral oil is recommended as cutting fluid. (b) See Table 2 for alloys in each group.

Types of Drills. The most important single requirement is that drills must be as short and as rigid as possible within the limiting requirements of the workpiece and setup. Stub-length screw-machine drills, type-C aircraft drills with accurately ground split points, rail drills, and extra-heavy-web drills are recommended. These heavy-duty drills give much better results than standard jobber's-length drills because of their greater rigidity. The importance of drill length on drill-life is shown in the following two examples and in Example 832.

Example 824. Shorter Unsupported Length of Drill for Longer Drill Life (Fig. 16)

A survey was made to determine the effect of unsupported length of drill on the life of M10 drills in drilling solution-treated-and-aged Astroloy (Rockwell C 42). As shown in Fig. 16, by decreasing unsupported length from 1.35 to 1.05 in., drill life was increased from 6 to 24 holes per grind. All drills were operated at 11.2 sfm with a feed of 0.002 ipr. Other details are included with Fig. 16.

Example 825. Effect of Drill Length on Drill Life in Drilling Waspaloy

To determine the effect of drill length on tool life in drilling ⅜-in.-thick Waspaloy, heavy-web, screw-machine drills of different flute lengths were used. The alloy was solution treated and aged to Rockwell C 40. In all tests, speed and feed were controlled at 25 sfm and 0.003 ipr, respectively, and a sulfurized cutting fluid was used. Details, other than flute length, for all drills were as follows:

Diameter	0.2010 in.
Point angle	118°
Lip relief angle	10° to 12°
Point style	Crankshaft

Tests showed that flute lengths of 1⅝ and 1¾ in. produced a drill life of 50 holes. When flute length was ⅞ and 1 in., drill life increased to 75 holes.

Drill Design. The crankshaft or split points, which are standard for type-C aircraft and heavy-web drills, are preferred for drilling all iron-base heat-resisting alloys harder than 400 Bhn and other heat-resisting alloys harder than 350 Bhn. Drills with standard chisel-edge points can be used for softer alloys.

Drill wear and life can be controlled to some extent by modifying the drill point. Chipping of drill corners can be reduced by decreasing the point angle, severe wear at the point can be reduced by increasing the point angle to 135°, and excessive margin wear can be eliminated by using a dual-angle (118°/90°) lip. All drills should be machine ground to very close accuracy. A

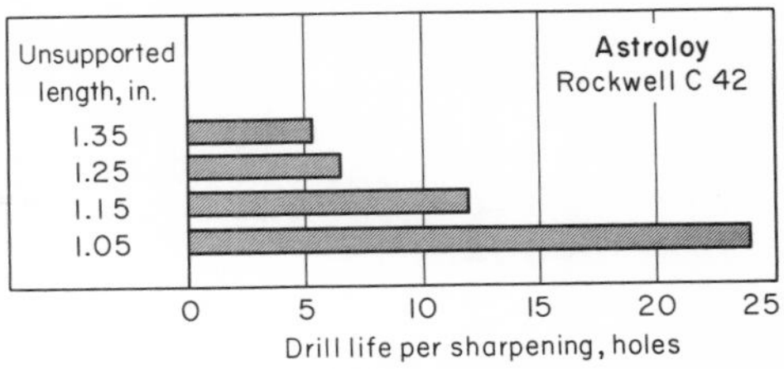

Hole depth was 0.310 in. Drills, which were made of M10 high speed steel, were 0.213 in. in diameter, with a notched point and 0.015-in. web; included point angles were 135°, and clearance was 9° to 10°. Sulfochlorinated mineral oil concentrate was used as cutting fluid.

Fig. 16. Effect of unsupported length of drill on drill life (Example 824)

slight amount of runout or point eccentricity will greatly reduce drill life. The three examples that follow demonstrate the importance of drill design in drill life.

Example 826. Drill Life for Rail Drills (Fig. 17)

For drilling rivet holes in ⅝-in.-thick A-286 (248 to 331 Bhn), low-helix, heavy-duty drills (rail drills) made of M7 high speed steel had an average tool life of 30 holes per grind, on the basis of 7000 holes drilled. In contrast, standard drills averaged only three to five holes per grind for the same operation. This difference in tool life was attributed to the greater strength and rigidity of the heavy-duty drills.

The drills had a lip relief angle of 12° to 14° (primary clearance) and were operated at a speed of 24.8 sfm in a hand-fed drill press, using a drill bushing and a soluble-oil cutting fluid. Figure 17 presents design details of these drills.

Example 827. Effect of Drill-Point Design on Drill Life (Fig. 18)

Drills with split points were tested against drills with notched points to determine the effect of point design on drill life in drilling solution-treated-and-aged Astroloy. The web

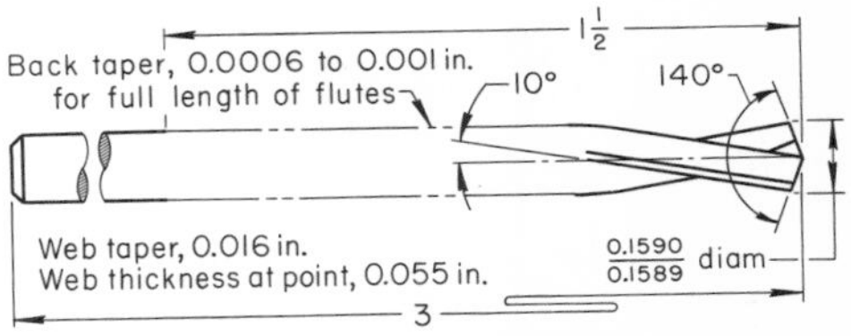

Fig. 17. Design of M7 high speed steel drill for machining A-286 alloy at 248 to 331 Bhn. Except for recommended 12° to 14° primary clearance, dimensions not given are manufacturer's standard. (Example 826)

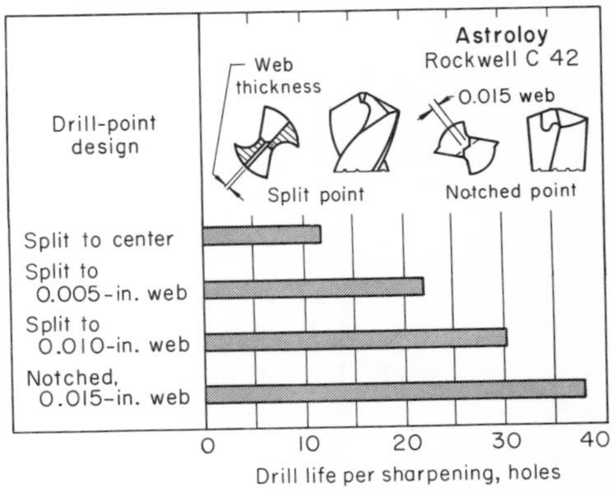

Fig. 18. Effect of drill-point design on life of T15 drills when drilling 0.310-in.-deep holes in 0.800-in.-thick Astroloy (Example 827)

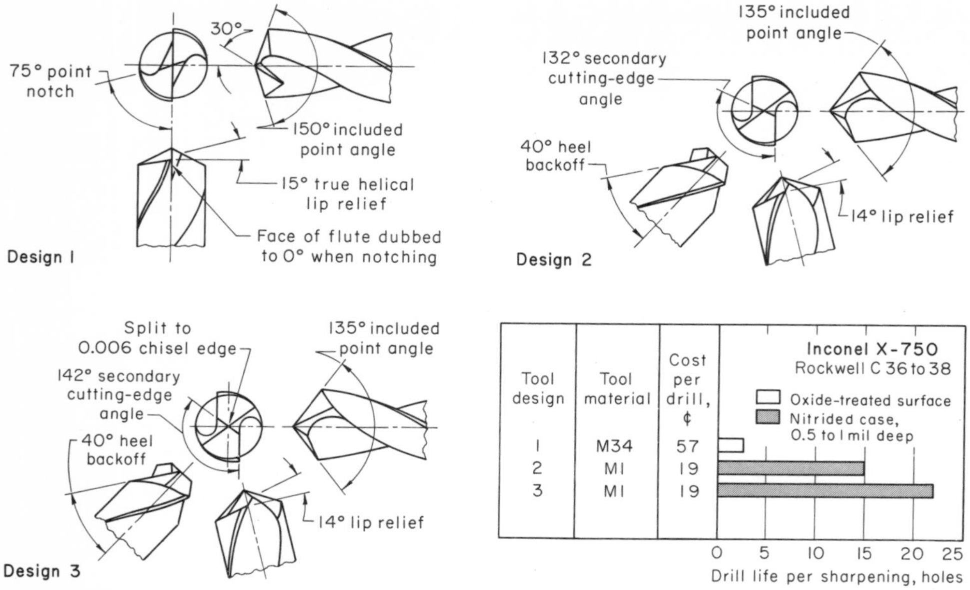

All drills were of screw-machine length, with a diameter of 0.098 in. and a flute helix angle of 29°. Designs 1 and 2 had a web thickness of 0.020 in. and a 132° secondary cutting-edge angle; design 3 had a web thickness of 0.024 in. and a secondary cutting-edge angle of 142°.

Fig. 19. Changes in drill design to reduce costs in hand drilling Inconel X-750. Graph shows effects on tool life. (Example 828)

thickness of the split point was varied from none to 0.010 in. The life of three split points and of one notched point is plotted in Fig. 18. Of the split points, least satisfactory results were obtained with a point split to center (no web thickness). Split point designs with web thicknesses of 0.005 and 0.010 in. had better life. However, a notched point, with a 0.015-in. web, yielded the best results. All drills had 135° point angles. Additional tests confirmed the finding that a 135° point angle is superior to 118°. Clearance angles of 9° to 10° proved superior in supplementary tests to clearance angles of 7° to 8° and 11° to 12°. All drills were made of T15 high speed steel and were operated at 11.2 sfm with a feed of 0.002 ipr. Cutting fluid was a sulfochlorinated concentrate of mineral and fatty oil.

Example 828. Effect of Drill Design on Cost of Drilling Inconel X-750 (Fig. 19)

For lower drilling costs in hand drilling parts made of heat treated Inconel X-750 (Rockwell C 36 to 38), changes in tool material and drill design were required. The workpieces ranged in thickness from 0.020 to 0.125 in., and a speed of 12.8 sfm was used with a 0.098-in.-diam drill. No cutting fluid was used.

The first drills tested were made of M34 high speed steel and had been developed under ideal conditions of rigid setup and positive feed. They performed satisfactorily under these conditions. These drills, however, proved impractical when used for hand drilling operations, using light, limited-production tooling. Brittleness of the tool material caused rapid deterioration of the drill, which, when coupled with the premium price of the special point (design 1, Fig. 19), resulted in tool costs that were prohibitive.

A change to a type-C aircraft drill (design 2, Fig. 19) made of M1 steel liquid nitrided to a depth of 0.0005 to 0.001 in. resulted in increased tool life and a reduction in costs. In operating the new drills, if the drill point was split past center, as permitted by the specification, tool life would usually be greatly shortened and the tool would chip just before it failed, at the point of intersection of the secondary cutting edge and the flute face.

These problems were overcome with the drill designated design 3 in Fig. 19. In this drill, the possibility of splitting past center was eliminated by the drill dimensions; the strength of the area that had chipped in the previous design was increased by enlarging the 132° secondary cutting-edge angle to 142°; and the web thickness also was increased, to improve the over-all stability of the tool. The change in web thickness helped considerably to extend tool life. Costs for each of the drill designs are shown in Fig. 19.

High speed steel drills are used for most drilling operations on heat-resisting alloys. In many applications, drills made of the general-purpose grades have proved satisfactory, judged by the number of holes drilled, and by initial cost of the drills and cost of resharpening. The premium grades of high speed steel, such as T15, M33 or M36, are preferred for drilling many of the heat-resisting alloys, and frequently their use is mandatory for obtaining acceptable drill life. The higher cost of drills made from the more highly alloyed high speed steels (commonly about four times the cost of their general-purpose counterparts) and the higher cost of resharpening are often warranted by increased tool life. The three examples that follow compare drills made of several grades of high speed steel, on the basis of performance under different drilling conditions (see also Example 836). Data in Examples 829 and 831 show better results for drills made of the more highly alloyed grades of high speed steel; in Example 830, no clear advantage was proved. Apparent inconsistencies such as these among the tool life data from different plants are not uncommon. Usually a new application will be started with drills made of a general-purpose high speed steel, and a premium grade will be used only when the need for it has been established.

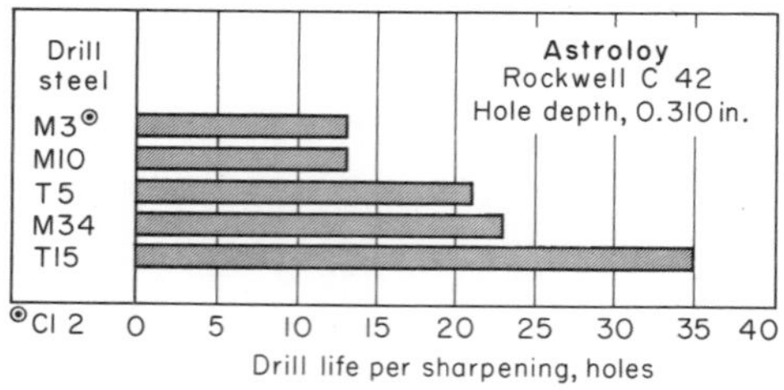

Fig. 20. Comparison of drill life for five high speed steels (Example 829)

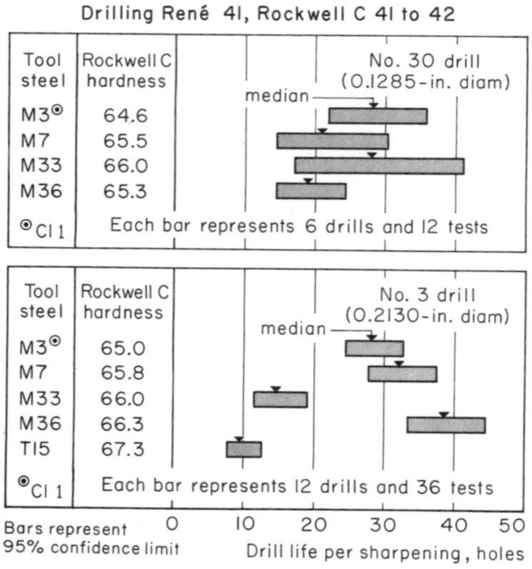

Fig. 21. Life of two sizes of rail drills tested to determine the performance of various grades of high speed steel in drilling ⅛-in.-thick sheet of René 41 (Example 830)

Example 829. General-Purpose vs Premium Grades of High Speed Steel for Drills (Fig. 20)

Drills made of five grades of high speed steel were compared for drilling 0.310-in.-deep holes, 0.201 and 0.213 in. in diameter, in solution-treated-and-aged Astroloy. Two drills of each material were tested. All drills had a 135° point angle, 9° to 10° clearance angle, and 0.015-in. web thickness, and were operated at 11.2 sfm with a feed of 0.002 ipr. Drills of M10 and M3 (class 2) did not perform satisfactorily in most of the tests. Drills of T15 performed best and those of M34 and T5 were also considered acceptable. Although they did not equal T15 drills in performance, M34 and T5 drills were reground at lower cost than the T15 drills.

Example 830. Effect of Drill Material and Size on Drill Life (Fig. 21)

Five grades of high speed steel — M3 (class 1), M7, M33, M36 and T15 — were tested for performance in drilling holes in ⅛-in.-thick René 41 sheet (Rockwell C 41 to 42). Two sizes of drills were used: No. 30 (0.1285-in.-diam) and No. 3 (0.213-in.-diam). Drills were tested in a drill press equipped with an electronically controlled variable-speed drive. The feeds were gear-driven positive with respect to spindle rotation. A drill bushing, about one drill diameter away from the work, was used. Each workpiece was clamped on two support blocks that were about 3 in. apart; this allowed some deflection of the workpiece, simulating actual operating conditions.

No. 30 (0.1285-In.-Diam) Drills. Twenty-four drills of this size (six drills of each of four grades of high speed steel) were tested. Drills in each group were operated for two grinds — the original point and one resharpening. Drills were rail drills with helix angle of 12°, over-all length of 2¾ in., and flute length of 1$\frac{5}{16}$ in. The drills were operated without cutting fluid, at a speed of 300 rpm and a feed of 0.001 ipr. A comparison of drill life obtained with the four steels is shown in the upper chart in Fig. 21.

The 95% confidence limits of all of the steels overlap, and therefore it cannot be assumed that there is any significant difference in the performance of the various steels. There is about a 50% probability that this test has revealed a real difference in the performance of grades M3 and M33 (each with a median drill life of 28 holes) and that of grades M7 and M36 (with median drill lives of 21 and 19 holes, respectively).

No. 3 (0.213-In.-Diam) Drills. Drills of this size were tested in the same setup as was used for the No. 30 drills, but a fifth grade of high speed steel (T15) also was tested, and more drills were used so as to provide a more reliable statistical comparison. Sets of six drills of each of the five grades of high speed steel were run four times (the original points and three regrinds). Other sets of six drills of the same grades were run twice (the original points and one regrind). These drills (also rail drills) had an 18° helix angle, over-all length of 3¾ in., and flute length of 1¼ in. They were operated without cutting fluid at a speed of 200 rpm and a feed of 0.002 ipr.

Drill life obtained is plotted in the lower chart in Fig. 21. M36 performed significantly better than any of the other grades except M7 (and there is about a 67% chance that its performance is better than that of grade M7). M3 also performed well. All drills of each grade were made from a single heat of high speed steel; the order of the three top grades might have interchanged if different heats had been used.

Grade M33 was disappointing in view of its excellent performance in drills of the No. 30 size. (The reason for this could not be detected in dimensional and metallurgical analysis of the drills; field tests have shown the performance of this grade to be generally good.)

The poor performance of T15 was not surprising. Tests on this grade over a period of several years had shown erratic performance of T15 as a tool material for small-diameter twist drills. T15 is capable of developing very high hardness, Rockwell C 67 or higher, and small drills of T15 usually failed by microscopic chipping of the cutting edges. This is probably the effect of the inherent lack of rigidity of small drills and of the slightly coarser grain structure of T15 high speed steel.

The general similarity in the performance of grades M3, M7 and M36 steels, which represent wide extremes in composition, suggests that tool material is a secondary factor in drilling heat treated René 41. Rigidity of the drill, achieved by design, is of primary importance.

Table 25. Nominal Speeds and Feeds for Drilling Heat-Resisting Alloys With High Speed Steel Tools (a)

Alloy group(b)	Condition(c)	Brinell hardness	Speed, sfm	Feed (ipr) for nominal diameter (in.) of: 0.125	0.250	0.500	0.750	1.000	1.500	2.000
Fe Wrt	ST	180 to 230	20	0.002	0.004	0.006	0.007	0.010	0.012	0.012
	ST, A	250 to 320	15	0.002	0.004	0.006	0.007	0.010	0.012	0.012
Ni Wrt 1	Ann or ST	200 to 300	20	0.001	0.001	0.003	0.005	0.007	0.010	0.010
	ST, A	300 to 400	15	0.001	0.001	0.003	0.005	0.007	0.010	0.010
Ni Wrt 2	Ann	140 to 220	30	0.002	0.004	0.006	0.007	0.010	0.012	0.012
	CD	280 to 310	20	0.001	0.002	0.003	0.005	0.007	0.010	0.010
Ni Cast	AC	250 to 350	10	0.001	0.001	0.002	0.004	0.006	0.007	0.008
Co Wrt	ST	180 to 230	25	0.002	0.004	0.006	0.007	0.010	0.012	0.012
	ST, A	270 to 320	15	0.001	0.002	0.003	0.005	0.007	0.010	0.010
Co Cast	AC	220 to 290	10	0.001	0.001	0.002	0.004	0.006	0.007	0.008
HR Cst 1	AC	160 to 210	40	0.002	0.003	0.005	0.008	0.009	0.011	0.013
HR Cst 2	AC	160 to 210	35	0.002	0.003	0.006	0.008	0.009	0.010	0.011

(a) High speed steels T15 and M33 for all alloy groups except HR Cst 1 and 2, for which M1, M7 and M10 tools are recommended. Tool design: 118° to 135° point angle, 9° to 12° lip relief angle, 125° to 135° chisel edge angle, 24° to 32° helix angle, crankshaft point. Stub-length drills are recommended whenever possible. A sulfochlorinated fat-containing mineral oil is recommended as the cutting fluid. (b) See Table 2 for alloys in each group. (c) ST = Solution treated; A = Aged; Ann = Annealed; CD = Cold drawn; AC = As cast.

Table 26. Nominal Speeds and Feeds for Gun Drilling Heat-Resisting Alloys With Grade C-2 Carbide Tools (a)

Alloy group(b)	Condition(c)	Brinell hardness	Speed, sfm	Feed (ipr) for nominal diameter (in.) of: Under 0.250	0.250 to 0.500	0.500 to 0.750	0.750 to 1.000	1.000 to 2.000
Fe Wrt	ST	180 to 230	150	0.0003	0.0005	0.0008	0.0012	0.0015
	ST, A	250 to 320	100	0.0003	0.0005	0.0008	0.0012	0.0015
Ni Wrt 1	Ann or ST	200 to 300	100	0.0003	0.0005	0.0008	0.0012	0.0015
	ST, A	300 to 400	60	0.0002	0.0004	0.0006	0.0008	0.001
Ni Wrt 2	Ann	140 to 220	100	0.0003	0.0005	0.0008	0.0012	0.0015
	CD	240 to 310	60	0.0003	0.0005	0.0008	0.0012	0.0015
Co Wrt	ST	180 to 230	100	0.0003	0.0005	0.0008	0.0012	0.0015
	ST, A	270 to 320	60	0.0003	0.0005	0.0008	0.0012	0.0015
HR Cst 1	AC	160 to 210	250	0.0003	0.0005	0.0006	0.0008	0.001
HR Cst 2	AC	160 to 210	200	0.0003	0.0005	0.0006	0.0008	0.001

(a) A sulfochlorinated fat-containing mineral oil is recommended as the cutting fluid. (b) See Table 2 for alloys in each group. (c) ST = Solution treated; A = Aged; Ann = Annealed; CD = Cold drawn; AC = As cast.

Example 831. M2 vs T15 Drills for Drilling René 41

A comparison was made of life of M2 and T15 high speed steel drills in machining 0.201-in.-diam through holes in ⅜-in.-thick René 41 (Rockwell C 41). Drills of both materials had crankshaft points, 30° helix angles, lip relief angles of 12° to 16°, and standard web thickness of approximately 17% of the drill diameter. The unsupported length was ⅞ to 1 in. The drills were operated at a speed of 20 sfm and a feed of 0.003 ipr, with sulfurized oil cutting fluid.

Only six holes were completed with the M2 drills, whereas 23 holes were made with the T15 drills. Although T15 is the more expensive of the two materials tested, the greater tool life obtained with it warranted its being selected for this application.

Carbide Drills. Whether or not carbide can be used for drills for heat-resisting alloys depends largely on the rigidity of the setup. In the two examples that follow, experience with carbide-tipped drills is described.

Example 832. High Speed Steel vs Carbide for Drilling A-286 (Fig. 22)

In drilling 2-in.-thick age-hardened A-286 (Rockwell C 31), carbide-tipped and high speed steel oil-hole drills were used.

The high speed steel drills tested were 33/64 in. in diameter and of two lengths — 8½ and 6¼ in. Drills of both lengths proved unsatisfactory when hole depth-to-diameter ratio exceeded 3 to 1. Tool details, speed and feed, and results with high speed steel drills were:

Item	8½-in. drills	6¼-in. drills
Flute length, in.	5	3¼
Unsupported length, in.	7	4¾
Speed, sfm	15 to 35	15
Feed, ipr	0.003 to 0.006	0.006
Tool life, No. of holes	1 to 2	17

The high speed steel drills contained one oil hole. They were of the screw-machine type (tube-style drills were not tested) and had a crankshaft point, a point angle of 118°, a web thickness of 0.090 in., and a lip relief angle of 17.5°. All were operated in an upright drill press, using the universal-applicator drill chuck shown in Fig. 22. Sulfurized oil under pressure of 20 to 40 psi was used as the cutting fluid.

Under these test conditions, more chatter and tool wear were encountered with the 8½-in. drills. Even though tool life was longer for the 6¼-in. drills, some chatter was observed.

Because the upright drill press used was not sufficiently rigid, carbide-tipped drills were tested in an engine lathe, using the same drill chuck (Fig. 22), but with a water-base cutting fluid. These drills were provided with a −28° rake and contained two oil holes. Other details of the carbide-tipped drills were as follows: total length, 5 in.; flute length, 3½ in.; unsupported length, 3⅜ in.; diameter, 33/64 in.; web thickness, 0.100 in.; chisel point, with point angle of 130°; lip relief angle, 30°.

Grades C-1 and C-2 carbides were tested. Grade C-1 had a hardness of Rockwell A 91.2

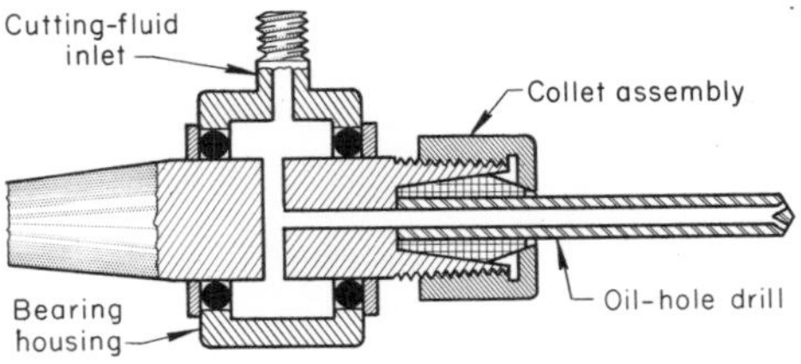

Fig. 22. Universal-applicator chuck used for both high speed steel and carbide-tipped oil-hole drills tested for performance in drilling A-286 (Example 832)

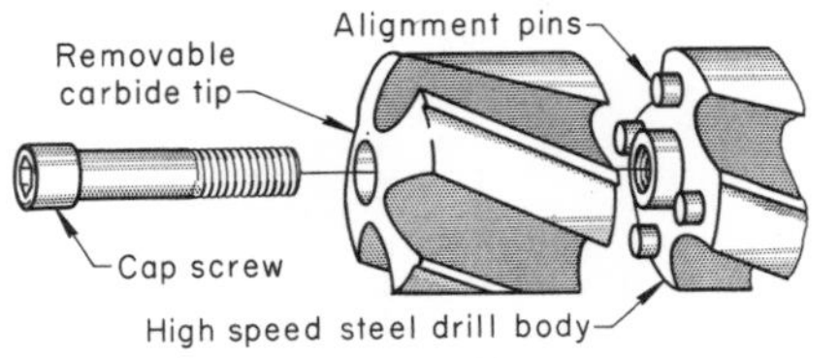

Fig. 23. Removable-carbide-tip core drill that replaced a high speed steel drill for machining Incoloy 901 (Example 833)

and a grain size of 3 microns; grade C-2, Rockwell A 91.8 and a grain size of 1 to 2 microns. Speeds ranged from 135 to 270 sfm; drilling rate was 2 ipm. Results obtained from the two grades of carbide were as follows:

Speed, sfm	Grade C-1	Grade C-2
135	5 holes drilled, good finish	....
200	2 holes drilled, fair finish	....
270	19 holes drilled, 0.026-in. wear land	37 holes drilled, good finish, 0.019-in. wear land

It was concluded that, when rigidity of the machine setup is sufficient, drills tipped with C-2 carbide should be used to drill holes ½ in. or more in diameter and 1 in. or more in depth. Other recommendations for drilling A-286 with carbide drills included: (*a*) a speed range of 250 to 275 sfm, (*b*) a feed of 0.0007 to 0.001 ipr, and (*c*) a water-base cutting fluid. The 2-ipm drilling rate achieved with the carbide drills used in these tests exceeded previous production rates on hardened A-286.

Example 833. Carbide vs High Speed Steel for Core Drills Used in Drilling Incoloy 901 (Fig. 23)

Core drills of solid high speed steel had a life of one hole per regrind when used for drilling Incoloy 901 (Rockwell C 30 to 34). Tool life increased to four holes per regrind when a core drill with a removable tip of tungsten carbide (Fig. 23) was used; thus, substantial savings in tool costs and grinding time were realized with the removable tip.

Both types of core drills were operated at a speed of 48 sfm and a feed of 0.0078 ipr to enlarge 1 3/32-in.-diam cored holes in Incoloy 901. The cutting fluid was a soluble-oil emulsion (1-to-20 ratio) containing lard additions, and full flow pressure was used. Except for web thickness, which was 0.670 in. for the high speed steel drills and 0.750 in. for the carbide-tipped drills, design details for both types were the same:

Diameter	1.3125 in.
Number of flutes	4
Lip relief angle	12° to 14°
Point angle	118°
Helix angle	15°

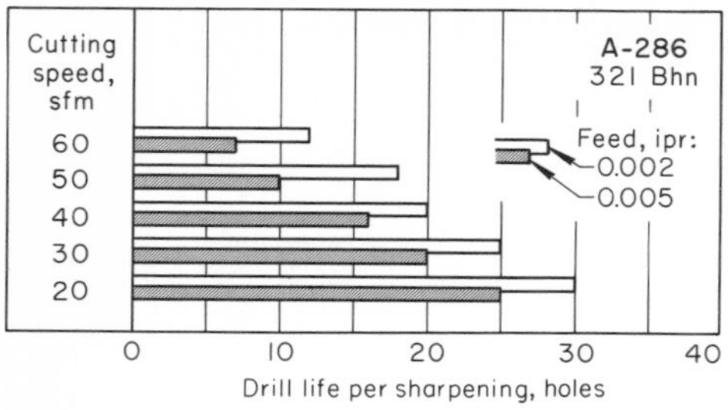

Depth of holes	0.500 in. (through)
Drill wear end point	0.015-in. wear land
Cutting fluid	Sulfurized and mineral oils (1:1)

Drill Details

Material	M2 high speed steel
Diameter	0.250 in.
Length	4 in.
Point angle	118°
Helix angle	29°
Primary clearance	7°
Point grind	Standard

Fig. 24. Effect of speed on drill life in drilling A-286 at two different speeds. See text for discussion.

Speed. The selection of optimum speed is one of the most important requisites for successful drilling of heat-resisting alloys. Nominal speeds for drilling eight groups of heat-resisting alloys with high speed steel drills are given in Table 25, which shows speeds ranging from 10 to 40 sfm for the various groups. Speeds of 15 to 30 sfm are extensively used for drilling with high speed steel drills, although in drilling the more difficult-to-machine alloys, such as René 41, speeds as low as 10 sfm may be required. On the other hand, speeds of more than 50 sfm have been used successfully for drilling some iron-base heat-resisting alloys. Speeds lower than 10 sfm are seldom feasible, because shear action is poor and the drills are likely to fail by chipping.

When carbide drills are used, speeds are usually four or more times as fast. Nominal speeds for gun drilling six groups of heat-resisting alloys with carbide-tipped drills are given in Table 26. Comparing Table 25 with Table 26, speeds for gun drilling with carbide drills are far higher than those used for conventional drilling with high speed steel, but feeds are relatively low for gun drilling. (See also the section on Gun Drilling, at page 81, in the article "Drilling".)

Figures 24 and 25 relate speed and feed to drill life in terms of number of holes drilled in four different metals. Although 17-22 (Fig. 25) is an alloy steel in terms of composition, it is frequently used for service temperatures higher than 1000 F, where other alloy steels would quickly lose their strength.

The next two examples describe the effects of speed on tool life and cost.

Example 834. Effect of Speed on Drill Life in Drilling Astroloy (Fig. 26)

In drilling Astroloy (Rockwell C 42), preliminary tests indicated that satisfactory drilling performance could be obtained at a speed near 12 sfm. To determine the range of speed within which acceptable performance and satisfactory tool life could be maintained, speeds ranging from 8.8 to 19 sfm were tested. Figure 26 shows a decrease in tool life at speeds above 15 sfm. At the highest speed (19 sfm), tool life was lowest. At the lowest speed (8.8 sfm), poor shearing action caused chipping of drills and premature drill failure.

All tests were run at a feed of 0.002 ipr; each drill had a split point (ground to a 0.005-in. web thickness), a 9° to 10° clearance, and 135° point angle.

The lightest feed available on the test equipment was 0.002 ipr. This feed and a feed of 0.003 ipr were tested at a speed of 11.2 sfm. The lighter feed proved far superior in terms of tool life. Because heavier feeds were obviously detrimental to tool life, no further tests of feed rate were made.

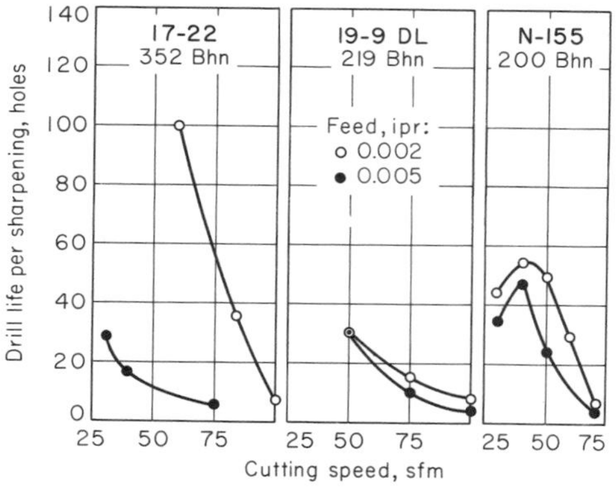

Depth of holes	0.500 in. (through)
Drill wear end point	0.015-in. wear land
Cutting fluid	Sulfurized and mineral oils (1:1)

Drill Details

Material	M2 high speed steel
Diameter	0.250 in.
Length	4 in.
Point angle	118°
Helix angle	29°
Primary clearance	7°
Point grind	Standard

Fig. 25. Effect of speed and feed on drill life in drilling 17-22 steel, 19-9 DL and N-155

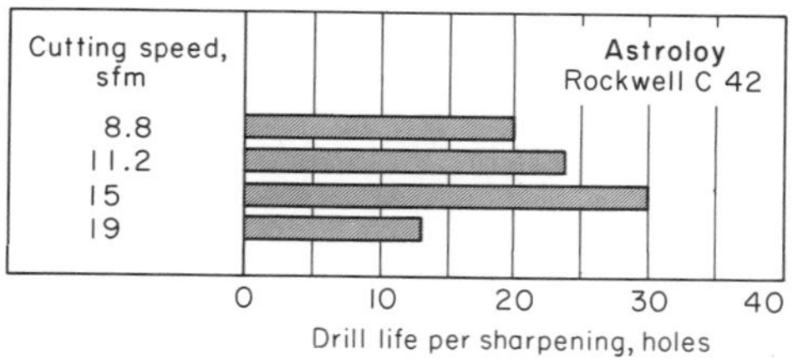

Fig. 26. Effect of speed on drill life in drilling 0.310-in.-deep holes in Astroloy with T15 high speed steel drills, using a feed of 0.002 ipr (Example 834)

Example 835. Effect of Speed on Drill Performance and Cost in Drilling Inconel X-750 (Table 27)

A test program was conducted to determine the most efficient operating speed of ¼-in.-capacity drill motors in the hand drilling of production parts (0.020 to 0.125 in. thick) made of heat treated Inconel X-750 (Rockwell C 36 to 38). The purchase of new drill motors was to be guided by the results of these tests.

New ¼-in.-capacity drill motors (air-powered and electric-powered), operated by experienced production personnel, were used in the test program. Although it was planned ultimately to use drills ranging in diameter from 0.098 to 0.250 in., only the 0.098-in. drill was tested. (A speed-reduction adjustment could be easily incorporated in each unit to accommodate drills of larger size.) The type-C aircraft drills were made of high speed steel, liquid nitrided to a depth of 0.0005 to 0.001 in.

Table 27 lists the results obtained in drilling through holes by direct hand feeding. On the basis of these results, drill motors with a speed of 600 rpm were purchased.

Table 27. Effect of Speed on Drill Performance and Cost in Drilling Inconel X-750 (Example 835) (a)

Item	Free speed of drill spindle, rpm: 500 / Corresponding cutting speed, sfm: 12.9	550 / 14.2	600 / 15.3	650 / 16.8
Average number of holes per minute	1.75	1.98	2.15	2.25
Average number of holes per drill	16.1	14.7	13.2	7.9
Labor cost per hole, @ $0.1073 per min	$0.0613	$0.0541	$0.0499	$0.0477
Drill cost per hole	0.0118	0.0129	0.0144	0.0241
Labor cost per drill change per hole	0.0022	0.0024	0.0027	0.0046
Total cost per hole	$0.0753	$0.0694	$0.0670	$0.0764

(a) Workpieces were production parts, 0.020 to 0.125 in. thick; drills, 0.098 in. in diameter, were of type C aircraft design, and had been liquid nitrided to a depth of 0.0005 to 0.001 in.

Feed. The selection of optimum feed requires more careful consideration for drilling heat-resisting alloys than for drilling steel or cast iron. Nominal feeds for drilling eight different groups of heat-resisting alloys with high speed steel drills are given in Table 25. Similar data for feeds used in gun drilling with carbide-tipped tools are given in Table 26. Tables 25 and 26 give feed as a function of hole diameter; type of cutting fluid and rigidity in the setup are also important factors.

Steady rate of feed is frequently more important than the average numerical value, especially when drilling alloys that work harden readily. Hand feeding, although sometimes used, is not recommended for drilling heat-resisting alloys.

The test data presented in Fig. 27 show the significant effect of feed on drill life in drilling three different heat-resisting alloys. All other variables (including speed) were held constant for each work metal, thus isolating the effect of feed. (See also Fig. 24 and 25 and examples where feeds are given for specific drilling operations.)

Torque and thrust are related to feed. Measurements taken when drilling through holes in ⅛-in. René 41 with T15 drills provided the data pre-

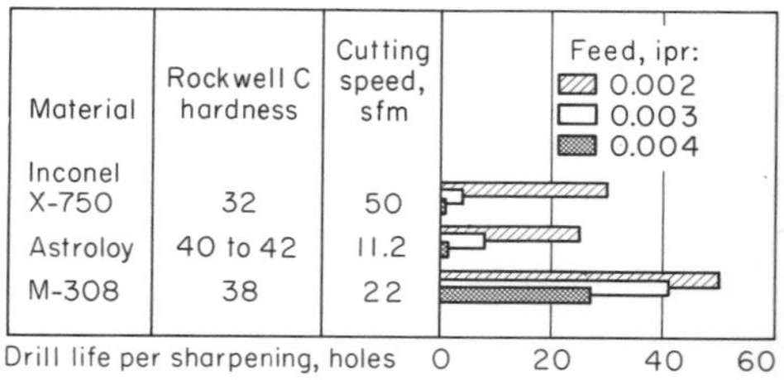

Condition(a)	Inconel X-750	Astroloy	M-308
Depth of holes, in.	0.400	0.310	0.500
Drill Details			
Material	M10	T15	T15
Diameter, in.	0.312	0.213	0.312
Length, in.	4.0	2.75	2.75
Point angle(b)	118°	135°	135°
Primary clearance	12°	12°	12°

(a) Thread-cutting oil diluted 1-to-1 with light machine oil was the cutting fluid. Drills were tested to failure. (b) Crankshaft point.

Fig. 27. Effect of feed on drill life in drilling three nickel-base alloys

sented in Fig. 28. All drilling was done in a vertical, electronic-control drill press.

Fixturing. Because successful drilling of most heat-resisting alloys depends on the rigidity of the workpiece, fixturing is important. The following example describes a fixturing procedure for drilling holes in forged rings.

Example 836. Fixturing and Drilling of Forged Rings of Waspaloy or Incoloy 901 (Fig. 29)

Holes were drilled radially through ¾-in.-thick forged rings of Waspaloy or Incoloy 901. Twenty-one holes of 1¹⁄₁₆-in. diameter reduced the weight of each 9-in.-diam ring from 5½ to 2½ lb.

A special holding fixture in a vertical milling machine provided the rigidity necessary to drill through the varying section of the ring. The ring contour and machining setup are shown in Fig. 29. Each ring was held in the clamping fixture, which, in turn, was mounted on the face plate of a turret-type indexing head. Because of the relatively short drills (5-in. flute length) and the rigidity of the machine spindle, it was unnecessary to employ drill bushings. An adjustment jack was placed under the holding fixture to relieve the indexing head of strain from the drill thrust. Drill details and machining conditions are given in the table accompanying Fig. 29.

Both M36 and T15 drills were tried in this operation, but M36 drills had only a third the life of T15 drills, and therefore T15 drills were used in production.

Rings of both materials were drilled in the age-hardened condition (Rockwell C 32 to 38 for both) after a preliminary turning operation. However, it was determined that a stress-relieving treatment (1000 F for 2 hr) prior to drilling increased drill life from 14 to 21 holes per grind in drilling Incoloy 901.

Fixturing is greatly simplified when the workpiece design is such that the piece will not distort appreciably when it is clamped. When the workpiece is too thin or too weak to withstand clamping forces, special techniques must be employed, such as filling portions of the workpiece with a low-melting alloy to give it added support and rigidity. An application of this technique is described in the next example:

Example 837. Use of Low-Melting Alloy Filler for Improved Workpiece Rigidity (Fig. 30)

For greater rigidity and better drill life in drilling 0.098-to-0.102-in.-diam holes in an HS-25 (AMS 5759) casting, the central portion of the piece, between the two webs, was filled with a low-melting alloy (Fig. 30). Before it was made rigid, the part could not properly support the pressure of the drill, and there was enough deflection to cause the alloy to work harden (initial hardness was Rockwell B 96). Consequently, life was less than one hole per drill.

Drills used in this operation were made of T15 high speed steel, with a ³⁄₃₂-in. diameter, a crankshaft point, a point angle of 118°, a lip relief angle of 10° to 12°, and a ¾-in. unsupported length. They were run in a 2-hp, 28-in. upright drill press, using sulfurized oil as cutting fluid. With improved rigidity of the workpiece, drill life increased appreciably, depending on operating speed and feed:

Speed, sfm	Feed, ipr	Holes per grind
5	0.0015	50
10	0.0015	50
10	0.003	10

Cutting Fluid. Active cutting oils — sulfurized, chlorinated or sulfochlorinated — usually provide better drill life and productivity than soluble-oil emulsions or other water-base cutting fluids. The superiority of active oils becomes more significant as the hardness of the work metal increases and as the depth of the drilled hole increases. When sulfochlorinated or other active oils are used as cutting fluids, all traces of oil must be removed from the workpiece before it is heat treated or put in service at high temperature. Blind holes require special attention.

Reaming

Rigidity is of prime importance in reaming heat-resisting alloys; consequently, unsupported lengths of tool holders and reamers should be kept at a minimum, for acceptable tool life.

Although it is generally desirable to use reamers having six or eight flutes, in reaming small holes (for example, less than ¼ in. in diameter), four-flute reamers are often used. Optimum tool angles may vary somewhat, depending on the alloy being reamed, size of hole, and number of flutes in the reamer. However, variation in angles is seldom great. For example, in one plant, eight-flute reamers with 2° radial rake, 12° radial relief, 42° chamfer, and 7° chamfer relief are successfully used for reaming ½-in. holes in A-286 and other iron-base alloys. The same angles are

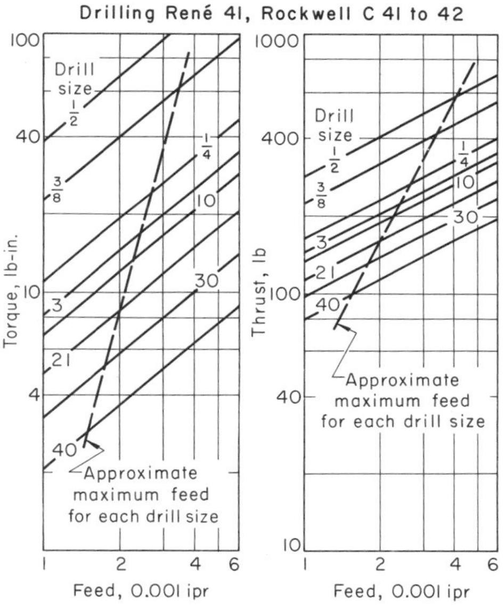

Fig. 28. Relations between torque and feed and between thrust and feed in drilling through-holes in heat treated ⅛-in.-thick René 41 with split-point rail drills

used for reaming ½-in. holes in nickel-base alloys, with the exception of the chamfer relief angle, which is reduced to 5°. For reaming ¼-in. holes in the same metals with four-flute reamers, the radial rake is increased to 3° and the radial relief is increased to 17°. Otherwise angles are the same as those used for reaming ½-in. holes. Narrow margins (0.007 to 0.009 in.) are used for reaming nickel-base alloys, but margin widths are increased to 0.010 to 0.017 in. for reaming iron-base alloys.

Nominal speeds and feeds for reaming heat-resisting alloys with six-flute reamers are presented in Table 28. Speeds of less than 10 sfm are seldom practical, because cutting edges are likely to chip. Feed must be great enough to maintain cutting action with a practical size of chip. Size of hole is the major factor influencing feed as indicated in Table 28. Relief angles, rake

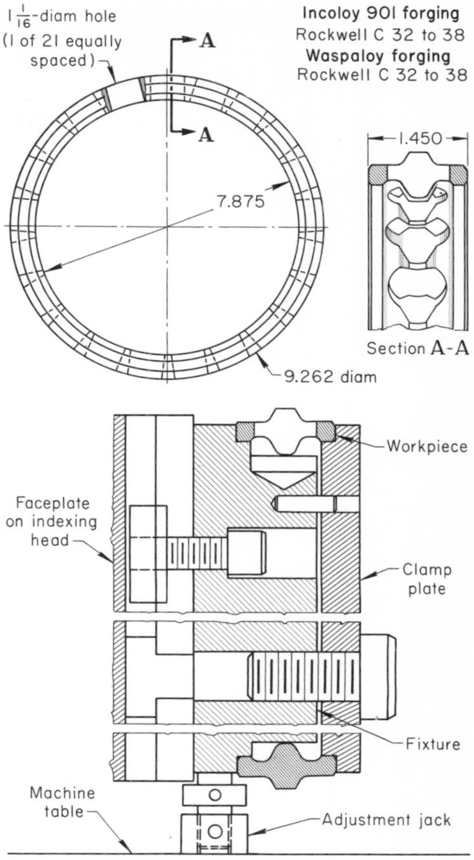

Drill Details

Drill material	T15 high speed steel
Drill diameter	1¹⁄₁₆ in. (tapered shank)
Flute length	5 in.
Point angle	135°
Lip relief angle	6°
Rake angle	5°
Chisel-edge thickness	0.090 in.

Drill Conditions

Speed	75 rpm (21 sfm)
Feed	0.0084 ipr
Cutting fluid	Soluble-oil:water (1:5)

Results

Machining rate, per hole	1.6 min
Machining rate, per ring	33.6 min (21 holes)
Floor-to-floor time, per ring	1 hr
Drill life in:	
Incoloy 901	21 holes per grind
Waspaloy	3 holes per grind

Fig. 29. Setup for drilling the 1¹⁄₁₆-in.-diam holes in rings of the section shown, in a vertical milling machine (Example 836)

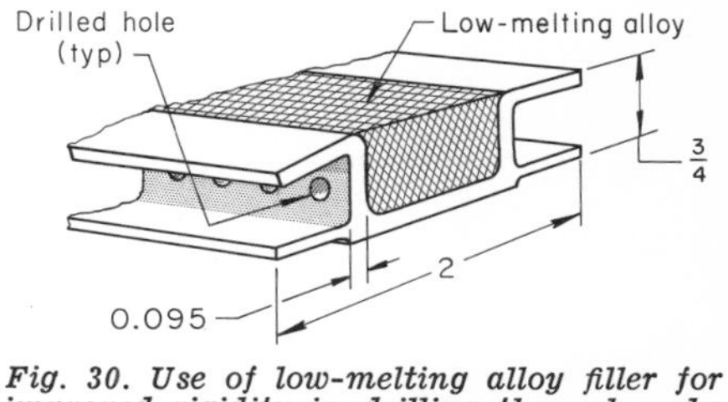

Fig. 30. Use of low-melting alloy filler for improved rigidity in drilling through webs of castings made of HS-25 (L-605) alloy (Example 837)

and clearances are enumerated in footnote (a) in Table 28.

The amount of stock left for reaming is especially critical with heat-resisting alloys. Removing an excessive amount of stock overloads the tools, whereas insufficient stock will cause burnishing,

Table 28. Nominal Speeds and Feeds for Reaming Heat-Resisting Alloys With 6-Flute Reamers(a)

Alloy group(b)	Condition(c)	Brinell hardness	Speed, sfm HSS tools(d)	Speed, sfm Carbide tools(e)	Feed (ipr) for nominal diameter (in.) of: 0.125	0.500	1.000	1.500	2.000
Fe Wrt	ST	180 to 230 ..	20	70	0.002	0.005	0.008	0.010	0.010
	ST, A	250 to 320 ..	15	50	0.002	0.005	0.008	0.010	0.010
Ni Wrt 1	Ann or ST	200 to 300 ..	15	50	0.002	0.005	0.008	0.010	0.010(f)
	ST, A	300 to 400 ..	10	40	0.002	0.005	0.008	0.010	0.010
Ni Wrt 2	Ann	140 to 220 ..	20	70	0.002	0.005	0.008	0.010	0.010
	CD	280 to 310 ..	15	60	0.002	0.005	0.008	0.010	0.010
Ni Cast	AC	250 to 350 ..	10	40	0.002	0.005	0.008	0.010	0.010
Co Wrt	ST	180 to 230 ..	15	50	0.002	0.005	0.008	0.010	0.010
	ST, A	270 to 320 ..	10	40	0.002	0.005	0.005	0.008	0.008
Co Cast	AC	220 to 290 ..	10	40	0.002	0.005	0.008	0.010	0.010
HR Cst 1	AC	160 to 210 ..	30(g)	100	0.003	0.007	0.010	0.012	0.015
HR Cst 2	AC	160 to 210 ..	25(g)	75	0.003	0.007	0.010	0.012	0.015

(a) High speed steel tool design: 0.007 to 0.009-in. margin width, 1⁄16-in. by 45° chamfer angle, 5° to 6° chamfer relief angle, 2° to 3° radial rake angle, 0° to 10° helix angle, 12° to 17° primary relief angle. Carbide tool design: 0.005 to 0.010-in. margin width, 3⁄16-in. by 2° lead angle, 7° to 10° radial rake angle, 5° to 8° helix angle, 7° to 15° primary relief angle. A chemical emulsion is recommended as the cutting fluid. (b) See Table 2 for alloys in each group. (c) ST = Solution treated; A = Aged; Ann = Annealed; CD = Cold drawn; AC = As cast. (d) T15 high speed steel. (e) Grade C-2. (f) Feed with carbide tools, 0.015 ipr. (g) M1, M2 and M7.

Table 29. Nominal Speeds and Feeds for Counterboring and Spotfacing Heat-Resisting Alloys(a)

Alloy group(b)	Condition(c)	Brinell hardness	Speed, sfm	Feed (ipr) for nominal diameter (in.) of: 0.250	0.500	1.000	2.000	3.000
High Speed Steel Tools(d)								
Fe Wrt	ST	180 to 230 ..	25	0.001	0.0015	0.002	0.0025	0.0035
	ST, A	250 to 320 ..	20	0.001	0.0015	0.002	0.0025	0.0035
Ni Wrt 1	Ann or ST	200 to 300 ..	10	0.001	0.0015	0.002	0.0025	0.0035
	ST, A	300 to 400 ..	10	0.001	0.0015	0.002	0.0025	0.0035
Ni Wrt 2	Ann	140 to 220 ..	35	0.001	0.0015	0.002	0.003	0.0035
	CD	240 to 310 ..	30	0.001	0.0015	0.002	0.003	0.0035
Ni Cast	AC	250 to 350 ..	10	0.0008	0.0015	0.002	0.003	0.003
Co Wrt	ST	180 to 230 ..	15	0.001	0.0015	0.002	0.0025	0.0035
	ST, A	270 to 320 ..	10	0.001	0.0015	0.002	0.0025	0.0035
Co Cast	AC	220 to 290 ..	10	0.0008	0.0015	0.002	0.003	0.003
HR Cst 1(e)	AC	160 to 210 ..	50	0.002	0.003	0.003	0.0035	0.004
HR Cst 2(e)	AC	160 to 210 ..	40	0.0015	0.002	0.0025	0.003	0.004
Carbide Tools(f)								
Fe Wrt	ST	180 to 230 .	100	0.002	0.003	0.004	0.005	0.007
	ST, A	250 to 320 .	90	0.002	0.003	0.004	0.005	0.007
Ni Wrt 1	Ann or ST	200 to 300 .	50	0.002	0.003	0.004	0.005	0.007
	ST, A	300 to 400 .	50	0.002	0.003	0.004	0.005	0.007
Ni Wrt 2	Ann	140 to 220 .	100	0.002	0.0025	0.004	0.006	0.008
	CD	240 to 310 .	80	0.002	0.0025	0.004	0.006	0.008
Ni Cast	AC	250 to 350 .	25	0.0015	0.003	0.004	0.006	0.006
Co Wrt	ST	180 to 230 .	65	0.002	0.003	0.004	0.005	0.007
	ST, A	270 to 320 .	50	0.002	0.003	0.004	0.005	0.007
Co Cast	AC	220 to 290 .	25	0.0015	0.003	0.004	0.006	0.006
HR Cst 1	AC	160 to 210 .	220	0.004	0.005	0.006	0.007	0.008
HR Cst 2	AC	160 to 210 .	180	0.003	0.004	0.005	0.006	0.008

(a) A sulfurized fat-containing mineral oil is recommended as the cutting fluid. (b) See Table 2 for alloys in each group. (c) ST = Solution treated; A = Aged; Ann = Annealed; CD = Cold drawn; AC = As cast. (d) T15, M41, M42, M43 and M44. (e) M2 and T5 tools. (f) Grade C-2.

which causes the alloy to work harden. The optimum amount varies with hole size, but 0.005 in. on the radius (0.010 in. on the diameter) should be the minimum, even for the smallest holes that can be reamed.

Counterboring and Spotfacing

Tools used for counterboring and spotfacing heat-resisting alloys are not necessarily different from those used for similar operations on other metals (see the articles "Counterboring" and "Spotfacing", pages 103 to 105). As in other machining operations, great emphasis should be placed on rigidity of setup in these two processes.

Nominal speeds and feeds for counterboring and spotfacing heat-resisting alloys, given in Table 29, show that carbide tools permit substantially higher speeds and feeds than high speed steel tools. The size of hole to be counterbored or spotfaced greatly influences the feed that should be used. Speeds and feeds given in Table 29 are based on the use of sulfurized, fat-containing mineral oil for cutting fluid; however, in practice, spotfacing is often done without a cutting fluid, because the process involves the removal of only a small amount of metal.

Tapping and Thread Milling

Machining internal threads in heat-resisting alloy workpieces is especially difficult, mainly because the surface to be threaded work hardens during the operation (drilling, reaming or boring) that prepares the hole for threading. Therefore, the preliminary operations should be planned so that the tools continuously cut chips of substantial thickness, to prevent burnishing of the workpiece. Because reamed holes are the most likely to cause difficulty in tapping (particularly in nickel-base and cobalt-base alloys), chip thickness in reaming should be no less than 0.005 in., and preferably 0.010 in. or more.

Most production problems in tapping heat-resisting alloys are more readily solved by some alteration in the method of preparing the holes than by changes in the tapping operation. Subject to the limitation on chip thickness mentioned in the preceding paragraph, holes should be made to maximum rather than minimum size to reduce the amount of metal to be removed, thus prolonging tap life.

General Tapping Practice. Drill presses are ordinarily used for tapping of heat-resisting alloys, because production lots are usually small. For large production lots, the cost of tapping may be decreased by using turret lathes or automatic chucking machines (Example 838). Regardless of the machine used, it should be equipped with a mechanical feed, such as lead control, and, whenever possible, torque-limiting tapping heads with axial float should be used in conjunction with automatic feed. (Devices for control of feed in tapping are discussed on page 108 in the article "Tapping".)

Tap Design. Spiral-point (or "gun") taps are preferred for tapping heat-resisting alloys. Hook angle of the tap should never exceed 15°, and should be less for higher work-metal hardness. For example, a hook angle of 4° to 6° is suitable for tapping of work metal having a hardness of about Rockwell C 40. Taps with lands of minimum width are preferred, to minimize work hardening of the metal being tapped.

The chamfer should be short — three to five threads is usually recommended. A chamfer longer than five threads does not permit cutting deep enough to penetrate the work-hardened layer, and chamfers shorter than three threads cause excessive tooth loads, resulting in chipped or broken taps.

When it is necessary to rough and finish tap heat-resisting alloys, the roughing tap should be undersize on the pitch diameter, and its sharp crests should be backed off. A plug tap should not be followed by a tap of the same pitch diameter, because tap and work are likely to bind and oversize holes may be produced. Tap design for specific applications is described in Examples 838 and 839.

Tap Material. For small production quantities, taps made of a general-purpose grade of high speed steel (such as M1) will produce satisfactory results in heat-resisting alloys, but surface treatment of the taps by liquid nitriding is recommended. When larger quantities are tapped, the higher cost of taps made of one of the more highly alloyed high speed steels (such as M4, M36 or T15) is usually warranted.

Speeds of 5 to 15 sfm are satisfactory for tapping most heat-resisting alloys. For tapping iron-base heat-resisting alloys, speeds near the high end of the range result in satisfactory tool life, and sometimes speeds higher than 15 sfm have been used. In tapping nickel-base and cobalt-base heat-resisting alloys, speeds near the low end of the range are necessary (see Example 839). The nominal tapping speeds listed in Table 30 are based on use of the tap design described in footnote (a) and of a sulfochlorinated cutting oil.

Cutting Fluid. Sulfochlorinated oils should be used for tapping all heat-resisting alloys, and the oil should be supplied in plentiful amounts during the tapping operation. Recommended practice is to force the cutting fluid under pressure of about 5 psi through a nozzle directly into the hole being tapped. If the sulfochlorinated oil is

Table 30. Nominal Speeds for Tapping Heat-Resisting Alloys With High Speed Steel Tools (a)

Alloy group(b)	Condi-tion(c)	Brinell hardness	Speed, sfm
Fe Wrt	ST	180 to 230	15
	ST, A	250 to 320	10
Ni Wrt 1	Ann or ST	200 to 300	8
	ST, A	300 to 400	5
Ni Wrt 2	Ann	140 to 220	10
	CD	280 to 310	5
Ni Cast	AC	250 to 350	5
Co Wrt	ST	180 to 230	15
	ST, A	270 to 320	8
Co Cast	AC	220 to 290	5
HR Cst 1	AC	160 to 210	20
HR Cst 2	AC	160 to 210	15

(a) Recommended tool materials: M10, M7 and M1 for all alloy groups. Tool design: 0° to 10° hook or rake angle, spiral point, 2 to 3 flutes, 4° to 6° chamfer relief, 9° chamfer angle on plug-style tap preferred. A sulfochlorinated fat-containing oil is recommended as cutting fluid. (b) See Table 2 for alloys in each group. (c) ST = Solution treated; A = Aged; Ann = Annealed; CD = Cold drawn; AC = As cast.

too viscous for the pressure system, it may be diluted with a thinner mineral oil without seriously impairing its characteristics. Chemically-active cutting fluids must be removed from the tapped holes to prevent damage to the work metal during subsequent heat treatment or high-temperature service.

Typical practices used in tapping are described in the next two examples.

Example 838. Tapping A-286: Drill Press vs Automatic Chucking Machine (Table 31)

A manual feed drill press with a tapping head was first used to tap ⅜–24, ¾-in.-length RH and LH through holes in turnbuckles (two holes per piece) made of aged A-286 bar stock (Rockwell C 32 to 33). Production quantities warranted changing from the drill press to an automatic chucking machine; tap design and tap material were changed at the same time. Production and cost details for the two methods are compared in Table 31. Total cost per piece for tapping in the chucking machine was less than half the cost for tapping in the drill press. In the chucking machine, workpieces were held in a collet, and both ends (two holes) were tapped in a total of 1.1 min.

Example 839. Tapping ¼-In.-Diam Through Holes in Hastelloy C

A drill press was used for tapping ¼–28 UNF-3B threads in annealed Hastelloy C (Rockwell B 95). The 0.500-in.-deep through holes were tapped with M1 standard spiral-point plug taps that had a pitch diameter of 0.2278 in. (0.001 in. over basic) and no relief on the pitch diameter. Chamfer angle was 8°; rake angle, +15°. Seventy-five holes were tapped before resharpening the tap. A speed of 5 sfm and a sulfochlorinated oil were used.

Thread Milling. Nominal speeds and feeds for thread milling heat-resisting alloys are given in Table 32.

Thread milling is used most for cutting external threads, but if tapping is impractical, because of alloy characteristics, high hardness, or work-hardened surfaces, thread milling is sometimes used for producing internal threads. The principal limitation of thread milling for internal threads is the size (diameter and length) of the hole to be threaded. It is unlikely that a milling cutter could be operated in holes much smaller than 1 in. in diameter. Length of the hole is also a limiting factor, because rigidity is reduced when the spindle is too long for its diameter. An application in which thread milling replaced tapping is described in Example 840, which follows.

Table 31. Comparison of Conditions and Results for Tapping A-286 in a Drill Press and in an Automatic Chucking Machine (Example 838) (a)

Condition or result	Chucking machine	Drill press
Tool Details		
Type of tap	3-flute, spiral point(b)	4-flute, plug
Tool material	M4	M1
Production Details		
Tool change, hr	0.02	0.02
Tool life, pieces per grind .	25	6
Production, pieces per hour	37.5	20
Costs		
Initial tool cost, per tap ...	$6.00	$3.50
Grinding cost, per tap	0.75	0.75
Costs per piece tapped(c):		
Tapping(d)	$0.26	$0.50
Tool change	0.008	0.033
Tool cost(e)	0.083	0.240
Total	$0.351	$0.773

(a) A speed of 150 rpm (12 sfm) was used for both machines; sulfochlorinated oil was the cutting fluid. Drilled hole size was 0.3299/0.3372 in. (b) A ⅜–24, GH3 tap with full eccentric thread relief; +10° hook in a spiral point; 10° chamfer angle; OD relief, 12° round spiral point angle; 0.0015 to 0.002-in. back taper. (c) Two holes per piece. (d) Includes labor and overhead at $10.00 per hour. (e) Based on life of three grinds per tap.

Table 32. Nominal Speeds and Feeds for Thread Milling Heat-Resisting Alloys With High Speed Steel Tools (a)

Alloy group(b)	Brinell hardness	Speed, sfm	Feed, ipt
Fe Wrt(c)	180 to 230	35	0.002
Fe Wrt(d)	250 to 320	35	0.001
Ni Wrt 1(d)	200 to 300	20	0.002
Ni Wrt 1(d)	300 to 400	20	0.001
Ni Wrt 2(d)	140 to 220	30	0.002
Ni Wrt 2(d)	240 to 310	30	0.002
Co Wrt(c)	180 to 230	20	0.002
Co Wrt(d)	270 to 320	20	0.001
HR Cst 1 & 2(c)	160 to 210	70	0.002

(a) Sulfochlorinated, fat-containing mineral oil is recommended as the cutting fluid. (b) See Table 2 for alloys in each group. (c) M2 and M7 tools. (d) T15 and M2 tools.

Example 840. Milling 1⅛–12 Threads in HS-31

Difficulty was encountered in tapping 1⅛–12 3B threads approximately 0.500 in. long (through holes) in HS-31 castings. When holes were tapped in one pass, either the casting cracked or the tap seized or broke off. Progressive tapping was tried, with some success, but tapping became more difficult with each succeeding pass, and picking up the previous thread became a problem. The work metal resisted any appreciable amount of stock removal, making it difficult to cut the work-hardened surface.

Ultimately, the thread-milling process was tried, and proved successful, partly because it decreased chip load per tooth. A tungsten carbide cutter and sulfochlorinated cutting fluid were used. Tool life was extended to 28 parts per grind. Threading required 13 min per piece. The cost of a new cutter was $125 to $150, and it could be reground eight times before it was discarded. Considering the difficulty of the operation, this tooling cost was acceptable. Approximately 3000 parts were successfully threaded by milling.

Multiple-Operation Machining in Automatic Chucking Machines

Machining of heat-resisting alloys in automatic machines is uncommon, because components made from these alloys seldom are produced in large quantities. However, because of their power, rigidity and capacity for performing several operations in a single chucking, turret lathes or automatic chucking machines are occasionally used. The three examples that follow describe procedures used in producing parts in multiple-operation machines.

Example 841. Machining Stellite J Bearing Races in a Turret Lathe (Fig. 31)

Bearing races cast of Stellite J, a cobalt-base heat-resisting alloy (Rockwell C 58), were machined in a 10-in. turret lathe. The workpieces were stress relieved before machining. Each part was held in a collet and machined in seven operations, using three carbide tools; one tool was operated from the cross slide and two from the turret. The machining was done in two chuckings, as shown in Fig. 31. Tool and processing details are given in the table accompanying Fig. 31.

Example 842. Machining Forged Rings of Incoloy 901 in a Turret Lathe (Fig. 32)

A turret lathe equipped with a hydraulic tracer attachment was used to turn, bore, face and chamfer Incoloy 901 ring forgings (Fig. 32). Three chuckings and 14 operations machined these rings from blanks weighing 15 lb each to finished pieces weighing 5½ lb.

As shown in Fig. 32, in the first chucking, rings were held on the outside in a three-jaw chuck. In the second and third chuckings,

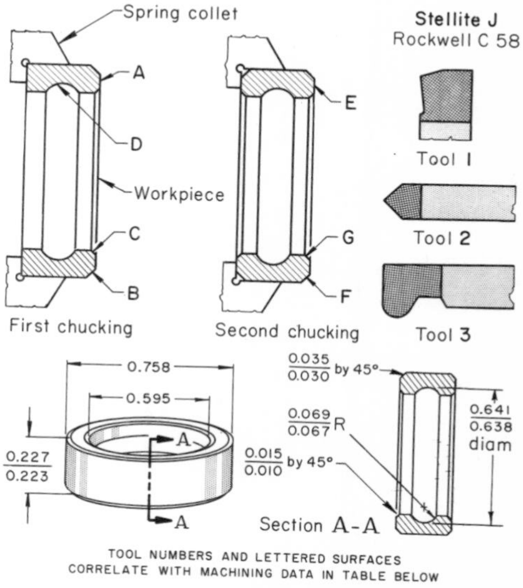

Tool Details

Facing (Tool 1). Style C, grade C-2 brazed carbide, altered to 15° lead angle, 8° side cutting-edge angle, 5° relief angles, 0° top rake angle, and 0.030-in. nose radius

Chamfering (Tool 2). Style D, grade C-2 brazed carbide, altered to 90° included angle, 0° top rake angle, and 7° relief angles

Forming Race (Tool 3). Style C, grade C-2 brazed carbide, altered to form race contour, 0° top rake angle; and 7° relief angle

Sequence of Operations

First chucking: Tool	Surface	Second chucking: Tool	Surface
1	Face A	1	Face E
2	Chamfer B	2	Chamfer F
2	Chamfer C	2	Chamfer G
3	Form D		

Machining Conditions

Speed, all operations .....300 rpm (59 sfm max)
Feed, all operations ....0.003 ipr
Cutting fluid ....Soluble-oil:water (1:5)
Tool life per grind, pieces:
Facing 6
Forming race 6
Chamfering 40
Production rate, pieces per hr 6

Fig. 31. Bearing race, and tool details and operations for machining it in a turret lathe (Example 841)

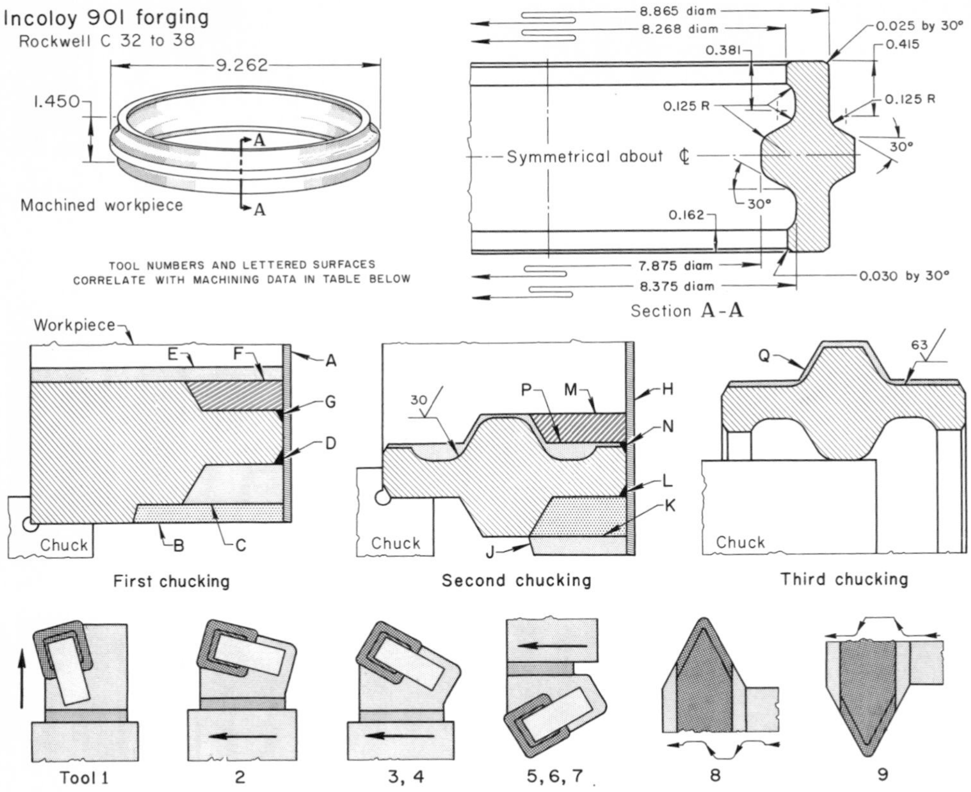

Item	Tool 1 (cross slide)	Tool 2 (cross slide)	Tool 4 (cross slide)	Tool 5 (turret)	Tool 6 (turret)	Tool 7 (turret)
First Chucking						
Surface(a)	A	B	C and D	E	F	G
Operation	Finish face	Rough turn	Rough turn; chamfer	Rough bore	Rough bore	Chamfer
Speed, sfm(b)	152	152	146	130	136	136
Feed, ipr	0.007	0.011	0.011	0.007	0.007	0.007
Lead angle	15°	15°	30°	30°	30°	30°
Rake angle	−5°	−5°	−5°	−5°	−5°	−5°
	Tool 1 (cross slide)	Tool 3 (cross slide)	Tool 4 (cross slide)	Tool 5 (turret)	Tool 6 (turret)	Tool 8 (rear cross slide)
Second Chucking(c)						
Surface(a)	H	J	K	M	N	P
Operation	Finish face	Rough turn	Rough turn(d)	Rough bore	Chamfer	Finish bore
Speed, sfm(b)	152	152	146	130	136	138 max
Feed, ipr	0.007	0.011	0.011	0.007	0.007	0.005

Third Chucking

Ring was turned (surface Q) by holding in a full-grip cast iron jaw chuck with tool 9 mounted in a hydraulic tracer attachment on the rear of the cross slide. Tool 9 was a precision-ground carbide insert, having a 55° included angle, −10° rake angle and 3/64-in. nose radius. Tool was held by a tracer turning insert holder. Speed was 63 rpm (152 sfm max), and feed was 0.005 ipr.

NOTE: All tools used disposable carbide inserts. Tool life was one to two rings per edge except for tools that did chamfering only (tool 7 in first chucking and tool 6 in second chucking); chamfering tools lasted for six rings per edge. Production rate was two rings per hour from each of the first and second chuckings, and four rings per hour from the third chucking. Cutting fluid was a soluble-oil emulsion (5 parts water to 1 part soluble oil) for all operations.

(a) Letters are correlated with those indicating machined surfaces in the above sketches. (b) Values are approximate maximums for spindle speed of 63 rpm. (c) Tool details are the same as for tools used in first chucking, except for tool 8, which was the same as tool 9 used in third chucking. (d) Also used to chamfer surfaces D and L, at feed of 0.007 ipr.

Fig. 32. Machined ring forging, and sequence of operations, tool details and operating details for machining it in three chuckings and 14 operations in a turret lathe (Example 842)

rings were held on the outside and inside diameters in a three-jaw chuck, using full-grip jaws. All of the tooling employed negative rake, disposable carbide inserts. Except for the tracer turning tool, all *original* tools had a +5° rake angle. With these tools, feeds were the same as those shown in the table below Fig. 32, but spindle speed was only 15 rpm. Changing tools to a −5° rake angle permitted a spindle speed of 63 rpm, without sacrificing tool life, and reduced machining time per piece to about a quarter of that required when speed was 15 rpm. Because negative-rake inserts offered twice the number of cutting edges at 75% of the cost of positive-rake inserts, cost per cutting edge was reduced to 37½% of that for the original tooling. Tool life was one to two rings per edge, except for the tools that did chamfering only (tool 7 in the first chucking and tool 6 in the second). Life of these tools was six rings per edge.

A hydraulic tracer attachment was employed, because it provided the only practical means for generating the contours in accordance with surface-finish requirements (63 micro-in. on outside surfaces and 30 micro-in. on inside surfaces). Form tools were not used, because the cost of regrinding would have been prohibitive and power requirements would have exceeded the 20 hp available. Two rings per hour were machined in chuckings 1 and 2, whereas four rings per hour were machined in the third chucking. The sequence of operations, tool details, and machining conditions are given in the table accompanying Fig. 32.

Example 843. Machining A-286 Turbine Disks in an Eight-Spindle Automatic Chucking Machine (Fig. 33)

First-stage turbine disks 12¼ in. in diameter, forged from A-286, were partially machined in an eight-spindle vertical chucking machine. The disk forging (Fig. 33) was reduced in weight from 43 to 30 lb in seven machining stations, using 19 cutting operations. (Loading and unloading were done at the first station.) Hardness of the forgings was 277 to 341 Bhn (Rockwell C 28 to 36). The order of operations and the machining data are with Fig. 33.

Milling

Climb milling is generally preferred to conventional milling if suitable equipment is available. Climb milling requires the ultimate in rigidity and a machine equipped with a backlash eliminator. However, cuts deeper than 0.060 in. are seldom attempted with climb milling of heat-resisting alloys, because it is virtually impossible to obtain the required rigidity.

Cutter Design. For milling heat-resisting alloys, two principles of cutter design must be given special consideration: Tooth strength must be greater than that required for milling steel or cast iron; and relief angles must be large enough to prevent rubbing action and consequent work hardening of the alloy being cut.

Regardless of the cutter material, inserted blades are used on nearly all but the smallest cutters, because even under the most favorable machining conditions, the life of cutting edges is short. Mechanical methods of securing the blades in the cutter body are preferred, because replacement of chipped or broken blades is easier.

Cutter life can sometimes be greatly increased by small design changes, as demonstrated in the next two examples.

Example 844. Serrated vs Straight End Mills for Profile Milling of Waspaloy (Fig. 34)

Waspaloy rings 46 in. in diameter were profile milled on the outside with a conventional cutter made of M3, class 2, high speed steel and with a serrated cutter made of the same material. Both tools are shown in Fig. 34.

Using the conventional cutter, four roughing cuts and one finishing cut were necessary to remove the required amount of metal. Total machining time was 12½ hr. Using the same speed (15 sfm) and feed (0.004 ipt), the serrated cutter removed the same amount of metal in 7½ hr, by eliminating two of the roughing passes. Given the same feed, the serrated cutter produced a thicker chip and penetrated the work-hardened layer better.

Both types of cutters required sharpening after 145 min of cutting, which produced a wear land of approximately 0.012 in. The serrated cutter was used only for roughing, because the finish produced by it was not acceptable as a final finish. However, this was not a disadvantage, because a freshly sharpened cutter had always been used for finish milling, and therefore no extra tool change was involved.

Example 845. Change of Carbide Cutter for Increased Tool Life (Fig. 35)

Chamfering the front cutting edge of the carbide tip of a 6-in.-diam face-milling cutter resulted in a 25% increase in tool life and a reduction in costs in climb milling aged Inconel X-750. The tip was of grade C-5 carbide. The improved cutter is shown in Fig. 35.

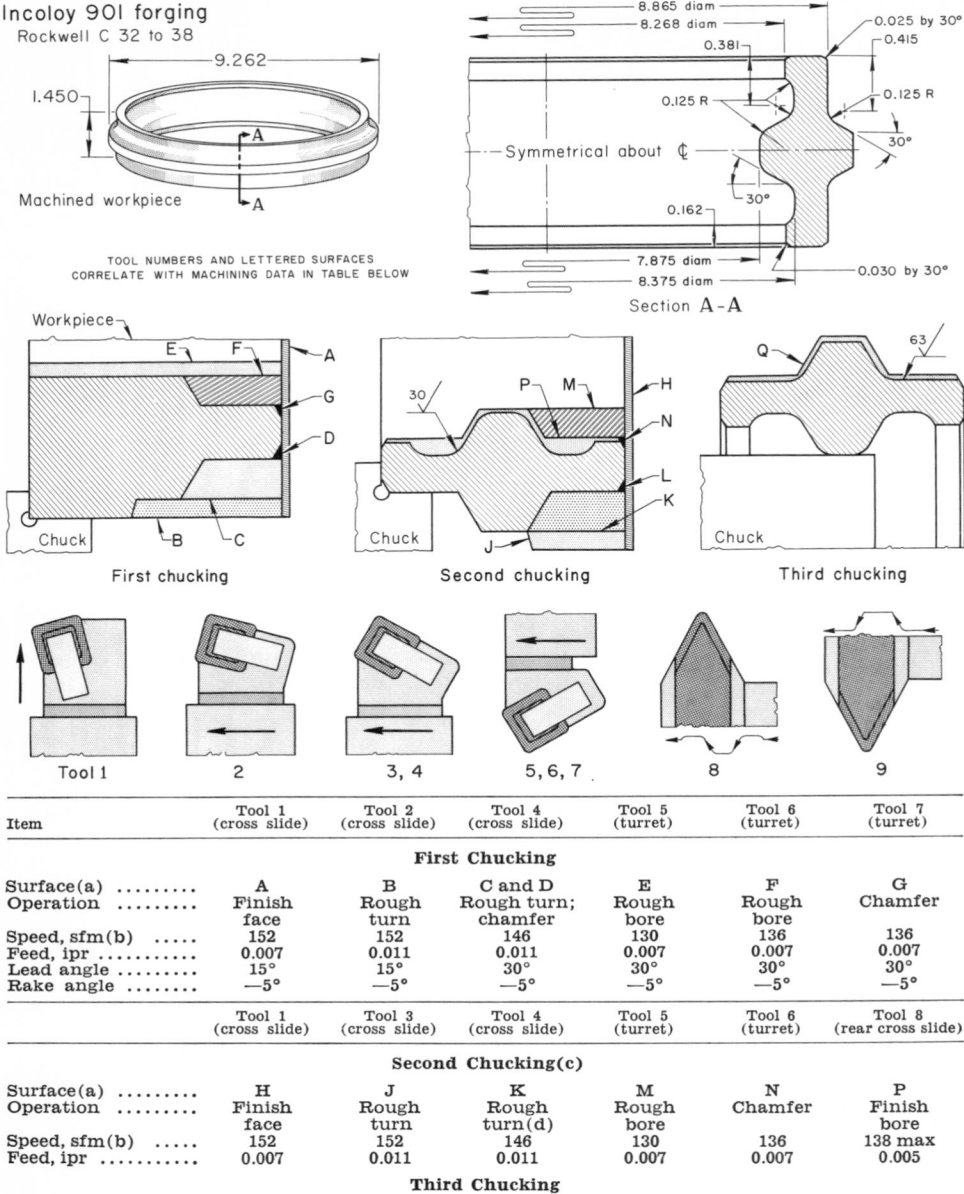

The use of a cutter that had been designed especially for climb milling, and of a soluble-oil cutting fluid (one part oil to 15 parts water), minimized cutter cratering and chiping. The major contribution to tool life, however, resulted from the chamfer (45° by 80% of feed, or 0.072 in.). The cutter was operated at a speed of 60 sfm, a feed of 0.009 ipt, and a depth of cut of 0.060 in. Width of cut was 2½ in. The cutting fluid was brushed on.

Cutter Material. High speed steel is used for cutters in most applications for milling heat-resisting alloys, but carbide is frequently superior to high speed steel in milling the more difficult-to-machine alloys, such as René 41. Small solid-carbide end mills have been used successfully in a few applications.

The more highly alloyed grades of high speed steel usually outperform the general-purpose grades, but there is less difference in performance between the two grades in milling cutters than in some other tools used for machining heat-resisting alloys.

In the first of the three examples that follow, five grades of high speed steel are compared for milling René 41. In the second, nine grades and two different speeds are compared for milling U-500. The third example compares M1 and T15 cutters for milling HS-25.

Example 846. Comparison of Five Grades of High Speed Steel for Cutters for End Milling René 41 (Table 33)

As the cutting edges of a milling cutter lose sharpness, the cutting load increases. The increase can be expressed as an increase in feed force over that originally required. In a test program on end milling of René 41 (Rockwell C 41 to 42), the feed-force increase was taken into consideration in comparing the performance of five high speed steels used in ¾-in.-diam end-milling cutters.

Table 33 shows the number of passes made at two points of feed-force increase, namely 200 lb and 300 lb. The length of each pass was 16 in., giving a metal-removal rate of 0.180 cu in. per pass. At both points, T15 gave the most satisfactory results (rated 100%).

All end mills failed by chipping, principally at the sharp corners. Sometimes, the chipping exposed a fresh cutting surface, and the end mill continued to cut without an increase (or sometimes even with a decrease) of feed force. However, finishes on surfaces that were cut by chipped edges were poor.

Example 847. Comparison of Nine Grades of High Speed Steel for Cutters for End Milling U-500 (Fig. 36)

A series of tests was conducted to compare cutter life for end mills made of cobalt-free high speed steels with those made of high speed steels containing cobalt. A nickel-base heat-resisting alloy, U-500, in the solution-treated-and-aged condition (Rockwell C 39), was milled. These tests indicated that U-500 could be end milled with reasonable tool life when *either* the cobalt-free or the more expensive cobalt-containing steels were employed. Steels of both types performed similarly at cutting speeds of 19 sfm, although at 37 sfm, two of the cobalt-containing types outperformed any cobalt-free steel tested.

Test Conditions and Methods. A conventional vertical-head milling machine (size 3) was used. The end mills were tested in making peripheral, slabbing cuts on U-500 test pieces ½ by ½ by 12 in. Five cobalt-containing high speed steels (M30, M33, M36, T5 and T15), from six manufacturers, and three cobalt-free high speed steels (M1, M2 and M7), from three manufacturers, were tested. All cutters were ½-in.-diam, four-flute, straight-shank end mills. These cutters were of conventional design, and before being tested were ground with a peripheral primary relief angle of 12° and a land width of 0.030 in.

The cuts, 0.050 in. deep, were made on the ½-by-12-in. surfaces of the test workpieces. Slabbing cuts were made because, with this type of cut, deflection could be held to a minimum and wear on the end of the cutter (which would have complicated the evaluation of tool wear) would not occur.

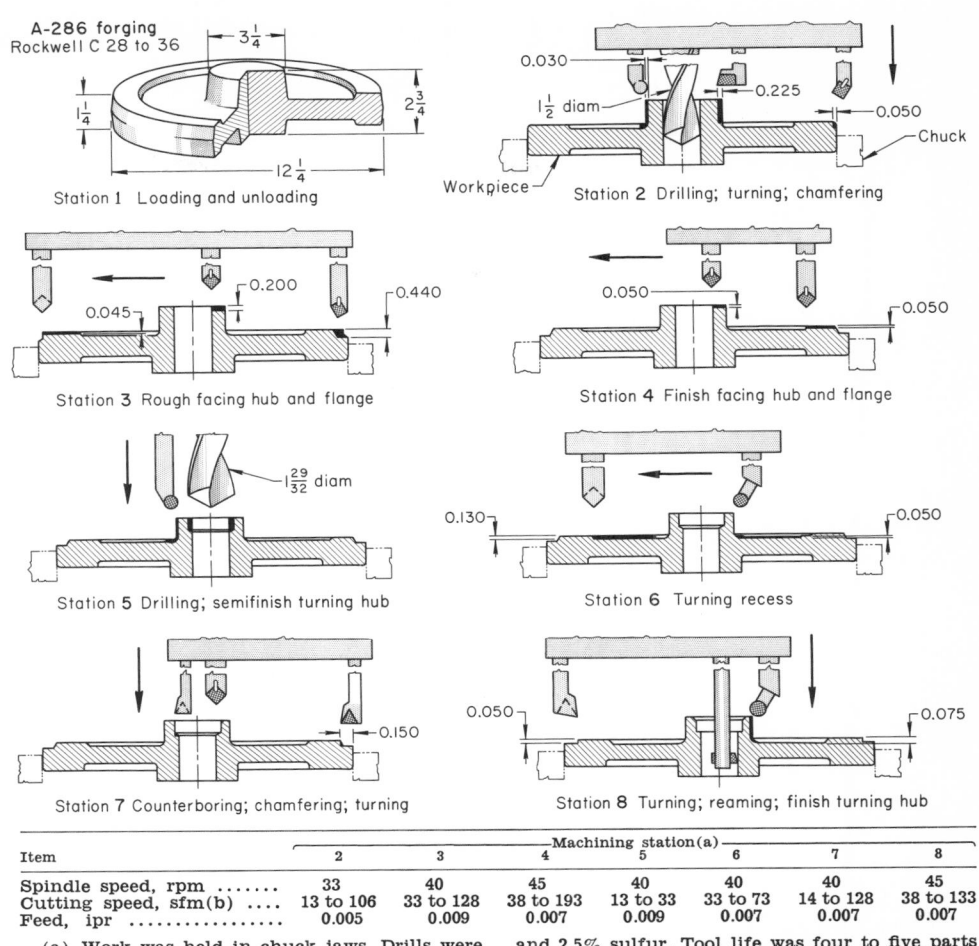

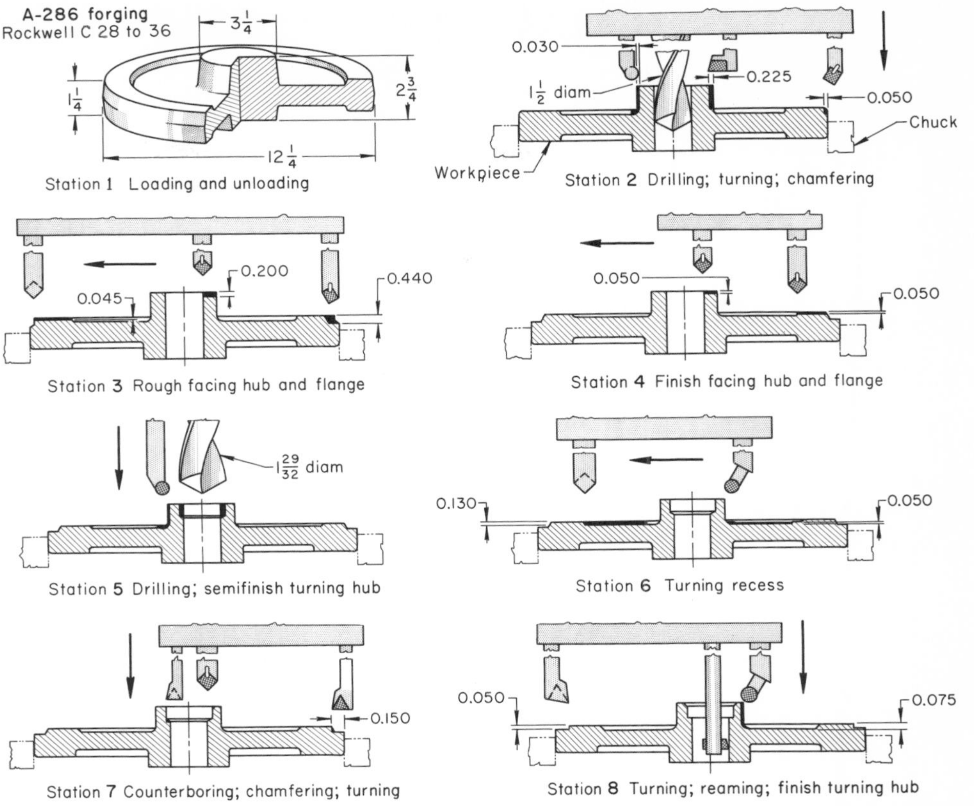

Item	Machining station(a) 2	3	4	5	6	7	8
Spindle speed, rpm	33	40	45	40	40	40	45
Cutting speed, sfm(b)	13 to 106	33 to 128	38 to 193	13 to 33	33 to 73	14 to 128	38 to 133
Feed, ipr	0.005	0.009	0.007	0.009	0.007	0.007	0.007

(a) Work was held in chuck jaws. Drills were made of M3 high speed steel; other tools were made with C-2 carbide disposable inserts. Cutting fluid was mineral oil with 12.25% lard oil and 2.5% sulfur. Tool life was four to five parts per edge, and total machining time was 18 min per piece. (b) Ranges for operations in the respective stations.

Fig. 33. Turning, facing, drilling, reaming, counterboring and chamfering turbine disk forging in an eight-spindle automatic chucking machine (Example 843)

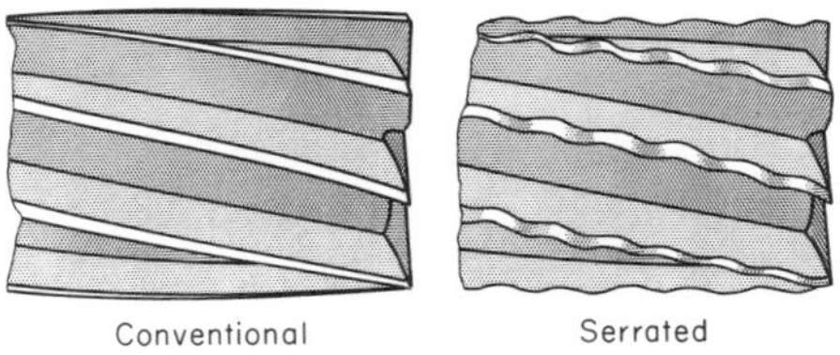

Fig. 34. Two types of high speed steel end mills used in profile milling of Waspaloy rings (Example 844)

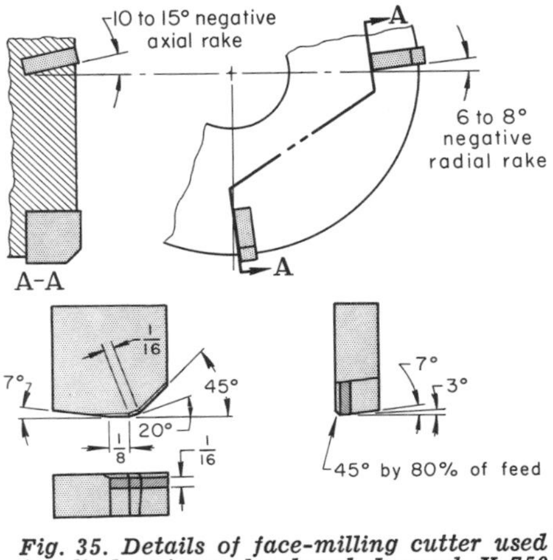

Fig. 35. Details of face-milling cutter used to climb-cut age-hardened Inconel X-750 (Example 845)

Table 33. Service Life of Five High Speed Steel Cutters in End Milling René 41 Hardened to Rockwell C 41 to 42 (Example 846)

Tool steel grade	Hardness, Rockwell C	Average life at feed-force increase of: 200 lb — Passes completed(a)	200 lb — Converted to %	300 lb — Passes completed(a)	300 lb — Converted to %
M3	65.5	3.2	46	3.8(b)	44
M7	65.2	5.2	75	8.7	100
M10	65.2	5.3	77	6.3	72
M36	65.5	5.2	75	7.1(c)	82
T15	67.2	6.9	100	8.7	100

(a) Length of each pass was 16 in., giving a removal rate of 0.180 cu in. per pass. Depth of cut was 0.015 in.; ¾-in. four-flute end mills. Speed was 97 rpm (19 sfm); feed, 1⅛ ipm (0.0029 ipt). (b) Estimated. (c) One tool only.

The unsupported length of each end mill (between the cutter holder and the workpiece) was held constant; other cutting conditions were as follows: climb cut; cutting speeds, 19 and 37 sfm; feed, 0.0027 ipt; depth of cut, 0.050 in.; width of cut, 0.5 in. A soluble-oil cutting fluid (one part oil to 20 parts water) was used in all tests. Cutter life was recorded in terms of work travel (in inches) up to the development of a 0.010-in. average wear land. Results reported are from three separate tests on each tool material at each of the two cutting speeds (19 and 37 sfm).

Test Results. In the top chart of Fig. 36, cutters are ranked in accordance with their tool life at the 19-sfm cutting speed. For all tool steels tested, life of the individual cutters decreased at 37 sfm; this decrease ranged from 4 in. of work travel for the M33 high speed steel cutters to 33 in. for the M2.

Table 34. Nominal Speeds and Feeds for Face Milling Heat-Resisting Alloys With High Speed Steel Cutters

Alloy group(a)	Condition(b)	Brinell hardness	For 0.150-in. depth: Speed, sfm	For 0.150-in. depth: Feed, ipt	For 0.025-in. depth: Speed, sfm	For 0.025-in. depth: Feed, ipt	HSS tool steel(c)
Fe Wrt	ST	180 to 230	50	0.007	65	0.005	M2, M7
	ST, A	250 to 320	50	0.006	65	0.004	T15, M33
Ni Wrt 1	Ann or ST	200 to 300	20	0.006	25	0.004	T15, M33
	ST, A	300 to 400	20	0.005	25	0.003	T15, M33
Ni Wrt 2	Ann	140 to 220	50	0.006	65	0.004	M2, M7
	CD	240 to 310	50	0.005	65	0.003	T15, M33
Co Wrt	ST	180 to 230	25	0.006	35	0.004	T15, M33
	ST, A	270 to 320	25	0.005	35	0.003	T15, M33
HR Cst 1	AC	160 to 210	75	0.010	100	0.008	M2, M7
HR Cst 2	AC	160 to 210	60	0.010	80	0.008	M2, M7

(a) See Table 2 for alloys in each group. (b) ST = Solution treated; A = Aged; Ann = Annealed; CD = Cold drawn; AC = As cast. (c) Cutter design: 10° axial and radial rake angles, 45° corner angle, 5° end cutting-edge angle, and 10° end and peripheral relief angles.

Table 35. Nominal Speeds and Feeds for Face Milling Heat-Resisting Alloys With Carbide Cutters(a)

Alloy group(b)	Condition(c)	Brinell hardness	For 0.150-in. depth: Speed (sfm) for: Brazed	For 0.150-in. depth: Speed (sfm) for: Disposable	For 0.150-in. depth: Feed, ipt	For 0.025-in. depth: Speed (sfm) for: Brazed	For 0.025-in. depth: Speed (sfm) for: Disposable	For 0.025-in. depth: Feed, ipt
Fe Wrt	ST	180 to 230	100	110	0.007	120	130	0.005
	ST, A	250 to 320	100	110	0.006	120	130	0.005
Ni Wrt 1	Ann or ST	200 to 300	50	55	0.006	60	65	0.005
	ST, A	300 to 400	50	55	0.006	60	65	0.005
Ni Wrt 2	Ann	140 to 220	100	110	0.006	120	130	0.005
	CD	240 to 310	100	110	0.006	120	130	0.005
Ni Cast	AC	250 to 350	30	35	0.005	35	40	0.005
Co Wrt	ST	180 to 230	60	65	0.006	70	80	0.005
	ST, A	270 to 320	60	65	0.006	70	80	0.005
Co Cast	AC	220 to 290	30	35	0.005	35	40	0.005
HR Cst 1	AC	160 to 210	350	385	0.012	465	510	0.010
HR Cst 2	AC	160 to 210	300	330	0.012	400	440	0.010

(a) C-2 grade. (b) See Table 2 for alloys in each group. (c) ST = Solution treated; A = Aged; Ann = Annealed; CD = Cold drawn; AC = As cast.

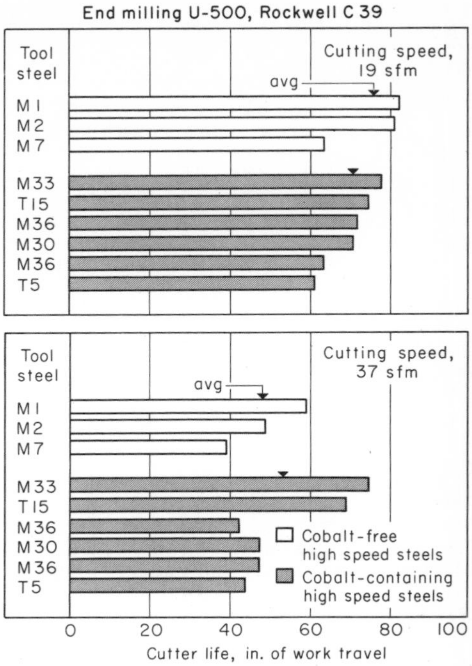

Fig. 36. Cutter life (to 0.010-in. wear land) of cobalt-free and cobalt-containing high speed steel, four-flute end mills at two cutting speeds. Each rating represents the average of three tests. (Example 847)

Table 36. Nominal Speeds and Feeds for Peripheral (Slab) Milling Heat-Resisting Alloys With High Speed Steel Cutters

Alloy group(a)	Condition(b)	Brinell hardness	For 0.150-in. depth: Speed, sfm	For 0.150-in. depth: Feed, ipt	For 0.025-in. depth: Speed, sfm	For 0.025-in. depth: Feed, ipt	HSS tool steel
Fe Wrt	ST	180 to 230	30	0.008	35	0.005	M2, M7
	ST, A	250 to 320	20	0.008	30	0.005	T15, M33
Ni Wrt 1	Ann or ST	200 to 300	20	0.005	25	0.003	T15, M33
	ST, A	300 to 400	20	0.005	25	0.003	T15, M33
Ni Wrt 2	Ann	140 to 220	40	0.006	55	0.004	M2, M7
	CD	240 to 310	30	0.006	40	0.004	T15, M33
Co Wrt	ST	180 to 230	20	0.005	25	0.003	T15, M33
	ST, A	270 to 320	30	0.008	35	0.005	M2, M7
HR Cst 1	AC	160 to 210	80	0.010	100	0.008	M2, M7
HR Cst 2	AC	160 to 210	65	0.010	80	0.008	M2, M7

(a) See Table 2 for alloys in each group. (b) ST = Solution treated; A = Aged; Ann = Annealed; CD = Cold drawn; AC = As cast.

At a cutting speed of 19 sfm, the average life for all cobalt-containing cutters was 70.5 in., whereas at the same speed the average life of cobalt-free cutters was somewhat higher (75.7 in.). At the 37-sfm cutting speed, however, the average life of cobalt-containing cutters (53.7 in.) exceeded the average life for cobalt-free cutters (48.7 in.).

Example 848. M1 vs T15 for End Milling HS-25

The tool life of M1 and T15 end mill cutters, based on 0.010-in. wear land, was compared in milling HS-25 (L-605) alloy (Rockwell B 97). Cutters were of the same diameter (1 in.) and were operated at the same speed (20 sfm) and feed (0.0025 ipt) to produce the same depth (0.100 in.), width (1 in.), and length (2 in.) of cut. A sulfurized oil was used as the cutting fluid in all tests. Under these conditions, the tool life to 0.010-in. wear land for M1 cutters was only 45 min, whereas the tool life of T15 cutters was 120 min. Relatively minor differences in the design of the two types of cutters were as follows:

	M1	T15
Tangential rake angle	17°	10°
Relief angle	10°	8°
Web thickness, in.	0.600	0.645

Speed, Feed and Depth of Cut. Nominal speeds and feeds for face, slab, end, and hollow milling of heat-resisting alloys are given in Tables 34 to 39. Speeds listed in these tables assume that the operations are conducted under conditions of best practice — that is, adequate rigidity in the setup, optimum tool angles, and a plentiful supply of cutting fluid.

When one or more factors are less favorable in a specific application (such as excessive work-metal hardness or inadequate rigidity), speed must be reduced. In some applications it is necessary to mill nickel-base and cobalt-base alloys at speeds as low as 5 sfm for acceptable tool life.

Optimum feed in inch per tooth (ipt) depends primarily on the type of milling operation and the depth of cut. Rough face milling of heat-resisting alloys at feeds of 0.007 to 0.012 ipt is common. This rate of feed is usually decreased for finishing cuts, as shown in Tables 34 and 35. Feeds used for peripheral or slab milling do not differ greatly from those used for face milling (Table 36).

Feeds used for end milling are necessarily less than those used for face and peripheral milling, because of the inherent lack of rigidity in end milling. In addition to depth of cut, the size of cutter is a significant variable influencing optimum feed in end milling. Nominal feeds for end milling, covering a range of cutter sizes, are given in Tables 37 and 38. Feeds used for hollow milling are affected to some extent by work-metal composition and hardness, although speed and tool material have an even greater influence on selection of feed (Table 39).

Depths of cut for rough face and peripheral (slab) milling are usually in the range of 0.060 to 0.100 in., although depths of cut as high as 0.150 in. are used. Availability of sufficient power is frequently a factor in limiting the depth of cut. Data given in Tables 34 to 36 for rough milling are based on 0.150-in. depth of cut. Finish face or peripheral milling is usually done with a depth of cut of 0.025 in. or less, depending to some extent on the required surface finish. To minimize transverse streaks and to obtain the best surface finish, depth of cut often ranges from 0.005 to 0.015 in. Depth of cut less than 0.005 in. is not recommended, because it is likely to result in excessive work hardening of the alloy being milled.

For end milling, depths of cut up to 0.050 in. for roughing and from 0.005 to 0.015 in. for finishing are common (Tables 37 and 38).

Cutting Fluid. Sulfochlorinated oil introduced in copious amounts at the exhaust side of the cutter is the preferred condition for milling heat-resisting alloys. Soluble-oil emulsions are often used (Examples 845 and 847), and they provide better cooling for the tools and workpieces than straight oils. However, some sacrifice in surface finish and tool life attends the use of soluble-oil emulsions, compared with sulfochlorinated oils. The latter are often diluted with mineral oil (up to 50%) to obtain fluidity with no large sacrifice in ability to promote cutting

Table 37. Nominal Speeds and Feeds for End Milling Heat-Resisting Alloys With High Speed Steel Cutters(a)

Alloy group(b)	Condi-tion(c)	Brinell hardness	For 0.050-in. depth: Speed, sfm	Feed (ipt) for diameter (in.) of: 0.250	0.500	0.750	1.0 to 2.0	For 0.015-in. depth: Speed, sfm	Feed (ipt) for diameter (in.) of: 0.250	0.500	0.750	1.0 to 2.0
Fe Wrt	ST	180 to 230	30	0.002	0.002	0.003	0.004	40	0.001	0.001	0.002	0.002
	ST, A	250 to 320	20	0.002	0.002	0.003	0.004	30	0.001	0.001	0.002	0.002
Ni Wrt 1	Ann or ST	200 to 300	15	0.002	0.002	0.003	0.004	25	0.001	0.001	0.002	0.002
	ST, A	300 to 400	12	0.0015	0.0015	0.002	0.003	20	0.0005	0.001	0.0015	0.002
Ni Wrt 2	Ann	140 to 220	40	0.002	0.002	0.003	0.004	55	0.001	0.001	0.002	0.002
	CD	240 to 310	30	0.002	0.002	0.003	0.004	40	0.001	0.001	0.002	0.002
Ni Cast	AC	250 to 350	10	0.0015	0.0015	0.002	0.003	15	0.0005	0.001	0.0015	0.002
Co Wrt	ST	180 to 230	20	0.002	0.002	0.003	0.004	25	0.001	0.001	0.002	0.002
	ST, A	270 to 320	15	0.0015	0.0015	0.002	0.003	20	0.0005	0.001	0.0015	0.002
Co Cast	AC	220 to 290	10	0.0015	0.0015	0.002	0.003	15	0.0005	0.001	0.0015	0.002
HR Cst 1	AC	160 to 210	60	0.001	0.002	0.004	0.005	80	0.0007	0.0015	0.003	0.004
HR Cst 2	AC	160 to 210	45	0.001	0.002	0.004	0.005	60	0.0007	0.0015	0.003	0.004

(a) T15 except for HR Cst 1 and 2, for which either M2 or M7 is recommended. As alternatives to T15, the following may be used: M33, M41, M42, M43 and M44. Cutter design: 35° helix angle, 15° radial rake, 3° end cutting-edge angle, 3° to 7° end relief angle, 10° peripheral relief. (b) See Table 2 for alloys in each group. (c) ST = Solution treated; A = Aged; Ann = Annealed; CD = Cold drawn; AC = As cast.

Table 38. Nominal Speeds and Feeds for End Milling Heat-Resisting Alloys With Carbide Cutters(a)

Alloy group(b)	Condi-tion(c)	Brinell hardness	For 0.050-in. depth: Speed, sfm	Feed (ipt) for diameter (in.) of: 0.250	0.500	0.750	1.0 to 2.0	For 0.015-in. depth: Speed, sfm	Feed (ipt) for diameter (in.) of: 0.250	0.500	0.750	1.0 to 2.0
Fe Wrt	ST	180 to 230	95	0.001	0.002	0.003	0.004	140	0.001	0.001	0.002	0.002
	ST, A	250 to 320	60	0.001	0.002	0.003	0.004	75	0.001	0.001	0.002	0.002
Ni Wrt 1	Ann or ST	200 to 300	50	0.001	0.002	0.003	0.004	70	0.001	0.001	0.002	0.002
	ST, A	300 to 400	40	0.0015	0.0015	0.002	0.003	60	0.0005	0.001	0.0015	0.002
Ni Wrt 2	Ann	140 to 220	110	0.001	0.002	0.003	0.004	165	0.001	0.001	0.002	0.002
	CD	240 to 310	90	0.001	0.002	0.003	0.004	165	0.001	0.001	0.002	0.002
Ni Cast	AC	250 to 350	30	0.0015	0.0015	0.002	0.003	40	0.0005	0.001	0.0015	0.002
Co Wrt	ST	180 to 230	60	0.001	0.002	0.003	0.004	75	0.001	0.001	0.002	0.002
	ST, A	270 to 320	50	0.0015	0.0015	0.002	0.003	65	0.0005	0.001	0.0015	0.002
Co Cast	AC	220 to 290	30	0.0015	0.0015	0.002	0.003	40	0.0005	0.001	0.0015	0.002
HR Cst 1	AC	160 to 210	300	0.002	0.0025	0.005	0.006	390	0.001	0.002	0.004	0.005
HR Cst 2	AC	160 to 210	250	0.002	0.0025	0.005	0.006	325	0.001	0.002	0.004	0.005

(a) C-2 grade. (b) See Table 2 for alloys in each group. (c) ST = Solution treated; A = Aged; Ann = Annealed; CD = Cold drawn; AC = As cast.

action and good surface finish. Workpieces milled with sulfochlorinated or other chemically active oils must be thoroughly cleaned before being heat treated or before being placed in service at elevated temperature.

Table 39. Nominal Speeds and Feeds for Hollow Milling Heat-Resisting Alloys
(Based on 0.125-in. width of cut using a four-tooth hollow milling cutter)

Alloy group(a)	Condi-tion(b)	Brinell hardness	High speed steel tools: Speed, sfm	Feed, ipr	Tool steel	Grade C-2 carbide tools: Speed, sfm	Feed, ipr
Fe Wrt	ST	180 to 230	25	0.004	M2, M7	80	0.008
	ST, A	250 to 320	20	0.003	T15, M33	65	0.006
Ni Wrt 1	Ann or ST	200 to 300	10	0.003	M2, M7	40	0.006
	ST, A	300 to 400	10	0.003	T15, M33	40	0.006
Ni Wrt 2	Ann	140 to 220	40	0.004	M2, M7	110	0.008
	CD	240 to 310	30	0.003	M2, M7	90	0.006
Ni Cast	AC	250 to 350	10	0.003	T15, M33	40	0.006
Co Wrt	ST	180 to 230	15	0.004	M2, M7	70	0.008
	ST	270 to 320	10	0.003	T15, M33	40	0.006
Co Cast	AC	220 to 290	10	0.003	T15, M33	40	0.006
HR Cst 1	AC	160 to 210	55	0.006	M2, M7	235	0.016
HR Cst 2	AC	160 to 210	50	0.006	M2, M7	200	0.016

(a) See Table 2 for alloys in each group. (b) ST = Solution treated; A = Aged; Ann = Annealed; CD = Cold drawn; AC = As cast.

Sawing

Because of their applications, heat-resisting alloys are less frequently machined by sawing than by most other processes.

Band Sawing. Nominal pitches (teeth per inch) and speeds for power band sawing of several groups of heat-resisting alloys are given in Table 40, which shows that speed depends mainly on composition and hardness, whereas pitch depends on the thickness of metal sawed. (See also Table 7, page 222.)

Table 40. Nominal Pitches and Speeds for Power Band Sawing Heat-Resisting Alloys With High Speed Steel Blades

Alloy group(a)	Condi-tion(b)	Brinell hardness	Pitch (teeth per in.) for material thickness (in.) of: Up to 0.250	0.250 to 1.500	Over 1.500	Speed, sfm
Fe Wrt	ST	180 to 230	6 to 8	4 to 6	2.5 to 4	80
	ST, A	250 to 320	6 to 8	4 to 6	2.5 to 4	70
Ni Wrt 1	Ann or ST	200 to 300	6 to 8	4 to 6	2.5 to 4	60
	ST, A	300 to 400	6 to 8	4 to 6	2.5 to 4	45
Ni Wrt 2	CD	140 to 310	6 to 8	4 to 6	2.5 to 4	75
Co Wrt	ST	180 to 230	6 to 8	4 to 6	2.5 to 4	70
	ST, A	270 to 320	6 to 8	4 to 6	2.5 to 4	50
HR Cst 1 and 2	AC	160 to 210	8 to 10	6 to 8	3 to 6	135

(a) See Table 2 for alloys in each group. (b) ST = Solution treated; A = Aged; Ann = Annealed; CD = Cold drawn; AC = As cast.

The effect of band speed on tool life and over-all cost is shown in the following tabulation for cutoff band sawing of bars of A-286 (Rockwell C 35) 1½ in. thick with a high speed steel band:

Band speed, sfm	Band life, sq in. cut	Cost per sq in. cut
70	168	$0.21
90	60	0.45

The sawing comparison was made at a hydraulically controlled feed rate of 1.0 ipm for a cutting rate of 1.5 sq in. per minute, with flow application of a 1-to-1 mixture of sulfurized and mineral oils. The 15-ft-long saw band was 1-in. wide, 0.035-in. thick, regular tooth, raker set, 4-pitch, with 0.060-in. set dimension. The over-all machining cost was based on a band cost of $22.10, tool change cost of $0.58, and operating cost of $0.116 per minute. Although increasing band speed from 70 to 90 sfm resulted in higher over-all sawing cost, as shown above, decreasing band speed substantially below 70 sfm could also give higher over-all cost; feed rate, too, can influence sawing-cost comparisons.

The two examples that follow compare sawing conditions for various heat-resisting alloys. In Example 849, a nickel-base (Inconel X-750), a cobalt-base (HS-25), and an iron-base (A-286) alloy are compared, and in Example 850, two nickel-base alloys are compared with a cobalt-base alloy.

Example 849 and 850. Band Sawing Heat-Resisting Alloys

Example 849 (Table 41). When 1½-in.-thick sections of alloy A-286, Inconel X-750, and HS-25 were machined on a band saw, the cutting rate and tool life data shown in Table 41 were obtained. For the alloys under comparison, metal composition had a greater effect on cutting rate and tool life than did hardness or tensile strength. The cobalt-base alloy was the most difficult to saw and resulted in the shortest tool life, despite its lower hardness and strength.

Table 41. Effect of Composition of Heat-Resisting Alloys in Band Sawing (Example 849) (a)

Item	Inconel X-750 (160,000 psi; Rockwell C 35)	HS-25 (L-605) (136,500 psi; Rockwell C 24)	A-286 (163,500 psi; Rockwell C 35)
Sawing Conditions			
Band speed, sfm ..	66	65	70
Feed, ipm	0.80	0.80	1.0
Area cut, sq in.(b) .	6.0	6.0	6.0
Cutting Rate and Tool Life			
Rate, sq in./min ..	1.2	1.0	1.5
Tool life:			
Area cut, sq in. .	246.0	164.0	168.0
Number of cuts .	41	27	28
Wear land, in.(c) .	0.030	0.030	0.030
Cost per sq in. cut	$0.25	$0.31	$0.20

(a) All alloys were sawed with high speed steel bands 1 in. wide, 4-pitch regular tooth form, and raker set. Bands used on Inconel X-750 and HS-25 were 0.032 in. thick; bands used on A-286 were 0.035 in. thick. Cutting fluid was a 1-to-1 mixture of sulfurized oil and mineral oil. (b) Cuts were 1½ by 4 in. (c) Point at which resharpening or replacement was considered economical in attainment of acceptable finish or cutting efficiency.

The low feed (0.80 ipm) and slow speed (66 sfm) employed in band sawing Inconel X-750 closely approximated those used in sawing hardened steel at Rockwell C 47 in Fig. 2 in the article "Cutoff Band Sawing". However, the nickel-base alloy at Rockwell C 35 was appreciably softer than the heat treated steel. Thus, factors other than hardness are significant for machinability in sawing.

The cobalt-base alloy HS-25 was sawed at essentially the same feed and speed employed for Inconel X-750. The lower machinability of HS-25 is probably caused by its higher rate of work hardening.

Example 850. Two nickel-base alloys (Hastelloy X and René 41) and one cobalt-base alloy (HS-25) were sawed. For sheet metal up to 0.060 in. thick, a speed of 50 to 60 sfm max was used with a manual feed at average to maximum force. Hard-edged low-carbon steel bands were used (¼ to ⅜ in. wide, 32-pitch, wavy set), and no cutting fluid. Band life (in linear inches cut) on sheet 0.040 to 0.060 in. thick was as follows:

Hastelloy X (Rockwell C 20) ......36 to 48 in.
HS-25 (Rockwell C 25) ....16 to 20
René 41 (Rockwell C 28) ....100 to 125

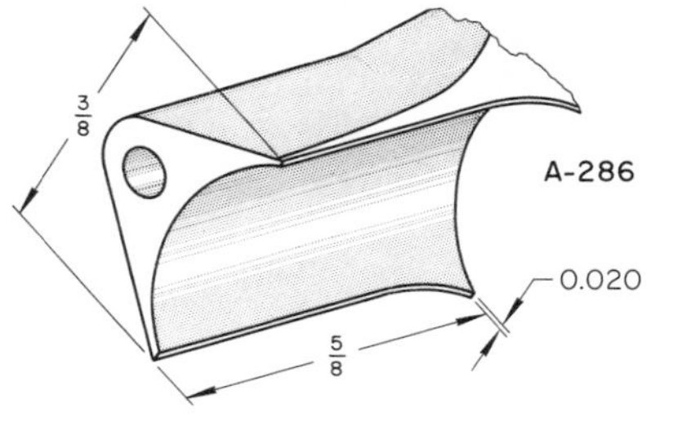

Fig. 37. Shape of bucket produced in turbine rotor by electrical discharge machining (Example 851)

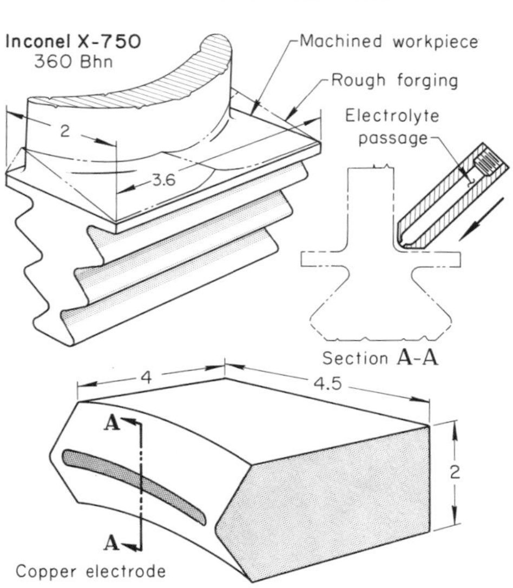

Machine	3000-amp capacity
Electrode	Copper, conforming
Current, amp	3000
Speed	0.060 ipm
Number of cuts	1
Length of cut	½ in.
Cycle time, per piece	15 min

Phantom lines in upper figure denote metal removed from platform area. Lower figure shows size and shape of electrode used, and its position during machining.

Fig. 38. Electrochemical machining of turbine blades (Example 852)

For plate or bar stock, a band speed of 25 to 50 sfm and a mechanical feed of 3 to 5 ipm were used. A high speed steel band (½ to 1 in. wide, 10-pitch, raker set) was preferred. Cutting fluid was soluble oil. When 1¾-in.-thick René 41 was band sawed, the best tool life obtained was 60 linear inches.

Circular Sawing and Slitting. Nominal pitches, speeds and feeds for circular sawing and slitting are presented in Table 42. Diameter or thickness of the work metal is the only variable affecting pitch and is the major variable affecting speed and feed, although work-metal composition and hardness also have some effect.

Hacksawing. Nominal speeds and feeds for power hacksawing are given in Table 43. As stated in the footnotes of Table 43, pitch of the saw is varied in accordance with work-metal thickness. Work-metal composition and condition are significant factors in the selection of speed and feed.

Cutting Fluids. Moderate-duty to heavy-duty chemical emulsions are widely used and are generally recommended as cutting fluids for sawing heat-resisting alloys. Plain soluble-oil emulsions have also provided satisfactory results. Regardless of the type of cutting fluid used, a plentiful supply at the area being sawed is important.

Electrical Discharge and Electrochemical Machining

Interest in special methods such as electrical discharge machining (EDM) and electrochemical machining (ECM) stemmed originally from their ability to remove metal that could not be removed by conventional cutting tools, or that could not be removed efficiently. Both EDM and ECM processes are useful production techniques in the machining of heat-resisting alloys, as illustrated by the three examples that follow. See also pages 227 to 240.

Example 851. Electrical Discharge Machining of A-286 Turbine Rotor Buckets (Fig. 37)

Seventy-six buckets of the size and shape shown in Fig. 37 were machined in the outer periphery of each turbine rotor by the electrical discharge method.

To produce the contour shown, a shaped electrode formed the outside contour, and a pin electrode formed the hole, which was blind and extended for a distance of about half the length of the machined bucket. Buckets were machined on a four-station machine that drew a total of 60 amp, split four ways so that 15 amp were supplied to each station. The dielectric fluid (two parts dielec-

Table 42. Nominal Pitches, Speeds and Feeds for Circular Sawing and Slitting of Heat-Resisting Alloys With High Speed Steel Saws (a)

Alloy group(b)	Condition(c)	Brinell hardness	Diameter or thickness of solid stock, in.: ¼ to 3	3 to 6	6 to 9	9 to 15
Saw Pitch, In.(d)						
All	All	.... ..	0.20 to 0.65	0.60 to 0.95	0.90 to 1.15	1.10 to 1.55
Cutting Speed, Sfm						
Fe Wrt	ST	180 to 230 ..	25	20	15	10
	ST, A	250 to 320 ..	20	20	15	10
Ni Wrt 1	Ann or ST	200 to 300 ..	15	10	7	5
	ST, A	300 to 400 ..	15	10	7	5
Ni Wrt 2	Ann	140 to 220 ..	30	25	20	15
	CD	240 to 310 ..	25	20	15	10
Co Wrt	ST	180 to 230 ..	20	15	15	10
	ST, A	270 to 320 ..	15	10	10	7
HR Cst 1 and 2	AC or Ann	140 to 210 ..	35	30	25	20
Feed, Ipm						
Fe Wrt	ST	180 to 230 ..	1.00 to 3.00	0.75 to 2.50	0.75 to 2.00	0.50 to 1.00
	ST,A	250 to 320 ..	1.00 to 3.00	0.75 to 2.50	0.75 to 2.00	0.50 to 1.00
Ni Wrt 1	Ann or ST	200 to 300 ..	0.75 to 2.50	0.75 to 2.00	0.50 to 1.00	0.50 to 1.00
	ST, A	300 to 400 ..	0.75 to 2.50	0.75 to 2.00	0.50 to 1.00	0.50 to 1.00
Ni Wrt 2	Ann	140 to 220 ..	1.00 to 3.00	0.75 to 2.50	0.75 to 2.00	0.50 to 1.00
	CD	240 to 310 ..	1.00 to 3.00	0.75 to 2.50	0.75 to 2.00	0.50 to 1.00
Co Wrt	ST	180 to 230 ..	0.75 to 2.50	0.75 to 2.00	0.50 to 1.00	0.50 to 1.00
	ST, A	270 to 320 ..	0.75 to 2.50	0.75 to 2.00	0.50 to 1.00	0.50 to 1.00
HR Cst 1 and 2	AC or Ann	140 to 210 ..	2.00 to 4.00	1.50 to 3.00	1.00 to 2.00	0.75 to 1.50

(a) Metal slitting includes cutters up to 8 in. in diameter. Circular sawing normally includes cutters larger than 8 in. in diameter.
(b) See Table 2 for alloys in each group. (c) ST = Solution treated; A = Aged; Ann = Annealed; CD = Cold drawn; AC = As cast. (d) Tooth-to-tooth distance, in inches.

Table 43. Nominal Speeds and Feeds for Power Hacksawing of Heat-Resisting Alloys With High Speed Steel Blades (a)

Alloy group(b)	Brinell hardness	Speed, strokes per min	Feed, in. per stroke
Fe Wrt	180 to 230	50	0.005
	250 to 320	40	0.005
Ni Wrt 1	200 to 300	35	0.006
	300 to 400	20	0.004
Ni Wrt 2	140 to 310	40	0.006
Co Wrt	180 to 230	40	0.006
	270 to 320	25	0.003
HR Cst 1 and 2	160 to 210	70	0.006

(a) Speeds and feeds for all materials in all conditions are given for saws with pitches as follows: 10-pitch (teeth per inch) for material up to ¾ in. thick (except 19-pitch for Co Wrt from ¼ to ¾ in.), 6-pitch for thickness of ¾ to 2 in., and 4-pitch for 2 in. and over. (b) See Table 2 for alloys in each group.

tric oil and one part silicone fluid) was fed through the hollow-pin portion of the electrode. The fluid flushed chips out of the gap between electrode and work metal, and provided the medium for electrical discharge. A roughing pass requiring 11 min was followed by a 4-min finishing pass to complete the bucket shape. At this rate each of the four stations completed a 76-bucket rotor in approximately 19 hr.

Surface finish after electrical discharge machining ranged from 250 to 300 micro-in. A finish of 125 micro-in. (or better) was required. Final finish requirements were obtained by blasting the machined rotor with aluminum oxide and then electropolishing.

Example 852. Electrochemical Machining of Platform Area of Inconel X-750 Turbine Blades (Fig. 38)

Electrochemical machining was selected as the method for developing the platform area shown in Fig. 38 on forged turbine blades of aged Inconel X-750 (360 Bhn). The blades (in a holding fixture) were placed in a 3000-amp ECM unit, together with a copper electrode formed to the required shape. The total power output of 3000 amp was used to remove metal at a rate of 0.060 ipm. The length of "cut" was ½ in., and it was completed in a single pass, in 15 min. Shape of the electrode used for this operation is also shown in Fig. 38.

Example 853. Mechanical Milling vs Electrochemical Machining of Root Form of Inconel X-750 Turbine Blades (Fig. 39)

The root form of turbine blades (Fig. 39), made from aged Inconel X-750 forgings (360 Bhn), was machined by two methods: conventional milling in a fixed-bed milling machine, and electrochemical machining in a 3000-amp ECM unit. The total time to produce the root form by electrochemical machining (45 min) was almost 25% less than that required to produce the form by conventional milling (56 min).

The setup used in electrochemical machining is shown in Fig. 39; machining conditions for both processes are compared in the accompanying table.

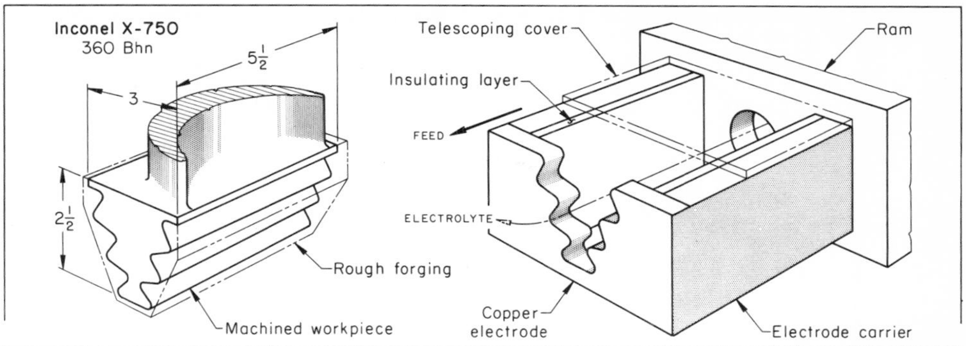

Item	Mechanical milling	Electrochemical machining
Machining Conditions		
Machine	Fixed-bed milling	3000-amp ECM
Tool material	M3, class 2	Copper
Tool description	10-tooth, form-relieved cutter	Form electrode
Speed or power input	30 sfm	2800 amp
Feed	⅝ ipm	⅛ ipm
Length of cut	18 in.(a)	5½ in.
Number of cuts or passes	2	1
Results		
Machining time	56 min	45 min
Tool life, pieces per grind	16	....

(a) Includes approach and overrun

Phantom lines in figure at left show outline of original forging and area of metal removal to obtain the root shape. The setup used for electrochemical machining is shown at right.

Fig. 39. Electrochemical machining of the root form of turbine blades, and comparison with mechanical milling (Example 853)

Examples of Machining Heat-Resisting Alloys Found Elsewhere in This Volume

Metal	Process	Ex. No.	Metal	Process	Ex. No.
AMS 5616 (Greek Ascoloy)	Boring	67	Inconel 901	Broaching	118
AMS 5356 (Lapelloy C)	Boring	83	A-286	Broaching	119
Hastelloy X, René 41, HS-255	Shaping	99	René 41	Broaching	125
AMS 5616 (Greek Ascoloy)	Broaching	110	AMS 5382 (HS-31)	Milling	324

Grinding of Heat-Resisting Alloys

EVEN WHEN operating conditions are favorable, heat-resisting alloys are more difficult and costly to grind than low-alloy steels. Most procedures for grinding heat-resisting alloys are similar to those for stainless steels (see the article "Machining of Stainless Steel", which begins on page 375); wheel speed, work speed and feed rates, however, are somewhat lower.

Typical iron-base, nickel-base and cobalt-base heat-resisting alloys are classified into five groups in Table 1. Compositions of the alloys discussed in this article are given in Table 1 of the article "Machining of Heat-Resisting Alloys", page 406.

Table 1. Alloy Groups Referred to in Tables 2, 3, 4 and 5

Designation	Typical alloys
Iron-Base Alloys	
Fe-1	A-286, 19-9 DL, 16-25-6
Nickel-Base Alloys	
Ni-1	René 41, Inconel X-750, Nimonic 90, U-500, U-700
Ni-2	M-252, R-235, Hastelloy B, Hastelloy C
Cobalt-Base Alloys	
Co-1	HS-31
Co-2	J-1570, J-1650, S-816, HS-21, HS-25

For compositions of these and other heat-resisting alloys, see Table 1 (page 406) in the article "Machining of Heat-Resisting Alloys".

Selection of Wheel

Aluminum oxide wheels are used for most grinding of heat-resisting alloys. Tables 2 to 5 identify wheels suitable for grinding five groups of alloys by four different methods. The marked superiority of aluminum oxide wheels is demonstrated by the data for grinding of seven alloys in Table 6.

Grain size of readily available wheels ranges from 10 to 600. Selection of grain size depends primarily on the surface finish required; wheels of finer grain sizes usually produce finer finishes. Although only two grain sizes (46 and 60) are indicated in Tables 2 to 5, wheels as fine as 180 are used to grind heat-resisting alloys.

This article was prepared from contributions of the ASM Committee on Machining of Heat-Resisting Alloys (see page 405 for committee list) and from the following paper by L. P. Tarasov: Effect of Grinding Variables on the Grinding Characteristics of Stainless Steels and Heat-Resistant Alloys, Chapter 21 in "Machining Difficult Alloys", American Society for Metals, 1962, pages 245 to 265. Figures 2 to 8 and Tables 6 to 11 are from this paper.

Grade (hardness) of the wheel is designated by letter, ranging from A (very soft) to Z (very hard). Most heat-resisting alloys are ground with medium-hard wheels (G to L).

Structure. Wheels with structure number from 5 to 13 are commonly used for grinding heat-resisting alloys;

Table 2. Nominal Processing Conditions for Surface Grinding of Heat-Resisting Alloys With Straight Wheels (a)

Alloy group(b)	Wheel: Classification	Wheel: Speed, sfm	Crossfeed per pass, fraction of wheel width
Iron-Base Alloys (180 to 320 Bhn)			
Fe-1	As-46-G-V	4000	1/10
Nickel-Base Alloys (200 to 400 Bhn)			
Ni-1	As-46-G-V	3000	1/12
Ni-2	As-46-G-V	3000 to 4000	1/10
Cobalt-Base Alloys (180 to 320 Bhn)			
Co-1	As-46-G-V	3000	⅛
Co-2	As-46-G-V	3000	⅛

(a) Conditions given in this table are for a unit downfeed of 0.001 in. per series of passes in roughing, and 0.0005 in. max in finishing. Table speed is 50 to 100 fpm. Grinding fluid may be water-base soluble-oil emulsion or synthetic solution, or sulfurized oil. (b) See Table 1 for designations of alloy groups and typical alloys in each group. (Data are adapted from tables compiled by Metcut Research Associates, Inc.)

Table 3. Nominal Processing Conditions for Cylindrical Grinding of Heat-Resisting Alloys (a)

Alloy group(b)	Wheel: Classification	Wheel: Speed, sfm	Infeed, in. per pass: Roughing	Infeed, in. per pass: Finishing (max)
Iron-Base Alloys at 180 to 320 Bhn				
Fe-1	A_s-60-H-V	4000	0.001	0.0002
Nickel-Base Alloys at 200 to 400 Bhn				
Ni-1	A_s-60-G-V	3000	0.001	0.0002
Ni-2	A_s-60-H-V	4000	0.001	0.0002
Cobalt-Base Alloys at 180 to 320 Bhn				
Co-1	A_s-60-G-V	3000	0.001	0.0002
Co-2	A_s-60-G-V	3000	0.002	0.0002

(a) Data given in this table are for a traverse rate of ⅕ of the wheel width per revolution of work in roughing, and 1/10 of the wheel width in finishing. Work speed is 50 sfm. Grinding fluid may be water-base soluble-oil emulsion or chemical solution, or sulfurized oil. (b) See Table 1 for identity of alloy groups and typical alloys. (Source of data: same as for Table 2)

Table 4. Nominal Processing Conditions for Through-Feed Centerless Grinding of Heat-Resisting Alloys

Wheel classification	A_s-60-J-V
Wheel speed for alloy group (a):	
Fe-1 (180 to 320 Bhn) (b)	4000 sfm
Ni-1 (200 to 400 Bhn) (c)	3000 sfm
Ni-2 (250 to 350 Bhn) (d)	3000 sfm
Co-1 and Co-2	3000 sfm
Infeed, roughing	0.003 in. per pass
Infeed, finishing	0.001 in. per pass
Work feed, approx	50 in. per min
Regulating-wheel angle	3°
Regulating-wheel speed	30 rpm
Grinding fluid	Water-base (e), or sulf. oil

(a) See Table 1 for designations of alloy groups and typical alloys in each group. (b) Solution treated or solution treated and aged. (c) Annealed, or solution treated, or solution treated and aged. (d) As cast. (e) Either soluble-oil emulsion or synthetic solution. (Source of data: same as for Table 2)

Table 5. Nominal Processing Conditions for Internal Grinding of Heat-Resisting Alloys (a)

Wheel classification	A_s-60-J-V
Wheel speed for alloy group (b):	
Fe-1 (180 to 320 Bhn) (c)	4000 sfm
Ni-1 (200 to 400 Bhn) (d)	3000 to 4000 (e)
Ni-2 (250 to 350 Bhn) (f)	3000 sfm
Co-1 and Co-2	3000 sfm
Infeed, roughing	0.0005 in. per pass
Infeed, finishing	0.0002 in. per pass
Traverse per work revolution:	
Roughing	⅓ wheel width
Finishing	⅙ wheel width
Grinding fluid	Water-base (f), or sulf. oil

(a) All data apply to holes of 2½-diam max length, and to grinding wheels of 1½-diam max width. (b) See Table 1 for identity of alloy groups. For all groups, work speed is 50 to 100 sfm. (c) Solution treated, or solution treated and aged.
(d) Cold drawn, annealed, solution treated, or solution treated and aged. (e) 4000 sfm for annealed and cold drawn; 5000 sfm for as-rolled. (f) Soluble-oil emulsion or synthetic solution. (SOURCE: same as for Table 2)

Table 7. Identification and Classification of Grinding Fluids

Fluid	Remarks
Soluble-Oil Emulsions (Regular)	
S1	Contains soap
S2	Contains soaps and fatty materials
S3	Emulsified kerosine
S4	Contains soap; a brand different from that in S1
Soluble-Oil Emulsions (Heavy-Duty)	
H1	Contains sulfur and chlorine
H2	Contains sulfurized fats; designed for stainless steel
H3	Contains sulfur and extreme-pressure additives, high percentage of fats
H4	Contains fatty materials, synthetic soaps; designed for stainless steel
H5	Contains lead additive but no sulfur or chlorine
Chemical ("Synthetic") Solutions	
C1	Contains 35% potassium nitrite (KNO_2) before dilution for use
C2	Contains 40% sodium nitrite ($NaNO_2$) before dilution for use; no organic compounds
C3	Contains a moderate percentage of sodium nitrite
C4	Based on synthetic wax
C5	Synthetic lubricant and sulfurized fatty acid
C6	Same as C5 but without sulfur
C7	Contains fatty acid
C8	Same as C7, with ionic additive
Grinding Oils	
G1	Transparent sulfochlorinated grinding oil containing fats, 4% sulfur and 2% chlorine (both active); viscosity, 230 SUS at 100 F
G2	Dark sulfochlorinated grinding oil containing fats, 3% sulfur and 0.5% chlorine (both active); 190 SUS at 100 F
G3	Inactive grinding oil containing fats, no added sulfur or chlorine; 300 SUS at 100 F

Table 8. Effect of Fluid on Grinding Ratio of Four Heat-Resisting Alloys

Grinding fluid(a)	Grinding ratio obtained for U-500 (wheel A-60-H8-V)	X-63 (wheel A-60-H8-V)	J-1570 (wheel A-60-H8-V)	J-1570 (wheel A-60-J8-V)	HS-31 (wheel A-60-J8-V)
C1	3.5	17	2.8	..	..
C2	..	..	..	4.8	16
C3	..	..	..	3.9	15
H1	3.3	..	..	..	..
H2	1.5	..	..	..	..
C4	..	13	1.7	..	..
C5	..	..	1.4	..	..
H3	..	15	1.3	..	..
C7	..	10	1.3	..	..
S1	..	..	1.1	2.6	14
S2	..	..	..	2.5	12
S3	..	10	1.1	..	..
C8	..	..	1.1	..	..
H4	..	..	..	2.4	12
S4	..	..	..	2.3	13
Air (b)	..	12	0.9	2.1	12
Water	..	..	..	1.7	7

(a) 10% concentration; see Table 7 for identification of fluids. (b) Dry grinding.

Table 6. Grinding Ratios for Seven Heat-Resisting Alloys

Alloy	Grinding fluid(a)	Concentration, %	Downfeed, 0.001 in.	Grinding ratio for indicated wheel(b)	
				A_s-46-J8-V	C-46-J5-V
S-590	H4	4	2	13	0.44
S-816	H4	4	2	9	0.35
16-25-6	H4	4	2	5.5	0.94
Nimonic 80	H4	4	2	2.3	0.34
				A_s-60-J8-V	C-60-J5-V
HS-21	G2	100	1	....	1.0
HS-21	G2	100	2	240	...
A-286	G2	100	1	27	2.0
A-286	G2	100	2	32	1.4
J-1570	G2	100	1	9.2	0.50
J-1570	G2	100	2	7.7	0.34

(a) Grinding fluids are identified in Table 7. (b) The grinding ratio is the volume of metal removed per volume of wheel wear. A high ratio thus indicates easier grinding than a low ratio.

this range is the same as for carbon steels. The definition of structure number varies among wheel manufacturers; however, they all agree that as structure number increases, the distance between grains increases. Structure numbers are omitted from some wheel designations in this article.

Bond. Vitrified bond (designated by letter V) is most commonly used for grinding heat-resisting alloys. Other types of bond (resinoid, for example) have been used. Resinoid bond is stronger than vitrified, and thus can be operated safely at higher speeds.

Grinding Fluid

Grinding fluids are of four principal types, as classified in Table 7. Because heat-resisting alloys have low thermal conductivity, grinding fluid must be applied at the grinding area in plentiful amounts, to prevent heat checking of the work surface.

For fast removal of heat, highly sulfurized water-base soluble-oil emulsions are the best fluid for any wrought heat-resisting alloy. Sulfurized oils are appropriate grinding fluids for all heat-resisting alloys, but they remove heat less rapidly than the water-base soluble-oil emulsions.

Chlorinated oil, generally about 1% chlorine, is particularly useful for wet dressing of form-grinding wheels to a tolerance of 0.0002 in. or less. Chlorinated water-base soluble-oil emulsions can be used in dressing form-grinding wheels within tolerances wider than 0.0002 in. Synthetic solutions and water-base soluble oil emulsions do not have this capability. The chlorinated straight oils and chlorinated soluble-oil emulsions also are applicable to other methods of grinding.

A disadvantage of chlorinated fluid is that any residual or entrapped fluid will react with the alloy during high-temperature service of the workpiece. Entrapment of fluid is especially likely in parts with small cavities such as blind holes and other difficult-to-clean recesses. For this reason some users of heat-resisting alloy parts do not permit the use of chlorinated grinding fluids.

In many applications, selection of the fluid is based on cost. Emulsions of soluble oil and water are the least expensive and grinding oils the most expensive grinding fluids.

Effect on Grindability.* Table 8 shows the effects of 15 water-base fluids on the grinding ratio of heat-resisting alloys U-500, X-63, J-1570 and HS-31. A few data are included for the use of plain water or air. All the grinding fluids were at 10% concentration, which is higher than normal. The magnitude of improvement in grinding ratio caused by grinding fluid increases with the concentration.

*The grindability index of a metal is a measure of the ease of removing stock by grinding, as expressed in terms of wheel wear. Numerically, it is equal to the grinding ratio, and is valid only for some specific set of grinding conditions. The grinding ratio is the volume of metal removed per volume of wheel wear. The higher this index, the easier the metal is to grind. It should be noted that the concept of grindability does not involve the grinding sensitivity, which is the susceptibility of the metal to cracking during or after grinding, nor does it involve the ease of obtaining a good surface.

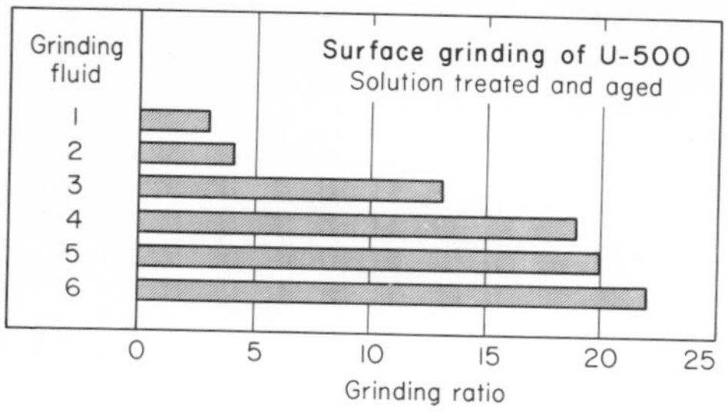

Identification of Grinding Fluids

1 Synthetic:water (1:40)
2 3½% KNO_2 solution
3 Highly chlorinated oil
4 Mixture of highly sulfurized oil and light machine oil (1:1)
5 Mixture of a different highly sulfurized oil and light machine oil (1:1)
6 Highly sulfurized oil of fluid 5 above

Operating Conditions. Wheel, A_s-46-L8-V; wheel speed, 6000 sfm; table speed, 40 fpm; crossfeed, 0.050 in./pass; downfeed, 0.001 in./pass.

Fig. 1. Effect of grinding fluid on surface grinding ratio for U-500 (Example 854)

Grinding dry proved less satisfactory than grinding with most of the water-base fluids, and grinding with plain water resulted in a very low grinding ratio. The highest ratios (greatest ease of grinding) were obtained with synthetic fluids containing nitrite ions in considerable quantity. The lowest ratios were obtained in grinding J-1570.

The influence of six grinding fluids on the grinding ratio for U-500 alloy is shown in Example 854.

Example 854. Effect of Fluid on Grinding Ratio for U-500 (Fig. 1)

Six fluids, identified below Fig. 1, were tested during surface grinding of U-500 alloy to determine their effect on the grinding ratio. The alloy was solution treated and aged. The highest ratio was obtained with a highly sulfurized oil. Results are shown in Fig. 1.

Surface Grinding

Table 2 shows conditions for surface grinding of heat-resisting alloys with straight wheels. The major differences are in wheel speed and crossfeed.

Usually, an increase in wheel hardness causes an increase in the grinding ratio and the grindability index. In the example that follows, effect of wheel hardness was demonstrated over the narrow range from hardness H to J.

Example 855. Effect of Wheel Hardness (Table 9)

U-500 alloy was surface ground in the solution treated and aged condition, to determine the effect of wheel hardness. Grinding ratios with three aluminum oxide wheels, each of a different hardness, are given in Table 9. Processing details were: wheel speed, 6000 sfm; table speed, 40 sfm; crossfeed, 0.050 in. per pass; downfeed, 0.001 in. per pass; grinding fluid, 1-to-1 mixture of highly sulfurized oil and light machine oil.

Although, in grinding certain alloys, wheel speed can exert an important influence on the grinding ratio, the effects of changes in downfeed,

Table 9. Effect of Wheel Grade (Hardness) on Surface Grinding Ratio for U-500 (Example 855)

Wheel	Grinding ratio
A_s-46-H8-V	13
A_s-46-I8-V	19.5
A_s-46-J8-V	15.5

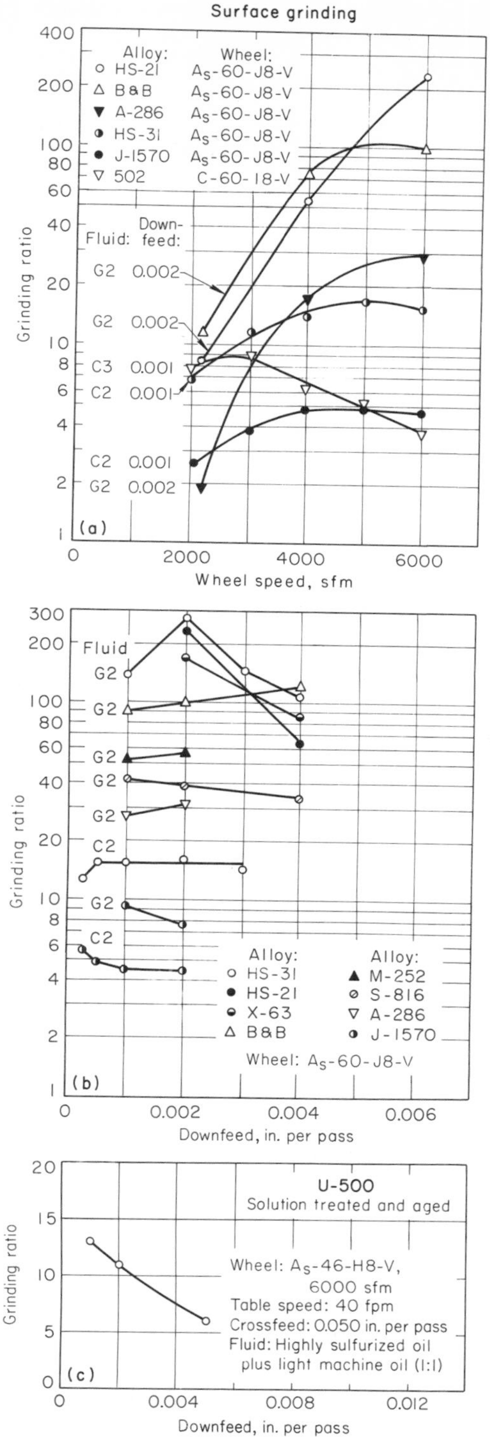

Fig. 2. Effects of wheel speed and downfeed on surface grinding ratio

crossfeed and traverse speed are variable. Data on the effects of speed and feed on the grinding ratio of various heat-resisting alloys in surface grinding are shown in Fig. 2 and 3.

Wheel Speed. As Fig. 2(a) shows, the grinding ratio decreased only moderately (or not at all), for all alloys shown except HS-21, when wheel speed was reduced from 6000 to 4000 sfm. Reductions in speed below 4000 sfm, however, resulted in a more precipitous drop in grinding ratio. The one exception, alloy HS-21, responded like carbon or low-alloy steel in that grinding ratio decreased continuously with decrease in wheel speed from 6000 to 2000 sfm.

Lowering the wheel speed is one way to reduce grinding heat and the probability of workpiece cracking. Thus, it is possible to minimize cracking in these alloys by grinding them at 4000 sfm, without significantly increasing wheel wear for a reasonable grinding rate.

Downfeed. The effects of changes in unit downfeed on grinding ratio, Fig. 2(b) and (c), indicate that no consistent effect is exerted by this variable. In some tests, grinding ratio decreased, rapidly or slowly, with larger downfeed increments; in others, it remained nearly constant or increased slowly. The curve for HS-31 went through a maximum at a unit downfeed of 0.002 in., and it may well be that HS-21 and X-63 would have shown the same behavior had they been tested at downfeeds of less than 0.002 in. The grinding ratio for the U-500 alloy was reduced by more than half — from 13.5 to 6 — as the downfeed increased from 0.001 to 0.005 in. per pass.

Crossfeed. The effect of crossfeed on the grinding ratio was not significant for HS-31 and J-1570 alloys, as shown in Fig. 3(a). The scatter of test results

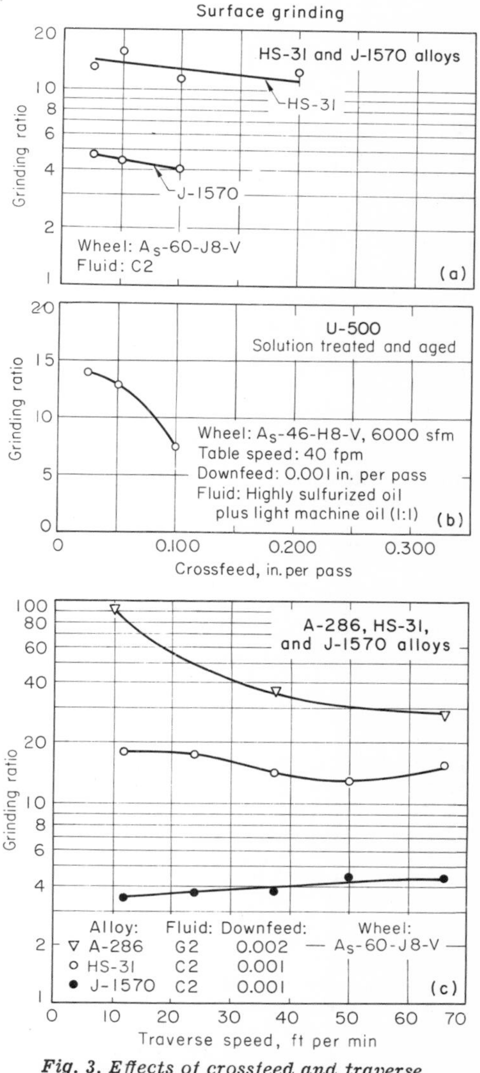

Fig. 3. Effects of crossfeed and traverse speed on surface grinding ratio

Table 10. Effect of Wheel Grade (Hardness) on Form Grinding Ratio for J-1570

Wheel	Grinding ratio
A_s-60-I8-V	6
A_s-60-J8-V	13
A_s-60-K8-V	15
A_s-60-L5-V	29

Grinding fluid was G1 (identified in Table 7).

obtained with HS-31 makes it difficult to ascertain whether the slight downward trend to the right shown for both alloys is significant.

A more pronounced effect of crossfeed on the grinding ratio for U-500 is shown by Fig. 3(b).

Traverse speed, as shown in Fig. 3(c), had relatively little effect on grinding ratio when a water-base grinding fluid was used; however, there was a considerable decrease in the grinding ratio with increasing traverse speed when A-286 was ground with an oil. It is questionable whether this difference in behavior should be attributed to the alloy or the grinding fluid. However, reducing traverse speed raises grinding temperature and introduces the possibility of damage to the work surface.

Form Grinding

In a series of tests on variables affecting form grinding, test blocks and grinding machine were the same as those used in the surface grinding tests previously discussed. (Test blocks were 4 to 5 in. long and 1 to 1½ in. wide.) The grinding wheels were 8 in. in diameter, diamond dressed to a 60° V-shape with a 0.030-in. flat. An A_s-60-L5-V wheel was used for all the tests except for the one on wheel grade, in which grades I, J, K and L were compared. Wheel speed was 6000 sfm, and traverse speed was 38 fpm. Unit downfeed was 0.002 in. at the end of each traverse, and the number of grooves ground was sufficient for adequate wheel wear — usually one to four grooves, but as many as 30 grooves when required.

Form Grinding Ratio. During the grinding of a groove with sloping sides, the grinding ratio increases as the total downfeed is increased. Thus, it is necessary to standardize on a constant total downfeed in order to obtain comparable values of grinding ratio. For a total downfeed of 0.060 in., which was convenient in these tests, a mathematical analysis showed that the grinding ratio was approximately twice as great as that for the same material in a plain surface grinding test. The rounding of the corners of the flat-bottomed V was closely related to the diametral wheel wear and was omitted from the calculation of grinding ratio in order to simplify the measurements and calculations, without significant loss of accuracy.

Wheel Grade. As shown in Table 10, increasing the hardness of the wheel increased the grinding ratio in the expected way when J-1570 cobalt-base alloy was form ground with grinding oil G1. The similarity of the ratios for the two intermediate grades indicates that hardnesses of the wheels used happened to be close to the boundary separating the two grades. Although the grade-L wheel is generally considered a little too hard for use in production grinding of heat-resisting alloys, it performed satisfactorily in these laboratory tests.

Grinding Fluid. The same alloy was ground using oils that contained various percentages of sulfur or chlorine, or both. The effect of the sulfur and chlorine contents of these oils on

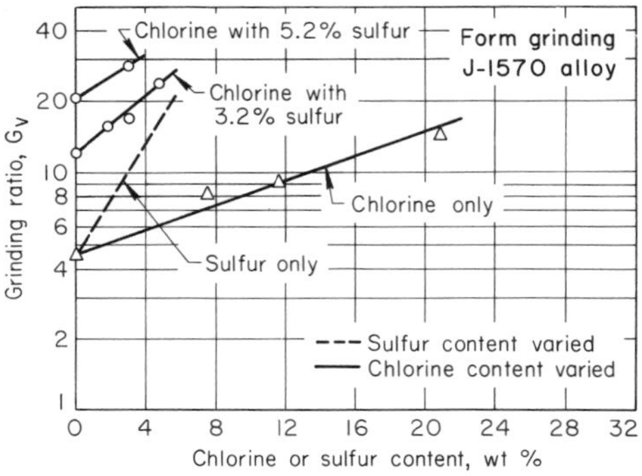

Fig. 4. Effects of grinding oil additives on form grinding ratio

Table 11. Grinding Ratios for Form Grinding Ten Alloys With Two Fluids

Alloy	Grinding fluid G1	Grinding fluid C1(a)
Iron-Base Alloys		
302 stainless	310	1.0
A-286	90	1.7
Nickel-Base Alloys		
Waspaloy	190	6.1
M-252	180	5.3
B & B	150	14
Cobalt-Base Alloys		
Vitallium	530	28
HS-31	290	28
X-63	250	28
S-816	170	21
J-1570	30	5.0

(a) Chemical solution of 10% concentration. See Table 7 for identification of fluids.

grinding ratio is shown in Fig. 4. A comparison of the lowest solid line with the broken line shows that sulfur was 5¼ times as effective as chlorine in raising the grinding ratio for J-1570 alloy. For example, either 4% sulfur or 21% chlorine was needed to make the grinding ratio equal 15. However, chlorine gained considerably in effectiveness when it was used in conjunction with sulfur. Note that the lines representing 3.2% and 5.2% sulfur are steeper than the line representing chlorine only.

Other variations in the formulation of an oil can affect its performance: among these are viscosity, the nature of the oil to which other ingredients are added, the amount of fatty materials, and the form in which sulfur and chlorine are present. These may explain why a grinding ratio of 30 was observed in another test with an oil containing 4% sulfur and 2% chlorine (J-1570 data of Table 11) for which Fig. 4 predicts a ratio of only 20. In a test dealing with viscosity, decreasing the viscosity of the oil from 300 to 120 sus, with everything else remaining the same, reduced the grinding ratio by 30%. Thus, although the results plotted in Fig. 4 illustrate the effects of sulfur and chlorine additions to certain oils, other oils containing the same percentages of sulfur and chlorine may not respond in the same manner. Moreover, the relationships indicated in Fig. 4 will not necessarily be applicable to heat-resisting alloys of types other than those tested.

Alloy Composition. Form grinding ratios for various alloys are listed in Table 11 for one grinding oil (G1) and one synthetic solution (C1). Although the grinding ratios were always far greater with the oil than with the synthetic solution, the relative effectiveness of oil over the solution varied with the alloy. Thus, the water-base fluid resulted in a higher grinding ratio for J-1570 than for A-286 alloy but the reverse was true when the grinding oil was used.

Speed and feed were evaluated primarily for J-1570, although in some tests data were obtained for M-252 and HS-31 alloys. The grinding fluids used in the speed and feed tests consisted of a grinding oil, G1; a synthetic solution of the nitrite type, C2, used in a 10% concentration; and a soluble oil, S1, used in a 2½% concentration. A decrease in wheel speed reduced the grinding ratio, as shown in Fig. 5. The only exception was a peak in the curve at 5000 sfm when grinding oil was used and the traverse speed was low.

Downfeed and Traverse Speed. The effect of unit downfeed depends on the traverse speed. This can be seen in Fig. 6(a) and (b), where, at a low traverse speed, grinding ratio either is nearly independent of the downfeed or else passes through a maximum value, while at higher traverse speeds it decreases with increasing units of downfeed. These same results are replotted in Fig. 7(a) and (b) to show unit downfeed as a function of traverse speed. It is clear that grinding ratio

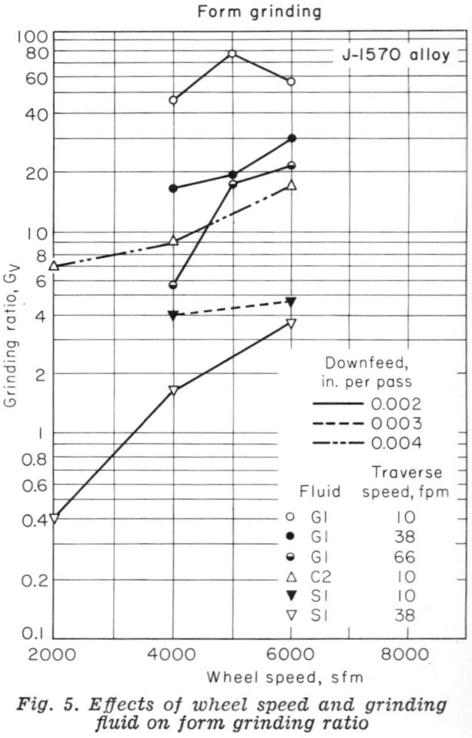

Fig. 5. Effects of wheel speed and grinding fluid on form grinding ratio

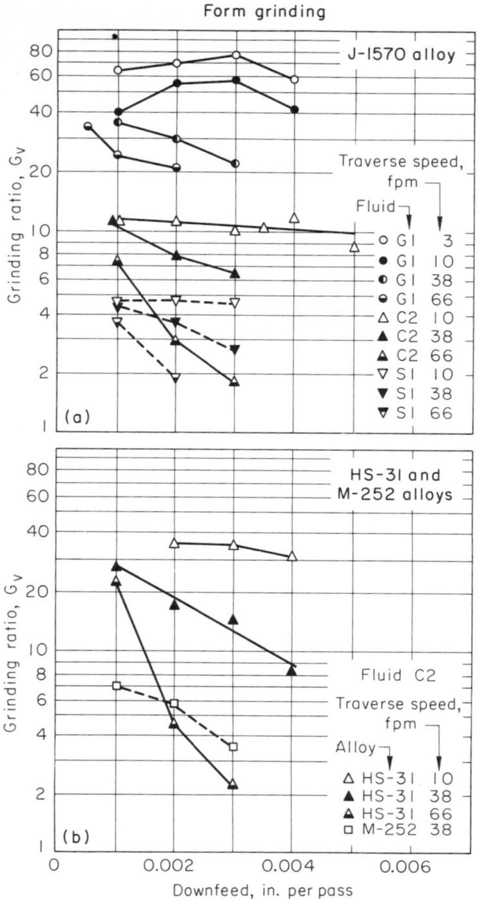

Fig. 6. Effect of unit downfeed on form grinding ratio

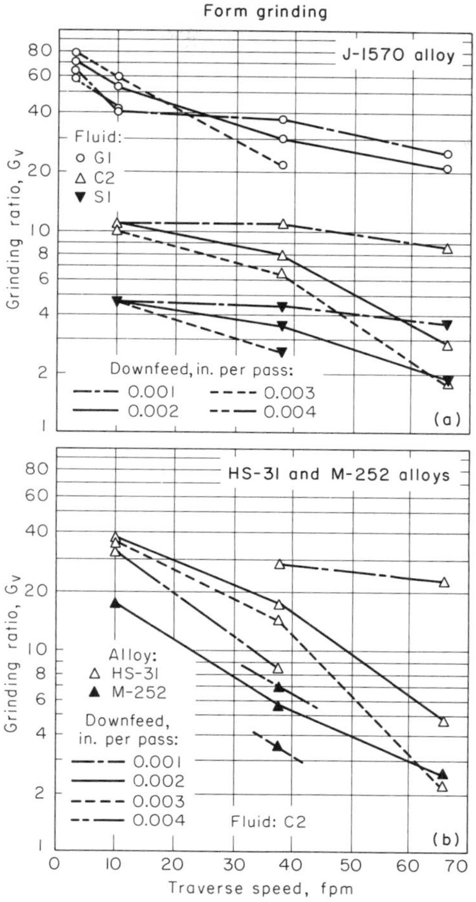

Fig. 7. Effects of traverse and unit downfeed on form grinding ratio

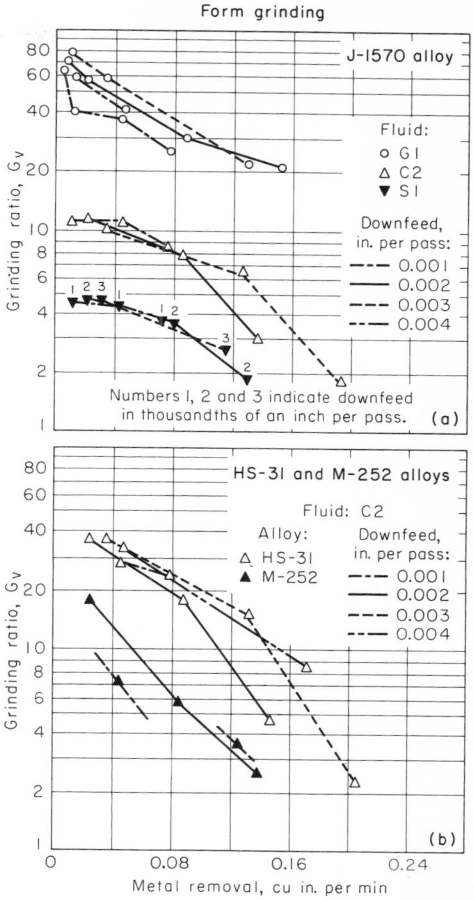

Fig. 8. Effect of rate of stock removal on form grinding ratio

decreases with increasing traverse speed, and that the rate of decrease itself increases as the unit downfeed is made higher.

Rate of production depends in part on the rate of stock removal, which is a function of traverse speed, downfeed, and the resultant wheel wear. The data discussed above are plotted in Fig. 8(a) and (b) against the volumetric rate of cut during the last traverse. (The average rate of cut for all the traverses required to complete a groove would have been about one third less.) The individual curves are similar to the corresponding ones in Fig. 7(a) and (b), but the relations between the curves for a single alloy and fluid are different because the abscissa of a point now depends not only on traverse speed but also on unit downfeed.

In Fig. 8(a), it can be seen that when alloy J-1570 was ground with oil G1, the highest grinding ratio at nearly every rate of cut was obtained when the downfeed was 0.003 in. On the other hand, grinding the same material with soluble oil S1 resulted in grinding ratios that were essentially independent of the downfeed. For both HS-31 and M-252, the highest grinding ratios for a particular rate of cut were obtained at the heavier downfeeds.

Although speed and feed appear to affect grinding ratio according to certain general patterns, in specific instances the relation is quite complex, and conclusions drawn from limited data may not hold when applied to apparently similar conditions. This is illustrated in the upper group of curves in Fig. 7(a), where the effect of downfeed on grinding ratio is changed when the traverse speed is increased beyond 20 or 30 fpm.

Although, as previously indicated, there may be some advantage gained from using a fairly heavy unit downfeed, reducing unit downfeed is sometimes necessary to prevent damage to the work surface from excessive heat, and to prevent loss of form, if this is affected differently from diametral wear by changes in grinding conditions.

Applications. Form grinding of two nickel-base alloys, a cobalt-base alloy, and a composite material of Inconel honeycomb compressed with pulverized quartz is discussed in the four examples that follow.

Example 856. Turbine Blade of R-235 Alloy (Table 12)

Tests were made to determine optimum procedures and wheel for form grinding fir-tree serrations (see cross-sectional view in Table 12) on R-235 alloy turbine blades. It was necessary to reproduce form and dimensions accurately, to avoid burning and grinding cracks, and to provide a 32-micro-in. finish. The grinding wheels that were used and the conditions that were varied in the four tests are summarized in Table 12.

Size of the grinding wheels used in all tests was 24 by ¾ by 12 in. The grinding fluid was a sperm-base oil containing 2.5% active sulfur and no chlorine (viscosity at 100 F was 145 to 155 SUS). Each test made use of a fixture designed to hold five turbine blades for simultaneous (batch) processing. The following is a brief discussion of the results obtained from these four tests:

Test 1 satisfactorily produced only two workpieces per load; this quantity was below production requirements.

Test 2 gave results considered good. As Table 2 shows, a coarser-grit, somewhat

Table 12. Form Grinding of Serrations in R-235 Alloy Turbine Blades (Example 856) (a)

Test No.	Grinding wheel	Grinding cycle time, min	Wheel speed, sfm	Work speed, sfm	Dresses per cycle	Dress per pass, in.	Infeed per pass, in.
1	As-180-K11-V (porous) As-180-J5-V(b)	6	6500	8	2	0.0006	0.004
2	As-150-L9-V	10	6500	15(c)	2	0.0006	0.002
3(c)	As-100-J8-V(d)	4	5500	7	1	0.001	0.004
3(d)	As-150-L9-V(e)	5.5	6500	10	2	0.0006	0.002
4(c)	As-60-H8-V(d)	3.5	6500	15(f)	2	0.001	0.004(g)
4(d)	As-150-K9-V(e)	5.5	6500	15(b)	2	0.0008	0.002(h)

Part:

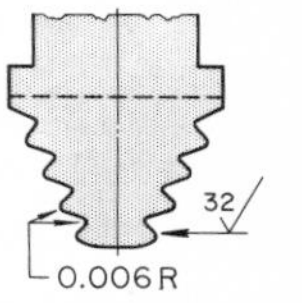

(a) Nominal composition of R-235 is 65 Ni, 15 Cr, 10 Fe, 5 Mo, 3 Al, 2 Ti. (b) Two wheels tried. (c) Work speed during the last two passes was 2 sfm. (d) Rough grinding. (e) Finish grinding. (f) Work speed during the last two passes was 4 sfm. (g) Infeed per pass during the last three passes was 0.002 in. (h) Infeed per pass during the last pass was zero.

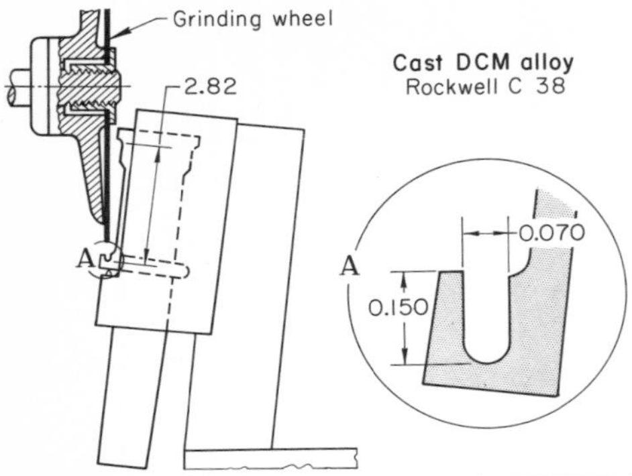

Wheel classification	A_t-54-K-B
Wheel size	8 by 0.070 in.

Operating Conditions

Wheel speed	3500 sfm
Work-rotation speed	30 sfm
Downfeed	0.001 in. per pass
Grinding fluid	Sulfurized oil
Production rate	6.3 min per piece(a)

(a) Includes setup time.

Fig. 9. Grinding a thin slot in a cast turbine blade (Example 857)

harder wheel was used than in test 1, and it was possible to grind a full load of five workpieces per cycle.

Test 3. The grinding procedure in this test was changed to two operations, roughing and finishing, each on a separate machine. Five blades were ground in each operation. Both operations were satisfactory, and the time cycles were such that one man could operate both machines. Tests were conducted on both the roughing and finishing procedures, varying the several conditions for each setup.

Test 4. The setup for rough and finish grinding procedures in this test was adopted for production. It made possible grinding five blades simultaneously in each operation.

Example 857. Slot Grinding vs Milling of DCM Alloy (Fig. 9)

Tests were made to determine whether grinding would be superior to milling in cost and production rate for making slots in the platforms of cast turbine-blade buckets made of DCM nickel-base alloy, solution treated and aged to Rockwell C 38. Figure 9 shows the size and location of one of tnese slots, and its position in relation to the grinding wheel.

To evaluate the grinding operation, and to analyze resultant residual stresses, cracks and surface finish, a number of similar slots were ground into the shank of a scrap part of the same material. For this operation, an aluminum oxide cutoff wheel was used, in a 6-by-18-in. surface grinder. Operating conditions are shown in Fig. 9. For producing these slots on a production basis, machine loading was six pieces per setup, and grinding time was 6.3 min per piece, including setup time.

This success in grinding contrasted favorably with previous experience in milling this difficult alloy. Six pieces were obtained per grind of the milling cutter, 5 min was necessary to machine one piece, 30 min was required for resharpening a cutter, and a milling cutter cost about five times as much as a grinding wheel. Added to this was the chipping or breakage of some carbide cutters and the difficulty of establishing a rigid milling setup.

Example 858. Slot Grinding vs Milling of HS-31 Alloy (Fig. 10)

A 0.062-in.-wide slot (Fig. 10), formerly milled, was successfully form ground in HS-31 investment castings. Milling was a slow operation and resulted in distortion of the part and heavy burring. Tool life in milling this alloy was extremely short.

In contrast, the grinding wheel wear was only 0.0005 in. per slot, and 60 slots per hour were ground without burrs or distortion. Thus, grinding was both faster and more economical than milling. For grinding, the slots were located by an indexing fixture. Each casting contained five slots. Grinding conditions are listed in the table that accompanies Fig. 10.

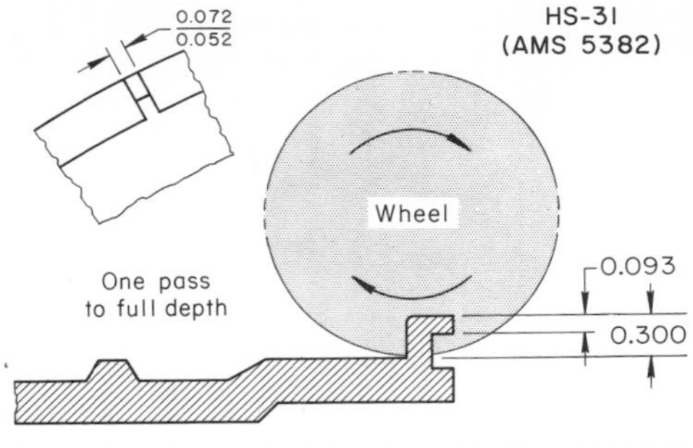

Wheel classification	A_t-54-S7-B
Wheel size	10 by 0.060 by 3 in.

Operating Conditions

Wheel speed	8200 sfm
Downfeed	0.300 in. per pass
Grinding fluid	None
Production rate	60 slots per hour(a)
Wheel wear	0.0005 in. per slot

(a) Five slots were ground in each casting.

Fig. 10. Form grinding of thin slots (Example 858)

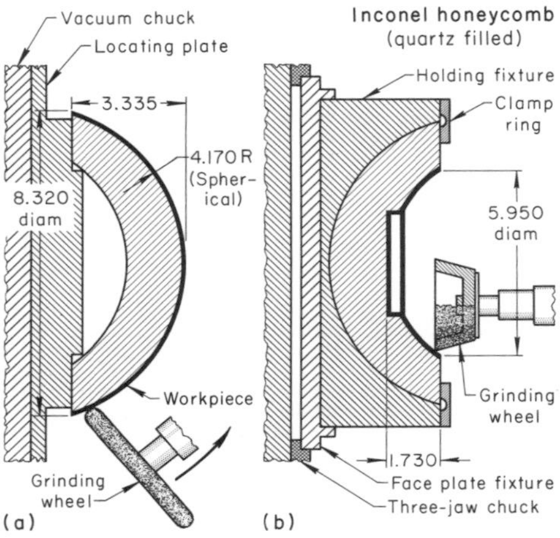

Wheel classification:	
External contouring	D-46-N100-M
Internal contouring	D-60-N100-M
Wheel size:	
External contouring	4 by ½ by 1¼ in.
Internal contouring	3-in.-diam cup(a)

Operating Conditions

Wheel speed:	
External contouring	150 rpm (157 sfm)
Internal contouring	100 rpm (79 sfm)
Feed, both operations	0.010 ipr
Grinding fluid	Tap water
Material removed, each surface	0.250 in.(b)
Wheel life per dressing(c)	50 pieces
Surface finish obtained	63 micro-in.
Tolerance	±0.005 in.

(a) 1¼ in. deep, 1¼-in.-diam hole. (b) In five passes; 0.050 in. removed per pass. (c) Wheel was dressed with a C-46-K-B dressing wheel.

Fig. 11. Form grinding a heat-shield cap (Example 859)

Example 859. Contouring an Inconel-Quartz Composite (Fig. 11)

The heat-shield cap (Fig. 11) was made of Inconel honeycomb with 250 cells into which pulverized quartz was compressed. The rough shape was press formed at 2250 F and 15 to 50 tons pressure. Compression of the composite was about 25%.

Machining of the heat-shield cap was first tried with various single-point tools, without success. Either tool wear or tool breakdown was excessive or the tools would not produce a satisfactory surface finish.

The cap was finished to required size, inside and outside, by grinding in a lathe with diamond wheels. This method produced parts of satisfactory quality and at a higher production rate than the previous method. Processing details are given with Fig. 11.

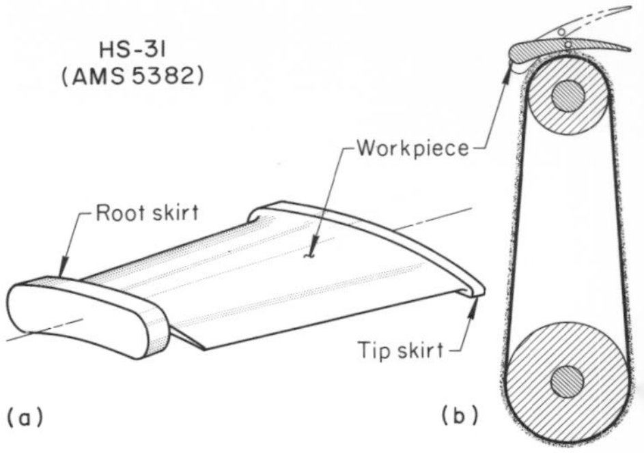

Belt type	60-grit aluminum oxide, resinoid bond(a)
Belt size	⅝ by 90 in.

Operating Conditions

Belt speed	6000 sfm
Metal removed, root skirt	0.015 in./side(b)
Metal removed, tip skirt	0.012 in./side(c)
Grinding fluid	None
Production rate	93 sec per piece(d)
Belt life	15 root skirts or 10 tip skirts

(a) Low-flexibility, heavy-duty belt. (b) 0.65 gram of metal removed. (c) 0.75 gram of metal removed. (d) Each piece required 33 sec for root end and 60 sec for tip end.

Fig. 12. Belt grinding of root and tip skirts of turbine nozzle vanes (Example 860)

Other Methods of Wheel Grinding

Conditions for grinding heat-resisting alloys by cylindrical, centerless and internal methods are given in Tables 3, 4 and 5. For a discussion of these three methods, see the article "Grinding", beginning on page 257.

Belt Grinding

Abrasive belt grinding can be applied successfully to heat-resisting alloys. The use of this method on vanes for the first stage of a turbine nozzle is described in the following example.

Example 860. Removal of Coating From Turbine Vanes (Fig. 12)

Investment cast turbine nozzle vanes made of HS-31 alloy were ground to remove the antioxidation diffusion coating from the tip-skirt and root-skirt sections (Fig. 12). Grinding was done in a turbine blade airfoil grinder equipped with a cloth-backed abrasive belt operating over a 1-in.-diam contact wheel. The vanes were ground singly in a mechanical fixture. Each vane weighed 21.65 grams before grinding and 20.25 grams after. Processing data are given in Fig. 12.

Abrasive Cutoff

Cutoff operations for nickel-base and iron-base alloys use rubber-bond aluminum oxide wheels of 54 grit and grade (hardness) N. Usually cutoff is done wet, using a soluble-oil emulsion, synthetic solution, or sulfurized oil.

HS-31 alloy can be cut either wet or dry using aluminum oxide wheels. Wet cutting is done with a rubber-bond wheel of 46 grain size and grade Q. The same cutting fluids used for nickel-base alloys are applicable to wet cutting of HS-31. Dry cutting is done with resinoid-bond wheels of 30 grain size and grade R.

Although the grade letters mentioned above are typical, they will vary among different wheel manufacturers.

Machining of Refractory Metals

*By the ASM Committee on Machining of Heat-Resisting Alloys**

THE REFRACTORY METALS — columbium, tantalum, molybdenum and tungsten — differ considerably in machining characteristics. Both tungsten and molybdenum lack ductility at room temperature, but molybdenum is less brittle than unalloyed tungsten. Furthermore, the brittleness of molybdenum varies considerably, depending on its condition. Pressed-and-sintered and arc-cast molybdenum are both brittle, but forging greatly reduces their room-temperature brittleness. Columbium and tantalum, on the other hand, are ductile and can be machined by methods similar to those used for other ductile metals.

For aerospace use, most parts made of tungsten and molybdenum are thin-walled and fragile. For this reason, and because of their brittleness at room temperature, they are easily damaged in handling and machining. Caution must be used to prevent damage to workpieces, particularly because of the high cost of the metals (as much as $100 per pound).

Maximum rigidity of machines and tools is essential in machining tungsten and molybdenum, to obtain satisfactory cutting and to minimize damage to work during processing.

Chucking and Fixturing. Workpieces of tungsten and molybdenum can be held in standard jaw-type chucks, provided sufficient pressure can be obtained and balanced. Chucking forces can cause cracking, and consequently a four-jaw chuck is often used for holding parts being machined from these metals, rather than a three-jaw chuck.

The use of copper shims is recommended for chucking or fixturing all refractory metal parts, especially parts made of tungsten or molybdenum. Thermoplastic supports are sometimes used for holding fragile parts made of these metals.

Cutting Tools. All refractory metals are abrasive (tungsten is the most abrasive). Accordingly, tool wear is more rapid and tool life is shorter than in machining carbon or alloy steel with similar tools.

For machining columbium and tantalum, high speed steel tools can be used in all operations. However, carbide tools are frequently used, especially for single-point cutting and face milling operations.

For machining molybdenum, carbide is preferred, and it is used almost exclusively in single-point cutting. On the other hand, high speed steel is used exclusively for drilling, reaming and tapping. Both tool materials have been successfully used in milling.

In machining tungsten, carbide tools are used for all operations except tapping. Solid carbide drills are required for drilling. Tapping is generally avoided, but if it is mandatory, high speed steel taps are used.

Grade C-2 carbide is recommended for machining all refractory metals except tungsten, for which C-4 is recommended. As in machining of other metals, disposable carbide tips are usually more economical than brazed tips.

For machining all refractory metals except tungsten, cutting tools normally have positive rake, although there are exceptions as noted later. In some operations, zero or negative rake has proved better for tungsten.

Sharp cutting tools are essential, to obtain best economy and surface finish and to minimize damage to the workpiece. When tungsten or molybdenum is being machined, the best tool life for any depth of cut is obtained from a combination of speed and feed for which flank wear of the cutting edge proceeds at the same rate as cratering of the tool face.

Cutting Fluids. Soluble-oil emulsions are satisfactory for most machining operations on refractory metals; exceptions are drilling, reaming and tapping. For these operations, cutting oils that contain sulfur or chlorine are preferred. Oils that contain sulfur or chlorine are also preferred for nearly all machining operations on columbium, except for turning, for which a soluble-oil emulsion is satisfactory.

Table 1. Comparative Machinability, Based on Turning With Single-Point Carbide Tools, of Five Refractory Alloys and Five Other Aerospace Materials

Workpiece metal	Hardness	Depth of cut, in.	Speed, sfm	Carbide tool: Type	Carbide tool: Feed, ipr	Carbide tool: Life, cu in.	Removal rate, cu in./min	Machinability rating(a): Removal rate	Machinability rating(a): Relative cost
Steels									
4130	200 Bhn	0.12	445	C-6	0.019	582	11.5	100	1
4340	Rc 54	0.12	90	C-6	0.004	19	0.62	5.4	19
Heat-Resisting Alloys									
HS-25	Rc 24	0.12	152	C-6	0.013	16	2.7	23	6
A-286	Rc 35	0.12	152	C-7	0.009	25	1.79	16	7
René 41	365 Bhn	0.06	70	C-2	0.009	16	0.47	4.1	25
Refractory Alloys									
Columbium	112 Bhn	0.12	300	C-2	0.005	151	2.2	19	6
D-31	207 Bhn	0.12	350	C-2	0.005	76	2.5	22	6
Ta – 10 W	240 Bhn	0.12	150	C-2	0.005	26	1.08	9.4	11
TZM	217 Bhn	0.06	350	C-2	0.009	99	2.3	20	5
Tungsten(b)	Rc 33	0.05	100	C-4	0.009	3.4	0.54	4.7	30

Source: F. W. Boulger, Machining of Refractory Metals, "The Science and Technology of Tungsten, Tantalum, Molybdenum, Niobium and Their Alloys", edited by N. E. Promisel, Macmillan Co., New York, 1964, p 527 to 540

(a) Ratings are based on metal-removal rate for 4130 steel at 100,000-psi tensile strength (200 Bhn), indicated as 100; lower numbers indicate poorer machinability. Relative costs are ratios of costs estimated for removing 1 cu in. of metal compared to 4130 steel at 1; higher ratios indicate higher cutting costs. The charges assumed for the estimates were: 26¢ per tool point; 10¢ per tool change; operating cost of 11.6¢ per minute.

(b) Unalloyed tungsten that was pressed and sintered to 93% of theoretical density.

Table 2. Compositions of Alloys Listed in Other Tables in This Article

Metal or alloy	C	Mn	Si	Cr	Ni	Co	Mo	W	Ti	Fe	Cb	Other
Steels												
4130	0.30	0.50	0.28	0.95	...	...	0.2	...	...	rem	...	...
4340	0.40	0.75	0.28	0.80	1.85	...	0.2	...	...	rem	...	...
D-6ac	0.45	0.80	0.25	1.15	0.55	...	1.0	...	...	rem	...	0.05 V
302 stainless.	0.10	2.0	1.0	18.0	9.0	...	...	...	...	rem	...	...
Heat-Resisting Alloys												
HS-25	0.15	1.5	0.5	20	10	rem	...	15	...	2	...	...
A-286	0.08	1.35	0.5	15	26	...	1.2	...	2.0	rem		0.2 Al, 0.3 V
René 41 ...	0.10	...	...	19	rem	11	10	...	3.0	5		1.5 Al, trace B
Refractory Alloys												
Cb-752	...	...	...	...	...	...	...	...	...	...	rem	2 Zr
D-31	...	...	...	...	...	...	10	...	10	...	rem	...
D-43	0.1	...	...	...	...	...	...	10	...	...	rem	1 Zr
Ta – 10 W ..	...	...	...	...	...	...	...	11.1	...	...	...	88.9 Ta
TZM	0.025	...	...	...	...	...	rem	...	0.5	...	...	0.10 Zr
TZC	...	...	...	...	...	...	rem	...	1.25	...	...	0.15 Zr
Mo – 0.5 Ti .	0.2	...	...	...	...	...	rem	...	0.5	...	...	...
Mo – 30 W ..	...	...	...	...	...	...	rem	30	...	...	...	...
Tungsten ..	0.005	0.001	0.01	...	...	0.01	0.02	rem	...	...	...	0.05 O_2
W – 2 Th ...	...	...	...	...	...	...	...	rem	...	...	...	2 Th
W – 15 Mo ..	...	...	...	...	...	...	15	rem	...	...	...	...
W – 10 Ag ..	...	...	...	...	...	...	...	rem	...	...	...	10 Ag

*For committee list, see page 405.

Table 3. Nominal Speeds and Feeds for Turning Refractory Alloys With High Speed Steel and Carbide Tools

Metal or alloy	Condition(a)	Brinell hardness	Single-point and box tools, Speed, sfm(b): Rough	Finish	Form tools: Speed, sfm	Feed, ipr, for tool width of: ½ in.	1 in.	2 in.	Cutoff tools: Speed, sfm	Feed, ipr, for tool width of: 1/16 in.	⅛ in.	¼ in.
High Speed Steel Tools(c)												
Cb-752(d)	SR	170 to 225	60(e)	80	45	0.0015	0.001	0.0007	45	0.001	0.001	0.0015
Ta – 10 W	SR	200 to 250	40(e)	50	30	0.002	0.0015	0.0007	30	0.001	0.0015	0.002
Carbide Tools(f)												
Cb-752(d)	SR	170 to 225	250(e)	300	185	0.003	0.0025	0.002	185	0.003	0.003	0.0045
Ta – 10 W	SR	200 to 250	75(e)	100	55	0.004	0.003	0.0015	55	0.003	0.005	0.006
Mo – 0.5 Ti(g)	SR	220 to 290	275(e)	300	205	0.004	0.003	0.0015	205	0.003	0.005	0.007
Tungsten (85% density)	PS	180 to 200	80	100	60	0.003	0.0025	0.001	60	0.003	0.003	0.0045
Tungsten (93% density)	PS	290 to 320	70	80	50	0.003	0.0025	0.001	50	0.003	0.003	0.0045
Tungsten (96% density)	AF	290 to 320	110	120	80	0.003	0.0025	0.001	80	0.003	0.003	0.0045
W – 2 Th	PS	260 to 320	120	150	90	0.003	0.0025	0.001	90	0.003	0.003	0.0045
W – 15 Mo	AC	260 to 320	120	150	90	0.003	0.0025	0.001	90	0.003	0.003	0.0045
W – 10 Ag	PS	290 to 320	220	250	165	0.004	0.003	0.0015	165	0.003	0.005	0.007

(a) AC = As cast; AF = As forged; PS = Pressed and sintered; SR = Stress relieved. (b) Rough turning at 0.060-in. depth of cut and finish turning at 0.015-in. depth of cut. (c) M2 high speed steel. (d) Or columbium alloy D-31 or D-43. (e) Rough turning at 0.100-in. depth of cut. (f) Grade C-2 carbide, except for tungsten, for which grade C-4 is preferred. (g) Or molybdenum alloy TZM, TZC or Mo – 30 W.

Table 4. Nominal Speeds and Feeds for Boring Refractory Alloys With High Speed Steel and Carbide Tools

Metal or alloy	Condition(a)	Brinell hardness	Rough boring, 0.100-in. depth of cut: Speed, sfm: HSS(b)	Carbide(c)	Feed, ipr: HSS(b)	Carbide(c)	Finish boring, 0.010-in. depth of cut: Speed, sfm: HSS(b)	Carbide(c)	Feed, ipr: HSS(b)	Carbide(c)
Cb-752(d)	SR	170 to 225	55	225	0.005	0.005	60	250	0.004	0.005
Ta – 10 W	SR	200 to 250	35	65	0.006	0.007	40	75	0.004	0.005
Mo – 0.5 Ti(e)	SR	220 to 290	..	250	....	0.007	..	275	....	0.005
Tungsten (85% dens.)	PS	180 to 200	..	70	....	0.008	..	80	....	0.004
Tungsten (93% dens.)	PS	290 to 320	..	65	....	0.008	..	70	....	0.004
Tungsten (96% dens.)	AF	290 to 320	..	100	....	0.008	..	110	....	0.004
W – 2 Th	PS	260 to 320	..	110	....	0.008	..	120	....	0.004
W – 15 Mo	AC	260 to 320	..	110	....	0.008	..	120	....	0.004
W –10 Ag	PS	290 to 320	..	200	....	0.009	..	220	....	0.005

(a) AC = As cast; AF = As forged; PS = Pressed and sintered; SR = Stress relieved. (b) M2 high speed steel. (c) Grade C-2 carbide, except for tungsten, for which C-4 is preferred. (d) Or columbium alloy D-31 or D-43. (e) Or molybdenum alloy TZM, TZC or Mo – 30 W.

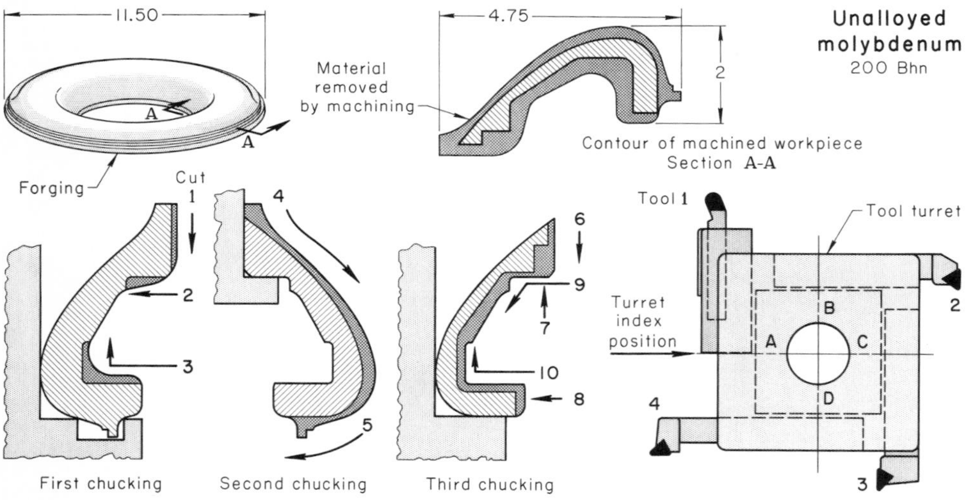

Cut	Speed, sfm	Feed, ipr	Depth of cut, in.	Tool no.	Turret position
1	350	0.005	0.040	4	A
2	300	0.005	Plunge	2	C
3	300	0.005	Plunge	1	B
4	300	0.007	0.150 max	4	A
	450	0.005	0.060	4	A
5	350	0.007	0.250 max	4	D
	450	0.005	0.060	4	D
6	450	0.005	0.060	4	A
7 ...	450	0.005	0.125	3	D
	450	0.005	0.060	3	D
8 ...	350	0.005	Plunge	2	C
9 ...	350	0.007	0.150 max	2	C
	400	0.005	0.060	2	C
10 ...	350	0.007	0.125 max	1	B
	400	0.005	0.060	1	B

Cutting tools had disposable carbide inserts with positive rake. Average tool life was three pieces. A soluble-oil cutting fluid (1 part oil to 20 parts water) was used in all operations.

Fig. 1. Molybdenum missile component turned in a tape-controlled lathe (Example 861)

When tungsten is heated for machining, no cutting fluid is used. When tungsten is not heated, a chlorinated cutting oil is preferred.

Precautions. To avoid chipping, flaking and damage at breakthrough in machining molybdenum and tungsten, special practice and special tools are often required. The probability of cracking at corners and other surfaces in single-point cutting or milling is reduced by observing these precautions:

1 Avoid machining to an external corner by cutting to the middle of a surface from opposite directions, especially when sharp corners are required. Climb milling, rather than conventional milling, should be used, so that the cutting forces are directed into the work metal. In conventional milling, work metal is likely to break at the point of entrance or exit of the cutter.
2 Use thermoplastic supports when it is necessary to machine to an external corner.
3 Machine a large chamfer on the corner before machining the adjacent surface. (This chamfer should be large enough so that some metal is left after the turning cut is completed.)
4 Use tools with high lead angles (about 45°), especially for roughing.

Turning and Boring

Table 1 compares conditions and results in turning operations on five refractory alloys with those on five other alloys commonly used in the aerospace industry. Typical compositions of the work metals are listed in Table 2.

As shown in Table 1, metal-removal rates for turning refractory metals are about 5 to 20% of those for normalized 4130 steel, and about the same as those for nickel-base and cobalt-base heat-resisting alloys. The cost of turning the various refractory metals, as shown in Table 1, is from 5 to 30 times that for 4130 steel at 200 Bhn. However, some of the values given in Table 1 are conservative. For instance, in turning molybdenum alloy TZM, depth of cut is often as great as 0.12 in. (0.060 in. is shown in Table 1), and metal-removal rate can be 40%, instead of 20%. Likewise, tungsten is often turned at 200 sfm, although 100 sfm is the speed used in Table 1 machinability rating.

Columbium and Tantalum. Nominal speeds and feeds for turning (single-point and box tools, form tools, and cutoff tools) are given in Table 3. High side rake on the tools is recommended for turning of both metals. Turning practice varies considerably from shop to shop. Sometimes better results are obtained by using speeds no greater than half those shown in Table 3, and doubling the feed rate. Regardless of technique, smooth finishes are difficult to obtain and finishing by grinding may be required.

Nominal speeds and feeds for rough and finish boring columbium and tantalum are given in Table 4.

Molybdenum is extremely abrasive, and all machining operations on it result in high rates of tool wear. Carbide tools with high side rake are preferred for turning and boring. Nominal speeds and feeds for Mo – 0.5 Ti are given in Tables 3 and 4. Practice used in turning of unalloyed molybdenum is described in the following example.

Example 861. Turning Molybdenum (Fig. 1)

Pressed-and-sintered unalloyed molybdenum rings (Fig. 1) were turned in a 25-hp tape-controlled lathe, with a four-position turret that held the four tools used for 15 cutting operations, which were carried out in three separate chuckings.

The conditions given in Fig. 1 represent a significant improvement in the efficiency of machining this part; one part was completely machined in 1½ hr, compared with the 6 hr that had been required when a tracer lathe was used. The special tooling and part programming costs were amortized in the production of 200 pieces.

Tungsten. Nominal speeds and feeds for turning and boring of unalloyed tungsten of three different densities and of three tungsten alloys are given in Tables 3 and 4. Density and composition of these materials markedly affect speed, and higher speeds are used for the harder grades.

Carbide tools with zero side rake and moderate back rake are usually best for turning and boring of tungsten.

Best tool life is obtained when chips show a heat color as they form. Therefore, cutting fluids are seldom used in turning tungsten. Color of the chips may range from a barely visible amber to a cherry red color.

Because of its room-temperature brittleness, tungsten is sometimes heated for turning or boring to reduce the danger of surface checking. Although parts are usually heated to 400 to 800 F for "warm machining" (see subsequent sections on Drilling and Tapping), heating to only slightly above room temperature has helped to reduce surface checking, as described in the following example.

Example 862. Turning a Tungsten Forging (Fig. 2)

A four-jaw chuck was used to hold the tungsten workpieces while they were contour turned in a tracer lathe, using disposable carbide inserts for both roughing and finishing cuts. Parts were heated to 150 F before turning, which helped to prevent surface checking. Other machining details are given in the table accompanying Fig. 2.

Drilling

Table 5 gives approximate rates and relative costs for drilling refractory alloys and several other difficult-to-machine metals. Except for tungsten, the difference between the refractory alloys and the soft steels is less in drilling than in turning, and columbium, tantalum and molybdenum are easier to drill than the heat-resisting alloys or steel at Rockwell C 50 to 55. Success in drilling refractory alloys depends primarily on rigidity of setup and drill design. Troubles are more common with portable drills and small holes, because of the difficulty of maintaining adequate rigidity and positive feed. Typical feeds, speeds, and other working details used in drilling refractory metals are given in Table 6.

Columbium. Accurately ground split-point drills should be used on columbium alloys, to minimize rubbing and accelerated wear at the drill margins. Cutting speeds and feeds given in Table 7 will provide good drill life for producing holes no deeper than three times their diameter. Highly active sulfurized or chlorinated cutting oils should be used.

Tantalum. Practice and results in drilling tantalum are influenced by the continuous, stringy chips formed. Because chips are likely to clog the holes, the usable range of cutting speeds for drilling small holes is closely related to the depth of the hole. Small-diameter holes up to one diameter deep can be drilled at 40 to 50 sfm. For holes more than one diameter deep, the speed should be reduced to 20 to 40 sfm (Table 6). Nominal speed, and feeds for three different hole sizes, for drilling alloy Ta – 10 W are given in Table 7.

Hole quality is affected by the drill point and the feed rate. Although drills with crankshaft or split points do not have longer life, they require less thrust force, thus helping to prevent the formation of burrs and extruded edges at the exit side of through holes. Drill feed should not exceed 0.002 ipr for drills up to ⅜ in. in diameter. Heavier feeds, although usable from the standpoint of longer drill life, will produce less accurate holes with poor surface finish.

Molybdenum is easier to drill than most other refractory metals. Nominal speeds and feeds are given in Table 7. Typical practice is summarized in Ta-

Table 5. Comparative Performance in Drilling 0.24-In.-Diam Holes ½ In. Deep in Refractory Alloys and Other Aerospace Materials

Workpiece metal	Hardness	Drill material(b)	Cutting fluid	Speed, sfm	Feed, ipr	Life, holes	Time, min	Rating(a) Time	Cost
Steels									
4130	200 Bhn	M2	Water-soluble oil	64	0.012	220	0.04	100	1
4340	Rc 54	C-2	Water-soluble oil	26	0.0015	16	0.81	5	22
Heat-Resisting Alloys									
HS-25	....	M36	Water-soluble oil	25	0.0036	144	0.35	12	6
A-286	....	M10	Water-soluble oil	27	0.0015	96	0.74	5.7	12
René 41	365 Bhn	T15	Chlorinated oil	16	0.002	56	0.96	4.3	16
Refractory Alloys									
D-31	225 Bhn	M1	Chlorinated oil	...	....	...	0.10	42	2
Ta – 10 W	240 Bhn	M1	Chlorinated oil	62	0.002	55	0.25	17	5
TZM	230 Bhn	M1	Chlorinated oil	110	0.005	96	0.06	70	2
Tungsten(c)	Rc 34	C-2	Chlorinated oil	150	0.001	7	0.19	23	25
(d)	Rc 26	C-2	Air + MoS_2	192	0.002	27	0.08	50	..

SOURCE: Same as for Table 1

(a) Ratings are based on 4130 steel at 100,000-psi tensile strength (200 Bhn); 4130 is rated 100 for drilling time and 1 for cost. Cost estimates are based on: operating cost of 11.6¢ per minute; 20¢ per drill change; 39¢ per point for high speed steel drills and 97¢ per point for carbide drills. (b) C-2 is a grade of carbide; other drill materials are high speed steels. (c) Unalloyed tungsten that was pressed and sintered to 96% of theoretical density. (d) Unalloyed tungsten that was pressed and sintered to 93% of theoretical density. The workpiece was machined at 800 F.

Table 6. Typical Practice for Drilling Refractory Metals

Item	Columbium	Tantalum	Molybdenum	Tungsten
Speed, sfm	75 to 90	40 to 50(a)	100 to 125	200 to 250
Feed, ipr	0.002 to 0.003(b)	0.002(c)	0.003 to 0.005(d)	0.001 to 0.002(e)
Cutting oil	Chlorinated or sulfochlorinated	Chlorinated or sulfochlorinated	Chlorinated	Chlorinated
Drill type	Stub-length	Stub-length	Stub-length	Stub; heavy-duty
Drill point	118° split	118° plain or split	118° plain or split(f)	118°/90° point(g)
Drill material	High speed steel	High speed steel	High speed steel	Solid carbide

(a) For drilling holes to a depth of one diameter. Decrease speed to 20 to 40 sfm for holes deeper than one diameter. (b) For drilling holes up to ⅜ in. in diameter. Use feed of 0.004 to 0.006 ipr for holes ⅜ in. in diameter and larger. (c) For drilling holes up to ⅜ in. in diameter. Use feed of 0.003 to 0.005 ipr for holes ⅜ in. in diameter and larger. (d) For drilling holes up to ⅜ in. in diameter. Use feed of 0.005 to 0.009 ipr for holes ⅜ in. in diameter and larger. (e) For drilling holes 3⁄16 to ⅜ in. in diameter. Use feed of 0.0005 to 0.001 ipr for drilling holes under 3⁄16 in. in diameter. (f) Use of split-point drill may result in less damage to work at breakthrough. (g) 90° extending from margin up one third of lip; notched point; 10°-to-12° lip clearance.

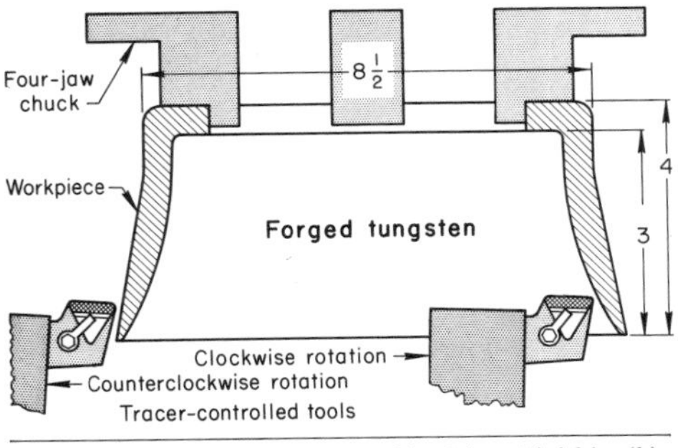

Machining condition	Roughing(a)	Finishing(b)
Speed, sfm	125	175
Feed, ipr	0.011	0.004
Depth of cut, in.	1⁄16 to ⅛	0.005 to 0.020
Tool life, minutes	2	2.5
Cutting fluid	None	None

(a) Roughing tool (not illustrated): square positive-rake carbide insert with 1⁄32-in. nose radius and 45° lead angle. (b) Finishing tool (shown above): triangular positive-rake carbide insert with 1⁄32-in. nose radius and 0° lead angle.

Fig. 2. Tungsten forging on which inside and outside surfaces were turned in a tracer lathe (Example 862)

Table 7. Nominal Speeds and Feeds for Drilling Refractory Alloys With High Speed Steel Drills(a)

Alloy(b)	Brinell hardness	Speed, sfm	Feed, ipr, for hole diameter of: ⅛ in.	¼ in.	½ in.
Cb-752(c)	170-225..	75	0.003	0.005	0.007
Ta – 10 W	200-250..	50	0.002	0.002	0.004
Mo – 0.5 Ti(d)	220-290..	100	0.003	0.005	0.007

(a) M33 or T15 high speed steel. (b) All alloys in the stress-relieved condition. (c) Or columbium alloy D-31 or D-43. (d) Or molybdenum alloy TZM, TZC or Mo – 30 W.

ble 6. Any of the standard high speed steels, such as M1, M3 and M10, are suitable for drills, under normal conditions. The standard 118°-point chisel-edge (plain) drill performs as well as drills with special points (except sometimes at breakthrough).

Table 8. Nominal Speeds and Feeds for Reaming Refractory Alloys With High Speed Steel and Carbide Reamers

Alloy(a)	Brinell hardness	Speed, sfm	Feed, ipr, for hole diam of: ¼ in.	½ in.
High Speed Steel Reamers(b)				
Cb-752(c)	170-225 ..	100	0.004	0.006
Ta – 10 W	220-250 ..	70	0.007	0.008
Mo – 0.5 Ti(d)	220-290 ..	60	0.006	0.010
Carbide Reamers(e)				
Cb-752(c)	170-225 ..	120	0.005	0.007
Ta – 10 W	200-250 ..	80	0.006	0.008
Mo – 0.5 Ti(d)	220-290 ..	120	0.006	0.010

(a) All alloys in the stress-relieved condition. (b) M1, M2 or M7 high speed steel. (c) Or columbium alloy D-31 or D-43. (d) Or molybdenum alloy TZM, TZC or Mo – 30 W. (e) Grade C-2 carbide was used for these reamers.

Table 9. Nominal Speeds for Tapping Refractory Alloys With High Speed Steel Taps(a)

Alloy(b)	Brinell hardness	Speed, sfm
Cb-752(c)	170 to 225	10
Ta – 10 W	200 to 250	3
Mo – 0.5 Ti(d)	220 to 290	50

(a) M1, M7 or M10 high speed steel. (b) All alloys in the stress-relieved condition. (c) Or columbium alloy D-31 or D-43. (d) Or molybdenum alloy TZM, TZC or Mo – 30 W.

Drill thrust is low in drilling molybdenum — approximately the same as in drilling pearlitic cast iron. Therefore, higher feed rates may be used without damaging the drill. However, when expensive metals are drilled, avoidance of damage to the workpiece, rather than maximum tool life, should receive primary consideration.

Chipping of the workpiece during breakthrough of the drill is a difficulty encountered in drilling the more brittle forms of molybdenum. Because 20 to 30% of the total thrust required by the standard drill results from the inefficient chisel edge at the point, damage to workpieces at breakthrough can sometimes be decreased by substituting a split-point drill for the chisel-edge drill. Decreasing the feed rate is less efficient in reducing thrust and it causes poor and erratic drill life. The use of sacrificial workpiece supports and prechamfering of the breakthrough area also help to prevent chipping at breakthrough.

Tungsten is more difficult to drill than the other refractory metals. Because tungsten begins a brittle-to-ductile transition at about 400 F, the workpiece is often heated to 400 to 800 F for machining. However, acceptable holes can be drilled on a production basis at room temperature if the proper procedure is followed and precautions are taken. Typical practice is summarized in Table 6. Because of possible damage to the workpiece and short drill life, design and manufacturing alternatives to avoid the drilling of holes should be considered.

The major problems encountered in conventional drilling of high-density unalloyed tungsten are:

1 Chipping at hole edges on the entrance side
2 Spalling on the exit side of through holes
3 Radial cracking, extending from holes to nearby discontinuities
4 Drill fracture, caused by excessive force, nonrigid setup, or chip interference in drill flutes.

The following procedures are recommended in drilling tungsten:

1 Use solid carbide drills that are accurately ground. (Drill lip runout should be less than 0.001 in.)
2 In drilling through holes, use one of the following to prevent spalling at breakthrough: (*a*) a tight-fitting backup plate of steel or similar metal clamped over the surface where breakthrough will occur, or (*b*) drill holes halfway through from each side.
3 Drill holes no closer than one drill diameter from any edge or other discontinuity.
4 Direct a heavy stream of cutting fluid into the hole to flush away chips. Retract the drill and flush out chips at least once for holes deeper than two diameters.
5 Locate and start holes with a carbide center drill. Do not use drill bushings, because they interfere with chip flow and cause drill fracture.
6 Replace drills at the first indication of chipping at hole edges or when the wear land at the drill corners reaches 0.016 in.

Reaming and Tapping

Nominal speeds and feeds for reaming of columbium, tantalum and molybdenum are given in Table 8. Tungsten should not be reamed. Carbide tools are most frequently used for reaming of refractory metals, but high speed steel reamers also can be used, at slightly lower speeds and feeds, as indicated in Table 8.

Nominal speeds and feeds for tapping of columbium, molybdenum and tantalum are given in Table 9. Tapping of tungsten is difficult and should be avoided; if it is unavoidable, the workpiece should be heated to 400 to 800 F, and a four-flute stub-type plug tap made of nitrided M10 or T15 high speed steel should be used. A speed of 5 sfm is recommended.

Milling

Machinability ratings based on metal-removal rates in turning (Table 1) also indicate performance to be expected in milling.

Columbium has been successfully milled with cutters of high speed steel and of carbide. Nominal speeds and

Table 10. Nominal Speeds and Feeds for Face Milling of Refractory Alloys With High Speed Steel and Carbide Cutters

Metal or alloy	Condition(a)	Brinell hardness	For 0.060-in. depth of cut: Speed, sfm		Feed, ipt	For 0.015-in. depth of cut: Speed, sfm		Feed, ipt
High Speed Steel Cutters(b)								
Cb-752(c)	SR	170-225 ..	120(d)		0.010	160		0.008
Ta – 10 W	SR	200-250 ..	60(e)		0.010(e)	80(e)		0.008(e)
Mo – 0.5 Ti(f)	SR	220-290 ..	90(d)		0.010	120		0.008
Carbide Cutters(g)			Brazed	Dispos.		Brazed	Dispos.	
Cb-752(c)	SR	170-225 ..	140(d)	155(d)	0.010	150	165	0.008
Mo – 0.5 Ti(f)	SR	220-290 ..	225(d)	250(d)	0.005	255	275	0.004
Tungsten (85% dens.)	PS	180-200 ..	80	90	0.010	100	110	0.008
Tungsten (93% dens.)	PS	290-320 ..	70	80	0.010	80	90	0.008
Tungsten (96% dens.)	AF	290-320 ..	110	120	0.009	120	130	0.007
W – 2 Th	PS	260-320 ..	120	130	0.010	150	165	0.008
W – 15 Mo	AC	260-320 ..	120	130	0.010	150	165	0.008
W – 10 Ag	PS	290-320 ..	220	240	0.010	250	275	0.008

(a) AC = As cast; AF = As forged; PS = Pressed and sintered; SR = Stress relieved. (b) M33 or T15 high speed steel, except as footnoted under (e). (c) Or columbium alloy D-31 or D-43. (d) Depth of cut, 0.100 in. (e) Use cutters of M41, M42, M43 or M44 high speed steel. (f) Or molybdenum alloy TZM, TZC or Mo – 30 W. (g) Grade C-2 carbide.

Table 11. Nominal Speeds and Feeds for End Milling of Refractory Alloys With High Speed Steel and Carbide Cutters

Metal or alloy	Condition(a)	Brinell hardness	For 0.050-in. depth of cut: Speed, sfm	Feed, ipt, for cutter diameter of: ¼ in.	½ in.	¾ in.	1 to 2 in.	For 0.015-in. depth of cut: Speed, sfm	Feed, ipt, for cutter diameter of: ¼ in.	½ in.	¾ in.	1 to 2 in.
High Speed Steel Cutters(b)												
Cb-752(c)	SR	170 to 225 ...	80	0.002	0.003	0.003	0.004	100	0.0015	0.002	0.0025	0.003
Ta – 10 W	SR	200 to 250 ...	55	0.002	0.002	0.003	0.004	65	0.001	0.0015	0.002	0.0025
Mo – 0.5 Ti(d)	SR	220 to 290 ...	160	0.002	0.003	0.004	0.004	190	0.001	0.001	0.0015	0.002
Carbide Cutters(e)												
Cb-752(c)	SR	170 to 225 ...	150	0.002	0.003	0.003	0.004	175	0.0015	0.002	0.0025	0.003
Mo – 0.5 Ti(d)	SR	220 to 290 ...	300	0.002	0.003	0.004	0.004	325	0.001	0.001	0.0015	0.002
Tungsten (85% density)	PS	180 to 200 ...	150	....	....	0.003	0.003	200	....	....	0.003	0.003
Tungsten (93% density)	PS	290 to 320 ...	150	....	....	0.003	0.003	200	....	....	0.003	0.003
W – 2 Th	PS	260 to 320 ...	150	....	....	0.003	0.003	200	....	....	0.003	0.003
W – 15 Mo	AC	260 to 320 ...	150	....	....	0.003	0.003	200	....	....	0.003	0.003
W – 10 Ag	PS	290 to 320 ...	200	....	0.002	0.003	0.005	250	....	0.001	0.001	0.001

(a) AC = As cast; PS = Pressed and sintered; SR = Stress relieved. (b) T15 high speed steel; M33, M41, M42, M43 or M44 can be used as an alternate. (c) Or columbium alloy D-31 or D-43. (d) Or molybdenum alloy TZM, TZC or Mo – 30 W. (e) Grade C-2 carbide.

feeds for face and end milling are given in Tables 10 and 11. Cutters having 0° axial rake and +30° radial rake have proved best for most applications. Most important for successful milling of columbium is the selection of cutting fluid: A highly chlorinated or sulfurized oil is recommended.

Tantalum can also be milled with either high speed steel or carbide tools. As shown in Tables 10 and 11, feeds for tantalum are approximately the same as for columbium, although tantalum is machined at slower speeds than is columbium. Cutting fluid should be a soluble-oil emulsion.

Molybdenum. Nominal speeds and feeds for face and end milling of molybdenum are given in Tables 10 and 11. Cutters with inserts of T15 high speed steel (or a similar highly alloyed grade) or C-2 carbide are used. Although speeds and feeds for the two cutter materials differ greatly (Tables 10 and 11), relatively high speeds and light feeds are generally used.

For the more brittle grades of molybdenum, cutters with zero axial and radial rakes give good results and minimize chipping. Positive rakes can be used for the more ductile grades.

Although climb milling, rather than conventional milling, is preferred for all refractory metals, it is especially important to use the climb technique for milling the more brittle grades of molybdenum, because chipping of the work metal at the entrance and exit of the cutter is minimized.

Use of cutting fluid is mandatory for milling of molybdenum. A soluble oil mixed 1 to 20 with water is satisfactory for most applications.

A typical procedure for face milling of a molybdenum alloy is described in the following example.

Example 863. Face Milling Molybdenum Alloy Bars (Table 12)

Arc-cast-and-rolled bars of Mo – 0.5 Ti were face milled in a horizontal milling machine. The bars were 2 by 1½ by 52 in. long; hardness was 220 Bhn. The 1½-in. faces were milled under the conditions shown in Table 12. These machining conditions proved to be near optimum for this application. Use of a cutting fluid was mandatory; attempts at dry milling reduced both cutter life and cutting speed about 50%.

Improved surface finish was obtained with a cutter having positive rake. However, cutting speed had to be reduced 20%. In addition, tool life decreased, because of edge chipping. The relation of cutting speed to tool life for this application was significantly affected by depth of cut. The cutting speed for equal tool life was only 30% higher for 0.030-in. depth of cut than for 0.060-in. depth.

Table 12. Cutter Details and Machining Conditions for Face Milling Arc-Cast-and-Rolled Mo – 0.5 Ti Bars (Example 863)

Cutter Details	
Size and type	4-in. diam, single-tooth
Material	Carbide insert
Axial rake	0°
Radial rake	0°
Cutting-edge angle	45°
End cutting-edge angle	10°
Milling Conditions	
Speed	230 sfm
Feed	0.005 ipt
Depth of cut	0.060 in.
Width of cut	1½ in.
Cutting fluid	Soluble-oil:water (1:20)
Tool life, per grind	120 linear in. of cut
Surface finish	150 micro-in. max

Table 13. Nominal Pitches, Speeds and Feeds for Power Sawing of Refractory Alloys With High Speed Steel Blades

Alloy(a)	Brinell hardness	Pitch (teeth/in.) for thickness (in.) of: Under ¼	¼ to ¾	¾ to 2	Over 2	Speed, strokes per min	Feed, in. per stroke	Pitch (teeth/in.) for thickness (in.) of: Under ¼	¼ to 1½	Over 1½	Speed, sfm
		Power Hacksawing						Power Band Sawing			
Cb-752(b)	170-225	10	10	6	4	50	0.006	8-10	6-8	3-6	90
Ta – 10 W	200-250	10	10	6	4	40	0.006	8-10	6-8	3-6	70
Mo – 0.5 Ti(c)	220-290	10	10	6	4	90	0.006	8-10	6-8	3-6	125

(a) All alloys in the stress-relieved condition. (b) Or columbium alloy D-31 or D-43. (c) Or molybdenum alloy TZM, TZC or Mo – 30 W.

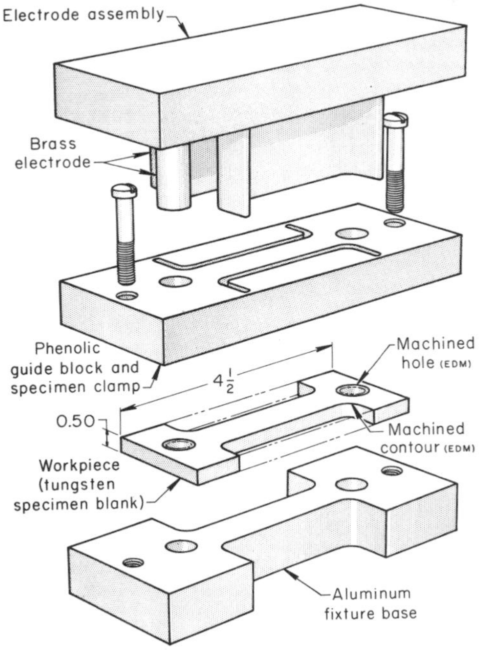

Operations

1 Saw 0.50-in.-thick tungsten plate into blanks, using a diamond-edged band saw.
2 Load blank into fixture and close components of assembly.
3 Electrical discharge machine contour and two holes, using 30-amp gap current (time required, 5 to 7 min per specimen).
4 Unload specimen, polish edges, and ream holes.

Fig. 3. Tungsten test specimen and setup for producing it from sheet by electrical discharge machining (Example 864)

Tungsten. As shown in Table 10, the composition and density of tungsten greatly affect the speed used for face milling at a given feed rate. For end milling (Table 11), composition and density have less effect on speed. The climb technique should always be used.

Carbide cutting edges are used exclusively for milling of tungsten. In room-temperature milling, best results are obtained with a copious supply of highly chlorinated cutting oil. Some success in warm milling (400 to 800 F) has been reported; under these conditions no cutting fluid is used.

Sawing

Columbium, tantalum and molybdenum can be sawed with power hacksaws or band saws, using high speed steel blades. Recommended pitch, based on work-metal thickness, and nominal speeds and feeds for hacksawing and band sawing are given in Table 13. Sawing is not recommended for tungsten (sawing blanks from plate in Example 864 was an unconventional operation).

Electrical Discharge Machining of Tungsten

Because unalloyed tungsten is extremely brittle at room temperature, and therefore presents problems in machining by conventional methods, electrical discharge machining is sometimes used. The principal advantage of this method is that it is essentially force-free, and therefore force-induced fracture and chipping of delicate parts is avoided. However, electrical discharge machining is extremely slow. Metal-removal rate for tungsten is approximately 0.0001 cu in. per ampere-minute with brass electrodes and is accompanied by a workpiece-to-electrode wear ratio of 1 to 2. By comparison, typical metal-removal rates and wear rates for a hardened steel workpiece and a brass electrode are 0.0003 cu in. per ampere-minute and 2.5 to 1, respectively. In the two examples that follow, electrical discharge machining was selected as the appropriate method.

Example 864. Electrical Discharge Machining of Tungsten Plate (Fig. 3)

The tool assembly shown in Fig. 3 was used to machine a contour and two holes in blanks of unalloyed tungsten. When a standard machine and a gap current of 30 amp were used, machining could be completed in 5 to 7 min. Other details related to the operation are included with Fig. 3.

Example 865. Electrical Discharge Trepanning of Tungsten Forgings (Fig. 4)

The setup shown in Fig. 4 was used for removing test specimens ⅝ in. in diameter by 3 in. long from tungsten forgings. The best technique was to trepan halfway through the forging from one side and then to complete the operation by trepanning from the opposite side. Operating details are included with Fig. 4.

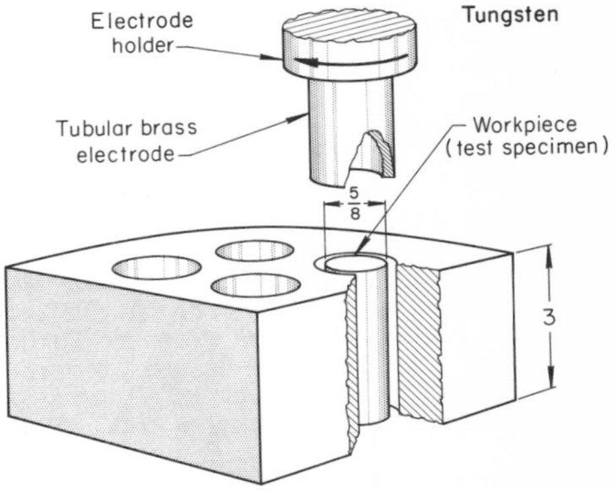

Operations

1 Electrical discharge trepan to 1½-in. depth, using 40 amp gap current (time: 2 hr).
2 Repeat operation 1, from opposite side of forging (time: 2 hr).

Fig. 4. Setup for trepanning cylindrical test specimens from a tungsten forging by electrical discharge machining (Example 865)

Grinding

Even with the best conditions, refractory metals are difficult and expensive to grind. Table 14 compares grinding ratios for refractory metals, three steels, and a nickel-base heat-resisting alloy. For refractory metals, grinding ratio is extremely sensitive to grinding fluid. In experiments with five different fluids, a threefold variation in grinding ratio was observed.

With the exception of tungsten, the refractory metals load grinding wheels rapidly; as a result, frequent dressing of wheels and plentiful quantities of grinding fluid are required. Water-base solutions (such as potassium nitrite) are effective in minimizing wheel loading. When the residue this solution leaves on the work is objectionable, soluble-oil emulsions or sulfurized or chlorinated grinding fluids can be used.

Columbium can be ground without surface cracking if the previously mentioned precautions are observed. Table 15 recommends an A_s-60-J-V wheel and a speed of 4000 sfm for cylindrical, internal, centerless and surface grinding. This wheel differs only slightly from the one referred to in Table 14. Other typical data are listed in Table 15.

Tantalum is sometimes difficult to grind, because chatter is likely to develop, especially in surface grinding. For this reason, speeds as low as 2000 sfm (Table 14) have been used. However, in a rigid setup and with a flood of grinding fluid (water-base synthetic is most commonly used), chatter can usually be overcome. A speed of 4000 sfm is recommended in Table 15 for all four types of grinding. Wheels with aluminum oxide abrasive and a vitrified bond are used exclusively for grinding tantalum.

Molybdenum is also likely to cause chatter in grinding. In some surface grinding, a harder wheel (N hardness, as shown in Table 14) and a slower speed have helped in minimizing chatter. However, with a rigid setup and a plentiful supply of grinding fluid (water-base synthetic), molybdenum can usually be ground successfully by using the data shown in Table 15.

Tungsten. Grinding is likely to cause surface cracking in tungsten, as a result of high thermal stresses. A wheel that is too soft is preferable to one that is too hard, because an excessively hard wheel will glaze more quickly and is more likely to cause cracking. Aluminum oxide wheels like A_s-46-N5-V, operated at 4000 sfm with a downfeed of 0.0005 in. per pass, have been used for surface grinding (Table 14). For most grinding of tungsten, however, silicon carbide wheels perform better than aluminum oxide wheels. In Table 15, silicon carbide wheels are recommended for all grinding of tungsten. This table also shows slow speeds (2000 sfm) for grinding of tungsten, regardless of the grinding method.

Because tungsten is brittle, even the lightest grinding pressure is likely to cause flaking at corners. Grinding toward sharp corners is never recommended. Soluble oil is acceptable as a cutting fluid; heating the fluid to about 100 F sometimes helps prevent surface cracking. Grinding practice that produced acceptable results in one application is described in the following example.

Example 866. Cylindrical Grinding of Tungsten (Table 16)

Practice for grinding the outside diameter of tungsten workpieces 9 in. in diameter and 3 in. long is summarized in Table 16. In this application, a silicon carbide wheel of medium hardness (J) provided acceptable results. A wheel of relatively large diameter (24 in.) was chosen because of rapid breakdown. Under the operating conditions shown in Table 16, about 0.002 in. could be removed from the 9-in. diameter of the workpiece before the wheel required dressing.

Table 14. Grinding Ratios for Surface Grinding Refractory and Other Alloys (a)

Workpiece metal	Hardness	Wheel: Classification	Wheel: Speed, fpm	Grinding fluid	Table speed, fpm	Downfeed, in.	Grinding ratio (b)
Steels							
D-6ac	R_C 57	A_s-46-H8-V	6000	Sulfurized oil	40	0.001	75
302 stainless	R_B 86	A_s-60-H8-V	6000	Sulfurized oil	60	0.001	20
302 stainless	R_B 86	A_s-60-H8-V	6000	Water-soluble oil	60	0.001	8
Heat-Resisting Alloy							
René 41	365 Bhn	A_s-46-J8-V	4000	KNO_2 solution	40	0.001	10
Refractory Metals							
Columbium	225 Bhn	A_s-46-K8-V	4000	Chlorinated oil	60	0.0005	4.0
D-31	225 Bhn	A_s-46-K8-V	2000	KNO_2 solution	40	0.0005	7.5
Ta – 10 W	240 Bhn	A_s-46-J8-V	2000	KNO_2 solution	40	0.001	4.8
TZM	232 Bhn	A_s-46-N5-V	2000	KNO_2 solution	40	0.001	25
Tungsten	R_C 26	A_s-46-N5-V	4000	KNO_2 solution	40	0.001	4.3

SOURCE: Same as for Table 1

(a) Crossfeeds were 0.05 in. per pass in all tests except for Ta – 10 W, which was ground at 0.025 in. per pass. Designations of grinding wheels are based on American Standard Marking Chart B5.17. (b) Ratio of the volume of metal removed in grinding to the volume of wheel wear. The higher this index, the easier the metal is to grind.

Table 15. Typical Conditions for Grinding Refractory Alloys

Grinding condition	Metal or alloy (a): Cb-752(b) (170-225 Bhn)	Ta – 10 W (200-250 Bhn)	Mo – 0.5 Ti(c) (220-290 Bhn)	Tungsten(d)
Cylindrical Grinding				
Wheel classification	A_s-60-J-V	A_s-60-J-V	A_s-60-J-V	C-60-J-V
Wheel speed, sfm	4000	4000	4000	2000
Work speed, sfm	50	50	50	50
Infeed per pass, in.:				
Roughing	0.001	0.001	0.001	0.001
Finishing (max)	0.0003	0.0003	0.0003	0.0003
Traverse per work revolution, fraction of wheel width:				
Roughing	1/5	1/5	1/5	1/5
Finishing	1/10	1/10	1/10	1/10
Internal Grinding				
Wheel classification	A_s-60-J-V	A_s-60-J-V	A_s-46-J-V	C-60-K-V
Wheel speed, sfm	4000	4000	4000	2000
Work speed, sfm	50 to 100	50 to 100	50 to 100	50 to 100
Infeed per pass, in.:				
Roughing	0.001	0.001	0.001	0.0005
Finishing (max)	0.0005	0.0005	0.0005	0.0002
Traverse per work revolution, fraction of wheel width:				
Roughing	1/3	1/3	1/3	1/3
Finishing	1/6	1/6	1/6	1/6
Centerless Grinding				
Wheel classification	A_s-60-J-V	A_s-60-J-V	A_s-60-J-V	C-60-J-V
Wheel speed, sfm	4000	2000 to 4000	2000 to 4000	2000
Work speed, sfm	50	50	50	50
Infeed per pass, in.:				
Roughing	0.001	0.001	0.001	0.001
Finishing (max)	0.0005	0.0005	0.0005	0.0003
Regulating wheel:				
Angle	3°	3°	3°	3°
Speed, rpm	30	30	30	30
Surface Grinding				
Wheel classification	A_s-46-J-V	A_s-46-J-V	A_s-46-J-V	C-60-K-V
Wheel speed, sfm	4000	4000	4000	2000
Table speed, sfm	50 to 100	50 to 100	40 to 80	50 to 100
Downfeed per pass, in.:				
Roughing	0.001	0.001	0.001	0.001
Finishing (max)	0.0005	0.0005	0.0005	0.0005
Crossfeed per pass, fraction of wheel width	1/2	1/2	1/2	1/2

(a) Alloys in the stress-relieved condition, except for tungsten. (b) Or columbium alloy D-31 or D-43. (c) Or molybdenum alloy TZM, CZM or Mo – 30 W. (d) Pure tungsten at 85%, 93%, 96% and 99% densities, and alloys W – 2 Th, W – 15 Mo and W – 10 Ag. Conditions and hardnesses are assumed to be the same as described in Table 3.

Table 16. Wheel Details and Grinding Conditions for Cylindrical Grinding of Tungsten (Example 866)

Wheel Details	
Classification	C-60-J5-V
Size	24-in.-diam by 1¼ in. wide
Dressing	Automatic single-point diamond
Grinding Conditions	
Wheel speed (a)	1045 rpm; 6600 sfm
Feed	0.0002 to 0.0005 in. per pass
Grinding fluid	Soluble oil heated to 100 F
Wheel life	Grinding of 0.002 in. from OD of workpiece 9-in. diam by 3 in. long

(a) Workpieces were rotated at 40 rpm opposite to direction of grinding-wheel rotation.

MACHINING OF NONFERROUS METALS

CONTENTS

Machining of Aluminum Alloys

*By the ASM Committee on Machining of Aluminum Alloys**

ALUMINUM alloys can be machined rapidly and economically; because of their complex metallurgical structure, their machining characteristics are superior to those of pure aluminum.

Effect of Microstructure. The microconstituents present in aluminum alloys have important effects on machining characteristics: Nonabrasive constituents have a beneficial effect, and insoluble, abrasive constituents exert a detrimental effect on tool life and surface quality. Constituents that are insoluble but soft and nonabrasive are beneficial, because they assist in chip breakage; such constituents are purposely added in formulating high-strength free-cutting alloys for processing in high-speed automatic bar and chucking machines.

In general, the softer alloys — and, to a lesser extent, some of the harder alloys — are likely to form a built-up edge on the cutting lip of the tool; this edge consists of aluminum particles that have become welded to the tool edge because they were melted by the heat generated in cutting. Edge buildup can be minimized by using effective cutting fluids and by employing tools with surfaces that are free of grinding marks and scratches.

Alloys containing more than 10% silicon are the most difficult to machine, because hard particles of free silicon cause rapid tool wear. Alloys containing more than 5% silicon will not finish to the bright machined surfaces of other high-strength aluminum alloys, but will have slightly gray surfaces with little luster. Chips are torn rather than sheared from the work, and special precautions (such as the use of lubricant-containing cutting fluids) must be taken to avoid buildup of burrs on cutting edges.

Cast Alloys. Cast alloys containing copper, magnesium or zinc as the principal alloying elements impose few machining problems. Tools with small rake angles normally can be used with little danger of burring the part or of developing buildup on the cutting edges of tools. Alloys having silicon as the major alloying element require tools with larger rake angles, and they are more economically machined at lower speeds and feeds.

Wrought Alloys. Most wrought aluminum alloys have excellent machining characteristics; several are well suited to multiple-operation machining. To utilize fully the free-machining qualities of aluminum alloys, thorough familiarity with recommended tool designs and machining practices is an essential requirement.

Strain-Hardenable Alloys. Alloys in this group (including commercially pure aluminum) contain no alloying elements that would render them hardenable by solution heat treatment and precipitation; however, they can be strengthened to some extent by cold work. In machining, a continuous chip is formed that must be directed away from the workpiece by tools with generous side and back rake angles, thus preventing scratching of the finished surface with the work-hardened chips. These alloys machine easily, although tool pressures are high as a result of high friction. To obtain good surface finish, sharp tools are mandatory, because the alloys are gummy. Machinability is improved by cold working; alloys in the full-hard temper are easier to machine to a good finish than those in the annealed condition.

Heat Treatable Alloys. Most of the alloys of this group contain fairly high percentages of alloying elements such as copper, silicon, magnesium and zinc. They can be machined to a good finish with or without cutting fluid, but a cutting fluid is recommended for most operations. Turnings usually occur as long, continuous curls, except for the free-machining alloys, which contain chip-breaking constituents.

Heat treatable alloys are more machinable in the heat treated tempers than in the softer as-fabricated or annealed condition.

Machinability groupings for aluminum alloys are useful in specifying tool forms. For this purpose, alloys are classified into five groups: A, B, C, D and E, in increasing order of chip length and in decreasing order of finish quality, as defined in the footnotes of Table 1. Ratings for most commercial aluminum alloys are given in Table 1, and typical chips for each rating are illustrated in Fig. 1.

Cutting Force and Power

The cutting force, and hence the power, required to machine aluminum is less than might be expected on the basis of its mechanical properties. Although the cutting force required to machine similar metals is often in direct proportion to tensile strength, this proportion is not necessarily valid with

*JOHN LONGABAUGH, *Chairman,* Chief Metallurgist, Outboard Marine Corp.; ALFRED A. BOULD, Assistant Section Chief, Facilities Dept., Grumman Aircraft Engineering Corp.; R. COUCHMAN, Assistant Chief, Fabricating Metallurgy Div., Alcoa Research Laboratories, Aluminum Co. of America.

JOHN H. DEN BOER, Metallurgical Supervisor, Alloys Plant, Reynolds Metals Co.; A. J. KAISER, Chief Tool Engineer – Metals, Pinsetter Plant, Bowling Div., Brunswick Corp.; VIRGIL J. KNIERIM, Staff Metallurgist, Elbeeco Plant, Aircraft Div., Aeroquip Corp.; JOSEPH KOCHANEK, Manager of Production Engineering, Chandler Evans Corp.; WILL LADD, Assistant Head, Production Engineering, Globe Industries, Inc.; E. R. LOEBACH, formerly with Automotive Div., Studebaker Corp.

CARL REXER, Department Head, Apparatus and Optical Div., Eastman Kodak Co.; EARL J. ROBERTS, Senior Manufacturing Research Engineer, Lockheed-Georgia Co. Div., Lockheed Aircraft Corp.; ALFRED SPOLIDORO, Senior Engineer, Merrimack Valley Works, Western Electric Co., Inc.

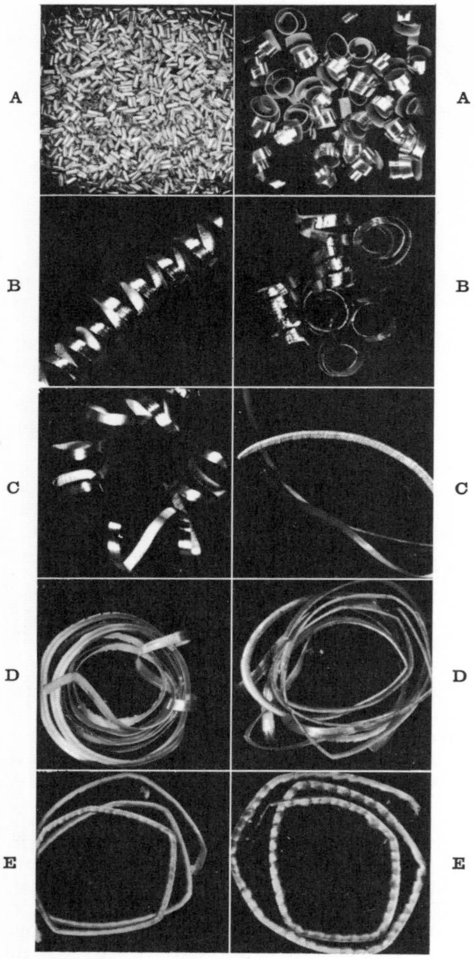

Machinability rating	Alloy	Speed, sfm	Feed, ipr Left photo	Feed, ipr Right photo
A	2011-T3	400	0.0026	0.0060
B	2024-T4	100	0.0060	0.0104
C	6061-T6	400	0.0060	0.0104
D	3004-H32	400	0.0060	0.0104
E	1100-H12	400	0.0060	0.0104

Fig. 1. Typical chips for machinability ratings A to E (Table 1) for aluminum alloys. All chips were made with 20°-rake tool and 0.100-in. depth of cut.

Table 1. Machinability Ratings of Aluminum Alloys

Alloy(a)	Tempers(a)	Rating(b)
Casting Alloys		
13, 43	F	E
108, A108	F	B
113, C113	F	B
A132	T551, T65	C
F132	T5	C
138	F	B
A140	F	A
142	T21, T571, T61, T77	B
195	T4, T6, T7, T62	B
214, A214	F	B
F214	F	B
218, B218	F	B
220	T4	B
319, 333	F	C
319, 333	T5, T6, T7	B
344	F	D
354	T61, T62	B
355	T51, T6, T61, T62, T7, T71	B
C355	T61	B
356	T51, T6, T7, T71	C
A356, A357	T61	B
357	T6	B
359	T61, T62	B
360	F	C
A360	F	C
364	F, T5	C
380, A380	F, T5	B
603, 607 (Ternalloy 5 & 7)	F	B
A612, C612	F	B
D612 (40E)	F	B
613 (Tenzaloy)	F	B
750, A750, B750	T5	A
Red X8	T4, T51	B
Red X11 & X20	T5	E
Tens 50	T6	B
Wrought Alloys		
EC	O, H111, H112, H12	E
EC	H14 to H19	D
1100	O, H112, H12	E
1100	H14 to H18	D
2011	T3, T4, T6, T8	A
2014(c)	O	C
2014(c)	T3, T4, T6	B
2017	O	C
2017	T4	B
2018	T61	B
2024(c)	T3, T4, T6, T8	B
2219	T3, T6, T8	B
2618	T6	B
3003(c)	O, H112, H12	E
3003(c)	H14 to H18	D
3004(c)	O, H112, H32	D
3004(c)	H34 to H38	C
5005	O, H112, H12, H32	E
5005	H14 to H18	D
5005	H34 to H38	D
5050	O, H112, H32	D
5050	H34 to H38	C
5052	O, H112, H32	D
5052	H34 to H38	C
5056	O	D
5056	H18, H38	C
5083	O, H112, H321, H323	D
5083	H131, H343	C
5086, 5154	O, H112, H32	D
5086, 5154	H34 to H38	C
5257, 5357	O	D
5257, 5357	H25, H28, H38	C
5454, 5456	O, H112, H311	D
5454, 5456	H343	C
5457	O	D
5457	H25, H28, H38	C
5557, 5657	O	E
5557, 5657	H25, H28, H38	D
6061(c)	O	D
6061(c)	T4, T6	C
6063	O, T2, T4	D
6063	T5, T6, T8	C
6262	T4, T9	B
6463	O, T1	D
6463	T4, T5, T6	C
7075(c)	T6, T73	B
7079	T6	B
7178(c)	T6	B

(a) Alloys and tempers are those commonly used. Alloy modifications designated by other second digits and temper variations designated by added numerals will have the same ratings.
(b) A, B, C, D and E are relative ratings in increasing order of chip length (see Fig. 1) and decreasing order of quality of finish and are defined as:
A – Free cutting, very small broken chips and excellent finish
B – Curled or easily broken chips and good-to-excellent finish
C – Continuous chips and good finish
D – Continuous chips and satisfactory finish
E – Optimum tool design and machine settings required to obtain satisfactory control of chip and finish.
(c) Includes clad alloys and tempers.

dissimilar metals. For example, the common mechanical properties of 2017-T4 aluminum alloy and of hot rolled low-carbon steel are quite similar (Table 2) but, as Fig. 2 shows, the cutting force required in turning aluminum is only about 35% that required in turning low-carbon steel. Consequently, as shown in Fig. 3, the number of cubic inches of metal that can be removed per minute per unit horsepower expended is approximately three times as great for aluminum alloy 2017-T4 as for hot rolled low-carbon steel of closely similar tensile strength.

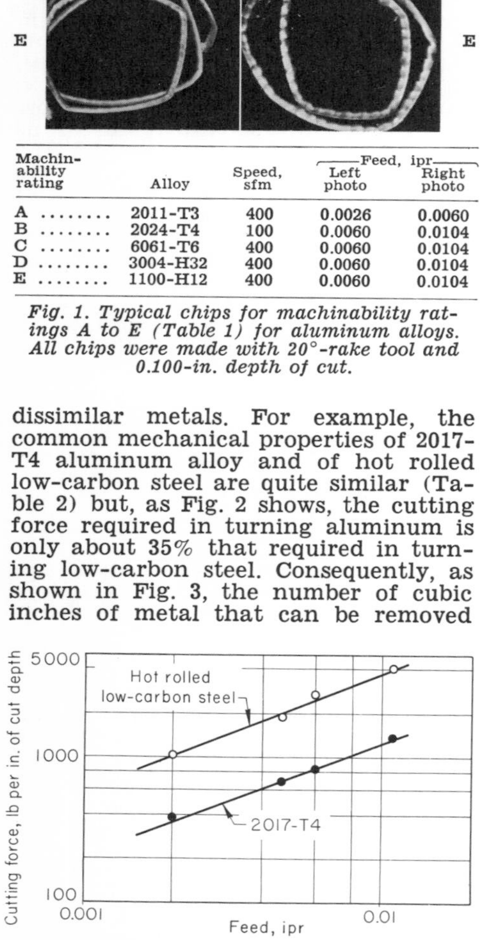

Fig. 2. Effect of feed on cutting force for low-carbon steel and aluminum alloy 2017-T4 with comparable mechanical properties

Selection of Alloy and Temper

An application often dictates the use of a specific alloy or temper, or both. Under these conditions, composition cannot be changed for the sake of improving machinability. However, there is often a marked difference in machinability among different tempers of the same alloy. Thus, it may be feasible to do some or all of the machining operations with the alloy in the most favorable condition for machining and then to convert the alloy to the temper specified for the end use.

Table 2. Comparison of Common Mechanical Properties of 2017-T4 Aluminum Alloy and Hot Rolled Low-Carbon Steel

Mechanical property	Aluminum alloy 2017-T4	Hot rolled low-carbon steel
Tensile strength, psi	63,800	65,200
0.2% yield strength, psi ..	40,300	40,200(a)
Elongation in 4 diam, % ..	26.0	32.7
Shear strength, psi	40,500	47,000
Brinell hardness number:		
500-kg, 10-mm ball	113	110
3000-kg, 10-mm ball	132	128

(a) Yield point is 44,800 psi.

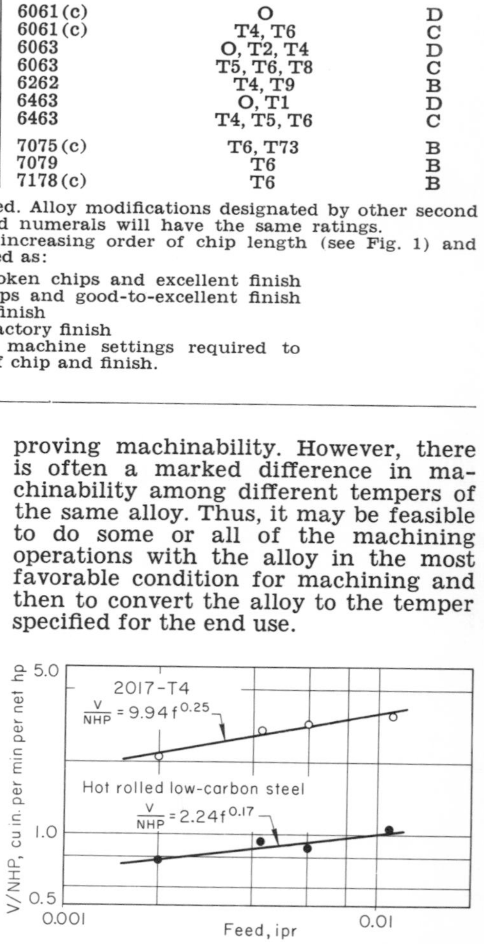

Fig. 3. Effect of feed on metal removal rate per net horsepower for low-carbon steel and aluminum alloy 2017-T4 with comparable mechanical properties

For some applications, two or more alloys are equally acceptable. Under these conditions, machinability can be a major consideration in making the final selection. For example, high-strength, free-cutting alloy 2011 can be machined to an excellent surface finish at high speed and feed, with a low rate of tool wear. The chips formed are finely broken. Alloy 2011 is therefore recommended for all general and high-production machining where a free-cutting alloy is desired. Alloy 2011 is especially desirable for multiple-operation machining, mainly because it machines with a broken chip.

Stock for multiple-operation machining is also available in alloys 2017, 2024, 6061 and 6262, in several heat treated tempers.

Alloys 2024-T4, 2017-T4 and 7075-T6 produce continuous chips that must be broken by a chip breaker in the tool. Alloys 6061-T6 and 5056-H38 are a little more difficult to machine, and they produce chips that are difficult to control. The softer alloys 5052, 3003 and 1100 are likely to produce gummy chips. Wrought alloy 4032 and cast alloys 220, 13 and A132 are quite abrasive, and high rates of tool wear result.

Examples 867 through 871, which follow, describe applications in which a change to an alloy and temper having better machinability improved results. In Examples 872 and 873, only temper was changed (see also Example 910).

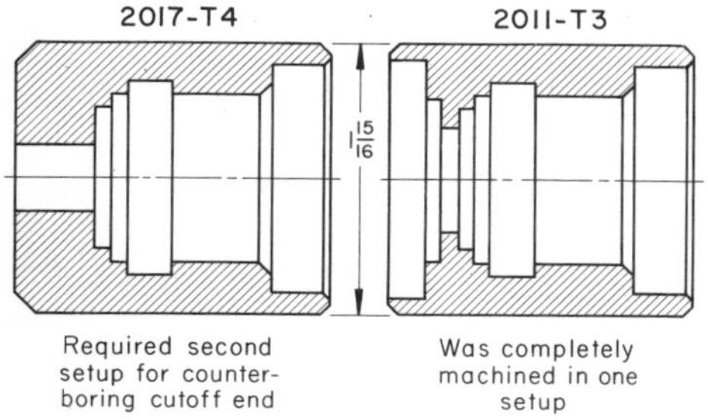

Operation	Tool material	Feed, ipr
Operations for Part Made of Alloy 2011-T3		
1 Subland drill ...	High speed steel	0.0035
Turn	High speed steel	0.0035
2 Step drill	Carbide	0.001
Form	Carbide	0.0007
3 Step drill	Carbide	0.001
4 Recess	Carbide	0.0006
5 Cutoff	High speed steel	0.0013

Speed was 915 rpm (460 sfm). Production rate was 103 pieces per hour (35 sec per piece).

Fig. 4. Substitution of alloy 2011-T3 for 2017-T4 to eliminate a second machining setup (Example 867)

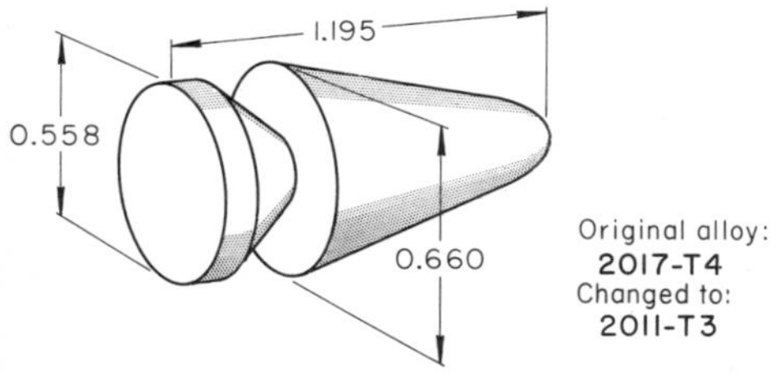

Fig. 5. Part for which a change from alloy 2017-T4 to 2011-T3 solved chip problem and increased production (Example 868)

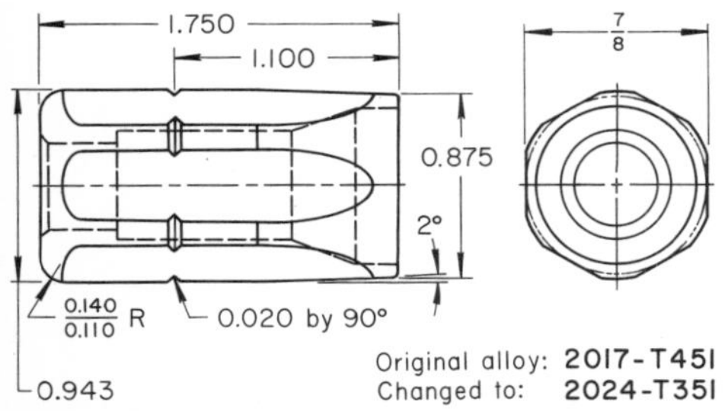

Fig. 6. Part for which change from alloy 2017-T451 to 2024-T351 increased production rate (Example 869)

Examples 867 to 873. Alloy and Temper Selection for Better Machinability

Example 867 — 2017-T4 to 2011-T3 (Fig. 4). When the part shown in Fig. 4 was made of alloy 2017-T4, it had to go through a second processing step (which involved realigning the part) for counterboring the cutoff end, because stringy chips were formed. With alloy 2011-T3, all machining could be completed in the first sequence of operations by use of a recessing tool. This change in alloy resulted in a 38% increase in production rate and a decrease of 23% in manufacturing costs.

Example 868 — 2017-T4 to 2011-T3 (Fig. 5). The part shown in Fig. 5 was originally specified in 2017-T4 rod. During rough forming and skiving, chips packed in the tool area and in the bed of the machine, requiring frequent stopping to remove them. Under these conditions, one man could operate two machines, and maximum production rate was 650 pieces per hour.

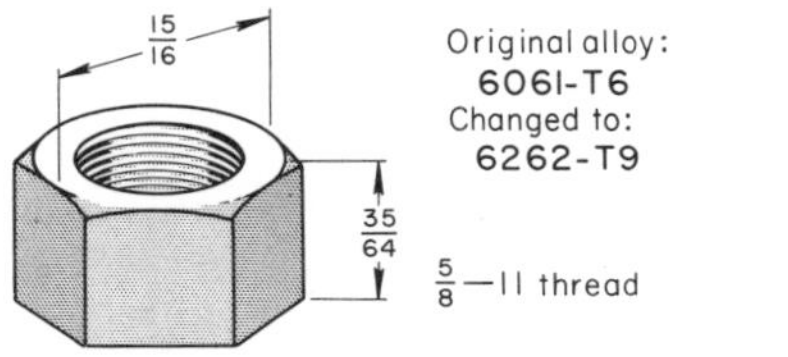

Fig. 7. Hexagonal nut for which a change from alloy 6061-T6 to 6262-T9 resulted in saving of material and less burring of the tapped thread (Example 870)

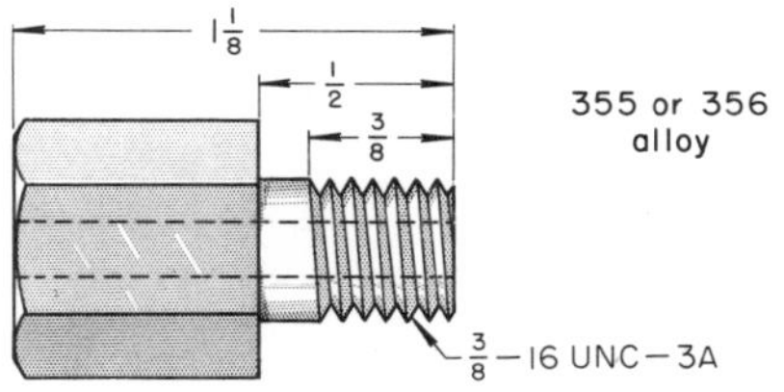

Operating conditions	Alloy 355	Alloy 356
Speed, sfm	150	130
Cutting fluid	Soluble oil	
Chaser life per set, pieces	800	750
Production, pieces per hr	300	275

Fig. 8. Threaded fitting produced from two different cast aluminum alloys (Example 871)

The alloy was changed to 2011-T3 to obtain smaller chips. It was then possible to reduce the cycle time from 3.2 to 2.8 sec by increasing speed from 2500 to 3000 rpm and changing feed. One man could then operate three machines, and production rate was increased to 1000 pieces per hour.

The weight of the blank, before it was machined, was 0.0472 lb; the weight of the part, after it was machined, was 0.0220 lb.

Example 869 — 2017-T451 to 2024-T351 (Fig. 6). In drilling and turning the part shown in Fig. 6 from ⅞-in. hexagonal bar stock, a change in material from 2017-T451 to 2024-T351 resulted in a large increase in production rate, because of increased speeds and feeds. Drilling feed was increased from 0.0035 ipr to 0.0068 ipr, and turning speed from 1062 rpm (280 sfm) to 1215 rpm (321 sfm). In addition, tool wear and size variation were reduced, and surface finish was improved.

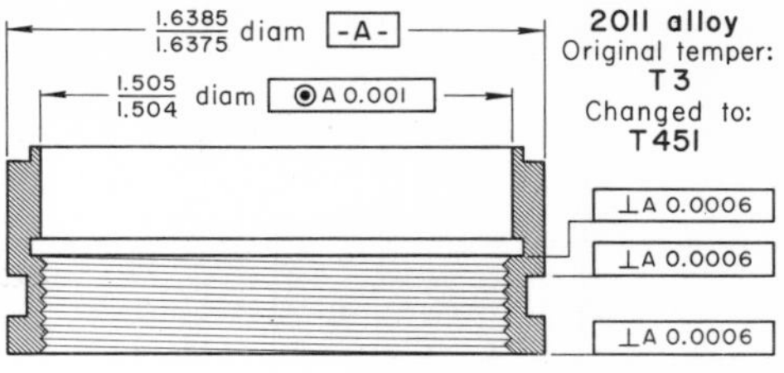

Operation	Tool material	Feed, ipr
1 Turn	High speed steel	0.0045
Drill	High speed steel	0.0045
2 Bore	Carbide	0.0045
Form	Carbide	0.001
3 Shave	Carbide	0.001
4 Internal form ..	Carbide	0.0009
5 Bore	Carbide	0.0015
Cutoff	High speed steel	0.001

Speed was 1277 rpm (550 sfm). Production rate was 300 pieces per hour (12 sec per piece).

Fig. 9. Part made of alloy 2011 for which change from T3 to T451 temper decreased cost 25% by eliminating bar-cutoff operation and 15-hr stress-relieving treatment for preventing out-of-roundness (Example 872)

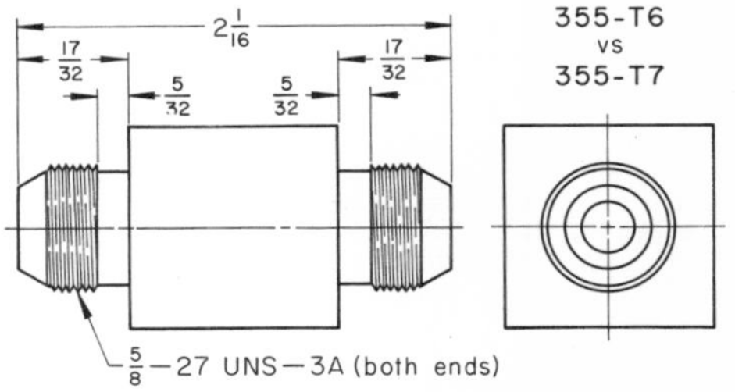

Item	T6 temper(a)	T7 temper(b)
Chasers used, sets(c)	1	2
Grinds, total number(d) ...	2	3
Total tool cost for run(e) ..	$5.60	$10.85
Tool life, pieces(f)	800	500
Production, pieces per hour	300	300

(a) Tensile strength, approximately 32,000 psi. (b) Tensile strength, approximately 35,000 psi. (c) Chasers cost $4.90 per set. (d) Cost for grinding $0.35 per grind per set. (e) 600 pieces per run. (f) Per set of chasers. Chasers not completely used during run.

Fig. 10. Part made of alloy 355 for which tool life in threading was improved by change from T7 to T6 temper (Example 873)

The blank weighed 0.117 lb, and 0.067 lb of stock was removed in machining in an automatic bar machine. When alloy 2017-T451 was used, 170 parts were produced per hour at a machining cost of 14¢ each. When alloy 2024-T351 was used production rate increased to 245 pieces per hour, and cost per piece decreased to 13¢.

Example 870 — 6061-T6 to 6262-T9 (Fig. 7). When alloy 6061-T6 was used for a hexagonal nut (Fig. 7), a lead of three threads chamfer on the tap form was required to produce a thread without tearing. A length of 3/16 in. had to be cut off after tapping. After changing to the freer-cutting 6262-T9, lead was reduced to 1½ threads, so that only ⅛ in. had to be cut off. Material saving was 8.5%. Because 6262-T9 produced fewer burrs on the tapped threads, frequency of tool grinding was reduced.

With 6061-T6, the workpiece before tapping weighed 0.0560 lb, and with 6262-T9, it weighed 0.0512 lb. The finished nut in both alloys weighed 0.0279 lb. Production rate was 890 pieces per hour with both alloys.

Example 871 — 356 vs 355 (Fig. 8). A turret lathe with a self-opening die was used to thread fittings made of two different cast aluminum alloys (355 and 356). As indicated in the table accompanying Fig. 8, tool life was greater in threading alloy 355, probably because of the lower content of silicon in 355. The increase in production rate was because of the greater speed used in thread-

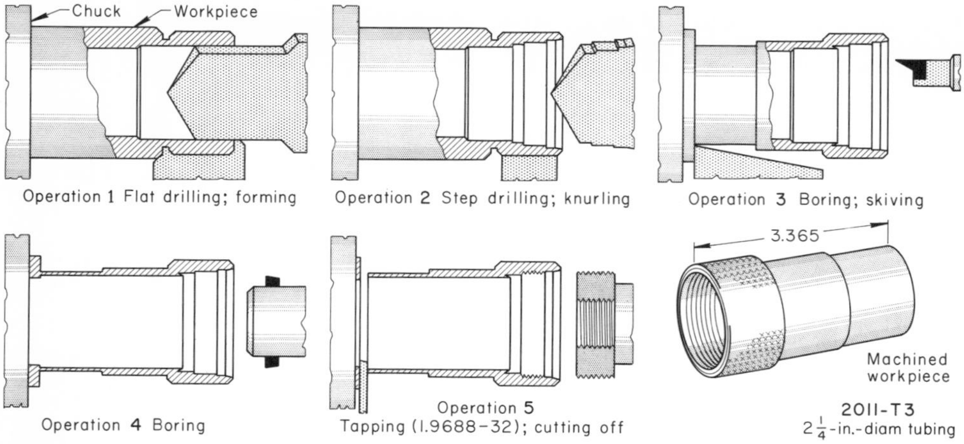

Operation(a)	Tool material	Feed, ipr
1 Flat drill	Carbide	0.004
Form	Carbide	0.001
2 Step drill	Carbide	0.004
Knurl	High speed steel	0.012
3 Bore	Carbide	0.0007
Skive	Carbide	0.002
4 Bore	Carbide	0.006
5 Tap	High speed steel	0.0015
Cutoff	High speed steel	0.001

(a) For all operations, speed was 1044 rpm (618 sfm max), and cutting fluid was a low-viscosity mineral oil with 5% fatty additive. Cycle time was 30 sec per piece.

Fig. 11. Machining a part from tubing, which resulted in greater production rate and lower metal cost than when part was machined from bar stock (Example 874)

ing the 355 alloy. To obtain acceptable thread finish, a slower speed was required for the 356 alloy. Chasers cost $4.90 per set and each sharpening cost $0.35 per set.

Example 872 — 2011-T3 to 2011-T451 (Fig. 9). The part shown in Fig. 9 was originally machined from 2011-T3 bar stock. Because of the relatively large diameter and thin wall, an out-of-round condition ranging from 0.004 to 0.010 in. TIR resulted. It was necessary to cut the bars and to stress relieve them at 325 F for 15 hr before machining, to reduce runout to within 0.001 in. However, by changing to alloy 2011-T451, the long and costly heat treating operation was eliminated and the runout condition was adequately controlled. This change in temper specification resulted in cost savings of about 25%.

The details of procedure used in machining this part in an automatic bar machine are given with Fig. 9.

Example 873 — 355-T6 vs 355-T7 (Fig. 10). In die threading of the workpiece shown in Fig. 10, the T6 temper machined with greater tool life than the T7 temper of cast alloy 355. However, the T7 temper was chosen, because thread finish requirements could be met more easily on the harder temper.

Bar vs Tubing

Many parts can be machined equally well from either bar stock or tubing. When either of these product forms can be used, cost per piece machined is the determining factor. To determine cost, initial cost of bar versus tube, cost of additional machining to make the part from bar stock, and value of the additional scrap that results from machining bar stock must be considered. Because of the high cost of producing small tubing, total cost per piece machined may be greater when tubing of small sizes (less than about 1¼-in.-diam) is used. For parts requiring a diameter greater than 1¼ in., tubing is usually cheaper.

The following example describes an application where an appreciable saving was effected by changing from bar to tubing.

Example 874. Tubing vs Bar Stock (Fig. 11)

The part shown in Fig. 11 was originally machined from 2011-T3 bar stock. Changing to tubing (2¼-in.-diam, ⅜-in. wall) of the same alloy and temper resulted in a 38.4% increase in production rate and a 16% reduction in metal cost.

A speed of 1044 rpm (618 sfm) was used for machining both bar and tube. Cycle time was 30 sec per part when the tubing was used. The sequence of operations, tool material, and rates of feed for machining the part from tubing are given with Fig. 11.

General Machining Conditions

Power requirements for machining are proportional to speed and cutting force, and the power lost in bearings and gears of the machine increases with speed. Power requirements for machining aluminum decrease somewhat as the rake angle of the cutting tool is increased. Typical power requirements for several wrought and cast alloys, as measured at the cutter, using single-point tools with 0° and 20° rake angles are given in Table 3.

Cutting force for aluminum alloys can vary widely at low speeds, such as 100 to 200 sfm, rising momentarily to peak values several times higher than normal. At higher speeds, cutting force for machining 2011-T3 alloy rises slightly with increasing speed, but for most alloys it decreases. The over-all effect of speed on cutting force is small: As speed increases up to about 1000 sfm, cutting force changes slightly; above 1000 sfm, the effect of speed is negligible. Increasing the speed does not produce much more heat, but it does shorten the time available for removing the heat from the tool. The effect of speed on cutting force for several aluminum alloys is plotted in Fig. 12. Heating of tool surfaces is not sufficient to have a harmful effect on a high speed steel tool until the speed exceeds about 700 sfm. High speed steel may be used for speeds well beyond this limit, but carbide tools are recommended for long tool life.

Table 3. Power Requirements for Machining Aluminum Alloys

Alloy	Power, hp/cu in./min, for: 0° rake	20° rake
F132-T5	0.20 to 0.50	0.20 to 0.40
356-T51	0.30 to 1.00	0.25 to 0.45
2011-T3	0.20 to 0.30	0.15 to 0.25
2024-T351	0.30 to 0.50	0.20 to 0.40
6061-T651	0.30 to 0.50	0.25 to 0.35

Cutting speed for aluminum alloys is determined by the limits of the machine tool and by the workpiece. Speeds as high as 15,000 sfm have been used in rare instances; even higher speeds have been achieved with experimental equipment. However, in most practice, mainly because of limitations imposed by available spindle speed, available horsepower, and dynamic balance of the part, machining speeds are seldom higher than 2000 sfm, and they are more commonly less than 1000 sfm, as indicated by the examples in this article.

Cutting speed should be as high as is practical, to save time and to minimize temperature rise in the part, as described later in connection with thermal expansion. As cutting speed is increased above 100 to 200 sfm, the probability of forming a built-up edge on the cutter is reduced, chips break more readily, and finish is improved.

Depth of cut should be as great as possible within the limits of part strength, chucking equipment, power of the machine tool, and amount of stock to be removed, to minimize the number of cuts required. As depth of cut is increased, cutting force increases. Depth of cut must be limited to a value that will not distort the workpiece or cause it to slip, nor overload the machine. Depth of cut in roughing may be as high as 0.250 in. for small work or up to 1.500 in. for medium or large work. At the opposite extreme, depth of cut in finishing is often less than 0.025 in.

Feed will depend on the finish desired, and the strength and rigidity of the workpiece and of the machine. Finishing cuts require a light feed of 0.002 to 0.006 ipr; rough cuts may use a feed of 0.006 to 0.080 ipr. Alloys with machinability ratings of D and E are best machined with a feed in the lower end of the range.

Tool Design

Tools intended for machining aluminum and its softer alloys should be ground to allow considerably more side rake and back rake than are customary when machining steel. Thus, they approach the contours of tools designed for cutting hardwood. The larger rake angles are recommended for finishing tools and for the machining of alloys that are not free-cutting, especially the softer alloys, which require exceptionally acute and keen cutting edges. Smaller rake angles can be used for the free-cutting alloys and for roughing cuts, where a sturdy tool is required for the heavier cuts and feeds employed. Suggested rake angles, as related to alloy machinability rating (see Table 1), are as follows:

Rating	Rake angle
A	0° to 20°
B	20°
C	20° to 30°
D	40°
E	40°

Tool forms for machining aluminum alloys with machinability ratings of A and B with single-point tools are given in Table 4. Variations of these may be desirable, depending on machining conditions or shape of the workpiece.

Clearance angle is important to proper functioning of the tool. Too small a clearance will permit the side or heel of the tool to rub the work and generate heat, whereas too large an angle will cause the tool to dig into the work and chatter. This angle must be carried around the side of the tool that advances into the work. For most applications, clearance angles of 6° to 10° are suitable. The side rake angle imparts to the tool a slicing action that assists materially in shearing the chip from the stock. This angle is important and should be held within the ranges recommended in subsequent sections of this article.

Cutting-Edge Finish. For maximum performance, it is essential that tool cutting edges be keen, smooth, and free from grinding-wheel scratches, burrs, or wire edges. Keen edges may be obtained by finish grinding on a fine abrasive wheel, and then lapping, or hand stoning with a fine oilstone. Neither the angles nor the contour of the cutting edge should be appreciably modified during tool finishing.

Tool Material

Water-hardening tool steel, such as W1, heat treated to Rockwell C 65 to 68, is an adequate cutting tool material when production runs are short and speeds are low. However, tool steels of this type soften rapidly if the temperature of the cutting edge exceeds 300 F. In addition, tools made from water-hardening tool steel have low resistance to edge wear.

High speed steel tools are generally satisfactory for machining all but the high-silicon alloys, which are quite abrasive and should be machined with carbide tools, unless runs are short; for short runs, high speed steel is usually satisfactory.

Carbide Tools. Because of the brittleness of the tool tip, the lip angle for carbide tools is usually greater than those recommended for high speed steel tools, in order to provide maximum support to the edge. This is shown in Table 4, where smaller relief angles are indicated for carbide tools. The rake angles can also be decreased to zero or negative to increase the lip angle, but negative rake angles are generally not recommended. When very light finishing cuts are made, it is sometimes feasible to reverse this practice and use higher rake angles and smaller lip angles.

Carbide tools retain sharp edges over a longer period between regrinds than carbon or high speed steel tools, provided they are not used for heavy intermittent cuts. A better finish is obtained, because of the great hardness of the tool tip compared to that of the stock. Carbide tools are particularly useful for machining alloys of high silicon content, many of which cannot otherwise be machined satisfactorily under production conditions.

Diamond tools are used only in operations where an exceptionally high finish is required, particularly on high-silicon alloys, in which particles of free silicon will, in time, slightly dull the cutting edge of even carbide tools. Finishing cuts with diamond tools seldom exceed a few thousandths of an inch.

Diamond tools are usually made with either circular or faceted cutting edges, the latter being the more common. With the faceted cutter, there may be as many as five facets on one cutting edge, each varying in size from 0.02 to 0.06 in. Cutting angles of 74° to 90° and top rake angles of 6° to 10° are used. Rake should not be less than −6°. The tool should be set on, or slightly above, the centerline of the work.

Cutting Fluid

Cutting fluid for aluminum can be a soluble-oil emulsion, a mineral oil, or an aqueous chemical solution. Cutting oils that contain compounds of sulfur or chlorine or both are seldom used, and are not usually required for machining aluminum. Also, many of them will leave stains on the work. There are exceptions, however, as indicated in Example 894.

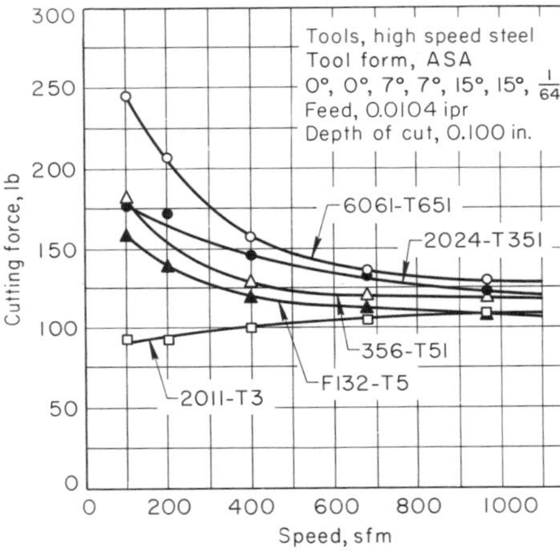

Fig. 12. Effect of speed on cutting force for five aluminum alloys

Soluble oil mixed with water in ratios of one part oil to 20 to 30 parts water is the cutting fluid most widely used for machining aluminum alloys. Soluble-oil emulsions are cheap, highly efficient for cooling and removing chips, and usually are adequate for preventing built-up edges. A soluble oil was used in most of the examples described in this article.

Mineral oil used as a cutting fluid may contain a fatty additive, such as lard oil, neat's-foot oil, oleic acid, or butyl stearate. However, mineral oil that contains no additive and that has a viscosity from 40 to 300 SUS at 100 F is most often used. As cutting speed is increased, viscosity of the oil should be decreased to provide easier flow, and therefore greater cooling. Straight mineral seal oil (viscosity of approximately 40 SUS at 100 F) has been effective in many applications (see Examples 885, 886 and 925). Kerosine, which is slightly less viscous than mineral seal oil, is also used (see Example 882).

Chemical solutions are effective as cutting fluids for machining aluminum, and are especially desirable when a transparent fluid is needed to permit viewing the work during machining. These solutions vary in composition, but most of them contain amines, nitrites, phosphates, borates, soaps, wetting agents, glycols and germicides. Some of these solutions stain aluminum alloys.

Table 4. Design of Single-Point Tools for Machining Aluminum Alloys of A and B Machinability Ratings

Tool details	High speed steel: Roughing	High speed steel: Finishing	Carbide: Roughing	Carbide: Finishing
Back rake	20°	20°	20°	20°
Side rake	20°	20°	20°	20°
End relief	10°	10°	7°	7°
Side relief	10°	10°	7°	7°
End cutting edge	5°	5°	5°	5°
Side cutting edge	10°	10°	10°	10°
Nose radius, in.	0.063	0.20	0.063	0.20

Continuous filtering of cutting fluids for removal of chips, slivers, grindings, and other foreign material is especially desirable, because aluminum alloys are relatively soft and are easily damaged by a contaminated cutting fluid.

Stick grease is sometimes used in band sawing, circular sawing, and abrasive-belt, abrasive-disk or abrasive-wheel polishing and grinding, when requirements are not too severe and a flood of lubricant is not required.

Distortion and Dimensional Variation

Because aluminum alloys have a low modulus of elasticity (about 10 million psi), they will distort more than most metals for a given clamping or chucking force. Moderate clamping forces should be used, to avoid dimensional variations due to distortion. High clamping pressures are not required, because cutting forces are low.

Thermal Expansion. The coefficient of thermal expansion of aluminum alloys (10 to 14 micro-in. per in. per °F) is higher than that of most metals commonly machined. Therefore, dimensional accuracy of finished parts requires that the part be kept cool during machining. When turning between centers, it is important to avoid expansion, which will put excessive pressure on the centers. High cutting speed helps keep the part cool, because most of the heat introduced into the part during a given rotation is removed with the chip during the next rotation, and the time for diffusion of heat is short. A cutting fluid is effective in removing heat that is not removed with the chips. Live centers are recommended to minimize frictional heating at the center. Dull tools cause a heat rise in the workpiece; therefore, cutting tools should be kept sharp.

Residual stress can be induced by a dull or improperly designed cutter that cold works the surface; by excessive chucking or clamping force; or by faulty clamping. Distortion from residual stress is most noticeable in slender parts.

Distortion resulting from machining stresses can be minimized or eliminated either by employing a series of light cuts as the part approaches finished size, or by stress relieving the part be-

Table 5. Design of Single-Point Tools for Turning Aluminum Alloys

(See text for discussion of applications for high and low ends of the ranges.)

Back rake angle	10° to 30°
Side rake angle	10° to 40°
End relief angle	7° to 10°
Side relief angle	7° to 10°
End cutting-edge angle	5° to 20°
Side cutting-edge angle	10° to 30°
Nose radius	0 to 0.20 in.

Table 6. Nominal Speeds for Turning Aluminum Alloys

Operation	Speed, sfm: Non-heat-treated cast alloys	Speed, sfm: All other alloys and tempers
High Speed Steel Tools (M2 or T5)		
Single-point roughing	750	600
Single-point finishing	1000	800
Forming and cutoff	550	450
Carbide Tools (C-2)		
Single-point roughing(a):		
Brazed tips	1600	1100
Disposable tips	2000	1400
Forming and cutoff	1200	825

NOTE: Speeds for single-point turning are based on 0.150-in. depth of cut and feed of 0.015 ipr for roughing, and 0.025-in. depth of cut and feed of 0.007 ipr for finishing. Speeds for form turning are based on feeds of 0.0035, 0.003 and 0.002 ipr for tool widths of ½, 1 and 2 in., respectively. Speeds for cutoff are based on a feed rate of 0.002 ipr.

(a) For finish turning, use maximum speed of the machine and C-3 carbide.

tween rough and finish machining. For heat treatable alloys, it is preferable to do all rough machining on material in the solution-treated-and-aged condition, rather than in the annealed condition, because the less ductile structure is more machinable.

Distortion resulting from machining stress often can be minimized by purchasing the alloy in a stress-relieved condition, normally designated by T451, T651 or T851 if the metal has been stress relieved by stretching. T*x*52 denotes stress relief by compression, and T*x*53, stress relief by heat treating.

A major source of dimensional variation arises from the presence of movement or "play" in the feed mechanism of the machine. When the machining conditions or the tool cause forces that take up the play completely, no variations in dimensions are encountered. However, when low cutting forces (typical of those required for machining aluminum) are combined with a small feed and light cut, the total force may be insufficient to overcome tool-slide friction. Then, some movement may still occur, and the tool may float.

Turning

As indicated in Fig. 2 and 3, the cutting force, and hence the power, required to turn aluminum is considerably less than for turning low-carbon steel of approximately the same hardness and tensile properties.

Tool Design. The recommended angles for a single-point lathe tool are given in Table 5. Cutting angles should be on the high end of the ranges for alloys that are not heat treatable or that are more ductile than the free-cutting alloys. (See Fig. 2 in the article "Turning" for definitions of the standard angles of a single-point tool.)

Because carbide tools are more brittle than high speed steel tools, they will chip or break when the cutting angles are too large. As a result, the lower half of each range given in Table 5 should be used for carbide tools. In turning free-cutting alloys, increasing the side relief or side rake angle, or both, will reduce the power required. Because the power needed for turning aluminum alloys is small (about one-third that needed for machining soft low-carbon steel), a turning tool ground with angles that are too large is likely to hog the work metal. The tool floats in operation, so that any backlash or play in the spindle or machine ways causes difficulty in holding tolerances. Tool life and surface finish also suffer. Surface finish can be improved by grinding a large nose radius on the turning tool. However, maximum nose radius depends partly on the allowable fillet on the workpiece when turning to a shoulder. As the nose radius is made larger, cutting force and horsepower requirement increase (see Fig. 3 in the article "Turning"). On small-diameter stock, increased cutting force may cause the work metal to

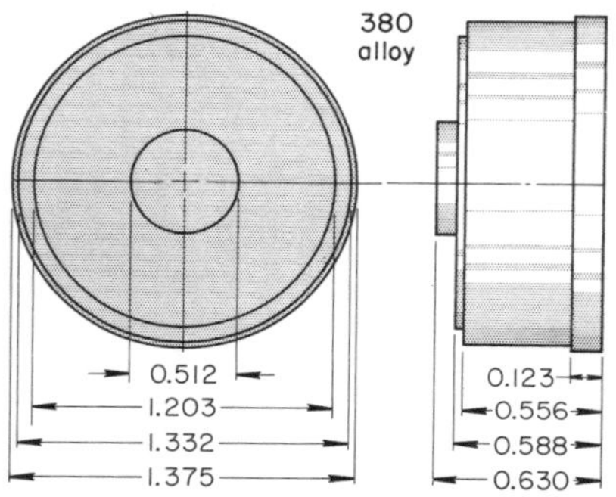

Item	Standard machine	Machine with tracer
Production, pieces per hour	19	67
Setup time, hr	2	½
Tooling cost	$10	$2
Total pieces per setup	1000	1000

Fig. 13. Die casting that was faced and turned in an eight-station chucking machine with and without a tracer attachment (Example 875)

bend away from the tool, so that stock supports or rests are required. A nose radius that is too large also causes chatter, which results in poor surface finish and, possibly, tool breakage.

Another way to improve surface finish is to grind the end cutting edge of the tool parallel to the work for a width equal to 1½ to 2 times the feed rate in inches per revolution. This flat edge will cut behind the nose of the tool to smooth out ridges caused by the feed. Too wide a flat will cause chatter, and a negative angle will leave a taper equal in length to the width of the flat, on the work at the end of the turn.

Tool Honing. Honing of a carbide tool with a diamond-impregnated stone will improve the surface finish on the workpiece and will extend the life of the tool. Disposable carbide inserts have a honed edge when purchased, and no additional honing is necessary.

Tool Material. Carbide tools, either brazed-insert or disposable-insert, last far longer than high speed steel tools for turning any aluminum alloy; for turning the high-silicon alloys, the use of carbide tools is mandatory for optimum results.

Speed used in turning aluminum alloys depends to some extent on the alloy and condition, but far more on tool material and type of tool — single-point, form or cutoff.

The effect of alloy composition and condition is small in selecting a turning speed, except for the non-heat-treated cast alloys. Nominal speeds for turning aluminum with high speed steel and carbide tools are given in Table 6. These speeds are based on feeds and depths of cut that are typical for turning aluminum alloys (footnote to Table 6), and on the assumptions that the setup is rigid, that a cutting fluid is used, and that the workpiece can be rotated to attain these surface speeds without causing excessive vibration. When conditions are below normal, speeds must be scaled down from those given in Table 6. Likewise, under nearly ideal conditions, higher speeds are often used successfully.

Feed. For rough turning with single-point tools, regardless of tool material, a feed of 0.015 ipr is common for all aluminum alloys. For finish turning, a feed of 0.007 ipr is recommended; this feed will usually result in a surface finish of 63 to 125 micro-in. Sometimes lighter feeds are used, to provide a better finish.

In form turning, width of the form tool is the major variable that affects the rate of feed. For all alloys and tool materials, a feed rate of 0.0035 ipr is generally satisfactory for form tools no wider than 0.500 in. Rate of feed should be decreased as width of the form tool increases. Feed rates of 0.003 and 0.002 ipr are recommended for form tool widths of 1 and 2 in., respectively.

For cutoff tools, a feed rate of 0.002 ipr is usually satisfactory, regardless of the alloy being turned, tool material, or width of the cutoff tool.

Depth of cut in turning aluminum often depends on the power available. The speeds given in Table 6 are based on 0.150-in. depth of cut for roughing and 0.025 in. for finishing. When power is available, roughing cuts of 0.250 in. are common. Finishing cuts of less than 0.025 often result in better surface finish.

Cutting fluid is recommended for turning all aluminum alloys (see section "Cutting Fluids" on the preceding page).

Procedures and equipment for turning that are the same for all metals are discussed in the article "Turning", which begins on page 1 of this volume. Because aluminum alloys are far less sensitive to abrupt changes in speed,

Table 7. Nominal Speeds and Feeds for Boring Aluminum Alloys

Boring operation	Speed, sfm: Non-heat-treated cast alloys	Speed, sfm: All other alloys and tempers
High Speed Steel Tools (M2 or T5)		
Roughing (feed, 0.015 ipr)	675	550
Finishing (feed, 0.008 ipr)	750	600
Carbide Tools (C-3)		
Roughing (feed, 0.020 ipr)	1450	1000
Finishing (feed, 0.010 ipr)	1600	1100

Depth of cut: rough, 0.10 in.; finish, 0.010 in.

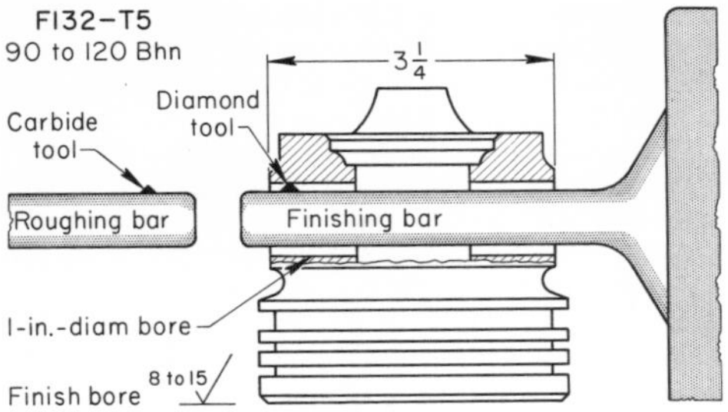

Speed, rough and finish	3340 rpm (870 sfm)
Feed, rough and finish	4.5 ipm
Metal removed:	
Rough boring	0.050 in.
Finish boring	0.010 in.
Length of cut	3¼ in.
Number of passes	1 rough, 1 finish
Cutting fluid	Soluble-oil:water (1:25)
Production rate	212 pieces per hour
Tolerance, rough bore	±0.001 in.
Tolerance, finish bore	±0.0004 in.

Fig. 14. Rough and finish boring of two in-line holes in a permanent mold casting (Example 876)

feed and depth of cut than many other metals, they are especially well adapted to turning in automatic equipment. The following example compares productivity, setup time, and tooling cost for turning and facing aluminum die castings in a standard chucking machine, compared with a chucking machine equipped with a tracer attachment. Various form turning and cutoff operations are described in the examples in the section on Multiple-Operation Machining, page 454 in this article.

Example 875. Turning With an Automatic Tracing Attachment (Fig. 13)

Use of an automatic tracing attachment on an eight-station chucking machine resulted in lower tooling costs and a higher production rate in machining the alloy 380 die casting shown in Fig. 13. Machining consisted of facing and turning the 0.512, 1.203, 1.332 and 1.375-in. diameters. A 1-to-20 mixture of soluble oil and water was used as the cutting fluid. Comparative data obtained in a standard chucking machine and in a similar machine with tracer are shown in the table accompanying Fig. 13.

Boring

Boring of aluminum alloys, particularly the alloys with high silicon content, requires the use of tools with acute rake and clearance angles. In general, rake angles are increased as silicon content is decreased. Recommended radial or side rake angles range from 5° to 15°; axial or back rake angles, from 0° to 30°. Clearance angles are held to 10°.

Tool Material. Although high speed steel tools are used to some extent for boring aluminum, carbide tools permit higher surface speeds (up to 1000 sfm or more), with markedly longer tool life. Carbide cutters readily yield surface finishes of 10 to 20 micro-in.

When used in conjunction with precision boring machines, diamond tools can produce surface finishes of 1 micro-in. They are also capable of holding size over a long production run. If the cut is continuous and the work metal contains no hard spots, diamond tools are most effective in boring the abrasive high-silicon alloys.

Tool Sharpening. For optimum tool life, cutting edges and adjacent surfaces must be free of burrs and scratches. Hand stoning of cutting edges with an oil stone is recommended. When a carbide boring tool is sharpened with a 400 or 500-grit diamond wheel, surface finishes of 3 to 4 micro-in. can be obtained.

Speed and Feed. The optimum speed for boring aluminum alloys depends somewhat on alloy and temper, but largely on tool material and whether the operation is roughing or finishing. Selection of feed depends largely on tool material and whether the operation is roughing or finishing.

Nominal speeds and feeds for rough and finish boring with high speed steel and carbide tools are given in Table 7. Speed is increased for a shallower depth of cut and lighter feed, regardless of alloy or tool material. Under some conditions, speeds much higher than those shown in Table 7 can be used successfully. For instance, in Example 880, speed of boring is 2930 sfm, which is nearly five times the average of the speeds given in Table 7 for boring with high speed steel tools; however, the boring tool used in Example 880 was engaged for only a fraction of each revolution.

Depth of Cut. Speeds and feeds given in Table 7 are based on a 0.10-in. depth of cut for roughing and 0.010 in. for finishing. Depth of cut is sometimes greater than 0.10 in. for rough boring if power is available and the setup can be made sufficiently rigid. Finishing cuts significantly less than 0.010 in. in depth are seldom used.

Cutting fluid is recommended but boring has been done dry. There is usually some sacrifice of productivity, dimensional accuracy or surface finish when aluminum is bored without a cutting fluid. A mixture of one part soluble oil to 20 to 30 parts water is most commonly used; also, mineral oil, or mineral oil mixed with up to 50% lard oil, is often used, especially when the best possible surface finish is desired. Sometimes mixtures of kerosine and lubricating oil are used, as in Example 880.

Procedures and equipment common to the boring of all metals are covered in detail in the article "Boring", in this volume. Types of machines that are used are listed on pages 20 and 21. Tools are discussed on page 22. Specific procedures for aluminum alloys are described in the five examples that follow.

Example 876. Boring of In-Line Holes in an Automotive Piston (Fig. 14)

Figure 14 shows the technique used for boring two in-line piston-pin holes. Rough boring was done with a carbide tool that entered from the left. As the rough boring tool retracted, a diamond finishing tool entered from the right and finish bored both holes. Boring was done in a six-spindle, double-end horizontal boring machine equipped with three fixtures for boring three pistons in one cycle. Details of the operation are given with Fig. 14.

Example 877. Multiple Boring of a Die Casting (Table 8)

Five different diameters were rough bored and three diameters were finish bored in an alloy 380 die-cast gear box. Boring tool details are shown in Table 8. Roughing and fin-

Table 8. Rough and Finish Boring of an Alloy 380 Die Casting (Example 877)

Conditions or Results for All Operations

Boring machine	2-spindle, driven by 15-hp motor, hydraulically operated across table	Tool life per grind, roughing	2000 pieces
Tools	Carbide, double-end(a)	Tool life per grind, finishing	1000 pieces
Tool angles, roughing:		Speed, roughing and finishing	1000 rpm
Radial rake	0°	Cutting fluid	Soluble-oil:water (1:25)
Axial rake	15°	Setup time (permanent setup)	3 hr
Clearance	10°	Downtime for changing tools	1 hr
Tool angles, finishing:		Cycle time, roughing and finishing:	0.0730 hr
Radial rake	15°	Production rate	14 pieces per hour
Axial rake	0°	Tolerance, significant dimensions	0.0006 in.
Clearance	10°	Surface finish	40 micro-in.
		Weight of finished casting	18 lb, 7 oz

Operation 1. Rough Bore 1.687-In.-Diam Clearance Hole

Speed	450 sfm
Feed	0.004 ipr
Depth of cut	1/16 to 1/8 in.

Operation 2. Rough Bore 1.860-In.-Diam Hole to 1.875-In. Diam

Speed	503 sfm
Feed	0.004 ipr
Depth of cut	1/16 in.

Operation 3. Rough Bore Clearance Hole to 2.125-In. Diam

Speed	556 sfm
Feed	0.004 ipr
Depth of cut	Up to 1/8 in.

Operation 4. Rough Bore 2.430-In.-Diam Hole to 2.4408-In. Diam

Speed	640 sfm
Feed	0.004 ipr
Depth of cut	1/16 to 1/8 in.

Operation 5. Rough Bore 3.610-In.-Diam Hole to 3.625-In. Diam

Speed	960 sfm
Feed	0.004 ipr
Depth of cut	Up to 0.590 in.

Operation 6. Finish Bore 1.875-In.-Diam Hole to +0.001, −0.000 In.

Speed	450 sfm
Feed	0.004 ipr
Depth of cut	0.007 in.

Operation 7. Finish Bore 2.4408-In.-Diam Hole to +0.0006, −0.0000 In.

Speed	640 sfm
Feed	0.004 ipr
Depth of cut	0.005 in.

Operation 8. Finish Bore 3.625-In.-Diam Hole to +0.002, −0.000 In.

Speed	960 sfm
Feed	0.004 ipr
Depth of cut	0.007 in.

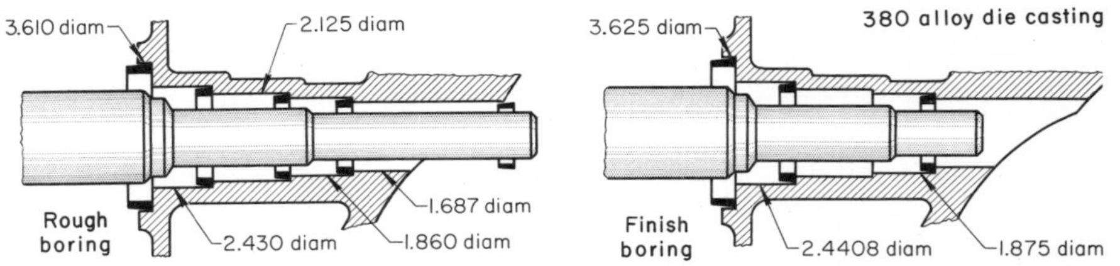

(a) Roughing tool, ½ by ⅝ in.; fixed. Finishing tool, mounted in bar with 0.003-in. float.

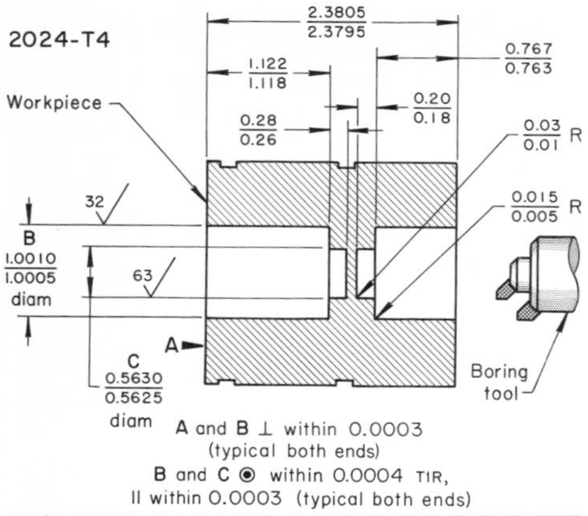

Speed	1200 rpm (318 sfm)
Feed	1.4 ipm
Cutting fluid	Kerosine plus proprietary oil
Production rate	9 pieces per hour
Tool life per grind	800 lineal in.

Fig. 15. Rough and finish boring of a heat treated aluminum alloy forging (Example 878)

ishing operations were done in the same machine. The roughing cutters were held in fixed position; finishing cutters were permitted to float about 0.003 in. Additional details of the boring operations are given in Table 8.

Example 878. Boring of Concentric Holes (Fig. 15)

Two small and two large holes were rough and finish bored from opposite sides of a heat treated aluminum forging, as shown in Fig. 15. It was required that the large and small holes be concentric within 0.0004 in. TIR, parallel within 0.0003 in., and square with the surface within 0.0003 in. The operation was done in a double-end, precision boring mill, and carbide tools were used. Details are given with Fig. 15.

Example 879. Boring With Numerical Control (Fig. 16)

A connecting-rod forging (Fig. 16) was loaded into a multiple-station milling fixture with numerical control that permitted milling all boss faces to required thickness at one setting by rotating the machine table through 180°. Hole locations were established by center drilling on the same program, and holes were drilled, leaving 0.040 in. of stock to be removed by a single-point boring tool. Boring speed was held to 196 sfm to minimize whip of the tool holder assembly. Machining and tooling details of the boring operation accompany Fig. 16.

Example 880. Boring to Produce a Concave Surface (Fig. 17)

The concave surface of a plunger top (Fig. 17), which was used to provide the shape of the bottom of aluminum ingots as they were cast, was produced by boring 6-in. plate in a 10-hp horizontal boring mill. The T4 high speed steel tools were hand ground, using a back rake angle of 25° to 30° and side rake angle of 0° for roughing. The same back rake angle was used for the finishing tool, but the side rake angle was increased to 30°. Additional details are given in Fig. 17.

Planing and Shaping

Techniques and equipment used for planing and shaping of other metals are generally applicable to aluminum alloys. Description of planing methods is presented in the article "Planing", starting on page 45. Similar information for shaping appears in the article "Shaping", starting on page 52.

Planing. Either high speed steel or carbide tools for planing aluminum usually have a back rake angle of 30° or more (sometimes as much as 60°) and 0° side rake. A speed of 300 sfm is generally recommended as maximum; however, this speed is higher than can be obtained with most planers.

Roughing feeds are about 0.090 in. per stroke when depth of cut is near the recommended maximum of ½ in. When shallow cuts are necessary (for lack of power or other reasons), a heavier feed can be used. For a 0.10-in. depth of cut, feed can be increased to about 0.125 in. per stroke.

Finish planing of aluminum alloys is usually done with a cut no deeper than 0.010 to 0.015 in. and a feed equal to three fourths the width of the broad-nose finishing tool (see the section on planer tools, in the article "Planing", in this volume).

Aluminum alloys are often planed without a cutting fluid. A cutting fluid is helpful in producing a better surface finish, but flooding with cutting fluid is seldom feasible. When surface finish is a primary objective, application of a mixture of kerosine and lubricating oil, or of kerosine and lard oil, by means of a swab is common practice. Sprayed cutting fluid is effective. Soluble-oil mixtures are ordinarily used in cutting-fluid spray systems.

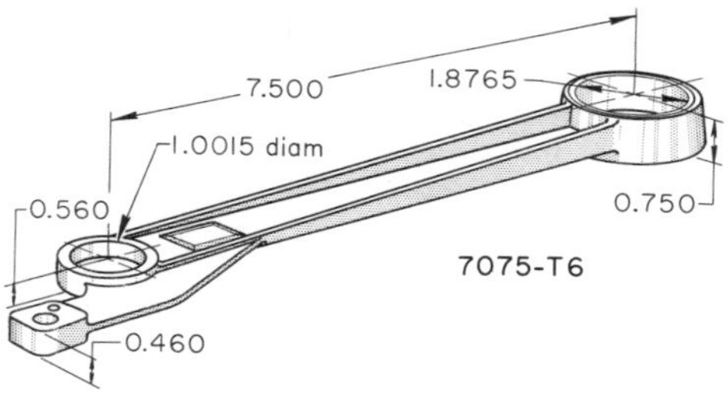

Tool material	High speed steel
Radial and axial rake angles	15°
Clearance angle	8°
Operating Conditions	
Speed	400 rpm (196 sfm max)
Feed	0.006 ipr
Cutting fluid	Soluble-oil:water (1:25); flood
Tolerance and Finish	
Tolerance	±0.0005 in.
Surface finish of bore	40 micro-in.

Fig. 16. Connecting-rod forging that was milled, drilled and bored (3 pieces per hour) with numerical control. Data in table are for boring. (Example 879)

Typical techniques and operating conditions for planing of aluminum are described in the following example.

Example 881. Planing a Mold Assembly (Table 9)

A subassembly of alloy 3003 sheet was used in a mold for direct chill casting of aluminum. The bottom edge of the mold had to be beveled so that water flowing down the mold would be directed toward the ingot. The bevel was planed on the sheet before it was rolled into a cylinder. Lengths and widths of the sheets to be beveled varied according to the size of mold being constructed. The surface of the bevel had to be smooth enough so that water could flow without deflection; surface roughness was 16 micro-in. In planing this workpiece, attempts were made to use more than one tool at a time, but this proved difficult because chips could not be disposed of readily. Tool and processing details are given in Table 9.

Shaping. Tool forms, tool materials, and cutting fluids for shaping aluminum are the same as for planing. Maximum speed in shaping is usually the maximum ram speed of the machine. Feed and depth of cut also depend to some extent on machine capabilities. A feed of 0.020 to 0.030 in. per stroke for roughing and about 0.010 in. per stroke for finishing are common. Depth of cut is often as much as 0.10 in. for roughing and 0.020 in. or less for finishing. Typical practice for shaping is given in the following example.

Example 882. Machining Ingot Slices in a Shaper (Table 10)

Cast ingot slices 10 in. square were shaped in a 12-in. crank shaper. The same shaping practice was used on all aluminum alloys, and production rate varied from 5 to 15 min per slice. Surface finish was 63 micro-in. Table 10 gives tool and processing details.

Broaching

All aluminum alloys can be broached successfully with standard broaching equipment, and by the same general procedures as for other metals. However, better surface finish and dimensional accuracy are obtained with heat treated alloys. Details of equipment and procedures that are common to broaching of all metals are dealt with in the article "Broaching", which begins on page 58 in this volume.

The principal limitation in broaching aluminum is the difficulty in maintaining an accurate relation between the broached hole and other surfaces of the workpiece, even when the starting hole is accurately located.

Tool Material. The general-purpose high speed steels, such as M2, are used for most tools for broaching aluminum. In some high-production operations, especially when broaching high-silicon alloys, broaches made of the more highly alloyed high speed steels or of carbide have proved economical. Surface treatments such as chromium plating or oxidizing help to prolong the life of high speed steel broaches.

A fine finish on the tool can be important. In one application, the life of a high speed steel broach was in-

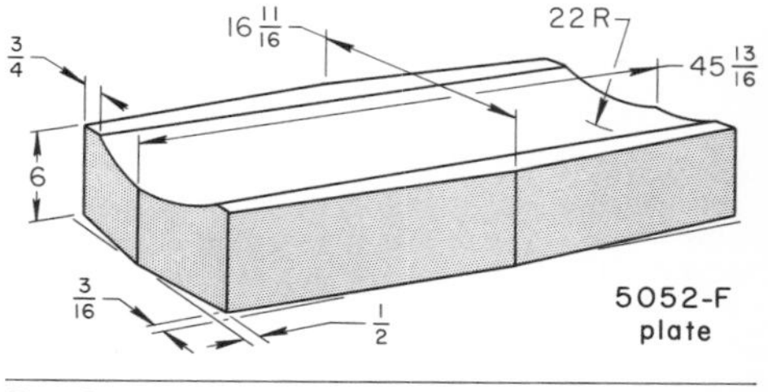

Speed	255 rpm (2930 sfm)
Feed, roughing	0.025 ipr
Feed, finishing	0.0125 ipr
Depth of cut, roughing	0.250 in.
Depth of cut, finishing	0.015 to 0.025 in.
Cutting fluid	Kerosine:lubricating-oil (1:1); 150 SUS at 100 F
Setup time	45 min
Downtime for changing tools	15 min
Production rate	2 to 3 pieces per hour
Tool material	T4 high speed steel
Tool life per grind	20 to 30 pieces
Tolerance on significant dimensions	1/64 in.
Surface finish	64 micro-in.

Rough boring was done in two or three passes, depending on setup; finish boring, in one pass. Roughing and finishing tools were on the same boring bar, which was 4 in. in diameter and supported at one end.

Fig. 17. Plunger top on which concave surface was produced by boring (Example 880)

creased from 2000 to 7400 pieces when the cutting edges were wet blasted with a superfine abrasive.

Broach Design. In rough broaching, a coarse tooth pitch is desirable, with only two or three teeth in contact and cutting at any one time. For internal finish broaching, best results are obtained if only two teeth are cutting; in external finish broaching, it is often best to have only one tooth engaging at a time.

Broaches used for aluminum should have a face angle of 10° and a land and clearance angle of 3½° for external surface broaching, and of 2° for internal broaching. Although a large clearance angle provides better cutting action, it markedly reduces broach life. Thus, clearance angles should be kept to a minimum to reduce loss of size when the broach is sharpened.

Speed and Feed. A speed range of 30 to 50 sfm is generally recommended for broaching aluminum alloys. When rigidity, supply of cutting fluid, and hardness of the work metal are nearly ideal, the upper portion of the range can be used. When one or more of these conditions is less than ideal, the speed may be reduced.

Greater feed per tooth (chip load) is recommended for broaching aluminum alloys than for steel. A feed of 0.006 in. per tooth is usually optimum for spline broaching and about 0.003 in. per tooth for broaching round holes.

Cutting fluid is required for best results. A copious supply of soluble oil mixed with water is satisfactory for most applications, although mineral oil, or mineral oil mixed with lard oil, will usually improve surface finish. (See the section on Cutting Fluids, in this article.)

Production Practice. The four examples that follow give details of typical practice in broaching aluminum. For the four different workpieces described in these examples, broaching was the most feasible and least costly method of obtaining the required results. See also Example 128 in "Broaching".

Example 883. Broaching of Internal Splines (Fig. 18)

Internal splines were broached in a 2017-T4 aluminum clutch housing (Fig. 18). The splined hole contained eight teeth with 32 diametral pitch, 20° pressure angle, and partial dedendum; internal diameter was 0.2185 in. The length of the broaching cut was 0.295 in. The pull broach (details in Fig. 18) was made of high speed steel, and broaching was done in a 1-ton vertical machine. Processing data are given in the table accompanying Fig. 18.

Example 884. Broaching of External Splines (Fig. 19)

External splines were broached in the 2.027-in. diameter of a workpiece made from 2¹⁄₁₆-in.-diam 2011-T3 bar stock (Fig. 19). Tolerance was ±0.001 in. and surface finish was 16 micro-in. The broach, made of M3 high speed steel, was pushed over the workpiece by a 1200-lb load. Processing details are given with Fig. 19.

Example 885. Broaching in a Single-Spindle Automatic Bar Machine (Fig. 20)

Internal splines were broached in a workpiece fabricated from 1-in.-diam 2011-T3 bar stock (Fig. 20). Broaching in a single-spindle automatic bar machine, in conjunction with other machining operations, proved the most economical procedure for making this workpiece, even though the machine spindle had to be completely stopped during broaching. The broach was made of M3 (class 1) high speed steel. Additional processing details are given in the table with Fig. 20.

Table 9. Planing Alloy 3003 Mold Assembly (Example 881)

Machine	Horizontal planing mill, 30-hp motor, 33-ft bed
Tool material	High speed steel
Tool angles	60° back rake, 0° side rake
Operating Conditions	
Speed	100 sfm
Feed	0.020 in. per stroke
Depth of cut	¼ in.
Cutting fluid	Kerosine:lubricating-oil (1:1); 150 SUS at 100 F
Setup time	4 to 5 min
Downtime for tool change	15 min per shift
Production rate	4 to 5 pieces per hour
Tool life	Approx 40 pieces per grind

Table 10. Shaping Aluminum Alloys (Example 882)

Machine	Shaper with 12-in. crank, 2-hp motor
Tool material	High speed steel
Tool design	30° back rake, 0° side rake, ⅛-in. nose radius
Operating Conditions	
Speed	120 strokes per min (220 sfm avg)
Feed:	
Roughing	0.025 in. per stroke
Finishing	0.010 in. per stroke
Depth of cut:	
Roughing	0.090 to 0.100 in.
Finishing	0.020 in.
Cutting fluid	Kerosine
Setup time	5 min
Downtime for changing tools	2 min
Production time	5 to 15 min per piece
Tool life	20 pieces per grind

Example 886. Broaching in a Multiple-Spindle Automatic Bar Machine (Fig. 21)

Both internal and external splines were broached in a workpiece made from ⅝-in.-diam 2011-T3 bar stock. Broaches were made of T2 tool steel, and broaching was done in a multiple-spindle automatic bar machine. During broaching, both workpiece and broach rotated at 3000 rpm. Details of the workpiece and the broaches are shown in Fig. 21; operating conditions and results are given in the table that accompanies Fig. 21.

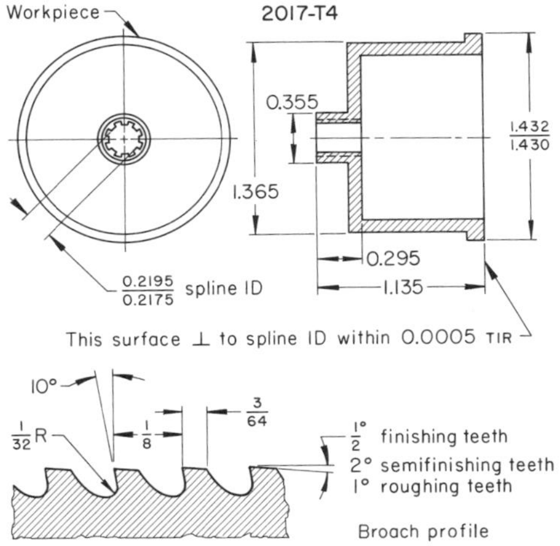

Speed	30 sfm
Feed per tooth	0.002 in.
Length of stroke	6 in.
Cutting fluid	Soluble-oil:water (1:25)
Setup time	30 min
Production rate	180 pieces per hour
Tool life per grind	2000 pieces
Total tool life	40,000 pieces

Fig. 18. Clutch housing and details of broach used for producing the internal splines (Example 883)

Drilling in Drill Presses

Although standard twist drills and drilling equipment used for steel may be employed in drilling aluminum alloys, optimum results require drills of special design, as well as higher rotational speeds and heavier feeds. Drills for aluminum normally are made with deep, well-polished flutes, narrow margins, and large helix angles. Proper drill design and drilling practice will frequently permit the removal of three to four times as much aluminum as steel per unit of power. The article

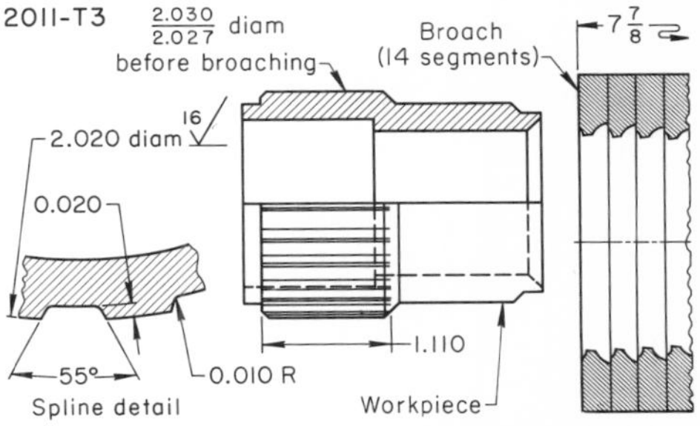

Speed	3½ strokes per min
Feed per tooth	0.020 in.
Cutting fluid	Soluble-oil:water (1:25)
Production rate	200 pieces per hour
Tool life per grind	1200 pieces

Fig. 19. Broaching external splines (Example 884)

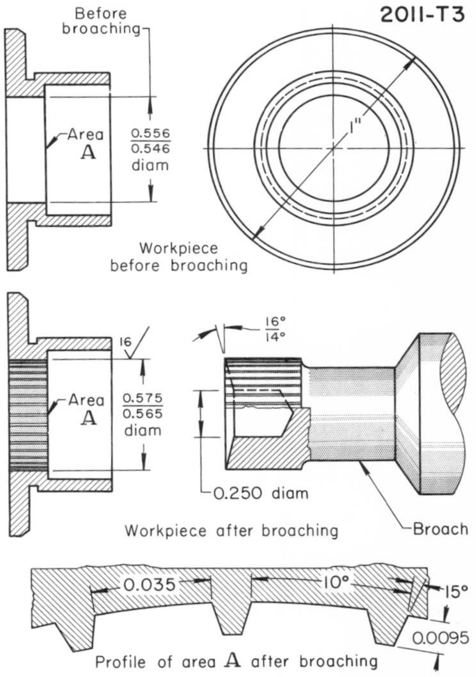

Feed (see note below)	0.015 ipr
Depth of cut	0.0095 in.
Cutting fluid	Mineral seal oil
Production rate	180 pieces per hour
Tool life per grind	25,000 pieces
Tolerance	±0.005 in.
Finish obtained	16 micro-in.

Note. Because of the short stroke, it was necessary to produce full tooth form with the front edge of the broach, as in push-pull broaching. Feed of 0.015 ipr refers to elapsed time based on normal spindle speed, although the spindle was stopped during broaching.

Fig. 20. Broaching internal splines in a single-spindle automatic bar machine (Example 885)

"Drilling", starting on page 75, discusses general equipment and practice.

For drilling in drill presses, the helix angle of the drill should be increased with the depth of the hole to be drilled, from a low-helix 24° angle for very shallow holes in thin stock, to a high-helix (40° to 48°) angle for deep holes — for which freer cutting is important (see Table 11).

The high-helix drill has a more acute cutting angle, resulting in more rapid penetration, and freer and cleaner cutting. Lands and margin are narrower than on the low-helix drill, resulting in reduced friction and increased chip space in the flutes. The slightly greater resistance to chip movement can be overcome by polishing the flutes and by supplying ample cutting fluid. This type of drill is recommended for deep holes, but is unsuitable for drilling thin stock because of its tendency to "hog in".

A twist drill with a 28° helix is suitable for holes of medium depth, up to about six drill diameters, whereas a drill with a 24° (or less) helix is recommended for thin stock, because it has less tendency to overfeed.

The point angle supplied on standard twist drills is 116° to 118°. The angle should be about 130° to 140° for drilling most aluminum alloys, to facilitate chip removal and minimize burring. However, drills for high-silicon alloys should have a less obtuse point, down to about 90°, for ease of penetration. For drilling thin sheet, the point angle should be very obtuse, to permit the drill to cut to its full diameter before the point breaks through. With this type of drill, a spur point may be necessary to assist in centering.

The standard lip clearance of 12° to 13° should be increased to about 17° for heavy feeds and for softer alloys. Insufficient lip clearance will cause excessive drill breakage. The drill cutting lips must be keen and smooth, and all surfaces over which the chip passes must be polished to minimize friction and chip buildup. Recommended point angles, helix angles, and lip clearances are summarized in Table 11.

Drill Material. Most drills for aluminum are made of high speed steel; M1, M7 and M10 are the most common grades. Only rarely can the extra cost for drills made of a more highly alloyed grade of high speed steel or of carbide be justified for conventional drilling in drill presses.

Speed and Feed. Because, with most drill presses, the peripheral speed of small-diameter drills is relatively low, they may be operated at the maximum efficient rotational speed of the machine. In general, high speed steel drills can be operated at a maximum of about 600 sfm. When variable speed is available, drill life can be increased in drilling deeper holes by bringing the drill up to speed gradually.

Because of the ease of penetrating most aluminum alloys, feeds up to twice those used for drilling steel can be employed. Feed varies with drill diameter, the larger-diameter drills permitting heavier feeds. A feed of 0.001 ipr is recommended for 1/16-in.-diam drills. The feed is increased to 0.003 ipr for 1/8-in.-diam drills, 0.007 for 1/4-in., 0.012 for 1/2-in., 0.016 for 3/4-in., 0.020 for 1 in., 0.025 for 1 1/2 in., and 0.030 for 2 in.

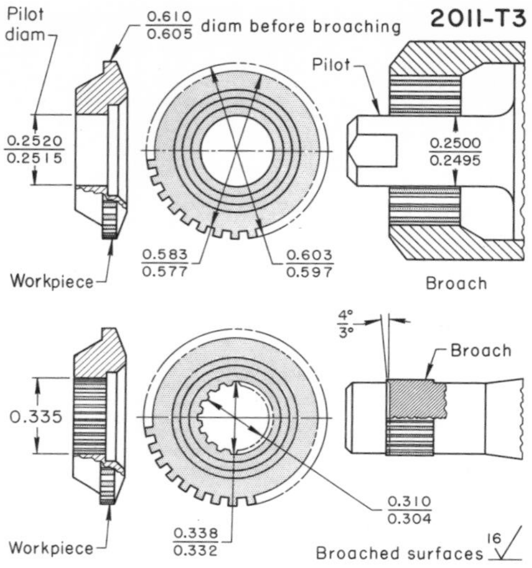

Feed(a):	
External broaching	0.0055 ipr
Internal broaching	0.007 ipr
Depth of cut(b):	
External broaching	0.010 in.
Internal broaching	0.014 in.
Cutting fluid	Mineral seal oil
Production rate	923 pieces per hour
Tool life per grind:	
External broaching	32,000 pieces
Internal broaching	47,500 pieces
Tolerance	±0.003 in.
Surface finish	16 micro-in.

(a) Broach feed per revolution of work spindle. (b) Depth of tooth form on part.

Fig. 21. Broaching internal and external splines in a multiple-spindle automatic bar machine (Example 886)

Cutting Fluid. Drilling of thin sections does not require a cutting fluid, but it is essential to drill life and hole quality that a copious supply of cutting fluid be provided for all deep-hole drilling. Soluble-oil emulsions or kerosine and lard-oil mixtures are satisfactory for general drilling. In drilling to a depth greater than six times the drill diameter, the workpiece should be kept cool by spraying. Also, the drill should be withdrawn several times during drilling to insure that the cutting fluid floods the hole completely.

Drilling in Automatic Bar and Chucking Machines

When drilling is done in multiple-operation machines, it is especially important that the tool be correctly ground and set. Standard twist drills are generally used for drilling holes up to six diameters deep. For drilling deeper holes, drills that pass the chips up the flutes more readily are recommended. When machining 2017-T4, 2024-T4 and 2011-T3, straight-flute drills generally are used for drilling holes deeper than six diameters. Either high-helix or low-helix drills can be used for drilling deep holes. The web of the high-helix drill is uniform in thickness the entire length of the body, providing large flutes for the chips. Wide flutes also characterize the low-helix drill. Both types give good results, particularly in the drilling of soft or gummy alloys. For holes with a high ratio of depth to diameter, half-round or gun drills are sometimes used.

Table 11. Tool Angles for Drilling Aluminum Alloys With High Speed Steel Drills in Drill Presses

Point angle (θ):	
Thin stock: 118° to 150°; thinned point(a)	
General work	118° to 140°
Al-Si alloys	Down to 90°
Helix angle:	
Thin stock	24°
Medium depth(b)	28°
Deep holes(c)	40° to 48°
Lip clearance:	
Soft alloys	17°
Strong alloys	15°
Al-Si alloys	12°

(a) Diameter ÷ 1.8 stock thickness = tan $\theta/2$. (b) Up to six times drill diameter. (c) Over six times drill diameter.

When standard twist drills are used for drilling deeper than three diameters, it may be necessary to enlarge the flutes. This may be done with a thin grinding wheel that has been dressed to a radius. The flute is held at an angle to the wheel to insure the proper curvature in the flute. All flutes on a drill should be ground alike.

Drill Margin. Margins along the edges of flutes support the drill in the hole and keep the drill cutting the correct diameter. When drilling aluminum alloys, standard drill margins often may be reduced in width without loss of necessary support. The narrower margin reduces friction between the drill and the hole, thus reducing the amount of heat generated. In many production jobs, a narrower margin has greatly increased drill life.

Web Thickness. For drilling aluminum alloys, web thickness at the point should be reduced as the drill is ground back. This will reduce the end pressure on the drill, because the chisel point does not cut but compresses the metal ahead of it. Generally, the web can be somewhat thinner at the point without making the drill susceptible to breakage when drilling aluminum alloys than when drilling steel.

For small-diameter drills, "notched-point" thinning is common. On larger drills, this type of point may produce a poor chip, and therefore the entire flute is ground at the point. The notched point is obtained by using the sharp corner of an abrasive wheel, the side of the wheel following the angle of the chisel point. The drill should be held at an angle to the wheel to form a slight rake for the new cutting edge, which is ground to the center of the point of the drill.

When the entire flute at the point is thinned by grinding, a thin wheel that has been dressed to a radius is used. The drill is held so that the flute is at an angle to the wheel, as when widening the flute. Most of the metal should be ground off the back of the land, and care must be taken not to grind the rake formed by the helix angle from the cutting edge or to destroy the shape of the cutting edge.

Thinning of the web must be done uniformly in each flute, to insure that the cut remains balanced on both sides of the centerline of the drill.

Cutting-Lip Angle. In general drilling practice, if holes are not too deep, a standard included cutting-lip angle of 118° will give satisfactory performance. However, if deeper holes are drilled with this cutting-lip angle, the chip produced does not come out easily. For drilling deeper holes, larger included cutting-lip angles are used, forming a narrower chip that readily passes up the flutes.

Occasionally, smaller cutting-lip angles may be employed, because the transverse forces at the cutting edges are greater and the tool can drill without runout. However, a broader chip is produced.

When several drills are used in the same hole, each succeeding tool should have a slightly more blunt cutting-lip angle than that of the preceding one, so that it can center at the outside of the cutting edges.

Clearance angle behind the cutting edges should be 12° to 20°. Larger clearances are used for straight-flute drills and for drills ground with large cutting-lip angles. Clearance should extend from periphery to center, so that the chisel point is at an angle of 130° to 145° with the cutting edges.

Rake angles are set by the helix angle of the drill. For standard twist drills, this is usually 20° to 25°; for high-helix drills, 40° to 43°; for low-helix drills, 7° to 15°; and for straight-flute and half-round drills, 0°.

Center Drills. When a drill starts against a flat surface, it may skid sideways before cutting, particularly if it is small or protrudes considerably from the holder. This may cause the drill to break or to cut off-center. Therefore, except with large, rigidly held drills, a center drill is recommended to provide an accurate start.

For maximum rigidity, center drills should be of relatively large diameter and short length. Unless a countersink of a special angle is to be left in the workpiece, an included cutting-lip angle of 90° should be used. In general, for proper centering, the outside of the cutting lips of the drill that follows the center drill should strike the stock first, insuring adequate support.

Depth of Hole. In multiple-operation machines, to prevent chips from jamming in the flutes and causing drill breakage when deep holes are being drilled, a limit must be set on the depth drilled with each entry of the tool. The maximum depths, in terms of drill diameter, that can be drilled per entry under normal production conditions are given in Table 12.

Before re-entry, the drill should be completely backed out of the hole, so that the chips can be washed away.

The type of workpiece, the number of positions on the machine available for drilling, and the type of machine determine practice for drilling deep holes. Sometimes it is economical to use several drills for drilling deep holes.

For holes more than eight diameters deep, half-round or gun drills are often used. To insure adequate support for the half-round drill when it starts cutting, another type of drill should be used to drill a starting hole, three diameters or more deep. The half-round drill can drill four diameters deeper in the first entry of the started hole.

Drill Speed. Generally, small-diameter, high speed steel drills can be operated at speeds up to 600 sfm. However, when larger drills are used to remove large quantities of metal at a rapid rate, lower speeds will give more economical drill life. A guide in choosing proper speeds for most conditions is the following:

Drill diameter	Speed
Less than 1 in.	600 sfm
1 to 1½ in.	550
Over 1½ in.	450

Feed for drilling in multiple-operation machines depends on the size and strength of the drill; finish, tolerance and concentricity desired; and power available. As feed is increased, torque on the drill increases, until the breaking point may be reached. On the other hand, lower feed produces thinner chips, which are more likely to clog the flutes than thicker chips. Clogging is likely to break the drill or mar the finish of the workpiece.

Recommended drill feeds are given in Table 13 for drill sizes up to 0.750 in. in diameter. Feeds for larger drills usually depend on the power available in the machine.

For greater accuracy and better finish, lower feed may be necessary. For deep holes, machined with several entries, feed should be decreased 15% for each successive entry. Lower feed should be used to drill thin-wall parts.

Power Requirements. When large quantities of metal are removed, lower feed may be necessary, to keep the power within the limits available in the machine. When drilling with standard drills (ground to 118° included cutting-lip angle and 15° clearance) to four diameters deep in 2017-T4 and 2024-T4, 1.5 to 2 cu in. of metal can be removed per minute per horsepower. For 2011-T3, the rate is 2.5 to 3 cu in. per minute per horsepower. These figures are based on a feed of 0.017 ipr. With lower feed, the rate of metal removal decreases.

Drill Size vs Hole Size. Drills, when properly ground and set, will cut aluminum alloys to size or not more than 0.002 in. oversize. However, any condition that causes overheating is likely to decrease the size of the hole when it is measured after the workpiece has cooled. This is especially noticeable when drilling large holes. Drilling of deep holes at high feed rate will decrease hole size in relation to drill size. Sometimes other tools working simultaneously will generate enough heat to cause the production of holes close to or even smaller than drill size, as measured after the workpiece has cooled to room temperature.

Table 12. Maximum Depths Per Drill Entry for Drilling in Automatic Bar and Chucking Machines

Drill type	Depth, in drill diameters — First drill: First entry	Second entry	Third entry	Second drill: First entry	Second entry	Third entry	Subsequent entries
Standard twist drill	4	1½	¾	....	....	....	....
High or low helix, or straight flute	5	2	1	1½	¾	½	½

Table 13. Feeds for Drilling Aluminum Alloys in Automatic Bar and Chucking Machines

Drill diam, in.	Tolerance, in.	Feed, ipr: 2011-T3	Other alloys
0.0625	±0.0015	0.0040	0.004
0.125	±0.002	0.0120	0.010
0.187	±0.002	0.0144	0.012
0.250	±0.002	0.0168	0.014
0.375	±0.0025	0.0204	0.017
0.500	±0.0025	0.0204	0.017
0.750	±0.003	0.0204	0.017

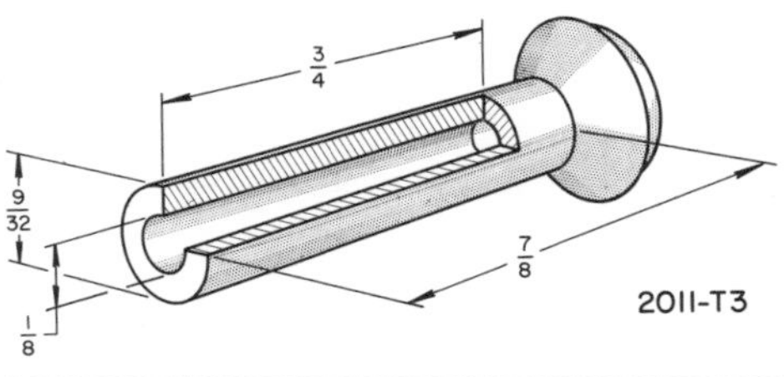

Drilling condition(a)	Original	Improved
Speed, rpm	6050	4365
Speed, sfm	198	143
Feed, ipr:		
First drilling(b)	0.0064	0.0088
Second drilling(c)	0.0057	0.0079
Cycle time, sec	10½	10½

(a) In both original and improved methods, ⅛-in.-diam tapered-shank high speed steel drills were used, and cutting fluid was a 1-to-25 mixture of soluble oil and water. (b) To depth of ½ in. (c) Remaining ¼-in. depth.

Fig. 22. Stud for which reduction of spindle speed eliminated drill breakage without reducing cycle time, because of increase in feed (Example 887)

Drilling Practice (Production Examples)

Because aluminum alloys are easily machined, rates of drill penetration are rapid and chip disposal can be a problem; for this reason, some sacrifice in speed may be necessary to permit disposal of the chips, as described in the following example.

Example 887. Decrease in Speed to Eliminate Drill Breakage (Fig. 22)

Repeated drill breakage occurred in the ⅛-in.-diam blind hole of the 2011-T3 stud shown in Fig. 22. Excessive spindle speed was the cause of drill failure. By reducing speed from 6050 to 4365 rpm and increasing the feed rate, the problem was eliminated without decreasing the cycle time. Drilling conditions at both speeds are given with Fig. 22.

Drill Design. The point angle of a drill can be a source of difficulty in drilling. When steel and other hard metals are drilled, a large included angle is used. With aluminum alloys such as 7075 and 2024, there is little difficulty in using the same point angle as for steel, but the softer, more gummy aluminum alloys require a smaller point angle. When a small angle is employed, abrasive wear is distributed more evenly over the cutting edge, thereby improving drill performance. A change in drill design that improved both drill life and the quality of drilled holes is described in the following example.

Example 888. Step Drill for Hand Drilling (Fig. 23)

In drilling holes in 7079 alloy, using portable hand tools with conventional twist drills having the standard recommended drill point, hole size could not be maintained and drill-point life was very short (one hole per grind).

As a result, operators used excessive pressure, which caused a heavy burr to appear on breakthrough of the drill point. Many holes had to be reamed after drilling, but frequently tolerances had already been exceeded in the drilling operation, and therefore the work had to be scrapped.

Drill design was modified. As shown in Fig. 23, the drill point was ground to a ⅜-in.-diam step with a 3° lip-relief clearance. High pressures were no longer needed. Tolerances could be maintained with the split-point step drill shown in Fig. 23.

Manufacturers' vs User's Standards. Drill life can sometimes be greatly improved by establishing standards of drill design more exacting than those of the manufacturer, as described in the example that follows.

Example 889. Effect of Drill-Design Standards on Tool Consumption (Table 14)

A user observed that when drills were purchased to manufacturers' standards, several details of design varied from lot to lot and from manufacturer to manufacturer. Because of these variations, drills could not be resharpened in an automatic drill grinder with precision, and many drills had to be discarded when they became dull.

When the user established his own standards for drill design and dimensions, the number of drills required for a given amount of work over a nine-month period decreased from 44,000 to 36,000. Furthermore, 50% of the drills made to the user's standard could be resharpened in an automatic drill grinder and reclaimed for further use. Details of this comparison are given in Table 14.

Workpiece Size and Shape. In the fabrication of airframe structures, part size and shape markedly affect the selection of drilling conditions and equipment. Although few problems are encountered when drilling holes in aluminum in standard bench or floor-type drilling machines, important benefits have accrued from the use of portable or other special tools. The two examples that follow describe techniques used in drilling large numbers of holes in aircraft components.

Examples 890 and 891. Techniques for Drilling Holes in Wing Panels and Skins

Example 890 — Color-Coded Templates. More than 11,000 fasteners — 22,000 holes — were required in an aircraft wing-panel assembly. Because these panels acted as fuel tanks, preparation of the holes was especially critical, to assure a leakproof assembly.

The original method of hole preparation on upper and lower wing panels involved three steps: (*a*) pilot holes were drilled, using a hand drill and drill block; (*b*) holes were drilled to size; and (*c*) holes were countersunk or counterbored, or both.

A revised method of hole preparation involved color-coded drill templates and an automatic tool that would drill, countersink and counterbore in one operation. The first hole in a panel was drilled by conventional means. The automatic tool was then locked into the drill template, using the first hole as the locating point. Because the tool provided a controlled feed and location for the next hole, the entire operation was semiautomatic.

Use of the color-coded templates was not complicated. For example, a yellow template might indicate drill and countersink only, and a blue ring around a hole in the yellow template might indicate drill, countersink and counterbore.

Two drill sizes were used: 0.187 in. +0.001, −0.000 in., and 0.187 in. +0.003, −0.000 in. Drill speed was varied, depending on the depth of the hole. Holes ¼ in. deep or less were drilled at 6000 rpm (295 sfm); those 5⁄16 in. deep or more were drilled at 3000 rpm (147 sfm). Time saved in drilling each panel assembly by the improved method amounted to 4000 hr.

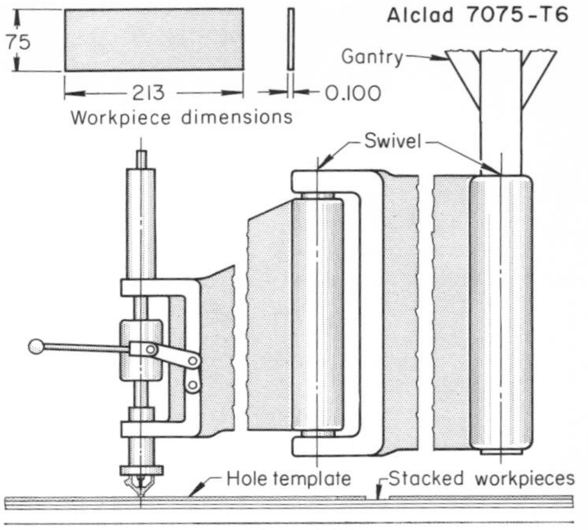

Drill Details

Material ....High speed steel
Diameter ....No. 40 (0.0980 in.)
Helix, land, web, and flute .....Same as user's standard in Table 14

Operating Conditions

Speed ....3700 rpm (96 sfm)
Feed ....Manual plunge
Depth of drilling ..0.200 in. (including pockets)
Cutting fluid ....Soluble-oil:water (1:30)
Setup time ....½ hr each for two operators
Drilling time ....2 hr for 12,000 holes

Fig. 24. Stack drilling aircraft wing skins (Example 891)

Example 891 — Stack Drilling (Fig. 24). To drill 5000 holes in an alclad 7075-T6 aircraft wing skin (213 in. long by 75 in. wide by 0.100 in. thick), two high-cycle, radial-arm drill units were employed. These units were equipped with double-swivel 6-ft arms (Fig. 24), independent overhead longitudinal-travel gantries, and a common overhead transverse-travel gantry. All motions were powered. The wing skins were stacked on an 8-by-24-ft table and were clamped with a hole template.

Holes were drilled in two stages. In the first stage, pilot holes and tooling holes for chemical milling were drilled in skins stacked five high. After chemical milling, the primary hole pattern was drilled through two-high stacks of skins. The chemically milled pockets limited the stack to two high in the second operation, because the drill was free to "walk" when passing through the pockets.

Because of the large number of holes to be drilled and the size of the parts, two operators and two drilling units were employed. The two operators drilled an average of 12,000 No. 40 holes in approximately 2 hr. This was equivalent to a hole every 1.2 sec, including the time for positioning of the drill units.

Handling the workpiece was facilitated by a vacuum lift suspended from one of the overhead traveling gantries. The vacuum lift also helped to protect the smooth surface of the parts.

Initially, a spray mist cutting fluid was applied near the top of the drill, through the open portion of the pilot bracket, but drill breakage was high. Therefore, a hole was drilled through the pilot bracket and pilot, and a small reservoir was counterbored in the pilot bracket, to feed cutting fluid by gravity to the drill, close to the work. Machining conditions and tool details are given with Fig. 24.

Combining Operations. For efficient production, drilling is often combined with one or more other machining operations, and some sacrifice in speed or feed may be required on one operation to accommodate another. This is offset by savings of tools and time. The next example describes a combination of drilling, reaming and spotfacing. For a combination drilling-and-countersinking application, see Example 161.

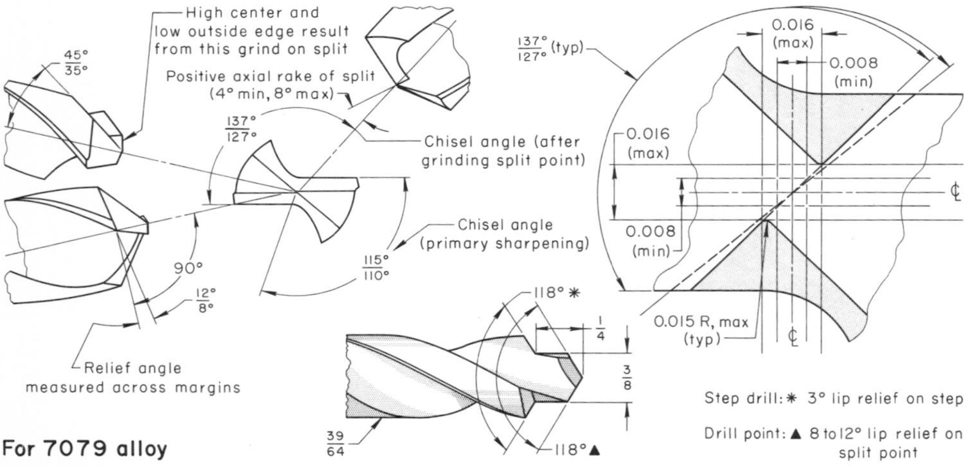

Fig. 23. Modified drill design that improved dimensional accuracy in hand drilling airframe structures of 7079 alloy (Example 888)

Table 14. Comparison of Manufacturers' and User's Standards for Drills (Example 889) (a)

Tool details	Manufacturers' standard	User's standard
Number of drills used in 9 months ..	44,000	36,000(b)
Drill diameters	No. 50 to ¼ in.	No. 50 to ¼ in.
Drill lengths	3 to 7½ in.	3 to 7½ in.
Flute lengths	1 to 3½ in.	1 to 3½ in.
Helix angle	33°	33° ± 30′
Land width	Not specified	40 to 50% of diameter, ±0.003 in.
Web thickness:		
Sizes No. 40 to 50	Not specified	23% of diameter parallel for ⅜ in. and subsequent increase of 0.013 ± 0.003 in. per in.
Sizes No. 30 to ¼ in.	Not specified	15% of diameter parallel for ⅜ in. and subsequent increase of 0.013 ± 0.003 in. per in.
Flute	Not specified	Polished, conforming to land width and web thickness

(a) Drills were used in the same machines, at the same speeds and feeds. (b) Of the drills, 50% could be automatically resharpened and reclaimed for further use.

Example 892. Combining Drilling With Reaming and Spotfacing (Table 15)

Originally, the procedure for machining the casting shown in the sketch with Table 15 was as follows: (*a*) straddle mill the 2-in. dimension in a milling machine; (*b*) drill the five holes in a drill press equipped with a multiple-spindle drill head; and (*c*) ream the five holes in a drill press, moving the fixture from spindle to spindle.

In an improved procedure, the workpiece was machined completely in a radial drilling machine with a 36-in. table. The sequence of operations and processing details are given in Table 15. Except for spotfacing one side of the hub, all operations were performed in one setting.

Production rate and perishable-tool costs for the two methods were:

	Original	Improved
Production, pieces per hr	18	82
Tools, cost per set	$116	$90
Cost of fixtures	$950	$2805

Deep-Hole Drilling

Gun drills, tipped with either carbide or high speed steel have replaced twist drills for many deep-hole drilling applications, regardless of the metal being drilled (see discussion of gun drilling on pages 81 and 82 in the article "Drilling", in this volume). In gun drilling, the maximum depth of hole that can be drilled successfully is generally related to drill size (Table 16). Length-to-diameter relationships shown in Table 16 are generally standard, although gun drills having much greater length-to-diameter ratios are often used — as in Examples 165 and 893.

Gun drills, with a single-flute cutting head and grooved shank, must have a sufficient flow of cutting fluid under high pressure at the point where the cutting edge contacts the work, to keep the cutting edge cool and to insure that the chips will be forced out through the chip groove. Cutting fluid is normally applied at a pressure of 500 to 600 psi for drills ⅜ in. in diameter or smaller and at 300 to 400 psi for larger drills. A pump of 5-hp capacity is usually required for average applications. A paraffin-base oil with a viscosity of 100 to 125 sus at 100 F has been used satisfactorily in gun drilling aluminum with a ⅜-in.-diam drill at a speed of 300 sfm (for high speed steel) or 600 sfm (for carbide) and feeds of 0.001 to 0.003 ipr.

Although deep-drilling problems have been alleviated to some extent by the development of gun drills and special gun-drilling equipment, this equipment is expensive and cannot always be justified. Example 148, in the article "Drilling", describes an application in which holes seven diameters deep were drilled in alloy 6061-T6 in a turret lathe. The following example describes another deep-hole drilling application that utilized available equipment (in this instance, a boring mill).

Example 893. Deep-Hole Drilling in a Boring Mill (Fig. 25)

The 36-in.-diam, 36-in.-long explosive forming die illustrated in Fig. 25 was originally made up from nine 4-in.-thick aluminum alloy plates. Because no plate stock obtainable was wide enough to make a 36-in.-diam one-piece plate, each round plate was made by doweling together two 4-in.-thick half-sections. As each 4-in. plate section was completed by machining the die cavity hole through its center and drilling 12 tie-bolt holes, it was mated to the next 4-in.-thick plate until the die was completed. Each individual plate was placed on the preceding plate so that the half-section cut lines were 90° from those in the preceding plate. Then each section was doweled with two pins to the next, completing the die.

Table 15. Seven-Operation Drilling, Reaming and Spotfacing of a Casting (Example 892) (a)

Operation 1
(Drilling hole A halfway)(b)

Speed	860 rpm (146 sfm)
Feed	0.006 ipr
Tool life per grind	500 pieces

Operation 2
(Through drilling hole A)(b)

Speed	860 rpm (146 sfm)
Feed	0.006 ipr
Tool life per grind	500 pieces

Operation 3
(Reaming hole A)(c)

Speed	500 rpm (90 sfm)
Feed	0.017 ipr
Tool life per grind	2500 pieces

Operation 4
(Spotfacing one side of hub)(d)

Speed	500 rpm (196 sfm)
Feed	0.017 ipr
Depth of cut	⅛ in.
Tool life per grind	5000 pieces

Operations 5 and 6
(Drilling and reaming holes B and C)(e)

Speed	1500 rpm (196 sfm)
Feed	0.010 ipr
Tool life per grind	500 pieces

Operation 7
(Spotfacing opposite side of hub)(d)

Speed	500 rpm (196 sfm)
Feed	0.017 ipr
Depth of cut	⅛ in.
Tool life per grind	5000 pieces

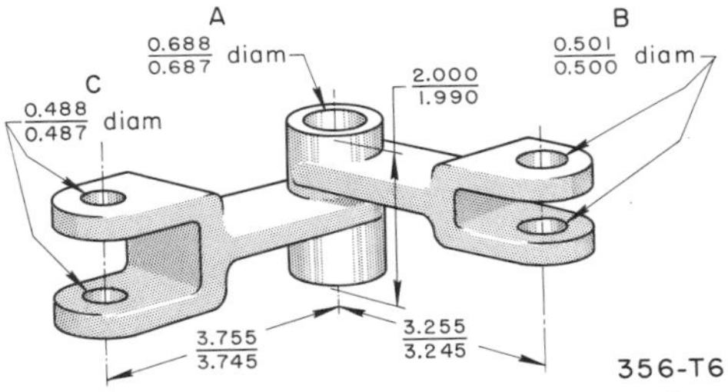

(a) Operations were performed on casting shown above, a distributing lever. Total setup time for all operations was 2 hr; cycle time for each operation was 0.732 min. Downtime for changing tools was 1½ hr; cutting fluid was a 1-to-25 mixture of soluble oil and water; finish obtained in reamed holes was 100 micro-in. (b) a 21/32-in.-diam high speed steel drill with high-spiral polished flutes and 125° point angle was used. (c) The six-flute reamer was 11/16 in. in diameter, with a 45° lead angle and 0.015-in. land. (d) Four-flute spotfacing tool was 1½ in. in diameter, with sharp land and 10° rake angle. Tool was used with a 0.686-in.-diam pilot, ½ in. long. (e) Holes B and C were drilled and reamed with subland drills having two-flute drill portions, four-flute reamer portions and 125° point angle. Drill portion for holes B was 31/64 in. in diameter; reamer portion was 0.500 in. Drill portion for holes C was 27/64 in. in diameter; reamer portion was 0.488 in.

By the improved method of producing these dies, four 36-in.-diam, 9-in.-thick forgings were obtained. These forgings were machined (as were the 4-in.-thick plates) individually and doweled to one another to maintain alignment. The assembly was then set up in a boring mill as shown in Fig. 25. Each of the 1⅝-in.-diam tie-bolt holes was drilled in one pass using a standard gun drill. Drilling time was reduced from 7 hr by the original method to ½ hr by the improved method.

The boring mill was modified by adding a hydraulic pump with a capacity of 40.6 gal per min to supply cutting fluid to the drill point at 300 psi. A baffle plate and filter system were installed to handle the flow of oil. This modification of the boring mill provided satisfactory deep-hole drilling at a cost of $1000 for the modification. Estimated cost for a new deep-hole drilling machine for this job was $25,000.

Reaming

The machines, basic designs of reamers, and techniques discussed in the article "Reaming", which begins on page 93 of this volume, are generally applicable to aluminum alloys.

Reamer Design. Because it is less likely to cause chatter, a spiral-flute reamer — either solid, expandable or adjustable — is generally preferable to a straight-flute reamer for finishing holes in aluminum alloys. In most applications, it is advantageous to use a reamer with a negative spiral (that is, one spiraled in the direction opposite to rotation), to prevent the reamer from feeding itself into the hole. Flutes should be large enough to pass the chips readily, and there should be enough flutes to provide adequate support to the tool. The margins of straight-flute reamers should be as narrow as possible, to reduce friction between tool and work.

Straight-flute reamers are designed with an even number of blades arranged opposite each other in pairs, but with flute spacing varied slightly to prevent chatter and marking.

Spiral flutes (right-hand cut, left-hand spiral) are frequently more effective than angular spacing in reducing chatter. However, a spiral-flute reamer must have sufficient spiral so that two or more flutes overlap in the length of the reamed hole. The spiral angle must be held to a minimum, because the steeper the angle, the more end pressure is required to feed the reamer through the hole. Additional reamer design data are given in Table 17.

Table 16. Relation of Drill Diameter to Approximate Maximum Depth of Hole in Gun Drilling

Drill diameter, in.	Depth of hole, in drill diameters	Drill diameter, in.	Depth of hole, in drill diameters
Up to ½	12	1½ to 2	5
½ to 1	7	2 to 2½	4
1 to 1½	6	2½ to 3	3

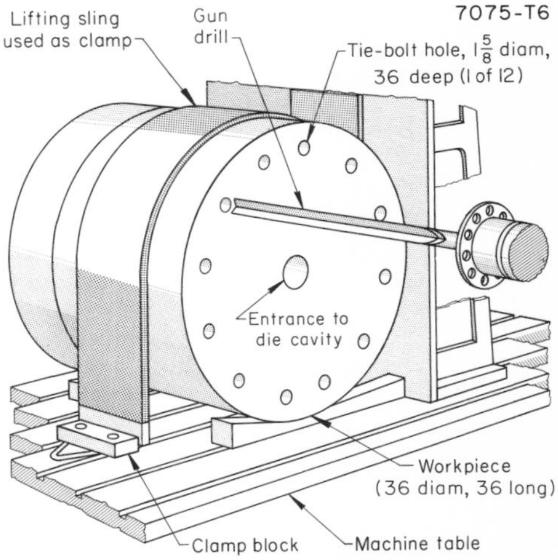

Fig. 25. Setup for deep-hole drilling an explosive forming die in a boring mill **(Example 893)**

Table 17. Reamer Design and Operating Conditions for Reaming Aluminum Alloys

Reamer Design	
Reamer size:	
Hand reaming	1.01 times drill diameter
Machine reaming	1.02 times drill diameter
Flute type	Straight to 10° spiral
Tooth spacing:	
Straight flute	Uneven (a)
Spiral flute	Even
Tooth style:	
Roughing	Solid or nicked
Finishing	Solid
Top rake	5° to 8°
Clearance angles:	
Primary	4° to 7°
Secondary	15° to 20°
Cutting angle	85° to 91°
Land width	0.020 to 0.060 in. (b)
Operating Conditions	
Speed, roughing:	
Hard alloys	Up to 200 sfm
Soft alloys	60 to 100 sfm
Speed, finishing:	
Straight reamers	Up to 400 sfm
Taper reamers	Up to 300 sfm
Feed:	
Roughing	0.013 to 0.035 ipr
Finishing	0.003 to 0.010 ipr

(a) To avoid chatter. (b) Land width is approximately 1/25 of reamer diameter.

When the hole has close tolerances and rigid surface finish requirements, reaming procedure must sometimes be altered. If the design of the workpiece permits, spiral-flute reamers with 7° hook will produce fine finishes, especially on angular surfaces. When reaming diameters of 0.750 in. or larger, a carbide-tipped expandable reamer will produce good finish and provide extended tool life.

Speed and Feed. Nominal speed for reaming the non-heat-treated cast alloys with high speed steel (M1, M7 or M10) reamers is 400 sfm. For all other cast and wrought alloys, speed should be about 300 sfm.

When reaming the non-heat-treated cast alloys with carbide tools, nominal speed is 850 sfm. For other cast and wrought alloys, nominal reaming speed is 700 sfm.

Feed rate in reaming aluminum alloys is generally the same for all alloys and tool materials; hole size, however, does affect optimum feed. A feed of 0.005 ipr is a good starting point in reaming ⅛-in.-diam holes. Nominal rate of feed increases as hole diameter increases: 0.008 ipr for ¼-in.-diam holes, 0.012 for ½-in., 0.016 for 1-in., 0.020 for 1½-in., and 0.030 for 2-in.

Cutting Fluid. At high reaming speed, a cutting fluid is required, to reduce temperature in the workpiece, minimize distortion, and prevent undersize reaming. For reaming with high speed steel reamers, mixtures of lard oil and paraffin oil or kerosine, or of petroleum and turpentine, are especially recommended. Sulfurized and chlorinated oils are often used (see Example 894), but they are likely to stain the work. With carbide reamers, emulsions of soluble oil and water are the most widely used cutting fluids.

Reaming and Burnishing. When difficulty is encountered in obtaining the desired tolerance and surface finish, it may be necessary to employ two-stage finishing — for instance, to ream the hole 0.0005 in. under the specified dimension, and then to burnish it to size and finish requirements (see the article "Roller Burnishing", which begins on page 105 of this volume). The following example describes two-stage ream-and-burnish finishing.

Example 894. Reaming and Burnishing to Close Tolerance (Fig. 26)

Two of the three inside diameters of the part shown in Fig. 26 were sized to tolerance (+0.005, −0.000 in.) by reaming. For the 1.122/1.121-in. diameter, however, a two-stage operation was required: reaming to 1.1210/1.1205 in. and then burnishing to final size and specified finish (63 micro-in.). All inside diameters were concentric within 0.002 in. TIR. A sulfurized and chlorinated mineral oil was used as cutting fluid in reaming.

Reaming in Automatic Machines. A finishing reamer for use in automatic bar and chucking machines is shown in Fig. 27. This reamer finishes three diameters and faces the part to length. A radial rake angle of approximately 7° helps improve surface finish, particularly in reaming angular surfaces. The varied angular spacing of the flutes is intended to minimize slip, deflection and chatter.

Burnishing

In the roller burnishing of aluminum, tools of hardened and polished steel are normally employed to finish a surface by compressing the surface while either the tool or the work is rotating. The burnishing of an in-line hole in a 356-T6 casting for accurate size control is described in Example 214, in the article "Roller Burnishing".

Holes in aluminum are also sometimes burnished in production by pressing a bearing-grade steel ball through the bore to improve the finish.

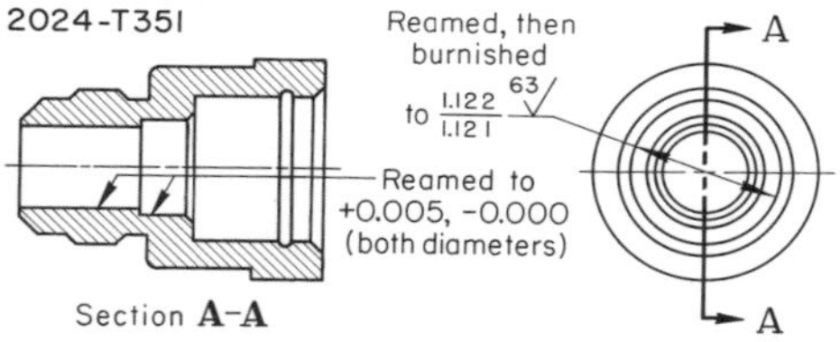

Fig. 26. Part in which two diameters were sized by reaming, and one by reaming and burnishing (Example 894)

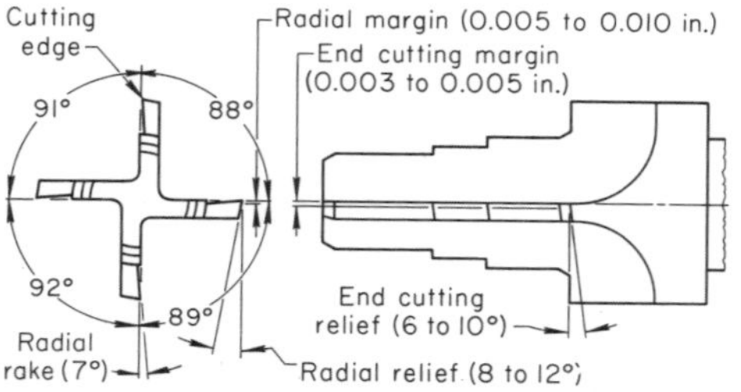

Fig. 27. Design of a finishing reamer used for reaming aluminum in automatic bar and chucking machines

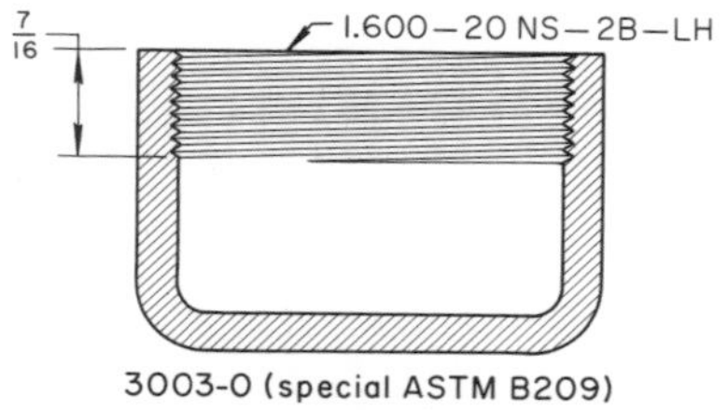

Fig. 28. Booster cup tapped by two different methods (Example 895)

Tapping

Taps for producing threads in aluminum are usually made of one of the general-purpose grades of high speed steel such as M1, M7 or M10. Taps should have polished flutes and ample backoff behind the land, to prevent pickup of work metal when the tap is withdrawn. Pitch diameters should be one thread class higher than those normally used for steel.

Taps with a diameter less than ⅜ in. should have no more than two flutes; larger taps should have the maximum number of flutes that will give the relationships of land width to circumference shown in the following table:

Tap circumference, in.	Optimum land, %
½ to 1	33
1 to 1¾	25
Over 1¾	20

Land width can also be expressed as 1½ to 3 times the pitch.

Taps for through holes and the harder aluminum alloys should be provided with a hook angle of 10° to 20°, a spiral point, 3 to 4 threads chamfer, and a pitch diameter of GH2 (basic plus 0.0005 to 0.001 in.) or GH3 (basic plus 0.001 to 0.0015 in.). Taps for blind holes and soft alloys should have 10° to 15° hook and 40° right-hand spiral flutes.

For tapping blind holes less than ⅛ in. in diameter, spiral flutes should be avoided. For best size control, it is preferable not to bring the chip up the flute but to push it ahead of the tap, with a spiral point.

Efficiency of tapping may be greatly improved by a change in tooling or method — for instance, a change from a solid tap to a collapsible tap, as in the following example:

Example 895. Solid vs Collapsible Tap (Fig. 28)

An extruded booster cup for high explosive (Fig. 28) was tapped originally in a single-spindle chucking machine with a thread-lead cam, using a solid tap. The machine was loaded by hand, and cycle time was 11½ sec. In backing out, the solid tap left chips attached to the part, so that a cleaning operation with a nylon brush was required. Also, chips wedged in the solid tap, and the tap had to be cleaned out after tapping only a few parts.

Replacement of the solid tap by a collapsible revolving tap (capacity, 1¾ in.) made it unnecessary to back out the tap. The job was changed to a six-spindle chucking machine, of 2⅜-in. capacity, which had a thread-lead cam. Cycle time was reduced to 4 sec per part.

Rotating the tap and collapsing it prevented the chips from sticking, eliminating the brushing operation and the cleaning of the tap. The cutting fluid, a light spindle oil, satisfactorily removed the chips during tapping. The chasers were ground with a lead like a solid gun tap (as was the original solid tap), to propel the chips forward.

Tapping speed recommended for aluminum is considerably higher than speeds used for steel. Alloy composition and condition, thread pitch, and method of tapping are major factors affecting tapping speed.

Assuming that the thread pitch is fine (18 to 24) and that the operation can be closely controlled (as in lead-screw tapping), the nominal speeds in the following table are generally suitable for use in tapping aluminum alloys:

Alloy	Speed, sfm
Non-heat-treated cast alloys	115
Heat treated cast alloys (solution treated and aged)	90
Cold drawn wrought alloys	125
Heat treated wrought alloys (solution treated and aged)	100

For coarser pitches, such as 8 to 12, any of the above speeds will be decreased, because of the difficulty in controlling the machine. For short thread lengths, speeds for tapping a coarse thread should be about one half the speeds given above. For long threads of the same pitch, the speed can be faster than for short threads, because of the longer time between starting and stopping. The use of lead-control devices permits higher tapping speeds than when no control is used. For instance, a speed of 115 sfm was used to tap 10–24 UNC threads in 2024-T4. The holes were blind and approximately ½ in. deep. However, lead-screw control was used. Under the same conditions but without lead-screw control, speed would have been 60 sfm max.

Cutting Fluid. Lard oil diluted with kerosine or other low-viscosity mineral oil is usually preferred for tapping aluminum. Low-viscosity commercial cutting oils are also used successfully. Soluble-oil emulsions are sometimes used, but they will not provide as good a finish as the other cutting fluids mentioned. However, the example that follows describes an application where a soluble oil was more effective than a mineral oil, probably because of the lower viscosity of the soluble-oil emulsion, which allowed it to penetrate more readily to the cutting edges of the tap and also allowed it to flow in greater volume for flushing away chips.

Example 896. Mineral Oil vs Soluble Oil for Tapping

An automatic tapping machine was used for cutting 6–32 UNC–2B threads in through holes (¼ in. deep) in alloy 2024-T4. Taps were straight-flute, spiral-point, with 15° chamfer angle and 18° hook, and were operated at 4150 rpm (122 sfm). Cutting fluid was mineral oil.

Chip congestion, together with buildup of work metal on the cutting edges of the tap, resulted in rough threads and tap breakage. Variations in tapping speed were tried, but did not alleviate these problems. However, by substituting soluble oil (in a 1-to-20 mixture with water) for mineral oil as the cutting fluid, thread finish became acceptable, and productivity and tap life were increased:

	Mineral oil	Soluble oil
Holes tapped per hour	1480	**1520**
Total tap life, holes	6250	**8900**

Best results are obtained when the cutting fluid is applied with pressure, especially when tapping blind holes.

Production Procedure. The three examples that follow describe the effect of thread size, close tolerances, and tapping blind versus through holes.

Example 897. Effect of Thread Size on Tap Life (Table 18)

Special tapping machines were used in a study to determine the effects of thread size on tap life in tapping two different aluminum alloys. Operating details and results are given in Table 18. As these data show, regardless of size, tap life was much less in tapping cast alloy 355-T6 than in tapping 6061-T6 bar stock. This agreed with experience in other machining operations in the plant.

Table 18. Effect of Thread Size on Tap Life in Alloys 355-T6 and 6061-T6 (Example 897)

Item	10–24 UNC–3B	⅜–24 UNF–3B	9/16–18 UNF–3B
Conditions Common to Both Materials(a)			
Diameter of tap-drilled hole, in.	0.155/0.151	0.334/0.328	0.508/0.502
Depth of thread, in.	7/16	Through	½
Speed of tap, rpm	250	200	150
Speed of tap, sfm	12.5	20	22
Taps for 355-T6 (AMS 4212) Aluminum Castings			
Number of flutes	3	3	4
Flute helix angle	55°	30°	0°
Hook angle	5°	7°	10°
Number of chamfered threads	1½	5	2
Tap life per grind, holes	*150*	*100*	*80*
Taps for 6061-T6 (AMS 4150) Aluminum Bar Stock			
Number of flutes (straight flutes)	2	3	4
Hook angle	10°	10°	10°
Number of chamfered threads	1½	5	2
Tap life per grind, holes	*200*	*300*	*200*

(a) Cutting fluid for all tapping operations consisted of lard oil and kerosine (1:1).

In tapping the cast alloy, tap life decreased as tap size increased — which is normal, because as size increases so does the amount of metal being removed. However, this relation did not hold true for tapping the bar stock; tap life was 300 holes per grind in tapping the ⅜–24 threads, whereas in tapping the 10–24 threads, tap life was only 200 holes per grind.

Example 898. Tapping Aluminum Castings to Close Tolerances

Turboprop-engine components made of alloy 355-T6 (AMS 4212) required stud fits in 20 blind holes (per casting) tapped to a depth of about ½ in. with ¼–20 UNC–5B threads. The completed assembly was required to withstand pressure of 4500 psi without leakage through the threads, and specifications permitted that only two holes per casting could be repaired by the use of inserts.

With the tapping procedure originally used, holes were undersize or bell-mouthed, and threads were torn. About 21% of the tapped castings required repair, and about 4% were beyond repair and were scrapped.

After experimentation, the following procedure was found to produce acceptable results, and was adopted:

1. Drill holes to 0.200/0.195-in. diameter.
2. Ream to 0.206/0.202-in. diameter.
3. Rough tap, leaving 0.005 to 0.008 in. of stock per side, for removal in finish tapping.
4. Finish tap to size.

Example 899. Tapping Blind vs Through Holes

Aircraft-engine components made of alloy 355-T6 (AMS 4212) had blind and through holes that required ¼–20 UNC–2B threads to a depth of ½ in. The blind holes (19/32 in. deep) were reamed after being drilled, to reduce the size and quantity of chips generated in tapping and thereby minimize the packing of chips in the 3/32-in. clearance space. The through holes (½ in. deep) were tapped without having been reamed. Tap life and cost, and production rate for the blind and through holes were as follows:

	Blind holes	Through holes
Tap life per grind, holes	275	**400**
Cost per tap	$2.14	**$1.81**
Holes tapped per hour	18	**22**

Example 900. Tapping a Thin-Wall Workpiece (Fig. 29)

A vertical tapping machine was used to tap the 3/64-in. wall portion of the workpiece shown in Fig. 29. The part was made of alloy 6063-T5, which has a yield strength of only 21,000 psi. Such relatively low strength, in combination with the thin wall, posed a size-retention problem in tapping: the outward pressure from tapping force caused the wall to expand, but the wall returned to normal size after the tap was removed, leaving the tapped holes undersize.

To avoid this problem, a tap ground oversize to GH7 pitch-diameter limit (see Table 4, page 110, in the article "Tapping") was used. As an additional precaution, an eight-flute tap was used, because the closer spacing of the lands provided extra support for the thin wall and distributed the cutting force more uniformly around the workpiece. Tap details and operating conditions are listed in the table that accompanies Fig. 29.

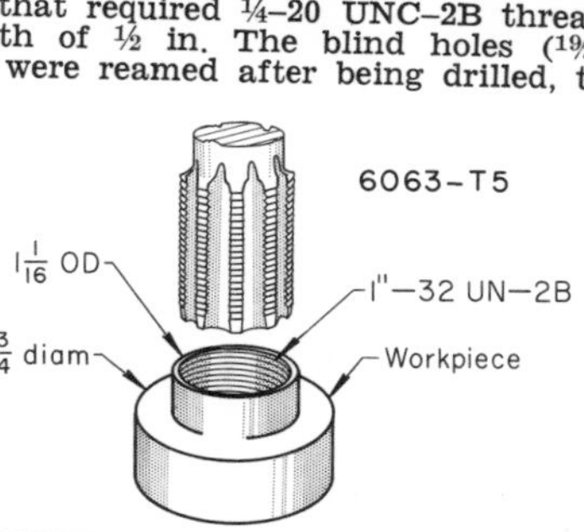

Tap Details

Material	M1 high speed steel
Number of flutes	8
Hook angle	12°
Chamfer angle	11° 15′ (approx 3½ threads)
Chamfer relief per land	0.006 to 0.008 in.
Pitch-diameter limit	GH7

Operating Conditions

Diameter of tap-drilled hole	31/32 in.
Wall thickness of threaded portion	3/64 in.
Length of threaded portion	⅜ in.
Per cent of full thread	76
Speed	344 rpm (90 sfm)
Cutting fluid	Mineral oil

Fig. 29. Tapping a thin-wall aluminum part (Example 900)

Form Tapping. If chips are a serious problem and if the hole wall is thick enough to support the pressure of the tool, a form (chipless) tap may be used (see page 118 in the article "Tapping", in this volume). Although a 75% thread is generally recommended for cut threads, tap drilling for 55 to 65% thread is practical for threads produced with a form tap. All aluminum alloys except the high-silicon (12%) die-casting alloys can be tapped with form taps.

In some applications, form taps have been successfully operated at speeds twice as fast as are used for their cutting-type counterparts. Limitations are the same for form tapping as for cutting tapping and the same cutting fluids are used. The following example compares performance of cutting taps and form taps.

Example 901. Tapping: Cutting vs Forming

Performance of No. 4-40 cutting taps was compared with that of form (chipless) taps in tapping a through hole in a ¼-in. section of alloy 380 die castings. Both taps were used in a lead-screw machine, at 3000 rpm. The cutting fluid was a high-grade cutting oil with low sulfur content. Although production rate for both taps was 400 pieces per hour, production rate per setup with the form tap (1200 pieces) was double the rate obtained when the cutting tap was used.

In tapping these die castings, a form tap was superior to a cutting tap in all sizes from No. 2 through No. 8, provided the hole wall was thick enough to support the pressure of the form tap.

Single-Point Threading

Single-point threading tools of conventional design are used to cut both internal and external threads on aluminum alloys. Speeds of 500 sfm are common, although higher speeds have been used. Typical practice is represented by the following example:

Example 902. Single-Point Threading of Die Castings (Fig. 30)

A fine-pitch thread (pitch diameter, 1.6580/1.6514 in.) was machined in an alloy 380 die casting (Fig. 30) with a single-point carbide tool. This alloy was susceptible to chipping and tearing if high cutting pressure was applied, particularly if the die casting was porous in the area being threaded.

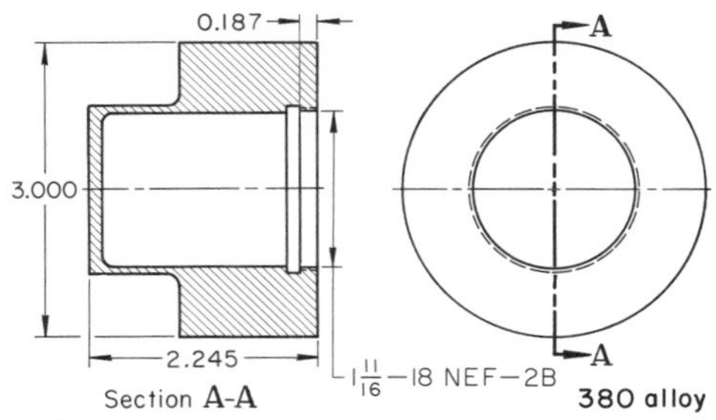

Details of Single-Point Threading Tool

Material	Carbide
Cutting-edge angle	60°
Top rake angle	20°
Clearance angle	7°

Operating Conditions

Speed	475 sfm
Diameter of bore	$1^{11}/_{16}$ in.
Length of threads	0.187 in.
Cutting fluid	Soluble-oil:water (1:25)
Setup time	1 hr
Cycle time	40 sec
Production rate	75 pieces per hour

Fig. 30. Die casting threaded in a single-spindle chucking machine with a threading attachment (Example 902)

Die Threading

Circular chasers for die threading aluminum alloys should have a hook angle of 20° and a face angle of 2°. When threading with tangential chasers, a combination of nominal back rake angle of 20° and 0° side rake angle is generally best.

To avoid damage to the first few threads, chasers should have a lead chamfer of 25° to 35° for 1½ threads. This chamfer will assure a smooth, even start.

Speeds up to 130 sfm for the non-heat-treated cast alloys and about 100 sfm for the other alloys can be used, if the length and pitch of the thread and the equipment used permit control at these speeds. Speeds no more than half of the above are more often used, because at the higher speeds control is more difficult, especially when threading short lengths or close to a shoulder.

Examples 871 and 873, in this article, compare two alloys and two tempers in die threading. In Example 871, alloys 355 and 356 were threaded in a turret lathe, and in Example 873, the threading characteristics of the T6 and T7 tempers of alloy 355 are compared.

Multiple-Operation Machining in Bar and Chucking Machines

The commercial aluminum alloys preferred for machining in automatic bar and chucking machines are 2011, 2017, 2024, 6061 and 6262. Alloy 2011 is the most widely used, because it produces chips that break easily without the aid of a chip breaker (see Fig. 1 and Table 1). Alloy 2011 is also heat treatable and usually is machined in the T3 temper, but if the part has thin walls or if distortion is probable, the stress-relieved T451 temper is recommended (Example 872). Although it is not always possible to change the alloy to improve machinability, when alloy 2011 will satisfy service requirements, substantial over-all savings are possible with its use (Examples 867 and 868).

Alloy 2017 machines well, but it produces chips that do not break readily unless a chip breaker is used. Alloy 2024 has similar machining characteristics. Example 869 describes an application where production rate increased and machining cost decreased when 2017 was replaced by 2024.

Alloy 6061 is the most ductile of the alloys recommended for multiple-operation machining, and consequently is the most difficult to machine. The chips produced are tough and stringy, and a chip breaker is essential. Alloy 6262 has slightly better machining characteristics than 6061, but still requires a chip breaker. When service requirements permit, 6262 can be substituted for 6061 (for instance, see Example 870, which involves tapping).

Table 19. Speeds and Feeds for Machining 2011 Aluminum Alloy Round Bar Stock in Automatic Bar and Chucking Machines

Width or depth of cut, in.	Size of hole, in.	High speed steel: Speed, sfm	High speed steel: Feed, ipr	Carbide: Speed, sfm	Carbide: Feed, ipr
Width:	**Form Tools, Circular or Dovetail**				
0.500	....	700	0.003	1000-1500	0.007-0.010
1.000	....	700	0.002	950-1450	0.006-0.009
1.500	....	650	0.001	950-1450	0.005-0.008
2.000	....	650	0.001	925-1425	0.004-0.005
	Twist Drills				
....	0.250	600	0.014	900-1400	0.012-0.016
....	0.500	600	0.017	850-1350	0.014-0.018
....	0.750	600	0.017	850-1350	0.016-0.019
....	1.000	550	0.019	800-1300	0.016-0.019
....	1.250	550	0.020	750-1250	0.018-0.022
Depth:	**Turning or Box Tools**				
0.125	....	700	0.008	1000-1500	0.017-0.024
0.250	....	700	0.006	950-1450	0.016-0.024
0.375	....	675	0.004	925-1425	0.013-0.019
0.500	....	650	0.002	900-1400	0.011-0.016
	Hollow Mills				
0.062	....	650	0.012	900-1400	0.036-0.048
0.125	....	625	0.010	850-1350	0.029-0.038
0.187	....	600	0.008	825-1325	0.025-0.034
0.250	....	600	0.007	800-1300	0.022-0.029
	Knurling Tools on Cross Slide				
....	....	700	0.010	1000-1500	0.060-0.080
....	....	700	0.020	1000-1500	0.120-0.160
....	....	700	0.010	1000-1500	0.060-0.080
	Chamfering and Facing				
....	....	700	0.002	1000-1500	0.024-0.030
	Reamers				
....	½ max	600	0.009	825-1350	0.026-0.034
....	½ min	600	0.015	825-1350	0.036-0.048
Width:	**Cutoff Tools**				
0.062	....	700	0.003	1000-1500	0.009-0.012
0.125	....	700	0.004	1000-1500	0.011-0.014
0.187	....	700	0.004	1000-1500	0.011-0.014
0.250	....	700	0.004	1000-1500	0.012-0.016

Speed and Feed. With carbide tools, speeds of 1000 to 1500 sfm are common; with high speed steel tools, speeds of 550 to 700 sfm are satisfactory. Table 19 gives speeds and feeds for machining 2011 aluminum alloy with high speed steel and carbide tools. The highest spindle speed possible is recommended for most automatic operations. Factors that determine maximum spindle speed include size and shape of the part, machining operations to be performed, and machine limitations.

Feeds employed vary with cutting conditions, dimensional tolerances, and the surface finish required. Overlapping operations, part size and shape, or machining conditions may require lower-than-normal feeds. The feeds shown in Table 19 are related to a specific tool and cut, and are applicable to most automatic machining operations. The lower feeds within the ranges are recommended for best surface finish and close dimensional tolerances, especially when machining the less free-cutting alloys, such as 6061 and 6262.

Cutting Fluid. A generous flow of cutting fluid is essential. A low-viscosity mineral oil is preferred for machining aluminum alloys in automatic machines; it dissipates heat quickly, washes away the chips, and — because of its low viscosity — allows fine chips to settle out in the sumps of larger equipment. This settling action prevents clogging of the sump drains.

When high temperatures or high pressures are encountered at the cutting point of the tool, special oils containing 5 to 10% of fatty additives in a light mineral oil are recommended. Among the fatty additives commonly used are oleic acid, neat's-foot oil, and lard oil. The flash point of cutting fluids should be above 270 F to reduce danger from fire.

Tool Design. The following suggestions for tools used on automatic machines provide initial guidance:

Cutoff Tools. A front angle of 23° and clearance angles of 8° to 12° are satisfactory. For deep cuts with heavy feeds, the front angle should be reduced to 10° to 15° and a chip breaker should be used for all alloys except 2011.

Form Tools. Rake angles of 5° to 10° are employed for all alloys recommended except 2011, which requires a rake angle of 0° to 3°. Where feasible, chip breakers are used for all alloys except 2011, or cams can be notched, provided the tool does not leave the work and make a plunge return.

Knee Tools. Clearance angles of 8° to 15° (usually provided on the holders) and rake angles of 15° to 20° are employed for all alloys except 2011.

Drills. See the section "Drilling in Automatic Bar and Chucking Machines", page 448 in this article.

Reamers. Standard twist drills can be used for reaming the smaller diameters. Straight reamers should employ rake angles of 5° to 10° and clearance angles of 10°. The lands on reamers should be made as narrow as possible, in order to reduce heating to a minimum in close-tolerance reaming.

Counterbores. Stepped counterbores with a rake angle of 7° are recommended for all alloys except 2011, which requires a 0° rake. Narrow lands are essential to reduce heat.

Taps and Chasers. Taps should be of the ground-thread type with polished flutes, narrow lands to reduce heat, ample chip room, and rake angles of 10° to 20°, depending on the alloy being machined. Threading ratios that are used for brass can also be used for aluminum, and thread rolling procedures are the same for both metals. Chaser dies and fluteless taps are suitable for use on aluminum.

Recessing tools, because of their fragility, should be made rigid and as large as possible; they should be provided with clearance angles of 5° to 10° and rake angles of 0° to 5°. Freer cutting can be obtained with larger rake angles, but chatter will develop unless the tool is extremely rigid. Chip breakers should be used for all alloys except 2011.

Box Tools. Tool holders for box tools commonly provide a front clearance angle of 8°; a cutting angle of 82° insures that the cutting face of the tool is parallel to the work axis. The top rake angle for machining 2011 alloy is 0°. Box tools for machining the other recommended alloys should be provided with a tapered V-groove ground on the face of the tool, parallel to the cutting edge; this groove will act as a chip breaker. If the groove is too wide, it will not break the chips.

Dimensional Control. Variations in the dimensions of consecutive pieces in one production lot machined in a single-spindle automatic bar machine are illustrated by the following example.

Example 903. Variation in Diameter of 29 Consecutive Pieces (Fig. 31)

Figure 31 shows the spread and distribution of variations in the form-turned 0.126/0.124-in. diameter on the 2011-T3 part shown in the inset sketch, as indicated by measurements made on 29 consecutively produced pieces. With a total variation range of 0.0009 in., the 29 parts were within less than half the allowable tolerance of ±0.001 in. on the 0.125-in. diameter. The reasonably even distribution of dimensions indicates that the ½-in. single-spindle automatic bar machine used was in good condition.

Where machining to close tolerances or to close relations between dimensions is imperative, careful selection of machine and the use of special procedures may be required, as shown in Example 904. In Example 905, the design of the part was changed so that close tolerances could be met, and in Example 906 close concentricity between turned and bored diameters was obtained by redesigning the part to be machined in a turret lathe.

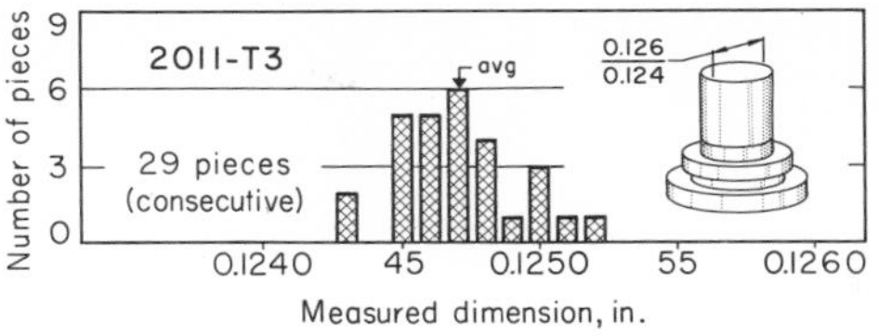

Fig. 31. Variation in diameter of parts produced in a single-spindle automatic bar machine (Example 903)

Example 904. Close Tolerances on 7075-T6 Gyro Cases (Fig. 32)

Figure 32 shows the close tolerances and dimensional relationships specified for gyro cases made from 2-in.-diam bar stock of alloy 7075-T6, and illustrates and gives details of the secondary machining operations by which these specifications were met. The cases were turned and bored in a prior operation, leaving about 0.040 in. on all diameters to be finish turned or bored.

The operations shown in Fig. 32 were performed in a 9-in. manually operated turret lathe that had spindle runout within 0.00005 in. and taper no more than 0.0001 in. in 6 in. An engine lathe of equivalent accuracy could have been used, but a turret lathe was preferred because all tools could be preset in the turret. Special equipment used on the turret lathe included a threading attachment and an air gage. (The use of either an air gage or an electronic gage insures greater speed and accuracy in repositioning than usually are obtainable when dial indicators are used.)

To prevent overheating and consequent dimensional change of a locating surface, three cuts were made in the initial boring operation (on diameter A, in operation 1 in Fig. 32); 0.005 in. was left after the first cut, and 0.0005 in. after the second, for finishing. Operations 3 and 4 were done using a nongalling friction-drive mandrel made by pressing a nylon sleeve over an aluminum arbor, the sleeve being held by a screw and washer.

Additional procedures used to assure meeting dimensional requirements were:

1 Rough machined workpieces were cooled to room temperature before further operations were performed, because a temperature rise of 10 F would increase a 2-in. diameter about 0.0002 in.
2 Spindle rotation and power feeds were kept in the same direction for all operations, because tolerances that could be held were not always the same for both directions.
3 Because tool-point radii could not exceed 0.005 in., the points were honed to produce acceptable surface finishes.

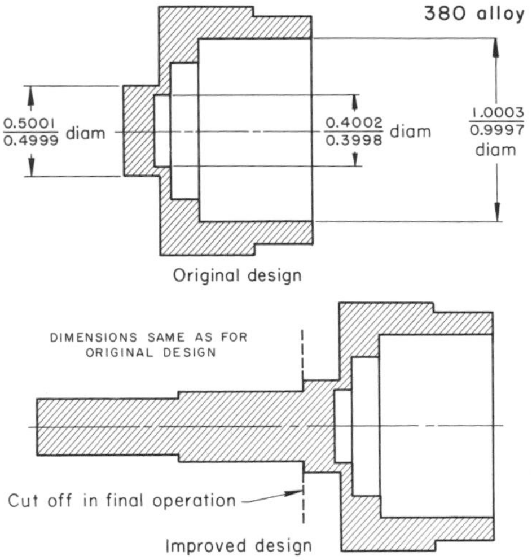

Fig. 33. Die casting redesigned to improve concentricity and dimensional accuracy in turning operations in an automatic chucking machine (Example 905)

Example 905. Design Change to Permit Use of Automatic Chucking Machine (Fig. 33)

The problem of holding size and concentricity in turning an alloy 380 die casting was solved by changing the design of the part, as shown in Fig. 33. The redesigned part could be machined in one setup, rather than two. Setup time and machining time were less, because turning was done in one chucking machine instead of two single-spindle turret lathes. By chucking at a location not over the bore, close control of size was possible. Also, close concentricity could be held in machining the revised part, because the pilot (0.5001-in. diameter) could be turned without unchucking the workpiece. The shank was cut off in a final operation. Cutting fluid was a 1-to-20 mixture of soluble oil and water.

Example 906. Close Concentricity Between Turned and Bored Diameters (Fig. 34)

Six machining operations were performed on the permanent mold casting for a gearbox cover shown in Fig. 34. Two boring operations (rough and finish) and chamfering were performed with tools set in the same holder. The 2.876/2.874-in. diameter had to be held concentric with the 7.5015/7.5005-in. diameter within 0.002 in. TIR. To accomplish this, both diameters were machined in the same setting. By machining on a turret lathe, it was possible to include the groove. Processing details are given in the table accompanying Fig. 34.

Production practices that have been followed in machining aluminum alloys in multiple-operation automatic machines under a variety of conditions are described in the three examples that follow. Other applications of multiple-operation machining are de-

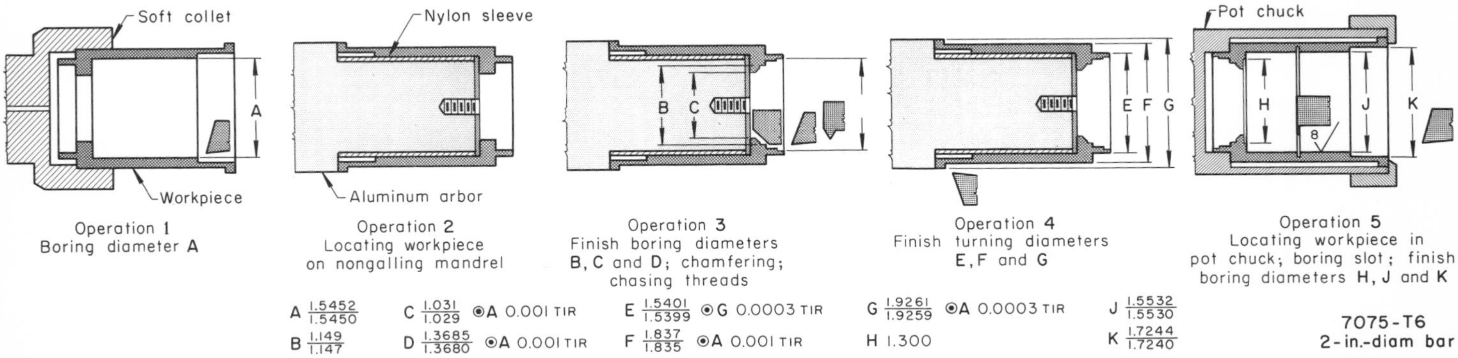

Speed, roughing	600 rpm (162 to 315 sfm)
Speed, finishing	1100 rpm (295 to 580 sfm)
Feed, roughing	1.5 ipm (0.0025 ipr)
Feed, finishing	0.75 ipm (0.0007 ipr)
Cutting fluid	None
Setup time	12 hr
Machining time per piece	1.5 hr

Tool Details	
Material	Carbide
Rake angle	Neutral
Clearance angle	5° to 7°
Cutting-edge angle	10° to 12°
Point radius	0.005 in. max

Fig. 32. Close-tolerance secondary machining of gyro cases in a manual turret lathe (Example 904)

scribed in Examples 867, 868, 869, 872, 895, 904, 905 and 906, in this article.

Example 907. Machining of Thin-Wall Parts From Bar Stock (Fig. 35)

The multiple-operation machining of thin-wall parts from 2011-T3 bar stock is illustrated in Fig. 35. For all operations, spindle speed was 2053 rpm (maximum surface speed, 676 sfm), and cutting fluid was a low-viscosity mineral oil with 5% fatty additive. Production rate was 240 pieces per hour. Tool materials and feeds are listed in the table with Fig. 35.

Example 908. Fourteen Operations to Produce a Thin-Wall Part From Bar Stock (Fig. 36)

The process used to machine the part shown in Fig. 36 resulted from about ten years of development. Except for straddle milling and anodizing, the part was completed when it left the automatic bar machine. The single-stage integrated machining operation produced concentric internal and external surfaces.

The first-station operations differed from conventional practice in that (*a*) an unusually wide forming cut was made, and (*b*) the use of a 45° spotting drill was eliminated, because the rigid bar to which the form drill was attached made spot drilling unnecessary.

Special features of the second-station operations included a form tool that closely controlled the width dimension and an adequate supply of cutting fluid to exterior surfaces and to the drill point, to insure dissipation of heat. Also, a slight angle was provided on the facing portion of the form tool to avoid a backoff tooling mark.

The operations at the third station were conventional form turning and form reaming; dimensional relations of diameters and lengths were fully controlled. The reamer left a maximum of 0.0012 in. of stock for the internal roller burnishing that followed.

The roller burnishing operation (at the fourth station) was selected in preference to ball burnishing because it required less end pressure (higher pressures could affect the drill slide adversely) and because minute shavings suspended in the cutting fluid were less likely to mar the surface finish. With roller burnishing, it was possible to obtain a 16-micro-in. surface finish and to meet a tolerance of 0.0003 in. without difficulty. The 0.707-in. diameter was shaved in preparation for thread rolling. An opposing roll on the shave tool holder served to maintain close dimensional tolerances, taking the place of the cross-slide cam-and-stop arrangement conventionally employed for this purpose in cross-forming operations.

The fifth-station operation consisted of thread rolling an outside surface and power recessing an inside surface. Because the part was made of one of the harder aluminum alloys (2024-T351), there was a probability that the two end (or outer) threads would shear or move outward during thread rolling. This was corrected by rolling an excess length of thread that was removed in the next operation. The power recessing operation was an improvement over stationary drawback recessing, because it provided an improved surface finish and eliminated chips that would normally hang in the O-ring groove.

The sixth-station operations removed the excess thread length and finish formed the sealing cone seat.

In the seventh station, the part number was marked on the workpiece; opposing support was provided to protect the thin-wall section.

Tapping of a 36-pitch internal thread and cutoff of the part were done in the eighth (final) station. The tapping operation was completed before the cutoff blade made contact with the work.

Example 909. Machining an Aircraft Forging (Fig. 37)

The forging shown in Fig. 37 was processed in two chucking operations in a six-spindle automatic chucking machine. Details of the machined part and of the operations are also given in Fig. 37, and in the table with it.

In machining this part, major considerations were rigidity of holding chucks, and elimination of heavy side feeds and vibration. As noted in the machining sequence, the long end of the forging was machined first and the short end was chucked, because this arrangement was more able to resist the leverage of side-cutting forces, particularly at the outer extremity of the part. In both chucking operations, the use of side-cutting tools was held to a minimum.

The 45° metal-to-metal sealing surface, shown in the fourth position of the first chucking operation, was highly critical. To eliminate chatter and out-of-roundness, this surface was machined with roller support.

To prevent chucking marks in the second chucking operation, the chuck jaws did not grip finish-machined surfaces.

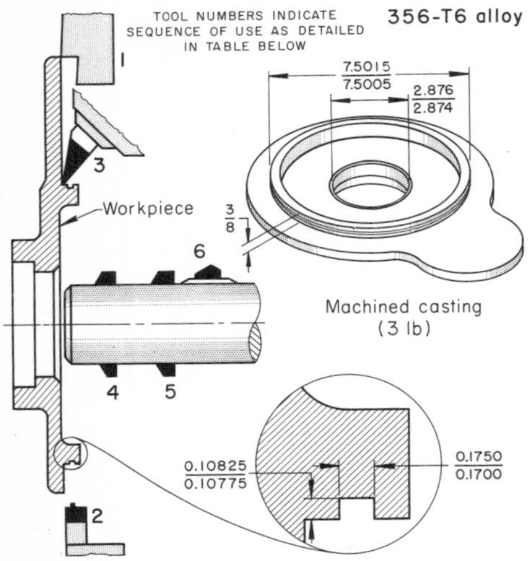

Production rate	11.3 pieces per hour
Cycle time	5.27 min
Setup time	2 hr
Cutting fluid	Soluble-oil:water (1:25)

Operation 1. Face Mounting Surface
(Front of cross slide)

Tool:

Type	Carbide insert (3/8-in. inscribed triangle)
Angles	0° rake, 10° clearance
Life per grind	1200 pieces (400 each index)

Operating conditions:

Speed	550 rpm (2100 sfm)
Feed	0.005 ipr
Depth of cut	0.060 in.

Operation 2. Machine Groove
(Rear of cross slide)

Tool:

Type	Carbide
Angles	0° rake, 10° clearance
Life per grind	2000 pieces

Operating conditions:

Speed	550 rpm (1100 sfm)
Feed	0.005 ipr
Depth of cut	0.100 in.

Operation 3. Turn 7.5015/7.5005-In. Diameter
(Turret)

Tool:

Type	Carbide in microbore cartridge
Angles	10° rake, 10° clearance
Life per grind	1500 pieces

Operating conditions:

Speed	550 rpm (1100 sfm)
Feed	0.005 ipr
Depth of cut	0.010 in.

Operations 4, 5 and 6. Rough and Finish Bore 2.876/2.874-In. Diameter, and Chamfer
(Turret)

Rough boring tool:

Type	Double-edged carbide cutter, fixed firm in boring bar
Angles	10° axial, 0° radial rake; 10° clearance
Life per grind	1500 pieces

Finish boring tool:

Type	Double-edged carbide cutter, with 0.003-in. float in boring bar
Angles	0° axial, 10° radial rake; 10° clearance
Life per grind	2000 pieces

Chamfering tool:

Type	Carbide
Angles	0° rake, 10° clearance
Life per grind	5000 pieces

Operating conditions:

Speed	550 rpm (415 sfm)
Feed	0.005 ipr
Depth of roughing cut	0.060 in.
Depth of finishing cut	0.010 in.

Fig. 34. Six-operation machining of a cast gear-box cover in a turret lathe
(Example 906)

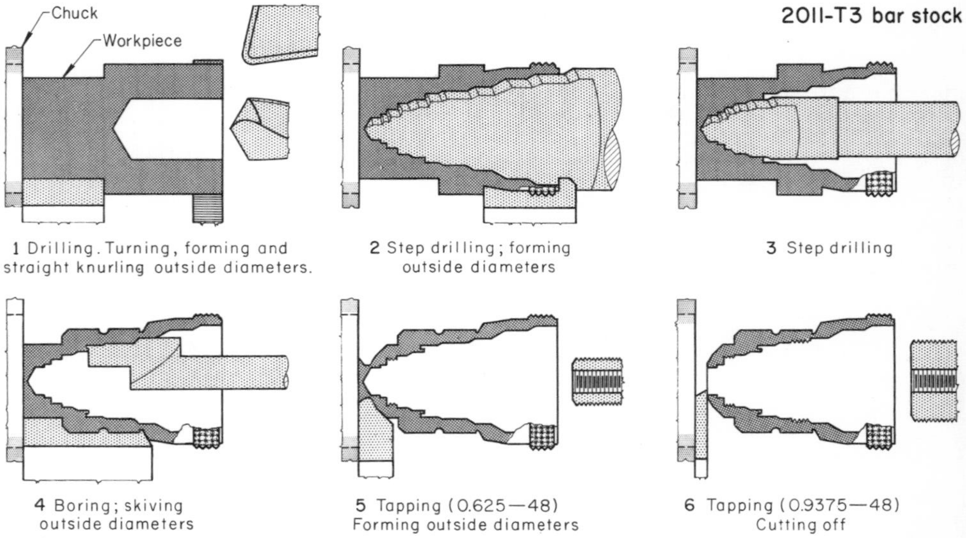

Operation	Tool material	Feed, ipr
Spindle Station 1		
Drill; turn	High speed steel	0.0045
Form; knurl	High speed steel	0.0016
Spindle Station 2		
Step drill	Carbide	0.0045
Form	Carbide	0.0015
Spindle Station 3		
Step drill	Carbide	0.0025
Spindle Station 4		
Bore	Carbide	0.001
Skive	Carbide	0.002
Spindle Station 5		
Tap	High speed steel	0.0022
Form	Carbide	0.0011
Spindle Station 6		
Tap	High speed steel	0.0015
Cut off	High speed steel	0.001

Fig. 35. Operations for producing a complicated thin-wall part in an automatic bar machine
(Example 907)

Milling

The characteristics of chip formation sometimes cause difficulty in milling of aluminum alloys. In some applications, chip ejection in the milling of deep slots or heavy cuts can be improved by changing from an alloy in the O or F temper to one in the T4 or T6 temper. In the T tempers, the chip is much less likely to clog the cutter. However, when aluminum is milled in the heat treated condition, production rate may be lower, because a lighter feed rate may be necessary, as demonstrated in the example that follows.

Example 910. Effect of Alloy Condition on Feed in End Milling (Fig. 38)

The alloy 7075 part shown in Fig. 38 was originally machined in the as-forged (F) condition. An engineering change required that the part have higher strength, and it was subsequently machined in the solution-treated-and-aged (T6) condition. As indicated by the data that accompany Fig. 38, the change in heat treatment necessitated a 50% reduction in feed; at the original feed, the higher strength of the T6 material produced excessive deflection in the end-milling cutters. When the part was machined in the F temper, the gummy nature of the chips had required close attention to cutter speed to utilize centrifugal force in ejecting chips from the path of the cutter.

If the operation described in Example 910 had been peripheral or face milling, it would probably have been unnecessary to reduce the feed rate, because the setup in peripheral or face milling usually has considerably greater rigidity than in end milling.

Power Requirements. Metal removal rates greater than 3.0 cu in. per horsepower per minute can be attained readily in production milling of aluminum alloys (see Example 915, where metal was removed at the rate of 6.75 cu in. per horsepower per minute). Some rules applicable to milling aluminum are:

1 If feed per tooth is doubled, the horsepower at the cutter must be increased in the ratio of 3 to 2, or 50%.
2 If the width of cut is doubled, the horsepower at the cutter must be doubled.
3 If the depth of cut is doubled, the horsepower at the cutter must be increased in the ratio of 1.9 to 1, or 90%.
4 If the depth of cut is halved and horsepower at the cutter remains the same, the feed may be increased by a factor of 2.5.
5 If the speed of the cutter is doubled and the feed per tooth is halved, the horsepower at the cutter must be increased by about 30%.

The example that follows illustrates the range of variables in slotting.

Example 911. Metal Removal Rates in Milling With Carbide Cutters (Table 20)

Tests were made with interlocking cutters of special design, using carbide inserts brazed to the cutter bodies. Each cutter half had two teeth, and its complement had two teeth of opposite helix. This gave each cutter unit four staggered teeth, with lapped faces and generous chip spaces for gang slotting. Cutters were 8 in. in diameter, with 25° positive axial rake, 15° radial rake, 0.06-in. corner radius, and 7° clearance on cutting edges. Spindle speed in all tests was 3600 rpm, using a 2.5-in.-diam arbor that was directly connected to a driving motor that provided a maximum of 100 hp to the milling cutter.

All tests were conducted on 7075-T6 aluminum plates (560 by 20 by 2 in.) that were mounted on vacuum chucks. A flood of soluble oil served as cutting fluid. Preliminary data are given in the upper portion of Table 20.

Based on the relationship between power requirement and optimum cutter life, the cutters employed in the tests were standardized in a production setup and additional data were obtained from production runs, as shown in the lower part of Table 20.

Cutter Design. For efficiency in milling aluminum, the cutter should have a radial rake angle of 10° to 20°, an axial rake angle of 15° to 45°, and end or peripheral clearance of 10° to 12°. Form-relieved cutters should have a relief of 10° on the profile.

Best results can be obtained with a cutter that has fewer teeth and larger positive rake angles than cutters for milling steel. Fewer teeth permit more chip space, which is especially important in milling aluminum, because speeds are usually much greater than those used in milling steel. To prevent chatter, however, the cutter should have enough teeth so that at least two teeth are engaged at all times.

Because of the high speeds used in milling aluminum, careful consideration must be given to the effect of centrifugal force on the cutter. This is more important with cutters of large diameter. Cutter bodies in which teeth are wedge locked and from which some of the teeth have been removed to provide greater chip space should not be operated at high speed. All cutters for high-speed milling that have inserted

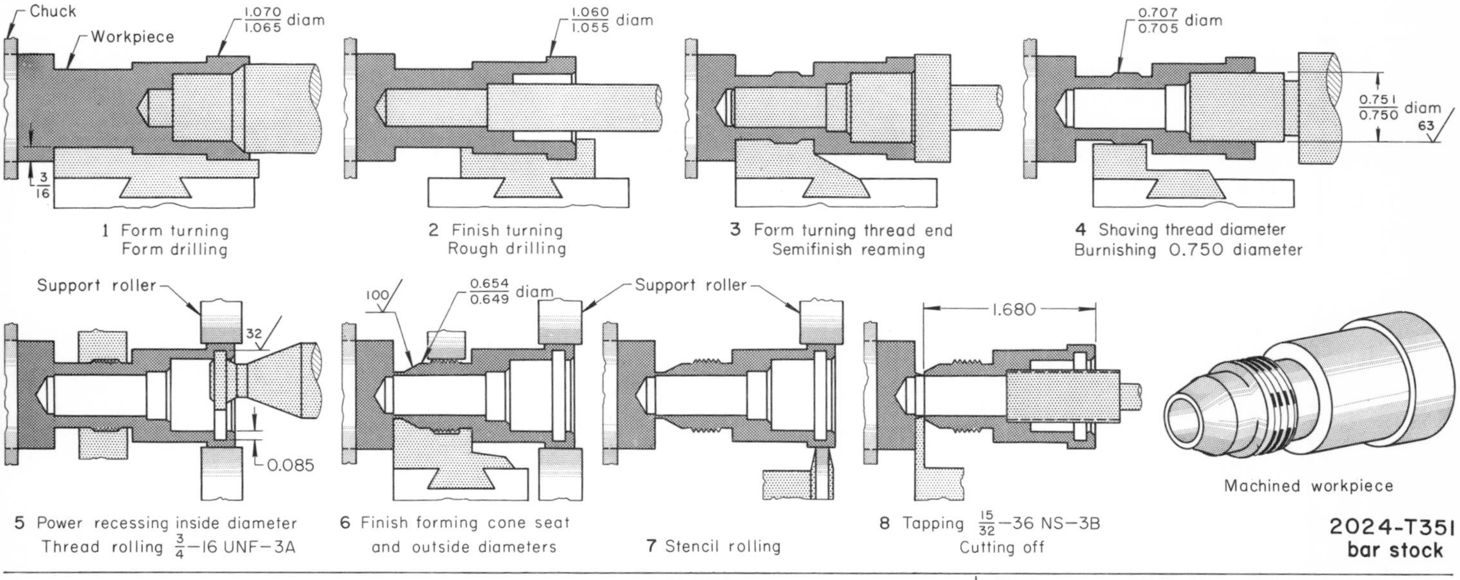

Operation	Speed, sfm	Feed, ipr	Tool data: Material	Type	Pieces per grind
1 Form turn	324	0.0019	M2 high speed steel	0° rake, dovetail	800
Form drill	226	0.0052	High speed steel	Standard 118°	1600
2 Finish turn(a)	324	0.0019	M2 high speed steel	0° rake, dovetail	800
Rough drill	138	0.0052	High speed steel	Standard 118°	1600
3 Form turn	219	0.0019	M2 high speed steel	0° rake, dovetail	800
Ream(b)	226	0.0052	M3 high speed steel	.....	1600
4 Shave	219	0.0019	M2 high speed steel	0° rake	800
Burnish(c)	230	0.0052	M10 high speed steel	Standard	1600
5 Power recess(d)	282	0.001	M3 high speed steel	12° rake	1000
Thread roll	216	0.014	High speed steel	Standard	....
6 Finish form(e)	219	0.0019	M2 high speed steel	0° rake, dovetail	800
7 Stencil roll(f)	...	.....	M1 high speed steel	(g)	(h)
8 Tap	47	0.0052	High speed steel	16° to 18° hook angle	1600
Cutoff	130	0.0019	M2 high speed steel	Standard	1000

Stock ....1⅛-in. bar, weighing 0.166 lb before, and 0.052 lb after, machining
Machine ....⅝-in. eight-spindle automatic bar machine
Spindle speed ....1169 rpm
Production rate ....211 pieces per hour

(a) Finish for both diameters to 0.005 in. TIR, with 0.005-in. depth of cut. (b) Ream all inside diameters to 0.002 in. TIR, leaving stock on 0.750-in. diameter for burnishing. (c) Burnish 0.750-in. diameter to 63-micro-in. finish. (d) Support rollers used with power recess tool to maintain 32-micro-in. finish and 0.002 in. TIR. Cut depth, 0.085 in. (e) Support rollers used to hold 0.005 in. TIR on all diameters on thread end and 100-micro-in. finish on 37° cone seat. Depth of cut, 0.068 in. (f) Support rolls used. (g) Sharp face, 3/32 in. high. (h) Minimum roll life of 15,000 pieces per grind.

Fig. 36. Setup, sequence of operations and machining details for producing a thin-wall coupling in an automatic bar machine (Example 908)

teeth (brazed or mechanically secured) should be dynamically balanced. Careful attention should be given to cutter adapters, cutter holders, arbors, spacers, and other components that rotate with the cutter.

End mills for aluminum should have sharp rake angles, with sufficient clearance to prevent "heeling". Neither rake nor clearance angles should be excessive, or "digging-in" will result. The cutter should contact the workpiece in such a manner that any torsional, or lateral, deflection will decrease the depth of cut.

Flute form and surface finish in the flute are important. Consequently, many of these cutters are made by grinding from the solid after heat treatment. The lips of an end mill (either plain two-flute or ball-nose) that is to be used for making plunge cuts directly into solid aluminum should have slightly greater clearances than is normal for these cutters, to prevent "heeling". Preferably, the faces of the cutting edges should have a surface finish of 1.5 micro-in., and should never be rougher than 3.5 micro-in.

In making plunge cuts directly into aluminum, the problem of chip ejection becomes acute. For this reason, it is best to feed the cutter into the material in such a way that, for each axial advance of the cutter (equal to about half the cutter diameter), the cutter is fed laterally about one diameter in an oscillating pattern, until the desired depth of cut is reached, rather than making a purely axial cut.

For milling slots, or pockets, where the end of the cutter is in contact with the workpiece, it is usually best to have the direction the same for the cut and the helix. However, when profiling with the periphery of the cutter, where the end of the cutter is not in contact with the workpiece, a combination of right-hand cut, left-hand helix gives the best results.

Router bits are a special type of end mill, modified to insure chip ejection at the speeds normally used for these cutters. Some cutters for general routing purposes may have two flutes with a helix angle of 25°. The best over-all performance in routing accurate slots or grooves is with a two-flute cutter having a 45° helix angle, with the direction of helix and of cut the same.

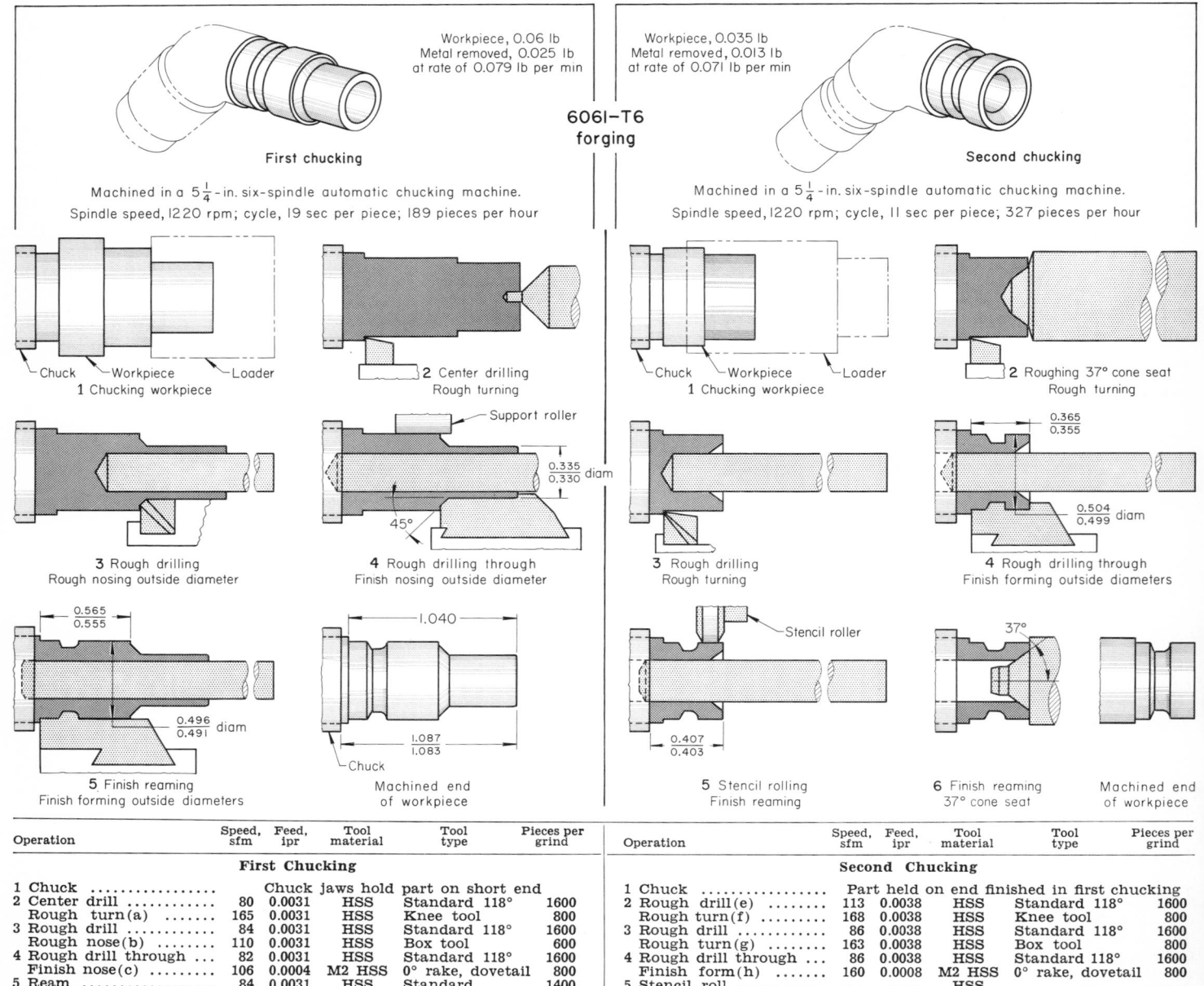

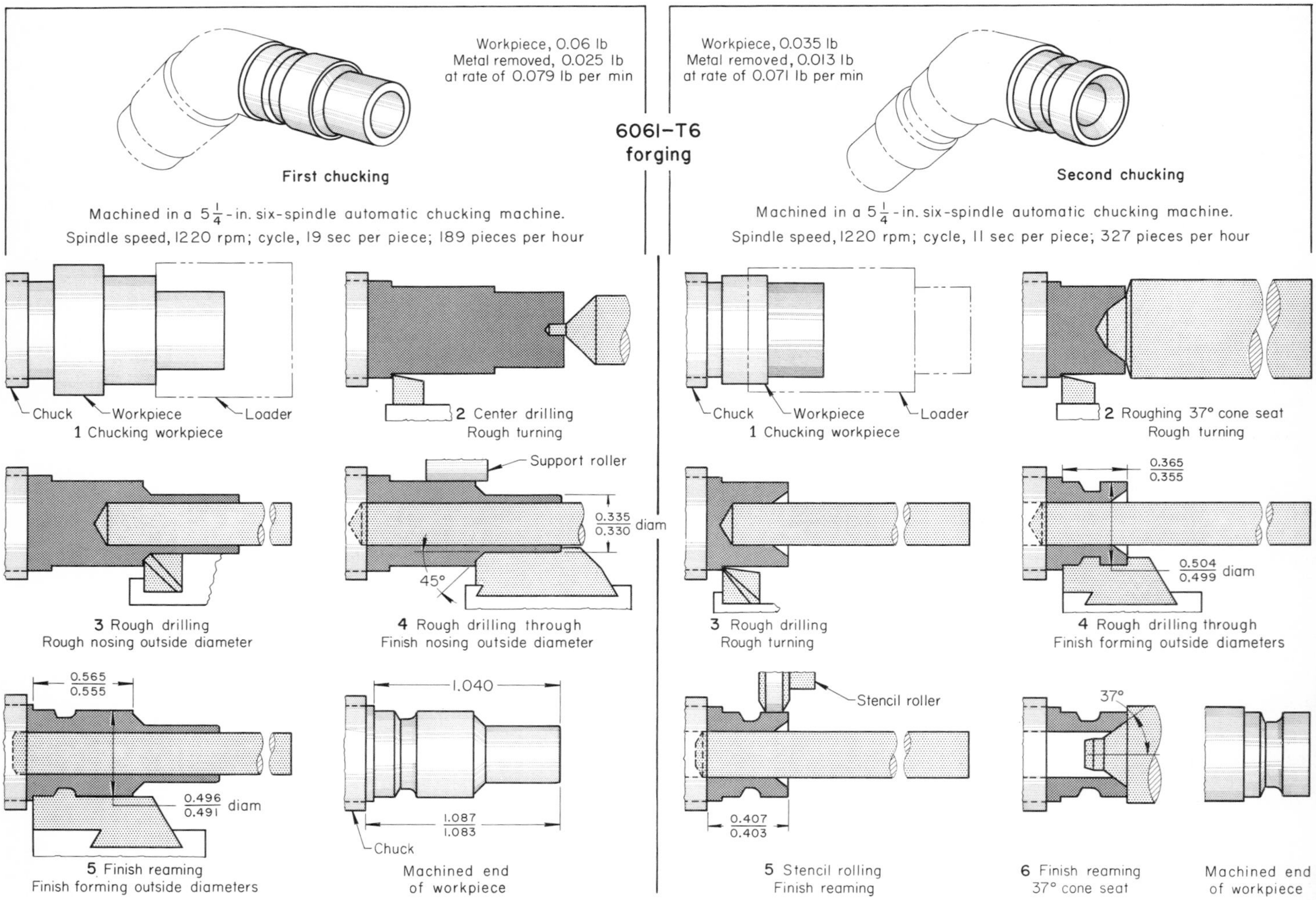

Operation	Speed, sfm	Feed, ipr	Tool material	Tool type	Pieces per grind
First Chucking					
1 Chuck	Chuck jaws hold part on short end				
2 Center drill	80	0.0031	HSS	Standard 118°	1600
Rough turn(a)	165	0.0031	HSS	Knee tool	800
3 Rough drill	84	0.0031	HSS	Standard 118°	1600
Rough nose(b)	110	0.0031	HSS	Box tool	600
4 Rough drill through	82	0.0031	HSS	Standard 118°	1600
Finish nose(c)	106	0.0004	M2 HSS	0° rake, dovetail	800
5 Ream	84	0.0031	HSS	Standard	1400
Finish form(d)	157	0.0004	M2 HSS	0° rake, dovetail	800

(a) To remove scale. Depth of cut, 1/8 in. (b) Box tool nose and 45° angle, to control amount of stock left for finish form tool. Depth of cut, 0.070 in. (c) Support roller used to hold 0.005 in. TIR on all diameters and 100-micro-in. finish on 45° angle. Depth of cut, 0.005 in.

Operation	Speed, sfm	Feed, ipr	Tool material	Tool type	Pieces per grind
Second Chucking					
1 Chuck	Part held on end finished in first chucking				
2 Rough drill(e)	113	0.0038	HSS	Standard 118°	1600
Rough turn(f)	168	0.0038	HSS	Knee tool	800
3 Rough drill	86	0.0038	HSS	Standard 118°	1600
Rough turn(g)	163	0.0038	HSS	Box tool	800
4 Rough drill through	86	0.0038	HSS	Standard 118°	1600
Finish form(h)	160	0.0008	M2 HSS	0° rake, dovetail	800
5 Stencil roll	...	.....	HSS	...	...
Ream	92	0.0038	HSS	Standard	1400
6 Ream(j)	116	0.0038	M3 HSS	7° rake, 3-flute	500

(d) Depth of cut, 0.055 in. (e) Rough drill 37° cone seat, to control amount of stock left for finish form tool. (f) To remove scale. Depth of cut, 0.016 in. (g) Depth of cut, 0.010 in. (h) Depth of cut, 0.058 in. (j) Finish ream 37° cone seat to 100-micro-in. finish and break corners.

Fig. 37. Machining a 6061-T6 forging in two chuckings in a six-spindle automatic chucking machine **(Example 909)**

Cutters for routing stacked sheet stock should be designed with a single flute and a helix angle of 25° to 45°. An integral pilot running in an outboard bearing is used on some of these cutters to help control deflection.

All cutters should have a 15° hook angle on the cutting lip. The flute should be of 0.09-in. uniform depth, with a smooth gullet extending ⅛ in. inward from the lip. The lips should be radially relieved on the periphery to 0.003 to 0.007 in. per $\frac{1}{16}$-in. width of land behind the cutting edge.

In the example that follows, an end mill assembly with an unsupported length of nine diameters was used.

Example 912. End Milling With a Long Unsupported Cutter (Fig. 39)

The angular aluminum alloy aircraft forging illustrated in Fig. 39 was end milled in a vertical, three-dimensional, numerically controlled profiler. Milling operations on surfaces other than indicated in Fig. 39 were also performed by end milling, but offered no problem because the spindle could be brought closer to the work. For end milling the portion shown, it was necessary to have an unsupported length of nine to one (cutter and adapter), to permit the spindle to clear the workpiece. Although greater unsupported length can be tolerated in milling aluminum than with harder metals, nine to one is unusual, and special techniques are needed. The special tapered adapter shown in Fig. 39 was helpful in maintaining rigidity. During all end milling of the area shown, and especially during roughing, the cutter was kept uniformly loaded, to minimize vibration and chatter. Acceptable surface finish was obtained by using an extremely light (0.007 in.) cut in the finishing operation. By using this technique, the finishing cutters had an indefinitely long life.

The heavy fixture to which the workpiece was clamped also added rigidity to the setup. The workpiece was clamped at various points on the edges. Cutter and operating details are given in the table with Fig. 39.

Speed. Nominal speeds for peripheral, face and end milling are given in Tables 21 and 22. Factors affecting speed are alloy being milled, tool material, and depth of cut (roughing or finishing). A major variable that is not reflected in the tables is chip disposal. Provided that chips can be adequately ejected from the cutting zone, speeds for carbide cutters are limited mainly by the capabilities of the machine. However, when the speed is too high for a particular setup, the cutter teeth may not have sufficient time to remove stock at the proper rate because of erratic feeding; the cutter teeth may "dig and ride" or "cut and skip". Optimum speed depends on the machine, work metal, depth of cut, and power.

Under certain conditions, milling speeds as high as 15,000 sfm have been used. However, speeds this high are rarely feasible. Speeds of 2000 to 4000 sfm are frequently used, as illustrated by the next two examples. In Example 913, metal was removed by face mills in a vertical position, and only a portion of the area presented to the cutter was milled. Thus, chip disposal was not a problem. In Example 914, two opposite sides of a casting were face milled simultaneously in a duplex machine.

Example 913. Face Milling a Die Casting at High Speed (Table 23)

The die-cast gear box shown in Table 23 required two surfaces to be milled parallel to each other within ±0.010 in. By using a milling machine with a large table, both sides of the gear box could be milled by placing two boxes on the machine table at one time, one side being milled in the first station and the opposite side in the second station. Because of the shape of the workpiece (relatively small surface to be milled in proportion to the total area presented to the cutters), chip disposal was not a problem, and speed could be higher than normal. Machine, cutter and operating details are given in Table 23.

Table 20. Performance Data for Carbide Milling Cutters Used in Slotting (Example 911)

Number of cutters on arbor	Width of slots, in.	Depth per slot, in.	Total feed per min, in.	Feed per tooth, in.	Power consumed at cutter, hp	Metal removed per min, cu in.	Metal removed per hp per min, cu in.
Preliminary Test Data							
5	1.370	0.640	72	0.010	80	315	3.94
5	1.370	0.640	60	0.0083	80	262	3.28
4	1.725	1.250	17	0.0023	53	150	2.83
4	1.725	0.880	120	0.0167	100	728	7.28
3	1.550	0.600	63	0.0087	65	177	2.72
Production Data							
11	1.695	0.231(a)	86	0.012	100	377	3.77
11	1.445	0.275(a)	86	0.012	100	377	3.77

(a) Depth of cut per pass

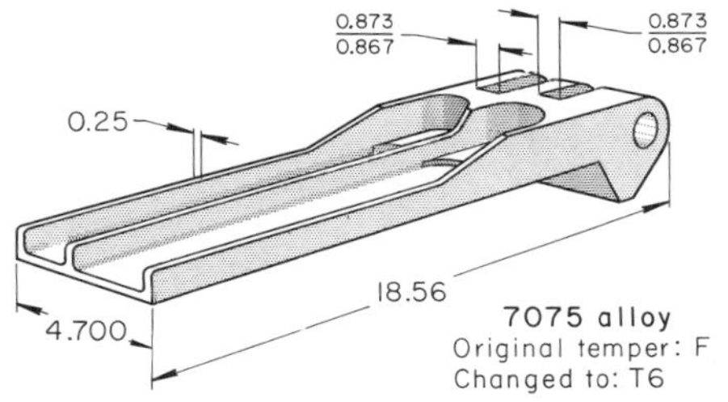

Operating condition	F temper	T6 temper
Speed, sfm	400	400
Feed, ipt	0.008	0.004
Depth of cut, in.	2.5	2.5
Width of cut, in.	0.870	0.870
Cutting fluid ....Soluble-oil:water		(1:25)
Setup time, min	20	20
Time per piece, hr	2	4.2

Machining was done in horizontal and vertical 15-hp milling machines. Cutters were radial, wheel-type end mills of high speed steel, 2.5 in. in diameter and 0.870 in. wide, with 10° radial rake, 30° axial rake. One drill jig and two milling fixtures were used for holding work.

Fig. 38. Forging for which change from F to T6 temper required a 50% reduction of milling feed (Example 910)

Example 914. Face Milling Parallel Sides Simultaneously in a Duplex Machine (Fig. 40)

Face milling two opposite sides was the first machining operation performed on the casting shown in Fig. 40. Maintaining required dimensions in subsequent operations depended greatly on the accuracy obtained in milling the sides. Parallelism was easily maintained by milling the two sides simultaneously, because the workpiece did not have to be moved and reclamped.

A 10-hp duplex machine was used for this operation. This type of machine afforded two advantages in addition to good dimensional control. First, after the initial cut, the spindles were advanced slightly to take a "skim" (finish) cut as the table returned to the start position. Second, milling both sides at one time increased productivity compared with milling each side separately. Details of the milling cutters and operation are tabulated below Fig. 40.

Feed. Nominal feeds for peripheral, face and end milling are given in Tables 21 and 22. For wheel-type cutters (peripheral and face), the alloy being milled has little effect on feed. Depth of cut has some effect, although usually this is not large. Some reduction in feed is usually made when high speed steel cutters are replaced by carbide cutters, mainly because the speeds are usually greater for carbide cutters. Depth of cut (roughing or finishing), particularly in face milling, has some effect on the rate of feed selected.

For end milling, the principal factor affecting rate of feed is cutter diameter (as shown in Table 22), because small end-milling cutters lack rigidity.

For additional information on feed, see pages 184 to 186, in "Milling".

Depth of cut is commonly about 0.250 in. for roughing and 0.025 in. or less for finishing. If power is available, depth of cut can be several times greater than the above when large amounts of metal are to be removed.

In machining aircraft components, skin milling, which involves deep cuts (sometimes 2 in. or more), is common practice. Machines used for skin milling are basically planer mills that have evolved into elaborate tracer-controlled machines. The milling is ordinarily done by means of large peripheral-type (slabbing) cutters.

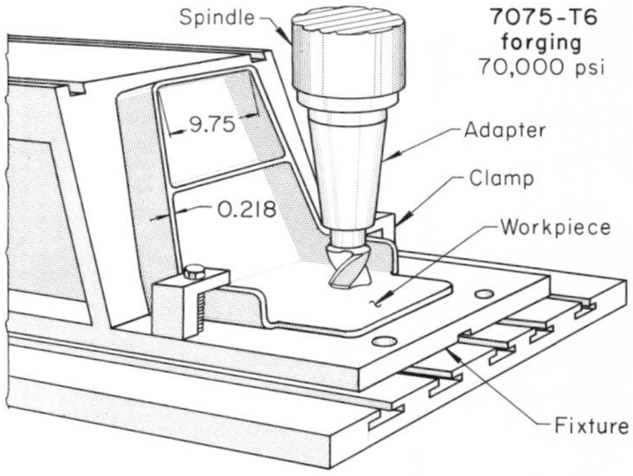

Cutter Details

Type	..............................End mill
Size	....2-in. diam with 0.187-in. corner radius, 4-in. cutter length, 1¼-in.-diam shank, 6½-in. over-all length
Number of teeth	2
Material	......................High speed steel

Operating Conditions

Speed	......................800 rpm (420 sfm)
Feed	..................................0.008 ipt
Depth of cut:	
Roughing	......................¼ in. approx
Finishing, first pass	.................0.050 in.
Finishing, second pass	..............0.007 in.
Cutting fluid	...............Soluble-oil:water
Setup time(a)	...................2 hr, 10 min
Production rate	.................4 hr per piece
Tool life per grind, roughing	.........12 pieces
Tolerance	............................±0.010 in.
Finish obtained	.....................63 micro-in.

(a) 2 hr for attaching project plate to table and 10 min for attaching workpiece to fixture

Fig. 39. Milling setup arranged so that the spindle cleared the workpiece (Example 912)

Table 21. Nominal Speeds and Feeds for Peripheral and Face Milling of Aluminum Alloys With High Speed Steel Cutters

Alloy	Speed(a), sfm Roughing	Speed(a), sfm Finishing	Feed(a), ipt Roughing	Feed(a), ipt Finishing	Speed(a), sfm Roughing	Speed(a), sfm Finishing	Feed(a), ipt Roughing	Feed(a), ipt Finishing
	Peripheral Milling(b)				Face Milling(c)			
Non-heat-treated, cast	900	1300	0.018	0.016	1000	1500	0.022	0.014
Heat treated, cast	900	1300	0.016	0.014	800	1200	0.022	0.014
Cold drawn, wrought	850	1200	0.016	0.014	800	1200	0.022	0.014
Heat treated, wrought	650	900	0.016	0.014	800	1200	0.022	0.014

(a) Roughing cuts, 0.250 in. deep; finishing cuts, 0.025 in. deep. (b) High speed steel cutters (M2 or M7). (c) High speed steel cutters (M2 or M7). If carbide cutters are used, maximum speed of the machine is allowed, but feed should be decreased 10 to 15%.

Table 22. Nominal Speeds and Feeds for End Milling of Aluminum Alloys With High Speed Steel and Carbide Cutters

Alloy	Speed(a), sfm Roughing	Speed(a), sfm Finishing	Feed(a), ipt Roughing, cutter diam, in. ¼	Roughing ¾	Roughing 1 to 2	Feed(a), ipt Finishing, cutter diam, in. ¼	Finishing ¾	Finishing 1 to 2
	High Speed Steel Cutters (M2 or M7)							
Non-heat-treated, cast	800	1000	0.004	0.008	0.010	0.003	0.005	0.007
Heat treated, cast	600	800	0.004	0.008	0.010	0.003	0.005	0.007
Cold drawn, wrought	600	800	0.004	0.008	0.010	0.003	0.005	0.007
Heat treated, wrought	600	800	0.003	0.008	0.010	0.002	0.005	0.007
	Carbide Cutters							
All castings	1000	1300	0.004	0.008	0.010	0.003	0.005	0.007
Cold drawn, wrought	1000	1300	0.004	0.008	0.010	0.003	0.005	0.007
Heat treated, wrought	1000	1300	0.003	0.008	0.010	0.002	0.005	0.007

(a) Roughing cuts, 0.050 in. deep; finishing cuts, 0.015 in. deep

The example that follows gives details of a skin milling operation in which the depth of cut was far greater than that made in conventional milling.

Example 915. Skin Milling of an Aircraft Wing Skin (Table 24)

Climb milling with a peripheral cutter was used to skin mill a billet of 7075-T6 alloy 133 in. long by 66 in. wide by 3 in. thick. A cutter having only four teeth was used, which reduced the chip problem when milling at high speed with an unusually deep (2 in.) cut. Metal removal was at the rate of 6.75 cu in. per horsepower per minute (675 cu in. per min in the 100-hp machine used). Table 24 gives details of the machine, cutter and operation.

Table 23. Processing Details for Face Milling a Die-Cast Gear Box (Example 913) (a)

Machine	Three-spindle profile-milling machine; table size, 132 by 28 in.
Cutter:	
Type:	Face, insert-blade, 14-in.-diam body
Material	C-2 carbide inserts, alloy steel body
Inserts	Mechanically secured, four cutting edges
Angles	5° pos axial and radial rake

Operating Conditions

Speed	650 rpm (2330 sfm)
Feed	0.011 ipt
Depth of cut:	
Roughing	⅛ to 3/16 in.
Finishing	0.015 in.
Cutting fluid	None
Setup time	1.5 hr
Downtime for changing tools	10 min
Production rate	11.3 pieces per hour
Cutter life	300 pieces per edge (four edges)

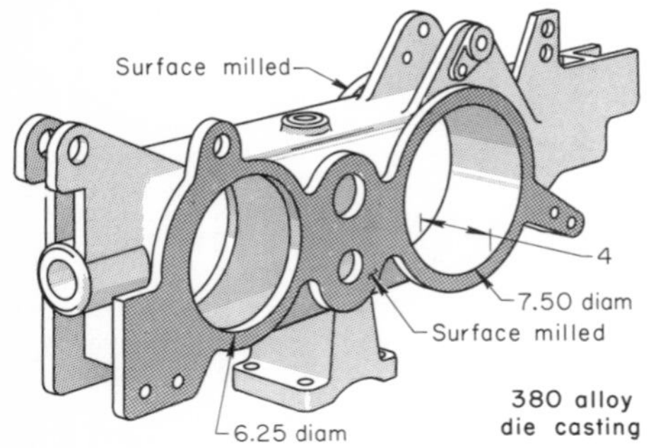

(a) Data are for milling the two faces of the gear box, illustrated above, to parallelism within ±0.010 in., and to a 45-micro-in. finish.

Cutting fluid should be supplied copiously and under pressure to the tool and workpiece. It is important, particularly with carbide cutters, that the cutting fluid be supplied uniformly and consistently to all parts of the cutter, to prevent overheating and sudden chilling of the carbide tips. Rapid heating and cooling is extremely detrimental to the life of carbide cutters.

For high-speed milling, emulsions of soluble oil and water at a 1-to-15 ratio are recommended; for low-speed milling, a ratio of 1 to 30 is recommended.

Kerosine is effective with form cutters. When modified T-slot cutters were used to mill a blade-root slot in aluminum wheels for axial-flow compressors to a tolerance of less than 0.001 in., no cutting fluid except kerosine could produce the required accuracy and surface finish (see the sections on cutting fluids on page 443 in this article and on page 188 in the article "Milling").

Form milling is often an economical method for machining complicated shapes in aluminum. The complexity of form that can be built into the design of a cutter is limited, as, for example, when the tangent of the curvature approaches 90° to the horizontal plane. As a result, secondary operations are sometimes required to complete a complex form.

Basic types of form cutters have cam-relieved teeth or shaped teeth. Cam-relieved teeth are sharpened by grinding the tooth faces without changing the form. If surface finish is a secondary consideration, straight-tooth cutters are used, because they are easier to sharpen. However, if surface finish is important, helical cutters must be used. Although helical cutters may be operated at higher speeds and greater feeds than straight-tooth cutters, they require considerably greater care when being sharpened.

Shape form cutters are made either with integral teeth or blade inserts. These cutters are less expensive than integral-tooth, cam-relieved cutters, but they require more equipment and more skill in grinding.

Feasibility of form milling depends on several variables, including cutter cost, volume of production, design of workpiece, and type of milling machine available. Thus, for small production lots, the cost of a single form cutter must be compared with the cost of several cutters of less complex shape. For form milling, the workpiece must be fairly large, have no thin sections, and must be capable of being well secured. Finally, form milling requires high-powered equipment that is rugged and in good operating condition.

The example that follows describes an application of form milling and shows the production quantity required to justify a high-cost form cutter.

Example 916. Cost of Standard vs Form Milling (Fig. 41)

The contour of the workpiece shown in Fig. 41 could be milled equally well by using five standard cutters for five separate operations or by using one specially designed form cutter that could mill the contour in a single operation. The operations performed by both methods are listed in the table accompanying Fig. 41. Although cost of cutters was the same for form and standard milling, time for form milling was only about one-third that for standard milling.

Automatic Control. The generally good machining characteristics of aluminum alloys make them especially well adapted to automatic control, by which extremely complex shapes can be milled efficiently. The two examples that follow give details of two widely different applications where automatic control was used. The first of the two examples deals with rise-and-fall mill-

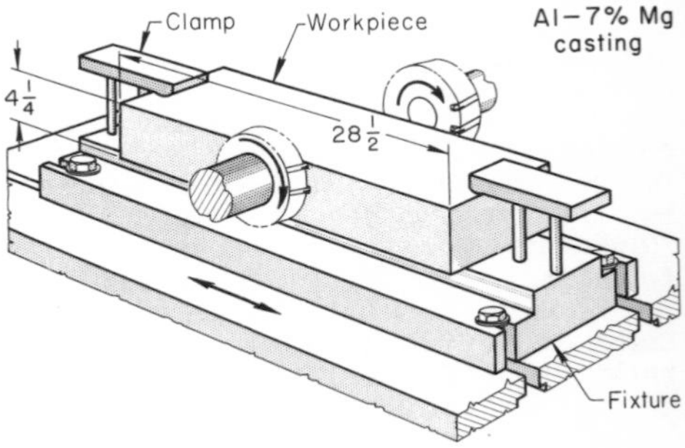

Cutter Details

Type	Face mill, inserted blade
Size	6-in. diam
Number of teeth	12
Material	Carbide-tipped blades

Operating Conditions

Speed	2345 rpm (3680 sfm)
Feed	0.0055 ipt
Depth of cut	⅛ in. max
Cutting fluid	None
Setup time	1.5 hr
Downtime for changing tools	15 min
Production rate	31 pieces per hour
Cutter life	100 pieces per grind (approx)
Tolerances:	
Flatness	Within 0.001 in.
Width	±0.003 in.
Parallelism error	0.005 in. max
Finish	63 micro-in. max

Fig. 40. Face milling parallel surfaces on opposite sides of a casting simultaneously (Example 914)

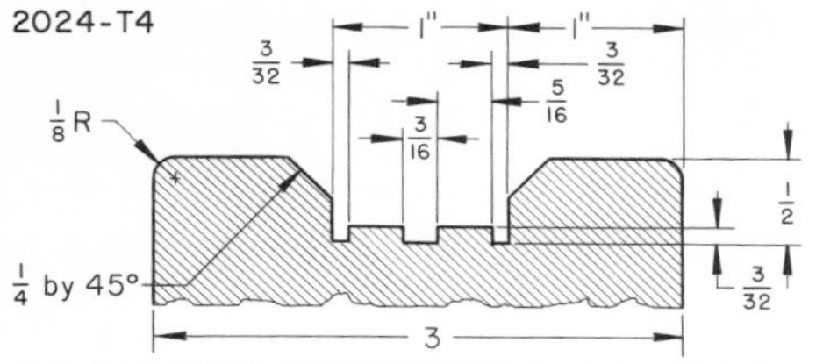

Operating Conditions(a)

Form milling (one pass)(b)	3 ipm feed
Standard milling (five passes)(c)	
1 Side mill slot	8 ipm feed
2 Side mill center slot	8 ipm feed
3 Straddle mill reliefs	5 ipm feed
4 Straddle mill two 1/4-in.-by-45° chamfers	8 ipm feed
5 Straddle mill two 1/8-in. radii	8 ipm feed

Time and Cost Analysis

Time per piece:	
Form milling	2.54 min
Standard milling	7.79 min
Time saved using form milling	5.25 min
Value of time saved per piece, using form cutter(d)	$0.877

(a) For all operations, cutter speed was 75 sfm, and sulfurized oil was used as cutting fluid. (b) Cutter cost $100. (c) Each cutter cost $20 (total, $100). (d) At $10 per hr.

Fig. 41. Contour that could be milled in a single pass using a form cutter or in five operations using standard milling cutters (Example 916)

ing of a relatively small part; the second example describes the milling of a large forging to about one-fourth of its as-forged weight.

Example 917. Milling a Channel-Shaped Part With Tracer Control (Fig. 42)

The channel-shaped part shown in Fig. 42 was machined from a 3-by-5-in. segment of alloy 7075-T6 bar stock. The machining sequence was as follows:

1 The channel portion was rough and finish milled to final dimensions.
2 One flange of the channel was milled to 0.160 in. thick and the opposite flange was milled to 0.100 in. thick.
3 The flanges were profiled to final contour and the ends milled to desired shape.

Other details are given with Fig. 42.

Example 918. Milling a 1670-Lb Forging With Numerical Control (Fig. 43)

The part shown in Fig. 43 was made from a 7075 alloy blocker forging that weighed 1670 lb. Over-all measurements of the forging were 133 by 68 by 16 in., and those of the finished part were 131 by 66 by 14 in. The weight of the finished part was 393 lb, 1277 lb of metal having been removed in machining.

With the part held in a special milling fixture, rough profile machining was performed in a tape-controlled three-axis profile milling machine. A special boring fixture was used for rough line boring the 5.50 and 8.75-in.-diam trunnion holes. After roughing cuts were completed, approximately 0.120 in. of metal remained to be removed by finish machining after the forging was heat treated to the T6 temper. Special fixtures prevented warpage during heat treating and in finish milling. Machining was completed using the same numerical-tape-controlled machine.

Details of the process, machine and cutter are given with Fig. 43.

Dimensional accuracy is affected by residual stress in the workpiece, induced stress caused by milling, built-up edge on cutters, and dull cutters. Workpieces with complex shapes or variable section thickness, especially in the aged condition, are more difficult to mill to close tolerances. To achieve dimensional stability and maintain close tolerances, residual stress must be avoided. Some of the methods include straddle or opposed-cutter milling,

Table 24. Processing Details for Skin Milling an Aircraft Wing Skin (Example 915)

Machine	Skin mill, 45 by 12 ft, gantry type; 100 hp; 3600 rpm; vacuum-chuck holding; original cost, $500,000
Cutter:	
Type	Peripheral
Material	C-2 carbide inserts, brazed to 4340 steel body
Number of teeth	4
Size	11-in.-diam, 6 in. wide
Rake angles	25° axial, 12° radial
Clearance	7° primary, 12° secondary
Hook angle	15°
Operating Conditions	
Speed	3600 rpm (10,400 sfm)
Feed	0.006 ipt (75 ipm)
Depth of cut	2 in.
Width of cut	4½ in.
Cutting fluid	Soluble-oil:water (1:30)
Setup time	1 hr(a)
Production time	40 hr per skin
Tolerance	±0.005 in.

(a) Average time for moving billet to table, locating billet, installing and setting cutter.

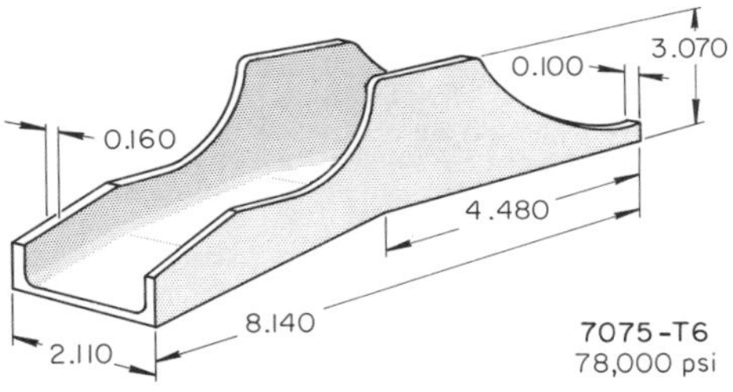

Machine	Horizontal-bed milling machine 22 by 96 in., with hydraulic tracer rise and fall
Cutter:	
Material	Modified M2 high speed steel
Size	12-in. diam
Rake angles	15° radial, 30° axial
Accessories	Contour templates and mill fixtures
Operating Conditions	
Speed	310 rpm (974 sfm)
Feed	0.005 ipt
Depth of cut	2.50 in.
Cutting fluid	Soluble-oil:water (1:25)
Production rate	1 piece per hour
Setup time	5 min
Tolerance on significant dimensions	±0.002 in.

Fig. 42. Channel-shaped part that was milled in a horizontal-bed machine equipped with hydraulic tracer (Example 917)

rough milling before heat treating, rough milling and straightening (hot or cold) before final milling, and milling and final straightening (hot or cold). The neutral axis of each increment of the workpiece should be the centerline for stock removal.

In the following example, distortion in a machined part was virtually eliminated by an improvement in the heat treating process — namely, by the use of a subzero quench in cooling the original forging from the solution-treating temperature.

Example 919. Eliminating Distortion in a Milled Part by Subzero Quenching (Fig. 44)

The fitting shown in Fig. 44 was forged of alloy 7075 and machined in the T6 condition. To overcome the distortion that resulted, the part had to be annealed, hot straightened, and heat treated a second time. In an attempt to avoid these corrective measures, premachining processing was changed to the following: Solution heat treat the as-received forging, quench in liquid nitrogen at −320 F, and age to the T6 condition. After machining, the finished part was again solution treated, water quenched, and aged to the T6 condition.

When the new method was employed, tooling holes were within ±0.002 in. of alignment, whereas the same holes in a part made by the old method had been out of alignment by as much as 0.020 in. Also, the new method saved about 9 hr per cycle. (Straightening time alone for the old method was 8 hr.)

Sawing

Contour cutting of aluminum alloys is usually done by band sawing; straight cutting is done on a circular saw, band saw, power hacksaw, or abrasive cutoff wheel. Circular saws or band saws are preferred for rapid cutoff of rod and bar stock; either can be readily adapted for high-speed, automatic work handling.

Linear feed rates as high as 30 to 80 in. per min are sometimes used in cutoff of stock 2 to 8 in. thick, for cutting rates of 50 to 250 sq in. per min.

Recommended tooth angles and contours for the three types of saws are given in Table 25.

Circular Sawing. Peripheral speeds are 2000 to 15,000 sfm for circular saws, depending on the saw material, the type of cut and the ability of the machine to withstand high speeds (Table 25). The limiting factor is usually the maximum *safe* operating speed of the machine and blade.

Feed rate for circular sawing ranges from 4 to 24 ipm, depending mainly on the alloy being sawed [see footnote (c) in Table 25]. Width of section being sawed and speed of the saw have some bearing on the rate of feed.

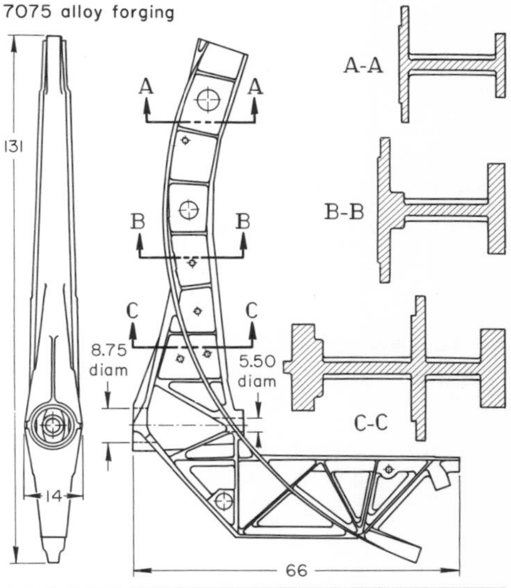

Machine	Three-axis profile milling machine, numerically controlled, 172 by 52 by 18 in.
Cutter:	
Material	Modified M2 high speed steel
Number of cutters	27
Size of cutters	0.75-in.-diam by 3¾ in. long to 3.00-in.-diam by 8 in. long
Rake angles	10° radial, 30° axial
Operating Conditions	
Speed	200 to 450 sfm
Feed	0.006 to 0.013 ipt
Depth of cut, axial dimension	0.12 to 7.00 in.
Width of cut, radial dimension	0.37 in. to cutter diam
Machining time, each part	91 hr(a)
Cutting fluid	Soluble-oil:water (1:25)
Tolerance on critical dimensions	±0.002 in.
Surface finish	60 to 120 micro-in.

(a) Roughing, 29 hr; finishing, 62 hr

Fig. 43. Part that was machined from a large blocker forging by numerically controlled profile milling (Example 918)

Recommended operating conditions for circular saws having carbide teeth are given also in Table 26. For smoother cuts, blades may have about twice as many teeth as indicated in Table 26 — especially blades of large diameter (24 to 84 in.).

In production sawing, carbide-tipped blades usually have much longer life than high speed steel blades, as shown in the example that follows. In this example, speed is less than half that recommended in Table 25 and feed is more than twice the rate shown in Table 25. The relative thinness of the plate (¼ in.) was probably the main reason for the marked deviation from the recommended speed and feed.

Example 920. High Speed Steel vs Carbide-Tipped Blades in Circular Sawing (Table 27)

Average blade life between grinds when sawing ¼-in. 7075-T6 plate with high speed steel blades was approximately 8 hr, because heat generated in sawing caused aluminum chips to weld to the blades. A carbide-tipped saw blade eliminated the chip-welding problem, and blade life between grinds was about 200 hr. Conditions of sawing with the carbide-tipped blades are shown in Table 27.

Selection of sawing machine and handling equipment can have a marked effect on efficiency, as demonstrated in the following example.

Example 921. Circular Sawing of Large Plates

Alloy 7075-T6 plates, 180 by 32 by 1½ in. and weighing about 800 lb, were cut on a diagonal with a table saw having a 14-in.-diam blade with carbide-tipped teeth. A stand equipped with rollers was used to support the plate, which was placed on the stand by a fork lift truck. Four men were required to guide, hold down, and push the plate through the sawing operation.

Production time was cut by one third (from 30 to 20 min per piece), and only one operator was required, when a special sawing machine with an over-arm clamping fixture with five pivot holddowns was installed. This special machine used a 28-in.-diam blade with carbide-tipped teeth. The automatic head feed, and swivel action of the fixture and holddowns, enabled the equipment to make longitudinal cuts of 16 ft in a single setup or 23 ft in two setups. The machine was capable of sawing plate up to 5 in. thick.

Band Sawing. Hard-tooth, flexible-back carbon steel bands are used at about 2500 sfm for heavy cuts, or 5000 sfm for medium cuts; spring temper bands, at speeds up to 7500 sfm, may be used in sawing thin sheet (Table 25). ("Friction" sawing may employ even higher speeds.) For data on speeds for contour band sawing various aluminum alloys in several ranges of thickness, see Table 8 on page 222.

Feed rates in band sawing usually range from 2 to 24 ipm, varying inversely with thickness of the section being cut. If the work-metal thickness is less than ¼ in., near-maximum feed can be used, whereas if the thickness is 2 in. or more, a feed near the low side of the above range should be used.

The two examples that follow compare milling and contour band sawing for producing a shape from an aluminum alloy plate and in fabricating a honeycomb core. In both applications, band sawing was faster and cheaper.

Example 922. Contour Sawing of a Large Plate (Fig. 45)

An aluminum alloy plate weighing 1440 lb and measuring 48 by 60 by 5 in. was rough machined in a milling machine to obtain the contour shown in Fig. 45. Milling required about 4½ hr. The same part was produced in 67 min in a contour band saw, cutting at a rate of 15 sq in. per min. The area cut was 1000 sq in.

Sawing was done with a high speed steel blade (hook tooth, raker set, 6 pitch, 1 in. wide, 0.035 in. thick), using a heavy-duty chemical solution as a cutting fluid. A dimensional tolerance of ±0.015 in. was maintained

Example 923. Fabrication of Aluminum Honeycomb Core for Bonded Aircraft Pod Fin (Fig. 46)

The core shown in Fig. 46 was made of 5052 alloy foil and expected production was 500 parts (not including parts scrapped or destructively tested). When a milling machine was employed, the time required for complete fabrication of one part was 40 hr, 12 hr of which was devoted exclusively to milling. The cost of milling, using a circular-knife cutter (so-called bologna slicer) and a depth of cut of 0.250 in. per pass, was $160.

When contour band sawing was employed, machining time was reduced to about 30 min (15 min per side) and machining cost was reduced to $4 per part. Details of the sawing process were as follows:

1 Precool fixture 1 hr before use by circulating a cold mixture of 60% ethylene glycol and 40% water through the fixture.
2 Load core into fixture.
3 Spray core cells with tap water so that each cell has 1/32 in. of water standing in the bottom.
4 Carefully lay lead weights on core to hold core firmly against fixture face.
5 Allow 3 to 5 min for water to freeze.
6 Remove weights.
7 Saw honeycomb with carbon steel band saw at speed of 10,000 sfm. (Blade: regular tooth, raker set, 14 pitch, 1 in. wide, 30½ ft long.)
8 After sawing, warm the fixture for 5 to 7 min by circulating warm mixture of 60% ethylene glycol and 40% water through it.
9 Remove core from fixture.
10 Repeat procedure for sawing other side, except that the sawed side is down on the second fixture.
11 After the second sawing operation, clean the core by spraying with tap water to remove all sawing particles, and blowing dry.

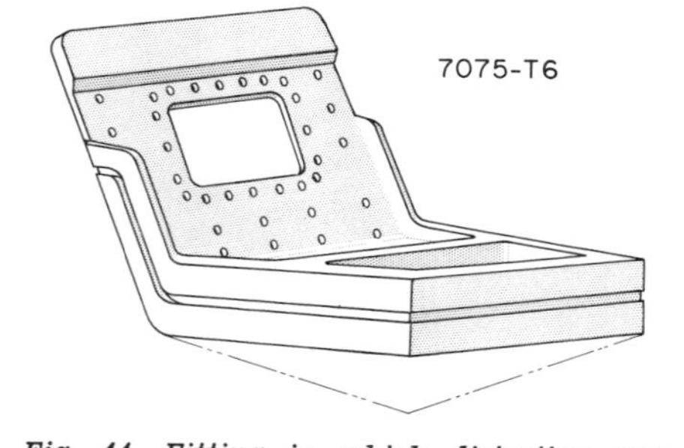

Fig. 44. Fitting in which distortion was eliminated by quenching from the solution-treating temperature in liquid nitrogen at —320 F before milling (Example 919)

Power hacksawing is commonly done at 140 to 160 strokes per min with a feed of 0.015 in. per stroke (Table 25). The higher speed is recommended for sawing non-heat-treated cast aluminum alloys and the lower speed (140 strokes per min) for all other aluminum alloys.

Cutting Fluid. Although circular saws can be operated satisfactorily on aluminum alloys at moderate speeds and medium cuts without a cutting fluid, it is advisable to supply copious amounts of soluble-oil:water emulsion (1:20) for all high-speed cutting. The cutting fluid should flood the blade and workpiece under slight pressure, and should be filtered or settled before recycling. In some applications, the addition of a little kerosine or lard oil to the emulsion has been beneficial. Soap solutions can be substituted for oil emulsions.

For band saws, some cutting fluid is essential for all but the lightest cuts. A wide selection of compounds is available, ranging from tallow or grease sticks to kerosine-thinned mineral-base lubricating oil or emulsions of soluble oil and water. It is often more convenient to use a fluid lubricant, supplied generously through a recycling system.

For hacksawing, procedures are similar to those for band sawing.

Grinding

The harder, free-cutting aluminum alloys are comparatively easy to grind. The non-free-cutting alloys, particularly in their softer tempers, are likely

Table 25. Recommended Tooth Angles, Contours and Practice for Sawing Aluminum Alloys

Tool material	Feed control	Tooth angles and contours: Cutting angle	Top rake	Clearance angles: Primary	Secondary	Side	Side rake	Tooth spacing	Set	Speed, sfm	Feed, ipm
Circular Saws											
High speed steel	Hand	69° to 79°	5° to 12°	6° to 9°	25° to 35°	1° to 2°	0° to 15°	(a)	(b)	2000 to 7000	4 to 24(c)
	Power	61° to 74°	10° to 20°	6° to 9°	25° to 35°	1° to 2°	0° to 15°	(a)	(b)	2000 to 7000	4 to 24(c)
Carbide-tipped	Hand	76° to 83°	1° to 5°	6° to 9°	25° to 35°	1° to 2°	0° to 10°	(a)	(b)	10,000 to 15,000	4 to 24(c)
	Power	71° to 79°	5° to 10°	6° to 9°	25° to 35°	1° to 2°	0° to 10°	(a)	(b)	10,000 to 15,000	4 to 24(c)
Band Saws											
Spring temper or hard-tooth, flexible back	Hand	72° to 80°	5° to 10°	5° to 8°	30° to 40°	....	5° to 15°(d)	(e)	(f)	2500 to 7500(g)	2 to 24
	Power	62° to 75°	10° to 20°	5° to 8°	30° to 40°	....	5° to 15°(d)	(e)	(f)	2500 to 7500(g)	2 to 24
Hacksaws											
Hard-tooth, flexible back	Hand or power	55° to 75°	10° to 25°	5° to 10°	30° to 40°	....	....	(h)	(j)	140 to 160 strokes per min	0.015 in. per stroke

(a) Coarse; generally two or three teeth should be engaged at all times. (b) Alternate set or chip-breaker teeth. (c) Feed for hard alloys, 4 to 17 ipm; for soft alloys, 17 to 24 ipm. (d) Resulting from alternate set. (e) Tooth spacing for heavy work, 4 to 5 per in.; for general work, up to 7 per in.; for thin stock, up to 11 per in. (f) Alternate set. (g) Speed for heavy work, up to 2500 sfm; for general work, 4000 to 5500 sfm; for thin stock, up to 7500 sfm. (h) For hand feed control, 10 to 15 per in.; for power feed, 5 to 10 per in. (j) Wavy set or alternate set.

Table 26. Recommended Conditions for Circular Saws With Carbide Teeth

Blade diameter, in.	Number of teeth(a)	Blade speed, sfm	Power requirement, hp
84	60	480 to 10,500	250 at 900 rpm
54	36	15,000	75 at 1200 rpm
36	36	16,000	75 at 1750 rpm
24	36	10,600	75 at 1750 rpm
12	50, 70, 80	5,000	20 at 1750 rpm
10	190	9,000	5 at 3450 rpm

(a) Feed is normally about 0.001 in. per tooth.

Table 27. Conditions for Circular Sawing ¼-In. Plate of Alloy 7075-T6 With Carbide-Tipped Blades (Example 920)

Machine ......Special table saw (144 by 60 by ½ in.) with automatic saw feed and pneumatic plate clamping

Saw blade:
- Material ....Carbide-tipped
- Blade diameter ....10 in.
- Number of teeth 60
- Tooth thickness ....0.120 in.
- Angles ....5° rake, 12° to 15° clearance

Operating Conditions

Speed ......1725 to 1825 rpm (4800 sfm max)
Feed ....60 ipm
Depth of cut ....0.250 in.
Length of cut ....144 in.
Cutting fluid ...Soluble-oil:water; spray mist
Cutting time ......2.4 min per plate (144 in.)
Setup time ....5 min
Tool life between grinds ....200 hr

to clog grinding wheels, and they do not finish to as bright and smooth a surface as the harder alloys.

Abrasive Wheels. For grinding aluminum alloys, a silicon carbide abrasive in a flexible base is generally preferred. Aluminum oxide is seldom recommended, except for piston grinding and in cutoff wheels. Wheels of medium hardness, about 30 grit size, and with a synthetic resin bond work best for roughing. For finishing, wheels of finer grit size (to about 54) and with a vitrified bond are generally used. Recommendations for wheels for several different types of grinding operations are given in Table 28. (For explanation of ASA system for identifying characteristics of grinding wheels, see Fig. 1 on page 258, in the article "Grinding".)

The following example describes specific grinding practice for pistons.

Example 924. Grinding Pistons (Fig. 47)

After extensive testing, an A-46-K5-V wheel was selected for grinding the skirt of permanent mold cast F132-T5 pistons. Requirements for the wheel were: (*a*) satisfactory performance without frequent redressing, (*b*) ability to hold the required profile, and (*c*) production of a 50-to-90-micro-in. finish. The A-46-K5-V wheel was capable of grinding 100 parts between redressings and met the other requirements.

A special hydraulic dresser, equipped with a profile bar, was used to dress the wheel. The dressing tool was a ¾-carat diamond that was turned in its holder after eight dressings to maintain a sharp point.

Details of this grinding operation are given in the table accompanying Fig. 47.

Cutoff Wheels. Abrasive cutoff wheels for aluminum are usually of aluminum oxide. For wet grinding, which is generally recommended, the bond is usually rubber. For dry grinding, either rubber or resinoid bond may be used. Typical specifications are A-20-U6-R (aluminum oxide, 20 grain size, U grade, 6 structure, rubber bond) and A-24-S7-B (aluminum oxide, 24 grain size, S grade, 7 structure, resinoid bond). Width of wheels ranges from 0.003 to 0.156 in.; diameter varies from 1 to 30 in. These wheels cut to an accuracy of a few thousandths of an inch.

A typical specification for an abrasive cutoff wheel for aluminum bars is C/A-24-S6-B (silicon carbide/aluminum oxide combination, 24 grain size, S grade, 6 structure, resinoid bond).

For wet cutting of intricate extrusions, a recommended specification is C-46-S7-R or A-46-S7-R.

Reinforced (Flexible) Wheels. In cutting off gates and sprues from castings of irregular shape, excessive wheel breakage can occur because of very high pressure on the sides of the wheel. To eliminate this problem and provide for safe operation, special reinforced, flexible, abrasive wheels have been developed. These wheels are manufactured from laminated sheets of cotton fiber filled with abrasive grain, and are used for operations ranging from heavy grinding to light sanding: cutting off, sharpening, deburring, and finishing. Such wheels used for aluminum are C-24-O14-B to C-24-U14-B.

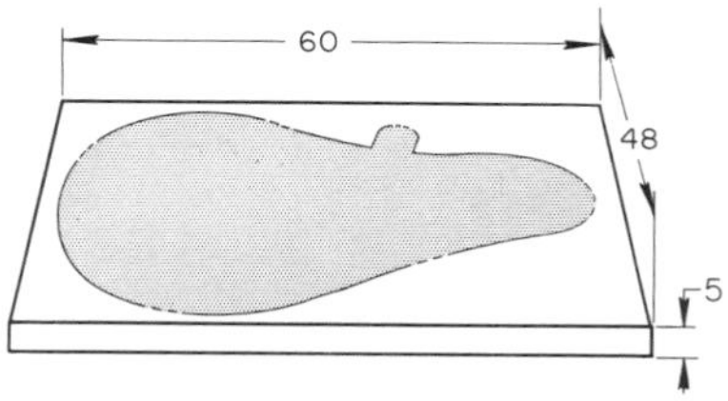

Fig. 45. Shape that was contour band sawed from aluminum plate (Example 922)

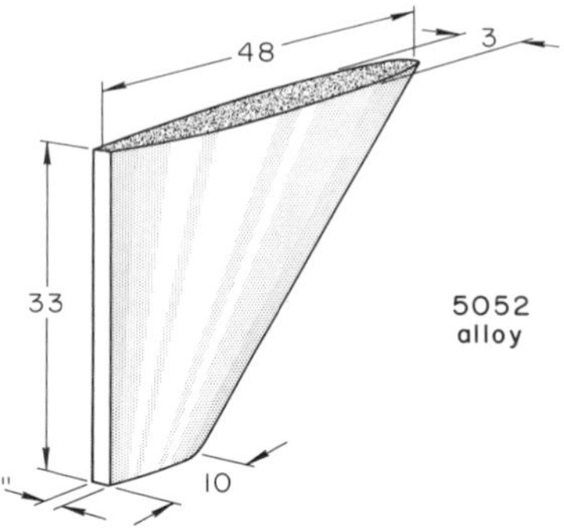

Fig. 46. Honeycomb core for aircraft pod fin (Example 923)

Speed. Typical wheel speeds for several types of grinding are given in Table 29. Sometimes, by adjusting the speed, a wheel that was previously unsuited for a particular operation can be made to grind satisfactorily. For example, if a wheel is too soft, increasing the speed will give a harder action.

Using the recommended speed for a wheel is important, not only from the standpoint of grinding results but also to insure safety. Stress from centrifugal force increases greatly as wheel velocity increases. The force tending to pull a wheel apart will be four times greater at 3600 rpm than at 1800 rpm.

Grinding Fluid. Neutral soluble-oil emulsions are satisfactory for grinding aluminum. Addition of a wetting agent (detergent) is sometimes helpful. Although an emulsion of 1 part soluble oil to 35 parts water is commonly used, a better cushioning effect, which also prevents clogging of the wheel, is obtained by using more oil and less water. One manufacturer, in grinding soft aluminum alloy castings, went progressively from a mixture of 1 part oil to 20 parts water to a mixture of 1 part oil to 6 parts water, before obtaining satisfactory results.

In rough grinding, where stock removal is the primary objective, generous application of wax or stick grease is often satisfactory. This type of lubricant is often used when the application of liquids is not feasible.

Belt Lubricant. Grinding fluids or stick lubricants improve the finish produced by a coated abrasive belt and prevent glazing of the belt. Lubricants used range from water to stick waxes; standard cutting oils and soluble-oil mixtures are often used in high-production belt machines.

Greases cushion the penetrating action of the abrasive into the work, and produce finer finishes than are obtained in dry grinding. Although the crest of each grain is free to cut, the grease prevents deep scratches.

Table 28. Recommended Wheels for Grinding Aluminum Alloys
(See Fig. 1, page 258, for explanation of wheel-classification system.)

Operation	Abrasive	Grain size	Grade and structure	Bond
General Grinding				
Centerless grinding	C	36	K8	V
Cylindrical grinding	C	36	K8	V
Surface grinding, cups and cylinders	C	24	J9	V-B
Surface grinding, disks	C or C/A	16 to 20	K19 to L4	B
Internal grinding	C	36	K19	V
Floor-stand grinders (5000 to 6500 sfm) ...	C	24	O	V
Floor-stand grinders (7000 to 9500 sfm) ...	C	24	P	B
Portable grinders (5000 to 6500 sfm)	C	24	O	V
Portable grinders (7000 to 9500 sfm)	C	30	O	B
Cutoff grinding, dry (9000 to 16,000 sfm) ..	A	24	S7	B
Cutoff grinding, wet (7500 to 12,000 sfm) ..	A	46	S7	R
Cutoff grinding, foundry machines	A	24	S7	B
Snagging, low-speed	C	24	O4	B
	A	24	O7	B
	C/A	24	O4	B
Snagging, high-speed	A	16	O7	B
Piston Grinding				
Cylindrical grinding	C	36 to 46	I to K8	V
Centerless grinding	C	36 to 46	I to K8	V
	C	60	J6	V
Regrinding	A or C	46	I to K8	V

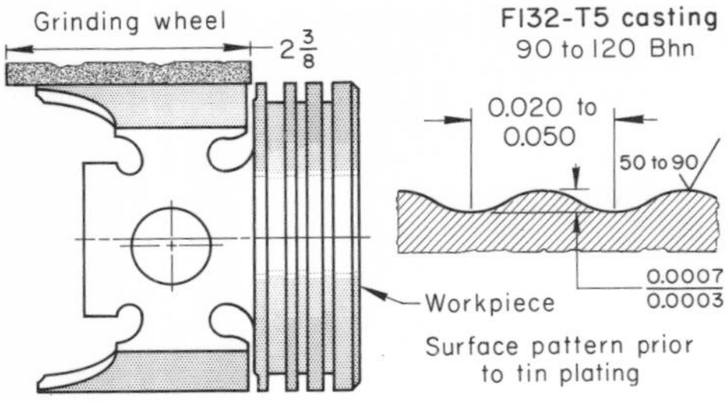

Machine	Cylindrical grinder, 6 by 18 in., with automatic infeed electric-cycle control and semiautomatic profile dresser
Wheel:	
Type	A-46-K5-V
Size	20 by 2⅜ by 12 in.
Life per dressing	100 pieces
Operating Conditions	
Wheel speed	1300 rpm (6800 sfm)
Work speed	96 rpm
Feed per pass	0.016 to 0.018 in.
Grinding fluid	Soluble-oil:water (1:25)
Production rate	106 pieces per hour
Time per pass(a)	20 sec
Surface finish	50 to 90 micro-in.

(a) Infeed set with automatic timer

Fig. 47. Permanent mold cast piston that was ground in a single pass, removing 0.016 to 0.018 in. of stock (Example 924)

Greases are used for offhand grinding of aluminum die castings. Where stock removal is the primary objective, a light grease should be used, preventing the belt from loading but permitting a maximum amount of abrasive penetration into the metal being ground. For a good finish, a heavy grease should be used.

Some operations use two types of grease, side by side, on the same abrasive belt. One side is used for a high rate of stock removal, and the other for a finer finish. If the belt becomes loaded despite the use of grease, an application of kerosine will free the belt of embedded particles.

Liquid lubricants are used primarily to prevent belt glazing. When water is used, a rust inhibitor should be added.

Soluble oil mixed with water is effective in grinding aluminum if stock removal is the primary objective.

Honing

Aluminum alloys are honed by methods similar to those used for other metals (see the article "Honing", which begins on page 288). Resin-bond abrasives are preferred; sulfurized mineral-base oil or lard oil mixed with kerosine is used to flush the abrasive sticks clean and to carry away heat.

Honing is used to finish anodized aluminum surfaces, primarily the bores of some small aluminum engine blocks, and most aircraft hydraulic cylinders. The example that follows describes the technique and conditions employed in honing of main bearing bores in aluminum engine blocks. The aluminum blocks and the gray iron bearing caps were honed simultaneously with a silicon carbide abrasive, even though, when honed separately, gray iron and aluminum would be honed with different abrasives.

Example 925. Simultaneous Honing of Aluminum and Gray Iron (Fig. 48)

Main-bearing bores in six-cylinder, die-cast aluminum engine blocks were honed with gray iron bearing caps bolted in place, as shown in Fig. 48. The blocks were fixtured for honing and were held in position by a light clamping force on the head faces. Each block was held securely so that it could resist torsional forces from the honing tool, but adjustment of clamping force was critical, because excessive force would distort the block. Hydraulic cone expanders automatically fed out the single bank of six carbon-bonded silicon carbide stones (2 by ¼ in., 120 grit). Fifteen fiber guides, each 3 by ¼ in., were incorporated in the honing tool. Processing details are given in the table with Fig. 48.

Table 29. Typical Wheel Speeds for Grinding Aluminum Alloys

Operation	Speed, sfm
Cylindrical grinding	5500 to 6500
Internal grinding	2100 to 6000
Snagging(a)	7000 to 9500
Surface grinding	4000 to 5000
Offhand grinding (large wheels)	4000 to 5000
Cutoff(b)	9000 to 16000

(a) Rubber and resinoid bonds. (b) Rubber, resinoid and shellac bonds.

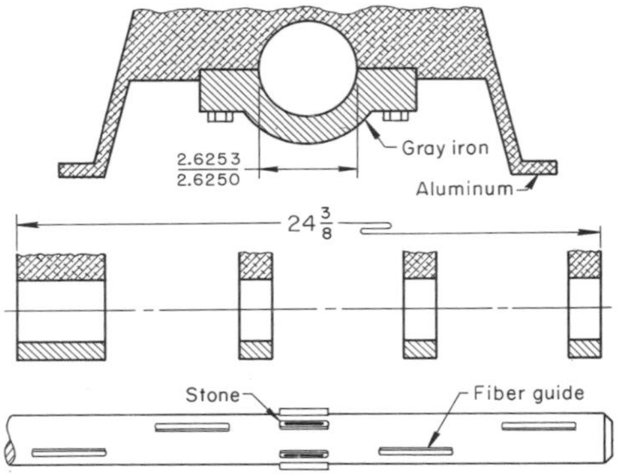

Speed	900 rpm (620 sfm)
Spindle reciprocation rate	60 strokes per min
Hone speed	70 ft per min
Stock removed	0.0015 to 0.020 in.
Honing time	25 sec
Cutting fluid	Mineral seal oil
Size-control method	Air gage
Stone life, per set (avg)	300 assemblies
Production rate	75 pieces per hour
Bore alignment before honing	0.002 in.
Bore alignment after honing	0.0007 in.
Specified tolerance	±0.0003 in.
Specified finish	20 to 25 micro-in.

Fig. 48. Die-cast engine block that was honed with gray iron bearing caps in place, and honing tool (bottom) used (Example 925)

Long anodized aluminum tubes that are components of in-flight refueling apparatus are finished by manual honing. The tubes are chucked in a lathe and the honing tool is moved manually. The oil supply is attached to the honing tool in such a manner that flow of oil is directed where most needed. This method of honing is also used for finishing connecting-rod journals or crankshafts in aircraft-overhaul shops.

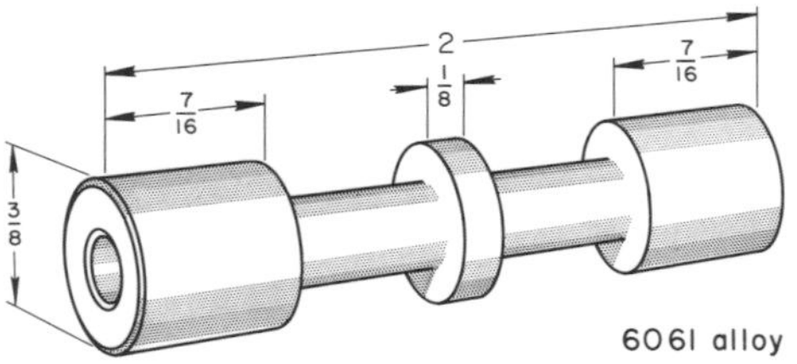

Fig. 49. Part from which 0.0002 in. of metal was removed by lapping to smooth the surface to 1 micro-in. (Example 926)

Lapping

The same methods are used for lapping aluminum as for other metals (see the article "Lapping", which begins on page 298). However, because similar finishes often can be produced by other methods at less cost, lapping is seldom used. In the example that follows, an extremely smooth finish of 1 micro-in. on an anodized part was produced by two methods of lapping.

Example 926. Lapping Hard-Anodized Alloy 6061 (Fig. 49)

The hard-anodized aluminum part (surface hardness equivalent to Rockwell C 65) shown in Fig. 49 required removal of 0.0002 in. from the three lands, to produce a finish of 1 micro-in. Diamond abrasive (8000-mesh) in a paste vehicle was used for both centerless roll lapping and lapping in a two-plate machine. The roll lapper, at a rotation speed of 100 rpm (large roll) and a stroke speed of 2 ipm, produced ten parts per hour. The two-plate machine, which had upper and lower cast iron laps 16 in. in diameter and 3 in. thick, lapped 1000 parts per hour.

Chemical Machining

Chemical contour machining (chemical milling), discussed in detail on pages 245 to 249, is used to etch preformed aerospace parts to obtain increased strength-to-weight ratio. Examples 465(a) and 466 on page 247 describe the application of chemical machining to parts made of aluminum alloys 7072 and 2024. In the latter example, etching was assisted by an auxiliary anodic current.

Figure 50 (below) presents a typical curve for choosing the most economical method (chemical vs mechanical) for removing metal from flat parts on which large areas having complex or wavy peripheral outlines are to be reduced in thickness. Fillet ratio and thickness of metal to be removed are used as the basis for evaluation. Metal thicknesses greater than 0.250 in. should be removed mechanically; thicknesses less than 0.125, chemically. Between these two values, choice depends on fillet ratio, which governs the weight penalty.

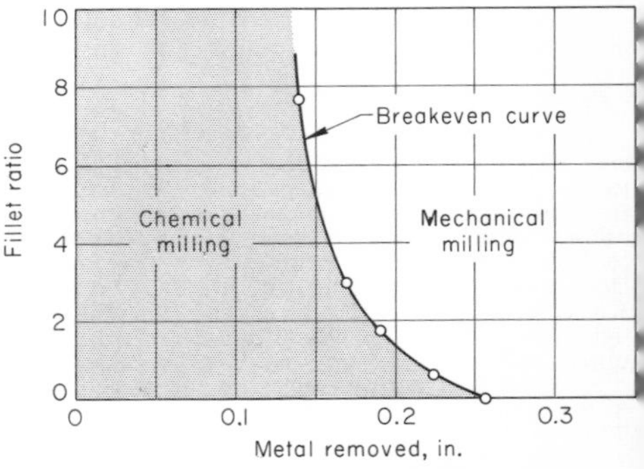

$$\text{Fillet ratio} = \frac{\text{total length of fillet (ft)}}{\text{total area of part (sq ft)}}$$

Fig. 50. Breakeven between chemical and mechanical milling. Choice between them depends on fillet ratio and depth of cut.

Other Examples of Machining Aluminum

Broaching	Example 128
Drilling	Example 148
Roller burnishing	Example 214
Tapping	Examples 231, 234
Contour band sawing	Example 442
Chemical machining	Examples 465(a), 466

Machining of Beryllium

*By the ASM Committee on Machining of Heat-Resisting Alloys**

CHARACTERISTICS of beryllium that require special attention in machining are given in the following list and discussed in subsequent paragraphs:

1 Beryllium is costly, indicating the need for good "housekeeping" and other procedures that prevent waste.
2 Beryllium is easily chipped or broken, and therefore is extremely sensitive to workpiece support and cutting technique.
3 Beryllium dust and chips are toxic, thus requiring the use of a tested exhaust system.
4 Because of the possibility that the workpiece may be harmed, cutting fluids must be carefully selected or not used at all.
5 Machining operations can cause surface microcracks that impair strength.

Saving Material. Because of the high metal cost (about $100 per pound), it is usually economical to have the workpiece roughed by the beryllium supplier to as near finished size as practical. By this method the manufacturer not only pays for less material that will become waste in machining, but also obtains better quality and fewer rejects in machining, thus decreasing cost per piece.

The vacuum system that must be used in machining beryllium also affords a means of salvaging metal (see Examples 928 and 930).

Mechanical Support. Rigid support for the workpiece is essential. Otherwise, chipping or breaking may result at the start or finish of a cut. Tools should be fed into the mass of material, rather than to an unsupported edge.

Health Hazard. No machining of beryllium should be done unless a tested exhaust system is used and quantitative measurements of beryllium dust in the atmosphere are regularly made. Beryllium dust in the atmosphere can cause a form of chemical pneumonitis (berylliosis) that can be fatal.

The U. S. Atomic Energy Commission's "Recommendations for Control of Beryllium Hazards" states:

1 The in-plant atmospheric concentration of beryllium should not exceed two micrograms per cubic meter as an average concentration throughout an eight-hour day.
2 Even though the daily average might be within the limits stated above, no personnel should be exposed to a concentration greater than 25 micrograms per cubic meter for any period of time, however short.

Cutting Fluid. Beryllium is usually machined dry. However, in some machining operations, such as deep-hole drilling, use of a cutting fluid is necessary: Soluble oil emulsions (usually 1 part oil mixed with 15 to 20 parts water) are used. The sulfurized and chlorinated grades of soluble oils are not recommended, because they may discolor or corrode the work metal. Whenever a cutting fluid is used, the workpiece should be thoroughly washed in water and dried after machining.

*For committee list, see page 405.

An advantage of using a cutting fluid is that it is helpful in suppressing beryllium dust. A disadvantage is that it makes chip salvage more costly.

Preserving Mechanical Properties. High strength in beryllium parts depends greatly on the surface condition after machining. Light cuts are helpful in preventing microcracking in the surface layers. However, microcracking sometimes develops even when machining cuts are extremely light.

Turning, Boring and Facing

Single-point tools used for turning, boring or facing beryllium must have keen cutting edges with a primary clearance angle of about 6° (or slightly higher) and a secondary clearance angle of about 10°. Tools usually give best results when a positive back rake (1° to 5°) is permissible, although sometimes a 0° back rake is used (see Example 927). To reduce the cutting pressure required, nose radius or chamfer should be as small as feasible for the job. Because of the abrasiveness of beryllium, live centers should be used.

Tool Material. For machining beryllium, carbide tools are used almost exclusively. The straight-tungsten grades are best.

Speed and Feed. Light cuts (under 0.030 in., even for roughing) and carbide tools permit the use of relatively high turning speeds. Beryllium is commonly rough turned, faced and bored at speeds of 200 to 300 sfm, although speeds as high as 350 sfm have been successfully used. For finish turning of critical dimensions, speeds of 100 to 150 sfm have been successful.

In roughing, feeds of 0.005 to 0.015 ipr are generally used. In finishing to minimum surface roughness, feeds as low as 0.0005 ipr are used.

Depth of cut should not exceed 0.030 in., to avoid developing excessive stress. Beryllium is susceptible to chipping as the cutting tool leaves the work at the end of the cut. This chipping may be reduced by (*a*) taking light cuts, (*b*) finish turning one end for a short distance and then reversing ends, (*c*) chamfering both ends prior to turning, or (*d*) using "runoff" material, like "runoff tabs" in welding. Increasing the side cutting-edge angle helps by distributing the impact load back from the nose. However, excessive increase of this angle causes chatter.

Examples. The two examples that follow demonstrate procedures and precautionary measures.

Example 927. Close Tolerances on Matched Housings (Fig. 1)

As shown in Fig. 1, close tolerances were assigned to numerous diameters of matched pairs of beryllium housings. These tolerances were met by turning, boring and facing the two items with carbide tools according to the sequence of operations given below Fig. 1. Machining was done in a 9-in. toolroom lathe, a special feature of which was a preloaded spindle that allowed runout error to be kept below 20 millionths of an inch. Parts were held in a collet chuck. Although carbide-tipped tools were satisfactory for turning and facing, the boring tool was of solid carbide, because a carbide-tipped steel bar lacked the necessary rigidity. During each phase of the operation, all chips were removed by vacuum.

The work material was purchased as hot pressed rod stock about 0.030 in. from finished dimensions. This was economical because:

1 By having the supplier furnish product forms near finish size, it was possible to detect flaws, thus minimizing the possibility of rejects during finish machining.
2 A minimum of material became generated scrap, which was significant because beryllium of this diameter (about 1½ in.) costs about $12 per lineal inch.

Example 928. Machining Blanks for Roll Forging (Fig. 2)

Converting cylindrical billets of commercially pure beryllium (2% BeO) into ring-shaped blanks for roll forging required trepanning, cutoff, turning, boring and facing. Figure 2 shows the workpiece, setup and tools employed for trepanning and cutoff; tool details and machining conditions for all of the operations are tabulated below Fig. 2.

Each billet, 17¾ in. in diameter and 27 in. long, weighed 396 lb before machining and 67 lb as two roll-forging blanks after machining. (The trepanning operation also produced a 27-in.-long core, or "log", 12½ in. in diameter.) After being chucked in a lathe (see Fig. 2), the billet was trepanned and, after removal of the core, parted with a cutoff tool. The two rings produced were then turned, bored and faced in a vertical turret lathe.

Figure 2 also shows that a vacuum pipe was located near the working area of the cutoff tool to remove all chips, and that the trepanning tool was provided with two nozzles, one at the end of each chip slot, for connection to a vent system. The trepanning tool had two replaceable carbide inserts, staggered — a notched chipper and an opposing raker.

Drilling

Drilling problems arise because of: (*a*) tool wear resulting from the abrasiveness of beryllium; (*b*) hole "breakthrough", or spalling (which occurs because beryllium is brittle); and (*c*) high torque and thrust requirements.

In addition to the operator variable when using manually operated equipment, other contributing variables are:

1 Drill material
2 Drill design
3 Dull or chipped drills
4 Bouncing entrance
5 Poor or changing alignment
6 Increased feed rate at exit.

Three breakthrough patterns are illustrated in Fig. 3.

Drill Material. With all other variables kept as nearly constant as possible, carbide is superior to high speed steel for drilling beryllium. For instance, when drilling with off-the-shelf, 118°-point-angle high speed steel drills, a breakthrough pattern no better than B (Fig. 3) was obtained. Drills of

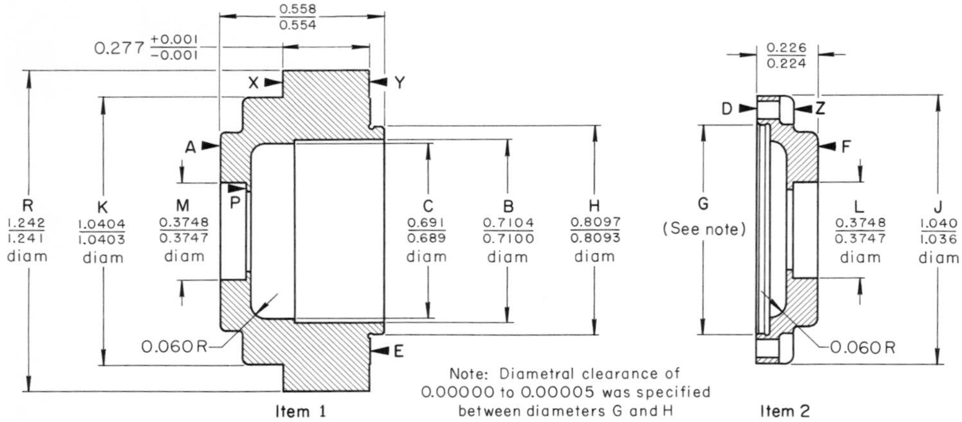

Sequence of Operations

1 Rough out both items 1 and 2 completely, with sharp carbide tools.
2 Stress relieve both items (1385 F, 20 min)
3 Machine inside contour of item 2 (including diameter G and surface D) to finish dimensions except for about 0.0001 in. (removed later by lapping).
4 Mount item 1 on stub arbor, using diameter B, and machine diameters K and R to size, then machine 0.277-in. dimension so that surfaces X and Y are parallel with each other and perpendicular to diameter R.
5 Drill a 2-in.-diam aluminum rod, held in a collet, 1.05-in. diam by 0.600 deep. Then counterbore 0.260 in. deep with a 0.0002-in. interference fit at room temperature on diameter R. (The bottom of the counterbore must be flat and square with the hole, and corner must be sharp and square.)
6 Heat aluminum holder sufficiently so it slips on diameter R, seating against surface X. Check surface Y with an indicator, to ascertain proper seating of item 1 in the aluminum holder with surface X firmly bottomed.
7 With item 1 held as described in step 6, finish machine diameters B, C and H, and surface E; then form 0.060-in. radius with separate tool (required because radius is too large to be formed by boring tool).
8 Assemble item 2 to item 1, applying equal torque to all mounting screws so that accuracy can be reproduced in later assembly.
9 Machine diameter L and surfaces F and Z on item 2, boring diameter L to, or slightly below, low limit. (Diameter L must be checked in machine — a method not always accurate — but after removal can be rechecked by a more accurate method and lapped to size if required.)
10 Reheat holder, remove and reverse assembly, and remount holder on diameter R, seating against surface Y. Check surface X with an indicator to insure alignment.
11 With assembly held as described in step 10, machine diameter M and surfaces A and P, on item 1, to complete the job.

Tool Angles(a)

Back rake	0°
Side rake	7° to 8°
Side cutting edge	12° to 15°
End cutting edge	8° to 15°
Side relief	7° to 10°
End relief	7° to 10°

(a) Carbide-tipped tools were used for turning and facing; boring tools were of solid carbide.

Machining Conditions(b)

Speed, roughing	60 to 100 sfm
Feed, roughing	0.010 to 0.015 ipr
Depth of cut, roughing	0.030 in. max
Tool life, roughing	25 in. (lineal)
Speed, finishing	100 to 150 sfm
Feed, finishing	0.0005 to 0.001 ipr
Depth of cut, finishing	0.0015 in. max
Total time per assembly	45 hr

(b) No cutting fluid was used.

Fig. 1. Turning, boring and facing of matched pairs of housing-assembly components to close tolerances (Example 927)

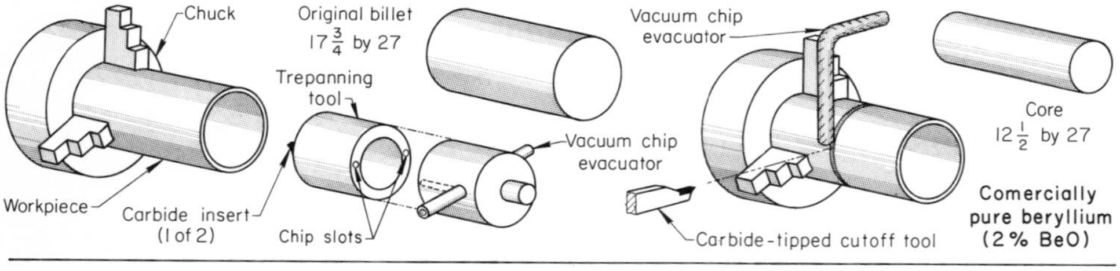

Item	Operation 1 Trepan	Operation 2 Cutoff	Operation 3 Turn, bore, face
Tool Angles(a)			
Lead	15°	15°	10° to 15°
Clearance:			
Primary	5°, 7°(b)	5°	7° to 10°
Secondary	7°, 10°(b)	7°	12° to 15°
Back rake	0°	0°	0° to +5°
Nose radius	....	....	1/32 in.
Machining Conditions(c)			
Speed, sfm	100	100	150 to 250
Feed, ipr	0.001 to 0.003	0.001	0.005 to 0.015
Width of cut, in.	0.520	0.500	....
Depth of cut, in.:			
Roughing	....	....	0.075 to 0.150
Finishing	....	....	0.005 to 0.015
Cutting fluid	None	None	None

(a) Carbide tools were used for all operations. Tools for trepanning and cutoff were provided with chip breakers, 0.010 in. deep by 0.030 in. wide. (b) Front and side, respectively. (c) Total machining time to produce two rings, 26 hr.

Fig. 2. Machining ring-shaped blanks from solid, cylindrical billets for roll forging (Example 928)

identical design made of carbide produced patterns more nearly like A under the same conditions.

Drill Design. Although standard 118°-point-angle drills have produced acceptable results, improved breakthrough pattern generally is obtained when these drills are modified by rounding the corners. Drills with thinned webs are sometimes used to reduce thrust force. Ball end drills (mills) have also been successfully used. A special drill of the design shown in Fig. 4 has also performed well, and eliminates the need for center drilling (see Example 929).

Speeds and feeds for drilling beryllium are not necessarily different from those used for drilling other metals. Various sources have reported successful results with speeds ranging from 25 to 80 sfm. In most applications, speeds are near the low end of this range (see Example 929).

Feed rates reported from several sources also vary over a wide range — 0.0006 to 0.0050 ipr, or even greater in

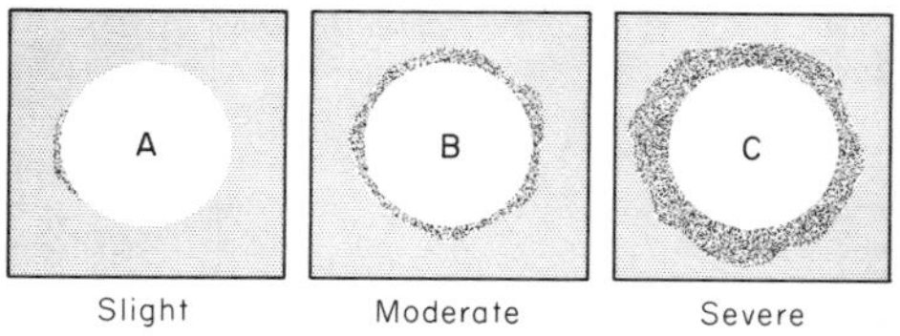

Fig. 3. Three degrees of exit-side spalling on beryllium, caused by breakthrough of drills

a few instances. In most applications feeds ranging from about 0.0006 to 0.0012 ipr are used.

Operating Variables. Drills must be sharp and free from nicks and chipped areas. Beryllium is more sensitive to these conditions than most metals.

Prior center drilling is often used to minimize a bouncing entrance, which will cause chipping at the hole entrance and may affect breakthrough, especially in drilling through thin walls in fragile workpieces.

Regardless of drill material and design, even the most skilled operators can only minimize the hazards of chipping at breakthrough when using conventional drill presses. No procedure will permit the free-hand drilling of beryllium when standards are high, as in the aerospace industry where the use of a torque-monitored drilling head has proved to be the best method. With this equipment, the upper limits of speed and feed are selected by trial. Feed rate is torque-dependent. As drilling proceeds and breakthrough begins, the reduced force will indicate to the monitoring computer that the drill is emerging, and feed is automatically reduced. Increased force will indicate a dull or chipped tool, which also reduces feed rate. A torque-monitored drilling head allows the entire cycle to be programmed and controlled automatically. The use of this type of drilling head is illustrated in the following example:

Example 929. Preventing Damage at Breakthrough (Fig. 4)

A missile component, ring rolled and machined to the form of a shell 32 in. in diameter, 12 in. high, and with a 0.160-in. wall, required 250 drilled holes 0.1875 in. in diameter. The drilling equipment consisted of a ¼-hp, torque-monitored drilling head (Fig. 4a), which was mounted on a vertical column in a manner to provide stepless vertical adjustment, and an adapter plate mounted on a standard rotary table.

Radial hole positioning was controlled by tool blocks and locator pins mounted on the rotary table. Vertical positioning was controlled by set-blocks and a dial indicator mounted on the drilling-head slide. Preliminary bench layout was used to avoid gross error in location. The use of the special drill illustrated in Fig. 4(b) made center drilling unnecessary, and hole location was easily held within 0.005 in.

All cutting was done dry, to simplify removal of dust and chips. Ventilation was accomplished using 1½-in. flexible vacuum lines, at both entrance and exit sides, located as close as possible to the drilling area. Face velocity of air across the work was 4000 to 6000 fpm. Other process details are given with Fig. 4.

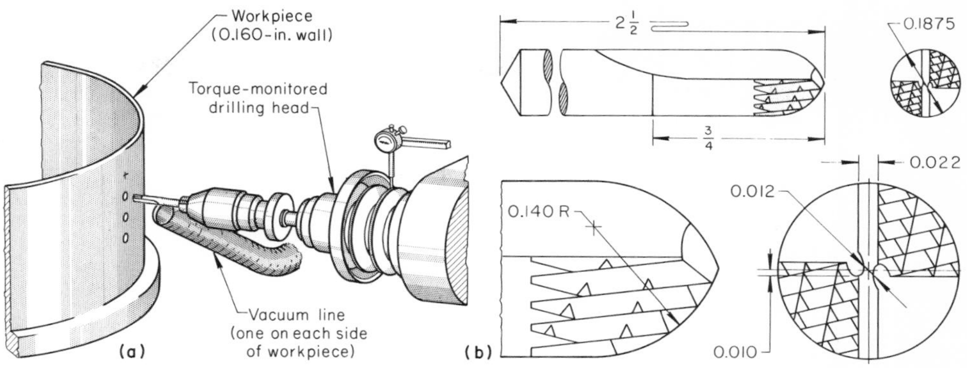

Machining Conditions	
Speed, no load	600 rpm (30 sfm)
Speed, average	500 rpm (25 sfm)
Feed	0.0006 to 0.0012 ipr
Feed, rapid	15 ipm
Feed, no load	8 ipm
Feed, cutting	3 ipm
Cutting fluid	None
Drill life per grind	10 to 100 holes(a)
Drilling time per hole	30 sec
Production rate(b)	24 holes per hour

Drill Details	
Material	Solid carbide
Number of flutes	2
Type of flutes	Straight
Number of burr teeth(c)	5 each side
Clearance angle, main tooth	8° to 10°
Clearance angle, burr teeth	5°

(a) Usual life, near 100 holes. (b) Includes positioning time. (c) Burr teeth concentric within 0.001 in. TIR.

Fig. 4. (a) *Setup, showing torque-monitored drilling head, and* (b) *details of special drill that eliminated need for center drilling, used for producing 250 holes in 32-in.-diam beryllium missile components* (Example 929)

Milling

Milling is often the most economical means of producing a desired size and providing the 125-micro-in. (max) finish required for penetrant and x-ray inspection. The work material is backed up and clamped in a sturdy universal fixture that supports close to the cut. Milling is usually done dry. A vacuum system for recovery of chips and dust must be used. (See Example 930 and the paragraph preceding it.)

Carbide insert-type cutters are recommended, and must be kept sharp to avoid disturbing the work metal to any appreciable depth.

Speed, Feed, and Depth of Cut. Beryllium is usually rough milled at speeds of 50 to 100 sfm. For finish milling, speed can be safely increased to 150 sfm when depth of cut is less than 0.030 in.

A feed rate up to 0.010 ipt is commonly used in roughing. Rate of feed is usually somewhat less (0.003 to 0.008 ipt) in finish milling.

Depth of cut in rough milling is preferably 0.100 in. or less. Although depth of roughing cut may range up to 0.250 in. (see Example 930), this would reflect the removal of irregularities; an entire surface would never be milled to this depth in a single pass. For finish milling, a depth of cut of less than 0.030 in. is recommended, and even with this shallow cut the work should be stress relieved (holding at 1385 F for 20 min) after being machined.

Typical practice for face milling of hot pressed vacuum sintered billets is described in Example 930, which follows. Most items of procedure shown in this example are similar to those used in face milling of other metals. The main differences are: (*a*) that the cutter rotates within a shroud to which nozzles are attached for vacuum removal of all chips (see Fig. 5); and (*b*) no cutting fluid is used, because it would be almost impossible to prevent most of the fluid from being evacuated from the shrouded cutter.

Example 930. Face Milling Rectangular Billets (Fig. 5)

Figure 5 shows the setup employed in face milling rectangular billets (7 by 10 by 14 in.) of commercially pure beryllium (2% BeO). The face mill, 8 in. in diameter, was used in a No. 4 hydraulic milling machine. The billet, secured to a universal adapter-plate fixture, was fed to the cutter as shown in Fig. 5.

Because depth of cut was relatively heavy in this operation (see conditions listed below Fig. 5), the inserted carbide teeth had a 1/32-in.

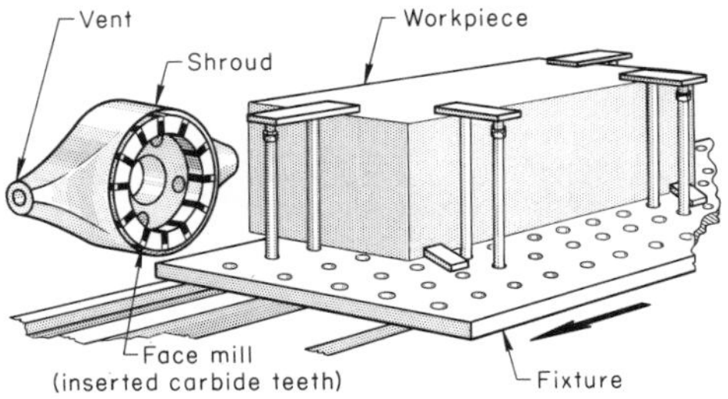

Cutter Details	
Diameter	8 in.
Number of teeth (carbide)	12
Radial rake angle	5°
Primary clearance angle	5° to 7°
Secondary clearance angle	10° to 12°

Machining Conditions	
Speed, roughing	60 to 100 sfm
Feed, roughing	0.005 to 0.010 ipt
Depth of roughing cut	0.100 to 0.250 in.
Speed, finishing	100 to 150 sfm
Feed, finishing	0.003 to 0.008 in.
Depth of finishing cut	0.010 to 0.030 in.
Cutting fluid	None

Fig. 5. Face milling hot pressed, vacuum-sintered beryllium billets (Example 930)

to 1/16-in. radius or chamfer to minimize chipping. As chips were formed, they were removed by vacuum through the vent in the shroud surrounding the cutter.

Tapping and Threading

Because beryllium chips and breaks easily, standard taps are not suitable. High speed steel taps with an eccentric relief are satisfactory. For external threading, single-point carbide tools should be used.

Chemical Machining

In several applications, chemical machining (see page 240 for a detailed description of the process) has proved ideal for removing excess metal, particularly from contoured surfaces or from thin sections. The example that follows describes a typical application.

Example 931. Reducing Dead Weight by Chemical Machining (Fig. 6)

A large missile component, a section of which is shown in Fig. 6, was reduced in weight from 13 to 6 lb by chemical machining over half the inside area from the original thickness of 0.160 in. to 0.080 in.

First, the workpiece was prepared for masking by being immersed in a sulfuric acid solution (15 to 20% H_2SO_4, rem H_2O), maintained between 72 and 90 F, until 0.0003 to 0.0005 in. of material was removed from all surfaces. Then the maskant, a proprietary resin compound reduced to a Zahn-cup viscosity of 30 to 35 sec, was dip applied in four coats to a total thickness of 0.015 to 0.020 in. Each of the first three coats was air dried for 10 min before the next was applied; the final coat was dried for 8 hr before scribing and peeling. Templates, of rigid plastic sheet, were designed to compensate for undercutting (which is normally 1.2 times the depth of material removed).

After the maskant had been peeled from areas to be reduced in thickness, the workpiece was reimmersed in the sulfuric acid solution (see above), and agitated to maintain uniform etching rate. Time in the solution varied from about 40 to 80 min, depending on the rate of metal removal. Normal rate was 0.001 to 0.002 in. per min; at or below 0.0005 in. per min, the solution was discarded.

Apart from reducing weight, chemical machining provided an additional benefit. As the component was originally designed, add-on doublers were needed to receive the doors for the openings in the component. With the use of chemical machining, integral doublers were provided, in a simpler design.

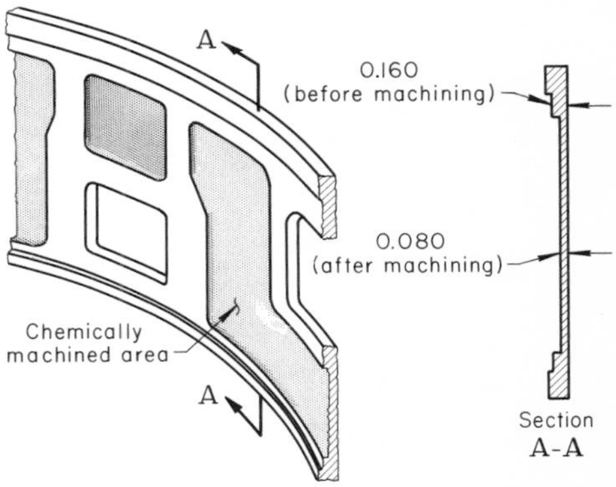

Fig. 6. Section of a chemically machined missile component (Example 931)

Machining of Copper and Copper Alloys

*By the ASM Committee on Machining of Copper and Copper Alloys**

COPPER and copper alloys are usually divided into three groups, with respect to machinability:

1. Free-cutting alloys, to which an appreciable amount of lead, sulfur, or tellurium has been added in order to improve the machining characteristics
2. Moderately machinable alloys, chiefly the nonleaded brasses containing 60 to 85% copper and the leaded nickel silvers
3. Alloys difficult to machine, including the nonleaded coppers, low-zinc brasses and nickel silvers, the phosphor bronzes and aluminum bronzes, cupro-nickel and beryllium copper.

Table 1 gives the nominal compositions and machinability ratings of the most widely used wrought coppers and copper alloys. Ratings are based on free-cutting brass (61.5 copper, 35.5 zinc, 3.0 lead) as 100.

Type of Chip. Group 1 alloys yield short, brittle chips. Because such chips readily free themselves from the tool or the machine, the alloys of group 1 are well suited to rapid machining.

Typical chips produced in machining group 2 alloys are a fairly open coil or a closely wound helix. These chips are relatively brittle, and a little more distortion will break them into separate fragments.

A typical chip from a group 3 alloy is long and continuous, and it is often tightly curled. Because it is strong and tough, such a chip will withstand considerable distortion without breaking, even to the extent of bending back flat.

Casting Alloys. Machinability ratings for copper casting alloys (Table 2) follow the same general pattern as for wrought alloys. Group 1 includes only those alloys containing lead, either as an alloying element or specifically for the purpose of improving machinability. As in wrought alloys, the lead additions facilitate chip breakage, thus making possible high machining speeds, good tool life, and good finish.

Alloys in group 2 contain secondary phases that are harder or more brittle than the matrix. In the machining of such alloys, short chips are produced. The silicon bronzes, several aluminum bronzes, and the high-tin alloys belong to this group.

Microstructure of the manganese bronzes would place them in group 2, but they produce a long spiral chip, smooth on both sides, which does not break. Some aluminum bronzes, on the other hand, produce a long spiral chip that is rough on the underside and breaks, thus acting like a short chip cut from an alloy in group 1.

Group 3, most difficult to machine, is composed mainly of the high-strength manganese and aluminum bronzes that are high in iron or nickel content.

Variation Within Machinability Groups

Marked effects on machinability are imparted by variations in structure and chemical composition within each of the three machinability groups of copper alloys. Furthermore, in a production machining operation, two alloys from the same group may differ considerably more in practice than is implied by the difference in their nominal machinability ratings. For instance, in the example that follows, free-cutting brass (alloy 360) was machined with a production rate and tool life 67% better than leaded copper, although these two group 1 alloys differ by only 20% in nominal machinability in Table 1.

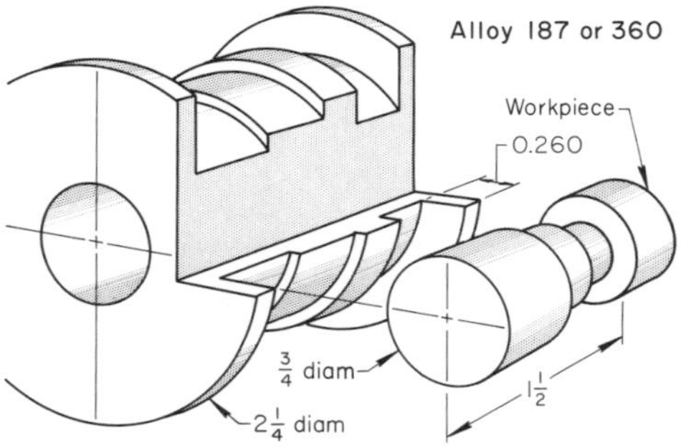

Condition or result(a)	Alloy 187(b)	Alloy 360(c)
Speed, rpm	1528	3300
Speed, sfm	300	650
Feed, ipr	0.001	0.0025
Cutting oil	Lt. mineral	Soluble
Setup time	5 hr	3.5 hr
Cycle time, sec:		
Handling	10	10
Machining	10	2
Production per hr, pcs	135	225
Tool life per grind, pcs	1080	1800

(a) Form tools were of T1 high speed steel, top rake 5° for leaded copper and 0° for alloy 360. Downtime for tool changes was 20 min. Cuts were to a maximum depth of 0.260 in., with tolerances of ±0.002 in. on significant dimensions and a maximum surface roughness of 50 micro-in. (b) Full hard temper, 51,000 psi tensile strength. (c) Half hard, 60,000 psi.

Fig. 1. Comparison of turning of alloy 187 and alloy 360 with a circular form tool (Example 932)

Example 932. Alloy 187 vs Alloy 360 (Fig. 1)

The part shown in Fig. 1 was produced in an engine lathe with a circular form tool of T1 high speed steel. The same part was machined from alloy 187 (leaded copper) and from alloy 360 (free-cutting brass) rod ¾ in. in diameter. As shown in the table with Fig. 1, the production rate and tool life with alloy 360 were 67% greater than with alloy 187.

Effects of copper content (from about 58 to 62%) on the machinability of free-cutting (3.25% Pb) alpha-beta alloys in drilling, sawing and milling tests are shown in the three lower curves of Fig. 2. The upper curve, plotted from ratings of two alpha-beta alloys from Table 1, indicates qualitative agreement with the tests on the other four leaded alloys in the same range of copper content.

The lack of precision in machinability ratings is shown by the variations among the three processes in Fig. 2.

In machining characteristics, most alloys of group 2 are closer to group 3 than to group 1. Leaded silicon bronze and nonleaded aluminum-silicon bronze (both rated 60) are exceptions.

Although all alloys in group 3 have the same nominal machinability rating of 20, they may differ considerably in production machining. For instance, tough pitch and other oxygen-bearing coppers contain cuprous oxide as a finely dispersed phase that functions somewhat like the lead particles in group 1 alloys, although to a much lesser degree. Because of this microstructural characteristic, the tough pitch coppers are better in machinability, type of chip, and surface finish than oxygen-free coppers.

Effect of Alloying Elements on Machinability

As indicated in the following paragraphs, machinability is improved by lead, sulfur, tellurium and zinc and deteriorates when tin and iron are used as alloying elements.

Lead. The function of lead in wrought copper alloys is to improve machinability by increasing the brittleness of the alloy, causing chips to break off readily and in short curls rather than in long stringers. Lead does not dissolve in copper alloys but is finely dispersed throughout the alloy matrix. It acts as a lubricant for the cutting tool and thus reduces tool wear. Although less tool pressure is

*H. J. HOLMES, *Chairman,* formerly Vice President – Engineering, Mueller Brass Co.; J. H. BAUER, Chief Metallurgist, Research and Engineering Dept., American-Standard Plumbing and Heating Div., American Radiator & Standard Sanitary Corp; R. R. CARNAHAN [retired], formerly Manager of Manufacturing Engineering, Mueller Brass Co.

L. V. COLWELL, Dept. of Mechanical Engineering, University of Michigan; A. H. COPELAND, Technical Advisor, Michigan Div., Revere Copper and Brass, Inc.; LOUIS SANTAGATA, Manager of Production, Budd Electronics Div., Budd Co., Inc.; EDWARD SHEPLER, formerly with Micro Switch Div., Honeywell Inc.; LEWIS E. THELIN, Manager of Technical Service, Bristol Brass Corp.; VINCENT P. WEAVER, Metallurgical Engineer, Research and Technical Center, Anaconda American Brass Co.; BERNARD A. WOODS, JR., President, Lawrenceville Screw Co.; J. H. ZALES [deceased], formerly Manufacturing Engineer, Imperial Eastman Corp.

necessary and an increase in brittleness accompanies *any* lead addition, chips are extremely short and brittle only when at least 2% lead is present in the alloy.

Figure 3 shows machinability as a function of lead content for brasses containing 62 to 65% copper; machinability improves rapidly at first, but the rate of improvement drops off rapidly to practically nothing at 3.25% lead. An increase in lead content beyond 3.25% is seldom advantageous. The use of less than 1% lead is common. For instance, the addition of 0.70% lead to naval brass increased machining rate by 50% in the following example.

Example 933. Low-Leaded vs Nonleaded Naval Brass (Alloy 464) (Table 3)

In producing a gear blank (see the inset view in Table 3) in a six-spindle automatic bar machine, a change in work metal from alloy 464 rod in the half-hard temper to naval brass rod containing 0.70% lead made increased speed and feed possible with a resulting 53% increase in production. Table 3 presents a comparison of machining conditions and results for the two alloys.

Sulfur and Tellurium. The effect of sulfur as an added element in copper is described in the following example.

Example 934. Effect of Sulfur in Alloy 122 Tubing on Machining Characteristics (Table 4)

In machining a reducing coupling (see illustration in Table 4) from tubing of alloy 122, congestion of stringy chips caused excessive downtime and a high rate of rejection for dimensional variations. Machining efficiency was consequently only 40%.

Efficiency was raised to 70% by changing to tubing containing 0.35% sulfur; the chip improvement from the sulfur addition eliminated the congestion. As a result, machining was within tolerance, and finish attained the required 35 to 45 micro-in. As shown by the comparison of machining data and results for the two materials in Table 4, the change also doubled production.

The effects of sulfur and tellurium on drilling of copper are compared in Fig. 4. The basis of appraisal was the number of turns of a drill under constant load required to penetrate 0.25 in. into the alloy indicated. For both elements, the number of turns dropped abruptly with small additions and then more gradually as increased amounts were added. There is no significant advantage in adding more than 0.5% of either of these elements.

Zinc. The hardness of alpha brass increases with addition of zinc up to the limit of alpha solubility, about 37% zinc. In lead-free brasses, increases in zinc content from 0 to 30% improve the machinability rating from 20 to 30.

Tin. Figure 5 shows the effect of tin content (up to 1.8%) in leaded commercial bronze (nominal composition: 89 copper, 9.25 zinc, 1.75 lead) in drilling, sawing and milling. The dashed curve shows the average effect of tin.

Iron. In drilling, sawing and milling tests, 1.6% iron in leaded commercial bronze was found to decrease machinability by about 10%.

Table 1. Compositions and Machinability Ratings of Wrought Copper and Copper Alloys

Alloy No.	Alloy name	Nominal composition, % Cu	Ni	Zn	Pb	Sn	Machinability(a)
	Group 1. Free-Cutting Alloys						
187	Leaded copper	99.00	....	....	1.00	....	80
145	Tellurium copper	99.40		(0.50 Te)			80
330	Low-leaded brass (tube)	66.00	....	33.50	0.50	....	60
335	Low-leaded brass	65.00	....	34.50	0.50	....	60
340	Medium-leaded brass	65.00	....	34.00	1.00	....	70
332	High-leaded brass (tube)	66.00	....	32.40	1.60	....	80
342	High-leaded brass	65.00	....	33.00	2.00	....	90
356	Extra-high-leaded brass	63.00	....	34.50	2.50	....	100
360	Free-cutting brass	61.50	....	35.50	3.00	....	100
365-368	Leaded Muntz metal	60.00	....	39.40	0.60	....	60
370	Free-cutting Muntz metal	60.00	....	39.00	1.00	....	70
377	Forging brass	59.00	....	39.00	2.00	....	80
485	Leaded naval brass	60.00	....	37.50	1.75	0.75	80
385	Architectural bronze	57.00	....	40.00	3.00	....	90
544	Free-cutting phosphor bronze	88.00	....	4.00	4.00	4.00	90
798	Leaded nickel silver, 10%	46.50	10.00	41.50	2.00	....	80
	Group 2. Moderately Machinable Alloys						
230	Red brass, 85%	85.00	....	15.00	...	....	30
240	Low brass, 80%	80.00	....	20.00	...	....	30
260	Cartridge brass, 70%	70.00	....	30.00	...	....	30
270	Yellow brass	65.00	....	35.00	...	....	30
280	Muntz metal	60.00	....	40.00	...	....	40
443-445	Inhibited admiralty	71.00	....	28.00	...	1.00	30
464	Naval brass	60.00	....	39.25	...	0.75	30
651	Low-silicon bronze, (B)	98.50	(1.50 Si)		...	....	30
655	High-silicon bronze, (A)	97.00	(3.00 Si)		...	....	30
675	Manganese bronze, (A)	58.50	(0.10 Mn)	39.00	(1.40 Fe)	1.00	30
534	Leaded phosphor bronze, 5% (B)	94.00	....	....	1.00	5.00	50
792	Leaded nickel silver, 12%	65.00	12.00	22.00	1.00	....	50
794	Leaded nickel silver, 18%	63.25	18.00	17.75	1.00	....	50
661	Leaded silicon bronze, (D)	95.60	(0.4 Pb, 1.5 Mn, 1.5 Zn, 3 Si)				60
639	Aluminum silicon bronze	91.00		(7.00 Al, 2.00 Si)			60
687	Aluminum brass	77.50	....	20.50	(2.00 Al)	....	30
	Group 3. Alloys Difficult to Machine						
110	Electrolytic tough pitch copper	99.90+	....	....	...	....	20
122	Phosphorus deoxidized copper	99.90+	(0.02 P)	....	...	....	20
102	Oxygen-free copper	99.95	....	....	...	....	20
113	Silver-bearing tough pitch copper	99.90	(8 oz Ag per ton)		...	....	20
114	Silver-bearing tough pitch copper	99.90	(10 oz Ag per ton)		...	....	20
116	Silver-bearing tough pitch copper	99.90	(25 oz Ag per ton)		...	....	20
182	Chromium copper	99.50	....	(0.80 Cr)	...	....	20
210	Gilding, 95%	95.00	....	5.00	...	....	20
220	Commercial bronze, 90%	90.00	....	10.00	...	....	20
226	Jewelry bronze, 87.5%	87.50	....	12.50	...	....	20
510	Phosphor bronze, 5% (A)	95.00	....	....	...	5.00	20
521	Phosphor bronze, 8% (C)	92.00	....	....	...	8.00	20
524	Phosphor bronze, 10% (D)	90.00	....	....	...	10.00	20
614	Aluminum bronze, (D)	91.00	(7.00 Al, 2.00 Fe)			....	20
628	Aluminum bronze, 10%	82.00	5.00	(1.00 Mn, 2.50 Fe, 9.50 Al)			20
706	Copper nickel, 10%	88.70	10.00	(1.30 Fe)	....	....	20
715	Copper nickel, 30%	70.00	30.00	....	....	....	20
745	Nickel silver, 65-10	65.00	10.00	25.00	....	....	20
752	Nickel silver, 65-18	65.00	18.00	17.00	....	....	20
754	Nickel silver, 65-15	65.00	15.00	20.00	....	....	20
757	Nickel silver, 65-12	65.00	12.00	23.00	....	....	20
770	Nickel silver, 55-18	55.00	18.00	27.00	....	....	20
...	Beryllium copper (not heat trtd)	97.60	0.35	(2.05 Be)	....	....	20

(a) Approximate relative machinability rating (free-cutting brass = 100)

Effect of Cold Work

The adverse effect of cold work on machinability of a typical free-cutting brass (62.3 copper, 3.5 lead, remainder zinc) is shown in Fig. 6. The 70% reduction by cold drawing that is indicated is well beyond the 25% maximum cold reduction normally given leaded brass bars of most sizes.

In drilling tests on a typical free-cutting brass rod, to determine the effect of cold work on machinability, the torque developed by a ¼-in. drill in penetrating alloys of four different tempers was recorded and is plotted in Fig. 7. The alloys were drilled to a depth of one inch under a wide range of axial loads. The lower curve shows torque to drill the low-strength rod to be about 50% of that to drill the high-strength rod, whereas the upper curve shows only about 15% difference caused by cold work; in all tests, the torque developed increased with the tensile strength of the alloy being drilled. In evaluating these drilling tests, it was concluded that high tool pressures and high cutting speeds could offset the effects of cold work.

Cutting Fluid

Some machining of copper alloys is done dry, but the use of a cutting fluid invariably increases the level of possible speed and feed, increases productivity, improves surface finish, enhances accuracy and lengthens tool life.

Unless otherwise noted, speeds and feeds shown in tables throughout this article are based on the use of water-soluble oil as cutting fluid. For most operations, water-soluble oil (20 parts water to 1 part oil) is adequate as an antiweld agent, especially for the group 1 alloys. When machining the alloys of groups 2 and 3 (more stringy chips) or when a very fine surface finish is required, results can be improved by using a light mineral oil, or mineral oil with 5 to 20% of lard oil. The higher content of lard oil is used for the alloys that produce extremely

Table 2. Compositions and Machinability Ratings of Copper Casting Alloys

Alloy name	Alloy No.(b)	Cu	Sn	Pb	Zn	Ni	Al	Others	Machinability(a)
		Nominal composition, %							
Group 1. Free-Cutting Alloys									
Leaded red brass	4A	85	5	5	5	....	....	....	90
Leaded red brass	4B	83	4	6	7	....	....	....	90
Leaded semi-red brass	5A	81	3	7	9	....	....	....	90
Leaded semi-red brass	5B	76	3	6	15	....	....	....	90
High-leaded tin bronze	3E	70	5	25	....	0.75 max	....	....	90
High-leaded tin bronze	3A	80	10	10	....	0.75 max	....	....	80
High-leaded tin bronze	3D	78	7	15	....	0.75 max	....	....	80
Leaded yellow brass .	6A	71	1	3	25	....	....	....	80
Leaded yellow brass .	6B	67	1	3	29	....	....	....	80
High-leaded tin bronze	33C	85	5	9	1	0.5 max	....	....	70
High-leaded tin bronze	3B	83	7	7	3	0.5 max	....	....	70
Leaded nickel brass .	10A	57	2	9	20	12.0	....	....	70
Group 2. Moderately Machinable Alloys									
Leaded tin bronze ..	2A	88	6	2	4	....	....	....	60
Leaded tin bronze ..	2B	87	8	1	4	....	....	....	60
Leaded high-strength manganese bronze .	7A	61	0.75	0.75	35.5	....	0.75	1.00 Fe, 0.25 Mn	60
Silicon-aluminum bronze	...	90	...	....	....	....	7.0	2.00 Si	50
Silicon-aluminum bronze	...	91	...	....	....	....	7.0	3.00 Si	50
Tin bronze	1A	88	10	0	2	....	....	0.35 P opt	50
Tin bronze	1B	88	8	0	4	....	....	....	50
Aluminum bronze ...	9B	89	...	....	....	....	10	1.00 Fe	35
High-strength manganese bronze .	8A	58	1 max	0.4 max	Rem	....	1.00	1.25 Fe, 1.5 Mn	30
High-strength manganese bronze .	8B	64	0.2 max	0.20 max	Rem	....	5.25	3.00 Fe, 3.75 Mn	30
Beryllium bronze	...	96.5	...	....	....	1.1	....	2.6 Be	20 to 40
Group 3. Alloys Difficult to Machine									
High-strength manganese bronze .	8C	64	0.2 max	0.20 max	Rem	....	7.5	3.00 Fe, 3.75 Mn	20
Aluminum bronze ..	9A	88	...	....	....	0	9	3.00 Fe	20
Aluminum bronze ..	9C	85	...	....	....	....	11	4.00 Fe	20
Aluminum bronze ..	9D	81	...	....	....	4	11	4.00 Fe	20

(a) Ratings are relative, based on free-cutting brass = 100. A material rated at 50 should be machined at roughly half the speed used for a material rated at 100, for equal tool life. (b) The alloy numbers refer to ASTM B143, B144, B145, B146, B147, B148, B149 and B198.

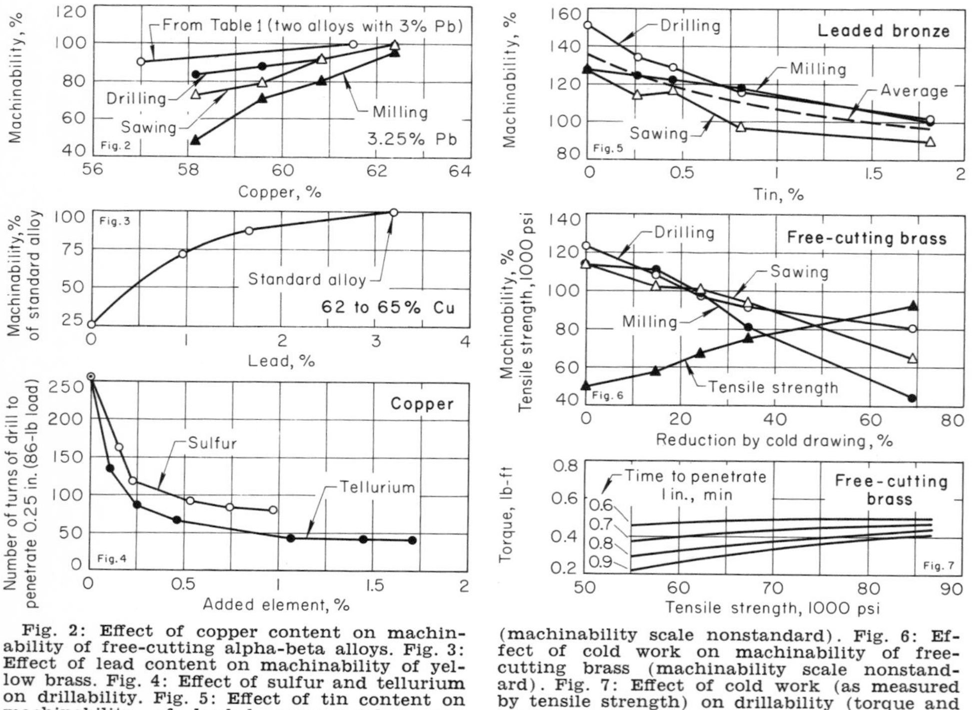

Fig. 2: Effect of copper content on machinability of free-cutting alpha-beta alloys. Fig. 3: Effect of lead content on machinability of yellow brass. Fig. 4: Effect of sulfur and tellurium on drillability. Fig. 5: Effect of tin content on machinability of leaded commercial bronze (machinability scale nonstandard). Fig. 6: Effect of cold work on machinability of free-cutting brass (machinability scale nonstandard). Fig. 7: Effect of cold work (as measured by tensile strength) on drillability (torque and time to penetrate) of free-cutting brass.

Fig. 2 to 7. Effect of variables on machinability

tough, stringy chips, or where finish is critical, as in cutting fine threads.

Sulfurized, chlorinated or sulfochlorinated oil is sometimes used as a cutting fluid, particularly for machining copper alloys that contain substantial amounts of nickel. When sulfurized or chlorinated oil is used for machining any copper alloy, the workpieces should be cleaned immediately after machining, to prevent staining. If the workpieces do become stained, the discoloration can be removed by immersing them for 20 min in a solution of 10% sodium cyanide in water.

Turning

Because of the wide variation in machining characteristics among the various coppers and copper alloys, tool design, as well as speed and feed, must be varied for best results.

Table 3. Effect of Lead on Machinability of Naval Brass (Example 933) (a)

Condition or result	Naval brass: Nonleaded	Naval brass: With 0.70% Pb
Spindle speed, rpm	848	1285
Surface speed, sfm (max) .	180	273
Feed, ipr (average):		
Cross-slide tools	0.0022	0.003
Main-slide tools	0.0039	0.0045
Machining time per pc, sec	11.5	7.5
Production per hour, pcs(b)	313	480

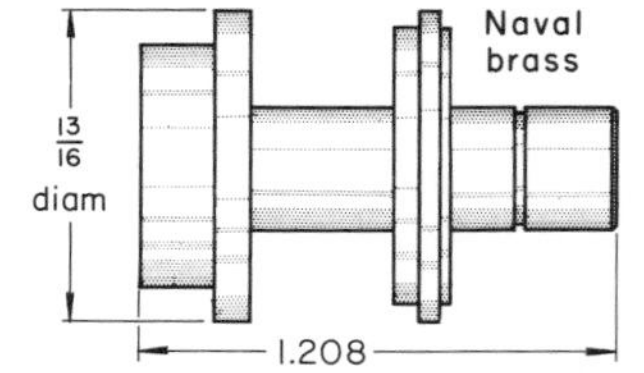

(a) Data are based on production of the gear blank shown above from rod stock in a six-spindle automatic bar machine. Nonleaded alloy (half hard temper) contained 60% copper, 39.25% zinc, 0.75% tin; leaded alloy contained 0.70% lead and 0.70% less zinc. (b) Gross.

Table 4. Effect of Sulfur on Machinability of Wrought Copper Tubing (Example 934) (a)

Condition or result	Type of copper tubing: Nonsulfurized(b)	Type of copper tubing: With 0.35% sulfur(c)
Speed, rpm	1928	1928
Speed, sfm (max)	189	189
Feed (average), ipr	0.0093	0.014(d)
Cycle time, sec	3.0	2.5
Gross production/hr, pcs	1200	1440
Efficiency	40%(e)	70%
Net production/hr, pcs...	480	1008

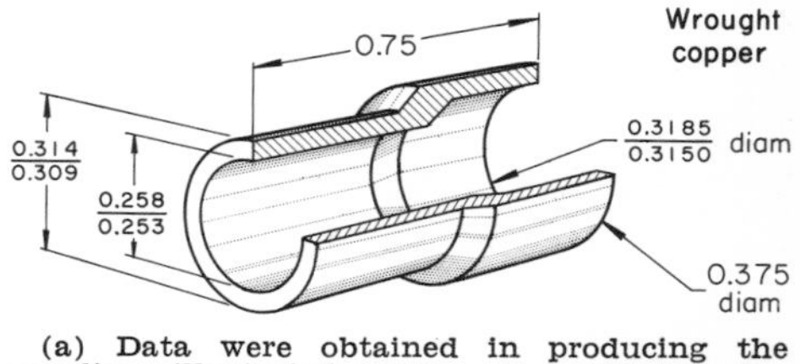

(a) Data were obtained in producing the coupling illustrated above, in a 9/16-in. six-spindle automatic bar machine, using carbide tools and a cutting fluid consisting of a 1-to-15 mixture of soluble oil and water. (b) Nominal composition: 99.90% min copper, 0.022% phosphorus. (c) Nominal composition: 99.63% copper, 0.35% sulfur, 0.02% phosphorus. (d) Estimated. (e) Low efficiency resulted from congestion of stringy chips formed by this material when machined, which caused excessive downtime and a high rate of rejection for dimensional inaccuracy.

Table 5. Design of Single-Point Tools for Turning Copper Alloys

Angle	Alloys machined: Group 1	Group 2	Group 3
High Speed Steel Tools			
Back rake	0°	5-10°	10-20°
Side rake	0-3°	5-10°	20-30°
End relief	6°	6-15°	10-15°
Side relief	0-5°	5-10°	10-20°
End cutting edge ...	8-15°	8-15°	8-15°
Side cutting edge ...	10-15°	10-15°	15°
Carbide Tools			
Back rake	0°	0-5°	4-8°
Side rake	2-6°	4-8°	15-25°
End relief	4-6°	4-8°	7-10°
Side relief	4-6°	4-8°	7-10°
End cutting edge ...	8-15°	8-15°	8-15°
Side cutting edge ...	10-15°	10-15°	10-15°

Table 6. Nominal Speeds for Turning Copper Alloys With Single-Point and Box Tools

Alloy group	Condition	Rockwell B hardness	Speed, sfm: HSS tools	Carbide tools: Brazed	Disposable
Rough Turning(a)					
1	Annealed	20-70	400	800	925
2	Annealed	20-70	275	550	625
3	Annealed	20-70	100	200	225
1	Cold drawn	60-100 ...	480	950	1100
2	Cold drawn	60-100 ...	300	600	680
3	Cold drawn	60-100 ...	115	225	250
Finish Turning(b)					
1	Annealed	20-70	480	960	1100
2	Annealed	20-70	350	700	800
3	Annealed	20-70	120	240	275
1	Cold drawn	60-100 ...	575	1125	1275
2	Cold drawn	60-100 ...	380	750	850
3	Cold drawn	60-100 ...	140	275	300

(a) Depth of cut, 0.150 in.; feed, 0.015 ipr. (b) Depth of cut, 0.025 in.; feed, 0.007 ipr. (SOURCE: Metcut Research Associates, Inc.)

Single-Point Turning. Zero to moderate rake angles are recommended for group 1 alloys, to reduce the probability that the tool will plow into the work. Rake angles are increased for turning alloys of groups 2 and 3, to provide a free flow of chips. Table 5 gives tool angles for turning copper alloys.

The speeds in Table 6 are intended as starting points in establishing procedures. In many instances, speeds can be increased with experience.

Form Turning. Both circular and dovetail form tools are used for turning copper and copper alloys; selection depends on the same factors that influence the choice in form turning of steel (see section on Form Tools on page 150, in the article on Multiple-Operation Machining). Form tools for turning copper alloys are shown in Fig. 8; speeds and feeds, in Table 7.

Cutoff tool designs for turning copper alloys are included in Fig. 8; feeds and speeds, in Table 8.

Tool Material. Both high speed steel and carbide are used as materials for tools to turn copper alloys. The use of carbide tools for facing a copper alloy ring, and a comparison of methods, is illustrated in the example that follows.

Example 935. Lathe vs Drill Press in Facing Forged Alloy 674 (Fig. 9)

Rings forged from alloy 674 (nominal composition: 57.50 copper, 2.75 manganese, 1.25 aluminum, 1.00 silicon, remainder zinc) were originally milled in a manually operated single-spindle drill press equipped with a special tool having two carbide bits, as shown in the left-hand view of Fig. 9. The production rate was 167 pieces per hour. Because tool

Table 7. Nominal Speeds and Feeds for Turning Copper Alloys With Form Tools

Alloy group	Condition(a)	Rockwell B hardness	Speed, sfm	Feed, ipr, for tool width, in., of: 0.500	1.000	2.000
High Speed Steel Tools						
1	Ann	20-70 ...	300	0.003	0.002	0.001
2	Ann	20-70 ...	205	0.002	0.002	0.001
3	Ann	20-70 ...	75	0.002	0.002	0.001
1	CD	60-100 ..	360	0.003	0.002	0.001
2	CD	60-100 ..	225	0.002	0.002	0.001
3	CD	60-100 ..	80	0.002	0.002	0.001
Carbide Tools						
1	Ann	20-70 ...	600	0.007	0.005	0.003
2	Ann	20-70 ...	410	0.007	0.005	0.003
3	Ann	20-70 ...	150	0.0025	0.0025	0.0015
1	CD	60-100 ..	700	0.007	0.005	0.003
2	CD	60-100 ..	450	0.007	0.005	0.003
3	CD	60-100 ..	170	0.0025	0.0025	0.0015

(a) Ann = Annealed; CD = Cold drawn. (SOURCE: same as for Table 6)

wear and breakage were excessive, and because chatter marks were produced on the machined surface, the operation was changed to an automatic lathe, as shown in the right-hand view of Fig. 9. A collet in the 5-in. spindle nose held the workpiece for facing with a carbide-tipped tool mounted in the rear cross slide. Tool wear decreased significantly, tool breakage was negligible, and no chatter marks were produced. In addition, production rate increased nearly 59%. Processing details are given in the table with Fig. 9.

Boring

Techniques used for boring of copper alloys do not differ greatly from those used for boring of ferrous metals (see article "Boring", page 20 in this volume). Recommended angles for high speed steel and carbide tools are: back rake, 0° to 10°; side rake, 5° to 20°; end relief, 8° to 13°; side relief, 5° to 8°; end cutting edge, 45°; side cutting edge, 45°. Table 9 lists speeds and feeds for boring of copper alloys.

Planing

Although planing is not used extensively on copper alloys, it may be preferred for some machining, such as on large workpieces, or when quantity requirements are too small to justify the cost of a milling cutter. Techniques for planing other metals are generally applicable to planing copper alloys (see the article "Planing", page 45). Tool angles for high speed steel and carbide planer tools are essentially the same as those for single-point turning (Table 5). Speeds for rough and finish planing of copper alloys are given in Table 10. For recommendations of speeds and feeds for planing hard and soft bronzes at depths of cut different from those in Table 10, see Table 1 on page 50.

Table 8. Nominal Speeds and Feeds for Turning Copper Alloys With Cutoff Tools

Alloy group	Condition(a)	Rockwell B hardness	Speed, sfm	Feed, ipr, for tool width, in., of: 0.062	0.125	0.250
High Speed Steel Tools						
1	Ann	20-70 ...	300	0.004	0.005	0.006
2	Ann	20-70 ...	205	0.004	0.005	0.006
3	Ann	20-70 ...	75	0.002	0.002	0.0035
1	CD	60-100 ..	360	0.004	0.005	0.006
2	CD	60-100 ..	225	0.004	0.005	0.006
3	CD	60-100 ..	80	0.002	0.002	0.0035
Carbide Tools						
1	Ann	20-70 ...	600	0.005	0.006	0.007
2	Ann	20-70 ...	410	0.005	0.006	0.007
3	Ann	20-70 ...	150	0.0025	0.0035	0.0045
1	CD	60-100 ..	700	0.005	0.006	0.007
2	CD	60-100 ..	450	0.005	0.006	0.007
3	CD	60-100 ..	170	0.0025	0.0035	0.0045

(a) Ann = Annealed; CD = Cold drawn. (SOURCE: same as for Table 6)

Table 9. Nominal Speeds and Feeds for Boring Copper Alloys

Alloy group	Condition(a)	Rockwell B hardness	Speed, sfm: HSS tools	Carbide tools	Feed, ipr: HSS tools	Carbide tools
Rough Boring(b)						
1	Ann	20-70 ...	360	720	0.015	0.020
2	Ann	20-70 ...	250	500	0.010	0.015
3	Ann	20-70 ...	90	180	0.008	0.010
1	CD	60-100 ..	440	855	0.015	0.020
2	CD	60-100 ..	270	540	0.010	0.015
3	CD	60-100 ..	105	205	0.008	0.010
Finish Boring(c)						
1	Ann	20-70 ...	400	800	0.008	0.010
2	Ann	20-70 ...	275	550	0.006	0.008
3	Ann	20-70 ...	100	200	0.005	0.007
1	CD	60-100 ..	480	950	0.008	0.010
2	CD	60-100 ..	300	600	0.006	0.008
3	CD	60-100 ..	115	225	0.005	0.007

(a) Ann = Annealed; CD = Cold drawn. (b) Depth of cut, 0.100 in. (c) Depth of cut, 0.010 in. (SOURCE: same as for Table 6)

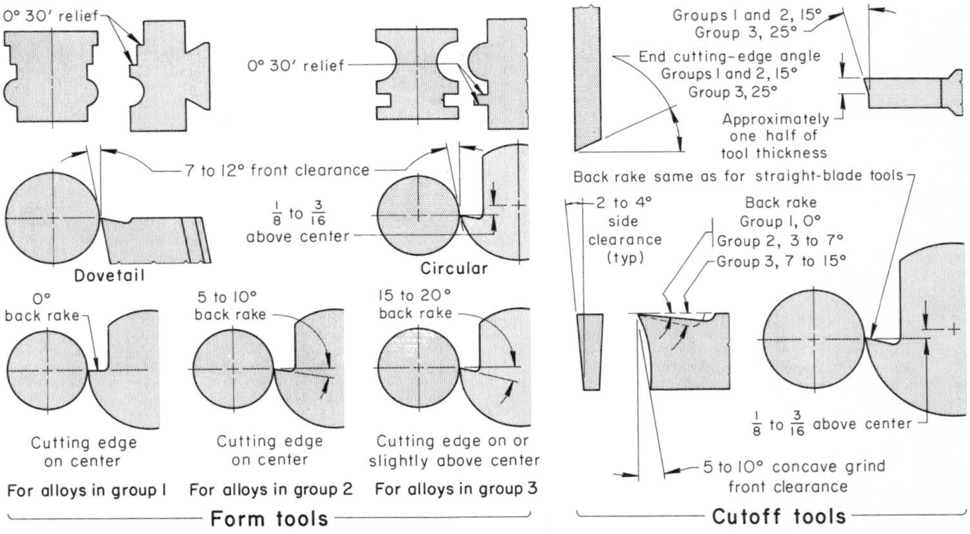

Fig. 8. Design of form and cutoff tools for turning copper and copper alloys

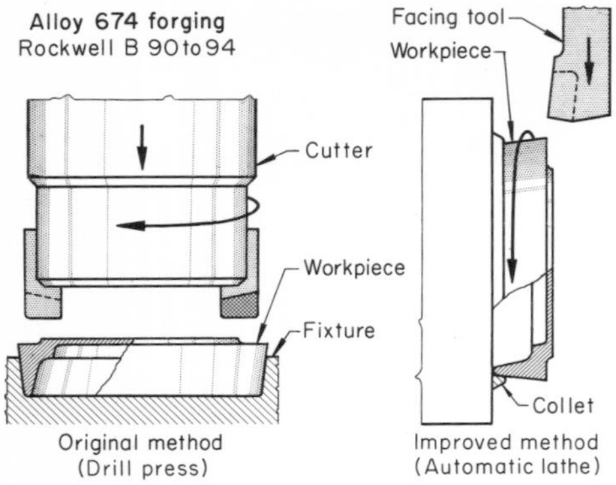

Condition or result(a)	Drill press	Automatic lathe
Spindle speed, rpm	....	1951
Quill speed, rpm	675	....
Infeed, ipr	....	0.015
Downfeed, ipr	0.008	....
Production rate, pieces/hr	167	265

(a) In both machines, carbide-tipped tools were used, depth of cut was 0.130 in. (tolerance, 0.010 in.), and a 125-micro-in. surface roughness was produced.

Fig. 9. Milling (left) replaced by facing (right) for removing web section and excess stock from a forged ring (Example 935)

Broaching

Internal broaching has been used to cut narrow grooves in copper electrical fittings and to cut square and hexagonal shapes for valve and plumbing fittings. (See also Examples 140 and 145, in the article "Broaching".) External broaching has been used in the manufacture of electric breaker arms. Sometimes broaching is one of a sequence of operations (see Example 958 in this article). Face and clearance angles for broaching copper alloys are given in Table 11; speeds, in Table 12.

Drilling

For drilling copper alloys of groups 1 and 2 the included angle of the drill point is 118°, with 12° to 15° lip clearance (Fig. 10). For group 3 alloys, the included angle is 100° to 110° (for pure copper, smaller angles are sometimes used), and the lip clearance is 12° to 20°. Flat and straight-flute drills with no rake angle are sometimes used for the free-machining alloys in group 1, but a slow spiral drill with a helix angle of 10° to 22° is preferred for deep-hole drilling of alloys in groups 1 and 2. For drilling group 3 alloys, drills with a greater helix angle (usually about 40°) are generally preferred. The greater angle is helpful in removing chips from deep holes. When drilling the group 3 alloys, it is sometimes helpful to notch the cutting edge, which splits the chips. Polished flutes are recommended for drilling copper and other tough group 3 alloys.

One application for which drills with a high helix angle (fast spiral) were appropriate is described in the example that follows.

Example 936. High-Helix Drills for Thin-Wall Blind Holes (Fig. 11)

In the part shown in Fig. 11, three small holes were required so close to the large center hole that there was danger of distorting the thin wall between them. A practice was developed that prevented bulging of the thin wall (0.033 in.) into the center hole. The pieces (alloy 510, hard temper) were drilled in a high-speed drill press. A chromium-plated high-helix drill of high speed steel was used at uniform feed for rapid and uninterrupted withdrawal of chips from the blind holes; drill deflection was slight, and hole size was maintained to the close tolerance specified (±0.001 in.). Pieces were submerged in a light mineral oil during drilling.

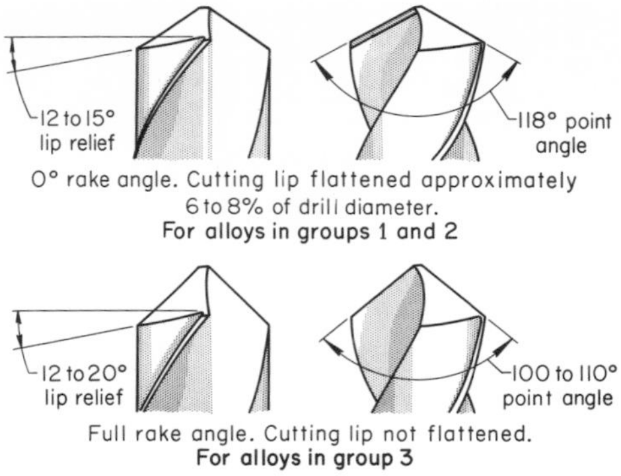

Fig. 10. Drill point and clearance angles for twist drills

Nominal speeds and feeds for drilling the three groups of copper alloys are given in Tables 13 and 14.

Type of machine or method of fixturing can contribute markedly to drilling efficiency. Mainly because of the shapes and sizes of workpieces commonly made from copper alloys, machines capable of performing several operations consecutively or simultaneously are often used. In the following examples, automatic machines did more operations, and faster, than would have been possible with manual machines.

Table 10. Nominal Speeds for Planing Copper Alloys

Alloy group	Condition	Rockwell B hardness	Speed, sfm HSS tools	Speed, sfm Carbide tools
Rough Planing(a)				
1	Annealed	20-70	180	300
2	Annealed	20-70	120	300
3	Annealed	20-70	50	250
1	Cold drawn	60-100	200	300
2	Cold drawn	60-100	130	300
3	Cold drawn	60-100	60	250
Finish Planing(b)				
1	Annealed	20-70	220	300
2	Annealed	20-70	160	300
3	Annealed	20-70	70	250
1	Cold drawn	60-100	270	300
2	Cold drawn	60-100	170	300
3	Cold drawn	60-100	75	250

(a) Depth of cut, 0.500-in.; feed, 0.060-in. per stroke. (b) Depth of cut, 0.010-in.; feed, ¾ the width of square-nose finishing tool. (Data are adapted from tables compiled by Metcut Research Associates, Inc.)

Table 11. Tool Angles for Broaching Copper Alloys

Alloy group	Face angle	Clearance angle
1	−5° to 5°	1° to 2°
2	0° to 10°	1° to 2°
3	10° to 15°	2° to 3°

Table 12. Nominal Speeds and Chip Loads for Broaching Copper Alloys With High Speed Steel Tools

Alloy group	Speed, sfm	Chip load, ipt
1	30	0.005
2	30	0.005
3	25	0.004

Example 937. Longitudinal and Cross Drilling in an Automatic Bar Machine (Table 15)

T1 high speed steel tools in a single-spindle automatic bar machine were used for machining lock tumblers (see sketch in Table 15) of alloy 360 rod, cold drawn to ¾-in. diameter (half-hard temper). Longitudinal drilling (⅜-in.-diam drill), cross drilling of three pairs of radially opposed holes (⅛-in.-diam drill) and cutoff operations were performed in sequence under conditions listed in Table 15.

Example 938. Manual vs Power Feed (Fig. 12)

A manually fed spindle on a bench drill press was originally used for drilling two flange holes 0.208/0.202 in. in diameter and 0.093 in. deep in the fuse head shown on the right in Fig. 12. The piece was made of alloy 360 (free-cutting brass) rod, half hard. In the original method, one hole was drilled and then the eccentric fixture holding the piece was moved to align the second hole for drilling. The production rate (252 pieces per hour) was too slow, and drill wear and breakage were excessive.

The operation was moved to a machine with two power-fed spindles and a rotating index table containing eight nests for holding pieces, as shown in the setup on the left in Fig. 12. A spring-loaded plate held pieces firmly for simultaneous drilling of the two holes. On completion of the machining cycle, the rotating table indexed and the completed pieces were stripped from the nests by a knockout.

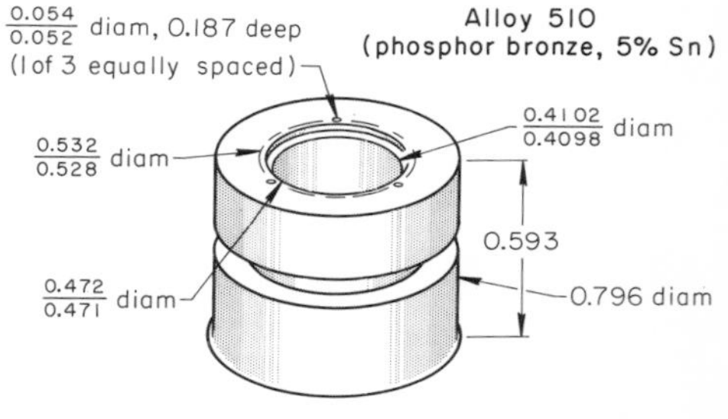

Fig. 11. Part in which thin-wall holes were drilled with a high-helix drill (Example 936)

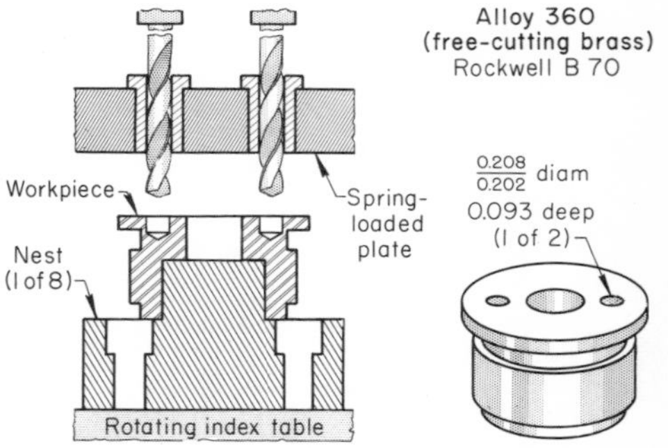

Machine	.........................Drill press(a)
Drill:	
Type	......Twist drill, straight shank, 0° rake
Diameter, in.	........................13/64 (std)
Number of flutes	2
Material	......................High speed steel
Operating Conditions	
Speed	......................5100 rpm (270 sfm)
Feed	................................0.005 ipr
Cutting fluid	..............................None
Tolerance on hole depth	............±0.005 in.
Finish obtained	..................125 micro-in.
Setup time	.................................4 hr
Downtime for tool change	..............10 min

(a) Power-fed, two-spindle drill press with ¾-hp motor and rotating index table.

Fig. 12. Automatic two-spindle drilling of two blind holes (Example 938)

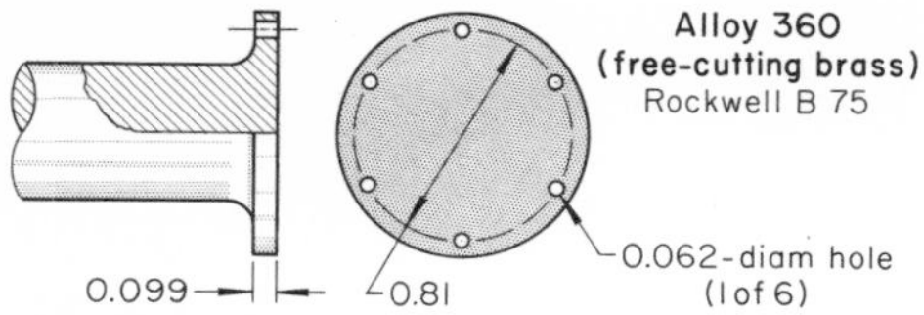

Fig. 13. Brake cylinder piston in which six through holes were drilled (Example 939)

With the improved method, tool life was extended and the production rate increased to 600 pieces per hour. Operating conditions for the index machine and results of the two methods are given with Fig. 12.

Example 939. Manual vs Automatic Feed and Indexing (Fig. 13)

Originally, six equally spaced through holes in the alloy 360 part shown in Fig. 13 were drilled in a bench hand drill press equipped with standard 1/16-in. twist drills. Three holes at a time were drilled, using manual feed, and the drill fixture was manually indexed for drilling the next three holes. Drill breakage was excessive because of varying feed and poor drill alignment — indexing the fixture required withdrawing the drills from the drill bushings. The production rate was 297 pieces per hour.

The drilling was transferred from manual control to a self-indexing machine with two drill heads and cam-controlled feed. Drills remained in the drill bushings when withdrawn from the workpiece. Drill breakage was significantly reduced and the production rate increased to 370 pieces per hour. The drills were run at a speed of 2810 rpm (46 sfm) and feed of 0.001 ipr; no cutting fluid was used.

Reaming

Reamers for finishing holes in copper alloy parts should have a right-hand spiral with positive-rake flutes. Polished cutting edges produce best results, especially on alloys that machine with stringy chips. Reamers with inserted carbide blades are best for copper alloys, but they cost more than high speed steel reamers, particularly in the smaller sizes, and therefore are usually used only in mass production. Reamer design is often altered to improve results as in the example that follows:

Example 940. Revised Reamer Design to Meet Close Tolerances (Fig. 14)

Close tolerance (±0.0005 in.) was specified on the diameter of the flat-bottomed blind hole reamed to 0.786/0.776-in. depth in the alloy 377 forging shown at the top of Fig. 14. Parts were rejected because the eight-flute reamer (lower left of Fig. 14) originally used was forced off center in bottoming out, causing out-of-roundness at the base of the hole.

Changing to a single-flute reamer (lower right of Fig. 14), and incorporating two wear strips to prevent the tool from being forced off center when bottoming out, resulted in parts meeting required tolerance. Both reamers had carbide cutting edges, and the same speed and feed were used (120 sfm and 0.005 ipr, respectively).

Nominal speeds and feeds for reaming copper alloys are given in Table 16.

Roller Burnishing

Bores in copper alloys are especially well suited to finishing by roller burnishing or simultaneous roller burnishing and peening, because copper alloys have low hardness and high ductility. See the article "Roller Burnishing", on page 105. Example 217 in that article describes finishing of bores of small copper alloy parts by roller peen burnishing in an automatic bar machine.

Table 13. Nominal Speeds and Feeds for Drilling Copper Alloys With High Speed Steel Tools

Alloy group	Speed, sfm: Annealed (a)	Speed, sfm: Cold drawn(b)	Feed, ipr, for nominal diameter, in., of: 0.062	0.125	0.250	0.500	0.750	1.000	1.500	2.000
1	140	140	0.001	0.003	....	....	....	....	....	....
	175	200	....	....	0.004	0.008	0.012	0.018	0.020	0.022
2	100	120	0.001	....	....	....	....	....	....	....
	120	140	....	0.003	0.006	0.010	0.010	0.015	0.015	0.020
3	50	60	0.001	....	....	....	....	....	....	....
	60	75	....	0.003	0.004	0.008	0.010	0.012	0.015	0.020

(a) Rockwell B 20 to 70. (b) Rockwell B 60 to 100. (SOURCE: same as for Table 10)

Table 14. Nominal Speeds for Gun Drilling Copper Alloys With Carbide Tools

Alloy group	Speed, sfm	Feed, ipr, for nominal diameter, in., of: Under 0.250	0.250 to 0.500	0.500 to 0.750	0.750 to 1.000	1.000 to 2.000
1	600	0.0010	0.003	0.005	0.008	0.010
2	500	0.0005	0.001	0.003	0.005	0.008
3	350	0.0005	0.001	0.003	0.005	0.008

Table 15. Details of Drilling and Cutoff Operations on an Alloy 360 Lock Tumbler (Example 937)

Condition	Drilling 3/8-in. diam	Drilling 1/8-in. diam	Cutting off
Speed, rpm	6000	3000	3300
Speed, sfm	589	98	649 max
Feed, ipr	0.005	0.005	0.005
Depth, in.	1.50	0.75	0.1875
Cycle time, min	0.05	<0.05	0.02

Conditions Common to All Operations

Tool material	T1 high speed steel
Cutting fluid	Soluble-oil emulsion
Finish	50 micro-in.
Setup time	16 hr
Downtime for tool change	20 min
Production rate per hour	378 pieces
Tool life per grind	3024 pieces

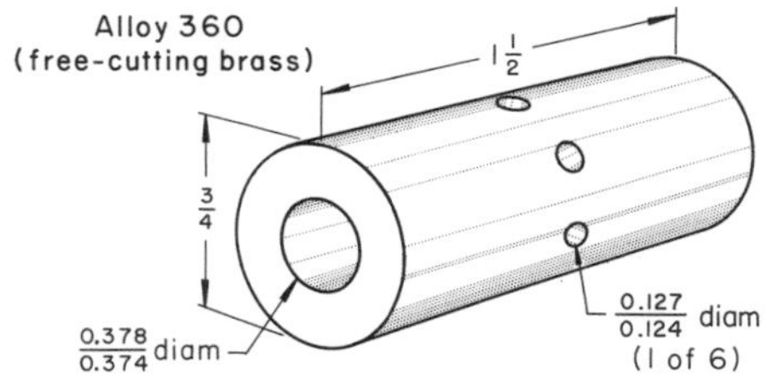

Tapping and Threading

Equipment, tools and techniques used for cutting internal and external threads in copper alloys are not greatly different from those used for ferrous metals (see the articles "Tapping" and "Die Threading", on pages 107 to 127).

Straight, four-flute taps with a rake angle of 3° to 6°, chamfer relief angle of 10°, and chamfer angles of 5° on taper taps, 15° on plug taps, and 30° on bottom taps are recommended for tapping copper alloys of group 1. For tapping alloys of groups 2 and 3, spiral-pointed taps with two or three flutes are preferred. Taps for group 2 should have rake angles of 9° to 12°, and for group 3 rake angles should be 15° to 18°. For tapping alloys of both groups 2 and 3, taps should have chamfer relief angles of 12°, with chamfer angles of 15° on plug taps and 30° on bottom taps.

General-purpose grades of high speed steel such as M1, M7 and M10 are used for taps for copper alloys. The more highly alloyed grades of high speed steel are rarely justified. However, nitriding or chromium plating of taps is often advantageous, especially for tapping the alloys of groups 2 and 3. One application in which surface-treated taps made higher speeds possible is described in the next example.

Example 941. Untreated vs Nitrided and Chromium-Plated Taps (Table 17)

In tapping the 5/8–11 UNC–2B threads in the alloy 637 (aluminum bronze) connector sleeve illustrated in Table 17, production rate was increased almost 40% when taps that had been nitrided and flash chromium plated were substituted for untreated taps. This increase was caused mainly by the higher speed at which the surface-treated taps could be operated (900 rpm, as compared with 575 rpm for the untreated taps).

The sleeves were tapped in a vertical drill press, under the conditions given in Table 17. The operator inserted the square shank end of the tap into the rotating tap driver and held the tap until it started threading the workpiece, which was held in an air-operated chuck. As the tap pulled itself through, the operator applied enough pressure to the handle to keep the tap driver engaged. The operator then retracted the tap driver, opened the chuck, and removed the workpiece over the shank end of the tap.

Tapping Speed. Conservative speeds used for tapping copper alloys are: 85 to 100 sfm for group 1 alloys, 60 to 75 sfm for group 2 alloys, and 40 to 50 sfm for group 3 alloys. However, higher speeds are often used successfully. For instance, in the preceding Example 941, speeds of 94 and 147 sfm were used for tapping a group 3 alloy. Pitch of

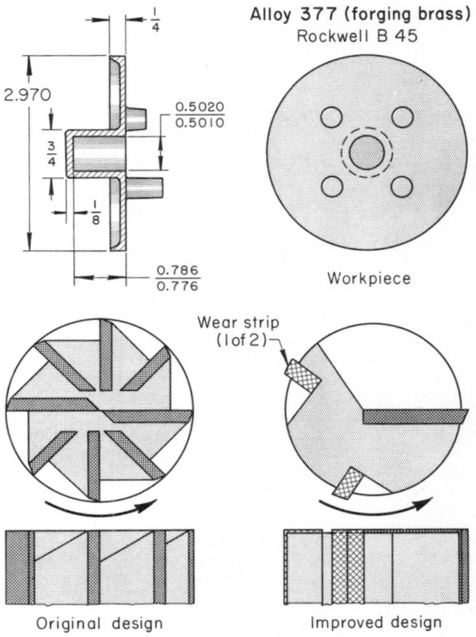

Fig. 14. Change from eight-flute reamer (bottom left) to single-flute reamer with wear strips (bottom right) eliminated out-of-roundness in reaming the blind hole in the forging shown at top (Example 940)

Table 16. Nominal Speeds and Feeds for Reaming Copper Alloys With Six-Flute Reamers

Alloy group	Speed, sfm: Annealed(a) HSS	Annealed(a) Carbide	Cold drawn(b) HSS	Cold drawn(b) Carbide	Feed, ipr, for nominal diameter, in., of: 0.125	0.250	0.500	1.000	1.500	2.000
1	160	320	180	360	0.003	0.006	0.009	0.012	0.015	0.020
2	110	250	120	275	0.003	0.006	0.009	0.012	0.015	0.020
3	50	180	60	200	0.003	0.005	0.007	0.010	0.012	0.015

(a) Rockwell B 20 to 70. (b) Rockwell B 60 to 100. (SOURCE: same as for Table 10)

Table 17. Untreated vs Nitrided and Chromium-Plated Taps (Example 941) (a)

Condition or result(b)	Untreated taps	Treated taps
Spindle speed, rpm	575	900
Surface speed, sfm	94	147
Production per hour, pieces	180	250
Tap life per grind, pieces	...	1000

Tap Details

Type ....Straight-shank plug, modified(c)
Size 5/8–11 UNC–2B (GH6)
Number of flutes 4
Rake angle ....Negative, 0° to 5°
Over-all length ....8 3/8 in.
Perfect-thread length ....1 5/8 in.
Material ....High speed steel

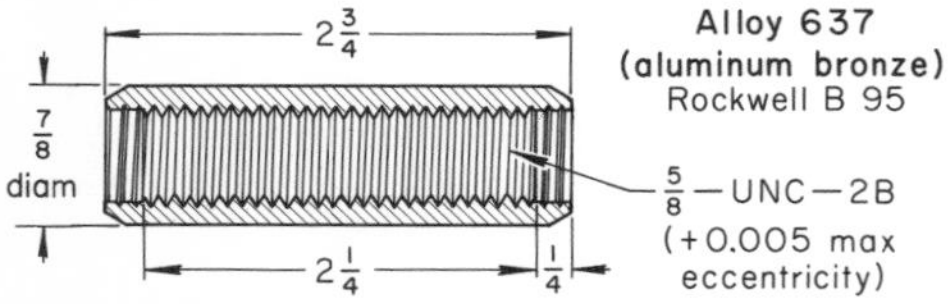

(a) Data were obtained in tapping the connector sleeve shown above, in a vertical drill press. (b) For both taps, feed was established by tap lead, with hand pressure applied only to maintain engagement of tap driver, and sulfochlorinated oil was used as cutting fluid. (c) End was chamfered 45° from a 5/32-in. diameter (to assure concentricity of first thread), beyond which point the tap had conventional plug chamfer (see Fig. 3, page 109).

thread, depth of hole, and type of cutting fluid all influence the selection of speed. Speed can usually be increased as thread pitch becomes finer.

The foregoing recommendations are based on the use of water-soluble oil as cutting fluid. Mineral oil with lard oil additions will usually improve efficiency and thread quality in either tapping or die threading.

Difficulty in disposing of chips when blind holes are being tapped is not unique to copper alloys, but because copper alloys produce soft chips, they are likely to pack in blind holes. The example that follows describes a change in procedure to eliminate a chip-disposal problem by converting blind holes into through holes.

Example 942. Blind Hole Tapping Eliminated by Change in Procedure (Fig. 15)

The use of an air-operated clamp (Fig. 15, right) for holding alloy 360 insert nuts enabled the tapping of 50 through holes per minute in a horizontal automatic tapping machine using a tapping speed of 68 sfm. Originally, the 3–48 UNC–2B threads were tapped before cutoff in an automatic bar machine, but drill chips in the long blind holes caused damage to the taps and the workpieces. By cutting off untapped blanks after drilling and transferring them to the hopper-fed automatic machine for tapping, the difficulty was avoided.

Cold form tapping is often more successful for copper alloys than for ferrous metals, because copper alloys are softer and more ductile. (For details of this process see page 118, in the article "Tapping".) The example that follows describes an application for which the cold form method resulted in better efficiency in tapping blind holes.

Example 943. Blind Hole Tapped by Cold Forming (Table 18)

A fluteless tap in a single-spindle automatic lathe was used for high-production cold forming of 5–40 UNC–2B threads in the blind hole in one end of the alloy 510 (phosphor bronze) mounting stud shown in Table 18. In previous runs using regular taps, downtime for tool changes averaged six minutes per 100 pieces and, in a secondary process, cleaning of chips from the holes required 15 minutes per 100 pieces. With the conditions given in Table 18, use of the fluteless tap resulted in a saving of 35 hr in a production run of 10,000 pieces.

Machines for Tapping. When volume requirements are high, as they are for many copper alloy parts for the plumbing goods and electrical industries, some type of automatic machine is often used for tapping. Examples 944 to 947, which follow, compare efficiency of a manual turret lathe and a single-spindle automatic machine for tapping small parts.

Examples 944 to 947. Manual Turret Lathe vs Single-Spindle Automatic for Tapping or Die Threading (Table 19)

Table 19 compares tooling and setup costs and production rates in the use of a manual turret lathe and a single-spindle automatic bar machine for tapping or die threading of four different plumbing parts. Three of these parts — a supply-pipe coupling (Example 944), a washer seat (Example 945), and a regulating screw (Example 946) — were machined from alloy 360 (free-cutting brass) rod in half-hard temper. The fourth part — a nipple (Example 947) — was produced from alloy 330 (low-leaded brass) seamless tubing.

The approximate production-quantity break point for more economical use of one machine rather than the other was 1000 for the parts in Examples 944, 945 and 946; for the nipples (Example 947) the production-quantity break point was 2000 pieces.

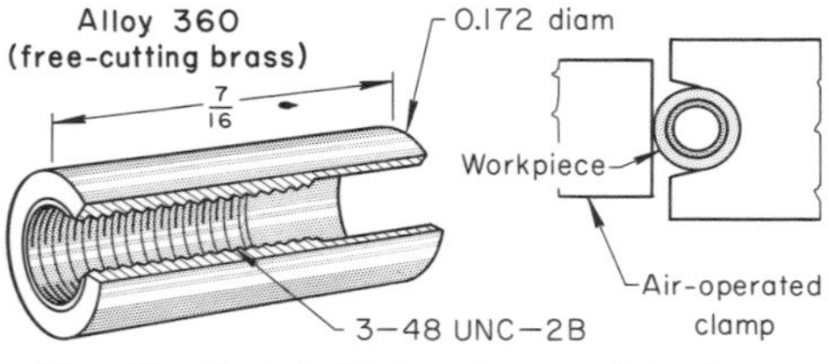

Fig. 15. Part held in air-operated clamp for horizontal tapping in an automatic tapping machine (Example 942)

Table 18. Cold Form Tapping a Blind Hole (Example 943)

Machine ......Single-spindle automatic lathe
Tool ....Fluteless tap, 0.125-in. diam
Speed ....3770 rpm (123 sfm)
Cutting fluid ....Light mineral oil
Setup time ....2 hr
Cycle time ....6.5 sec per piece
Production rate ....500 pieces per hour
Tool life ....(a)
Time saved:
Cleaning chips ....25 hr/10,000 pieces
Tool change downtime ..10 hr/10,000 pieces

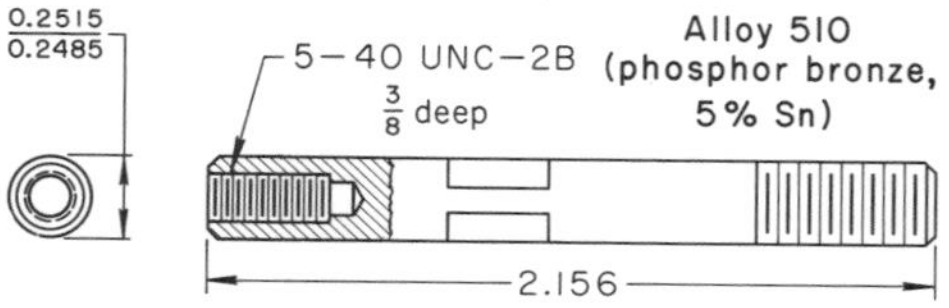

(a) Because data are for 10,000 pieces, tool life was not determined to point of failure or regrind; the tap used maintained thread size, quality and concentricity with outside diameter within 0.003 in., as specified, through the entire production run.

Threading With Dies. When threading copper alloys of group 1 with tangential chasers, the rake angle should be 0° to 10° (positive). For threading alloys of group 2 the rake angle should be increased to 20° to 25°, and for threading commercially pure copper or other alloys of group 3 the rake angle should be 30° to 35° for tangential chasers. On circular chasers, face angles of 1½° to 2° are satisfactory for threading alloys of all three groups. The hook angle on circular chasers should be about zero for threading the alloys of group 1 (up to 5° negative for free-cutting brass) and 15° to 20° positive for threading alloys of groups 2 and 3.

Soluble oil is often used as the cutting fluid for die threading, although low-viscosity mineral oil or mineral oil with an addition of about 10% lard oil will usually give better finish and tool

Table 19. Manual Turret Lathe vs Single-Spindle Automatic for Tapping or Die Threading (Examples 944 to 947)

Item	Manual turret lathe	Single-spindle automatic
TAPPING		
Example 944 — Pipe Coupling (Alloy 360)		
Tool cost per set	$525	$600
Pieces machined per setup	1000	25,000
Setup cost per 1000 pieces(a)	$2.57	$0.34
Production per hour, pieces	111	476
Example 945 — Washer Seat (Alloy 360)		
Tool cost per set	$350	$400
Pieces machined per setup	850	6500
Setup cost per 1000 pieces(a)	$3.02	$1.31
Production per hour, pieces	156	400
DIE THREADING		
Example 946 — Regulating Screw (Alloy 360)		
Tool cost per set	$600	$650
Pieces machined per setup	850	6500
Setup cost per 1000 pieces(a)	$3.02	$1.31
Production per hour, pieces	144	400
Example 947 — Nipple (Alloy 330)		
Tool cost per set	$400	$500
Pieces machined per setup	1000	10,000
Setup cost per 1000 pieces(a)	$2.57	$0.86
Production per hour, pieces	252	599

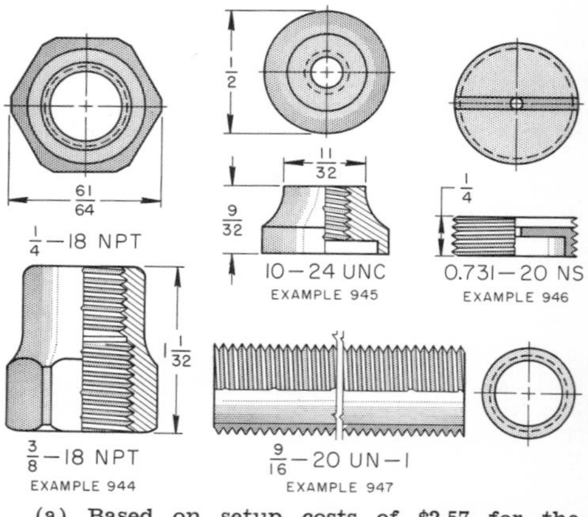

(a) Based on setup costs of $2.57 for the manual turret lathe and of $8.55 for the single-spindle automatic machine.

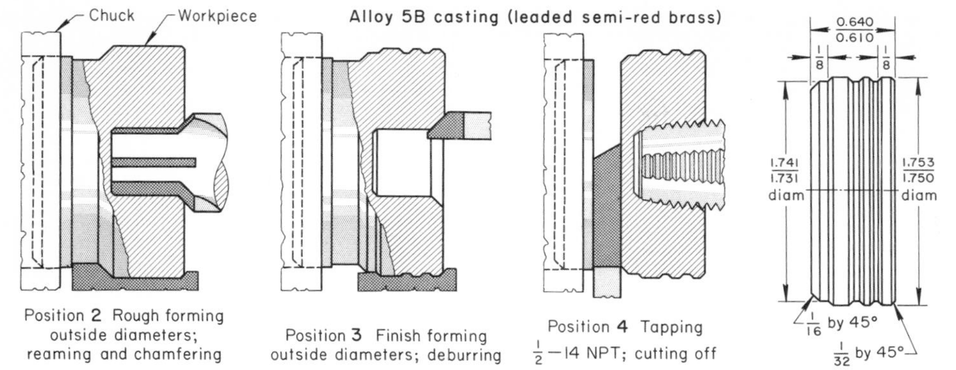

Speed(a) ....1007 rpm (486 sfm max)	Tool material:
Feed, ipr:	Tapping ....High speed steel(b)
Rough forming; deburring 0.0028	All other operations ....Carbide tips(c)
Reaming 0.0079	Tool life per grind, pieces:
Finish forming 0.0020	Rough forming 800
Cutting off 0.0036	Reaming and chamfering 1200
Depth of cut, in.:	Finish forming 1000
Rough forming 3/32	Deburring 2200
Reaming 0.005	Tapping 1400
Chamfering 1/32	Cutting off 950
Finish forming 0.010	Downtime for tool change ....30 min
Deburring 0.005	Setup time ....4 hr
Cutting fluid ....Soluble-oil emulsion	Production pieces per hour(d) 434

(a) All machining positions. First spindle position was used for loading and unloading. (b) Tap, 1/2–14 NPT, was held in No. 2 holder; tap bushing, 1-in. OD. (c) Tips for rough and finish forming tools were of tungsten carbide (hardness, Rockwell A 92.0; density, 14.90 g per cu cm); rake angle for finish forming tool was 2°. Tips for reaming-and-chamfering and deburring tools were tungsten carbide (hardness, Rockwell A 91.8); front clearance angle of reaming-and-chamfering tool was 7°. Deburring tool was 1/2 by 1/2 in.; cutoff tool, 3/32 in. (d) Rate of production was based on spindle-position cycle time of 8.3 sec.

Fig. 16. Seven-operation machining of an alloy 5B spout adapter in a four-spindle automatic chucking machine (Example 948)

life, especially when alloys of groups 2 and 3 are being threaded.

In external threading of group 1 alloys, a speed of 50 sfm is recommended for cutting a 7-pitch thread, whereas speed may be about 180 sfm for a 24-pitch thread. For the same pitches, recommended speeds are 30 and 100 sfm for alloys of group 2 and for those group 3 alloys that produce less stringy chips. For commercially pure copper, speeds of 15 and 40 sfm, respectively, for the 7 and 24 thread pitches are recommended. Speeds for threads of other pitches can be determined by interpolation.

Productivity in the threading of regulating screws and nipples on a manual machine and on an automatic machine are given in Examples 946 and 947 (Table 19).

Multiple-Operation Machining

Copper alloys, particularly the leaded alloys, are especially well-suited to machining in multiple-operation equipment such as turret lathes and automatic bar and chucking machines. The next two examples illustrate the efficiency that can be achieved in machining small brass castings in multiple-spindle chucking machines.

Examples 948 and 949. Multiple-Spindle Automatic Chuckers for Machining Alloy 5B Castings

Example 948 — Complete Machining of Spout Adapter in One Setup (Fig. 16). The sequence of operations for machining an alloy 5B spout adapter casting in three of the four spindle positions of an automatic chucking machine is illustrated in Fig. 16. Processing details for the seven operations performed — rough forming, reaming, chamfering, finish forming, deburring, tapping and cutting off — are given with Fig. 16. The cast blanks were loaded and unloaded in the first position.

Example 949 — Hollow Mills and Box Tools Used in Multiple-Operation Machining of Drain Seal (Fig. 17). The carbide tooling and conditions used for machining an alloy 5B drain seal casting in four positions on a six-spindle automatic chucker are shown in Fig. 17 and listed in the tabulation accompanying this figure. The first spindle position was used for loading a casting onto a special expanding arbor. In the sixth position, the machined casting was automatically grasped by a rotating pick-off attachment.

Semifinish turning, in position 3, was done with a hollow mill through which an air hose was used to remove chips. In position 5, the cutters were held in a box tool with a C-shaped guide bushing for steadying the workpiece during machining.

Because of the high spindle speeds at which multiple-operation machines can be operated, carbide tools are usually better than high speed steel for machining copper alloys (drills are an exception). The example that follows describes an application in which changing from high speed steel to carbide tools increased productivity by about 50%.

Example 950. High Speed Steel vs Carbide Tools for Machining Alloy 360 (Free-Cutting Brass) (Fig. 18)

The adapter shown in Fig. 18 was produced from 7/8-in. hexagonal brass rod in ten operations on a six-spindle automatic bar machine. Changing from M2 high speed steel tools to carbide tools for the turning operations not only decreased downtime for tool sharpening, but also made possible an increase in speed and resulted in decreased machining time, as shown in the following comparison:

	HSS	Carbide
Spindle speed, rpm	1832	2425
Surface speed (max), sfm .	480	635
Cycle time, sec	4.4	2.87
Production per hour, pcs .	818	1254

Manual vs Automatic Machines. Although it is often possible to perform as many different operations in a manually operated machine as in an automatic, high-volume production usually warrants the use of automatic machines. The four examples that follow deal with comparisons between hand-operated and automatic machines.

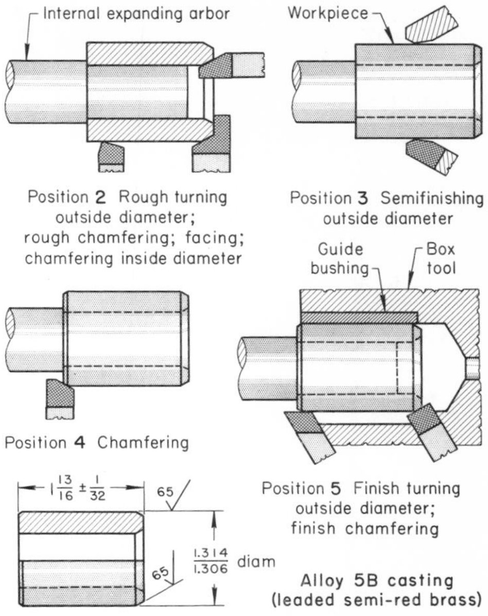

Speed, all positions(a)	1007 rpm (346 sfm max)
Feed, ipr:	
Rough turning	0.0128
Chamfering and facing	0.0029
Chamfering bore	0.0128
Semifinish turning	0.0128
Chamfering (position 4)	0.0019
Finish turning	0.002
Chamfering (position 5)	0.0128
Depth of cut, in.:	
Rough turning	3/64
Chamfering and facing	1/32
Chamfering bore	1/32
Semifinish turning	0.002
Chamfering (position 4)	1/32
Finish turning	0.005
Chamfering (position 5)	1/32
Cutting fluid(b)	Soluble-oil emulsion
Tool material(c)	Carbide (tips)
Tool life per grind, pieces:	
Rough turning	925
Chamfering and facing	2200
Chamfering bore	2200
Semifinish turning	1400
Chamfering (position 4)	2100
Finish turning	2300
Chamfering (position 5)	2200
Downtime for tool change	30 min
Setup time	5 hr
Production per hour(d)	348 pieces

(a) First position used for loading, sixth for unloading. (b) Heavy flow was used in position 5. (c) Form tool used for chamfering and facing (position 2) and chamfering tool in position 5 had 2° rake angle; turning tool in position 5 had 1° rake angle. Form tools in positions 2 and 4 were 3/4 in. square; hollow mill in position 3 had 1 1/2-in. shank; turning tool in position 5 was 1/2 in. square. (d) Based on spindle-position cycle time of 10.3 sec.

Fig. 17. Eight-operation machining of a drain seal casting in a six-spindle automatic chucking machine (Example 949)

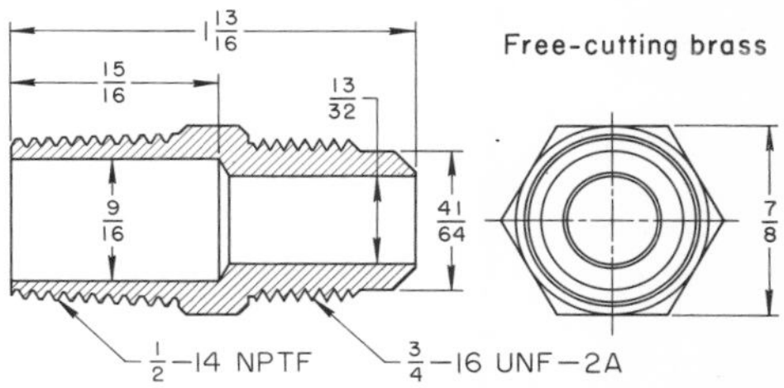

Fig. 18. Adapter that was produced in 35% less time when carbide tools replaced high speed steel tools, for turning operations (Example 950)

In these examples, automatic machines produced 2 to 28 times as fast as hand-operated machines.

Examples 951, 952 and 953. Manual Turret Lathes vs Automatic Bar Machines for Machining Alloy 360 (Free-Cutting Brass) Bars

Example 951 — Internally Threaded Couplings (Fig. 19). The tooling and processing conditions for the multiple-operation production of a coupling from 1-in. hexagonal free-cutting brass bar in a manual turret lathe and in a six-spindle automatic bar machine are compared in Fig. 19. Because of the shorter setup time, the turret lathe was the more economical for short production runs — 50 pieces or less. The bar machine, with 28 times the production rate of the turret lathe, was preferable for large-quantity runs — especially of 1000 pieces or more.

Although somewhat different in sequence, the operations in the two machines were the same in number and type except for the preliminary rough forming in position 1 on the bar machine (see Fig. 19), and the couplings, used for adapting ¼-in.-OD tube to ½–14 taper-threaded pipe, were identical. For every 100 couplings, 38.33 lb of bar stock was used. About 28% remained as net weight (10.56 lb per 100 pieces); turnings accounted for 22.77 lb, and scrap or ends of bars for 5 lb.

Examples 952 and 953 — Stems and Nipples (Table 20). Productivity and tooling costs for manufacturing stems (Example 952) and nipples (Example 953) on a manual turret lathe were compared with those for the use of a single-spindle automatic bar machine. Results are presented in Table 20. Both parts were made from bar stock of alloy 360 (free-cutting brass) in the half-hard temper.

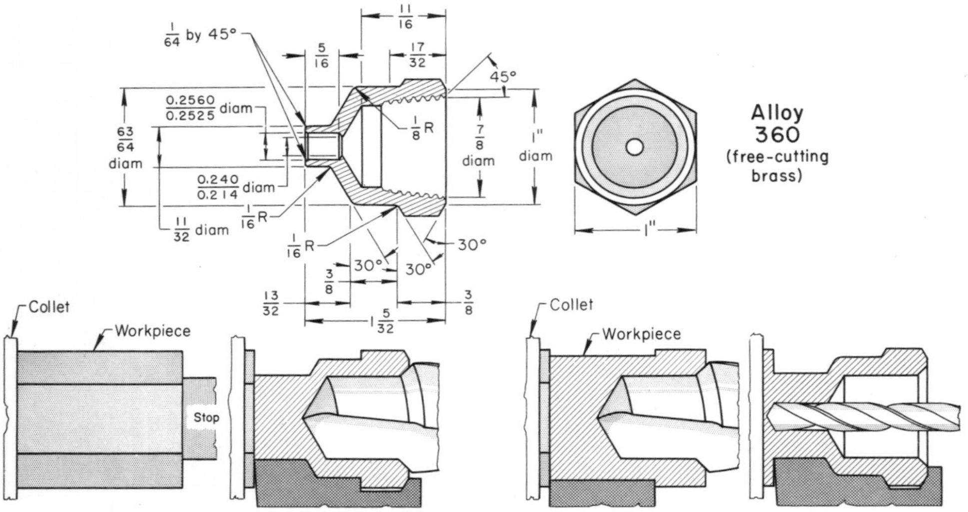

Condition or result	Manual turret lathe(a)	Six-spindle bar machine(b)
Machine speed, rpm	600	1072
Surface speed (max), sfm	186	333
Cutting fluid	Soluble oil(c)	Mineral oil(d)
Surface finish for formed diameters and cutoff, micro-in.	125	125
Setup time, hr	5	16
Production rate per hour, pieces	18.6	504

(a) Universal turret lathe with six-position indexing turret and saddle-type cross slide; one position on cross slide had a square turret that could accommodate four tools. (b) Six-spindle automatic with maximum capacity of 1¼-in.-diam bar and maximum speed of 2370 rpm. (c) Mixed in 1-to-20 ratio with water. (d) Viscosity, 150 SUS at 100 F.

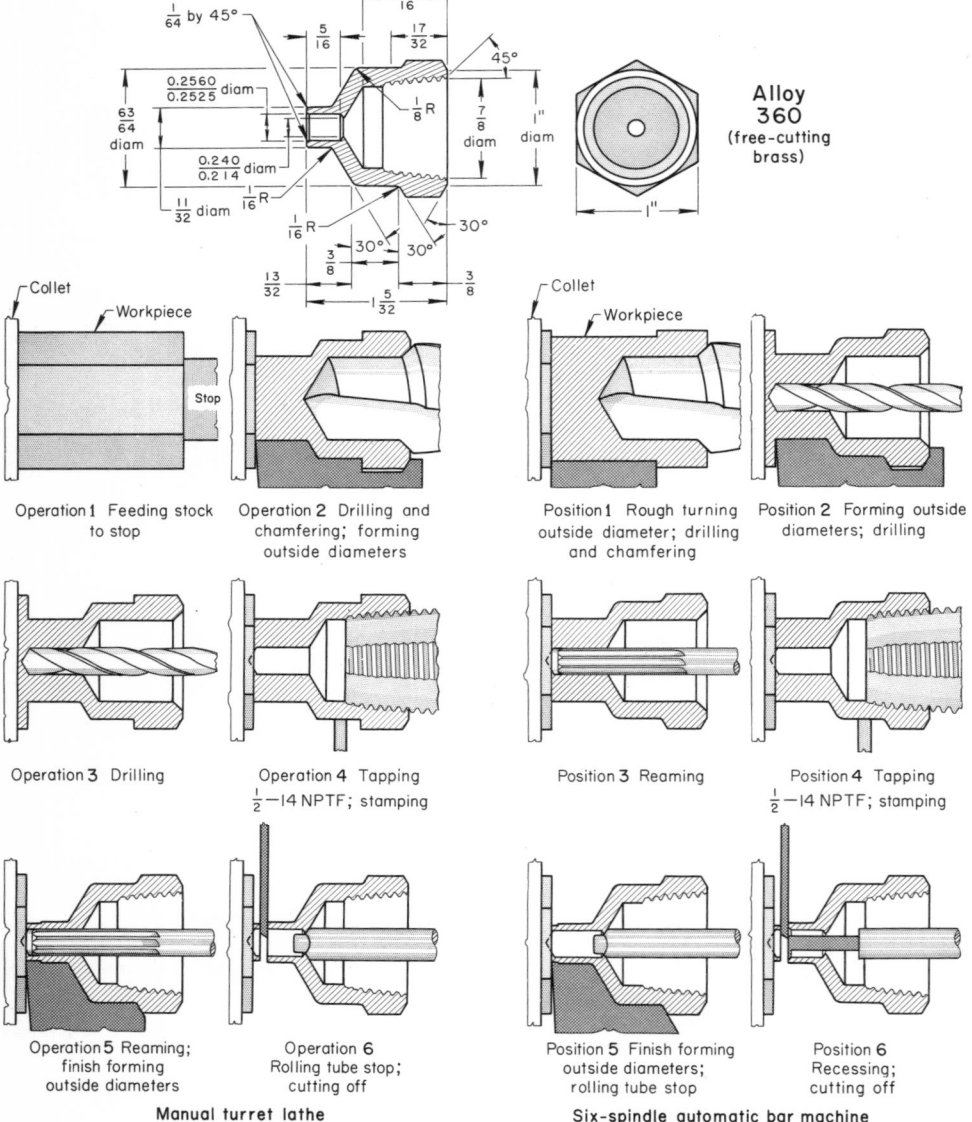

Fig. 19. Manual turret lathe compared with a six-spindle automatic bar machine for producing a coupling from 1-in. hexagonal bar. Turret lathe was more economical for quantities of 50 pieces or less, bar machine for 1000 pieces or more. (Example 951)

Table 20. Manual Turret Lathe vs Single-Spindle Automatic Bar Machine for Producing Stems and Nipples From Alloy 360 (Free-Cutting Brass) Bars (Examples 952 and 953)

Item	Manual turret lathe	Single-spindle automatic
Example 952 — Stems		
Tool cost per set	$600	$650
Setup cost per machine	$2.57	$8.55
Pieces machined per setup	1000	20,000
Setup cost per 1000 pieces	$2.57	$0.43
Production per hour, pieces	119	449
Example 953 — Nipples		
Tool cost per set	$400	$500
Setup cost per machine	$0.86	$8.55
Pieces machined per setup	250	5000
Setup cost per 1000 pieces	$3.44	$1.71
Production per hour, pieces	252	500

Example 954. Manual Turret Lathe vs Multiple-Spindle Chucking Machine for Machining a Sand Casting (Fig. 20)

Sequences of operations, processing details, and cost data for the use of a manual turret lathe and of a five-spindle semiautomatic chucking machine for drilling, chamfering and tapping ¾-in. pipe union nuts sand cast from alloy 4A (ASTM B145) are compared in Fig. 20 and the accompanying table. As shown by the cost data, the turret lathe was more economical in quantities of 500, and the chucking machine for 5000-piece runs. Break point was about 1100 pieces.

A finish of 125 micro-in. was specified for machined surfaces, and tolerance was ±0.010 in. Rough castings weighed 42.13 lb per hundred; 100 machined castings, 32.42 lb.

Machining and forming characteristics of copper alloys are generally better than those of ferrous metals. Therefore, it is often possible to use procedures and to incorporate operations in multiple-operation sequences for machining copper alloys that would not be practical for harder and less formable metals.

The four examples that follow describe procedures to increase processing efficiency. In Example 955 a method is described for using coil stock (invariably cheaper than straight lengths) for feeding a bar machine. Examples 956 and 957 describe procedures in which the ductility of copper alloys was used to advantage in saving time or material in multiple-operation machining. Broaching and turning simultaneously, an unusual combination of procedures, is described in Example 958. Milling can also be done in automatic machines, as described in Example 963.

Example 955. Wire Feeder for an Automatic Bar Machine Performing a Four-Operation Sequence (Fig. 21)

The alloy 342 part shown in Fig. 21 was machined from ⅛-in.-diam coiled wire in a single-spindle automatic bar machine equipped with a wire straightener. The workpiece was drilled, knurled and form turned. A cam-actuated single-point tool did both turning and cutoff. A pick-off collet removed the workpiece. Processing details and machining-cost data are given in the table with Fig. 21.

Example 956. Swaging That Eliminated Drilling and Reaming (Fig. 22)

Figure 22 shows the swaged end of a nozzle produced in a turret lathe from tellurium copper tubing (½-in. OD, 7/32-in. ID). Originally, the ¼-in.-long hole was produced after the

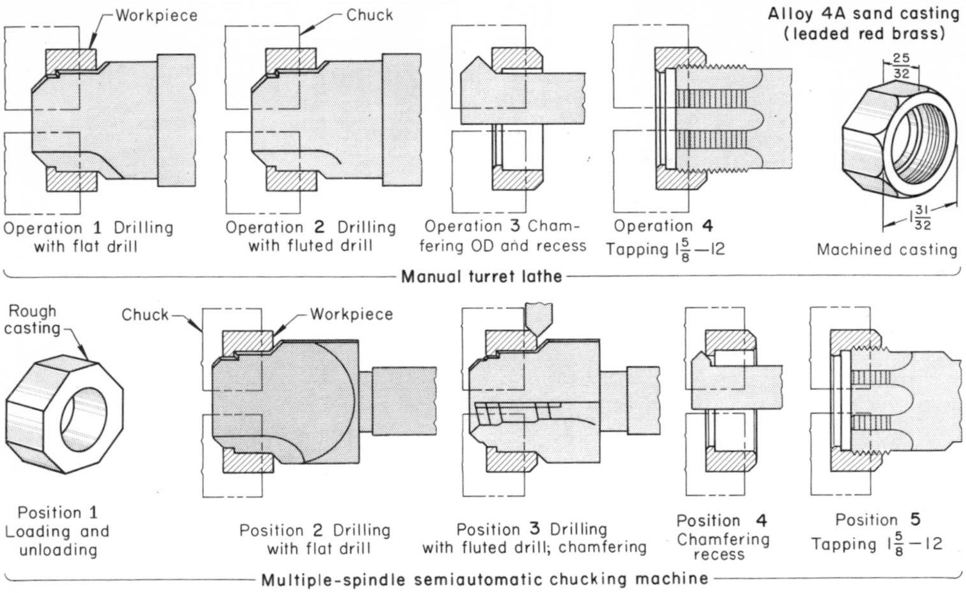

Item	Turret lathe	Chucking machine
Processing Details		
Machine speed, rpm	500	900
Surface speed (max), sfm	258	465
Cutting fluid	Soluble-oil:water	(1:20)
Setup time, hr	2	8
Cycle time, sec	37	6
Production per hour, pieces	96	420(a)
Cost Data		
Tooling	$200(b)	$340(c)
Setup	$ 16(d)	$ 80(e)

Item	Turret lathe	Chucking machine
Cost of Machining 500 Pieces		
Machining	$41.65(f)	$11.90(g)
Setup	16.00	80.00
Total	$57.65	$91.90
Cost per piece	$ 0.115	$ 0.184
Cost of Machining 5000 Pieces		
Machining	$416.50(f)	$119.00(g)
Setup	16.00	80.00
Total	$432.50	$199.00
Cost per piece	$ 0.087	$ 0.040

(a) At 70% efficiency. (b) Including one pair of chuck jaws. (c) Including five pairs of chuck jaws. (d) At $8 per hour. (e) At $10 per hour. (f) 96 pieces per hour, at $8 per hour. (g) 420 pieces per hour, at $10 per hour.

Fig. 20. Manual turret lathe compared with a multiple-spindle semiautomatic chucking machine for machining a cast union nut (Example 954)

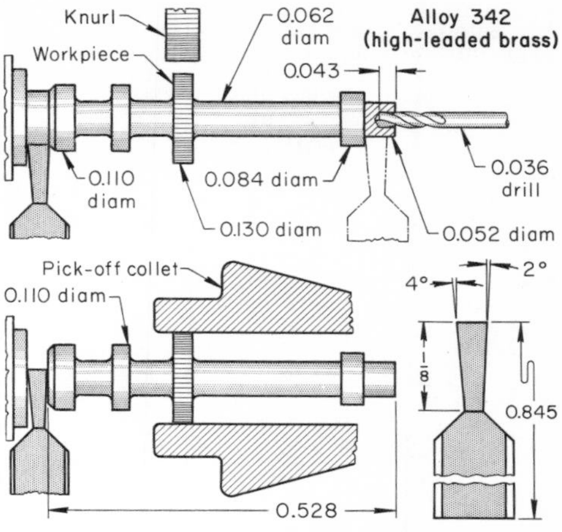

Tool Details

Turning tool:
- Type .... Turn and cutoff
- Material .... Carbide
- End relief .... 12°
- Side relief .... 1° to 2° per side
- Back rake .... 1°

Drill:
- Type .... Screw machine or stub
- Size .... No. 64
- Number of flutes 2
- Material .... High speed steel

Knurl:
- Type .... Push
- Material .... High speed steel

Operating Conditions

Speed .... 6000 rpm(a)
Feed .... (b)
Tool life per grind .... 500,000 pieces
Finish .... 63 micro-in.
Cutting fluid .... Mineral oil
Setup time .... 6 hr
Downtime for tool change .... 1 hr
Production rate .... 15 pieces per minute

(a) 196 sfm turning and knurling, 56 sfm drilling, 173 sfm max cutting off. (b) 0.0025 ipr turning, 0.0016 ipr drilling, 0.001 ipr knurling and cutting off.

Fig. 21. Four-operation machining of a part from coiled alloy 342 wire stock in a bar machine (Example 955)

end had been swaged, by drilling to 0.029-in. diameter and then reaming to size. Drilling required 17 sec, reaming 15 sec.

Drilling and reaming were eliminated by revising the processing so that the hole was formed to size during swaging by the use of a mandrel of 0.033-in.-diam music wire. Insertion and removal of the wire required only 3 sec, which resulted in a saving of 29 sec in machining time per piece. The improved method also eliminated tool and downtime costs for the drills and reamers.

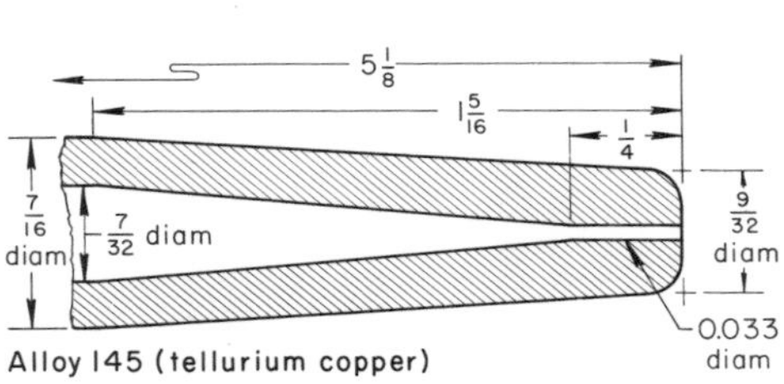

Fig. 22. Swaged end of a spout produced from copper tubing. Production time was reduced by swaging the ¼-in.-long hole over 0.033-in.-diam music wire, instead of producing the hole by drilling and reaming after swaging (Example 956)

Example 957. Spin-Flaring That Saved Material (Fig. 23)

Figure 23 illustrates the technique used on a small multiple-spindle automatic bar machine for providing an insert nut made from 3/16-in. bar stock of alloy 342 (high-leaded brass) with one end flared to ¼ in. in diameter. This technique (spinning, followed by trimming and facing with a form tool) enabled a 43.7% saving in material that would have been required had the part been more conventionally produced by turning ¼-in.-diam bar.

Spinning was done with a two-lip, cam-ground, form-relieved tool, at 75 sfm and 0.0025-ipr feed. Other machining operations included drilling, tapping, knurling, recessing and cutting off; production rate was 1200 pieces per hour.

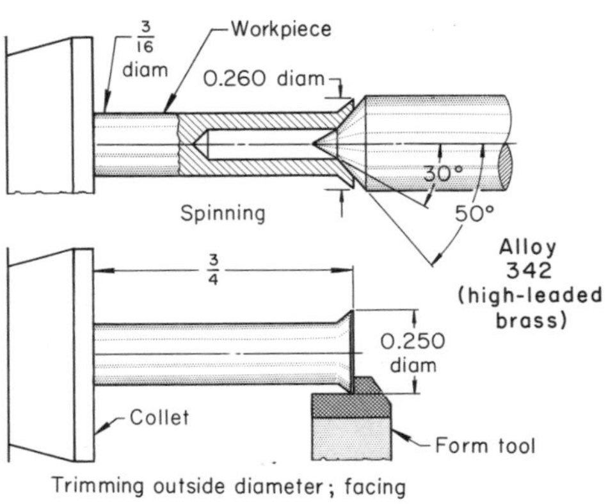

Fig. 23. Spinning and trimming that eliminated necessity for oversize bar stock and material waste by machining (Example 957)

Example 958. Broaching of Splines in a Six-Spindle Automatic Bar Machine (Fig. 24)

Figure 24 shows the use of an external broach in a 6-spindle automatic bar machine for producing a 16-tooth (120°) spline on one end of a valve stem machined from alloy 360 (free-cutting brass) rod. The operations for producing these pieces included turning, threading, chamfering and cutting off, in addition to broaching. During broaching, the tool and workpiece rotated at the same speed (2804 rpm), so that the part could be turned at the same time that it was broached; broach feed was 0.0053 ipr.

The broach, a ⅜-in., 16-spline tool, was made of M1 high speed steel; specified tool hardness was Rockwell C 60 to 62.

Dimensional accuracy that can be maintained in machining copper alloys in automatic machines is similar to that obtained when machining similar shapes from other metals. The condition of the machine is usually the major controlling factor. Common practice for maintaining dimensions within specified tolerance is to measure the significant dimensions of a predetermined number of parts during a production run. From the distribution pattern of these measurements it is possible to judge machine condition, as shown in the following example.

Example 959. Diameter and Length Variations of Brass Studs Produced in an Automatic Bar Machine (Fig. 25)

Figure 25 shows the variations in a form-turned step diameter and in cutoff length of an alloy 360 (free-cutting brass) stud (inset illustration in Fig. 25), as determined by measuring 26 consecutively produced parts from a total run of 150,000 pieces in a ¾-in. single-spindle automatic bar machine.

The range and distribution of variation on the 0.312-in. nominal diameter were considered normal and indicated the form turning operation to be under control. The wider range and unbalanced distribution of variation in the cutoff length indicated some axial movement in the spindle; but because the cutoff length was well within the relatively wide tolerance, no corrective action was taken.

Milling

High speed steel cutters, either solid or with inserted blades, are used for most applications in milling copper alloys, regardless of the type of milling

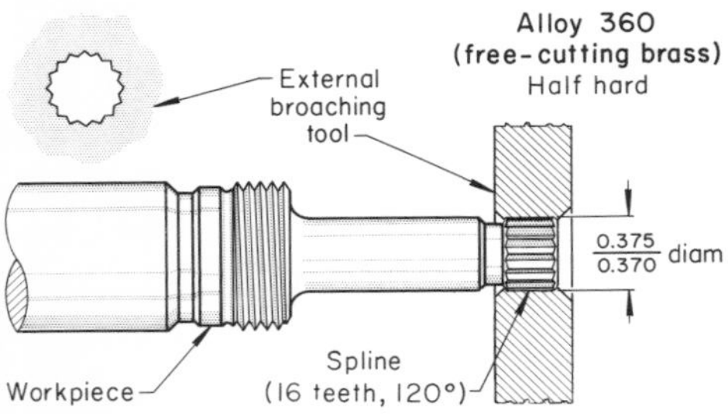

Fig. 24. Spline broaching combined with other operations in an automatic bar machine (Example 958)

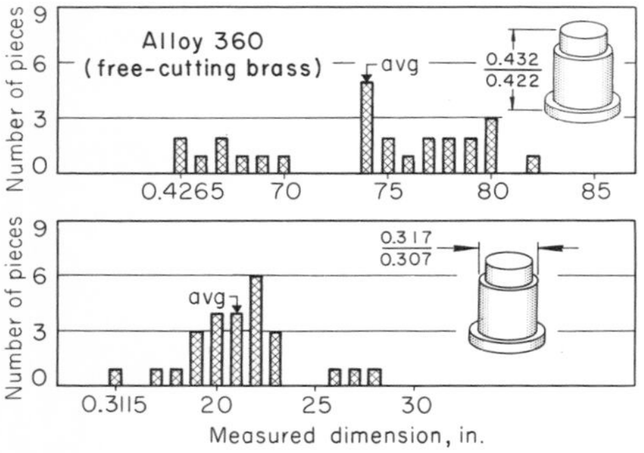

Fig. 25. Variation in dimensions of 26 brass studs produced consecutively in a single-spindle automatic bar machine representing a run of 150,000 pieces (Example 959)

(peripheral, face or end). However, cutters with carbide inserts are more efficient than high speed steel for some applications. The usual practice is to begin with high speed steel cutters, and change to carbide only when the setup can be made rigid enough or when advantages are strongly indicated by experience.

Peripheral Milling. Angles and land width recommended for peripheral and side milling cutters for use in milling copper alloys are given in Fig. 26.

Nominal speeds and feeds for peripheral milling copper alloys with high speed steel cutters are given in Table 21. These values are conservative (as are other speeds and feeds tabulated in this section) and may often be increased under favorable conditions, such as maximum rigidity, a flood of cutting fluid, or a shallow cut. In the first three examples that follow, speeds were several times greater than those recommended in Table 21, although in Example 963 cutter speed was close to the value given in Table 21 for peripheral milling of group 1 alloys.

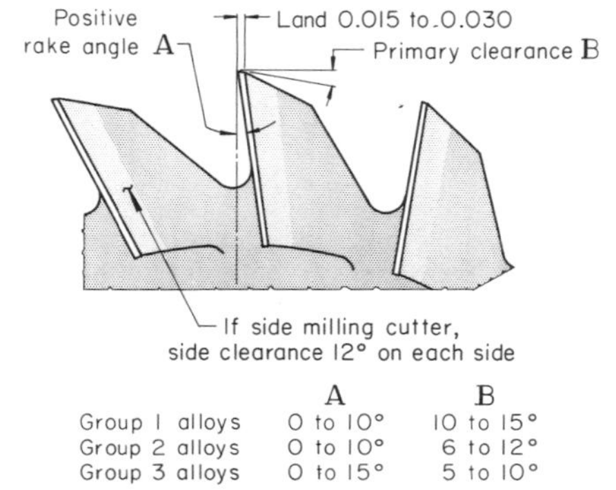

Fig. 26. Recommended angles and land width for peripheral and side milling cutters

Examples 960 and 961. Milling Four Slots at a Time in Commutators Made of Two Different Alloys (Fig. 27)

Figure 27 shows the setups used in a commutator-slotting machine for milling 28 equally spaced lead-wire slots, four at a time, in the commutator of an automotive starter of alloy 110 (Example 960) and a generator commutator of alloy 114 (Example 961). In each setup, the workpiece, held on an expanding vertical arbor, was lowered into the path of four rotating slitting saws mounted on four spindles spaced radially 90° apart. After the

Table 21. Nominal Speeds and Feeds for Peripheral Milling of Copper Alloys With High Speed Steel Cutters

Alloy group	Condition	Rockwell B hardness	Speed, sfm	Feed, ipt
Depth of Cut, 0.125 In.				
1	Annealed	20-70	430	0.018
2	Annealed	20-70	300	0.011
3	Annealed	20-70	120	0.007
1	Cold drawn	60-100	510	0.018
2	Cold drawn	60-100	350	0.011
3	Cold drawn	60-100	140	0.007
Depth of Cut, 0.025 In.				
1	Annealed	20-70	525	0.016
2	Annealed	20-70	375	0.009
3	Annealed	20-70	165	0.005
1	Cold drawn	60-100	625	0.016
2	Cold drawn	60-100	425	0.009
3	Cold drawn	60-100	200	0.005

Data are adapted from tables compiled by Metcut Research Associates, Inc.

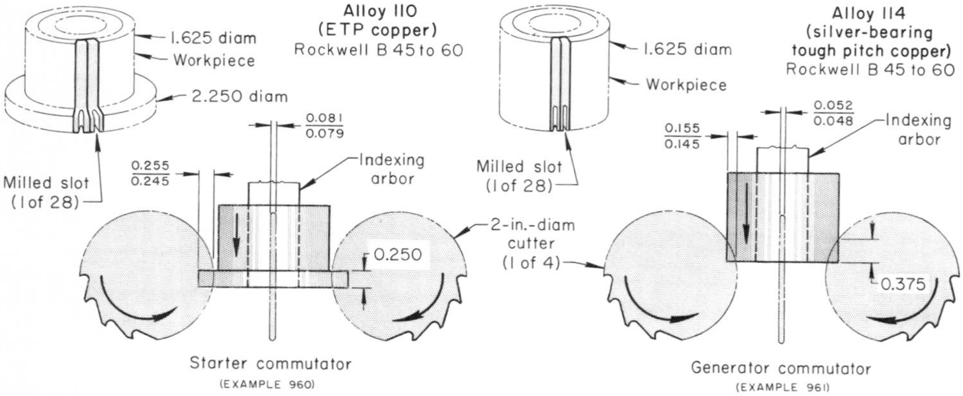

Condition or result(a)	Example 960 (Starter, alloy 110)	Example 961 (Generator, alloy 114)
Speed	7000 rpm (3665 sfm), for both parts	
Feed	0.0015 ipt for both parts	
Depth of cut (max), in.	0.250	0.150
Metal removed per slot, lb	0.0016	0.0004
Cutting fluid	None	None
Production per hour, pieces	360 (100% efficiency)	450 (100% efficiency)
Tool life per grind:		
Number of slots	30,000	224,000
Number of pieces (28 slots each)	1070	8000
Metal removed, lb	48.45	89.6

(a) Cutters for both parts were 2.002/1.998-in.-OD (½-in. hole diam) slitting saws with 14 teeth, made of high speed steel and nitrided to Rockwell C 62 to 64. Teeth were radiused to half of width and ground with 45° relief on alternate sides; both sides were hollow ground 1½° by 0.31 in. deep; rake angle was 10°, and tooth height 0.150/0.140 in.

Fig. 27. Milling lead-wire slots four at a time, in 28-bar commutators of two different alloys (Examples 960 and 961)

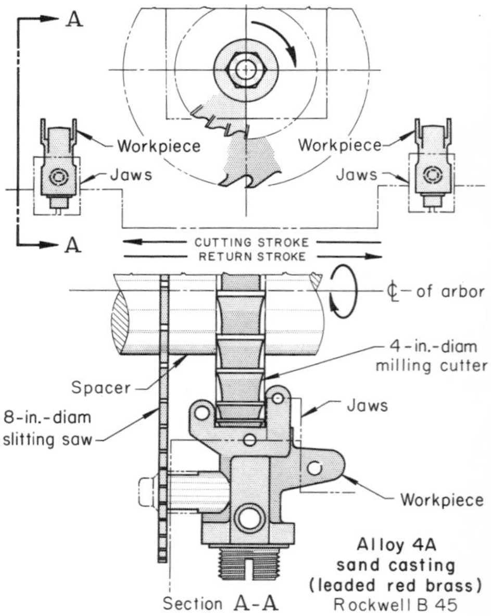

Tool Details(a)

Milling cutter:
- Type .... Side mill
- Width .... 0.690/0.684 in.
- Number of teeth 20

Slitting saw:
- Width .... ⅛ in.
- Number of teeth 48

Operating Conditions

Speed, milling .... 1500 rpm (1575 sfm)
Speed, sawing .... 1500 rpm (3150 sfm)
Cutting fluid .... None
Setup time .... 2 hr
Downtime for tool change .... 15 min
Cycle time (machine only) .... 22.2 sec(b)
Production per hour(c) .... 226 pieces

(a) Both tools were of high speed steel and had 1¼-in.-diam arbor bores. (b) Two pieces machined per cycle. (c) At 70% efficiency.

Fig. 28. Simultaneously milling a slot in and sawing-off a boss from an alloy 4A cast valve body (Example 962)

Table 22. Straddle Milling in an Automatic Bar Machine (Example 963)

Cutter Details

Type	Helical side mills (two)
Diameter	1⁹⁄₁₆ in.
Number of teeth	60
Helix angle	15°
Material	High speed steel

Milling Conditions

Speed	1200 rpm (491 sfm)
Feed	0.00007 ipt (5.04 ipm)
Depth of cut, max	³⁄₃₂ in.
Cutting fluid	Mineral oil
Cycle time per piece	3 sec
Production rate	17 pieces per min
Cutter life per grind	500,000 pieces

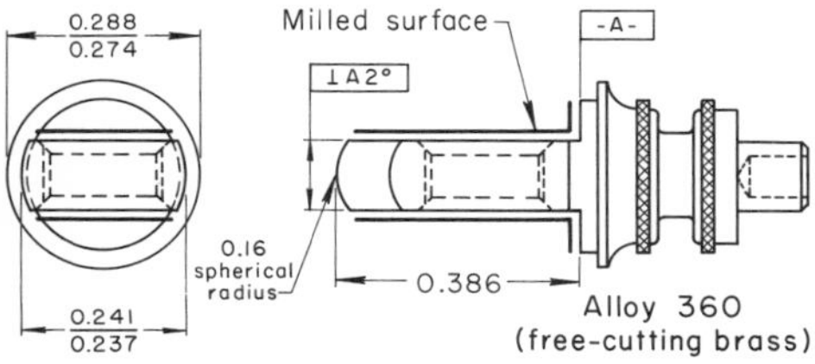

Data are for straddle milling the 0.097/0.091-in.-wide flat section on the nut insert sketched above, during production of this part from ⁹⁄₁₆-in.-diam rod in a multiple-spindle automatic bar machine. Spindle-stopping attachment was used during milling.

Table 23. Nominal Speeds and Feeds for Face Milling of Copper Alloys With High Speed Steel Cutters

Alloy group	Condition	Rockwell B hardness	Speed, sfm	Feed, ipt
Depth of Cut, 0.125 In.				
1	Annealed	20-70	450	0.020
2	Annealed	20-70	325	0.014
3	Annealed	20-70	100	0.010
1	Cold drawn	60-100	500	0.020
2	Cold drawn	60-100	350	0.014
3	Cold drawn	60-100	115	0.010
Depth of Cut, 0.025 In.				
1	Annealed	20-70	550	0.012
2	Annealed	20-70	425	0.010
3	Annealed	20-70	130	0.008
1	Cold drawn	60-100	600	0.012
2	Cold drawn	60-100	450	0.010
3	Cold drawn	60-100	150	0.008

SOURCE: same as for Table 21

four slots were cut, the arbor was raised and indexed and then lowered for the next cuts. After seven sets of cuts (28 slots) had been made, the arbor was raised to release the part for unloading. Processing details are given with Fig. 27.

Example 962. Milling and Sawing Combined in One Operation (Fig. 28)

Figure 28 shows the setup used in a horizontal automatic milling machine for simultaneously milling a slot in and sawing-off a side boss from a valve body sand cast from alloy 4A. As shown at the top in Fig. 28, two castings were held at opposite ends of the reciprocating table of the machine, which had 30-in. travel. These were machined successively (conventional milling cut) in one cycle (22.2 sec), during which the operator had enough time to unload finished parts and to reload the two quick-clamping, manually operated fixtures.

Tool details and operating conditions are given in the tabulation with Fig. 28.

Example 963. Straddle Milling in an Automatic Bar Machine (Table 22)

A spindle-stopping attachment enabled a straddle-milling operation to be included in the machining sequence for the production of a nut insert (sketch in Table 22). These inserts were machined from ⁹⁄₃₂-in.-diam alloy 360 rod stock in half-hard temper. After turning and knurling operations, the spindle was stopped and the flat section was produced by two side milling cutters (tool and operating details in Table 22). During cutoff, in which the 0.16-in. spherical radius was produced on the end of the part, milling and cutoff burrs were removed by the use of a skiving tool; for this combined operation, the part was held in a rotating pick-off collet.

Table 24. Nominal Speeds and Feeds for Face Milling of Copper Alloys With Carbide Cutters

Alloy group	Condition	Rockwell B hardness	Speed, sfm: Brazed	Speed, sfm: Disposable	Feed, ipt
Depth of Cut, 0.125 In.					
1	Annealed	20-70	900	990	0.018
2	Annealed	20-70	600	660	0.014
3	Annealed	20-70	250	275	0.010
1	Cold drawn	60-100	1000	1100	0.018
2	Cold drawn	60-100	650	715	0.014
3	Cold drawn	60-100	300	330	0.010
Depth of Cut, 0.025 In.					
1	Annealed	20-70	1200	1320	0.012
2	Annealed	20-70	800	880	0.010
3	Annealed	20-70	300	330	0.008
1	Cold drawn	60-100	1300	1430	0.012
2	Cold drawn	60-100	850	935	0.010
3	Cold drawn	60-100	350	385	0.008

SOURCE: same as for Table 21

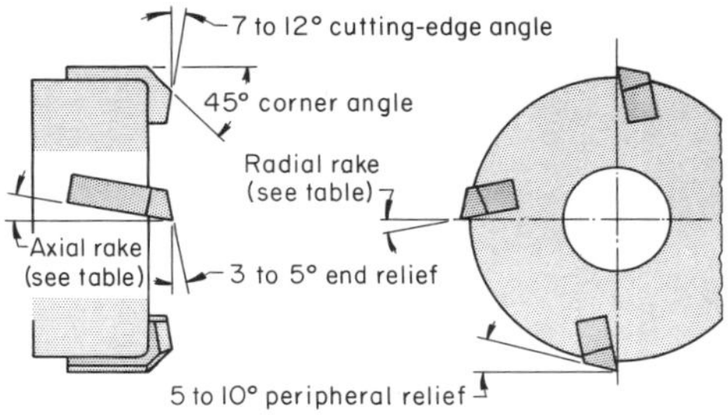

Angle	High speed steel	Disposable carbide	Brazed carbide
Axial rake	12° to 25°	5° to 7°	3° to 10°
Radial rake	10° to 12°	0° to 5°	3° to 10°

Fig. 29. Recommended angles for face milling cutters; all angles are positive.

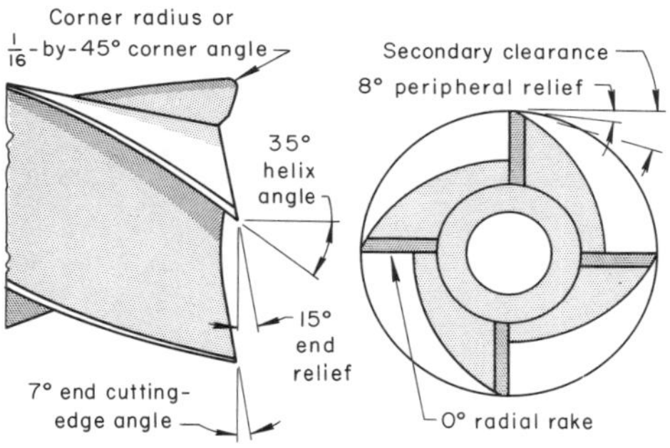

Fig. 30. Recommended angles for end milling cutters

Face Milling. Angles for cutters (high speed steel and carbide) for face milling copper alloys are presented in Fig. 29. Nominal speeds and feeds for face milling with high speed steel cutters are given in Table 23; speeds and feeds for carbide cutters are given in Table 24.

End Milling. Recommended angles for end milling cutters used for copper alloys are shown in Fig. 30. Although these recommendations are for high speed steel cutters, the same angles are applicable to carbide-tipped cutters. Speeds for end milling of copper alloys with high speed steel and carbide cutters are given in Tables 25 and 26.

Table 25. Nominal Speeds and Feeds for End Milling of Copper Alloys With High Speed Steel Cutters

Alloy group	Condition	Rockwell B hardness	Speed, sfm	Feed, ipt, for cutter diam, in., of: 0.250	0.750	1.0-2.0
Depth of Cut, 0.050 In.						
1	Ann	20-70	375	0.003	0.008	0.010
2	Ann	20-70	250	0.002	0.006	0.008
3	Ann	20-70	125	0.0015	0.005	0.007
1	CD	60-100	400	0.003	0.008	0.010
2	CD	60-100	275	0.002	0.006	0.008
3	CD	60-100	125	0.0015	0.005	0.007
Depth of Cut, 0.015 In.						
1	Ann	20-70	450	0.002	0.005	0.007
2	Ann	20-70	325	0.002	0.005	0.006
3	Ann	20-70	150	0.001	0.004	0.005
1	CD	60-100	500	0.002	0.005	0.007
2	CD	60-100	350	0.002	0.005	0.006
3	CD	60-100	175	0.001	0.004	0.005

SOURCE: same as for Table 21

Table 26. Nominal Speeds and Feeds for End Milling of Copper Alloys With Carbide Cutters

Alloy group	Condition	Rockwell B hardness	Speed, sfm	Feed, ipt, for cutter diam, in., of: 0.250	0.750	1.0-2.0
Depth of Cut, 0.050 In.						
1	Ann	20-70	750	0.003	0.008	0.010
2	Ann	20-70	500	0.003	0.007	0.009
3	Ann	20-70	300	0.002	0.006	0.008
1	CD	60-100	800	0.003	0.008	0.010
2	CD	60-100	525	0.003	0.007	0.009
3	CD	60-100	350	0.002	0.006	0.008
Depth of Cut, 0.015 In.						
1	Ann	20-70	900	0.002	0.005	0.007
2	Ann	20-70	700	0.003	0.006	0.007
3	Ann	20-70	350	0.0015	0.005	0.006
1	CD	60-100	950	0.002	0.005	0.007
2	CD	60-100	750	0.003	0.006	0.007
3	CD	60-100	400	0.0015	0.005	0.006

SOURCE: same as for Table 21

Slitting and Circular Sawing

Copper alloys are sawed with relative ease, and because chips are removed rapidly, coarse-tooth saws are preferred. When sawing leaded alloys, saws with no hook angle are best. For sawing commercially pure copper or copper alloys that produce stringy chips, the hook angle should be as much as 18°. When surface finish on the cut surfaces is critical, the use of metal-slitting saws with side chip clearance will minimize rubbing and chip wash. Recommended shapes for solid and inserted saw teeth are shown in Fig. 31.

General-purpose high speed steels such as M2 and M7 are most often used for saws for copper alloys, although for some alloys, such as aluminum-silicon bronze, carbide-tipped saws have proved more efficient (see Example 966, on the next page).

The free-cutting alloys like high-leaded brass are often sawed without a cutting fluid, although fluids are recommended for most circular sawing or slitting operations (see section on Cutting Fluid in this article).

Nominal pitches, speeds and feeds for slitting and circular sawing of various compositions and thicknesses of copper alloys with high speed steel and carbide-tipped saws are given in Tables 27 and 28. Speeds several times as great as those shown in Table 27 are often used successfully in production applications (see Examples 964 to 974).

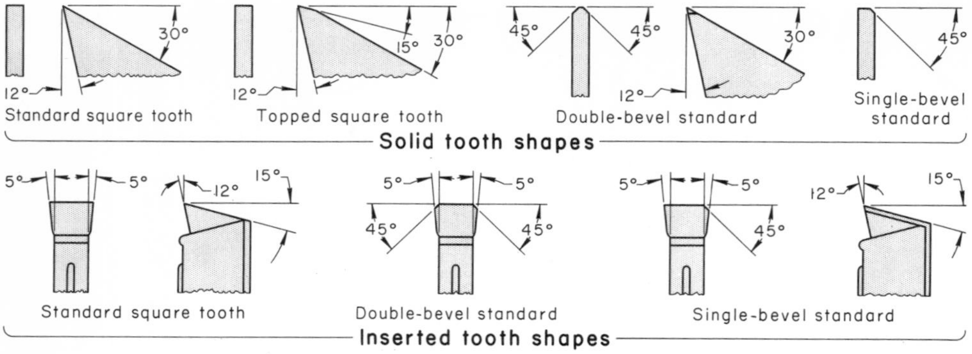

Fig. 31. Solid and inserted tooth shapes for circular saws

Typical practices for circular sawing copper alloys of several compositions and shapes are given in the 11 examples that follow:

Example 964. Sawing Three Parts at a Time in an Automatic Bar Machine (Table 29)

Three high speed steel saws, each driven by an air motor, simultaneously cut spacing washers (view in Table 29) from three lengths of alloy 360 bar stock. The saws were mounted on three of the spindles of a six-spindle automatic bar machine.

Production rate was one piece per second. The saws were rotated opposite to spindle rotation. They were ground to remove the hook and insure concentricity. Tool and processing details are given in Table 29.

Table 27. Nominal Pitches, Speeds and Feeds for Circular Sawing and Metal Slitting of Copper Alloys With High Speed Steel Saws(a)

Alloy group	Condition	Rockwell B hardness	Diameter or thickness of solid stock, in. ¼ to 3	3 to 6	6 to 9	9 to 15
Saw Pitch, In.(b)						
All	All	....	0.200-0.650	0.600-0.950	0.900-1.150	1.100-1.550
Cutting Speed, Sfm						
1	Ann	20-70	350	300	250	200
2	Ann	20-70	250	200	175	150
3	Ann	20-70	100	80	65	50
1	CD	60-100	375	325	275	225
2	CD	60-100	275	250	225	200
3	CD	60-100	125	100	80	60
Feed, Ipt						
1	Ann	20-70	15-25	10-20	8-15	5-10
2	Ann	20-70	10-20	8-15	5-10	4-7
3	Ann	20-70	8-15	6-10	4-8	2-5
1	CD	60-100	15-25	10-20	8-15	5-10
2	CD	60-100	10-20	8-15	5-10	4-7
3	CD	60-100	8-15	6-10	4-8	2-5

(a) Metal slitting includes cutters up to 8-in. diam. Circular sawing normally includes cutters larger than 8-in. diam. (b) Tooth-to-tooth distance, in inches. (Data are adapted from tables compiled by Metcut Research Associates, Inc.)

Table 28. Nominal Pitches, Speeds and Feeds for Circular Sawing of Copper Alloys With Carbide-Tipped Plate Saws

Saw Pitch, In. (All Alloys)(a)	
¼ to 1½-in. plate	0.500 to 0.750
1½ to 3½-in. plate	0.750 to 1.000
3½ to 5-in. plate	1.000 to 1.500
5 to 6-in. plate	1.500 to 2.000
Speed, Sfm (¼ to 6-In. Plate)	
Copper (R_B 20 to 60)	1500 to 3000
Brasses (R_B 60 to 100)	500
Bronzes (R_B 60 to 100)	400
Feed, Ipt (¼ to 6-In. Plate)	
Copper (R_B 20 to 60)	0.0065
Brasses (R_B 60 to 100)	0.006
Bronzes (R_B 60 to 100)	0.006

(a) Tooth-to-tooth distance, in inches. (SOURCE: same as for Table 27)

Examples 965 and 966. Production Sawing of Slugs From Bar Stock in an Automatic-Feed Saw

Example 965 — Free-Cutting Brass (Table 30). The tool details, operating conditions, and results listed in Table 30 represent the practice employed in one plant for high-production sawing of slugs from free-cutting brass bars of various diameters, with high speed steel saws.

Example 966 — Aluminum-Silicon Bronze (Table 31). For cutting slugs from aluminum-silicon bronze bars, carbide-tipped saws as detailed in Table 31 were used for stock up to 2 in. in diameter. Feed was considerably less than for the free-cutting brass in Example 965.

Examples 967 to 974. Sawing Slugs From Shapes Extruded From Four Alloys (Table 32)

Table 32 gives operating conditions and costs for cutting 1-in.-long slugs from eight different extruded shapes (two each from four different copper alloys) with high speed steel slitting saws.

Circular Sawing Compared With Alternative Methods. Cutoff operations are commonly performed in sequence with other operations, as in a multiple-spindle bar machine, although when cutoff is the principal operation (or the only one) a sawing machine is more efficient, as shown in Example 975.

A choice between circular sawing and abrasive cutting for copper alloys depends greatly on the work metal composition. Some copper alloys, particularly the softest and most ductile, cause excessive loading of abrasive wheels. Under these conditions circular sawing is more efficient than abrasive-wheel cutting. On the other hand, for the most abrasive copper alloys, such as the aluminum bronzes or silicon bronzes, abrasive cutting is more efficient than sawing.

The next two examples compare methods of cutting off copper alloys.

Table 29. Sawing Off Spacing Washers Three at a Time in a Bar Machine (Example 964) (a)

Details of Each Saw	
Type	Slotting saw(b)
Size	2¾-in. OD, 0.020 in. wide
Number of teeth	72
Material	High speed steel
Operating Conditions	
Speed(c):	
Workpieces	3560 rpm (700 sfm max)
Saws	18,000 rpm (12,960 sfm)
Feed	0.003 ipr
Depth of cut	0.120 in.
Cutting fluid	Sulfurized mineral oil(d)
Cycle time, each spindle	3 sec
Production per hour (total)	3600 pieces(e)
Tool life per grind(f)	5000 pieces
Downtime for tool change	5 min

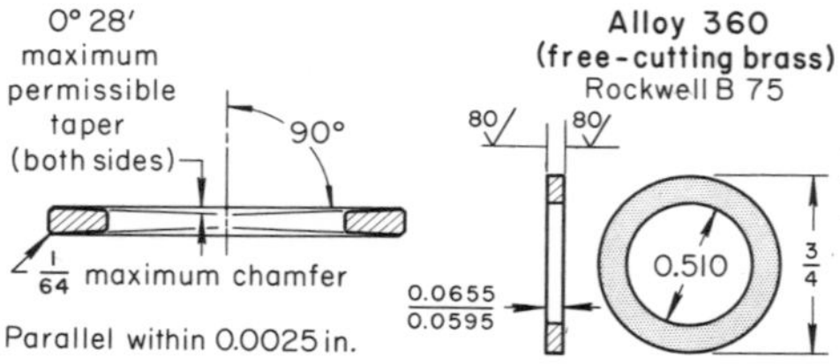

(a) Three washers (sketch above) were cut off simultaneously by air-motor-driven saws at three of the six spindles of a 1-in.-capacity automatic bar machine. (b) Hook removed by grinding, to insure concentricity. (c) Saws and spindles rotated in opposite directions; combined cutting speed was 13,660 sfm. (d) Specially prepared to prevent staining of copper alloys. (e) 1200 pieces each saw. (f) Saws were reground when unable to cut to specified flatness and parallelism.

Examples 975 and 976. Sawing vs Alternative Methods for Cutting Off

Example 975 — Change from Milling to Sawing (Table 33). In cutting slugs from wrought bars of sulfurized copper, setup time was reduced by 98%, and production rate was nearly quadrupled when the operation was transferred from a four-spindle automatic bar machine to a sawing machine. Comparative data for the original and improved methods are presented in Table 33.

Example 976 — Change from Saw to Abrasive Wheel. When a circular saw was used for cutting two types of 1-by-4-in. wrought aluminum bronze bar stock (10.0 to 11.2% aluminum, 3.0 to 4.25% iron; and 12.5 to 13.6% aluminum, 3.5 to 5.0% iron) to various lengths, results were unsatisfactory. Not only did each cut take 20 min, but the cut edges were chipped and the stock broke off before the last ¼ in. had been cut. Saws wore excessively.

By changing to an abrasive cutoff wheel in the sawing machine, completely satisfactory results were obtained. Tool life was increased by 75%, and cutting time per piece was reduced almost 95% to 68 sec per piece. Setup took 12 min; wheel speed was 1910 rpm; maximum roughness of the cut surface was 80 micro-in. No cutting fluid was used.

Table 30. Sawing Slugs From Free-Cutting Brass Bars (Example 965)

Condition or result	Bar diameter, in. 5/8	1-5/16	2-1/2
Length of slug, in.	4	2⁵⁄₁₆	1
Area of cut, sq in.	0.307	1.353	4.908
Feed, ipr	0.1042	0.1094	0.0139
Time per cut, sec	0.2	0.4	6.0
Cycle time, sec	1.3	2.0	8.0
Production, pcs/hr	2400	1500	450

Conditions for Bars of All Diameters

Machine	Automatic-feed saw
Saw details:	
Material	High speed steel
Diameter	10 in.
Number of teeth	60
Face width	0.062 in.
Face angle	15° to 18°
Top angle	8°
Speed	1800 rpm (4712 sfm)
Cutting fluid	Water-soluble oil (flooded on)

Saw blades were straight ground for cutting bars up to 1¼-in. diameter; for bars 1¼ to 2½ in.-diameter, a triple-chip grind was used.

Table 31. Sawing Slugs From Aluminum-Silicon Bronze Bars (Example 966)

Machine	Automatic-feed saw
Saw details:	
Material	Carbide (tipped)
Diameter	8 in.
Number of teeth	60
Face width	0.110 in.
Face angle	10° to 15°
Top angle	8°
Speed	1800 rpm (3770 sfm)
Cutting fluid	Water-soluble oil (flooded on)

Data are for sawing stock up to 2-in. diam.

Table 32. Conditions and Costs for Circular Sawing 1-In. Slugs From Extruded Shapes of Four Copper Alloys (Examples 967 to 974) (a)

Shape (see drawing)	Weight per ft, lb	No. of saw teeth	Feed, ipr(b)	Cost of cutting 1000 slugs
A (Example 967)	1.51	180	0.0166	$25.22
B (Example 968)	5.02	110	0.0166	43.36
C (Example 969)	2.82	110	0.0055	35.96
D (Example 970)	3.19	110	0.0055	38.90
E (Example 971)	0.94	180	0.0166	$20.11
F (Example 972)	3.79	180	0.0166	28.94
G (Example 973)	2.24	80	0.0055	31.11
H (Example 974)	10.20	50	0.0055	92.87

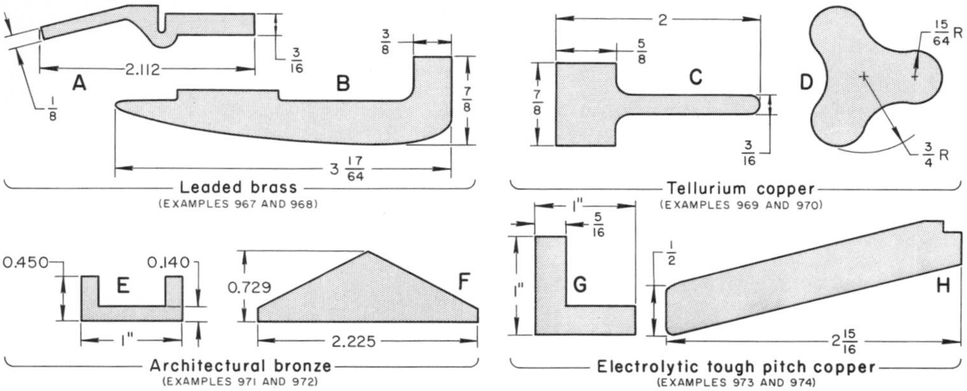

(a) Data were obtained in cutting 1-in.-long slugs from the eight extruded shapes illustrated above, with high speed steel slitting saws in an automatic cutoff machine. All saws were 10 in. in diameter, had tooth thickness of 0.100 in. and hook angle of 12° to 15°, and cut a 13/64-in. kerf. For all materials, saw speed was 3600 rpm (9425 sfm), and spindle oil sprayed on saw blade was used as cutting fluid. (b) Lighter feed will produce burr-free edges and smoother surfaces.

Power Band Sawing and Power Hacksawing

Nominal pitches and speeds that are successful for band sawing copper alloys are given in Table 34. (See also Table 8, page 222, and Table 3, page 225.) Similar data for power hacksawing are shown in Table 35. The figures in these tables are for conditions that include the use of soluble oil as a cutting fluid. Speeds are based on an indefinitely long cut. If the length of cut is short (say only ¼ in.) and there is time between cuts, speed can be increased.

Abrasive Cutoff

The use of an abrasive cutoff wheel may be more economical than sawing, as in Example 976. Aluminum oxide wheels are recommended, resinoid-bond for dry cutting and rubber-bond for wet cutting. Wheels should be relatively hard (grades N to R). Typical wheel recommendations are:

Work metal hardness, R_B	Dry cutting	Wet cutting
30 to 70	A-30-R-B	A-46-N-R
60 to 100	A-46-R-B	A-46-N-R

Grinding

Grinding of copper alloys is not common, but in some applications grinding is the best means of getting accuracy and finish. Sometimes, when finish grinding must supplement machining, one grinding operation can be used to replace both operations.

Speeds, feeds and wheels are given in Table 36. Aluminum oxide wheels are recommended for all types of grinding except for surface grinding softer alloys. For these conditions, silicon carbide wheels are preferred. In all instances, vitrified-bond wheels of medium grade (J to N) are recommended. Emulsions of soluble oil and water are satisfactory grinding fluids.

Table 33. Bar Machine vs Saw for Cutoff of Sulfurized Copper Bar Slugs (Example 975) (a)

Condition or result	Bar machine(b)	Sawing machine
Speed, rpm	1566	1800
Speed, sfm	378	4850
Feed, ipr	0.005	0.032
Cutting fluid	Mineral oil	Soluble oil(c)
Tool material	Carbide	M35 HSS
Setup time	8 hr	10 min
Cycle time, sec	5.5	1.6
Production, pcs/hr	458(d)	1765(e)
Tool life/grind, pcs	1830	7500

Saw Details

Diameter	10.8 in.
Face width	0.093 in.
Number of teeth	60
Face angle	15°
Top angle	9°
Method of grinding	Triple chip

(a) Data are for cutting slugs 0.200 in. long from 0.950-in.-diam wrought bars of sulfurized copper (99.7 Cu, 0.3 S). (b) 4-spindle automatic, 1-in. bar capacity. (c) Mixed 1:4 with water. (d) At 70% efficiency. (e) At 78% efficiency.

Honing

Honing is frequently used to finish bores to close dimensions, particularly in hard alloys like aluminum bronze.

Honing Stones (Sticks). Resinoid-bond silicon carbide stones of grade R should be used for honing all copper alloys. Selection of grain size depends on finish requirements as follows:

Finish, micro-in.	Grain size	Finish, micro-in.	Grain size
3 to 5	600	15 to 20	320
6 to 9	500	21 to 26	280
10 to 14	400	27 to 30	220

For a finish of over 31 micro-in., a grain size of 180 is recommended.

Speed. A reciprocating speed of 80 sfm is recommended regardless of alloy hardness. Rotational speeds of 160 to 210 sfm are recommended for alloys with hardness of 120 to 140 Bhn (Rockwell B 67 to 77). For honing alloys of 180 to 200 Bhn (Rockwell B 89 to 93) lower speeds (150 to 180 sfm) are better.

Table 34. Power Band Sawing Copper Alloys

Alloy group	Condition (a)	Rockwell B hardness	Type of steel(b)	Pitch, teeth/in., for thickness, in., of: Under ¼	¼ to 1½	Over 1½	Speed, sfm
1	Ann	20-70	HC	18-24	6-14	3-6	500
2	Ann	20-70	HSS	8-10	6-8	3-6	250
3	Ann	20-70	HSS	8-10	6-8	3-6	200
1	CD	60-100	HC	18-24	6-14	3-6	550
2	CD	60-100	HSS	8-10	6-8	3-6	300
3	CD	60-100	HSS	8-10	6-8	3-6	225

(a) Ann = Annealed; CD = Cold drawn. (b) HC = High-carbon steel; HSS = High speed steel. (Data are adapted from tables compiled by Metcut Research Associates, Inc.)

Table 35. Power Hacksawing of Copper Alloys With High Speed Steel Blades

Alloy group	Pitch, teeth/in., for thickness, in., of: Up to ¼	¼ to ¾	¾ to 2	Over 2	Speed, strokes/min	Feed, in./stroke
Annealed Alloys (Rockwell B 20 to 70)						
1	10	6	6	4	130	0.012
2	10	6	6	4	100	0.012
3	10	6	6	4	90	0.010
Cold Drawn Alloys (Rockwell B 60 to 100)						
1	10	10	6	4	150	0.012
2	10	10	6	4	120	0.012
3	10	10	6	4	100	0.010

SOURCE: same as for Table 34

Table 36. Conditions for Grinding of Copper Alloys

Surface Grinding

Wheel classification:
- Workpiece 20 to 70 R_B C-46-K-V
- Workpiece 60 to 100 R_B A-46-K-V

Wheel speed .... 5500 to 6500 sfm
Table speed .... 50 to 100 fpm
Downfeed:
- Rough .... 0.003 in./pass
- Finish .... 0.0005 in./pass (max)

Crossfeed .... ⅓ wheel width/pass

Cylindrical Grinding

Wheel classification:
- Workpiece 20 to 70 R_B A-60-N-V
- Workpiece 60 to 100 R_B A-46-L-V

Wheel speed .... 5500 to 6500 sfm
Work speed .... 100 sfm
Infeed:
- Rough .... 0.002 in./pass
- Finish .... 0.0005 in./pass (max)

Traverse:
- Rough .... ⅓ wheel width/work rev.
- Finish .... ⅙ wheel width/work rev.

Centerless Grinding

Grinding wheel classification A-60-L-V
Wheel speed .... 5500 to 6500 sfm
Work feed .... 50 ipm
Infeed:
- Rough .... 0.005 in./pass
- Finish .... 0.0015 in./pass (max)

Regulating wheel:
- Angle .... 3°
- Speed .... 30 rpm

Internal Grinding

Wheel classification:
- Workpiece 20 to 70 R_B A-46-J-V
- Workpiece 60 to 100 R_B A-60-L-V

Wheel speed .... 5000 to 6500 sfm
Work speed .... 100 to 200 sfm
Infeed:
- Rough .... 0.002 in./pass
- Finish .... 0.0002 in./pass (max)

Traverse:
- Rough .... ⅓ wheel width/work rev.
- Finish .... ⅙ wheel width/work rev.

SOURCE: same as for Table 34

Other Examples of Machining Copper Alloys

Boring .... Example 45
Broaching .... Examples 140, 145
Drilling .... Examples 160, 181
Roller burnishing .... Examples 216, 217
Tapping .... Examples 221, 222, 225, 229, 230
Die threading .... Examples 248, 252, 255

Machining of Lead Alloys

BY ROBERT WILLIAMS*

MOST LEAD ALLOYS that are machined are bearing alloys. The resistance of these alloys to cutting is low, but speeds and feeds are limited by difficulties in chip disposal and by the need for accuracy and good finish.

Lead-base bearing alloys usually contain 10 to 15% antimony, 1 to 10% tin, and small amounts (generally less than 0.5%) of copper or arsenic, or both. In making babbitted pillow-block bearings, boring is the most important operation. Boring techniques are similar for pillow blocks from ½ to 12 in. in diameter and up to 20 in. long.

Equipment for Boring. Rigidity is a primary requirement in boring of babbitted bearings, just as in most other boring operations (see the article "Boring", which begins on page 20). Production lathes are often used for boring of smaller bearings, particularly when outboard support for the boring bar is not needed. For larger bearings, especially for those that require outboard support, horizontal boring mills are generally used.

As a rule, bores up to 6 in. long are bored with no outboard support. A 6-in.-long bore requires a boring bar 1½ in. in diameter, to keep within the generally accepted 4-to-1 ratio of length to diameter.

Boring Tools. Carbide-tipped tools are nearly always used in production boring of lead alloys. Because machining of lead alloys seldom involves any substantial shock load, even in interrupted cuts, the brittleness of carbide is not a problem.

Tools should have adequate relief, to prevent chip congestion. The two tools shown in Fig. 1 are typical for use when more than ⅛-in. thickness of babbitt must be removed. Note that these tools are similar except for the sharp hook on the top face of the finisher. In machining of small bores, where no more than about 1/16 in. of babbitt is to be removed, roughing and finishing are often done with the same tool. Under these conditions, a tool like that shown in Fig. 2 is used; note that both side and back rake are 0°, but that relief is liberal.

*Assistant Superintendent, Machine Shop, Dodge Manufacturing Corp.

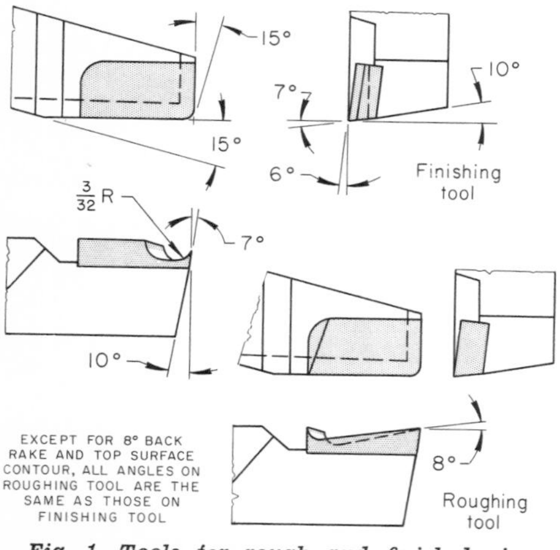

Fig. 1. Tools for rough and finish boring of lead-base alloys

Boring Speed, Feed, and Depth of Cut. Speeds usually range from 400 to 650 sfm. The use of higher speeds depends largely on machine condition and ability to prevent chip congestion.

Feed rate is usually 0.010 ipr, although lighter feeds are sometimes used for higher speeds. Occasionally, when roughing and finishing are separate operations, 0.010 ipr is used for roughing and 0.007 ipr for finishing.

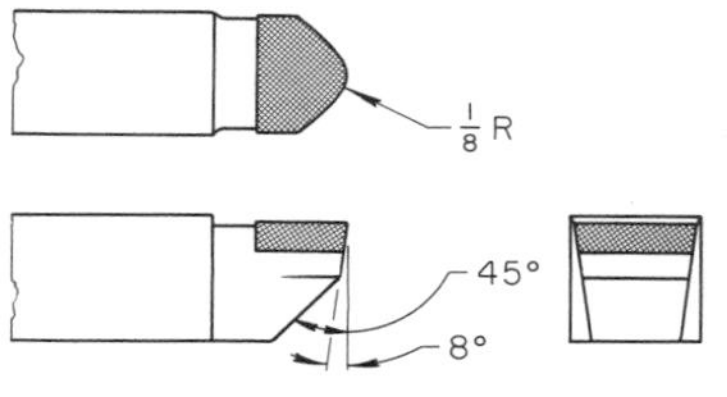

Fig. 2. Tool for both roughing and finishing of small bores in lead-base alloys (see Production Example and Fig. 3 for typical application)

Depth of cut is often ⅛ in. or more for rough boring. When the babbitt to be removed is substantially thicker than ⅛ in., two cuts are generally made.

In finish boring without outboard support, cuts 0.006 to 0.008 in. deep are common. When outboard support is used, the depth of cut for finishing may be as great as 0.015 in.

Avoiding Chip Congestion. Chip congestion is more likely to occur in the machining of lead alloys than in the machining of harder metals that have higher fusion temperatures. If a lead alloy chip becomes entrapped, it will probably fuse and promote further congestion and fusing, ultimately damaging the workpiece or the tool, or both.

To prevent chip congestion, tools must be ground with adequate relief (see Fig. 1 and 2), and there must be enough clearance (⅛ in. minimum) between the boring bar and the workpiece to permit free flow of chips.

A jet of air directed at the cutting tool (see Fig. 3) helps move chips away from the tool. Cutting fluids are not used in machining of lead alloys.

Dimensional Accuracy and Finish. Diameter of bore for babbitted bearings is expressed as standard plus a minimum and maximum oversize, standard referring to the diameter of the shaft that will operate in the specific bearing. The bore of the pillow block in the production example that follows was specified as standard plus 0.003 to 0.005 in. Since shaft diameter for this bore was 15/16 in. (0.9375 in.), the bore diameter had to be 15/16 in. plus 0.003 to 0.005 in. (oversize tolerance of 0.002 in.). As bore diameter becomes larger, tolerances are more liberal. For instance, for a 6-in.-diam bore the amount of oversize may be 0.004 to 0.007 in., for a tolerance of 0.003 in.

A surface finish of 75 micro-in. or better is commonly specified, and 50 micro-in. is common after finish boring. For bearing applications, smoother surfaces may not retain an adequate lubrication film in service.

Production Example. The following example is typical for boring of small babbitted bearings.

Rough and Finish Boring of 15/16-In.-Diam Babbitted Pillow Blocks (Fig. 3)

Figure 3 shows a typical setup used for rough and finish boring of small babbitted pillow blocks. The workpiece was held securely on a riser block by means of four locating pins and two toggle clamps. The riser block was mounted on the carriage of a production lathe. A boring tool of the type shown in Fig. 2 was rotated by a boring bar from the headstock. The block was roughed by being moved toward the headstock; then direction of the carriage was reversed, and the block was finish bored on the return stroke. Additional processing details are given with Fig. 3.

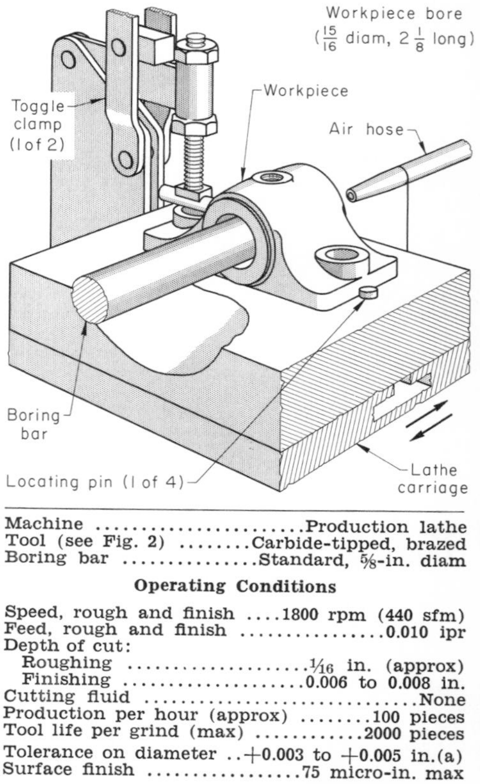

Machine .... Production lathe
Tool (see Fig. 2) .... Carbide-tipped, brazed
Boring bar .... Standard, ⅝-in. diam

Operating Conditions

Speed, rough and finish .... 1800 rpm (440 sfm)
Feed, rough and finish .... 0.010 ipr
Depth of cut:
Roughing .... 1/16 in. (approx)
Finishing .... 0.006 to 0.008 in.
Cutting fluid .... None
Production per hour (approx) .... 100 pieces
Tool life per grind (max) .... 2000 pieces
Tolerance on diameter .. +0.003 to +0.005 in.(a)
Surface finish .... 75 micro-in. max

(a) Oversize for 15/16-in.-diam shaft

Fig. 3. Rough and finish boring of a babbitted pillow block (see Production Example)

Machining of Magnesium Alloys

*By the ASM Committee on Fabrication of Magnesium**

MAGNESIUM alloys can be machined at extremely high speeds, and deeper cuts and a higher rate of feed are used than for other structural metals. Because magnesium is a free-cutting metal, chips produced are well broken.

Less power is required for removing a given volume of magnesium by machining than for any other commonly machined metal, as indicated below:

Metal	Relative power, %	Metal	Relative power, %
Nickel alloys ..	100	Brass	23
Mild steel	63	Aluminum ...	18
Cast iron	35	Magnesium ...	10

The power required for removing 1 cu in. of magnesium per minute is usually from 0.15 to 0.3 hp.

Smooth surfaces are produced by machining at high or low speeds, with or without a cutting fluid.

Tools

Usually, tools of standard design for machining steel can be used for machining magnesium. However, because of the low resistance of magnesium to cutting, and its comparatively low heat capacity, tools should have smooth faces, large peripheral relief angles, large chip spaces, few blades (in milling cutters), and small rake angles.

When a tool is ground, the cutting edge must be kept as sharp and as smooth as possible, and it must be free of scratches, burrs or wire edges. In addition, the tool surfaces along which the chips move should be kept as smooth as possible. The edges and surfaces are best obtained by finish grinding on a fine or very fine abrasive wheel and then, if necessary, hand stoning them with a fine or extrafine oilstone.

Carbide-tipped tools are usually preferred, because they last longer and are more accurate than high speed steel tools. Tools that have been used for other metals should always be resharpened before being used to cut magnesium, even if the cutting angles of the tools are not changed.

Cutting Fluids

Most machining of magnesium is done without a cutting fluid. Although less heat is generated in cutting magnesium than in cutting other metals, the high cutting speeds used and the high thermal expansion and low heat capacity of magnesium make it necessary, in some machining operations, to dissipate the heat developed.

Efficient machining practice demands that high feeds be used whenever possible. When high speeds are used, there is danger of fire, particularly when fine chips are being produced, although sharp tools greatly reduce this danger. Cutting feeds below 0.001 ipr, or tools rubbing on the work, are more likely to cause fires, and iron or steel inserts and sand cast surfaces are likely to spark when hit with a cutting tool. A stream of 4 to 5 gal of oil cutting fluid per minute per tool will virtually eliminate the fire hazard. If a particular job or machine tool prohibits the use of a cutting fluid, cutting speed should be reduced to less than 500 sfm, and the recommendations regarding tools and feeds should be followed carefully.

Table 1. Speeds, Feeds and Depths of Cut for Turning and Boring Magnesium Alloys

Speed, sfm	Feed, ipr	Maximum depth of cut, in.
Roughing		
300 to 600	0.030 to 0.100	0.500
600 to 1000	0.020 to 0.080	0.400
1000 to 1500	0.010 to 0.060	0.300
1500 to 2000	0.010 to 0.040	0.200
2000 to 5000	0.010 to 0.030	0.150
Finishing		
300 to 600	0.005 to 0.025	0.100
600 to 1000	0.005 to 0.020	0.080
1000 to 5000	0.003 to 0.015	0.050

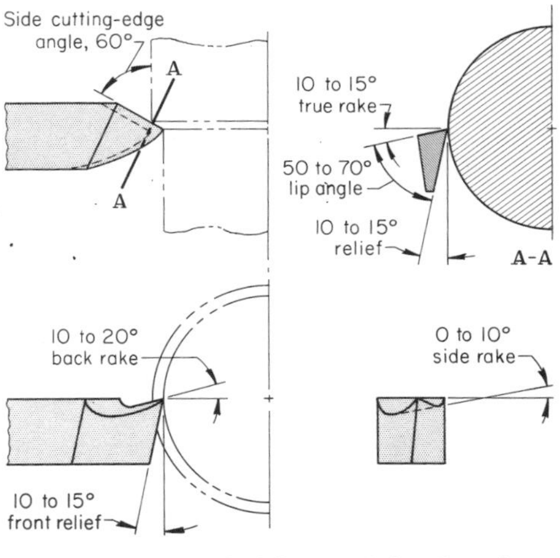

Fig. 1. Lathe tool for rough turning of magnesium

Various mineral-oil cutting fluids are used on magnesium. To secure adequate cooling, the cutting oil should have low viscosity. To prevent corrosion of the magnesium, free acid content of cutting fluids should be less than 0.2%. Vegetable or animal oils should not be used.

In a few applications soluble-oil emulsions have been used successfully in machining magnesium, but this practice is dangerous and is not recommended. Water will greatly intensify any chip fires and will also make the reclaiming of machining scrap very inefficient. The presence of moisture on turnings generates a small volume of hydrogen, which presents a definite hazard during shipment or storage.

Turning and Boring

Figure 1 shows a typical lathe tool for rough turning. The large relief (10° to 15°) and the small back rake (10° to 20°) are important. A larger back rake often causes feeding of the tool into the work. In some plants, 0° back rake is used, to break chips and prevent curling. This practice is seldom recommended, because it increases the roughness of the machined surface and increases power consumption. The side rake may vary from 0° to about 10°.

A typical finishing tool differs from a roughing tool in that it has a round nose and thus produces a smoother surface finish. Tool noses narrower than those used in turning aluminum produce comparably smooth finishes on magnesium.

The design of form tools for taking wide cuts or for turning specially shaped contours is similar to that of single-point finishing tools except that the back rake should be reduced to about 3° to 8° to avoid chatter.

Figure 2 shows a typical parting tool. The large relief angles are important, because they reduce friction and prevent tool breakage.

Speeds, feeds and depths of cut commonly used for rough and finish turning or boring of magnesium are given in Table 1.

The three examples that follow describe production practice for turning and boring magnesium.

*L. W. Hudson, *Chairman,* Chief Metallurgist, Goodyear Aerospace Corp.; Robert O. Hughes, Supervisor of Production Engineering, AC Spark Plug Div., General Motors Corp.; C. E. Lehnhardt, Manager, Fabrication Div., Magnesium Aerospace Products, Inc.; Lloyd F. Lockwood, Metallurgical Laboratory, Dow Metal Products Co. Div., Dow Chemical Co.

J. A. Mallen, Materials Engineer, Sperry Gyroscope Co. Div., Sperry Rand Corp.; E. L. Moyer, Chief Engineer, Aircraft Wheels and Brakes, Bendix Products Aerospace Div., Bendix Corp.; John R. Powers, Section Head, Tool Engineering, Wheel and Brake Div., Goodyear Aerospace Corp.; Stuart T. Ross, Vice President, Brooks and Perkins, Inc.; Frank Sheara, Executive Vice President, Magnesium Elektron, Inc.; V. M. Tardiff, Project Engineer, Magline, Inc.

Gordon Vivian, Chief Metallurgist, Outboard Marine Corp. of Canada, Ltd.; Elliott Willner, Specialist, Materials and Processes, Missiles and Space Co. Div., Lockheed Aircraft Corp.; J. P. Young, Process and Equipment Engineering, Thomson Engineering Laboratory, Small Aircraft Engine Dept., General Electric Co.

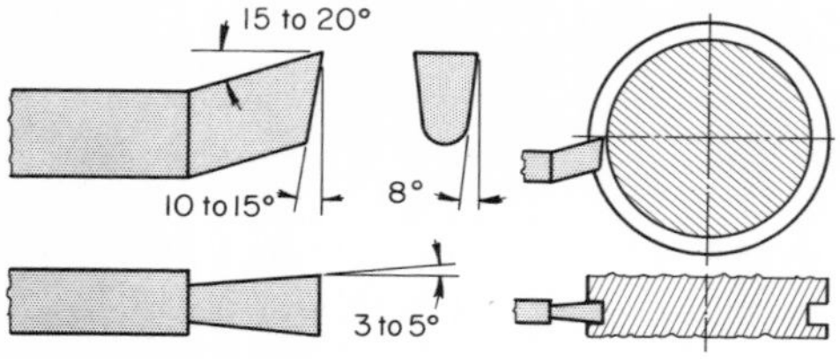

Fig. 2. Lathe tool for parting of magnesium

Example 977. Form Turning AZ91B Die Castings (Fig. 3)

The die casting shown in Fig. 3 was turned to remove parting-line flash and to form a sealing surface for a rubber gasket. A feed of 0.008 ipr was used to obtain the gasket surface and to produce a chip that could be easily handled. Because of the type of chip desired, the dwell normally used at the bottom of such a cut was omitted. No cutting fluid, as such, was used; however, chips were flushed away by a fire-resistant oil. Other processing details are given with Fig. 3.

Example 978. Turning, Boring and Facing AZ91B Die Castings (Fig. 4)

A satisfactory surface finish without chatter marks and dimensional accuracy within ±0.0005 in. were produced on the turned and bored surfaces of the magnesium die casting shown in Fig. 4. Carbide-tipped tools of the designs shown were used in a four-spindle machine (No. 3 size) that had a boring bar with a fly cutter. An air clamp held the workpiece during machining. Two pieces were machined while two pieces were being loaded. Other processing details are given with Fig. 4.

Example 979. Turning a Wheel Forging (Fig. 5)

The setup for machining the outer surface of a forged wheel-half is shown in Fig. 5. A 32-by-60-in. lathe equipped with a 30-hp motor and an air-actuated tracer was used. The workpiece was centered by the headstock pilot and held between the headstock plate and the tailstock pilot, which was used as a support. The carbide tool, ¾ by 1 in., had top rake of 10°, primary clearance of 12°, and secondary clearance of 15°.

The form was cut with one pass of the tool, and about ¼ to 5⁄16 in. (radial depth) of stock was removed. Feed was relatively light, because of the part shape and the finish and accuracy required, and because no cutting fluid was used. The forging weighed 133 lb before machining, and 86.5 lb afterward. Other processing details are given with Fig. 5.

Planing and Shaping

Single-point tools for planing and shaping have essentially the same angles as the tools used for turning and boring (Fig. 1). Cutting fluids are seldom used for planing or shaping.

Planing. Because the maximum cutting speeds in planing are much lower than those for turning and boring, operating economy is obtained by heavy feeds and deep cuts. Depths of roughing cuts are commonly about 0.50 in., at a speed of 300 sfm and a feed of 0.90 in. per stroke. To obtain best surface finish, depth of cut for finish planing should be 0.010 in. These heavy feeds and deep cuts are possible because of the low power needed for planing magnesium. Rigidity of the setup is the main limitation on maximum size of cut.

Shaping. Operating conditions for planing are generally applicable to shaping also. Speed is limited only by the capability of the shaper. Feed and depth of cut are more often limited by workpiece design or rigidity of the setup. In the next example, a light feed was necessary because of workpiece shape.

Example 980. Use of a Shaper for Cutting Slots (Fig. 6)

Sixteen slots, ⅞ in. wide, 9⁄32 in. deep, and 1⅝ in. long, were machined in the bosses of cast wheels with a flat-nose carbide shaping tool. These wheels were 23¼ in. in outside diameter and 915⁄32 in. long; the bosses were 21⅜ in. in inside diameter. A vertical shaping machine with a 5-hp motor and a maximum ram stroke of 12 in. was used. The workpiece was mounted on a register plate and held by a stud through the center and a clamping washer on the hub, as shown in Fig. 6. Slot spacing was controlled by a master indexing unit attached to the rotary table of the machine. Other details are given with Fig. 6.

Broaching

Broaches for magnesium are usually made from M2 high speed steel. Face (hook) angles of 10° to 15° are recommended. Relief angles are usually 1° to 3°. Broaching is done dry or with a broaching oil.

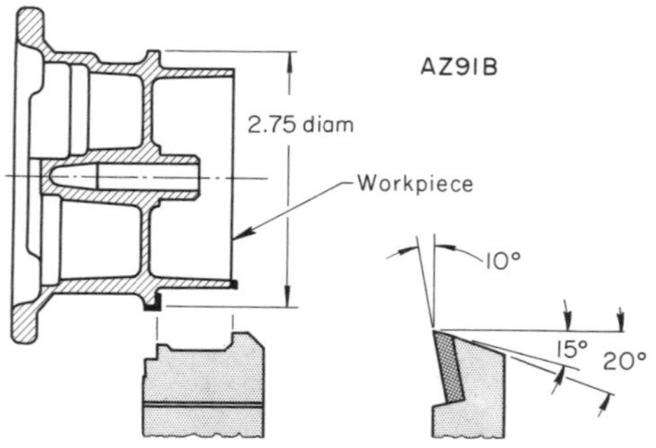

Speed	1120 rpm (800 sfm, approx)
Feed	0.008 ipr
Metal removed	0.015 in. (approx)
Cutting fluid	None
Production rate	700 pieces per hour
Tool life per grind	100,000 pieces

Fig. 3. Die casting that was machined by the carbide form tool shown (Example 977)

Speeds ranging from 20 to 50 sfm are generally used, machine capability being the major factor limiting maximum speed. A rise per tooth (chip load) of 0.006 in. is usually near optimum. A chip load that is too light will cause burnishing, which will shorten broach life and distort the workpiece.

The following example describes practice for broaching splines in a magnesium alloy part.

Example 981. Broaching Internal Splines (Fig. 7)

A horizontal, variable-speed broaching machine with a 64-in. stroke was used to cut splines in a casting of magnesium alloy AZ92A. The hydraulically powered broaching machine was equipped with a 10-hp motor, and had a pulling capacity of 41,000 lb and a maximum cutting speed of 20 sfm.

Figure 7 shows the workpiece and broaching setup. The pull broach used, which was made of M3 high speed steel, was 5.080 in. in diameter and 68 in. long, and had 131 rows of roughing teeth and five rows of finishing teeth. Each row of cutting teeth on the broach produced an internal form consisting of 19 teeth, with one space omitted, 30° involute spline, 4/8 diametral pitch, and 4.750-in. pitch diameter. Broach-teeth details and operating conditions are given with Fig. 7.

Drilling

Magnesium alloys can be easily drilled with twist drills made of any high speed steel. Speeds most commonly used are shown in Table 2. Feed depends on hole size and is usually from 0.001 to 0.030 ipr for holes 1⁄16 to 2 in. in diameter, as shown in Table 2.

Deep Holes. Twist drills of the design shown at the left in Fig. 8 are suitable for drilling holes of depth-to-diameter ratio up to 20 to 1. A web of uniform thickness is preferred. The clearance (relief behind the land) should be twice as deep as that of standard drills, and the margin should be half the standard width. A point angle of 118° and a lip relief of 15° are recommended. A spur or pilot can be ground on the point to prevent drill marks and to keep the drill straight. Chisel-edge angles must be 135° to 150°, to provide good surface finish and to minimize spiraling in the holes. When chisel-edge angles are smaller or larger, difficulties result, because of improper relief at the cutting edge and lack of proper centering of the drill.

A drill of this design cuts freely and will readily clear chips. Raising the drill to remove the chips is unnecessary unless the depth of the hole is more than about 20 diameters. If the drill bushing and the surface of the drilled part are too close, however, the chips may not flow out readily and can jam in the flutes. An approximate minimum distance of 1½ times the hole diameter is recommended. However, if a flat

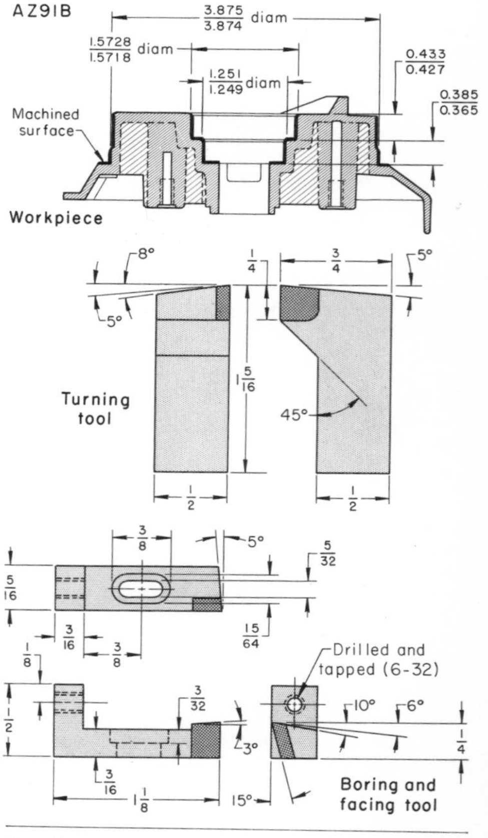

Speed	1500 rpm (1500 sfm, max)
Feed	0.002 ipr
Cutting fluid	Mineral oil(a)
Tolerance	±0.0005 in.
Production rate	50 pieces per hour
Tool life per grind	500 to 600 pieces
Labor cost per piece, machining	$0.045

(a) Viscosity, 50 SUS at 100 F

Fig. 4. Die casting that was machined by turning, boring and facing with the tools shown (Example 978)

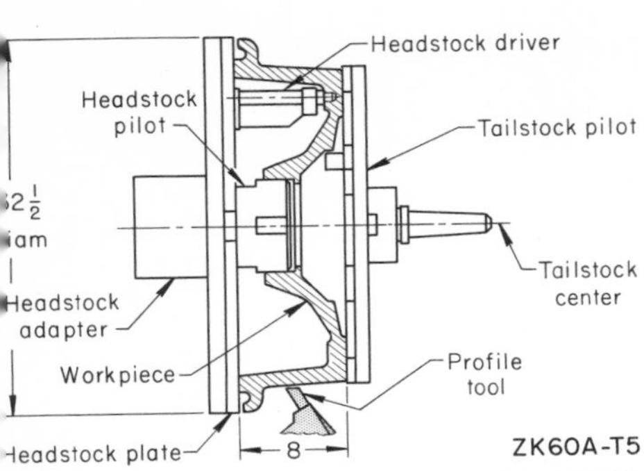

Speed	250 sfm
Feed	3 ipm
Metal removed	¼ to 5/16 in.
Cutting fluid	None
Tolerance	±0.003 in.
Production rate	7.5 pieces per hour(a)

(a) Includes loading and unloading

Fig. 5. Machining the outer surface of a forged wheel-half (Example 979)

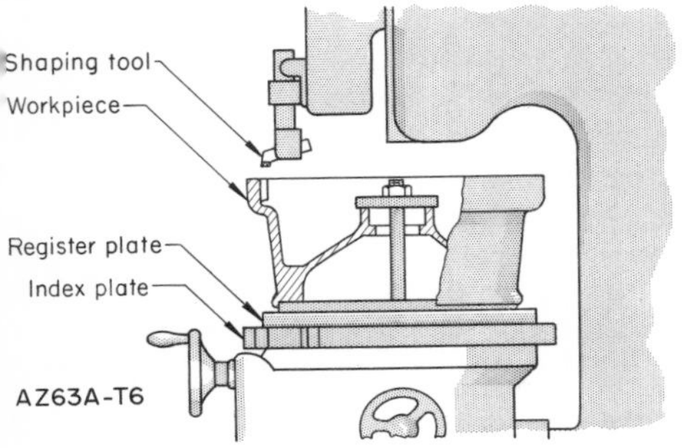

Details of Carbide Tool

Width	0.875 in.
Corner radius	0.020 in.
Top thickness	⅛ in.
Rake angle	0°
Nose clearance angle	10°
Side clearance angle	5°
Side relief angle	4°

Operating Conditions

Speed	76 strokes per min (25 sfm, approx)
Feed	0.008 in. per stroke
Cutting fluid	None
Tolerance, slot depth	±0.005 in.
Tolerance, slot width	+0.000, −0.001 in.
Tolerance, slot spacing	Within 0.003 in. of true position
Production rate	2.26 pieces per hour
Tool life per grind	80 pieces

Fig. 6. Machining internal slots in a cast wheel on a vertical shaper (Example 980)

machined face is available, the drill bushing may be held tightly against the machined face during drilling. This allows chips to be brought back through the bushing.

Shallow Holes. Drilling holes in magnesium to a depth less than four times the diameter presents few difficulties, and standard twist drills (center of Fig. 8) can be used. Polished flutes are recommended, to aid in clearing chips, and cutting edges must be kept sharp.

The two examples that follow describe modifications in operating conditions or in drill design that resulted in increased efficiency in drilling shallow holes in die castings.

Example 982. Increased Feed for Greater Efficiency in Drilling Magnesium Die Castings

At a feed of 0.0088 ipr, the machining time for drilling two 0.218-in.-diam holes through an AZ91B die casting was 4.17 sec. This time was reduced by nearly a third, to 2.85 sec, by increasing feed rate to 0.0115 ipr and slightly reducing total stroke.

Cam-feed heads and a high speed steel drill with a 42° helix angle were used at 3500 rpm. Mineral oil with an addition of sperm oil, previously used in machining aluminum, flooded the tool and the workpiece during drilling.

The drills were removed and reground at the end of each shift to reduce breakage and to prevent burrs on the breakthrough side of the hole. An average of 4000 pieces were drilled between regrinds.

Example 983. Modified Drills for Reduced Clogging and Wear (Fig. 9)

Slow-spiral, wide-flute, narrow-land drills, similar to those used for plastics, were modified for drilling three holes in die castings before tapping, as shown in Fig. 9. This modification reduced clogging of drills, excessive wear on the outside diameter, and the breakage usually experienced with drills with conventional spirals and lands. Drill bushings were required, to prevent wander. Each workpiece was mounted in an air clamping fixture and was then drilled using automatic air feed. Drills were changed when they could no longer maintain dimensional accuracy.

After being drilled, the holes were tapped as described in Example 991. Both operations were performed on a special drilling-and-tapping machine. Additional processing details are given with Fig. 9.

Table 2. Nominal Speeds and Feeds for Drilling, Gun Drilling, Reaming and Counterboring of Magnesium Alloys

Operation	Speed, sfm(a)	Feed, ipr, for hole diameter of: 1/16 in.	⅛ in.	¼ in.	½ in.	¾ in.	1 in.	1½ in.	2 in.
Drilling	140 to 330	0.001	0.003	0.007	0.012	0.016	0.020	0.025	0.030
Gun drilling	650	0.001	0.001	0.003	0.005	0.008	0.010	0.010	0.010
Reaming	400(b)	....	0.005	0.008	0.012	....	0.016	0.020	0.030
Counterboring:									
High speed steel	640(c)	....	....	0.005	0.006	0.007	0.0085	0.011	0.013
Carbide	1600(c)	....	....	0.006	0.007	0.008	0.010	0.012	0.014

(a) Limitations of machine or rigidity or both may require lower speeds. (b) For high speed steel; for carbide reamers, speed is 850 sfm. (c) For 3-in.-diam holes use 0.016 ipr. (Data are adapted from tables compiled by Metcut Research Associates, Inc.)

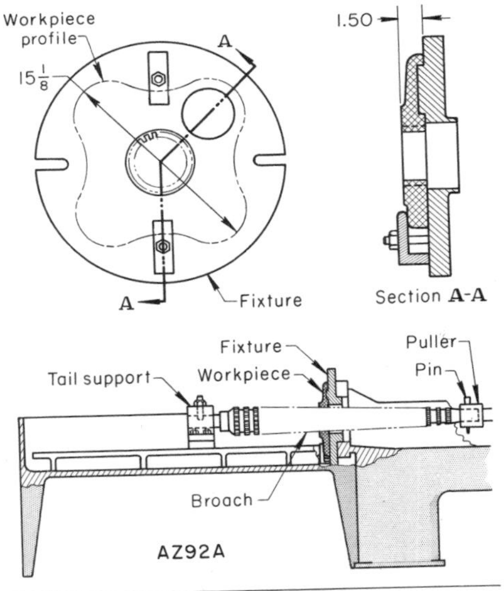

Details of Broach Teeth

Pitch	13/32 in.
Land	⅛ in.
Face (hook) angle	15°
Backoff angle	1°
Side relief angle	1°

Operating Conditions

Speed	20 sfm(a)
Cutting fluid	Sulfurized oil
Tolerance on pitch diameter	±0.001 in.
Maximum permissible involute error	0.0008 in.
Time per piece	3.75 min(b)
Production rate	16 pieces per hour
Tool life per grind	500 pieces(c)
Machining cost per piece	$1.49(d)

(a) Maximum speed for this machine. (b) 16 sec for the stroke; 5 sec for the ram to return to the fixture; 10 sec for unpinning the broach and retracting it; 14 sec for pinning the broach; 3 min for loading, unloading and cleaning. (c) Estimated; sharpening not required for production quantity. (d) Includes setup cost of $40.80.

Fig. 7. Broaching spline teeth in a cast magnesium part (Example 981)

Drilling of Sheet. Magnesium sheet can be drilled with a sharp, standard twist drill (118° point angle), but a slightly modified drill (at right in Fig. 8) is recommended for mass production of accurate holes with a good finish and minimum burr. The point angle of this drill is reduced to approximately 60° to prevent "walking" of the drill, to reduce thrust, and to prevent abrupt change of thrust when breaking through. The chisel-edge angle is 120° to 135°. The web is thinned and the ends of the cutting edges rounded. A thin web at the point helps to center the drill and reduce thrust; the rounded corners provide a smooth finish and reduce burrs. A helix angle of about 10° prevents the work from climbing the drill on breakthrough.

Gun Drilling. A typical gun drill for magnesium (Fig. 10) consists of a cylindrical driver with a flat cutout, a crimped tubular shank through which cutting fluid can flow, and a carbide head or tip. Typical angles are shown

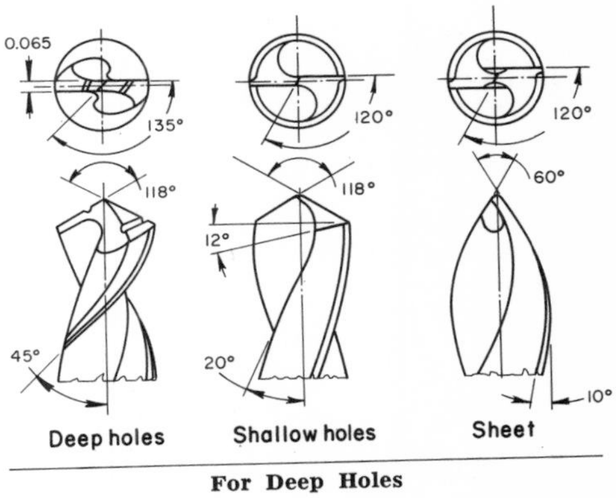

For Deep Holes

Point angle	118°
Helix angle	40° to 50°
Chisel-edge angle	135° to 150°
Web	Constant thickness
Flutes	Polished

For Shallow Holes

Point angle	118°
Helix angle	10° to 30°
Chisel-edge angle	120° to 135°
Relief angle	12°
Flutes	Polished

For Sheet

Point angle	60°
Helix angle	10°
Chisel-edge angle	120° to 135°
Web	Thinned at point
Corners	Rounded

Fig. 8. Recommended designs of twist drills for magnesium

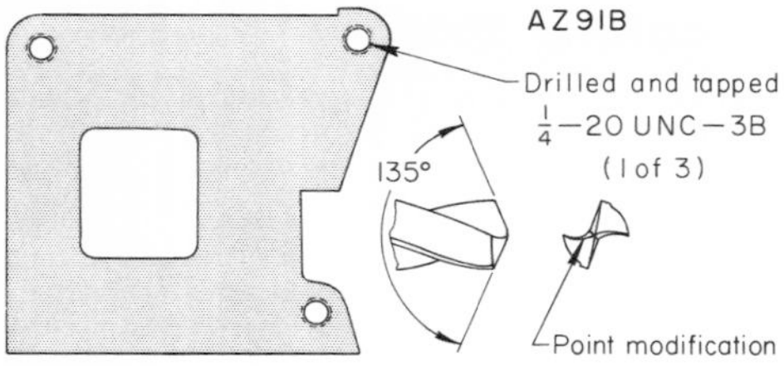

Drilling Conditions

Speed	300 sfm
Feed	0.004 ipr
Cutting fluid	Mineral oil(a)
Drill life per grind	1000 pieces

(a) Viscosity, 50 sus at 100 F

Holes were drilled through (9/16-in. nominal depth) with a No. 7 drill (0.201-in. diam), then tapped with 1/4–20 UNC–3B threads.

Fig. 9. Holes in the die casting shown were drilled with drills of the modified design shown (Example 983), *and then tapped.* (Example 991)

in Fig. 10, although these vary in practice in different plants. For example, in one plant cutting-edge angles of 10° and 10° are used, instead of 20° and 42° as shown in Fig. 10. Dimensional tolerance of the drill tip is from −0.0002 to +0.0000 in. Gun drills are end-cutting tools with an outer cutting angle and an inner angle, and with no back or side rake and only one axial flute.

In gun drilling, the tip of the drill passes through an accurate starting bushing and into the workpiece. The inside diameter of the bushing, which should be replaced when it becomes 0.0006 in. oversize (depending on required accuracy), has a tolerance of −0.0000 to +0.0002 in. After the tip enters the workpiece, the hole it has cut acts as a guide. The cutting fluid is delivered to the cutting point by a high-pressure system (400 psi minimum for 1/4-in.-diam holes and higher pressure for smaller holes) that contains filters for removing metal chips and foreign particles. Cutting speeds for average machining conditions are usually 650 sfm or less (depending on the capability of the machine).

A speed of 650 sfm is suggested in Table 2, along with feeds of 0.001 to 0.010 in., depending on hole size.

Production applications of gun drilling deep holes in magnesium are described in the following two examples.

Example 984. Gun Drilling Holes 37 Diameters Long in Brake Housings (Fig. 11)

The setup shown in Fig. 11 was used for gun drilling a hole 3/16 in. in diameter and 7 in. deep in a magnesium alloy brake housing. The gun drill had a solid-carbide tip 3/16 in. in diameter, a standard steel shank with a center section made of round alloy steel tubing, a 110° V-shaped flute for chip clearance and a V-shaped cutting edge. One side of the cutting edge was about one fourth of the tool diameter and was ground to an angle of 42°; the other side was ground to 21°. The over-all length of the drill was 13 in.

A single-end precision boring machine with a 3-hp, 3600-rpm spindle adapted for gun drilling was used for the operation.

Drills were changed when cutting edges became dull enough to cause an increase in tool pressure and therefore an increase in torque, which could cause the hollow center section of the drill to be distorted and the brazed carbide tip to be severed from the hollow center section. Additional processing details are given with Fig. 11.

Example 985. Gun Drilling Holes 29 Diameters Long in Brake Carriers (Fig. 12)

Eight holes 7¼ in. deep by ¼ in. in diameter were gun drilled in sand cast aircraft brake carriers 15½ in. in diameter by 3 in. thick. Figure 12 shows the workpiece and the drilling setup. The work was mounted in a fixture that located it on a center bore. A 7½-hp deep-hole drilling machine and a carbide-tipped gun drill with a top rake of 10°, a side clearance angle of 15°, and a chip breaker were used. The workpiece was indexed at each of eight locations to drill the required holes. The cutting fluid and pressure of the gun drill cleared the chips. Further details are given with Fig. 12.

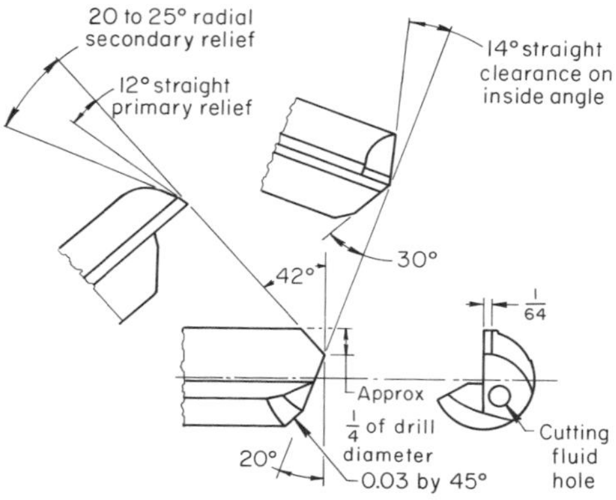

Fig. 10. Gun drill for magnesium

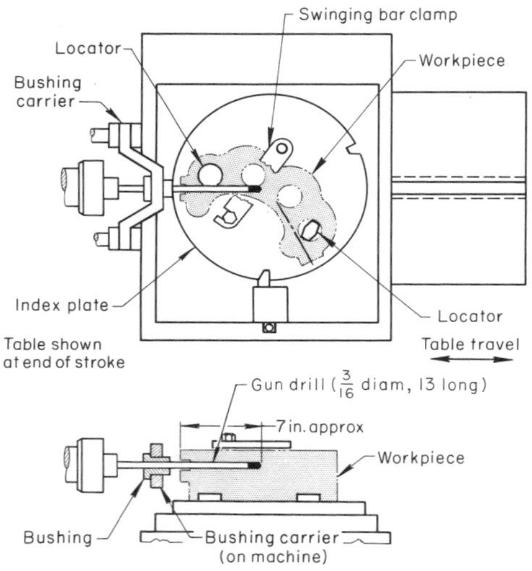

Speed	176 sfm
Feed	0.003 ipr
Cutting fluid	Sulfurized oil
Production rate	20 pieces per hour
Downtime for changing tools	15 min
Drill life per grind	400 pieces

Fig. 11. Gun drilling a magnesium alloy brake housing (Example 984)

Reaming

Reamers for magnesium should have fewer flutes than those used for most metals so as to provide more chip space. Reamers under 1-in. in diameter usually have four or six flutes. There should be an even number of flutes with opposing cutting edges spaced at 180° (Fig. 13).

Reamers for machining magnesium usually have 45° chamfer, 7° rake, a 0.006 to 0.012-in. margin with no relief, a primary relief angle of 5° to 8°, and a secondary relief angle of approximately 20°. Flutes can be straight or have a negative helix of up to −10°. Reamers with either high speed steel or carbide cutting edges are suitable for magnesium, the choice depending on the number of holes to be reamed.

Holes drilled for reaming should allow enough stock for the reamer to take a definite cut (a minimum of 0.010 in. from the diameter), because with less stock for reaming, burnishing is likely to occur. A maximum allowance of 0.015 in. on the diameter is preferred, although greater amounts are often removed. If too much stock is removed, chips will build up in the flutes and eventually jam the reamer.

Cutting speeds generally are from 100 to 400 sfm for high speed steel reamers and up to 850 sfm for reamers with carbide cutting edges. Table 2 shows speeds of 400 and 850 for high speed steel and carbide, respectively, but, these speeds are maximum, and in many operations the machine used is not capable of such speeds. Sometimes lower speeds must be used because of lack of rigidity in the setup. As a rule, the best surface finish and the most accurate holes are obtained by reaming at high speeds and medium feeds.

Feeds are 0.005 to 0.030 ipr, depending on hole size, as shown in Table 2.

Typical production practice for reaming magnesium is described in the two examples that follow.

Example 986. Reaming Cast Brake Carriers With High Speed Steel (Fig. 14)

A six-flute high speed steel reamer was used in a variable-speed 5-hp drill press for reaming 7/8-in.-deep through holes in sand cast magnesium aircraft brake carriers. Figure 14 shows the setup used.

The reamer, 0.6750 +0.0003, −0.0000 in. in diameter, had polished flutes, a 0.020-in. margin with a 10° primary clearance and a chamfer lead of 45°.

Although a small buildup of metal sometimes occurred on the cutting edge of the

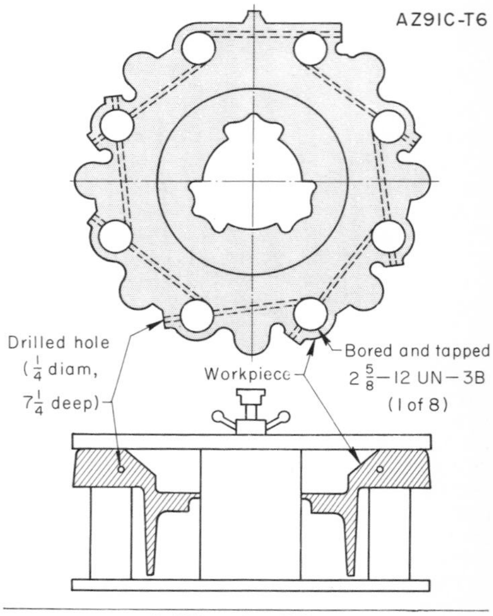

Drilling Conditions

Speed	313 sfm
Feed	0.0015 ipr
Cutting fluid	Mineral oil
Tolerance	Straightness within 0.005 in.
Specified finish	30 micro-in. max

Fig. 12. Aircraft brake carrier drilled with carbide-tipped gun drill. Large holes were tapped as described in Example 990. (Example 985)

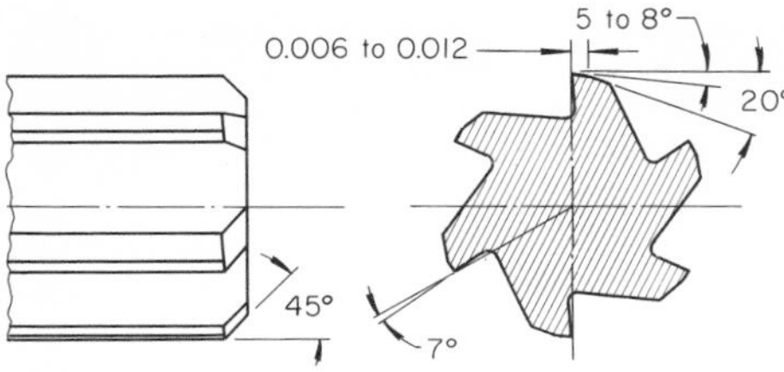

Fig. 13. Reamer design recommended for magnesium

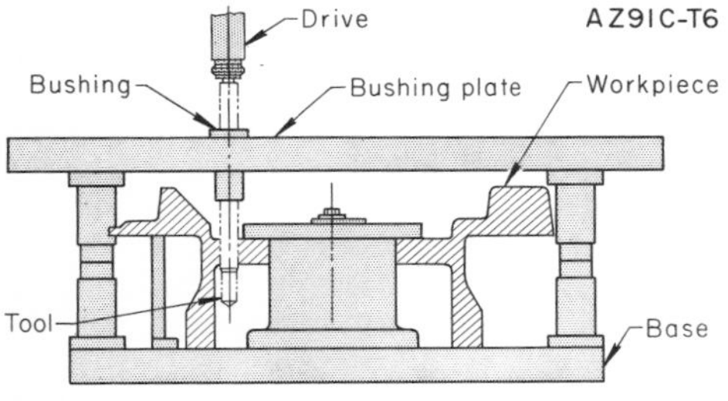

Speed	106 sfm
Feed	0.004 in. per flute
Metal removed from diameter	1/64 in.
Cutting fluid	Low-viscosity mineral oil
Reamer life	600 holes per grind

Fig. 14. Reaming a 1/8-in.-deep through hole in a brake carrier (Example 986)

reamer, periodic removal of the buildup enabled the reamer to hold size and finish for about 600 holes. Additional processing details are given with Fig. 14.

Example 987. Boring-Reaming With a Solid Carbide Tool (Fig. 15)

In the magnesium alloy casting shown in Fig. 15, a 0.218-in.-diam through hole was drilled from two sides and then bored and reamed simultaneously from one side. A single-flute solid-carbide tool (Fig. 15), which had a high surface finish, was used for the boring-reaming operation. The tool and work were flooded with cutting fluid. Additional processing details are tabulated with Fig. 15.

Counterboring

A tool recommended for counterboring of magnesium is illustrated in Fig. 16. A narrow margin of approximately 0.015 in. (not shown in Fig. 16), with adequate relief and clearance angles, allows adequate chip space and eliminates rubbing. Counterbores of many different designs, however, are used. For instance, the counterbore illustrated in Fig. 17 resembles a reamer.

Counterbores with cutting edges of either high speed steel or carbide can be used, depending on the number of holes to be counterbored.

Speeds often can be as high as 640 sfm for counterboring with high speed steel and 1600 sfm with carbide (Table 2). However, many machines cannot develop these high speeds, and lower speeds must be used. Feed rates are 0.005 to 0.014 ipr, depending on hole size and tool material. Recommended feeds are given in Table 2.

Typical practice for counterboring magnesium is described in the following example.

Example 988. Counterboring Cavities in AZ91B Die Castings (Fig. 17)

Two cavities in the AZ91B die casting shown in Fig. 17 were counterbored to a diameter of 0.996 in. on a two-station nonindexing machine. The workpiece was placed by hand in the first station, and one cavity was counterbored while Dryseal threads were tapped in a cored hole. (The tapping operation is described in Example 989.) The work was then manually placed in the second station, and the second cavity was counterbored, after which the workpiece was ejected automatically. Both stations cycled simultaneously, producing one finished part per cycle.

A six-flute carbide counterbore (see Fig. 17) with a cam-feed head was used. A 4° dwell on the highest point of the cam feed produced a smooth finish on the gasket surface at the bottom of the cavity, although an undesirable ribbon-type chip was produced. Fixtures were mounted at a 15° angle and had enough clearance to flush chips. Additional operating details are given with Fig. 17.

Roller Burnishing

Holes in magnesium alloy workpieces can be finished to close accuracy and low roughness by roller burnishing. (See the article "Roller Burnishing", and in particular Example 215.)

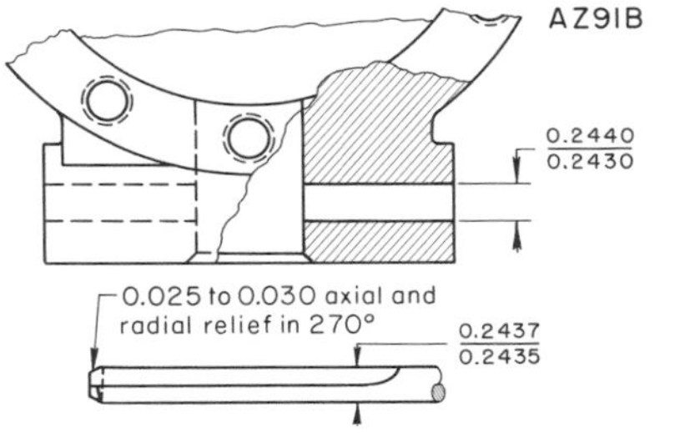

Reaming Conditions

Speed	200 sfm
Feed	0.0188 ipr
Metal removed from diameter	0.0245 in.
Cutting fluid	Mineral oil, with sperm oil added
Tolerance	±0.0005 in.
Production rate	500 holes per hour
Reamer life	Changed after each 8-hr shift

Fig. 15. Previously drilled hole in magnesium alloy casting at top was bored and reamed to finished size with combination tool of design shown (Example 987)

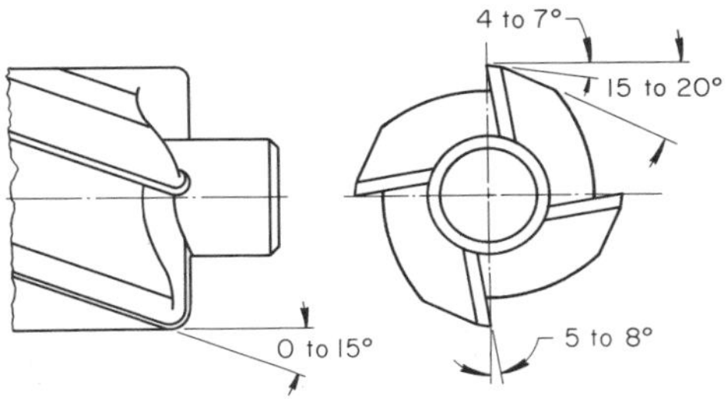

Fig. 16. Recommended design of tool for counterboring magnesium

Tapping and Die Threading

Standard taps are adequate if production quantities are small and if high-quality tapping is not required. When a large number of parts or close tolerances are involved, standard taps must be modified or taps designed especially for magnesium must be used.

Taps made of a general-purpose grade of high speed steel such as M1, M7 or M10 are usually adequate. Sometimes, for long production runs, taps are made of T5 or T15. Carbide taps are rarely used for magnesium alloys.

Straight-flute or helical-flute taps are recommended. The number of flutes is determined by limiting the total land width to about 30% of the tap circumference. Generally, two flutes are used for taps up to 3/16-in. diameter, three flutes for taps up to 3/4-in. diameter, and four flutes for taps over 3/4-in. diameter.

The tap design shown in Fig. 18(a) usually gives good finish and accuracy. However, if chips jam in the hole as the tap is being removed, a heel rake angle of 3° to 5° is recommended (Fig. 18b). This heel rake (with no relief) provides cutting action as the tap is removed, and results in a clean, accurately tapped hole.

If the tap cuts oversize, the rake angle should be decreased, and, conversely, increasing the rake angle will make the tap cut larger. Sometimes, taps on the high side of pitch-diameter tolerance are used, because tapped holes in magnesium are likely to close-in slightly after the tap is removed. This is especially true if high tapping speeds have been used.

Tapping speeds are 75 to 175 sfm; the lower speeds are used (*a*) when taps are small (because of their low capacity to conduct the heat of cutting), (*b*) when no cutting fluid is used, and (*c*) when the alloy is tough or abrasive. A cutting fluid is recommended, to improve surface finish, to increase tap life, and to produce accurate threads.

The four examples that follow describe production tapping.

Example 989. Tapping Dryseal Threads in Die Castings (Fig. 17)

Tapping produced 1/8–27 Dryseal (NPTF) threads in a cored hole in the die casting shown in Fig. 17. Tapping was done while

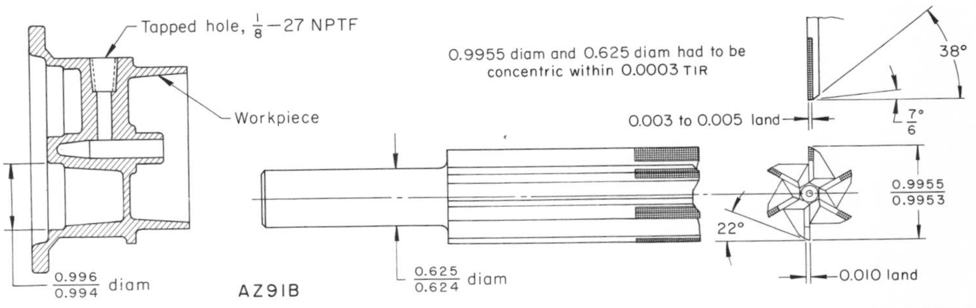

Counterboring Conditions

Speed	1500 rpm (390 sfm)
Feed	(0.010 ipr
Metal removed: 0.020 in. from sides and bottom	
Cutting fluid	Mineral oil, with sperm oil added
Tolerance	+0.000, −0.002 in.
Production rate	414 pieces per hour
Counterbore life	500,000 pieces per grind (1 million holes)

Fig. 17. Two cavities in die casting at left were counterbored to 0.996-in. diam with six-flute counterbore shown at right (Example 988). *Cored hole was tapped while casting was in position for counterboring of first cavity* (Example 989).

the workpiece was in the first station of a nonindexing machine for counterboring, as described in Example 988.

A five-flute high speed steel tap with a lead-screw unit, 0.3691-to-0.3701-in. pitch diameter, 15° hook angle, and no eccentric relief was used to produce a minimum of 0.31 in. of full threads. Cutting fluid was mineral oil with sperm oil added. Checking was done with a standard taper plug gage that had to enter 1¾ to 3¼ turns. Tap speed was 37 sfm and tap life was between 90,000 and 100,000 parts per grind.

A three-flute tap and the same cutting fluid had been tried, but there was no significant difference in tool life or thread quality.

Example 990. Tapping 2⅝–12 UN–3B Blind Holes in Sand Castings (Fig. 12 and 19)

A vertical drilling machine equipped with a 5-hp motor was used for tapping holes in a sand cast magnesium aircraft brake carrier. This casting (also discussed in Example 985 and shown in Fig. 12) was clamped in a fixture for tapping (Fig. 19). The solid, high speed steel tap used was adjustable and had a 2⅝-in. diameter, a 4-in. threaded segment, a 15° radial hook, and a three-thread lead.

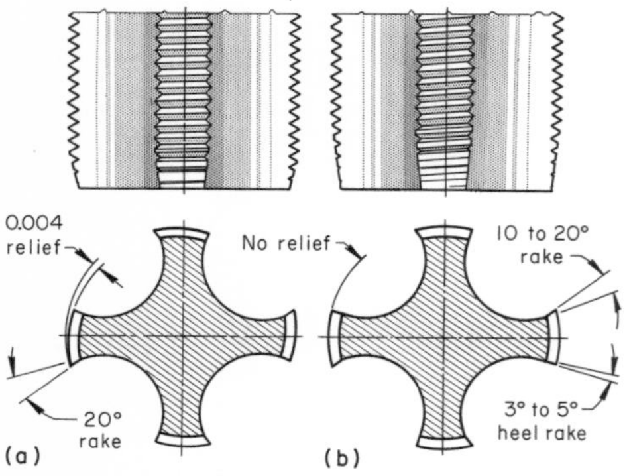

Fig. 18. (a) *Eccentric-ground tap for magnesium.* (b) *Heel-cutting tap, a concentric tap with no relief.*

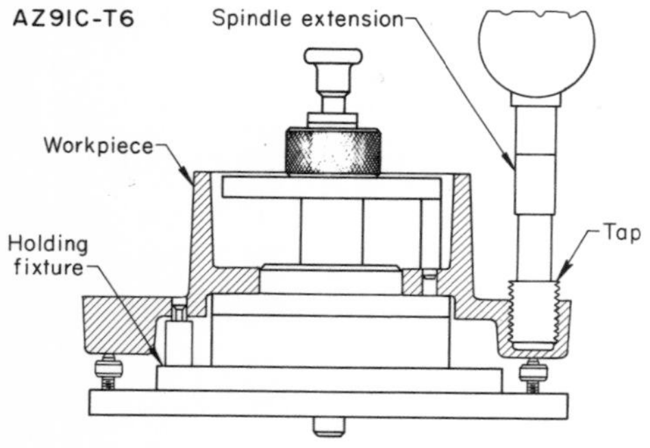

Fig. 19. Tapping a sand cast aircraft brake carrier (Example 990)

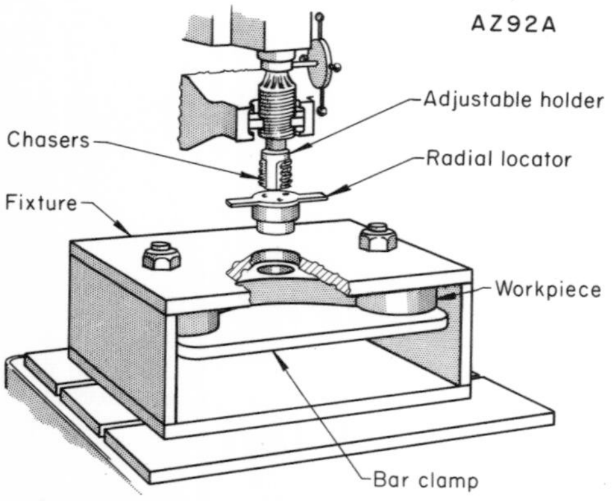

Fig. 20. Tapping six cavities in a 3-in.-thick cast brake housing (Example 992)

A light mineral oil was used as cutting fluid. Surface roughness was 60 micro-in. or lower. Tool life was about 1500 holes per grind.

Example 991. Tapping ¼–20 UNC–3B Threads In Die Castings (Fig. 9)

The drilled holes in the die casting described in Example 983 (Fig. 9) were tapped with a ¼–20 GH3 tap, using a lead screw. A special machine that both drilled and tapped was used, as in Example 983, and the same cutting fluid (mineral oil, with viscosity of 50 SUS) was used. It was important that the drills cut efficiently so that the life of the taps could be extended. Tap life was 1700 pieces.

Example 992. Tapping 3⅛–16 UN–3B Holes in AZ92A (Fig. 20)

A precision tapping-and-threading machine was used to tap six cavities in a 3-in.-thick brake housing cast of AZ92A alloy (Fig. 20). This machine was equipped with a rapid-reversing drive motor, and had a tapping capacity of ⅜ to 4⅛-in. diam, a maximum spindle stroke of 5½ in., a maximum tapping stroke of 3½ in., and 16 forward and 8 reverse spindle speeds.

The holding fixture, a rectangular, boxlike unit enclosed on all sides except the front, was mounted on the machine table so that a precision-bored hole in its top plate was aligned with the machine spindle. The workpiece was loaded and unloaded through the front of the fixture. A bar clamp held the workpiece loosely under the top plate. A radial locator plug was inserted through the hole in the top plate into the first cavity of the workpiece, to align the cavity with the machine spindle. The workpiece was then clamped securely in position, and the radial plug was removed before tapping was started. This procedure was repeated for each cavity.

Solid, adjustable holders capable of accommodating thread chasers ranging from 1⁵⁄₁₆ to 4⅛ in. in major diameter were used. For this operation, a chaser with a 22° chamfer and a 33° hook was best for producing the 3⅛–16 UN–3B threads required for each cavity. Oil was used as cutting fluid.

Machining time (including loading and unloading) was 11.76 min per piece; production rate was 5.10 pieces per hour. Tool life was about 100 pieces per grind. Tool change and adjustment required 1 hr.

Cold form tapping (see the article "Tapping", in this volume) is not recommended for magnesium, unless a 45% thread will have enough holding power for the application. Attempting to form a fuller thread is likely to cause embrittlement and subsequent spalling of the metal.

Because of the excellent machinability of magnesium, the life of thread-cutting taps is usually greater than for other metals. Thus, the only advantage in using the cold forming method is to eliminate the need for removing chips from the tapped hole.

Die Threading. Threading dies for magnesium should have approximately the same cutting angles as taps. A cutting-edge relief of 0.004 in. is generally recommended, although there are applications that require extremely good surface finishes and high accuracy. Under these conditions, a 3° rake angle on the heel side of the land will clean up the thread when the die is removed. Self-opening dies help to provide smooth threads.

Cutting angles of chasers for die threading should be about the same as those on single-point turning tools.

Multiple-Operation Machining

When magnesium is being machined in multiple-operation bar or chucking machines, the maximum speed of the machine is usually permissible. Heavy feeds are preferred, because they produce well-broken chips; feeds 40% higher than those used in machining free-cutting brass are common. Feeds of 0.015 ipr produce short coils; below this rate, chips are likely to be long coils or ribbons.

Alloy AZ31B is preferred for multiple-operation bar machining, although any of the other extruded magnesium alloys can be cut satisfactorily. The use of a mineral-oil type of cutting fluid is recommended.

Tools used for cutting magnesium in multiple-operation machines require little if any modification from those used for brass or used for single operations discussed in this article.

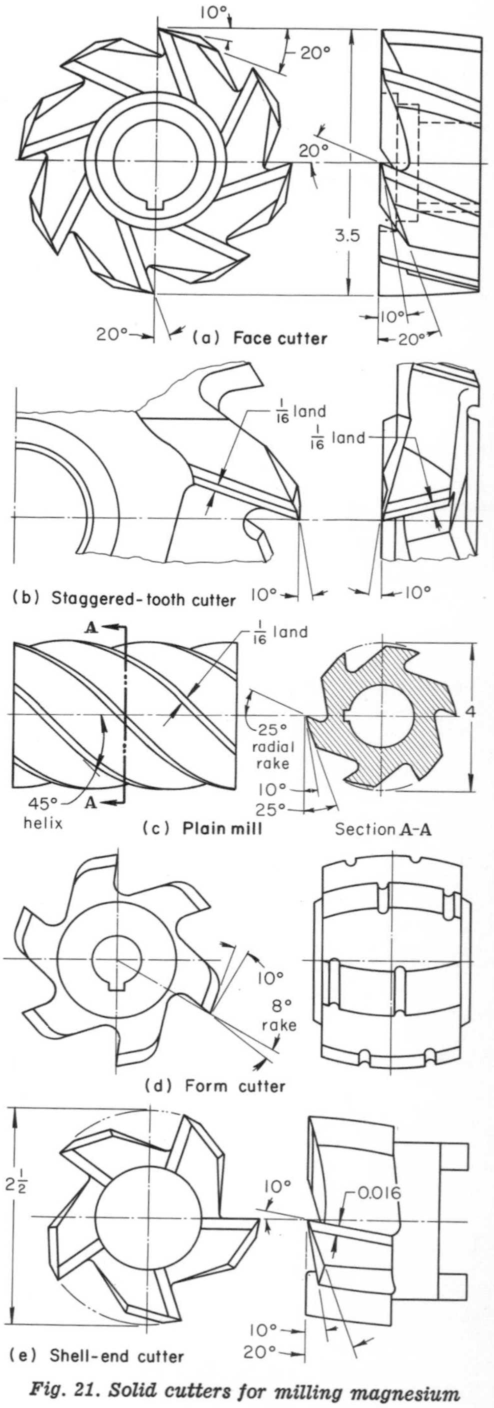

Fig. 21. Solid cutters for milling magnesium

Milling

Milling cutters for magnesium should have fewer teeth than conventional cutters used for steel or other metals — preferably only a half to a third as many. The larger chip space and the heavier cut resulting from the smaller number of teeth cause a reduction in frictional heat and an increase in chip clearance, and consequently to higher speeds, decreased distortion, lower power consumption, and smoother finish. Milling cutters for magnesium commonly have a 10° relief angle, 1/16-in. land width, and a 20° secondary clearance (Fig. 21a).

Solid Cutters. Figure 21 shows tool angles for five types of solid cutters for milling magnesium. Form cutters have a much smaller rake angle than plain cutters, because the heavier cutting pressure of form cutters would cause chatter if a larger rake angle were used.

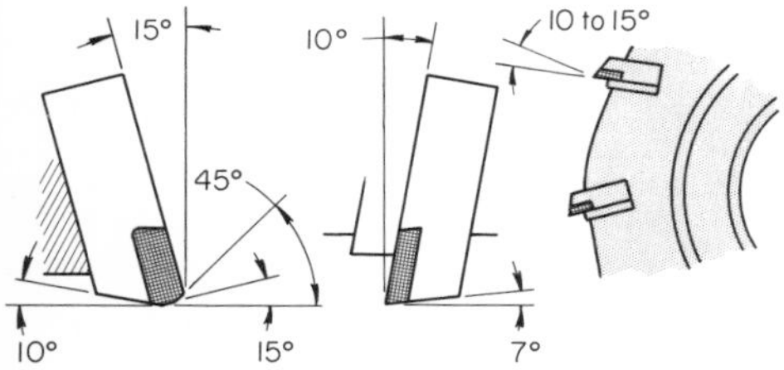

Fig. 22. Inserted-blade cutter for face milling of magnesium at high peripheral speeds

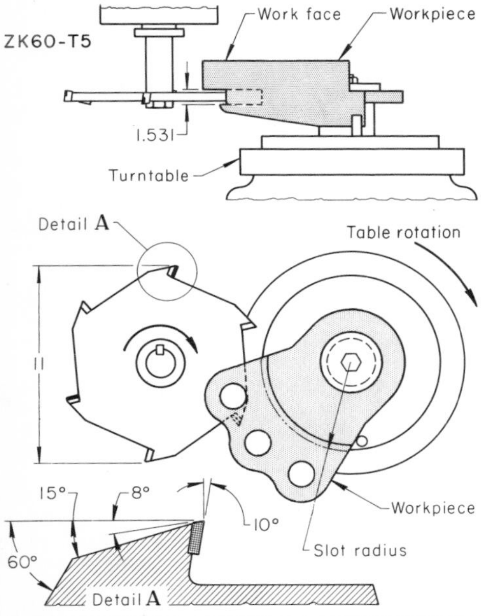

Cutter Details

Peripheral cutting-edge angle .... 10°
Face relief angle .... 3°
Radial rake angle .... 10°
Face cutting-edge angle .... 5°
Peripheral relief angle .... 8°
First peripheral relief angle .... 15°
Second peripheral relief angle .... 60°

Operating Conditions

Speed .... 1074 rpm (3100 sfm)
Feed .... 0.005 ipt
Cutting fluid .... None
Tolerance, side of slot to outer face: ±0.005 in.
Surface finish .... 100 micro-in. max
Production rate .... 4.36 pieces per hour
Downtime for changing cutters .... 25 to 36 min
Cutter life .... 200 to 250 pieces per grind

Fig. 23. Milling an irregular-shaped forging (Example 993)

Table 3. Nominal Speeds and Feeds for Face and Peripheral (Slab) Milling of Magnesium Alloys

Operation	Roughing (0.250-in. depth) Speed, sfm	Roughing Feed, ipt	Finishing (0.025-in. depth) Speed, sfm	Finishing Feed, ipt
Face milling, high speed steel cutters	900	0.022	1500	0.014
Face milling, carbide cutters	Max	0.025	Max	0.012
Peripheral milling, high speed steel cutters	900	0.018	1300	0.016

Details of an inserted-blade cutter for face milling are shown in Fig. 22.

Operating Conditions. Under ordinary circumstances, magnesium alloys can be milled with standard equipment at maximum spindle speeds, and with a feed rate and depth of cut as great as the capacity of the machine permits. As a rule, the only reason for using slower speeds is that higher speeds are likely to cause high residual stresses in the work metal.

Nominal speeds, feeds and depths of cut used for face, peripheral and end milling of magnesium alloys are given in Tables 3 and 4.

Examples. Equipment and operating conditions employed in milling of magnesium alloy parts are described in the two examples that follow.

Example 993. Peripheral Milling an Irregular-Shaped Forging (Fig. 23)

An 11-in.-diam carbide-tipped side-milling cutter was used on a vertical milling machine to produce a slot 1.531 in. wide in an irregular-shaped forging. The workpiece and setup are shown in Fig. 23. The milling machine, which had a 15-hp motor and 17¾-in. throat clearance, was capable of spindle speeds of 13 to 1300 rpm and table feeds of ¼ to 60 ipm.

The workpiece was clamped in a fixture that was mounted on a power-driven 24-in. turntable on top of the machine table. The fixture registered on the machine face and the bore of the workpiece, as shown in Fig. 23. Angular rotation of the turntable was 116°.

The forging weighed 15.5 lb before machining and 12.1 lb after machining. Tools were changed when they were worn enough to produce surface roughness greater than 100 micro-in. Additional processing details are given with Fig. 23.

Example 994. Face Milling of AZ91B Die Castings (Fig. 24)

A carbide-tipped cutter with a hardened steel body was used on a horizontal milling machine with a special setup to machine die castings (Fig. 24). Air clamps were used to hold the workpiece during machining. Cutters were changed when dull enough to produce burrs, which created a fire hazard. Additional processing details are given with Fig. 24.

Sawing

Magnesium can be cut readily with hand or power saws. Because only low cutting pressure is required, large cuts can be taken. This means that saws must have large chip spaces for a free cutting action. Too small a chip space rapidly loads the teeth and causes the saw to ride over the work. The set of the teeth on band saws and hacksaws must be relatively large, but no set is recommended for circular saw teeth. Relief angles on the teeth of circular saws must be adequate to minimize friction. Designs of circular saws, band saws, and power and hand hacksaws are summarized in Table 5.

Blades of circular saws may be made of high speed steel or may have carbide inserts.

For general cutting of magnesium plate, the saw teeth should have square tops with the face either straight or tilted 5°, with an alternate bevel (Fig. 25). For slotting operations a triple-chip blade with alternating chamfered roughing teeth and square finishing teeth is used to provide both cutting and clearing of the slot. Figure 26 shows the design of teeth for a 12-in.-diam slotting saw with 72 teeth.

Speed and Feed. For circular saws, high speed steel blades are limited to a

Table 4. Nominal Speeds and Feeds for End Milling of Magnesium Alloys

Operation	Speed, sfm	Feed, ipt, for cutter diameter of: ¼ in.	¾ in.	1 to 2 in.
High Speed Steel Cutters				
Roughing (a)	800	0.004	0.009	0.011
Finishing (b)	1000	0.003	0.005	0.008
Carbide Cutters				
Roughing (a)	Max	0.004	0.010	0.012
Finishing (b)	Max	0.003	0.005	0.009

(a) 0.050-in. depth. (b) 0.015-in. depth.

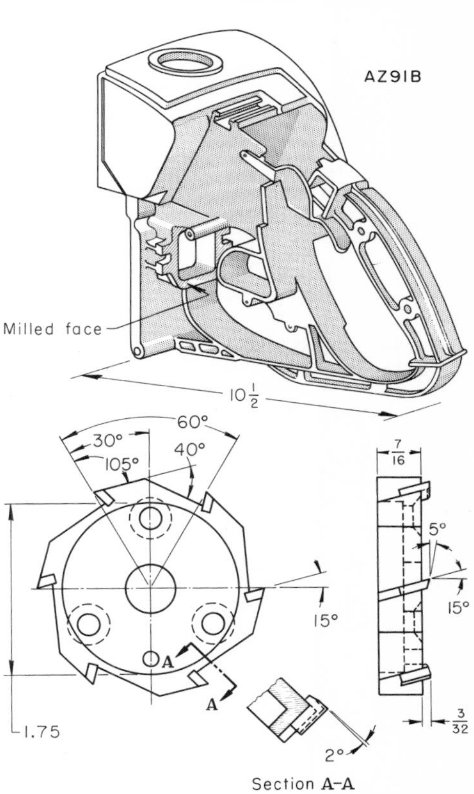

Speed .... 2800 rpm (1475 sfm, approx)
Feed .... 0.004 ipt
Cutting fluid .... None
Tolerance .... ±0.005 in.
Production rate .... 50 pieces per hour
Downtime to change cutters: 5% of mach'g time
Cutter life per grind .... 1000 to 1500 pieces
Labor cost per piece, machining $0.038

Fig. 24. Area indicated on die casting at top was milled with the carbide-tipped cutter shown at bottom, in a horizontal milling machine. (Example 994)

Table 5. Saws for Cutting Magnesium Alloys

Circular Saws	
Pitch (teeth per inch)	½ to 4
Tooth set	None
End relief angle	9° to 11°
Side relief (HSS saws)	1° to 1° 30′
Clearance angle	10° to 30°
Rake angle	5° to 20°
Face bevel angle	0° to 5°
Kerf	0.080 to 0.600 in.
Band Saws	
Pitch (teeth per inch)	4 to 6
Tooth set	0.02 to 0.05 in.
End relief angle	10° to 12°
Clearance angle	20° to 30°
Power Hacksaws	
Pitch (teeth per inch)	2 to 6
Tooth set	0.015 to 0.030 in.
Clearance angle	20° to 30°
Hand Hacksaws	
Pitch (teeth per inch)	12 to 18
Clearance angle	20° to 30°

peripheral speed of 2000 sfm; carbide-tipped blades can be operated at speeds as high as 10,000 sfm. Magnesium requires only one tenth the power required for sawing soft steel. A 12-in. carbide-tipped blade of proper design can cut 1-in.-thick plate at 250 linear inches per minute.

Power hacksaws are commonly used for sawing magnesium and can be operated at speeds as high as 160 strokes per minute, using a feed of 0.015 in. per stroke. Power band saws are commonly operated at 1200 sfm.

Grinding

It is seldom necessary to grind magnesium, because machining produces good finishes. When required, magnesium can be ground by any method.

Aluminum oxide grit is most widely used, although silicon carbide has also proved successful in many grinding applications. A relatively coarse grit is usually best, the surface finish being controlled mainly by the rate of feed, as in grinding most other metals. Wheels of hardness J or K are most commonly used. Most wheels for grinding magnesium have vitrified bond, although resinoid-bond wheels are sometimes used.

Typical conditions for grinding of magnesium are given in Table 6.

Dust Collection During Grinding

Because magnesium dust ignites readily and may explode if ignited while suspended in air, every precaution should be taken to insure its proper collection and disposal.

Wet Grinding. If magnesium is to be ground wet on a belt sander or disk grinder, sufficient cutting fluid should be used to collect all the dust and convey it to a collection point. The dust should always be kept wet with a copious supply of fluid, and no dry or damp dust should be allowed to collect on the machine. Mineral oil can be used as the cutting fluid. The sludge formed by the mixture of magnesium dust with cutting fluid must be disposed of by being burned according to safe practice (National Fire Protection Assoc., "Standards for Magnesium").

Dry Grinding. If magnesium is ground dry, the magnesium dust created must be collected in an approved dust collector, in which a water spray washes the dust from the air stream. The ducts should be short and as straight as possible. Connecting a number of dust-producing units to one exhaust system is not recommended.

Fig. 25. Design of 12-in.-diam, 48-tooth carbide (tipped) circular saw for cutoff operations at 1880 rpm (5900 sfm) on magnesium plate and extrusions

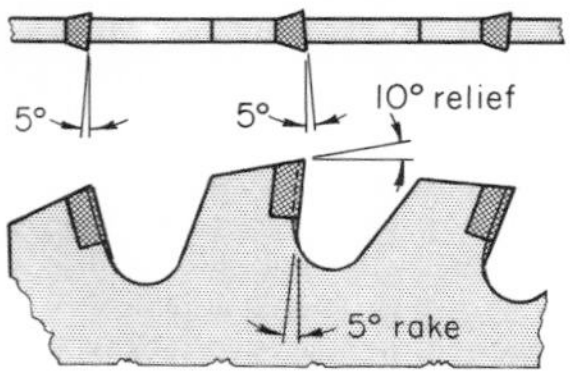

The electrical controls of collecting systems should be interconnected so that the grinders cannot be operated unless the water spray and exhaust system are working. Dust collectors should be kept clean and should be vented to the outdoors. The magnesium-water sludge should be collected to prevent excessive accumulation. This sludge should be kept under water.

The following safety precautions also should be observed in dry grinding.

1 Wheels should be used for magnesium alloys only. Before wheels are dressed, the collector should be cleaned thoroughly.
2 An adequate supply of recommended fire-extinguishing compound (Underwriters' Laboratories listed) should be available. Water must *never* be used in an attempt to extinguish a magnesium fire. It may cause an explosion.
3 Warning signs should be displayed in order to prevent unnecessary fire hazards.

Fire Precautions

By following correct machining practice, ignition of magnesium chips or shavings may be easily avoided. Magnesium must reach the melting point before it ignites. In roughing operations, it is very difficult to attain such temperatures, because the high heat conductivity of magnesium rapidly dissipates any frictional heat generated.

In finishing operations, however, where light shavings are produced, temperatures high enough for ignition may be reached. Factors that will produce such temperatures include very fine feeds or cuts, excessive dwell, dull or chipped tools, tools with small relief angles and small chip space, and high cutting speeds in the absence of a cutting fluid.

Sharp tools with ample clearance will reduce the fire risk. Coarser feeds, deeper cuts, and lower speeds will have a similar effect; where fine feeds and cuts and highest speeds are essential, an oil cutting fluid is recommended.

In turning, ignition may occur if cutting is interrupted and the feed is stopped while the work revolves with the tool still in contact. When cutting must be interrupted, to prevent ignition the tool should be backed away from the revolving work. In machining magnesium parts with an insert of ferrous metal, sparking may occur when the tool strikes the insert. The hazard presented by this sparking is minimized by the use of an oil cutting fluid.

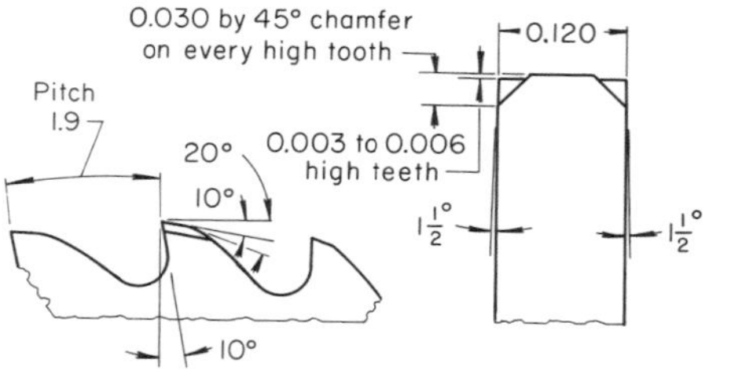

Fig. 26. Design of 72-tooth high speed steel or carbide-tipped circular saw for slotting magnesium

Table 6. Typical Wheels and Grinding Conditions for Magnesium Alloys

Surface Grinding	
Wheel classification	At-46-K-V
Wheel speed	5500 to 6500 sfm
Table speed	50 to 100 sfm
Downfeed per pass, roughing	0.003 in.
Downfeed per pass, finishing	0.001 in.
Crossfeed per pass, in.	⅓ wheel width
Cylindrical Grinding	
Wheel classification	C-46-J-V
Wheel speed	5500 to 6500 sfm
Work speed	150 sfm
Infeed per pass, roughing	0.002 in.
Infeed per pass, finishing	0.0005 in.
Traverse per work revolution:	
Roughing	⅓ wheel width
Finishing	⅙ wheel width
Centerless Grinding	
Wheel classification	C-60-K-V or At-60-J-V
Wheel speed	5500 to 6500 sfm
Infeed per pass, roughing	0.005 in.
Infeed per pass, finishing	0.0015 in.
Work feed	50 ipm
Regulating wheel	30-rpm rotation; 3° angle
Internal Grinding	
Wheel classification	At-36-K-V
Wheel speed	5000 to 6500 sfm
Work speed	80 to 160 sfm
Infeed per pass, roughing	0.003 in.
Infeed per pass, finishing	0.0002 in.
Traverse per work revolution:	
Roughing	⅓ wheel width
Finishing	⅙ wheel width

Under no circumstances should water or any "standard" fire extinguisher (of the pressurized or liquid type) be used to combat a magnesium fire. To extinguish a magnesium fire, cover the burning chips with dry graphite powder, dry cast iron turnings, or graphite-base or other approved proprietary compounds. Another method is to cover the burning magnesium with chloride-base dry powder. This material forms an air-excluding crust over the burning metal. This powder is commercially available and contains other ingredients that prevent water absorption and insure free-flowing characteristics. It can be discharged through hose lines or fixed piping, or from portable containers. It is suggested that a container full of a recommended extinguisher be at each machine and that the operator be trained to use the extinguisher.

If a fire does occur, the smothering material should be applied gently, to avoid scattering the fire. In its initial stage, the fire should be localized by scraping away adjacent turnings.

Accumulation of magnesium chips or turnings on, under or around machines should be avoided; spreading of a fire will be minimized if the quantity of chips near the machine is small. The chips should be removed from the machine at regular and frequent intervals and should be stored in tightly covered metal cans until reclaimed. Avoiding accumulation of magnesium dust on the operator's body or clothing is also important. (See also "Dust Collection During Grinding", on this page.)

Machining of Nickel and Nickel Alloys

By R. W. BREITZIG*

NICKEL-BASE ALLOYS can be machined by techniques used for iron-base alloys. However, certain requirements are imposed by the high strength of the nickel alloys, their tendency to work harden, and their "gumminess" in some conditions.

Work Hardening. Nickel alloys, like austenitic stainless steels, work harden rapidly. The high pressures developed during machining produce a hardening effect that retards further machining and may also cause distortion in parts that have small cross sections.

One method of reducing work hardening during machining is to work harden the material before machining, by cold deformation. Cold drawn, stress-relieved material is always preferred for machining, particularly when the smoothest finish is desired. Hot rolled material is next best, and annealed material is least desirable in most applications (however, solution annealing improves machinability by dissolving hard phases). On age-hardenable alloys, the best finish is produced by machining in the aged condition. The high strength and hardness of the aged material prevent heavy cuts; therefore, most roughing is done before age hardening.

A second method of minimizing work hardening during machining is to employ careful machining practices. Sharp tools with positive rake angles, which cut the metal instead of pushing it, are required. Feed rate and depth of cut must be sufficient to prevent burnishing or glazing. Tools should not be allowed to rub the work, either because of improper clearance or by being allowed to dwell in the cut.

Distortion. Even with the best machining conditions, some stresses are produced that may cause subsequent distortion of the work. For maximum dimensional stability, it is best to rough out the part almost to size, stress relieve it, and then finish it to size. Stress relieving has little effect on dimensions but may affect mechanical properties.

Microstructure. Grain size has little direct effect on the machinability of nickel alloys. In general, microstructure affects machinability in two ways:

1 The presence of graphite or sulfide phases greatly improves machinability.
2 Hard phases, such as carbides, nitrides, carbonitrides, oxides, silicates, and possibly also the gamma-prime phase $Ni_3(Al,Ti)$, are abrasive and cause rapid tool wear.

The nickel-chromium and nickel-chromium-iron alloys are less abrasive than the common grades of austenitic stainless steel, because they have lower carbon content and therefore fewer carbide particles. Probably the hardest and most abrasive of all the phases is titanium carbide (TiC), which is present in most of the age-hardenable alloys; another hard phase is columbium carbide (CbC). These carbides are usually present in as-rolled or mill-annealed products. Solution annealing at high temperature (2000 F or above) is required to dissolve them. Age hardening precipitates greater amounts of columbium and titanium carbide, along with chromium carbide and the gamma-prime phase. The refractory nature of these phases, together with their strengthening effect, makes age-hardened material less machinable, although chip action is improved.

These refractory phases have little or no effect on finishes obtainable. Softer and gummier alloys, such as those in the A, B and C groups identified below, are likely to have torn surfaces after roughing operations, and greater care is necessary in finishing operations. With proper technique, however, finishes of 4 to 8 micro-in. and finer can be obtained by grinding, honing and lapping. It may not always be possible to produce these finishes on Monel R-405 and Monel 501, because these alloys are likely to have sulfide and graphite inclusions.

Classification of Alloys

Table 1 classifies 38 nickel alloys with respect to machining characteristics. Except as noted in subsequent discussion, all alloys in a given group require similar machining practices.

Group A consists of alloys containing 95% or more nickel. These alloys have moderate mechanical strength and high toughness. They are hardened only by cold work. The alloys are quite gummy in the annealed and the hot worked condition, and cold drawn material is recommended for best machinability and smoothest finish.

Group B consists of most of the nickel-copper alloys. The alloys in this group have higher strength and slightly lower toughness than those in group A. They are hardened only by cold work. Cold drawn or cold drawn and stress-relieved material gives the best machinability and smoothest finish.

Group C consists largely of the nickel-chromium and nickel-chromium-iron alloys, which are similar to the austenitic stainless steels. They are hardened only by cold work, and are machined most readily in the cold drawn or cold drawn and stress-relieved condition.

Group D, which consists of the age-hardenable alloys, has two subgroups:

D-1 — Alloys in the unaged condition
D-2 — The alloys of Group D-1 in the aged condition, plus several other alloys in both the aged and unaged conditions.

The alloys in group D have high strength and hardness, particularly when aged. Material that has been solution annealed and quenched or rapidly air cooled is in the softest condition, and machines most easily. Because of its comparative softness, the unaged condition is necessary for greater ease in drilling, tapping and external threading.

Age-hardenable alloys take heavy machining best when they are either *(a)* solution annealed or *(b)* hot worked and quenched.

Although fully age-hardened material is usually too hard for tools with weak cutting edges, such as small drills and taps, and also for rough machining, it can be finish machined to fine finishes and close tolerances.

The best way to machine the alloys of group D, therefore, is to machine almost to size in the unaged condition, age harden, and then finish to size. Because the age-hardening treatment will relieve machining stresses, allowance must be made for warpage. A permanent contraction (about 0.0002 in. per inch) occurs during aging. Aged material has good dimensional stability.

Group E contains Monel R-405 only. This alloy and Monel 501 (graphitized condition) are designed for high production rates in automatic bar and chucking machines. These alloys are discussed separately in the section on Multiple-Operation Machining.

Cutting Fluids

Almost any cutting fluid, or none, can be used in machining nickel alloys.

In many applications, nickel alloys respond well to ordinary sulfurized mineral oil; sulfur imparts improved lubricity and antiweld properties. If the temperature of the oil and workpiece becomes high enough during machining to cause brown sulfur staining of the work, the stain can be readily removed with a cleaning solution of the sodium cyanide or chromic-sulfuric acid type. This should be done before any thermal treatment, including welding, because during further exposure to high temperature, the staining may cause intergranular surface attack. To avoid intergranular corrosion, the parts should be immersed in cleaning solution only long enough to remove the stain. High-speed machining operations that create high temperatures might preclude the use of a sulfurized oil because of sulfur embrittlement of carbide tools. (Many sintered carbides have a nickel or cobalt matrix that is sensitive to sulfur attack at high temperature.) However, flooding the cutting area with cutting fluid generally cools the tool enough to avoid breakdown of the carbide bond.

Water-base fluids are preferred in high-speed turning, milling and grinding, because of their greater cooling

* Technical Service Representative, Huntington Alloy Products Div., International Nickel Co.

Table 1. Classification of Nickel Alloys by Machining Characteristics

Alloy	Ni	C	Mn	Fe	S	Si	Cu	Cr	Ti	Al	Co or Cb	Mo or Mg
Machining Group A												
Nickel 200	99.5	0.06	0.25	0.15	0.005	0.05	0.05	...	...	...	...	...
Nickel 201	99.5	0.01	0.20	0.15	0.005	0.05	0.05	...	...	...	...	...
Nickel 204	95.2	0.06	0.20	0.05	0.005	0.02	0.02	...	...	...	4.50 Co	...
Nickel 205	99.5	0.06	0.20	0.10	0.005	0.05	0.05	...	0.02	...	...	0.04 Mg
Nickel 211	95.0	0.10	4.75	0.05	0.005	0.05	0.03	...	...	...	...	...
Nickel 220	99.5	0.06	0.12	0.05	0.005	0.03	0.03	...	0.02	...	...	0.04 Mg
Nickel 230	99.5	0.09	0.10	0.05	0.005	0.03	0.01	...	0.003	...	...	0.06 Mg
Nickel 233	99.5	0.09	0.18	0.05	0.005	0.03	0.03	...	0.003	...	...	0.07 Mg
Machining Group B												
Monel 400	66.0	0.12	0.90	1.35	0.005	0.15	31.5	...	...	...	...	...
Monel 401	44.5	0.03	1.70	0.20	0.005	0.01	53.0	...	...	...	0.50 Co	...
Monel 402	58.0	0.12	0.90	1.20	0.005	0.10	40.0	...	...	...	...	...
Monel 403	57.5	0.12	1.80	0.50	0.005	0.25	40.0	...	...	...	...	...
Monel 404	55.0	0.06	0.01	0.05	0.005	0.02	44.0	...	...	0.02	...	...
Monel 501, graphitized	65.0	0.23	0.60	1.00	0.005	0.15	29.5	...	0.50	2.80	...	...
Machining Group C												
Nickel 270	99.97	0.02	Trace	Trace	Trace	Trace	Trace	Trace	...	...	...	...
Monel K-500, unaged	65.0	0.15	0.60	1.00	0.005	0.15	29.50	...	0.50	2.80	...	...
Inconel 600	76.0	0.04	0.20	7.20	0.007	0.20	0.10	15.8	...	...	...	...
Inconel 604	74.0	0.04	0.20	7.20	0.007	0.20	0.10	15.8	...	...	2.0 Cb	...
Incoloy 800	32.0	0.04	0.75	46.0	0.007	0.35	0.30	20.5	...	...	...	...
Incoloy 801	32.0	0.04	0.75	44.5	0.007	0.35	0.15	20.5	1.00	...	...	...
Incoloy 804	42.6	0.06	0.85	25.4	0.007	0.50	0.40	29.3	0.40	0.25	...	...
Incoloy 825	41.8	0.03	0.65	30.0	0.007	0.35	1.80	21.5	0.90	0.15	...	3.00 Mo
Machining Group D-1												
Permanickel 300, unaged	98.6	0.25	0.10	0.10	0.005	0.06	0.02	...	0.50	...	...	0.35 Mg
Duranickel 301, unaged	94.0	0.15	0.25	0.15	0.005	0.55	0.05	...	0.50	4.50	...	...
Ni-span-C 902, unaged	42.0	0.02	0.40	48.50	0.008	0.50	0.05	5.4	2.40	0.65	...	...
Machining Group D-2												
Permanickel 300, aged	98.6	0.25	0.10	0.10	0.005	0.06	0.02	...	0.50	...	...	0.35 Mg
Duranickel 301, aged	94.0	0.15	0.25	0.15	0.005	0.55	0.05	...	0.50	4.50	...	...
Monel K-500, aged	65.0	0.15	0.60	1.00	0.005	0.15	29.50	...	0.50	2.80	...	...
Monel 501, aged	65.0	0.23	0.60	1.00	0.005	0.15	29.50	...	0.50	2.80	...	...
Inconel 700	46.0	0.12	0.10	0.70	0.007	0.30	0.05	15.0	2.20	3.00	28.5 Co	3.75 Mo
Inconel 702	79.5	0.04	0.05	0.35	0.007	0.20	0.10	15.6	0.70	3.40	...	...
Inconel 718	52.5	0.04	0.20	18.00	0.007	0.20	0.10	19.0	0.80	0.60	5.2 Cb	3.0 Mo
Inconel 721	71.0	0.04	2.25	7.20	0.007	0.12	0.10	16.0	3.00	...	...	...
Inconel 722	75.0	0.04	0.55	6.50	0.007	0.20	0.05	15.0	2.40	0.60	...	...
Inconel X-750	73.0	0.04	0.70	6.75	0.007	0.30	0.05	15.0	2.50	0.80	0.85 Cb	...
Inconel 751	72.5	0.04	0.70	6.75	0.007	0.30	0.05	15.0	2.50	1.20	1.00 Cb	...
Ni-span-C 902, aged	42.0	0.02	0.40	48.50	0.008	0.50	0.05	5.4	2.40	0.65	...	...
Machining Group E												
Monel R-405	66.0	0.18	0.90	1.35	0.050	0.15	31.5	...	...	...	...	...

effect. These may be soluble oils or chemical solutions. Except for grinding, which depends almost entirely on cooling and flushing, some chemical activity is always desired, and is generally provided by chlorine, amines or other chemicals.

For slower operations, such as drilling, boring, tapping and broaching, heavy lubricants and very rich mixtures of chemical solutions are needed. Oils should be used when drilling Nickel 200 and Inconel X-750. In the drilling and tapping of small-diameter holes, and in other operations in which lubricant flow and chip flushing are restricted, chlorinated hydrocarbon solvents such as trichlorethylene and 1,1,1-trichloroethane will improve performance. These less viscous fluids can be used alone or can be used for diluting mineral and lard oils.

A cutting fluid of the spray-mist type serves adequately for simple turning operations on all alloys.

Turning

Single-point turning tools used for cutting nickel alloys should have positive rake angles (Table 2), so that the metal is cut instead of pushed, as would occur if negative rake angles were used. A secondary function of the rake angle is to guide the chip away from the finished surface. The side cutting-edge angle is second in importance only to the rake angle.

The nose radius, which joins the end and side cutting edges, strengthens the tool nose and helps to dissipate the heat generated in cutting. A guide for size of nose radii is given with other recommended tool angles in Table 2.

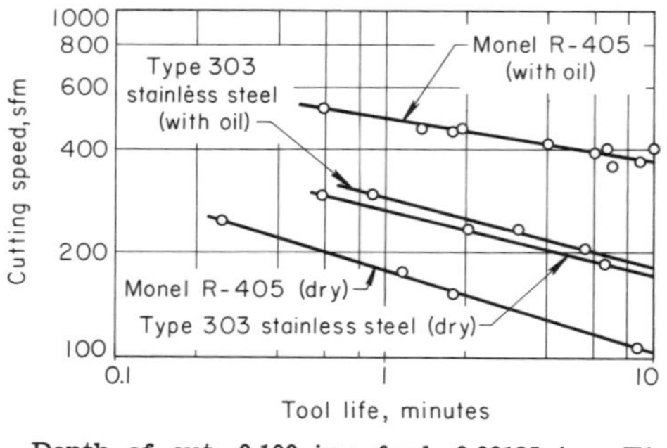

Depth of cut, 0.100 in.; feed, 0.00125 ipr; T1 high speed steel tools ground with 0° back rake angle and 0° side rake angle. Tool life was taken as the time required to develop a wear land of 0.050 in. Work was cold drawn bars.

Fig. 1. Effect of cutting oil on the relation of tool life to cutting speed of single-point turning tools

Chip Control. Nickel alloys present a minimum of chip disposal problems when cut with tools that have properly designed chip curlers or breakers. High speed steel tools require chip curlers, commonly referred to as lipped tools. The lip should include the proper rake angles for the alloy and should be wide and deep enough to cause the chip to curl and break but not to force it into a wad or tight knot.

Carbide tools should have chip breakers. With them, tool rake angles are plane surfaces that terminate at the chip breaker wall. The radius joining the chip-breaker wall and the rake-angle plane must be kept very small. The angle between the two surfaces must be 125° to 135°. A small radius and the proper angle will usually prevent the chip from welding in the chip breaker. Width and depth of the chip breaker depend on the feed rate used (Table 3).

Tool Material. Carbide tools permit the highest cutting rates and are recommended for most turning operations involving uninterrupted cuts. Cast alloy tools are recommended for turning group A alloys at optimum cutting rates. As with carbide tools, interrupted cutting is not included in this recommendation. High speed steel tools

Table 2. Design of Single-Point Tools for Turning Nickel Alloys

Angle	Roughing	Finishing
Back rake	0°	8°
End relief	6°	8°
Side relief	6°	8°
End cutting-edge	6°	60°
Side cutting-edge	To 45° (a)	To 45° (a)

Hardness	Alloy group	Positive side rake angle(b): HSS	Cast(c)	Carbide
45 R_B...	A	45°	22°	...
50 R_B...	A	40°	20°	...
65 R_B...	A, B	30°	15°	...
70 R_B...	A, B	30°	15°	20°
80 R_B...	A, B, C, D-1	25°	12°	20°
95 R_B...	A, B, C, D-1	25°	10°	20°
100 R_B...	B, C, D-1, D-2	20°	10°	10°
25 R_C...	C, D-1, D-2	15°	10°	10°
40 R_C...	D-2	12°	10°	10°
45 R_C...	D-2	10°	10°	5°

Depth of cut, in.	Nose radius, in.	Ratio of diameter to length	Nose radius, in.
1/32	0.013	1-to-30	0.010
1/16	0.020	1-to-25	0.012
3/32	0.031	1-to-20	0.015
1/8	0.035	1-to-15	0.018
3/16	0.040	1-to-10	0.023
1/4	0.062	1-to-5	0.029

(a) Depending on job requirements and chip load. (b) For finishing cuts and light-to-medium roughing cuts. Feed rates are up to 0.025 ipr and depth of cut to 0.250 in. (c) Cast cobalt-base alloy tools.

Table 3. Typical Depth and Width of Chip Breakers on Turning Tools

Feed rate, ipm	Depth, in.	Width, in.
0.005	0.015	0.060
0.010	0.020	0.080
0.020	0.030	0.150

should be used for interrupted cuts such as occur in the roughing of an uneven surface. They also are used for finishing to close tolerances, finishing to the smoothest surfaces, and cutting with the least work hardening.

Feeds and speeds for turning nickel alloys are given in Table 4. The centers of the ranges in Table 4 should be used as starting points in establishing the best conditions for specific jobs.

Tool Life. The effects of several machining variables on tool life in turning Monel R-405 are shown in Fig. 1, 2 and 3, in comparison with data for other materials. All material was machined in the cold drawn condition.

Planing and Shaping

The tools used for planing and shaping are similar to lathe tools.

For rough planing, the top rake angle of the tool is the most important; it must be positive and of large magnitude to achieve good cutting action. The optimum chip, resulting from a suitable combination of side cutting-edge angle and rake angle, is a small curl that curves over ahead of the tool and breaks as it hits the work.

The gooseneck type of planer tool should be used for finishing. Its spring action makes smooth cuts. The cutting edge of a gooseneck tool should be behind the centerline of the clapper-box pin, so that the tool will spring away from the cut and not dig in.

Cutting fluids are not essential for roughing, but sulfurized oil should be applied to the workpiece for smooth finishing cuts. Table 5 lists feeds, speeds and depths of cut used for planing. Speeds are generally 80 to 85% of those used for turning.

Heavy sections may be parted in a planer with the aid of a gooseneck finishing tool. Only light cuts (0.005 to 0.010 in. per stroke) may be taken. Continuous soluble-oil lubrication should be provided.

Practice for shaping operations is similar to that for planing.

Broaching

Although group D alloys are broached more cleanly in the age-hardened condition, high pressures are required for these materials in either the aged or unaged condition. For example, when broaching fir-tree profiles in a jet engine turbine wheel of solution-annealed Inconel X-750 (Rockwell B 93), pressures of 8 to 6 tons were required for roughing and 4 to 3 tons for finishing. When broaching the same section in fully age-hardened Inconel X-750 (Rockwell C 31), pressures of 6 to 3 tons were required. The decrease in power requirements for the harder material was attributed to cleaner cutting and less drag on the broach.

Sulfurized mineral oil is recommended as cutting fluid. Broaching speeds and face angles are as follows:

Alloy group	Speed, sfm	Face angle
A and B	10 to 18	12° to 18°
C and D-1	5 to 12	10° to 15°
D-2	6	8° to 10°

Drilling

In drilling nickel alloys, steady feed rates should be used. If the drill is allowed to dwell, excessive work hardening of the metal at the bottom of the hole will make it difficult to resume cutting and may result in breaking of the drill when it does take hold. The setup should be as rigid as possible. Stub drills are recommended. Drill jigs should be used whenever possible.

Standard high speed steel drills are satisfactory for general-purpose drilling of the alloys of groups A and B. These drills have a 118° point angle, a helix of about 30°, a 12° lip relief angle, and a chisel-edge angle of 125° to 135°.

Heavy-duty, high speed steel drills with a heavy web are recommended for drilling the alloys of groups C and D. Cobalt-bearing high speed steel drills give longer tool life. Cutting pressures are reduced and a positive effective rake maintained if the web is thinned

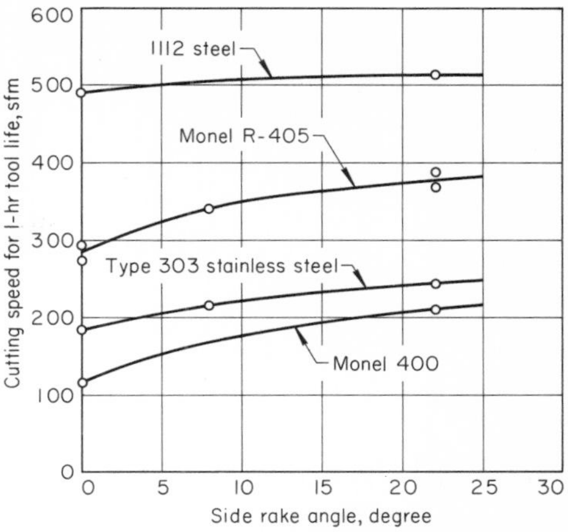

Depth of cut, 0.100 in.; feed, 0.00125 ipr; T1 high speed steel tools; sulfurized chlorinated cutting oil. Tool life was taken as the time required to develop a wear land of 0.050 in. Work was cold drawn bars.

Fig. 2. Effect of side rake angle on the speed for 1-hr tool life of single-point turning tools

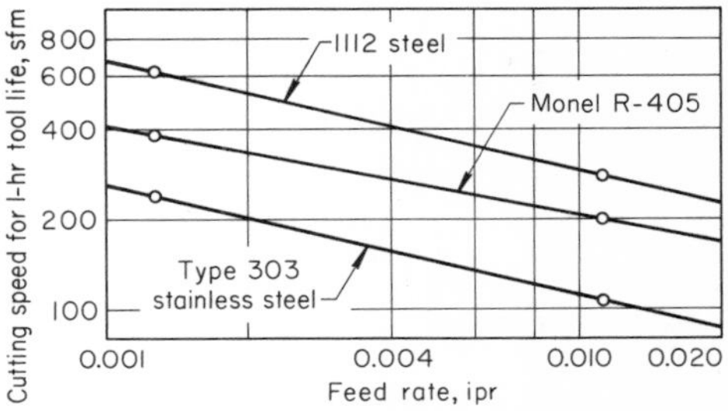

Depth of cut, 0.100 in.; T1 high speed steel tools ground with 8° back rake angle and 22° side rake angle; sulfurized chlorinated cutting oil. Tool life was taken as the time required to develop a wear land of 0.050 in. Work was cold drawn bars.

Fig. 3. Effect of feed rate on the speed for 1-hr tool life of single-point turning tools

Table 4. Conditions for Turning Nickel Alloys With Single-Point Tools

Alloy (any condition)	Hardness	Depth of cut, in.	High speed steel: Tool material	Speed, sfm	Feed, ipr	Cutting fluid	Cast alloy: Speed, sfm	Feed, ipr	Cutting fluid	Carbide: Tool material	Speed, sfm: Brazed	Disposable	Feed, ipr	Cutting fluid
A	45 R_B	0.250	T5	50 to 60	0.030	(a)	(c)	(c)	(c)	(c)	(c)	(c)	(c)	(c)
	95 R_B	0.050	M36	170 to 200	0.008	(a) (b)	370 to 400	0.008	(a) (b)	(c)	(c)	(c)	(c)	(c)
B	65 R_B	0.250	T5	60 to 70	0.030	(a)	(c)	(c)	(c)	C-6	250 to 300	275 to 325	0.020	(a)
	100 R_B	0.050	M36	90 to 100	0.010	(a)	150 to 200	0.008	(a)	C-7	300 to 350	350 to 400	0.008	(a)
C	75 R_B	0.250	T5	25 to 35	0.030	(a)	(c)	(c)	(c)	C-6	150 to 200	175 to 225	0.020	(a)
	30 R_C	0.050	M36	50 to 60	0.010	(a)	100 to 150	0.008	(a)	C-2	325 to 375	375 to 425	0.008	(a)
D-1 ..	80 R_B	0.250	T5	40 to 50	0.030	(a)	(c)	(c)	(c)	C-6	175 to 225	200 to 250	0.020	(a)
	35 R_C	0.050	M36	60 to 70	0.010	(a)	100 to 150	0.008	(a)	C-8	225 to 275	250 to 300	0.008	(a)
D-2 ..	85 R_B	0.250	T5	12 to 18	0.010	(a)	(c)	(c)	(c)	C-2	30 to 40	40 to 60	0.010	(a)
	45 R_C	0.050	M36	15 to 20	0.008	(a)	(c)	(c)	(c)	C-2	40 to 50	50 to 100	0.008	(a)
E	65 R_B	0.250	T5	70 to 80	0.030	(a)	(c)	(c)	(c)	C-6	250 to 300	275 to 325	0.020	(a)
	100 R_B	0.050	M36	120 to 130	0.010	(a)	175 to 225	0.008	(a)	C-7	300 to 350	350 to 400	0.008	(a)

(a) Water-base cutting fluid, oil emulsion or chemical solution. (b) Sulfurized or chlorinated oil, or mixed oils. (c) Not recommended.

Table 5. Speeds and Feeds for Planing Nickel Alloys

Alloy group	Roughing: Depth of cut, in.	Roughing: Table speed, sfm	Roughing: Feed, in.	Finishing: Depth of cut, in.	Finishing: Table speed, sfm	Finishing: Feed, in.	Parting: Table speed, sfm	Parting: Feed, in.
A	5/8	50 to 60	0.050	0.010	50	0.250	50	0.005 to 0.010
B	5/8	40 to 50	0.050	0.010	40	0.250	40	0.005 to 0.010
C	3/8	15 to 20	0.050	0.010	15	0.250	15	0.005 to 0.010
D-1	3/8	20 to 30	0.050	0.010	20	0.250	20	0.005 to 0.010
D-2, unaged	3/8	5 to 10	0.040	0.010	5	0.250	5	0.005 to 0.010
D-2, aged	3/8	5 to 10	0.040	0.010	5	0.250	5	0.005 to 0.010

Table 6. Feeds and Speeds for Drilling Nickel Alloys With Twist Drills

Drill diameter, in.	Feed, ipr
Less than 1/16	0.0005 to 0.001
1/16 to 1/8	0.001 to 0.002
1/8 to 3/16	0.002 to 0.004
1/4 to 5/16	0.003 to 0.005
3/8 to 7/16	0.004 to 0.007
1/2 to 11/16	0.006 to 0.010
3/4 to 1	0.008 to 0.015

Alloy group	Speed, sfm	Alloy group	Speed, sfm
A	55 to 75	D-2, unaged	10 to 12
B	45 to 55	D-2, aged	8 to 10
C	25 to 35	E	50 to 70
D-1	20 to 30		

Table 7. Speeds and Feeds for Spade and Gun Drilling of Nickel Alloys

Alloy group	Speed, sfm	Feed, ipr
Spade Drilling (1-to-2-In.-Diam Tool of M2 HSS)		
A	55 to 75	0.005 to 0.007
B	45 to 55	0.005 to 0.007
C	25 to 35	0.005 to 0.007
Gun Drilling (1/16-to-2-In. Drill)		
A	220	0.0001 to 0.002
B	300	0.00015 to 0.004
C	320	0.0002 to 0.005
D-1	220	0.0001 to 0.003
D-2, unaged	100	0.0001 to 0.003
D-2, aged	60	0.0001 to 0.003

Alloy group	Insert material for gun drills
A	Cast alloy (40 Co – 30 Cr – 18.5 W)
B	C-6 carbide
C, D-1, D-2	C-2 carbide

at the chisel point. Increasing the point angle to 135° is helpful.

Crankshaft drills are useful for producing deep holes. These drills have a heavy web and a helix angle slightly higher than normal; the web is thinned at the chisel point. Cutting action with drills larger than 3/4 in. in diameter will be improved by grinding several small grooves through the lip, extending back along the lip clearance. The spacing of the grooves should be staggered between the two cutting edges. The effect of this serration will be to produce narrow chips with less tendency to foul in the helical flutes.

Speeds and feeds for drilling with twist drills are given in Table 6.

Spade drills are regularly used for deep-hole and heavy drilling — 1½ in. in diameter and greater. The drill is secured in a steel head, which is attached to a rigid bar, with bearing support between the work and tailstock. Spade drills are made of high speed steel; the cutting edges may be tipped with carbide. Lead holes should be made with a drill having a point smaller than that of the spade drill. Table 7 shows speeds and feeds for spade drilling.

Gun drills are used mostly for producing deep holes of diameter up to and including 2 in., but they are occasionally used for holes as large as 2½ in. in diameter. Appropriate speeds and feeds are cited in Table 7.

A highly sulfurized oil is recommended for gun drilling and other deep-hole drilling and finishing. Cutting fluid pressure should be about 800 psi for 3/16-in. holes, decreasing to about 200 psi for 2-in. holes.

Reaming

Fluted reamers for nickel alloys are produced as standard items and are characterized by:

1 High speed steel tool material
2 Right-hand cut
3 Right-hand helix (positive axial rake)
4 Positive radial rake.

Operating speed for reaming should be about two thirds the speed for drilling the same material (Table 6), but not so high as to cause chatter. Other factors contributing to chatter are lack of rigidity in the setup, misalignment, and dull tools.

Reamer feed into the work should be 0.0015 to 0.004 in. per flute per revolution. Too low a feed rate will result in glazing of the work and excessive wear of the tool. An excessive feed rate reduces the accuracy of hole dimensions and the quality of the finish. In reaming nickel alloys, sufficient stock must be removed so that non-work-hardened or nonglazed material is being cut. Good starting points for stock removal are 0.010 in. for a 1/4-in. hole, 0.015 in. for a 1/2-in. hole, and up to 0.025 in. for a 1½-in. hole.

Reamers must be kept sharp; honed reamers produce smoother surfaces and last longer between grinds.

Flat (solid) reamers and built-up (inserted-blade) reamers are used for holes 1½ in. in diameter or larger. Blind holes are reamed with flat reamers, and through or stepped holes with built-up reamers. A reaming allowance of 1/16 to 1/8 in. on the diameter should be provided for both types.

Conventional fluted reamers, flat solid reamers, and insert tools for built-up reamers are made of high speed steel (usually M2 and M10). Composite tools having steel shanks tipped with carbide are also used for all types of reamers and are recommended for group D-2 alloys. Grades C-2 and C-6 carbide give good results. Sulfurized or chlorinated oil should be used as cutting fluid.

Because flat and built-up reamers constitute a specialized area of finishing inside diameters, cutting speeds and feeds must be developed for each job. Speeds of about two thirds those listed for turning with similar tool material and feeds of 0.008 to 0.010 ipr should be used as a starting point.

Tapping and Threading

The most important factor in tapping is the selection of the proper drill size. The standard tap drill selection tables, in use for many years, are based on 75% of full thread depth and were established by experience with low-strength materials such as brass. Modern high-strength materials, however, provide adequate holding strength with less thread depth. For most requirements, 55% is sufficient, and more than 60% is seldom required. This is particularly true for holes tapped to a length of 1½ times the bolt diameter. Tests of thread strength show that any increase in thread depth above 60% for the tapped member does not increase the static strength of a threaded joint. In general, the bolt will break first (before threads strip) in holes tapped to 55% of full thread.

Decreasing thread profile depth decreases the torque necessary to drive the tap and markedly decreases tap breakage. As a general rule, torque is doubled when thread depth is increased from 60 to 72% and tripled when thread depth is raised to 80%.

Suggested percentages of thread depth for nickel alloys are given in Table 8.

For most applications, standard high speed steel four-flute taps are recommended. These standard taps are readily obtained with a 7° hook angle. The alloys of group D-2 are best tapped with serial taps, which are standard taps modified in diameter so that each successive tap increases the thread diameter proportionately.

Tapping speeds are shown in Table 8. The age-hardenable alloys should be tapped in the unaged condition whenever possible. Ample cutting fluid is essential for both hand and machine tapping, with liquid chlorinated wax preferred.

Lathe Threading. Thread-cutting lathe tools are ground according to the principles described for turning tools, but the angles on threading tools are smaller than on turning tools so that the small nose of the threading tool is well supported. Because of the weakness of the tool nose and the small volume of tool available to dissipate heat, single-point threading must be done at lower speeds and feeds than those used for turning. Conventional single-point lathe practices for threading steel are adequate for threading nickel alloys.

The tool nose should be flooded with sulfurized oil during threading. If the machine is not equipped to pump oil on the work, the workpiece should be brushed with a sulfurized oil during the cutting operation.

Threading speeds are listed in Table 9. The depth of cut will vary, becoming less as the work progresses and more of the tool cutting edge is engaged in removing metal.

Die Threading. Threading dies must be kept sharp and flooded with cutting fluid (sulfurized oil or a rich mixture of soluble oil or chemical solution) during use.

A chamfer angle of 15° to 20° is recommended for producing V-threads where no shoulder is involved. The rake angle is 15° for threading mate-al of Rockwell C 30 hardness, and it is creased to 30° for threading material soft as Rockwell B 65.

The workpiece diameter should be to 1½% undersize to prevent binding the die. The exact undersize required ill vary with alloy and temper, but in be determined by one or two trials.

Speeds shown in Table 9 for single-oint threading apply also to die ıreading.

Thread Grinding. External threads ay be produced in group D-2 alloys ny condition) by form grinding. Aluinum oxide (150 to 320 grit) vitrified-ond grinding wheels (medium hard, pen structure) are used. The recomended grinding fluid is an oil of out 300 SUS viscosity at 70 F; it ould be filtered.

Multiple-Operation Machining

Monel R-405 and Monel 501 were deeloped for good machinability, and re recommended for machining in auomatic bar and chucking machines. ther alloys in groups A, B, C and D-1 an be machined in automatics, but e lower speeds required are seldom ossible with this type of equipment.

Monel R-405 combines the toughness, trength, and corrosion resistance of Ionel 400 with excellent machinability. his "free-machining" characteristic is btained by careful adjustment of mi-or alloying constituents, including the ontrolled addition of a small amount f sulfur. The resulting nickel-copper ulfides in the alloy act as chip reakers. Because of these inclusions, he surface finish on a machined Moiel R-405 part is inferior to that on a art made of Monel 400. Recommended utting speeds and feeds for Monel R-405 are shown in Table 10. Results of ctual production runs in automatic ar machines are given in the three xamples that follow.

Examples 995, 996 and 997. Multiple-Operation Machining of Monel R-405 Bars (Table 11)

Example 995. Monel R-405 bars ⅝ in. in liameter were machined in an automatic bar achine. Operations included turning, drilling, hreading and cutting off. High speed steel ools were used, and a sulfochlorinated cutting luid. A total of 575 parts were produced at he rate of 75 sec of machine time per piece. Tools were not excessively worn after 11.8 hr.

Example 996. Hexagonal ⅝-in. bars of Monel R-405 were form turned, drilled, reamed, hreaded and cut off in an automatic machine imilar to the one used in Example 995. Again high speed steel tools were used, but the utting fluid was a sulfurized mineral-base sperm oil. In this application, 495 parts were produced at the rate of 60 sec of machine time per piece. Surface finish was equal to or better than that in Example 995. Tools were not excessively worn after 8.2 hr.

Example 997. Workpieces similar to those machined in Example 996 were form turned, drilled, reamed, tapped and cut off; the same machine, tool material, and cutting fluid were used as in Example 996. In this application, 543 parts were produced at the rate of 45 sec of machine time per piece. Surface finish was equal to or better than that in Example 995. Tools required refinishing after 6.7 hr.

Monel 501 is a modification of Monel K-500, with machinability improved by increasing the carbon content and heat treating the alloy to precipitate graphite particles throughout the matrix. Because of the graphite particles, machined surfaces may not be as bright and smooth as those of machined Monel K-500. Recommended speeds and feeds are shown in Table 12.

Table 8. Speeds and Thread-Depth Percentages for Tapping Nickel Alloys

Alloy group	Tapping speed, sfm	Per cent of full thread
A and B	15 to 25	60
C and D-1	10 to 15	55
D-2	5 to 10	50

Table 9. Speeds for Single-Point and Die Threading

Alloy group	Speed, sfm
A, B and E	25 to 30
C and D-1	12 to 18
D-2	3.0 to 3.5

Monel 501 should be machined in the as-received condition. It can then be age hardened. The alloy can be rough machined, age hardened, and then finish machined. However, the age-hardened alloy can be cut only at the rates shown in Table 4 for group D-2 alloys.

Form tools, which are extensively used for automatic machining, must be sturdy, and a rigid setup must be maintained to achieve efficient operation and adequate tool life.

Recommended angles for form tools are shown in Fig. 4. The cutting edge of the form tool is set in line with the centerline of the work. Form tools with positive top rake angles are more efficient than those with no top rake. Sharp corners should be eliminated, because they lead to early tool breakdown. Figure 4(c) shows a modified form tool design that will aid in minimizing the drag encountered on a conventional circular or dovetail form tool, because of its lack of side clearance. The excess stock left in the form by the modified tool can be removed by a typical cutoff or parting tool. The flat form tool shown in Fig. 4(d) is used for forms of simple design where there is sufficient side clearance.

The recommended maximum width for form tools is 1½ to 2 times the minimum diameter that is to be machined. The use of wider form tools is likely to result in chatter and consequently short tool life. When a wider form is to be cut, this should be done in two separate operations, using tools that have a combined width that is equal to the width of the form.

The plunge-cutting action of form tools is less desirable than longitudinal cutting, as with single-point tools. It might be possible to first rough with a longitudinal cut so that the least possible stock is removed in forming. If this cannot be done, separate tools for rough and finish forming will be more economical than a single form tool.

Box tools with V-shaped or roller work supports are used for both roughing and finishing cuts. Box tools are preferred to balance turning tools, because they provide greater rigidity. Details of a suitable box tool cutter are shown in Fig. 5.

Balance turning tools are used primarily for roughing cuts. They offer no support for the work and should not be used on long slender parts. The blades are held in the tool holder at a fixed angle, which must be considered when the tools are ground. Figure 6 shows cutting-edge angles suitable for a balance turning tool, and the reduction of front relief, when a heavier cutting edge is desired.

Cutoff Tools. Circular cutoff tools are suitable for nickel alloys, but straight cutoff tools afford greater clearance and are preferred. The blade thickness should be greater than is used for cutting equivalent sections of carbon steel. A next-heavier-size blade than would be used for the same diameter of carbon steel is recommended.

Table 10. Speeds and Feeds for Monel R-405

Operation	Speed, sfm	Feed, ipr
Turning(a)	140 to 160	0.003 to 0.005
Forming(a)	140 to 160	0.0004 to 0.001
Drilling	60 to 80	0.001 to 0.005
Reaming	30 to 45	0.003 to 0.012
Tapping	30 to 40	....
Threading	30 to 40	....
Cutoff	140 to 160	0.0005 to 0.001

(a) For a single-spindle automatic bar machine handling stock 1 in. in diameter and under, using high speed steel tooling. For a multiple-spindle machine or a lathe handling stock over 1 in. in diameter, speeds of 90 to 125 sfm should be used.

Table 11. Machining Monel R-405 in Automatic Bar Machines (Examples 995, 996 and 997)

Operation	Speed, sfm	Feed, ipr
Example 995		
Box turning	143	0.004
Spot drilling	65	0.0035
Forming(a)	143	0.001
Drilling 0.261-in. diam(b)	60	0.003
Drilling 0.199-in. diam(c)	46	0.0025
Threading 7/16–14	33	0.071
Cutting off(d)	143	0.001
Example 996		
Forming	161	0.0007
Drilling 3/8-in. diam	84	0.004
Drilling 9/32-in. diam	62	0.0035
Reaming 3/8 to 1/2-in. step	21	0.0075
Threading 9/16–20	25	0.050
Cutting off	100	0.0008
Example 997		
Forming	176	0.006
Drilling 1/2-in. diam	112	0.005
Drilling 3/8-in. diam	84	0.0045
Reaming 17/32-in. diam	38	0.018
Tapping 9/16–20	41	0.050
Cutting off	140	0.0008

(a) Surface finish: first piece, 25 to 45 micro-in.; last piece, 100 micro-in. (b) Surface finish: first piece, 8 to 20 micro-in.; last piece, 30 to 60 micro-in. (c) Surface finish, first piece, 45 micro-in. (d) Surface finish: first piece, 40 to 80 micro-in.; last piece, 30 micro-in.

Table 12. Speeds and Feeds for Machining Unhardened Monel 501

Operation	Speed, sfm(a)	Feed, ipr
Turning	70 to 80	0.003 to 0.005
Forming	70 to 80	0.0004 to 0.001
Drilling	30 to 40	0.001 to 0.010(b)
Reaming	15 to 20	0.003 to 0.012
Tapping	15 to 20	....
Threading	15 to 20	....
Cutoff	70 to 80	0.005 to 0.001

(a) For high speed steel tools. (b) Depending on drill diameter.

Milling

The essential requirements of milling are accuracy and smooth finish, and therefore it is imperative to have sharp tools and rigid machines and fixtures. High speed steel cutters (M2 and M10)

Table 13. Speeds and Feeds for Milling Nickel Alloys

Operation	Group A (Speed, 80 to 100 sfm)	Group B (Speed, 60 to 80 sfm)	Group C (Speed, 30 to 40 sfm)	Group D-1 (Speed, 25 to 35 sfm)	D-2, unaged (Speed, 10 to 20 sfm)	D-2, aged (Speed, 5 to 15 sfm)
	Feed per tooth, in.					
Helical milling	0.003	0.007	0.005	0.005	0.003	0.003
Face milling	0.004	0.008	0.006	0.006	0.004	0.004
Side milling	0.002	0.005	0.004	0.004	0.003	0.003
End milling	0.002	0.004	0.003	0.003	0.002	0.002
Slotting	0.002	0.005	0.004	0.004	0.003	0.003
Sawing	0.002	0.002	0.002	0.002	0.001	0.001

Table 14. Band Sawing of Nickel Alloys

Alloy group	1/16 in. Pitch	1/16 in. Speed, sfm	¼ in. Pitch	¼ in. Speed, sfm	1 in. Pitch	1 in. Speed, sfm	3 in. Pitch	3 in. Speed, sfm
	Thickness of work							
A	14	105	10	75	8	50	6	50
B	18	125	14	75	10	50	8	50
C	14	90	12	75	10	50	8	50
D-1	18	75	12	40	10	30	8	30
Inconel X-750, cold rolled and annealed	For 0.093-in. work thickness, 32 pitch and 60 sfm							

Table 15. Friction Sawing of Nickel Alloys (a)

Alloy	Work thickness, in.	Blade width, in.	Blade speed, sfm	Cutting rate(b), in./min
Monel 400	3/16	1	9,000	43
Monel K-500(c)	3/16	1	10,000	43
Inconel 600(c)	3/16	1	9,000	72
Inconel X-750(c)	⅛	⅝	9,500	31

(a) 10-pitch, raker-set blade. (b) Approximate lineal inches per minute. (c) Annealed alloy.

are most suitable, particularly for interrupted cutting action.

Feeds and speeds are shown in Table 13. Too light a feed, approximating "rubbing", will cause an excessively work-hardened layer. Because rubbing at the beginning of the cut is avoided by climb milling, this technique is preferred to conventional (up) milling. In addition, the downward motion of the cut assists rigidity and diminishes chatter. The disadvantage of climb milling is the need for positive control of backlash in the table drive. Face milling is preferable to slab milling, because it reduces work hardening and chatter.

Chip problems in milling are the same as in turning. Standard milling cutters provide adequate clearance for chips.

Heavy-duty milling cutters with 12° positive radial rake and 45° axial rake are preferred for rough milling all alloys except those of group D-2. Light-duty cutters with 12° positive radial rake and 18° axial rake (helical flutes) are best for the high-strength alloys of this group. They require low cutting speeds (10 to 20 sfm) and light chip loads. The light-duty cutters have more teeth than the heavy-duty type; consequently, light-duty cutters operate at higher cutting rates for the cutting speeds allowed.

Finishing cutters for all alloys should be of the high-helix type with 15° positive radial rake and 52° to 65° helical flutes (positive axial rake). Staggered-tooth cutters, with alternate teeth of opposite helix, are best for milling grooves. High speed steel slitting saws with side chip clearance are recommended for narrow slotting.

Face-milling cutters with inserted teeth of high speed steel should be designed so that the inserted teeth have positive rake and helix angles. A typical tool is made with cutters set into the head at a positive axial rake angle or helix of 7° and a positive radial rake angle of 15°. Primary relief angles should be 7° to 8°; secondary relief angles should be 12° to 14° on all except end mills and small-diameter cutters.

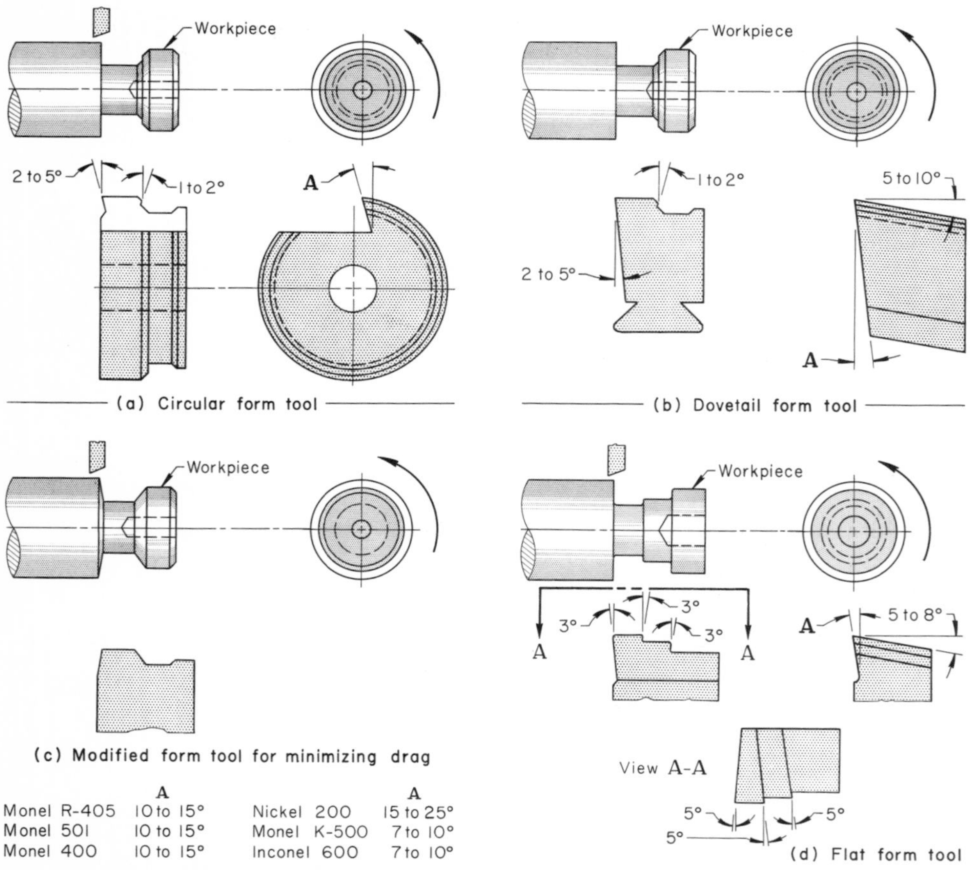

Fig. 4. Form tools for turning nickel alloys in automatic bar and chucking machines

Sawing and Cutting Off

Nickel alloys can be sawed or cut off by conventional methods.

Hacksawing. Hand and power hacksaws are suitable for cutoff operations involving the alloys of groups A, B, C and D-1. Alloys of group D-2 are not readily cut by these tools.

Hand hacksaw blades should be made of high speed steel. Blades with 14 to 18 pitch (teeth per inch), raker set, are used for general work. Blades with 24 to 32 pitch, wavy set, are used for sawing thin-wall tube.

Power hacksaws may be operated at 90 strokes per minute for the alloys of groups A and B and about 60 strokes per minute for groups C and D-1. High speed steel blades give satisfactory service. Heavy-duty power hacksaw blades with 6 to 10 pitch, raker set, should be used for cutting bar stock. The same type of blade with 14 to 18 pitch, raker or wavy set, is suitable for cutting off tube with a 1/16-in. or heavier wall. Tube with less than 1/16-in. wall thickness is not generally cut off on power hacksaws, but if necessary a blade with at least 18 pitch, wavy set, should be used.

The work should be kept flooded with water-soluble or sulfurized cutting oil.

Circular Sawing. The best method for cold cutting heavy sections (such as forgings, ingots and blooms) of the alloys of groups A, B, C and D-1 is by circular saws with insert teeth. A typical installation uses a 44-in.-diam blade with 56 inserted high speed steel teeth. The teeth are ground and set into the blade to give a 15° rake angle. Square and round teeth alternate, with the round teeth projecting about 1/16 in. beyond the cutting edge of the square teeth. This saw cuts alloys of groups A and B at a speed of 50 sfm with a feed of 0.33 ipm; a water-soluble cutting oil is used. Alloys of group C and D-1 are cut at 25 sfm with the same feed, but sulfurized oil is used as cutting fluid.

Band sawing can be used for cutting off all nickel alloys, although it is not recommended for group D-2 alloys of thick section. High speed steel saws with flexible backs are recommended. Raker-set teeth are suggested for sawing all forms of material other than light-gage sheet and thin-wall tube. Saws with wavy-set teeth are best for sawing thin sections.

The speeds shown in Table 14 may be used as a guide. Medium feeding pressures should be used. The saw should constantly bite into the work; otherwise the blade will work harden the material. The blade and workpiece should be flooded with a soluble oil. A sulfurized or sulfochlorinated oil may be brushed on the saw teeth to prevent chip welding.

Friction Sawing. The nickel alloys can be readily cut by friction sawing. Irregular as well as straight cuts can be made in material up to 1 in. thick. Material less than ½ in. thick can be fed by hand; hydraulic or power feeds should be used for material ½ to 1 in. thick. If it is necessary to use hand feed for thicker material, the workpiece should be rocked up and down slowly to expose a smaller surface to the saw.

Friction sawing depends on the heat developed between the saw and the workpiece; consequently, cutting fluids are not used for this type of cutting. A new saw blade is not required for friction sawing; the saw is efficient only after its teeth become blunt and create the necessary frictional heat to soften the material.

Saw blades with raker-set teeth should be used. The teeth may be 10, 14 or 18 pitch; the 10-pitch saw is used for the thicker materials and the 18-pitch saw for the thinnest stock. Generally, teeth of 10 pitch are used for sawing material ⅝ in. thick and heavier. For straight cutting, a 1-in.-wide blade is the most desirable for all thicknesses. However, for both straight and contour cutting, a blade at least ⅛ in. wider than the thickness of the material to be cut is preferred. Saw blades less than ½ in. wide should be used only to cut contours with radii under 3 in.

Representative saw speeds are:

5,000 sfm, for 1/32-in. material
9,000 sfm, for 3/16-in. material
11,000 sfm, for ½-in. material
15,000 sfm, for 1-in. material.

Table 15 gives data for friction sawing four nickel alloys.

Lathe Cutoff. Rounds larger than ⅞ in. can be cut off more rapidly on cutoff lathes than by hacksawing. These lathes usually have two high speed steel blades 3/16 to ¼ in. thick, which should be set to give a positive rake. One tool should have a square nose, the other a rounded nose. Operating speeds are 50 to 60 sfm for alloys of groups A and B, and 30 to 35 sfm for those of groups C and D-1. Water-soluble oil is an adequate cutting fluid.

Abrasive Cutoff. All nickel alloys can be cut off with abrasive wheels. For dry cutting small sections (up to 1 in.), aluminum oxide resinoid-bond wheels, such as A-301-R6-B and A-602-Q8-B, are satisfactory.

Wet cutting is preferred for sections over 1 in. thick, and for groups D-1 and D-2 alloys in all thicknesses. Aluminum oxide rubber-bond wheels such as A-602-M-R are recommended. Water with a rust inhibitor is a satisfactory grinding fluid. Speed should be about 5000 to 5500 sfm; feed, the maximum permitted by machine capability.

Table 16. Surface Grinding Conditions for Four Nickel Alloys

Factor	Nickel 200, Monel 400, Inconel 600 — Rotary	Nickel 200, Monel 400, Inconel 600 — Reciprocating	Inconel X-750(a) — Rotary(b)	Inconel X-750(a) — Reciprocating
Machine	Vertical spindle	6 by 8 in.	Surface grinder	Surface grinder
Wheel	A-60-K8-V	A-60-I8-V (Nickel 200, Monel 400) C-80-L5-V (Inconel 600)	A-36-E12-V	A-60-G12-V
Wheel size	8-in. diam, 3-in. face, 4-in. arbor hole; cup with ⅝-in. rim	8-in. diam, ½-in. face, 1½-in. arbor hole	11-in. diam by 5 in. by 1-in. rim	7¾ by ¾ by 1¼ in.
Finish	....	....	50 micro-in.	17 micro-in.
Wheel speed	4200 sfm	5000 sfm	3200 sfm	5400 sfm
Cross speed	....	0.050 in. every other stroke	....	0.050 in. per stroke
Work speed	50 rpm	400 in. per min	24 rpm	35 sfm
Downfeed	Roughing: 0.001 in. per min	Roughing: 0.001 in. per pass	0.0016 in. per min	0.005 in. max
Dressing	Mechanical, fine	Diamond, fine	Star-type	Diamond
Grinding condition	Wet	Wet	....	....
Wheel wear/metal removal	7-to-3	....	....	Negligible

(a) Tests were made on both annealed (Rockwell B 84 to 86) and age-hardened (Rockwell C 32 to 34) alloys; there was no appreciable difference on the action of the grinding wheel in grinding the two types of alloys. (b) A lean solution of a water-soluble oil was used as grinding fluid.

Grinding

Methods of grinding nickel alloys do not differ greatly from those for steel.

For best results, nickel alloys should be ground wet. A solution of 25 gal of water and 1 lb of sal soda or 50 parts of water to 1 part of soluble oil is a suitable grinding fluid for operations other than crush and thread grinding. Grinding oil is the best fluid for crush and thread grinding. Sodium chromate may be added to the sal soda solution to inhibit rusting of the machine and circulation system.

Recommendations for the principal types of grinding are listed in Tables 16, 17, 18 and 19. The data for Inconel X-750 are generally applicable to all alloys of group D.

Surface Grinding. The materials to be ground should be stress relieved to keep them flat. Table 16 shows preferred wheels and grinding conditions for several nickel alloys. The finer-grit aluminum oxides produce the best ground surfaces.

Low wheel contact and wheel pressure are desirable, to avoid distortion during grinding, especially with material in the annealed condition. Because there is greater wheel contact in surface grinding on a rotary table than on a reciprocating table, the latter is often preferred; less heat is generated, and consequently distortion is minimized.

Cylindrical Grinding. For cylindrical grinding of most alloys, silicon carbide wheels are superior to those of aluminum oxide. Table 17 lists cylindrical grinding conditions for nickel alloys. A grinding fluid must be used.

The samples used for cylindrical grinding in the tests described in Table 17 were 1½ in. in diameter and 12 in. long. A steady rest had to be used, to support the work and eliminate vibration. Transverse and plunge grinding were both done equally well with the use of a steady rest.

Internal Grinding. The best finishes on cold drawn Monel 400, Nickel 200 and Inconel 600 seamless tubing have been obtained with a C-60-K5-V silicon carbide vitrified-bond wheel, for both roughing and finishing. If a relatively poor finish can be tolerated, an A-60-K5-V aluminum oxide wheel can remove metal more rapidly in roughing Monel 400 and Nickel 200 only. Grinding conditions for these alloys are shown in Table 18.

Centerless Grinding. Conditions for centerless grinding of Inconel X-750 with a silicon carbide wheel are summarized in Table 19. In roughing, the workpiece is likely to become out-of-round unless a mild breakdown of the wheel face occurs occasionally. Out-of-roundness occurs almost immediately after a wheel face has been diamond dressed. However, this condition can be corrected by proper wheel dressing.

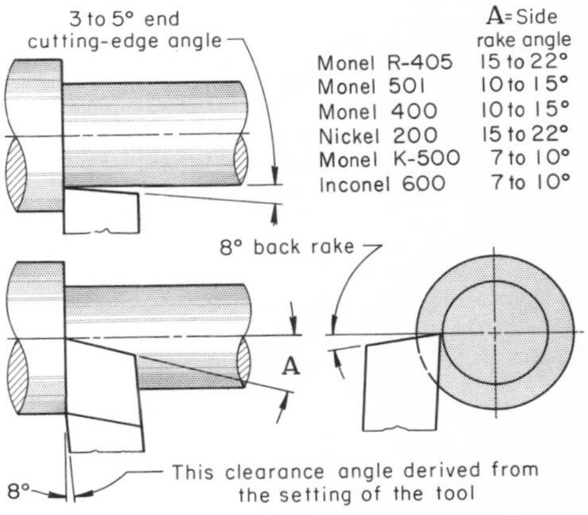

Fig. 5. Box tool for turning nickel alloys in automatic bar and chucking machines

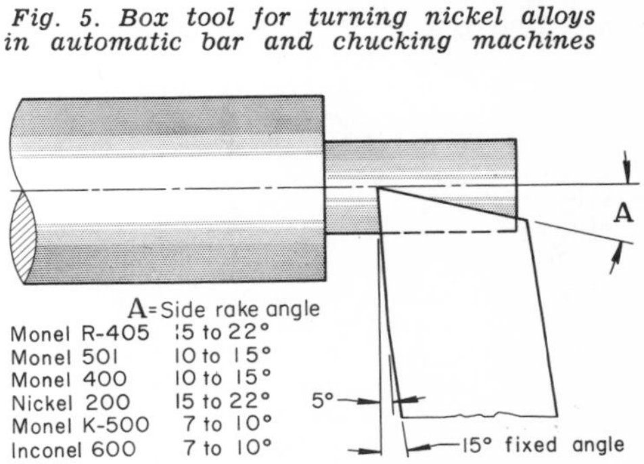

Fig. 6. Balance tool for turning nickel alloys in automatic bar and chucking machines

Table 17. Cylindrical Grinding Conditions for Nickel Alloys

Factor	Alloy groups A, B, C, D-1	Inconel X-750(a)
Machine	10 by 36 in.	Cylindrical grinder
Wheel	C-60-J7-V	A-602-J8-V
Wheel size	18 by 2 by 4 in.	20 by 2 by 5 in.
Finish	....	8 to 10 micro-in.
Wheel speed	6000 sfm	6000 sfm
Work speed	88 rpm (2-in.-diam workpiece)	150 rpm
Table traverse	90 ft/min (roughing); 63 to 77 ft/min (finishing)	50 in./min
Feed:		
Roughing	0.001 to 0.005 in./pass	0.001-in. index/pass
Finishing	0.00025 in./pass	0.0005 in./pass
Wheel dressing	Diamond, wet	Diamond
Grinding condition	Wet	....
Grinding fluid	....	Water-soluble oil, lean solution
Wheel wear	....	0.004-in. for 0.030-in. index feed

(a) Tests were made on both annealed (Rockwell B 90) and fully age-hardened (Rockwell C 30) alloy; there was no significant difference in their grinding characteristics.

Table 18. Internal Grinding of Nickel 200, Monel 400, and Inconel 600 Seamless Tubing

Wheel classification	C-60-K5-V
Wheel size	1 by ¾ by ¼ in.
Wheel speed	3200 sfm
Work speed	156 rpm
Traverse speed	40 in. per min
Feed rate	0.0003 to 0.0004 in./pass on diam
Grinding condition	Wet
Size of tubing	1-in. IPS (Iron Pipe Size)

Table 19. Centerless Grinding of Inconel X-750

Machine	Centerless grinder
Wheel	C-46-K5-V
Wheel size	20 by 6 by 12 in.
Wheel finish	Commercial
Wheel speed	6500 sfm
Work speed	22 rpm
Wheel feed:	
Roughing	0.003 in./pass infeed
Finishing	0.001 in./pass infeed
Wheel dressing	3° angle dressed on regulating wheel
Wheel wear	Approximately 0.014 in. on wheel diameter for 14 passes at 0.003-in. infeed and 18 passes at 0.001-in. infeed
Grinding condition	Wet
Traverse speed	35 in. per min
Grinding fluid	Water-soluble, lean solution

Tests were made on 1-in.-diam annealed material (Rockwell B 90 to 92) and fully age-hardened material (Rockwell C 30); similar results were obtained for the two materials.

In finish grinding, a commercial finish can be obtained without redressing the wheel face after the roughing operation, merely by taking light cuts.

Offhand and Snag Grinding. Offhand and snag grinding tests have been made on Inconel X-750 in the annealed condition (Rockwell B 84 to 86) and fully age-hardened (Rockwell C 32 to 34). The machines used were a bench grinder (aluminum oxide A-24-N5-V wheel) and a portable grinder (aluminum oxide A-24-Q5-V wheel); grinding was done dry.

Crush Grinding. Aluminum oxide vitrified-bond grinding wheels of medium-to-soft grade and medium-to-open structure are satisfactory. Grinding oil should be continuously filtered during all operations. Aluminum oxide wheels (medium-to-soft grade, open structure) have also been used successfully for internal grinding.

Grinding With Abrasive Belts. Abrasive belts (cloth belts coated with aluminum oxide) can be used for finishing group D alloys. Precision-forged airfoil turbine blades have been finished by rough grinding with 80-grit abrasive, semifinishing with 120 to 150-grit abrasive, and final finishing with 180 to 220-grit abrasive. Rough grinding can be done dry. Semifinish and finish grinding are done with a grinding fluid, for instance, cottonseed oil. The addition of kerosine imparts greater fluidity. For rough grinding, a light machine oil is suitable if needed.

Honing

Honing is done with aluminum oxide vitrified-bond honing stones of medium to soft grade. Ample honing fluid must be supplied; various honing fluids as-supplied or diluted by 2 to 3 parts kerosine are recommended. A mixture of 50% oleic acid, 35% kerosine, and 15% turpentine is also suitable.

Speeds for rotation of the honing tool are 150 to 250 sfm, and for stroke (reciprocation) 35 to 50 sfm. The lower speeds should be used for roughing and the higher speeds for finishing. Pressure should be about 40 psi.

Chemical and Electrical Metal-Removal Techniques

Several processes that remove metal without producing chips have been developed for shaping high-temperature, high-strength alloys that are difficult to machine by conventional methods. A few of these techniques have potential application to nickel alloys, particularly to supplement conventional practice with the more difficult-to-machine alloys like those of groups D-1 and D-2.

Electrochemical machining (ECM) is essentially electrolytic deplating in which the "tool" is a shaped cathode, usually of copper, and the workpiece is anodic. (See the article on page 233.) For nickel alloys, electrolytes are salt solutions (sodium or potassium nitrate or chloride) or dilute acid (sulfuric).

The resistance of most nickel alloys to chemical attack does not seem to retard electrochemical solution. Some differences occur in processing the various alloys, because of differences in their current-carrying capacities. For example, the nickel and nickel-copper alloys have fair-to-good electrical conductivity, whereas the chromium-bearing materials are essentially resistance alloys. Compensation must be made for greater power loss, voltage drop and electrolyte heating with the latter alloys. Because mechanical properties do not affect the process, alloys can be shaped in the fully cold worked and age-hardened conditions as easily as in the annealed condition. This is particularly advantageous with the group D-2 alloys and permits operations not feasible by conventional methods.

Electrochemical grinding (ECG) is a specialized form of ECM in which the cathode is a current-conducting grinding wheel impregnated with particles of abrasive. (See the article on page 281.) Because about 90% of the metal removal is accomplished by electrolytic solution and about 10% by abrasion, wheel life is relatively long. The principal effect of the abrasive action is to grind off any passive film, especially on chromium-bearing alloys, produced by the electrochemical action.

Electrical discharge machining (EDM), or spark erosion, originally developed for removing broken taps from holes and later adapted for the shaping of carbide and hard, relatively brittle tool steel, has been refined for machining all current-carrying materials. (See the article on page 227.) Experiments have indicated that the nonchromium alloys in the D-2 group require approximately 75% more power than tool and die steels, and that metal-removal rates of about 12 to 14 cu in. per hour can be achieved on group C alloys at higher power settings.

Chemical machining (CHM) is controlled, selective metal removal by etching. (See the article on page 240.) Because nickel alloys are generally resistant to chemical attack, they require strong acids for metal removal at practical rates. These acids can cause intergranular attack or severe pitting if not properly used, especially on the chromium-bearing alloys. Quality control should include metallographic examination of a finished sample. Even with the best conditions, chemical machining will lower fatigue life slightly.

One of the major problems to be overcome in chemical machining the chromium-bearing alloys is the prevention of preferential attack at grain boundaries. The age-hardenable alloys should be solution-treated or unaged to be chemically machined.

Electron beam machining (see the article on page 253) and plasma-arc cutting are two similar techniques that remove metal by localized melting and vaporization with high-temperature, high-velocity beams of electrons or ionized gas. Plasma-arc torches are capable of cutting nickel alloys several inches thick at very high speed, and are superior to all other methods in the rough cutting of plate and sheet.

Ultrasonic machining (USM) is impractical on nickel alloys, which are all relatively tough and ductile. Ultrasonic grinding, on the other hand, shows promise of improving cutting rates and wheel life in grinding nickel alloys. In this process, vibrations are superposed on the conventional grinding process through an ultrasonic transducer.

Machining of Heat-Resisting Alloys

Procedures for machining nickel alloys used in turbojet engines and for other high-temperature applications are described in the article "Machining of Heat-Resisting Alloys", which begins on page 405 of this volume.

Machining of Titanium Alloys

*By the ASM Committee on Fabrication of Titanium**

THE following characteristics of titanium affect machining procedures:

1 Titanium reacts rapidly at high temperature with oxygen, nitrogen and constituents in cutting tools. In machining, this chemical activity contributes to seizing, galling and abrasion, and to the pyrophoric behavior of small particles of titanium.
2 Chips of titanium ordinarily exhibit less shear deformation than those of other metals. The thinner chips cause higher sliding velocities and smaller tool-chip contact areas. These conditions, in conjunction with the relatively high strength of titanium, produce high contact pressures and unusually high temperatures at the tool tip.
3 Titanium has relatively poor thermal conductivity. This contributes to high temperatures at the tool tip.
4 Titanium has a relatively low modulus of elasticity. This means that slender titanium parts are more likely than slender steel parts to distort from clamping and machining forces.

Although the characteristics listed above apply generally to all grades of titanium and titanium alloys, these metals are by no means equal in machinability. Variations in composition or hardness, or both, cause large differences in machinability.

In Table 1, commercially pure titanium, alpha and alpha-beta alloys, and a beta alloy are grouped according to hardness ranges. These groupings represent similar machinability as referred to in tables of nominal speeds and feeds for various machining operations presented in this article.

Tool Material. For turning, boring, planing, reaming, counterboring and milling of titanium, high speed steel or carbide cutting tools may be used. High speed steel tools are used almost exclusively for trepanning, broaching, twist drilling, tapping and sawing. Gun drilling is done with carbide-tipped drills.

General-purpose high speed steels (such as M1, M2, M7 and M10) are generally suitable for machining titanium. However, because titanium is highly abrasive, tool cost per piece machined is often lower with a more highly alloyed grade (such as T5 or T15) — especially for machining titanium alloys that have been hardened by solution treating and aging.

Carbide grade C-2 is the most widely used for machining of titanium, although C-3 is better for some operations, such as finish turning.

Cutting Fluid. Titanium alloys develop higher temperature in the cutting zone than other metals, because of the characteristically smaller chip-tool contact area and poorer thermal diffusivity of titanium. For this reason, cutting fluid is particularly important.

Soluble-oil emulsions (1 part oil to 20 parts water) are generally used when cutting conditions are not severe. Low-viscosity sulfurized oils, chlorinated and sulfochlorinated oils, water-soluble waxes and various synthetic fluids have also been used.

Chlorinated fluids and solvents should be avoided in processing titanium workpieces when nonchlorinated fluids satisfy the requirements, because chloride residues may remain on the parts after subsequent heating operations and contribute to stress-corrosion cracking in service. Although this point is controversial and unsettled, some companies restrict the use of chlorinated fluids and solvents. On the other hand, chlorinated fluids have been widely used in production operations. It is always good practice to remove all cutting fluid or lubricant from titanium workpieces, especially if they are to be heated later.

A water-base solution of barium hydroxide is effective as a cutting fluid for titanium. However, because some barium compounds are toxic, fumes should be exhausted from the cutting area to protect the operator. Whether such fluids may affect the surfaces of machined workpieces has not been thoroughly investigated. Therefore, as with chlorinated fluids, careful cleaning of machined parts before subsequent processing is important.

Turning and Boring

For turning, facing and boring, carbide tools are usually used. Grade C-2 performs well for most operations, although C-3 is sometimes preferred for finish turning. High speed steel tools have also been used successfully. Little success has been reported with ceramic tools. Standard negative-rake inserts are best for work at a hardness of 360 Bhn or more; positive-rake tools usually are preferred for softer work. For turning in which continuous, tough, noncurling chips are produced, tools must have efficient chip breakers.

A flood of cutting fluid at the cutting edge is essential to adequate tool life. Because of the galling characteristics of titanium, tools must be resharpened or replaced after about half the tool-flank wear allowable with other metals. Galling also often necessitates the use of machine tools with live centers.

Nominal speeds and feeds for single-point turning, form turning and cutting off, are listed in Tables 2 and 3, for high speed steel and carbide tools, respectively. Work-metal hardness is the major factor influencing feed and speed, especially speed. Speeds and feeds in Tables 2 and 3 are based on maximum rigidity in the setup, uniform depth of cut, sharp tools and a flood of cutting fluid. When one or more of these conditions is less than optimum, the speed for any given set of conditions shown in Tables 2 and 3 must be reduced.

The size and surface condition of some workpieces demand the use of turning speeds much slower than shown in Tables 2 and 3; this is especially true for rough turning of large workpieces, as in the next example:

Example 998. Machining Large Rings (Fig. 1)

Two vertical boring mills were used for machining rings forged and rolled from Ti – 5 Al – 2.5 Sn alloy, of the shape and dimensions shown at the left in Fig. 1, to produce two finished rings and a test ring, as shown at the right in Fig. 1. The rings to be machined were produced from 855-lb billets for use in a nuclear engine. Machining entailed four operations: rough scaling, rough finishing, slicing and finishing; maximum speeds, feeds and depths of cut are listed in the table below Fig. 1.

The first three operations were done in a 35-hp boring mill with a 60-in.-diam table. Finishing was done on a 50-hp boring mill with a 52-in.-diam table. Conventional boring-mill practice was employed for leveling, blocking and clamping of the rings. Single-point cutting tools with brazed carbide tips were used. A 20-to-1 mixture of water and soluble oil was the cutting fluid on the 60-in. mill, and plain cold water was used on the 52-in. mill. With both machines, flow of cutting fluid was adjusted to flood the tool and chip.

In rough scaling, the forged and rolled rings were machined to remove surface cracks, eliminate low spots caused by scarfing and

*FRANCIS W. BOULGER, *Chairman,* Chief, Metalworking Div., Battelle Memorial Institute; N. F. BRATKOVICH, Allison Div., General Motors Corp.; S. R. CARPENTER, Design Specialist, Astronautics Div., General Dynamics; J. E. COYNE, JR., Manager of Metallurgical Development and Evaluation Dept., Wyman-Gordon Co.

ERNEST DELL, General Manager, TRI-D Corp. (formerly Chief Project Engineer, Wright Aeronautical Div., Curtiss-Wright Corp.); V. V. DONALDSON, Senior Application Engineer, Alco Products, Inc.; GENE ERBIN, Assistant Manager, Technical Service and Development, Titanium Metals Corp. of America; GLENN FAULKNER, Aerojet General Corp., Sacramento; REX FORD, Senior Manufacturing Research Engineer, LTV Vought Aeronautics Div., Chance Vought Corp.; GERALD GARFIELD, Director of Manufacturing Engineering, Douglas Aircraft Co., Inc.; LARRY S. KLASS, Senior Metallurgical Engineer, Aerospace Structures Div., Avco Corp.; W. F. OSTERLOH, Tool Engineer, Aircraft Div., Douglas Aircraft Co., Inc.; G. PFANNER, Section Head, Manufacturing Research Dept., Republic Aviation Corp.

R. M. POTTER, Senior Research Engineer, Columbus Div., North American Aviation, Inc.; I. J. STEWART, Physical Research Laboratory, Cincinnati Milling Machine Co. (formerly Manager of Materials Processing, Ingersoll-Rand Co.); VERNON R. THOMPSON, Metallurgist, Process Research Laboratory, Crucible Steel Co. of America; THOMAS L. WILE, Project Chief, Manufacturing Development and Research Section, Airplane Div., Boeing Co.

Table 1. Hardness-Range Groupings of Alloys as Referred to in Tables of Speed and Feed in This Article

Hardness range, Bhn	Typical alloy	Other alloys in group
Commercially Pure Titanium		
110 to 170	99.5 Ti	None
140 to 200	99.2 Ti with 0.15 Pd	99.0 Ti with 0.15 Pd
200 to 275	99.0 Ti	98.9 Ti
Alpha and Alpha-Beta Alloys		
150 to 200	Ti – 2.5 Al – 16 V	Ti – 3 Al – 2.5 V
200 to 260	Ti – 2.5 Al – 16 V	Ti – 3 Al – 2.5 V
300 to 340	Ti – 2 Fe – 2 Cr – 2 Mo	Ti – 5 Al – 2.5 Sn; Ti – 5 Al – 2.5 Sn (low O); Ti – 7 Al – 2 Cb – 1 Ta; Ti – 4 Al – 3 Mo – 1 V
310 to 350	Ti – 6 Al – 4 V	Ti – 7 Al – 12 Zr; Ti – 4 Al – 4 Mn
320 to 370	Ti – 7 Al – 4 Mo	Ti – 8 Al – 1 Mo – 1 V; Ti – 5 Al – 1.25 Fe – 2.75 Cr; Ti – 5 Al – 1.5 Fe – 1.4 Cr – 1.2 Mo; Ti – 6 Al – 6 V – 2 Sn – 1 (Fe, Cu)
320 to 380	Ti – 1 Al – 8 V – 5 Fe	None
350 to 400	Ti – 6 Al – 4 V	Ti – 4 Al – 4 Mn
375 to 420	Ti – 2 Fe – 2 Cr – 2 Mo	Ti – 5 Al – 1.25 Fe – 2.75 Cr; Ti – 6 Al – 6 V – 2 Sn – 1 (Fe, Cu); Ti – 5 Al – 1.5 Fe – 1.4 Cr – 1.2 Mo; Ti – 7 Al – 4 Mo; Ti – 4 Al – 3 Mo – 1 V
375 to 440	Ti – 1 Al – 8 V – 5 Fe	None
Beta Alloy		
310 to 350	Ti – 3 Al – 13 V – 11 Cr	None
375 to 440	Ti – 3 Al – 13 V – 11 Cr	None

chipping, and correct for about ⅜-in. eccentricity. Tool details were as follows:

Back rake, 0°; side rake, +5°
Side cutting-edge angle, 12° to 15°
End cutting-edge angle, 5° minimum
End relief, 8°; side relief, 8°
Nose radius, ⅛ in. max; no chip breaker.

Chip form ranged from a spiral through figure-six to C-shape. Speed and feed were adjusted frequently to produce a figure-six chip, which resulted in the longest tool life (average, 40 to 50 min).

For rough finishing, the rings had to be recentered, because of low spots left by the rough-scaling operation. Tool details were the same as for the rough-scaling cuts except for a reduction in nose radius (1⁄16 to 3⁄32 in., instead of ⅛ in.).

In slicing, standard boring-mill practice was followed to part the rings and the test ring. The cutting tool was ¼ in. wide with more than 2 in. of steel under the insert to provide rigidity. This tool was ground square (with a slight break on corners), relieved to 8° from 6° on the end and sides, and provided with a +5° back rake angle. Speed and feed were varied inversely to keep the chip string from becoming a tight spiral. Loose open spirals gave the best tool life. Edge buildup was not excessive as long as the cutting fluid flooded the tool-chip area.

In finishing, the parted rings were machined individually on the 52-in. mill to produce the contour required (Fig. 1). Tool details were the same as for the rough-scaling cuts, except nose radius was 0.030 in. Tool life, using plain cold water as the cutting fluid, was 55 to 60 min. This was more than twice the tool life (20 to 25 min) obtained when finishing had been done with no fluid.

Boring. Tool angles are essentially the same as for turning (see text above and Example 998). As in any boring, the end relief angle must be increased as hole size decreases.

Nominal speeds and feeds for boring with high speed steel and carbide tools are given in Table 4.

Planing and Shaping

Typical tool angles for rough and finish planing of titanium are given in Fig. 2, in conjunction with Example 999. High speed steel or carbide can be used as tool material, the choice often depending on the rigidity of the setup.

Planing speed is influenced mainly by work-metal hardness and tool material. Assuming maximum rigidity and use of a cutting fluid, commercially pure titanium and some of the alloys in the annealed condition can be planed at 35 to 40 sfm with high speed steel tools. For planing the harder alloys (solution treated and aged), a speed of about 15 sfm is the practical maximum. With rigid setups, these speeds may be increased as much as four times when carbide tools are used. Speeds for rough and finish planing are usually the same.

Feed depends largely on depth of cut. In rough planing, with depth of cut up to 0.250 in., crossfeed usually ranges from 0.060 to 0.090 in. per stroke. In finish planing, depth of cut is shallow (0.003 to 0.015 in.), because a broad-nose finishing tool is used (Example 999), and feed generally ranges from ½ to 1 in. per stroke.

Because of the inconvenience of using cutting fluid on a planer, planing is sometimes done dry, at decreased speed. However, a cutting fluid is recommended. Spray mist is often used (Example 999).

One airframe producer used planing for preparing 12-ft-long structural Z-sections because milling equipment

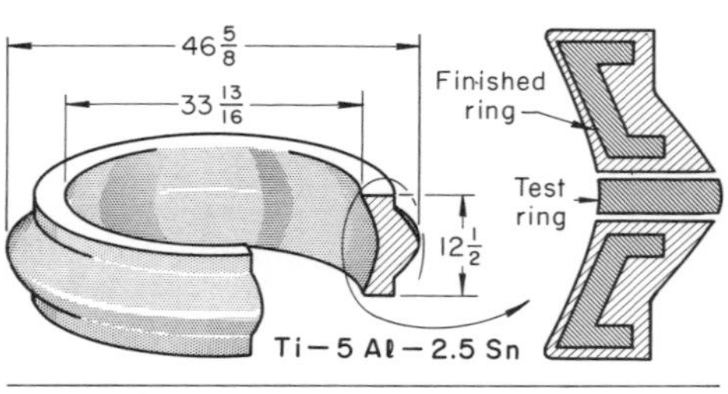

Operation (carbide tools)	Speed, sfm	Feed, ipr	Depth of cut, in.
1 Rough scaling:			
First cut	40-50	1⁄32	0-3⁄16
Subsequent cuts	90	1⁄64	⅛
2 Rough finishing	90-120	1⁄64	1⁄32-3⁄16
3 Slicing	125-135	0.006-0.008	...
4 Finishing	180	0.015	1⁄32

Fig. 1. Forged and rolled ring (left) machined in four operations in two boring mills to produce two finished rings and a test ring (cross section at right) (Example 998)

with adequate rigidity and the necessary bed length was not available. Details of the operation are described in the example that follows.

Example 999. Planing a 52-Lb Z-Section to 23 Lb (Fig. 2)

An open-side planer, equipped with a 4-by-20-ft bed, rack-and-pinion drive, two heads on the rail, one head on the vertical column, and a 15-hp main drive motor, was used to prepare structural Z-sections of Ti – 8 Al – 1 V – 1 Mo alloy. The size of the section before and after planing is shown in the upper two sketches in Fig. 2.

Each section was 12 ft long and weighed 52 lb before machining and 23 lb after. These workpieces had to be well supported and clamped to prevent deflection by machining forces. Tolerances on the planed section were ±0.010 in. for the flange and web thickness and ±0.030 in. for the other dimensions. Specified finish was 230 micro-in.

Planing comprised roughing and finishing operations under conditions tabulated below Fig. 2. Details of the roughing and finishing tools are shown in the lower two sketches in Fig. 2. Tools for both operations consisted of carbide inserts brazed on a tool steel holder.

Tools were changed when wear caused an increase in power consumption and deterioration in surface finish. Tool change and repositioning required about 10 min. Total time for setup, machining and tool changes was about 12 hr per piece.

Shaping. Angles for single-point shaper tools should be the same as those for planer tools (see Fig. 2). When metal removal is the primary objective, and the work metal is commercially pure titanium or one of the softer alloys, a ram speed of 30 to 40 sfm for roughing and 40 to 50 sfm for finishing is used. For shaping hardened (aged) alloys, roughing speed is usually 10 to 20 sfm and finishing speed is 20 to 30 sfm. All these speeds are based on a feed of 0.020 in. per stroke and 0.250-in. depth of cut for roughing, and a feed of 0.010 in. per stroke at 0.060-in. depth of cut for finishing. Use of a spray-mist or swab-applied cutting fluid is recommended.

Broaching

Although titanium alloys can be broached with tools designed for steel, better results are obtained if tool angles are modified. Face angles of 8° to 10° are recommended; clearance angles of 3° for roughing and 2° for finishing have given good results. Broaches made of M2, M10 or T1 high speed steel are satisfactory for commercially pure titanium and are often used for the softer alloys. For machining the harder alloys, the more highly alloyed high speed steels such as T5 or T15 are generally recommended.

In some applications, broaches made of a higher-carbon grade of general-purpose high speed steel such as M2 have longer life. Also, carburized broaches made of ordinary M2 have lasted longer than standard broaches (see Examples 1000 and 1001).

Nominal speeds and chip loads are given in Table 5 for broaching titanium alloys with high speed steel broaches. These speeds and chip loads are based on rigid setup, use of a cutting fluid and the broach materials named in footnote (a).

Flooding the workpiece with a cutting fluid minimizes welding of chips to the cutting edges of the broach. A prior application of a high-film-strength oil

Table 2. Nominal Speeds and Feeds for Turning Titanium Alloys With High Speed Steel Tools(a)

			Single-point and box tools — Speed, sfm		Form tools				Cutoff tools		
Typical alloy(b)	Condition(c)	Brinell hardness	Roughing (feed, 0.015 ipr; 0.150-in. cut)	Finishing (feed, 0.007 ipr; 0.025-in. cut)	Speed, sfm	Feed, ipr, for tool width of: ½ in.	1 in.	2 in.	Speed, sfm	Feed, ipr, for tool width of(d): ⅛ in.	¼ in.
99.5 Ti	Ann	110 to 170	200	250	150	0.0025	0.0015	0.001	150	0.0015	0.002
99.2 Ti with 0.15 Pd	Ann	140 to 200	160	180	120	0.0025	0.0015	0.001	120	0.0015	0.002
99.0 Ti	Ann	200 to 275	100	110	75	0.0025	0.0015	0.001	75	0.0015	0.002
Ti – 2 Fe – 2 Cr – 2 Mo	Ann	300 to 340	70	80	50	0.002	0.0015	0.001	50	0.0015	0.002
	ST,A	375 to 420	40(e)(f)	50(f)	30	0.0015	0.0015	0.0007	30	0.0015	0.0015
Ti – 6 Al – 4 V	Ann	310 to 350	60	70	45	0.002	0.0015	0.001	45	0.0015	0.002
	ST,A	350 to 400	55	65	40	0.0015	0.0015	0.0007	40	0.0015	0.0015
Ti – 7 Al – 4 Mo	Ann	320 to 370	50	60	35	0.002	0.0015	0.001	35	0.0015	0.002
Ti – 1 Al – 8 V – 5 Fe	Ann	320 to 380	20	30	15	0.002	0.0015	0.001	15	0.0015	0.002
	ST,A	375 to 440	25(e)(f)	35(f)	20	0.0015	0.0015	0.0007	20	0.0015	0.0015
Ti – 3 Al – 13 V – 11 Cr	ST	310 to 350	25(e)	35	20	0.002	0.0015	0.001	20	0.0015	0.002
	ST,A	375 to 440	25(f)	35(f)	20	0.0015	0.0015	0.0007	20	0.0015	0.0015

(a) High speed steel M3 or T15, unless footnoted otherwise. (b) Typical alloy may represent a group of alloys in a specific hardness range. See Table 1 for alloys in each hardness-range group. (c) Ann = Annealed; ST = Solution heat treated; A = Aged. (d) Feed for tools 1/16 in. wide is 0.001 ipr for all alloys. (e) Feed, 0.010 ipr. (f) With high speed steel T15, M41, M42, M43 or M44. (SOURCE: same as for Table 3)

Table 3. Nominal Speeds and Feeds for Turning Titanium Alloys With Carbide Tools(a)

			Single-point and box tools — Speed, sfm — Roughing (feed, 0.015 ipr; 0.150-in. cut)		Finishing (feed, 0.007 ipr; 0.025-in. cut)		Form tools				Cutoff tools			
Typical alloy(b)	Condition(c)	Brinell hardness	Brazed	Disposable	Brazed	Disposable	Speed, sfm	Feed, ipr, for tool width of: ½ in.	1 in.	2 in.	Speed, sfm	Feed, ipr, for tool width of: 1/16 in.	⅛ in.	¼ in.
99.5 Ti	Ann	110 to 170	450	500	500	550	340	0.005	0.003	0.0025	340	0.003	0.0045	0.006
99.2 Ti with 0.15 Pd	Ann	140 to 200	375	425	425	475	280	0.005	0.003	0.0025	280	0.003	0.0045	0.006
99 0 Ti	Ann	200 to 275	250	310	275	350	185	0.005	0.003	0.0025	185	0.003	0.0045	0.006
Ti – 2 Fe – 2 Cr – 2 Mo	Ann	300 to 340	180	220	215	250	135	0.004	0.0025	0.002	135	0.003	0.0045	0.006
	ST,A	375 to 420	100(d)	120(d)	120	150	75	0.002	0.002	0.001	75	0.002	0.003	0.004
Ti – 6 Al – 4 V	Ann	310 to 350	150	180	170	210	110	0.004	0.0025	0.002	110	0.003	0.0045	0.006
	ST,A	350 to 400	120	160	145	185	85	0.002	0.002	0.001	85	0.002	0.003	0.004
Ti – 7 Al – 4 Mo	Ann	320 to 370	130	165	155	185	95	0.003	0.0015	0.002	95	0.0025	0.0035	0.005
Ti – 1 Al – 8 V – 5 Fe	Ann	320 to 380	90	110	115	135	65	0.003	0.0015	0.002	65	0.0025	0.0035	0.005
	ST,A	375 to 440	80(d)	100(d)	100	120	60	0.002	0.002	0.001	60	0.002	0.003	0.004
Ti – 3 Al – 13 V – 11 Cr	ST	310 to 350	100(d)	120(d)	125	150	75	0.004	0.0025	0.002	75	0.003	0.0045	0.006
	ST,A	375 to 440	80	100	100	120	60	0.002	0.002	0.001	60	0.002	0.003	0.004

(a) Single-point and box tools, carbide grade C-2 for roughing, C-3 for finishing; form and cutoff tools, grade C-2. (b) Typical alloy may represent a group of alloys in a specific hardness range. See Table 1 for alloys in each hardness-range group. (c) Ann = Annealed; ST = Solution heat treated; A = Aged. (d) Feed, 0.010 ipr. (Data are adapted from tables compiled by Metcut Research Associates, Inc.)

to the surface to be broached also helps to prevent chip welding and prolongs broach life.

Lack of rigidity in the setup will cause poor surface finish and poor broach life. Rigidity can be improved by preliminary machining of the workpiece locating surfaces, and by the use of broaches as short as practical. For additional information on the process and tooling, see "Broaching", page 58.

Solutions to problems in production broaching of titanium alloys are described in the next three examples:

Table 4. Nominal Speeds and Feeds for Boring Titanium Alloys With High Speed Steel and Carbide Tools

			Rough boring (0.100-in. cut) — Speed, sfm		Feed, ipr		Finish boring (0.010-in. cut) — Speed, sfm		Feed, ipr	
Typical alloy(a)	Condition(b)	Brinell hardness	HSS(c)	Carbide(d)	HSS(c)	Carbide(d)	HSS(c)	Carbide(d)	HSS(c)	Carbide(d)
99.5 Ti	Ann	110 to 170	180	405	0.008	0.010	200	450	0.005	0.007
99.2 Ti with 0.15 Pd	Ann	140 to 200	140	335	0.008	0.010	160	375	0.005	0.007
99.0 Ti	Ann	200 to 275	90	225	0.008	0.010	100	250	0.005	0.007
Ti – 2 Fe – 2 Cr – 2 Mo	Ann	300 to 340	65	160	0.007	0.009	70	180	0.004	0.005
	ST,A	375 to 420	35(e)	90	0.005(e)	0.007	40(e)	100	0.003(e)	0.004
Ti – 6 Al – 4 V	Ann	310 to 350	55	130	0.007	0.009	60	150	0.004	0.005
	ST,A	350 to 400	50	110	0.005	0.007	55	120	0.003	0.004
Ti – 7 Al – 4 Mo	Ann	320 to 370	45	115	0.007	0.009	50	130	0.004	0.005
Ti – 1 Al – 8 V – 5 Fe	Ann	320 to 380	20	80	0.007	0.009	20	90	0.004	0.005
	ST,A	375 to 440	20(e)	70	0.005(e)	0.007	25(e)	80	0.003(e)	0.004
Ti – 3 Al – 13 V – 11 Cr	ST	310 to 350	20(e)	90	0.007(e)	0.009	25(e)	100	0.004(e)	0.005
	ST,A	375 to 440	20(e)	70	0.005(e)	0.007	25(e)	80	0.003(e)	0.004

(a) Typical alloy may represent a group of alloys in a specific hardness range. See Table 1 for alloys in each hardness-range group. (b) Ann = Annealed; ST = Solution heat treated; A = Aged. (c) High speed steel M3 or T15, unless footnoted otherwise. (d) Carbide grade C-3. (e) With high speed steel T15, M41, M42, M43 or M44. (SOURCE: same as for Table 3)

Example 1000. Increased Backoff Angle for Reducing Springback

In broaching alloys Ti – 6 Al – 4 V, Ti – 2.5 Al – 16 V, and Ti – 5 Al – 2.5 Sn with M2 high speed steel broaches provided with a 2° backoff angle, accuracy was difficult to maintain because of "springback", or closing-in of the slot being broached. The springback was caused by the low modulus of elasticity of the alloys in relation to their strength, and by the appreciable deflection imposed by the high cutting forces required.

Increasing the backoff angle to 3° provided sharper cutting and slightly reduced force, which reduced the deflection. The modification in broach design, however, caused increased wear on the cutting edges, more sharpenings, and increased setup and broach costs. These difficulties were overcome by carburizing the M2 broaches.

Example 1001. Broach Modification for Increased Life

Broaching D-shaped holes in a ⅜-in. length of cut in Ti – 6 Al – 4 V alloy (350 to 400 Bhn) involved a production run of 10,000 pieces. T15 high speed steel broaches with a 2° backoff angle had a maximum tool life of only 40 pieces between sharpenings. Tool life was increased to 1000 pieces per sharpening by substituting carburized M2 broaches with a 3° backoff angle. Broaches of both designs were operated under the same conditions; speed was 8 sfm, and cutting fluid was a high-viscosity, active sulfochlorinated oil with polar and wetting additives.

Example 1002. Broach Modification and Increased Speed for Better Finish and Increased Production

A T15 high speed steel broach produced poor surface finish in bulb-slot form broaching of Ti – 6 Al – 4 V compressor wheels. These wheels were 23 in. in diameter and 1.9 in. thick, and had a maximum hardness of Rockwell C 38. Sixty-nine slots were broached in each wheel, at a 16° 40′ broaching angle and a machine speed of 15 sfm. The design of the broach was conventional.

To improve the poor surface, the broach was modified slightly by increasing the backoff clearance angle to 3°, and by specifying a 16-micro-in. maximum roughness on the broach. The machine speed was increased to 18 sfm. The new tools lasted an average of 150 slots per grind. Along with improved surface finish, production was increased 120%.

Drilling

When it is feasible, titanium workpieces should be backed up with a piece of aluminum or soft steel at the face opposite the drill entry. The backup prolongs drill life by providing a heat sink, and by minimizing burrs or damage where the drill breaks through.

Dwell of the drill, which frequently occurs in hand drilling, causes excessive work hardening and high temperature at the tip of the drill — both of which lead to premature drill failure. Best results are obtained with positive-feed equipment, which often provides four times the tool life obtained in hand drilling.

Drill life may vary appreciably with small differences in operating condi-

Table 5. Nominal Speeds and Chip Loads for Broaching Titanium Alloys With High Speed Steel Broaches (a)

Typical alloy (b)	Condi-tion (c)	Brinell hardness	Speed, sfm	Chip load, ipt
99.5 Ti	Ann	110-170	25	0.003
99.2 Ti	Ann	140-200	25	0.003
99.0 Ti	Ann	200-275	25	0.003
Ti – 2 Fe – 2 Cr – 2 Mo	Ann	300-340	10	0.003
	ST,A	375-420	5	0.001
Ti – 6 Al – 4 V	Ann	310-350	10	0.003
	ST,A	350-400	5	0.001
Ti – 7 Al – 4 Mo	Ann	320-370	8	0.003
Ti – 1 Al – 8 V – 5 Fe	Ann	320-380	5	0.002
	ST,A	375-440	5	0.001
Ti – 3 Al – 13 V – 11 Cr	ST	310-350	5	0.001
	ST,A	375-440	5	0.001

(a) High speed steel T5 or T15, except M2 for alloys below 300 Bhn. (b) Typical alloy may represent a group of alloys in a specific hardness range. See Table 1 for alloys in each hardness-range group. (c) Ann = Annealed; ST = Solution heat treated; A = Aged. (Data are adapted from tables compiled by Metcut Research Associates, Inc.)

Table 6. Typical Details of High Speed Steel Drills for Titanium Alloy Sheet

Helix angle	29°
Relief angle	7° to 12°
Cutting angle	0°
Point angle, power drilling:	
Hole diam ¼ in. or less	135°
Hole diam ¼ to ½ in.	118°
Point angle, hand drilling:	
Hole diam ¼ in. or less	150°
Hole diam ¼ to ½ in.	135°
Body clearance:	
Power drilling	Yes
Hand drilling	No

tions. In one study, for example, high speed steel drills were used for drilling 5⁄16-in.-diam holes through 0.10-in. sheets of heat treated Ti – 4 Al – 3 Mo – 1 V alloy. Life per drill averaged 8 holes but varied from 3 to 37 holes.

In tests to evaluate the effect of point angle on drill life in drilling Ti – 2.5 Al – 16 V, a point angle of 105° was best and was arbitrarily established as 100%. In comparison, a 95° point angle was rated at 10%, a 115° angle at 75%, and a 125° angle at 40%. Other tests on the same alloy showed that the helix angle also exerted a strong influence on drill life. A helix angle of 25° was established as 100%. In comparison, a 20° angle decreased drill life to 65%, a 30° angle to 70%, and a 35° angle to 50%. All tests were made with a ¾-in.-diam drill.

Drills with crankshaft-type split points and thinned webs or with spiral points are more suitable than ordinary chisel-point drills. High speed steel drills give satisfactory results in most drilling and countersinking. Chromium plating or oxide coating to resist galling on the drill margin may be beneficial.

Clean, spiral chips are desirable; other types indicate that the drill requires resharpening or that its design should be modified. When it is necessary to clear the chips periodically from deep holes, the drill should be retracted at the same time the feed is stopped, to avoid dwelling. After clearing the chips, the power feed should be started before the drill touches the bottom of the hole.

Hand grinding of drill points is rarely accurate enough to insure the proper point angles; machine grinding of points is recommended.

Typical design details of high speed steel drills for holes in sheet are given in Table 6.

Speed and Feed. Nominal speeds and feeds for conventional drilling with

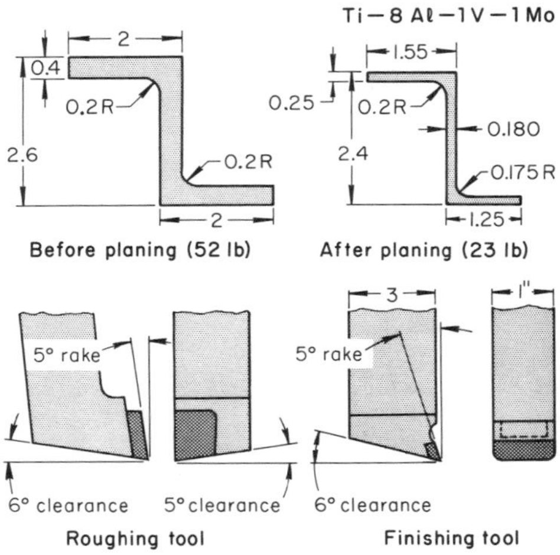

Operating condition	Roughing	Finishing
Speed, sfm:		
Without cutting fluid	20	20
With cutting fluid (a)	35	35
Crossfeed, in.	0.08 max	0.5 to 1.0
Depth of cut, in.	0.08 max	0.010
Tool life, hr	1	1

(a) Synthetic spray mist

Top: Size of section before and after planing. *Bottom:* Details of carbide-insert tools used for rough and finish planing.

Fig. 2. Planing of a 12-ft-long extruded Z-section (Example 999)

Table 7. Nominal Speeds and Feeds for Drilling Titanium Alloys With High Speed Steel Drills (a)

Typical alloy (b)	Condi-tion (c)	Brinell hardness	Speed, sfm	Feed, ipr, for hole diameter of: ⅛ in.	¼ in.	½ in.	¾ in.	1 in.	1½ in.	2 in.
99.5 Ti	Ann	110 to 170	100	0.0005	0.002	0.006	0.007	0.008	0.010	0.013
99.2 Ti with 0.15 Pd	Ann	140 to 200	80	0.0008	0.003	0.006	0.007	0.008	0.010	0.013
99.0 Ti	Ann	200 to 275	50	0.002	0.005	0.006	0.007	0.008	0.010	0.013
Ti – 2.5 Al – 16 V	ST	150 to 200	70	0.002	0.005	0.006	0.008	0.009	0.010	0.012
	Ann	200 to 260	50	0.002	0.005	0.006	0.008	0.009	0.010	0.012
Ti – 2 Fe – 2 Cr – 2 Mo	Ann	300 to 340	40	0.002	0.005	0.006	0.007	0.008	0.010	0.011
	ST,A	375 to 420	20 (d)	0.001	0.002	0.003	0.004	0.004	0.005	0.005
Ti – 6 Al – 4 V	Ann	310 to 350	30	0.002	0.005	0.006	0.007	0.008	0.009	0.010
	ST,A	350 to 400	25 (d)	0.001	0.002	0.004	0.005	0.006	0.007	0.008
Ti – 7 Al – 4 Mo	Ann	320 to 370	20	0.002	0.005	0.006	0.007	0.008	0.009	0.010
Ti – 1 Al – 8 V – 5 Fe	Ann	320 to 380	15 (d)	0.002	0.004	0.005	0.006	0.007	0.008	0.009
	ST,A	375 to 440	15 (d)	0.0005	0.001	0.0015	0.0015	0.002	0.002	0.003
Ti – 3 Al – 13 V – 11 Cr	ST	310 to 350	20	0.001	0.003	0.004	0.005	0.006	0.007	0.008
	ST,A	375 to 440	15 (d)	0.0005	0.001	0.0015	0.0015	0.002	0.002	0.003

(a) High speed steel M1, M7 or M10, unless footnoted otherwise. (b) Typical alloy may represent a group of alloys in a specific hardness range. See Table 1 for alloys in each hardness-range group. (c) Ann = Annealed; ST = Solution heat treated; A = Aged. (d) With high speed steels T15 and M33. (Data are adapted from tables compiled by Metcut Research Associates, Inc.)

high speed steel drills are given in Table 7. As these data indicate, work-metal hardness is significant to both speed and feed, and hole size has a large bearing on rate of feed. Speeds and feeds given in Table 7 are based on a rigid setup, sulfochlorinated oil as cutting fluid, and holes not deeper than about four times drill diameter.

Cutting Fluid. Sulfochlorinated oils, extreme-pressure chlorinated oils, and soluble-oil emulsions are satisfactory as cutting fluids. In some applications, high-viscosity, high-film-strength oils have been applied to tools before drilling. This precaution minimizes galling or welding and prolongs drill life. Titanium parts drilled with fluids containing chlorine must be cleaned immediately and thoroughly.

Deep-Hole Drilling. Gun drills tipped with carbide (usually grade C-2) are used for deep-hole drilling of titanium alloys. A single-lip drill with a relief angle of 6° to 8°, and a point angle of 42° outside and 20° inside, is generally recommended.

Commercially pure titanium can be gun drilled at 200 sfm; speeds of 100 to 170 sfm are recommended for solution treated or annealed alloys, and 75 to 150 sfm for aged alloys. Feed is usually 0.0005 ipr for all speeds.

Deep-hole drilling with gun drills requires that a cutting fluid be supplied under pressure to the drill point.

Reaming, Counterboring and Spotfacing

Sufficient reaming stock must be allowed so that the reamer constantly cuts a chip and is never allowed to burnish. Otherwise, the hole will be inaccurate and the reamer will wear prematurely. Both high speed steel and carbide reamers are satisfactory. Spiral-flute reamers, which produce wide, thin chips, generally have longer life than straight-flute reamers.

Most reamers have a clearance angle of 10° to 15°, relief angle of 5° to 10°, and a margin (land) width of 0.010 to 0.015 in. Nominal speeds and feeds for reaming titanium alloys with high speed steel and carbide reamers are given in Table 8.

A flood of sulfochlorinated oil is a preferred cutting fluid. When it is used, the workpieces should be thoroughly washed, with particular attention given to blind holes. Soluble-oil emulsions have provided acceptable results in many reaming applications.

Counterboring and Spotfacing. Speeds and feeds for high speed steel and carbide tools are given in Table 9.

Tapping

A hole to be tapped in titanium must not be work hardened during drilling or reaming. Tapers and variations in diameter also cause trouble in tapping. The tap should be relieved so that its threads will not rub on the hole surface and work harden as the tap moves into the hole.

Conventional two-flute, spiral-point, plug-style GH2 taps can be used for holes up to ⅜-in. diam; three-flute taps with spiral points should be used for larger holes. Taps are more effecive if modified by grinding away the hreads behind the cutting edges down to the minor diameter, leaving ull-thread lands only 0.015 in. wide acking up the cutting edges). Nitrided aps made from M1 or M10 high speed steel are often used.

Through holes can be machine-tapped in sizes ranging from 4–40 UNC–2B to 10–32 UNF–2B, provided the drilled holes are as large as good practice will permit. No attempt should be made to machine-tap holes to full thread depth.

Blind holes have been tapped successfully by machine-tapping down as far as possible (without compacting the chips in the bottom of the holes) with plug taps, then hand-tapping to within three threads of the bottom of the holes with similarly modified bottoming taps.

Twisting of the workpiece (caused by tap pressure) leads to work hardening, which causes rapid tap wear or breakage. For this reason, taps must be replaced as soon as they are worn enough to exert appreciable torque on the work when the tap reverses.

Speed. Nominal tapping speeds range from 7 to 50 sfm, depending mainly on composition and hardness of the work metal. Speeds shown in Table 10 assume the use of nitrided taps made from a general-purpose grade of high speed steel.

Cutting Fluid. Good results have been obtained by applying a coating of lithopone paste (a mixture of lithopone and oil) on the taps immediately before tapping. Taps should be cleaned with an air blast and recoated with lithopone paste before succeeding holes are tapped.

Chlorinated or sulfochlorinated oils have also been used successfully for tapping titanium and its alloys. Parts tapped with a cutting fluid containing chlorine should be thoroughly cleaned to avoid embrittlement or stress corrosion in later operations or in service.

Milling

Titanium parts in a variety of shapes and sizes are milled to thickness tolerances of ±0.010 in. On bars and plates, it is relatively easy to produce finishes of 60 micro-in. in rough milling and 15 micro-in. in finishing.

Cutting speed is the most critical factor controlling milling operations on titanium alloys. Slower speed minimizes cutting temperature and tool wear caused by chipping. Feed rate also is important, especially for light cuts; uniform, positive feed is mandatory for successful milling of titanium. Cutters should not be allowed to stop or dwell in the cut and should be retracted before being returned across the workpiece, to avoid rubbing.

Cutting Fluid. Water-base cutting fluids are generally recommended for milling titanium and its alloys. Heavy-duty soluble-oil emulsions, rust-inhibitor types of fluids, and barium hydroxide in water perform well. Water-base cutting fluids can be applied as a flood or a mist. Spray mists should be applied ahead of the peripheral cutter in climb milling and at both entrance and exit in face milling.

Table 8. Nominal Speeds and Feeds for Reaming Titanium Alloys With High Speed Steel and Carbide Reamers

Typical alloy(a)	Condition(b)	Brinell hardness	Speed, sfm: HSS (c)	Speed, sfm: Carbide(d)	Feed, ipr(e), for hole diameter of: 1/8 in.	1/4 in.	1/2 in.	1 in.	1 1/2 in.	2 in.
99.5 Ti	Ann	110 to 170	100	375	0.003	0.006	0.009	0.012	0.015	0.020
99.2 Ti with 0.15 Pd	Ann	140 to 200	80	300	0.003	0.006	0.009	0.012	0.015	0.020
99.0 Ti	Ann	200 to 275	70	250	0.003	0.005	0.008	0.011	0.014	0.016
Ti – 2.5 Al – 16 V	ST	150 to 200	70	200	0.003	0.006	0.008	0.011	0.014	0.017
	Ann	200 to 260	60	250	0.003	0.005	0.007	0.009	0.012	0.015
Ti – 2 Fe – 2 Cr – 2 Mo	Ann	300 to 340	45	175	0.002	0.005	0.007	0.009	0.012	0.015
	ST,A	375 to 420	25	100	0.002	0.005	0.007	0.009	0.012	0.015
Ti – 6 Al – 4 V	Ann	310 to 350	35	150	0.002	0.005	0.007	0.009	0.012	0.015
	ST,A	350 to 400	30	120	0.002	0.005	0.007	0.009	0.012	0.015
Ti – 7 Al – 4 Mo	Ann	320 to 370	30	120	0.002	0.005	0.007	0.009	0.012	0.015
Ti – 1 Al – 8 V – 5 Fe	Ann	320 to 380	30	120	0.002	0.005	0.007	0.009	0.012	0.015
	ST,A	375 to 440	25	100	0.002	0.004	0.006	0.008	0.010	0.012
Ti – 3 Al – 13 V – 11 Cr	ST	310 to 350	30	150	0.002	0.005	0.007	0.009	0.012	0.015
	ST,A	375 to 440	25	100	0.002	0.004	0.006	0.008	0.010	0.012

(a) Typical alloy may represent a group of alloys in a specific hardness range. See Table 1 for alloys in each hardness-range group. (b) Ann = Annealed; ST = Solution heat treated; A = Aged. (c) High speed steel M1, M2 or M7. (d) Carbide grade C-2. (e) Based on the use of a six-flute reamer of either high speed steel or carbide. (SOURCE: same as for Table 7)

Table 9. Nominal Speeds and Feeds for Counterboring and Spotfacing Titanium Alloys With High Speed Steel and Carbide Tools

Typical alloy(a)	Condition(b)	Brinell hardness	Speed, sfm	Feed, ipr, for tool diameter of: 1/4 in.	1/2 in.	1 in.	2 in.	3 in.
High Speed Steel Tools(c)								
99.5 Ti	Ann	110 to 170	160	0.002	0.0025	0.003	0.004	0.005
99.0 Ti	Ann	200 to 275	80	0.0015	0.002	0.0025	0.0035	0.0045
Ti – 2 Fe – 2 Cr – 2 Mo	Ann	300 to 340	55	0.001	0.0015	0.002	0.003	0.0045
	ST,A	375 to 420	30(d)	0.001	0.0015	0.002	0.003	0.0035
Ti – 6 Al – 4 V	Ann	310 to 350	50	0.001	0.0015	0.002	0.003	0.0045
	ST,A	350 to 400	45	0.001	0.0015	0.002	0.003	0.0035
Carbide Tools(e)								
99.5 Ti	Ann	110 to 170	360	0.004	0.005	0.006	0.008	0.010
99.0 Ti	Ann	200 to 275	200	0.003	0.004	0.005	0.007	0.009
Ti – 2 Fe – 2 Cr – 2 Mo	Ann	300 to 340	145	0.002	0.003	0.004	0.006	0.009
	ST,A	375 to 420	80	0.002	0.003	0.004	0.005	0.007
Ti – 6 Al – 4 V	Ann	310 to 350	120	0.002	0.003	0.004	0.006	0.009
	ST,A	350 to 400	95	0.002	0.003	0.004	0.005	0.007

(a) Typical alloy may represent a group of alloys in a specific hardness range. See Table 1 for alloys in each hardness-range group. (b) Ann = Annealed; ST = Solution heat treated; A = Aged. (c) High speed steel M3 or T15, unless footnoted otherwise. (d) High speed steel T15, M41, M42, M43 or M44. (e) Carbide grade C-2. (SOURCE: same as for Table 7)

Table 10. Nominal Speeds for Tapping Titanium Alloys With High Speed Steel Taps(a)

Typical alloy(b)	Condition(c)	Brinell hardness	Speed, sfm
99.5 Ti	Ann	110-170	50
99.2 Ti with 0.15 Pd	Ann	140-200	40
99.0 Ti	Ann	200-275	30
Ti – 2.5 Al – 16 V	ST	150-200	35
	Ann	200-260	25
Ti – 2 Fe – 2 Cr – 2 Mo	Ann	300-340	25
	ST,A	375-420	10
Ti – 6 Al – 4 V	Ann	310-350	20
	ST,A	350-400	10
Ti – 7 Al – 4 Mo	Ann	320-370	15
Ti – 1 Al – 8 V – 5 Fe	Ann	320-380	10
	ST,A	375-440	7
Ti – 3 Al – 13 V – 11 Cr	ST	310-350	15

(a) Nitrided M1, M7 or M10 high speed steel. (b) Typical alloy may represent a group of alloys in a specific hardness range. See Table 1 for alloys in each hardness-range group. (c) Ann = Annealed; ST = Solution heat treated; A = Aged. (SOURCE: same as for Table 7)

Sulfurized mineral oils also are used extensively, and are usually applied in a flood. Carbon dioxide blasts and refrigerated fluids can also be used. Fumes, especially those from barium hydroxide mists, should be removed from the cutting area by a suitable exhaust system.

Peripheral Milling. Peripheral milling is done with plain, helical, side, slab, form-relieved, and formed-profile cutters. Peripheral milling usually requires more complex fixtures and lower feed than does face milling. Climb milling is generally preferred for all peripheral milling of titanium.

Table 11. Helical Cutters for Peripheral and End Milling of Two Mill-Annealed Titanium Alloys

(Ti – 8 Al – 1 Mo – 1 V and Ti – 6 Al – 4 V)

Item	Type of helical cutter: Peripheral milling: Slab mill	Wheel mill	End milling
Material	Carbide(a)		HSS(b)
Diameter, in.	4 to 6	6 to 12	2 to 4
Flutes/in. of diam.	4	6	3
Angles			
Axial rake, helix	15°		15° to 30°
Radial rake	0°		−4° to 0°
Clearance	6° to 12°		6° to 12°
End cutting edge	5° to 10°		5° to 10°
Corner	30°		45°

(a) Grade C-2; brazed inserts. (b) T5 or T6 high speed steel is suitable for these cutters.

The arbors used with cutters for peripheral milling of titanium should be of the largest practical diameter and supported on both sides of the cutter. Slab milling cutters should be used so that the cutting force will be against the spindle. This is accomplished by using cutters with a left-hand helix for a right-hand cut, and vice versa.

Typical cutter angles for two types of peripheral cutters (helical slab and helical wheel) used for milling high-strength titanium alloys are given in Table 11.

Most slab milling of titanium is done with high speed steel cutters, although carbide cutters are sometimes used. Nominal speeds and feeds for slab milling at 0.150-in. and 0.025-in. depths of

Table 12. Nominal Speeds and Feeds for Peripheral (Slab) Milling of Titanium Alloys With High Speed Steel Cutters(a)

Typical alloy(b)	Condi-tion(c)	Brinell hardness	Roughing (0.150-in. cut) Speed, sfm	Roughing Feed, ipt	Finishing (0.025-in. cut) Speed, sfm	Finishing Feed, ipt
99.5 Ti	Ann	110 to 170	110	0.008	155	0.004
99.2 Ti with 0.15 Pd	Ann	140 to 200	90	0.006	125	0.004
99.0 Ti	Ann	200 to 275	65	0.006	100	0.004
Ti – 2 Fe – 2 Cr – 2 Mo	Ann	300 to 340	45	0.006	55	0.004
	ST,A	375 to 420	20	0.006	30	0.004
Ti – 6 Al – 4 V	Ann	310 to 350	35	0.006	45	0.004
	ST,A	350 to 400	30	0.006	40	0.004
Ti – 7 Al – 4 Mo	Ann	320 to 370	25	0.006	35	0.004
Ti – 1 Al – 8 V – 5 Fe	Ann	320 to 380	20	0.006	30	0.004
	ST,A	375 to 440	20	0.006	25	0.004
Ti – 3 Al – 13 V – 11 Cr	ST	310 to 350	20	0.006	30	0.004
	ST,A	375 to 440	20	0.006	25	0.004

(a) High speed steel M2 or M7 for alloys up to 275 Bhn; T15 or M33 for alloys at 300 Bhn and higher hardness. (b) Typical alloy may represent a group of alloys in a specific hardness range. See Table 1 for alloys in each hardness-range group. (c) Ann = Annealed; ST = Solution heat treated; A = Aged. (Data are adapted from tables compiled by Metcut Research Associates, Inc.)

cut (rough and finish) with high speed steel cutters are given in Table 12. If cutters with inserted carbide blades are used, feeds will be about the same as those shown for high speed steel cutters, but speeds should be about three times as fast for carbide.

Face and Skin Milling. In face milling of titanium, the cutter should not be appreciably wider than the width of the cut. On the other hand, the cutter should not be buried. An overhang of about 10% on at least one side of the cutter is desirable. Climb milling is recommended for widths of cut less than three-fourths the width of the cutter; for wider cuts, conventional milling ("up" milling) is preferred.

Table 13 gives details of carbide-insert face milling cutters that have performed satisfactorily on two titanium alloys, producing tightly curled, easily disposable chips.

The surface finish on titanium parts improves slightly with increases in milling speed and considerably with decreases in feed. In skin milling, light cuts of 0.010 to 0.020 in. produce less distortion than deeper cuts. Tools are normally replaced or reground when the wear land on the flank of the cutter reaches 0.010 in. on carbide cutters or 0.015 in. on high speed steel cutters.

Table 13. Typical Angles for Carbide Cutters Used in Face Milling Two Titanium Alloys

Cutter angle	Ti-8Al-1Mo-1V or Ti-6Al-4V, annealed	Ti-6Al-4V, solution treated and aged
Axial rake	0°	0° to 10°
Radial rake	(a)	0° to 10°
Clearance	12°	10°
End cutting edge	5° to 10°	5° to 10°
Corner	30°	45°

(a) For Ti-8Al-1Mo-1V, 0° to −10°. For Ti-6Al-4V, 0° to +12°.

Nominal speeds and feeds for face milling of titanium alloys at two different depths of cut are presented in Table 14; the speeds for high speed steel cutters are based on the use of one of the more highly alloyed grades, except for milling of commercially pure titanium. When carbide cutters are used, the disposable-insert type is preferred. This type is generally more economical than cutters having blades secured by brazing. In addition, the disposable type can be operated at higher speeds, as indicated in Table 14.

End Milling. When chip crowding and disposal are troublesome, helical-flute cutters usually perform better than straight-flute cutters. When the end of the cutter is doing the work, the helix and the cut should be in the same direction (for example: left-hand helix, left-hand cut). But if most of the metal is removed by the periphery of the cutter, the opposite is true (for example: left-hand helix, right-hand cut).

Typical angles for helical cutters made of high speed steel and used for end milling two titanium alloys are given in Table 11. Angles for both high speed steel and carbide cutters used for slotting operations are given in Table 15. Both carbide and high speed steel end milling cutters give satisfactory performance under specific conditions.

Grade C-2 carbide is preferred, and small end mills are made from solid carbide. However, solid carbide should not be used when length of contact between the workpiece and the side of the cutter exceeds two-thirds the diameter of the end mill.

General-purpose types of high speed steel may be used for end milling cutters, but for milling very hard work metals, cutters made of a more highly alloyed grade generally will give better results.

Regardless of cutter material used, end mills should be as short as practical, and the shank diameter should equal the outside cutting diameter. Breakage can be reduced by having the shank of the end mill softer than the flutes of the cutter. Cutters last longer if they have axial holes through which to inject cutting fluid at the cut.

Nominal speeds and feeds for end milling, using two different depths of cut, are given in Table 16.

In profile milling, speeds considerably higher than those given in Table 16 have been used in experimental work. Life of 2-in.-diam cutters with carbide blades and a helix angle of 15° was studied under varying conditions of speed, chip load and depth of cut. In milling Ti – 8 Al – 1 Mo – 1 V alloy at a given cutter speed, cutter life increased as chip load was increased from 0.004 to 0.017 in. per tooth per revolution. At a speed of 350 sfm and a chip load of 0.008 in. per tooth per revolution, cutter life decreased from a lineal cut of 400 ft for a 0.025-in. depth of cut to 50 lineal ft when depth of cut was increased to 1 in. At higher cutting speeds, with other conditions constant, cutter life decreased as speed was increased; cutter speeds of 250, 350 and 500 sfm resulted in cutter lives of 177, 108 and 62 lineal feet, respectively.

Titanium alloys are sometimes milled at subzero temperatures. The following example describes a subzero procedure.

Example 1003. Use of Subzero Temperature in Profile Milling (Fig. 3)

Structural shapes and flat parts made of Ti – 6 Al – 4 V and Ti – 8 Al – 1 Mo – 1 V alloys were profile milled at subzero temperatures using a vertical machine equipped with a hydraulic tracer, as shown in Fig. 3. The low temperature made cutting easier, produced uniform curls, and reduced tool wear.

Low temperature was achieved by flowing a 1-to-1 mixture of Stoddard solvent and trichlorethylene at −60 F or lower, over the workpiece and cutter. This mixture cooled the workpiece to a temperature varying from −40 to −70 F. The fluid was cooled by dry ice in a 50-gal container, the temperature of which was never higher than −60 F. Control of cutting-fluid temperature was important, because the machined dimensions had to be within tolerance after the workpiece expanded when it warmed to room temperature.

Tool details and operating conditions are given below Fig. 3. To prevent chatter, it was essential that the workpiece be held in a rigid fixture. Total cutter runout was consistently within 0.001 in.

With the subzero treatment, tool life was six to nine times that obtained in room-temperature milling; individual cutters lasted for up to 1000 lineal ft. Surface finish was 63 micro-in. or smoother.

Tape-controlled end milling is well adapted to the milling of pockets and

Table 14. Nominal Speeds and Feeds for Face Milling Titanium Alloys With High Speed Steel and Carbide Cutters

Typical alloy(a)	Condi-tion(b)	Brinell hardness	High speed steel cutters(c) Roughing (0.150-in. cut) Speed, sfm	HSS Roughing Feed, ipt	HSS Finishing (0.025-in. cut) Speed, sfm	HSS Finishing Feed, ipt	Carbide cutters(d) Roughing (0.150-in. cut) Speed, sfm Brazed	Carbide Roughing Speed, sfm Disposable	Carbide Roughing Feed, ipt	Carbide Finishing (0.025-in. cut) Speed, sfm Brazed	Carbide Finishing Speed, sfm Disposable	Carbide Finishing Feed, ipt
99.5 Ti	Ann	110 to 170	125	0.008	165	0.004	400	440	0.008	530	585	0.004
99.2 Ti with 0.15 Pd	Ann	140 to 200	100	0.006	135	0.004	300	330	0.006	400	440	0.004
99.0 Ti	Ann	200 to 275	75	0.006	100	0.004	200	220	0.006	265	310	0.004
Ti – 2 Fe – 2 Cr – 2 Mo	Ann	300 to 340	50	0.006	65	0.004	170	190	0.006	225	245	0.004
	ST,A	375 to 420	25	0.007	35	0.004	80	90	0.006	105	115	0.004
Ti – 6 Al – 4 V	Ann	310 to 350	40	0.006	50	0.004	130	145	0.006	170	185	0.004
	ST,A	350 to 400	35	0.007	45	0.004	110	120	0.006	145	160	0.004
Ti – 7 Al – 4 Mo	Ann	320 to 370	30	0.006	40	0.004	110	120	0.006	145	160	0.004
Ti – 1 Al – 8 V – 5 Fe	Ann	320 to 380	20	0.006	30	0.004	90	100	0.006	120	130	0.004
	ST,A	375 to 440	20	0.007	30	0.004	60	65	0.006	80	85	0.004
Ti – 3 Al – 13 V – 11 Cr	ST	310 to 350	25	0.006	35	0.004	100	110	0.006	130	145	0.004
	ST,A	375 to 440	20	0.007	25	0.004	60	65	0.006	80	90	0.004

(a) Typical alloy may represent a group of alloys in a specific hardness range. See Table 1 for alloys in each hardness-range group. (b) Ann = Annealed; ST = Solution heat treated; A = Aged. (c) High speed steel M2 or M7 for alloys to 275 Bhn; T15 or M33 for alloys at 300 Bhn and harder. (d) Carbide grade C-2. (Data are adapted from tables compiled by Metcut Research Associates, Inc.)

Table 15. Typical Cutter Angles for End Milling of Slots in Titanium Alloys

Cutter angle	Cutter material: M2 HSS	Cutter material: C-2 carbide
Helix	30°	15°
Radial rake	10°	0°
End clearance	5°	12°
Peripheral clearance	5°	12°
End cutting edge	3°	3°
Corner	45°	45°

complex contours on aircraft components made from titanium alloys:

Example 1004. Tape-Controlled End Milling to Maintain Uniform Wall Thickness (Fig. 4)

The titanium aircraft part shown in Fig. 4 was end milled in a horizontal-spindle profiler with punched-tape control. Machining of the three pockets was controlled to meet the requirement of constant wall thickness in the part. Machining details and descriptions of the cutters used are included with Fig. 4.

Sawing

Powerful, rigid saws with positive feed should be used for sawing titanium. Water-soluble cutting fluids and slower feeds than those used for steel should be employed. Power hacksaws should be adjusted so that the saw blade does not drag on the back stroke.

Nominal speeds for power band sawing of titanium alloys are given in Table 17. Table 18 presents speeds and feeds for power hacksawing.

Abrasive Cutoff

A machine equipped with an oscillating head is preferred for cutting thick sections of titanium, especially for sections thicker than 2 in. Satisfactory results can be obtained with rubber-bond wheels containing 60-grit silicon carbide and flooded with a 10% solution of nitrite-amine in water. Some special blades with diamonds mounted in nickel have also given good results. In a machine not equipped with an oscillating head, bars larger than 2 in. in diameter should be rotated during cutting, to minimize heating and wheel breakage.

Electrical Discharge Machining

In electrical discharge machining (EDM), metal is removed from workpieces by the action of a spark. (See the article "Electrical Discharge Machining", page 227 in this volume). The use of this process for simultaneous drilling of multiple holes is described in the following example.

Example 1005. Electrical Discharge Drilling of Aircraft Skin Assemblies (Fig. 5)

The setup shown in Fig. 5 was used for electrical discharge drilling of holes in compound-curved, tack-riveted skin assemblies made of Ti – 8 Mn alloy. Inner and outer surfaces of the assembly were drilled simultaneously in two separate machines, which were operated by one man. The holes were reamed conventionally after drilling.

The machine used for electrical discharge drilling was a four-post hydraulic type, 4 by 8 ft, equipped with a 60-amp power pack. Spring-loaded, disposable yellow brass electrodes, 0.098 to 0.182 in. in diameter, were fed downward by a ram shaped to the contour of the workpiece (Fig. 5). The ram was actuated by the servo-controlled platen of the machine. The springs in the electrode assembly kept the assembly in contact with the ram. Transformer oil was the dielectric fluid in which the

Table 16. Nominal Speeds and Feeds for End Milling Titanium Alloys With High Speed Steel and Carbide Cutters

Typical alloy(a)	Condition(b)	Brinell hardness	For 0.050-in. depth of cut: Speed, sfm	Feed, ipt, for cutter diam of: ¼ in.	½ in.	1 to 2 in.	For 0.015-in. depth of cut: Speed, sfm	Feed, ipt, for cutter diam of: ¼ in.	½ in.	1 to 2 in.
High Speed Steel Cutters(c)										
99.5 Ti	Ann	110 to 170	125	0.002	0.004	0.007	150	0.0015	0.004	0.007
99.2 Ti with 0.15 Pd	Ann	140 to 200	120	0.002	0.004	0.007	150	0.0015	0.004	0.007
99.0 Ti	Ann	200 to 275	60	0.0015	0.003	0.006	75	0.001	0.002	0.005
Ti – 2 Fe – 2 Cr – 2 Mo	Ann	300 to 340	55	0.0015	0.003	0.006	70	0.001	0.002	0.005
	ST,A	375 to 420	35(d)	0.0015	0.003	0.006	45(d)	0.001	0.002	0.004
Ti – 6 Al – 4 V	Ann	310 to 350	50	0.0015	0.003	0.006	65	0.001	0.002	0.005
	ST,A	350 to 400	35(d)	0.0015	0.003	0.006	45(d)	0.001	0.002	0.004
Ti – 7 Al – 4 Mo	Ann	320 to 370	45	0.0015	0.003	0.006	55	0.001	0.002	0.005
Ti – 1 Al – 8 V – 5 Fe	Ann	320 to 380	35(d)	0.0015	0.003	0.006	45(d)	0.001	0.002	0.005
	ST,A	375 to 440	35(d)	0.001	0.002	0.005	45(d)	0.0007	0.0015	0.004
Ti – 3 Al – 13 V – 11 Cr	ST	310 to 350	45(d)	0.0015	0.003	0.006	55(d)	0.001	0.002	0.005
	ST,A	375 to 440	35(d)	0.001	0.002	0.005	45(d)	0.0007	0.0015	0.004
Carbide Cutters(e)										
99.5 Ti	Ann	110 to 170	325	0.002	0.003	0.006	375	0.001	0.003	0.006
99.2 Ti with 0.15 Pd	Ann	140 to 200	300	0.002	0.003	0.006	375	0.001	0.003	0.006
99.0 Ti	Ann	200 to 275	160	0.0015	0.003	0.008	190	0.001	0.002	0.007
Ti – 2 Fe – 2 Cr – 2 Mo	Ann	300 to 340	140	0.0015	0.003	0.008	175	0.001	0.002	0.007
	ST,A	375 to 420	90	0.0015	0.004	0.007	115	0.001	0.002	0.006
Ti – 6 Al – 4 V	Ann	310 to 350	125	0.0015	0.003	0.008	165	0.001	0.002	0.007
	ST,A	350 to 400	90	0.0015	0.003	0.007	115	0.001	0.002	0.006
Ti – 7 Al – 4 Mo	Ann	320 to 370	115	0.0015	0.003	0.008	140	0.001	0.002	0.007
Ti – 1 Al – 8 V – 5 Fe	Ann	320 to 380	90	0.0015	0.003	0.008	115	0.001	0.002	0.007
	ST,A	375 to 440	90	0.001	0.002	0.006	115	0.0007	0.0015	0.005
Ti – 3 Al – 13 V – 11 Cr	ST	310 to 350	115	0.0015	0.003	0.008	140	0.001	0.002	0.007
	ST,A	375 to 440	90	0.001	0.002	0.006	115	0.0007	0.0015	0.005

(a) Typical alloy may represent a group of alloys in a specific hardness range. See Table 1 for alloys in each hardness-range group. (b) Ann = Annealed; ST = Solution heat treated; A = Aged. (c) High speed steel M2 or M7, unless footnoted otherwise. (d) High speed steel T15, M33, M41, M42, M43 or M44. (e) Carbide grade C-2. (SOURCE: same as for Table 14)

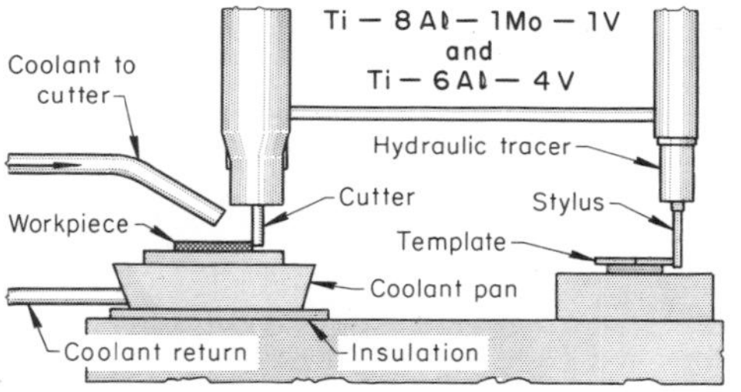

Details of End Milling Cutter

Diameter	⅜ in.
Material	Solid carbide
Number of flutes	4

Operating Conditions

Speed	3400 rpm (330 sfm)
Feed	0.0027 ipt (36 ipm)
Depth of cut	Up to 5/16 in.

Fig. 3. Subzero profile milling of structural shapes and flat parts (Example 1003)

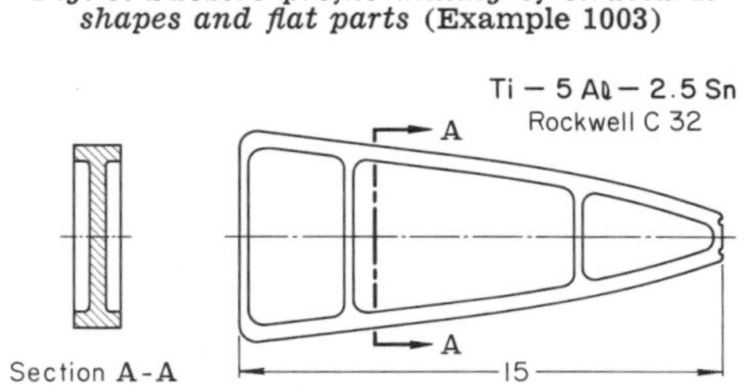

Operating condition	Roughing pockets and outside contour	Finishing: Pockets	Finishing: Outside contour
Cutter diameter, in.(a)	1½	1	1½
Speed, rpm	114	148	155
Speed, sfm	45	38	60
Feed, ipt	0.008	0.0067	0.0065
Feed, ipm	3¼	4	3¼

Other Conditions

Cutting fluid	Soluble-oil:water (1:20)
Cutter life per grind (approx)	250 linear in.
Tolerance	±0.005 in.
Surface finish obtained	125 micro-in.

(a) Four-flute end mills, T15 high speed steel

Fig. 4. Airfoil contour end milled in an aircraft component (Example 1004)

tools and workpiece were immersed. The brass electrode rods machined an average of 20 pieces before eroding sufficiently to require replacement.

Machining time for each surface of the assembly was 1.5 hr. Conventional drilling had required 14.2 and 11.8 man-hr for the inner and outer surfaces, respectively. In addition to the saving in time, the electrical discharge method also enabled a saving in tool cost; the disposable brass electrodes cost about 2¢ each, as against $1.75 each for the T5 high speed steel drills used in conventional drilling. Total savings amounted to $169.74 for the assemblies required per airplane.

Chemical Machining

Chemical machining (CHM) can be used for removing metal to shallow depths from large areas and from parts of complex shape (see the article on Chemical Machining, page 240 in this volume, for details of the process).

The customary etchants for titanium are aqueous solutions containing hydrofluoric acid, either alone or mixed with nitric or chromic acid, together with additives to speed up etching and

Table 17. Nominal Speeds for Power Band Sawing of Titanium Alloys With High Speed Steel Bands

Typical alloy(a)	Condition(b)	Brinell hardness	Speed, sfm(c)
99.5 Ti	Ann	110-170	200
99.2 Ti with 0.15 Pd	Ann	140-200	175
99.0 Ti	Ann	200-275	130
Ti – 2 Fe – 2 Cr – 2 Mo	Ann	300-340	100
Ti – 6 Al – 4 V	Ann	310-350	90
	ST,A	350-400	70
Ti – 7 Al – 4 Mo	Ann	320-370	80
Ti – 1 Al – 8 V – 5 Fe	Ann	320-380	70
Ti – 3 Al – 13 V – 11 Cr.	ST	310-350	60

(a) Typical alloy may represent a group of alloys in a specific hardness range. See Table 1 for alloys in each hardness-range group. (b) Ann = Annealed; ST = Solution heat treated; A = Aged. (c) Speed based on use of bands with 8 to 10 pitch for sawing material less than ¼ in. thick, 6 to 8 pitch for material ¼ to 1½ in. thick, and 3 to 6 pitch for material more than 1½ in. thick. (Data are adapted from tables compiled by Metcut Research Associates, Inc.)

Table 18. Nominal Speeds and Feeds for Power Hacksawing of Titanium Alloys With High Speed Steel Blades (a)

Typical alloy(b)	Condition	Brinell hardness	Speed, strokes per min(c)	Feed, in. per stroke(c)
99.5 Ti	Annealed	110 to 170	180	0.009
99.2 Ti with 0.015 Pd	Annealed	140 to 200	150	0.009
99.0 Ti	Annealed	200 to 275	120	0.009
Ti – 2 Fe – 2 Cr – 2 Mo	Annealed	300 to 340	70	0.006
Ti – 6 Al – 4 V	Annealed	310 to 350	60	0.006
	Solution heat treated and aged	350 to 400	30	0.003
Ti – 7 Al – 4 Mo	Annealed	320 to 370	50	0.005
Ti – 1 Al – 8 V – 5 Fe	Annealed	320 to 380	30	0.003
Ti – 3 Al – 13 V – 11 Cr	Solution heat treated	310 to 350	25	0.003

(a) Speeds and feeds are based on use of blades with 10 pitch for sawing material less than ¼ in. thick, 6 pitch for material ¼ to 2 in. thick, and 4 pitch for material more than 2 in. thick. (b) Typical alloy may represent a group of alloys in a specific hardness range. See Table 1 for alloys in each hardness-range group. (SOURCE: same as for Table 17)

Table 19. Typical Wheels and Operating Conditions for Grinding of Titanium Alloys

Grinding condition	Alloys, condition(a), and hardness: Commercially pure Ti (Ann; 110-275 Bhn)	Alpha and alpha-beta: Ann or ST; 150-380 Bhn	Alpha and alpha-beta: ST,A; 350-440 Bhn	Beta: ST; 310-350 Bhn	Beta: ST,A; 375-440 Bhn
Surface Grinding(b)					
Roughing:					
Wheel speed, 1500 to 2500 sfm.	A_s-46-J-V	A_s-46-J-V	....	A_s-46-J-V	....
Wheel speed, 3000 to 6000 sfm.	C-46-J-V	C-46-J-V	C-46-J-V	C-46-J-V	C-46-J-V
Finishing:					
Wheel speed, 1500 to 2500 sfm.	A_s-60-J-V	A_s-60-L-V	....	A_s-60-L-V	....
Wheel speed, 3000 to 6000 sfm.	C-70-L-V	C-70-L-V	C-60-K-V	C-70-L-V	C-60-K-V
Cylindrical(c), Centerless(d), or Internal(e) Grinding					
Roughing or finishing:					
Wheel speed, 1500 to 2500 sfm.	A_s-60-J-V	A_s-60-J-V	....	A_s-60-J-V	....
Wheel speed, 4000 to 6000 sfm.	C-60-J-V	C-60-J-V	C-60-J-V	C-60-J-V	C-60-J-V

(a) Ann = Annealed; ST = Solution heat treated; A = Aged. For all alloys, wheels and speeds: table speed is 40 sfm, downfeed per pass is 0.001 in. in roughing and 0.0005 in. (max) in finishing, and crossfeed per pass is 1/10 wheel width. (c) For all alloys, wheels and speeds: work speed is 50 sfm, infeed per pass is 0.001 in. in roughing and 0.0005 in. (max) in finishing, and traverse per revolution of work is ⅕ wheel width in roughing and 1/10 wheel width in finishing. (d) For all alloys, wheels, and speeds: work feed is 50 in. per min, infeed per pass is 0.001 in. in roughing and 0.0005 in. (max) in finishing, regulating wheel angle is 3°, and regulating wheel speed is 30 rpm. (e) For all alloys, wheels and speeds: work speed is 20 to 40 sfm, infeed per pass is 0.0005 in. in roughing and 0.0002 in. (max) in finishing, and traverse per revolution of work is ⅓ wheel width in roughing and ⅙ wheel width in finishing. Conditions for internal grinding are based on maximum hole length of 2½ hole diameters and maximum wheel width of 1½ wheel diameters. (Source of data is same as for Table 17.)

Table 20. Production Grinding of Two Ti – 6 Al – 4 V Parts (Example 1007) (a)

Conditions	Part A: Cylindrical grinding of 17-in. OD	Part A: Side grinding of 15.25-in. flange	Part B: Cylindrical grinding of 4.25-in. OD
Grinder size, in.	26 by 36	30 by 46	30 by 48
Wheel classification	A_s-60-I8-V	A_s-80-J5-V	A_s-80-J5-V
Wheel size, in.	24 by 2 by 12	30 by 3 by 12	30 by 3 by 12
Wheel speed, sfm	1760	2200	1880
Work speed, rpm	12	16	32
Infeed, ipr	0.0002	0.0002	0.0002
Type of cut	Traverse(b)	Side	Plunge

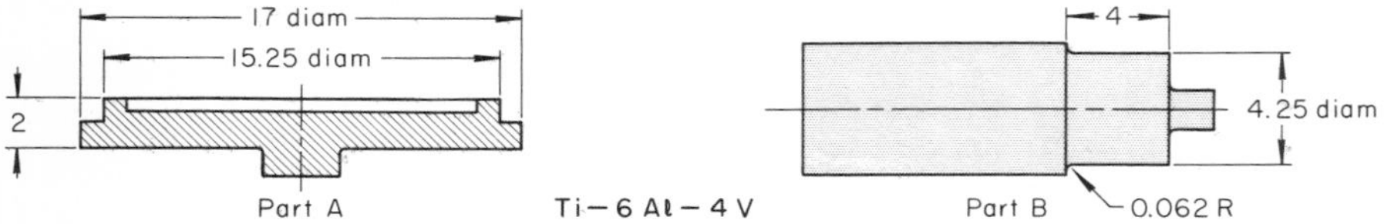

(a) Both parts were in the annealed condition. For all operations on both parts, grinding fluid was an aqueous nitrite-amine solution at a concentration of 1 part to 40 parts water. (b) Manual.

minimize pitting. Usually, the solutions are circulated and the parts moved, to insure uniform attack. Temperature and bath composition must be controlled carefully to obtain predictable results.

Production etching rates for titanium range from 0.0010 to 0.0015 in. per min. Tolerances of ±0.002 in. on etch depth and finishes of 15 to 50 micro-in. are typical. Because there is some lateral etching attack, the minimum width of narrow cuts is ordinarily about three times the depth.

Chemical machining may cause pitting or intergranular attack of Ti – 6 Al – 4 V, Ti – 7 Al – 4 Mo, and Ti – 5 Al – 2.5 Sn alloys. Titanium alloys may pick up hydrogen during chemical machining. The amount of hydrogen absorbed depends on the amount of beta phase present, the composition of the etchant, and the time and temperature of exposure. In one study under standardized etching conditions, the alpha alloy Ti – 5 Al – 2.5 Sn was not embrittled, the alpha-beta alloy Ti – 6 Al – 4 V was slightly embrittled, and the all-beta alloy Ti – 3 Al – 13 V – 11 Cr was severely embrittled. Ductility was restored to the all-beta alloy by vacuum annealing. Thus, care should be taken to insure that conditions used for chemical machining do not cause enough hydrogen absorption and embrittlement to be harmful.

Grinding

Titanium alloys can be ground with abrasive wheels or belts. Metal-removal rates are comparable to those for grinding alloy tool steel, but slower than those for soft constructional steel.

Wheel Grinding. Light cuts are recommended. Excessive wheel loading and other improper grinding conditions can cause burning, cracking and high residual stress.

Typical conditions for surface, cylindrical, centerless and internal grinding of titanium are presented in Table 19. Pronounced chemical action occurs in grinding titanium with an aluminum oxide wheel at conventional speeds. This results in severe wheel wear and dulling of the wheel face. Wear can be decreased markedly, and the abrasive can be kept sharp, by using aluminum oxide wheels at the slower speeds shown in Table 19, and by using a chemically active grinding fluid.

Grit sizes of 46 to 70 are shown in Table 19, but grit size as fine as 80 is sometimes used to obtain extremely fine finish. Wheel hardnesses of J to L are generally satisfactory, although softer wheels sometimes must be used (as in Example 1006). Vitrified-bond wheels are used almost exclusively for grinding titanium. Resinoid-bond wheels are used only for special applications.

Production grinding of titanium is described in the two examples that follow.

Example 1006. Surface Grinding Large Disks Flat and Parallel Within 0.001 In.

A disk 25 in. in diameter and 0.375 in. thick, made of Ti – 6 Al – 4 V alloy in the hot rolled and annealed condition (120,000-psi yield strength), was surface ground on both sides. Surfaces had to be flat and parallel within 0.001 in., and surface roughness could be no greater than 20 micro-in.

These requirements were met by grinding in a 36-in. rotary surface grinder equipped with an aluminum oxide wheel (A_s-80-G8-V) 16 by 8 by 2½ in. Operating details were as follows: wheel speed, 2000 sfm; work speed, 40 rpm; wheel traverse, 12 in. per min; down-

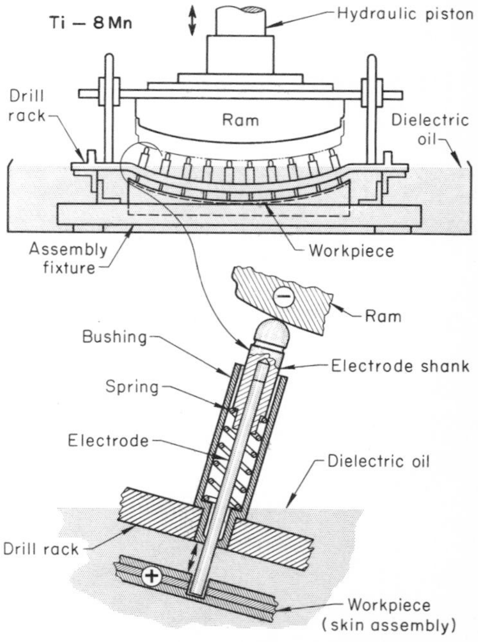

Fig. 5. Setup for electrical discharge machining of holes in aircraft skin assemblies (Example 1005)

feed, 0.0003 in. per pass; grinding fluid, a 1-to-20 mixture of heavy-duty soluble oil and water. A total of 0.005 in. of stock was removed from each side of the disk in 1½ hr. The wheel was dressed after every 40 passes.

In testing, a harder wheel (grade K) with a coarser abrasive (60-grit) loaded excessively. Speed was reduced gradually from 6000 to 2000 sfm to minimize wheel loading and breakdown, and to obtain better grinding action.

Example 1007. Cylindrical and Side Grinding of Ti – 6 Al – 4 V (Table 20)

The two different production parts made of Ti – 6 Al – 4 V alloy illustrated in Table 20 were both ground in the annealed condition. Cylindrical and side grinding operations were performed on part A; part B was cylindrical ground only. Table 20 gives details of conditions used in these two applications.

Belt Grinding. Resin-bond, cloth-backed belts with silicon carbide abrasive are recommended for normal feeds; aluminum oxide is better for very heavy feeds. Roughing and spotting operations are normally done with medium or fine abrasive (40 to 80 grit); extra-fine abrasive (120 to 220 grit) is used for finishing operations.

The contact wheel should be as small in diameter and as hard as practicable. Contact wheels with plain rather than serrated faces are ordinarily used for titanium.

Belt speed is from 1000 to 2200 ft per min (but is usually below 1500); pressure is 80 to 120 psi. High speed takes less pressure and a softer wheel.

Grinding Fluid. Titanium alloys should never be ground dry. Dry grinding damages the workpiece and constitutes a fire hazard from titanium powder. Grinding fluid cools and inhibits surface reactions between abrasive and workpiece. Nitrite-amine water solutions can be used with aluminum oxide wheels, but highly chlorinated or sulfochlorinated oil is recommended for high-speed silicon carbide wheels. Enough grinding fluid should always be supplied to prevent sparking. Fluid should be filtered and should be changed more frequently than is customary when grinding steel.

Aqueous solutions containing 5% sodium nitrite or potassium nitrite, or 15% tripotassium phosphate are suitable for use with waterproof belts.

Honing

Titanium is honed like the more common metals, with the same equipment. Typical practice is described in Example 546, in the article "Honing".

Machining of Zinc Alloy Die Castings

THE COMPLEX forms, accurate details, and superior surface finishes obtainable in the die casting of zinc alloys make extensive machining unnecessary. Flash that is formed at the parting surfaces of dies has to be removed. Critical surfaces may need truing to correct for die-clearance drafts or for distortion caused by nonuniform shrinkage in cooling. Holes that are not readily cored may have to be drilled. Undercuts or threads that are impossible or costly to cast have to be cut. Broaching, reaming or facing may be needed to bring critical dimensions within tolerance. However, because zinc alloys are free-cutting and comparatively soft (80 to 100 Bhn), they are machined more easily than most other metals.

Built-Up Edges. The formation of built-up edges on tools is one of the most common difficulties encountered in machining zinc. Built-up edges cause decreased accuracy, poor surface finish, and reduced tool life, and contribute to tool breakage. Edge buildup can be minimized by the proper setting of the tool, by providing proper rake and clearance angles, by polishing tool surfaces, by reducing drag through reduction of the amount of tool surface in contact with the work, by using proper lubricants, or by a combination of these practices. In designing tools, provisions should be made to divert chips from cutting edges and for adequate chip clearance.

Cutting Fluids. Dry machining of zinc die castings is common practice, especially when only small amounts of metal are being removed. However, when large amounts of metal are being removed, as in drilling, reaming or tapping of deep holes, the use of a cutting fluid is recommended. The cutting fluids most often used for machining of zinc alloy castings are:

1 Mineral seal oil (a "cut" taken between kerosine and light lubricating oil in the refinery)
2 Kerosine and light machine oil (50:50)
3 Straight kerosine
4 Soluble-oil emulsions (one part oil to 10 parts water)
5 Kerosine with additions of lard oil (50:50)
6 Mixtures of turpentine and kerosine.

Mixtures of kerosine and lard oil are highly efficient, but they cost more than mineral seal oil, kerosine, or soluble-oil mixtures. Lard-oil mixtures are difficult to remove from machined workpieces. Mixtures of turpentine and kerosine are expensive and are therefore infrequently used.

The removal of cutting fluids from complex parts is likely to be a problem, and is a major consideration in the selection of a cutting fluid, because parts must be thoroughly cleaned before any finish coating can be applied. Under normal conditions, soap, tallow or wax should not be used as a lubricant in place of a cutting fluid. A notable exception is for parts that must be machined after plating or some other finishing operation, where cutting fluids may spot the finish, thus justifying the use of a small quantity of tallow, soap or wax, which is usually applied to the cutting tool.

Turning and Boring

Turning Tool Angles. For turning tools of high speed steel or cast cobalt alloy, a back rake of 0° to 20° and an end relief angle of 8° to 20° (15° is typical) are commonly recommended. An end relief angle of 7° may be sufficient for some applications, but this angle must always be large enough to prevent drag on the heel of the tool. Where side cutting is involved, a side relief angle of 4° is recommended.

Cutting about ¼ in. above center and tilting the tool down at an angle of about 15° are recommended. With this setup, any chatter throws the tool outward instead of causing it to dig into the work. However, the closest accuracy usually is obtained with the tool set horizontal and on center, or slightly below center.

With carbide turning tools (in which the carbide tip must be rigidly supported), the end relief angle should not exceed 6° to 8° and the back rake should be within the range of 5° to 10°. The side cutting-edge angle may be from 10° to 20°, but is not critical, sometimes being 45° or more. The end cutting-edge angle is commonly from 5° to 10°. The nose of the tool is rounded to a maximum of 1⁄32-in. radius. Figure 1 shows the basic carbide-tipped tool for turning zinc alloys (see Fig. 2 in the article "Turning" for nomenclature of the standard shapes and tool angles for turning tools).

Turning Speed and Feed. For roughing cuts, using high speed steel or cast alloy tools, a speed of 200 sfm is recommended. For finishing, this speed may be increased to 400 sfm or higher. When using carbide tools, speeds of 400 to 600 sfm are common, and range as high as 800 sfm after experience is gained on a specific job.

Feeds of 0.005 to 0.010 ipr are most commonly used, mainly because cuts taken on die castings are usually light. When heavier cuts must be taken, feeds as high as 0.0625 ipr are feasible.

Boring. For boring tools, rake and relief angles usually are about the same as for tools used in turning. The same speeds can be employed. As in other machining of zinc alloys, light cuts and high speeds are recommended and commonly used to avoid seizure.

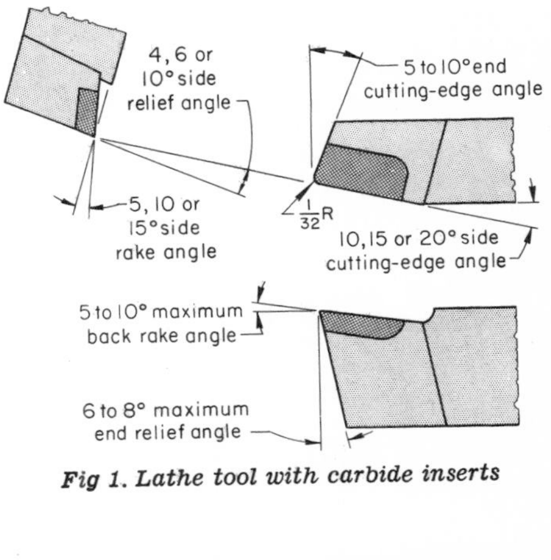

Fig 1. Lathe tool with carbide inserts

The illustrations and much of the text of this article are based on "Practice in Machining Zinc Die Castings", by New Jersey Zinc Co.

Diamond tools are infrequently used for boring of zinc, although they produce surfaces of exceptional smoothness, and when a precision machine is used, extreme accuracy can be held. Diamond tools are expensive and must be lapped, but when properly applied they can bore many thousands of holes without relapping. Table 1 contains an illustration of a diamond boring tool and gives data on the dimensions of diamond tools for boring holes of different diameters.

Diamond tools should be supported as rigidly as possible and should be brought gradually into contact with the rotating workpiece. The work should never be stopped while in contact with the tool. Any sign of a chipped edge should be the signal to remove the tool for lapping. Every effort should be made to prevent chatter. Although a cutting fluid is not required, a light oil emulsion is sometimes used to aid in chip removal. Diamonds are not recommended for intermittent cuts.

For boring of zinc alloys, speeds of 800 to 1500 sfm are recommended. Speed should be as high as possible consistent with freedom from vibration and chatter. Very fine feeds of 0.004 to 0.005 ipr are recommended, and cutting depth should not exceed 0.008 to 0.025 in. With very fine feeds, bright surfaces with finishes of 1.0 micro-in. have been attained.

Results almost as good as with diamond tools can be produced with carbide tools in precision boring machines.

Drilling

Drilling is the most widely used operation in machining of zinc die castings. Holes may be produced completely by drilling, or cored holes may be deepened. High-spiral drills made of a general-purpose high speed steel are generally recommended (see the article "Drilling", page 75 in this volume). Carbide-tipped drills can also be used.

Drill Angles. Any design that helps to clear chips and to keep them feeding away from the cutting edge is advantageous. If, with standard drills, a built-up edge forms, polishing of the flute next to the cutting edge is often helpful. Drill grinding methods are usually conventional. The standard 118° point is generally recommended (Fig. 2a); for special work, this angle may be varied from 90° to 136°. The flatter points are used to minimize runout when drilling deep sections of castings in which porosity may be encountered. The sharper points are used to minimize the burr in breaking through at the end of the hole. With such sharper points, especially when drilling thin sections, a flat should be ground along the lip to provide a zero or slightly negative rake along the cutting edge (Fig. 2b), and thus to counteract any "corkscrew" or "grabbing". Whatever the angle of the drill point, grinding a flat on the lip is common to minimize drill breakage. Grabbing is sometimes reduced by increasing the speed of the drill.

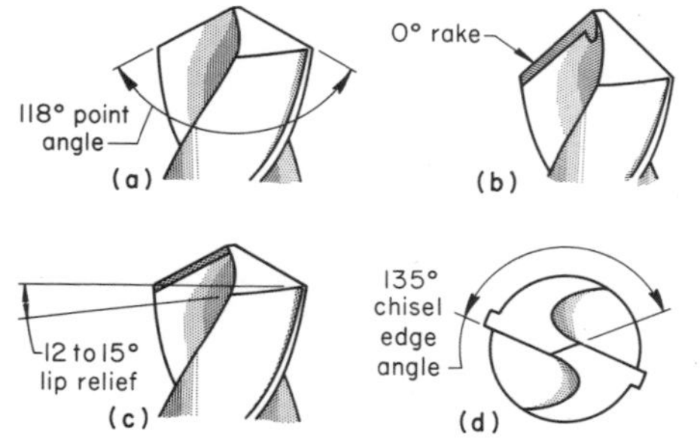

Fig. 2. Drill angles for drilling zinc

A lip clearance angle of 12° works satisfactorily in most drilling (Fig. 2c) but is often increased to 15°, and in at least one instance a lip clearance of 20° proved advantageous. In another application, a gradual increase of the lip clearance angle toward the center of the drill was best. The chisel edge angle should be 120° to 135° (Fig. 2d).

Flutes larger than normal are sometimes advantageous for chip clearance. Some drill manufacturers use steel slightly harder than regular grades to make special thin-web drills with wide flutes and narrow lands for drilling zinc die castings. Thick-web drills have an advantage in strength over thin-web types, but when thick webs are used, it is desirable, if not essential, to thin the web near the point.

One large producer of machined die castings recommends two-flute drills up to 1/4-in. diameter, three-flute drills in 1/4 to 3/8-in. sizes and four-flute drills for all work above 3/8 in. One manufacturer of drills recommends that two-flute drills be used for all drilling of new holes and that three or four flutes be used for enlarging holes. These two recommendations are not necessarily consistent, because cored holes are often less than 1/4 in. in diameter; drilling practice varies considerably among different shops.

Straight flutes sometimes give service superior to that obtained with spiral flutes. One machine shop has reported that straight-flute drills in sizes up to 3/16-in. diameter are much more efficient than spiral-flute drills. A drill manufacturer recommends that straight-flute drills be used only for enlarging existing holes. Trouble from chip packing may result if deep holes are drilled from the solid with straight-flute drills. One maker recommends a fast-spiral drill with a point angle of 130° for drilling deep holes.

Carbide-tipped drills are sometimes used for long runs. Details of such a drill are shown in Fig. 3.

Speed and Feed. Speeds of 200 to 300 sfm are generally satisfactory for high speed steel drills. One plant reports a speed of 12,000 rpm (580 sfm) in drilling deep holes 3/16 in. in diameter, but this is much higher than normal.

Cutting Fluids. Although a cutting fluid is usually recommended, much drilling, especially of shallow holes, is done dry with satisfactory results (see paragraphs on cutting fluids, page 507).

Reaming

In zinc die castings, holes are often cored to reaming size, thus eliminating the need for drilling. Reamers made of solid high speed steel are used exclusively in many shops. High speed steel reamers have produced 30,000 reamed

Table 1. Typical Details of Diamond Tools for Boring Holes of Various Diameters in Zinc Alloys (a)
(Nose angle, C, for all diameters: 80° ± 1°. Nose radius, R, for all diameters: 0.015 to 0.020 in.)

Diameter of bored hole, in.	Tool shank diameter, D, in.	Primary clearance angle, a	Second-ary clearance angle, b	Max height of top face above center, H, in.	Max stone thick-ness, T, in.	Diameter of hole for shank in boring bar, in.	Over-all length of tool, L, in.
3/8 to 1/2	3/16: −0.0002, +0.0005	20° ± 1°	25°	0.002	0.045	3/16: +0.0003, −0.0000	5/16, 3/8
1/2 to 3/4	1/4: −0.0002, +0.0005	18° ± 1°	23°	0.003	0.060	1/4: +0.0003, −0.0000	3/8, 1/2, 5/8
3/4 to 1	5/16: −0.0002, +0.0006	15° ± 1°	20°	0.004	0.080	5/16: +0.0004, −0.0000	1/2, 5/8, 3/4, 7/8
1 to 1 1/2	5/16: −0.0002, +0.0006	13° ± 1°	18°	0.006	0.080	5/16: +0.0004, −0.0000	5/8, 7/8, 1 1/8, 1 3/8
1 1/2 to 2 1/2	5/16: −0.0002, +0.0006	10° ± 1°	0°	0.008	0.100	5/16: +0.0004, −0.0000	3/4, 1, 1 3/8, 1 7/8
Over 2 1/2	5/16: −0.0002, +0.0006	7° ± 1°	0°	0.010	0.100	5/16: +0.0004, −0.0000	3/4, 1, 2
Over 2 1/2	3/8: −0.0002, +0.0006	7° ± 1°	0°	0.010	0.100	3/8: +0.0004, −0.0000	2, 2 3/8

Boring tool

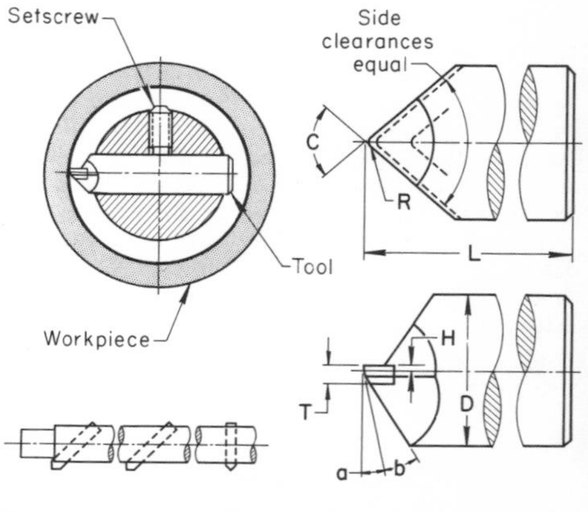

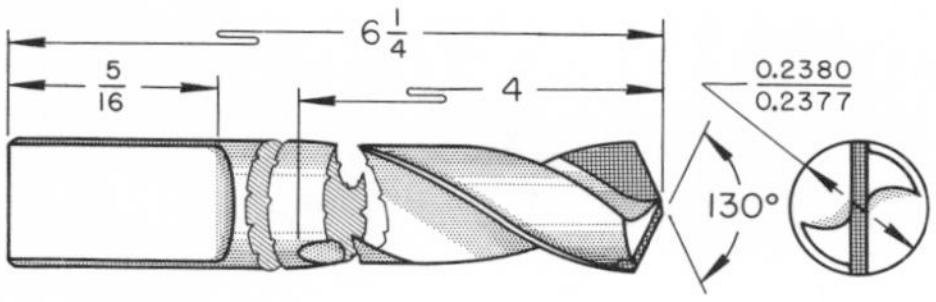

Fig. 3. Carbide-tipped drill for high-production drilling of zinc castings

holes before being resharpened, although more frequent sharpening is usually required. Reamers with inserted blades of either high speed steel or carbide are also used for reaming zinc, provided the size of the holes to be reamed permits insert construction (see the article "Reaming", which begins on page 93).

Some work is permitted to float during reaming, to avoid drift of the hole. The uniform cutting action of the reamer holds the center fixed.

Reamer Design. Machine reamers most commonly used have four, five or six straight flutes; eight flutes, irregularly spaced, have also been satisfactory. Spiral flutes are sometimes recommended, and are required for parts having irregularities such as keyways. A very marked spiral is considered essential if any is used. One machine shop has reported obtaining best results, in deep-hole reaming, with a reamer having left-hand spiral flutes but cutting right hand. Rose reamers are not recommended.

Deep flutes are recommended, to allow sufficient chip space. Polishing of flutes aids in preventing built-up edges. Chromium plating of reamer flutes, after polishing, has also helped to prevent built-up edges.

Sharp cutting edges are necessary for successful reaming of zinc alloys. The face of flutes is usually made radial (zero rake) and the clearance angle behind the land generally approximates 10°. Back taper from nose to shank of about 0.001 in. is generally used.

Many standard reamers have a land that is too wide for best results in zinc alloys. A land about 0.015 in. wide is frequently recommended, but this is often ground down to 0.005 to 0.007 in. to aid in preventing built-up edges and to reduce the amount of heat generated. Wide lands produce burnishing and generate heat. If heating is sufficient to cause the hole to expand, the hole may be too small after the reamer has been removed and the workpiece has cooled.

If 1/32 in. or more of metal is to be removed by reaming, one procedure is to grind a stepped portion at the end, about 0.005 in. smaller than the body of the reamer. The step cuts away most of the metal, leaving the body portion to size the hole with a light cut. This practice, however, may cause excessive reamer wear. The alternative is to remove all metal in one cut with a single-land reamer, using a feed per revolution that will yield the desired finish, based on trial.

Stepped reamers are used for simultaneously reaming stepped holes. Reamers are sometimes combined with spotfacing tools. Figure 4 shows a combination tool used for two-step reaming and simultaneous spotfacing of a 3° conical valve seat.

In reaming, most of the cutting is done by the reamer nose, which is chamfered to provide a lead. This chamfer is usually 45°. Once the initial grinding of the flutes and lands is correct, little other grinding is required, except at the lead end, although a very light cut may be taken off the radial face of the flutes. In grinding the lead chamfer, a clearance angle of about 10° is recommended.

For holes large enough to permit the use of inserted-blade reamers, this type is usually preferred, but blades should be firmly supported. The blade can be shaped to perform a facing operation at the bottom or at the top of the hole, as well as to ream the hole.

Speed and Feed. Wide ranges of speed and feed have produced successful results in reaming zinc. Optimum speeds and feeds are usually determined by trial. Speeds of 300 to 400 sfm have often been used for high speed steel reamers and up to twice these speeds for carbide-blade reamers.

Tapping

It is nearly always cheaper to tap than to cast threads around a core that would subsequently have to be unscrewed. Only very coarse threads and those of special shape are cored.

Cored Holes. Holes for tapping are usually cored in zinc die castings except when coring would greatly increase die cost. Because core pins require some taper, cored holes are smaller at the bottom than at the top. Hence, unless allowance is made for taper, or the hole is drilled or reamed before tapping, tap breakage or a poor thread may result, especially in deep or blind holes. Holes slightly larger than standard help to avoid "crowding" of taps. Hole size is commonly such as to yield 75 to 80% of full thread.

Taps are nearly always standard, and the grinding need seldom be special. Ground-thread taps, although not essential, are often used (especially in sizes above 1/4 in.) because they produce a smoother thread and minimize galling. Opinions differ as to whether or not the added cost of ground taps is offset by increased tap life and more precise threads. One plant uses ground taps for all blind holes; others use them only where close limits must be met. For class 3 fits, the use of a lead-screw control is recommended.

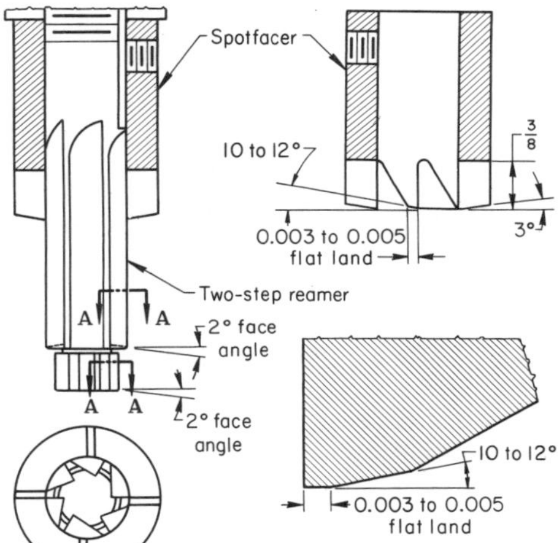

Fig. 4. Combination tool for reaming a two-step hole and spotfacing a valve seat

Generous chip clearance is mandatory for successful tapping. Two-flute taps for holes up to about 5/16 in. in diameter and taps with one less flute than standard for holes of other sizes are commonly preferred. According to one large manufacturer, however, three-flute taps in sizes below 1/4 in. have longer life than two-flute taps because less surface bears on the threads cut in the casting.

Selection of Taps. In selecting the type of tap, the hole is the most important consideration. For through holes, especially when they are not more than two diameters deep, there are advantages in spiral-point taps. These taps are pointed and the ends of the flutes are ground off at an angle, instead of being straight. This results in shearing the metal and curling the chips, which are forced ahead of the tap. Under these conditions the chips are kept out of the flutes, thus allowing the flutes to be shallower than could be permitted if chips accumulated in the flutes. Taps that have shallow flutes are stronger than those with deep flutes. Taps larger than 5/16 in. in diameter usually have three flutes.

Because the lands are wide in taps with only two or three flutes, there may be considerable friction; hence they are recommended only for short holes. Furthermore, although spiral-point taps can be used for blind holes (if adequate chip space is left in the bottom of the hole), the chips are more difficult to remove when packed in the bottom of the hole.

Spiral-point taps cut rapidly, but are more difficult to grind than those with straight flutes. One manufacturer recommends regrinding spiral-point taps after each 2000 holes. Such taps generally have five or six lead threads. The spiral point should include at least the first full thread.

For blind holes, especially those in which the thread must come close to the bottom, a straight-flute tap with a lead of only 1 1/2 to 2 1/2 threads is generally employed.

One maker of taps recommends high speed steel ground-thread taps with right-hand spiral flutes for smooth and precise threads in blind holes. Flutes should be large enough for good chip clearance, and the lands should be narrow to minimize friction. Taps of this design break up chips. Usually such taps have three flutes for holes under 3/8-in. diam, and four flutes for larger holes. The same type of tap with more taper (taper or plug chamfer) can be used for tapping blind holes for which the thread need not come close to the bottom, and for tapping long through holes.

It is generally good practice to hook or undercut the cutting faces of any tap, giving a rake of 12° to 15° (Fig. 5). Eccentric relief and a slight back taper, as shown in Fig. 5, are also commonly used in tapping zinc. This design narrows the land to a mere line, reducing friction and galling. Eccentric clearance also facilitates removal of

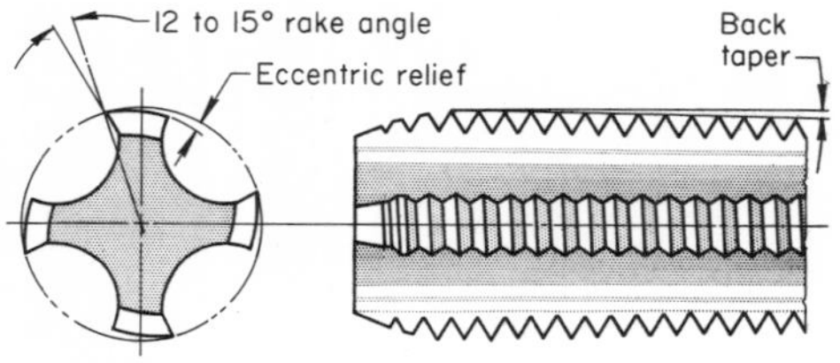

Fig. 5. Tap for use in zinc

the tap from the hole and prevents the tap from sticking. With small, conventionally ground taps, sticking can be reduced by grinding off or "breaking" the back corner of the lands at the opposite side of the flute from the cutting edge. Steep right-hand spiral flutes sometimes prove advantageous, because they are effective in carrying the chips out of the hole.

Built-up edges on taps can be minimized by using sharp taps and a cutting fluid (see the section early in this article on cutting fluids).

For holes 1¼ in. in diameter or larger, adjustable or collapsible taps are often used to advantage. Collapsible taps make it easy to vary the size and fit of the thread, and eliminate the need for reversing the tap.

In selecting taps for taper pipe threads, the general recommendations for bottoming taps should be followed. Some rake and some relief are desirable. One maker especially recommends interrupted-thread pipe taps.

Speed. Definite recommendations for tapping speeds have not been established for zinc alloys. A speed of 150 sfm has been suggested by some shops, but for high-speed tappers speeds higher than 150 sfm are common.

Die Threading

Many die castings require external threading. The die threading operation may be only for breaking fins and "cleaning up" a cast thread at the die parting line. Die threading may also be used to produce full threads on studs or projections where casting of the threads is not feasible. Because zinc alloys are easily machined and chasing is likely to be needed anyway, it is often more economical to cast the stud or projection to threading size and then to chase the full thread, rather than to cast rough threads that still require chasing to obtain acceptable results.

Dies. Threading can be done successfully with button or acorn dies in small sizes; but for sizes larger than ¼ in., chaser dies are recommended. Chasers made by milling are preferred for threading zinc, although those made by other methods are sometimes used.

Chasers may be of either the radial or the tangential type. For the radial type, one tool manufacturer recommends a 10° radial hook for straight threads and a 7° radial hook for tapered threads.

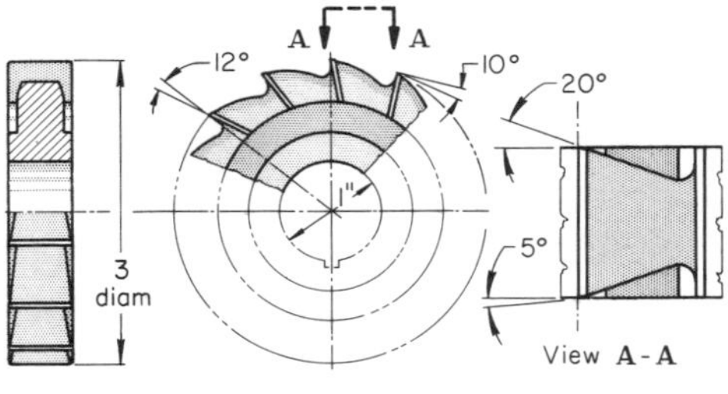

Fig. 6. Typical cutter for milling zinc

A maker of tangential chasers states that, with zinc alloys, the cutting edge of the chaser must be on or very near the center to avoid rapid wear of the chasers just beyond the cutting edge, whereas with other materials the cutting edge must be above the center. The type of grinding recommended for this type of chaser involves a 5° positive rake. Using this rake, about thirty thousand ¾–24 threads have been cut between grinds.

For round dies, one manufacturer recommends a rake of 15° to 20° with narrow cutting sections and eccentric relief for 7/16-in. diameter and larger. Self-opening dies or solid adjustable dies are recommended for cutting the larger sizes of threads.

Speed. Dies for threading zinc castings are commonly operated 10 to 15% slower than taps used for cutting similar internal threads. When radial chasers are to be used, one manufacturer recommends a speed of 100 sfm for 8 to 11 threads per inch and 200 sfm for 12 to 32 threads per inch.

Milling

Compared with drilling and tapping, milling is used to a small extent for machining zinc.

Cutters. Stock cutters can be used if the teeth are given an extra amount of primary clearance. About 10° is usual (Fig. 6), although a larger angle is employed for special form cutters. Coarse teeth help to provide the space needed for chip removal. Although the radial rake angle of 10°, as used for most stock cutters, is satisfactory, a 15° positive radial rake angle is often used. A higher spiral angle than for standard cutters is preferred for milling of zinc.

One plant recommends staggered-tooth cutters for deep slots, because they make finer chips and give a better finish than if the chips are the full width of the slot. A similar effect can be obtained with nonstaggered cutters by nicking or chamfering the corners of alternate teeth. Details of a typical cutter used for milling zinc are shown in Fig. 6. For 3-to-5-in.-diam cutters a land width of 1/32 in. is recommended; for 5-to-7-in.-diam cutters land width is increased to 3/64 in. For cutters less than 3 in. in diameter, land width ranges from 0.020 to 0.030 in. Cutters are usually made of high speed steel.

Speed and Feed. A speed of about 1000 sfm is common for milling of zinc alloys. Higher speeds are sometimes used. Feeds vary considerably, depending on the type of operation being performed; about 0.016 ipr is often used for operations such as milling of slots.

Cutting fluids are recommended for best results in milling of zinc (see the section on cutting fluids that appears near the beginning of this article).

Machining of Powder Metallurgy Parts

*By the ASM Committee on Powder Metallurgy**

PARTS made by powder metallurgy generally require machining methods that differ from those used for wrought or cast parts of similar composition, largely because the powder metallurgy parts are inherently porous.

The structure of powder metallurgy parts causes problems in machining for the following reasons: (*a*) pores may be closed by smearing of the metal surface; (*b*) cutting fluids may cause difficulties by entering the pores; and (*c*) parts may become charged with abrasive if ground, honed or lapped.

Preserving Porosity. Many machine parts such as bearings are made by powder metallurgy mainly because porosity can be obtained and controlled. Because these parts either have been or will be impregnated with lubricant, a minimum of machining is preferred because of the danger of closing the pores. If pores are even partially closed, it is difficult to obtain adequate

*WALTER A. STADTLER, *Chairman,* Director of Technical Services, International Business Machines Corp.; NORBERT A. ARNOLD, Manager, Powdered Metal Engineering, Keystone Carbon Co.; LOUIS W. BAUM, JR., Research Metallurgist, Remington Arms Co., Inc.; W. J. DOELKER, Head of Metallurgical Research Dept., National Cash Register Co.

FRANK EMLEY, Research Laboratory, C. K. Williams Div., Chas. Pfizer & Co., Inc.; E. G. GIBSON, Vice President, Zenith Sintered Products, Inc.; W. A. IRVINE, Manager of Production Engineering, Maytag Co.; J. K. LANGFITT, Divisional Superintendent, Ewart Plant, Link-Belt Co.; PETER V. SCHNEIDER, Manager, Powdered Metals Engineering, Systems Manufacturing Div., International Business Machines Corp.

PAUL J. SHIPE, Supervisor, Physical Science Laboratories, Delco Moraine Div., General Motors Corp.; E. F. SWAZY, Section Engineer, Advanced Metallurgical Development, Mallory Metallurgical Co. Div., P. R. Mallory & Co., Inc.; FRANK I. ZALESKI, Supervisor, Powder Metallurgy Laboratory, Frankford Arsenal.

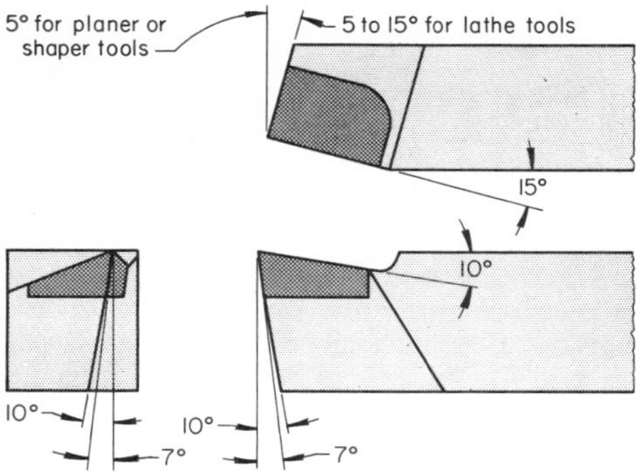

Fig. 1. Tool for turning, boring, shaping or planing of powder metallurgy parts

impregnation after machining. If the parts are impregnated with lubricant before machining and the pores become closed to a significant extent, the lubricant will not be released as needed during service.

When machining is required and porosity must be maintained, the following procedure should be used:

1 Review manufacturing sequence carefully for the purpose of minimizing machining.
2 Use the sharpest possible cutting tools (see later sections on specific operations).
3 Make sure that all cutting tools have a good surface finish and are free from "saw-tooth" effect.
4 Use light cuts (not more than 0.015 in. for single-point tools).

Cutting fluids are less often required in machining powder metallurgy parts, because they are inherently freer-machining than wrought parts. If a specific machining operation indicates the need for a fluid, a stream of low-pressure air will usually suffice for cooling the tools and removing chips. Cutting fluids should not be used for machining powder metallurgy parts that have been or will be impregnated with a lubricant. If the lubricant is present before machining, it will be contaminated by a cutting fluid. If a cutting fluid is used on nonimpregnated parts, pores will absorb the cutting fluid, which must then be removed before impregnation with a lubricant can be successful.

When porosity is incidental or minimal and no impregnated lubricant is required for the end use, a cutting fluid may be used if needed; however, subsequent processing operations must be considered. If porous parts are to be painted or plated, the pores must be kept free of cutting fluid; if the parts become contaminated, they cannot be satisfactorily painted or plated unless they are thoroughly cleaned. Cleaning is difficult and expensive. When porous parts have become contaminated with cutting fluid, solvent cleaning with agitation is effective in removing the absorbed fluids. Such a method is described on page 314 of Volume 2 of this Handbook.

If powder metallurgy parts have been infiltrated, or porosity serves no functional purpose, or they will not be finished by painting or plating, a cutting fluid can be used as needed.

The main requirement for the cutting fluid, when used, is that it be compatible with the metal being machined so that corrosion will not occur. Under special circumstances, light mineral oil is used, partly as an aid in machining and partly as a means of preventing rust or corrosion during subsequent processing and storage.

Contamination by Abrasive. Porous parts may become charged with minute particles of metal or abrasive during grinding, honing or lapping. This condition is discussed in the sections of this article that deal with grinding, honing and lapping.

Turning and Boring

Turning or boring is sometimes required in finishing powder metallurgy parts to make projections, re-entrant angles, and tapers, or for accuracy not obtainable by pressing.

For the turning or boring of parts in which porosity must be maintained at

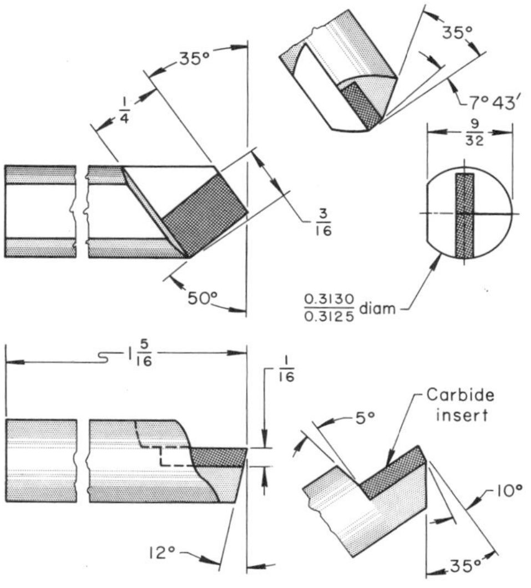

Fig. 2. Tool for boring porous bronze bearings in high production

the surface, tools of carbide or diamond should be used; carbide is the more common. After being ground, the tool faces should be honed or polished to obtain the sharpest and smoothest edges that are possible. "Saw-tooth" edges on cutting tools can be avoided by advancing the grinder perpendicular to the tool face, never at an angle. All sharpened edges of turning or boring tools should be examined at a magnification of 25 to 40 diameters to make sure that smooth, sharp edges have been obtained.

Some experimenting generally is needed to develop optimum tool shape and feed. The tool design shown in Fig. 1 will serve as a starting point in making carbide tools for turning or boring. The design illustrated in Fig. 2 has proved satisfactory for boring porous bronze bearings in high production.

Optimum feeds are influenced by the shape of the tool. For instance, when a nose radius of 1/16 in. is used, a feed of 0.010 to 0.015 ipr will be suitable. If the nose radius is decreased to 0.010 in., feed should be between 0.003 and 0.005 ipr to obtain clean-cut surfaces. Nose radii between 0.010 and 1/16 in. require feeds between the extremes given above. Feeds of 0.005 to 0.015 ipr are usually selected when preservation of porosity is critical. For roughing, or when a porous surface is not required, feeds of up to 0.030 ipr can be used.

Speeds of 175 to 350 sfm are most commonly used for turning or boring iron-base and copper-base powder metallurgy parts with sharp carbide tools. If maintenance of a porous surface is not required, speeds up to 500 sfm can be used. The two examples that follow give the essential details of recommended practice for boring porous bearings of sintered bronze.

Example 1008. Boring Noncritical Surfaces (Table 1)

A two-spindle precision boring machine was used to bore porous bronze bearings 0.605 in. in diameter. Workpiece, tool and operating details are given in Table 1. The bearings were subjected to relatively low speeds and light loads in service. Thus, the amount of porosity retained was not critical and some smearing of the metal could be tolerated in machining.

Example 1009. Boring Critical Surfaces (Table 1)

A four-spindle precision boring machine was used to bore porous bronze bearings 1.730 in. in diameter. Workpiece, tool and operating details are given in Table 1. The bearings were subjected to high speeds and heavy loads in service. Thus, smearing of the metal could not be tolerated and maintenance of surface porosity in machining was critical.

In comparing Examples 1008 and 1009, it is evident that similar practices were used for the two different parts. Except for size, the major difference was the surface requirement. The penalty for obtaining better surfaces (not smeared) was lower tool life. Assuming the same number of spindles, the same tools would produce three times as many of the smaller parts as of the larger, because of the difference in circumference (approximately 1 to 3). However, four tools (spindles) were used to bore 190 of the larger parts, whereas two were used for boring 600 of the smaller parts. Therefore, because of the need for more frequent tool sharpening when surfaces were critical, tool life was reduced by 50%.

Table 1. Boring Sintered Bronze Bearings (Examples 1008 and 1009)

Item	Example 1008	Example 1009
Workpiece Details		
Length, in.	1.5	2.0
Bore diameter, in.:		
Originally	0.605-0.607	1.730-1.732
After boring	0.621-0.623	1.754-1.755
Operating Conditions(a)		
Speed, rpm	2030	800
Speed, sfm	330	366
Feed, ipr	0.005	0.0069
Depth of cut (max), in.	0.008	0.0115
Average tool life per run, pieces	600	190

(a) Grade C-3 carbide tools were used for both workpieces. No cutting fluid was used.

Planing and Shaping

A carbide or high speed steel tool (usually carbide) ground as shown in Fig. 1 may be used as a starting point for planing or shaping, at the maximum speeds available on most machines. If the machine does not provide for automatic lifting of the tool on the return stroke, the tool must be lifted manually to prevent marring of the finish of the workpiece.

Planer and shaper feeds are too coarse to provide good surface finishes on powder metallurgy parts. However, surface finish may be improved by changing the end cutting-edge angle of the tool (Fig. 1) from 5° to 2°, so that the heel will barely clear the work and feed marks will be removed.

Drilling

Speeds of 70 sfm for high speed steel drills and 200 sfm for carbide drills will produce satisfactory holes in powder metallurgy parts. Drills with a low right-hand helix angle, or sometimes a left-hand helix angle, will prevent the drill from digging in. The cutting edges should be "dubbed" or ground to reduce axial rake sufficiently to prevent digging into the work.

Mechanical feed should be used whenever possible, and should be selected to achieve the desired finish if the drill is used for the final sizing operation, especially for larger drills. Satisfactory feeds are:

Drill diameter	Feed
⅛ to ¼ in.	0.002 ipr
5/16 to ½	0.004
9/16 to ¾	0.006
13/16 to 1	0.010

Reaming

To control bore accuracy in powder metallurgy parts, reaming is sometimes used instead of pin sizing, ball sizing, or burnishing. Standard reamers are satisfactory; left-hand spiral reamers have also proved successful. The cutting edges should have the best possible finish to minimize edge buildup, which results in oversize holes. The drill should leave a reaming allowance depending on hole size as follows:

Hole diameter	Allowance
¼ in. or less	0.002 in. on diameter
¼ to ½	0.002 to 0.004
½ to 1	0.004 to 0.006

When possible, reamers should be used in floating holders and be run at 25 to 50 sfm. Recommended feeds are:

Hole diameter	Feed
Up to ¼ in.	0.005 ipr
5/16 to ½	0.007
9/16 to ¾	0.010

Burnishing

When the clearance between a shaft and a powder metallurgy bearing is ±0.0005 in. or less, burnishing the bearing bores after they have been installed in the housing is preferred for correcting the bore size. No more than 0.002 in. per inch of diameter should be displaced, and the smallest amount of displacement that will produce the true diameter is desirable. The type of burnishing tool recommended for this operation is illustrated in Fig. 3.

Assume a finished bore diameter of 1.500 in. +0.0002, −0.0000 in. (B in Fig. 3). The diameter of the starting end of the burnishing tool then becomes 1.5000 in. − 0.0020 in., or 1.4980 in., and bearings would be bored to 1.4990 in. +0.0005, −0.0000 in. Thus, there would be a minimum clearance of 0.001 in. at the entering end of the tool and the first land would be a line-to-line fit. The tool then becomes progressively larger and the bearing is expanded. If there were no springback, the operation would be stopped at the fourth or fifth tool land. However, the bearing would ordinarily be burnished to 0.0004-in. oversize, to allow for springback.

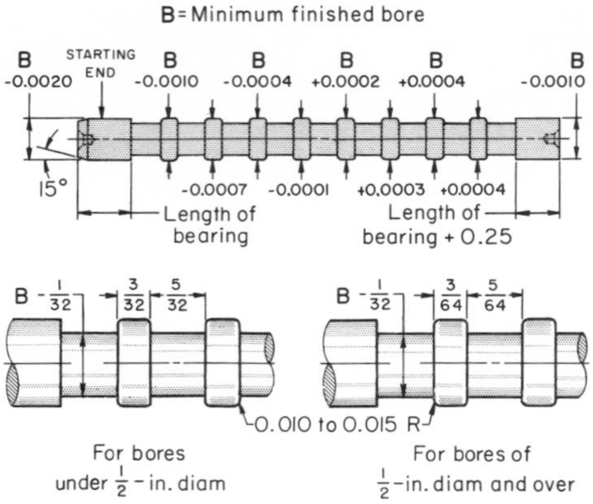

Fig. 3. Ball broach for burnishing bores in powder metallurgy parts

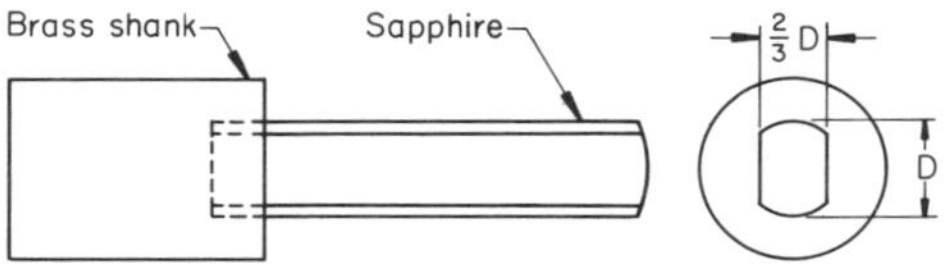

Fig. 4. Tool for high-speed burnishing of holes in powder metallurgy parts

A sapphire tool used for burnishing holes ½ in. in diameter or smaller in powder metallurgy parts is shown in Fig. 4. This tool can be operated in a high-speed lathe or a drill press. A drop of lubricating oil serves as a fluid, and the workpiece is pushed onto the rotating tool by hand.

Tapping

Conventional tap drill charts should be followed to maintain 65 to 75% depth of thread. Two-flute taps are recommended for diameters up to 5/16 in. Three-flute taps should be used for diameters of 5/16 to ½ in. Spiral-point taps are desirable, because they throw the chip out instead of driving it into the pores of the workpiece. Some experimenting may be required in tapping powder metal parts, to determine which tap is best for a specific metal.

Milling

Powder metallurgy parts are frequently milled to provide slots or undercuts that cannot be formed in pressing. For best results, carbide-tipped cutters are recommended, and helical-tooth cutters provide the best chip disposal. Cutters must be kept sharp and ground with minimum corner radii or, better still, with beveled corners.

For general-purpose milling with carbide cutters, speeds of 250 to 300 sfm are recommended. If high speed steel cutters are used, speeds should be no greater than 70 sfm. Feeds of 0.010 to 0.015 ipt for rough milling, and of 0.002 to 0.005 ipt for finish milling, are common.

If wear lands 1/64 in. wide appear on the back of the cutter teeth, or if wear becomes visible on the cutting edges, cutters should be replaced or sharpened. Dull cutters will cause smearing of the workpiece surface.

Grinding

Grinding operations are frequently used for maintaining close dimensions on powder metallurgy parts. However, some parts present problems in grinding because they lose porosity or become charged with abrasive particles. As the density of the parts decreases, these problems increase.

Heat treated high-density iron powder parts are being successfully ground with aluminum oxide wheels that have a medium grit size, porous structure, and vitrified bond. Operating speeds of 1750 to 1900 sfm with feeds of 0.002 in. per pass are satisfactory. The grinding fluids used for grinding similar wrought materials are generally satisfactory for high-density parts.

Parts that have been infiltrated with a copper-base alloy can be ground successfully, but they cause the wheel to load. Wheel loading can be minimized by using coarse-grit, open-structure wheels.

Grinding of low-density parts is not recommended, because some surface porosity will be lost and pores will become charged with abrasive particles that will dislodge in service and cause damage to bearing surfaces.

In special applications where grinding of porous parts is mandatory, solvent cleaning with long-cycle agitation or in an ultrasonic unit is effective for removing abrasive particles (see the methods described on pages 313 and 314, and on other pages indexed under ultrasonic cleaning, in Volume 2 of this Handbook).

Although surfaces of powder metallurgy parts that have become smeared in grinding have been successfully "opened up" by acid etching, if all of the acid is not removed, serious corrosion will result, and therefore etching is seldom advisable.

Honing and Lapping

Holes requiring extreme accuracy can be honed or lapped by normal techniques if retention of porosity is not required. However, size control of holes in powder metallurgy parts can usually be obtained more economically by reaming or burnishing.

High-density ferrous metal parts, especially when hardened, have been successfully honed and lapped, using conventional procedures.

Honing of infiltrated parts is seldom practical, because the stones become loaded. Neither lapping nor honing is recommended for porous parts, because either of these processes will cause the pores to become charged with abrasive particles. For special applications that require the use of lapping or honing, see discussion of cleaning in the preceding section, on Grinding.

Other Examples of Machining of Powder Metallurgy Parts in This Volume

Boring sintered alloy iron .... Example 76
Ball burnishing bronze .... Example 145
Roller burnishing bronze .... Example 216

Index

The major entries in this index are primarily machining processes, machines, tools and tool materials, and the metals being machined. (Products are indexed too, but only those most widely used, such as gears.) Details of machining that vary for different processes are listed under the processes; the major entry for speeds is a cross reference only, but under **Broaching,** there is a subordinate entry "speeds" giving page numbers. Metal removal rates, feeds, tolerances and surface finish are also listed under the process.

A few alloys designated by number are given at the beginning of the index, under "Numbered Alloys". Numbered aluminum alloys are listed under **Aluminum alloys, specific types;** numbered steels, under **Steels, AISI-SAE specific types;** tool steels, under **Tool steels, specific types;** and so on. Certain nonferrous alloys that are usually designated by name (rather than number) are listed alphabetically under this name — for instance, **Aluminum bronze** and **Nickel 200.** Heat-resisting alloys are listed alphabetically — even those incorporating numbers: **A-286** is in the A's and **K-42-B** in the K's.

The letter E, F, or T following an index entry means that information is in an Example, Figure or Table, and the letter A following an entry means that the topic is the subject of an article.

B

C

G

T

U

Some Abbreviations and Symbols Used in This Volume

ac	alternating current
amp	ampere
approx	approximately
asf	amperes per sq ft
asi	amperes per sq in.
avg	average
Bé	Baumé (specific-gravity scale)
Bhn	Brinell hardness number
BR	back rake angle
Btu	British thermal unit
C	Centigrade
cm	centimeter
cps	cycles per second
cu	cubic
dc	direct current
diam	diameter
ECEA	end cutting-edge angle
ER	end rake angle
est	estimated
Ex.	Example
F	Fahrenheit
fps	feet per second
ft	foot
ft-lb	foot-pound
g	gram
gal	gallon
gpm	gallons per minute
>	greater than
hp	horsepower
hr	hour
IC	inscribed circle
ID	inside diameter
in.	inch
ipm	inches per minute
ipr	inches per revolution
ips	inches per second
ipt	inches per tooth
kc	kilocycles
Khn	Knoop hardness number
kv	kilovolt
kw	kilowatt
lb	pound
LH	left-hand
<	less than
max	maximum
mfd	microfarad
mg	milligram
microamp	microampere
micro-in.	micro-inch
microsec	microsecond
min	minimum
min	minute
mm	millimeter
NC	National coarse thread
neg	negative (−)
NF	National fine thread
No.	number
NPS	National pipe straight thread
NPSC	National pipe straight coupling thread
NPT	National pipe taper thread
NPTF	National pipe taper fuel thread
NR	nose radius
NS	National special thread
OD	outside diameter
oz	ounce
pc	piece
PD	pitch diameter
pH	hydrogen-ion concentration
pos	positive (+)
ppm	parts per million
psi	pounds per sq in.
R_A	Rockwell A scale
R_B	Rockwell B scale
R_C	Rockwell C scale
R-C	resistance-capacitance circuit
rem	remainder
RH	right-hand
rpm	revolutions per minute
rpt	rise (step) per tooth
SCEA	side cutting-edge angle
sec	second
sfm	surface feet per minute
sq	square
SR	side rake angle
SRF	side relief angle
SUS	Saybolt universal second
temp	temperature
TIR	total indicator reading
tpi	teeth per inch
typ	typical
UN	Unified thread
UNC	Unified coarse thread
UNEF	Unified extra fine thread
UNF	Unified fine thread
UNS	Unified special thread
v	volt
Vhn	Vickers hardness number
vol	volume
w	watt
wt	weight

Geometric Characteristic Symbols

Characteristic	Symbol
Flatness	▱
Straightness	—
Roundness (circularity)	○
Cylindricity	⌭
Profile of any line	⌒
Profile of any surface	⌓
Parallelism	∥
Perpendicularity (squareness)	⊥
Angularity	∠
Runout	↗
True position	⌖
Concentricity	◎
Symmetry	⌯
Surface roughness, micro-in.	√

Pages in This Volume That Contain Tables of Nominal Speeds and Feeds for Machining Operations on Various Work Metals

(a) See page 105 for thickness and hardness limitations. (b) Feeds listed for power band sawing refer to cutoff sawing or straight cutting. For contour cutting, speeds should be somewhat lower, depending on the radius of cut.

Reference

DATE DUE

LORD   PRINTED IN U.S.A.

[redacted]

Speed Conversions

Diameter, inches	100 sfm	110 sfm	120 sfm	130 sfm	140 sfm	150 sfm	160 sfm	170 sfm	180 sfm	190 sfm	200 sfm	220 sfm	240 sfm	260 sfm	280 sfm	300 sfm	320 sfm	Diameter, inches
	Rotational speeds (rpm) for surface speeds of:																	
0.010 ...	38200	42000	45800	49700	53500	57300	61100	64900	68800	72600	76400	84000	91700	99300	107000	115000	122000	... 0.010
0.020 ...	19100	21000	22900	24800	26700	28600	30600	32500	34400	36300	38200	42000	45800	49700	53500	57300	61100	... 0.020
0.030 ...	12700	14000	15300	16600	17800	19100	20400	21600	22900	24200	25500	28000	30600	33100	35700	38200	40700	... 0.030
0.0625 ...	6110	6720	7330	7950	8560	9170	9780	10400	11000	11600	12200	13400	14700	15900	17100	18300	19600	... 0.0625
0.125 ...	3060	3360	3670	3970	4280	4580	4890	5190	5500	5810	6110	6720	7330	7950	8560	9170	9780	... 0.125
0.1875 ...	2040	2240	2440	2650	2850	3060	3260	3460	3670	3870	4070	4480	4890	5300	5700	6110	6520	... 0.1875
0.25 ...	1530	1680	1830	1990	2140	2290	2440	2600	2750	2900	3060	3360	3670	3970	4280	4580	4890	... 0.25
0.3125 ...	1220	1340	1470	1590	1710	1830	1960	2080	2200	2320	2440	2690	2930	3180	3420	3670	3910	... 0.3125
0.375 ...	1020	1120	1220	1320	1430	1530	1630	1730	1830	1940	2040	2240	2440	2650	2850	3060	3260	... 0.375
0.4375 ...	873	960	1050	1140	1220	1310	1400	1480	1570	1660	1750	1920	2100	2270	2440	2620	2790	... 0.4375
0.50 ...	764	840	917	993	1070	1150	1220	1300	1380	1450	1530	1680	1830	1990	2140	2290	2440	... 0.50
0.5625 ...	679	747	815	883	951	1020	1090	1150	1220	1290	1360	1490	1630	1770	1900	2040	2170	... 0.5625
0.625 ...	611	672	733	795	856	917	978	1040	1100	1160	1220	1340	1470	1590	1710	1830	1960	... 0.625
0.6875 ...	556	611	667	722	778	833	889	945	1000	1060	1110	1220	1330	1440	1560	1670	1780	... 0.6875
0.75 ...	509	560	611	662	713	764	815	866	917	968	1020	1120	1220	1320	1430	1530	1630	... 0.75
0.8125 ...	470	517	564	611	658	705	752	799	846	893	940	1030	1130	1220	1320	1410	1500	... 0.8125
0.875 ...	437	480	524	568	611	655	698	742	786	829	873	960	1050	1140	1220	1310	1400	... 0.875
0.9375 ...	407	448	489	530	570	611	652	693	733	774	815	896	978	1060	1140	1220	1300	... 0.9375
1.00 ...	382	420	458	497	535	573	611	649	688	726	764	840	917	993	1070	1150	1220	... 1.00
1.0625 ...	360	395	431	467	503	539	575	611	647	683	719	791	863	935	1010	1080	1150	... 1.0625
1.125 ...	340	373	407	441	475	509	543	577	611	645	679	747	815	883	951	1020	1090	... 1.125
1.1875 ...	322	354	386	418	450	482	515	547	579	611	643	708	772	836	901	965	1030	... 1.1875
1.25 ...	306	336	367	397	428	458	489	519	550	581	611	672	733	795	856	917	978	... 1.25
1.3125 ...	291	320	349	378	407	437	466	495	524	553	582	640	698	757	815	873	931	... 1.3125
1.375 ...	278	306	333	361	389	417	444	472	500	528	556	611	667	722	778	833	889	... 1.375
1.4375 ...	266	292	319	345	372	399	425	452	478	505	531	585	638	691	744	797	850	... 1.4375
1.50 ...	255	280	306	331	357	382	407	433	458	484	509	560	611	662	713	764	815	... 1.50
1.5625 ...	244	269	293	318	342	367	391	416	440	464	489	538	587	636	684	733	782	... 1.5625
1.625 ...	235	259	282	306	329	353	376	400	423	447	470	517	564	611	658	705	752	... 1.625
1.6875 ...	226	249	272	294	317	340	362	385	407	430	453	498	543	589	634	679	724	... 1.6875
1.75 ...	218	240	262	284	306	327	349	371	393	415	437	480	524	568	611	655	698	... 1.75
1.8125 ...	211	232	253	274	295	316	337	358	379	400	421	464	506	548	590	632	674	... 1.8125
1.875 ...	204	224	244	265	285	306	326	346	367	387	407	448	489	530	570	611	652	... 1.875
1.9375 ...	197	217	237	256	276	296	315	335	355	375	394	434	473	513	552	591	631	... 1.9375
2.00 ...	191	210	229	248	267	286	306	325	344	363	382	420	458	497	535	573	611	... 2.00
2.125 ...	180	198	216	234	252	270	288	306	324	342	360	395	431	467	503	539	575	... 2.125
2.25 ...	170	187	204	221	238	255	272	289	306	323	340	373	407	441	475	509	543	... 2.25
2.375 ...	161	177	193	209	225	241	257	273	289	306	322	354	386	418	450	482	515	... 2.375
2.50 ...	153	168	183	199	214	229	244	260	275	290	306	336	367	397	428	458	489	... 2.50
2.625 ...	146	160	175	189	204	218	233	247	262	276	291	320	349	378	407	437	466	... 2.625
2.75 ...	139	153	167	181	194	208	222	236	250	264	278	306	333	361	389	417	444	... 2.75
2.875 ...	133	146	159	173	186	199	213	226	239	252	266	292	319	345	372	399	425	... 2.875
3.00 ...	127	140	153	166	178	191	204	216	229	242	255	280	306	331	357	382	407	... 3.00
3.125 ...	122	134	147	159	171	183	196	208	220	232	244	269	293	318	342	367	391	... 3.125
3.25 ...	118	129	141	153	165	176	188	200	212	223	235	259	282	306	329	353	376	... 3.25
3.375 ...	113	124	136	147	158	170	181	192	204	215	226	249	272	294	317	340	362	... 3.375
3.50 ...	109	120	131	142	153	164	175	186	196	207	218	240	262	284	306	327	349	... 3.50
3.625 ...	105	116	126	137	148	158	169	179	190	200	211	232	253	274	295	316	337	... 3.625
3.75 ...	102	112	122	132	143	153	163	173	183	194	204	224	244	265	285	306	326	... 3.75
3.875 ...	98.6	108	118	128	138	148	158	168	177	187	197	217	237	256	276	296	315	... 3.875
4.00 ...	95.5	105	115	124	134	143	153	162	172	181	191	210	229	248	267	286	306	... 4.00
4.25 ...	89.9	98.9	108	117	126	135	144	153	162	171	180	198	216	234	252	270	288	... 4.25
4.50 ...	84.9	93.4	102	110	119	127	136	144	153	161	170	187	204	221	238	255	272	... 4.50
4.75 ...	80.4	88.5	96.5	105	113	121	129	137	145	153	161	177	193	209	225	241	257	... 4.75
5.00 ...	76.4	84.0	91.7	99.3	107	115	122	130	138	145	153	168	183	199	214	229	244	... 5.00
5.25 ...	72.8	80.0	87.3	94.6	102	109	116	124	131	138	146	160	175	189	204	218	233	... 5.25
5.50 ...	69.4	76.4	83.3	90.3	97.2	104	111	118	125	132	139	153	167	181	194	208	222	... 5.50
5.75 ...	66.4	73.1	79.7	86.4	93.0	99.6	106	113	120	126	133	146	159	173	186	199	213	... 5.75
6.00 ...	63.7	70.0	76.4	82.8	89.1	95.5	102	108	115	121	127	140	153	166	178	191	204	... 6.00
6.50 ...	58.8	64.6	70.5	76.4	82.3	88.1	94.0	99.9	106	112	118	129	141	153	165	176	188	... 6.50
7.00 ...	54.6	60.0	65.5	70.9	76.4	81.9	87.3	92.8	98.2	104	109	120	131	142	153	164	175	... 7.00
7.50 ...	50.9	56.0	61.1	66.2	71.3	76.4	81.5	86.6	91.7	96.8	102	112	122	132	143	153	163	... 7.50
8.00 ...	47.7	52.5	57.3	62.1	66.8	71.6	76.4	81.2	85.9	90.7	95.5	105	115	124	134	143	153	... 8.00
8.50 ...	44.9	49.4	53.9	58.4	62.9	67.4	71.9	76.4	80.9	85.4	89.9	98.9	108	117	126	135	144	... 8.50
9.00 ...	42.4	46.7	50.9	55.2	59.4	63.7	67.9	72.2	76.4	80.6	84.9	93.4	102	110	119	127	136	... 9.00
9.50 ...	40.2	44.2	48.2	52.3	56.3	60.3	64.3	68.4	72.4	76.4	80.4	88.5	96.5	105	113	121	129	... 9.50
10.0 ...	38.2	42.0	45.8	49.7	53.5	57.3	61.1	64.9	68.8	72.6	76.4	84.0	91.7	99.3	107	115	122	... 10.0
10.5 ...	36.4	40.0	43.7	47.3	50.9	54.6	58.2	61.8	65.5	69.1	72.8	80.0	87.3	94.6	102	109	116	... 10.5
11.0 ...	34.7	38.2	41.7	45.1	48.6	52.1	55.6	59.0	62.5	66.0	69.4	76.4	83.3	90.3	97.2	104	111	... 11.0
11.5 ...	33.2	36.5	39.9	43.2	46.5	49.8	53.1	56.5	59.8	63.1	66.4	73.1	79.7	86.4	93.0	99.6	106	... 11.5
12.0 ...	31.8	35.0	38.2	41.4	44.6	47.7	50.9	54.1	57.3	60.5	63.7	70.0	76.4	82.8	89.1	95.5	102	... 12.0
13.0 ...	29.4	32.3	35.3	38.2	41.1	44.1	47.0	50.0	52.9	55.8	58.8	64.6	70.5	76.4	82.3	88.1	94.0	... 13.0
14.0 ...	27.3	30.0	32.7	35.5	38.2	40.9	43.7	46.4	49.1	51.8	54.6	60.0	65.5	70.9	76.4	81.9	87.3	... 14.0
15.0 ...	25.5	28.0	30.6	33.1	35.7	38.2	40.7	43.3	45.8	48.4	50.9	56.0	61.1	66.2	71.3	76.4	81.5	... 15.0
16.0 ...	23.9	26.3	28.6	31.0	33.4	35.8	38.2	40.6	43.0	45.4	47.7	52.5	57.3	62.1	66.8	71.6	76.4	... 16.0
17.0 ...	22.5	24.7	27.0	29.2	31.5	33.7	36.0	38.2	40.4	42.7	44.9	49.4	53.9	58.4	62.9	67.4	71.9	... 17.0
18.0 ...	21.2	23.3	25.5	27.6	29.7	31.8	34.0	36.1	38.2	40.3	42.4	46.7	50.9	55.2	59.4	63.7	67.9	... 18.0
19.0 ...	20.1	22.1	24.1	26.1	28.1	30.2	32.2	34.2	36.2	38.2	40.2	44.2	48.2	52.3	56.3	60.3	64.3	... 19.0
20.0 ...	19.1	21.0	22.9	24.8	26.7	28.6	30.6	32.5	34.4	36.3	38.2	42.0	45.8	49.7	53.5	57.3	61.1	... 20.0
21.0 ...	18.2	20.0	21.8	23.6	25.5	27.3	29.1	30.9	32.7	34.6	36.4	40.0	43.7	47.3	50.9	54.6	58.2	... 21.0
22.0 ...	17.4	19.1	20.8	22.6	24.3	26.0	27.8	29.5	31.3	33.0	34.7	38.2	41.7	45.1	48.6	52.1	55.6	... 22.0
23.0 ...	16.6	18.3	19.9	21.6	23.3	24.9	26.6	28.2	29.9	31.6	33.2	36.5	39.9	43.2	46.5	49.8	53.1	... 23.0
24.0 ...	15.9	17.5	19.1	20.7	22.3	23.9	25.5	27.1	28.6	30.2	31.8	35.0	38.2	41.4	44.6	47.7	50.9	... 24.0